MIDDLE AND JUNIOR HIGH
CORE COLLECTION

FIFTEENTH EDITION

CORE COLLECTION SERIES

FORMERLY
STANDARD CATALOG SERIES

SHAUNA GRIFFIN, MLS, GENERAL EDITOR

CHILDREN'S CORE COLLECTION
MIDDLE AND JUNIOR HIGH CORE COLLECTION
SENIOR HIGH CORE COLLECTION
FICTION CORE COLLECTION
PUBLIC LIBRARY: NONFICTION CORE COLLECTION
GRAPHIC NOVELS CORE COLLECTION

MIDDLE AND JUNIOR HIGH
CORE COLLECTION

FIFTEENTH EDITION

EDITED BY

KENDAL SPIRES

H. W. Wilson

A Division of EBSCO Information Service, Inc.

Ipswich, Massachusetts

2021

GREY HOUSE PUBLISHING

Printed in the United States of America

ISBN 978-1-64265-805-7

Abridged Dewey Decimal Classification and Relative Index, Edition 15 is © 2004-2012 OCLC Online Computer Library Center, Inc. Used with Permission. DDC, Dewey, Dewey Decimal Classification, and WebDewey are registered trademarks of OCLC.

Middle and Junior High Core Collection, 2021, published by Grey House Publishing, Inc., Amenia, NY, under exclusive license from EBSCO Information Services, Inc.

A catalog record for this title is available from the Library of Congress.

PRINTED IN CANADA

TABLE OF CONTENTS

PREFACE

MIDDLE AND JUNIOR HIGH CORE COLLECTION is a curated list of fiction and nonfiction books recommended for young people in grades five through nine. It also includes professional aids for librarians and library media specialists addressing children's librarianship in public and school libraries, collection development for the age group, and related issues.

This Core Collection is an abridgment of the database available from EBSCO Information Services, which has an additional two recommendation levels, Lexile measures, book reviews and articles, and expanded metadata. It is updated weekly. Contact your EBSCO or NoveList sales rep for a free trial, or visit https://www.ebscohost.com/novelist/our-products/core-collections for more information. EBSCO also invites feedback from Core Collections customers at novelist@ebsco.com.

What's in this Edition?

This edition continues to emphasize equity, diversity, and inclusion, representing and reflecting a varied community in which many voices can be heard. Significant weeding is undertaken to ensure that older, outdated books are removed in favor of more relevant recommendations. This 15th edition includes more than 6,000 fiction and nonfiction titles, which includes a generous selection of graphic novels.

New metadata includes precise genres and subgenres, and subject headings that consistently include both location and time period where appropriate. Books will be much easier to find through the index, and the metadata associated with each record offers better insight into the contents of the book.

Additionally, beginning with this volume, all entries for fiction titles in series will also include the name of that series.

New in this edition is an expanded selection of professional materials, now including titles relevant to the needs of school teachers and administrators, on such topics as developing skills and classroom management.

As always, a star (★) at the start of an entry indicates that a book is an Essential title, our highest recommendation level. These titles are the essential books in a given category or on a given subject; while there are often a number of recommended titles, this designation helps users who want only a small selection. Non-starred entries represent Recommended titles, which provide a fuller list of recommended books.

History

JUNIOR HIGH SCHOOL LIBRARY CATALOG, first published in 1965, was developed to address the unique needs of younger adolescents. It developed from the STANDARD CATALOG FOR HIGH SCHOOL LIBRARIES, which was subsequently modified in scope and renamed SENIOR HIGH SCHOOL LIBRARY CATALOG. With the seventh edition in 1995, the title of the JUNIOR HIGH SCHOOL LIBRARY CATALOG was changed to MIDDLE AND JUNIOR HIGH SCHOOL CATALOG to reflect the prevalence of middle school programs and the extension of coverage to grades five and six. With the ninth edition in 2009, the title was changed to MIDDLE AND JUNIOR HIGH SCHOOL CORE COLLECTION.

The collection subsequently evolved, along with other Core Collections, into an online resource called WilsonWeb. EBSCO Information Services acquired H.W. Wilson in 2011, and the collections became EBSCOhost databases in 2012. In 2020, the readers' advisory experts at NoveList applied their expertise: while Core Collections continues to provide impartial collection development guidance by experts in their fields, this marriage of readers advisory and collection development expertise strengthened the application of genre and subject headings, expanded awards content, and improved search and browse capabilities in the online Core Collections databases.

Scope

This Core Collection is intended to serve the needs of any library serving readers of children's literature. School, public, and even academic libraries, such as those with teacher education or library science degree programs, use the MIDDLE AND JUNIOR HIGH CORE COLLECTION to identify the highest quality books. Recommendations contains herein stand as a basic or "opening day" collection, with Essential and Recommended titles. The newer titles help in identifying areas in a collection that can be updated or strengthened, while the retention of useful material from the previous edition enables the librarian to make informed decisions about weeding a collection. With its classified arrangement, complete bibliographical data, and descriptive and evaluative annotations, the Core Collection provides useful information for the acquisitions librarian, the reference librarian, and the cataloger.

The librarians of Core Collections are committed to creating and maintaining collections that reflect the diversity of human experience. We consider a multitude of factors when choosing a title for the Core Collections, such as the books' critical consensus and its contribution to the breadth and depth of viewpoints available. We mitigate biases to the best of our ability by seeking out multiple opinions on books and actively staying educated on issues of diversity and representation in publishing.

This Core Collection excludes the following: non-English-language materials, with the exception of bilingual materials; dictionaries and similar items; and works of adult fiction, unless they are commonly read by young people or are widely used in the curriculum. Textbooks, books about individual computer programs, and other content than dates quickly have also been excluded. This collection also excludes most works recognized as "classic" literature for two reasons – to concentrate on recommending titles that are perhaps less well-known, and due to extensive conversations with school media specialists, who indicated that additions of classics to their collections were primarily based on local curricula, not on recommendations from Core Collections. While some classics do remain in the print edition, more can be found in the full EBSCOhost database under the "Supplemental" recommendation level.

Books are listed with an ISBN--most frequently for a hardcover edition published in the United States, or published in Canada or the United Kingdom and distributed in the U.S. Out-of-print titles are retained in the belief that good books are not obsolete simply because they happen to go out of print.

Database

This Core Collection is derived from the database available from EBSCO Information Services. Metadata for the titles in this volume is provided by the metadata librarians at NoveList, who manage and apply a controlled vocabulary that adapts as terms come in and out of style, or as events require new ones. There are additional, browsable access points, plus full-text book reviews and articles, full-color cover art, Lexile measures, and all of the Supplemental book recommendations and Weeded titles. It is updated weekly. For more information or for a free trial, contact your EBSCO or NoveList sales rep, or visit https://www.ebscohost.com/novelist/our-products/core-collections. EBSCO also invites feedback from Core Collections customers at novelist@ebsco.com.

Preparation

Books included in Core Collections are selected by experienced librarians representing public library systems, school libraries, and academic libraries across the United States and Canada, as well as NoveList staff. These librarians also act as advisors on library policy, trends, and special projects. The names of participating librarians and their affiliations are listed in the Acknowledgements.

Core Collections Products

For recommendations for books for children and teens, librarians are encouraged to investigate the following databases and their associated print versions:
CHILDREN'S CORE COLLECTION
MIDDLE AND JUNIOR HIGH CORE COLLECTION
SENIOR HIGH CORE COLLECTION

For young adult fiction specifically, consult the YOUNG ADULT FICTION CORE COLLECTION, available only in print.

For adult nonfiction for the general reader, try the database NONFICTION CORE COLLECTION or the associated print volume PUBLIC LIBRARY CORE COLLECTION: NONFICTION. For fiction, please use FICTION CORE COLLECTION, either as a database or the associated print version.

For Graphic Novels for all ages, try the GRAPHIC NOVELS CORE COLLECTION in print or database form, which includes both fiction and nonfiction recommendations.

PURPOSE AND ORGANIZATION

PURPOSE

CORE COLLECTIONS is designed to serve a number of purposes:

As an aid in purchasing. Core Collections is designed to assist in the selection and ordering of titles. Summaries and evaluative excerpts are provided for each title along with information regarding the publisher, ISBN, page count, and publication year. In evaluating the suitability of a work, each library will want to consider the needs of the unique patron base it serves.

As an aid in verification of information. For this purpose, bibliographical information is provided in the list of works. Entries also include recommended subject headings based on NoveList's proprietary subject vocabulary. Notes may describe editions available and other content; for the most up-to-date metadata, please consult the EB-SCOhost database.

As an aid in curriculum or programming support. The classified approach, subject indexing, annotations, and evaluative excerpts are helpful in identifying materials appropriate for classroom support, for book discussions, and other programming.

As an aid in collection maintenance. Information about titles available on a subject facilitates decisions to rebind, replace, or discard items. If a book has been demoted to the Supplemental or Weeded recommendation levels and therefore no longer appears in the print abridgement of the database, that demotion is not intended as a sign that the book is no longer valuable or that it should necessarily be weeded from your library's collection.

As an aid in professional development or instruction. The Core Collection is useful in courses or professional training that deal with collection development and readers' advisory; it may also be used in course that deal with literature and book selection, especially in the creation of bibliographies and reading lists.

As an aid to readers' advisory. Every title in this Core Collection is a recommended work and can be given with confidence to a user who expresses a need based on topic, genre, etc. Readers' advisory and user service are further aided by series and awards information, by the descriptive summaries and evaluative excerpts from trusted review sources, and by the subject headings in the Title and Subject Index applied by professional metadata librarians at NoveList.

ORGANIZATION

This Core Collection is organized into two parts: a Classified Collection and an Author, Title, and Subject Index.

As in previous editions, the MIDDLE AND JUNIOR HIGH CORE COLLECTION contains graphic novels: most fiction graphic novels can be found in 741.5, while most nonfiction graphic novels are found either in the biography section (B) or under specific Dewey headings by subject.

Part 1. Classified Collection

The Classified Collection is arranged with nonfiction books first, classified according to the Dewey Decimal Classification in numerical order from 000 to 999. Individual biographies are classed at B and follow the Dewey Classified section. Fiction follows the biographies. Within classes, works are arranged alphabetically under the main entry, usually the author. Biographies are arranged alphabetically under the biography's subject.

An Outline of Classification, which serves as a table of contents for the Classified Collection, is reproduced following this explanation. It should be noted that many topics can be classified in more than one discipline. If a particular title is not found where it might be expected, the Index should be consulted to determine if it is classed elsewhere.

The information supplied for each book includes a bibliographic description, suggested subject headings, and, where relevant, series names and publication history. Subject headings are derived from NoveList's extensive curated vocabulary. Also included is a suggested classification number from the *Abridged Dewey Decimal Classification and Relative Index*. Whenever possible, a summary and an evaluative excerpt from a quoted source are also included. The following is an example of a typical entry and a description of its components.

> **Woodson, Jacqueline**
> ★   **Before** the ever after. Jacqueline Woodson. Nancy Paulson Books, 2020. 176 p. Grades: 5 6 7 8   **Fic**
> 1. 2000s (Decade) 2. Fathers and sons 3. Memory 4. African American boys 5. Football 6. Chronic traumatic encephalopathy 7. Realistic fiction 8. Novels in verse 9. African American fiction
> ISBN 9780399545436
>   LC 2020018310
> Coretta Scott King Award, Author Category, 2021.
> ZJ's friends Ollie, Darry and Daniel help him cope when his father, a beloved professional football player, suffers severe headaches and memory loss that spell the end of his career.
> "Woodson again shows herself to be a masterful writer, and her meaningful exploration of concussions and head injuries in football, a subject rarely broached in middle-grade fiction, provides young athletes with necessary insights into sport's less glamorous side." Booklist

The name of the author, Jacqueline Woodson, is given in conformity with Library of Congress Authorities. The star at the start of the title indicates that this is an *Essential* title. The title of the book is *Before the Ever After*. The book was published by Nancy Paulson Books in 2020. The book has 176 pages. If it were part of a series, the series name would follow the page count. The book is recommended for any of the following grade levels: 5 6 7 8. At the end of the last line in the body entry is the figure Fic in bold face type, indicating the section the book is found in. If this were nonfiction, the appropriate Dewey Decimal Classification number would be found here.

The numbered terms "1. 2000s (Decade)," etc. are recommended subject headings for this book based on NoveList's database of subject headings. An ISBN (International Standard Book Number) is included to facilitate ordering; however, there will often be many editions and formats of a given title; due to space constraints these ISBNs are not provided in the print edition, though many can be found in the corresponding database. The Library of Congress control number is provided when available.

Next are the awards this title has won, followed by a brief summary and an evaluative excerpt from a critical reviewing source, in this case Booklist. Such summaries and excerpts are useful in evaluating books for selection and in determining which of several books on the same subject is best suited for the individual reader or purchasing library. Notes are also made to describe special features, such as publication history, film adaptations, or series order. In this case, none are noted.

Part 2. Author, Title, and Subject Index

The title, author, and subject index is a single alphabetical list of all the books entered in the Core Collection. Each book can be found under their author entry, title, and subjects. The classification number, displayed in boldface, is the key to the location of the main entry for the book in the Classified Collection.

The following are examples of index entries for the book cited above:

Author	**Woodson, Jacqueline** Before the ever after	**Fic**
Title	**Before** the ever after. Woodson, J.	**Fic**
Subject	**AFRICAN AMERICAN FICTION** Woodson, J. Before the ever after	**Fic**

OUTLINE OF CLASSIFICATION

Reproduced below is the Second Summary of the Dewey Decimal Classification. * As Part 1 of this Core Collection is arranged according to this classification, the outline will serve as a table of contents for it. Please note, however, that the inclusion of this outline is not to be considered a substitute for consulting the Dewey Decimal Classification itself.

* Reproduced from Edition 15 of the Abridged Dewey Decimal Classification and Relative Index, published in 2012, by permission of OCLC Online Computer Library Center, Inc., owner of copyright.

ACKNOWLEDGMENTS

H.W. Wilson, NoveList, and EBSCO Information Services express special gratitude to the following librarians who both advised in editorial matters and assisted in the selection and weeding of titles for this Core Collection.

Steven Ashley
Librarian
Carrboro, North Carolina

Robin Brenner
Editor-in-chief, No Flying No Tights
Teen Librarian
Brookline Public Library
Brookline, Massachusetts

Heather Cunningham
Teen Services Librarian
Saratoga Spring Public Library
Saratoga Springs, New York

Gail de Vos
Storyteller & Adjunct Instructor, SLIS
University of Alberta, Edmonton
Canada

Elizabeth Elsbree
Elementary Library Media Specialist
East Aurora School District
East Aurora, Illinois

Francisca Goldsmith
Library and Media Consultant
Worcester, Massachusetts

Natalie Harvey
Freelance Librarian
Raleigh, North Carolina

Christen Higgins
School Library Media Coordinator
Charlotte-Mecklenburg Schools
Charlotte, North Carolina

Michael Jenkins
Consultant
Wilmington, North Carolina

Abby Johnson
Collection Development Leader
The Floyd County Library
New Albany, Indiana

Joquetta Johnson
High School Media Specialist
Baltimore County Public Schools
Baltimore, Maryland

Angela Leeper
Director, Curricular Materials Center
University of Richmond
Richmond, Virginia

Marcela Peres
Director
Lewiston Public Library
Lewiston, Maine

Sarah Polace
Children's Services Supervisor
Cuyahoga County Public Library
Cleveland, Ohio

Natalie Romano
Librarian
Denver Public Library
Denver, Colorado

Jennie Stevens
Teen Librarian
Naperville Public Library
Naperville, Illinois

Sarah Bean Thompson
Youth Services Manager
Springfield-Green County
Springfield, Missouri

Kay Weisman
Youth Services Librarian
West Vancouver Memorial Library
Vancouver, BC, Canada

Susie Wilde
Children's Book Specialist
Chapel Hill, North Carolina

Barbie Zinkovich
School Library Media Specialist
Spartanburg School District
Spartanburg, South Carolina

The editors would also like to thank NoveList Readers' Advisory Librarian Rebecca Honeycutt and Amy Morgan Assistantship recipient Helen Sharma for their help in creating this collection.

MIDDLE AND JUNIOR HIGH CORE COLLECTION
FIFTEENTH EDITION
CLASSIFIED COLLECTION

000 COMPUTER SCIENCE, KNOWLEDGE & SYSTEMS

001.9 Controversial knowledge

Barton, Chris

Can I see your I.D.?: true stories of false identities. by Chris Barton; illustrated by Paul Hoppe. Dial Books for Young Readers, c2011. 144 p.

Grades: 6 7 8 9   **001.9**
   1. Impostors 2. False personation 3. Identity (Psychology) 4. Fraud 5. Deception 6. Illustrated books 7. Books for reluctant readers
   ISBN 9780803733107

"In 10 impeccably crafted profiles, Barton . . . shares the stories of individuals—many just teenagers—who adopted false identities for amusement, profit, or survival. . . . Barton reveals the motivations behind and the consequences of each deception. The use of second-person narration is very effective, allowing readers to assume the identities of each individual. Barton's prose captures the daring, ingenuity, and quick thinking required of each imposter. . . . Hoppe contributes dynamic comic book style panel art." Publishers Weekly.

Includes bibliographical references.

Eaton, Gale, 1947-

A **history** of ambition in 50 hoaxes. Gale Eaton. Tilbury House Publishers, 2019. 288 p.: History in 50

Grades: 6 7 8 9 10   **001.9**
   1. Hoaxes -- History 2. Ambition 3. History 4. Curiosities and wonders
   ISBN 9780884484929

                                                  LC 2016015590

Shares the stories of fifty hoaxes from history and the motivations behind them, including the Piltdown man, the cursed tomb of the last Aztec emperor, and crop circles.

Gee, Joshua

★ **Encyclopedia** horrifica: the terrifying truth! about vampires, ghosts, monsters, and more. Joshua Gee. Scholastic, c2007. 129 p.

Grades: 4 5 6 7   **001.9**
   1. Vampires 2. Ghosts 3. Monsters 4. Books for reluctant readers
   ISBN 0439922550

                                                  LC 2007061733

A visual reference contains true stories of such creatures as vampires, aliens, werewolves, and ghosts, accompanied by photographic evidence, eyewitness accounts, and original interviews.

"Each topic is replete with color illustrations and photos and is accompanied by a light, readable text that tries to separate fact from fiction." Voice of Youth Advocates.

Includes bibliographical references (p. [130-132]) and index.

Stewart, Gail B., 1949-

Vampires: do they exist? Gail B. Stewart. ReferencePoint, 2010. 80 p.: Vampire library

Grades: 7 8 9 10   **001.9**
   1. Vampires 2. Monsters 3. Cryptozoology 4. Mythical creatures 5. Curiosities and wonders
   ISBN 9781601521101

"Energetic and surprisingly educational, this lively [book] seizes upon a zeitgeist topic and takes it as far as possible." Booklist.

Includes bibliographical references and index.

001.94 Mysteries

Hawkins, John

Atlantis and other lost worlds. by John Hawkins. PowerKids Press, 2012. 32 p.: Mystery hunters (PowerKids Press)

Grades: 4 5 6 7   **001.94**
   1. Atlantis (Legendary place) 2. Geomythology 3. Curiosities and wonders
   ISBN 9781448864294

                                                  LC 2011021292

Explores the mythology and lore of Atlantis and other supposed lost cities and civilizations, including Lemuria and Thule.

Hulick, Kathryn

Strange but true: 10 of the world's greatest mysteries explained. written by Kathryn Hulick; illustrated by Gordy Wright. Frances Lincoln Children's Books, 2019. 128 p.

Grades: 4 5 6 7 8   **001.94**
   1. Curiosities and wonders 2. Paranormal phenomena 3. Supernatural 4. Metaphysics 5. History
   ISBN 9781786037848

Prepare to have your mind blown! As you explore ten of the world's greatest unsolved mysteries, you'll witness a UFO encounter, search for the lost city of Atlantis, tour a haunted house, and discover the kraken's true form. Along the way, you'll use the scientific method and sharp thinking to separate fact from fiction and explain the unexplainable.

"Scientific explanations for mysteries that have given rise to fantastical stories." Kirkus.

Includes bibliographical references (pages 124-127).

001.942 Unidentified flying objects (UFOs)

Karst, Ken

Alien abductions. Ken Karst. Creative Education, 2019 48 p.

Grades: 5 6 7 8   **001.942**
1. Human-alien encounters 2. Alien abduction 3. Unidentified flying objects -- Sightings and encounters
ISBN 9781640260054

LC 2017060031

An investigative approach to the curious phenomena and mysterious circumstances surrounding alien abductions, from abductees' hypnotic recollections to conspiracy theories to hard facts. Provided by publisher.

001.944 Monsters and related phenomena

Beccia, Carlyn

★ **Monstrous**: the lore, gore, and science behind your favorite monsters. Carlyn Beccia. Carolrhoda Books, 2020. 148 p.

Grades: 4 5 6 7 8   **001.944**
1. Monsters 2. Science and paranormal phenomena 3. Explanations, Unusual 4. Imaginary creatures 5. Supernatural 6. Books for reluctant readers
ISBN 9781512449167

LC 2019002795

This fascinating encyclopedia of monsters delves into the history and science behind eight legendary creatures, from Bigfoot and the kraken to zombies and more.

"A fantastically researched, absolutely delectable approach to science education." Booklist.

Includes bibliographical references and index.

Halls, Kelly Milner, 1957-

★ **Tales** of the cryptids: mysterious creatures that may or may not exist. by Kelly Milner Halls, Rick Spears, Roxyanne Young; [illustrated by Rick Spears]. Darby Creek Pub., c2006. 72 p.

Grades: 4 5 6 7   **001.944**
1. Cryptozoology 2. Monsters 3. Mythical creatures 4. Books for reluctant readers
ISBN 1581960492

Cryptozoology is the study of animals that may or may not be real: familiar animals like Bigfoot and the Loch Ness Monster, and those that are less familiar like the Marozi of Kenya, the Orang-pendek of Sumatra and the Thylacine of Tasmania. Meet these and more in this introduction to cryptozoology.

"The conversational text makes for fun reading, and a plethora of pictures . . . will prove enticing." School Library Journal.

Johnson, Hal, 1972-

The **big** book of monsters: the creepiest creatures from classic literature. by Hal Johnson; illustrated by Tim Sievert. Workman Publishing, 2019 170 p.

Grades: 5 6 7 8   **001.944**
1. Monsters 2. Characters and characteristics in literature 3. Imaginary creatures 4. Supernatural 5. Mythical creatures
ISBN 9781523507115

An illustrated compendium of monster profiles from 25 works of classic literature offers playful story summaries, full-color illustrations and literary sidebars for such creatures as Dracula, Cyclops and the Invisible Man.

"Johnson has an eyeball for the details—informative, entertaining, frightfully funny—and humor buoys the work throughout, with tongue-in-cheek sarcasm employed to relay the often-absurd tales." Booklist.

O'Meara, Stephen James, 1956-

Are you afraid yet?: the science behind scary stuff. written by Stephen James O'Meara; illustrated by Jeremy Kaposy. Kids Can Press, 2009. 80 p.

Grades: 5 6 7 8   **001.944**
1. Monsters 2. Science 3. Curiosities and wonders 4. Vampires 5. Mummies 6. Books for reluctant readers
ISBN 9781554532940

LC oc2008111679

"This book cleverly weaves together the supernatural and the scientific in an entertaining read that answers questions about ghosts, UFOs, vampires, werewolves, and how long a decapitated head can remain conscious. Examples depicting such things in classical fiction and popular movies are seamlessly interjected between the factual explanations. Each page is filled with detailed black-and-white illustrations, emphasizing the sometimes-humorous, yet often-macabre descriptions." School Library Journal.

005.1 Software development

Saujani, Reshma

★ **Girls** who code: learn to code and change the world. by Reshma Saujani; illustrations by Andrea Tsurumi. Viking, 2017. 176 p.: Girls who code

Grades: 4 5 6 7 8 9   **005.1**
1. Computer programming 2. Women computer programmers 3. Girls and computers 4. Computer science 5. Illustrated books
ISBN 9780425287538

The founder of the Girls Who Code nonprofit organization presents a graphically illustrated introduction to the relevance of coding that shares down-to-earth explanations about coding principles and real-life stories of women programmers who work at such places as Pixar and NASA.

"An encouraging supplementary resource for young coders." Kirkus.

Whitney, David

Get coding!: learn HTML, CSS & JavaScript & build a website, app & game. written by David Whitney; illustrations by Duncan Beedie. Candlewick Press, 2017, c2016. 208 p.

Grades: 4 5 6 7 8   **005.1**
1. HTML (Document markup language) 2. Cascading style sheets 3. JavaScript (Computer program language) 4. Coding theory 5. Computer programming
ISBN 9780763692766

Learn how to write code and then build your own website, app and game using HTML, CSS and JavaScript in this essential guide to coding for kids. In bite-size chunks learn important real-life coding skills and become a technology star of the future.

"There's been considerable demand for resources on kids and coding, and this new entry deserves center stage." Booklist.

005.1092 Computer software developers

Redding, Anna Crowley

Google it: a history of Google. Anna Crowley Redding. Feiwel and Friends, [2018] 272 p.

Grades: 7 8 9 10 **005.1092**
1. Brin, Sergey, 1973- 2. Page, Larry, 1973- 3. Google (Firm) 4. Computer programmers 5. Internet programming 6. Telecommunications engineers 7. Webmasters 8. Businesspeople
ISBN 9781250148223

LC 2017041741

An Emmy Award-winning investigative reporter chronicles the history of Google, from its origin as a thesis project made out of knock-off LEGOs to becoming one of the world's most influential companies, sharing insights into its innovation and likely next steps.

005.13 Programming languages

McManus, Sean, 1973-
How to code in 10 easy lessons: learn how to design and code your very own computer game. Sean McManus. Walter Foster Jr., 2015. 64 p.: Super skills (Walter Foster)
Grades: 4 5 6 7 8 **005.13**
1. Computer programming 2. Websites -- Design 3. Computer games -- Programming 4. Scratch (Computer program language) 5. HTML (Document markup language)
ISBN 9781633220508

Offers an introduction to computer programming using Scratch software and creating web pages using HTML in ten lessons that each introduce a different coding skill.

"The book is made more accessible with plenty of colorful graphics as visual references, information divided into manageable chunks, and a concluding list of useful web links. Kids will bite at this first taste of coding." Booklist.

005.7 Data in computer systems

Martin, Brett S.
Big data and machine learning. Brett S. Martin. Norwood House Press, 2019 48 p.
Grades: 5 6 7 8 **005.7**
1. Big data 2. Machine learning
ISBN 9781599539386

LC 2018003241

"These books are clearly written and informative, with a glossary and additional resource list appended." Booklist.

006.3 Artificial intelligence and natural computing

Brown, Don, 1949-
Machines that think! Don Brown Amulet Books, 2020 128 p.
Grades: 3 4 5 6 7 **006.3**
1. Computers -- History 2. Technology 3. Artificial intelligence 4. Comics and Graphic novels
ISBN 9781419740985

Machines That Think! explores machines from ancient history to today that perform a multitude of tasks, from making mind-numbing calculations to working on assembly lines. Included are fascinating looks at the world's earliest calculators, the birth of computer programming, and the arrival of smartphones. From the abacus to artificial intelligence, machines through the ages have pushed the boundaries of human capability and creativity.

"Accessible, occasionally funny, and always thoughtful, this speedy but thorough trip through time is a must for budding scientists." School Library Journal

006.7 Multimedia systems

Maxwell, Lucas
Podcasting with youth: a quick guide for librarians and educators. Lucas Maxwell. Libraries Unlimited, 2020. 90 p.
Grades: Professional **006.7**
1. Children's libraries -- Activity programs 2. Podcasting -- Library applications
ISBN 9781440870354

LC 2020003262

Learn how to set up a student-led podcast in your library, involve staff from several subject areas, market effectively, what challenges you are likely to face, and how podcasting will benefit the students and school overall. Provided by publisher.

011.62 Works for young people

Chance, Rosemary
Young adult literature in action: a librarian's guide. Rose Brock. Libraries Unlimited, 2019 xvii, 219 p.
Grades: Professional **011.62**
1. Teenagers -- Books and reading 2. Young adults -- Books and reading 3. Young adult literature 4. Young adult literature, American 5. High school libraries
ISBN 9781440866937

LC 2019018612

Taking a genre approach, this overview of young adult literature shows new librarians and library science students the criteria to use for selecting quality books, including recommended titles.

016 Bibliographies and catalogs of works on specific subjects

McCollough, Carole J
★ The **Coretta** Scott King awards: 50th anniversary. edited by Carole J. McCollough and Adelaide Poniatowski Phelps. ALA Editions, 2019. 214 p.
Grades: Professional **016**
1. Coretta Scott King Award 2. American literature -- African American authors 3. American literature -- African American authors -- Awards 4. Children's literature, American 5. Children's literature, American -- Awards
ISBN 9780838918692

LC 2019010142

Marking the 50th anniversary of the Coretta Scott King (CSK) Book Awards, this invaluable guide celebrates the legacy of these prestigious honors, which have enlarged the prominence of literature for children and youth about the Black experience. Provided by publisher.

016.80883 Bibliographies—Novels

Goldsmith, Annette Y

Reading the world's stories: an annotated bibliography of international youth literature. Annette Y. Goldsmith, Theo Heras, Susan Corapi [compilers]. Rowman & Littlefield, 2016 xiii, 285 p.

Grades: Professional   **016.80883**
   1. Children's stories 2. Children -- Books and reading
   ISBN 9781442270848

                 LC 2016013427

Reading the World's Stories?is an annotated bibliography of high-quality international children's and adolescent literature. Centered around the theme of the importance of stories, the book is a resource for discovering global books that fit many reading tastes and educational needs.

016.8093 Bibliographies—Genre fiction

Fichtelberg, Susan

Encountering enchantment: a guide to speculative fiction for teens. Susan Fichtelberg. Libraries Unlimited, 2015 xix, 392 p.

Grades: Adult Professional   **016.8093**
   1. Fantasy fiction 2. Science fiction 3. Speculative fiction
   ISBN 9781610691130

                 LC 2015015833

The most current and complete guide to a favorite teen genre, this book maps current releases along with perennial favorites, describing and categorizing fantasy, paranormal, and science fiction titles published since 2006. Provided by publisher.

021.2 Relationships with the community

Harrod, Kerol

Library youth outreach: 26 ways to connect with children, young adults and their families. edited by Kerol Harrod and Carol Smallwood; foreword by Leslie S.J. Farmer. McFarland & Company, Inc., Publishers, 2014 viii, 202 p.

Grades: Professional   **021.2**
   1. Library outreach programs 2. Libraries and teenagers 3. Libraries and families 4. Libraries and community 5. Libraries and minorities
   ISBN 9780786473458

                 LC 2013046141

The outreach methods detailed by the authors of this book range from simple actions to detailed processes. Each of the 26 chapters provides helpful information for both those new to library outreach and those with years of experience. Provided by publisher.

025.04 Information storage and retrieval systems

Brown, Christopher C., 1953-

Librarian's guide to online searching: cultivating database skills for research and instruction. Christopher C. Brown and Suzanne S. Bell. Libraries Unlimited, 2018 xxiii, 374 p.

Grades: Professional   **025.04**
   1. Database searching 2. Electronic information resource searching
   ISBN 9781440861567

                 LC 2018011054

This book describes the background of how databases work; how they are constructed and in the case of some databases; how they transitioned from the legacy print world to an online environment; how technologies within databases can interact with other products like bibliography citation services, outbound linking to full text content, and social media mentions; and the methods used by libraries to provide access to licensed content from anywhere in the world. Provided by publisher.

025.1 Administration

Repman, Judi

★ **School** library management. Judi Repman and Gail K. Dickinson, editors. Linworth, 2015 xvii, 335 p.

Grades: Professional   **025.1**
   1. School libraries -- Administration
   ISBN 9781610691406

                 LC 2014037465

This book compiles selected articles from Library Media Connection to help school librarians implement best practices for school library management. Provided by publisher.

Woolls, Blanche

The **school** library manager: surviving and thriving. Blanche Woolls and Sharon Coatney. Libraries Unlimited, 2018 xvi, 269 p.

Grades: Professional   **025.1**
   1. School libraries -- Administration
   ISBN 9781440852565

                 LC 2017024832

This sixth edition of Library Unlimited's classic school library management text describes new approaches to management and addresses the realities that school librarians face in today's quickly evolving information-based world.

025.2 Acquisitions and collection development

Gallaway, Beth, 1975-

Game on!: gaming at the library. Beth Gallaway. Neal-Schuman Publishers, c2009. xiv, 306 p.

Grades: Adult Professional   **025.2**
   1. Libraries -- Special collections -- Electronic games 2. Video games
   ISBN 9781555705954

                 LC 2009014110

"An essential guide for any librarian who plans on embracing the video-game phenomenon, or at the very least, understanding it. . . . [The chapters] are well organized and contain an abundance of practical information. The sections on selection, collection, and circulation of video games include relevant advice on policy, cataloging, marketing, storage, and displays. . . . The annotated list of video games for a core collection is wonderful for selection purposes." School Library Journal.

Includes bibliographical references and index.

Goldsmith, Francisca

The **readers'** advisory guide to graphic novels. Francisca Goldsmith. ALA Editions, an imprint of the American Library Association, 2017. xvi, 215 p.

Grades: Adult Professional   **025.2**

    1. Readers' advisory services 2. Graphic novels

ISBN 9780838915097

               LC 2016042034

"This is a book to spend time with, not flip through, although a strong index and table of contents make it easily consultable for patron interactions as well." Voice of Youth Advocates.

Includes bibliographical references and index.

Hughes-Hassell, Sandra

★ **Collection** management for youth: equity, inclusion, and learning. Sandra Hughes-Hassell. ALA Editions, 2020. 164 p.

Grades: Professional   **025.2**

    1. Constructivism (Education) 2. Educational change 3. Instructional materials centers -- Collection development 4. School librarian participation in curriculum planning 5. School libraries -- Collection development

ISBN 9780838947500

               LC 2020000768

Hughes-Hassell provides models and tools for collection managers that will enable library staff who serve youth to put in place, demonstrate, and create learner-centered collections that are inclusive and provide equitable access to all youth. Provided by publisher.

Kerby, Mona

★ An **introduction** to collection development for school librarians. Mona Kerby. ALA Editions/American Association of School Librarians, 2019. xii, 104 p.

Grades: Professional   **025.2**

    1. School libraries -- Collection development 2. Instructional materials centers -- Collection development

ISBN 9780838918920

               LC 2019019817

This guide introduces school librarians to collection development. It explains tasks to do first; how to prepare orders by knowing standards, learners, and the curriculum and identifying selection criteria; sources for selecting new materials and filling in collection gaps; how to weed and evaluate the collection; and how to deal with complaints.?

Magi, Trina J

★ **Intellectual** freedom manual. Compiled by the Office for Intellectual Freedom of the American Library Association; Trina Magi, Editor; Martin Garnar, Assistant Editor. ALA Editions, an imprint of the American Library Association, 2015. xxii, 273 p.

Grades: Professional   **025.2**

    1. Libraries -- Censorship 2. Intellectual freedom

ISBN 9780838912928

               LC 2014037437

"All libraries should have a copy of this book to use when writing or revising policies; indispensable." Library Journal.

Includes bibliographical references (pages 257-260) and index.

Smith, Karen M., 1975-

Creating a tween collection: a practical guide for librarians. Karen M. Smith. Rowman & Littlefield, 2019 xv, 147 p.

Grades: Professional   **025.2**

    1. Libraries -- Special collections -- Children's literature 2. Preteens -- Books and reading 3. Middle school students -- Books and reading 4. Children's libraries -- Collection development 5. Middle school libraries -- Collection development

ISBN 9781538116937

               LC 2018055639

Creating a Tween Collection shows librarians how to evaluate their current juvenile and teen collections; meet all tween needs for recreation, education, and life skills; and carve out space, market, budget, and justify the need for a tween collection.

025.4 Subject analysis and control

Bristow, Barbara A

Sears list of subject headings. Barbara A. Bristow, editor; Christi Showman Farrar, associate editor. Grey House Publishing, 2014. liii, 946 p.

Grades: Professional   **025.4**

    1. Subject headings

ISBN 9781619251908

               LC oc2014024574

This resource lists subject headings used by small and medium-sized libraries, with patterns, examples, and notes on usage. The subject headings are listed alphabetically and aligned with the Dewey Decimal Classification system and include a list of canceled and replacement headings, as well as a discussion of the theoretical foundations of the list and the general principles of subject cataloging.?

025.5 Services and programs for users

Fitzgerald, Katie, 1982-

Successful summer reading programs for all ages: a practical guide for librarians. Katie Fitzgerald. Rowman & Littlefield, 2018 xvii, 131 p.

Grades: Professional   **025.5**

    1. Libraries -- Activity programs 2. Summer reading programs

ISBN 9781442281677

               LC 2017048326

This book provides the tools necessary to put together successful summer reading programs for each of these different age groups. It also helps librarians to simplify their summer reading programs in order to minimize the amount of preparation they willneed to do each year and to maximize their patrons' enjoyment of the program. Provided by publisher.

026 Specific kinds of institutions

Phoenix, Jack

Maximizing the impact of comics in your library: graphic novels, manga, and more. Jack Phoenix. Libraries Unlimited, 2020 248 p.

Grades: Professional   **026**

    1. Libraries -- Special collections -- Comic books, strips, etc 2. Libraries -- Special collections -- Graphic novels 3. Libraries -- Activity programs

ISBN 9781440868856

               LC 2019056103

This unique guide offers fresh insights on how graphic novels and comics differ from traditional books and require different treatment in the library—from purchasing, shelving, and cataloging to readers' advisory services, programs, and curriculum. Provided by publisher.

"Marrying in-depth knowledge of comics and libraries, Phoenix has produced a practical, user-friendly read that's essential book for school and public librarians." School Library Journal.

Includes bibliographical references and index.

027.8 School libraries

Miller, Shannon (Shannon McClintock)

Leading from the library: help your school community thrive in the digital age. Shannon McClintock Miller and William Bass. International Society for Technology in Education, 2019 xii, 110 p.

Grades: Professional   **027.8**
1. School libraries 2. Libraries and schools 3. School libraries -- Information technology 4. School librarian participation in curriculum planning 5. School librarians -- Effect of technological innovations on
ISBN 9781564847096

     LC 2019000377

Written by a seasoned librarian and an education leader, this book guides librarians in becoming leaders in their school communities, with strategies on developing partnerships, empowering students and more.

"This slim but engaging volume offers a concise discussion of how school librarians and administrators alike can 'advance leadership through library programs.' Miller, a school librarian, and Bass, a district administrator, incorporate two different points of view, as well as tips and strategies to build partnerships and support the school community through the library." School Library Journal

Includes bibliographical references (pages 97-98) and index.

028 Reading and use of other information media

Krashen, Stephen D.

The **power** of reading: insights from the research. Stephen D. Krashen. Libraries Unlimited, 2004. xi, 199 p.

Grades: Professional   **028**
1. Books and reading 2. Literacy
ISBN 9781591581697

     LC 2004044207

Describes trends and research on the topic of reading, covering such topics as reading and cognitive development, libraries, light reading, and the effects of television.

028.1 Reviews

Horning, Kathleen T.

From cover to cover: evaluating and reviewing children's books. Kathleen T. Horning. Collins, c2010. 229 p.

Grades: Professional   **028.1**
1. Book reviewing 2. Children's literature -- History and criticism 3. Children -- Books and reading
ISBN 9780060777579

     LC 2009027564

Describes the field of children's books; suggests the points to consider in judging non-fiction, traditional literature, verse, picture books, and fiction for different ages; and provides tips on writing reviews.

028.5 Reading and use of other information media by young people

Carstensen, Angela

The **readers'** advisory guide to teen literature. Angela Carstensen. ALA Editions, 2018. x, 190 p.

Grades: Professional   **028.5**
1. Readers' advisory services 2. Libraries and teenagers 3. Teenagers -- Books and reading 4. Young adult literature
ISBN 9780838917268

     LC 2018006318

This book combines an introduction to readers' advisory language, vocabulary and techniques with information about what teens like to read and why, followed by an examination of the appeal lurking within each genre. All in service to the goal of using readers' advisory to help teens find the right books at the right time. Provided by publisher.

Harlan, Mary Ann

★ The **girl-positive** library: inspiring confidence, creativity, and curiosity in young women. Mary Ann Harlan. Libraries Unlimited, 2019 viii, 161 p.

Grades: Professional   **028.5**
1. Girls -- Books and reading 2. Teenage girls -- Books and reading 3. Libraries -- Special collections -- Young adult literature 4. Libraries -- Special collections -- Girls 5. Libraries and teenagers
ISBN 9781440860638

     LC 2018037626

Providing a model of critique useful in readers advisory, collection development, and book clubs, this title encourages the inclusion of young adult titles advancing a positive representation of girls in programming and instruction.

"This well-researched, straightforward work offers librarians guidance in reading, critiquing, and recommending YA books that advance positive and accurate representation of girls and young women. Harlan discusses complex issues: character archetypes that define norms of adolescent behavior, bodily autonomy and sex positivity, and the importance of reading YA fiction through a lens of intersectional feminism." School Library Journal

Includes bibliographical references and index.

Khailova, Ladislava N.

The **stories** we share: a guide to PreK-12 books on the experience of immigrant children and teens in the United States. Ladislava N. Khailova. ALA Editions, 2018. x, 235 p.

Grades: Professional   **028.5**
1. Immigrants in literature 2. Children's literature, American 3. Young adult literature, American 4. Immigrants -- Juvenile literature 5. Immigrants
ISBN 9780838916513

     LC 2017052427

Children who are first- and second-generation immigrants can be at risk of experiencing identity crisis, self-depreciation, and low self-esteem due to intergenerational and inter-cultural conflicts. These young readers need books that show them that their experiences are not unique—and these books also carry the important potential of promoting general understanding of and tolerance toward immigrant groups. Provided by publisher.

028.7 Use of books and other information media as sources of information

Dorr, Christina H.

LGBTQAI+ books for children and teens: providing a window for all. Christina Dorr and Liz Deskins; foreword by Jamie Campbell Naidoo. ALA Editions, 2018. xxix, 132 p.

Grades: Professional   **028.7**

1. Children -- Books and reading 2. Children's literature -- Study and teaching 3. Libraries -- Special collections -- Gay men and lesbians 4. Characters and characteristics in children's literature 5. LGBTQIA persons

ISBN 083891649X

LC 2017052430

This resource not only surveys the best in LGBTQAI+ lit but, just as importantly, offers guidance on how to share it in ways that encourage understanding and acceptance among parents, school administrators, and the wider community. Provided by publisher.

"Despite some limitations, this volume does a superb job on many fronts. An essential purchase for public and school libraries, especially given that few other selections on this topic exist." School Library Journal.

Includes bibliographical references and indexes.

031.02 Books of miscellaneous facts

Boyer, Crispin

Why not? Crispin Boyer. National Geographic, 2018 223 p.: National Geographic Kids

Grades: 4 5 6 7   **031.02**

1. Questions and answers 2. Curiosities and wonders

ISBN 9781426331916

LC 2018288866

Shares the answers to over one thousand questions on such topics as animals, natural resources, technology, and history.

Farndon, John

Do not open: an encyclopedia of the world's best kept secrets. John Farndon. DK Publishing, 2007. 192 p.

Grades: 4 5 6 7   **031.02**

1. Curiosities and wonders 2. Trivia and miscellaneous facts 3. Books for reluctant readers

ISBN 9780756632052

"This encyclopedic tome catalogues the mysterious and unusual. . . . Flaps, foldout pages and varied styles of illustration—from photomontage to digital cartoons and more conventional line art—keep the book visually fresh and ably complement the subject matter. . . . Taking in everything from weird weather like St. Elmo's fire and raining frogs to possible locations of Atlantis, the book incites curiosity—and expansively rewards it." Publishers Weekly.

National Geographic Kids Almanac 2022

National Geographic Kids Almanac 2022. National Geographic, 2021 352 p.: National Geographic Kids Almanac

Grades: 4 5 6 7 8   **031.02**

1. Almanacs 2. Curiosities and wonders

ISBN 9781426372032

Provides the latest information on a wide range of topics, including animals, culture, geography, the environment, history, and science.

"This gathering of upbeat, vividly illustrated, browser-friendly dips into topics ranging from black holes to blue-footed boobies to Bolivian street food is hard to put down, and the pop quizzes and research guides at each chapter's end will give studious sorts a leg up, too." Kirkus

Reynolds, Toby

Wonders of the world. Toby Reynolds and Paul Calver. Barron's Educational Series, 2016. 32 p.: Visual explorers

Grades: 4 5 6 7   **031.02**

1. Civilization, Ancient 2. Curiosities and wonders 3. Seven Wonders of the World 4. Historic sites 5. Historic buildings

ISBN 9781438008301

"Inexpensive and relatively sturdy, these large-format paperbacks make for a visually enticing series." Booklist.

Winterbottom, Julie

Frightlopedia: an encyclopedia of everything scary, creepy, and spine-chilling, from arachnids to zombies. Julie Winterbottom, illustrated by Stefano Tambellini Workman Publishing, 2016 ix, 213 p.

Grades: 4 5 6   **031.02**

1. Monsters 2. Paranormal phenomena 3. Curiosities and wonders 4. Dangerous animals 5. Ghosts

ISBN 9780761183792

Combining fact, fiction and hands-on activities, this illustrated A-Z collection of some of the world's most frightening places, scariest stories and most gruesome creatures—both real and imagined—is perfect for kids who love scary stuff—whether it's telling ghost stories around a campfire; discovering the origins of various vampires, monsters and witches; or reading creepy tales under the covers with a flashlight.

"A prime source of thrills and chills, equally suitable for casual browsing or quick reference." Booklist.

070.4 Journalism

Bausum, Ann

Muckrakers: how Ida Tarbell, Upton Sinclair, and Lincoln Steffens helped expose scandal, inspire reform, and invent investigative journalism. by Ann Bausum. National Geographic, c2007. 111 p.

Grades: 6 7 8 9   **070.4**

1. Tarbell, Ida M. (Ida Minerva), 1857-1944 2. Sinclair, Upton, 1878-1968 3. Steffens, Lincoln, 1866-1936 4. Investigative journalism -- History 5. Journalists 20th century

ISBN 1426301383

LC 2007011391

Golden Kite Award for Nonfiction, 2007.

Examines the birth of investigative journalism in America at the turn of the 20th century, discussing the work of the dedicated journalists who, through their exposés, forced responsible changes in the industrial practices and politics of that period.

"This describes muckrakers, 20th-century journalists who investigated corruption and called for reform. . . . The well-captioned, black-and-white illustrations, mainly photos, are sometimes reproduced with a sepia tone. . . . Clearly written, this offers a very readable and informative introduction to American muckrakers." Booklist.

Includes bibliographical references (p. 104-105) and index.

Miller, Michael, 1958-

Fake news: separating truth from fiction. Michael Miller. Twenty-First Century Books, 2019. 80 p.

Grades: 8 9 10 11 12 **070.4**
  1. Fake news 2. Misinformation 3. News media 4. Mass media
  5. Journalistic ethics
  ISBN 9781541528147

This title explores journalistic and fact-checking standards, Constitutional protections, and real-world case studies, helping readers identify the mechanics, perpetrators, motives, and psychology of fake news. A final chapter explores methods for assessing and avoiding the spread of fake news.

Otis, Cindy L.
  True or false: a CIA analyst's guide to spotting fake news. Cindy L. Otis. Feiwel & Friends 2020 336 p.
Grades: 5 6 7 8 9 **070.4**
  1. Fake news 2. Misinformation 3. News media 4. Mass media
  5. Journalistic ethics
  ISBN 9781250239495

LC 2019036127

A YA Nonfiction book about the history of Fake News and tips for how to spot it. Provided by publisher.

"Most of the mini lessons herein gain their impact from Otis' engaging storytelling, with historical episodes illustrating the various ways truth has been altered for public consumption followed by observations on how technological innovations steadily speed up the dissemination of fake news, and once discussion arrives at the Internet Age, tips and checklists and self quizzes that encourage readers to hone their own skills at unmasking humbugs." Bulletin of the Center for Children's Books

Includes bibliographical references.

070.9 History and biography of journalism and newspapers

Brown, Robin Terry
  Breaking the news: what's real, what's not, and why the difference matters. Robin Terry. National Geographic Kids, 2020. 160 p.
Grades: 5 6 7 8 9 **070.9**
  1. Journalism 2. Fake news 3. Misinformation 4. Propaganda 5. Mass media bias
  ISBN 9781426338885

In this timely and relevant title, National Geographic Kids shines a light on the history of news to reveal where we started, how far we've come, and the serious impact that misinterpretation and misinformation can have on the world.

"With color-coded info boxes and brightly colored pages, Terry-Brown provides a sharp-looking survey that examines the history of news—how it began, how it evolved, and what consumers of all ages must consider before accepting a truth as the truth." Kirkus

Includes bibliographical references and index.

100 PHILOSOPHY

109 History and collected biography

Blackburn, Simon
  Philosophers: their lives and works.. Dorling Kindersley Publishing, Incorporated, 2019. 360 p.

Grades: 9 10 11 12 **109**
  1. Philosophy 2. Philosophers 3. Illustrated books
  ISBN 9781465482037

From Confucius and Plato to Karl Marx and Noam Chomsky, this book brings together more than 100 illustrated biographies of the world's great philosophers. Introduced with a stunning portrait of each featured philosopher, the biographies trace the ideas, friendships, loves, and rivalries that inspired the great thinkers and influenced their work, providing revealing insights into what drove them to question the meaning of life, and come up with new ways of understanding the world and the history of ideas.

"As an introductory work, Philosophers stands out, making it an excellent choice for middle- and high-school students, general readers, and even those looking for a thoughtful coffee-table book." Booklist

133.4 Demonology and witchcraft

Schanzer, Rosalyn
  Witches!: the absolutely true tale of disaster in Salem. Roaslyn Schanzer. National Geographic, c2011. 144 p.
Grades: 6 7 8 9 **133.4**
  1. 17th century 2. Witchcraft -- History 3. Puritans -- History 4. Trials (Witchcraft) 5. Salem, Massachusetts -- History
  ISBN 9781426308697

LC 2011012989

"With text that flows like a dramatic novel, Schanzer brings readers into the famous Salem trials, asking them to ponder the motivations of the accusers and the tribulations of the accused. Black-and-white ink prints and red accents are wonderfully evocative and set an appropriately horrific tone." School Library Journal.

Includes bibliographical references (p. 138-141) and index.

150 Psychology

Weeks, Marcus
  Heads up psychology. written by Marcus Weeks; consultant, Dr. John Mildinhall. DK Publishing, 2014. 160 p.
Grades: 7 8 9 10 **150**
  1. Psychology 2. Human behavior
  ISBN 9781465419934

LC bl2014012182

An introduction to psychology surveys the ideas of over sixty famous psychologists, discussing topics ranging from psychoanalysis and intelligence to groundbreaking experiments and mental disorders.

"By interspersing explanations of topics and research studies with biographies of great thinkers, psychological pioneers, and researchers, Weeks helps readers connect fields of psychological study with names they may have heard or read. In true DK fashion, format, graphics, text boxes, pixelated portraits of scientists, bubbles, and balloons all contribute to making this a busy but appealing companion for high-school psychology textbooks." Booklist.

152.1 Sensory perception

Jackson, Donna M., 1959-
  Phenomena: secrets of the senses. by Donna M. Jackson. Little, Brown and Co., 2008. 174 p.
Grades: 6 7 8 9 **152.1**
  1. Senses and sensation 2. Science and paranormal phenomena 3.

Extrasensory perception 4. Intuition 5. Coincidence
ISBN 9780316166492

LC 2008031215

Learn how to interpret your senses and explore the ways that technology is changing the way we experience the world.

"Students with an interest in the weird and unusual will find this book fascinating. It begins with an introduction to human senses and continues with chapters devoted to phenomena such as the sixth sense, synethesia, and intuition. One of the most interesting sections discusses animals that use their senses in unusual ways. . . . The black-and-white illustrations and photographs are plentiful enough to make the text accessible to reluctant readers. Accurate, entertaining nonfiction." School Library Journal.

Includes bibliographical references and index.

152.14 Visual perception

Wick, Walter

★ **Walter** Wick's optical tricks, Anniversary ed.. by Walter Wick Scholastic, 2008. 43 p.

Grades: 4 5 6 7   **152.14**
1. Optical illusions 2. Visual perception 3. Photography 4. Picture puzzles
ISBN 9780439855204

"The author has produced a stunning picture book of optical illusions. With crystal-clear photographs, he creates a series of scenes that fool the eye and the brain." Booklist. [review of 1998 ed.]

152.4 Emotions

Chopra, Mallika

Just feel: how to be stronger, happier, healther, and more. Mallika Chopra; illustrated by Brenna Vaughan; afterword by Deepak Chopra. RP Kids, 2019. xiii, 113 p.

Grades: 5 6 7 8   **152.4**
1. Emotions in children 2. Emotions 3. Mind and body 4. Self-actualization (Psychology) in children
ISBN 9780762494743

LC bl2019029868

The daughter of Deepak Chopra and author of Just Breathe presents a fully illustrated guide to empowerment that counsels middle grade students on how to harness their inner strengths and emotional awareness to promote independence and problem-solving.

"With such a wealth of material from which to pick and choose, this resource stands out in offering something for everybody." Kirkus.

Includes bibliographical references (page 112).

153.6 Communication

Jackson, Donna M., 1959-

★ **Every** body's talking: what we say without words. by Donna M. Jackson, with Carol Kinsey Gorman, PhD. Twenty-First Century Books, 2014 64 p.

Grades: 5 6 7 8 9   **153.6**
1. Body language 2. Nonverbal communication 3. Interpersonal communication 4. Interpersonal relations
ISBN 9781467708586

LC 2013019674

"Nonverbal clues including stance, facial expression, posture, eye contact, and others add meaning to our words, or sometimes contradict them. Using second-person narration to engage readers, suggestions for interpreting body language is followed by a chapter explaining how cultural differences affect interpretations. A final chapter encourages readers to practice physical positions to increase confidence. Plentiful full-color pictures illustrate concepts." Horn Book.

Includes bibliographical references and index.

155.2 Individual psychology

Kay, Katty

The **confidence** code for girls: taking risks, messing up, & becoming your amazingly imperfect, totally powerful self. Katty Kay & Claire Shipman with JillEllyn Riley; illustrated by Nan Lawson. Harper, an imprint of HarperCollinsPublishers, 2018. 320 p.

Grades: 4 5 6 7 8   **155.2**
1. Self-confidence in girls 2. Self-esteem in girls 3. Self-help psychology 4. Self-fulfillment 5. Self-acceptance
ISBN 9780062796981

Offers inspiration and practical advice to encourage girls to take risks, have big adventures, and challenge themselves in ways they never imagined.

"There's a lack of books on this subject for tweens and young teens, so this, with its endnotes and helpful resource list, invaluably fills the gap." Booklist

Includes bibliographical references.

155.3 Sex psychology; psychology of people by gender or sex, by sexual orientation

Wambach, Abby, 1980-

Wolfpack: how young people will find their voice, unite their pack, and change the world. Abby Wambach. Roaring Brook, 2020. 112 p.

Grades: 5 6 7 8 9   **155.3**
1. Leadership 2. Success (Concept) 3. Attitude (Psychology) 4. Courage in girls 5. Leadership in girls
ISBN 9781250766861

Updated with stories that trace the Olympic gold medalist's journey from youth soccer to the Hall of Fame, an adaptation of the best-selling Wolfpack inspires readers to harness their inner strength, forge their own path and band together with teammates to make the world a better place.

"In this young readers' edition, the two-time Olympic gold medalist and FIFA World Cup champion delivers eight guiding principles for leading, working through life, and changing the world. . . . Wambach makes each point salient and accessible through short, personal stories of strife and success." Booklist

155.4 Psychology of specific ages

Cain, Susan

Quiet power: the secret strengths of introverts. Susan Cain with Gregory Mone and Erica Moroz. Dial Books for Young Readers, 2016. 288 p.

Grades: 6 7 8 9   **155.4**
1. Interpersonal relations 2. Introversion 3. Self-acceptance in

teenagers 4. Self-acceptance in children 5. Introverts
ISBN 9780399186721

Illuminates the strengths and struggles of being an introverted child or teen, sharing the stories of real-life kids who have met the challenges and made their mark in quiet ways.

"Many will find value in this title that emphasizes that being an introvert is not a blemish on one's personality but a benefit. An excellent addition." School Library Journal.

Lewis, Carrie

All about anxiety. written by Carrie Lewis; illustrated by Sophia Touliatou. Augsburg Fortress Pub 2020 88 p.

Grades: 4 5 6 7   **155.4**
1. Anxiety in children 2. Stress in children 3. Coping in children
4. Worry in children 5. Emotions in children
ISBN 9781506463209

LC 2019042628

Anxiety. It's an emotion that rears its head almost every day, from the normal worries and concerns that most of us experience, to outright fear when something scary happens, to the anxiety disorders that many kids live with daily. But what causes anxiety? And what can we do about it?

Telgemeier, Raina

★ **Guts**. Raina Telgemeier; with color by Braden Lamb. Graphix, 2019. 224 p.

Grades: 3 4 5 6 7   **155.4**
1. Telgemeier, Raina 2. Stress in children 3. Fourth grade girls
4. Anxiety in children 5. Child psychotherapy 6. Children -- Physiology 7. Autobiographical comics 8. Comics and Graphic novels
ISBN 9780545852500

LC 2018050676

Developing a chronic upset stomach that she initially dismisses as a bug, young Raina discovers that her symptoms are related to her anxieties about school, food and changing friendships, in a story based on the Eisner Award-winning author's childhood.

"After a particularly bad bout of the flu in fourth grade, Raina keeps having stomach aches and intense feelings about food and germs. The thought of being near a sick person sends her into a panic, and conflicts among her friends at school and embarrassment about bodily functions in general certainly don't help matters. In this third graphic memoir, Telgemeier describes her childhood anxiety in an approachable, nonjudgmental way and emphasizes how useful talk therapy can be." Booklist.

155.5 Psychology of young people twelve to twenty

Andrus, Aubre

Project you: more than 50 ways to calm down, de-stress, and feel great. by Aubre Andrus, with Karen Bluth, Ph.D. Switch Press, a Capstone imprint, [2017] 160 p.

Grades: 8 9 10 11 12   **155.5**
1. Stress management for teenagers 2. Stress in teenagers 3. Health 4. Stress management 5. Exercise
ISBN 9781630790912

LC 2017003996

Written with insights from a mindfulness educator, a guide to navigating stress and living a life of healthy balance counsels middle-grade readers on such techniques as making protein smoothies for busy mornings, writing in a journal, practicing yoga, scheduling priorities and developing a sleep-supporting nighttime routine.

"The authors have designed a self-help book for students interested in ways to combat the everyday stresses of school, family, and friends." School Library Journal.

Bluth, Karen

The **self-compassionate** teen: mindfulness & compassion skills to conquer your critical inner voice. Karen Bluth, PhD. Instant Help Books, 2020 xiv, 165 p.: Instant help solutions

Grades: 7 8 9 10 11 12   **155.5**
1. Self-esteem in teenagers 2. Self-acceptance 3. Compassion 4. Mindfulness (Psychology) 5. Self-esteem
ISBN 9781684035274

LC 2020015695

Teens can be extremely self-critical, and are often nicer to others than they are to themselves. In The Self-Compassionate Teen, psychologist Karen Bluth offers powerful, everyday self-compassion and mindfulness tools to help teen readers overcome self-judgment, stop comparing themselves to others, and cultivate the courage to be themselves. Provided by publisher.

"The author both criticizes how social media can add to teen anxiety as well as offers up ways to harness the power of social media for self-kindness practice, offering a balanced approach. Importantly, the author is explicitly reassuring toward and supportive of LGBTQ+ youth." Kirkus

Includes bibliographical references.

De la Bedoyere, Camilla

Balancing work and play. Camilla de la Bedoyere. Amicus, 2011. 46 p. : Healthy lifestyles

Grades: 7 8 9 10 11 12   **155.5**
1. Stress 2. Stress management 3. Stress management for teenagers 4. Stress in teenagers
ISBN 9781607530831

LC 2009047569

Discusses the importance of and gives tips for managing stress in your teenage years to achieve a balance between studies, jobs, family and friends, hobbies, and other leisure activities.. Provided by publisher.

"This book is well-written and satisfyingly informative. . . . [The] magazine-like format includes numerous sidebars, color photos, and charts." School Library Journal.

Harris, Ashley Rae

Cliques, crushes & true friends: developing healthy relationships. by Ashley Rae Harris. ABDO Pub. Co., 2008. 112 p. : Essential health: strong beautiful girls

Grades: 6 7 8 9   **155.5**
1. Cliques 2. Interpersonal relations 3. Peer pressure 4. Friendship 5. Crushes (Interpersonal relations)
ISBN 9781604530995

LC 2008012103

Brings widespread issues to life through character narratives and discussion questions to help readers develop positive ways to deal with common scenarios while also building self-esteem.

"Each chapter tells a personal narrative, with a consulting doctor giving insight and making suggestions. The topics are well selected, the design is attractive, and the stories feature girls from a variety of cultures." Booklist.

Ottaviano, Patricia

Girl world: how to ditch the drama and find your inner amazing! Patricia Ottaviano. Sourcebooks Fire, 2015. 160 p.

Grades: 6 7 8 9 **155.5**
   1. Self-esteem in teenage girls 2. Self-acceptance in teenage girls
3. Self-perception in teenage girls 4. Self-esteem in teenagers 5.
Self-acceptance in teenagers
ISBN 9781492609636

                                            LC 2015012961

Counsels teen girls on how to navigate issues ranging from friendship and drama to self-confidence and negative social media messages.

Owens, L. L.

Frenemies: dealing with friend drama. by Lisa L. Owens; content consultant, Robyn J.A. Silverman. ABDO Pub., c2010. 112 p.: Essential health: strong, beautiful girls

Grades: 6 7 8 9 **155.5**
   1. Interpersonal conflict 2. Interpersonal relations 3. Friendship 4.
Teenage girls -- Psychology 5. Frenemies
ISBN 9781604537505

                                            LC 2009002132

Offers advice on how to cope with friendship problems including moving, different backgrounds, rumors, boyfriend stealing, suspected abuse, and the end of a friendship.

"In this book about friendships each chapter tells a personal narrative, with a consulting doctor giving insight and making suggestions. The topics are well selected, the design is attractive, and the stories feature girls from a variety of cultures." Booklist.

Includes bibliographical references (p. 106-107) and index.

Wagenen, Maya van

Popular: a memoir: vintage wisdom for a modern geek. Maya Van Wagenen. Dutton, an imprint of Penguin Group (USA), LLC, [2014] 259 p.

Grades: 7 8 9 10 **155.5**
   1. Wagenen, Maya van. 2. Teenage girl misfits 3. Etiquette 4.
Social status 5. Self-confidence 6. Life skills
ISBN 9780525426813

                                            LC 2014000236

Documents a high school student's year-long attempt to change her social status from that of a misfit to a member of the "in" crowd by following advice in a 1950s popularity guide, an experiment that triggered embarrassment, humor and unexpected surprises.

"The clash of eras and cultures is funny: the author wears a girdle, hat, and pearls to class; learns how to apply makeup; improves her posture and poise; and tries a diet. But the best lessons she learns . . . are about how to talk to and understand the people around her." School Library Journal.

155.9 Environmental psychology

Gootman, Marilyn E.

When a friend dies: a book for teens about grieving & healing. Marilyn E. Gootman; edited by Pamela Espeland. Free Spirit Pub., c2005. vii, 118 p.

Grades: 7 8 9 10 **155.9**
   1. Grief in teenagers 2. Coping in teenagers 3. Teenagers and death
4. Bereavement in teenagers 5. Death -- Psychological aspects
ISBN 1575421704

                                            LC 2005000447

"This offers information on subjects including: How can I stand the pain? How should I be acting? What is normal? What if I can't handle my grief on my own? and How can I find a counselor or a therapist? Interspersed throughout the book . . . are quotes by teenagers who

have experienced grief. . . . Quotes from well-known writers and philosophers give insight into the grieving process and healing." School Library Journal.

Includes bibliographical references (p. 112-113) and index.

158.1 Personal improvement and analysis

Chopra, Mallika

Just breathe: meditation, mindfulness, movement, and more. Mallika Chopra; foreword by Deepak Chopra, MD; illustrated by Brenna Vaughan. RP Kids, 2018. 128 p.

Grades: 4 5 6 7 8 **158.1**
   1. Stress management for children 2. Meditation for children 3.
Mindfulness (Psychology) 4. Emotions in children 5. Awareness
ISBN 9780762491582

A fully illustrated go-to meditation guide, written by Deepak Chopra's wellness-expert daughter, counsels children ages 8-12 on how to use breathing techniques and guided meditations for stress management, better sleep, self-confidence and improved focus.

"Adults sharing mindfulness with children and preteens will find a treasure trove of scripts for guided practice. Young people of various skin tones, genders, and religious expressions are included in the illustrations." Kirkus

158.2 Interpersonal relations

Amblard, Odile

Friends forever?: why your friendships are so important. by Odile Amblard; illustrated by Andree Prigent; edited by Andrea Bussell. Amulet Books, c2008. 95 p.: Sunscreen

Grades: 5 6 7 8 **158.2**
   1. Friendship 2. Interpersonal relations 3. Teenagers -- Friendship
4. Making friends 5. Teenagers -- Interpersonal relations
ISBN 9780810994805

                                            LC 2007043138

"The importance of friendship is stressed in the opening of Friends Forever?, followed by brief discussions on the types of friendships and how they are formed and maintained. . . . The tone of the [book] is breezy and light without being flippant. The [author] never [talks] down to the teen reader." Voice of Youth Advocates.

170 Ethics (Moral philosophy)

Abell, Tracy

Artificial intelligence ethics and debates. Tracy Abell. Focus Readers, 2020. 48 p.

Grades: 5 6 7 8 9 **170**
   1. Artificial intelligence -- Moral and ethical aspects
ISBN 9781644930731

                                            LC 2019027291

Describes possible ethical concerns of Artificial Intelligence, including applications in medical fields, the military, criminal justice systems, or in hiring practices. Includes fun facts and 'Leading the Way' special features. Provided by publisher.

"Compelling, very readable, and ideal for research about human/AI interaction. Highly recommended." School Library Journal

Includes bibliographical references (page 48) and index.

Latham, Irene

Dictionary for a better world: poems, quotes, and anecdotes from A to Z. Irene Latham & Charles Waters; illustrated by Mehrdokht Amini. Carolrhoda Books, 2020 119 p.

Grades: 4 5 6 7 8 9 10 11 12   **170**

    1. Personal conduct 2. Multiculturalism 3. Words 4. Social justice

    ISBN 9781541557758

                        LC 2019000739

Organized as a dictionary, entries in this book for middle-grade readers present words related to creating a better, more inclusive world. Each word is explored via a poem, a quote from an inspiring person, and a short personal anecdote from one of the co-authors, a prompt for how to translate the word into action, and an illustration. Provided by publisher.

Nevertheless, we persisted:

Nevertheless, we persisted: 48 voices of defiance, strength, and courage. foreword by Senator Amy Klobuchar. Alfred A. Knopf, 2018. 320 p.

Grades: 8 9 10 11 12   **170**

    1. Personal conduct 2. Persistence 3. Courage 4. Discrimination 5. Essays

    ISBN 9781524771973

A powerful collection of essays from actors, activists, athletes, politicians, musicians, writers, and teens, each writing about a time in their youth when they were held back because of their race, gender, or sexual identity— but persisted. Among others: actress Alia Shawkat was told she was too "ethnic" for parts. Former NFL player Wade Davis bullied other gay classmates in an attempt to hide his own sexuality. Holocaust survivor Fanny Starr tells of her harrowing time in Auschwitz, where she watched her family disappear, one by one. They tell how they rose through the hate, overcoming the obstacles of their childhood to the hard-won lives they live today.

170.84 Ethics — Young Adults

Weinstein, Bruce D.

Is it still cheating if I don't get caught?: straight answers to life's sticky questions from the Ethics Guy. Bruce Weinstein; illustrated by Harriet Russell. Roaring Brook Press, 2009. 144 p.

Grades: 8 9 10 11 12   **170.84**

    1. Ethics 2. Teenagers -- Personal conduct 3. Advice 4. Options, alternatives, choices 5. Personal conduct

    ISBN 9781596433069

Whether it is about the use of the Internet, sports, family, school, or affairs of the heart, five simple and clear ethical principles provide the basis for answers to tough choices teens face every day.

"This appealing guide speaks to the ethical dilemmas that all young people experience in their daily lives, and it should prompt considerable conversation and reflection." Kirkus.

174.2 Medical and health professions

Uschan, Michael V., 1948-

The **Tuskegee** experiments: forty years of medical racism. Michael V. Uschan. Lucent Books, c2006. 112 p.: Lucent library of Black history

Grades: 8 9 10 11 12   **174.2**

    1. Tuskegee Syphilis Study 2. Human experimentation in medicine

-- History 3. Syphilis -- Research -- History 4. Syphilis -- History 5. African American men -- Diseases -- History

    ISBN 1590184866

                        LC 2004010678

Describes the history behind the "Tuskegee Study of Untreated Syphilis in the Negro Male," the study itself, and the uproar it created when the ethics behind the study were challenged.

"This is an account of the Tuskegee Study of Untreated Syphilis in the Negro Male. . . . Halftone photographs of participants and of the persons who designed, conducted, or criticized the project supplement the text. Informational sidebars provide additional descriptions and photographs of some of the damage done by untreated syphilis." School Library Journal.

Includes bibliographical references and index.

Wittenstein, Vicki O., 1954-

For the good of mankind?: the shameful history of human medical experimentation. Vicki Oransky Wittenstein. Twenty-First Century Books, [2014] 96 p.

Grades: 7 8 9 10 11 12   **174.2**

    1. Human experimentation in medicine -- History 2. Medical research -- History 3. Experimental medicine -- History 4. Medicine -- History

    ISBN 9781467706599

                        LC 2012043413

Discusses the several medical advances that were achieved through unethical medical experimentation on humans.

176 Ethics of sex and reproduction

Evans, Keisha

Consent: deal with it. Keisha Evans, illustrations by Jenny Chan. Lorimer Children and Teens, 2020 32 p.

Grades: 5 6 7 8 9   **176**

    1. Human body 2. Sexual consent 3. Autonomy 4. Personal space 5. Personal conduct

    ISBN 9781459415065

"A mixed delivery engages readers with illustrations, comics, quizzes, Q&As, and lists of do's and don'ts. This ensures the book never feels dense; it has both good pacing and opportunities to pause and contemplate the information being shared. . . . Empowering and useful." Kirkus.

Freitas, Donna

The **big** questions book of sex and consent. Donna Freitas. Levine Querido, 2020. 320 p.

Grades: 7 8 9 10 11 12   **176**

    1. Sex education for teenagers 2. Sexuality 3. Sexual ethics 4. Sexual consent 5. Body image

    ISBN 9781646140183

What this book is NOT: The fear-based How-To on sex and consent, oversimplified and focused on technicalities, that represents so much of our sexual education today. What this book IS: A journey into the Big Questions that will turn you into a thinking person about sex and consent, with the ability to wrestle towards the answers that work for YOU and continue to wrestle towards them for the rest of your life. What is the meaning and purpose of sex? How does it intersect with who I am? Why are people so afraid of it? What does a healthy and joyful approach to sex look like for me? Why is consent so much more than a yes or no question? Who this book is FOR: Everybody!! No matter your sexuality, gender, religion, or race. What could be more essential?

"This is a well-considered, authoritative, and exhaustive look at a very complex subject, and it will be of interest to teens, parents, teachers, counselors, and anyone grappling with what constitutes consent." Booklist.

177 Ethics of social relations

Fox, Annie, 1950-
Real friends vs. the other kind. Annie Fox. Free Spirit Pub., c2009. 90 p.
Grades: 5 6 7 8   **177**
    1. Friendship in children 2. Interpersonal relations in children 3. Middle school students -- Psychology
    ISBN 9781575423197
         LC 2008031368
Along with graphic-novel-style illustrations, a title filled with quizzes, quotes from real kids, and further resources offers insider information on making friends, resolving disputes, and dealing with other common middle school concerns, such as gossip, exclusion, and cyberbullying. Original.

"Jack, Abby, Mateo, Jen, Chris, and Michelle are the middle school students of various ethnicities who take readers through this slim, interactive guide. Chapters cover such topics as friendship dilemmas, so-called friends, when friendships aren't working, crushes, and making new friends. Each chapter opens with a scene played out by the students in cartoon panels. Next, bits of text, along with a multitude of side boxes, address the topic at hand. . . . Lists of questions are offered, along with the answers. There's a lot packed into this colorful title that falls somewhere between self-help and peer advice." School Library Journal.

Lady Gaga
Channel kindness: stories of kindness and community. Born This Way Foundation Reporters with Lady Gaga. Feiwel and Friends, 2020. 304 p.
Grades: 7 8 9 10 11 12   **177**
    1. Kindness 2. Community activism 3. Compassion 4. Personal conduct 5. Helpfulness 6. Anthologies 7. Essays
    ISBN 9781250245588
The global superstar and her mother collect stories from their Channel Kindness nonprofit to celebrate the quiet influence of kindness in today's world and the examples of young people whose acts of bravery and resilience demonstrate the universal power of caring for others.

"Each piece is truly inspiring, whether because of the identified need (climate change awareness, suicide prevention, grief mitigation, menstrual acceptance), the innovator (high school and college students, friends, neighbors, siblings, roommates), or the ability to recreate these initiatives in other communities." Booklist
Includes bibliographic references.

Vermond, Kira
Half-truths and brazen lies: an honest look at lying. Kira Vermond; illustrated by Clayton Hanmer. OwlKids Books, 2016. 48 p.
Grades: 5 6 7 8   **177**
    1. Truthfulness and falsehood 2. Honesty 3. Personal conduct
    ISBN 9781771471466
Offers historical anecdotes, scientific studies, and sociocultural analyses to help reveal the complex world of lying.

"Rich with evidence, explanation, and food for thought, this well-documented approach to an issue not often covered in-depth for this age group will be enjoyed for curiosity's sake as well as a resource for study." Booklist.

179.7 Respect and disrespect for human life

Tate, Nikki, 1962-
Choosing to live, choosing to die: the complexities of assisted dying. Nikki Tate; illustrations by Belle Wuthrich. Orca Book Pub., 2019. 276 p.
Grades: 7 8 9 10 11 12   **179.7**
    1. Right to die 2. Euthanasia 3. Assisted suicide 4. Medical ethics 5. Physician-assisted suicide 6. Illustrated books
    ISBN 9781459818897
Examines the complex issue of medical assistance in dying from multiple perspectives, including the author's own story.

"Focusing primarily on the Western world, despite noting in passing that Japan has the world's largest right-to-die group, this is a frank, dispassionate, and accessible guide that respects the ability of teen readers to understand the nuances surrounding a complex topic. A thought-provoking, easy-to-understand resource." Kirkus.
Includes bibliographical references and index.

181 Eastern philosophy

Whitfield, Susan
Philosophy and writing. Susan Whitfield. Sharpe Focus, 2009. 80 p.
Grades: 7 8 9 10   **181**
    1. China -- Civilization -- 221 B.C.E.-960 C.E. 2. China -- Civilization -- To 221 B.C.E.
    ISBN 9780765681683
         LC 2008031167
Looks at the philosophy of ancient China, showing how this knowledge has been passed down over the years through writing.

"Whitfield covers religion and philosophy [of ancient China] and how they have been passed down using various precursors to books and printing. . . . [This is illustrated with] fine and frequent color photographs and reproductions. Readers will be rewarded . . . with clear, accessible writing, peppered liberally with entertaining stories from history." School Library Journal.
Includes bibliographical references and index.

200 RELIGION

Bowker, John Westerdale
World religions: the great faiths explored and explained. John Bowker. DK Pub., c2006. 216 p.
Grades: 8 9 10 11 12 Adult   **200**
    1. Religions 2. Religion -- Handbooks, manuals, etc
    ISBN 9780756617721
A comprehensive overview of the beliefs and practices of a variety of different world religions draws on religious artifacts, explanations of sacred texts, paintings, architecture, and other teachings to provide explanations of Christianity, Judaism, Islam, Hinduism, Buddhism, Jainism, Sikhism, and other faiths.

"This book is a bold attempt to meld religious information with expressive art and to use the art as a tool for pedagogy. . . . World Religions has generous discussions of the ancient Egyptian, Greek, Roman, Norse, and Celtic religions, topics not even included in the Oxford

Dictionary. . . . Ultimately, World Religions is the more commendable publication, though both books are recommended for most libraries." Library Journal.

Breuilly, Elizabeth

Religions of the world: the illustrated guide to origins, beliefs, traditions & festivals. Elizabeth Breuilly, Joanne O'Brien, Martin Palmer. Facts On File, c2005. 160 p.

Grades: 7 8 9 10   **200**
    1. Religions
    ISBN 9780816062584

                 LC 2005051101

A guide to modern-day religions explores the beliefs, traditions, festivals, and practices of major faiths and covers the main branches and divisions of each religion, all accompanied by photographs and illustrations.

"This is a valuable resource, covering the beliefs and practices of 10 major religions and lavishly illustrated with color photos, maps, diagrams, and charts." School Library Journal.

Includes bibliographical references and index.

What do you believe?

What do you believe? DK Pub., 2011. 96 p.

Grades: 4 5 6 7   **200**
    1. Religions 2. Religion 3. Faith 4. Philosophy 5. Christianity
    ISBN 9780756672287

"This extensive guidebook covers the beliefs and history of the world's major religions. Focusing in particular on Buddhism, Christianity, Hinduism, Islam, Judaism, and Sikhism, the book also explores atheism and agnosticism, indigenous belief systems, East Asian religions, philosophy, and morality. . . . The graphically bold format—which mixes photographs, cartoons, and sidebars—will keep kids' attention, whether they are seeking truth, knowledge, or more to ponder." Publishers Weekly.

200.9 Religion—History, geographic treatment, biography

Mooney, Carla, 1970-

Comparative religion: investigate the world through religious tradition. Carla Mooney; illustrated by Lena Chandhok. Nomad Press, [2015] vii, 120 p.: Inquire and investigate

Grades: 5 6 7 8   **200.9**
    1. Religions 2. Christianity 3. Judaism 4. Islam 5. Hinduism
    ISBN 9781619303010

                LC bl2015041375

Compares and contrasts the cultural, spiritual, and geographical underpinnings of Christianity, Judaism, Islam, Hinduism, and Buddhism, encouraging a deeper understanding of the world's religions.

"By examining complex beliefs and doctrine in an accessible and reader-friendly format, Mooney effectively teases out the commonalities among major world religions." Booklist.

Includes bibliographical references (pages 116-117) and index.

200.973 Religion—United States

Capaccio, George

Religion in colonial America. George Capaccio. Cavendish Square, 2015. 80 p.: Life in colonial America

Grades: 6 7 8   **200.973**
    1. Puritans 2. Puritanism 3. Anglicans 4. Great Awakening (United States religious history) 5. Religion 6. United States -- Religion -- To 1800
    ISBN 9781627128889

                LC 2013050650

Looks at the role of religion in colonial America, from the Puritanism of Massachusetts to the tolerance of the Mid-Atlantic to the Anglicanism of the South.

"Thoroughly researched and expertly executed, this series describes in rich detail the lives of Native Americans, African Americans, and white settlers, including children, women, and criminals. The introductory material that prefaces each title is of particular value, as it demonstrates that the colonists were part of a larger world picture. For instance, Religion takes readers back to Jerusalem to chronicle the expansion of Protestantism and Catholicism there and abroad. . . . Strong, attractive titles for those looking for more coverage of Colonial America." School Library Journal.

Includes bibliographical references (pages 72-77) and index.

Haugen, David M.

Religion in America. David Haugen and Susan Musser, book editors. Greenhaven Press, c2010. 240 p.: Opposing viewpoints series

Grades: 8 9 10 11 12   **200.973**
    1. Religion and politics 2. Religion and culture 3. Religion and state 4. United States -- Religion.
    ISBN 9780737749885

                LC 2010016975

This volume explores the topics relating to religion in the United States by presenting varied expert opinions that examine many of the different aspects that comprise these issues. The viewpoints are selected from a wide range of highly respected and often hard-to-find sources and publications. Allows the reader to attain the higher-level critical thinking and reading skills that are essential in a culture of diverse and contradictory opinions.

201 Specific aspects of religion

Hamilton, Virginia, 1936-2002

★ **In** the beginning: creation stories from around the world. told by Virginia Hamilton; illustrated by Barry Moser. Harcourt Brace Jovanovich, 1988. 161 p.

Grades: 5 6 7 8   **201**
    1. Creation (Religion) 2. Mythology
    ISBN 0152387404

                LC 88006211

An illustrated collection of twenty-five myths from various parts of the world explaining the creation of the world.

"Hamilton has gathered 25 creation myths from various cultures and retold them in language true to the original. Images from the tales are captured in Moser's 42 full-page illustrations, tantalizing oil paintings that are rich with somber colors and striking compositions. Included in the collection are the familiar stories (biblical creation stories, Greek and Roman myths), and some that are not so familiar (tales from the Australian aborigines, various African and native American tribes, as well as from countries like Russia, China, and Iceland). At the end of each tale, Hamilton provides a brief commentary on the story's origin and originators." Booklist.

Willis, Roy G.

World mythology: the illustrated guide. Roy Willis , general editor. Oxford University Press, 2006. 311 p.

Grades: Adult **201**

1. Mythology 2. Mythology, folklore, and legends

ISBN 9780195307528

LC 2005030779

This work offers readers an authoritative and wide-ranging guide to these enduring mythological traditions, combining the pure narrative of the myths themselves with the background necessary for more complete understanding. Beautifully illustrated with more than 500 color photographs, works of art, charts, and maps, World Mythology offers readers the most accessible guide yet to the heritage of the world's imagination.

202 Doctrines

Boughn, Michael

Into the world of the dead: astonishing adventures in the underworld. Annick, 2006. 48 p.

Grades: 5 6 7 8 **202**

1. Death 2. Heroes and heroines 3. Gods and goddesses 4. Monsters 5. Mythology

ISBN 1550379585

"Boughn retells stories from many cultures on every continent except South America, including quite a few from Mesoamerica, Asia, Africa, and Oceania. Readers will find heroes who have traveled to and returned from the underworld as well as the gods and monsters who dwell there. Full-color and black-and-white illustrations, including reproductions, photos, and plenty of graphics of skulls, appear on every page. . . . This is a book that many young people may find appealing." School Library Journal.

Hackney Blackwell, Amy

Lent, Yom Kippur, and other Atonement days. Amy Hackney Blackwell. Chelsea House, 2009. 120 p. : Holidays and celebrations (Chelsea House)

Grades: 6 7 8 9 **202**

1. Lent 2. Yom Kippur 3. Religious holidays 4. Atonement 5. Religion

ISBN 9781604131000

LC 2009010109

"This presents a welcome worldview of various atonement days, headlined by Lent, Yom Kippur, and the Buddhist holiday Rains Retreat. . . . Each gets an introduction to its associated religion, a brief history of the holiday, and a rundown of the significant days, rituals, and practices of observation. Then, readers are treated to a trip around the world . . . to investigate the unique ways in which different cultures observe similar holidays. The layout is text-dominated but dotted with colorful quality photos and a few informational insets. A good choice to help explain the significance behind holidays, . . . illuminating the many similarities lurking behind cultural and religious differences." Booklist.

Includes bibliographical references and index.

220.5 Modern versions and translations

Carroll, Robert P.

The **Bible**: Authorized King James Version. with an introduction and notes by Robert Carroll and Stephen Prickett. Oxford University Press, 2008. lxxiv, 1039, 248, 445 p.

Grades: 5 6 7 8 9 10 11 12 Adult **220.5**

ISBN 9780199535941

LC 2008273825

This unique edition offers an exciting new approach to the most influential of all English biblical texts—the Authorized King James Version, complete with the Apocrypha. Its wide-ranging Introduction and the substantial notes to each book of the Bible guide the reader through the labyrinth of literary, textual, and theological issues, using the most up-to-date scholarship to demonstrate how and why the Bible has affected the literature, art and general culture of the English-speaking world.—From publisher description

220.5205 Confraternity Bible and New American Bible

Confraternity of Christian Doctrine

The **new** American Bible: translated from the original languages with critical use of all the ancient sources including the revised Psalms and the revised New Testament. authorized by the Board of Trustees of the Confraternity of Christian Doctrine and approved by the Administrative Committee Board of the National Conference of Catholic Bishops and the United States Catholic Conference. Oxford University Press, 2005 xxiii, 1514 p.

Grades: 8 9 10 11 12 Adult **220.5205**

ISBN 9780195289046

This edition is perfect for anyone needing a straightforward text of the New American Bible, whether for reading or personal devotions. It includes a presentation section, prayers and devotions of the Church, the Dogmatic Constitution on Divine Revelation (Dei Verbum), a select NAB concordance, an essay on using the lectionary, and weekday and Sunday lectionary readings.—From publisher description

220.9 Geography, history, chronology, persons of Bible lands in Bible times

Murphy, Claire Rudolf

Daughters of the desert: stories of remarkable women from Christian, Jewish, and Muslim traditions. Claire Rudolf Murphy ... [et al.]. SkyLight Paths Pub., c2003. ix, 178 p.

Grades: 7 8 9 10 **220.9**

1. Women in the Bible 2. Women in the Qur'an

ISBN 1893361721

LC 2002153821

Women—though seldom educated—played key roles in the development of these three great faiths, but their lives and contributions are rarely honored. The men who recorded and copied the sacred Scriptures and other important texts included very little about how women passed on their experiences of God through storytelling, song, and ritual. With the help of imagination and careful research, Daughters of the Desert introduces us to the lives and loves, personalities and dreams of women who are only hinted at in the Scriptures, but whose faith and strength were vital to the growth of their beliefs.

"Using sacred writings as their basis, the five women authors have reshaped the stories of such individuals as Sarah, Mary Magdalene, Eve, and Khadiji, the wife of Mohammed. . . . The stories are short and simply told, but they are intriguing and invite discussion." Booklist.

Includes bibliographical references (p. 169-172).

Napoli, Donna Jo, 1948-

Treasury of Bible stories: Prophecy and Peril, Exile and Forgiveness. Donna Jo Napoli; illustrations by Christina Balit. National Geographic, 2019 208 p.

Grades: 4 5 6 7   **220.9**

    1. Bible stories

    ISBN 9781426335389

                         LC bl2019031929

Presents stories from the Bible, including Adam and Eve's expulsion from Eden, the Tower of Babel, Moses and the Ten Commandments, and Daniel in the lions' den.

"Balit's bold illustrations accompany each tale and feature a diversity of skin tones that reflects the many lands from northeast Africa to the Middle East where the drama unfolds; Adam and Eve appear to be sub-Saharan Africans, echoing current thinking on human origins." Kirkus.

Includes bibliographical references (pages 202-203) and index.

221.9 Geography, history, chronology, persons of Old Testament lands in Old Testament times

Ehrlich, Amy, 1942-

With a mighty hand: the story in the Torah. Amy Ehrlich. Candlewick Press, 2013. 224 p.

Grades: 2 3 4 5 6 7 8   **221.9**

    1. Bible stories

    ISBN 9780763643959

                         LC bl2013033227

An adaptation of the first five books of the Hebrew Bible presents the stories of Adam and Eve, Abraham, Moses, and other primary figures in a continuous narrative that upholds the complexities of the original text.

Lottridge, Celia Barker

Stories from Adam and Eve to Ezekiel. retold from the Bible by Celie Barker Lottridge. Douglas & McIntyre, 2004 192 p.

Grades: 4 5 6 7   **221.9**

    1. Bible stories

    ISBN 0888994907

"Lottridge uses her storyteller's ear to bring ancient stories from the Hebrew Bible to a young audience, tailoring them to make them more age appropriate. . . . The numerous, well-drawn ink-and-watercolor illustrations are reminiscent of Warwick Hutton's work. Some pictures . . . are quite spectacular." Booklist.

222 Historical books of Old Testament

Feiler, Bruce, 1964-

★ **Walking** the Bible: an illustrated journey for kids through the greatest stories ever told. by Bruce Feiler; illustrated by Sasha Meret. HarperCollinsPublishers, c2004. 108 p.

Grades: 5 6 7 8   **222**

    1. Voyages and travels 2. Pilgrims and pilgrimages 3. Christianity 4. Travelers 5. Middle East -- Description and travel.

    ISBN 9780060511180

The author describes his journey through places mentioned in the Old Testament.

"In this version of his adult book with the same title (Morrow, 2001), Feiler largely succeeds in slimming rather than dumbing down his account of his trip across the 10,000-mile setting of the earliest Bible sto-

ries. The author's unpretentious . . . tone and astute pacing help make the volume accessible, and his sincerity is palpable." School Library Journal.

223 Poetic books of Old Testament

Dillon, Leo

To every thing there is a season: verses from Ecclesiastes. illustrations by Leo & Diane Dillon. Blue Sky Press, [1998] 40 p.

Grades: 4 5 6 7 8   **223**

    1. Purpose in life

    ISBN 0590478877

                         LC 97035124

Presents the selection from Ecclesiastes which relates that everything in life has its own time and season; depicts each verse with a different style of art from around the world.

"The Dillons compellingly convey the relevance of the Ecclesiastes verse throughout history, via a stunning array of artwork that embraces motifs from cultures the world over." Publishers Weekly.

225.9 Geography, history, chronology, persons of New Testament lands in New Testament times

Lottridge, Celia Barker

Stories from the life of Jesus: retold from the Bible. Celia Barker Lottridge. Douglas & McIntyre, 2004 128 p.

Grades: 4 5 6 7   **225.9**

    1. Jesus Christ 2. Bible stories

    ISBN 0888994974

"This is an exceptional collection. . . . Each story is retold in three or four pages of clear, concise prose that is meant to be read aloud. . . . Each selection is enhanced by dramatic and atmospheric, mixed-media illustrations that are executed in warm earth tones." School Library Journal.

226.7 Miracles

Connolly, Sean, 1956-

New Testament miracles. Sean Connolly. Enchanted Lion Books, 2004. 32 p.: Art revelations

Grades: 7 8 9 10   **226.7**

    1. Jesus Christ 2. Miracles (Christianity) 3. Bible stories

    ISBN 9781592700127

                         LC 2003049414

Presents brief retellings of the miracles of Jesus Christ, accompanied by paintings by eminent artists from the past and details about each work.

"The 12 miracles discussed . . . include Jesus healing the man born blind, Jesus raising Lazarus from the dead, and the conversion of Paul. Each one is told from verses in the four Gospels or the Book of Acts, with explanatory paragraphs, sidebars, and captions by the author. Art masterpieces . . . illustrate each story. Works by El Greco, Rembrandt, Tintoretto, and Witz, among others, are featured. . . . Visually stunning." School Library Journal.

230 Christianity

Self, David
★ **Christianity**. David Self. World Almanac Library, 2006. 48 p.: Religions of the world (World Almanac)
Grades: 5 6 7 8   **230**
    1. Christianity 2. Religions
    ISBN 0836858662

LC 2005041712

Describes the origins, principal teachings, scriptures, important figures, historical events, holidays, places of worship, and community life of Christianity.

"Wonderfully colorful in images, language, and fact. . . . [This is] enumerated with full-color photographs on every page, charts, maps, and tables." School Library Journal.

Includes bibliographical references (p. 47) and index.

232.9 Family and life of Jesus

Spirin, Gennady
    Jesus: his life in verses from the King James holy Bible. art by Gennady Spirin. Marshall Cavendish Children, c2010. 36 p.
Grades: 5 6 7 8   **232.9**
    1. Jesus Christ 2. Christianity 3. Bible stories
    ISBN 9780761456308

LC 2009005956

Tells the story of the life of Jesus from his birth through his resurrection through excerpts from the Gospels, accompanied by sections from an oil painting by Gennady Spirin, that depict thirteen definitive events in his life.

"In an unusual project, a tempera painting by Spirin has been digitally dissected to create individual images for this picture book that portrays 13 events from the life of Jesus. . . . Details from the larger work illustrate key moments—including the Annunciation, Jesus' baptism, and the raising of Lazarus, among others—beside passages from the King James Bible (Jesus' words are printed in red). The result is an elegant, large-format volume that offers a reverent and arresting visual interpretation of biblical events." Publishers Weekly.

235.2 Saints

Wallace, Carey, 1974-
    Stories of the saints: bold and inspiring tales of adventure, grace, and courage. Carey Wallace; illustrated by Nick Thornborrow. Workman Publishing Company, Incorporated, 2020. 232 p.
Grades: 3 4 5 6 7 8 9   **235.2**
    1. Catholic Church 2. Christian saints 3. Saints 4. Canonization 5. Faith (Christianity)
    ISBN 9780761193272

A chronologically organized collection of stories about the Christian saints places their unexpectedly adventurous experiences against a backdrop of history, in a volume that includes biographical introductions to Francis of Assisi, Joan of Arc and Mother Teresa.

"Wallace presents them all with quiet confidence that the stories matter, and she convinces us that they do. Thornborrow's illustrations combine traditional iconography with modern graphic art, effectively dramatizing each tale. Unusual, well done, and useful in many settings." Kirkus.

248.8 Guides to Christian life for specific groups of people

Finke, Leigh
    Queerfully and wonderfully made: a guide for LGBTQ+ Christian teens. Leigh Finke; foreword Jennifer Knapp. Beaming Books, 2020 260 p.: Queerfully and Wonderfully Made Guides
Grades: 7 8 9 10 11 12   **248.8**
    1. LGBTQIA persons 2. Christian teenagers -- Religious life 3. Gay teenagers -- Religious life 4. Identity (Psychology) -- Religious aspects -- Christianity 5. Sexuality -- Religious aspects -- Christianity
    ISBN 9781506465241

LC 2020007058

Written by a group of queer adults, and featuring testimony from young LGBTQ+ Christians, Queerfully and Wonderfully Made looks to educate young queer people of faith and to help them stay safe, healthy, and secure. Provided by publisher.

"This guide for Christians seeks to provide counsel, understanding, and gentle guidance across a series of 40-plus chapters that address everything from coming out in a variety of contexts, positive ways to deal with haters, and helping start the conversation about gender-neutral bathrooms at school, to living authentically." Kirkus

270.1 Historical periods

Nardo, Don, 1947-
    The **birth** of Christianity. by Don Nardo. Morgan Reynolds Pub., c2011. 112 p. : World religions and beliefs
Grades: 7 8 9 10   **270.1**
    1. Church history Primitive and early church, ca. 30-600 2. Christianity 3. Religions 4. Religion
    ISBN 9781599351452

LC 2010038443

"This covers the beginnings of Christianity in an impartial way. The [context] in which the [religion] developed [is] explained, offering insight into how [Christianity] came to be and introducing major concepts from the [religion]." School Library Journal.

Includes bibliographical references.

274 Christianity in Europe

Schomp, Virginia
    The **Church**. Virginia Schomp Marshall Cavendish Benchmark, 2011. 80 p.: Life in Victorian England
Grades: 6 7 8 9   **274**
    1. Church of England -- Customs and practices. 2. Church of England -- History. 3. Christianity -- Rites and ceremonies 4. Evolution -- Religious aspects -- Christianity 5. Great Britain -- History -- Victoria, 1837-1901. 6. England -- Religion.
    ISBN 9781608700318

LC 2010006901

Describes the role of religion in the lives of Victorians, including how it influenced the way they lived, how they observed special occasions, and how they coped with the many changes and challenges of their times. Provided by publisher.

"This is clearly written, thorough, and informative. The visually rich layout includes photographs and paintings from the time period, full-page illustrations, and attention-grabbing sidebars. Most appealing are the primary source quotations, which are plentiful and relevant." Library Media Connection.

Includes bibliographical references and index.

280 Denominations and sects of Christian church

Brown, Stephen F.

Catholicism & Orthodox Christianity. Stephen F. Brown and Khaled Anatolios. Chelsea House Publishers, c2009. 144 p.
Grades: 7 8 9 10 11 12   **280**
   1. Catholic Church 2. Catholic Church -- Relations -- Orthodox Eastern Church -- History 3. Orthodox Eastern Church 4. Orthodox Eastern Church -- Relations -- Catholic Church -- History
ISBN 9781604131062

LC 2008043046
Traces Catholicism and Orthodox Christianity from their roots in early Christian churches to the way these religions are observed today.

Protestantism. Stephen F. Brown. Chelsea House Publishers, c2009. 144 p.
Grades: 7 8 9   **280**
   1. Protestantism 2. Protestants 3. Christianity
ISBN 9781604131123

LC 2008029659
Examines the history and customs of Protestantism from its beginnings in the 16th century to present day. Includes discussions of contemporary issues such as birth control, abortion, relationship between religion and politics, diversity among protestants, and more.

289.3 Latter-Day Saints (Mormons)

Bial, Raymond

Nauvoo: Mormon city on the Mississippi River. Raymond Bial. Houghton Mifflin, 2006. 47 p.
Grades: 5 6 7 8   **289.3**
   1. Mormon Church -- History -- 19th century. 2. Mormon Church -- History. 3. Mormon Church 4. Mormons 5. Religion 6. Nauvoo, Illinois -- Church history -- 19th century. 7. Nauvoo, Illinois -- History.
ISBN 0618396853

LC 2005027528
Learn about this city that many Mormons consider the birthplace of their religion.

"Bial introduces readers to a city that was established by the Church of Jesus Christ of Latter Day Saints in 1839. . . . This effectively written account provides a sympathetic but balanced introduction to Mormon beliefs. . . . Excellent color photographs grace almost every page." School Library Journal.

Includes bibliographical references (p. [44-47]).

Bushman, Claudia L.

Mormons in America. Claudia Lauper Bushman and Richard Lyman Bushman. Oxford University Press, c1999. 142 p.: Religion in American life
Grades: 7 8 9 10   **289.3**
   1. Mormon Church 2. Mormon Church -- History 3. Mormons 4. Religion 5. United States -- Religion.
ISBN 0195106776

LC 98018605

Chronicles the history of the Church of Jesus Christ of Latter-Day Saints beginning in America in the early 1800s and continuing to the present day throughout the world.

"A solid resource for libraries. Illustrated with historical material and black-and-white photos. Time line and bibliography appended." Booklist.

Includes bibliographical references (p. 136-137) and index.

292 Classical religion (Greek and Roman religion)

O'Connor, George

Hephaistos: God of fire. George O'Connor. First Second, 2019. 76 p.: Olympians
Grades: 5 6 7 8   **292**
   1. Hephaestus (Greek deity) 2. Gods and goddesses, Greek 3. Comics and Graphic novels 4. Mythology
ISBN 9781626725270

LC 2018938079
Traces the story of the god of forge and fire, Hephaistos, who is scorned by his fellow gods despite making beautifully crafted gifts and weapons, before he orchestrates a plan to win their respect.

★ **Zeus**: king of the gods. George O'Connor. First Second, 2010. 76 p.: Olympians
Grades: 5 6 7 8   **292**
   1. Zeus (Greek deity) 2. Gods and goddesses, Greek 3. Ancient Greece 4. Comics and Graphic novels 5. Mythology
ISBN 9781596434318

LC bl2010000098
Retells in graphic novel format stories from Greek mythology about the exploits of the young Zeus and how he rallied an army and overthrew his father, Kronos, to become king of the gods.

"It's [the] balance between respect for myth and adherence to comic-book form that works so wonderfully well here." Bulletin of the Center for Children's Books.

Includes bibliographical references (p. 76).

292.1 Specific elements

Daly, Kathleen N.

Greek and Roman mythology, A to Z. Kathleen N. Daly; revised by Marian Rengel. Chelsea House Publishers, c2009. xiii, 162 p.
Grades: 5 6 7 8 9 10 11 12   **292.1**
   1. Mythology, Classical 2. Gods and goddesses, Greek 3. Heroes and heroines, Greek 4. Gods and goddesses, Roman 5. Heroes and heroines, Roman 6. Mythology
ISBN 9781604134124

LC 2009008243
An illustrated dictionary of the gods, heroes, and legends of the Greek and Roman peoples.

Evans, Hestia

The **mythology** handbook: a course in ancient Greek myths. by Hestia Evans; edited by Dugald A. Steer and Clint Twist. Candlewick Press, c2009. 71 p.
Grades: 4 5 6 7   **292.1**
   1. Gods and goddesses, Greek 2. Heroes and heroines, Greek 3.

Creative activities for children and students 4. Mythology
ISBN 9780763642914

LC 2008935650

This highly informative, interactive handbook explores the amazing myths of ancient Greece. Brimming with facts and special features, it also contains maps and many heroic and monstrous activities.

"This follow-up to Mythology (Candlewick, 2007) again uses the voice of a fictional 19th-century scholar. Here, Lady Hestia Evans offers a guide to elements of Greek myth for her two children, providing information in lessons . . . with exercises based on each topic. Some of the activities encourage students to do further research . . . while others suggest that they draw new monsters, write hymns with the Muses' help, or design a new pentathlon for the Olympics. Mazes and a word search (using Greek letters) are also included. . . . The activities are engaging, and the illustrations of creatures and maps of the ancient world will add to the knowledge of even more experienced myth fans." School Library Journal.

Hamby, Zachary, 1982-
Mythology for teens: classic myths in today's world. written and illustrated by Zachary Hamby. Prufrock Press, c2009. xv, 167 p.
Grades: Professional   **292.1**
1. Mythology, Classical 2. Mythology, folklore, and legends
ISBN 9781593633639

LC 2008049537

Examines classical mythology through scripts and activities designed to make the ancient stories feel relevent.

293 Germanic religion

D'Aulaire, Ingri, 1904-1980
D'Aulaires' book of Norse myths. by Ingri and Edgar Parin D'aulaire; preface by Michael Chabon. New York Review of Books, 2005. xiii, 154 p.
Grades: 4 5 6 7 8   **293**
1. Gods and goddesses, Norse 2. Creation (Norse religion) 3. Chaos 4. Mythology
ISBN 9781590171257

LC 2004029214

"The d'Aulaires manage to capture the wildness and strangeness of the Norse pantheon with their bold lithographs and no-nonsense prose." Horn Book.

294 Religions of Indic origin

Mann, Gurinder Singh
Buddhists, Hindus, and Sikhs in America. Gurinder Singh Mann, Paul David Numrich & Raymond B. Williams. Oxford University Press, c2001. 158 p.: Religion in American life
Grades: 7 8 9 10   **294**
1. Asian Americans -- Religion 2. Buddhism 3. Hinduism 4. Sikhism 5. Immigrants -- Religious life 6. United States -- Immigration and emigration. 7. United States -- Religious life and customs
ISBN 0195124421

LC 2001045151

Presents the basic tenets of these three Asian religions and discusses the religious history and experience of their practitioners after immigration to the United States.

"Solid information, a large selection of historical and contemporary photographs, interesting readings from primary sources, and accounts from school-age Buddhists, Hindus, and Sikhs combine to make this is a valuable resource." Booklist.

Includes bibliographical references (p. 152-154) and index.

294.3 Buddhism

Eckel, Malcolm David, 1946-
Buddhism. Malcolm David Eckel. Rosen Pub., 2010. 112 p.: Understanding religions (Rosen Publishing Group)
Grades: 7 8 9 10   **294.3**
1. Buddhism 2. Buddhism -- History 3. Buddhism -- Social aspects 4. Religions
ISBN 9781435856196

Describes the origins, principal teachings, scriptures, important figures, historical events, and festivals of Buddhism.

"Thorough research and concise writing brand this series. Each volume discusses origins and historical development; aspects of the divine; sacred texts, persons, space, and time; ethical principles; death and the afterlife; and society and religion. Each chapter includes an extract from a sacred text followed by analysis and commentary. Terms and ideas that are unique to the religion are explained clearly within context." School Library Journal.

Includes bibliographical references and index.

Ganeri, Anita, 1961-
Buddhism. Anita Ganeri. World Almanac Library, 2006. 48 p.: Religions of the world (World Almanac)
Grades: 5 6 7 8   **294.3**
1. Buddhism 2. Religions
ISBN 0836858654

LC 2005041708

Describes the origins, principal teachings, scriptures, important figures, historical events, holidays, places of worship, and community life of Buddhism.

"The author presents a survey of Buddhist history, beliefs, sacred texts, festivals, and lifecycle events. . . . There is discussion of the art and folk literature associated with the religious tradition. Colorful photographs, illustrations, and art reproductions appear throughout." School Library Journal.

Includes bibliographical references (p. 47) and index.

Lee, Jeanne M.
I once was a monkey: stories Buddha told. Jeanne M. Lee. Farrar, Straus and Giroux, 1999. 40 p.
Grades: 4 5 6 7   **294.3**
1. Gautama Buddha. 2. Monkeys 3. Animals 4. Buddhism 5. Asia 6. Folklore
ISBN 0374335486

LC 98017651

A retelling of six Jatakas, or birth stories, which illustrate some of the central tenets of Buddha's teachings, such as compassion, honesty, and thinking clearly before acting.

"The appealing character of the monkey will pull children into the tales, which convey lessons in a direct yet gentle way that is never preachy. The accompanying linocut illustrations are lovely." Booklist.

294.5 Hinduism

Ganeri, Anita, 1961-

The **Ramayana** and Hinduism. Anita Ganeri. Smart Apple Media, c2004. 30 p. : Sacred texts

Grades: 5 6 7 8 9   **294.5**
    1. Valmiki. Ramayana 2. Hinduism 3. Sacred books 4. Hinduism -- History 5. Hinduism -- Rites and ceremonies
    ISBN 158340242X

                        LC 2003042352

Explains the history and practices of the religion of Hinduism, especially as revealed through its sacred book, the Ramayana.

Nardo, Don, 1947-

Understanding Hinduism. By Don Nardo. ReferencePoint Press, 2019. 80 p.

Grades: 8 9 10 11 12   **294.5**
    1. Hinduism 2. Hinduism -- Doctrines 3. Hinduism -- Rituals 4. Hinduism -- Customs and practices 5. Hinduism -- Relations
    ISBN 9781682824634

                        LC 2018017161

"This entry in the Understanding World Religions series reveals Hinduism's origins, beliefs, common practices, and the challenges its adherents face. While not a comprehensive examination of Hinduism, appended notes help make this additionally useful as a supplement for student reports." Booklist

Includes bibliographical references and index.

Rasamandala Das

★ **Hinduism**. Rasamandala Das. World Almanac Library, 2006. 48 p.: Religions of the world (World Almanac)

Grades: 5 6 7 8   **294.5**
    1. Hinduism 2. Religions
    ISBN 0836858670

                        LC 2005041749

Describes the origins, principal teachings, scriptures, important figures, historical events, holidays, places of worship, and community life of Hinduism.

"Hinduism is explored in an accessible introductory manner, including information on [its] history, teachings, religious practices, culture and lifestyle, and the [faith's role] in today's global society. Vibrant full-color photographs are appropriately placed within the [text]. Ideal for . . . school reports or for general interest." School Library Journal.

Includes bibliographical references (p. 47) and index.

Sattar, Arshia

Ramayana: an illustrated retelling. Arshia Sattar; illustrated by Sonali Zohra. Restless Books, 2018 181 p.

Grades: 5 6 7 8 9   **294.5**
    1. Brothers 2. Kidnapping 3. Demons 4. Rama (Hindu deity) 5. Sita (Hindu deity) 6. India -- Social life and customs. 7. Epic fiction 8. Translations Sanskrit to English
    ISBN 9781632061775

Retells the story of Rama, a young prince forced into exile, who travels into a mysterious forest and encounters strange and dangerous creatures.

Singh, Rina, 1955-

Diwali: festival of lights. Rina Singh. Orca Book Publishers, 2016. 64 p.

Grades: 4 5 6 7   **294.5**
    1. Divali 2. Hindu holidays
    ISBN 9781459810075

                        LC oc2016011084

Discusses the festival Diwali and how it is celebrated. "An exceptionally valuable resource." Kirkus.

295 Zoroastrianism (Mazdaism, Parseeism)

Hartz, Paula

Zoroastrianism. Paula R. Hartz. Chelsea House Publishers, c2009. 144 p.

Grades: 7 8 9   **295**
    1. Zoroastrianism
    ISBN 9781604131161

                        LC 2008035811

Traces the history and beliefs of Zoroastrianism and its followers' determination through centuries of persecution and hardship into the present day. The Iranian and Indian Zoroastrian communities in which the religion has thrived without missionary efforts or vast numbers of believers is also explored.

296 Judaism

Berlin, Adele

The **Oxford** dictionary of the Jewish religion. editor in chief, Adele Berlin. Oxford University Press, c2011. xxiv, 934 p.

Grades: Adult   **296**
    1. Judaism
    ISBN 9780199730049

                        LC 2010035774

Under the editorship of Adele Berlin, nearly 200 internationally renowned scholars have created a new edition that incorporates updated bibliographies, biographies of 20th-century individuals who have shaped the recent thought and history of Judaism, and an index with alternate spellings of Hebrew terms. Entries from the previous edition have been be revised, new entries commissioned, and cross-references added, all to increase ease of navigation research. Provided by publisher

Ehrlich, Carl S.

Judaism. Carl S. Ehrlich. Rosen Pub., 2010. 112 p.: Understanding religions (Rosen Publishing Group)

Grades: 7 8 9 10   **296**
    1. Judaism 2. Judaism -- History 3. Religions
    ISBN 9781435856226

                     LC   2009010055

Describes the origins, principal teachings, scriptures, important figures, historical events, and holidays of Judaism.

"Far from a quick overview, this detailed title in the Understanding Religions series is quite dense and scholarly at times, with authoritative discussion on origins and history and with separate chapters on sacred texts, persons, space, and time, as well as on ethical principles, death and the afterlife, and society and religion." Booklist.

Includes bibliographical references and index.

Rosinsky, Natalie M. (Natalie Myra)

Judaism. by Natalie M. Rosinsky. Compass Point Books, 2009. 48 p. : World religions (Compass Point Books)

Grades: 5 6 7 8   **296**
1. Judaism 2. Judaism -- History 3. Jewish way of life 4. Religions
ISBN 9780756542405

LC 2009015813

"The colorful, attractive layout includes high-quality reproductions of photographs, maps, and paintings. Students who are new to religious studies, as well as those doing reports, will find that this . . . meets their needs." School Library Journal.

296.4 Traditions, rites, public services

Kimmel, Eric A.
★ **Wonders** and miracles: a Passover companion. compiled by Eric A. Kimmel. Scholastic Press, c2004. 144 p.
Grades: 4 5 6 7   **296.4**
1. Passover 2. Seder 3. Jewish holidays 4. Haggadah 5. Judaism
ISBN 0439071755

LC 2002004732

Presents the steps performed in a traditional Passover Seder, plus stories, songs, poetry, and pictures that celebrate the historical significance of this holiday to Jews all over the world.

"The marvelous selection of art—paintings, photographs, artifacts, and illustrations from historical Haggadahs—illuminates each step in the service. . . . Both the presentation of information and the overall design attest to the careful and loving attention given to every detail. This inviting, handsome, and informative compendium should find a place of honor in every library." School Library Journal.

Includes bibliographical references and index.

Metter, Bert
Bar Mitzvah, Bat Mitzvah: the ceremony, the party, and how the day came to be. by Bert Metter; illustrated by Joan Reilly. Clarion Books, c2007. ix, 70 p.
Grades: 4 5 6 7   **296.4**
1. Bar Mitzvah 2. Bat Mitzvah 3. Jewish girls 4. Jewish boys 5. Judaism -- Rites and ceremonies
ISBN 0618767738

LC 2006032942

Traces the history of this coming-of-age event for young Jews through a review of its origins, traditions, and evolution throughout the years.

"The author describes a typical ceremony and explains how this custom began for boys during the Middle Ages and how it was adapted for girls beginning in 1922. He also discusses the recent custom of adult bar and bat mitzvahs and celebratory parties. The writing is clear and concise; ink illustrations . . . help break up the text." Booklist.

Includes bibliographical references (p. 62-68) and index.

297 Islam, Babism, Bahai Faith

Ashkar, Michael
Islam. Michael Ashkar. Mason Crest, 2018 112 p.
Grades: 10 11 12   **297**
1. Islam 2. Islam -- Essence, genius, nature
ISBN 9781422238196

LC 2016048088

Discusses the origins of Islam, the major sects that follow the faith, important religious centers such as Mecca and Medina, and the elemental religious practices that unite all members of the umma, or Islamic community.

Gordon, Matthew
Islam. Matthew S. Gordon. Rosen Pub., 2010. 112 p.: Understanding religions (Rosen Publishing Group)
Grades: 7 8 9 10   **297**
1. Islam 2. Islam -- History 3. Islam -- Social aspects 4. Religions
ISBN 9781435856189

LC 2009010043

"This book about Islam discusses origins and historical development; aspects of the divine; sacred texts, persons, space, and time; ethical principles; death and the afterlife; and society and religion. . . . There is enough substance here to make this . . . a key resource for reports." School Library Journal.

Includes bibliographical references and index.

Islam. Matthew S. Gordon. Chelsea House, 2009. 144 p.
Grades: 7 8 9   **297**
1. Islam
ISBN 9781604131093

LC 2008035810

Discusses the founding of Islam, the various sects, and its continued growth and strength throughout the world today.

Pickthall, Marmaduke William
The **meaning** of the glorious Koran. an explanatory translation by Marmaduke Pickthall; with an introduction by William Montgomery Watt. A.A. Knopf, 1992. xxviii, 693 p., 6 p. of plates
Grades: 7 8 9 10 11 12 Adult   **297**
ISBN 0679417362

LC 92052928

While in the service of India's Nizam of Hyderabad, Marmaduke Pickthall converted to Islam and, with the help of Muslim theologians and linguists, produced this clear and lovingly precise English interpretation of the Holy Koran. His work is honored by believer and nonbeliever alike for its unique combination of piety, scholarly rigor in its translation and explanatory notes, and deep feeling for the poetic beauty and moral grandeur of its Arabic original.—From publisher description.

Radley, Gail
Understanding Islam. Gail Radley; content consultant, Sana Tayyen, Visiting Scholar, School of Religion, University of Southern California, Visiting Assistant Professor, University of Redlands. Essential Library, 2019 112 p.
Grades: 7 8 9 10 11 12   **297**
1. Islam -- Doctrines 2. Islam -- Customs and practices 3. Islam and culture
ISBN 9781532114267

LC 2017961411

"Perhaps the most relevant chapters to understanding Islam are those on the religion's core beliefs, how it is practiced, its spread to Western countries, and numerous debates and misconceptions." Booklist.

297.03 Islam—Encyclopedias, . . .

Marshall Cavendish Reference
Illustrated dictionary of the Muslim world.. Marshall Cavendish Corporation Marshall Cavendish Reference, c2011. 192 p.

Grades: 7 8 9 10 11 12   **297.03**
   1. Islam 2. Islamic civilization
ISBN 9780761479291

                  LC 2010008613

Alphabetic entries discuss the basic concepts and ideas, key events, and important people and places of the Muslim world.

297.09 Islam, Babism, Bahai Faith—History, geographic treatment, biography

Nardo, Don, 1947-

The **birth** of Islam. by Don Nardo. Morgan Reynolds Pub., 2011. 112 p. : World religions and beliefs

Grades: 7 8 9 10   **297.09**
   1. Islam -- History 2. Muslims 3. Religions 4. Religion 5. Islamic Empire -- History
ISBN 9781599351469

                  LC 2010038442

"This covers the beginnings of Islam in an impartial way. The [context] in which the [religion] developed [is] explained, offering insight into how [Islam] came to be and introducing major concepts the [religion]." School Library Journal.

Includes bibliographical references.

297.2 Islamic doctrinal theology (Aqaid and Kalam) Islam and secular disciplines Islam and other

Barnard, Bryn

★ The **genius** of Islam: how Muslims made the modern world. Bryn Barnard. Random House Childrens Books, 2011. 32 p.

Grades: 4 5 6 7   **297.2**
   1. Muslims 2. Inventions 3. Islam 4. Civilization, Islamic 5. Islam -- History
ISBN 9780375840722

"This is a concise and eloquent exploration of the far-reaching influence of Islam over the centuries. Each spread is devoted to a different subject (writing, Arabic numerals, architecture, astronomy, agriculture), while captioned spot art homes in on specific inventions and innovations (the zither, the astrolabe, advanced medical knowledge)." Publishers Weekly.

297.3 Islamic worship

Ali, S. K.

★ **Once** upon an Eid: stories of hope and joy by 15 Muslim voices. edited by S.K. Ali and Aisha Saeed. Amulet Books, 2020 272 p.

Grades: 4 5 6 7   **297.3**
   1. Islamic holidays 2. Islam -- Customs and practices 3. Family traditions 4. Religious life -- Islam 5. Muslim families 6. Short stories 7. Anthologies
ISBN 9781419740831

                  LC 2019026811

Featuring contributions by such established genre authors as Hena Khan, Randa Abdel-Fattah and Ashley Franklin, a collection of short stories celebrates Muslim culture and the joyful holiday traditions of Eid.

"This special anthology about family traditions, sharing meals, giving presents, and delighting in the cultural uniqueness of people all over the world isn't just for those who celebrate Eid; it's for all who want to share and learn about the holidays." Booklist.

Jeffrey, Laura S.

Celebrate Ramadan. Laura S. Jeffrey. Enslow Publishers, c2007. 112 p.: Celebrate holidays

Grades: 5 6 7 8   **297.3**
   1. Ramadan 2. Id al-Fitr 3. Islamic holidays 4. Islam -- Rites and ceremonies
ISBN 0766027740

                  LC 2006028107

Discusses the significance of Ramadan, a month-long observance celebrated in the Islamic faith.

"This book opens by introducing a contemporary Muslim, Bushra, who celebrated Ramadan as a girl growing up in England [and] later immigrated to the United States. . . . An informative chapter surveys the history, beliefs, and practices of Islam. . . . The remainder of the book offers a detailed discussion of Ramadan, prayer, and spiritual awareness, and of I'Id al Fitr. . . . Punctuated by sidebars and illustrated with color photos, this clearly written book offers a good overview of how the holidays of Islam are celebrated." Booklist.

Includes bibliographical references (p. 108-109) and index.

297.9 Babism and Bahai Faith

Hartz, Paula

Baha'i faith. Paula Hartz. Chelsea House Publishers, c2009. 144 p.

Grades: 7 8 9   **297.9**
   1. Bahai Faith
ISBN 9781604131048

                  LC 2008043045

Explores all aspects of the Baha'i faith, from the original teachings of its founder, Baha'u'llah, to the modern-day communities that exist in 236 countries and territories throughout the world.

299 Religions not provided for elsewhere

Harpur, James

Celtic myth: a treasury of legends, art, and history. James Harpur. M.E. Sharpe, c2008. 96 p.: The world of mythology

Grades: 8 9 10 11 12   **299**
   1. Civilization, Celtic 2. Celts 3. Mythology
ISBN 9780765681027

                  LC 2007006015

"With lots of heroic adventures and exciting, sometimes gruesome detail, Harpur retells stories of the Irish and Welsh Celts and weaves in facts about their culture and the history of their struggle for dominence. The dense text is broken up with beautiful, color images on every page, including paintings and photos of the settings, sculptures, weapons, and other artifacts." Booklist.

Includes bibliographical references and index.

Martin, Joel W., 1956-

Native American religion. Joel W. Martin. Oxford University Press, 1999. 157 p.: Religion in American life

Grades: 7 8 9 10   **299**
   1. Indians of North America -- Spiritual life 2. Traditional religion

3. Indians of North America -- Religion
ISBN 0195110358

LC 98050155

Discusses the world view and beliefs of various Native American religions and their role in promoting survival of the devastation caused by the arrival of Europeans.

"An examination of religious life and practices from ancient times through the Colonial period and the Western Expansion, and into the 20th century. Martin acknowledges the importance of religion in all aspects of Native American daily life and explores some of the differences among the various cultures. He also addresses the impact of the arrival of Europeans on spiritual life." School Library Journal.

Includes bibliographical references (p. 151-153) and index.

Napoli, Donna Jo, 1948-

★ **Treasury** of Egyptian mythology: classic stories of gods, goddesses, monsters & mortals. Donna Jo Napoli; illustrated by Christina Balit. Natl Geographic Soc Childrens books 2013 192 p.

Grades: 3 4 5 6 **299**

    1. Gods and goddesses, Egyptian 2. Mythology
    ISBN 9781426313806

An elaborately illustrated tableau of Egyptian myths, vividly recreated by the award-winning author of Beast, combines narrative accounts of the stories of the Sun God Ra, the Sphinx and numerous pharaohs and queens with informative sidebars that provide historical, cultural and geographic facts.

299.5 Religions of East and Southeast Asian origin

Hartz, Paula

Daoism. Paula R. Hartz. Chelsea House Publishers, 2009. 144 p.

Grades: 7 8 9 **299.5**

    1. Taoism
    ISBN 9781604131154

LC 2008035809

Discusses the history, basic beliefs, and traditional practices of Daoism as well as the renewed interest and growth in modern China and the world.

Shinto. Paula R. Hartz; series editors, Joanne O'Brien and Martin Palmer. Chelsea House Publishers, c2009. 144 p.

Grades: 7 8 9 **299.5**

    1. Shinto 2. Shinto -- Customs and practices 3. Shinto -- History
    4. Japan -- Religion. 5. Japan -- History.
    ISBN 9781604131130

LC 2008029661

Developed in prehistoric times, Shinto is the true expression of what it means to be Japanese. Less a formal religious statement than a deeply ingrained way of life, the rituals, traditions, and values of Shinto have both shaped and been shaped by Japanese culture.

Hoobler, Dorothy

Confucianism. Dorothy and Thomas Hoobler. Chelsea House Publishers, c2009. 144 p.

Grades: 7 8 9 **299.5**

    1. Confucianism
    ISBN 9781604131079

LC 2008029656

Examines Cufucianism in conjunction with its resurgence in China and the rest of the world. Presents its history, basic beliefs, and evolutionin response to historical events in China.

299.6 Religions originating among Black Africans and people of Black African descent

Lugira, Aloysius Muzzanganda

African traditional religion. Aloysius M. Lugira. Chelsea House Publishers, c2009. 144 p.

Grades: 7 8 9 10 11 12 **299.6**

    1. Africa -- Religion 2. Africa -- Religious life and customs
    ISBN 9781604131031

LC 2008051188

Explores the many manifestations of African religious belief and their expressions, in the past and in the present, as well as the hopes for the future.

Lynch, Patricia Ann, 1936-

African mythology, A to Z. Patricia Ann Lynch; revised by Jeremy Roberts. Chelsea House, c2010. xxiv, 149 p.

Grades: 7 8 9 **299.6**

    1. Mythology, African 2. Mythology
    ISBN 9781604134155

LC 2009033612

Alphabetically listed entries discuss the myths, traditions, beliefs, and characters of African mythology.

299.7 Religions of North American native origin

Hartz, Paula

Native American religions. Paula R. Hartz. Chelsea House Publishers, c2009. 144 p.

Grades: 7 8 9 **299.7**

    1. Indians of North America 2. Indians of North America -- Religion
    3. Indians of North America -- Rites and ceremonies
    ISBN 9781604131116

LC 2008051197

Presents the history of the Native American religions, starting from their roots as tribal religions, and then details the detrimental effects of European colonization, the annihilation of the Native Americans that threatened the religions, and their restoration in the 20th century

300 SOCIAL SCIENCES, SOCIOLOGY & ANTHROPOLOGY

302 Specific topics in sociology and anthropology

Hale, Shannon

★ **Friends** forever. written by Shannon Hale; illustrated by LeUyen Pham. First Second 2021 304 p.: Friends (Hale)

Grades: 4 5 6 7 8 **302**

    1. Hale, Shannon 2. Best friends 3. Preteen girls 4. Cliques 5. Popularity 6. Social acceptance in children 7. Autobiographical comics 8. Comics and Graphic novels
    ISBN 9781250317551

Following up their mega-bestselling Real Friends and Best Friends graphic memoirs, Shannon Hale and LeUyen Pham are back with Friends Forever, a story about learning to love yourself exactly as you are.

"With the combination of Hale's lucid writing and Pham's masterful portrayal of body and language and facial expression, this book homes in squarely and affirmingly on teen angst and worries." Booklist

302.23 Media (Means of communication)

DiPiazza, Francesca, 1961-

Fandom: fic writers, vidders, gamers, artists, and cosplayers. by Francesca Davis DiPiazza, illustrated by Shauna Lynn Panczyszyn. Lerner Pub Group 2018 120 p.
Grades: 7 8 9 10   302.23
  1. Subcultures 2. Fans (Persons) 3. Popular culture 4. Mass media -- Social aspects 5. Live action role play
  ISBN 9781512450491
                                LC 2017010738
"This book fills a need for a positive, informative resource that covers the breadth of fandom in one book." Booklist
Includes bibliographical references and index.

Ratcliffe, Amy

A **kid's** guide to fandom: exploring fan-fic, cosplay, gaming, podcasting, and more in the geek world! Amy Ratcliffe; illustrated by Dave Perillo Running Pr Book Pub 2021 160 p.
Grades: 4 5 6 7   302.23
  1. Media fandom 2. Fans (Persons) 3. Entertainments 4. Popular culture 5. Hobbyists
  ISBN 9780762498758
"Throughout the upbeat and accessible text, digital illustrations in blues and reds feature cartoonish young people with a range of skin tones, hairstyles, and physical abilities. . . . It's game on for proud geeks!" Booklist

Rojas, Meridith

Selfie made: your ultimate guide to social media stardom. Meridith Rojas. Wednesday Books, 2018 272 p.
Grades: 8 9 10 11 12   302.23
  1. Social media 2. Online social networks 3. Internet industry and trade 4. Digital media 5. Online identities
  ISBN 9781250196743
The founder of DigiTour offers stories, tips, and tricks to starting a social media company, discussing how to grow an audience and build a brand in front of and behind the camera.

302.30285 Computer applications

Leavitt, Amie Jane

Combatting toxic online communities. Amie Jane Leavitt. Rosen Publishing, 2017. 64 p.: Combatting shaming and toxic communities
Grades: 6 7 8 9 10   302.30285
  1. Online social networks 2. Online hate speech
  ISBN 9781508171171
                                LC 2015050278
Discusses the characteristics of toxic online communities and the psychology behind them, and provides guidance on how to respond to and avoid them.

"Useful advice is also offered on building healthy relationships to foster a sense of self-worth. This set is top of the line. The back matter of each title is extensive and includes a contact information list for relevant social agencies." School Library Journal.
Includes bibliographical references and index.

302.34 Social interaction in primary groups

Bazelon, Emily

Sticks and stones: defeating the culture of bullying and rediscovering the power of character and empathy. Emily Bazelon. Random House, c2013. 256 p.
Grades: Adult Professional   302.34
  1. Bullying and bullies -- Prevention 2. Schools 3. Aggressiveness (Psychology) 4. Interpersonal relations
  ISBN 9780812992809
                                LC 2012022773
Offers insights into teen bullying in the Internet era, counseling parents, educators, advocates, and kids on how to understand its dynamics and consequences and take appropriate protective measures.
"While less prescriptive than other books on the topic, very useful FAQs are included, as are resource lists for readers. Masterfully written, Bazelon's book will increase understanding, awareness, and action." Publishers Weekly.
Includes bibliographical references and index.

Scherer, Lauri S.

Cyberbullying. Lauri Scherer, book editor. Greenhaven Press, a part of Gale, Cengage Learning, 2015 137 p.
Grades: 7 8 9   302.34
  1. Cyberbullying 2. Internet and teenagers 3. Bullying and bullies
  ISBN 9780737772340
                                LC 2014030230
Explores the issues surrounding cyberbullying—bullying through the Internet—by placing opinions from a wide range of sources in a pro/con format.

Strauss, Susan, 1946-

Sexual harassment and bullying: a guide to keeping kids safe and holding schools accountable. Susan L. Strauss. Rowman & Littlefield Publishers, c2012. xii, 290 p.
Grades: Adult Professional   302.34
  1. Bullying and bullies -- Prevention 2. Bullying and bullies 3. Sexual harassment in education 4. Sexual harassment -- Prevention
  ISBN 9781442201620
                                LC 2011031731
Despite headlines that label all harassment among youth as bullying, there is in fact a difference between sexual harassment and bullying. This book discusses the similarities and important differences between the two, offering firsthand accounts from victims and others involved in combating the activities that victimize students. It provides parents, youth advocates, scout leaders, and other concerned adults with practical steps to partner with schools to prevent and intervene on the behaviors to help keep kids safe. The book clearly identifies the steps to take to hold schools accountable when a student has been harassed or bullied, even when the school is not stopping the behavior. Providing examples throughout the work, Strauss helps readers become better acquainted with the various activities that constitute sexual harassment and bullying and what they can do to combat the problem.

303.48 Causes of change

Hill, Laban Carrick, 1960-2021

America dreaming: how youth changed America in the 60s. by Laban Carrick Hill. Little, Brown & Company, 2007. 176 p.

Grades: 6 7 8 9 10   **303.48**

1. 1960s 2. Social movements -- History 20th century. 3. Baby boom generation -- Political activity 4. Social change -- History 20th century. 5. United States -- History -- 1961-1969.
ISBN 0316009040

LC 2006027898

Describes how the young Americans of the 1960s found creative ways to express their beliefs and views on political and social fronts that impacted and changed the course of history with regard to civil rights, women's rights, and other political issues.

"An excellent textbook for the children and, probably, grandchildren of baby boomers who want to know what the youth culture of the time as all about." New York Times Book Review.

Includes bibliographical references and index.

Kluger, Jeffrey

Raise your voice: 12 protests that shaped America. Jeffrey Kluger. Penguin Group USA 2020 224 p.

Grades: 5 6 7 8 9   **303.48**

1. Protest movements -- History 2. Political participation -- History 3. Social movements 4. Political activists 5. Social participation 6. United States -- History
ISBN 9780525518303

LC 2019030850

The best-selling author of Apollo 13 shares the stories of 12 protests and marches that shaped history, detailing the activists, movements and events that enabled change on behalf of civil rights, climate change, gun control and more.

"Descriptions of how early protests succeeded without the aid of the internet—and sometimes, as in the case of the Stonewall Uprising, without organization at all—show how one person can inspire many to exercise constitutional rights to 'peaceably... assemble and petition the government for a redress of grievances.'" Publishers Weekly

Mooney, Carla, 1970-

Globalization: why we care about faraway events. Carla Mooney; illustrated by Sam Carbaugh. Nomad Press, 2018 vii, 120 p.: Inquire & Investigate

Grades: 6 7 8 9 10   **303.48**

1. Globalization 2. International relations 3. International communication 4. Diplomacy
ISBN 9781619306646

Is your salad drizzled with olive oil imported from Italy? What country made the car that your parents drive? Globalization connects us today more than ever before, and in ways we never expected, and populations around the world are questioning whether this is a purely beneficial circumstance or if we should take steps to scale back our interrelatedness. Globalization: Why We Care About Faraway Events delves into the nature and history of interconnected relationships between the governments, businesses, media, and industries all around the world and asks pressing questions about the future. Provided by publisher

"A comprehensive social studies selection for middle and high school." School Library Journal

Includes bibliographical references (pages 116-117) and index.

303.49 Social forecasts

Schutten, Jan Paul, 1970-

Hello from 2030: the science of the future and you. Jan Paul Schutten. Aladdin; Hillsboro, Oregon: Beyond Words, 2014, 224 p.

Grades: 4 5 6 7   **303.49**

1. Forecasting 2. Scientific forecasting 3. Technological forecasting 4. Social forecasting
ISBN 9781582704746

LC 2013044906

"Extremely detailed source notes for each chapter draw on current research and news articles and include links to further reading. The engaging text is supported by plenty of full-color visuals presented in a dynamic format. Presenting an overwhelmingly optimistic outlook on the future, the book reminds us that we might as well welcome change with open arms." Booklist.

Includes bibliographical references and index.

303.6 Conflict and conflict resolution

Dawson, Eric David

Putting peace first: seven commitments to change the world. by Eric David Dawson. Viking, 2018. 160 p.

Grades: 5 6 7 8 9   **303.6**

1. Children and peace 2. Peace-building 3. Toleration 4. Peace
ISBN 9781101997338

LC 2017033431

Presents seven strategies that children can use to make a difference in their communities and promote peace and tolerance, including putting peace first, taking a stand, and working with enemies.

"Issues of cyberbullying, gun violence, and attacks on immigrant students are ones that are faced in these pages and also every day in schools around the world. By internalizing the seven commitments, standing up, and taking action—choosing to put peace first—Dawson argues, the world could change, one student at a time. These anecdotes are inspirational, but Dawson also includes a practical starting guide for any readers who need concrete steps on how to begin to think and plan for change. Dawson is careful to point out (the seventh commitment is Keep Trying, and the epilogue is aptly named Pending Disasters) that nothing is perfect. Change is difficult, especially if you are trying to right an injustice, but this manual helps readers past excuses." Kirkus.

Ellis, Deborah, 1960-

Off to war: voices of soldiers' children. Deborah Ellis. Groundwood Books, 2008. 175 p.

Grades: 5 6 7 8   **303.6**

1. Children of military personnel 2. War 3. Family relationships 4. Soldiers 5. Parent-separated children 6. Canada -- Social life and customs -- 21st century. 7. United States -- Social life and customs -- 21st century.
ISBN 9780888998941

LC 2017301345

The wars in Iraq and Afghanistan have impacted the children of soldiers—men and women who have been called away from their families to fight in a faraway war. In their own words, some of these children describe how their experience has marked and shaped their lives.

"Accessible and utterly readable. . . . The book is an excellent resource for opening discussions about the current events." School Library Journal.

Includes bibliographical references (pages 174-175).

Hasak-Lowy, Todd, 1969-

We are power: how nonviolent activism changes the world. Todd Hasak-Lowy. Abrams Books for Young Readers, 2020. 320 p.

Grades: 5 6 7 8   **303.6**
     1. Nonviolence 2. Civil disobedience 3. Protest movements 4. Political participation 5. Social change
     ISBN 9781419741111

An inspiring introduction to nonviolent activism and how it works traces the examples of history-shaping international movements as well as such practitioners as Mahatma Gandhi, Martin Luther King, Jr. and César Chavez to reveal how nonviolent demonstrations have repeatedly succeeded.

"These examinations are not simply overviews; Hasak-Lowy's writing gives life to both the people and issues involved, taking time to explain historical backgrounds and the ways the lessons from one movement affected future ones . . . A thoughtful and inspiring book." Booklist.

O'Brien, Anne Sibley

After Gandhi: one hundred years of nonviolent resistance. Anne Sibley O'Brien and Perry Edmond O'Brien; [illustrations by Anne Sibley O'Brien]. Charlesbridge, 2018, c2009. ix, 181 p.

Grades: 7 8 9 10   **303.6**
     1. Nonviolence 2. Civil disobedience 3. Peace activists 4. Pacifism 5. Resistance to government
     ISBN 9781580891295

                 LC 2008010660

Explores Gandhi's work and legacy through fifteen profiles of activists who chose nonviolent resistance as the path to change, focusing on individuals who were in direct physical danger and chose to respond with nonviolence.

"Using Gandhi as its starting point, this large-format book traces the history of nonviolent resistance by looking at significant adherents from 1908 to 2003 including Martin Luther King, Jr., Nelson Mandela, Charles Perkins, César Chvez, Aung San Suu Kyi, Vaclav Havel, and Wangari Maathi and groups such as the student activists of Tiananmen Square and the Madres de Plaza de Mayo (Mothers of the Disappeared) in Argentina. . . . The handsome design and striking black-and-white illustrations are strong visuals that complement the story of nonviolent resistance in action." Booklist.

Includes bibliographical references (p. 168-174) and index.

303.60835 Adolescents—Social conflict

Omnigraphics, Inc

Abuse and violence information for teens: health tips about the causes and consequences of abusive and violent behavior including facts about the types of abuse and violence, the warning signs of abusive and violent behavior, health concerns of victims, and getting help and staying safe. Keith (EDT) Jones. Omnigraphics, 2017 xi, 325 p.

Grades: 8 9 10 11 12   **303.60835**
     1. Youth and violence 2. Youth and violence -- Prevention
     ISBN 9780780814561

                 LC 2016049906

Provides basic consumer health information for teens about risk factors, consequences, and prevention of various types of abuse and violence. Includes index, resource information and recommendations for further reading. Provided by publisher.

304.2 Human ecology

Auld, Mary

Pathways through Asia. Mary Auld. Crabtree Publishing Company, 2019. 32 p.: Human Path Across the Continents

Grades: 4 5 6   **304.2**
     1. Nature -- Effect of human beings on 2. Physical geography 3. Human ecology -- Asia 4. Asia -- Environmental conditions
     ISBN 9780778766469

                 LC 2019030382

This incredible journey through the continent of Asia helps show how humans affect, and are affected by, the environments in which they live. Readers will gain an understanding of the continent's various landforms, resources, and human activities. Examples featured include traveling on a high-speed train through China, sailing on a riverboat along the Mekong River, and walking in the Himalayas. Provided by publisher.

Carson, Mary Kay

Inside Biosphere 2: earth science under glass. by Mary Kay Carson; with photographs by Tom Uhlman. Houghton Mifflin Harcourt, [2015] 79 p.: Scientists in the field (Houghton Mifflin)

Grades: 7 8 9 10   **304.2**
     1. Biosphere 2 (Project) 2. Closed ecological systems (Space environment) 3. Human ecology 4. Ecology -- Research 5. Arizona
     ISBN 9780544416642

                 LC 2014047046

In the 1990s, scientists lived inside Biosphere 2 (Biosphere 1 is the Earth itself) for two years, trying to figure out if colonizing Mars would ever be possible. Now scientists don't live there but instead conduct all sorts of studies and experiments aimed to help us better understand our environment and especially understand what sort of things are happening to it due to climate change and other man-made problems. It's a unique take on the Scientists in the Field mission statement—in this case, the field/lab is a replica that allows the scientists to conduct large scale experiments that would otherwise be impossible. Provided by publisher.

"Well-chosen, clearly captioned photographs support the text, while flashback boxes inform readers of what came before. For middle and high school readers, an encouraging example of earth scientists working to understand and deal with climate change in new and amazing ways." Kirkus.

Hudak, Heather C., 1975-

Pathways through Africa. Heather C. Hudak. Crabtree Publishing Company, 2019. 32 p.: The Human Path Across the Continents

Grades: 4 5 6   **304.2**
     1. Human ecology 2. Transportation 3. Africa
     ISBN 9780778766445

                 LC 2019023297

This exciting journey through the continent of Africa helps show how humans affect, and are affected by, the environments in which they live. Readers will gain an understanding of the continent's various landforms, resources, and human activities. Examples featured include driving along the Trans-Sahelian Highway in West Africa, walking to get water in Malawi, and riding a camel in Morocco. Provided by publisher.

Pathways through South America. Heather C. Hudak. Crabtree Publishing Company, 2020 32 p.: Human Path Across the Continents

Grades: 4 5 6   **304.2**
     1. Human ecology 2. Nature -- Effect of human beings on

3. Physical geography 4. Continents 5. South America --
Environmental conditions
ISBN 9780778766506

LC 2019023330

This fantastic journey through the continent of South America helps show how humans affect, and are affected by, the environments in which they live. Readers will gain an understanding of the continent's various landforms, resources, and human activities. Examples featured include walking along the Inca Trail in Peru, riding a cable car in Bolivia, and taking a water taxi in Suriname. Provided by publisher.

Miles, John C. (John Christian), 1960-

Pathways through Antarctica. John C. Miles. Crabtree Publishing, 2019. 32 p.: Human Path Across the Continents
Grades: 4 5 6 **304.2**
1. Human ecology 2. Nature -- Effect of human beings on 3. Physical geography 4. Antarctica -- Environmental conditions
ISBN 9780778766452

LC 2019023322

This stunning journey through the continent of Antarctica helps show how humans affect, and are affected by, the environments in which they live. Readers will gain an understanding of the continent's landforms, resources, and human activities. Examples featured include flying by helicopter to Bird Island, skiing to the South Pole, and sailing to the edge of the ice sheet. Provided by publisher.

Pathways through Europe. John C. Miles. Crabtree Publishing Company, 2019. 32 p.: The Human Path Across the Continents
Grades: 4 5 6 **304.2**
1. Human ecology 2. Nature -- Effect of human beings on 3. Physical geography 4. Continents 5. Europe -- Environmental conditions
ISBN 9780778766353

LC 2019023326

This engaging journey through the continent of Europe helps show how humans affect, and are affected by, the environments in which they live. Readers will gain an understanding of the continent's various landforms, resources, and human activities. Examples featured include traveling by train through a tunnel in the Alps, riding a water bus in the canals of Venice, and cycling along the Danube River. Provided by publisher

Morganelli, Adrianna, 1979-

Pathways through Australia. Adrianna Morganelli. Crabtree Publishing, 2019. 32 p.: The Human Path Across the Continents
Grades: 4 5 6 **304.2**
1. Human ecology 2. Nature -- Effect of human beings on 3. Physical geography 4. Continents 5. Australia -- Environmental conditions
ISBN 9780778766346

LC 2019023324

This awe-inspiring journey through the continent of Australia helps show how humans affect, and are affected by, the environments in which they live. Readers will gain an understanding of the continent's various landforms, resources, and human activities. Examples featured include traveling on horseback through the Outback, bushwalking through Kakadu National Park, and flying by seaplane over the Great Barrier Reef. Provided by publisher.

O'Brien, Cynthia (Cynthia J.)

Pathways through North America. Cynthia O'Brien. Crabtree Publishing Company, 2020 32 p.: The Human Path Across the Continents
Grades: 4 5 6 **304.2**
1. Human ecology 2. Nature -- Effect of human beings on 3. Physical geography 4. Continents 5. North America -- Environmental conditions
ISBN 9780778766490

LC 2019023328

This amazing journey through the continent of North America helps show how humans affect, and are affected by, the environments in which they live. Readers will gain an understanding of the continent's various landforms, resources, and human activities. Examples featured include dog sledding in Greenland, floating on a barge down the Mississippi River, and driving by truck along the Pan American Highway. Provided by publisher.

304.8 Movement of people

Butler, George

Drawn across borders: true stories of human migration. George Butler Candlewick Studio, 2021 46 p.
Grades: 6 7 8 9 10 **304.8**
1. Immigrants 2. Refugees 3. Disasters 4. Communities 5. Immigration and emigration 6. Essays
ISBN 9781536217759

LC 2021933581

Resisting his own urge to walk away, the author, an artist, took his sketchbook and made, over the course of a decade, a series of pen-and-ink and watercolor portraits in war zones, refugee camps, and on the move. While he worked, his subjects—migrants and refugees in the Middle East, Europe, Africa, and Asia—shared their stories. Theirs are the human stories behind the headlines that tell of fleeing poverty, disaster, and war, and of venturing into the unknown in search of jobs, education, and security. Whether sketching by the hospital bed of a ten-year-old Syrian boy who survived an airstrike, drawing the doll of a little Palestinian girl with big questions, or talking with a Masai herdsman forced to abandon his rural Kenyan home for the Kibera slums, the author turns reflective art and sensitive reportage into a cry for understanding and empathy.—Publisher's description.

"This is a work of art, compassion, and activism, with journalist and illustrator Butler using his craft to bear witness to and build awareness of the effects of war on civilians whose lives are treated as mere collateral for those in power." Booklist

304.80973 Emigration—United States

Osborne, Linda Barrett, 1949-

This land is our land: the history of American immigration. Linda Barrett Osborne. Abrams Books for Young Readers, 2016. 124 p.
Grades: 5 6 7 8 9 10 **304.80973**
1. Immigrants -- History 2. Immigration and emigration 3. United States -- Immigration and emigration -- History
ISBN 9781419716607

LC 2015017877

Explores the way government policy and popular responses to immigrant groups have evolved throughout U.S. history, from 1800 to today.

"Well researched, clearly written, and informative, the discussion is particularly useful in offering the broad look at immigration over time, showing how similar arguments and legal restrictions have been used against different groups in different periods. Throughout the book, the perspectives of individual immigrants emerge in paragraphs detailing their personal stories and including quotes. Handsomely designed, the book offers many captioned period illustrations, especially photos. A strong introduction to American immigration." Booklist.

Includes bibliographical references and index.

305.23 Young people

Dias, Marley (Marley Emerson)

Marley Dias gets it done: and so can you! by Marley Dias, with Siobhan McGowan. Scholastic Press, 2018. 208 p.

Grades: 5 6 7 8 9   305.23
1. Dias, Marley (Marley Emerson) 2. African American girls 3. Equality 4. Social action 5. Social justice 6. Teenage girl social advocates
ISBN 9781338136890

LC 2017016415

The young organizer of the #1000blackgirlbooks campaign explores the power of activism, social justice, volunteerism, equality, inclusion and positive social media, drawing on her personal experiences to counsel other kids on how they can work together to make positive changes in their communities in the areas of literacy and diversity.

Ewald, Wendy

America, border, culture, dreamer: the young immigrant experience from A to Z. Wendy Ewald [editor and photographer]. Little, Brown and Company, 2018. 64 p.

Grades: 5 6 7 8 9   305.23
1. Child immigrants 2. Children of immigrants 3. Americanization 4. Immigrants 5. Racism
ISBN 9780316484954

LC 2018010742

Carter G. Woodson Book Awards: Middle Level, 2019.

Profiles eighteen immigrant teenagers in an alphabet that defines their experiences, journeys, and perspectives.

"This unique alphabet book is the result of collaboration between Ewald and 18 high school teenagers who attend Al-Bustan Seeds of Culture, an arts and education organization in Philadelphia." School Library Journal.

Yousafzai, Malala, 1997-

We are displaced: my journey and stories from refugee girls around the world. Malala Yousafzai. Little, Brown and Company, 2019. 224 p.

Grades: 8 9 10 11 12   305.23
1. Refugees 2. Forced relocations 3. Violence 4. Child refugees 5. Political violence 6. Books for reluctant readers
ISBN 9780316523646

LC 2018043763

The Nobel Peace Prize winner presents an urgent reminder about the plight of the world's refugees that draws on her own experiences and the stories of some of the remarkable refugee girls she has met through the course of her advocacy journey.

"In this uplifting work Yousafzai shares the survival stories of female refugees from around the world." Kirkus.

305.23086 Children by miscellaneous social attributes

Ellis, Deborah, 1960-

Children of war: voices of Iraqi refugees. Deborah Ellis. Groundwood Books, c2008. 128 p.

Grades: 7 8 9 10 11 12   305.23086
1. Children and war 2. Child refugees 3. Iraq War, 2003-2011 -- Children 4. Refugees, Iraqi 5. War 6. Iraq -- Social conditions -- 21st century. 7. Iraq -- History -- 21st century.
ISBN 9780888999078

"Ellis interviews child refugees from Iraq, now living in Jordan, and a few who have made it to Canada. . . . Accompanying each of the . . . interviews with young people is a brief introduction and a photo. . . . What is haunting are their graphic recent memories of what they witnessed. . . . An important, current title that will have lasting significance." Booklist.

305.235 Young people twelve to twenty

Alifirenka, Caitlin

I will always write back: how one letter changed two lives. by Caitlin Alifirenka and Martin Ganda; with Liz Welch. Little, Brown and Company, 2015. 400 p.

Grades: 6 7 8 9 10 11 12 Adult   305.235
1. Pen pals 2. Letter writing 3. Friendship 4. Teenagers 5. Zimbabwe 6. United States
ISBN 9780316241311

LC 2014030355

Traces the friendship between an American girl and her pen pal from an impoverished region of Zimbabwe, describing how 12-year-old Caitlin wrote to an unknown student for a class assignment and shared a life-changing six-year correspondence.

"Sensitively and candidly demonstrating how small actions can result in enormous change, this memoir of two families' transformation through the commitment and affection of long-distance friends will humble and inspire." Publishers Weekly.

Burton, Bonnie, 1972-

Girls against girls: why we are mean to each other and how we can change. Bonnie Burton. Orange Avenue Pub., 2009. 128 p.

Grades: 7 8 9 10   305.235
1. Personal conduct 2. Teenage girls -- Personal conduct 3. Cruelty in teenage girls 4. Cruelty in girls 5. Nastiness in teenage girls
ISBN 9780979017360

Examines the topic of cruel behavior amongst girls and the reasons why it happens, offers tips for handling such problems when they arise, and provides suggestions for team building, enhanced with topic-related quotes and stories from celebrities and role models.

"This offers excellent coping techniques. . . . Burton never talks down to her readers, nor does she pull her punches. Readers will respond to the author's clear respect for the painful nature of the problem." Booklist.

Ellis, Deborah, 1960-

Kids of Kabul: living bravely through a never-ending war. Deborah Ellis. Groundwood Books/House of Anansi Press, 2018. c2012. 143 p.

Grades: 6 7 8 9 10 11 12   305.235
1. Children and war 2. War 3. Afghan War, 2001- 4. Afghanistan

-- Social conditions
ISBN 9781554981823

Children in Afghanistan, ranging in age from ten to seventeen, talk candidly about their lives since the fall of the Taliban.

Rosenwald, Laurie, 1955-

All the wrong people have self esteem: an inappropriate book for young ladies (or, frankly, anybody else). by Laurie Rosenwald. Bloomsbury Children's Books, 2008. 144 p.

Grades: 6 7 8 9   **305.235**

1. Teenage girls 2. Teenage girls -- Personal conduct 3. Teenage girls -- Interpersonal relations
ISBN 9781599902401

LC 2008014386

With chapter headings such as "Reasons To Be Cheerful" and "Just Plain Bizarre," this guide provides guidance, tips, and amusing anecdotes for everyday teen dilemmas and challenges, from saving the earth to understanding the "meaning" of breasts.

"Rosenwald tackles political correctness, the follies of prevailing wisdom and her favorite peeves using all the tools in her arsenal: her spread-size collages feature fonts on sterioids, magazine cut-outs, photos and cartoons paired with witty diatribes [and] confessions. . . . Funny, fresh and impossible not to read cover to cover." Publishers Weekly.

Sokolower, Jody

Determined to stay: Palestinian youth fight for their village. Jody Sokolower; introduction by Nick Estes. Olive Branch Press, an imprint of Interlink Publishing Group, Inc., 2021. 208 p.

Grades: 7 8 9 10 11 12   **305.235**

1. Palestinian teenagers 2. Arab-Israeli conflict 3. Arab-Israeli relations 4. Palestinians 5. Jerusalem, Israel
ISBN 9781623718886

LC 2021010013

Palestinian youth and the fight for their village. Silwan is a Palestinian village located just outside the ancient walls of the Old City of Jerusalem. As Silwani youth and community members share their lives with us, their village becomes an easily accessible way to understand Palestinian history and current reality. Written with young people in mind, the richly illustrated text stresses connections between the lives of youth in the US and Palestine: criminalization of youth, forced relocation, the impact of colonialism on Indigenous communities, efforts to bury history, and inspiring examples of resistance and resilience. Provided by publisher.

"The harrowing and heartbreaking true stories told by the Palestinian children reveal the obvious parallels between the treatment of Indigenous people by the U.S. government in the past and the current racial injustices, especially toward Black people, prevalent in the U.S. now. . . . Necessary reading that is highly recommended." Booklist

305.235092 Young people—Biography

Villalobos, Juan Pablo, 1973-

The **other** side: stories of Central American teen refugees who dream of crossing the border. Juan Pablo Villalobos; translated by Rosalind Harvey. Farrar Straus Giroux, 2019. 147 p.

Grades: 7 8 9 10 11 12   **305.235092**

1. Teenage refugees 2. Teenage immigrants 3. Refugees 4. Immigrants 5. Central America -- Emigration and immigration 6.

United States -- Emigration and immigration
ISBN 9780374305734

LC 2018058988

Recounts the experiences of eleven teenagers who navigated the immigration process, while exploring the issues that lead refugees from Central America to flee to the United Sates.

"The fear and dangers of crossing the border are palpable, but not all depictions are dire. Villalobos makes a point to include a thread of hopefulness that pushes the protagonists forward." Kirkus.

305.3 People by gender or sex

Bornstein, Kate, 1948-

My new gender workbook: a step-by-step guide to achieving world peace through gender anarchy and sex positivity. Kate Bornstein. Routledge, 2013. xiii, 293 p.

Grades: Adult   **305.3**

1. Gender identity 2. Sex (Psychology)
ISBN 9780415538640

LC 2012033355

Since its first publication in 1997, My Gender Workbook has been challenging, encouraging, questionning, and handholding those trying to figure out how to become a "real man," a "real woman," or "something else entirely." In this updated edition of her classic text, Bornstein re-examines gender in light of issues like race and class. With new quizzes, new puzzles, new exercises, and plenty of Kate's over-the-top style, My Gender Workbook,

Second Edition promises to help a new generation create their own unique place on the gender spectrum. Provided by publisher.

305.42 Social role and status of women

Sands, Crystal

Women and feminism today. by Crystal Sands. ReferencePoint Press, Inc., 2019 80 p.: Women and society

Grades: 8 9 10 11 12   **305.42**

1. Feminism -- History 2. Women's rights 3. Gender role
ISBN 9781682825471

LC 2018038249

"The portrayal of women in the media, the evolution of feminism, and the changing face of the American family are thoroughly explored. The continuing struggle for representation in the sports field, as well as harassment, victimization, violence, and the recent #TimesUp and #MeToo movements are covered." School Library Journal

Includes bibliographical references and index.

305.48 Specific groups of women

Arce, Julissa

Someone like me: how one undocumented girl fought for her American dream. Julissa Arce. Little, Brown and Company, 2018. 240 p.

Grades: 6 7 8 9   **305.48**

1. Arce, Julissa 2. Undocumented immigrants 3. Mexican American girls 4. Women social advocates 5. Immigrants 6. Mexican Americans
ISBN 9780316481748

LC 2018007526

Explores the author's days in Mexico separated from her parents, and her daily fears while growing up undocumented in Texas.

"Offering young people a clear autobiographical viewpoint of a controversial issue, this is a must for all collections." Booklist.

Charleyboy, Lisa

#NotYourPrincess: voices of Native American women. edited by Lisa Charleyboy and Mary Beth Leatherdale. Annick Press, 2017. 116 p.

Grades: 7 8 9 10 11 12   **305.48**
1. Native American women 2. Indigenous peoples 3. Ethnic identity 4. Social perception 5. Stereotypes (Social psychology) 6. Anthologies
ISBN 9781554519583

A collection of powerful voices of Indigenous women across North America.

"The vital message that it offers is that Indigenous women continue to shatter stereotypes through their personal successes and creative expression. Both testament to the complexity of Indigenous women's identities and ferocious statement that these women fully inhabit the modern world." Kirkus.

305.5 People by social and economic levels

Hansen, Joyce

Breaking ground, breaking silence: the story of New York's African burial ground. Joyce Hansen and Gary McGowan. Henry Holt, 1998. 130 p.

Grades: 8 9 10 11 12 Adult   **305.5**
1. 18th century 2. Enslaved people 3. African Americans -- History 18th century 4. Cemeteries -- History 18th century 5. Material culture 6. Excavations (Archaeology) 7. New York City -- Antiquities
ISBN 0805050124

LC   97019105

Describes the discovery and study of the African burial site found in Manhattan in 1991, while excavating for a new building, and what it reveals about the lives of black people in Colonial times.

"This book is well written and attractively designed, and readers should have access to it in social studies classrooms as well as in libraries. It will generate lots of class discussion and writing projects." Voice of Youth Advocates.

Includes bibliographical references (p. [119]) and index.

Miller, Michael, 1958-

Exposing hate: prejudice, hatred, and violence in action. Michael Miller. Tweny-First Century Books, 2019. 144 p.

Grades: 8 9 10 11 12   **305.5**
1. Hate groups 2. Hate crimes 3. Right-wing extremists 4. Violence 5. Violent crimes
ISBN 9781541539259

"The book does not sensationalize; it just gives solid facts on how injustices are committed due to ignorance, fear, and misinformation. Stories of how people have reformed after interacting with those they have learned to hate give the factual text emotional heft. A necessary book on a hot-button social issue that can help students develop critical thinking skills while they learn more about heinous organizations." Booklist..

305.8 Ethnic and national groups

Hudson, Wade

The **talk**: conversations about race, love & truth. edited by Wade Hudson & Cheryl Willis Hudson Crown Books for Young Readers, 2020. 128 p.

Grades: 5 6 7 8 9   **305.8**
1. Racism 2. Race relations 3. Marginalized people 4. Ethnic identity 5. Self-esteem in children 6. Anthologies 7. Short stories 8. Essays 9. Antiracist literature
ISBN 9780593121610

LC 2020011095

Thirty diverse and award-winning authors and illustrators capture frank discussions about racism, identity, and self-esteem. Provided by publisher.

"Approaches range from emotional direct address to warmly remembered anecdote to thoughtful lecture and accompanying art includes graphic novel styled panels, incorporated line drawings, and tender portraiture. This will be validating for readers already familiar with these kinds of talks and importantly enlightening for those to whom the ideas of such restrictions are new." Bulletin of the Center for Children's Books

Includes bibliographical references.

Joseph, Frederick

The **Black** friend: on being a better white person. Frederick Joseph. Candlewick Press, 2020. xviii, 254 p.

Grades: 7 8 9 10 11 12   **305.8**
1. Joseph, Frederick (Activist) 2. Race awareness 3. Antiracism 4. Racism 5. Institutional racism 6. African American men 7. United States -- Race relations 8. Antiracist literature
ISBN 9781536217018

Presents race-related anecdotes from the author's past, weaving in his thoughts on why they were hurtful and how he might handle things differently now, in hopes of bringing more race awareness to Americans.

"Readers will appreciate the comradely tone of this meaty yet accessible, challenging yet enjoyable book addressed to white people trying to do better at understanding race and racism." Bulletin of the Center for Children's Books

Includes bibliographic references (pages 245-247) and index.

Rodger, Marguerite

Racism and prejudice. Marguerite Rodger and Jessie Rodger. Crabtree Pub., c2011. 48 p.: Straight talk about...

Grades: 7 8 9 10   **305.8**
1. Racism 2. Race relations 3. Prejudice 4. Discrimination 5. Race (Social sciences)
ISBN 9780778721291

"The authors cover topics ranging from overt racism to homophobia to the treatment of people with mental and physical disabilities. They discuss the history of hate and include personal accounts from those who've dealt with being stereotyped. The book is well laid out and easy to read. . . . Readers will appreciate the relevant photos of teens, the quotes, and the honest writing style." School Library Journal.

305.800973 Ethnic groups—United States

Burton, Erica

Race relations. Erica Burton. Mason Crest, 2020. 112 p.

Grades: 7 8 9   **305.800973**
1. Race relations 2. Political science -- Race relations 3. Prejudices

4. Racism 5. Instructional and educational works
ISBN 9781422244005

LC 2019275215

The United States has a long and difficult history of race relations. Although slavery was ended after the American Civil War in 1865, its legacy continues today in education, employment, housing, and the criminal justice system. This book examines the roles that society and government could play in changing attitudes toward race and creating a country where people are judged on the content of their character, rather than the color of their skin."—Back cover.

Jewell, Tiffany

This book is anti-racist: 20 lessons on how to wake up, take action, and do the work. by Tiffany Jewell; illustrated by Aurelia Durand. Frances Lincoln Children's Books, 2020. 160 p.

Grades: 7 8 9 10   **305.800973**

1. Antiracism 2. Racism 3. Race relations 4. Stereotypes (Social psychology) 5. Discrimination 6. United States -- Race relations 7. Antiracist literature
ISBN 9780711245211

Who are you? What is racism? Where does it come from? Why does it exist? What can you do to disrupt it? Learn about social identities, the history of racism and resistance against it, and how you can use your anti-racist lens and voice to move the world toward equity and liberation.

"Combining the disruption of common fallacies, spotlights on change makers, the author's personal reflections, and a call to action, this powerful book has something for all young people no matter what stage they are at in terms of awareness or activism." Kirkus.

Includes bibliographical references (pages 158-159).

Kendi, Ibram X.

Stamped: racism, antiracism, and you. Ibram X. Kendi and Jason Reynolds. Little, Brown and Company, 2020. 304 p.

Grades: 7 8 9 10 11 12   **305.800973**

1. Race relations 2. Discrimination 3. Racism 4. Antiracism 5. Stereotypes (Social psychology) 6. United States -- Race relations -- History 7. Antiracist literature
ISBN 9780316453691

LC 2019033917

A history of racist and antiracist ideas in America, from their roots in Europe until today, adapted from the National Book Award winner Stamped from the Beginning.

"Readers will undoubtedly experience a mixture of feelings after finishing this book, but the encouragement to emerge as critical thinkers who can decipher coded language and harmful imagery stemming from racist ideas, which still linger in modern society and popular culture, will be the most empowering result." Booklist

Includes bibliographical references and index.

305.868 Spanish Americans

Hutchison, Patricia

Central American immigrants: in their shoes. Patricia Hutchison. Child's World, 2019 32 p.

Grades: 4 5 6 7   **305.868**

1. Central Americans 2. Emigration and immigration -- Social aspects 3. Immigrants -- History 4. Immigrants
ISBN 9781503827950

LC bl2019003242

Looks into the lives, challenges, and successes of Central American immigrants.

305.895 East and southeast Asian peoples

Yoo, Paula

From a whisper to a rallying cry: the killing of Vincent Chin and the trial that galvanized the Asian American movement. Paula Yoo. Norton Young Readers, 2021. 352 p.

Grades: 8 9 10 11 12   **305.895**

1. Chin, Vincent, -1982 2. 1980s 3. Hate crimes 4. Chinese American men 5. Murder 6. Trials 7. Racism
ISBN 9781324002871

LC 2020053662

America in 1982. Japanese car companies are on the rise and believed to be putting American autoworkers out of their jobs. Anti-Asian American sentiments simmer, especially in Detroit. A bar fight turns fatal, leaving Vincent Chin—a Chinese American man—beaten to death at the hands of two white men, autoworker Ronald Ebens and his stepson Michael Nitz.

"This clear and lucid account, based on in-depth research, superlatively conveys the context and significance of the events. The conflicting accounts and explanations are presented evenhandedly, offering readers the opportunity to weigh the evidence and draw their own conclusions." Kirkus

Includes bibliographical references and index.

305.896 Africans and people of African descent

Coates, Ta-Nehisi

The beautiful struggle. Ta-Nehisi Coates. Random House Childrens Books 2021 176 p.

Grades: 8 9 10 11 12   **305.896**

1. Coates, Ta-Nehisi. 2. African American authors 3. African Americans -- Social conditions 4. Fathers and sons 5. African American young men -- Family relationships 6. African American parenting 7. Baltimore, Maryland -- Social life and customs -- 20th century
ISBN 9781984894021

LC 2020040484

Adapted for teen readers, a father-son memoir documents the National Book Award-winning author's youth in the "murder capital" of 1980s Baltimore and his relationship with his father, Vietnam veteran Paul Coates, throughout the latter's activism as a Black Panther and Afrocentric scholar.

"A beautiful meditation on the tender, fraught interior lives of Black boys." Kirkus

Marcovitz, Hal

Black in America. by Hal Marcovitz. ReferencePoint Press, 2021. 80 p.: Bias in America

Grades: 7 8 9 10 11 12   **305.896**

1. Racism -- History 2. African Americans -- Social conditions 21st century. 3. Racial profiling 4. Police brutality 5. United States -- Race relations -- History
ISBN 9781682828915

LC 2020011941

Racial bias against African Americans remains part of the fabric of American life, 400 years after the first African slaves stepped off a ship docking near Jamestown, Virginia. Black people often face violent attacks simply because they are Black. Provided by publisher.

"Discussing topics such as being victimized by police, and racism in retail and on school campuses, this book speaks to the ways that racism pervades every aspect of Black American life." Booklist

Includes bibliographical references and index.

Osborne, Linda Barrett, 1949-

Miles to go for freedom: segregation and civil rights in the Jim Crow years. by Linda Barrett Osborne. Abrams Books for Young Readers, 2011. ix, 118 p.

Grades: 6 7 8   **305.896**

1. 20th century 2. 19th century 3. Racism 4. Segregation -- History 20th century 5. African Americans -- Civil rights -- History 20th century 6. Prejudice 7. United States -- Race relations
ISBN 9781419700200

           LC 2011022854

Told through first-person accounts, Library of Congress records and other primary sources, an overview of racial segregation and early civil rights efforts in Jim Crow America examines the period from various perspectives while explaining the impact of legal segregation and discrimination.

305.897 North American native peoples

Leatherdale, Mary Beth

Urban tribes: Native Americans in the city. edited by Lisa Charleyboy and Mary Beth Leatherdale. Annick Press, [2015] 136 p.

Grades: 7 8 9 10 11 12   **305.897**

1. First Nations (Canada) 2. Indians of North America -- Urban residence 3. City life 4. Urban teenagers 5. Ethnic identity 6. Canada 7. Anthologies
ISBN 9781554517503

Over 30 young urban Natives share stories, poems, and art chronicling how they connect to their culture, break down stereotypes, and use their indigenous world views to create a better future for all.

"A refreshingly authentic, edgy, and captivating work that will appeal to young people." School Library Journal.

Includes bibliographical references.

305.9 People by occupation and miscellaneous social statuses; people with disabilities and illnesses, gifted people

Leatherdale, Mary Beth

Stormy seas: stories of young boat refugees. Mary Beth Leatherdale and Eleanor Shakespeare. Annick Press, [2017] 56 p.

Grades: 5 6 7 8 9   **305.9**

1. Refugees 2. Immigration and emigration 3. Poverty
ISBN 1554518962

Presents five true stories, from 1939 to today, about young people who lived through the harrowing experience of setting sail in search of asylum: Ruth and her family board the St. Louis to escape Nazism; Phu sets out alone from war-torn Vietnam; José tries to reach the United States from Cuba; Najeeba flees Afghanistan and the Taliban; and after losing his family, Mohamed abandons his village on the Ivory Coast in search of a new life.

"Together, the words and images offer an affecting perspective on the plight of refugees and emphasizes that this human-rights crisis is an ongoing, urgent issue." Booklist.

Includes bibliographical references and Internet addresses.

Wilkes, Sybella

Out of Iraq: refugees' stories in words, paintings and music. Sybella Wilkes. Evans Brothers, 2010. 70 p.

Grades: 4 5 6 7   **305.9**

1. Refugees, Iraqi 2. War 3. Iraq War, 2003-2011 4. Military occupation 5. Refugees 6. Iraq -- History -- 2003- 7. Jordan
ISBN 9780237539306

"Provides a concise overview of events before and during the invasion, interspersed with first-person narratives of Iraqi refugees, gathered while Wilkes worked with the United Nations Refugee Agency in Syria. . . . Moving photographs and artwork, quotations from political figures, and accessible language form a harrowing window into lives rarely paid witness." Publishers Weekly.

306 Culture and institutions

Paul, Caroline

You are mighty: a guide to changing the world. by Caroline Paul; illustrated by Lauren Tamaki. Bloomsbury, 2018. 128 p.

Grades: 5 6 7 8 9   **306**

1. Social problems 2. Social advocacy 3. Community activism 4. Children 5. Social action
ISBN 9781681198224

           LC 2017034366

Shares tips and inspiration for aspiring activists, offering anecdotes about young activists from different world regions and historical periods while outlining a range of legal activist tactics.

306.096 Culture—Africa

Bowden, Rob, 1973-

African culture. Rob Bowden and Rosie Wilson. Heinemann Library, c2010. 48 p.

Grades: 4 5 6   **306.096**

1. Africa -- Civilization 2. Africa -- Social life and customs
ISBN 9781432924409

           LC 2008048310

Describes the culture of Africa, discussing ancient traditions, languages, family life, eating customs, education, diseases, the arts, recreation, religion, and the influence of African culture on the rest of the world.

"This book presents a clear and timely overview of the diverse and complex continent. The full-color photographs are of exceptional quality. [The] book also includes interesting fact boxes, sidebars, maps, and a time line. [It] focuses on traditions and how they are relevant for today. Highlights include family and daily life; religion, beliefs, and customs; and the performing and visual arts." School Library Journal.

Includes bibliographical references (p. 46) and index.

306.3 Economic institutions

Conkling, Winifred
Passenger on the Pearl: the true story of Emily Edmonson's flight from slavery. Winifred Conkling. Algonquin Young Readers, 2015. 176 p.
Grades: 7 8 9 10 **306.3**
    1. Edmonson, Emily, 1835-1895 2. Edmondson family 3. Pearl (Schooner) 4. Freedom seekers 5. Anti-slavery movements -- History 19th century 6. Slavery 7. Enslaved people 8. African Americans 9. United States -- History -- 19th century
ISBN 9781616201968
    LC 2014029246
Carter G. Woodson Book Awards: Secondary Level, 2016.
Documents the turbulent events of the 1848 escape attempt by 13-year-old Emily Edmonson, her siblings and dozens of other enslaved people on board the Pearl, discussing the contributions made by Harriet Beecher Stowe, Emily's subsequent education and her history-changing teaching career.
    "By examining the intersecting experiences of enslaved people, abolitionists, free people of color, slave owners, and slave traders, this book provides an effective antidote to the oversimplified picture of slavery in America painted by some outdated textbooks." Booklist.
    Includes bibliographical references.

Huey, Lois Miner
Forgotten bones: uncovering a slave cemetery. Lois Miner Huey. Millbrook Press, 2016. 112 p.
Grades: 4 5 6 7 **306.3**
    1. Cemeteries 2. Enslaved people 3. Human remains (Archaeology) 4. Forensic anthropology 5. African Americans 6. Northeastern States -- History.
ISBN 9781467733939
    LC 2014009379
"Together with chronicles of two other noted northern slave cemeteries and full-color photos of the excavation in process, this account provides a vivid description of both the eighteenth-century slave experience and the field of archaeology." Booklist.
    Includes bibliographical references and index.

Lester, Julius
    ★ **To** be a slave. Julius Lester; paintings by Tom Feelings. Dial Books, 1998, c1968. 160 p.
Grades: 6 7 8 9 **306.3**
    1. Slave trade 2. Slavery 3. Enslaved people 4. United States -- History -- Race relations.
ISBN 0803723474
    LC 98005213
A compilation, selected from various sources and arranged chronologically, of the reminiscences of slaves and ex-slaves about their experiences from the leaving of Africa through the Civil War and into the early twentieth century.

McClafferty, Carla Killough, 1958-
Buried lives: the enslaved people of George Washington's Mount Vernon. by Carla Killough McClafferty. Holiday House, 2018. x, 144 p.
Grades: 6 7 8 9 **306.3**
    1. Judge, Oney, 1773-1848 2. Washington, George, 1732-1799 3. Early America (1784-1819) 4. 18th century 5. Enslaved people 6. Slavery 7. Presidents 8. Freedom seekers 9. Slaveholders 10. Mount Vernon 11. Virginia -- History
ISBN 9780823436972
    LC 2016058471
Draws on primary source documents and photographs of historical artifacts to examine the lives of men and women enslaved by the Washington family, and includes information on the present-day archeological survey of Mount Vernon's Slave Cemetery.

Sylvester, Kevin
Follow your stuff: who makes it, where does it come from, how does it get to you? Kevin Sylvester, Michael Hlinka. Annick Press, 2019. 100 p.
Grades: 5 6 7 8 9 **306.3**
    1. Products 2. Wages 3. Work environment
ISBN 9781773212548
Takes on a tour of the global economy, examining the often complex journey of everyday objects, from production right to our doorsteps.

306.4 Specific aspects of culture

Chang, Jeff
Can't stop won't stop: a hip-hop history. Jeff Chang, with Dave "Davey D" Cook. St Martins Pr 2021 320 p.
Grades: 8 9 10 11 12 **306.4**
    1. Rap music -- History and criticism 2. Hip-hop culture 3. Music and society 4. Popular music
ISBN 9781250790514
    LC 2020048553
The American Book Award winner, now completely adapted for a young adult audience! From award-winning author Jeff Chang, Can't Stop Won't Stop is the story of hip-hop, a generation-defining movement and the music that transformed American politics and culture forever. Hip hop is one of the most dominant and influential cultures in America, giving new voice to the younger generation. It defines a generation's worldview. Exploring hip hop's beginnings up to the present day, Jeff Chang and Dave "Davey D" Cook provide a provocative look into the new world that the hip hop generation has created. Based on original interviews with DJs, b-boys, rappers, activists, and gang members, with unforgettable portraits of many of hip hop's forebears, founders, mavericks, and present day icons, this book chronicles the epic events, ideas and the music that marked the hip hop generation's rise. Provided by publisher.
    "The authors show the oft-underrepresented ways that Black women have shaped hip-hop, and new chapters chart its championing in the 21st century as a lifestyle built around being anti-establishment grappled with commercial success, political influence, and social change." Kirkus
    Includes bibliographical references and index.

Jensen, Kelly
Body talk: 37 voices explore our radical anatomy. edited by Kelly Jensen. Algonquin Young Readers, 2020. 256 p.
Grades: 8 9 10 11 12 **306.4**
    1. Human body -- Social aspects 2. Human body -- Political aspects 3. Body image 4. Anthologies 5. Essays 6. Comics and graphic novels
ISBN 9781616209674
    LC 2020009794
Thirty-seven contributors—including model Tyra Banks, gymnast Aly Raisman, and bestselling YA authors—explore the world in their unique bodies through essays, lists, comics, and art.

"Each author fully and impressively engages with their intersecting identities and the ways in which these intersections affect the way their bodies are treated by society. Taken together with short FAQ sections that address everything from the difference between body positivity and fat acceptance to respectful terms to use when discussing disability, the anthology is a comprehensive, compulsively readable guide to growing into our bodies in a politically fraught world." Kirkus

Includes bibliographical references.

Manfredi, Angie

The **(other)** F word: a celebration of the fat & fierce. edited by Angie Manfredi. Amulet Books, 2019. 224 p.

Grades: 8 9 10 11 12   **306.4**
1. Body image 2. Body size 3. Self-confidence 4. Overweight persons 5. Influencers 6. Anthologies
ISBN 9781419737503

LC 2019011713

A crossover anthology for teens and activists shares essays, prose, fashion tips and art to offer strategies for overcoming today's narrow definitions of beauty and styling oneself in accordance with body positivity and acceptance of all sizes.

306.6 Religious institutions

Marshall Cavendish Reference

Modern Muslim societies.. Marshall Cavendish Reference, 2011. 46 p.

Grades: 7 8 9   **306.6**
1. Islamic sociology 2. Islam -- Customs and practices 3. Muslims -- Social life and customs 4. Islamic law 5. Economics -- Religious aspects -- Islam
ISBN 9780761479277

LC 2010008612

Discusses the major features of Muslim society, including family life, Islamic law, economic practices, and government relations, and profiles Muslim life in each region of the world.

306.70835 Adolescents—Sexual relations

Mirk, Sarah

You do you: figuring out your body, dating, and sexuality. Sarah Mirk. Twenty-First Century Books, 2019. 120 p.

Grades: 8 9 10 11 12   **306.70835**
1. Sex education for teenagers 2. Reproductive health 3. Sexuality 4. Teenagers -- Health 5. Puberty
ISBN 9781541540224

Every person—and every body—is different. Deciding what's right for you in dating and relationships means learning how your body works. It also means thinking about your gender and sexual identity. Mirk provides information that will help you move with respect and joy through the world of friendship, romance, and sex. Adapted from jacket

"An affirming, up-to-date book for teens that encourages smart, informed decision-making about their own bodies. . . . Highly recommended for teens and the adults who care for them." Kirkus.

Includes bibliographical references (page 111) and index.

Murray, Craig

Sexpectations: sex stuff straight up. Craig Murray and Leissa Pitts. Allen & Unwin, 2011. 111, 111 p.

Grades: 7 8 9 10 11 12   **306.70835**
1. Family life education 2. Sex education for teenagers 3. Teenagers -- Sexuality 4. Reversible books
ISBN 9781741751437

LC bl2012017863

Examines issues involving sexual exploration, sexual desire, and making positive, responsible choices, in a guide that provides straightforward facts on everything from keeping safe to understanding sexual identity.

Pardes, Bronwen

Doing it right: making smart, safe, and satisfying choices about sex. Bronwen Pardes. Simon Pulse, 2013. 146 p.

Grades: 9 10 11 12   **306.70835**
1. Sex education for teenagers 2. Teenagers -- Sexual behavior 3. Teenagers 4. Sexuality -- Questions and answers
ISBN 9781442483705

LC bl2013002491

Provides information and advice for young adults on sex-related issues, including sexual anatomy, sexual readiness, STDs, birth control, sexual and gender identity, masturbation, and rape.

306.76 Sexual orientation, transgender identity, intersexuality

Bausum, Ann

Stonewall: breaking out in the fight for gay rights. Ann Bausum. Penguin Group USA, 2015. 128 p.

Grades: 8 9 10 11 12   **306.76**
1. Stonewall Riots, New York, NY, 1969 2. LGBTQIA rights 3. Gay and Lesbian Movement -- History 4. Homosexuality -- History 5. United States -- History -- 20th century
ISBN 9780670016792

In 1969 being gay in the United States was a criminal offense; it meant living a closeted life or surviving on the fringes of society. People went to jail, lost jobs, and were disowned by their families for being gay. A police raid on the Stonewall Inn, a gay bar in Greenwich Village, turned into a riot. Ann Bausum's riveting exploration of the Stonewall Riots and the national Gay Rights movement that followed is eye-opening, unflinching, and inspirin

"Bausum begins her history of the gay rights movement with a careful, detailed exposition of the June 1969 Stonewall riots, laying out the events leading up to the clash between the Greenwich Village gay community and the police and putting those events in the context of time and place. She dedicates the first half of the book to the riots themselves, drawing on reports, interviews, and other first-person accounts to put together a candid linear narrative that takes into consideration the perspectives of both sides of the conflict. . . . Bausum writes with the precision of a journalist; there is never any doubt as to what she wonders, what she conjectures, and what she knows." Horn Book.

Chevat, Richie

A **queer** history of the United States for young people. Michael Bronski; adapted by Richie Chevat. Beacon Press, 2019. xx, 316 p.

Grades: 7 8 9 10 11 12   **306.76**
1. LGBTQIA rights -- History 2. Homosexuality -- History 3. Gay and Lesbian Movement 4. Lesbians -- History 5. Gay men -- History 6. United States -- Social life and customs.
ISBN 9780807056127

Through engrossing narratives, letters, drawings, poems, and more, the book encourages young readers, of all identities, to feel pride at the accomplishments of the LGBTQ people who came before them and to use history as a guide to the future.

"Now here's an attention getting title. Be they erstwhile researchers, concerned adults, or curious kids, readers will find a straightforward, documented, nonsensational celebration of the contributions of LGBTQ people in the U.S. over the past three centuries." Booklist.

Includes bibliographical references and index.

Harris, Duchess

Being transgender in America. Duchess Harris, JD, PhD; with Kristin Marciniak. Essential Library, an imprint of Abdo Publishing, 2020 112 p.

Grades: 6 7 8 9 10 11 12 **306.76**

1. Transgender people 2. Transgender people -- Social conditions 3. Transgender people -- Legal status, laws, etc 4. Gender identity
ISBN 9781532119033

LC 2018966009

Examines how people who are transgender—who have a gender identity that doesn't match their sex assigned at birth—have experiences that are unique compared to those of the rest of the population. Publisher's website.

Huegel, Kelly

LGBTQ: the survival guide for lesbian, gay, bisexual, transgender, and questioning teens. Kelly Huegel Madrone. Free Spirit Pub., 2018, c2003. 272 p.

Grades: 7 8 9 10 11 12 **306.76**

1. Gay teenagers 2. Lesbian teenagers 3. Homosexuality 4. Coming out (Sexual or gender identity) 5. Gay teenagers -- Coming out
ISBN 9781631983023

LC 2002156692

Describes the challenges faced by gay, lesbian, bisexual, and transgendered teens, offers practical advice, real-life experiences, and accessible resources and support groups.

"This sensitive, frank, and supportive volume belongs in every library." School Library Journal.

Includes bibliographical references.

Hurt, Avery Elizabeth

Confronting LGBTQ+ discrimination. Avery Elizabeth Hurt. Rosen YA, 2018. 64 p.: Speak up! Confronting discrimination in your daily life

Grades: 7 8 9 10 **306.76**

1. LGBTQIA persons 2. Discrimination 3. Empowerment (Social sciences) 4. Homophobia 5. Homosexuality
ISBN 9781538381748

LC 2017017641

"This entry in the Speak Up! Confronting Discrimination in Your Daily Life series (7 titles) is a fact-based introduction to an important issue. This is generously illustrated, replete with sidebars, and offers helpful appended matter. A useful book that belongs in school and public library collections." Booklist

Includes bibliographical references and index.

Jennings, Jazz

Being Jazz: my life as a (transgender) teen. Jazz Jennings. Crown, 2016 265 p.

Grades: 6 7 8 9 **306.76**

1. Jennings, Jazz 2. Transgender teenagers 3. Transgender persons

4. Teenage social advocates 5. Transgenderism 6. Teenage girls 7. Teenagers' writings
ISBN 9780399554643

"A great introduction to trans life for middle schoolers and a balancing addition to the more harrowing stories available." School Library Journal.

Kuklin, Susan

Beyond magenta: transgender teens speak out. Susan Kuklin. Candlewick Press, 2014. 182 p.

Grades: 7 8 9 10 11 12 **306.76**

1. Transgenderism 2. Transgender teenagers 3. Gender identity 4. Genderqueer 5. Intersexuality
ISBN 9780763656119

Draws on six first-person interviews to share compassionate insights into the teen transgender experience, tracing each individual's emotional and physical journey as it was shaped by family dynamics, living situations and the transition each teen made during the personal journey toward acknowledgement of gender preference.

"The level of detail about their lives, and the diversity of their identities—including gender, sexuality, ethnicity, religion, and geography—provide a powerful antidote to the isolation and stigma that some transgender youth experience." School Library Journal.

McKenna, Miles

Out!: how to be your authentic self. by Miles McKenna. Harry N Abrams Inc., 2020 224 p.

Grades: 7 8 9 10 11 12 **306.76**

1. Coming out (Sexual or gender identity) 2. YouTubers 3. Gay transgender persons 4. Identity (Psychology) 5. Transgender persons
ISBN 9781419739941

LC 2019034837

Activist Miles McKenna came out on his YouTube channel in 2017, documenting his transition to help other teens navigate their identities and take charge of their own coming out stories. From that wisdom comes Out!, the ultimate YA guide to the queer lifestyle. Find validation, inspiration, and support for your questions big and small—whether you're exploring your identity or seeking to understand the experience of an awesome queer person in your life. Provided by publisher.

"McKenna, a queer, white, trans YouTube personality, presents a new generation of tween and teen readers with an updated coming-out guide that's fun, fresh, and incredibly useful. Celebrity-authored books can be hit or miss, but this one will be a hit thanks to the warmth and personality that infuse it." Kirkus

Pitman, Gayle E

The Stonewall Riots: coming out in the streets. Gayle E Pitman; foreword by Fred Sargeant Abrams Books for Young Readers, 2019. 224 p.

Grades: 6 7 8 9 **306.76**

1. Stonewall Riots, New York, NY, 1969 2. LGBTQIA rights 3. Gay and Lesbian Movement -- History 4. Homosexuality -- History 5. Gay men -- History 20th century 6. United States -- History -- 20th century 7. Greenwich Village, New York City -- History 8. Books for reluctant readers
ISBN 9781419737206

LC 2019000932

A chronicle of gay history in America draws on news clippings, first-hand testimonies and other period sources, in a 50th anniversary account of the Stonewall Riots and other pivotal events that shaped the beginning of the LGBTQ+ movement.

"A substantive look at a key moment in the history of the LGBTQ-IAP-equality movement." Kirkus

Includes bibliographical references and index.

Savage, Dan

It gets better: coming out, overcoming bullying, and creating a life worth living. edited by Dan Savage and Terry Miller. Plume, 2012, c2011. x, 338 p.

Grades: 6 7 8 9 10 11 12   **306.76**
1. Gay teenagers 2. Coming out (Sexual orientation) 3. Bullying and bullies 4. Quality of life 5. Happiness
ISBN 9780452297616

LC bl2012003218

A collection of essays and testimonials written to teens from celebrities, political leaders, and everyday people, stresses to gay and lesbian youth that they can lead fulfilling lives free of bullying, and that their adult years will get better.

"I wish I could have told you things get better. The words that became a call to action were born in the comments section on a blog post written by Savage about 15-year-old Billy Lucas. Savage, an author (The Kid, 1999), gay activist, and sex-advice columnist, together with his partner, Miller, launched the It Gets Better project on YouTube as a reaction to Lucas and two other suicides precipitated by gay bullying during the summer of 2010. . . . It Gets Better—the book—expands on a selection of those videos, capturing stories from people of every background, including a startling collection of famous writers, entertainers, and politicians. Particularly noteworthy are essays from President Obama and David Sedaris and a bilingual entry from a Mexican student now living in Canada. This a resource every Library should have on hand." Booklist.

Testa, Rylan Jay

The **gender** quest workbook: a guide for teens and young adults exploring gender identity. Rylan Jay Testa, Deborah Coolhart, and Jayme Peta. Instant Help, [2015] 168 p.: Instant help solutions series

Grades: 7 8 9 10 11 12 Adult Professional   **306.76**
1. Gender identity 2. Sex differences (Psychology) 3. Sexuality 4. Transgenderism 5. Genderqueer
ISBN 9781626252974

LC 2015032696

"From inconspicuous activities such as people watching to more task-oriented ideas for encouraging young people to broach their concerns to family members, this volume serves as a valuable resource. While this isn't the best acquisition for libraries (it is truly a workbook), librarians would do well to be informed of its availability" Library Journal.

306.85 Family

Lynette, Rachel

What makes us a family?: living in a nontraditional family. Rachel Lynette; content consultant, Robyn J.A. Silverman. ABDO Pub., c2010. 112 p.

Grades: 6 7 8 9   **306.85**
1. Families
ISBN 9781604537567

LC 2009004416

Discusses a variety of nontraditional families and emotional issues that children who are adopted, have an autistic sibling, or are raised by grandparents may face.

"The topics are well selected, the design is attractive, and the stories feature girls from a variety of cultures." Booklist.

Includes bibliographical references (p. 106-107) and index.

306.874 Parent-child relationship

Shantz-Hilkes, Chloe

My girlfriend's pregnant!: a teen's guide to becoming a dad. Chloe Shantz-Hilkes, Willow Dawson. Firefly Books Ltd., 2015. 128 p.

Grades: 7 8 9 10 11 12   **306.874**
1. Teenage fathers -- Psychology 2. Pregnancy -- Psychological aspects 3. Parenthood -- Psychological aspects 4. Teenage fathers
ISBN 9781554517435

For male teens confronted with an unplanned pregnancy and faced with a future filled with fear, doubt, and guilt, My Girlfriend's Pregnant! provides much-needed information and support as they are suddenly thrust into the role of father. Based on interviews with teenage dads, social workers, and medical professionals, this book explores topics such as what to expect during pregnancy and childbirth, parenthood, stress, abortion, and adoption. With an extensivce list of further readings and resources to help with issues ranging from child support to bonding with your child, this book illustrates to young dads that they are not alone and that there are positive ways of dealing with the difficult choices that lie ahead.—Page [4] of cover.

"Intended to provide teen fathers-to-be some support and guidance, this book sheds light on a variety of topics: pregnancy, childbirth, and parenting; the different options ahead (keeping the baby, adoption, abortion), how to deal with the relationship with the mother, and how to manage stress. Interspersed throughout are firsthand accounts from men who became fathers in their teens or early twenties." School Library Journal.

306.875 Sibling relationships

Miller, Sarah Elizabeth, 1979-

The **miracle** & tragedy of the Dionne quintuplets. Sarah Miller. Schwartz & Wade Books, an imprint of Random House Children's Books, 2019 320 p.

Grades: 7 8 9   **306.875**
1. Dionne quintuplets. 2. Quintuplets 3. Child custody 4. Exploitation 5. Public guardianship 6. Guardian and ward 7. Ontario 8. Canada
ISBN 9781524713829

A sobering account of the lives of the Dionne quintuplets describes how the government of 1934 Canada seized custody of the sisters to prevent their exploitation only to render them a popular tourist attraction.

"Miller (The Borden Murders, 2016) offers another impeccably researched look into a cultural phenomenon, digging into the heart of a story surrounded by rumor and exaggeration." Booklist.

Telgemeier, Raina

★ **Sisters**. Raina Telgemeier. Graphix, 2014. 208 p.

Grades: 5 6 7 8   **306.875**
1. Telgemeier, Raina. 2. Sisters 3. Family relationships 4. Automobile travel 5. Girls -- Family relationships 6. Interpersonal relations 7. Autobiographical comics 8. Comics and Graphic novels
ISBN 9780545540599

LC 2013008700

"The author's narrative style is fresh and sharp, and the combination of well-paced and well-placed flashbacks pull the plot together, moving the story forward and helping readers understand the characters' point of view. The volume captures preadolescence in an effortless and uncanny way and turns tough subjects, such as parental marriage problems, into experiences with which readers can identify." School Library Journal.

306.9 Institutions pertaining to death

Noyes, Deborah

Encyclopedia of the end: mysterious death in fact, fancy, folklore, and more. by Deborah Noyes. Houghton Mifflin Co., 2008. 160 p.

Grades: 7 8 9 10 11 12 **306.9**
1. Death -- Social aspects 2. Funerals
ISBN 9780618823628

LC 2008001872

Perfect for Halloween, this beautifully rendered—and unexpectedly lively—compendium explores all things death, including the afterlife, forensic science, funeral foods, rigor mortis, reincarnation, and much more.

"This stylish A-to-Z encounter with all things related to death and dying shows Noyes . . . at her liveliest. . . . The author offers a broad illumination of spiritual, historical and biological aspects of death. Photos, paintings and engravings in homage to the end make the book dynamic visually, too." Publishers Weekly.

Thornhill, Jan

I found a dead bird: the kids' guide to the cycle of life & death. Jan Thornhill Maple Tree Press, 2006. 64 p.

Grades: 4 5 6 **306.9**
1. Death 2. Children and death 3. Life cycles (Biology) 4. Death -- Psychological aspects 5. Dead
ISBN 1897066708

Explores the cycle of life and death and how the process is necessary in nature while also commenting on how death effects people personally and the skills they use to cope with such a trauma when it occurs.

"This straightforward, no holds barred approach to the subject will captivate children. Chock-full of color photographs, the well-designed book contains boxes with tidbits of information on a wide variety of topics, such as death of a species, human destruction, plant decomposition, trapped in time, and learning from death." School Library Journal.

307.1 Planning and development

Reilly, Kathleen M.

Cities: discover how they work. Kathleen M. Reilly; illustrated by Tom Casteel. Nomad Press, 2014 128 p.: Build it yourself

Grades: 4 5 6 **307.1**
1. Cities and towns 2. Urban planning 3. Civil engineering 4. City life
ISBN 9781619302136

An introduction to the inner workings of urban areas profiles the systems that work together to keep things running safely, discussing how cities have evolved since the first riverside settlements while outlining projects that explain basic facts about transportation, water systems and architecture.

"According to the 2010 Census, 80% of Americans live in urban areas. But do they know what it takes to make a city run? From this well-organized and engaging text, readers will learn how cities developed and grew...The simple black-and-white illustrations are helpful, but young readers accustomed to photos might pass on it when leafing through the book. Even so, this is a worthy title for any library collection." School Library Journal.

307.76 Urban communities

Bial, Raymond

Tenement: immigrant life on the Lower East Side. Raymond Bial. Houghton Mifflin, c2002. 48 p.

Grades: 4 5 6 7 **307.76**
1. Poor people 2. Immigrants -- History 19th century 3. Immigrants -- History 20th century 4. Tenement houses 5. Lower East Side, New York City -- Social conditions. 6. New York City -- Social conditions
ISBN 0618138498

LC 2002000407

Presents a view of New York City's tenements during the peak years of foreign immigration, discussing living conditions, laws pertaining to tenements, and the occupations of their residents.

"The writing is particularly clear and sharp. Calling upon and quoting the writing of reformer Jacob Riis (and featuring his compelling photographs), Bial explains simply, yet engagingly, what tenement life was like. . . . Along with Riis' photographs, Bial provides some of his own, taken at the Lower East Side Tenement Museum in New York City." Booklist.

Includes bibliographical references.

320 Political science

Styron, Alexandra

Steal this country: a handbook for resistance, persistence, and fixing almost anything. by Alexandra Styron. Viking, 2018. 224 p.

Grades: 7 8 9 10 11 12 **320**
1. Teenage social advocates 2. Social action 3. Teenagers -- Political activity 4. Community organization 5. Social movements
ISBN 9780451479372

LC 2017060705

Discusses contemporary American problems such as LGBTQIA rights, climate change, immigration, and racial justice, and describes how young activists can make a difference right now.

320.082 Women in politics

Cooper, Ilene

A woman in the House and Senate: how women came to the United States Congress, broke down barriers, and changed the country. by Ilene Cooper; with illustrations by Elizabeth Baddeley. Abrams Books for Young Readers, 2020, 2014. 144 p.

Grades: 5 6 7 8 **320.082**
1. United States. Congress -- History 2. Women legislators -- History 3. Political science 4. Women -- Political Activity
ISBN 9781419742668

Tracing the period between the women's suffrage movement through the results of the 2012 election, a chronicle of women's contributions to politics in the United States features archival photographs and portraits of such luminaries as Hattie Caraway, Patsy Mink and Shirley Chisholm.

320.973 Politics—United States

Khan, Khizr, 1950-

This is our Constitution: discover America with a Gold Star father. Khizr Khan. Random House Childrens Books 2017 256 p.

Grades: 6 7 8 9   **320.973**
1. United States. Constitution 2. Constitutional amendments 3. Constitutional law 4. Constitutions 5. Constitutional history
ISBN 9781524770914

The popular DNC speaker presents an accessible introduction to the Constitution that explains how it represents America's deepest democratic values, tracing the story of his own family's immigration to the U.S. and his views on the Constitution's history, the Bill of Rights and why they are important to today's young people.

321 Systems of governments and states

Gelletly, LeeAnne

Monarchy. LeeAnne Gelletly. Mason Crest, c2013. 64 p.: Major forms of world government

Grades: 6 7 8 9 10   **321**
1. Monarchy 2. Rulers 3. Monarchy -- History
ISBN 9781422221419

LC 2012027846

Examines the history of monarchies and discusses the various forms they have taken.

Oligarchy. LeeAnne Gelletly. Mason Crest, c2013. 64 p.: Major forms of world government

Grades: 6 7 8 9 10   **321**
1. Elite (Social sciences) 2. Rulers 3. Upper class 4. Elitism
ISBN 9781422221426

LC 2012027858

Examines the history of oligarchy and questions if the few wealthy elite constitute a new threat to undermine democracy.

321.8 Democracy

Meersman, Erika

Majority rule vs. individual rights. Erika Meersman. PowerKids Press, 2018. 32 p.

Grades: 5 6 7 8   **321.8**
1. Majorities 2. Civil rights 3. Political rights 4. United States -- Politics and government
ISBN 9781508163947

LC 2017027522

Explores the basic and inalienable rights that United States citizens have that cannot be violated by the government and discusses how those rights are protected in a country of majority rule.

321.9 Authoritarian government

Bailey, Diane, 1966-

Dictatorship. Diane Bailey. Mason Crest, c2013. 64 p.: Major forms of world government

Grades: 6 7 8 9 10   **321.9**
1. Dictatorship 2. Dictators 3. Authoritarianism 4. Totalitarianism 5. Dictatorship -- History
ISBN 9781422221389

LC 2012027899

Examines the history of dictatorships and discusses authoritarianism and totalitarianism.

321.9092 Authoritarian government

Davis, Kenneth C.

Strongman: the rise of five dictators and the fall of democracy. Kenneth C. Davis. Henry Holt & Co 2020 304 p.

Grades: 7 8 9 10 11 12   **321.9092**
1. Hitler, Adolf, 1889-1945 2. Stalin, Joseph, 1879-1953 3. Mao, Zedong, 1893-1976 4. Hussein, Saddam, 1937-2006 5. Mussolini, Benito, 1883-1945 6. Dictators 7. Dictatorship 8. Democracy -- History 9. Political leadership 10. World politics
ISBN 9781250205643

LC 2020009793

A nonfiction account of some of the deadliest dictators in modern history. Provided by publisher.

"Readers learn that each of the five was unspeakably vile in his own way, but together they did share areas of commonality: all of them developed a cult of personality, all of them created new generations of loyal young people (Hitler youth, for example), placed blame on a single group (as Hitler did with the Jews), called for 'law and order,' took control of the media, etc." Booklist

Includes bibliographical references and index.

322.4 Political action groups

Bartoletti, Susan Campbell

They called themselves the K.K.K.: the birth of an American terrorist group. by Susan Campbell Bartoletti. Houghton Mifflin Harcourt, 2010. 172 p.

Grades: 7 8 9 10   **322.4**
1. Ku-Klux Klan -- History -- 19th century. 2. Ku-Klux Klan -- History -- 20th century. 3. Ku-Klux Klan. 4. Racism -- History 5. Hate groups -- History 6. Reconstruction (United States history) 7. United States -- Race relations.
ISBN 9780618440337

LC 2009045247

"In this comprehensive, accessible account, . . . [the author] draws from documentary histories, slave narratives, newspapers, congressional testimony, and other sources to chronicle the origins and proliferation of the Ku Klux Klan against the charged backdrop of Reconstruction politics and legislation. . . . The author lives up to her introductory promise to avoid censoring racist language and images, and includes some horrifying descriptions of lynchings and murders perpetuated during KKK raids. . . . Her account of attending a Klan meeting while researching the book is chilling to the core." Publishers Weekly.

323 Civil and political rights

Archer, Jules

They had a dream: the civil rights struggle, from Frederick Douglass to Marcus Garvey to Martin Luther King, and Malcolm X. Jules Archer. Puffin Books, 1996, c1993. ix, 258 p.

Grades: 6 7 8 9   **323**

   1. Douglass, Frederick, 1818-1895 2. Garvey, Marcus, 1887-1940 3. King, Martin Luther, Jr., 1929-1968 4. Malcolm X, 1925-1965 5. Civil rights workers 6. African Americans -- Civil rights -- History 7. Civil Rights Movement 8. African Americans

ISBN 0140349545

                             LC BL 99769754

Traces the progression of the civil rights movement and its effect on history through biographical sketches of four prominent and influential African Americans: Frederick Douglass, Marcus Garvey, Martin Luther King, Jr., and Malcolm X.

"This discussion of the contributions of four pivotal civil rights activists is balanced and substantive." Publishers Weekly.

Includes bibliographical references and index.

Brimner, Larry Dane

Blacklisted!: Hollywood, the Cold War, and the First Amendment. Larry Dane Brimner. Calkins Creek, 2018. 176 p.

Grades: 7 8 9 10 11 12   **323**

   1. United States. Congress. House. Committee on Un-American Activities 2. United States. Constitution. 1st Amendment. 3. 1940s 4. Civil rights 5. Hollywood Ten 6. Hollywood Blacklist 7. Film industry and trade 8. Communism 9. United States -- Foreign relations -- Soviet Union.

ISBN 9781620916032

                             LC 2018931176

Recounts the 1947 government investigation into the motion picture industry by the House Un-American Activities Committee.

"A chilling look at a time when the government waged war on civil liberties, with the public a complicit ally." Kirkus.

Includes bibliographical references (pages 143-145), filmography (page 145), and index.

Robinson, Mary

Every human has rights: a photographic declaration for kids. by the editors of National Geographic; foreword by Mary Robinson. National Geographic, 2009. 1 v. (unpaged)

Grades: 4 5 6 7 8   **323**

   1. Human rights 2. Children's rights 3. Citizen of the world (Concept) 4. Human rights (International law)

ISBN 9781426305108

                             LC bl2008033100

Based on the thirty rights listed in the "United Nations Universal Declaration of Human Rights," explores the basic freedoms of human beings, especially children, with examples of how these rights have been implemented around the world.

"On the sixtieth anniversary of the Universal Declaration of Human Rights, this full-color photo-essay combines prize-winning poems by young people with beautiful photographs from all over the world. . . . The stirring pictures will stimulate classroom discussion about the declaration, which is quoted in full at the back." Booklist.

323.092 Civil rights leaders

Aretha, David

Martin Luther King Jr. and the 1963 March on Washington. David Aretha. Morgan Reynolds Publishing, [2013] 112 p.: The Civil Rights Movement

Grades: 7 8 9 10 11 12   **323.092**

   1. King, Martin Luther, Jr., 1929-1968. 2. King, Martin Luther, Jr., 1929-1968. I have a dream. 3. March on Washington for Jobs and Freedom, 1963 4. Civil rights demonstrations -- History 20th century. 5. African Americans -- Civil rights 6. Civil Rights Movement 7. Racism

ISBN 9781599353722

                             LC 2012035355

Looks at the rise of Martin Luther King Jr. and the civil rights movement leading up to the 1963 March on Washington where King delivered his famous "I have a dream" speech, presenting details about the march and those who took part.

"Aretha offers considerable detail about the march, including the peaceful, racially integrated crowd and the rousing speeches, which culminated with Dr. King's "Dream" speech. Each chapter opens with lyrics from a protest song, and large sepia-toned photos illustrate the text. Chapter notes document sources, and a lengthy bibliography will aid researchers." School Library Journal.

Includes bibliographical references (p. 102-106) and index.

Bausum, Ann

Marching to the mountaintop: how poverty, labor fights, and civil rights set the stage for Martin Luther King, Jr.'s final hours. Ann Bausum; with a foreword by James Lawson. National Geographic, c2012. 104 p.

Grades: 7 8 9 10   **323.092**

   1. King, Martin Luther, Jr., 1929-1968 2. Garbage Workers' Strike, Memphis, Tennessee, 1968 3. Labor movement -- History 20th century 4. African Americans -- Social conditions 20th century 5. Race relations 6. Civil Rights Movement 7. Memphis, Tennessee -- Race relations -- History -- 20th century

ISBN 9781426309403

                             LC 2011024661

Carter G. Woodson Book Awards: Middle Level, 2013.

Explores how the media, politics, the civil rights movement, and labor protests all converged to set the scene for one of Dr. King's greatest speeches and for his tragic death on April 4, 1968, in Memphis.

323.0973 Civil rights—United States

Turck, Mary

Freedom song: young voices and the struggle for civil rights. Mary C. Turck. Chicago Review Press, c2009. 160 p.

Grades: 7 8 9 10   **323.0973**

   1. Chicago Children's Choir -- History 2. Freedom Singers -- History 3. African Americans -- Civil rights -- History 20th century 4. Civil Rights Movement 5. African American music -- Political aspects -- History 20th century 6. Music -- Political aspects -- History 20th century 7. Singing -- Political aspects -- History 20th century 8. United States -- History -- 20th century.

ISBN 9781556527739

                             LC 2008029673

"The book is divided into chapters that represent the history of the Civil Rights Movement. Sunday of Song, Singing in the Churches, and South Africa, for example, contain information about the factual events while including how the evolution of the music captured the mood and sentiment of the time. The importance of music in the lives of African Americans is described in depth. . . . The accompanying CD allows students to internalize the words and their emotional impact as they listen. Overall, this informative and well-written book is an excellent addition to any collection." School Library Journal.

Includes bibliographical references and index.

323.1 Civil and political rights of nondominant groups

Downing, David, 1946-

Apartheid in South Africa. David Downing. Heinemann Library, c2004. 56 p.: Witness to history

Grades: 7 8 9 10   **323.1**

1. Anti-apartheid Movement 2. Apartheid 3. South Africa -- Race relations -- History.
ISBN 1403448701

LC 2003018235

Examines the historical forces that led to the development of the system of apartheid, what life was like under the system for both blacks and whites, and the efforts that caused the end of this system.

"This dense volume is an excellent narrative overview of the apartheid struggle, drawing extensively on primary sources that provide depth, detail, drama, and authenticity." Booklist.

Includes bibliographical references (p. 53-54) and index.

323.11 Civil and political rights of nondominant groups— Ethnic and national groups

Brimner, Larry Dane

Twelve days in May: Freedom Ride 1961. Larry Dane Brimner. Calkins Creek Books, 2017. 112 p.

Grades: 5 6 7 8 9 10   **323.11**

1. Freedom Riders (Civil rights movement) 2. Civil Rights Movement 3. Civil rights demonstrations 4. African Americans -- Civil rights 5. Freedom Rides (Civil rights movement) 6. Southern States -- Race relations
ISBN 9781629795867
Carter G. Woodson Book Awards: Secondary Level, 2018.
Robert F. Sibert Informational Book Medal, 2018.

For twelve history-making days in May 1961, thirteen black and white civil rights activists, also known as the Freedom Riders, traveled by bus into the South to draw attention to the unconstitutional segregation still taking place. Despite their peaceful protests, the Freedom Riders were met with increasing violence the further south they traveled.

"While the introductory and concluding sections offer helpful summaries of four major Supreme Court rulings on segregation from 1896 to 1960 and short biographies of the 13 Freedom Riders, the heart of the book is its straightforward, concise, day-by-day reporting of the journey. A memorable presentation of inherently dramatic and historically significant events." Booklist.

323.1196 African Americans—Civil and human rights

Bausum, Ann

The **March** against Fear: the last great walk of the civil rights movement and the emergence of Black power. by Ann Bausum. National Geographic Partners, [2017] 128 p.

Grades: 7 8 9 10 11 12   **323.1196**

1. Meredith, James Howard, 1933- 2. 1960s 3. Civil rights demonstrations 4. Racism 5. African American civil rights workers 6. African American college students 7. Black power 8. Mississippi
ISBN 9781426326660

LC 2016027880

Mississippi. 1966. On a hot June afternoon an African-American man named James Meredith set out to walk through his home state, intending to fight racism and fear with his feet. A seemingly simple plan, but one teeming with risk. Just one day later Meredith was shot and wounded in a roadside ambush. Within twenty-four hours, Martin Luther King, Jr., Stokely Carmichael, and other civil rights leaders had taken up Meredith's cause, determined to overcome this violent act and complete Meredith's walk. Provided by publisher.

"This compelling account will be equally engaging for classroom resource material or individual research." Booklist.

Includes bibliographical references and index.

Blohm, Craig E., 1948-

The **civil** rights movement. Craig E. Blohm. ReferencePoint Press, 2019 80 p.

Grades: 7 8 9 10 11 12   **323.1196**

1. African Americans -- Civil rights -- History 2. Civil rights movements -- History 20th century 3. United States -- Race relations
ISBN 9781682824191

LC 2018017166

Since its founding, America has championed the ideal of equality for all its citizens. But ideals do not become reality by simply wishing them to be so; it is hard and often unsung work by dedicated people that brings an ideal to fruition. Through The Civil Rights Movement, equality for all Americans was finally made the law of the land. Provided by publisher.

Bowers, Rick, 1952-

The **spies** of Mississippi: the true story of the spy agency that tried to destroy the Civil Rights movement. by Rick Bowers. National Geographic, 2010. 128 p.

Grades: 7 8 9 10   **323.1196**

1. Mississippi State Sovereignty Commission -- History. 2. 1950s 3. States' rights (American politics) -- History 4. Civil Rights Movement 5. Spies 6. African Americans -- Civil rights 7. Administrative agencies 8. Mississippi -- Politics and government -- 1951- 9. Mississippi -- Race relations.
ISBN 9781426305955

LC 2009018944

"Bowers draws upon archival material, supplemented with his own extensive research, to document the activities of the Mississippi State Sovereignty Commission, a Civil Rights-era state agency that disseminated segregationist propaganda and used Soviet-style methods to spy upon, harass, and harm those who challenged white supremacy. . . . This book's unique perspective will help students understand the previously unknown history of the despicable actions of Mississippi leaders who opposed civil rights and the silent citizens who supported their activities." School Library Journal.

Includes bibliographical references and index.

Brimner, Larry Dane

Birmingham Sunday. Larry Dane Brimner. Calkins Creek, c2010. 48 p.

Grades: 5 6 7 8   **323.1196**

1. Ku Klux Klan -- History -- 20th century 2. 16th Street Baptist Church (Birmingham, Ala.) 3. African Americans -- Civil rights -- History 20th century 4. Crimes against African Americans 5. Bombings -- History 20th century 6. Hate crimes -- History 7. Racism -- History 8. Birmingham, Alabama -- History
ISBN 9781590786130

LC 2009035716

Describes the bombing of the Sixteenth Street Baptist Church in 1963 by Ku Klux Klan members, which killed four girls and sparked race riots in Birmingham, and discusses how the event contributed to the civil rights movement.

"This moving photo-essay covers much more than just an account of the Birmingham, Alabama, Baptist Church bombing that killed four young girls in 1963. The detailed text, illustrated with black-and-white photos on every spacious double-page spread, sets the shocking assassination of the children within a general overview of both the racist segregation of the times and the struggle against it." Booklist.

Includes bibliographical references (p. 46).

Black & white: the confrontation between Reverend Fred L. Shuttlesworth and Eugene "Bull" Connor. Larry Dane Brimner. Boyds Mills Press, 2011. 112 p.

Grades: 7 8 9 10 11 12   **323.1196**

1. Shuttlesworth, Fred L., 1922- 2. Connor, Eugene, 1897-1973. 3. Civil Rights Movement 4. African Americans -- Civil rights -- History 20th century. 5. Racism 6. Civil rights workers 7. Race relations 8. Birmingham, Alabama -- Race relations.
ISBN 9781590787663

LC 2011924006

Carter G. Woodson Book Awards: Secondary Level, 2012.

Examines a significant confrontation between Reverend Fred Shuttlesworth and Commissioner Bull Connor in Birmingham, Alabama, during the Civil Rights Movement that brought about violence and change to this southern city.

"Reverend Fred L. Shuttlesworth led the civil rights struggle for equality in Birmingham, Alabama. . . . Eugene Bull Connor, backed by the Ku Klux Klan, became a symbol of racist hatred and violence against Shuttlesworth. With a spacious design that includes archival pictures and primary-source documents on almost every page, this accessible photo-essay recounts the events in three sections, which focus first on the preacher, then on the commisioner, and finally, on their confrontation. . . . Never simplistic in his depictions, Brimner shows the viewpoints from all sides. . . . A penetrating look at elemental national history." Booklist.

Includes bibliographical references (p. 105-107) and index.

Freedman, Russell

★ **Freedom** walkers: the story of the Montgomery Bus Boycott. Russell Freedman. Holiday House, 2006. 114 p.

Grades: 4 5 6 7   **323.1196**

1. King, Martin Luther, Jr., 1929-1968. 2. Parks, Rosa, 1913-2005. 3. African Americans -- Civil rights -- History 20th century. 4. Civil Rights Movement 5. Segregation 6. Segregation in transportation 7. Montgomery Bus Boycott 8. Montgomery, Alabama -- Race relations. 9. Montgomery, Alabama -- History -- 20th century.
ISBN 0823420310

Carter G. Woodson Book Awards: Middle Level, 2007.

"This offers expertly paced text, balanced but impassioned. . . . The narrative arc is compelling; well-captioned black-and-white photographs enhance the impact." Horn Book.

Goldstone, Lawrence, 1947-

Separate no more: the long road to Brown v. Board of Education. Lawrence Goldstone. Scholastic, 2021. 304 p.

Grades: 7 8 9 10 11 12   **323.1196**

1. Brown, Oliver, 1918-1961 2. Topeka, Kansas Board of Education 3. Segregation in education 4. African Americans -- Civil rights 5. Racism 6. Civil Rights Movement 7. Discrimination in education -- Law and legislation 8. United States -- History -- 1950-1959. 9. United States -- Race relations.
ISBN 9781338592832

Since 1896, in the landmark outcome of Plessy v. Ferguson, the doctrine of "separate but equal" had been considered acceptable under the United States Constitution. African American and white populations were thus segregated, attending different schools, living in different neighborhoods, and even drinking from different water fountains. However, as African Americans found themselves lacking opportunity and living under the constant menace of mob violence, it was becoming increasingly apparent that segregation was not only unjust, but dangerous. In this thrilling examination of the path to Brown v. Board of Education, Constitutional law scholar Lawrence Goldstone highlights the key trials and players in the fight for integration. Written with a deft hand, this story of social justice will remind readers, young and old, of the momentousness of the segregation hearings.

"Crucial historical information wrapped in well-written, inviting prose." Kirkus

Kimmel, Allison Crotzer

The **Montgomery** Bus Boycott: a primary source exploration of the protest for equal treatment. Allison Crotzer Kimmel. Capstone Press, 2015. 32 p.

Grades: 6 7 8 9 10   **323.1196**

1. Parks, Rosa, 1913-2005 2. 1950s 3. Montgomery Bus Boycott 4. Race relations 5. African Americans 6. Civil Rights Movement 7. Civil rights 8. Montgomery, Alabama 9. Montgomery, Alabama -- Race relations -- History -- 20th century
ISBN 9781491420430

LC 2014019815

The Montgomery Bus Boycott began when Rosa Parks was arrested for refusing to give up her seat on the bus. The campaign that followed was one of the most important protests against racial segregation in the United States. The boycotters endured violence and vicious words. But they stood up for their beliefs. Explore the points of view of the boycotters and the people who opposed them through powerful primary sources and historical photos.—From publisher description

"Heavy with quotes from those directly involved, the books balance both sides (activist Rosa Parks presented along with bus driver James Blake). Tons of relevant photos—some of which may be difficult viewing for sensitive readers (burning crosses, for instance)—break up the text and immerse readers in the period." School Library Journal.

Includes bibliographical references (page 30) and index.

Levinson, Cynthia

We've got a job: the 1963 Birmingham Children's March. Cynthia Levinson. Peachtree Publishers, c2012. 176 p.

Grades: 6 7 8 9   **323.1196**

1. 1960s 2. Civil Rights Movement 3. African American students -- History 20th century 4. African Americans -- Civil rights 5.

Birmingham, Alabama -- History. 6. Antiracist literature
ISBN 9781561456277

LC 2011031738

Discusses the events of the 4,000 African American students who marched to jail to secure their freedom in May 1963.

Lowery, Lynda Blackmon, 1950-

Turning 15 on the road to freedom: my story of the Selma Voting Rights March. Lynda Blackmon Lowery; as told to Elspeth Leacock and Susan Buckley; illustrated by PJ Loughran. Dial Books, an imprint of Penguin Group (USA) LLC, 2015. 128 p.

Grades: 7 8 9 10 11 12   **323.1196**

1. Lowery, Lynda Blackmon, 1950- 2. African Americans -- Civil rights -- History 20th century 3. African American women 4. African Americans -- Suffrage 5. Selma, Alabama -- Race relations
ISBN 9780803741232

LC 2013047316

A 50th-anniversary tribute shares the story of the youngest person to complete the momentous Selma to Montgomery March, describing her frequent imprisonments for her participation in nonviolent demonstrations and how she felt about her involvement in historic Civil Rights events.

"The illustrations are a mix of photographs and cartoonish drawings, which bring a graphic novel-like feel to this memoir. A concluding chapter explains the fight for voting rights and contains short biographies of those who died for the cause. This is an honest, powerful historical work, straight from the source." School Library Journal.

Mayer, Robert H., 1950-

When the children marched: the Birmingham civil rights movement. Robert H. Mayer. Enslow Publishers, c2008. 176 p.

Grades: 7 8 9 10   **323.1196**

1. African Americans -- Civil rights -- History 20th century 2. African American children -- History 20th century 3. African American civil rights workers 4. Civil rights workers 5. Birmingham, Alabama -- Race relations
ISBN 0766029301

LC 2007025590

Discusses the Birmingham civil rights movement, the great leaders of the movement, and the role of the children who helped fight for equal rights and to end segregation in Birmingham. Provided by publisher.

"Children played a significant role in Birmingham's crucial civil rights struggle, and this stirring history of the movement, with many photos, news reports, and quotes from all sides, emphasizes the connections between the young people's power and that of the big leaders. . . . From the cover picture of police escorting African American children to jail, the numerous photos of youth in nonviolent confrontation—marching, attacked by dogs and fire hoses, crammed in prisons—will draw readers with their gripping drama." Booklist.

Includes bibliographical references and index.

Partridge, Elizabeth

Marching for freedom: walk together, children, and don't you grow weary. by Elizabeth Partridge. Viking, c2009. 80 p.

Grades: 6 7 8 9 10 11 12   **323.1196**

1. African Americans -- Civil rights -- History 20th century 2. Suffrage 3. Civil Rights Movement 4. African American children -- Political activity -- History 20th century. 5. Protests, demonstrations, vigils, etc 6. Alabama -- Race relations.
ISBN 9780670011896

LC 2009009696

"This is a stirring photo-essay. . . . The vivid text is filled with quotes collected from Partridge's personal interviews with adults who remember their youthful experiences. . . . Filled with large black-and-white photos, every spread brings readers up close to the dramatic, often violent action." Booklist.

Includes bibliographical references and index.

Rubin, Susan Goldman

Freedom summer: the 1964 struggle for Civil Rights in Mississippi. Susan Goldman Rubin. Holiday House 2014 144 p.

Grades: 5 6 7 8 9 10   **323.1196**

1. Mississippi Freedom Project 2. Civil Rights Movement 3. Civil rights workers 4. African Americans -- Civil rights 5. African Americans -- Suffrage 6. Civil rights 7. Mississippi -- History -- 20th century.
ISBN 9780823429202

"This work gives a real sense of the time and place, the issues and the opposing sides, and the impact on the nation. Including myriad period photos and drawings, facsimiles of reports and records, meticulous source notes, an extensive bibliography, picture credits, and an extensive index, this title is the epitome of excellent historical reporting, with the human element never forgotten." School Library Journal.

Tougas, Shelley

Birmingham 1963: how a photograph rallied civil rights support. by Shelley Tougas. Compass Point Books, c2011. 64 p. : Captured history

Grades: 6 7 8 9   **323.1196**

1. Moore, Charles, 1931-2010. 2. Civil Rights Movement 3. African American teenagers -- History 20th century. 4. Photographs 5. African Americans -- Civil rights -- History 20th century. 6. Civil Rights Movement -- Protests, demonstrations, vigils, etc 7. Birmingham, Alabama -- Race relations -- History -- 20th century.
ISBN 9780756543983

LC 2010038574

Explores and analyzes the historical context and significance of the iconic Charles Moore photograph. Provided by publisher.

"This book about Charles Moore's 1963 photograph of young African American civil rights protesters being blasted with a fire hose places the photo in historical context, profiles the photographer, describes the conditions under which it was taken, and analyzes both its immediate and its continuing impact. The [text includes] ample background information and details and [is] enhanced by large photos and sidebars." School Library Journal.

Includes bibliographical references and index.

Venable, Rose

The **civil** rights movement. by Rose Venable. The Child's World, 2021. 32 p.: Black American Journey

Grades: 4 5 6 7   **323.1196**

1. African Americans -- Civil rights -- History 20th century 2. Civil Rights Movement 3. United States -- Race relations
ISBN 9781503853690

The Civil Rights Movement was a time of drastic change in America. From the end of Reconstruction, when blacks were denied their rights in the South, through the Montgomery bus boycott and Dr. Martin Luther King's 'I Have a Dream' speech, to the election of the first black president of the United States, witness the events that forever changed the way we look at race.

"The writing is approachable and the texts are evenhanded. Period photos, drawings, and maps are generous. Historical illustrations are

devastating at times. . . . This is true Black American history everyone should know about. Highly recommended." School Library Journal
Includes bibliographical references (page 31) and index.

Watson, Bruce, 1953-

Freedom Summer for young people: the savage season of 1964 that made Mississippi burn and made America a democracy. Bruce Watson; adapted by Rebecca Stefoff. Random House Inc 2020 400 p.

Grades: 6 7 8 9 10   **323.1196**
1. Mississippi Freedom Project 2. Student Nonviolent Coordinating Committee (U.S.) 3. 1960s 4. African American civil rights workers 5. African American college students 6. Civil Rights Movement 7. African Americans -- Civil rights -- History 20th century. 8. African Americans -- Suffrage -- History 20th century. 9. United States -- Race relations -- History -- 20th century. 10. Southern States -- Race relations -- History -- 20th century.
ISBN 9781644210093

LC 2020032394

In the summer of 1964, as the Civil Rights movement boiled over, the Student Nonviolent Coordinating Committee (SNCC) sent more than seven hundred college students to Mississippi to help Black Americans already battling for democracy, their dignity and the right to vote. The campaign was called "Freedom Summer." But on the evening after volunteers arrived, three young civil rights workers went missing, presumed victims of the Ku Klux Klan. The disappearance focused America's attention on Mississippi. In the days and weeks that followed, volunteers and local Black activists faced intimidation, threats, and violence from white people who didn't believe African Americans should have the right to vote. As the summer unfolded, volunteers were arrested or beaten. Black churches were burned. More Americans came to Mississippi, including doctors, clergymen, and Martin Luther King. A few frightened volunteers went home, but the rest stayed on in Mississippi, teaching in Freedom Schools, registering voters, and living with Black people as equals. Freedom Summer brought out the best and the worst in America. The story told within these pages is of everyday people fighting for freedom, a fight that continues today. 'Freedom Summer for Young People' is a riveting account of a decisive moment in American history, sure to move and inspire readers. Provided by publisher.

"An underlying sense of urgency pervades the writing as the narrative progresses, reflecting the tension building throughout the summer as an array of forces, including the Klan, the FBI, and competing political factions, came into play. A fascinating account of a pivotal civil rights initiative." Booklist

323.1197 Native Americans—Civil rights

Edwards, Judith, 1940-

The **history** of the American Indians and the reservation. Judith Edwards. Enslow Publishers, c2008. 128 p.: From many cultures, one history

Grades: 6 7 8 9   **323.1197**
1. Indian Removal, 1813-1903 2. Indian reservations 3. Government relations with indigenous peoples 4. United States -- Interethnic relations. 5. United States -- Race relations.
ISBN 9780766027985

LC 2007028275

Explores the difficult changes American Indians were forced to make, including moving off their land, adapting to life on reservations, and how those reservations have changed since their creation. Provided by publisher.

323.3 Civil and political rights of other social groups

Dionne, Evette

Lifting as we climb: Black women's battle for the ballot box. Evette Dionne. Viking, 2020 170 p.

Grades: 5 6 7 8 9   **323.3**
1. Suffragists 2. Suffragist movement 3. Women's rights -- History 4. African American women -- Civil rights -- History
ISBN 9780451481542

LC 2020288838

Describes a history of the role of African American women as a significant force in the suffrage movement and their efforts to be accepted as equal partners by their fellow activists.

"A lively and critical addition as the United States commemorates the centennial of women's suffrage." Kirkus
Includes bibliographical references (pages 150-156) and index.

Gitlin, Marty

Transgender rights. Martin Gitlin, book editor. Greenhaven Publishing, 2018. 110 p.

Grades: 7 8 9 10   **323.3**
1. Transgender persons -- Legal status, laws, etc 2. LGBTQIA persons -- Legal status, laws, etc 3. Human rights
ISBN 9781534502222

LC 2017031275

Transgender rights are not just limited to bathroom bills, though the controversial issue has dominated news headlines for the past few years. What basic human rights are afforded to transgender and nonbinary U.S. citizens is a mystery to many. The viewpoints in this resource lay out the issues in a concise and informative way, offering measured arguments as to why trans Americans are a protected class, as well as arguments for why they don't need special treatment. Workplace discrimination, marriage equality, and adoption, as they relate to transgender identities, are also touched upon.

Hayes, Amy

Disability rights movement. Amy Hayes. PowerKids Press, 2017. 32 p.: Civic participation: working for civil rights

Grades: 4 5 6 7   **323.3**
1. People with disabilities -- Legal status, laws, etc 2. Discrimination 3. Services for people with disabilities 4. People with disabilities -- Social conditions
ISBN 9781499428506

LC 2016037017

Traces the history of people with disabilities from the discrimination they endured during much of history through the earliest efforts at change to the Americans with Disabilities Act of 1990 and the current situation.

"A fine introductory survey of civil rights issues that prompts reader involvement. Consider for report writers." School Library Journal.

323.4 Specific civil rights limitation and suspension of

King, Martin Luther

The **words** of Martin Luther King, Jr.. selected by Coretta Scott King. Newmarket Press, c1983. 112 p.

Grades: 8 9 10 11 12 Adult   **323.4**
1. King, Martin Luther, Jr., 1929-1968 2. African Americans -- Civil rights 3. United States -- Race relations
ISBN 9780937858288

LC 83017306

Gathers selections from King's writings, speeches and sermons about racism, civil rights, justice, freedom, faith, nonviolence, and peace

323.44 Freedom of action (Liberty)

Kyi, Tanya Lloyd, 1973-

Eyes & spies: how you're tracked and why you should know. Tanya Lloyd Kyi; art by Belle Wuthrich. Annick Press, [2017] 135 p.
Grades: 6 7 8   **323.44**
1. Data protection 2. Privacy rights 3. Surveillance 4. Cyberbullying 5. Internet -- Safety measures
ISBN 1554519101
Investigates the way information and data is collected and used by individuals, governments, companies and organizations. Arguments for both increased security and increased privacy are offered, encouraging readers to think critically about the issues. Topics relevant to children are included, such as being tracked at school, cyberbullying and online safety.

Osborne, Linda Barrett, 1949

Guardians of liberty: freedom of the press and the nature of news. Linda Barrett Osborne. Abrams Books for Young Readers, 2020 176 p.
Grades: 7 8 9 10   **323.44**
1. Freedom of the press 2. Press and politics
ISBN 9781419736896
                                                LC 2020011306
Guardians of Liberty explores the essential and basic American ideal of freedom of the press. Allowing the American press to publish—even if what they're reporting is contentious—without previous censure or interference by the federal government was so important to the Founding Fathers that they placed a guarantee in the First Amendment to the Constitution. Citing numerous examples from America's past, from the American Revolution to the Vietnam War and the Civil Rights Movement to Obama's and Trump's presidencies, Linda Barrett Osborne shows how freedom of the press has played an essential role in the growth of this nation, allowing democracy to flourish. She further discusses the diversity of American news and explores why freedom of the press is still imperative to uphold today. Provided by publisher.
"The accessible, mostly chronological text is full of short quotations from both primary and secondary sources. It includes excellent definitions, informative sidebars, and archival photographs." Kirkus
Includes bibliographical references and index.

324.6 Election systems and procedures; suffrage

Anderson, Carol (Carol Elaine)

One person, no vote: how not all voters are treated equally. by Carol Anderson and Tonya Bolden. Bloomsbury, 2019. 288 p.
Grades: 7 8 9 10 11 12   **324.6**
1. African Americans -- Suffrage 2. Suffrage 3. Civil rights 4. Racism -- Political aspects 5. Political activists 6. United States -- Politics and government.
ISBN 9781547601073
                                                LC 2019019145
Carol Anderson chronicles the rollbacks to African American participation in the vote since the 2013 Supreme Court decision that eviscerated the Voting Rights Act of 1965. Adapted from publisher description.

"Bolden's adaptation will fire up a new generation of civic activists through its gripping presentation. A significant people's history and call to action for youth." Kirkus.

Bausum, Ann

With courage and cloth: winning the fight for a woman's right to vote. by Ann Bausum. National Geographic, 2004. 112 p.
Grades: 5 6 7 8 9   **324.6**
1. Paul, Alice, 1885-1977. 2. Suffragists 3. Voting 4. Women's rights 5. Women -- Suffrage -- History 6. Gender role 7. United States -- History -- 20th century.
ISBN 0792276477
                                                LC 2004001191
"Bausum's lucid and nuanced study focuses on 1913-20, the last years of the more than seven decades when women in the US fought for the right to vote. She summarizes what went before and she teases out, remarkably clearly, how hard it was. . . . Bausum focuses on Alice Paul and some other lesser-known lights of the movement, and all the while she makes the history live as she explains, exhorts, and lets nothing drop by the wayside. The entire volume is put together wonderfully, using some never-before-published photos and a lively layout. . . . Excellent." Kirkus.
Includes bibliographical references.

Chambers, Veronica

Finish the fight!: the brave and revolutionary women who fought for the right to vote. Veronica Chambers, The Staff of the New York Times. Versify/Houghton Mifflin Harcourt, [2020] 132 p.
Grades: 5 6 7 8 9   **324.6**
1. Women -- Suffrage 2. Women's rights 3. Suffrage 4. Suffragist movement 5. Women -- Social conditions
ISBN 9780358408307
"In addition to recognizing the contributions of well-known figures such as Susan B. Anthony and Elizabeth Cady Stanton, it widens the spotlight, profiling leaders who have represented minoritiese. . . . The text, written with clarity and verve, also acknowledges racist attitudes within the mainstream women's suffrage organizations of the nineteenth and twentieth centuries, while showing how the voting-rights movement was intertwined with other important causes.

Conkling, Winifred

Votes for women!: American suffragists and the battle for the ballot. Winifred Conkling. Algonquin Young Readers, 2018. 240 p.
Grades: 6 7 8 9 10   **324.6**
1. United States. Constitution. 19th Amendment 2. Women's rights 3. Women -- Suffrage -- History 4. Voting 5. Suffrage 6. Election law 7. United States -- Politics and government.
ISBN 9781616207342
Relates the story of the 19th Amendment and the nearly eighty-year fight for voting rights for women, covering not only the suffragists' achievements and politics, but also the private journeys that led them to become women's champions.
"Looking for a comprehensive, well-written history of women's fight for the right to vote? You've found it." Booklist.

Fleischer, Jeff

Votes of confidence: a young person's guide to American elections. Jeff Fleischer. Zest Books, 2020, c2016. 240 p.

Grades: 6 7 8 9 10 11 12 **324.6**
1. Elections 2. Voting 3. Representative government and representation 4. Citizenship
ISBN 9781541578968
"Fleischer's well-contextualized, nonpartisan approach results in a valuable resource for readers looking to understand and become involved in a complicated system while avoiding spin." Publishers Weekly.

Goldstone, Lawrence, 1947-
Stolen justice: the struggle for African-American voting rights. Lawrence Goldstone; foreword by Henry Louis Gates, Jr. Scholastic Focus, 2020. 288 p.
Grades: 8 9 10 11 12 **324.6**
1. African Americans -- Suffrage -- History 2. Voting 3. Suffrage 4. Electoral reform 5. Elections 6. United States
ISBN 9781338323481
LC 2019027535
A thrilling and incisive examination of the post-Reconstruction era struggle for and suppression of African American voting rights in the United States.
"Goldstone has provided new and compelling insight into the societal impact of the U.S. Supreme Court's decisions related to voting rights. A must-buy for all high school collections." School Library Journal.
Includes bibliographical references and index.

Hollihan, Kerrie Logan
Rightfully ours: how women won the vote, 21 activities. Kerrie Logan Hollihan. Chicago Review Press, 2012. 130 p.
Grades: 4 5 6 7 8 **324.6**
1. Women -- Suffrage -- History 2. Women's rights -- History 20th century 3. Suffragists 4. Creative activities for children and students
ISBN 9781883052898
LC 2012006044
This guide tells of the century-long struggle for women's suffrage in the United States, a movement that began alongside the abolitionist cause and continued through the ratification of the 19th amendment on August 18, 1920, the amendment that granted women the right to vote.

Zimet, Susan
Roses and radicals: the epic story of how American women won the right to vote. by Susan Zimet & Todd Hasak-Lowy. Viking Books for Young Readers, 2018. 160 p.
Grades: 6 7 8 9 **324.6**
1. United States. Constitution. 19th Amendment. 2. Suffragist movement 3. Suffragists 4. Women -- Suffrage -- History
ISBN 9780451477545
LC 2017013719
Presents the seventy-year history of the suffrage movement in the United States, profiling its prominent leaders and describing the ridicule and imprisonment their supporters had to endure before women were granted the right to vote in 1920.

324.973 Elections—United States

Burgan, Michael
TV shapes presidential politics in the Kennedy-Nixon debates: an augmented reading experience. Michael Burgan. Compass Point Books, 2019 64 p.

Grades: 5 6 7 8 9 **324.973**
1. Nixon, Richard M. (Richard Milhous), 1913-1994 2. Kennedy, John F. (John Fitzgerald), 1917-1963 3. Presidents -- Election 1960 4. Campaign debates -- History 5. Television in politics -- History 6. Political campaigns -- History 20th century 7. United States -- Politics and government -- 20th century.
ISBN 9780756558239
LC 2018006449
On-point historical photographs combined with strong narration bring the story of the Nixon-Kennedy presidential debates to life. TV was new in those days, and these were both the first debates ever held between two presidential candidates and the first to be televised. About 60 million people tuned into the first debate, or more than 1/4 of the country's population. Readers will learn just how much effect seeing the debates had on the results of the election and how they changed presidential campaigning forevermore. Readers will understand the significance behind this event through text and clips of the event itself via the Capstone 4D augmented reality app. Provided by publisher.

325.73 International migration—United States

Bausum, Ann
Denied, detained, deported: stories from the dark side of American immigration. Ann Bausum; with a poem foreword by Naomi Shihab Nye. National Geographic, c2009. 111 p.
Grades: 6 7 8 9 10 11 12 **325.73**
1. Immigration policy 2. Undocumented immigrants 3. Deportation 4. Aliens (Law) 5. Immigrant workers 6. United States -- Immigration and emigration -- History
ISBN 9781426336591
LC 2008048433
Carter G. Woodson Book Awards: Secondary Level, 2010.
Examines the history of American immigration, particularly those lesser-known stories of immigrants who were denied entrance into the United States or detained for security reasons, including the story of a ship of Jewish refugees.
"This volume deals frankly with the more troubling aspects of United States immigration policy. The author chose the stories of three immigrants. . . . Twelve-year-old German-Jew Herb Karliner was denied entry to the United States at the border when he attempted to escape Nazi Germany. Sixteen-year-old Japanese-American Mary Matsuda was detained with the rest of her family during World War II. Labor-activist Emma Goldman was deported for her un-American views. . . . The themes of the three stories are unified by the introduction and conclusion, which deal with Chinese immigration during the late 19th century and the history of immigration across the southern border of the United States, respectively. Photographs throughout will help students relate to the narrative. . . . This is an interesting and readable book." School Library Journal.
Includes bibliographical references (p. 102-103) and index.

Eboch, M. M
Immigration and travel restrictions. MM Eboch, book editor. Greenhaven Press, 2019 120 p.
Grades: 7 8 9 10 **325.73**
1. Travel restrictions -- Government policy 2. Travel restrictions -- Government policy 3. Travel restrictions -- Social aspects 4. United States -- Emigration and immigration -- Government policy 5. United States -- Emigration and immigration -- Social aspects
ISBN 9781534504233
LC 2018023285

Essays examine both sides of the questions raised about immigration and travel restrictions.

327.1 Foreign policy and specific topics in international relations

Wilson, Janet, 1952-
   One peace. Janet Wilson. Orca Book Publishers, 2008. 48 p.
Grades: 4 5 6 7   **327.1**
   1. Child social advocates 2. Teenage social advocates 3. Peace 4. Pacifists 5. Children and peace
   ISBN 9781551438924

                                LC 2008927399
   "The stories of young people who have been refugees from war, injured by land mines, or learned about the consequences of violence through other means are interspersed with children's poems, quotes, artwork, and photographs. The brief, powerful accounts document how these children ages 8 to 15 worked for or became symbols of peace." School Library Journal.

327.12 Espionage and subversion

Favreau, Marc, 1968-
   Spies: the secret showdown between America and Russia. Marc Favreau. Little, Brown and Co., 2019. 320 p.
Grades: 8 9 10 11 12   **327.12**
   1. CIA -- History. 2. KGB -- History. 3. Cold War 4. Espionage -- History 5. Spies -- History 20th century. 6. Spies -- History 7. Undercover operations 8. United States -- Foreign relations -- Soviet Union. 9. Soviet Union -- Foreign relations -- United States.
   ISBN 9780316545921

                                LC 2019005698
   An account of the Cold War spies whose survival depended on carefully orchestrated deceptions as they fought in the shadows to help avert global nuclear war and, in so doing, changed the global landscape in ways that are still felt today. Provided by publisher.
   "The facts behind the fantastic lives of spies born from Cold War friction." Kirkus.
   Includes bibliographical references.

Langston-George, Rebecca
   Spies!: the history of secret agents and double-crossers. by Rebecca Langston-George and Allison Lassieur. Capstone Young Readers, a Capstone imprint, 2017 240 p.
Grades: 6 7 8   **327.12**
   1. Spies 2. Espionage -- History 3. Intelligence service -- History
   ISBN 9781623709112

                                LC 2017015907
   A look at the world of espionage highlights some of the most famous spies in history, from Blinker Hall to modern-day cyber spies.

327.73 Foreign relations—United States

Janeczko, Paul B.
   The **dark** game: true spy stories from the Revolution to the 21st century. Paul B. Janeczko. Candlewick Press, 2010. 256 p.
Grades: 5 6 7 8   **327.73**
   1. Spies 2. Espionage -- History 3. Intelligence service -- History

   4. Military intelligence -- History 5. United States -- History, Military.
   ISBN 9780763629151

                                LC 2009049102
   "From Benedict Arnold and Mata Hari to the lesser-known Elizabeth Van Lew and Juan Pujol, Janeczko delves into [spies'] stories with delicious detail, drawing readers into a world of intrigue and danger. Did you ever wonder why invisible ink works? How a code breaker deciphers a message? Or whether dentistry could affect a secret agent's success? The answers to these questions and more can be found here. Each chapter covers a historical era and chronicles the maturation of spying, while primary-source photographs are interspersed throughout, lending an authentic feel to each section." School Library Journal.

330 Economics

Sylvester, Kevin
   Follow your money: who gets it, who spends it, where does it go? Kevin Sylvester and Michael Hlinka. Annick Press, c2013. 56 p.
Grades: 5 6 7 8   **330**
   1. Money 2. Capital market 3. Banks and banking 4. Economics
   ISBN 9781554514816
   An introduction to the way money flows, exploring where the money you spend actually goes and following its path as it pays for everything involved in creating and selling a product.

330.9 Economic situation and conditions

Mooney, Carla, 1970-
   The **Industrial** Revolution: investigate how science and technology changed the world: with 25 projects. Carla Mooney; illustrated byJen Vaughn. Nomad Press, 2011. 120 p. : Build it yourself
Grades: 4 5 6 7   **330.9**
   1. Technology -- History 2. Industrialization -- History 3. Industries -- History 4. Industrial revolution 5. Science projects
   ISBN 9781936313815
   Beginning with the Industrial Revolution in England, a guide follows its progression to North America, illustrating the societal changes that occurred as a result of the shift in the way goods and services were created and consumed.
   "The crisp, clear format, featuring ample black-and-white sketches and diagrams and pleasingly arranged type in a large font, is in sync with the straightforward text." Booklist.

330.973 Economic conditions—United States

Bair, Sheila
   The **bullies** of Wall Street: this is how greedy adults messed up our economy. Sheila Bair. Simon & Schuster Books for Young Readers, 2015. 288 p.
Grades: 8 9 10 11 12   **330.973**
   1. Working class -- Economic conditions 2. Global Financial Crisis, 2008-2009 3. Financial crises 4. Economic policy 5. United States -- Economic conditions -- 2009-
   ISBN 9781481400855

                                LC 2014005948

"Her analysis of the crisis (particularly the "Too Big to Fail" mentality) and the six case studies are very perceptive. Readers are given keen insight into the link between banking and the economy. An excellent selection that puts a human face on the economic crisis." School Library Journal.

Riggs, Kate

The **great** recession. by Kate Riggs. Creative Education, 2016. 48 p.: Turning points (Creative Education)

Grades: 5 6 7 8   **330.973**

   1. Financial crises -- History 2. Global Financial Crisis, 2008-2009 3. Recession (Economics) 4. Economic history 5. World economy 6. United States -- Economic conditions -- 2009-

   ISBN 9781608187492

LC 2016002552

A historical account of the Great Recession, including the causes of the economic downturn, the role played by the Federal Reserve and other government offices, and the lingering aftermath. Provided by publisher.

"Despite the complicated nature of the subject matter, this account stays engaging thanks to clear writing, glossy photographs, and helpful sidebars throughout." Horn Book.

Includes bibliographical references and index.

331.3 Labor force by personal attributes

Bartoletti, Susan Campbell

Growing up in coal country. Susan Campbell Bartoletti. Houghton Mifflin Co., 1996. 127 p.

Grades: 5 6 7 8   **331.3**

   1. 19th century 2. 20th century 3. Child labor -- History 4. Coal miners -- History 5. Coal mines and mining -- History 6. Boy coal miners -- History 7. Immigrants -- History 8. Pennsylvania -- History -- 20th century.

   ISBN 0395778476

LC 96003142

Describes what life was like, especially for children, in coal mines and mining towns in the nineteenth and early twentieth centuries.

"With compelling black-and-white photographs of children at work in the coal mines of northeastern Pennsylvania about 100 years ago, this handsome, spacious photo-essay will draw browsers as well as students doing research on labor and immigrant history." Booklist.

Includes bibliographical references (p. 123-126).

Burgan, Michael

Breaker boys: how a photograph helped end child labor. written by Michael Burgan. Compass Point Books, c2012. 64 p.: Captured history

Grades: 6 7 8 9   **331.3**

   1. Hine, Lewis Wickes, 1874-1940 2. Child labor -- History 3. Coal mines and mining -- History 4. Documentary photography -- History

   ISBN 9780756544393

LC 2011003316

"This is model nonfiction. . . . The design is fresh and inviting, the writing clear, and the back matter . . . is useful and extensive. An all-around winner." Booklist.

Includes bibliographical references and index.

331.4 Women workers

Colman, Penny

Rosie the riveter: women working on the home front in World War II. Penny Colman; illustrated with photographs. Crown Publishers, c1995. 120 p.

Grades: 5 6 7 8   **331.4**

   1. 1940s 2. Women -- Employment -- History 20th century. 3. World War II -- Women 4. World War II -- Economic aspects 5. Gender role -- History 6. Sexual harassment of women 7. United States -- Social conditions

   ISBN 051759790X

LC 94003614

An account, based on interviews and other sources, of the women who replaced men in defense plants, factories, and offices and on farms during the Second World War.

"A thoughtfully prepared look at women's history and wartime society, this dynamic book is characterized by extensive research." Horn Book.

Includes bibliographical references (p. [110]-113) and index.

331.7 Labor by industry and occupation

Hopkinson, Deborah

★ **Up** before daybreak: cotton and people in America. Scholastic, 2006. 120 p.

Grades: 5 6 7 8   **331.7**

   1. Cotton 2. Cotton growing 3. Cotton textile industry and trade -- History 4. Cotton industry and trade -- History 5. Economics 6. United States -- History.

   ISBN 0439639018

"From the industrial revolution to the 1950s demise of the Lowell cotton mills, Hopkinson discusses the history and sociology of king cotton, frequently emphasizing the children who labored under slave masters, endured dead-end mill jobs, or helped sharecropping parents claw out a living. . . . Stories of real people . . . sharply focus the dramatic history, as do arresting archival photos of stern youngsters manipulating hoes, cotton sags, or bobbins." Booklist.

Pawlewski, Sarah

Careers: the graphic guide to finding the perfect job for you. consultant and principal author, Sarah Pawlewski. DK Publishing, 2015. 320 p.

Grades: 6 7 8 9 10 11 12   **331.7**

   1. Vocational guidance for teenagers 2. Vocational guidance 3. Occupations 4. Professions 5. Teenagers

   ISBN 9781465429735

"A typical Library's collection of career books can quickly become dated or out of touch. Enter this manual. With simple graphics, bright colors, and a vast compendium of information, this guide will engage teens who are wondering, What now? . . . This strong addition will be fun for browsers as well as for those selecting college majors and making job decisions." School Library Journal.

331.8 Labor unions, labor-management bargaining and disputes

Brimner, Larry Dane

Strike!: the farm workers' fight for their rights. Larry Dane Brimner. Boyds Mills Press, 2014. 172 p.

Grades: 6 7 8 9   **331.8**

1. United Farm Workers Union -- History 2. Migrant agricultural laborers -- Labor unions 3. Strikes 4. Migrant workers 5. Immigrant workers 6. Agricultural laborers 7. California -- History -- 20th century
ISBN 9781590789971

"Brimner's inclusion of information about the Filipino workers who began the movement, quotes and balanced discussion of Chavez's strengths and weaknesses provides a fresh perspective on the movement, making this book a first-purchase choice for middle-level researchers." School Library Journal.

331.892 Strikes

Bartoletti, Susan Campbell

★ **Kids** on strike! Susan Campbell Bartoletti. Houghton Mifflin, 1999. 208 p.

Grades: 5 6 7 8   **331.892**

1. Jones, Mother, 1837-1930 2. Strikes -- History 3. Child labor -- History 4. Child labor exploitation -- History 5. Child labor -- Law and legislation -- History
ISBN 0395888921

LC 98050575

Describes the conditions and treatment that drove workers, including many children, to various strikes, from the mill workers strikes in 1828 and 1836 and the coal strikes at the turn of the century to the work of Mother Jones on behalf of child workers.

"This well-researched and well-illustrated account creates a vivid portrait of the working conditions of many American children in the 19th and early 20th centuries." School Library Journal.

Includes bibliographical references (p. [197]-203) and index.

332.024 Personal finance

Holyoke, Nancy

A **smart** girl's guide: money: how to make it, save it, and spend it. by Nancy Holyoke; illustrated by Brigette Barrager. American Girl Publishing, 2014 96 p.: Smart girl's guides

Grades: 4 5 6 7   **332.024**

1. Personal finance 2. Money 3. Teenage girls -- Personal finance 4. Money-making projects for children
ISBN 9781609584078

LC 2013025896

A practical reference for young girls helps them identify personal spending styles while outlining strategies for earning money, saving funds and making smart shopping choices as recommended through the quotes and tips of other girls.

Scott, Elaine, 1940-

Dollars and sense: a kid's guide to using--not losing--money. by Elaine Scott; illustrated by David Clark. Charlesbridge, [2015] 112 p.

Grades: 4 5 6 7   **332.024**

1. Personal finance 2. Money 3. Economics 4. Banks and banking 5. Debt
ISBN 9781580893961

LC 2013022069

"An informative primer on how money functions that doesn't trigger the dismal science's snooze button." Kirkus.

332.4 Money

Cribb, Joe

Money. written by Joe Cribb. DK Publishing, 2016. 72 p.

Grades: 4 5 6 7   **332.4**

1. Money
ISBN 9781465451798

LC bl2016014681

Examines the symbolic and material meaning of money, from shekels, shells, and beads to gold, silver, checks, and credit cards, and discusses how coins and banknotes are made, the value of money during wartime, and how to collect coins.

January, Brendan, 1972-

Cryptocurrencies and the blockchain revolution: Bitcoin and beyond. Brendan January. Lerner Pub Group 2020 96 p.

Grades: 8 9 10 11   **332.4**

1. Electronic commerce 2. Digital currency 3. Bitcoin 4. Money 5. Exchange
ISBN 9781541578777

LC 2019046569

When Bitcoin was first released in January 2009, each digital coin was worth only a few pennies. A single Bitcoin is now valued at over ten thousand dollars. This book examines digital cryptocurrency and the blockchain technology that makes them possible. Provided by publisher.

"This book clearly explains what Bitcoin is, its advantages and disadvantages as a digital cryptocurrency, how it's being used, and its impact on financial and other institutions." Booklist

Includes bibliographical references and index.

Jenkins, Martin, 1959-

The **history** of money: from bartering to banking. Martin Jenkins; illustrated by Satoshi Kitamura. Candlewick Press, 2014. 64 p.

Grades: 4 5 6 7 8   **332.4**

1. Money -- History 2. Commerce -- History 3. Banks and banking 4. Money -- Social aspects 5. Money
ISBN 9780763667634

A lighthearted chronicle of the history of money includes coverage of topics ranging from currency forms and the relationship between money and writing to the way taxes work and the practices of modern banking systems.

"This cleverly designed picture book uses just the right balance of information and explanation to guide students through both the global history of currency and the application of market pressures on exchange methods." Booklist

332.64 Exchange of securities and commodities; speculation

Blumenthal, Karen, 1959-2020

Six days in October: the stock market crash of 1929. Karen Blumenthal. Atheneum Books for Young Readers, c2002. 156 p.: Wall Street journal books

Grades: 7 8 9 10   **332.64**

1. New York Stock Exchange -- History. 2. 1920s 3. Stock market crash, October 1929 4. Depressions 1929-1941 5. Economics -- History 20th century. 6. Economics -- History 7. United States -- Economic conditions -- 1918-1945.

ISBN 0689842767

LC 2001046360

A comprehensive review of the events, personalities, and mistakes behind the Stock Market Crash of 1929, featuring photographs, newspaper articles, and cartoons of the day.

"This fast-paced, gripping . . . account of the market crash of October 1929 puts a human face on the crisis." Publishers Weekly.

Includes bibliographical references (p. 148-150) and index.

333.72 Conservation and protection

Giannella, Valentina

Green Nation revolution: use your future to change the world. by Valentina Giannella and Lucia Esther Maruzelli; illustrated by Manuela Marazzi. Chronicle Books Llc, 2020. 128 p.

Grades: 5 6 7 8   **333.72**

1. Environmentalists 2. Environmental protection 3. Nature -- Effect of humans on

ISBN 9781786277657

"Dedicated to environmental activist Greta Thunberg, this book offers snapshots of social actions that can help save the planet, from tree plantings to no-waste fashion and ecotourism." Booklist

Petronis, Lexi

47 things you can do for the environment. Lexi Petronis with Jill Buck. Zest Books, 2012. 128 p.

Grades: 6 7 8 9   **333.72**

1. Environmentalism 2. Sustainable living 3. Conservation of natural resources 4. Environmental protection -- Citizen participation 5. Nature -- Effect of humans on

ISBN 9780982732212

Identifies numerous everyday practices that can be employed to protect and clean up the earth, counseling teens on such options as eating less meat, shopping for vintage clothing and organizing an environmental task force at school.

"Divided into categories revolving around habits at home, school, in the community, or on the road, [this book] offers such suggestions as shopping at vintage or secondhand stores, eating less meat, donating old cellphones, and carpooling. Each green venture is followed by concrete ideas . . . that encourage direct action. Cheerful cartoon spot art underscores the positive tone." Publishers Weekly.

Try this at home:

Try this at home: planet-friendly projects for kids. Jackie Farquhar, D.I.Y. editor. Owlkids, c2008. 93 p.

Grades: 5 6 7 8   **333.72**

1. Environmental education -- Activity programs 2. Environmental protection

ISBN 9782895791928

"Many of these projects are unique or innovative, featuring ideas like growing your own pizza ingredients and making a foosball game out of recycled corks, clothespins, and plastic fruit baskets. One of the best projects provides tips on making sure a bike is road ready, offering advice on checking the cables, gears, and oiling the chain. The book also includes sections designed to increase environmental awareness, including information on carbon footprint and eco all-stars. Interactive elements, like a game board, should appeal to children. Illustrations are hip collages of full-color photographs and cartoons." School Library Journal.

333.72092 Conservationists

Rao, Anuradha S., 1975-

One Earth: people of color protecting our planet. Anuradha Rao. Orca Book Publishers, 2020. 208 p.

Grades: 6 7 8 9 10 11 12   **333.72092**

1. Environmentalists 2. Indigenous peoples' rights 3. Environmentalism 4. Environmental protection 5. Environmental movement

ISBN 9781459818866

This nonfiction book for teens profiles twenty environmental defenders of color from around the world. Their individual stories show that the intersection of environment and ethnicity is an asset to protecting our planet. Illustrated with photos of each of the people profiled.

"The content is neatly sorted into six sections like community involvement, the defense of ancestral lands, and wildlife conservation. One section even goes, without preaching, into sustainable meat-eating practices. There?s something for everyone." Booklist

Includes bibliographical references and index.

333.75 Forest lands

Hand, Carol, 1945-

Bringing back our tropical forests. by Carol Hand. Essential Library, an imprint of Abdo Publishing, 2017. 112 p.: Conservation success stories

Grades: 7 8 9 10   **333.75**

1. Rain forest ecology 2. Habitat conservation 3. Endangered ecosystems 4. Deforestation 5. Habitat (Ecology) 6. Tropics

ISBN 9781532113161

"The design of these books is roomy and attractive, featuring many high-quality photos, 'Science Connection' spreads, and relevant fact boxes—often highlighting indigenous people's rights and plights within vulnerable areas." Booklist.

Includes bibliographical references and index.

MacCarald, Clara, 1979-

Bringing back our deserts. by Clara MacCarald. Essential Library, an imprint of Abdo Publishing, 2017. 112 p.: Conservation success stories

Grades: 7 8 9 10   **333.75**

1. Desert ecology 2. Habitat conservation 3. Endangered ecosystems 4. Arid regions 5. Habitat (Ecology)

ISBN 9781532113130

Explains some of the ways deserts are in danger, and shares the ways people are combating invasive species and restoring damaged areas.

333.78 Recreational and wilderness areas

Carson, Mary Kay

The **park** scientists: Gila Monsters, Geysers, and Grizzly Bears in America's Own Backyard. Mary Kay Carson; with photographs by Tom Uhlman. Houghton Mifflin Harcourt, 2014 80 p.: Scientists in the field (Houghton Mifflin)

Grades: 4 5 6 7 8 9   **333.78**
    1. Park rangers 2. Naturalists 3. Natural resources 4. Scientists 5. National parks and reserves
ISBN 9780547792682

              LC 2013039895

The national parks have been called "America's best idea," and in this book, kids can meet up with scientists studying geysers, grizzlies, salamanders, cacti and fireflies in some of America's most treasured places.

"The National Park System is often known as the nation's own backyard due to the possibilities it provides for leisure, recreation, and scientific study. This entry into the long-running Scientists in the Field series celebrates this by focusing on three specific parks: Yellowstone, Saguaro, and the Great Smoky Mountains... With a conservationist bent, Carson describes just how accessible these real-life natural laboratories and living museums are and how each individual can act with the same spirit of inquiry as the scientist-explorers detailed here." Booklist.

McHugh, Erin, 1969-

National parks: a kid's guide to America's parks, monuments, and landmarks. Erin McHugh; art by Neal Aspinall, Doug Leen, and Brian Maebius. Black Dog & Leventhal Publishers: 2019, c2012. 128 p.

Grades: 4 5 6   **333.78**
    1. National parks and reserves 2. United States -- Description and travel
ISBN 9780762494705

              LC bl2012013440

Presents a guide to some of the national parks of the United States, designated by state, and includes information on the history of each site and the plants and animals that can be found there.

333.79 Energy

Dickmann, Nancy

Using renewable energy. Nancy Dickmann. Crabtree Publishing Company, [2018] 32 p.: Putting the Planet First

Grades: 4 5 6 7   **333.79**
    1. Renewable energy sources 2. Alternative energy development 3. Renewable energy industry and trade 4. Biomass energy 5. Fuel cells
ISBN 9780778750321

              LC 2018021422

In the series Putting the Planet First, this book highlights the different ways renewable energy is used around the globe.

McPherson, Stephanie Sammartino

Arctic thaw: climate change and the global race for energy resources. Stephanie Sammartino McPherson. Twenty-First Century Books, 2015. 64 p.

Grades: 6 7 8 9 10   **333.79**
    1. Global warming -- Political aspects 2. Natural resources 3. International relations 4. Global warming -- Economic aspects 5.

Energy resources 6. Arctic regions
ISBN 9781467720434

              LC 2013025164

Describes how global warming has made the Arctic's oil, gas, natural resources, and minerals more accessible and how competition between nations and corporate interests for control of the resources is endangering the Arctic's fragile ecosystems.

"Succinct and clearly written, the text offers up-to-date information, illustrated with clear color photos and useful maps. An articulate introduction to the Arctic in a time of profound, striking changes." Booklist.

Includes bibliographical references (pages 59-60) and index.

Sneideman, Joshua

Renewable energy: discover the fuel of the future with 20 projects. Joshua Sneideman and Erin Twamley; illustrated by Heather Jane Brinesh. Pgw 2016 128 p.: Build It Yourself

Grades: 4 5 6 7   **333.79**
    1. Renewable energy sources 2. Energy resources 3. Energy conservation 4. Energy consumption 5. Energy production
ISBN 9781619303560

"Links to online sources couple with essential questions and writing prompts about a range of interdisciplinary topics to make this book a quality choice for both the classroom and pleasure reading." Booklist.

333.9 Other natural resources

Woll, Kris

Wind energy. by Kris Woll Core Library, an imprint of Abdo Publishing, [2017] 48 p.: Alternative energy (Core Library)

Grades: 4 5 6 7   **333.9**
    1. Wind power 2. Renewable energy sources 3. Energy resources
ISBN 9781680784602

              LC bl2016057113

Explains what wind power is, the history of the technology, how it generates electricity, and its future uses.

"With its impeccable content, this dynamic series is a must for school and public libraries." School Library Journal.

Includes bibliographical references (page 47) and index.

333.91 Water and lands adjoining bodies of water

Amstutz, Lisa J.

Bringing back our freshwater lakes. by Lisa J. Amstutz. Essential Library, an imprint of Abdo Publishing, 2017. 112 p.: Conservation success stories

Grades: 7 8 9 10   **333.91**
    1. Lake ecology 2. Habitat conservation 3. Endangered ecosystems 4. Stream ecology 5. Habitat (Ecology)
ISBN 9781532113147

Explains some of the ways freshwater lakes are in danger, and shares the ways people are combating overfishing, pollution, and climate change.

Burgan, Michael

Not a drop to drink: water for a thirsty world. Michael Burgan. National Geographic, 2008. 64 p.: National Geographic investigates

Grades: 4 5 6 7   **333.91**
    1. Water supply 2. Water use 3. Global environmental change 4.

Climate change 5. Water conservation
ISBN 9781426302671

Water is one of Earth's hot environmental topics. The scarcity of clean drinking water will have dramatic consequences for humanity in the 21st century: water disputes could spark regional conflict, while increased desertification and drought could affect world food supplies and the future of farming. Not a Drop to Drink conveys a clear message to young readers about this precious commodity and our urgent need to conserve it.

Hand, Carol, 1945-

Bringing back our oceans. by Carol Hand. Essential Library, an imprint of Abdo Publishing, 2017. 112 p.: Conservation success stories

Grades: 7 8 9 10   333.91

1. Marine ecology 2. Habitat conservation 3. Endangered ecosystems 4. Oceans 5. Habitat (Ecology)
ISBN 9781532113154

Explains why the oceans are at risk, and shares the ways people are combating plastics pollution and restoring marine biodiversity.

"These wonderfully researched titles are valuable resources that allow readers to see the big picture surrounding complex environmental and social issues with hopeful eyes." Booklist.

Includes bibliographical references and index.

Kallen, Stuart A., 1955-

Running dry: the global water crisis. Stuart A. Kallen. Twenty-First Century Books, 2015. 64 p.

Grades: 4 5 6 7 8   333.91

1. Water-supply 2. Water consumption 3. Water conservation 4. Conservation of natural resources 5. Global warming
ISBN 9781467726467

LC 2014003223

"This title provides a clear and concise look at the importance of fresh water in sustaining life on earth . . . the book will appeal to those with little or no background on the subject. An excellent source for student research." School Library Journal.

Includes bibliographical references and index.

Kaye, Cathryn Berger

Going blue: a teen guide to saving our oceans, lakes, rivers, & wetlands. by Cathryn Berger Kaye; with Philippe Cousteau & EarthEcho International. Free Spirit Pub., c2010. 151 p.

Grades: 7 8 9   333.91

1. Water conservation 2. Water-supply 3. Marine pollution -- Prevention 4. Marine ecology 5. Environmentalism
ISBN 9781575423487

LC 2010016589

Teaches young people about the Earth's water crisis and provides practical suggestions on how readers can identify water-related needs in the community and transform their ideas into action.

"This valuable how-to manual is suitable for an individual student, a family, a youth group, or a school wishing to protect our precious resource of water. This upbeat treasure will challenge anyone interested in environmental activism, whether water related or not. It is a must for any Library serving youth." Voice of Youth Advocates.

Includes bibliographical references and index.

Mulder, Michelle, 1976-

★ **Every** last drop: bringing clean water home. Michelle Mulder. Orca Book Publishers, 2014. 48 p.

Grades: 4 5 6 7   333.91

1. Water quality management 2. Water resources development 3. Water
ISBN 9781459802230

LC oc2013127374

"Divided into four chapters, this book explores the history of water use by humans; the natural cycle of water on earth; how people access, clean, and desalinate water; and ways in which we can conserve and preserve our water resources. Plenty of well-captioned photos, including some from the author's own travels, illustrate and personalize the accessible text." Horn Book.

Includes bibliographical references and index.

333.95 Biological resources

Castaldo, Nancy F. (Nancy Fusco), 1962-

Back from the brink: saving animals from extinction. Nancy F. Castaldo. Houghton Mifflin Harcourt, 2018. 176 p.

Grades: 6 7 8 9   333.95

1. Rare and endangered animals 2. Wildlife conservation 3. Extinction (Biology)
ISBN 9780544953437

LC 2017015664

Explores the threats to seven species and the scientific and political efforts to bring the threatened animals back from the brink of extinction.

Conley, Kate A., 1977-

Biofuels. by Kate Conley; content consultant, Richard M. Amasino, College of Agricultural Arts and Sciences, University of Wisconsin-Madison. Core Library, an imprint of Abdo Publishing, [2017] 48 p.: Alternative energy (Core Library)

Grades: 4 5 6 7   333.95

1. Biomass energy 2. Renewable energy sources 3. Energy resources
ISBN 9781680784534

LC bl2016057098

Explains what biofuels are, the history of the technology, how they generate electricity, and their future uses.

"Text-heavy yet comprehensible, each book delves into the specific energy source's origins, current applications, and outlook; addresses its benefits and drawbacks; and encourages readers to come to their own conclusions." School Library Journal.

Includes bibliographical references (page 47) and index.

Debbink, Andrea

The **wild** world handbook: how adventurers, artists, scientists--and you--can protect Earth's habitats. by Andrea Debbink; illustrated by Asia Orlando. Random House Distribution childrens 2021 232 p.

Grades: 4 5 6 7   333.95

1. Nature 2. Ecology 3. Explorers 4. Climate change 5. Nature conservation
ISBN 9781683692461

LC 2020052824

A middle-grade guide to environmental stewardship and protecting diverse habitats.

"This beautifully illustrated book of nature and ecology is full of fascinating facts, activities, and suggestions on how to save nine different habitats around the world." Booklist

Includes bibliographical references and index.

Kallen, Stuart A., 1955-

What is the impact of declining biodiversity? Stuart A. Kallen. ReferencePoint Press, 2021 80 p.: Environmental impact

Grades: 7 8 9 10 11 12   **333.95**

    1. Biodiversity conservation 2. Biodiversity 3. Biotic communities 4. Population -- Environmental aspects

    ISBN 9781682828618

In 2019 there were about 7.7 billion humans on Earth, more than double the number of people alive in 1969. During that fifty-year period the impact of humanity on the natural environment has increased proportionately. Human activity is causing a loss of biodiversity—the diversity of plant, animal, algae, fungi, and microbe species. But the survival of humanity—and all life on earth—is directly related to biodiversity. Provided by publisher.

"The book defines what biodiversity is and where biodiversity hot spots are and describes how species loss affects various ecosystems." Booklist

Includes bibliographical references and index.

Kurlansky, Mark

World without fish. Mark Kurlansky, illustrated by Frank Stockton. Workman Publishing Company, 2011. 183 p.

Grades: 5 6 7 8 9 10   **333.95**

    1. Overfishing 2. Water -- Pollution 3. Nature -- Effect of humans on 4. Bottom fishing -- Environmental aspects 5. Sustainable fisheries

    ISBN 9780761156079

Examines the threats to the survival of fish in the world's oceans, discussing the damage caused by various types of fishing equipment, the impact of politics on the regulation of fishing, and the harmful effects of overfishing, pollution, and global warming.

"Brief sections in graphic-novel format follow a young girl, Ailat, and her father over a couple of decades as the condition of the ocean grows increasingly dire, eventually an orange, slimy mess mostly occupied by jellyfish and leatherback turtles. At the end, Ailat's young daughter doesn't even know what the word fish means. This is juxtaposed against nonfiction chapters with topics including types of fishing equipment and the damage each causes, a history of the destruction of the cod and its consequences, the international politics of the fishing industry and the effects of pollution and global warming... Depressing and scary yet grimly entertaining." Kirkus.

Laidlaw, Rob, 1954-

Saving lives & changing hearts: animal sanctuaries and rescue centres. Rob Laidlaw. Fitzhenry & Whiteside, 2012. 62 p.

Grades: 4 5 6 7 8   **333.95**

    1. Wildlife refuges 2. Animal rescue 3. Animal sanctuaries 4. Human/animal relationships

    ISBN 9781554552122

From a donkey sanctuary in Canada to a bear rescue centre in China, this book examines numerous efforts by animal sanctuaries around the world to rescue and care for animals in need and shows the positive side of the human-animal relationship.

Perdew, Laura

Bio diversity: explore the diversity of life on Earth with environmental science activities for kids. Laura Perdew; illustrated by Tom Casteel. Nomad Press, 2019 v, 122 p.

Grades: 4 5 6 7 8   **333.95**

    1. Biodiversity 2. Science -- Experiments

    ISBN 9781619307483

                         LC bl2019004864

Explores the concept of biodiversity and enforces key ideas through science experiments.

"Biodiversity is placed under the microscope—sometimes literally—in a text that makes daunting concepts, such as evolution, levels of biodiversity (genetic, species, or ecosystem), and why biodiversity matters, easy to understand without sacrificing scientific precision." Booklist.

Includes bibliographical references (page 119) and index.

Pobst, Sandra

Animals on the edge: science races to save species threatened with extinction. Sandra Pobst. National Geographic, 2008 64 p.: National Geographic investigates

Grades: 4 5 6 7   **333.95**

    1. Wildlife conservation 2. Rare and endangered animals 3. Animal welfare 4. Wildlife habitats 5. Zoology

    ISBN 9781426303586

Stresses the importance of saving endangered species and discusses how scientists are using the latest technology to survey animal populations, to track down and arrest those who prey on endangered wildlife, and to breed animals in captivity.

"This eye-catching [title features] full-color photographs. . . . The approach is to understand the challenges to protecting endangered animals, including global warming, destruction of habitat, tagging and tracking, poaching, captive breeding, and cloning." Voice of Youth Advocates.

338.09 Production—History, geographic treatment, biography

Pringle, Laurence, 1935-

Ice!: the amazing history of the ice business. Laurence Pringle. Calkins Creek, c2012. 74 p.

Grades: 4 5 6 7 8   **338.09**

    1. Ice industry and trade -- History 2. Ice manufacture 3. Ice 4. Ice harvesting

    ISBN 9781590788011

                         LC bl2012021606

Presents a history of the ice business, detailing the process of harvesting, storage, and distribution.

338.2 Extraction of minerals

Goldstein, Margaret J.

Fuel under fire: petroleum and its perils. Margaret Goldstein. Twenty First Century Books, 2015. 104 p.

Grades: 7 8 9 10 11 12   **338.2**

    1. Fossil fuels 2. Nonrenewable natural resources 3. Energy resources 4. Fuel 5. Energy

    ISBN 9781467738316

"Though concise, a solid purchase for schools and public libraries." Booklist.

338.3 Other extractive industries

Foster, Mark

    ★ **Whaleport**: a history of Tuckanucket. by Mark Foster; illustrated by Gerald L. Foster. Houghton Mifflin, 2007. 64 p.

Grades: 4 5 6 7   338.3
  1. Whalers 2. Humans and whales 3. Whaling -- History 4. City
life -- History
  ISBN 9780618547227

                                                LC 2006018772
  "The village is depicted in precisely detailed ink and crayon pictures.
. . . The Fosters . . . have elegantly synthesized a tremendous amount of
information into a beguiling format." Horn Book.

338.7 Business enterprises

Frydenborg, Kay
  Chocolate: sweet science and dark secrets of the world's
favorite treat. by Kay Frydenborg. Houghton Mifflin Harcourt,
2015. 272 p.
  Grades: 7 8 9 10   338.7
  1. Chocolate 2. Chocolate industry and trade 3. Cacao 4.
Manufacturing processes
  ISBN 9780544175662

                                                LC 2014015885
  A fascinating account for teen readers that captures the history, science, and economic and cultural implications of the harvesting of cacao
and creation of chocolate. Readers of Chew On This and The Omnivore's Dilemma will savor this rich exposé. Provided by publisher.
  "Covering controversy over labor laws, the chemical makeup of
chocolate, and recent attempts to map the cacao genome, Frydenborg offers a wealth of information that will likely encourage students to think
critically about the ecological and human cost of their favorite candies
and maybe even prompt them to choose sustainable alternatives." Booklist.
  Includes bibliographical references.

339.4 Factors affecting income and wealth

Sharif, Meghan
  Poverty and economic inequality. Meghan Sharif. Lucent
Press, 2019. 104 p.
  Grades: 6 7 8 9   339.4
  1. Income inequality 2. Poverty
  ISBN 9781534563551

                                                LC 2017058899
  "Each volume is similarly laid out, with plenty of photographs and
graphics where appropriate, as well as notes citing sources. The discussion questions are a scaffold for teachers using these for class work,
while the organizations to contact and the 'More Information' sections
will help students doing research on these topics to expand their resources." VOYA
  Includes bibliographical references and index.

340.092 Biography

Stevenson, Bryan
  Just mercy: adapted for young adults: a true story of the fight
for justice. Bryan A. Stevenson. Delacorte Press, 2018. 288 p.
  Grades: 7 8 9 10 11 12   340.092
  1. Stevenson, Bryan 2. Equal Justice Initiative 3. Justice 4.
Redemption 5. Lawyers 6. Social reformers 7. Sentences

(Criminal procedure) 8. Alabama 9. Antiracist literature
  ISBN 9780525580041

                                                LC 2018015248
  Details the author's personal experience, challenges, and efforts
as a lawyer and social advocate to find justice for America's most
marginalized people.

342.73 Constitutional law—United States

Krull, Kathleen, 1952-2021
  A **kids'** guide to America's Bill of Rights. Kathleen Krull;
illustrated by Anna DiVito. HarperCollins, 2015, c1999. 240 p.:
Kids' guide to American history
  Grades: 4 5 6 7 8   342.73
  1. United States Constitution 1st-10th Amendments. 2. Civil rights
3. Civics 4. Political science
  ISBN 9780062352316

                                                LC 99017324
  Examines the ten amendments to the United States Constitution that
make up the Bill of Rights, explaining what the amendments mean, how
they have been applied, and the rights they guarantee.

Ohnaka, Kathryn
  Key civil rights laws. Kathryn Ohnaka. Cavendish Square,
2020 80 p.: Laws that changed history
  Grades: 7 8 9 10 11   342.73
  1. Civil rights 2. Civil Rights Movement 3. Civil rights -- History
4. African Americans -- Civil rights -- History
  ISBN 9781502655219
  The ability to vote, the freedom to attend school and have a job,
the independence to be exactly who you are. These rights seem fundamental to us, but when the nation was beginning, only certain people
were granted full rights. It's been a fight for everyone else, and we're
still fighting today. This essential resource explores how these key civil
rights came to be, how they are still being fought for today, and how
they changed the nation forever. It includes a list of resources for more
exploration and a timeline of important dates for an even deeper dive.
Provided by publisher.

342.7302 Constitutions—United States

Levinson, Cynthia
  Fault lines in the constitution: the framers, their fights, and
the flaws that affect us today. written by Cynthia Levinson and
Sanford Levinson. Peachtree Publishers, 2017. 192 p.
  Grades: 6 7 8 9 10 11 12   342.7302
  1. United States. Constitution 2. Constitutional law 3.
Constitutional history 4. Civics 5. Political science -- History 6.
United States -- Politics and government
  ISBN 9781561459452

                                                LC 2017011413
  Many of the political issues we struggle with today have their roots
in the US Constitution. Husband-and-wife team Cynthia and Sanford
Levinson take readers back to the creation of this historic document and
discuss how contemporary problems were first introduced—then they
offer possible solutions.
  "A fascinating, thoughtful, and provocative look at what in the Con-
stitution keeps the United States from being 'a more perfect union.'"
Kirkus.
  Includes bibliographical references and index.

Ritchie, Donald A., 1945-

Our Constitution. Donald A. Ritchie & JusticeLearning.org. Oxford University Press, c2006. 255 p.

Grades: 7 8 9 10   **342.7302**

1. United States. Constitution 2. Constitutional law
ISBN 0195223853

LC 2005031885

An in-depth look at the entire text of the U. S. Constitution, annotated with detailed explanations of its terms and contents. Each Amendment and Article is accompanied by sidebar material on the history of its application, including profiles of important Supreme Court cases, texts of related primary source documents, and contemporary news articles. Double-page timelines for several of the Articles and all the Amendments highlight important events and legal cases. Includes facsimile reproductions of primary source documents, paintings, phots, and historical artifacts.—From publisher description.

"This volume begins with five chapters of background (Why have a constitution? How has it changed?) and then goes on to discuss the preamble, articles, and amendments, using a What It Says (word for word) and What It Means format. Every spread contains photos, reproductions, and sidebars, all of which invite students to read and understand this living document. . . . This is an excellent, well-documented addition for most libraries." School Library Journal.

Includes bibliographical references (p. 244-248) and index.

342.7308 Constitutional law—United States—Groups of people

Baxter, Roberta, 1952-

The **Bill** of Rights. Roberta Baxter. Heinemann/Raintree, 2012. 48 p.: Documenting U.S. history

Grades: 4 5 6 7   **342.7308**

1. United States. Constitution. 1st-10th Amendments. 2. Constitutional amendments 3. Civil rights 4. United States -- Politics and government.
ISBN 9781432967512

This fascinating series examines some of the most influential documents in U.S. history, with each book providing in-depth information about a famous primary source document and including material about the value of studying these sources.

Blumenthal, Karen, 1959-2020

Jane against the world: Roe v. Wade and the fight for reproductive rights. Karen Blumenthal. Roaring Brook Press, 2020. 385 p.

Grades: 8 9 10 11 12   **342.7308**

1. McCorvey, Norma, 1947- 2. Wade, Henry 3. United States. Supreme Court 4. Trials (Abortion) 5. Abortion -- Law and legislation 6. Reproductive rights 7. Women's rights 8. Birth control -- History
ISBN 9781626721654

A history of the fight for reproductive rights in the United States. Tracing the path to the landmark decision in Roe v. Wade and the continuing battle for women's rights, Blumenthal examines the root causes of the current debate around abortion and repercussions that have affected generations of American women. This book intends to facilitate difficult discussions and awareness of a topic that is rarely touched on in school but affects each and every young person. Includes a glossary of legal and medical terms, timeline, and information about significant Supreme Court cases.

"Written in clear, accessible language, as lively as it is thorough, the book presents the issue as far more nuanced and complex than the often sharply divided 'pro-choice' and 'pro-life' stances it is often boiled down to." Publishers Weekly

Includes bibliographical references (pages [335]-345) and index.

Cates, David, 1963-

Plessy v. Ferguson: segregation and the separate but equal policy. by David Cates; content consultant, Margalynne Armstrong. ABDO Pub., 2012. 160 p.: Landmark Supreme Court cases

Grades: 8 9 10 11 12   **342.7308**

1. Plessy, Homer Adolph 2. United States. Supreme Court 3. Segregation in transportation -- Law and legislation -- History 19th century 4. Plessy Case, 1896 5. African Americans -- Civil rights 6. Segregation
ISBN 9781617834752

LC 2012001279

Describes the landmark Supreme Court case of Plessy v. Ferguson, challenging the "separate but equal" national policy, and includes the events leading up to the case, the Supreme Court's ruling, and how it affected future cases and the history of the United States.

Jacobs, Thomas A.

Every vote matters: the power of your voice, from student elections to the Supreme Court. Tom Jacobs and Natalie Jacobs. Free Spirit Pub. Inc., 2016. 208 p.: Teens & the Law

Grades: 7 8 9 10 11 12   **342.7308**

1. United States. Supreme Court 2. Voting 3. Elections 4. Trials 5. Law
ISBN 9781631980695

LC 2015032349

Encourages teens to recognize the importance of voting and making their voices heard in the democratic process, focusing on Supreme Court decisions that came down to a single vote.

"Clear explanations, relevant supplemental cases, reader-directed questions, and suggested resources help make the legal issues at play relevant and readily accessible. Whether readers finish the book inspired to exercise their own future voting rights, it's a fascinating window into recent U.S. legal history." Publishers Weekly.

Includes bibliographical references and index.

Lusted, Marcia Amidon

Tinker vs. Des Moines: the right to protest in schools. Marcia Amidon Lusted; content consultant: Gerald Thain. ABDO Pub., c2013. 160 p.

Grades: 7 8 9 10 11 12   **342.7308**

1. Tinker, John Frederick 2. Des Moines Independent Community School District -- Trials, litigation, etc. 3. High school students -- Civil rights 4. Freedom of speech 5. Vietnam War, 1961-1975 -- Protest movements 6. Trial and arbitral proceedings
ISBN 9781617834776

LC 2012001280

Describes the landmark Supreme Court case of Tinker v. Des Moines, which involved student protests in schools, and includes the events leading up to the case, the Supreme Court's ruling, and how it affected future cases and the history of the United States.

344.73 Labor, social service, education, cultural law—United States

Rubin, Susan Goldman

Brown v. Board of Education: a fight for simple justice. Susan Goldman Rubin. Holiday House, 2016. 160 p.

Grades: 5 6 7 8 **344.73**

1. Brown, Oliver, 1918-1961 2. Marshall, Thurgood, 1908-1993. 3. School desegregation decision, 1954 4. Segregation in education -- Law and legislation 5. African Americans -- Civil rights 6. Plessy Case, 1896 7. Racism

ISBN 9780823436460

LC 2016004631

Traces the lesser-known stories of advocates and activists who risked significant danger and hardship to uphold the 1954 desegregation ruling by the Supreme Court, sharing additional information on how the NAACP carefully strategized their own responses to period racism.

"A rich, compelling story of the many people who stood up to racial inequality, risking significant danger and hardship for the cause of justice." Kirkus.

345.73 Criminal law—United States

Higgins, Melissa, 1953-

Roe v. Wade: abortion and a woman's right to privacy. Melissa Higgins; content consultant Joseph Dellapenna. ABDO Pub., c2013. 160 p.

Grades: 7 8 9 **345.73**

1. Roe, Jane, 1947-2017 2. Wade, Henry 3. Trials (Abortion) 4. Abortion -- Law and legislation 5. Trial and arbitral proceedings

ISBN 9781617834769

LC 2012001275

Presents the history of the landmark case, discussing the key players and challenges to the decision.

Jacobs, Thomas A.

They broke the law, you be the judge: true cases of teen crime. Thomas A. Jacobs; edited by Al Desetta. Free Spirit Pub., c2003. 213 p.

Grades: 7 8 9 10 **345.73**

1. Juvenile justice system 2. Juvenile delinquents 3. Crime 4. Juvenile courts 5. Personal conduct 6. Books for reluctant readers

ISBN 1575421348

LC 2003004814

Letters from and interviews with twenty-one children and teenagers who broke the law reveal what it is like to be arrested, attend legal proceedings, and be held accountable for one's actions.

"An excellent introduction to how juvenile justice works, this will be a great resource for classroom and group discussions." Booklist.

Includes bibliographical references (p. 203-205) and index.

Marguiles, Phillip

The **devil** on trial: witches, anarchists, atheists, communists, and terrorists in America's courtrooms. by Phillip Marguiles and Maxine Rosaler. Houghton Mifflin Co., 2008. 218 p.

Grades: 7 8 9 10 11 12 **345.73**

1. Trials 2. Criminal justice system 3. Racism in the criminal justice system 4. Courts 5. Trials (Witchcraft)

ISBN 9780618717170

LC 2008001870

Featuring five famous trials, this book examines the way an individual's right to a fair trial can be threatened when people are tempted to abandon their principles in the name of safety.

"The authors examine five highly emotional court cases, each of which served as a litmus test for the health of America's justice system at the time it occurred. . . . Each chapter gives historical context of the court proceeding, describes its progression in some detail, and comments on the political and intellectual aftermath. . . . [This is] a highly relevant and riveting book." School Library Journal.

Includes bibliographical references (p. [177]-207) and index.

345.761 Criminal law—Alabama

Aretha, David

The **trial** of the Scottsboro boys. by David Aretha. Morgan Reynolds Pub., c2007. 128 p.: The civil rights movement

Grades: 7 8 9 10 11 12 **345.761**

1. Scottsboro Trial, Scottsboro, Ala, 1931 2. Trials (Rape) 3. African Americans -- Civil rights -- History

ISBN 1599350580

"Aretha writes clearly, with objectivity and compassion." School Library Journal.

Includes bibliographical references and index.

Brimner, Larry Dane

Accused!: the trials of the Scottsboro Boys: lies, prejudice, and the Fourteenth Amendment. Larry Dane Brimner. Calkins Creek, 2019 189 p.

Grades: 8 9 10 11 12 **345.761**

1. 1930s 2. Scottsboro Trial, Scottsboro, Ala, 1931 3. Trials (Rape) 4. African Americans -- Civil rights 5. Malicious accusation 6. Race relations 7. Scottsboro, Alabama 8. Alabama

ISBN 9781629797755

Tells the story of the Scottsboro Boys, nine African-American teenagers who, when riding the rails during the Great Depression, found their lives destroyed after two white women falsely accused them of rape. The author explains how it took more than eighty years for their wrongful convictions to be overturned.

"Tightly wound, compelling, and comprehensive, Brimner's meticulously documented narrative re-creates the menacing atmosphere of Depression-era segregated courtrooms, atrocious carceral facilities, and a riven public. . . . An essential acquistion." School Library Journal.

346.7301 Private law—United States—Persons and domestic relations

Brimner, Larry Dane

Finding a way home: Mildred and Richard Loving and the fight for marriage equality. Larry Dane Brimner. Calkins Creek, 2020. 112 p.

Grades: 7 8 9 10 11 **346.7301**

1. Loving, Richard Perry 2. Loving, Mildred Jeter 3. United States. Supreme Court 4. Interracial marriage 5. Intermarriage 6. Virginia 7. United States -- Race relations

ISBN 9781629797519

When Mildred and Richard Loving are arrested, jailed, and exiled from their home simply because of their mixed-race marriage, they must challenge the courts and the country in order to secure their civil rights.

"A concise, well-organized account of the landmark Loving v. Virginia case, its significance, and the people at the heart of the story." Booklist

Includes bibliographical references and index.

346.7304 Property law—United States

Butler, Rebecca P.

Copyright for teachers & librarians in the 21st century. Rebecca P. Butler. Neal-Schuman Publishers, c2011. xvii, 276 p.

Grades: Adult Professional   **346.7304**
1. Copyright 2. Fair use (Copyright) 3. Teachers -- Legal status, laws, etc
ISBN 1555707386

LC 2011012600

Here is a practical copyright handbook designed to help librarians, media specialists, technology coordinators and specialists, and teachers stay within copyright law while making copyrighted print, non-print, and Web sources available to students and others.

Russell, Carrie

Complete copyright for K-12 librarians and educators. Carrie Russell. American Library Association, 2012. xi, 173 p.

Grades: Professional   **346.7304**
1. Copyright 2. Fair use (Copyright) 3. Librarians -- Legal status, laws, etc 4. School libraries -- Law and legislation
ISBN 0838910831

LC 2012016674

Advises school librarians on the issue of copyright, including fair use, infringement, digital copyright, and student work.

347.73 Civil procedure and courts of the United States

Ortiz, Victoria, 1942-

Dissenter on the bench: Ruth Bader Ginsburg's life and work. Victoria Ortiz. Clarion Books, 2019. 192 p.

Grades: 6 7 8 9 10 11 12   **347.73**
1. Ginsburg, Ruth Bader. 1933-2020 2. United States. Supreme Court -- Justices 3. Judges 4. Feminists 5. Dissenting opinions 6. Civil rights 7. Women's rights
ISBN 9780544973640

LC 2018035167

The life and career of the fiercely principled Supreme Court Justice, now a popular icon, with dramatic accounts of her landmark cases that moved the needle on legal protection of human rights, illustrated with b/w archival photographs. Provided by publisher.

"Ortiz offers detailed accounts of cases Ginsburg either heard as a Supreme Court justice or argued as a lawyer defending individuals' rights under the Constitution. The descriptions of noteworthy legal cases and significant court decisions are particularly well done." Booklist.

Includes bibliographical references (pages 187-192) and index.

Panchyk, Richard

Our Supreme Court: a history with 14 activities. Richard Panchyk. Chicago Review Press, c2007. xii, 195 p.

Grades: 7 8 9 10   **347.73**
1. United States. Supreme Court 2. Constitutional law 3. Civics 4. Creative activities for children and students
ISBN 1556526075

LC 2006009018

Activity book for young readers on how the Supreme Court works, organized by the principles of the Constitution the Court has dealt with over the years.

"The history and evolution of the court and how it works are discussed in the first chapter. Thematic sections follow, covering such topics as free speech, privacy, and civil rights, with significant decisions included. . . . This a solid work that makes a complex and important subject accessible to students." School Library Journal.

Includes bibliographical references (p. 188-189) and index.

353.9 Public administration of safety, sanitation, waste control

Jarrow, Gail

The **poison** eaters: fighting danger and fraud in our food and drugs. Gail Jarrow. Calkins Creek, an imprint of Highlights, 2019 160 p.

Grades: 5 6 7 8 9 10   **353.9**
1. Wiley, Harvey Washington, 1844-1930 2. United States. Food and Drug Administration 3. Food contamination 4. Food industry and trade 5. Food safety 6. Consumer protection 7. Government regulation 8. Books for reluctant readers
ISBN 9781629794389

Documents the achievements of government chemist Harvey Washington Wiley, revealing how his hard work and determination created the FDA and rendered foods safer from contamination by dangerous toxins that were commonly used a century ago.

"Revolting and riveting in turns, Jarrow's masterfully crafted narrative will fundamentally alter how readers view their food." Kirkus.

355.009 Military science—History, geographic treatment, biography

Goldsmith, Connie, 1945-

Women in the military: from drill sergeants to fighter pilots. Connie Goldsmith. Twenty-First Century Books, 2019 120 p.

Grades: 7 8 9 10 11 12   **355.009**
1. Military life 2. Women soldiers 3. Sexism in the military 4. Women in combat 5. Women's rights 6. United States Armed Forces -- Women. 7. United States Armed Forces -- Military life.
ISBN 9781541528123

In 2015 the Pentagon changed a historical ruling, allowing American women to serve in front-line ground combat troops. Women have served in the military throughout history. Yet no matter their title, they face discrimination and even sexual assault. Meet the women who serve their country and stand up for fairness.

355.1 Military life and customs

Engdahl, Sylvia

Military families. Sylvia Engdahl, book editor. Greenhaven Press, a part of Gale, Cengage Learning, 2014 240 p.: Current controversies

Grades: 8 9 10 11 12   **355.1**
1. Families of military personnel -- Social conditions 2. Soldiers -- Pay, allowances, etc 3. Military life 4. Armed forces 5. Families

of military personnel -- Services for -- Evaluation
ISBN 9780737768787

LC 2013041402

Collects essays that discuss different aspects of military family life, including the benefits available to them, the impact of being a child of a military parent, and the resources available through the government.

355.8 Military equipment and supplies

Sullivan, Edward T., 1966-
The **ultimate** weapon: the race to develop the atomic bomb. Ed T. Sullivan. Holiday House, c2007. 182 p.
Grades: 6 7 8 9   **355.8**
1. Manhattan Project (U.S.) -- History 2. Atomic bomb -- History 3. Generals 4. Military engineers 5. Nuclear power research 6. Nuclear physics -- Research -- History 7. United States -- History, Military -- 20th century.
ISBN 9780823418558

LC 2005050330

"This history of the Manhattan Project effectively distills the science behind the development of the atomic bomb into understandable terms that turns the human story behind the project into compelling drama." Booklist.
Includes bibliographical references (p. 163-168) and index.

358.4 Air forces and warfare

Karst, Ken
Area 51. Ken Karst. Creative Education, 2014. 48 p.: Enduring mysteries
Grades: 5 6 7 8   **358.4**
1. UFOs 2. Aliens 3. Curiosities and wonders 4. UFOs -- Sightings and encounters 5. Conspiracy theories 6. Area 51 region, Nevada 7. Nevada
ISBN 9781608183999

LC 2013036073

An investigative approach to the curious phenomena and mysterious circumstances surrounding Area 51, from conspiracy theories to claims of extraterrestrial sightings to hard facts.
"With only the barest dashes of skepticism, these handsomely produced surveys present budding cryptozoologists and conspiracy theorists with rich arrays of historical anecdotes and encounters, supposed evidence, 'scientific' explanations of varying plausibility, and tantalizing speculations." School Library Journal.
Includes bibliographical references (page 47) and index.

Schwartz, Heather E.
Women of the U.S. Air Force: aiming high. by Heather E. Schwartz. Capstone Press, c2011. 32 p.: Snap books.
Grades: 4 5 6   **358.4**
1. United States. Air Force -- Women 2. Armed forces 3. Women
ISBN 9781429654494

LC 2010040749

Describes the past, present, and future of women in the U.S. armed forces. Provided by publisher.

362.1988 Obstetrical surgery and abortion

Merino, Noel
Abortion. Noel Merino, book editor. Greenhaven Press, 2013. 240 p.: Opposing viewpoints series
Grades: 8 9 10 11 12   **362.1988**
1. Abortion 2. Abortion -- Moral and ethical aspects 3. Abortion -- Law and legislation
ISBN 9780737769395

LC 2013037282

Opposing Viewpoints is the leading source for libraries and classrooms in need of current-issue materials. The viewpoints are selected from a wide range of highly respected sources and publications. Provided by publisher.

Stevenson, Robin, 1968-
My body my choice: the fight for abortion rights. Robin Stevenson; illustrations by Meags Fitzgerald. Orca Book Pub., 2019. 176 p.
Grades: 7 8 9 10 11 12   **362.1988**
1. Abortion 2. Pro-choice movement 3. Reproductive rights 4. Abortion -- History 5. Pro-choice movement -- History 6. Illustrated books
ISBN 9781459817128

This nonfiction book for teens examines the ongoing fight for abortion rights and reproductive justice. Provided by publisher.
"Reproductive rights have a long history of conflict and controversy around the globe, and this exceptional installment in the Orca Issues series (2 titles) provides an in-depth look at abortion rights and services, both historically and as they exist today." Booklist.

Wilcox, Christine
Thinking critically: abortion. by Christine Wilcox. ReferencePoint Press, Inc., 2017 80 p.: Thinking Critically
Grades: 8 9 10 11 12   **362.1988**
1. Abortion -- Moral and ethical aspects 2. Abortion
ISBN 9781682822616

LC 2016052613

Examines the issue of abortion, asking if fetuses should be considered persons, if the procedure endangers women, if it harms society, and whether state laws should be made more or less restrictive.

362.2 People with mental illness and disabilities

Flath, Camden, 1987-
21st-century counselors: new approaches to mental health & substance abuse. by Camden Flath. Mason Crest Publishers, c2011. 64 p.: New careers for the 21st century: finding your role in the global renewal
Grades: 7 8 9 10   **362.2**
1. Counseling -- Vocational guidance 2. Psychology -- Vocational guidance 3. Counselors 4. Mental health services 5. Drug abuse counseling
ISBN 9781422218259

LC 2010021812

"Chapters identify and emphasize specific careers: important strengths, necessary aptitudes and interests, education and training, projected earnings, closely related occupations, type of work environment, and predictions for the future of the field. . . . Color photos have a small role amid the many statistics, figures, graphs and charts that support and supplement the . . . [text]." School Library Journal.

Includes bibliographical references (p. 59-61) and index.

362.28 Suicide

Chandler, Matt

Understanding suicide. Matt Chandler. Cherry Lake Publishing, 2020 32 p.

Grades: 4 5 6   **362.28**

1. Suicide -- Prevention 2. Suicidal behavior 3. Teenagers -- Suicidal behavior

ISBN 9781534148000

LC 2019008065

In Understanding Suicide, readers will explore the history and social aspects of suicide, teen suicide, and ways to help themselves and others. Sidebars challenge and expand readers' thinking while relating topics to 21st Century skills and themes—from creativity and innovation to financial literacy.

"Candidly explains, without preachiness, how these issues harm body and mind, social life, and future prospects." School Library Journal

Nelson, Richard E.

The **power** to prevent suicide: a guide for teens helping teens. Richard E. Nelson & Judith C. Galas; foreword by Bev Cobain; edited by Pamela Espeland. Free Spirit Pub., c2006. xi, 115 p.

Grades: 7 8 9 10 11 12   **362.28**

1. Teenagers -- Intervention 2. Suicide -- Prevention 3. Suicidal behavior

ISBN 1575422069

LC bl2006018547

Provides information about teen suicide, describes the warning signs and the situations in which people are most likely to be at risk, and provides advice and information on how to help people considering suicide.

"The authors' premise is that, as trusted and caring friends, YAs have a special role in the prevention of suicide among their peers, and discuss what to do if they observe the danger signals. . . . This book provides clear, practical information and advice." School Library Journal.

Includes bibliographical references and index.

362.29 Substance abuse

Bjornlund, Lydia, 1961-

Marijuana. by Lydia Bjornlund. ReferencePoint Press, 2012. 96 p. : Compact research series.

Grades: 7 8 9 10 11 12   **362.29**

1. Decriminalization of drugs 2. Marijuana 3. Marijuana -- Law and legislation 4. Marijuana abuse 5. Drug control policy

ISBN 9781601521606

LC 2011007743

Discusses the legalization of marijuana, debates the effect of legalizing it on both the economy and society, and questions if medicinal use of the drug is adequate justification.

Cashin, H. John

The **heroin** crisis. John Cashin. Mason Crest, 2018 64 p.

Grades: 10 11 12   **362.29**

1. Heroin 2. Opioids 3. Drug abuse 4. Opioid abuse 5. Narcotics

ISBN 9781422238257

LC bl2017042426

Explores the ways in which the abuse of prescription opioids has also led to an increased and changed heroin addiction problem, and discusses the history of the drug, the role of organized crime, and possible solutions.

Espejo, Roman

Tobacco and smoking. Roman Espejo, book editor. Greenhaven Press, 2015. 240 p.: Opposing viewpoints series

Grades: 8 9 10 11 12   **362.29**

1. Smoking 2. Tobacco 3. Teenage smokers 4. Smoking -- Health hazards 5. Nicotine

ISBN 9780737772944

LC 2014026089

Presents conflicting opinions on issues related to smoking, including whether or not smoking is a serious problem, how smoking alternatives should be regulated, and how media impacts the choice to smoke.

Harris, Duchess

The **opioid** crisis. Duchess Harris, JD, PHD with John L. Hakala. Essential Library, 2019 112 p.

Grades: 7 8 9 10   **362.29**

1. Medication abuse 2. Opioid abuse 3. Drug abuse -- Social aspects

ISBN 9781532116797

LC 2018948307

"The Opioid Crisis is a probing examination of this problem, featuring a wide-ranging discussion that looks at everything from pain management to poverty, race, and class issues to Big Pharma." Booklist.

Includes bibliographical references (pages 104-109) and index.

Lundquist-Arora, Stephanie

Addiction: a problem of epidemic proportions. Stephanie Lundquist-Arora. ReferencePoint Press, 2021 80 p.

Grades: 8 9 10 11 12   **362.29**

1. Drug addiction 2. Drug abuse 3. Drug abuse

ISBN 9781682829219

LC 2020011901

Drug addiction is a pervasive problem across the United States. Addiction in the United States is a pandemic. It is taking lives, ruining health, and destroying families. Provided by publisher.

"This title provides teens with well-researched, detailed information about addictions, their causes, and the devastating effects they can have—and not only drug addictions, but behavioral addictions as well, including gambling, video gaming, shopping, eating, and using social media." Booklist

Includes bibliographical references (pages 68-71) and index.

Marcovitz, Hal

The **opioid** epidemic. by Hal Marcovitz. ReferencePoint Press, Inc., 2018. 80 p.

Grades: 7 8 9 10 11 12   **362.29**

1. Opioids 2. Drug abuse 3. Drug addiction 4. Drug abusers 5. Opioid abuse

ISBN 9781682822999

LC 2017017982

"Marcovitz offers a timely exploration of the issue. . . . Both reasoned and impassioned." Kirkus.

Includes bibliographical references and index.

Parks, Peggy J., 1951-

Bath salts and other synthetic drugs. Peggy J. Parks. ReferencePoint Press, [2014] 96 p.: Compact research series.

Grades: 8 9 10 11 12   **362.29**
  1. Drugs 2. Drug abuse 3. Designer drugs 4. Synthetic drugs
ISBN 9781601525161

      LC 2013015820
Examines the history, health effects, social issues, and legal status of different types of synthetic drugs through objective overviews, primary sources, and illustrated statistics.
  "Backed by current facts, statistics, and first-person experiences, every chapter includes further documentation with concluding Primary Source Quotes, from former addicts and law enforcement to health care workers and government officials. In this visual, by-the-numbers era, the series responds with end-of-chapter charts and graphs that display drug-related information." Booklist.
  Includes bibliographical references (pages 86-90) and index.

Quinones, Sam, 1958-
  Dreamland: the true tale of America's opiate epidemic. by Sam Quinones. Bloomsbury Childrens Books 2019 224 p.
Grades: 7 8 9   **362.29**
  1. Drug traffic 2. Drug addiction 3. Opioid abuse 4. Opioids 5. Heroin addiction 6. Books for reluctant readers
ISBN 9781547601318

      LC 2018045397
A young-adult adaptation of the award-winning Dreamland uses comprehensive language and informed examples to trace how the rise of prescription painkiller use has triggered crisis levels of addiction.

Scott, Celicia, 1957-
  Caffeine: energy drinks, coffee, soda, & pills. Celicia Scott. Mason Crest, 2015. 48 p.: Downside of drugs
Grades: 6 7 8   **362.29**
  1. Caffeine 2. Caffeine addiction 3. Stimulants 4. Drugs 5. Drug abuse
ISBN 9781422230183
  "Written with a Harvard Medical School consultant, this series discusses drugs in a tone that is appropriately sober yet not alarmist or condescending." School Library Journal.

Sommers, Michael A., 1966-
  The **NFL**: steroids and human growth hormone. Michael Sommers. Rosen Central, 2010. 48 p. : Disgraced! the dirty history of performance-enhancing drugs in sports
Grades: 5 6 7 8   **362.29**
  1. Football -- Corrupt practices 2. Doping in sports 3. Anabolic steroids in sports 4. Football players -- Drug use 5. Athletes -- Drug use
ISBN 9781435853041
  "Amazing statements from athletes giving reasons why they took illegal drugs are good for discussion topics. . . . Concludes with thoughts regarding future additional legislation. [A] useful [update]." School Library Journal.
  Includes bibliographical references and index.

Watkins, Christine
  Addiction. Christine Watkins, book editor. Greenhaven Press, 2014 240 p.: Opposing viewpoints series
Grades: 8 9 10 11 12   **362.29**
  1. Drug abuse 2. Interpersonal relations 3. Addiction
ISBN 9780737769418

      LC 2013036319
  Each title in the highly acclaimed Opposing Viewpoints series explores a specific issue by placing expert opinions in a unique pro/con format; the viewpoints are selected from a wide range of highly respected and often hard-to-find publications. This title addresses various issues related to addiction, including what some causes and sources of addiction are, how addiction can be prevented, how addictions affect relationships, and how addictions can be treated.

362.5 Poor people

Senker, Cath
  Poverty and hunger. Cath Senker. Smart Apple Media, c2012. 46 p.: Mapping global issues
Grades: 6 7 8   **362.5**
  1. Poverty 2. Poor people 3. Hunger 4. Food security
ISBN 9781599205113

      LC 2011017066
  Describes the worldwide problem of poverty and food shortages that affect the population. Includes current statistics, maps, and charts. Provided by publisher.

362.7 Young people

Banigan, Melissa
  Coping with teen pregnancy. Melissa Banigan. Rosen Young Adult, 2019 112 p.
Grades: 7 8 9 10   **362.7**
  1. Pregnancy 2. Teenage parents 3. Teenage pregnancy 4. Teenagers -- Sexuality
ISBN 9781508183259

      LC 2018017290
  Providing teens with comprehensive fact-based sexual education can help them make informed choices about their reproductive health and futures. This thoughtful and informative book helps eliminate the stigma associated with teen parenthood, and a Myths and Facts sidebar helps correct common misconceptions about the topic.

362.734 Adoption

Langwith, Jacqueline
  Adoption. Jacqueline Langwith, book editor. Greenhaven Press, A part of Gale, Cengage Learning, 2014 240 p.: Introducing issues with opposing viewpoints
Grades: 7 8 9 10   **362.734**
  1. Adoption 2. Families
ISBN 9780737769180

      LC 2013033191
  Discusses issues regarding adoption, including the ethics of international adoption, transracial adoption, same-sex couple adoption, and open adoptions.

362.82 Families

Zehr, Howard
  What will happen to me? by Howard Zehr and Lorraine Stutzman Amstutz; portraits by Howard Zehr. Good Books, c2011. 94 p.
Grades: 7 8 9 10   **362.82**
  1. Children of prisoners 2. Children of prisoners -- Services for 3.

Prisoners' families
ISBN 9781561486892

LC 2010012419

Pairs portraits of children whose parents are incarcerated with the reflections of grandparents who are caring for them and includes resources for caregivers and advice on dealing with the unique emotions of these children.

"This discusses issues facing children of incarcerated parents. . . . In part one, the statements from the children interviewed are accompanied by full-color photo portraits. What comes through is that they all love their parents unequivocally, but here it is tangible and poignant both in their words and faces. . . . Part two offers advice for caregivers and includes 10 questions often asked by children whose parents are in jail." School Library Journal.

Includes bibliographical references (p. 92-93).

362.87 Displaced persons

McPherson, Stephanie Sammartino

The **global** refugee crisis: fleeing conflict and violence. Stephanie Sammartino McPherson. Twenty-First Century Books, 2019. 128 p.

Grades: 7 8 9 10 11 12 　　　　　　　**362.87**
　　1. Refugees 2. Immigration and emigration 3. Immigration policy 4. Forced relocations 5. Political refugees
ISBN 9781541528116

LC 2018016059

The Syrian civil war as well as armed conflicts in Nigeria, Afghanistan, Yemen, Somalia, and the Central African Republic contributed to the continuing exodus of people into Europe and North America. Learn more about these modern mass exoduses, what is fueling them in the 21st century, how nations are addressing the crises, how refugees contribute to and strain communities, and what kinds of solutions could help. Along the way, you'll meet actual refugees and the people who are trying to help.

"An excellent resource for researchers, report writers, and school debate members." Booklist.

Includes bibliographical references and index.

362.883 Rape

Conley, Kate A., 1977-

Date rape drugs. Kate Conley; content consultant, R.E. Gaensslen, PhD, Professor Emeritus, Forensic Science, University of Illinois at Chicago. Essential Library, 2019 112 p.

Grades: 8 9 10 11 　　　　　　　**362.883**
　　1. Date rape drugs 2. Dating violence 3. Drug control 4. Drug control 5. Rape
ISBN 9781532114151

LC bl2019026597

Looks at the issue of date rape drugs, providing information about the three most common types, how they affect the body, and what the legal system is doing about them.

363.11 Occupational and industrial hazards

Aronson, Marc

★ **Trapped**: how the world rescued 33 miners from 2,000 feet below the Chilean desert. Marc Aronson. Atheneum, 2011. 144 p.

Grades: 4 5 6 7 　　　　　　　**363.11**
　　1. Mine accidents 2. Mine rescue work 3. Survival (after airplane accidents, shipwrecks, etc) 4. San Jose Mine Accident, Chile, 2010 5. Copper mines and mining -- Accidents 6. Chile 7. Copiapo Region, Chile
ISBN 9781416913979

LC 2011000777

Describes the rescue of thirty-three miners trapped in a copper-gold mine in San Jose, Chile and how experts from around the world, from drillers, to astronauts, to submarine specialists, came together to make their remarkable rescue possible.

"This is a riveting, in-depth recounting of the events that held the world rapt. . . . Twelve short chapters with photos and diagrams keep the story well-paced." Publishers Weekly.

Includes bibliographical references and index.

Bodden, Valerie

The **Deepwater** Horizon oil spill. Valerie Bodden. Creative Education, 2018. 48 p.

Grades: 4 5 6 7 8 　　　　　　　**363.11**
　　1. BP Deepwater Horizon Explosion and Oil Spill, 2010 2. Oil spills
ISBN 9781640260030

A historical account—including eyewitness quotes—of the devastating 2010 explosion on the Deepwater Horizon oil rig and the resulting oil spill's harmful environmental impact, ending with how the disaster's victims are memorialized today. Provided by publisher.

Scott, Elaine, 1940-

★ **Buried** alive!: how 33 miners survived 69 days deep under the Chilean desert. Elaine Scott. Clarion Books, 2012. 80 p.

Grades: 4 5 6 7 8 　　　　　　　**363.11**
　　1. San Jose Mine Accident, Chile, 2010 2. Mine rescue work 3. Mine accidents 4. Gold mines and mining -- Accidents 5. Copper mines and mining -- Accidents 6. Chile 7. Copiapo Region, Chile
ISBN 9780547707785

LC 2011025945

Describes the 2010 mining accident in San Jose, Chile, in which thirty-three men became trapped underground for over sixty days, and details the rescue efforts and the worldwide media coverage of the event.

363.12 Transportation hazards

Burgan, Michael

The **Hindenburg** in flames: how a photograph marked the end of the airship. by Michael Burgan. Compass Point Books, an imprint of Capstone Press, [2017] 64 p.: Captured world history

Grades: 5 6 7 8 　　　　　　　**363.12**
　　1. Hindenburg (Airship) 2. Airships -- History 3. Mass media 4. Photography 5. Documentary photography -- History
ISBN 9780756554415

LC 2016008220

Discusses the iconic photograph of the German airship Hindenburg in flames as it attempted to land in New Jersey in May 1937. Provided by publisher.

"The fact-filled texts are inviting but never talk down to the audience. Mark this series as a great way to discuss history, photography, and the way both shape public perception." Booklist.

Includes bibliographical references and index.

363.17 Hazardous materials

Langeland, Deirdre

Meltdown: earthquake, tsunami, and nuclear disaster in Fukushima. Deirdre Langeland. Henry Holt & Co 2021 208 p.

Grades: 5 6 7 8 9   363.17

1. Fukushima Nuclear Disaster, Japan, 2011 2. Nuclear power plants -- Accidents 3. Nuclear accidents 4. Tsunamis 5. Disasters 6. Japan

ISBN 9781626727007

Draws on first-person testimony to document the harrowing events of the 2011 earthquake and tsunami that damaged the Fukushima power plant, triggering a nightmare nuclear meltdown.

"A well-researched, sharply written, engrossing account of natural and nuclear disaster." Kirkus

Moore, Kate

The **radium** girls: the scary but true story of the poison that made people glow in the dark. Kate Moore. Sourcebooks eXplore, 2020. 352 p.

Grades: 5 6 7 8 9   363.17

1. 20th century 2. Radioactive pollution 3. Employee rights 4. Occupational health and safety 5. Womens rights 6. Radium 7. United States

ISBN 9781728210346

LC 2020016986

Amid the excitement of the early twentieth century, hundreds of young women spend their days hard at work painting watch dials with glow-in-the-dark radium paint. The painters consider themselves lucky—until they start suffering from a mysterious illness. As the corporations try to cover up a shocking secret, these shining girls suddenly find themselves at the center of a deadly scandal.

"Published for adults in 2017, Moore's bestseller is now updated for readers closer to the age of the doomed dial painters. Clipped sentences and uncomplicated language make for an easily readable text, and Moore's matter-of-fact descriptions of the girls' physical declines are more harrowing for their lack of sensationalist gore." Bulletin of the Center for Children's Books

Includes bibliographical references and index.

Newton, Michael, 1951-

Bomb squad. Michael Newton. Chelsea House Publishers, 2010. 128 p. : Law enforcement agencies

Grades: 6 7 8 9   363.17

1. Bomb squads 2. Explosives -- Detection 3. Bombings -- Prevention 4. Explosives -- Safety measures 5. Terrorism -- Prevention

ISBN 9781604136241

LC 2010022102

"Solidly and comprehensively researched. . . . Bomb Squad shows that explosives have always been a means of striking terror throughout history. The volume covers the making and defusing of bombs, nuclear devices, and headline-making acts of terror. . . . An attractive design, plenty of photos, and solid back matter complete [the] package. Extremely useful for students and appealing for browsers." Booklist.

Includes bibliographical references and index.

Perritano, John

Bomb squad technician. by John Perritano. Mason Crest, 2016. 48 p.: On a mission

Grades: 4 5 6 7   363.17

1. Bomb squads 2. Bomb threats 3. Explosives -- Detection 4. Bomb reconnaissance 5. Bombing investigation

ISBN 9781422233924

"Excitement never flags in this book, as every chapter is accompanied by explosive stories, such as Guy Fawkes and the Boston Marathon bombing." Booklist.

363.2 Police services

Behnke, Alison

Racial profiling: everyday inequality. Alison Marie Behnke. Twenty-First Century Books, 2017. 160 p.

Grades: 8 9 10 11 12   363.2

1. Racial profiling 2. Discrimination in law enforcement 3. Inequality 4. White privilege 5. Antiracist literature

ISBN 9781512402681

LC 2016009454

"A courageous historical examination of one of the most critical civil rights issues of our time." Kirkus.

Includes bibliographical references and index.

Gallagher, Jim

Policing and race: the debate over excessive use of force. Jim Gallagher ReferencePoint Press, [2021] 80 p.

Grades: 7 8 9 10 11 12   363.2

1. Race relations 2. Police brutality 3. Racism 4. African Americans -- Social conditions 21st century. 5. African Americans -- Civil rights 6. United States -- Race relations.

ISBN 9781678200442

There is a long and ugly history of violent encounters between law enforcement officers and Americans of color, particularly Black Americans. About 1,000 Americans are killed each year by law-enforcement officers, and numerous studies have found a link between race and police killings. Provided by publisher.

"A solid introduction for readers seeking a broad outline of the subject." Kirkus

Includes bibliographical references and index.

Johnson, C. M. (Cheri M.)

Law enforcement. Cheri Johnson. Full Tilt Press, [2017] 48 p.: Origins.

Grades: 4 5 6 7   363.2

1. Crime prevention 2. Law enforcement 3. Criminal investigation

ISBN 9781629206134

Presents the world of today's crime-fighters, and examines how and why different divisions of law enforcement were created.

Newton, Michael, 1951-

SWAT teams. Michael Newton. Chelsea House, c2010. 128 p. : Law enforcement agencies

Grades: 6 7 8 9   363.2

1. Police -- Special weapons and tactics units 2. Law enforcement 3. Law enforcement agencies 4. Vocational guidance 5. Occupations

ISBN 9781604136258

LC 2010026511

Traces the history of special police teams worldwide, examining their techniques, tools, successes, and failures.

363.25 Detection of crime (Criminal investigation)

Evans, Colin, 1948-
Crime lab. Colin Evans. Chelsea House, 2011. 134 p.: Law enforcement agencies
Grades: 6 7 8 9   363.25
1. Crime laboratories 2. Criminal evidence 3. Criminal investigation 4. Forensic sciences 5. Laboratories
ISBN 9781604136128
LC 2010043271
"The Law Enforcement Agencies series is as formidable as the various groups it introduces. Solidly and comprehensively researched. . . . An attractive design, plenty of photos, and solid back matter complete each package. Extremely useful for students and appealing for browsers." Booklist.
Includes bibliographical references and index.

Harris, Elizabeth Snoke, 1973-
Crime scene science fair projects. Elizabeth Snoke Harris. Lark Books, c2006. 112 p.
Grades: 6 7 8 9 10   363.25
1. Criminal investigation 2. Forensic sciences 3. Science projects
ISBN 1579907652
LC 2006016803
Presents more than twenty great experiments—broken into topics such as blood and guts, eyewitness accounts, and physical evidence—that allow students to use real CSI techniques to find clues, analyze the data, and come to their own conclusions.
"Harris begins with an explanation of forensic science and how it's applied in the everyday world, followed by a discussion of how to plan for a successful project. The projects involve lie detection, lifting fingerprints, recovering data from burned documents, and so on. . . . The author's concise, lively style will even engage students who aren't fond of reading nonfiction." School Library Journal.

Johnson, C. M. (Cheri M.)
Forensics. Cheri Johnson. Full Tilt Press, [2017] 48 p.: Origins.
Grades: 4 5 6 7   363.25
1. Forensic sciences 2. Criminal investigation 3. Crime scenes
ISBN 9781629206127
Explores the science involved in crime-fighting and how it has impacted the way crimes are both solved and committed. Includes glossary and quiz.

MacLeod, Elizabeth
Bones never lie: how forensics helps solve history's mysteries. Elizabeth MacLeod. Firefly Books Ltd., 2013. 160 p.
Grades: 4 5 6 7 8   363.25
1. Criminal investigation 2. Forensic sciences 3. Criminal investigation
ISBN 9781554514830
Describes how forensic sciences can explain the fate of seven people whose deaths have intrigued observers, including King Tut, Napoleon, and the Man in the Iron Mask.
"In real life, forensics can be slow and tedious, but MacLeod invests these high-profile deaths with considerable vim and drama. A good selection of staged and archival photographs and artwork accompany the

stories. A fully fleshed and crisply told story of forensics at its romantic best." Kirkus.

Newton, Michael, 1951-
Drug Enforcement Administration. Michael Newton. Chelsea House Publishers, 2011. 128 p.: Law enforcement agencies
Grades: 6 7 8 9   363.25
1. United States. Drug Enforcement Administration 2. Drug control 3. Drug traffic
ISBN 9781604136418
LC 2010036940
"The Law Enforcement Agencies series is as formidable as the various groups it introduces. Solidly and comprehensively researched. . . . An attractive design, plenty of photos, and solid back matter complete each package. Extremely useful for students and appealing for browsers." Booklist.
Includes bibliographical references and index.

363.250973 United States. Federal Bureau of Investigation

Ricciuti, Edward R.
Federal Bureau of Investigation. Edward R. Ricciuti. Chelsea House Publishers, c2010. 128 p. : Law enforcement agencies
Grades: 6 7 8 9   363.250973
1. FBI 2. Criminal investigation 3. Law enforcement agencies 4. Law enforcement 5. Vocational guidance 6. Occupations
ISBN 9781604136364
LC 2010030397
"Solidly and comprehensively researched. . . . Federal Bureau of Investigation is a broad and deep look at the agency from its inception. Many of its most famous cases, including the Rosenbergs' arrest, terror cases, and the fight against organized crime, are discussed. Common criticisms, such as the overreach of the agency (J. Edgar Hoover in particular) are included. . . . An attractive design, plenty of photos, and solid back matter complete [the] package. Extremely useful for students and appealing for browsers." Booklist.
Includes bibliographical references and index.

363.28 Services of special kinds of security and law enforcement agencies

Newton, Michael, 1951-
U.S. marshals. Michael Newton. Chelsea House, c2011. 128 p.
Grades: 6 7 8 9   363.28
1. United States. Marshals Service 2. Law enforcement 3. United States marshals
ISBN 9781604136272
LC 2010038195
Describes the history of the United States Marshals Service, its initial purpose and how its function has evolved over the years, and their current responsibilities in modern law enforcement and in the war on terror.
"The Law Enforcement Agencies series is as formidable as the various groups it introduces. Solidly and comprehensively researched. . . . An attractive design, plenty of photos, and solid back matter complete each package. Extremely useful for students and appealing for browsers." Booklist.
Includes bibliographical references (p. 122-123) and index.

Ryan, Bernard, 1923-
The **Secret** Service. Bernard Ryan, Jr. Chelsea House Publishers, 2010. 128 p. : Law enforcement agencies
Grades: 6 7 8 9   **363.28**
1. United States. Secret Service. 2. Secret service 3. Law enforcement agencies 4. Law enforcement 5. Vocational guidance 6. Occupations
ISBN 9781604136234
     LC 2010029372
"The Law Enforcement Agencies series is as formidable as the various groups it introduces. Solidly and comprehensively researched. . . . An attractive design, plenty of photos, and solid back matter complete each package. Extremely useful for students and appealing for browsers." Booklist.
Includes bibliographical references and index.

Weir, William
Border patrol. William Weir. Chelsea House, c2010. 128 p. : Law enforcement agencies
Grades: 6 7 8 9   **363.28**
1. U.S. Customs and Border Protection. 2. Border patrols 3. Law enforcement agencies 4. Law enforcement 5. Vocational guidance 6. Occupations
ISBN 9781604136357
     LC 2010030051
"Solidly and comprehensively researched. . . . Border Patrol takes on a topic much in the news. The hottest issues of border control are all examined: drugs, bandits, and smuggling of goods and people. There is also great information on the technology used, as well as a levelheaded discussion on the terror threat presented by illegal immigrants. . . . An attractive design, plenty of photos, and solid back matter complete [the] package. Extremely useful for students and appealing for browsers." Booklist.
Includes bibliographical references and index.

363.31 Censorship

Gottfried, Ted
Censorship. Ted Gottfried. Marshall Cavendish Benchmark, c2006. 143 p.: Open for debate
Grades: 7 8 9 10   **363.31**
1. United States. Constitution. 1st Amendment. 2. Freedom of speech 3. Censorship 4. Internet and freedom of speech
ISBN 0761418830
     LC 2004021818
Discusses how censorship relates to the First Amendment and freedom of speech, historic fights for and against censorship in the United States, and how censorship has become an increasingly inflammatory issue with regards to the Internet.

363.33 Control of firearms

Atkin, S. Beth
Gunstories: life-changing experiences with guns. interviews and photographs by S. Beth Atkin. Harper Tempest, c2006. ix, 245 p.
Grades: 7 8 9 10 11 12   **363.33**
1. Guns -- Social aspects 2. Gangs 3. Gang members 4. Teenagers and guns 5. Violence in gangs 6. United States -- Social life and customs -- 21st century. 7. Essays
ISBN 0060526599
     LC 2005002076
A collection of stories, interviews, and photographs that share the mixed impact guns have on young people's lives. Provided by publisher.
"This book should be useful for students involved in the debate about guns in our culture as well as for those with a general interest in the subject." School Library Journal.

Doeden, Matt
Gun violence: fighting for our lives and our rights. Matt Doeden. Twenty-First Century Books, 2019 112 p.
Grades: 7 8 9 10 11 12   **363.33**
1. Violence and guns 2. Violent crimes 3. Gun control 4. Guns 5. Gun ownership -- Government policy
ISBN 9781541555549
"While examining escalating gun violence and mass shootings, Doeden presents a balanced approach to the debates concerning gun control and differing interpretations of the U.S. Constitution's Second Amendment. He offers the perspectives and arguments from one side and immediately follows with the other, raising tough questions on both fronts." Booklist.

363.330973 Gun control—United States

Allen, John, 1957-
Thinking critically: gun control. John Allen. ReferencePoint Press, 2018 80 p.: Thinking critically
Grades: 8 9 10 11 12   **363.330973**
1. Gun control 2. Guns -- Social aspects
ISBN 9781682823378
     LC 2017041159
Examines the issue of gun control, asking if control laws reduce deaths, if background checks should be expanded, if military-style assault weapons should be banned, and if concealed handguns should be permitted.

McCann, Michelle Roehm, 1968-
Enough is enough: how students can join the fight for gun safety. Michelle Roehm McCann; foreword by Shannon Watts, founder of Moms Demand Action for Gun Sense in America. Simon Pulse; xx, 300 p.
Grades: 7 8 9 10 11 12   **363.330973**
1. Gun control 2. School shootings 3. Students -- Political activity 4. Protest movements 5. United States
ISBN 9781582707006
     LC 2019009560
"A timely, thoughtful, far-reaching, and inclusive look at gun control and gun violence issues." School Library Journal.
Includes bibliographical references.

363.34 Disasters

Brown, Don, 1949-
Drowned City: Hurricane Katrina and New Orleans. Don Brown. Houghton Mifflin Harcourt, 2015. 96 p.
Grades: 7 8 9 10   **363.34**
1. Hurricane Katrina, 2005 2. Survival (after hurricanes) 3. Responsibility 4. Hurricanes 5. Hurricane damage 6. New

Orleans, Louisiana 7. Comics and Graphic novels
ISBN 9780544157774
NCTE Orbis Pictus Nonfiction Award, 2016.

"Brown's narrative is clear and precise, relying exclusively on data and statistics interspersed with quotes from residents, rescue crews, journalists, and news reports. Alone, the text might lack impact, but combined with the haunting imagery, it hits readers like a punch in the gut." Booklist.

Fradin, Judith Bloom

Droughts. Judy and Dennis Fradin. National Geographic, 2008. 48 p. : Witness to disaster

Grades: 4 5 6 7   **363.34**

1. 1930s 2. Droughts 3. Droughts -- History 4. Dust Bowl (South Central United States)
ISBN 9781426303395

LC 2008020424

Presents an introduction to droughts, discussing their causes, government responses and the recommendations of scientists for dealing with them, and a review of some of the worst droughts of the early twenty-first century.

Langley, Andrew, 1949-

Hurricanes, tsunamis, and other natural disasters. Andrew Langley; foreword by Bill McGuire. Kingfisher, 2006. 63 p.: Kingfisher knowledge

Grades: 5 6 7 8   **363.34**

1. Hurricanes 2. Tsunamis 3. Natural disasters
ISBN 9780753459751

Stunning photographs help take readers into the world of natural disasters.

"This book presents a high-interest topic in an attractively designed format that features colorful, eye-catching graphics and a solidly written text." Booklist.

Markle, Sandra

Rescues! Sandra Markle. Millbrook Press, c2006. 88 p.

Grades: 4 5 6 7   **363.34**

1. Rescue work 2. Mountain rescue operations 3. First responders 4. Search and rescue operations 5. Survival (after airplane accidents, shipwrecks, etc)
ISBN 0822534134

LC 2005009707

Looks at how emergency workers use their specialized training, equipment, and the latest technology to rescue victims of accidents or disasters in eleven different situations ranging from an earthquake to a tsunami.

"From the collapse of a Pennsylvania coal mine in 2002 to the tsunami that struck 11 countries in 2004 to Hurricane Katrina in 2005, the 11 disasters Markle describes are straight from news headlines. In this full-color photo-essay, she uses individual experiences of rescue and survival to bring each drama close." Booklist.

Includes bibliographical references (p. 84-86) and index.

Mooney, Carla, 1970-

Surviving in cold places. Carla Mooney. Lerner Publications Company, [2014] 32 p.: Shockzone.

Grades: 5 6 7 8   **363.34**

1. Survival 2. Survival skills 3. Winter survival 4. Arctic regions 5. Polar regions
ISBN 9781467714341

LC 2013019868

Provides tips on surviving in freezing environments, discusses different types of cold weather emergencies, and shares the stories of survivors.

"Each thin volume shares six to eight (mostly) contemporary stories of extreme survival, including a 2005 grizzly bear attack on a father and daughter and a boy's eight-day ordeal buried in rubble in the 2010 Haiti earthquake. Readers will be grabbed by a mix of harrowing details and eye-catching color photographs. The stories and appended safety tips are superficially presented but are nonetheless fascinating." Horn Book.

Includes bibliographical references (page 30) and index.

Rusch, Elizabeth

★ **Eruption!**: volcanoes and the science of saving lives. text by Elizabeth Rusch; photographs by Tom Uhlman. Houghton Mifflin Harcourt, c2013. 76 p. : Scientists in the field (Houghton Mifflin)

Grades: 5 6 7 8   **363.34**

1. Volcanic eruptions 2. Volcanoes 3. Natural disasters 4. Volcanologists 5. Crisis management
ISBN 9780547503509

LC 2012034055

Recounting the harrowing 1985 eruption of Colombia's Nevado del Ruiz volcano that claimed 23,000 lives, an account of the work of volcanologists Andy Lockhart, John Pallister and their team describes their life-risking efforts to investigate dangerous volcanoes that pose constant threats to more than one billion people worldwide.

363.37 Fire hazards

Cooper, Michael L., 1950-

Fighting fire!: ten of the deadliest fires in American history and how we fought them. Michael L. Cooper. Henry Holt and Company, 2014 144 p.

Grades: 5 6 7 8   **363.37**

1. Fire fighting -- History 2. Fire fighters 3. Fires
ISBN 9780805097146

LC 2013043580

Recounts the histories of 10 of America's most formidable fires while paying tribute to the bravery of firefighters, sharing insights into how each catastrophic blaze led to new firefighting practices and technologies.

"Throughout history, fires have wreaked destruction but have also sparked innovation and reform. The Great Chicago Fire (1871) destroyed a third of the city but brought about a new architecture style; the Triangle Shirtwaist Factory Fire (1911) killed 146 people but led to the passage of laws protecting workers. Entries are lively, with dramatic illustrations to match." Horn Book.

Includes bibliographical references and index.

Thiessen, Mark

Extreme wildfire: smoke jumpers, high-tech gear, survival tactics, and the extraordinary science of fire. Mark Thiessen. National Geographic Partners, 2016 111 p.

Grades: 4 5 6 7 8   **363.37**

1. Wildfire fighters 2. Wildfires -- Prevention and control 3. Fire ecology 4. Fire fighters 5. Occupations
ISBN 9781426325311

An introduction to wildfires and their ecological impact describes the prevention and containment methods of fire science and the cutting-edge technologies that are being used to predict and track fire behavior, sharing additional information about the survival tactics and bravery of today's elite firefighters.

"Wildfires are an incredible force of nature that inevitably create life-and-death situations for humans, and this book's stunning images and insider insight provide an in-depth introduction to understanding and controlling them." Booklist

363.4 Controversies related to public morals and customs

Blumenthal, Karen, 1959-2020

Bootleg: murder, moonshine, and the lawless years of prohibition. Karen Blumenthal. Roaring Brook Press, c2011. 160 p.

Grades: 8 9 10 11 12   **363.4**

1. Prohibition 2. Liquor industry and trade 3. Temperance movements -- History 20th century. 4. Sobriety 5. Alcoholic beverage law violations 6. United States -- History -- 1919-1933.

ISBN 9781596434493

LC 2010032687

Offers information about Prohibition, temperance movements at the end of the eighteenth century, the Eighteenth Amendment, bootlegging, and gangsters.

"The author offers a highly readable, well-shaped look at the Eighteenth Amendment. . . . She provides concise, clearly written insights into the seeds of temperance movements in the late eighteenth century. . . . The section on Al Capone will satisfy readers hungry for the gangster-warfare side of Prohibition. A closing chapter makes an argument that despite the mostly disastrous results, there were bright points to Prohibition. . . . Plenty of archival images lend to the book's pleasant design, and an ample bibliography and source notes close out this top-notch resource." Booklist.

363.45 Drug traffic

Martin, Claudia

Drug wars. Claudia Martin. Cavendish Square, 2018 48 p.

Grades: 6 7 8 9   **363.45**

1. Drug control 2. Drug traffic 3. Drug use 4. Violence and drugs 5. Violence

ISBN 9781502632586

The violence that surrounds drug dealing and drug trafficking has decimated whole communities, and, in some cases, reshaped daily life in entire countries. This volume takes a closer look at the people affected by the drug trade and the efforts being made to combat it. The book includes firsthand stories, critical thinking questions, and a summative activity, all with the aim of showing the human toll of the drug economy.

363.7 Environmental problems

Fleischman, Paul

Eyes wide open: going behind the environmental headlines. Paul Fleischman. Candlewick Press, 2014. 208 p.

Grades: 8 9 10 11 12   **363.7**

1. Environmental responsibility 2. Consumer education 3. Information behavior 4. Environmentalism 5. Information resources

ISBN 9780763671020

"With simple, matter-of-fact language, an attractive layout and an abundance of references, this compact guide to addressing climate change is a must-read for millennials and for all who seek solutions to global warming. . . . Readers are offered advice on how to analyze and interpret what they hear in person and discover through the media." Kirkus.

Jankeliowitch, Anne

Kids who are changing the world. Anne Jankeliowitch; photographs by Yann Arthus-Bertrand. Sourcebooks Jabberwocky, 2014, 144 p.

Grades: 4 5 6 7   **363.7**

1. Child environmentalists 2. Environmentalism 3. Environmentalists 4. Environmental protection -- Citizen participation 5. Nature conservation

ISBN 9781402295324

LC 2014011237

"Each story is styled as an interview with direct quotes from the kids involved. Photographs are dynamic and stunning, and background information and statistics on environmental issues are included in the margins." Booklist.

Includes bibliographical references and index.

Reilly, Kathleen M.

Planet Earth: 25 environmental projects you can build yourself. Kathleen M. Reilly. Nomad Press, c2008. 128 p.

Grades: 4 5 6 7   **363.7**

1. Environmental sciences 2. Environmental sciences -- Experiments 3. Pollution 4. Global warming 5. Conservation of natural resources

ISBN 9781934670057

"Both comprehensive and approachable, this title . . . combines explanations of science concepts and environmental issues with hands-on projects. . . . Elementary- and middle-school students will find the succinct overview of the facts very useful, and they'll welcome the clearly presented projects." Booklist.

363.72 Sanitation

Albee, Sarah

Poop happened!: a history of the world from the bottom up. by Sarah Albee; illustrated by Robert Leighton. Walker, 2010. 176 p.

Grades: 4 5 6 7   **363.72**

1. Toilets -- History 2. Bathrooms -- History 3. Sewage disposal -- History 4. Bathing customs -- History 5. Sanitation 6. Grossology

ISBN 9780802798251

LC 2009034172

History finally comes out of the water-closet in this exploration of how people's need to relieve themselves shaped human development from ancient times to the present; through a blend of historical photos and humorous illustrations, the author traces human civilization using a fascinating (albeit revolting) theme.

"Albee deposits a heaping history of human sanitation—or rather lack thereof—and its effects. . . . She pumps out a steady stream of comments on the miasmic effects of urbanization, waste disposal, and the roles of (not) bathing in ancient Greece, Rome, medieval Europe, . . . and the Reeking Renaissance. She then digs into the gradual adoption of better practices in the nineteenth century. . . . The cartoon illustrations feature sludgy green highlights." Booklist.

Eamer, Claire, 1947-

What a waste!: where does garbage go? Claire Eamer; illustrated by Bambi Edlund. Annick Press, 2017. 96 p.

Grades: 4 5 6 7   **363.72**
1. Solid waste disposal 2. Garbage collection 3. Solid waste 4. Environmentalism
ISBN 9781554519194
"This selection will be useful for environmentally minded upper elementary and middle school readers as well as those needing a resource for science and classroom projects." School Library Journal.

Goldstein, Margaret J.

Garbage in space: a space discovery guide. Margaret J. Goldstein. Lerner Publications, [2017] 48 p.: Space Discovery Guides
Grades: 5 6 7 8   **363.72**
1. Space debris 2. Space pollution 3. Pollution 4. Waste-products 5. Near-Earth objects 6. Space 7. Earth
ISBN 9781512425901

LC 2016018175
This book explores the problem of space junk that clutters outer space and details the ways in which NASA and other organizations are trying to deal with and solve this problem. Provided by publisher.
"A thoroughly researched and authoritative addition to science collections." School Library Journal.
Includes bibliographical references (page 46) and index.

Kallen, Stuart A., 1955-

Trashing the planet: examining our global garbage glut. Stuart A. Kallen. Twenty-First Century Books, 2018 104 p.
Grades: 6 7 8 9 10   **363.72**
1. Refuse and refuse disposal
ISBN 9781512413144

LC 2016033032
Introduces the problems of global waste disposal, describing the hazards of toxins associated with landfills, plastics floating in the oceans, and debris orbiting the planet, with some of the solutions proposed by scientists.

363.738 Pollutants

Bow, James

Earth's climate change: carbon dioxide overload. James Bow. Crabtree Publishing, 2016. 32 p.: Next generation energy
Grades: 5 6 7 8   **363.738**
1. Greenhouse effect, Atmospheric 2. Carbon dioxide 3. Global warming 4. Climate change
ISBN 9780778719786

LC 2015020964
We live in an energy-rich age, in which we can turn on a light with the flick of a switch or drive anywhere by turning a key. But, our vehicles, factories, and power stations, which create the electricity needed to light and heat our buildings, pump carbon dioxide into Earth's atmosphere. Carbon dioxide overload from these human activities is making our planet hotter and hotter—and is causing the Earth's climate to change. Find out what scientists are doing to find sustainable new forms of energy that will secure our planet's future. Provided by publisher.

Chiang, Mona

Oil spill: disaster. [written by Mona Chiang ... et al.]. Scholastic, c2010. 31 p.
Grades: 4 5 6 7 8   **363.738**
1. Oil spills 2. Oil pollution 3. Pollution -- Environmental aspects 4. Oil spills -- Environmental aspects 5. Oil spills -- Cleanup 6. Gulf of Mexico
ISBN 9780545317764

LC bl2010026660
Examines the consequences of the April 2010 Gulf of Mexico oil spill, when the offshore oil rig Deepwater Horizon exploded, causing environmental and economical damage along the Gulf coast of the United States.
"While text and color photographs convey the extent of the devastation to the Gulf, the book also highlights some innovative attempts to clean up oil spills and profiles two middle school students, who researched cleaning up oil in their own neighborhood." Publishers Weekly.

David, Laurie

The **down-to-Earth** guide to global warming. Laurie David and Cambria Gordon. Orchard Books, 2007. xiii, 112 p.
Grades: 4 5 6 7   **363.738**
1. Global warming 2. Environmental education
ISBN 0439024943

LC 2006035705
Presents facts about global warming and its disastrous consequences, and suggests steps readers and their parents can take to help reverse the problem.
"The authors put forth the basics on global warming, climate change, and how readers can green up the environment. They temper the book's often troubling subject matter with kid-friendly humor, some celebrity shout-outs, and explanations of the scientific underpinnings. An amply illustrated layout, featuring attention-grabbing sidebars, dramatic photos, and diagrams, will sustain reader interest." Booklist.
Includes bibliographical references (p. 102-107) and index.

Delano, Marfe Ferguson

Earth in the hot seat: bulletins from a warming world. by Marfé Ferguson Delano. National Geographic, 2009. 64 p.
Grades: 5 6 7 8   **363.738**
1. Global warming 2. Global temperature changes 3. Greenhouse effect, Atmospheric 4. Climate change 5. Nature -- Effect of humans on
ISBN 9781426304347
Explains global warming, discussing its current signs, its effect on climate and animals, and identifying efforts being made around the world to try to control it and minimize its impact.
"This book lays out . . . the evidence for global warming and the part that human activity plays in it. Five chapters lay out the signs and evidences of a warming world. . . . Subsequent chapters of the book are devoted to what humankind can expect in a warming world and steps that must be taken to avert catastrophe for humans and the planet. . . . The illustrative photos are fully up to National Geographic high standards. This [is a] fine book, reasonably priced and carefully researched." Voice of Youth Advocates.
Includes bibliographical references and index.

Gore, Albert, 1948-

★ An **inconvenient** truth: the crisis of global warming. Al Gore. Viking, 2007. 191 p.
Grades: 5 6 7 8   **363.738**
1. Global warming 2. Climate change 3. Environmental policy 4. Environmental protection 5. Climatology
ISBN 0670062715

LC 2006103242
The former vice-president details the factors contributing to the growing climate crisis, describes changes to the environment caused by global warming, and discusses the shift in environmental policy that is needed to avert disaster.

"This is illustrated with easy-to-grasp graphics and revealing before-and-after photos. . . . O'Connor rephrases Gore's arguments in briefer, simpler language without compromising their flow." School Library Journal.

Includes bibliographical references and index.

Our choice: how we can solve the climate crisis. Al Gore; text adapted by Richie Chevat. Puffin Books, 2009. 207 p.

Grades: 6 7 8 9 10   **363.738**
1. Global warming 2. Greenhouse effect, Atmospheric 3. Environmental policy 4. Environmental protection 5. Human ecology
ISBN 9780142409817

LC bl2009030414

Explores the extent of the impending environmental crisis and outlines the Nobel Peace Prize-winning former vice president's comprehensive and urgent global strategy for implementing solutions to it.

"This colorful, well-designed volume presents the climate crisis in an easy-to-understand format. Covering many aspects of this complex problem, it addresses the effects of pollution on the environment, the search for alternative energy sources, and offers suggestions for conserving power and reducing the impact of human habitation on the planet. . . . Although the urgency of the current global situation is stressed, the chapters are also laced with hope. Suggestions for change offer positive steps that anyone can take to reduce his carbon footprint, and extend a call to unite globally to save the planet for future generations." Voice of Youth Advocates.

Heos, Bridget
It's getting hot in here: the past, the present, and the future of global warming. Bridget Heos. HMH Books for Young Readers, 2016. 224 p.

Grades: 7 8 9 10   **363.738**
1. Global warming
ISBN 9780544303478

LC 2014035584

This hard-hitting look at climate change tackles the past, present, and future of global warming, examining the effects it's having across the world, the politics behind denial, and the ways in which we can all work to lessen the harsh effects of our warming world. Perfect for young environmentalists looking to learn about the ways in which we can take action against global warming. Provided by publisher.

Klein, Naomi, 1970-
How to change everything: the young human's guide to protecting the planet and each other. Naomi Klein; adapted by Rebecca Stefoff. Atheneum Books for Young Readers, 2021. 336 p.

Grades: 5 6 7 8 9 10 11   **363.738**
1. Environmentalism 2. Green movement 3. Climate change 4. Environmental protection 5. Conservation of natural resources
ISBN 9781534474529

LC 2020030304

Young people are not just part of the climate change movement. They are leading the way. Will you be one of them? Forget everything you think you know about climate change. This book explains why the planet desperately needs our help and how you can use your power to change the world through climate activism.

"With its wide focus and pull-no-punches real talk, this book stands out among climate change books for its uniquely inclusive perspective that will inspire conviction, passion, and action." Kirkus

Includes bibliographical references.

McPherson, Stephanie Sammartino
Hothouse earth: the climate crisis and the importance of carbon neutrality. Stephanie Sammartino McPherson. Lerner Pub Group 2021 136 p.

Grades: 7 8 9 10   **363.738**
1. Climate change 2. Greenhouse effect, Atmospheric 3. Global warming 4. Climatology 5. Environmentalists
ISBN 9781541579170

LC 2019046586

The past, present, and future of Earth is a result of climate change. Climate change affects our everyday lives, and scientists and young people are looking into what we can do to fix it. Provided by publisher.

"This attractive offering considers climate change through scientific, political and personal responsibility lenses." Booklist

Includes bibliographical references and index.

Morris, Neil, 1946-
Global warming. Neil Morris. World Almanac Library, 2007. 48 p.: What if we do nothing?

Grades: 5 6 7 8   **363.738**
1. Global warming 2. Global temperature changes 3. Climate change 4. Global environmental change
ISBN 0836877551

LC 2006030444

"This boasts an attractive format, with large pages that allow room for pictures, excellent charts and graphs, as well as a thoughtful, clear discussion of the topic." Booklist.

Includes bibliographical references (p. 47) and index.

Nardo, Don, 1947-
Planet under siege: climate change. Don Nardo. Referencepoint Press, 2020 80 p.

Grades: 7 8 9 10 11 12   **363.738**
1. Climate change 2. Global warming 3. Nature -- Effect of humans on 4. Global environmental change 5. Environmentalism 6. Earth
ISBN 9781682827574

"Readers already interested in the topic will devour this volume; for others, the large font, clear subheadings, and numerous color photographs make it easy to engage with. Fact-based, well-documented, and accessible, this publication serves its purpose well." Kirkus

Newman, Patricia
Plastic, ahoy!: investigating the great Pacific garbage patch. Patricia Newman; photographs by Annie Crawley. Millbrook Press, [2014] 48 p.

Grades: 5 6 7 8 9 10   **363.738**
1. Marine pollution 2. Ocean waste disposal 3. Pollution 4. Plastic marine debris -- Environmental aspects 5. Plastic scrap -- Environmental aspects 6. Pacific Ocean
ISBN 9781467712835

LC 2013017773

A team of scientists explores the Great Pacific Garbage Patch, where millions of pieces of plastic have gathered, having drifted there from rivers, beaches, and ocean traffic all over the world.

"Here readers travel to the Pacific Garbage Patch with three graduate-student scientists as they try to determine the effect of plastics on the sea. There's solid explanation of their hypotheses and research, and emphasis on the researchers' experiences lends a personal feel. Questions of how plastic may harm the oceans, its inhabitants, and even humans encourage further inquiry." Horn Book.

Includes bibliographical references (page 46) and index.

Simon, Seymour

Climate action: what happened and what we can do. Seymour Simon. Harpercollins Childrens Books, 2021. 56 p.

Grades: 4 5 6 7 8   **363.738**

1. Climate change 2. Global warming 3. Hope 4. Greenhouse gases 5. Social advocacy
ISBN 9780062943316

"A veteran science writer describes some of the environmental effects of our changing climate, introduces some teen activists, and offers suggestions and examples of what can be done. . . . An effective introduction clearly designed and organized for its audience." Kirkus

363.9 Population problems

Lasky, Jack

Birth control. Jack Lasky, book editor. Greenhaven Press, 2016. 224 p.: Opposing viewpoints series

Grades: 7 8 9 10 11 12   **363.9**

1. Birth control 2. Contraception 3. Sexuality 4. Birth control
ISBN 9780737775068

LC 2015025016

Collects articles on topics related to birth control that represent diverse viewpoints on issues relating to it, including access to birth control, the Affordable Care Act in relation to it, concerns related to it, and its social consequences.

364 Criminology

Denson, Bryan

The **Unabomber**: Agent Kathy Puckett and the hunt for a serial bomber. Bryan Denson. Roaring Brook Press, 2019 xi, 162 p.

Grades: 4 5 6 7   **364**

1. Kaczynski, Theodore John, 1942- 2. Puckett, Kathy 3. Puckett, Kathleen M. 4. United States. Federal Bureau of Investigation -- Officials and employees 5. Serial murder investigation 6. Terrorism 7. Bombing investigation 8. Bombers (Terrorists) 9. Serial murderers
ISBN 9781250199140

LC 2018955824

[The author] presents the story of the FBI's investigation of the Unabomber and the agent who helped bring him to justice.. Publisher's description.

"An enthralling, well-researched introduction to true crime for upper elementary/middle school readers." School Library Journal.

Includes bibliographical references (pages [143]-149) and index.

364.1 Criminal offenses

Gallagher, Jim, 1969-

Thinking critically: illegal immigration. James Gallagher. ReferencePoint Press, 2019. 80 p.: Thinking Critically

Grades: 7 8 9 10 11 12   **364.1**

1. Undocumented immigrants
ISBN 9781682825372

LC 2018038621

Illegal immigration remains one of the most controversial and divisive issues today. There is strong disagreement among Americans about the effects on the nation. Both Republicans and Democrats recognize that something must be done about the 11.3 million illegal immigrants living in the country, although there is no consensus over whether that should involve a path to citizenship, mass deportation, or some other option or combination. Clearly, questions like these will continue to be asked until solutions are found. Provided by publisher.

"Illegal Immigration asks whether the practuce hurts US workers or puts a strain on public services, stronger border enforcement measures are needed, and illegal immigrants should be given a path to citizenship." Booklist

Includes bibliographical references and index.

364.1317 Terrorism

Sullivan, Tom

Escape at 10,000 feet: D.B. Cooper and the missing money. Tom Sullivan. Balzer + Bray, 2021. 94 p.

Grades: 4 5 6 7   **364.1317**

1. Cooper, D. B. 2. Hijacking of aircraft 3. Missing persons 4. Criminal investigation 5. Cold cases (Criminal investigation) 6. Comics and graphic novels
ISBN 9780062991522

A minute-by-minute account of the only unsolved airplane hijacking in the United States uses reproductions of FBI files and investigation photographs to chronicle the events surrounding an unidentified extortionist's 1971 hijacking and disappearance.

"This stranger-than-fiction saga thrives thanks to spectacular design choices. . . . A compulsively readable series debut." Kirkus

Includes bibliographical references.

364.15 Offenses against the person

Bascomb, Neal

The **Nazi** hunters: how a team of spies and survivors captured the world's most notorious Nazi. Neal Bascomb. Scholastic 2013 256 p.

Grades: 6 7 8 9 10   **364.15**

1. Nazi hunters 2. Spies 3. Undercover operations 4. War criminals 5. Holocaust (1933-1945) 6. Germany
ISBN 9780545430999

Sydney Taylor Book Award for Teen Readers, 2014.

Recounts how, sixteen years after the end of World War II, a team of undercover Israeli agents captured the Nazi war criminal, Adolf Eichmann, in a remote area of Argentina and brought him to trial in Israel for crimes committed during the Holocaust.

"This is a splendid example of fascinating storytelling blended with significant historical events." Booklist.

Blumenthal, Karen, 1959-2020

Bonnie and Clyde: the making of a legend. Karen Blumenthal. Viking, an imprint of Penguin Random House, 2018 256 p.

Grades: 7 8 9 10   **364.15**

1. Parker, Bonnie 1910-1934 2. Barrow, Clyde, 1909-1934 3. Criminals 4. Outlaws -- History 20th century 5. Bank robberies -- History 20th century 6. Depressions 1929-1941
ISBN 9780451471222

Describes the life and crimes of the outlaw duo Bonnie and Clyde, detailing their spree of robbery and murder that ended in their brutal deaths.

"That Bonnie and Clyde were young people, close to their families, often kind, and placed in extraordinarily difficult circumstances is not disputed, but neither is the extent of their crimes; in sidebars, Blumenthal profiles each of the people that the Barrow Gang killed. Additional sidebars investigate some of the legends surrounding the duo, and the circumstances that led to their popularity. An extraordinarily successful resource about a painful time in history and a complicated, infamous pair." Booklist.

Crowe, Chris

Getting away with murder: the true story of the Emmett Till case. by Chris Crowe. Phyllis Fogelman Books, c2003. 128 p.

Grades: 7 8 9 10   **364.15**

1. Till, Emmett, 1941-1955 2. Lynching -- History 20th century 3. Crimes against African Americans 4. African American teenage boys 5. Racism -- History 20th century 6. Trials (Murder) 7. Mississippi -- Race relations

ISBN 0803728042

LC 2002005736

When fourteen-year-old Emmett Till left Chicago to visit family in a small town in Mississippi and was soon murdered for whistling at a white woman, a series of events took place that changed the ways of the south and the nation forever.

"This is the story of the Black 14-year-old from Chicago who was brutally murdered while visiting relatives in the Mississippi Delta in 1954. . . . The gruesome, racially motivated crime and the court's failure to convict the white murderers was a powerful national catalyst for the civil rights movement. . . . Crowe's powerful, terrifying account does justice to its subject in bold, direct telling, supported by numerous archival photos and quotes from those who remember." Booklist.

Includes bibliographical references (p. 125-128).

Marcovitz, Hal

Hate crimes. by Hal Marcovitz. ReferencePoint Press, [2018] 80 p.

Grades: 8 9 10 11 12   **364.15**

1. Hate crimes -- Prevention 2. Hate 3. Prejudice 4. Hate groups 5. Crime

ISBN 9781682824719

LC 2018021023

Crimes committed against people because of their race, ethnicity, or religion have become common in the United States. Marcovitz examines the nature of hate crimes, their consequences, and possible methods of preventing or prosecuting such offenses.

"Written in an accessible, episodic style, the message is powerful and disturbing, and this work is a worthy purchase." Kirkus.

Includes bibliographical references and index.

364.152 Homicide

Harris, Duchess

Mass shootings in America. Duchess Harris, JD, PHD with Jennifer Simms. Essential Library, 2019 112 p.

Grades: 7 8 9 10   **364.152**

1. Mass shootings 2. Firearms -- Law and legislation 3. School shootings

ISBN 9781532116780

LC 2018948306

Mass Shootings in America looks at the history of mass shootings, from the 1966 mass shooting at the University of Texas, Austin, to the 2018 MSD High School shooting. The debates surrounding gun rights are also explored. The book encourages readers to form their own opinions. Features include a glossary, references, websites, source notes, and an index. Aligned to Common Core Standards and correlated to state standards. Essential Library is an imprint of Abdo Publishing, a division of ABDO. Provided by publisher.

"Attractively designed with well-chosen stock photos, these excellent books will certainly be useful for reports; but, perhaps more important, they may well be picked up by readers who want to be better informed about current events—and they will be." Booklist.

Includes bibliographical references (pages 104-109) and index (pages 110-111).

364.36 Juvenile delinquents

Ellis, Deborah, 1960-

My story starts here: voices of young offenders. Deborah Ellis. Groundwood Books, 2019. 224 p.

Grades: 8 9 10 11 12   **364.36**

1. Juvenile delinquents 2. Juvenile corrections 3. Teenage prisoners 4. Juvenile justice system 5. Juvenile delinquency

ISBN 9781773061214

Representing diverse socioeconomic backgrounds, genders, orientations and ethnicities, a collection of stories by juvenile offenders reveals the complicated factors, from abuse and gangs to the foster system and corruption, that changed the course of their lives.

"A sensitive and informed look at court-involved youth with writing that is thought provoking and precise." School Library Journal.

364.4 Prevention of crime and delinquency

Doeden, Matt

Whistle-blowers: exposing crime and corruption. by Matt Doeden. Twenty-First Century Books, [2015] 96 p.

Grades: 5 6 7 8 9   **364.4**

1. Whistle blowing 2. Whistle blowers 3. Corruption -- Prevention 4. Crime prevention 5. Leaks (Disclosure of information)

ISBN 9781467742092

LC 2014011850

"In addition to telling what happened in each case, Doeden reflects on matters such as the complex motivations of individual whistle-blowers and the degrees of risk that they were willing to take. This thought-provoking volume will fill a gap in many Library collections." Booklist.

Includes bibliographical references and index.

364.66092 Capital punishment—Biography

Kuklin, Susan

No choirboy: murder, violence, and teenagers on death row. Susan Kuklin. Henry Holt and Co., 2008. 212 p.

Grades: 8 9 10 11 12   **364.66092**

1. Capital punishment 2. Juvenile justice system 3. Teenage prisoners 4. Death row prisoners 5. Juvenile delinquents 6. Collective autobiographies and memoirs 7. Books for reluctant readers

ISBN 9780805079500

LC 2007046940

In-depth interviews with teenage prisoners who have been sentenced to death and are awaiting execution on death row provides a powerful look at life behind bars, the effects their decisions have had on themselves and others, and their personal views on the death penalty itself.

"The book opens with candid interviews that introduce three inmates, all of them teenagers when they committed their crimes. . . . This eye-opening account will likely open minds. . . . The book concludes with solid back matter notes, glossary, bibliography, and index." Horn Book.

Includes bibliographical references and index.

365 Penal and related institutions

Lasky, Jack

America's prisons. Jack Lasky, book editor. Greenhaven Press, 2016 202 p.

Grades: 8 9 10 11 12   **365**
  1. Prisons 2. Imprisonment 3. Alternatives to imprisonment 4. Criminals -- Rehabilitation 5. Mass incarceration
  ISBN 9780737775365

                                             LC 2015021383
Collects articles on issues related to the American prison system that represent diverse viewpoints on the issues relating to it, including the problems that prisons pose, who is imprisoned, humane treatment, and alternatives to imprisonment.

370.11 Education for specific objectives

Kaye, Cathryn Berger

The **complete** guide to service learning: proven, practical ways to engage students in civic responsibility, academic curriculum, & social action. Cathryn Berger Kaye. Free Spirit Pub., c2010. xii, 275 p.

Grades: Professional   **370.11**
  1. Service learning 2. Civics -- Study and teaching
  ISBN 9781575423456

                                             LC 2010000213
An award-winning reference provides a blueprint that can be used by teachers and youth workers to motivate young people to become involved in community-service projects in such areas as literacy tutoring and senior assistance to animal care and environmental protection.

Serafini, Frank

Reading the visual: an introduction to teaching multimodal literacy. Frank Serafini; foreword by James Paul Gee. Teachers College Press, 2014 xiii, 189 p.

Grades: Professional   **370.11**
  1. Visual literacy 2. Visual learning 3. Literacy -- Philosophy 4. Critical pedagogy
  ISBN 9780807754719

                                             LC 2013025440
"Reading the Visual addresses the need for teachers and literacy educators to analyze their instructional strategies by addressing the challenges of theoretical, curricular, and pedagogical frameworks that do not make sense of the multimodal images in today's school settings." Choice

Includes bibliographical references and index.

370.117 Multicultural education and multilingual education

Hammond, Zaretta

★ **Culturally** responsive teaching and the brain: promoting authentic engagement and rigor among culturally and linguistically diverse students. Zaretta Hammond; foreword by Yvette Jackson. Corwin, a SAGE company, 2015 xi, 173 p.

Grades: Professional   **370.117**
  1. Multicultural education 2. Educational equalization 3. Teaching -- Social aspects
  ISBN 9781483308012

                                             LC 2015413518
In this book, Zaretta Hammond draws on cutting-edge neuroscience research to offer an innovative approach for designing and implementing brain-compatible culturally responsive instruction.

370.15 Educational psychology

LaGarde, Jennifer

Fact vs. fiction: teaching critical thinking skills in the age of fake news. Jennifer LaGarde and Darren Hudgins. International Society for Technology in Education, 2018 xi, 147 p.

Grades: Adult Professional   **370.15**
  1. Critical thinking -- Study and teaching 2. Fake news -- Study and teaching 3. Information literacy -- Study and teaching 4. Mass media -- Study and teaching
  ISBN 9781564847041

                                             LC 2018051063
"A thought-provoking resource for teachers and librarians seeking to foster their students' critical thinking." School Library Journal

Includes bibliographical references (pages 133-140) and index.

370.71 Education

Abilock, Debbie

Growing schools: librarians as professional developers. Debbie Abilock, Kristin Fontichiaro, and Violet H. Harada, editors. Libraries Unlimited, 2012. xxiii, 390 p.

Grades: Professional   **370.71**
  1. Teachers -- In-service training 2. Teachers -- Training of 3. Educational technology -- Study and teaching 4. Information technology -- Study and teaching 5. Technological literacy -- Study and teaching
  ISBN 9781610690416

                                             LC 2012016191
Presenting examples of school librarians leading professional learning in numerous contexts and for diverse learning goals with remarkable success, this book will inspire other practitioners to initiate and refine professional learning in their schools and districts.

"This book promotes the role of the school librarian as a leader in school, district, and online professional development in 16 essays. A rich smorgasbord of ideas, this book would be invaluable for an individual librarian looking to become a professional development leader, and for district librarians to use in planning and implementing meaningful district-wide professional development." Library Media Connection

Includes bibliographical references and index.

370.9173 Urban and rural education

Emdin, Christopher
★ **For** white folks who teach in the hood-- and the rest of y'all too: reality pedagogy and urban education. Christopher Emdin. Beacon Press, 2016. 224 p.
Grades: Professional   **370.9173**
   1. Urban education 2. Urban school teachers 3. Race (Social sciences) 4. Antiracist literature
ISBN 9780807006405
                   LC 2015033466

Merging real stories with theory, research, and practice, a prominent scholar offers a new approach to teaching and learning for every stakeholder in urban education. Drawing on his own experience of feeling undervalued and invisible in science classrooms as a young man of color, Christopher Emdin offers a new lens on and approach to teaching in urban schools. Putting forth his theory of Reality Pedagogy, Emdin provides practical tools to unleash the brilliance and eagerness of youth and educators alike—both of whom have been typecast and stymied by outdated modes of thinking about urban education.

371.102 Teaching

Minor, Cornelius
★ **We** got this.: equity, access, and the quest to be who our students need us to be. Cornelius Minor; foreword by Kwame Alexander. Heinemann, 2019 xvi, 144 p.
Grades: Professional   **371.102**
   1. Teacher effectiveness 2. Classroom management 3. Education -- Social aspects 4. Marginalized children 5. Education -- Social aspects
ISBN 9780325098142
                   LC 2018289574

While challenging the teacher as hero trope, We Got This shows how authentically listening to kids is the closest thing to a superpower that we have. Cornelius identifies tools, attributes, and strategies that can augment our listening.

371.14 Organization of teaching force

Harada, Violet H.
Inquiry learning through librarian-teacher partnerships. Violet H. Harada and Joan M. Yoshina. Linworth Pub., c2004. xii, 172 p.
Grades: Professional   **371.14**
   1. Questioning 2. Teaching teams 3. School libraries 4. Curriculum planning
ISBN 9781586831349
                   LC 2004000662

Begin a school-wide movement toward collaborative instruction and ultimate student success! Challenge yourself and teachers to build learning environments that focus on realistic issues and themes. Build a strong case for the role of the library media specialist in implementing curriculum changes.

"While the gestalt of inquiry learning feels subversively open-ended and creative in these days of standardized tests and lockstep curricula, the required elements are all actually there. Wonderful teachers could take this book, soar with it, and still manage to cross and dot the requisite t's and i's." School Library Journal

Includes bibliographical references (p. 165-169) and index.

371.2 School administration; administration of student academic activities

Brulles, Dina
The **cluster** grouping handbook: how to challenge gifted students and improve achievement for all: a schoolwide model. Dina Brulles, Susan Winebrenner; foreword by Scott J. Peters. Free Spirit Publishing, 2019 xii, 258 page
Grades: Professional   **371.2**
   1. Gifted children -- Education 2. Mainstreaming in education 3. Group work in education 4. Academic achievement
ISBN 9781631983566
                   LC 2018060610

The Schoolwide Cluster Grouping Model is explained as well as how the model differs from grouping practices of the past. Offers teacher-tested classroom strategies and detailed information on identifying gifted students for clusters, gaining support, and providing ongoing professional development. Provided by publisher.

Odden, Allan
Improving student learning when budgets are tight. Allan R. Odden. Corwin, c2012. xxi, 184 p.
Grades: Adult Professional   **371.2**
   1. School budgets 2. School improvement programs
ISBN 9781452217086
                   LC 2011045908

This book offers a comprehensive framework to enhance student achievement in good times and in bad. The author provides a school improvement action plan and then shows how to target resources to implement that plan. More than just a 'theory' book, this text describes concrete, specific actions that can be taken immediately.?

"Odden provides a comprehensive handbook for teachers, school administrators, and concerned citizens outlining a school improvement action plan focused on student learning. Moving beyond vague theory, Odden delivers concrete, specific suggestions that schools and districts can implement immediately to improve student learning, recruit top teachers, provide ongoing professional development, and utilize new and existing educational technologies." VOYA

Includes bibliographical references and index.

371.27 Classroom and school examinations and tests; marking systems

Stevens, Dannelle D.
Introduction to rubrics: an assessment tool to save grading time, convey effective feedback, and promote student learning. Dannelle D. Stevens, Antonia Levi; foreword by Barbara E. Walvoord. Stylus, c2013. xxiii, 211 p.
Grades: Professional   **371.27**
   1. Grading and marking (Students) 2. Students -- Rating of
ISBN 9781579225889
                   LC 2012010840

This new edition retains the appeal, clarity and practicality that made the first so successful, and continues to provide a fundamental introduction to the principles and purposes of rubrics, with guidance on how to construct them, use them to align course content to learning outcomes, and apply them in a wide variety of courses, and to all forms of assignment.

Wormeli, Rick

Fair isn't always equal, second edition: assessing and grading in the differentiated classroom. Rick Wormeli. Stenhouse Publishers, 2018 xii, 308 p.

Grades: Professional   **371.27**
1. Grading and marking (Students) 2. Educational tests and measurements 3. Students -- Rating of
ISBN 9781625310170

LC 2017023613

Rick [examines] current grading and assessment practices in differentiated classrooms. Coherent and effective standards-based grading practices for a high-stakes, accountability-focused world are also outlined. Recognizing the importance of having a shared school vision for assessment and grading, Rick addresses the challenges for teachers and administrators alike.

371.3 Methods of instruction and study

Brulles, Dina

A **teacher's** guide to flexible grouping and collaborative learning: form, manage, assess, and differentiate in groups. Dina Brulles, PH.D, Karen L. Brown, M.ED. Free Spirit Publishing, 2018 xvi, 182 p.

Grades: Professional   **371.3**
1. Group work in education 2. Group work in education -- Evaluation
ISBN 9781631982835

LC 2017035588

This guide helps teachers implement and use flexible grouping and differentiation strategies to respond to students' diverse learning needs. Included are methods for creating groups based on assessment data, planning group lessons, supporting personalized learning, and grading collaborative work. Digital content contains forms from the book and a PDF presentation. Provided by publisher.

Fox, Janet S.

Get organized without losing it. by Janet S. Fox; edited by Pamela Espeland. Free Spirit Pub., c2006. 105 p.: Laugh & learn

Grades: 5 6 7 8   **371.3**
1. Study methods 2. Homework 3. Time management 4. Students -- Time management 5. Students
ISBN 1575421933

LC 2005032809

Provides students with tips on ways to manage their time, locker, and desk, and get organized.

"In this handbook for students, Fox uses humor to provide practical, easy-to-follow ideas for organizing desks, backpacks, and lockers; managing time for homework and after school activities; planning long-term projects; and taking better notes. . . . Fox writes in a conversational style. . . . Humorous illustrations complement the text." Voice of Youth Advocates.

Includes bibliographical references (p. 99-101) and index.

Tucker, Catlin R

Blended learning in action: a practical guide toward sustainable change. Catlin R. Tucker, Tiffany Wycoff, Jason T. Green. Corwin, 2017 xviii, 203 p.

Grades: Professional   **371.3**
1. Blended learning 2. Educational change
ISBN 9781506341163

LC 2016027423

Blended learning has the power to reinvent education, but the transition requires a new approach to learning and a new skillset for educators. Loaded with research and examples, Blended Learning in Action demonstrates the advantages a blended model has over traditional instruction when technology is used to engage students both inside the classroom and online.

Tucker, Catlin R.

★ **Power** up blended learning: a professional learning infrastructure to support sustainable change. Catlin R. Tucker. Corwin, 2019 xvii, 166 p.

Grades: Professional   **371.3**
1. Blended learning 2. Teachers -- In-service training 3. Professional learning communities
ISBN 9781506396767

LC 2018018140

This book will establish the need for rethinking professional development in schools/districts shifting from traditional instruction to blended learning. It limits the scope of the conversation about professional development to three elements: targeted training, 1:1 coaching, and participation in a personal learning community with non-evaluative peer feedback. This book helps school leaders think about and articulate a long-term professional development plan and emphasizes the importance of creating a "coaching culture" where experimentation and failure are celebrated, which is particularly important when it comes to using technology. Provide by publisher.

Wallace, Virginia, 1938-

★ **Collaborating** for inquiry-based learning: school librarians and teachers partner for student achievement. Virginia L. Wallace and Whitney N. Husid. Libraries Unlimited, 2017 v, 134 p.

Grades: Professional   **371.3**
1. Inquiry-based learning 2. Libraries and teachers 3. Libraries and education 4. School librarian participation in curriculum planning
ISBN 9781440852848

LC 2016030617

This newly revised and expanded practical resource links pedagogical theory, research, and practical application of Inquiry-Based Learning (IBL). An important resource for school librarians, classroom teachers, and school library preparation programs, this thoroughly updated second edition of Collaborating for Inquiry-Based Learning explores Inquiry-Based Learning in greater depth and addresses new educational insights.

371.37 Recitation and discussion

Hale, Michael S.

The **teacher's** guide to leading student-centered discussions: talking about texts in the classroom. Michael S. Hale, Elizabeth A. City. Corwin Press, c2006. xiii, 120 p.

Grades: Professional   **371.37**
1. Active learning 2. Student-centered learning 3. Discussion
ISBN 9781412906357

LC 2005031710

Highlights the basics of planning for text-based discussion and provides tips for improving facilitation skills.

371.39 Other methods of instruction

Daniels, Harvey, 1947-
★ **Literature** circles: voice and choice in book clubs and reading groups. Harvey Daniels. Stenhouse Publishers, c2002. xii, 260 p.
Grades: Professional   **371.39**
   1. Group reading 2. Book clubs (Discussion groups) 3. Literature -- Study and teaching -- United States 4. Children -- Books and reading 5. Group work in education
ISBN 9781571103338
LC 2001049385
A guide to launching and managing literature circles offers strategies, tools, structures, and stories and includes new models and procedures for primary, middle, and high school grades.

371.7 Student welfare

Falkowski, Melissa
We say #never again: reporting by the Parkland student journalists. edited by MSD teachers Melissa Falkowski and Eric Garner. Crown, 2018. 272 p.
Grades: 7 8 9 10 11 12   **371.7**
   1. Marjory Stoneman Douglas High School Shooting, Parkland, Florida, 2018 2. School shootings 3. High school students 4. College and school journalism 5. Teenage social advocates 6. Florida 7. Teenagers' writings 8. Essays
ISBN 9781984849960
Demonstrating the growing journalistic prowess of teens directly impacted by school shootings, an anthology of school newspaper articles, journalism class writings, student broadcasts and social media op-eds recounts the day's tragedy and related fight for stricter gun control.
"Throughout, the students express appreciation for peers and faculty who exhibited courage during the shootings, and they stress the importance of journalistic integrity. An impressive roundup of eloquent, well-reasoned, and inspiring writing." Publishers Weekly.

Lerner, Sarah
Parkland speaks: survivors from Marjory Stoneman Douglas share their stories. edited by MSD teacher Sarah Lerner. Crown Books for Young Readers, 2019. 192 p.
Grades: 8 9 10 11 12   **371.7**
   1. Teenage social advocates 2. School shootings 3. Gun control 4. Mass shootings 5. Social movements 6. Florida 7. Essays 8. Teenagers' writings
ISBN 9781984849991
LC 2018050403
A collection of art and writing from the students of the Parkland, Florida shooting reflects how the students dealt with grief, anger, determination, and hope in the wake of tragedy.

March for Our Lives (Organization)
Glimmer of hope: how tragedy sparked a movement. by the March for Our Lives founders Razorbill, 2018 xiv, 218 p., 16 unnumbered p. of plates
Grades: 8 9 10 11 12   **371.7**
   1. Teenage social advocates 2. Student movements 3. School shootings 4. Mass shootings 5. Gun control 6. Essays
ISBN 9781984836090
LC 2018044805

Tells the story of how a group of teenagers raced to channel their rage and sorrow into action, and went on to create one of the largest youth-led movements in global history.

McPherson, Stephanie Sammartino
Stressed out in school?: learning to deal with academic pressure. Stephanie Sammartino McPherson. Enslow Publishers, c2009. 112 p. : Issues in focus today
Grades: 7 8 9 10   **371.7**
   1. Students -- Mental health 2. Educational tests and measurements 3. Stress -- Prevention 4. Stress management 5. Standardized tests
ISBN 9780766030695
LC 2008040339
Examines the stress and academic pressure students of all ages encounter, including early education, homework, standardized tests, college applications, peer pressure, and alternative learning styles. Provided by publisher.

371.81 Student movements

Kallen, Stuart A., 1955-
Teen guide to student activism. Stuart A. Kallen. ReferencePoint Press, 2019 80 p.
Grades: 7 8 9 10 11 12   **371.81**
   1. Teenage social advocates 2. Teenagers -- Political activity 3. Student movements 4. Teenage volunteers 5. Social action
ISBN 9781682825419
Looks at some of the best known student and youth movements enacting change in the world today, discussing how these groups organize, reach out, and find the balance between activism and school.

371.826 Students by miscellaneous social attributes

Cianciotto, Jason
LGBT youth in America's schools. Jason Cianciotto and Sean Cahill. The University of Michigan Press, 2012. 236 p.
Grades: Adult Professional   **371.826**
   1. Bisexual students 2. Gay students 3. Homosexuality and education 4. Lesbian students 5. LGBTQIA persons -- Education
ISBN 0472031406
LC 2011045478
Jason Cianciotto and Sean Cahill, experts on lesbian, gay, bisexual, and transgender public policy advocacy, combine an accessible review of social science research with analyses of school practices and local, state, and federal laws that affect LGBT students. In addition, portraits of LGBT youth and their experiences with discrimination at school bring human faces to the issues the authors discuss.—From publisher description.
"Organized into three sections (research, current policies, and an agenda for looking forward), Cianciotto and Cahill's treatise is an informative and compelling basis for continuing the discussion (especially as regards LGBT students of color) of how best to protect the rights of a vulnerable and largely disenfranchised group. While their approach is accessible enough for the concerned lay reader, policymakers and educational professionals will likely get the most out of this study." Publishers Weekly.
Includes bibliographical references (p. 181-226) and index.

371.829 Ethnic and national groups

Finkelstein, Norman H.

Schools of hope: how Julius Rosenwald helped change African American education. Norman H. Finkelstein. Calkins Creek, an imprint of Highlights, 2014. 80 p.

Grades: 5 6 7 8   **371.829**
    1. Rosenwald, Julius, 1862-1932. 2. African Americans -- Education 3. Schools -- History 4. Philanthropists 5. Jewish men
    ISBN 9781590788417

"This straightforward narrative is substantially supported with many photographs of the period, especially of the schools and the students. Source notes, a bibliography (which could have used a few more titles for the target readership), a list of websites, an index and picture credits add to its authenticity. Clean layout and design augment a quality introduction to an important chapter in the history of American education." Kirkus

Stokes, John A., 1931-

Students on strike: Jim Crow, civil rights, Brown, and me. by John A. Stokes and Lois Wolfe with Herman Viola. National Geographic, 2008. 127 p.

Grades: 4 5 6 7   **371.829**
    1. African American students -- History 2. Segregation in education -- History 3. School environment -- History 4. Strikes 5. Civil Rights Movement 6. Virginia -- History -- 20th century.
    ISBN 9781426301537

                  LC 2007034677
Presents an eyewitness account of the 1951 "Manhattan Project," a strike at R.R. Moton High School in Virginia which led to the historic civil right case "Brown v. Board of Education" and ended separate schooling for blacks and whites throughout the United States.

"In 1951, a group of African-American high school students in Prince Edward County, VA, went on strike to protest the substandard conditions in their segregated schools. They eventually became plaintiffs in a lawsuit that was one of the five that were part of the 1954 Brown decision . . . Fear of retribution and lingering bitterness has kept the strike leaders silent, but Stokes, who was among them, has decided that the story of the strike and its aftermath need to be told. . . . Stoke's inspiring story reveals an almost completely unreported part of one of the most important court cases of the 20th century." School Library Journal.

Includes bibliographical references and index.

371.9 Special education

Billingsley, Bonnie S.

A **survival** guide for new special educators: grades K-12. Bonnie S. Billingsley, Mary T. Brownell, Maya Israel, Margaret L. Kamman. Jossey-Bass, a Wiley Imprint, 2013. xxii, 410 p.

Grades: Professional   **371.9**
    1. First year teachers 2. Special education
    ISBN 9781118095683

                  LC 2012048512
A Survival Guide for New Special Educators provides relevant, practical information for new special education teachers across a broad range of topic areas. Drawing on the latest research on special educator effectiveness and retention, this comprehensive, go-to resource addresses the most pressing needs of novice instructors, resource teachers, and inclusion specialists.

Fox, Jenifer

The **differentiated** instruction book of lists. Jenifer Fox, Whitney Hoffman. Jossey-Bass, c2011. xvi, 268 p.: J-B Ed: Reach and Teach

Grades: Professional   **371.9**
    1. Individualized instruction 2. Inclusive education 3. Mainstreaming in education 4. Classroom management
    ISBN 9780470952399

                  LC 2011017902
Hundreds of useful ideas for meeting the needs of each child, The Differentiated Instruction Book of Lists is the definitive reference for DI for teachers in grades K-12. Ready for immediate use, it offers over 150 up-to-date lists for developing instructional materials, lesson planning, and assessment. Organized into 12 convenient sections, the book is full of practical examples, teaching ideas, and activities that can be used or adapted to meet students' diverse needs. Coverage includes curriculum design, lesson planning, instructional strategies, assessment, classroom management, strategies by subject area (from Language Arts to Math to Physical Education), new media, etc. Offers an easy-to-use guide that gives quick tips and methods to plan effectively for delivering truly differentiated lessons. Filled with helpful DI lists, lesson plans, strategies, assessments, and more Jennifer Fox is the author of the bestselling book Your Child's Strengths. The Differentiated Instruction Book of Lists is a hands-on guide for meeting the instructional needs of all students so that they can reach their full potential. Provided by publisher.

Maanum, Jody L.

The **general** educator's guide to special education. Jody L. Maanum. Corwin Press, 2009. xv, 236 p.

Grades: Professional   **371.9**
    1. Children with disabilities -- Education 2. Special education
    ISBN 9781412971379

                  LC 2009006702
Provides information on disability categories, the referral and placement process, teaching strategies, and behavioral adaptations to the curriculum.

Mannix, Darlene

Social skills activities for secondary students with special needs. Darlene Mannix. Jossey-Bass, c2009. xvi, 348 p.

Grades: Professional   **371.9**
    1. Developmentally disabled children -- Life skills guides 2. Developmentally disabled children -- Education (Secondary) 3. Life skills -- Study and teaching (Secondary) 4. Social skills -- Study and teaching (Secondary)
    ISBN 9780470259368

                  LC 2012439265
Provides teachers with a series of activities to help their special needs students develop social skills and coping techniques for a variety of social situations and interactions with teachers, family, and peers.

371.91 Students with physical disabilities

Mannix, Darlene

Life skills activities for secondary students with special needs. Darlene Mannix. Jossey-Bass, c2009. xxii, 513 p.

Grades: Professional   **371.91**
    1. Teenagers with disabilities 2. Life skills -- Study and teaching (Secondary) 3. Life skills
    ISBN 9780470259399

                  LC 2012439266

Presents a series of activities for teachers to help disabled teenage students acquire life skills needed for independence, covering such tasks as managing money, making living arrangements, succeeding in school, and interviewing for a job.

Marschark, Marc

★ **How** deaf children learn: what parents and teachers need to know. Marc Marschark and Peter C. Hauser. Oxford University Press, 2012. ix, 156 p.

Grades: Adult Professional   **371.91**
    1. Deaf children -- Language 2. Deaf children -- Means of communication 3. Deaf -- Education 4. Parents of deaf children
ISBN 9780195389753

                                        LC 2011012553

"The authors believe the best way to lead deaf children to academic success is by understanding who they are, what they know, and how they think. After reading this book, parents who may be feeling inadequate about their parenting skills or fearful about providing a good education for their deaf or hard-of-hearing child should be more at ease, and teachers will gain insight into the complexities involved in deaf education and be better equipped to teach these children." Library Journal.

Includes bibliographical references and index.

371.92 Students with mental disabilities

Craig, Susan E

Trauma-sensitive schools for the adolescent years: promoting resiliency and healing, grades 6-12. Susan E. Craig; foreword by Jim Sporleder. Teachers College Press, 2017. x, 158 p.

Grades: Professional   **371.92**
    1. Children with mental disabilities -- Education (Secondary) 2. Psychic trauma in children 3. Post-traumatic stress disorder in children 4. Educational psychology 5. Community and school
ISBN 9780807758250

                                        LC 2017024039

Susan Craig provides secondary school teachers and administrators with practical ideas for how to improve students' achievement by implementing a trauma-sensitive approach to instruction. Provided by publisher.

371.94 Students with emotional disturbances

Rief, Sandra F.

How to reach & teach children & teens with ADD/ADHD: practical techniques, strategies, and interventions. Sandra F. Rief. Jossey-Bass, 2016 xxvi, 465 p.

Grades: Professional   **371.94**
    1. Attention-deficit-disordered children -- Education 2. Attention-deficit-disordered youth -- Education 3. Hyperactive children -- Education 4. Classroom management
ISBN 9781118937785

                                        LC 2016018130

Provides information on how to help improve the academic, social, and behavioral performance of children and teens with attention-deficit hyperactivity disorder.

371.95 Gifted students

Galbraith, Judy

When gifted kids don't have all the answers: how to meet their social and emotional needs. Judy Galbraith, M.A. and Jim Delisle, Ph.D. Free Spirit Publishing, 2015 viii, 279 p.

Grades: Professional   **371.95**
    1. Gifted children -- Education -- Psychological aspects 2. Classroom environment
ISBN 9781575424934

                                        LC 2014037117

Gifted kids are so much more than test scores and grades. Still, it's sometimes difficult to see past the potential to the child who may be anxious, lonely, confused, or unsure of what the future might bring. This book, now fully revised with updated information and new survey quotes, offers practical suggestions for addressing the social and emotional needs of gifted students. The authors present ways to advocate for gifted education; help gifted underachievers, perfectionists, and twice-exceptional students; and provide all gifted kids with a safe, supportive learning environment. Complete with engaging stories, strategies, activities, and resources, this book is for anyone committed to helping gifted students thrive. Includes online digital content. Provided by publisher.

Roberts, Julia L.

Differentiating instruction with centers in the gifted classroom K-8: K-8. edited by Julia Link Roberts & Julia Roberts Boggess. Prufrock Press, c2012. 146 p.

Grades: Professional   **371.95**
    1. Gifted children -- Education 2. Individualized instruction
ISBN 9781593638399

                                        LC 2011044720

This work provides teachers with tons of ideas and guidance for creating unique classroom centers that will challenge gifted learners and encourage high-level, independent thinking. Implementing centers in the gifted classroom gives elementary and middle school teachers the opportunity to develop in-depth learning experiences on a variety of topics, encouraging students' passion areas with hands-on, minds-on extensions.

371.96 Special education—Students by socioeconomic status

Stanley, Jerry, 1941-

Children of the Dust Bowl: the true story of the school at Weedpatch Camp. Jerry Stanley; illustrated with photographs. Crown, c1992. 85 p.

Grades: 5 6 7 8   **371.96**
    1. 1930s 2. Children of migrant farm workers -- Education -- History 20th century. 3. Droughts -- History 20th century. 4. Depressions 1929-1941 5. Migrant labor 6. Dust Bowl (South Central United States) 7. United States -- Economic conditions -- 1929-1939.
ISBN 0517587815

                                      LC 92000393

NCTE Orbis Pictus Nonfiction Award, 1993.

Describes the plight of the migrant workers who traveled from the Dust Bowl to California during the Depression and were forced to live in a federal labor camp and discusses the school that was built for their children.

"Stanley's text is a compelling document. . . . The story is inspiring and disturbing, and Stanley has recorded the details with passion and dignity." Booklist.

Includes bibliographical references (p. 78-80) and index.

372.133 Instructional materials—Primary education

Cornwall, Phyllis

Super smart information strategies.. by Phyllis Cornwall. Cherry Lake Pub., c2010. 32 p.: Information explorer

Grades: 3 4 5 6   **372.133**
1. Report writing
ISBN 9781602796430

LC 2009027806

"The appealing layout includes manageable paragraphs, a variety of engaging illustrations, and examples that clearly guide readers through each topic. In [this book], strategies include gathering resources, organizing information, and ways of presenting discoveries." School Library Journal.

Includes bibliographical references (p. 31) and index.

372.3 Knowledge, computer science, library and information sciences, science, technology

Ansberry, Karen Rohrich, 1966-

★ **Picture-perfect** science lessons, expanded 2nd edition: using children's books to guide inquiry, 3-6. Karen Ansberry and Emily Morgan. NSTA, c2010. xviii, 403 p.

Grades: Professional   **372.3**
1. Science -- Study and teaching (Elementary) 2. Children's books
ISBN 9781935155164

LC 2010014284

This book of twenty lesson plans for grades three through six combines children's literature and reading with standards-based science education to provide educators with ready to use units for their science curriculum.

Brooks-Young, Susan

Teaching with the tools kids really use: learning with Web and mobile technologies. Susan Brooks-Young. Corwin, c2010. xi, 137 p.

Grades: Professional   **372.3**
1. Teachers -- Training of 2. Technological literacy -- Standards 3. Educational technology -- Standards 4. Mobile computing 5. Web 20
ISBN 9781412972758

LC 2009043856

Designed to help educators deliver relevant instruction through the use of 21st-century technologies, this resource examines available low-cost hardware, explores free Web 2.0 tools, and sheds light on the pros and cons of using mobile technologies for instructional support.

"In this book, we see how technology can be used, but we also see the responsibility of the educator to make sure it is done appropriately, so 21st-century skills are addressed. The author addresses technologies and applications, and also discusses their ethical uses and how to think ahead to make adjustments for the future." Library Media Connection

Includes bibliographical references and index.

372.35 Science and technology

Altieri, Jennifer L

Reading science: practical strategies for integrating instruction. Jennifer L. Altieri. Heinemann, 2016 xlv, 130 p.

Grades: Professional   **372.35**
1. Science -- Study and teaching (Elementary) 2. Science -- Study and teaching (Middle school) 3. Language arts (Elementary) 4. Language arts (Middle school) 5. Reading (Elementary)
ISBN 9780325062587

LC 2015039640

How can we prepare our students to think, read, and write like scientists? Altieri reminds us that literacy skills aren't add-ons to the science class—they are critical parts of instruction. She addresses the need to prepare students for future science classes and the world beyond by using literacy as a tool to help students access science content, communicate their ideas precisely, and apply their discoveries in new contexts.

Mackey, Bonnie

A **librarian's** guide to cultivating an elementary school garden. Bonnie Mackey and Jennifer Mackey Stewart. Linworth Pub., c2009. xii, 124 p.

Grades: Professional   **372.35**
1. School gardens
ISBN 9781586833282

LC 2008034963

A guidebook for school librarians looks at how school gardens can improve students' academic performance; offers tips on justifying, designing, and implementing a school garden; and provides information on funding sources.

Vasquez, Jo Anne, 1943-

STEM lesson essentials, grades 3-8: integrating science, technology, engineering, and mathematics. Jo Anne Vasquez, Cary Sneider and Michael Comer; foreword by Rodger Bybee. Heinemann, 2013 xi, 178 p.

Grades: Professional   **372.35**
1. Science -- Study and teaching (Elementary) 2. Technology -- Study and teaching (Elementary) 3. Engineering -- Study and teaching (Elementary) 4. Mathematics -- Study and teaching (Elementary)
ISBN 9780325043586

LC 2012046403

Vasquez, Sneider, and Comer have created this book for professionals teaching third through eighth grade. In seventeen chapters, the authors discuss such topics as STEM literacy, guiding principles, STEM practices, technology and engineering, project-based learning, STEM assessment, implementing STEM, and creating STEM curricula. The book has a lesson planning map, lesson plan template, and a complete list of resources with websites.

372.4 Reading

Fountas, Irene C.

★ **Guided** reading: responsive teaching across the grades. Irene C. Fountas & Gay Su Pinnell. Heinemann, 2017 viii, 620 p.

Grades: Professional   **372.4**
  1. Reading (Elementary)
ISBN 9780325086842

      LC 2016011903

In the highly anticipated second edition of Guided Reading, Fountas and Pinnell remind you of guided reading's critical value within a comprehensive literacy system, and the reflective, responsive teaching required to realize its full potential.

Grover, Sharon

Listening to learn: audiobooks supporting literacy. Sharon Grover, Lizette D. Hannegan. American Library Association, 2012. xi, 188 p.

Grades: Professional   **372.4**
  1. Reading   2. Literacy -- Study and teaching   3. Educational technology   4. Audiobooks   5. Libraries -- Special collections -- Audiobooks
ISBN 9780838911075

      LC 2011041814

Audiobooks not only present excellent opportunities to engage the attention of young people but also advance literacy. Learn how the format can support national learning standards and literacy skills in the K-12 curricula.

Lemov, Doug, 1967-

Reading reconsidered: a practical guide to rigorous literacy instruction. Doug Lemov, Colleen Driggs, Erica Woolway. Jossey-Bass, 2016 xxii, 416 p.

Grades: Professional   **372.4**
  1. Reading   2. Reading comprehension   3. Language arts -- Correlation with content subjects
ISBN 9781119104247

      LC 2015038419

In the 2010 article "Building a Better Teacher," the article that "launched" Teach Like a Champion, journalist Elizabeth Green compared two schools of thought—one that teaching skills were the most important driver of classroom learning, the other that content knowledge was the true driver. Some readers saw a conflict between these two perspectives. The authors of Reading Reconsidered have always thought that the answer was more complex: that technique was irreplaceable and helped teachers maximize the application of their subject knowledge but there was also no substitute for content knowledge. Moreover, they believed, there were in fact techniques specific to each of the content areas that drive results and could be delineated and learned like the general techniques in Teach Like a Champion. Reading Reconsidered is the authors' first effort to take on the challenge of defining subject-specific methods. It is an anxious time for many teachers but also a time of great opportunity. This book will provide a road map from confusion to success. Provided by publisher.

"The authors call on educators to focus on 'the core of the core': harder texts, close reading, more nonfiction, and frequent writing in response to reading as the main approach to ameliorate declining SAT scores. Part 1 details this instructional core, while part 2 gets into the nitty-gritty of teaching strategies: vocabulary instruction, approaches to 'independent' reading, text annotation, and more." School Library Journal

Includes bibliographical references and index.

Miller, Donalyn

Reading in the wild: the book whisperer's keys to cultivating lifelong reading habits. Donalyn Miller with Susan Kelley; foreword by Teri S. Lesesne. Jossey-Bass, 2013. xxvii, 273 p.

Grades: Professional   **372.4**
  1. Reading (Elementary)   2. Reading (Middle school)   3. Children -- Books and reading   4. Motivation in education
ISBN 9780470900307

      LC 2013031978

Teaching students to become lifelong readers, a companion to the bestselling The Book Whisperer, Reading in the Wild explores whether or not we are truly instilling lifelong reading habits in our students and provides practical strategies for teaching "wild" reading. Based on survey responses from over 900 adult readers and classroom feedback, Reading in the Wild offers solid advice and strategies on how to develop, encourage and assess key lifelong reading habits, including dedicating time for reading, planning for future reading, and defining oneself as a reader. Includes advice for supporting the love of reading by explicitly teaching lifelong reading habits Contains accessible strategies, ideas, tips, lesson plans and management tools along with lists of recommended books. Co-published with Editorial Projects in Education, publisher of Education Week and Teacher Magazine. Packed with ideas for helping students choose their own reading material, respond to text, and build capacity for lifelong reading. Provided by publisher.

"Miller and Kelley's favorable volume will prove to be essential for the practitioner or preparing practitioner looking for verified approaches to reading that will engage all students." Library Journal

Includes bibliographical references (pages 248-253) and index.

372.41 Instructional materials, reading readiness, methods of instruction and study

Daniels, Harvey, 1947-

Mini-lessons for literature circles. Harvey Daniels, Nancy Steineke. Heinemann, c2004. x, 292 p.

Grades: Professional   **372.41**
  1. Group reading   2. Book clubs (Discussion groups)   3. Literature -- Study and teaching   4. Children -- Books and reading
ISBN 9780325007021

      LC 2004009666

Daniels and Steineke team up to focus on one crucial element of the Literature Circle model: the short, teacher-directed mini lessons that begin, guide and follow up every successful book club meeting. Each of these forty-five short, focused, and practical lessons includes Nancy and Harvey's actual classroom language and is formatted to help busy teachers with point-by-point answers to the questions they most frequently ask.

Richardson, Jan

★ The **next** step forward in guided reading: an assess-decide-guide framework for supporting every reader grades K-8. Jan Richardson. Scholastic, 2016. 335 p.

Grades: Professional   **372.41**
  1. Guided reading -- Study and teaching (Preschool)   2. Guided reading -- Study and teaching (Primary)   3. Guided reading -- Study and teaching (Elementary)   4. Guided reading -- Study and teaching (Middle school)   5. Reading comprehension
ISBN 9781338161113

      LC 2017277955

Using the guided reading approach, a guide to improve reading skills for students in grades K to 8.

Thompson, Terry, 1970-

Adventures in graphica: using comics and graphic novels to teach comprehension, 2-6. Terry Thompson. Stenhouse Publishers, c2008. xi, 188 p.

Grades: Professional   **372.41**
  1. Comic books, strips, etc, in education 2. Reading comprehension -- Study and teaching (Elementary)
ISBN 9781571107121

                   LC 2007051350
Drawing on his own success using graphica with elementary students, literacy coach Terry Thompson introduces reading teachers to this popular medium and suggests sources of appropriate graphica for the classroom and for particular students. This work provides a roadmap for teachers to the medium that the New York Times recently hailed as possibly 'the next new literary form.'

372.46 Word-attack strategies (Decoding strategies)

Blevins, Wiley

Teaching phonics & word study in the intermediate grades: grades 3-8. Wiley Blevins. Scholastic, 2017 368 p.

Grades: Professional   **372.46**
  1. Phonics 2. Word recognition 3. Phonetics
ISBN 9781338113488

                   LC 2017446290
Revised and updated, this companion book to the best-selling Phonics From A to Z contains everything teachers need to help struggling readers in the upper grades. In addition to ready-to-use lessons, extensive word lists, and quick assessments, this new edition offers step-by-step syllabication support, daily activities and games for combining multisyllabic word and vocabulary learning, a comprehensive phonics survey, technology resources, and more! An invaluable resource!

372.47 Reading comprehension strategies

Boyles, Nancy N., 1948-

That's a great answer!: teaching literature-response strategies to elementary, ELL, and struggling readers. Nancy N. Boyles. Maupin House, c2012. xiv, 354 p.

Grades: Professional   **372.47**
  1. Reading comprehension -- Study and teaching 2. Motivation in education
ISBN 9781936700448

                   LC 2011037381
The ability to comprehend and to respond meaningfully to text is a skill students need every day—not just on test day. This book provides complete and ready-to-go support to help teachers get great answers to open-ended comprehension questions from the students who need help the most—elementary students, struggling older readers, and English language learners.?

Bryan, Trevor Andrew, 1975-

Art of comprehension: exploring visual texts to foster comprehension, conversation, and confidence. Trevor Andrew Bryan. Stenhouse Publishers, 2019 xv, 139 p.

Grades: Professional   **372.47**
  1. Reading comprehension -- Study and teaching (Elementary) 2. Reading (Elementary) 3. Picture books for children 4. Children

-- Books and reading
ISBN 9781625311689

                   LC 2018036001
This book shows how picture and chapter books work in conjunction with the text to deepen children's understanding of meaning. Its aim is to improve the reading skills of students in grades K-5. Provided by publisher.

Gallagher, Kelly, 1958-

Deeper reading: comprehending challenging texts, 4-12. Kelly Gallagher. Stenhouse Publishers, c2004. xii, 228 p.

Grades: Professional   **372.47**
  1. Reading comprehension 2. Reading (Middle school) 3. Reading (Secondary)
ISBN 9781571103840

                   LC 2004052469
"Although geared toward English language arts teachers in grades 4-12, the reading and writing activities can be used with modifications by teachers of other subjects and even in college classes." Choice
Includes bibliographical references (p. 217-219) and index.

Harvey, Stephanie

Strategies that work: teaching comprehension for understanding, engagement, and building knowledge, Grades K-8. Stephanie Harvey & Anne Goudvis. Stenhouse Publishers, 2017 xxi, 298 p.

Grades: Professional   **372.47**
  1. Reading comprehension 2. Reading (Elementary) 3. Thought and thinking -- Study and teaching (Elementary) 4. Children -- Books and reading
ISBN 9781625310637

                   LC 2017004524
Steph and Anne tackle close reading, close listening, text complexity, and critical thinking in a new chapter on building knowledge through thinking-intensive reading and learning. Other fully revised chapters focus on digital reading, strategies for integrating comprehension and technology, and comprehension across the curriculum.

372.5 The arts

Hogan, Jillian

Studio thinking from the start: the K-8 art educator's handbook. Jillian Hogan, Lois Hetland, Diane B. Jaquith, Ellen Winner; foreword by David P. Nelson; illustrations by Nicole Gsell. Teachers College Press, 2018 vii, 152 p.

Grades: Professional   **372.5**
  1. Art -- Study and teaching (Elementary)
ISBN 9780807759158

                   LC 2018016980
This new publication shows how the eight Studio Habits of Mind and four Studio Structures can be used successfully with younger students in a range of socioeconomic contexts and school environments. Provided by publisher.

Sousa, David A.

From STEM to STEAM: brain-compatible strategies and lessons that integrate the arts. David A. Sousa, Tom Pilecki. Corwin, 2018 xii, 248 p.

Grades: Professional   **372.5**
  1. Arts -- Study and teaching 2. Science -- Study and teaching 3.

Interdisciplinary approach in education 4. Cognitive learning
ISBN 9781506322452

LC 2017045273

Arts activities enhance the skills critical for achieving STEM success, but how do busy STEM educators integrate the arts into sometimes inflexible STEM curriculum? This new edition of From STEM to STEAM explores emerging research to detail the way, and includes sample frameworks for transitioning schools from STEM to STEAM.

372.6 Language arts (Communication skills)

Beers, G. Kylene, 1957-

Notice & note: strategies for close reading. Kylene Beers & Robert E. Probst. Heinemann, 2013 ix, 274 p.

Grades: Professional **372.6**
    1. Language arts 2. English language -- Study and teaching (Secondary) 3. Literature -- Study and teaching 4. English literature -- History and criticism -- Theory, etc
    ISBN 9780325046938

LC 2012035466

Presents lessons intended to help students read literature with deeper understanding, introducing signposts that help them identify significant moments in literature and anchor questions that encourage them to read more closely.

Casey, Heather Kenyon

Literacy learning clubs in grades 4-8: engaging students across the disciplines. Heather Kenyon Casey; Series Editors' Note by Linda B. Gambrell and Lesley Mandel Morrow. The Guilford Press, 2017 xvi, 182 p.

Grades: Professional **372.6**
    1. Language arts (Elementary) 2. Language arts (Middle school) 3. Language arts -- Correlation with content subjects 4. Reading (Elementary) 5. Reading (Middle school)
    ISBN 9781462529940

LC 2017004982

Literacy learning clubs are highly motivating small-group collaborations that can improve tweens' and teens' academic achievement, support their social-emotional development, and increase their enjoyment of reading and writing. This book explains the research basis for the author's approach and offers practical instructions for implementation in English language arts, social studies, science, and mathematics classrooms, illustrated with detailed case examples. Links to the Common Core State Standards are identified, and multimodal methods and new literacies emphasized throughout. User-friendly features include end-of-chapter reflection questions and suggested activities. The Appendix provides reproducible planning forms and handouts that can be downloaded and printed in a convenient 8 1/2" x 11" size. Provided by publisher.

Culham, Ruth

Traits of writing: the complete guide for middle school. Ruth Culham. Scholastic, c2010. 336 p.

Grades: Professional **372.6**
    1. English language -- Composition and exercises -- Study and teaching 2. Language arts (Middle school)
    ISBN 9780545013635

LC bl2012036992

Provides teachers with trait-specific assessment materials, including scoring guides, benchmark papers, and sample conference comments, along with warm-up exercises, focus lessons, and activities for the middle school classroom.

Dorfman, Lynne R., 1952-

Mentor texts: teaching writing through children's literature, K-6. Lynne R. Dorfman & Rose Cappelli, foreword by Linda Hoyt. Stenhouse Publishers, 2017 xiv, 368 p.

Grades: Professional **372.6**
    1. Language arts (Elementary) 2. Children's literature -- Study and teaching (Elementary) -- Activity programs 3. English language -- Composition and exercises -- Study and teaching (Elementary)
    ISBN 9781625311313

LC 2016050295

It's been a decade since Lynne Dorfman and Rose Cappelli wrote the first edition of Mentor Texts and helped teachers across the country make the most of high-quality children's literature in their writing instruction. In the second edition of this important book, Lynne and Rose show teachers how to help students become confident, accomplished writers by using literature as their foundation. The second edition includes brand-new "Your Turn Lessons," built around the gradual release of responsibility model, offering suggestions for demonstrations and shared or guided writing. Reflection is emphasized as a necessary component to understanding why mentor authors chose certain strategies, literary devices, sentence structures, and words. Lynne and Rose offer new children's book titles in each chapter and in a carefully curated and annotated Treasure Chest. At the end of each chapter a "Think About It—Talk About It—Write About It" section invites reflection and conversation with colleagues. The book is organized around the characteristics of good writing—focus, content, organization, style, and conventions. Rose and Lynne write in a friendly and conversational style, employing numerous anecdotes to help teachers visualize the process, and offer strategies that can be immediately implemented in the classroom. This practical resource demonstrates the power of learning to read like writers. Provided by publisher.

Miller, Donalyn

★ The **book** whisperer: awakening the inner reader in every child. Donalyn Miller; foreword by Jeff Anderson. Jossey-Bass, c2009. xi, 227 p.

Grades: Professional **372.6**
    1. Reading (Elementary) 2. Reading (Middle school) 3. Children -- Books and reading 4. Motivation in education
    ISBN 9780470372272

LC 2008055666

From the Publisher: Donalyn Miller says she has yet to meet a child she couldn't turn into a reader. No matter how far behind Miller's students might be when they reach her 6th grade classroom, they end up reading an average of 40 to 50 books a year. Miller's unconventional approach dispenses with drills and worksheets that make reading a chore. Instead, she helps students navigate the world of literature and gives them time to read books they pick out themselves. Her love of books and teaching is both infectious and inspiring. The book includes a dynamite list of recommended "kid lit" that helps parents and teachers find the books that students really like to read.

"Miller provides many tips for teachers and parents and includes a useful list of ultimate reading suggestions picked by her students. This outstanding contribution to the literature is highly recommended for teachers, parents, and others serving young students." Library Journal

Includes bibliographical references (p. [213-215]) and index.

Serravallo, Jennifer

The **literacy** teacher's playbook, grades 3-6: four steps for turning assessment data into goal-directed instruction. Jennifer Serravallo; foreword by Ellin Oliver Keene. Heinemann, 2014 xvii, 173 p.

Grades: Professional   **372.6**

   1. Language arts (Elementary) -- Evaluation
ISBN 9780325043531

LC 2013024162

Serravallo, a literacy consultant, speaker, and author, leads third through sixth grade literacy teachers through a four-step assessment process that focuses on meeting the needs of students and planning for students based on what they already know, understand, and are able to do.

Ziemke, Kristin

Read the world: rethinking literacy for empathy and action in a digital age. Kristin Ziemke & Katie Muhtaris. Heinemann, 2020 ix, 229 p.

Grades: Professional   **372.6**

   1. Language arts 2. Literacy -- Study and teaching 3. Empathy -- Study and teaching 4. Language arts -- Social aspects 5. Internet in education
ISBN 9780325108919

LC 2019026083

The book traces an arc from (1) teaching students to make sense of today's influx of information with the help of comprehension skills to (2) broadening students' empathy and their understanding of the world by teaching them how to listen to the diverse voices that technology brings us to (3) using their technological skills and broadened understanding of the world to take action in the world. Provided by publisher.

372.61 Grammar

O'Conner, Patricia T.

Woe is I Jr.: the younger grammarphobe's guide to better English in plain English. Patricia T. O'Conner; drawings by Tom Stiglich. Puffin Books, 2016, c2007. 176 p.

Grades: 4 5 6 7 8   **372.61**

   1. Grammar 2. English language -- Usage
ISBN 9780147519160

A grammar reference for middle-grade students shares accessible guidelines organized under such chapter names as "Incredible Shrinking Words," in a lighthearted guide that pairs English-language rules with whimsical instructional elements.

"The author covers pronouns, plurals, possessives, verb usage, subject-verb agreement, capitalization, and punctuation with jargon-free explanations and entertaining examples. . . . She knows her subject, can convey her message with wit and ease, and does it all in a compact, easy-to-read format." School Library Journal.

372.62 Written and spoken expression

Culham, Ruth

 ★ **6+1** traits of writing: the complete guide: grades 3 and up. Ruth Culham. Scholastic Professional Books, c2003. 304 p.

Grades: Professional   **372.62**

   1. English language -- Composition and exercises -- Study and teaching (Elementary) 2. Language arts (Elementary)
ISBN 9780439280389

LC bl2004114391

Describes the traits of good writing in any genre and includes information on assessing student writing skills, lesson planning, and activities.

Dorfman, Lynne R., 1952-

Nonfiction mentor texts: teaching informational writing through children's literature, K-8. Lynne R. Dorfman & Rose Cappelli; foreword by Tony Stead. Stenhouse Publishers, c2009. xii, 292 p.

Grades: Professional   **372.62**

   1. English language -- Study and teaching (Elementary) 2. English language -- Composition and exercises -- Study and teaching (Middle school) 3. Exposition (Rhetoric) -- Study and teaching (Elementary) 4. Exposition (Rhetoric) -- Study and teaching (Middle school) 5. Children's literature -- Study and teaching (Elementary)
ISBN 9781571104960

LC 2008054528

Lynne and Rose guide teachers through a variety of projects, samples, and classroom anecdotes that demonstrate how teachers can help students become more effective writers of good nonfiction. The Your Turn lessons at the end of each chapter use the gradual release of responsibility model to guide and empower student writers.

Fletcher, Ralph J.

Boy writers: reclaiming their voices. Ralph Fletcher. Stenhouse Publishers; c2006. ix, 190 p.

Grades: Professional   **372.62**

   1. English language -- Composition and exercises -- Study and teaching (Elementary) 2. Creative writing (Elementary education) 3. Boys -- Education (Elementary) 4. Sex differences in education
ISBN 9781571104250

LC 2006024168

Suggests ways to create writing classrooms that are boy friendly and offers techniques to engage boys in the writing process.

Craft lessons: teaching writing K-8. Ralph Fletcher, JoAnn Portalupi. Stenhouse Publishers, c2007. xiv, 177 p.

Grades: Professional   **372.62**

   1. English language -- Study and teaching (Elementary) 2. Creative writing (Elementary education)
ISBN 9781571107060

LC 2007033883

Since its publication in 1998, Craft Lessons has become a mainstay of writing teachers, both new and experienced. Readers value the pithy, practical lessons printed on one page and appreciate the instructional language geared to three grade-level groupings: K and 2, 3 and 4, and 5 and 8.

Linder, Rozlyn

The **big** book of details: 46 moves for teaching writers to elaborate. Rozlyn Linder, foreword by Harvey "Smokey" Daniels. Heinemann, 2016 ix, 238 p.

Grades: Professional   **372.62**

   1. English language -- Composition and exercises -- Study and teaching 2. Description (Rhetoric) -- Study and teaching
ISBN 9780325077666

LC 2015042708

To help our students use details and elaborate effectively,' author Roz Linder writes, "We need to find out what they want their writing to do, and then show them explicit moves to make it happen." This work supports planning and on-the-go teaching for one-on-one conferences, whole-class instruction, and more. Its lessons are organized to help kids understand each move quickly.

Portalupi, JoAnn

Nonfiction craft lessons: teaching information writing K-8. JoAnn Portalupi, Ralph Fletcher. Stenhouse Publishers, c2001. xi, 148 p.

Grades: Professional   372.62

1. English language -- Composition and exercises -- Study and teaching (Elementary) 2. English language -- Composition and exercises -- Study and teaching (Middle school) 3. Exposition (Rhetoric) -- Study and teaching (Elementary) 4. Exposition (Rhetoric) -- Study and teaching (Middle school)
ISBN 9781571103291

LC 2001017018

This book will help students breathe voice into lifeless 'dump-truck' writing and improve their nonfiction writing by making it clearer, more authoritative, and more organized. Nonfiction Craft Lessons gives teachers a wealth of practical strategies to help students grow into strong writers as they explore and explain the world around them.

Stern, Rebecca

Breakfast on Mars and 37 other delectable essays. edited by Rebecca Stern & Brad Wolfe. Roaring Brook Press, 2013. xii, 211 p.

Grades: 6 7 8 9 10 11 12   372.62

1. English language -- Study and teaching (Elementary) 2. English language -- Study and teaching (Middle school) 3. Essay writing 4. Essays
ISBN 9781596437371

LC 2012040918

Presents a collection of unconventional essays by leading writers to challenge how students think about essays using imaginative, rule-breaking, and unconventional examples.

"This handy volume fills a gap. Thirty-eight essays for young readers by contemporary writers demonstrate that 'essays can be just as enjoyable to read as fiction . . . An important collection that ought to become a staple in writing classes." Kirkus.

372.63 Spelling and handwriting

Mary Elizabeth (Mary Elizabeth Podhaizer)

Painless spelling. Mary Elizabeth. Barron's Educational Series, c2011. xv, 284 p.: Barron's painless series

Grades: 7 8 9 10   372.63

1. Spelling 2. Spelling ability
ISBN 9780764147135

LC bl2011019821

Analyzes sound and letter patterns, diphthongs, silent letters, homophones and homographs, compound and abbreviated words, contractions, prefixes, suffixes, and base words to teach spelling skills.

372.64 Literature appreciation

Alexander, Kwame

The **write** thing: Kwame Alexander engages students in writing workshop and you can too! Kwame Alexander; foreword by Kylene Beers, Ed. D.. Shell Education, 2019 208 p.

Grades: Adult Professional   372.64

1. Poetry -- Authorship -- Study and teaching (Elementary) 2. Poetry -- Authorship -- Study and teaching (Middle school) 3. Poetry -- Authorship -- Study and teaching (Secondary) 4. Poetry

-- Study and teaching (Elementary) 5. Poetry -- Study and teaching (Middle School)
ISBN 9781493888429

LC bl2019009873

A Newbery Award winner instructs teachers on how to use poetry to inject life into their school writing programs.

Chatton, Barbara

Using poetry across the curriculum: learning to love language. Barbara Chatton. Libraries Unlimited, c2010. xx, 241 p.

Grades: Professional   372.64

1. Poetry -- Study and teaching (Elementary) 2. Language experience approach in education 3. Interdisciplinary approach in education
ISBN 9781591586975

LC 2009036711

This comprehensive listing and discussion of poetic works supports the standards of all areas of the curriculum, helping librarians and teachers working with kindergarten through middle school students.

"With the emphasis in most schools on improving literacy, fluency, and reading and writing test scores, this book is extremely valuable. Sections are divided into various curricula areas. Each section begins with the national standards for that discipline, then a few paragraphs explain how the poetry in the extensive listings can be used." Library Media Connection

Includes bibliographical references and index.

Fountas, Irene C.

Genre study: teaching with fiction and nonfiction books: grades K-8 +. Irene C. Fountas & Gay Su Pinnell. Heinemann, c2012. xii, 524 p.

Grades: Professional   372.64

1. Literary form -- Study and teaching 2. Literature -- Study and teaching 3. Youth -- Books and reading
ISBN 9780325028743

LC 2011048022

Fountas and Pinnell describe how to teach genre study through an inquiry-based approach within a readers' workshop in which students in grades K-8 read, make choices about what to read, and see reading as thinking. They focus on using picture books as mentor texts and the instructional contexts of various settings.

Hopkins, Lee Bennett

Pass the poetry, please! Lee Bennett Hopkins. HarperCollins Publishers, c1998. x, 277 p.

Grades: Adult   372.64

1. Poetry -- Study and teaching (Elementary) 2. Poetry -- Authorship -- Study and teaching (Elementary) 3. Education, Elementary -- Activity programs 4. Interdisciplinary approach in education
ISBN 9780060277468

LC 98019617

Explores the importance of poetry in the lives of children, discusses contemporary poets, and collects activities successfully used by educators in the classroom

372.652 English as a second language

Echevarria, Jana, 1956-

★ **Making** content comprehensible for English learners: the SIOP Model. Jana Echevarria, Professor Emerita, California State University, Long Beach; MaryEllen Vogt, Professor Emerita, California State University, Long Beach; Deborah Short, Director, Academic Language Research & Training. Pearson, 2017 xviii, 358 p.

Grades: Professional   372.652
    1. English language -- Study and teaching (Elementary) -- Foreign speakers 2. Language arts -- Correlation with content subjects
    ISBN 9780134045238

                             LC 2015034338

Using a writing style that is practical and applicable to all kinds of classrooms, this widely popular book presents a user-friendly approach for planning and implementing lessons for teaching English learners and other students. It provides students with access to grade-level content, develops their academic English skills, and prepares them to be college and career ready.?

372.67 Other oral presentations

Hostmeyer, Phyllis
    Storytelling and QAR strategies. Phyllis Hostmeyer and Marilyn Adele Kinsella. Libraries Unlimited, c2011. viii, 123 p.

Grades: Professional   372.67
    1. Storytelling -- Methodology
    ISBN 9781598844948

                             LC 2010036576

Promotes a Question-Answer Relationship (QAR) between teachers and students and offers an explanation of this reading comprehension framework, and also provides the tools needed to incorporate a QAR into the educational setting.

372.7 Mathematics

Chapin, Suzanne H.
    Classroom discussions: using math talk to help students learn, grades K-6. Suzanne H. Chapin, Catherine O'Connor, Nancy Canavan Anderson. Math Solutions, c2009. xxv, 286 p.

Grades: Professional   372.7
    1. Mathematics -- Study and teaching (Elementary) 2. Discussion
    ISBN 9781935099017

                             LC 2009022068

This best seller offers an unparalleled look at the significant role that classroom discussions can play in teaching mathematics and deepening students' mathematical understanding. Based on a four-year research project funded by the U.S. Department of Education, the second edition includes more examples of classroom talk focusing on pre-algebra and early grade levels, an expanded range of vignettes, and more.

    Math matters: understanding the math you teach, grades K-8. Suzanne H. Chapin, Art Johnson. Math Solutions Publications, c2006. xvii, 358 p.

Grades: Professional   372.7
    1. Mathematics -- Study and teaching (Elementary)
    ISBN 9780941355711

                             LC 2006001876

This must-have resource is widely acknowledged for helping teachers, coordinators, and college faculty deepen their understanding of the mathematical concepts they teach. Over 100 activities give readers an opportunity to connect ideas, compare and contrast concepts, and consider how students understand the mathematics presented.

Harris, Pamela Weber
    Lessons and activities for building powerful numeracy. Pamela Weber Harris. Heinemann, 2014 xiii, 306 p.

Grades: Professional   372.7
    1. Numeracy -- Study and teaching
    ISBN 9780325048048

                             LC 2014018873

Pam Harris continues her work by offering lessons and activities that promote her strategies for teaching as much mathematics as possible with as little memorization as possible. Student Workouts include reproducible worksheets that students can work on independently or in pairs, followed by robust class discussion to promote understanding of the ideas.

Lempp, Jennifer
    Math workshop: five steps to implementing guided math, learning stations, reflection, and more, grades K- 5 with video streaming. Jennifer Lempp; foreword by Sherry Parrish. Math Solutions, 2017 xxxviii, 233 p.

Grades: Professional   372.7
    1. Mathematics -- Study and teaching (Elementary)
    ISBN 9781935099611

                             LC 2017040495

This work shows teachers how to successfully implement the transformational math workshop model of instruction through five accessible, manageable steps. Educators are invited to embrace this resource as their own personal and instructional coach for establishing and running a highly successful math workshop.

McNamara, Julie
    Beyond invert & multiply: making sense of fraction computation, grades 3-6: a multimedia professional learning resource. Julie McNamara; foreword by Deborah Loewenberg Ball. Math Solutions, 2015 206 p.

Grades: Professional   372.7
    1. Fractions -- Study and teaching (Elementary) 2. Video tapes in education
    ISBN 9781935099574

                             LC 2014046881

This volume builds on the foundational understandings that are described in Beyond Pizzas & Pies: 10 Essential Strategies for Supporting Fraction Sense, Second Edition, and applies them to situations involving fraction computation. This resource features more than 30 online video clips filmed in actual classrooms.

372.89 Other studies—History and geography

Monte-Sano, Chauncey
    Reading, writing, and thinking about history: teaching argument writing to diverse learners in the common core classroom, grades 6-12. Chauncey Monte-Sano, Susan De La Paz, Mark Felton. Teachers College Press, 2014 xi, 228 p.: Common Core State Standards for Literacy

Grades: Professional   372.89
    1. History -- Study and teaching (Elementary) 2. History -- Study and teaching (Secondary) 3. History -- Study and teaching -- Standards 4. Language arts -- Correlation with content subjects
    ISBN 9780807755303

                             LC 2013047386

This practical guide presents six research-tested historical investigations along with all corresponding teaching materials and tools that have improved the historical thinking and argumentative writing of academically diverse students. Provided by publisher.

373 Secondary education

Lemov, Doug, 1967-

★ **Teach** like a champion 2.0: 62 techniques that put students on the path to college. Doug Lemov; foreword by Norman Atkins. Jossey-Bass, 2015 xxxii, 468 p.

Grades: Professional   **373**

   1. Teacher effectiveness 2. Student achievement 3. College preparation programs

ISBN 9781118901854

LC 2014024321

One of the most influential teaching guides ever—updated! Teach Like a Champion 2.0 is a complete update to the international bestseller. This teaching guide is a must-have for new and experienced teachers alike. Over 700,000 teachers around the world already know how the techniques in this book turn educators into classroom champions. With ideas for everything from classroom management to inspiring student engagement, you will be able to perfect your teaching practice right away. The first edition of Teach Like a Champion influenced thousands of educators because author Doug Lemov's teaching strategies are simple and powerful. Now, updated techniques and tools make it even easier to put students on the path to college readiness. Here are just a few of the brand new resources available in the 2.0 edition: Over 70 new video clips of real teachers modeling the techniques in the classroom A selection of never before seen techniques inspired by top teachers around the world Brand new structure emphasizingthe most important techniques and step by step teaching guidelines Updated content reflecting the latest best practices from outstanding educators With the sample lesson plans, videos, and teachlikeachampion.com online community, you will be teaching like a champion in no time. The classroom techniques you'll learn in this book can be adapted to suit any context. Find out why Teach Like a Champion is a "teaching Bible" for so many educators worldwide. Provided by publisher.

373.18 Students—secondary education

Glasser, Debbie

New kid, new scene: a guide to moving and switching schools. by Debbie Glasser and Emily Schenck. Magination Press, c2012. 112 p.

Grades: 5 6 7 8   **373.18**

   1. New students 2. Moving, Household 3. Children 4. Children -- Social life and customs 5. Making friends

ISBN 9781433810398

LC 2011013608

Provides advice for children moving to a new school, including tips for navigating new surroundings, making new friends, and keeping in touch with old friends.

"Students making the transition to new schools, new communities, or new homes will always experience a bit of anxiety, and this self-help book offers practical advice on how to make those changes smoother. The ideas and suggestions are sound and practical. . . . The eye-catching layout will keep students flipping through the pages." School Library Journal.

375 Curricula

Bishop, Kay, 1942-

Connecting libraries with classrooms: the curricular roles of the media specialist. Kay Bishop. Linworth, 2011 xvi, 122 p.

Grades: Professional   **375**

   1. School librarian participation in curriculum planning 2. Media programs (Education)

ISBN 9781598845990

LC 2010051623

This book provides an in-depth exploration of the topics that are currently relevant in K-12 curricula, including the school librarian's role in dealing with these issues, collaborating with teachers, and connecting to classrooms. Provided by publisher.

378 Higher education (Tertiary education)

Burgan, Michael

Death at Kent State: how a photograph brought the Vietnam War home to America. by Michael Burgan; Content Adviser: Alan Canfora, Director, Kent May 4 Center. Compass Point Books, Capstone Press, 2017. 64 p.: Captured History

Grades: 6 7 8 9   **378**

   1. Kent State shootings, May 4, 1970 2. College students -- Political activity -- History 20th century 3. Vietnam War, 1961-1975 -- Protest movements 4. Student movements -- History 20th century 5. Kent, Ohio

ISBN 9780756554248

LC 2016008213

Discusses the shooting deaths of Kent State University students by the National Guard in 1970 and the iconic photograph that became a symbol of the antiwar movement. Provided by publisher.

"The approachable text, appealing layout, and fascinating lens through which to explore history are all bolstered by extensive source notes and additional resources." Booklist.

Includes bibliographical references and index.

379.2 Specific policy issues in public education

Aretha, David

With all deliberate speed: court-ordered busing and American schools. David Aretha. Morgan Reynolds Pub., c2012. 128 p.: Civil Rights Movement

Grades: 7 8 9 10   **379.2**

   1. Busing (School integration) 2. School integration 3. Race relations 4. Civil Rights Movement 5. United States -- History -- 20th century.

ISBN 9781599351810

LC 2011019530

Examines the origins of residential and school segregation even where it was not enforced by law, the drive for integrated schools through busing children of both races to other neighborhoods, the often violent response, and the mixed results.

"The latest books from the Civil Rights Movement series offer well-researched and clearly-written discussions of events and issues that helped define their times." Booklist.

Includes bibliographical references (p. 114-124) and index.

Beals, Melba

March forward, girl: from young warrior to Little Rock Nine. Melba Pattillo Beals; illustrated by Frank Morrison. Houghton Mifflin Harcourt 2018 208 p.

Grades: 6 7 8 9 10   **379.2**

1. Beals, Melba 2. Civil Rights Movement 3. African Americans -- Civil rights 4. School integration -- History 5. Child civil rights workers 6. Segregation 7. Little Rock, Arkansas -- History
ISBN 9781328882127

From the legendary civil rights activist and author of the million-copy selling Warriors Don't Cry comes a powerful, timely new memoir about growing up in the segregated South. Civil rights heroine Melba Patillo Beals puts readers right in her saddle oxfords as she struggles to understand—and fight back against—the laws that told her she was less just because of the color of her skin. Includes photos and illustrations.

Boyce, Jo Ann Allen

This promise of change: one girl's story in the fight for school equality. Jo Ann Allen Boyce and Debbie Levy. Bloomsbury Children's Books, 2019. 320 p.

Grades: 5 6 7 8 9   **379.2**

1. Boyce, Jo Ann Allen 2. 1950s 3. Civil Rights Movement 4. School integration 5. African American teenage girls 6. Segregation in education 7. High schools 8. Tennessee
ISBN 9781681198521

LC 2018026349

In 1956, one year before federal troops escorted the Little Rock 9 into Central High School, fourteen year old Jo Ann Allen was one of twelve African-American students who broke the color barrier and integrated Clinton High School in Tennessee. At first things went smoothly for the Clinton 12, but then outside agitators interfered, pitting the townspeople against one another.

"Engrossing, informative, and important for middle-grade collections." Booklist.

Howard, Gary R.

We can't teach what we don't know: white teachers, multiracial schools. Gary R. Howard; foreword by Sonia Nieto; reflection and discussion Guide by Victoria E. Romero and Rachel Powers. Teachers College Press, 2016 xix, 204 p.

Grades: Professional   **379.2**

1. Discrimination in education 2. Multicultural education 3. European Americans -- Identity 4. Racism
ISBN 9780807757314

LC 2016003970

Making a case for the "fierce urgency of now," this new edition deepens the discussion of race and social justice in education with new and updated material. Aligned with our nation's ever more diverse student population, it speaks to what good teachers know, what they do, and how they embrace culturally responsive teaching. Provided by publisher.

Magoon, Kekla

Today the world is watching you: the Little Rock Nine and the fight for school integration, 1957. by Kekla Magoon. Twenty-First Century Books, 2011. 160 p.: Civil rights struggles around the world

Grades: 6 7 8 9   **379.2**

1. Central High School, Little Rock, Arkanas -- History 2. School integration -- History 3. African American students -- History 4. African Americans -- History 5. Arkansas -- History 6. Little Rock, Arkansas -- History
ISBN 9780761357674

LC 2010028443

"Well-paced and engaging, the book is broken up into manageable chapters and gives background information on racial tensions in America starting with slavery. The information is carefully documented. . . . Black-and-white photographs and text boxes give additional information and context. . . . An ideal purchase for research purposes." School Library Journal.

Includes bibliographical references and index.

Tougas, Shelley

Little Rock girl 1957: how a photograph changed the fight for integration. by Shelley Tougas. Compass Point Books, c2012. 64 p.: Captured history

Grades: 6 7 8 9   **379.2**

1. Eckford, Elizabeth, 1941- 2. Central High School, Little Rock, Arkanas -- History. 3. School integration 4. African American high school students 5. Race relations 6. Little Rock, Arkansas -- Race relations
ISBN 9780756544409

LC 2010054303

Explores and analyzes the historical context and significance of the newspaper photograph of African American Elizabeth Eckford trying to enter Little Rock, Arkansas's all-white Central High School in 1957.

"This is model nonfiction. . . . The design is fresh and inviting, the writing clear, and the back matter . . . is useful and extensive. An all-around winner." Booklist.

Includes bibliographical references (p. 61-63) and index.

Walker, Paul Robert

Remember Little Rock: the time, the people, the stories. by Paul Robert Walker. National Geographic, 2008. 64 p.

Grades: 5 6 7 8 9   **379.2**

1. Central High School, Little Rock, Arkanas -- History. 2. 1950s 3. School integration -- History 4. African American students -- History 5. African Americans -- Education -- History 6. Little Rock, Arkansas -- History
ISBN 9781426304033

LC 2008024959

Uses eyewitness accounts and on-the-scene news photography to examine the history-making integration of Central High School in Little Rock, Arkansas, in 1957, as well as explores what has happened in the last fifty years, what has changed, what hasn't, and why.

"The story of the battle to integrate Central High School in 1957 Little Rock, Arkansas, is presented through photographs and firsthand accounts from those who were there. . . . The multitude of eyewitness accounts, the poignant photographs, and the contextual background make this text a must-have addition to any classroom or library." Voice of Youth Advocates.

Includes bibliographical references and index.

382 International commerce (Foreign trade)

Cooke, Tim, 1961-

Money and trade. Tim Cooke. Cavendish Square 2017. 48 p.: What's the big idea? (Cavendish Square)

Grades: 6 7 8   **382**

1. Commerce 2. Free trade 3. International trade 4. Money
ISBN 9781502628169

Outlines the practice of commerce and international trade and traces their development, the use of currency through history, and their status in the world today.

382.44 Slave trade

Cottman, Michael H.

Shackles from the deep: tracing the path of a sunken slave ship, a bitter past, and a rich legacy. by Michael H. Cottman. National Geographic Partners, 2017 127 p.

Grades: 6 7 8 9 **382.44**

1. Henrietta Marie (Ship) 2. Slave ships 3. Shipwrecks 4. Underwater archaeology 5. Slave trade -- History 6. Excavations (Archaeology)

ISBN 9781426326646

A Pulitzer Prize-winning journalist and avid scuba diver recounts his investigation into the wreck of the Henrietta Marie and how it reflects the tragic history of slavery in England, West Africa, the Caribbean and America.

"Cottman wrote a well-received version of this story for adults... and this retelling for young readers is just as intriguing." Kirkus.

384.5 Wireless communication

Steffens, Bradley, 1955-

Thinking critically: cell phones. Bradley Steffens. Referencepoint Press, Inc., 2018. 80 p.: Thinking critically

Grades: 7 8 9 10 11 12 **384.5**

1. Cell phones -- Social aspects 2. Smartphones -- Social aspects 3. Interpersonal relations 4. Technology and children

ISBN 9781682823354

LC 2017040656

Examines the issues raised by the widespread use of cell phones, asking if they harm or enhance relationships, intelligence, and health, and whether they increase or impede efficiency.

"Timely, relevant, and thought-provoking, these volumes in the ongoing Thinking Critically series use a pro-con approach to analyze four issues related to a broader, controversial topic...Cell Phones considers whether the devices are affecting human relationships, intelligence, and health and are impacting efficiency. Each title concludes with copious back matter, including source notes, related organizations and websites, a bibliography, and bulleted facts about key issues, which are especially helpful. The reliable resources will bolster student debates and research." Booklist.

Includes bibliographical references and index.

385 Railroad transportation

Spilsbury, Louise

Maglev trains. Louise and Richard Spilsbury. Gareth Stevens Publishing, 2017. 48 p.: Cutting-edge technology (Gareth Stevens Pub.)

Grades: 5 6 7 8 **385**

1. Trains -- Technological innovations 2. Magnetic levitation vehicles

ISBN 9781482451597

LC oc2016038104

"Rock-solid choices that will update and deepen science and technology collections." School Library Journal.

Includes bibliographical references (page 47) and index

Zimmermann, Karl R.

All aboard!: passenger trains around the world. Karl Zimmermann; photography by the author. Boyds Mills Press, 2004. 48 p.

Grades: 5 6 7 8 **385**

1. Railroads -- Passenger cars 2. Trains 3. Transportation 4. Railroads

ISBN 1590783255

LC 2005024990

Discusses the history of passenger train travel and the current state of passenger rail.

"Zimmermann has traveled by train across six continents, and his beautiful, big color photos appear on every double-page spread of this enthusiastic account, which blends history, geography, business, and engineering with his personal focus." Booklist.

385.0979 Railroad transportation—Pacific Slope (U.S.)

Sandler, Martin W.

Iron rails, iron men, and the race to link the nation: the story of the transcontinental railroad. Martin W. Sandler. Candlewick Press, 2015. 224 p.

Grades: 6 7 8 **385.0979**

1. Union Pacific Railroad -- History -- 19th century. 2. Central Pacific Railroad -- History -- 19th century. 3. 19th century 4. Transcontinental railroad (United States) 5. Railroads -- History 19th century. 6. Trains

ISBN 9780763665272

"A fascinating epilogue relates what later happened to each of the key players introduced in the narrative, and a thorough timeline serves as a summary of important events. A dramatic story related in dramatic fashion." Kirkus.

387.1 Ports

House, Katherine L. (Katherine Lucille)

Lighthouses for kids: history, science, and lore with 21 activities. Katherine L. House. Chicago Review Press, 2008. x, 118 p.

Grades: 4 5 6 7 8 **387.1**

1. Lighthouses 2. Lighthouses -- Action projects for children 3. Lighthouses -- History

ISBN 9781556527203

LC 2007027093

"This book is noteworthy for the way in which the activities are related to the information in the text. . . . Readers learn about the challenges of building . . . [lighthouses], inventions to make them more reliable, and how lighthouses function as historical relics today." School Library Journal.

Includes bibliographical references (p. 115-117) and index.

388.4 Local transportation

Sandler, Martin W.

Secret subway. by Martin W. Sandler. National Geographic, 2009. 96 p.

Grades: 5 6 7 8   **388.4**
1. Beach, Alfred E. (Alfred Ely), 1826-1896 2. Subways 3. Subway tunnels 4. New York City -- History.
ISBN 9781426304620

In 1869, Alfred Beach wanted to build America's first air-powered railway below New York City, but Boss Tweed, powerful politician and notorious crook, opposed. Working under night cover, Beach and his crew carved a three-hundred-foot tunnel beneath a department store. Before long, the project was discovered and the public raved about its potential. But no further tunnels were ever built. What happened to Beach's railway, and where is it now?

"Sandler takes an in-depth look at the building of New York's first subway. . . . [He] writes about the subway in a well-put-together book with interesting information, great pictures, and a compelling true story." Voice of Youth Advocates.

Includes bibliographical references and index.

391 Customs

Clancy Steer, Deirdre

Colonial America. Deirdre Clancy Steer and Amela Baksic. Chelsea House, c2009. 64 p.: Costume and fashion source books

Grades: 6 7 8 9   **391**
1. Fashion -- History 2. Clothing -- History Colonial period, 1600-1775 3. Military uniforms 4. United States -- Social life and customs -- To 1775. 5. United States -- History -- Colonial period, 1600-1775
ISBN 9781604133806

"This is written in a clear, engaging style. . . . [The] volume is profusely and gorgeously illustrated with period paintings and photographs, movie and TV stills, design sketches, and photographs from period re-enactments. Each illustration is captioned with intriguing, relevant facts that enhance the text." School Library Journal.

391.009 History, geographic treatment, biography

Albee, Sarah

Why'd they wear that?: fashion as the mirror of history. Sarah Albee National Geographic Society Children's Books, 2015. 160 p.

Grades: 5 6 7 8 9   **391.009**
1. Fashion -- History 2. Fashion design -- History 3. Fashion designers 4. Textile fabrics 5. Social indicators
ISBN 9781426319198

A narrative chronicle of fashion through the ages describes the outrageous, politically perilous and life-threatening creations people have worn in different historical eras, from spats and togas to hoop skirts and hair shirts.

"As the subtitle says, this hefty, extensively illustrated book uses fashion to discuss the ways and whys people dress and how it reflects what's happening in their civilization. . . . The many photographs are well chosen and reproduced, and Albee writes in a conversational style that, though occasionally repetitive, is instantly appealing to readers. Tim Gunn writes the foreword, and a timeline and bibliography conclude." Booklist.

Croll, Jennifer

Fashion that changed the world. Jennifer Croll. Prestel, 2014. 192 p.

Grades: Adult   **391.009**
1. Fashion design -- History 2. Celebrities 3. Popular culture 4. Fashion -- Social aspects
ISBN 9783791347899

LC 2014940422

What did Vogue's first cover look like? When did film stars become part of the fashion industry? What led to the development of ready-to-wear clothing? How did the paintings of Mondrian, Dali and Warhol end up on the runway? These and other questions are answered in this eye-opening look at different aspects of the history of fashion—from Elizabeth I's "Mask of Youth," to Lady Gaga's "meat dress." Arranged by topic, the lavishly illustrated chapters explore themes such as war and the military; ready-to-wear; fashion in film, art, and sports; celebrity; gay and lesbian fashion; globalization; and the internet. Fashion That Changed the World digs into a multitude of social, economic, and cultural factors that changed the course of fashion over the last few hundred years.

Platt, Richard

They wore what?!: the weird history of fashion and beauty. Richard Platt. Two-Can, 2007. 48 p.

Grades: 4 5 6   **391.009**
1. Fashion -- History 2. Beauty care -- History 3. Manners and customs 4. Beauty 5. Clothing
ISBN 9781587285820

LC 2006039159

Describes changing ideas of fashion and beauty through history and around the world. Provided by publisher.

"Busy, colorful pages recount the historical, social, and political sides of clothing, hair, hats, and shoes, from legal and moral issues such as wearing fur to dangerous practices like cinched waists and bound feet. . . . Ever-fluctuating ideas of beauty and body image are also explored." Horn Book Guide.

Includes bibliographical references (p. 45) and index.

391.1 Costume of men

Croll, Jennifer

Bad boys of fashion: style rebels and renegades through the ages. Jennifer Croll; illustrated by Aneta Pacholska. Annick Press, 2019. 184 p.

Grades: 6 7 8 9 10 11 12   **391.1**
1. Fashion 2. Clothing 3. Celebrities 4. Influencers 5. Men's clothing
ISBN 9781773212432

A fiercely fabulous look at men's fashion rule-breakers and icons.

391.6 Personal appearance

Bailey, Diane, 1966-

Tattoo art around the world. Diane Bailey. Rosen Pub., 2011. 64 p.: Tattooing

Grades: 7 8 9 10   **391.6**
1. Tattooing 2. Culture
ISBN 9781448846184

LC 2010048428

Tattoos have gone from a symbol of shame and isolation to a widely accepted art form all over the world. The book looks at tattoo techniques and styles, from honored religious and cultural traditions of the East to the pop-culture inspired body art of the West. Colorful images provide an interesting glimpse at unique and traditional tattoo styles as they evolve through history into what they are today.

"Tattoo Art around the World discusses how different cultures have used tattoos, ranging widely in place and time from a Siberian mummy, to the Tahitians found by Captain Cook, to people in the present day. The design and the reading level are accessible without talking down to the audience, so this is a good choice for enticing reluctant readers with an interest in body art." Booklist.

Includes bibliographical references (p. 56-61) and index.

Nagle, Jeanne
  Why people get tattoos and other body art. Jeanne Nagle. Rosen, 2011. 64 p.: Tattooing
  Grades: 7 8 9 10   **391.6**
    1. Tattooing 2. Body modification 3. Culture
    ISBN 9781448846177

                                            LC 2011000276
  Looks at some of the cultural, aesthetic, expressive, and religious motivations that people have for getting tattoos and body art.

  "Why People Get Tattoos explains the appeal of tattoos for a wide variety of people as a way of expressing themselves aesthetically, religiously, or for other reasons... The design and the reading level are accessible without talking down to the audience, so this is a good choice for enticing reluctant readers with an interest in body art." Booklist.

  Includes bibliographical references (p. 56-61) and index.

392.3 Customs relating to dwelling places and domestic arts

Hepplewhite, Peter
  Loos, poos, and number twos: a disgusting journey through the bowels of history! Peter Hepplewhite. Gareth Stevens Pub., 2015. 32 p.: Awfully ancient
  Grades: 4 5 6 7 8   **392.3**
    1. Feces 2. Toilets -- History 3. Sewage disposal 4. Feces -- History 5. Grossology
    ISBN 9781482431186
  "A lively, surprisingly informative, high-interest volume that manages to both entertain and educate." Booklist.

393 Death customs

Colman, Penny
  Corpses, coffins, and crypts: a history of burial. Penny Colman. Henry Holt, 1997. 212 p.
  Grades: 7 8 9 10   **393**
    1. Funerals -- History 2. Burial -- History 3. Cremation 4. Death -- Social aspects 5. Death -- Psychological aspects -- History
    ISBN 0805050663

                                            LC   97007842
  Documents the burial process throughout the centuries and in different cultures.

  "The author is both candid and detailed in her handling of the gruesome nitty-gritty. . . . Many of the photographs in the liberally illustrated text are from her own explorations, and all are captioned, some in great detail. . . . She's filled her sensitive, solid book with answers to ques-

tions people often need and want to know but are too reluctant to ask." Booklist.

  Includes bibliographical references (p. 196-201) and index.

Halls, Kelly Milner, 1957-
  Mysteries of the mummy kids. by Kelly Milner Halls. Darby Creek Pub., c2007. 72 p.
  Grades: 4 5 6 7   **393**
    1. Mummies 2. Human remains (Archaeology) 3. Children -- Death
    ISBN 158196059X

                                            LC bl2007003775
  Explores the worldwide practices of mummification, introducing famous mummies of children and the events surrounding their deaths, describing the social or religious reasons behind mummification, and explaining how bodies become mummified.

  "Halls presents an eerily fascinating exploration of mummified children and teens found in South and North America, Europe, and Asia. . . . The writing style is plain yet absorbing, presenting scientific and historical information in simple terms." Voice of Youth Advocates.

  Includes bibliographical references (p. 67-69) and index.

Sloan, Christopher
  Mummies: dried, tanned, sealed, drained, frozen, embalmed, stuffed, wrapped, and smoked-- and we're dead serious. by Christopher Sloan. National Geographic, c2010. 48 p.
  Grades: 4 5 6 7   **393**
    1. Mummies 2. Embalming 3. Funerals
    ISBN 9781426306952

                                            LC 2010008498
  Presents some of history's most significant mummy discoveries reveal the science behind mummification and what has been determined about each mummy's life and death.

  "A gratifyingly grisly album of choice photos accompanies Sloan's lucid, informative text as he describes not only the mummification processes but also individual mummies produced whether by intent or by chance. From the dried Beauty of Krorn in China to the bundled Lady of Cao in a Peruvian pyramid or the familiar Boy King Tut in Egypt, a global variety is offered to fascinated readers. . . . [This is a] well-written, heavily illustrated glimpse into the world of after-death preservation, either by accident or design." School Library Journal.

  Includes bibliographical references (p. 47) and index.

394.1 Eating, drinking; using drugs

Augustin, Byron
  The **food** of Mexico. Byron Augustin. Marshall Cavendish Benchmark, c2010. 64 p.: Flavors of the world
  Grades: 4 5 6 7   **394.1**
    1. Food habits 2. Festivals 3. Food 4. Mexico -- Social life and customs
    ISBN 9781608702374

                                            LC 2010013830
  Explores the culture of Mexico through its food. Provided by publisher.

Chevat, Richie
  The **omnivore's** dilemma: the secrets behind what you eat. Michael Pollan; adapted by Richie Chevat. Dial Books for Young Readers, 2015, c2009. 377 p.

Grades: 5 6 7 8 9 10 11 12　　　　　394.1
   1. Food industry and trade 2. Food chains (Ecology) 3. Food consumption 4. Food supply 5. Food values
ISBN 9781101993828

                    LC 2009009283

Delves into facts about food, life expectancy as it relates to consumption and global health implications resulting from food choices made by people around the world, encouraging readers to consider their food choices and eating habits.

"Adopting the role of food detective, the author peers behind the curtain of the modern food industry and finds that the industrial approach to the food chain imperils our health and planet. ... Clear organization and lively writing rooted in fascinating examples make this accessible and interesting." Kirkus.

Includes bibliographical references (pages 355-377) and index.

Orr, Tamra

   The **food** of China. Tamra B. Orr. Marshall Cavendish Benchmark, 2011. 64 p.: Flavors of the world
Grades: 4 5 6 7　　　　　394.1
   1. Food habits 2. Festivals 3. Food 4. China -- Social life and customs.
ISBN 9781608702343

"Numerous high-quality, close-up color photos of outdoor vegetable markets, food in various stages of preparation, and families gathering around the table will keep readers engaged (and hungry) throughout the accessible and enlightening food tour." Booklist.

Schlosser, Eric

   Chew on this: everything you don't want to know about fast food. by Eric Schlosser and Charles Wilson. Houghton Mifflin Co., 2006. 304 p.
Grades: 6 7 8 9 10　　　　　394.1
   1. Junk food 2. Food habits 3. Fast food restaurants, chains, etc 4. Fast food restaurants, chains, etc -- History 5. Food industry and trade
ISBN 0618710310

A behind-the-scenes look at the fast food industry.

"An adaptation of Schlosser's Fast Food Nation (Houghton, 2001), Chew on This covers the history of the fast-food industry and delves into the agribusiness and animal husbandry methods that support it. . . . Equally disturbing is his revelation of the way that the fast-food giants have studied childhood behavior and geared their commercials and free toy inclusions to hook the youngest consumers. The text is written in a lively, layout-the-facts manner. Occasional photographs add bits of visual interest." School Library Journal.

394.262 Holidays of March, April, May

Peterson, Christy

   Earth Day and the global environmental movement: standing up for Earth. Christy Peterson. Twenty-First Century Books, 2020 120 p.
Grades: 6 7 8 9 10 11 12　　　　　394.262
   1. Earth Day -- History 2. Environmentalism -- History
ISBN 9781541552814

                    LC 2019003593

Published to mark the 50th anniversary of Earth Day, a cautionary report on the threatened state of earth protections cites the political divides and disinformation that are compromising urgently needed responses to climate change. Illustrations.

394.263 Holidays of June, July, August

Dolbear, Emily

   Juneteenth. by Emily Dolbear. The Child's World, 2021 32 p.: Black American Journey
Grades: 4 5 6 7　　　　　394.263
   1. Juneteenth 2. African Americans -- Social life and customs 3. Enslaved people -- Emancipation 4. African Americans -- History 5. Slavery 6. Texas -- Social life and customs.
ISBN 9781503853799

                    LC bl2021005690

Learn the basics about Juneteenth, also called Emancipation Day or Freedom Day, and how the holiday celebrates the emancipation of slaves in the United States." Providedby publisher.

394.3 Recreational customs

Pheasant-Neganigwane, Karen

   Powwow: a celebration through song and dance. Karen Pheasant-Neganigwane. Orca Book Pub 2020 88 p.: Orca origins
Grades: 4 5 6 7 8 9　　　　　394.3
   1. Powwows 2. Indians of North America -- Rites and ceremonies 3. Native American dancers 4. Powwow dancers 5. First Nations (Canada) -- Rites and ceremonies
ISBN 9781459812345

Part of the nonfiction Orca Origins series for middle readers. Illustrated with photographs, Powwow is a celebration of Indigenous song and dance in North America. Provided by publisher.

"The gallery of photos throughout the book gives readers seats at a powwow, an event that is described as a continual space to restore kinship and preserve Indigenous identity." Kirkus.

395.1 Etiquette for people by gender or sex; for age groups

Packer, Alex. J., 1951-

   How rude!: the teen guide to good manners, proper behavior, and not grossing people out. Alex J. Packer, Ph.D. Free Spirit Publishing Inc., 2014 xiv, 489 p.
Grades: 7 8 9 10 11 12　　　　　395.1
   1. Etiquette 2. Etiquette for teenagers 3. Social skills 4. Teenagers -- Personal conduct
ISBN 9781575424545

                    LC 2014001602

A humorous but practical guide to good manners and social skills, discussing such areas as family life, behavior in public, manners in school, eating, and clothes.

Post, Peggy, 1945-

   Emily Post's the guide to good manners for kids. by Peggy Post & Cindy Post Senning. Harper Collins Publishers, c2004. 144 p.
Grades: 4 5 6 7　　　　　395.1
   1. Etiquette for children 2. Etiquette 3. Behavior
ISBN 0060571969

                    LC 2003026426

Presents guidelines for proper etiquette in various situations, including weddings, after-school events, after-school jobs, and parties.

"The writing is clear, friendly, and sometimes clever. . . . The advice is consistently practical and simple." School Library Journal.

Senning, Cindy Post

Teen manners: from malls to meals to messaging and beyond. by Cindy Post Senning and Peggy Post. Harper Collins Publishers, c2007. 134 p.

Grades: 7 8 9 10 **395.1**
1. Etiquette for teenagers 2. Teenagers -- Personal conduct
ISBN 0060881984

LC 2007010991

Provides etiquette guidelines for teenagers, covering such topics as using polite language; cell phone, e-mail, and IM usage; table manners; and how to act during job interviews.

395.5 Etiquette by situations

Post, Peggy, 1945-

Emily Post's table manners for kids. by Peggy Post & Cindy Post Senning. Harpercollins Childrens Books, 2009. 96 p.

Grades: 4 5 6 7 **395.5**
1. Etiquette for children 2. Table manners 3. Etiquette 4. Dinners and dining 5. Personal conduct
ISBN 9780061117091

"This deceptively slim guide teems with advice about everything from meal courses to table settings, from the art of conversation to dining out. The tone is measured and mildly proscriptive, offset by Bjorkman's amusing cartoons. . . . A strength: the excellent troubleshooting for specific concerns, such as eating fondue and using chopsticks." Kirkus.

398 Folklore

Bryant, Megan E.

She's all that!: a look-it-up guide to the goddesses of mythology. Megan E. Bryant. Scholastic Library Pub., 2009. 128 p.: Mythlopedia

Grades: 4 5 6 7 **398**
1. Gods and goddesses, Greek 2. Heroes and heroines, Greek 3. Mythology
ISBN 9781606310595

The superstars of Greek myth meet the modern age—complete with profiles, headshots, and family trees; fascinating sidebars; and irreverent surprises, this series is for readers who love action, deception, romance, power struggles, and more!

"This spices things up with sassy artwork, a pastel color scheme, and an OMG sensibility. . . . Aside from the heaps of information coming from all angles on just about every page, . . . [this] book also contains a decent family tree, a rudimentary star chart, and lists of further reading. . . . For kids unconvinced that anything so old and gray could have any bearing on their lives, . . . [this provides] a feisty . . . guide to the many cultural references lingering from antiquity." Booklist.

Currie, Stephen, 1960-

African American folklore. Stephen Currie. Lucent Books, c2009. 103 p.: Lucent library of Black history

Grades: 7 8 9 10 **398**
1. African Americans 2. Culture 3. United States -- Race relations.

4. Folklore
ISBN 9781420500820

LC 2008020201

Introduces the oral tradition of African American culture in the United States, discussing stories, songs, rhymes, jokes, its roots in African folklore and slavery, and its continuing influence on the present.

"The book is highly accessible and [provides] cultural context to help readers understand [the] topic. . . . [The] book includes captioned color and black-and-white photographs and reproductions on every spread. Well-organized and clearly written." School Library Journal.

Includes bibliographical references (p. 90-96) and index.

Etingoff, Kim

Howling at the moon: vampires and werewolves in the New World. Kim Etingoff. Mason Crest Publishers, 2010. 64 p.: Making of a monster: vampires & werewolves

Grades: 7 8 9 10 **398**
1. Vampires 2. Werewolves 3. Monsters 4. Curiosities and wonders
ISBN 9781422218051

"The writing is engaging and accessible, and peppered easily with teen vernacular. . . . Large, clear photographs and period and contemporary drawings appear on every other page or so. . . . First-rate entertainment." School Library Journal.

Includes bibliographical references and werewolves

The **science** of the beast: the facts behind the fangs. by Kim Etingoff. Mason Crest Publishers, 2010. 63 p.: Making of a monster: vampires & werewolves

Grades: 7 8 9 10 **398**
1. Vampires 2. Werewolves 3. Monsters 4. Curiosities and wonders
ISBN 9781422218082

LC 2010023660

"The writing is engaging and accessible, and peppered easily with teen vernacular. . . . Large, clear photographs and period and contemporary drawings appear on every other page or so. . . . First-rate entertainment." School Library Journal.

Includes bibliographical references (p. 62) and index.

Indovino, Shaina Carmel

Trannsylvania and beyond: famous vampires & werewolves in old Europe. Shaina Carmel Indovino. Mason Crest Publishers, 2010. 64 p.: Making of a monster: vampires & werewolves

Grades: 7 8 9 10 **398**
1. Vampires 2. Werewolves 3. Monsters
ISBN 9781422218099

"The writing is engaging and accessible, and peppered easily with teen vernacular. . . . Large, clear photographs and period and contemporary drawings appear on every other page or so. . . . First-rate entertainment." School Library Journal.

Includes bibliographical references and index.

Kallen, Stuart A., 1955-

Vampire history and lore. by Stuart A. Kallen. ReferencePoint Press, 2011. 80 p.: Vampire library

Grades: 7 8 9 10 **398**
1. Vampires 2. Curiosities and wonders 3. Undead 4. Vampires -- History 5. Monsters
ISBN 9781601521323

LC 2010005866

"Energetic and surprisingly educational, this lively [book] seizes upon a zeitgeist topic and takes it as far as possible." Booklist.

Includes bibliographical references and index.

Kelly, Sophia

What a beast!: a look-it-up guide to the monsters and mutants of mythology! Sophia Kelly. F. Watts, 2009. 128 p. : Mythlopedia

Grades: 4 5 6 7   **398**

    1. Monsters 2. Mutants 3. Mythology

    ISBN 9781606310601

                  LC 2009020998

A thoroughly new series where the superstars of Greek myth meet the modern age—complete with profiles, headshots, and family trees; fascinating sidebars; and irreverent surprises, this series is for readers who love action, deception, romance, power struggles, and more!

"This spices things up with sassy artwork, a pastel color scheme, and an OMG sensibility. . . . [This title is] loaded with information on the inspired methods with which various nasty creatures could put an end to bothersome heroes. Aside from the heaps of information coming from all angles on just about every page, . . . [the] book also contains a decent family tree, a rudimentary star chart, and lists of further reading. . . . For kids unconvinced that anything so old and gray could have any bearing on their lives, . . . [this book provides] a feisty . . . guide to the many cultural references lingering from antiquity." Booklist.

Martin, Nicholas, 1988-

Fighting the fangs: a guide to vampires and werewolves. by Nicholas Martin. Mason Crest Publishers, c2011. 64 p.: Making of a monster: vampires & werewolves

Grades: 7 8 9 10   **398**

    1. Vampires 2. Werewolves 3. Monsters 4. Paranormal phenomena 5. Curiosities and wonders

    ISBN 9781422218044

                  LC 2010025187

"The writing is engaging and accessible, and peppered easily with teen vernacular. . . . Large, clear photographs and period and contemporary drawings appear on every other page or so. . . . First-rate entertainment." School Library Journal.

Includes bibliographical references and index.

Robson, David, 1966-

Encounters with vampires. David Robson. ReferencePoint Press, c2011. 80 p.: Vampire library

Grades: 7 8 9 10   **398**

    1. Vampires 2. Curiosities and wonders 3. Vampires -- History 4. Undead

    ISBN 9781601521330

                  LC 2010010100

Collects stories of vampire sightings, vampire attacks, and vampire hunting.

"The author lays out both folklore and real-world reports of bloodsucking beings. Expanding beyond familiar Transylvanian tales and stories of vampires in strictly human form, the author's survey is global, from the Malaysian langsuyar, believed to be responsible for many newborn deaths, to the red-eyed, monstrous Latin American chupacabra, notorious for preying on livestock. . . . Young vampire-fiction fans will find much to ponder here, while the accounts of contemporary murders with purported vampire links may emerge as the most chilling and grisly." Booklist.

Includes bibliographical references (p. 74-76) and index.

Sanna, Ellyn, 1957-

Latino folklore and culture: stories of family, traditions of pride. by Ellyn Sanna. Mason Crest Publishers, c2006. 112 p.: Hispanic heritage

Grades: 7 8 9 10   **398**

    1. Latin Americans 2. Latin Americans -- Social life and customs 3. Latin America -- Social life and customs

    ISBN 1590849329

                  LC 2004024248

"This book begins with a description of the place of folklore in culture and the differences between the terms Latino and Hispanic. Specific folktales, such as the many versions of La Llorona, and dominant themes, such as machismo, strong women, and religion, are described in subsequent chapters. . . . [This is] an excellent resource both for students researching Latino arts for reports and for general readers." School Library Journal.

Includes bibliographical references (p. 107-108) and index.

Sanna, Emily

Pop monsters: the modern-day craze for vampires and werewolves. Emily Sanna. Mason Crest Publishers, 2011 64 p.: Making of a monster: vampires & werewolves

Grades: 7 8 9 10   **398**

    1. Vampires 2. Werewolves 3. Monsters 4. Popular culture 5. Curiosities and wonders

    ISBN 9781422218068

"The writing is engaging and accessible, and peppered easily with teen vernacular. . . . Large, clear photographs and period and contemporary drawings appear on every other page or so. . . . First-rate entertainment." School Library Journal.

Includes bibliographical references and index.

Stewart, Sheila, 1975-

The **psychology** of our dark side: humans' love affair with vampires & werewolves. Sheila Stewart. Mason Crest Publishers, 2010. 64 p.: Making of a monster: vampires & werewolves

Grades: 7 8 9 10   **398**

    1. Vampires 2. Werewolves 3. Superstition -- Psychological aspects 4. Monsters 5. Curiosities and wonders

    ISBN 9781422218075

"The writing is engaging and accessible, and peppered easily with teen vernacular. . . . Large, clear photographs and period and contemporary drawings appear on every other page or so. . . . First-rate entertainment." School Library Journal.

Includes bibliographical references and index.

398.2 Folk literature

Abrahams, Roger D.

African folktales: traditional stories of the Black world. selected and retold by Roger D. Abrahams. Pantheon Books, c1983. xviii, 354 p.

Grades: 8 9 10 11 12 Adult   **398.2**

    1. Mythology, folklore, and legends

    ISBN 0394721179

                  LC 83002474

Gathers stories about ghosts, kings, clever animals, mischief makers, devils, foolish humans and the origin of things

Brown, Dee, 1908-2002
Dee Brown's folktales of the Native American, retold for our times. illustrated by Louis Mofsie. H. Holt, 1993. 174 p.
Grades: 7 8 9 10   **398.2**
    1. Folklore
    ISBN 080502607X
                            LC 93012449
A collection of thirty-six stories, interpreted by the author communicate the oral traditions of a variety of Native American tribes

Bryan, Ashley
★ **Ashley** Bryan's African tales, uh-huh. retold and illustrated by Ashley Bryan. Atheneum Books for Young Readers, c1998. 198 p.
Grades: 4 5 6   **398.2**
    1. Animals 2. Frogs 3. Hens 4. Anansi (Legendary character) 5. Folklore
    ISBN 0689820763
                            LC 97077743
"This collection of African folktales is told with Bryan's distinctive rhythmic word patterns and filled with humor, life lessons, and the antics of trickster Ananse. . . . Quality reproductions of the original woodcuts enrich this handsome volume." Horn Book Guide.

Bryant, Megan E.
Oh my gods!: a look-it-up guide to the gods of mythology. Megan E. Bryant. Franklin Watts, c2009. 128 p.: Mythlopedia
Grades: 4 5 6 7   **398.2**
    1. Gods and goddesses, Greek 2. Heroes and heroines, Greek 3. Mythology
    ISBN 9781606310588
A thoroughly new series where the superstars of Greek myth meet the modern age—complete with profiles, headshots, and family trees; fascinating sidebars; and irreverent surprises, this series is for readers who love action, deception, romance, power struggles, and more!
"The book is organized around entries on major gods and titans, each with vital stats and a Top 10 Things to Know about Me, followed by a few highlights from their lore and sidebars that delve into their cultural relevance. Illustrations abound, from embellished stock images to original cartoons, and the pastel-heavy color scheme may entice readers otherwise resistant to the grays and ivories that tend to dominate classicism." Booklist.

Burns, Batt
★ The **king** with horse's ears and other Irish folktales. Batt Burns. Sterling Pub. Co., 2009. 96 p.
Grades: 4 5 6 7   **398.2**
    1. Fairy tales 2. Folklore
    ISBN 9781402737725
                            LC 2007035258
"These 13 Irish tales retold by storyteller Burns follow fairies and warriors, heroes and clever thieves. . . . The stories are cleanly retold in contemporary, accessible language, and each is introduced with a short paragraph providing cultural or other information. . . . Oleynikov's paintings have a rough texture that suits the energy of the retellings and adds to the lively tone. This is a hearty collection, handsomely produced with Celtic-knot borders and gouache full-page and spot illustrations." Booklist.

Chase, Richard
The **Jack** tales: told by R.M. Ward and his kindred in the Beech Mountain section of western North Carolina and by other descendants of Council Harmon (1803-1896) elsewhere in the southern mountains with three tales from Wise County, Virigina. set down from these sources and edited by Richard Chase; with an appendix compiled by Herbert Halpert; and illustrated by Berkekey Williams, Jr. Houghton Mifflin, 2003, c1943. xviii, 216 p.
Grades: 5 6 7 8 9 10 11 12 Adult   **398.2**
    1. Giants 2. Boys and giants 3. Folklore
    ISBN 9780618346936
                            LC 43012028
A collection of folk tales from the southern Appalachians that center on a single character, the irrepressible Jack.
"Humor, freshness, colorful American background, and the use of one character as a central figure in the cycle mark these 18 folk tales, told here in the dialect of the mountain country of North Carolina. A scholarly appendix by Herbert Halpert, giving sources and parallels, increases the book's value as a contribution to American folklore. Black-and-white illustrations in the spirit of the text." Booklist.
Includes bibliographical references.

Delacre, Lulu
Golden tales: myths, legends, and folktales from Latin America. Retold and illustrated by Lulu Delacre. Scholastic Press, 1996. 73 p.
Grades: 5 6 7 8   **398.2**
    1. Creation (Taino religion) 2. Folklore 3. Mythology
    ISBN 059048186X
                            LC 9436724
Presents twelve tales from thirteen countries and "the four native cultures from which they sprung": Taino, Zapotec, Muisca, and Quechua.
"This includes 12 stories from four native cultures (Taino, Zapotec, Muisca, and Quechua), including pourquoi tales, legends of the conquistadores, and folktales from before and after the age of Columbus. . . . [The author's] . . . retellings are done in a clear and confident voice and are accompanied by her robust, colorful oil paintings. . . . This impressively presented and referenced collection will inspire readers and tellers alike." Booklist.

Erdoes, Richard
American Indian myths and legends. selected and edited by Richard Erdoes and Alfonso Ortiz. Pantheon Books, c1984. xv, 527 p.
Grades: 8 9 10 11 12 Adult   **398.2**
    1. Indians of North America 2. Tricksters 3. Monsters 4. Creation (Native American religion) 5. Mythology
    ISBN 0394507967
                            LC 84042669
"This volume comprises 160 tales of native folklore and myth ranging from one geographical end of our continent to the other. The book is organized according to type of myth. . . . Erdoes and Ortiz seek to keep Indian myth intact and pure through their retellings, using, as often as possible, primary sources." Booklist.

Fleischman, Paul
Dateline: Troy. Paul Fleischman; collages by Gwen Frankfeldt & Glenn Morrow. Candlewick Press, 2006, c1996. 80 p.
Grades: 7 8 9 10   **398.2**
    1. Trojan War 2. World politics 3. Heroes and heroines, Greek 4. Achilles (Greek mythology) 5. War and society 6. Troy (Extinct

city) 7. Ancient Greece 8. Mythology
ISBN 9781564024695

LC 95036356

A retelling of the story of the Trojan War illustrated with collages featuring newspaper clippings of modern events from World War I through the Persian Gulf war.

Forest, Heather

Wisdom tales from around the world. Heather Forest. August House Publishers, 1996. 156 p.

Grades: 7 8 9 10   **398.2**
   1. Folklore
   ISBN 0874834783

LC 96-31141

A collection of traditional stories from around the world, reflecting the cumulative wisdom of Sufi, Zen, Taoist, Buddhist, Jewish, Christian, African, and Native American cultures.

"Forest retells folktales, proverbs, and parables in a thoughtful and satisfying style that amuses as it deftly imparts lessons for living." School Library Journal.

García Esperón, María

The **sea-ringed** world: sacred stories of the Americas. by María García Esperón; illustrated by Amanda Mijangos and translated by David Bowles. Levine Querido, 2021 240 p.

Grades: 4 5 6 7 8 9 10 11 12   **398.2**
   1. Indians of North America 2. Indians of South America 3. Indigenous peoples 4. Creation 5. Western Hemisphere 6. Folklore
   ISBN 9781646140152

Fifteen thousand years before Europeans stepped foot in the Americas, people had already spread from tip to tip and coast to coast. Like all humans, these Native Americans sought to understand their place in the universe, the nature of their relationship with the divine, and the origin of the world into which their ancestors had emerged. The answers lay in their sacred stories. Author María García Esperón, illustrator Amanda Mijangos, and translator David Bowles have gifted us a treasure. Their talents have woven this collection of stories from nations and cultures across our two continents—the Sea-Ringed World, as the Aztecs called it—from the edge of Argentina all the way up to Alaska. The Em Querido list seeks to introduce the finest books in translation from around the world to an American audience. We feel lucky to be bringing you this book on our inaugural list, which we hope will be a true window and mirror. Provided by publisher.

"These retellings, most three to four pages in length, are generous in spirit. García Esperón, a lauded Mexican poet, evokes a harshly beautiful world, and Bowles' finely rendered translation begs to be read aloud." Kirkus

Goss, Linda

Talk that talk: an anthology of African-American storytelling. edited by Linda Goss & Marian E. Barnes. Simon & Schuster, c1989. 521 p.

Grades: 8 9 10 11 12 Adult   **398.2**
   1. African Americans -- History 2. Mythology, folklore, and legends
   ISBN 0671671685

LC 89010582

Gathers fables, sermons, historical anecdotes, humorous tales, and modern raps and rhymes by Black storytellers

"The selections included range from slave stories and the animal legends of Brer Rabbit and Brer Fox to the comedy monologues of Dick Gregory and rap routines. . . . Interspersed throughout are brief sections of commentary and analysis." Booklist.

Includes bibliographical references (p. 507-511).

Hamilton, Virginia, 1936-2002

★ The **people** could fly: American Black folktales. Virginia Hamilton; illustrated by Leo and Diane Dillon. A. A. Knopf, 1985. 178 p.

Grades: 5 6 7 8   **398.2**
   1. Freedom 2. Slavery 3. Folklore
   ISBN 0375804714

LC 84025020

Coretta Scott King Award, Author Category, 1986.

Retold African-American folktales of animals, fantasy, the supernatural, and desire for freedom, born of the sorrow of the slaves, but passed on in hope.

"The author has been successful in her efforts to write these tales in the Black English of the slave storytellers. Her scholarship is unobtrusive and intelligible. She has provided a glossary and notes concerning the origins of the tales and the different versions in other cultures. Handsomely illustrated." New York Times Book Review.

Hayes, Joe

Dance, Nana, dance = Baila, Nana, baila: Cuban folktales in English and Spanish. retold by Joe Hayes; illustrated by Mauricio Trenard Sayago. Cinco Puntos Press, 2007. 96 p.

Grades: 5 6 7 8 9   **398.2**
   1. Cubans 2. Cuba 3. Spain -- Social life and customs. 4. Bilingual materials English/Spanish 5. Folklore
   ISBN 9781933693170

LC 2007038295

A collection of stories from Cuban folklore, representing the cultures of Spain, Africa, and the Caribbean.

"Each tale is accompanied by a full-page illustration that is colorful and contributes to the text. This book is a great addition to folktale and Spanish language collections. Students will enjoy these stories that could easily be incorporated into the curriculum." Library Media Connection.

Hirschmann, Kris, 1967-

Medusa. Kris Hirschmann. ReferencePoint Press, c2012. 80 p.: Monsters and mythical creatures

Grades: 6 7 8 9   **398.2**
   1. Monsters 2. Mythical creatures 3. Medusa (Greek mythology) 4. Perseus (Greek mythology) 5. Gorgons (Greek mythology) 6. Mythology
   ISBN 9781601521811

LC 2011020993

Desribes the history of the legend of Medusa, including the ancient Greek myth of Perseus and the Gorgons, representations of Medusa in art, and modern versions of the monster in popular culture.

"This is an ideal starting point for young researchers interested in the weird, mysterious, and paranormal. Using fleet, descriptive prose to communicate the impressively researched (and sourced) information, [this] medium-length [work manages] to rope in just about everything, from folklore to history to pop culture. . . . Medusa goes into the monster's roots in Greek storytelling before delving more deeply into Homer's Iliad, the story of Perseus, and the Gorgan's appearance in art, theater, opera, and more. . . . The illustrations are fine and varied, the sidebars always illuminating, and the back matter robust." Booklist.

Includes bibliographical references (p. 67-71) and index.

Jennings, Ken, 1974-

Greek mythology. Ken Jennings; illustrated by Mike Lowery. Little Simon, 2014 160 p.: Ken Jennings' junior genius guides

Grades: 3 4 5 6 **398.2**
1. Characters and characteristics in mythology 2. Mythology
ISBN 9781442498495

Provides facts on the classic myths of the Greeks, from how Prometheus outsmarted the gods to how Achilles's heel led to his death.

Johnson, Hal, 1972-

Fearsome creatures of the Lumberwoods: 20 chilling tales from the wilderness. Hal Johnson, Tom Mead. Workman Pub Co., 2015. 208 p.

Grades: 5 6 7 8 **398.2**
1. Imaginary creatures 2. Curiosities and wonders 3. Forest animals
ISBN 9780761184614

Collects illustrated tales of the strange and terrifying wild creatures living in the Lumberwoods, including the shadow-eating snoligoster and the speedy hoop snake.

"Look out for what's lurking around every corner. The book is told from the perspective of a cryptozoologist who focuses on the lumberwoods of North America and who recounts many painful and horrifying incidents he witnessed during his years of seeking the most bizarre creatures. . . . A captivating collection for fans of Alvin Schwartz's Scary Tales to Tell in the Dark, this is also ideal for those looking for something fresh, creative, and deliciously creepy." School Library Journal.

Krasno, Rena, 1923-

Cloud weavers: ancient Chinese legends. Rena Krasno and Yeng-Fong Chiang; illustrations from the collection of Yeng-Fong Chiang. Pacific View Press, c2003. 96 p.

Grades: 5 6 7 8 **398.2**
1. Culture 2. China 3. Short stories 4. Folklore
ISBN 1881896269

LC 2002035911

Presents legends and tales from China, including ancient folktales, stories that reflect Chinese traditions and virtues, historical tales, and selections from literature.

"This collection provides a showcase for some remarkable pieces of Chinese calendar art and advertising posters from the 1920s and 1930s. . . . Prefaces provide cultural insight for some stories, and the brisk retellings weave important background unobtrusively into the narrative." Booklist.

Landmann, Bimba

★ The **incredible** voyage of Ulysses. Bimba Landmann. J. Paul Getty Museum, 2010. 60 p.

Grades: 4 5 6 7 **398.2**
1. Voyages and travels 2. Adventurers 3. Monsters 4. Odysseus (Greek mythology) 5. Heroes and heroines, Greek 6. Adventure stories 7. Comics and Graphic novels 8. Mythology
ISBN 9781606060124

LC 2009932972

"With narrative restraint and illustrative power, Landmann's . . . retelling of Homer's Odyssey follows Ulysses as he battles frightening creatures and endures the treachery of the gods while sailing home to Ithaca. . . . The paintings, worked with swift, bold strokes, combine the solemn stiffness of Greek statuary with the prophetic sweep of William Blake's imaginings." Publishers Weekly.

Lester, Julius

★ **Uncle** Remus: the complete tales, with a new introduction. as told by Julius Lester; Illustrated by Jerry Pinkney. P. Fogelman, 1999. 686 p.

Grades: 4 5 6 7 **398.2**
1. Tricksters 2. Forest animals 3. Rabbits 4. Brer Rabbit 5. Foxes 6. Folklore
ISBN 0803724519

"This is a landmark collection. . . . Lester's retellings are sharp and flavorful and grounded in the here and now." Booklist.

Livo, Norma J.

Folk stories of the Hmong: peoples of Laos, Thailand, and Vietnam. [compiled by] Norma J. Livo, Dia Cha. Libraries Unlimited, 1991. xii, 135 p.

Grades: 8 9 10 11 12 Adult **398.2**
1. Hmong (Southeast Asian people) 2. Southeast Asia 3. Folklore
ISBN 0872878546

LC 91000370

Describes the culture of the Hmong people, and gathers some of their folk tales.

Marshall, James Vance, 1924-1992

Stories from the Billabong. James Vance Marshall; illustrated by Francis Firebrace. Frances Lincoln, 2009. 64 p.

Grades: 3 4 5 6 **398.2**
1. Animals 2. Australia 3. Mythology
ISBN 9781845077044

"With the help of Aboriginal storytellers who have collected the tales and myths of their people, Marshall has assembled 10 fascinating stories of the Dreamtime. . . . Each selection is beautifully told and is illustrated by a traditional artist who uses the distinctive symbols and colors of the Aboriginal people. . . . This is an engaging, colorful book that belongs in most libraries." School Library Journal.

Martin, Rafe, 1946-

The **world** before this one: a novel told in legend. Rafe Martin; with paper sculpture by Calvin Nicholls. Arthur A. Levine Books, 2002. x, 195 p.

Grades: 4 5 6 7 **398.2**
1. Seneca boys 2. Seneca Indians 3. Indians of North America 4. Boy orphans 5. Pariahs 6. Folklore
ISBN 0590379763

LC 2001023403

"Written in the style of a novel, this collection of 14 Seneca tales is presented through the retelling of one central story into which all of the others are artfully woven. . . . Martin offers sources for the tales along with an introductory note by Seneca Elder Peter Jemison. Each chapter includes a painstakingly detailed white paper sculpture of a character (often an animal) from one of the stories." School Library Journal.

McCaughrean, Geraldine

★ **Gilgamesh** the hero. retold by Geraldine McCaughrean; illustrated by David Parkins. Eerdmans Books for Young Readers, 2003. 95 p.

Grades: 5 6 7 8 **398.2**
1. Heroes and heroines 2. Immortality 3. Quests 4. Floods 5. Death 6. Sumer -- Rulers 7. Mesopotamia -- History -- To 330 B.C.E. 8. Epic poetry
ISBN 0802852629

LC 2003001086

A retelling, based on seventh-century B.C. Assyrian clay tablets, of the wanderings and adventures of the god king, Gilgamesh, who ruled in ancient Mesopotamia (now Iraq) in about 2700 B.C., and of his faithful companion, Enkidu.

"This is clearly a telling for our time, but one that honors its source. Parkins captures the epic's primitive power and universal emotions in rough, broadly rendered portraits." Horn Book.

★ **Hercules**. retold by Geraldine McCaughrean. Cricket Books, c2005. 142 p.: Heroes (Geraldine McCaughrean)
Grades: 5 6 7 8   **398.2**
  1. Heroes and heroines, Greek 2. Hercules (Roman mythology) 3. Strong men 4. Gods and goddesses, Greek 5. Punishment 6. Mythology
ISBN 0812627377

                             LC 2005004524
"This volume does a creditable job of making Hercules a dimensional character whose struggles against fate and the vindictiveness of the gods arouse readers' sympathy. . . . McCaughrean enlivens the familiar story with arresting imagery." School Library Journal.

★ **Odysseus**. retold by Geraldine McCaughrean. Cricket Books, c2004. 148 p.: Heroes (Geraldine McCaughrean)
Grades: 5 6 7 8   **398.2**
  1. Odysseus (Greek mythology) 2. Heroes and heroines, Greek 3. Adventure 4. Monsters 5. Voyages and travels 6. Mythology
ISBN 0812627210

                             LC 2004010734
"With mounting suspense, wild action, and simple, rhythmic prose, this dramatic retelling of Homer's classic makes a gripping read-aloud as well as an exciting introduction to the story." Booklist.

★ **Perseus**. retold by Geraldine McCaughrean. Carus Pub., c2005. 118 p.: Heroes (Geraldine McCaughrean)
Grades: 5 6 7 8   **398.2**
  1. Heroes and heroines, Greek 2. Oracles 3. Perseus (Greek mythology) 4. Medusa (Greek mythology) 5. Quests 6. Mythology
ISBN 0812627350

                             LC 2004020690
"This makes a thrilling read-aloud. . . . McCaughrean blends the colloquial and contemporary into the heroic quest." Booklist.

Mhlophe, Gcina

African tales. Gcina Mhlophe; [illustrations by] Rachel Griffin. Barefoot Books, 2009. 96 p.
Grades: 5 6 7 8   **398.2**
  1. Africa 2. Folklore
ISBN 9781846861185

                             LC 2008028042
A collection of folktales, each from a different region in Africa.

"Each of these eight tales is preceded by information and interesting facts about the country from which it originated. A basic map of Africa helps orient readers to the location of the various countries represented. Extensive source notes are appended. . . . There are many choices that could be read aloud or told using a call-and-response format. The book design . . . is a feast for the eyes. Griffin employs a collage technique using colored beads, sewn fabric, and textured papers, and incorporates them into shapes and faces of animals and humans. . . . This compilation contains a wealth of information and will enhance folklore collections." School Library Journal.

Monte, Richard

The **mermaid** of Warsaw: and other tales from Poland. retold by Richard Monte; illustrated by Paul Hess. Frances Lincoln Children's Books, 2011. 105 p.
Grades: 4 5 6 7   **398.2**
  1. Mythical creatures 2. Supernatural 3. Folklore
ISBN 9781847801647
Collects folklore from Poland, including the story of a mermaid kidnapped and brought to Warsaw, a miner who meets the guardian spirit of a mine, and an orphan who finds a mysterious golden coin.

"A gratifying and unusual collection of folktales from Poland. There are a number of good stock characters in these pages: beautiful princesses who get themselves into trouble, warty-nosed ogres, . . . buffoons who overstep themselves or commit one-too-many deadly sins. There are also talking trees, dark forests, miraculous springs and . . . monsters. . . . The tales are told . . . in an unwavering voice, with portent enough to keep an audience listening close, and Hess' artwork has the right spidery look and sinister atmosphere. . . . That the locales are ancient and real gives the whole collection added wallop." Kirkus.

Includes bibliographical references (pages 103-105).

Morpurgo, Michael

★ **Beowulf**. as told by Michael Morpurgo; illustrated by Michael Foreman. Candlewick Press, 2006. 92 p.
Grades: 5 6 7 8   **398.2**
  1. Heroes and heroines 2. Courage in men 3. Strong men 4. Warriors 5. Monsters
ISBN 0763632066

                             LC 2006046289
A retelling in prose of the Anglo-Saxon epic about the heroic efforts of Beowulf, son of Edgetheow, to save the people of Heorot Hall from the terrible monster, Grendel.

"Morpurgo retells the classic story of the courageous young warrior . . . who used his brute strength to save the neighboring Danes, then his own kinsmen, by slaying two horrible monsters, a sea serpent, and a massive dragon. . . . Many attractive full-page watercolor and pastel paintings illustrate important action-filled scenes. . . . This is a fine retelling." School Library Journal.

★ **Sir** Gawain and the Green Knight. as told by Michael Morpurgo; illustrated by Michael Foreman. Candlewick Press, 2004. 114 p.
Grades: 5 6 7 8   **398.2**
  1. Arthur, King. 2. Gawain (Legendary character) 3. Knights and knighthood 4. Honor in men 5. Temptation 6. Courage 7. Arthurian legends
ISBN 0763625191

                             LC 2003065527
The quest of Sir Gawain for the Green Knight teaches him a lesson in pride, humility, and honor.

"Morpurgo's sprightly writing brings out all the humor as well as the horror of the original tale, and Foreman's profuse, evocative watercolor-and-pastel illustrations highlight the drama in each scene." School Library Journal.

Napoli, Donna Jo, 1948-

★ **Tales** from the Arabian nights: stories of adventure, magic, love, and betrayal. by Donna Jo Napoli; illustrated by Christina Balit. National Geographic Partners, 2016. 208 p.

Grades: 5 6 7 8   **398.2**

    1. Fairy tales 2. Illustrated books 3. Folklore

ISBN 9781426325403

LC 2016016718

A collection of tales told by Scheherazade to amuse the cruel sultan and stop him from executing her as he had his other daily wives.

"A brilliant tapestry woven not of yarn but of stories, both fresh and faithful to its historical roots." Kirkus.

★ **Treasury** of Greek mythology: classic stories of gods, goddesses, heroes & monsters. by Donna Jo Napoli; illustrated by Christina Balit. National Geographic Society, 2011. 192 p.

Grades: 5 6 7 8   **398.2**

    1. Gods and goddesses, Greek 2. Heroes and heroines, Greek 3. Mythology

ISBN 9781426308444

LC 2011024327

Combines lyrical retellings of classic Greek tales by an award-winning writer with sumptuously detailed illustrations in an introduction to mythology that is complemented by informative sidebars containing character profiles, historical insights, cultural facts and more.

"Napoli presents 25 tales introducing the major players of the Greek pantheon along with an assortment of celebrated heroes and mortals. . . . At once eloquent and elemental, these lyrically written portraits deftly detail each character's origins, realm of power, and legendary story lines. Filled with sensual imagery, the language is poetic, yet balanced by amusing asides and wry observations that add a contemporary, almost conversational accessibility. . . . Stunning stylized paintings featuring luminous colors, rich patterns, and star-infused motifs add depth and drama to the text. . . . Interesting sidebars appear throughout, providing historical, scientific, and cultural information." School Library Journal.

Includes bibliographical references and index.

Treasury of Norse mythology: stories of intrigue, trickery, love, and revenge. by Donna Jo Napoli; illustrated by Christina Balit. National Geographic, 2015. 192 p.

Grades: 5 6 7 8   **398.2**

    1. Gods and goddesses, Norse 2. Mythology

ISBN 9781426320996

LC 2015013321

Classic stories and dazzling illustrations of gods, goddesses, heroes and monsters come to life in a stunning tableau of Norse myths, including those of the thunder god Thor, the one-eyed god and Allfather Odin, and the trickster god Loki. The lyrical storytelling of award-winning author Donna Jo Napoli dramatizes the timeless tales of ancient Scandinavia. This book is the third in the trilogy that includes the popular National Geographic Treasury of Greek Mythology and National Geographic Treasury of Egyptian Mythology. Provided by publisher.

"Buy it, and if space is an issue, weed to make it fit." School Library Journal.

Includes bibliographical references and index.

Oberman, Sheldon

    Solomon and the ant: and other Jewish folktales. Boyds Mills, 2006. 165 p.

Grades: 5 6 7 8   **398.2**

    1. Jewish way of life 2. Jews 3. Folklore

ISBN 1590783077

"This collection of 43 traditional Jewish stories is authoritative as well as immensely entertaining. . . . The stories, from both Ashkenazi and Sephardic traditions, are arranged more or less chronologically— from biblical days through the talmudic period to more contemporary

times. There are legends, medieval fables, trickster tales, and more. . . . The stories, wonderful for storytelling and sharing, are accessible even to listeners younger than the target audience, and the notes and commentary will provide older children with context and history." Booklist.

Ollhoff, Jim, 1959-

    Indian mythology. Jim Ollhoff. ABDO Pub., c2011. 32 p.: World of mythology

Grades: 5 6 7 8   **398.2**

    1. Mythology, Indic -- History and criticism 2. Hinduism 3. India -- Religion. 4. India 5. Mythology

ISBN 9781617147227

LC 2010041628

"Ollhoff writes in a clear and engaging fashion, presenting complex issues in a way that will be easy for youngsters to grasp. . . . The photographs and reproductions of art tie directly to the [text]." School Library Journal.

Orr, Tamra

    The **monsters** of Hercules. Tamra Orr. Mitchell Lane Publishers, c2011. 48 p.: Monsters in myth

Grades: 4 5 6 7   **398.2**

    1. Heracles (Greek mythology) 2. Heroes and heroines, Greek 3. Monsters 4. Gods and goddesses, Greek 5. Hercules (Roman mythology) 6. Mythology

ISBN 9781584159278

LC 2010028764

"This book about the monsters of Hercules is thorough and respectful of a number of ancient and modern sources and [bends] over backward to navigate often contradictory, interlinked legends. . . . A number of paintings and photos break up the otherwise text-heavy pages, and copious chapter notes and reading suggestions conclude. This is by no means entry-level stuff, but for kids handy with the basics and ready to delve deeper, [this book] will be of great use." Booklist.

Includes bibliographical references (p. 45-47) and index.

    The **sirens**. by Tamra Orr. Mitchell Lane Publishers, c2011. 48 p.: Monsters in myth

Grades: 4 5 6 7   **398.2**

    1. Sirens (Mythology) 2. Monsters 3. Mythology

ISBN 9781584159308

LC 2010026965

"This book is thorough and respectful of a number of ancient and modern sources and [bends] over backward to navigate often contradictory, interlinked legends. . . . A number of paintings and photos break up the otherwise text-heavy pages, and copious chapter notes and reading suggestions conclude. This is by no means entry-level stuff, but for kids handy with the basics and ready to delve deeper, [this book] will be of great use." Booklist.

Includes bibliographical references and index.

Otfinoski, Steven

    All in the family: a look-it-up guide to the in-laws, outlaws, and offspring of mythology. Steven Otfinoski. F. Watts, 2009. 128 p. : Mythlopedia

Grades: 4 5 6 7   **398.2**

    1. Family relationships 2. Gods and goddesses, Greek 3. Heroes and heroines, Greek 4. Mythology

ISBN 9781606310571

LC 2009020999

A thoroughly new series where the superstars of Greek myth meet the modern age—complete with profiles, headshots, and family trees;

fascinating sidebars; and irreverent surprises, this series is for readers who love action, deception, romance, power struggles, and more!

"Jam-packed with trivia, brief profiles, god and goddess relationships, stories, Top 10 Things to Know About Me facts, and entertaining illustrations, this title explores 20 heroes and mortals of classic Greek mythology. The selections include the well-known Achilles, Heracles, Odysseus, and Pandora and the more obscure Meleager, Orion, Atalanta, and Bellerophon; each one is given lively treatment. . . . The lighthearted style and humorous collage and cartoon illustrations may draw even the most reluctant of readers." School Library Journal.

Philip, Neil

Celtic fairy tales. retold with an introduction by Neil Philip; illustrated by Isabelle Brent. Viking, 1999. 137 p.

Grades: 4 5 6 7   **398.2**
1. Celts 2. Fairy tales 3. Folklore
ISBN 9780670883875

               LC 98050081
An illustrated collection of twenty stories from many Celtic regions.

"There's a mix of the almost familiar and nicely exotic in this collection, which is lavishly illustrated with a glowing full-page painting for each tale and Celtic motifs on every page." Booklist.

Pyle, Howard, 1853-1911

The **merry** adventures of Robin Hood. Howard Pyle; illustrated by Scott McKowen. Sterling Pub., 2004. viii, 335 p.

Grades: 8 9 10 11 12   **398.2**
1. Robin Hood (Legendary character)
ISBN 1402714564

            LC 2004016213
Recounts the legend of Robin Hood, who plundered the king's purse and poached his deer and whose generosity endeared him to the poor.

Raven, Nicky

Beowulf: a tale of blood, heat, and ashes. retold by Nicky Raven; illustrated by John Howe. Candlewick Press, 2007. 72 p.

Grades: 7 8 9 10 11 12   **398.2**
1. Warriors 2. Heroes and heroines, Norse 3. Northmen and Northwomen 4. Monsters 5. Battles 6. Epic poetry
ISBN 0763636479

            LC 2007027094
A modern, illustrated retelling of the Anglo-Saxon epic about the heroic efforts of Beowulf, son of Ecgtheow, to save the people of Heorot Hall from the terrible monster, Grendel.

"This is a gripping rendition of the Anglo-Saxon epic. . . . Raven takes some liberties that add welcome nuance to the story. . . . Howe's artwork . . . is . . . spectacular, easily capturing the heroic grandeur and horrific gruesomeness of the tale." Booklist.

Rumford, James, 1948-

★ **Beowulf**, a hero's tale retold. by James Rumford. Houghton Mifflin Company, 2007. 48 p.

Grades: 4 5 6 7   **398.2**
1. Dragons 2. Anglo-Saxons 3. Monsters 4. England 5. Epic poetry
ISBN 9780618756377

            LC 2006026084
A simplified and illustrated retelling of the exploits of the Anglo-Saxon warrior, Beowulf, and how he came to defeat the monster Grendel, Grendel's mother, and a dragon that threatened the kingdom.

"Superb on all counts—from the elegant bookmaking to the vigorous, evocative prose . . . to the pen-and-ink and watercolor illustrations that strikingly recall the work of Edmund Dulac." Horn Book.

Rylant, Cynthia

The **beautiful** stories of life: six Greek myths, retold. Cynthia Rylant; illustrations by Carson Ellis. Harcourt, c2009. 71 p.

Grades: 5 6 7 8   **398.2**
1. Gods and goddesses, Greek 2. Heroes and heroines, Greek 3. Ancient Greece 4. Mythology
ISBN 9780152061845

            LC 2007034808
Retells the myths about Pandora, Persephone, Orpheus, Pygmalion, Narcissus, and Psyche.

"Rylant retells the stories of Pandora, Persephone, Orpheus, Pygmalion, Narcissus, and Psyche in this trim, handsome book. Written in a modern style with an old-fashioned feel, the selections sit well with other titles in the genre. . . . Accompanied by full-page black-and-white illustrations and sprinkled with decorations, the whole package is nicely done." School Library Journal.

Shelby, Anne

The **adventures** of Molly Whuppie and other Appalachian folktales. Anne Shelby; illustrations by Paula McArdle. The University of North Carolina Press, 2007. 88 p.

Grades: 4 5 6 7   **398.2**
1. Appalachian Region -- Social life and customs. 2. Folklore
ISBN 9780807831632

            LC 2007013789
Retells fourteen folktales that star the famous Appalachian character of Molly Whuppie.

"Shelby has captured the language of Appalachia. . . . Her adaptations are true to the traditional folktales. . . . Young readers and listeners will make these stories their own and enjoy retelling them." School Library Journal.

Includes bibliographical references.

Smith, Charles R.

The **mighty** 12: superheroes of Greek myth. by Charles R. Smith, Jr.; illustrated by P. Craig Russell. Little, Brown, 2008. 48 p.

Grades: 5 6 7 8   **398.2**
1. Gods and goddesses, Greek 2. Gods and goddesses 3. Heroes and heroines, Greek 4. Heroes and heroines 5. Comics and Graphic novels 6. Mythology
ISBN 9780316010436

            LC 2007048729
Introduces readers to the ancient gods and goddesses of Olympus through an examination of their incredible skills and superhero strength, enhanced with comic book-style illustrations and poetic verse.

"Future students of Homer get a handy checklist of musclebound Greek gods in this combo of mythology, comics and loose rhyme. . . . Smith and Russell make the pairing of classical material and a comics-like format look completely natural, with a gee-why-didn't-we-think-of-that simplicity." Publishers Weekly.

Includes bibliographical references (p. 48).

Tchana, Katrin

Changing Woman and her sisters. by Katrin Tchana; illustrated by Trina Schart Hyman. Holiday House, 2006. 80 p.

Grades: 5 6 7 8   **398.2**
1. Gods and goddesses 2. Women 3. Empowerment 4.

Supernatural 5. Mythology
ISBN 0823419991

LC 2005052504

An illustrated collection of traditional tales which feature goddesses from different cultures, including Navajo, Mayan, and Fon. Notes explain each goddess's place in her culture, the reason for the book, and how the illustrations were developed.

"This large, handsome volume assembles well-chosen, well-told stories. . . . Hyman . . . contributed distinctive portrayals of the goddesses using a technique that melded photographs and found materials into full-page ink and acrylic paintings." Booklist.

Includes bibliographical references.

Tingle, Tim
Spirits dark and light: supernatural tales from the five civilized tribes. Tim Tingle. August House, 2006. 160 p.

Grades: 6 7 8 9 **398.2**
1. Spirits 2. Shapeshifters 3. Witches 4. Talking animals 5. Healers 6. Folklore
ISBN 0874837782

LC 2006042709

"Choctaw storyteller Tingle tells 25 deliciously scary tales collected from the five major Native American tribes of the southeastern U.S.the Cherokee, Chickasaw, Choctaw, Creek, and Seminole. . . . For each tribe, Tingle begins with background on history, culture, and folklore. The language is clear and informal, and the dialogue is immediate." Booklist.

Turnbull, Ann
★ **Greek** myths: retold by Ann Turnbull. Ann Turnbull; illustrated by Sarah Young. Candlewick Press, 2011. 165 p .

Grades: 5 6 7 8 9 10 **398.2**
1. Gods and goddesses, Greek 2. Mythology
ISBN 9780763651114

LC 2010039178

"Sixteen Greek myths . . . are retold here with stylistic grace well matched to beautiful visual presentation. . . . Turnbull narrates with . . . vibrancy. . . . Sarah Young's mixed-media artwork—regal, yet sensuous compositions in richly textured earthtones touch[ed] with gold—is sufficiently representational to assist younger readers with context clues, and sufficiently elegant and sophisticated to satisfy seasoned readers." Bulletin of the Center for Children's Books.

Yep, Laurence, 1948-
The **rainbow** people. Laurence Yep; illustrated by David Wiesner. Harper & Row, c1989 194 p.

Grades: 4 5 6 7 **398.2**
1. Tricksters 2. Virtues 3. Vices 4. Love 5. Folklore
ISBN 0060267607

LC 88021203

Twenty Chinese folk tales passed on by word of mouth for generations, as told by some oldtimers newly settled in the United States.

"Twenty Chinese folktales, selected and retold by Yep from those collected in the 1930s in the Oakland Chinatown as part of a WPA project. . . . The tales, while drawn from the depicting Chinese culture, present a variety of familiar motifs and types: wizards and saints, shape changing and magical objects, pourquoi tales and lessons. An Afterword provides suggestions for further reading on Chinese folktales. This is an excellent introduction to Chinese and Chinese-American folklore." School Library Journal.

Includes bibliographical references (p. 194).

Yolen, Jane
Mightier than the sword: world folktales for strong boys. Jane Yolen; with illustrations by Raul Colon. Harcourt, 2003. 112 p.

Grades: 4 5 6 7 **398.2**
1. Boys 2. Men 3. Teenage boys 4. Heroes and heroines 5. Strength and weakness 6. Folklore
ISBN 0152163913

LC 2002009886

A collection of fourteen folktales from around the world which demonstrate the triumph of brains over brawn.

"Yolen's versions of these stories are lively, expressively written, ready for reading aloud or telling, and illustrative of her point." School Library Journal.

398.2089 Ethnic and national groups

Houston, James, 1921-2005
James Houston's treasury of Inuit legends. Harcourt, c2006. 268 p.

Grades: 5 6 7 8 **398.2089**
1. Inuit -- Social life and customs 2. Inuit 3. Arctic peoples 4. Inuit mythology 5. Arctic regions 6. Canada 7. Folklore
ISBN 9780152059248

"This collection includes four previously published stories: Tiktaliktak (1965), The White Archer (1967), Akavak (1968), and Wolf Run (1971). Noted artist Houston lived among the Inuit people for fourteen years and brought their culture to life through his books and artwork." Horn Book Guide.

398.20943 Folk literature—Germany

Gaiman, Neil
Hansel & Gretel. Neil Gaiman, Lorenzo Mattotti. Toon Books, [2014] 48 p.

Grades: 2 3 4 5 6 **398.20943**
1. Abandoned children 2. Witches 3. Brothers and sisters 4. Fairy tales 5. Illustrated books 6. Folklore
ISBN 9781935179658

Two abandoned children come upon a gingerbread cottage inhabited by a cruel witch who wants to eat them.

"Mattotti contributes elegant b&w ink spreads that alternate with spreads of text. His artistry flows from the movement of his brush and the play of light and shadow. . . . Gaiman makes the story's horrors feel very real and very human, and Mattotti's artwork is genuinely chilling." Publishers Weekly.

398.21 Tales and lore of paranatural beings of human and semihuman form

Curran, Robert
The **zombie** handbook. Robert Curran. Barron's, 2011. 80 p.

Grades: 6 7 8 9 **398.21**
1. Zombies
ISBN 9780764164095

LC bl2011014472

Offers tips and advice about how to survive a zombie attack, how to avoid becoming a zombie, and what to do if confronted by the living dead.

"This compact book does a good job of introducing zombies: what they are, how they look, where you find them. . . . The text is highly readable, the interspersed artwork is creepy and plentiful." Booklist.

Hearne, Betsy Gould

Beauties and beasts. [collected] by Betsy Hearne; illustrated by Joanne Caroselli. Oryx Press, 1993. xi, 179 p.: The Oryx multicultural folktale series

Grades: Adult   **398.21**
    1. Cupid and Psyche (Tale) 2. Beauty and the beast(Tale) 3. Fairy tales 4. Folklore 5. Mythology
    ISBN 9780897747295

                  LC 93000016
Presents several versions of "Beauty and the Beast" and "Cupid and Psyche," and provides several tales that reverse traditional gender roles. Includes commentary on each tale, activities, bibliographies, and a list of sources.

San Souci, Robert D.

★ **Cut** from the same cloth: American women of myth, legend, and tall tale. collected and told by Robert D. San Souci; illustrated by Brian Pinkney; introduction by Jane Yolen. Philomel Books, 1993. xvi, 140 p.

Grades: 4 5 6 7   **398.21**
    1. Women 2. Heroes and heroines, American 3. Tall tales 4. Folklore
    ISBN 9780399219870

                  LC   92005233
A collection of twenty stories about legendary American women, drawing from folktales, popular stories, and ballads.

398.22 Tales and lore of persons without paranormal powers

DiPrimio, Pete

The **sphinx**. Pete DiPrimio. Mitchell Lane Publishers, c2011. 48 p.: Monsters in myth

Grades: 4 5 6 7   **398.22**
    1. Sphinxes 2. Monsters 3. Mythical creatures 4. Mythology
    ISBN 9781584159315

                  LC 2010006560
"This book is thorough and respectful of a number of ancient and modern sources and [bends] over backward to navigate often contradictory, interlinked legends. . . . A number of paintings and photos break up the otherwise text-heavy pages, and copious chapter notes and reading suggestions conclude. This is by no means entry-level stuff, but for kids handy with the basics and ready to delve deeper, [this book] will be of great use." Booklist.

Includes bibliographical references and index.

Gavin, Jamila

Tales from India. Jamila Gavin; illustrated by Amanda Hall. Candlewick Press, 2011. vii, 88 p.

Grades: 5 6 7 8   **398.22**
    1. India 2. Mythology 3. Folklore
    ISBN 9780763655648

                  LC   2010047651

"Gavin, . . . presents 10 classic Hindu stories, accompanied by Hall's lush and elegant gouache illustrations. . . . . Readers should be drawn toward the valor, action, and dramatic transformations in these powerful tales." Publishers Weekly.

Horowitz, Anthony, 1955-

Heroes and villains. Anthony Horowitz; illustrated by Thomas Yeates. Kingfisher: c2011. 165 p.: Legends (Anthony Horowitz)

Grades: 6 7 8   **398.22**
    1. Heroes and heroines 2. Villains 3. Knights and knighthood 4. Mythical creatures 5. Mythology
    ISBN 9780753465462
"Balancing the heroic and the macabre, these dryly humorous, sometimes gory retellings hold particular appeal for reluctant readers. The conversational language also lends itself well to reading aloud. Black-and-white illustrations provide occasional breaks in the text while adding visual interest." Horn Book Guide.

Rapunzel and other magic fairy tales

Rapunzel and other magic fairy tales. selected and illustrated by Henriette Sauvant; translated by Anthea Bell. Trafalgar Square, 2008. 157 p.

Grades: 5 6 7 8   **398.22**
    1. Magic 2. Fairy tales 3. Illustrated books 4. Folklore
    ISBN 1405227028
"Sauvant has selected 14 tales of German, English, and French origin, many of them written down by the Grimm brothers. While most of them are familiar . . . others will be unknown to most readers. . . . The illustrations, which range in size from tiny fillers to full-page and double-page pictures, appear to be painted in watercolor or acrylic on a textured surface. While some are painted in classic fairy-tale style, others are best described as surreal. . . . The sophistication of both stories and artwork makes this collection most suitable for older readers." School Library Journal.

398.24 Tales and lore of plants and animals

Baynes, Pauline

Questionable creatures: a bestiary. Pauline Baynes. William B. Eerdmans Pub., 2006. 47, 1 p.

Grades: 4 5 6 7   **398.24**
    1. Animals 2. Mythical creatures 3. Bestiaries
    ISBN 080285284X

                  LC 2005033658
A modern rendition of a medieval bestiary provides illustrations of animals, both real and mythical, along with common myths associated with them.

"Baynes introduces readers to the creatures and myths found in medieval bestiaries and explains how the books were made and how they were viewed by the general public. The rest of the volume details the commonly held beliefs that both peasants and scholars embraced about specific animals. . . . Baynes's detailed gouache and colored-pencil illustrations . . . are done in the style of medieval illuminations. . . . The artist shows great respect for the early bestiary creators while also giving the stories relevance for modern readers." School Library Journal.

Includes bibliographical references (p. [48]).

Hausman, Gerald

Horses of myth. by Gerald and Loretta Hausman; illustrated by Robert Florczak. Dutton Children's Books, 2004. 100 p.

Grades: 4 5 6 7   **398.24**

1. Horses 2. Folklore
ISBN 0525469648

LC 2002040809

"These five tales each feature a different type of horse, remarkable for both its individuality and the qualities representative of its breed. . . . Florczak's illustrations adapt characteristics appropriate to the locations and time periods of each selection's origins. . . . This is an attractive volume, useful to teachers and librarians for read-alouds and of interest to horse-loving youngsters." School Library Journal.

Laskow, Sarah

The **very** short, entirely true history of unicorns. by Sarah Laskow; illustrated by Sam Beck. Penguin Workshop, 2019 88 p.

Grades: 4 5 6 7   **398.24**

1. Unicorns 2. Mythology, folklore, and legends
ISBN 9781524792732

LC bl2019023631

A look at unicorns throughout history discusses the mythical creature's role in mythology, science, and popular culture.

"If the mythical animals' enduring resonance proves anything, Laskow suggests, unicorns are in no danger of leaving the realms of collective imagination any time soon." Publishers Weekly

Includes bibliographical references.

398.2454 Legendary animals

Aronson, Marc

The **griffin** and the dinosaur: how Adrienne Mayor discovered a fascinating link between myth and science. Marc Aronson with Adrienne Mayor; illustrated by Chris Muller. National Geographic, 2014. 48 p.

Grades: 5 6 7 8   **398.2454**

1. Griffins 2. Fossils 3. Archaeology 4. Mythology, Scythian 5. Mythology
ISBN 9781426311086

Traces the research scientist co-author's explorations in Greece and the Gobi Desert for the origins of the mythical griffin, relating the story of the ancient Scythians and the griffins that were said to have guarded their treasure.

398.25 Ghost stories

San Souci, Robert D.

A **terrifying** taste of short & shivery: thirty creepy tales. retold by Robert D. San Souci; illustrated by Lenny Wooden. Delacorte Press, 1998. 159 p.

Grades: 4 5 6 7   **398.25**

1. Ghosts 2. Supernatural 3. Horror 4. Ghost stories
ISBN 0385326351

A collection of scary traditional tales from all over the world, including Apparitions from Germany, The Hundreth Skull from Ohio, and The Ogre's Arm from Japan.

"Drawing on urban legends, myths, folktales, and ghost stories from around the world and across time, the reteller serves up 30 tales of the supernatural that range from eerie to downright scary. . . . Suspenseful, accessible, and energetic, the tales are uniformly brief and gripping." School Library Journal.

Schwartz, Alvin, 1927-1992

★ **Scary** stories to tell in the dark. collected by Alvin Schwartz; drawings by Stephen Gammell J.B. Lippincott, 1981. 111 p.

Grades: 4 5 6   **398.25**

1. Horror 2. Folk songs 3. Musical scores 4. Folklore
ISBN 9780062682826

LC 80008728

Yarns about ghosts and witches, "jump" stories, scary songs, and modern-day scary tales. Includes song lyrics and music.

398.28 Tales and lore of other topics

Horowitz, Anthony, 1955-

Death and the underworld. Anthony Horowitz; illustrated by Thomas Yeates. Kingfisher, c2011. 133 p.: Legends (Anthony Horowitz)

Grades: 6 7 8   **398.28**

1. Hell 2. Life after death 3. Death 4. Mythical creatures 5. Mythology
ISBN 9780753465424

"Balancing the heroic and the macabre, these dryly humorous, sometimes gory retellings hold particular appeal for reluctant readers. The conversational language also lends itself well to reading aloud. Black-and-white illustrations provide occasional breaks in the text while adding visual interest." Horn Book Guide.

398.45 Paranormal beings of human and semihuman form

Kallen, Stuart A., 1955-

The **sphinx**: part of the Monsters and mythical creatures series. Stuart A. Kallen. ReferencePoint Press, 2012. 80 p.

Grades: 4 5 6 7 8   **398.45**

1. Sphinxes (Mythology) 2. Mythology
ISBN 9781601522221

LC 2011026636

Traces the history of the sphinx, an ancient mythological half-human, half-lion figure usually associated with ancient Egypt, but one whose aura continues to fascinate in modern times.

"Children will get a well-rounded look at the featured subjects and how they have evolved into the creatures that still fascinate many today." School Library Journal.

Includes bibliographical references and index.

400 LANGUAGE

401 Philosophy and theory

Lunge-Larsen, Lise

★ **Gifts** from the gods: ancient words & wisdom from Greek and Roman mythology. written by Lise Lunge-Larsen; illustrated by Gareth Hinds. Houghton Mifflin Harcourt/Childrens, 2011. 90 p.

Grades: 4 5 6 7 **401**
1. Vocabulary 2. Etymology 3. Mythology
ISBN 9780547152295

LC 2010031635

"Lunge-Larsen and Hinds explain what words like echo, grace, hypnotize, and janitor have in common, tracing the origins of common words and expressions to Greek and Roman myths. . . . Lunge-Larsen provides additional context, including dictionary definitions, and quotes from children's literature. Hinds incorporates graphic novel style elements into his dynamic illustrations, including dialogue balloons and filmic perspectives. A treat for myth lovers and language lovers alike, this smart and well-executed compilation should provide readers with a deeper understanding of the ways in which language evolves and of the surprising symbolism behind certain words." Publishers Weekly.

411 Writing systems of standard forms of languages

Donoughue, Carol
The **story** of writing. Carol Donoughue. Firefly Books, c2007. 48 p.
Grades: 4 5 6 7 **411**
1. Writing -- History 2. Signs and symbols -- History 3. Writing materials and instruments -- History 4. Writing -- Social aspects
ISBN 1554073065

LC bl2007022583

Provides the story of how writing was invented, how it developed over the centuries, how it has changed people's lives over time, and what it means in today's cultures.

"This is an introduction to the history of the Roman alphabet. . . . Beginning sections about early civilizations' alphabets, starting with Sumerian cuniforms, include a you-are-there narrative. . . . Later spreads cover European illuminated manuscripts and the development of printing technology. A final section [covers] Chinese characters. . . . Numerous carefully chosen color photos of artifacts . . . greatly enhance the book's appeal." Booklist.

Includes bibliographical references (p. 48) and index.

418 Standard usage (Prescriptive linguistics)

Beers, G. Kylene, 1957-
Disrupting thinking: why how we read matters. Kylene Beers & Robert E. Probst. Scholastic Inc., 2017 174 p.
Grades: Professional **418**
1. Reading 2. Critical thinking -- Study and teaching 3. Teaching -- Aids and devices
ISBN 9781338132908

LC bl2018086354

A guide for teachers and administrators in changing the way they teach students to become thoughtful, skillful, attentive, and responsive readers.

Blaz, Deborah
Differentiated instruction: a guide for world language teachers. Deborah Blaz. Routledge, 2016. vii, 192 p.
Grades: Professional **418**
1. Individualized instruction 2. Languages, Modern -- Study and teaching
ISBN 9781138906181

LC 2015036077

In this new edition of a bestseller, author Deborah Blaz helps teachers differentiate lessons for their world language students based on their learning styles, interests, prior knowledge, and comfort zones. This practical book uses brain-based teaching strategies to help students of all ability levels thrive in a rigorous differentiated learning environment.?

419 Sign languages

Warner, Penny
Signing fun: American Sign Language vocabulary, phrases, games & activities. Penny Warner; illustrations by Paula Gray. Clerc Books/Gallaudet University Press, 2006. ix, 225 p.
Grades: 4 5 6 7 8 **419**
1. American Sign Language 2. American Sign Language -- Vocabulary 3. American Sign Language
ISBN 9781563682926

LC 2006041269

Offers over four-hundred useful signs on a variety of topics and includes practice sentences, games and activites, use of numbers, and information on communicating with deaf people.

420.9 English language—History

Dubosarsky, Ursula, 1961-
The **word** snoop. Ursula Dubosarsky; illustrated by Tohby Riddle. Dial Books, 2009. 246 p.
Grades: 5 6 7 8 **420.9**
1. English language -- History 2. Language and languages -- Origin
ISBN 9780803734067

LC 2009008306

A tour of the English language from the beginning of the alphabet in 4000 BC to modern text messaging and emoticons.

"Short chapters, clear explanations, and humorous examples bring the subject to life, while word puzzles and coded messages at the end of each section invite reader participation. The attractive design adds to the appeal." Booklist.

422 Etymology of standard English

Hitchings, Henry, 1974-
The **secret** life of words: how English became English. Henry Hitchings. John Murray, 2008. 448 p.
Grades: 8 9 10 11 12 Adult **422**
1. Lexicography -- History 2. Etymology 3. Language and culture 4. Communication 5. Language and languages
ISBN 9780374254100

LC 2008026055

A wide-ranging history of English language and vocabulary reveals hidden etymologies to reveal how English has absorbed words from hundreds of other languages and reflects key social changes.

423 Dictionaries of standard English

Brewer, Ebenezer Cobham, 1810-1897
Brewer's dictionary of phrase & fable. edited by Susie Dent. Brewer's, c2012. xxii, 1480 p.

Grades: 6 7 8 9 10 11 12 Adult **423**
1. Allusions 2. English language 3. Literature 4. Mythology
ISBN 0550107649

LC 2012464049

Provides definitions of typical phrases and words and explains their historical origins.

Corbeil, Jean-Claude

Merriam-Webster's visual dictionary. under the direction of Jean-Claude Corbeil. Merriam-Webster, Incorporated, 2012. 1112 p.
Grades: 6 7 8 9 10 11 12 Adult **423**
1. Picture dictionaries, English
ISBN 0877791511

LC 2013498156

25,000 terms and their definitions with 8,000 full-color illustrations of a wide variety of objects from all aspects of life.

Merriam-Webster, Inc

★ **Merriam-Webster's** intermediate dictionary. Merriam-Webster. Merriam-Webster, Incorporated, 2016 1008 p.
Grades: 5 6 7 8 **423**
1. English language
ISBN 9780877796978

LC 2016299963

An updated edition of a best-selling reference for grades 6-8, ages 11-14, features nearly 70,000 entries and includes nearly 200 newly revised words and meanings across a variety of fields including technology, social media, science, health and popular culture; 23,000 usage examples; over 1,000 carefully drawn illustrations to clarify and expand understanding; and abundant word history and synonym paragraphs. This great study aid for students helps them build vocabulary and engage with more complex text. New words added include cloud computing, derecho, selfie and tweet.

Merriam-Webster's school thesaurus.. Merriam-Webster Merriam-Webster, Incorporated, 2017 16, 1007 p.
Grades: 9 10 11 **423**
1. English language -- Synonyms and antonyms
ISBN 9780877793656

LC 2016043885

Provides more than 154,000 alphabetically-arranged synonyms and antonyms.

Terban, Marvin

Scholastic dictionary of idioms. Marvin Terban. Scholastic Reference, [2006], c1996. 298 p.
Grades: 4 5 6 7 **423**
1. English language -- Idioms 2. English language -- Terms and phrases 3. Figures of speech
ISBN 9780439770835

LC bl2006015172

An alphabetical listing of common figures of speech, along with their definitions and origins.

★ **Scholastic** dictionary of spelling. Marvin Terban. Scholastic Reference, [2006], c1998. 272 p.
Grades: 4 5 6 **423**
1. English language -- Orthography and spelling 2. English language -- Spelling 3. Spellers
ISBN 9780439764216

LC bl2006015142

In addition to the more than 15,000 words provided, an updated illustrated reference tool for middle readers offers helpful spelling tricks and tips, rules for spelling, a list of commonly misspelled words, and more.

425.55 English language—Pronouns

Bongiovanni, Archie

A **quick** & easy guide to they/them pronouns. Archie Bongiovanni and Tristan Jimerson. Limerence Press, 2018. 60 p.
Grades: 7 8 9 10 11 12 Adult **425.55**
1. Gender expression 2. Gender identity 3. Gender-nonconforming people 4. Gender nonconformity 5. Comics and Graphic novels
ISBN 9781620104996

A quick, easy and important educational comic guide to using gender-neutral pronouns.

"In addition to supplying best practices for allies, situational examples illustrate what its like to be misgendered and how that feels to someone who identifies as nonbinary." Library Journal.

428 Standard English usage (Prescriptive linguistics)

Atwell, Nancie

In the middle: a lifetime of learning about writing, reading, and adolescents. Nancie Atwell. Heinemann, 2015. x, 629 p.
Grades: Professional **428**
1. Language arts (Secondary) 2. English language -- Study and teaching (Secondary) 3. English language -- Composition and exercises
ISBN 9780325028132

LC 2014026845

Just as the second edition documented Nancie Atwell's evolution from 1987, this book shows how she continues to shape and refine her teaching, based on her perceptions of what students need and her growing knowledge of literature and the craft of writing. As Nancie describes it, 'The third edition of In the Middle is everything I've learned over the past three decades that makes writing-reading workshop the only logical way to teach English.'

Bernadowski, Carianne

Teaching literacy skills to adolescents using Coretta Scott King Award winners. Carianne Bernadowski. Libraries Unlimited, c2009. xix, 136 p.
Grades: Professional **428**
1. Language arts (Secondary) 2. Young adult literature, American -- Study and teaching (Secondary) 3. African Americans in literature -- Study and teaching (Secondary) 4. African American teenagers -- Books and reading 5. African American teenagers -- Education
ISBN 9781586833374

LC 2009015279

This volume offers ready-made, standards-based, academically sound lessons and activities based on Coretta Scott King Award winning books.

"This book contains information to help the classroom teacher and library media specialist develop a program around the Coretta Scott King books. This book would be a great professional resource, and a must have for those educators that teach adolescents." Library Media Connection

Includes bibliographical references and indexes.

Burke, Jim, 1961-

The **English** teacher's companion: a completely new guide to classroom, curriculum, and the profession. Jim Burke. Heinemann, 2013 xvi, 373 p.

Grades: Professional   **428**

1. English philology -- Study and teaching
ISBN 9780325028408

LC 2012033297

The fourth edition of this text for pre-service and in-service English teachers is founded on the Common Core State Standards and contains new material on how to help struggling and special needs students and ELLs. Material on technology is integrated throughout the curriculum rather than confined to a separate chapter.

Ferlazzo, Larry

The **ELL** teacher's toolbox: hundreds of practical ideas to support your students. Larry Ferlazzo and Katie Hull Sypnieski. Jossey-Bass, 2018 xxxi, 512 p.

Grades: Professional   **428**

1. English as a second language
ISBN 9781119364962

LC 2017057348

The ELL Teacher's Toolbox is a practical, valuable resource to be used by teachers of English Language Learners, in teacher education credential programs, and by staff development professionals and coaches. It provides hundreds of innovative and research-based instructional strategies you can use to support all levels of English Language Learners.?

The **ESL/ELL** teacher's survival guide: ready-to-use strategies, tools, and activities for teaching English language learners of all levels. Larry Ferlazzo, Katie Hull-Sypnieski. Jossey-Bass, c2012. xiv, 322 p.

Grades: Professional   **428**

1. English as a second language
ISBN 9781118095676

LC 2012011534

A much-needed resource for teaching English to all learners. The number of English language learners in U.S. schools is projected to grow to twenty-five percent by 2025. Most teachers have English learners in their classrooms, from kindergarten through college. The ESL/ELL Teacher's Survival Guide offers educators practical strategies for setting up an ESL-friendly classroom, motivating and interacting with students, communicating with parents of English learners, and navigating the challenges inherent inteaching ESL students. Provides research-based instructional techniques which have proven effective with English learners at all proficiency levels Offers thematic units complete with reproducible forms and worksheets, sample lesson plans, and sample student assignments The book's ESL lessons connect to core standards and technology applications This hands-on resource will give all teachers at all levels the information they need to be effective ESL instructors. Provided by publisher.

428.1 Vocabulary—English language—Usage (Applied linguistics)

Hellweg, Paul

The **American** Heritage student thesaurus. Paul Hellweg, Joyce LeBaron, Susannah LeBaron. Houghton Mifflin Harcourt, 2016 vi, 378 p.

Grades: 7 8 9   **428.1**

1. English language -- Synonyms and antonyms
ISBN 9780544336643

LC bl2015024235

Presents alphabetically arranged entries containing synonyms, definitions, and parts of speech, with example sentences for each synonym to distinguish shades of meaning.

Robb, Don

★ **Ox,** house, stick: the history of our alphabet. Donald Robb; illustrated by Anne Smith. Charlesbridge, 2007. 48 p.

Grades: 4 5 6 7   **428.1**

1. Alphabet 2. Alphabet -- History 3. Writing methods and systems
ISBN 9781570916090

LC 2005006015

"Robb traces the history of each letter from its origin to its modern appearance in the Roman alphabet. He explains the birth of writing in pictogram form and the eventual transition to written symbols that stand for sounds. . . . Smith's whimsical paintings are a fitting companion to Robb's lighthearted text." School Library Journal.

428.2 English language grammar

Fogarty, Mignon

Grammar Girl presents the ultimate writing guide for students. Mignon Fogarty, Erwin Haya. Henry Holt & Co., 2011. 294 p.

Grades: 6 7 8 9 10   **428.2**

1. Writing 2. Grammar, Comparative and general 3. Language arts
ISBN 9780805089431

"This text is evenly divided into five sections: parts of speech, sentence structure, punctuation, usage, and a final segment on how readers can improve their writing. Fogarty's style mimics her podcasts with pithy but helpful rules and advice laced with examples. Pop quizzes and cartoon illustrations are also included. Libraries should purchase this book for reference use if nothing else, but budding writers will find it invaluable." School Library Journal.

Truss, Lynne

Eats, shoots & leaves: the zero tolerance approach to punctuation. Lynne Truss; Pat Byrnes, illustrator. Gotham Books, 2009, c2004. 176 p.

Grades: 8 9 10 11 12 Adult   **428.2**

1. Language and languages -- Grammars 2. English language -- Usage 3. Language arts 4. Writing -- Philosophy
ISBN 9781592404889

LC 2009291769

Looks at the history of punctuation and the rules governing the use of apostrophes, commas, dashes, hyphens, colons, and semicolons.

"The author dissects common errors that grammar mavens have long deplored (often, as she readily points out, in isolation) and makes . . . arguments for increased attention to punctuation correctness. . . . Truss serves up delightful, unabashedly strict and sometimes snobby little book, with cheery Britishisms (Lawks-a-mussy!) dotting pages that express a more international righteous indignation." Publishers Weekly.

428.4 Reading—English language

Bernadowski, Carianne

Research-based reading strategies in the library for adolescent learners. Carianne Bernadowski and Patricia Liotta Kolencik. Libraries Unlimited, c2010. xxv, 108 p.

Grades: Professional   **428.4**
    1. Reading (Secondary) 2. Content area reading 3. School libraries
ISBN 9781586833473

LC 2009021198

Provides information to help school librarians and classroom teachers in a collaborative effort to increase reading comprehension and vocabulary skills through nine research-based reading strategies.

Farwell, Sybil M.

Supporting reading in grades 6-12: a guide. Sybil M. Farwell and Nancy L. Teger. Libraries Unlimited, 2012. xiii, 358 p.

Grades: Professional   **428.4**
    1. Reading (Secondary) 2. Children -- Books and reading 3. School librarian participation in curriculum planning 4. Motivation in education
ISBN 9781598848038

LC 2012010826

This book presents a curricular framework for students grades 6-12 that school librarians and teachers can use collaboratively to enhance reading skill development, promote literature appreciation, and motivate young people to incorporate reading into their lives beyond simply being required schoolwork. Provided by publisher.

Gallagher, Kelly, 1958-

180 days: two teachers and the quest to engage and empower adolescents. Kelly Gallagher and Penny Kittle. Heinemann, 2018 xxii, 233 p.

Grades: Professional   **428.4**
    1. Reading (Secondary) 2. Language arts (Secondary) 3. English language -- Composition and exercises -- Study and teaching (Secondary)
ISBN 9780325081137

LC 2017056660

East Coast and West Coast teachers discuss how they "get it all in" with their respective high school classes. Provided by publisher.

Gallagher, Kelly, 1958-

Readicide: how schools are killing reading and what you can do about it. Kelly Gallagher; foreword by Richard Allington. Stenhouse Publishers, c2009. x, 150 p.

Grades: Professional   **428.4**
    1. Reading 2. Literacy 3. Reading promotion
ISBN 9781571107800

LC 2008040694

Argues that the decline in reading by children in the United States is furthered by schools by focusing on test-taking and focusing solely on academic texts with guidance for educators on how to conteract this trend.

Robb, Laura

Teaching reading in middle school: a strategic approach to teaching reading that improves comprehension and thinking. Laura Robb; [foreword by P. David Pearson]. Scholastic, c2010. 335 p.

Grades: Professional   **428.4**
    1. Reading (Middle school) 2. Middle school students -- Books and reading
ISBN 9780545173551

LC bl2012043658

Presents strategy lessons and learning experiences to teach reading in middle school classrooms, covering such topics as motivation, assessment, classroom management, and differentiation.

Serravallo, Jennifer

★ The **reading** strategies book: your everything guide to developing skilled readers. Jennifer Serravallo. Heinemann, 2015. xii, 388 p.

Grades: Professional   **428.4**
    1. Reading 2. Books and reading
ISBN 9780325074337

LC 2016498719

Collects 300 strategies to share with readers in support of thirteen goals—everything from fluency to literary analysis. Each strategy is cross-linked to skills, genres, and Fountas & Pinnell reading levels to give you just-right teaching, just in time.

Tovani, Cris

I read it, but I don't get it: comprehension strategies for adolescent readers. Cris Tovani; foreword by Ellin Oliver Keene. Stenhouse Publishers, c2000. xii, 140 p.

Grades: Professional   **428.4**
    1. Reading comprehension 2. Reading (Secondary) 3. Reading -- Remedial teaching
ISBN 9781571100894

LC 00058798

I Read It, but I Don't Get It is a practical, engaging account of how teachers can help adolescents develop new reading comprehension skills. In a time when students need increasingly sophisticated reading skills, this book will provide support for teachers who want to incorporate comprehension instruction into their daily lesson plans without sacrificing content knowledge.

443 Dictionaries of standard French

Girard, Denis

Cassell's French dictionary: French-English, English-French. completely rev. by Denis Girard, with the assistance of Gaston Dulong, Oliver Van Oss, and Charles Guinness. Macmillan, 1977, c1973. xvi, 762, 655 p.

Grades: 8 9 10 11 12 Adult   **443**
    1. French language -- English 2. English language -- French
ISBN 9780025226203

LC 77007669

French-Canadian terms are included in this French dictionary which also affords a comprehensive coverage of classical literary language

"New words including colloquialisms, slang, American English and French-Canadian terms [are included]. . . . There are also sections on French verbs and French and English abbreviations. Reliable, standard dictionary. A first choice. N Y Public Libr. Ref Books for Child Collect. 2d edition

Bibliography: p. vi.

453 Dictionaries of standard Italian

Rebora, Piero

Cassell's Italian dictionary: Italian-English, English-Italian. compiled by Piero Rebora, with the assistance of Francis M. Guercio and Arthur L. Hayward. Macmillan, 1977. xxi, 1096 p.

Grades: 8 9 10 11 12 Adult   **453**
   1. Italian language -- English 2. English language -- Italian
   ISBN 9780025225404

                                      LC 77007405

Verb tables supplement entries offering comprehensive coverage of the language of contemporary Italy while including treatment of obsolete terms found in classic Italian writings.

463 Dictionaries of standard Spanish

Gooch, Anthony

Cassell's Spanish-English, English-Spanish dictionary =: Diccionario espanol-ingles, ingles-espanol. compiled by Anthony Gooch, Angel Garcia De Paredes. Macmillan, 1978. xxv, 1109 p.

Grades: 8 9 10 11 12 Adult   **463**
   1. Spanish language -- English 2. English language -- Spanish
   ISBN 9780025229105

                                      LC 77018453

Over forty-five thousand entries provide Spanish and English equivalents, and include technical as well as conversational words and phrases

493 Non-Semitic Afro-Asiatic languages

Giblin, James Cross, 1933-

The **riddle** of the Rosetta Stone: key to ancient Egypt: illustrated with photographs, prints, and drawings. James Cross Giblin. HarperTrophy, 1992, c1990. 85 p.

Grades: 5 6 7 8   **493**
   1. Egyptian hieroglyphics
   ISBN 0064461378

                                      LC BL 99734822

Describes how the discovery and deciphering of the Rosetta Stone unlocked the secret of Egyptian hieroglyphics.

"Suspense keeps the reader glued to this fine piece of nonfiction as the mystery of hieroglyphs is slowly unraveled. . . . The author has done a masterful job of distilling information, citing the highlights, and fitting it all together in an interesting and enlightening look at a puzzling subject." Horn Book.

Bibliography: p. 78-79.

495.1 Chinese

Manser, Martin H.

Oxford Chinese dictionary: English-Chinese, Chinese-English = [Ying Han, Han Ying]. monolingual English text edited by Martin H. Manser; English-Chinese dictionary edited and translated by Zhu Yuan, Wang Liangbi, Ren Yongchang; Chinese-English dictionary edited by Wu Jingrong ... [et al.] Oxford University Press, 2003. 10, 512, 33, 614 p.

Grades: 8 9 10 11 12 Adult   **495.1**
   1. Chinese language -- English 2. English language -- Chinese
   ISBN 9780195964592

                                      LC 2005295454

The third edition of this reference text is designed for intermediate-level Chinese-speaking learners of English and English-speaking learners of Chinese, travelers, translators, and language professionals. Now featuring some 90,000 words and phrases and 130,000 translations, the text has been updated to take account of new vocabulary and recent developments in Chinese and English.

495.7 Korean

Adelson-Goldstein, Jayme

Oxford picture dictionary: English/Korean. Jayme Adelson-Goldstein, Norma Shapiro. Oxford Univ Press, c2009. 305 p.

Grades: Adult   **495.7**
   1. English language -- Korean 2. Korean language -- English 3. Picture dictionaries
   ISBN 9780194740166

                                      LC 2009292655

Content is organized within 12 thematic units, including Everyday Language, People, Housing, Food and Recreation. Rich visual contexts recycle words from the unit. This structure is designed to address the needs of multilevel classrooms.

500 SCIENCE

500 Natural sciences and mathematics

Bryson, Bill

A **really** short history of nearly everything. Bill Bryson; illustrated by Daniel Long, Dawn Cooper, Jesus Sotes, and Katie Ponder. Puffin, 2020 176 p.

Grades: 4 5 6 7   **500**
   1. Science -- History 2. Scientific discoveries 3. Firsts (Events, inventions, etc) 4. Science
   ISBN 9780241451946

Ever wondered how we got from nothing to something? Or thought about how we can weigh the earth? Or wanted to reach the edge of the universe? Uncover the mysteries of time, space and life on earth in this extraordinary book—a journey from the centre of the planet to the dawn of the dinosaurs, and everything in between. And discover our own incredible journey, from single cell to civilisation, including the brilliant (and sometimes very bizarre) scientists who helped us find out the how and why.

Grossman, Emily

What breathes through its butt?: mind-blowing science questions answered. Emily Grossman; [illustrated by] Alice Bowsher. Bloomsbury Childrens Books 2020 224 p.

Grades: 3 4 5 6 7 **500**
1. Science 2. Curiosities and wonders 3. Questions and answers
ISBN 9781547604524

LC 2020027006

Why is your elbow called your funny bone? How could you escape the grip of a crocodile's jaw? Which animal can breathe through its butt? This book uncovers the amazing scientific explanations behind all sorts of questions that can pop into our heads. Can an egg bounce? How can a giraffe's ridiculously long neck contain the same number of bones as a human's? How much does the Internet weigh? With delightful interactive features that invite readers to guess answers to questions and make links between different scientific concepts, this is a great book for reluctant readers and STEAM lovers alike. Provided by publisher.

"Sure to hook those who already love science and lure in skeptics." Kirkus

Nye, Bill
Bill Nye's great big world of science. by Bill Nye and Gregory Mone. Abrams Books for Young Readers, 2020. 256 p.
Grades: 6 7 8 9 **500**
1. Science 2. Curiosities and wonders 3. Trivia and miscellaneous facts
ISBN 9781419746765

Science educator, TV host, and New York Times bestselling author Bill Nye is on a mission to help kids understand and appreciate the science that makes our world work. Featuring a range of subjects—physics, chemistry, geology, biology, astronomy, global warming, and more—this profusely illustrated book covers the basic principles of each science, key discoveries, recent revolutionary advances, and the problems that science still needs to solve for our Earth. Nye and coauthor Gregory Mone present the most difficult theories and facts in an easy-to-comprehend, humorous way. They interviewed numerous specialists from around the world, in each of the fields discussed, whose insights are included throughout. Also included are experiments kids can do themselves to bring science to life! Features photographs, illustrations, diagrams, glossary, bibliography, and index.

"Wordplay and wry wit put extra fun into a trove of fundamental knowledge." Kirkus

Includes bibliographical references (pages 248-249) and an index.

Rice, Dona
What a scientist sees. Dona Herweck Rice. Shell Education, 2015. 32 p.: Science readers.
Grades: 4 5 6 **500**
1. Scientists 2. Science -- Methodology 3. Research
ISBN 9781480746916

"Smartly written, these innovative and imaginative volumes make learning fun... First-rate nonfiction." School Library Journal.

Wood, Matthew Brenden
The **science** of science fiction. Matthew Brenden Wood; illustrated by Tom Casteel. Pgw 2017 128 p.: Inquire and investigate
Grades: 6 7 8 9 **500**
1. Science fiction writing 2. Science 3. Technology 4. Clones and cloning 5. Time travel
ISBN 9781619304666

Early science fiction imagined a world with space travel, video calls, and worldwide access to information, things we now know as NASA's human spaceflight program, Skype, and the Internet. What next? Could we really bring back the dinosaurs, travel to a distant star, or live on Mars?

"This latest addition to the award-winning Inquire and Investigate series will be a welcome acquisition for librarians wanting to spice up their STEAM collections." Booklist.

500.5 Space sciences

Perritano, John
Space science. John Perritano. Mason Crest, [2017] 64 p.: STEM in current events
Grades: 6 7 8 9 10 **500.5**
1. Space sciences
ISBN 9781422235959

"A great fit for classroom or school libraries and a strong consideration for public libraries interested in the integration of STEM into everyday life." School Library Journal.

503 Science—Dictionaries, encyclopedias, concordances

Tamm, Vali
The **American** heritage student science dictionary.. Vali Tamm, editor. Houghton Mifflin Harcourt, c2009. viii, 376 p.
Grades: 5 6 7 8 9 10 11 12 **503**
1. Science
ISBN 9780547002439

LC 2009278788

Entries with definitions of basic scientific terms are accompanied by illustrations, "Did You Know" sidebars, and explanatory notes.

507 Science—Education, research, related topics

Isabella, Jude
Hoaxed!: fakes & mistakes in the world of science. by the editors of YES mag; illustrated by Howie Woo. Kids Can Press, c2009. 48 p.
Grades: 5 6 7 8 **507**
1. Science fraud 2. Hoaxes 3. Scientific errors 4. Science -- History 5. Misconceptions
ISBN 9781554532063

"Piltdown man, Richard Meinertzhagen the light-fingered bird collector, Stone Age Tasaday in the Philippines, crop circles in England, cold fusion energy and UFOs in Roswell, N.M., are the fakes and mistakes described in this lively introduction to fraud in science. The breezy text opens with a clear description of the scientific process of hypothesis, experiment, publication in professional magazines and replication of results before proceeding to the many colorful fakes exposed." Kirkus.

507.8 Use of apparatus and equipment in study and teaching

Challoner, Jack
★ **Maker** lab: 28 super cool projects. Jack Challoner DK Publishing, 2016. 160 p.
Grades: 3 4 5 6 7 8 **507.8**
1. Science projects 2. Science -- Experiments 3. Science
ISBN 9781465451354

"Though not all projects are innovative, what sets this book apart is that each experiment is accompanied by real-world applications that tie

new observations to kids existing understanding and offer endless opportunities for STEM-related discussions. Not only are young scientists
encouraged to experiment, they are challenged to apply the information
gleaned to real-world problem-solving." Booklist.

Cobb, Vicki

We dare you!: hundreds of fun science bets, challenges, and
experiments you can do at home. Vicki Cobb and Kathy Darling.
Skyhorse Pub., c2008. xiii, 321 p.

Grades: 4 5 6 7   **507.8**
1. Science -- Experiments 2. Science fun 3. Science projects
ISBN 9781602392250

LC 2007051236

Provides over two hundred experiments that use such principles as
gravity, mechanics, geometry, and perception, and which can be performed in the home using readily available objects and materials.

"Divided into chapters with titles such as The Human Wonder, Fluid
Feats, Energy Entrapments, and Mathematical Duplicity, this volume
has more than 200 experiments with clear how-to instructions. All of
the projects are doable and the science behind them is explained in a kid-
accessible manner. . . . Black-and-white line drawings add humor and
clarify instructions. This is a great resource for teachers, parents, and
budding scientists—and for any youngster who can't resist a challenge."
School Library Journal.

Connolly, Sean, 1956-

The **book** of wildly spectacular sports science: 54 all-star
experiments. Sean Connolly. Workman Publishing, 2017. 240 p.

Grades: 4 5 6 7 8   **507.8**
1. Sports sciences 2. Sports 3. Science -- Experiments 4.
Experiments
ISBN 9780761189282

"The chatty tone, clear scientific explanations, and broad range of
athletics discussed mean there's something here for just about every
kind of sports fan." Publishers Weekly.

Leavitt, Loralee

Candy experiments. Loralee Leavitt Andrews McMeel Publishing, 2012. 146 p.

Grades: 4 5 6   **507.8**
1. Candy 2. Science projects 3. Chemistry 4. Experiments 5.
Science -- Experiments
ISBN 9781449418366

Presents scientific experiments that use candy to demonstrate such
concepts as color, density, size, heat, crystalization, and stickiness.

McCallum, Ann, 1965-

Eat your science homework: recipes for inquiring minds.
Ann McCallum; illustrated by Leeza Hernandez. Charlesbridge,
2014. 48 p.

Grades: 5 6 7 8   **507.8**
1. Cooking 2. Science -- Experiments 3. Cooking and children
4. Recipes
ISBN 9781570912986

LC 2013022070

A companion to Eat Your Math Homework explains such upper-
elementary science concepts as subatomic particles, black holes, and
acids and bases while providing simple recipes, activity sidebars and a
glossary of terms.

"Scientific terms are explained in each chapter, and recipes are given
and reinforced with a glossary. Bright illustrations and clear instructions
will appeal to younger readers, while older readers will find the concepts

and vocabulary educational; the recipes will appeal to a wide range of
ages." School Library Journal.

Messner, Kate

★ **Solve** this: forensics: super science and curious capers for
the daring detective in you. Kate Messner and Anne Ruppert.
Natl Geographic Soc Childrens books 2020 160 p.

Grades: 4 5 6 7   **507.8**
1. Forensic sciences 2. Problem solving 3. Science -- Experiments
4. Criminal investigation 5. Criminal evidence
ISBN 9781426337444

LC 2019007820

Science experiments for children that help them learn to solve problems. Provided by publisher.

Williams, Jennifer, 1971-

Oobleck, slime & dancing spaghetti: twenty terrific at-home
science experiments inspired by favorite children's books. Jennifer Williams. Bright Sky Press, c2009. 192 p.

Grades: 4 5 6   **507.8**
1. Science -- Experiments
ISBN 9781933979342

LC 2009000876

Presents twenty activities that test the scientific properties of elements of popular children's books, including creating slime, shaking
cream into butter, and constructing an air balloon.

"Using children's literature as a springboard, this title provides a
series of science experiments designed to explore concepts and ideas
that spring from various stories. At the beginning of each chapter, a children's book is nicely summarized. The author then explains a related science concept, suggests discussion questions that connect the experiment
to the story, and offers ideas for taking the project further. This is serious
science. . . . The experiments do a really wonderful job of emphasizing the importance of observation and data collection. The writing is
relatively clear. . . . This book is great choice for home use and science
units." School Library Journal.

Includes bibliographical references.

508 Science—Natural history

Lloyd, Christopher, 1968-

The **nature** timeline wallbook: Unfold the Story of Nature
- from the Dawn of Life to the Present Day! written by Christopher Lloyd and Patrick Skipworth; illustrated by Andy Forshaw.
What on Earth Publishing Ltd., 2017. unpaged

Grades: 5 6 7 8   **508**
1. Natural history 2. Nature 3. Pictorial works
ISBN 9780993284731

LC bl2017030819

Presents a six-foot timeline of the natural history of the world, along
with a copy of "The Wallbook Chronicle," featuring stories of notable
philosophers and scientists.

"This utterly browsable and very engaging large-format title is
chock-full of scientific facts and stories." School Library Journal.

Paquette, Ammi-Joan

Two truths and a lie: it's alive! Ammi-Joan Paquette and
Laurie Ann Thompson; illustrated by Lisa K. Weber. Walden
Pond Press, an imprint of HarperCollins Childrens Books, 2017.
176 p.

Grades: 4 5 6 7   **508**
1. Nature 2. Nature and science 3. Questions and answers 4. Truthfulness and falsehood 5. Natural history 6. Trivia and miscellaneous facts
ISBN 9780062418791

Blends strange but true facts about the natural world with a handful of fictional accounts, challenging readers to discover which two out of every three stories are true.

"The authors' casual tone should easily draw readers in, and activities at the end of each chapter underscore a key goal underneath all the fun: developing critical thinking skills." Publishers Weekly.

508.092 Natural history—Biography

Beil, Karen Magnuson
What Linnaeus saw: a scientist's quest to name every living thing. Karen Magnuson Beil. Norton Young Readers, 2019. 256 p.
Grades: 8 9 10 11 12   **508.092**
1. Linne, Carl von, 1707-1778. 2. 18th century 3. Naturalists 4. Natural history 5. Biology 6. Scientists 7. Sweden
ISBN 9781324004684

LC 2019014206

Chronicles the scientist's life and career as he sought to name every plant and animal on Earth, and describes how he developed a system of classifying these names that inspired generations of scientists.

508.866 Natural history—Galapagos Islands

Chin, Jason, 1978-
★ **Island**: a story of the Galapagos. Jason Chin. Henry Holt & Co., 2012. 40 p.
Grades: 3 4 5 6   **508.866**
1. Natural history 2. Botany 3. Wildlife 4. Zoology 5. Islands of the Pacific 6. Galapagos Islands
ISBN 9781596437166

Presents a painstakingly researched visual tribute to the evolving terrain and animals of the Galapagos that traces the island's fiery origins, its rise and decline as an environment and the emergence of life on new islands.

509 Science—History, geographic treatment, biography

Blanchard, Anne
Arab science and invention in the golden age. Anne Blanchard; Emmanuel Cerisier; translated by R.M. Brent. Enchanted Lion Books, 2008. 65 p.
Grades: 6 7 8 9   **509**
1. Muḥammad, Prophet, d. 632. 2. Science -- History 3. Civilization, Islamic -- History 4. Ancient science 5. Mathematics -- History 6. Islamic Empire -- History
ISBN 9781592700806

LC 2008026431

Examines the cities of the ancient Arab world that became flourishing Muslim metropolises which were key locations for the development of algebra, the decimal system, astronomy, medicine, and other sciences from the eighth to the fifteenth centuries.

"The Muslim world led an amazing scientific revolution for hundreds of years with breakthroughs in math, geography, physics, astronomy, and medicine. This large-size, attractive volume packs in a wealth of information about the rise and fall of the immense empire. . . . The open format, with lots of boxed inserts and detailed illustrations on each double-page spread, is dense with information." Booklist.

Includes bibliographical references.

Hakim, Joy
Aristotle leads the way. Joy Hakim. Smithsonian Books, c2004. xiii, 282 p.: Story of science
Grades: 8 9 10 11 12   **509**
1. Aristotle 2. Science -- History 3. Scientists
ISBN 1588341607

LC bl2004113209

Presents the influence of of ancient Greek, Hindu, and Arab thinkers on the evolution of science in the fields of math, astronomy, and physics, with charts, diagrams, and excerpts from the writings of scientists.

"Hakim has interwoven creation myths, history, physics, and mathematics to present a seamless, multifaceted view of the foundation of modern science. . . . The entire volume is beautifully organized." School Library Journal.

Includes bibliographical references (p. 271-273) and index.

Einstein adds a new dimension. Joy Hakim. Smithsonian Books, 2006. 256 p. : Story of science
Grades: 8 9 10 11 12   **509**
1. Science -- History 2. Scientists
ISBN 1588341623

LC bl2006015136

A critical study of the contributions of Albert Einstein explores the evolution of science in the twentieth century, telling the story of the people and ideas who dramatically changed our view of both the universe and ourselves.

"Hakim delivers a brisk, intellectually challenging account of the development of quantum theory and modern cosmology. . . . She introduces a teeming cast of deep thinkers who . . . delivered a series of brilliant experiments and insights. . . . Supplemented by a digestible resource list and a generous assortment of illustrations." Booklist.

Includes bibliographical references and index.

Krull, Kathleen, 1952-2021
Leonardo da Vinci. by Kathleen Krull; illustrated by Boris Kulikov. Viking, c2005. 124 p.: Giants of science (Viking)
Grades: 5 6 7 8   **509**
1. Leonardo, da Vinci, 1452-1519 2. Medieval period (476-1492) 3. Scientists 4. Artists 5. Renaissance science 6. Civilization, Medieval 7. Curiosity 8. Italy
ISBN 067005920X

LC 2005007244

Krull presents a vivid and highly accessible portrait of a true renaissance man—an artist, scientist, and inventer of unparalleled genius.

"This is a biography of Leonardo da Vinci that highlights his scientific approach to understanding the physical world. The first half of the book describes Leonardo's apprenticeship and his work as an artist in Milan. The second half relates events in his later life, emphasizing his observation and investigation of the human body and nature. . . . Six excellent ink drawings illustrate this attractive volume. A very readable, vivid portrait set against the backdrop of remarkable times." Booklist.

Includes bibliographical references (p. 120-124) and index.

509.2 Scientists

Allman, Toney

Women scientists and inventors. Toney Allman. Reference-Point Press, [2017] 80 p.: Collective biographies (Reference-Point Press)

Grades: 6 7 8 9   **509.2**

1. Women scientists 2. Women inventors 3. Scientists 4. Inventors
ISBN 9781682820322

LC 2015050839

"Clearly written and well-documented short narratives suitable for formal research." School Library Journal.

Includes bibliographical references and index.

Gow, Mary

The **great** thinker: Aristotle and the foundations of science. Mary Gow. Enslow Publishers, c2011. 128 p.: Great minds of ancient science and math

Grades: 6 7 8 9   **509.2**

1. Aristotle 2. Scientists 3. Philosophy and science 4. Ancient philosophers 5. Science -- Philosophy 6. Philosophers 7. Ancient Greece -- History.
ISBN 9780766031210

LC 2009023813

A biography of ancient Greek philosopher and scientist Aristotle, whose writings on zoology, logic, the philosophy of nature, metaphysics, ethics, politics, and literary criticism influenced Western thought for hundreds of years. Provided by publisher.

"Presents a biography of the fourth-century B.C.E. Greek philosopher and scientist Aristotle, whose writings on logic, metaphysics, ethics, politics, and literary criticism influenced Western thought for hundreds of years. . . . [This] colorful, attractive book includes simple, straightforward text with nice illustrations and appendixes of suggested activities, a supplemental chronology, chapter notes, and glossary." Voice of Youth Advocates.

Includes bibliographical references and index.

Jackson, Donna M., 1959-

Extreme scientists: exploring nature's mysteries from perilous places. by Donna M. Jackson. Houghton Mifflin Harcourt, c c2009. 80 p. : Scientists in the field (Houghton Mifflin)

Grades: 5 6 7 8   **509.2**

1. Scientists 2. Science -- Vocational guidance 3. Meteorologists 4. Microbiologists 5. Botanists
ISBN 9780618777068

LC 2008036796

Offers a look at the exciting, dangerous, and important jobs that three different extreme scientists do around the world, the reasons they do it, and the benefits the world has gained as a result of their research.

"This volume profiles three scientists working far out in the field. Hurricane hunter Paul Flaherty, . . . Hazel Barton, a microbiologist specializing in single-cell organisms living in extreme conditions, . . . [and] ecologist and college professor Steve Sillett, who . . . climbs into the canopies to study redwoods. While the clearly written text includes vivid passages about the dangers these scientists face, it goes on to discuss what drives them to pursue their subjects and what they have discovered along the way. . . . The many excellent color photos portray these adventures as scientists intently focused on their work." Booklist.

Lawlor, Laurie

Super women: six scientists who changed the world. Laurie Lawlor. Holiday House, 2017 57 p..

Grades: 7 8 9 10   **509.2**

1. Burbidge, E. Margaret 2. Tharp, Marie. 3. Ellis, Florence Hawley 4. Johnson, Katherine G. 1918-2020 5. Elion, Gertrude B. 6. Clark, Eugenie, 1922- 7. Women scientists 8. Scientists
ISBN 9780823436750

LC 2016027036

Profiles six women scientists who persevered in the face of prejudice, including ichthyologist Eugenie Clark and mathematician Katherine Coleman Johnson.

"This compilation of short biographies of six pioneering women scientists is a welcome and fascinating addition to STEM resources." School Library Journal.

Noyce, Pendred

Remarkable minds: seventeen more pioneering women in science & medicine. Pendred Noyce. Independent Pub Group 2015 192 p.

Grades: 6 7 8 9 10   **509.2**

1. Women scientists 2. Scientists 3. Women
ISBN 9780990782902

"This scholarly look at 17 remarkable, intelligent women devoted to research in science and medicine will round out science or biography collections." School Library Journal.

510 Mathematics

McKellar, Danica

Math doesn't suck: how to survive middle school math without losing your mind or breaking a nail. Danica McKellar. Hudson Street Press, 2007. 297 p.

Grades: 5 6 7 8   **510**

1. Mathematics 2. Mathematics -- Study and teaching (Middle school)
ISBN 1594630399

Demystifies middle-school math concepts that are most challenging, sharing step-by-step instructions for developing real-world math skills, providing time-saving tips and tricks, and offering practice problems with detailed answers and explanations.

"This covers some of the most basic ideas of middle-grade math, including concepts relating to fractions, decimals, and ratios, making each comprehensible, interesting, and fun. Using real-world constructions, such as tangled necklaces, boyfriends, and pizza, concepts are thoroughly explained." Voice of Youth Advocates.

Young, Tracie

Cool math: 50 fantastic facts for kids of all ages. Tracie Young, Katie Hewett. Pavilion Children's Books, 2020 112 p.

Grades: 7 8 9   **510**

1. Mathematics
ISBN 9781843654483

This lively, engaging book is illustrated throughout to help bring math to life, and topics include how to tip, how to work out the distance of a storm, Fibonacci sequences, cracking codes, and many more! From simple multiplication to complex calculus, math has never been easier. Excerpted from publisher description

"Clever section headings such as 'You're So Mean!' offer a laugh for those who find math a bit dry. Perfect for library collections or classroom use." School Library Journal

510.23 Math—Careers

Hynson, Colin
Dream jobs in math. Colin Hynson. Crabtree Publishing Company, 2017. 32 p.: Cutting-edge careers in STEM
Grades: 5 6 7 8   **510.23**
  1. Mathematics 2. Vocational guidance 3. Occupations
ISBN 9780778729631

LC 2016045933

"The book's information is light but grounded, making it a useful preliminary resource to get mathematically inclined readers thinking about their futures." Booklist.

510.71 Mathematics—Education

Aungst, Gerald
5 principles of the modern mathematics classroom: creating a culture of innovative thinking. Gerald Aungst; foreword by Mark Barnes. Corwin Mathematics, 2016 xxvi, 172 p.
Grades: Professional   **510.71**
  1. Mathematics -- Study and teaching 2. Motivation in education
ISBN 9781483391427

LC 2015027594

Creating a math classroom filled with confident problem solvers starts with challenges discovered in the real world, not a sequence of prescribed problems. In this groundbreaking book, Gerald Aungst offers five powerful principles for instilling a culture of learning in your classroom: Conjecture, Collaboration, Communication, Chaos, and Celebration.

Humphreys, Cathy
Making number talks matter: developing mathematical practices and deepening understanding, grades 4-10. Cathy Humphreys & Ruth Parker; foreword by Jo Boaler. Stenhouse Publishers, 2015 xii, 200 p.
Grades: Professional   **510.71**
  1. Mathematics -- Study and teaching (Elementary) 2. Mathematics -- Study and teaching (Middle school)
ISBN 9781571109989

LC 2014044584

Making Number Talks Matter?is about the myriad decisions facing teachers as they make this fifteen-minute daily routine a vibrant and vital part of their mathematics instruction. Throughout the book, Humphreys and Parker offer practical ideas for using Number Talks to help students learn to reason numerically and build a solid foundation for the study of mathematics.

510.92 Mathematicians

Edwards, Sue Bradford
Hidden human computers: the black women of NASA. by Sue Bradford Edwards and Duchess Harris, JD, PhD. Essential Library, an imprint of Abdo Publishing, 2017. 112 p.: Hidden heroes
Grades: 7 8 9 10 11 12   **510.92**
  1. United States. National Aeronautics and Space Administration -- Officials and employees 2. Women mathematicians 3. African American women 4. Space programs -- International competition 5. Women astronauts 6. African American astronauts 7. United States -- History -- 20th century
ISBN 9781680783872

LC bl2017002465

Tells the story of the African American women who worked as mathematicians at NASA and proved invaluable to the American effort during the space race.
"An essential purchase for STEM collections." Booklist.
Includes bibliographical references (pages 106-109) and index.

519.2 Probabilities

Wingard-Nelson, Rebecca
Graphing and probability word problems: no problem! Rebecca Wingard-Nelson. Enslow Publishers, c2011. 64 p.: Math busters word problems
Grades: 6 7 8 9   **519.2**
  1. Word problems (Mathematics) 2. Graphic methods 3. Problem solving -- Graphic methods 4. Problem solving -- Statistical methods
ISBN 9780766033726

LC 2010003281

Presents a step-by-step guide to understanding word problems with graphing and probability. Provided by publisher.

520 Science—Astronomy

Aguilar, David A.
Cosmic catastrophes: seven ways to destroy a planet like earth. David Aguilar. Viking, published by the Penguin Group, 2016 79 p.: Smithsonian
Grades: 5 6 7 8   **520**
  1. Natural disasters 2. Catastrophism 3. Planets 4. Astronomy 5. Disasters 6. Earth 7. Solar system
ISBN 9780451476845

LC 2015044536

A lively exploration of seven cosmic catastrophes that could hit Earth and any of the other 20 billion Earth-like planets in our galaxy.. Provided by publisher.
"A wild and thought-provoking look at what potential calamities await our planet. A good addition for collections in need of browsables titles on space." School Library Journal.

Gater, Will
The **practical** astronomer: explore the wonders of the night sky. Will Gater and Anton Vamplew; consultant, Jacqueline Mitton. DK, 2017. 264 p.
Grades: Professional   **520**
  1. Astronomy
ISBN 9781465445131

LC bl2018048658

Presents a guide to observing the night sky using the naked eye and a telescope, with instructions on setting up equipment and taking pictures, along with maps showing planets and constellations throughout the year.

Gilliland, Ben
Rocket science for the rest of us. written by Ben Gilliland; consultant, Jack Challoner. DK, 2015. 192 p.
Grades: 7 8 9 10   **520**
  1. Astronomy 2. Astrophysics 3. Space exploration 4. Antimatter

5. Black holes (Astronomy)
ISBN 9781465433657

LC bl2015006053

Presents a common-sense guide to astronomy and astrophysics that provides comprehensive explanations of such topics as black holes, antimatter, and space exploration.

Green, Dan, 1975 June 20-

Astronomy: out of this world! Dan Green; created by Simon Basher. Kingfisher, 2009. 128 p.: Basher science

Grades: 5 6 7 8   **520**

1. Astronomy 2. Planets 3. Galaxies 4. Stars 5. Sun 6. Solar system
ISBN 9780753462904

"Basher has created a portrait gallery of personified planets, comets, space probes, galaxies, several kinds of stars, and an array of other celestial bodies in a hyper-cute, pastel cartoon style. . . . Along with short bulleted lists of additional information, each figure offers a fact-based self-description. . . . Green's astro-narrative is both accurate and spiced with seldom-mentioned details." School Library Journal.

Miller, Ron, 1947-

Natural satellites: the book of moons. Ron Miller Lerner Pub Group 2021 104 p.

Grades: 7 8 9 10 11 12   **520**

1. Astronomy 2. Moon 3. Solar system
ISBN 9781728419435

"While laying a scientific foundation through brief asides on the likes of Newton and Galileo, Miller utilizes research from as recently as 2020 as he takes readers through time and space. . . . An excellent resource for teen selenophiles." Booklist

Mitchell, Chris

How do astronauts wee in space? Chris Mitchell. Trafalgar Square Books, 2016. 116 p.: Dr Dino's Learnatorium

Grades: 4 5 6 7 8   **520**

1. Astronomy 2. Space environment 3. Planets 4. Solar system 5. Space
ISBN 9781784186531

This book is packed with the wildest, weirdest, funniest, filthiest, foulest, wisest, grossest, brainiest, biggest and best facts about space and the universe.

"Frequent comic spot art keeps things light, and as for that title question? The answer is more involved than you might think." Booklist.

520.9 Astronomy—History

Carson, Mary Kay

Beyond the solar system: exploring galaxies, black holes, alien planets, and more: a history with 21 activities. Mary Kay Carson. Chicago Review Press, c2013. 127 p.

Grades: 5 6 7 8   **520.9**

1. Astronomy -- History 2. Planets 3. Solar system
ISBN 9781613745441

LC 2012046330

Traces the evolution of humankind's astronomical knowledge from its origins to current findings, suggesting a range of educational projects while providing profiles of famous astronomers, a timeline of major discoveries and a glossary of technical terms.

Jenkins, Martin, 1959-

Exploring space: from Galileo to the Mars Rover and beyond. written by Martin Jenkins; illustrated by Stephen Biesty. Candlewick Press, 2017. 59 p.

Grades: 5 6 7 8   **520.9**

1. Galilei, Galileo, 1564-1642. 2. International Space Station 3. Space exploration -- History 4. Astronomy -- History 5. Space flight -- History 6. Astronauts 7. Space vehicles 8. Solar system
ISBN 9780763689315

Presents a brief history of space exploration, covering such topics as the first human missions, life on the International Space Station, and settling on Mars.

"In exceptionally clear prose, Jenkins surveys the history and possible future of space exploration ... The subject matter is thrilling on its own, but this expert portrayal of the facts makes it all the more captivating." Booklist.

Includes bibliographical references and index.

520.92 Astronomers

Saucier, C. A. P., 1954-

Explore the cosmos like Neil DeGrasse Tyson: a space science journey. C.A.P. Saucier. Prometheus Books, 2015. 120 p.

Grades: 4 5 6   **520.92**

1. Tyson, Neil deGrasse. 2. Astrophysicists 3. African American scientists 4. Scientists 5. Astronautics 6. Cosmology 7. Solar system
ISBN 9781633880146

LC 2014039219

"Perhaps a bit overly ambitious, this guide is nonetheless an excellent jumping-off point for those pursuing a deeper interest in space, while its level of detail may deter others. Its focus is brought back to Earth in Tyson's belief that knowledge and curiosity are of the utmost importance, challenging readers to grab some binoculars, go outside, and start asking questions." Booklist.

Includes bibliographical references and index.

522 Techniques, procedures, apparatus, equipment, materials

Scott, Elaine, 1940-

Space, stars, and the beginning of time: what the Hubble telescope saw. Elaine Scott. Clarion Books, 2011. 66 p.

Grades: 5 6 7 8   **522**

1. Hubble Space Telescope 2. Space vehicles 3. Space exploration 4. Telescopes 5. Space
ISBN 9780547241890

LC 2010008040

Through the eye of the Hubble, the author guides readers through the evolution of the universe, investigating the deepest mysteries of the cosmos.

"This examines some of the data that has been collected over the two decades of the Hubble Telescope's operation. Opening chapters discuss the satellite's instrumentation and its 2009 repairs, and then the real fun begins with sections on calculating the age of the universe and its speed of expansion; the nature of dark matter, dark energy, and black holes; star formation; and planet formation, particularly outside our solar system. . . . Gasp-worthy photographs should fire up the most sluggish imaginations." Bulletin of the Center for Children's Books.

Includes bibliographical references (p. [63]) and index.

523 Specific celestial bodies and phenomena

Jennings, Ken, 1974-

Outer space. Ken Jennings; illustrated by Mike Lowery. Little Simon, 2015. 160 p.: Ken Jennings' junior genius guides
Grades: 3 4 5 6   **523**
1. Astronomy 2. Space exploration 3. Solar system 4. Space 5. Trivia and miscellaneous facts
ISBN 9781481401715

Now you can become a junior genius with Ken Jennings' first children's series! With this book you'll become an expert and wow your friends and teachers with out-of-this-world facts: Did you know that Mars has a volcano bigger than the state of Arizona? Or that there's a star with a diamond the size of our moon at its core? With great illustrations, cool trivia, and fun quizzes to test your knowledge, this guide will have you on your way to whiz-kid status in no time! Provided by publisher.

523.1 The universe, galaxies, quasars

Garlick, Mark A. (Mark Antony), 1968-

Atlas of the universe. Mark. A. Garlick. Simon & Schuster Books for Young Readers, 2008, c2007. 128 p.: Insiders
Grades: 5 6 7 8   **523.1**
1. Astronomy 2. Cosmology 3. Space exploration 4. Solar system 5. Space
ISBN 1416955585

LC bl2008016200

Presents the latest findings about the Universe, covering such topics as the solar system and its stars, other galaxies, supernovas, star clusters, nebulas, and black holes, and examines man's effort to explore outer space and find signs of life on other planets.

"Seamlessly commingling luscious, color space photographs and dramatic, sharply detailed digital imagery, this tour of the universe earns high marks for visual impact. It's not too shabby in breadth of coverage either." School Library Journal.

Includes index.

523.2 Science—Astronomy and allied sciences—Specific celestial bodies and phenomena—Planetary systems

Carroll, Michael W., 1955-

Envisioning exoplanets: searching for life in the galaxy. Michael Carroll; foreword by Elisa Quintana; illustrated by Michael Carroll and members of the International Association of Astronomical Artists. Smithsonian Books, 2020 224 p.
Grades: 6 7 8 9 10 11 12 Adult   **523.2**
1. Extrasolar planets 2. Habitable planets 3. Life on other planets 4. Planets
ISBN 9781588346919

LC 2020007210

Envisioning Exoplanets traces the journey of astronomers and researchers on their quest to explore the universe for a planet like Earth. Provided by publisher.

"The most outstanding feature of this book is its high-quality, full-color pictures that include artistic renderings of scientifically accurate exoplanets." Booklist

Includes bibliographical references (page 218) and index.

Kenney, Karen Latchana

Exoplanets: worlds beyond our solar system. by Karen Latchana Kenney. Twenty-First Century Books, [2017] 88 p.
Grades: 8 9 10 11   **523.2**
1. Extrasolar planets 2. Planets 3. Astronomy 4. Milky Way 5. Solar system
ISBN 9781512400861

LC 2016010442

Learn about the planets that exist outside of our solar system, and the actions scientists are taking to learn more about them. Provided by publisher.

"Perfect for outer space enthusiasts and out of this world for report writers." School Library Journal.

Includes bibliographical references and index.

523.4 Science—Astronomy and allied sciences—Specific celestial bodies and phenomena—Planets, asteroids, trans-Neptunian objects of solar system

Siy, Alexandra

Voyager's greatest hits: the epic trek to interstellar space. by Alexandra Siy. Charlesbridge, 2017. 80 p.
Grades: 6 7 8   **523.4**
1. Project Voyager 2. Space probes 3. Space exploration 4. Planets -- Exploration 5. Sense of wonder 6. Space
ISBN 9781580897280

LC 2016013223

A brief history and discussion of the planets and outer space objects encountered by spacecraft Voyager.

"Writing in a conversational style, Siy presents a good deal of information in an accessible way. She creates a sense of discovery as scientists interpret data, and images are sent back by the probes." Booklist.

523.43 Mars

Aldrin, Buzz

Welcome to Mars: making a home on the red planet. Buzz Aldrin and Marianne Dyson. National Geographic Society Childrens books, 2015. 96 p.
Grades: 4 5 6 7 8   **523.43**
1. Space exploration 2. Space flight to Mars 3. Space colonies 4. Astronauts 5. Planets 6. Mars (Planet) 7. Solar system
ISBN 9781426322075

"Colorful images, a time line, and a map of Mars enhance the text. . . . A solid option for readers doing school reports or those curious about exploring a new frontier." School Library Journal.

Rusch, Elizabeth

★ The **mighty** Mars rovers: the incredible adventures of spirit and opportunity. Elizabeth Rusch. Houghton Mifflin Harcourt, 2012. 80 p. : Scientists in the field (Houghton Mifflin)
Grades: 4 5 6   **523.43**
1. Space flight to Mars 2. Mars probes 3. Space exploration 4. Astronautics 5. Mars (Planet) -- Exploration.
ISBN 9780547478814

An edge-of-your-seat adventure story about the relentless team who gave us our first in-depth look at the Martian landscape is filled with awesome pictures from NASA and the author's personal collection.

523.7 Sun

Loomis, Ilima

Eclipse chaser: science in the Moon's shadow. Ilima Loomis; with photographs by Amanda Cowan. Houghton Mifflin Harcourt, 2019 79 p.

Grades: 4 5 6 7 8   **523.7**
   1. Habbal, Shadia Rifai 2. Total solar eclipses 3. Solar eclipses 4. Astrophysicists 5. Total solar eclipses
   ISBN 9781328770967

                         LC 2019000890

The August 2017 solar eclipse is the chance of a lifetime for astronomer Shadia Habbal—years of planning come down to one moment of totality. Will everything go off as planned? Provided by publisher.

523.8 Science—Astronomy and allied sciences—Specific celestial bodies and phenomena—Stars

Dickinson, Terence

Nightwatch: a practical guide to viewing the universe. Terence Dickinson; foreword by Timothy Ferris; illustrations by Adolf Schaller ... [et al.]; principal photography by Terence Dickinson. Firefly Books, c2006. 192 p.

Grades: 8 9 10 11 12 Adult   **523.8**
   1. Astronomy 2. Stars
   ISBN 9781554071470

                       LC bl2006021073

A reference guide for stargazers offers star charts and information on equipment, planets, and stellar photography.

"This handbook for amateur astronomers combines a text both meaty and hard to put down with a great array of charts, boxes, tables, and dazzling full-color photos of the sky." School Library Journal. [review of 1998 edition]

Includes bibliographical references (p. 186-189) and index.

Jackson, Ellen B., 1943-

The **mysterious** universe: supernovae, dark energy, and black holes. text by Ellen Jackson; photographs and illustrations by Nic Bishop. Houghton Mifflin Books, 2008. 60 p.: Scientists in the field (Houghton Mifflin)

Grades: 5 6 7 8 9   **523.8**
   1. Supernovae 2. Dark energy (Astronomy) 3. Black holes (Astronomy) 4. Astronomy
   ISBN 9780618563258

                       LC 2007041165

Follows Dr. Alex Fillippenko and his High-Z Supernova Search Team as they use the Keck telescope in Hawaii to look for supernovae, find black holes, and study the effects of dark energy.

"Splitting its attention evenly between the scientist and his field, this handsomely designed volume displays the joys of being fascinated by one's work in a way that will encourage students to seek similar professional satisfaction for themselves." Booklist.

Includes bibliographical references (p. 54-55) and index.

Latta, Sara L.

Black holes: the weird science of the most mysterious objects in the universe. Sara Latta. Twenty-First Century Books, [2018] 120 p.

Grades: 6 7 8 9   **523.8**
   1. Black holes (Astronomy) 2. Astronomy
   ISBN 9781512415681

                       LC 2016038386

Introduces black holes, discussing the relativity theory of Albert Einstein, the discovery of black holes, the data that scientists use to study them, and scientists' studies of the black hole at the center of the Milky Way.

525 Earth (Astronomical geography)

Nardo, Don, 1947-

The **blue** marble: how a photograph showcases a fragile planet. by Don Nardo. Compass Point Books, 2014 64 p.: Captured history

Grades: 5 6 7 8 9   **525**
   1. Apollo 17 (Spacecraft) 2. Photographs -- History 3. Space flight 4. Earth
   ISBN 9780756547325

                       LC 2013031184

Discusses the iconic Blue Marble photo of Earth taken by the Apollo 17 astronauts in December 1972. Provided by publisher.

"This outstanding follow-up to Capstone's 'Captured History' series continues the same format, focusing on a single, emblematic photograph that defines an era or event. . . . This set will show students how a single image can 'capture' history and influence the perceptions and actions of those who see it. The books will certainly draw a large readership and are must-buys for all middle-level and secondary collections." School Library Journal.

Includes bibliographical references and index.

Simon, Seymour

Earth: our planet in space. Seymour Simon. Simon & Schuster Books for Young Readers, c2003. 1 v. (unpaged)

Grades: 4 5 6 7   **525**
   1. Planets 2. Astronomy 3. Earth
   ISBN 0689835620

                       LC 2001031304

Photographs of Earth help explain our home planet, tell what it looks like and furnish information on its composition and its place in the universe.

529 Chronology

Formichelli, Linda, 1969-

Timekeeping: explore the history and science of telling time with 15 projects. Linda Formichelli, W. Eric Martin, Sam Carbaugh. Independent Pub Group, 2012. 120 p.: Build it yourself

Grades: 4 5 6 7 8   **529**
   1. Time -- History 2. Clocks and watches 3. Calendars 4. Time measurements 5. Creative activities for children and students
   ISBN 9781619301368

A cultural history of time imparts facts in engaging and accessible ways while outlining numerous hands-on activities, from making a shadow clock and a candle clock to measuring time with water and using a protractor to create a sundial.

530 Science—Physics

Claybourne, Anna

The **nature** of matter. Anna Claybourne. Gareth Stevens Pub., 2007. 48 p.: Gareth Stevens vital science: physical science
Grades: 4 5 6 7   **530**
   1. Matter 2. Atoms 3. Physical chemistry 4. Molecules
ISBN 9780836880885

              LC 2006033732

Discusses matter, from atoms and elements and how they bond to the properties of solids, liquids, and gases.

   "This is straightforward and clear. . . . The layout is bright and colorful, with photographs and illustrations on almost every page." School Library Journal.

   Includes bibliographical references (p. 46) and index.

Field, Andrea R.

Matter. edited by Andrea R. Field. Britannica Educational Pub. in association with Rosen Educational Services, c2013. 77 p.: Introduction to physics
Grades: 7 8 9 10   **530**
   1. Matter -- Properties 2. Physics 3. Atoms 4. Molecules
ISBN 9781615308392

              LC 2011052216

Examines the physics of matter, its various states, how forces act upon it, how it relates to energy, and the different theories behind it.

The **science** of physics. edited by Andrea Field. Britannica Educational Pub., 2012. 80 p.: Introduction to physics
Grades: 7 8 9 10   **530**
   1. Physics 2. Physical sciences
ISBN 9781615306763

              LC 2011026548

Presents an introduction to the science of physics, covering the history, important concepts, main branches, and applied technology of the field.

Lee, Cora

The **great** motion mission: a surprising story of physics in everyday life. by Cora Lee; illustrated by Steve Rolston. Annick Press, c2009. 114 p.
Grades: 4 5 6   **530**
   1. Physics 2. Professional conferences 3. Teenagers 4. Summer 5. Exchange students
ISBN 9781554511846

   "This book is a combination of narrative and concepts about physics. . . . Jeremy and his friends are distraught when the local summer fair is canceled in order to host a physics conference. While Jeremy helps his uncle campaign to save the fair, his new neighbor, Aubrey, sets out to prove that physics isn't only necessary, but also fun. The text is chatty and accessible to students. Topics include Physics and Sight, Physics and Sound, and Physics in Motion. Each chapter profiles a featured physicist, from Albert Einstein to Richard Feynman. . . . Cartoon illustrations help to explain concepts such as the water cycle and wave patterns. Photographs are scattered throughout, and boxed areas highlight specific topics. This title would be especially useful for students wanting a good introduction to physics." School Library Journal.

530.078 Physics experiments

Brown, Jordan

Science stunts: fun feats of physics. Jordan D. Brown; illustrated by Anthony Owsley. Charlesbridge Publishing, 2016. 80 p.
Grades: 4 5 6 7   **530.078**
   1. Physics 2. Experiments 3. Science
ISBN 9781623540647

   "Magical science that's amazing, astounding, and sure to appeal to middle-grade and middle school readers." Kirkus.

Gardner, Robert, 1929-

Solids, liquids, and gases experiments using water, air, marbles, and more: one hour or less science experiments. Robert Gardner. Enslow Publishers, 2012. 48 p.: Last-minute science projects
Grades: 4 5 6 7   **530.078**
   1. Change of state (Physics) -- Experiments 2. Matter 3. Science -- Experiments
ISBN 9780766039629

              LC 2011019957

Provides simple experiments to learn about the changing states of matter, density, viscosity, and the conduction of electricity by solids. Provided by publisher.

530.092 Physicists

Bailey, Diane, 1966-

Physics. by Diane Bailey; foreword by Malinda Gilmore, Ph. D., Executive Board Chair, and Mel Poulson, Executive Board Vice-Chair, National Organization for the Professional Advancement of Black Chemists and Chemical Engineers (NOBCChE). Mason Crest, an imprint of National Highlights, Inc., [2017] 64 p.: Black achievement in science
Grades: 7 8 9 10 11 12   **530.092**
   1. African American physicists 2. African American scientists 3. Physicists 4. African Americans 5. Scientific discoveries
ISBN 9781422235621

              LC oc2016025654

   "This book is well suited to reports, with a list of text-dependent questions, suggested research projects, a bibliography of websites and books, a series glossary of key terms, and QR codes that link to videos about the scientists." Booklist.

   Includes bibliographical references and index.

530.11 Relativity theory

Hunter, Nick

Is time travel possible? Nick Hunter. Capstone, [2016] 48 p.: Ignite: top secret!
Grades: 5 6 7 8   **530.11**
   1. Time travel 2. Physics 3. Space and time 4. Special relativity (Physics) 5. Questions and answers
ISBN 9781410981622

              LC 2015024556

   "The discourse is, unsurprisingly, only ankle deep, but readers will be swept off their feet by the flood of big ideas, cosmic theories, silly speculations, and tantalizing hints of awesome scientific discoveries waiting just around the corner." Booklist.

Includes bibliographical references and index.

531 Classical mechanics

Rooney, Anne

You wouldn't want to live without gravity! written by Anne Rooney; illustrated by Mark Bergin. Franklin Watts, an imprint of Scholastic Inc., [2016]. 40 p.: You wouldn't want to...

Grades: 3 4 5 6   **531**

1. Gravity 2. Weightlessness
ISBN 9780531214879

"The books feature a time line and numerous ancillaries, but the myriad entertaining facts are the real hit. Who wouldn't want to read them?" Booklist.

535 Light and related radiation

Caes, Charles J.

Discovering the speed of light. Charles J. Caes. Rosen Pub., 2012. 112 p.: The scientist's guide to physics

Grades: 5 6 7 8   **535**

1. Light -- Speed -- Measurement 2. Light 3. Optics
ISBN 9781448846993

LC 2010048426

Introduces the study of light, explores the various experiments used to explain it, and looks at theories from Max Planck, Albert Einstein, and Lene Hau.

Sitarski, Anita

Cold light: creatures, discoveries, and inventions that glow. Anita Sitarski. Boyds Mills Press, c2007. 48 p.

Grades: 5 6 7 8   **535**

1. Boyle, Robert, 1627-1691. 2. Luminescence
ISBN 1590784685

LC bl2007024610

Explores the science and wonder of cold light—the chemistry of animals and things that make light but not heat—by recounting the many stories of alchemist and chemist Robert Boyle who discovered this phenomenon in the seventeenth century.

"A clearly written, chatty text not only discusses the expected bioluminescent critters (think fireflies), but delves into the realms of chemiluminescence, photoluminescence, and LEDs (light-emitting diodes) as well. . . . The text lays out the historical hows and whys of cold light, its success in the natural world, and its application in medicine and domestic/industrial illumination. Clear color photos and information boxes abound." School Library Journal.

Includes bibliographical references (p. 45) and index.

Winterberg, Jenna

★ **Light** and its effects. Jenna Winterberg. Shell Education, 2015. 32 p.

Grades: 4 5 6   **535**

1. Light 2. Light and darkness
ISBN 9781480746855

"Smartly written, these innovative and imaginative volumes make learning fun... First-rate nonfiction." School Library Journal.

535.078 Optics—Science experiments

Canavan, Thomas, 1956-

Super experiments with light and sound. Thomas Canavan; illustrated by Adam Linley. Gareth Stevens Publishing, 2017. 32 p.: Mind-blowing science experiments

Grades: 4 5 6 7   **535.078**

1. Light 2. Sound 3. Experiments 4. Optics 5. Waves
ISBN 9781538207451

Collects hands-on experiments that exhibit scientific principles that deal with such light and sound properties as refraction, centripetal force, sound waves, and heat absorption.

537 Electricity and electronics

Anderson, Michael

Electricity. edited by Michael Anderson. Britannica Educational Pub. in association with Rosen Educational Services, 2012. 79 p.: Introduction to physics

Grades: 7 8 9 10   **537**

1. Electricity 2. Electric power 3. Science
ISBN 9781615306657

LC 2011017090

Presents an introduction to Electricity and magnetism, covering the history of their study, important concepts related to them, and applied technology that utilizes these forces.

"...Features clear diagrams and is a narrow enough topic to be well covered, with chapters on circuits, magnetic fields, and generators." Booklist.

Includes bibliographical references (p. 76) and index.

Galiano, Dean

Electric and magnetic phenomena. Dean Galiano. Rosen Central, 2011. 64 p.: Science made simple

Grades: 5 6 7 8   **537**

1. Electricity 2. Magnetism 3. Physics
ISBN 9781448812318

LC 2010014546

Presents an introduction to electricity and magnetism, the physics behind them, and how they work at an everyday level.

"This introduction to electric and magnetic phenomena includes a lot of detailed information, making [it] useful as [a] resource . . . for science projects and reports. . . . The [book] also [includes a] brief discussion of scientists important in the field, the history of the topic, and current and future applications. . . . The straightforward, no-nonsense [narrative] and simple design make this . . . a nice package for basic science." School Library Journal.

Includes bibliographical references (p. 59-61) and index.

539.7 Atomic and nuclear physics

Campbell, Margaret Christine

Discovering atoms. Margaret Christine Campbell and Natalie Goldstein. Rosen Pub., 2012. 112 p.: Scientist's guide to physics

Grades: 5 6 7 8 9   **539.7**

1. Atoms 2. Atomic theory 3. Matter -- Constitution 4. Physical

chemistry
ISBN 9781448847006

LC 2010048416

Provides a history of atoms, explores the properties and laws of chemicals, and discusses the new subatomic particles.

Conkling, Winifred

Radioactive!: how Irene Curie and Lise Meitner revolutionized science and changed the world. by Winifred Conkling. Algonquin Young Readers, an imprint of Algonquin Books of Chapel Hill, 2016. 176 p.

Grades: 7 8 9 10 **539.7**
1. Joliot-Curie, Irene, 1897-1956 2. Meitner, Lise, 1878-1968 3. Radioactivity 4. Nuclear fission 5. Women scientists 6. Scientists
ISBN 9781616204150

LC 2015017256

"Black-and-white period photos, scientific asides and diagrams, and a time line enhance the well-cited text." Booklist.

Includes bibliographical references and index.

Latta, Sara L.

SMASH!: exploring the mysteries of the universe with the Large Hadron Collider. Sara Latta; illustrated by Jeff Weigel. Graphic Universe, a division of Lerner Publishing Group, Inc., 2017. 72 p.

Grades: 6 7 8 9 **539.7**
1. European Organization for Nuclear Research. 2. Large Hadron Collider (France and Switzerland) 3. Particles (Nuclear physics) 4. Nuclear physics 5. Particle accelerators 6. Quantum theory 7. Comics and Graphic novels
ISBN 9781467785518

LC 2016017321

Nick and Sophie, two cousins from the United States, visit the European Organization for Nuclear Research and learn about the Large Hadron Collider. Throughout their tour, they chat about the mysteries of particle physics and the building blocks of matter. Provided by publisher.

"An accessible look at the Large Hadron Collider (LHC) and particle physics." School Library Journal.

Includes bibliographical references.

Manning, Phillip, 1936-

Atoms, molecules, and compounds. Phillip Manning. Chelsea House Publishers, c2008. 137 p.: Essential chemistry

Grades: 7 8 9 10 **539.7**
1. Atoms 2. Molecules 3. Matter -- Constitution 4. Chemical reactions
ISBN 0791095347

LC 2007011403

Discusses what atoms are and how they were discovered and explores reactions between atoms, the properties of the resulting molecule, and the importance of the interactions between molecules to life on Earth.

"In relatively few pages, and with lots of colorful, clear illustrations, Manning takes us from Thompson's plum-pudding model of the atom to Rutherford's model to the quantum model, and through the discovery of atomic particles and the teasing out of atomic forces, in a very clear, compelling path. . . . The clear linkages he makes between the different types of chemical bonds and the nature of various materials will remain with the reader." Science Books & Films.

Includes bibliographical references (p. 126-129) and index.

540 Science—Chemistry—Chemistry and allied sciences

Green, Dan, 1975 June 20-

Chemistry:[getting a big reaction!]. [created by Basher; written by Dan Green]. Kingfisher, c2010. 128 p.: Basher science

Grades: 4 5 6 7 **540**
1. Chemistry 2. Chemical reactions 3. Science
ISBN 9780753464137

"This begins with a short overview of [chemistry] and information on Antoine Lavoisier's 18th-century scientific findings. Concepts are grouped by associations: Basic States (solid, liquid, etc.), Nuts and Bolts (atom, ion, etc.), Nasty Boys (acid, base, etc.), and more. The individual concepts are each introduced over a spread that features a computer-generated cartoon of a character representing the idea and a brief introduction to its characteristics and personality. . . . The information is presented in a chatty, first-person voice." School Library Journal.

Mooney, Carla, 1970-

Chemistry: investigate the matter that makes up your world. Carla Mooney, Samuel Carbaugh. Nomad Press, 2016. 128 p.: Inquire and investigate

Grades: 6 7 8 9 10 **540**
1. Chemistry 2. Matter 3. Chemical elements 4. Atoms 5. Organic compounds
ISBN 9781619303614

Have you ever wondered what makes up everything in the world around you? Or what exactly is the difference between solids, liquids, and gases? Have you wanted to know what causes two substances to react or change? Chemistry: Investigate the Matter that Makes Up Your World introduces readers 12 through 15 to the fascinating world of protons, neutrons, and electrons. Learn how these molecules combine to form ordinary objects such as the chair you're sitting on, the water in your glass, even you! Through hands-on, investigative projects, readers delve into the world of chemical reactions and changing matter, learning how these principles are used in many areas of science, from biochemistry to nuclear science. Combining hands-on science inquiry with chemistry, mathematics, and biology, projects include building models of molecules and bonds, identifying acids and bases, investigating the effect of temperature on reaction rate, and observing how a chemical reaction from vinegar, water, and bleach can accelerate the rusting of steel. Chemistry offers entertaining illustrations and fascinating sidebars to illuminate the topic and engage readers further, plus integrates a digital learning component by providing links to primary sources, videos, and other relevant websites.

"Those with a science bent will find the information easily accessible and concise, while those with little interest will be drawn to the colorful graphic illustrations and highlighted sidebars. The experiments provided will inspire and encourage further discovery of the world of science." School Library Journal.

Rae, Rowena

Chemical world: science in our daily lives. Rowena Rae. Orca Book Publishers, 2020. 48 p.: Orca Footprints

Grades: 4 5 6 7 **540**
1. Chemistry 2. Chemicals
ISBN 9781459821576

Part of the nonfiction Footprints series for middle readers, this book examines the good and the bad of the chemicals we come into contact with in our daily lives. Provided by publisher.

"In this Orca Footprints offering, Rae not only demystifies chemistry in our everyday lives but also emphasizes how it affects our environment by using everyday language to clarify technical jargon. Numerous color photos, sidebars, and the author's personal interactions with chemistry keep the topic accessible and relatable." Booklist

Stefoff, Rebecca, 1951-

Alchemy and chemistry. Rebecca Stefoff. Cavendish Square, 2014. 48 p.

Grades: 6 7 8   **540**

    1. Alchemy -- History 2. Chemistry 3. Pseudoscience -- History 4. Scientific errors

ISBN 9781627125093

"Each volume is heavily illustrated with period images and modern photographs, and each closes with particularly generous lists of further resources." School Library Journal.

541 Physical chemistry

Heinecke, Liz Lee

Chemistry for kids: homemade science experiments and activities inspired by awesome chemists, past and present. Liz Lee Heinecke; photography: Amber Procaccini Photography; illustrations: Kelly Anne Dalton. Quarry Books, an imprint of The Quarto Group, 2020. 128 p.: The kitchen pantry scientist

Grades: 3 4 5 6 7   **541**

    1. Chemists 2. Chemistry -- Experiments 3. Chemistry -- History

ISBN 9781631598302

                        LC 2019050167

The kitchen pantry scientist's guide to chemistry features biographies of 25 leading chemists, past and present, accompanied by accessible, hands-on experiments and activities to bring the history and principles of chemistry alive. Provided by publisher.

Richardson, Gillian

Kaboom!: explosions of all kinds. by Gillian Richardson. Annick Press, 2009. 83 p.

Grades: 4 5 6 7   **541**

    1. Explosions 2. Volcanoes 3. Bombs 4. Halifax Explosion, December 6, 1917 5. Seeds 6. Earth 7. Space

ISBN 9781554512041

"With comic-style sound-effect headings and fact boxes galore, Kaboom! highlights the supercharged of the natural and manmade worlds, from astronomy, geology, biology, herbology, and entomology to chemistry, mechanics, pyrotechnics, and art. Text is broken into asymmetrical panels for bite-size explanations. Some explosions are captured in sequence and detail with historical and high-speed photography and illustrations in comic-style panel frames. . . . Kaboom! is an engrossing attention-getter, effectively tapping the sensationalism of all types of blasts." School Library Journal.

546 Inorganic chemistry

Dingle, Adrian, 1967-

The **complete** periodic table: more elements with style! created by Basher; written by Adrian Dingle and Dan Green. Kingfisher, 2014, c2007. 192 p.: Basher science

Grades: 4 5 6 7   **546**

    1. Periodic law 2. Chemical elements 3. Chemistry 4. Books for

reluctant readers

ISBN 9780753471975

                        LC 2006022515

"After a brief introduction to Mendeleev's famous table and a spread on the chart-topping loner, hydrogen, Dingle presents the elements by group. . . . Data on featured elements includes symbol, atomic number and weight, color, standard state, classification, density, boiling and melting points, . . . a diagram of the position in the periodic table, a full-page original anime-styled icon, . . . and descriptive paragraphs that rise from informative all the way to entertaining." Bulletin of the Center for Children's Books.

Just add water:

Just add water: science experiments you can sink, squirt, splash, sail.. from the editors of the New Book of Popular Science. Children's Press, c2008. 32 p.: Experiment with science

Grades: 5 6 7 8   **546**

    1. Water -- Experiments 2. Hydrodynamics 3. Science projects 4. Physical sciences 5. Science -- Experiments

ISBN 9780531185452

                        LC 2007021682

Presents nine science projects designed to help students learn about the properties and interactions of water and the scientific method.

"The book consists of nine hands-on activities that target physical science concepts inherent in water (e.g. density, buoyancy, and hardness.) . . . Students . . . will likely find the age-appropriate activities engaging and purposeful. . . . The colorful photos augment the narrative and the science is sound." Science Books & Films.

Includes bibliographical references (p. 29) and index.

Oxlade, Chris

Metals. Chris Oxlade. Heinemann Library, c2007. 48 p.: Chemicals in action

Grades: 6 7 8 9   **546**

    1. Metals 2. Chemistry 3. Chemical elements

ISBN 9781432900540

Provides an introduction to metals, including their physical properties, their place in the periodic table, their uses in everyday life, and how they react with other substances. Includes experiments.

Thomas, Isabel, 1979-

Exploring the elements: a complete guide to the periodic table. words by Isabel Thomas; pictures by Sara Gillingham. Phaidon Press, 2020. 223 p.

Grades: 4 5 6 7 8   **546**

    1. Periodic table of the elements 2. Chemical elements 3. Periodic law

ISBN 9781838662318

A comprehensive introduction explaining what elements are and the design and purpose of the periodic table. Each of the 118 elements is visually presented with its respective letter symbol and atomic number, as well as a map of where it's located in the periodic table. Additional details showing where each element is found in the universe (from food on our plates to the center of a star), its unique properties, atomic diagram, secret chemistry, and working examples of how its's used or changing the world." Amazon.com.

"Chic, minimalist illustrations and clear, engaging text combine in a striking and attractive design. . . . Could make a chemist out of anyone." Kirkus

550 Science—Earth sciences & geology—Earth sciences

Allaby, Michael

National Geographic visual encyclopedia of Earth. Michael Allaby. National Geographic, 2008. 256 p.

Grades: 7 8 9 10   **550**

    1. Earth sciences 2. Ecosystem management 3. Climate change 4. Rain forests 5. Global environmental change 6. Earth
    ISBN 9781426303678

A single-volume reference provides the latest research on Earth's fragile ecosystems and climate shift and includes coverage of the world's oceans, landforms, weather, and resources.

    "This overview of the earth . . . cover[s] all aspects of earth science. . . . [This] is a feast for the eyes and an exceptional introduction to earth science. It will be a useful resource for science teachers who want to engage their students in this subject matter." Library Media Connection.

Reilly, Kathleen M.

Natural disasters: investigate Earth's most destructive forces with 25 projects. Kathleen M. Reilly, Tom Casteel. Independent Pub Group, 2012. 128 p.: Build it yourself

Grades: 4 5 6 7   **550**

    1. Natural disasters 2. Disasters 3. Hurricanes 4. Volcanoes 5. Wildfires
    ISBN 9781619301467

Instructive, hands-on activities enable young science enthusiasts to explore the causes and impact of natural disasters through table-shaking exercises, a cake batter lava flow experiment, a wind tunnel re-creation and more.

551.1 Gross structure and properties of the earth

Reilly, Kathleen M.

Fault lines & tectonic plates: discover what happens when the Earth's crust moves. Kathleen M. Reilly; illustrated by Chad Thompson. Pgw 2017 128 p.: Build It Yourself

Grades: 4 5 6 7   **551.1**

    1. Faults (Geology) 2. Plate tectonics 3. Geology 4. Physical sciences 5. Earth sciences
    ISBN 9781619304611

Explains how plate tectonics causes earthquakes and volcanoes, discussing the movement of the Earth's crust and offering twenty-five science activities to explore geological principles.

551.2 Science—Earth sciences & geology—Geology, hydrology, meteorology—Volcanoes, earthquakes, thermal waters and gases

Nargi, Lela

  ★ **Volcanoes**: all the latest facts from the field. Lela Nargi; with National Geographic explorer Arianna Soldati. National Geographic, 2018 112 p.

Grades: 4 5 6 7 8   **551.2**

    1. Volcanoes
    ISBN 9781426331428

                 LC bl2018146361

Introduces volcanoes, describing how they form, why they erupt, and some of the most explosive eruptions throughout history.

"The book's attractive design and tone will appeal to casual readers, but even those with serious interests will unearth scads of new information." Booklist.

Includes bibliographical references (page 108) and index.

551.21 Volcanoes

Fradin, Judith Bloom

Volcanoes. [Judy & Dennis Fradin]. National Geographic, c2007. 48 p.: Witness to disaster

Grades: 4 5 6 7   **551.21**

    1. Volcanoes 2. Geology 3. Natural disasters
    ISBN 0792253779

                 LC 2006102817

Describes what volcanoes are, what causes them to erupt, and their effect on the landscape.

    "This introduces readers to these violent eruptions, using eyewitness accounts to explain the history and science involved. They begin with a report of the 1943 birth of a volcano in Paricutn, Mexico. . . . Subsequent chapters describe other celebrated volcanoes, explain their causes and types, note the benefits of these eruptions, and clarify how they are currently predicted. . . . Numerous clear, well-chosen photographs and diagrams help to convey the great power of volcanic activity and the consequences to humans. . . . This will be useful for report writers, and a fascinating pick for browsers." Booklist.

Includes bibliographical references (p. 45-46) and index.

551.22 Earthquakes

Fradin, Judith Bloom

Earthquakes: witness to disaster. by Judy and Dennis Fradin. National Geographic, c2008. 48 p. : Witness to disaster

Grades: 4 5 6 7   **551.22**

    1. Earthquakes 2. Earthquakes
    ISBN 1426302126

                 LC 2007044164

Uses eyewitness accounts to bring readers into the heart of an earthquake. The first chapter documents the 1964 Alaskan quake that shook Prince William Sound with a 9.2 magnitude force, and set off a tsunami that ultimately caused most of the deaths attributed to this frightening act of nature. The following chapters explore the history of earthquakes and the seismic and geological science of this phenomenon.

    "The combination of good writing and excellent graphics paired with archival and personal perspectives makes this book a valuable addition." School Library Journal.

Includes bibliographical references.

Stewart, Melissa

Inside earthquakes. By Melissa Stewart; illustrations throughout by Cynthia Shaw. Sterling Children's Books, 2011. 48 p.: Inside series

Grades: 5 6 7 8   **551.22**

    1. Earthquakes
    ISBN 9781402758775

                 LC 2010046452

    "This book about earthquakes explores its topic in an engaging way, and the many illustrations work well with adjacent text and captions. . . . The [book's] varied page layouts are attractive and the quality of photos, computer-generated images, original illustrations, and charts is . . . excellent. . . . [The book] looks at the geology of the earth's crust as well as the effects of quakes on people and cities, landforms and coast-lines." Booklist.

Includes bibliographical references (pages 46-47) and index.

Winchester, Simon

When the earth shakes: earthquakes, volcanoes, and tsuna-mis. Simon Winchester. Viking, [2015] 80 p.: Smithsonian

Grades: 5 6 7 8   **551.22**

1. Earthquakes 2. Volcanoes 3. Tsunamis 4. Natural disasters 5. Earth sciences

ISBN 9780670785360

LC 2014039743

"A must-buy for libraries serving middle school, this title works both as a basic overview of earth science and as a fine example of how to incorporate personal narrative into nonfiction." School Library Journal.

551.3 Surface and exogenous processes and their agents

Rusch, Elizabeth

Impact!: asteroids and the science of saving the world. Elizabeth Rusch; photographs by Karin Anderson. Houghton Mifflin Harcourt 2017 80 p.: Scientists in the field (Houghton Mifflin)

Grades: 6 7 8 9 10   **551.3**

1. Natural disasters 2. Asteroids -- Collisions with Earth

ISBN 9780544671591

"Accompanied by photographs of scientists in action and requisite space shots, the book concludes with citizen science connections and re-sources and is sure to have an impact on young astronomers." Booklist.

551.46 Oceanography and submarine geology

Burns, Loree Griffin

Tracking trash: flotsam, jetsam, and the science of ocean motion. Loree Griffin Burns. Houghton Mifflin, 2007. 56 p.: Scientists in the field (Houghton Mifflin)

Grades: 5 6 7 8   **551.46**

1. Ocean currents 2. Marine debris 3. Pollution

ISBN 0618581316

LC 2006011534

Describes the work of a man who tracks trash as it travels great dis-tances by way of ocean currents.

"The book profiles two oceanographers who devised experiments using computer-modeling programs of ocean surface current movement to predict the landfall of . . . drifting objects. . . . Spacious layout, excep-tionally fine color photos, and handsome maps give this book an inviting look. . . . A unique and often fascinating book." Booklist.

Includes bibliographical references (p. 56) and index.

Earle, Sylvia A., 1935-

Extreme ocean: amazing animals, high-tech gear, record-breaking depths, and much more! Sylvia Earle, Glen Phalen. National Geographic Children's Books, 2020 112 p.: National Geographic kids

Grades: 4 5 6 7 8   **551.46**

1. Oceans 2. Underwater exploration 3. Conservation of natural resources 4. Marine ecology 5. Oceanography

ISBN 9781426336867

Discover the most outrageous aspects of the deep blue—-from re-cord-breaking depths to towering tsunamis, underwater giants to tiny sea creatures—along with ocean conservation challenges and what you can do to help.

MacQuitty, Miranda

Eyewitness ocean. written by Dr. Miranda MacQuitty; pho-tographed by Frank Greenaway. DK Publishing, 2014. 72 p.

Grades: 4 5 6 7   **551.46**

1. Marine animals 2. Oceans

ISBN 9781465420541

LC 2015300894

Explores the diversity of life in the sea, including predators and prey, the coral reef, and life in the twilight zone of the ocean, with informa-tion on products of the ocean, ocean explorers, and preservation of this natural resource.

Mallory, Kenneth

At home beneath the sea: seven days in an underwater labo-ratory. Kenneth Mallory; photographs by Brian Skerry. Boyds Mills Press, c2009. 48 p.

Grades: 4 5 6 7   **551.46**

1. Oceanographic submersibles 2. Underwater exploration 3. Oceanography 4. Deep diving 5. Ocean bottom 6. Florida Keys National Marine Sanctuary (Fla)

ISBN 9781590786079

LC 2009024226

"The author invites readers to squeeze into Aquarius, a venerable science-station habitat resting on the sea floor at a depth of 60 feet in the Florida Keys. The readable text explains the complexities of training for a weeklong stay, the aims of the scientists on the team, and what it is like to spend 24/7 in squashed companionship in a 43' 9' cylinder as part of a crew of seven. . . . Sidebars contain interesting information. . . . Full-color photos abound." School Library Journal.

Includes bibliographical references and index.

551.48 Hydrology

Peters, Marilee, 1968-

10 rivers that shaped the world. Marilee Peters; art by Kim Rosen. Annick Press, 2015. 132 p.

Grades: 4 5 6 7   **551.48**

1. Rivers 2. Streams 3. Earth sciences

ISBN 1554517397

Learn how rivers shaped human civilizations by introducing the 10 most famous rivers in the world.

"Each of the 10 rivers detailed in this book has its own chapter, which includes chronological narratives about the groups of people who have called the river home. Full-color maps show each river's head-waters and terminus, and photographs detail major cultural attractions, wildlife, and artifacts. . . . The book is intent on helping young readers make the connection between physical and human geography and on understanding the myriad of forces that shape a peoples culture. With a colorful, engaging layout and a unique approach to its topic, this title is a solid entry point to both geography and world history." Booklist.

Includes bibliographical references, Internet addresses and index.

551.5 Meteorology

Hackney Blackwell, Amy
   U-X-L encyclopedia of weather and natural disasters. Amy Hackney Blackwell, editor; Elizabeth Manar, project editor. U-X-L, a part of Gale Cengage Learning, 2016 888 p.
Grades: 7 8 9   **551.5**
   1. Meteorology 2. Natural disasters
   ISBN 9781410332905
                                                 LC 2015032053
Presents comprehensive, up-to-date information on weather and climate basics, weather conditions and phenomena, natural disasters, forecasting, and human influences on weather and climate.

551.55 Atmospheric disturbances and formations

Carson, Mary Kay
   Inside hurricanes. by Mary Kay Carson. Sterling, c2010. 48 p.: Inside series
Grades: 5 6 7 8   **551.55**
   1. Hurricanes 2. Weather 3. Natural disasters
   ISBN 9781402758805
                                                 LC bl2010026258
Examines the nature of hurricanes, what they look like, how they occur, and how to stay safe in a storm.
   "This trip into the eye of the storm is enveloping in more ways than one. . . . The pages fold up, or down, or left, or right, with every turn guided by an icon familiar to anyone who lives in a storm zone: a circular blue Hurricane Evacuation Route road sign. This constant motion can't help but engage. . . . The design and layout is well above par, featuring excellent cutaways of storm systems, meteorological maps, thrilling photography, and a spectacular foldout Saffir-Simpson Hurricane Scale. The text is packed with info, data, and case studies broken into digestible chunks, and boxes and sidebars . . . make this . . . very appealing." Booklist.
Includes bibliographical references (p. 46) and index.

   Inside tornadoes. Mary Kay Carson. Sterling, 2010. 48 p.: ill. (some col.), col. maps; 26 cm.: Inside series
Grades: 5 6 7 8   **551.55**
   1. Tornadoes 2. Storms 3. Meteorology 4. Disasters 5. Earth sciences
   ISBN 9781402758799
"This visually tempting title defines and explains the storms people call twisters, gives examples of four particularly devastating ones in this country, describes tornado watchers at work, offers hands-on activity and suggests precautions for tornado safety. . . . It includes step-by-step explanatory text, striking images and helpful graphics." Kirkus.

Fradin, Judith Bloom
   Tornado!: the story behind these twisting, turning, spinning, and spiraling storms. by Judith Bloom Fradin & Dennis Brindell Fradin. National Geographic, c2011. 63 p.
Grades: 4 5 6 7   **551.55**
   1. Tornadoes 2. Natural disasters 3. Severe storms 4. Storms
   ISBN 9781426307799
                                                 LC 2010042813
Presents information about tornadoes and the damage that they can cause, with facts, scientific explanations, photographs, first-person accounts, and historical reports of deadly tornadoes.

"Two of the four chapters describe deadly twisters in the U.S., while the others discuss the science and predictability of tornadoes. Throughout, there are first-person accounts. . . . Excellent color photos make this book a magnet for browsers, while the informative text and diagrams bring meaning to the images and provide content that students will find helpful for reports." Booklist.
Includes bibliographical references (p. 60-61) and index.

Prokos, Anna
   Tornadoes. by Anna Prokos. Gareth Stevens Pub., 2009. 48 p.: Ultimate 10.
Grades: 5 6 7 8   **551.55**
   1. Tornadoes 2. Storms 3. Severe storms 4. Natural disasters
   ISBN 9780836891539
                                                 LC 2008018949
"Tornadoes are described, while color photos illustrate the resulting damage, conveying a significant part of the information through their captions. . . . Explanations of weather terms . . . are included; additional facts are boxed off from the text; and preparation/safety tips are appended. . . . An especially useful book." School Library Journal.
Includes bibliographical references and index.

Roker, Al, 1954-
   Al Roker's extreme weather: tornadoes, typhoons, and other weather phenomena. Al Roker. Harper, 2017 48 p.
Grades: 3 4 5 6   **551.55**
   1. Meteorology 2. Severe storms 3. Weather
   ISBN 9780062484994
                                                 LC bl2017035782
The popular weather forecaster examines extreme and rare weather phenomena that covers such subjects as spider lightning, derechos, and fogsicles.

Shoals, James
   Extreme weather. James Shoals. Mason Crest, 2020 48 p.
Grades: 6 7 8 9   **551.55**
   1. Weather -- Effect of human beings on 2. Severe storms 3. Climatic changes 4. Natural disasters
   ISBN 9781422243558
                                                 LC 2019013904
Climate change and natural disasters, such as heat waves, droughts, floods, earthquakes, hurricanes, and thunderstorms, have been occurring since the dawn of time. But global warming is a phenomenon induced by humankind. Scientists across the world have been thoroughly examining the changing climate, and have found close links between global warming and extreme climatic events. Global warming induced by humans has drastically altered global climatic patterns. Natural disasters that used to occur once in a hundred years are now occurring more frequently, more extensively, and with greater intensity. The destruction and damage caused by such events are also increasing. Frequent extremities in weather events are drastically affecting the global population by increasing the death toll each passing year. Provided by publisher.

551.56 Atmospheric electricity and optics

Stewart, Melissa
   Inside lightning. Melissa Stewart; illustrations by Cynthia Shaw. Sterling Children's Books, 2011. 48 p.: Inside series
Grades: 5 6 7 8   **551.56**
   1. Lightning 2. Weather
   ISBN 9781402758782

"This book about lightning explores its topic in an engaging way, and the many illustrations work well with adjacent text and captions. . . . The [book's] varied page layouts and attractive and the quality of photos, computer-generated images, original illustrations, and charts is . . . excellent. . . . Featuring a step-by-step, illustrated explanation of lightning formation as well as comments from people who have had close encounters with the phenomenon, Inside Lightning provides a vivid and unusually informative introduction to the subject." Booklist.

551.6 Climatology and weather

Cherry, Lynne

How we know what we know about our changing climate: scientists and kids explore global warming. by Lynne Cherry and Gary Braasch; photographs by Gary Braasch. Dawn Publications, c2008. 64 p.

Grades: 4 5 6 7   **551.6**
    1. Climate change 2. Global warming
    ISBN 1584691034

Describes where scientists look to find evidence of climate change—from changes in bird migration patterns and fruit blossom dates, to obtaining tree rings and mud cores—and especially how students and other citizen-scientists are assisting to monitor climate change, as well as what can be done to mitigate global warming.

"The can-do emphasis helps to make the topic less depressing, and the intriguing color photographs are thoughtful and upbeat." Booklist.
Includes bibliographical references.

Danneberg, Julie, 1958-

The **science** of weather and climate: rain, sleet, and the rising tide. Julie Danneberg; illustrated by Michelle Simpson. Nomad Press, 2020 120 p.: Inquire & investigate

Grades: 7 8 9   **551.6**
    1. Weather 2. Climatology
    ISBN 9781619308473

Complemented by STEM-based activities, from creating a barometer to testing the effects of air pressure, an introduction to the science and impact of today's turbulent weather provides introductory coverage of meteorology, climatology and global climate change. Index.

Drimmer, Stephanie Warren

National Geographic kids ultimate weather-pedia: the most complete weather reference ever. Stephanie Warren Drimmer. National Geographic, 2019 272 p.

Grades: 4 5 6 7   **551.6**
    1. Weather
    ISBN 9781426335433

                    LC bl2019031975

Shares in-depth information about weather, including extreme weather, climate change, and animal adaptation behaviors.

551.7 Historical geology

Brown, Don, 1949-

Older than dirt: a wild but true history of Earth. by Don Brown & Professor Mike Perfit. Houghton Mifflin Harcourt, [2017] 112 p.

Grades: 4 5 6 7 8   **551.7**
    1. Earth sciences 2. Geology 3. History 4. Big Bang Theory

(Astronomy) 5. Global warming 6. Earth 7. Comics and Graphic novels
ISBN 9780544805033

                    LC 2016018643

Sibert-Honor winner Don Brown brings us a graphic novel about world geology. Perfect for science class as well as anyone curious about our globe, a humble groundhog guides us on a tour through the planet's natural history and describes the different stages of the Earth's evolution as well as the incredible natural forces constantly at work.

"In 100 fact-crammed but surprisingly zippy pages, nonfiction graphic novelist extraordinaire Brown covers 14 billion years of Earth's development. From the big bang to our planet's origin to landmass formation to the appearance of life, Brown and scientific consultant Perfit provide an astonishingly comprehensive overview and manage to humanize it with witty asides from the woodchuck and worm who serve as surrogate teacher and student, as well as quick visits with important historical scientists." Booklist.

552 Petrology

Chesterman, Charles W. (Charles Wesley), 1913-1991

The **Audubon** Society field guide to North American rocks and minerals. Charles W. Chesterman; scientific consultant, Kurt E. Lowe. Knopf, 1978. 850 p.

Grades: Adult   **552**
    1. Rocks -- Collection and preservation 2. Minerals -- Collection and preservation
    ISBN 9780394502694

                    LC 78054893

Displays rocks, minerals, variant forms, and major gemstones

Dorling Kindersley, Inc

Rocks & minerals. Dorling Kindersley Publishing. DK Pub., 2008. 72 p.: Eyewitness experts

Grades: 5 6 7 8   **552**
    1. Rocks 2. Mineralogy 3. Minerals 4. Geology
    ISBN 9780756631321

Examines rocks and minerals for budding geologists and fossil hunters everywhere.

Hirsch, Andy, 1987-

Rocks and minerals: geology from caverns to the cosmos. Andy Hirsch. First Second, 2020 128 p.: Science comics

Grades: 5 6 7   **552**
    1. Rocks 2. Minerals 3. Geology 4. Mineralogy 5. Earth sciences 6. Comics and Graphic novels
    ISBN 9781250203960

Join a crystal-crazy fanboy and a famous rock hunter on a geological journey that will take them to the summit of a volcano, deep within the earth, and even into outer space! They'll learn about the unstoppable forces that shape our planet and they might even pick up a gemstone or meteorite along the way.

"Readers intrepid enough to follow from the bottom of our planet's oceans to the top of one of its tallest peaks will come away with clear ideas of the distinctive conditions that lead to the formation of dozens of minerals, rocks, and crystals, as well as a coherent overview of the complex processes that have been shaping Earth's surface for billions of years—and will continue to do so for billions more." School Library Journal.

Hirsch, Rebecca E

The **rock** cycle. by Rebecca E. Hirsch; conetent consultant, Dr. Kevin Theissen, Associate Professor and Chair of Department of Geology, University of Saint Thomas. Core Library, an imprint of Abdo Publishing, [2015] 48 p.: Rocks and minerals (Core Library (Firm))

Grades: 5 6 7   **552**

    1. Rocks 2. Sedimentary rocks 3. Metamorphic rocks 4. Igneous rocks

    ISBN 9781624033896

                               LC bl2014030413

Identifies the three types of rock present on Earth—sedimentary, metamorphic, and igneous—discussing their properties, where they can be found, and how they are formed.

"Aligned to Common Core and state standards, the series provides ample opportunity for additional research (Stop and Think), hands-on experimentation (In the Field), and critical thinking (Changing Minds) that will have readers looking at the world around them with a better understanding of just what exactly they're seeing." School Library Journal.

Includes bibliographical references (page 47) and index.

Sedimentary rocks. by Rebecca E. Hirsch; content consultant, Dr. Kevin Theissen, Associate Professor and Chair, Department of Geology, University of Saint Thomas. Core Library, an imprint of Abdo Publishing, [2015] 48 p.: Rocks and minerals (Core Library (Firm))

Grades: 5 6 7   **552**

    1. Sedimentary rocks 2. Rocks

    ISBN 9781624033902

                               LC bl2014030393

Introduces sedimentary rocks, discussing their characteristics; types; the rock cycle; how and where they are formed; how they are classified, identified, and used; and landforms that are composed of them.

Owings, Lisa

Igneous rocks. by Lisa Owings; content consultant, Alan Boudreau, Earth and Ocean Sciences, Duke University. Core Library, an imprint of Abdo Publishing, [2015] 48 p.: Rocks and Minerals

Grades: 5 6 7   **552**

    1. Igneous rocks 2. Volcanoes 3. Rocks 4. Geology 5. Volcanic eruptions

    ISBN 9781624033872

                               LC bl2014030400

Introduces igneous rocks, discussing their characteristics; types; the rock cycle; how they are formed, classified, identified, and used; and landforms that are composed of them.

"Aligned to Common Core and state standards, the series provides ample opportunity for additional research ('Stop and Think'), hands-on experimentation ('In the Field'), and critical thinking ('Changing Minds') that will have readers looking at the world around them with a better understanding of just what exactly they're seeing. Despite a few issues, these are solid choices." School Library Journal.

Includes bibliographical references (page 47) and index.

Reynolds, Toby

Rocks, crystals and gems. Toby Reynolds and Paul Calver. Barron's Educational Series, 2016. 32 p.: Visual explorers

Grades: 4 5 6 7   **552**

    1. Rocks 2. Crystals 3. Gems 4. Precious stones 5. Minerals

    ISBN 9781438008288

                               LC bl2016015595

Provides facts and figures about the types of rocks, crystals, and gems found on Earth and describes the natural processes required to create them.

"Inexpensive and relatively sturdy, these large-format paperbacks make for a visually enticing series." Booklist.

Swanson, Jennifer

Metamorphic rocks. by Jennifer Swanson; content consultant, Dr. Kevin Theissen, Associate Professor and Chair, Department of Geology, University of Saint Thomas. Core Library, an imprint of Abdo Publishing, [2015] 48 p.: Rocks and minerals (Core Library (Firm))

Grades: 5 6 7   **552**

    1. Metamorphic rocks 2. Rocks

    ISBN 9781624033889

                               LC bl2014030401

Introduces metamorphic rocks, discussing their characteristics and types, how they are formed, and what they can be used for.

"Despite a few issues, these are solid choices." School Library Journal.

Includes bibliographical references (page 47) and index.

552.0075 Petrology—Collecting

Callery, Sean

Rocks, minerals & gems. Sean Callery and Gary Ombler. Scholastic, 2016. 224 p.

Grades: 6 7 8 9 10   **552.0075**

    1. Rocks 2. Minerals 3. Gems 4. Precious stones

    ISBN 9780545947190

In Rocks, Minerals, and Gems, readers will learn about hundreds of rocks, minerals, crystals, and gems that were forged by the most powerful events in prehistory. Explore what specimens look like and how they're used today—readers can use the information to identify rocks and minerals themselves and open up a spectacular new world.

"A browser's delight but less useful for reference, this hefty album features hundreds of sharply reproduced close-up photos of geological specimens—including fossils, meteorites, China's terra-cotta army, and amber with small animals inside." School Library Journal.

Honovich, Nancy

Rocks & minerals. Nancy Honovich. National Geographic, 2016. 160 p.: National Geographic kids

Grades: 4 5 6 7 8   **552.0075**

    1. Rocks 2. Minerals 3. Geology 4. Mineralogy

    ISBN 9781426323027

A fact-filled guide to common rocks and minerals includes each mineral's chemical formula, where it can be naturally found, and activities to help explore different proerties of rocks and minerals.

"A useful supplement for elementary and middle-school science curricula, the book includes a well-considered glossary and further resources." Booklist.

553.2 Carbonaceous materials

Belton, Blair

How coal is formed. by Blair Belton. Gareth Stevens Publishing, 2017. 32 p.: From the Earth: how resources are made
Grades: 5 6 7   **553.2**
     1. Coal 2. Carbon cycle (Biogeochemistry) 3. Coal mines and mining 4. Natural resources 5. Energy resources
     ISBN 9781482447071

                       LC 2016000747
"This series would be a great addition to school or public libraries, as it makes an often dull topic really shine." School Library Journal.
     Includes bibliographical references and index.

Nagelhout, Ryan

How natural gas is formed. by Ryan Nagelhout. Gareth Stevens Publishing, 2017. 32 p.: From the Earth: how resources are made
Grades: 5 6 7   **553.2**
     1. Natural gas -- Geology 2. Gas industry and trade
     ISBN 9781482447187

                       LC 2016012598
Looks at how natural gas forms, how it is extracted from the ground, and how it is used to create electricity.
     "This series would be a great addition to school or public libraries, as it makes an often dull topic really shine." School Library Journal.
     Includes bibliographical references (page 31) and index.

Rajczak Nelson, Kristen

How oil is formed. Kristen Rajczak Nelson. Gareth Stevens Publishing, 2017. 32 p.: From the Earth: how resources are made
Grades: 5 6 7   **553.2**
     1. Petroleum -- Geology 2. Oil industry and trade
     ISBN 9781482447248

                       LC 2016011773
Looks at how oil forms, how it is extracted from the ground, and how it is used to create electricity.
     "This series would be a great addition to school or public libraries, as it makes an often dull topic really shine." School Library Journal.
     Includes bibliographical references (page 31) and index.

553.3 Iron

Kennon, Caroline

How iron ore forms. by Caroline Kennon. Gareth Stevens Publishing, 2017. 32 p.: From the Earth: how resources are made
Grades: 5 6 7   **553.3**
     1. Iron ores 2. Iron
     ISBN 9781482447156

                       LC 2016006959
"This series would be a great addition to school or public libraries, as it makes an often dull topic really shine." School Library Journal.

553.8 Gems

Keppeler, Jill

How gems are formed. by Jill Keppeler. Gareth Stevens Publishing, 2017. 32 p.: From the Earth: how resources are made
Grades: 5 6 7   **553.8**
     1. Gems 2. Precious stones 3. Geology
     ISBN 9781482447118

                       LC 2015046972
Informs readers about gemstones, including why they are valuable, how they are formed, and how they can be used.
     "This series would be a great addition to school or public libraries, as it makes an often dull topic really shine." School Library Journal.
     Includes bibliographical references (page 31) and index.

557 Earth sciences of North America

Collier, Michael, 1950-

Over the mountains: an aerial view of geology. Michael Collier; foreword by John S. Shelton. Mikaya Press, c2007. 127 p.
Grades: 9 10 11 12   **557**
     1. Geology 2. Mountains 3. Aerial photography in geology
     ISBN 9781931414180

                       LC 2006047151
Geology is thrilling. It's the Earth in all its splendor. Unfortunately, geology texts rarely communicate that sense of excitement. Enter Michael Collier, geologist, writer and one of America's premier aerial photographers. For over 20 years, he has piloted his Cessna 180 to inaccessible locations and returned with stunning photographs that lay bare the Earth's workings. Over the Mountains, the first book in Michael Collier's new series, focuses on geology's most spectacular subject in a most spectacular way. It includes: detailed and breathtaking large-format color photographs covering the geology of every major mountain range in the United States and clear, easy-to-understand text, diagrams and captions that explain and illuminate the geologic processes shown in the photographs. After exploring the pages of Over the Mountains, readers will never think of mountains—or geology—in the same way again.

557.9132 Geology—Grand Canyon

Chin, Jason, 1978-

★ **Grand** Canyon. Jason Chin. Roaring Brook Press, 2017. 56 p.
Grades: 1 2 3 4 5 6   **557.9132**
     1. National parks and reserves 2. Canyons 3. Fathers and daughters 4. Hiking 5. Grand Canyon 6. Grand Canyon National Park
     ISBN 9781596439504

                       LC 2016025024
NCTE Orbis Pictus Nonfiction Award, 2018.
     An exploration of the Grand Canyon on a grand scale, as only Jason Chin can illustrate and explain. Provided by publisher.
     "With vivid imagination, a crystal-clear grasp of the facts, and brilliant artwork, this illuminating look at one of the planet's most fascinating features will entrance young readers." Booklist.

559.9 Earth sciences of extraterrestrial worlds

Simon, Seymour

The **moon**. Seymour Simon. Simon & Schuster Books for Young Readers, 2003. 1 v. (unpaged)
Grades: 4 5 6 7   **559.9**
     1. Satellites 2. Astronomy 3. Moon 4. Solar system
     ISBN 0689835639

                       LC 2001031303

Contains the most current information about the Earth's only natural satellite, with photographs to provide a close-up look at the Moon.

"The digitally remastered color photographs in this update are incredible. . . . The text has undergone minimal change. . . . The facts remain true and relevant, and the writing reflects the graphics: beautiful. This is a must-have for astronomy sections." School Library Journal.

560 Paleontology

Fretland VanVoorst, Jenny, 1972-

Fossils. by Jenny Fretland VanVoorst; concent consultant, Dr. Kevin Theissen, Associate Professor and Chair, Department of Geology, University of Saint Thomas. Core Library, an imprint of Abdo Publishing, [2015] 48 p.: Rocks and minerals (Core Library (Firm))

Grades: 5 6 7 **560**

1. Fossils 2. Paleontology
ISBN 9781624033858

LC bl2014030418

Presents general information about fossils, explaining how they are formed, how they are extracted from the sites where they are discovered, and how scientists use them to gain an understanding of Earth's past.

"Aligned to Common Core and state standards, the series provides ample opportunity for additional research (Stop and Think), hands-on experimentation ('In the Field'), and critical thinking ('Changing Minds') that will have readers looking at the world around them with a better understanding of just what exactly they're seeing. Despite a few issues, these are solid choices." School Library Journal.

Includes bibliographical references (page 47) and index.

Taylor, Paul D.

Eyewitness fossil. written by Paul D. Taylor; [special photography, Colin Keates]. DK Pub., 2017 72 p.: Eyewitness books

Grades: 4 5 6 7 **560**

1. Fossils 2. Paleontology
ISBN 9781465462473

LC 2004302380

A photo essay about different types of fossils, including bacteria, algae, birds, mammals and more.

560.9 History, geographic treatment, biography

Johnson, Rebecca L.

Battle of the dinosaur bones: Othniel Charles Marsh vs. Edward Drinker Cope. by Rebecca L. Johnson. Twenty-First Century Books, 2012. 64 p.: Scientific rivalries and scandals

Grades: 5 6 7 8 **560.9**

1. Marsh, Othniel Charles, 1831-1899. 2. Cope, E. D. (Edward Drinker), 1840-1897. 3. Paleontology -- History 19th century. 4. Paleontologists 5. Fossils -- Collection and preservation 6. Academic rivalry 7. Competition
ISBN 9780761354888

LC 2011045648

Relates the competition between Othniel Marsh and Edward Cope to discover more fossils, name more species, and publish more papers that brought out the best and worst in them and provided the world with a new view of life on Earth.

Lendler, Ian

The **first** dinosaur: how science solved the greatest mystery on earth. Ian Lendler; illustrated by C. M. Butzer. Margaret K. McElderry Books, 2019. 224 p.

Grades: 5 6 7 8 9 **560.9**

1. Paleontology -- History 2. Paleontologists 3. Scientific discoveries 4. Dinosaurs 5. Fossils
ISBN 9781534427006

LC 2019023595

The First Dinosaur tells the story of the idea of dinosaurs, and the chain of fossil discoveries and advances in science that led to that idea. Be prepared to meet eccentric men and overlooked women who uncovered the pieces to a puzzle so much bigger than themselves, a puzzle far stranger and more spectacular than they could have ever imagined.

"An outstanding case study in how science is actually done: funny, nuanced, and perceptive." Kirkus

Includes bibliographical references and index.

565 Fossil Arthropoda

Bradley, Timothy J.

Paleo bugs: survival of the creepiest. written and illustrated by Timothy J. Bradley. Chronicle Books, c2008. 44 p.

Grades: 4 5 6 7 **565**

1. Insects 2. Arthropods 3. Fossils 4. Fossil insects 5. Paleoentomology
ISBN 9780811860222

LC 2007018174

The companion title to Paleo Sharks introduces budding entomologists to the rather large and disgusting creepy crawlies that crawled upon the earth in the time of the dinosaurs, millions of years ago.

"This offers an eye-widening gallery of extinct arthropods, from the mayfly-like heptagenia to a seven-foot-long arthropleura. . . . Bradley decks out each of his painted figures in bright hues, poses them in natural settings . . . and sets them aside a human hand or body in silhouette to suggest scale. . . . Readers will . . . pore over the pictures and come away knowing more about both these extinct animals and their modern descendants." Booklist.

567.9 Reptiles

Berkowitz, Jacob

Jurassic poop: what dinosaurs (and others) left behind. written by Jacob Berkowitz; illustrated by Steve Mack. Kids Can Press, c2006. 40 p.

Grades: 4 5 6 7 **567.9**

1. Coprolites 2. Feces 3. Fossils 4. Dinosaurs 5. Paleontology 6. Grossology
ISBN 1553378601

LC bl2006023295

Describes what coprolites are and where they are often found, and explains the different ways they may have become fossilized and why they are important to paleontologists.

"Berkowitz' style is goofy and lighthearted, but there's plenty of real information. . . . The browsable format combines cartoony digital art, photographs . . . and design elements such a spiky borders and background shading." Bulletin of the Center for Children's Books.

Bonner, Hannah

When dinos dawned, mammals got munched, and Pterosaurs took flight: a cartoon pre-history of life in the Triassic. Hannah Bonner. National Geographic Children's Books, 2012. 48 p.
Grades: 3 4 5 6 7   **567.9**
1. Paleontology Triassic 2. Dinosaurs 3. Prehistoric animals 4. Comics and Graphic novels
ISBN 9781426308628
LC 2011029212

In the style of WHEN BUGS WERE BIG and WHEN FISH GOT FEET this book discusses all the exciting developments of the Triassic Age, from the split of Pangaea into Gondwanaland and Laurasia, to the first appearance of the dinosaurs. There were pterosaurs (flying reptiles), the first flowering plants, humongous sea creatures, early turtles, and the first coral reefs. Early mammals also appeared in the Triassic, and there were several dramatic extinction events. With the books' signature blend of humor and clearly presented information, cartoon illustrations help keep the fact-filled material extra fun. Provided by publisher.

Guiberson, Brenda Z.

Feathered dinosaurs. Brenda Z. Guiberson; illustrated by William Low. Henry Holt and Company, 2016. 32 p.
Grades: 2 3 4 5   **567.9**
1. Dinosaurs 2. Feathers 3. Birds -- Origin
ISBN 9780805098280
LC 2015003535

A beautiful exploration of recently-discovered feathered dinosaurs—the ancient ancestors of birds today! Provided by publisher.

"An intriguing introduction to the evolutionary connection between dinosaurs and birds, as well as the process of ongoing scientific discovery." Booklist.

Lessem, Don

National Geographic kids ultimate dinopedia: the most complete dinosaur reference ever. "Dino" Don Lessem; reviewed by paleontologist Dr. Darren Nash; illustrated by Franco Tempesta. National Geographic, 2017. 296 p.
Grades: 3 4 5 6   **567.9**
1. Dinosaurs
ISBN 9781426329050
LC bl2017041859

Shares in-depth information about all currently known dinosaur species organized under major periods, providing details on such topics as physical characteristics, diet, and discovery dates.

"In the opening chapter, Lessem presents broad basics on [dinosaur] behavior and habitats as well as a look at major discoveries in paleontology. However, it's the later chapters, which devote two pages each to specific dinosaurs, that will hook hard-core dino lovers. . . . Tempesta's full-page illustrations appear on every spread and jump off the page, and the dynamic layout . . . is immensely appealing. . . . Lessem's comprehensive overview will satisfy the interested browser as much as the ardent dinosaur enthusiast." Booklist.

Includes bibliographical references (page 288) and index.

Malam, John, 1957-

Dinosaur atlas: an amazing journey through a lost world. author, John Malam and John Woodward; consultant, Michael Benton. DK, 2006. 96 p.
Grades: 5 6 7 8   **567.9**
1. Dinosaurs 2. Dinosaurs -- Extinction -- Causes 3. Dinosaurs --

Geographical distribution 4. Extinct animals 5. Prehistoric animals
ISBN 0756622352
LC 2006285529

"The atlas is organized by continent. Each section is prefaced with a large map showing where various species are found, with a picture and a brief synopsis of each species on the facing page. . . . Each introductory map is followed by several regional maps, surveying important local fossil sites and formations. Each section provides attractive diorama snapshots for a wide range of periods and locations." Science Books & Films.

Manning, Phillip Lars, 1967-

Dinomummy: the life, death, and discovery of Dakota, a dinosaur from Hell Creek. Phillip Lars Manning; foreword by Tyler Lyson. Kingfisher, 2007. 64 p.
Grades: 4 5 6 7   **567.9**
1. Dinosaurs 2. Fossils 3. Paleontology 4. Dinosaurs 5. Mummies 6. North Dakota
ISBN 0753460475
LC 2007002878

Documents the story of two men and a very special dinosaur, whose fossil remains were found in the year 2000 in the remote hills of the Hell Creek Formation in North Dakota.

"The color photographs and simple text offer a detailed account of carefully unearthing the fossil and transporting it safely to the laboratory, where many tests were performed. Dinosaurs buffs and young scientists will love this book. It is a thrilling story that is part narrative, part mystery, and part science lesson." Voice of Youth Advocates.

Nardo, Don, 1947-

Deadliest dinosaurs. Don Nardo. ReferencePoint Press, [2017] 80 p.: Deadliest predators
Grades: 6 7 8 9 10   **567.9**
1. Dinosaurs 2. Predatory dinosaurs 3. Prehistoric animals 4. Paleontology
ISBN 9781682820483
LC 2016004075

Profiles some of the deadliest dinosaurs, including Predator x, Troodon, and Spinosaurus.

"First-rate nonfiction on a high-interest topic." School Library Journal.

Includes bibliographical references (pages 67-68) and index.

Reed, M. K.

Dinosaurs: fossils and feathers. MK Reed; Joe Flood. First Second, 2016. 117 p.: Science comics
Grades: 4 5 6 7 8   **567.9**
1. Dinosaurs 2. Prehistoric animals 3. Paleontology 4. Fossils 5. Comics and Graphic novels
ISBN 9781626721449
LC bl2016012765

Introduces dinosaurs, including how they may have lived and died millions of years ago, and explores the history of paleontology.

Thimmesh, Catherine

Scaly spotted feathered frilled: how do we know what dinosaurs really looked like? by Catherine Thimmesh. Houghton Mifflin Books for Children, Houghton Mifflin Harcourt, 2013. 64 p.

Grades: 4 5 6 7   **567.9**
1. Paleoart 2. Dinosaurs 3. Paleontology 4. Prehistoric animals
ISBN 9780547991344

LC 2012048466

Through illustrated full-color images, unravels the mystery of how we bring to life creatures that no one has ever seen before.

Woodward, John, 1954-

Dinosaur!: dinosaurs and other amazing prehistoric creatures as you've never seen them before. written by John Woodward; consultant, Darren Naish; illustrators, Peter Minister, Arran Lewis, Andrew Kerr, Peter Bull, Vlad Konstantinov. DK Publishing, 2014. 176 p.

Grades: 5 6 7 8   **567.9**
1. Dinosaurs 2. Prehistoric animals
ISBN 9781465420473

Created in partnership with the Smithsonian Institution, a fact-filled introduction to prehistoric animals combines photo-realistic, computer-generated imagery with detailed cross sections and concise annotations that profile a range of dinosaur species from the Triassic, Jurassic and Cretaceous Eras.

"For those budding paleontologists and dinosaur fans willing to dig a little, this a wealth of material on this ever-evolving subject." Booklist.

567.918 Pterosauria (Flying reptiles)

Peterson, Sheryl

Pterodactyl. Sheryl Peterson. Creative Education, c2011. 48 p.: Age of dinosaurs (Creative Education)

Grades: 5 6 7 8   **567.918**
1. Pterodactyls 2. Dinosaurs
ISBN 9781583419755

LC 2009025175

An introduction to the life and era of the flying contemporaries of dinosaurs known as pterodactyls, starting with the creatures' 1784 discovery and ending with present-day research topics. Provided by publisher.

"Peterson nicely balances the known with conjecture. . . . The inviting design, on glossy pages, elegantly detours from the main text into details tantalizing . . .; informative . . .; and incredible. . . . The illustrations, from sharp diagrams to dramatic paintings to B-movie-worthy recreation scenes, add some nice flair to this solid entry." Booklist.

Includes bibliographical references (p. 47) and index.

569 Fossil mammals

Turner, Alan, 1947-

National Geographic prehistoric mammals. Alan Turner; illustrated by Mauricio Anton. National Geographic, c2004. 192 p.

Grades: 5 6 7 8   **569**
1. Fossil mammals 2. Prehistoric animals
ISBN 9780792271345

LC 2004001189

Provides a prehistoric journey through time to visit one hundred creatures that walked the Earth, from the saber-toothed cat and woolly mammoth to the hornless rhinoceros and giant ground sloth.

"Dramatic full-color pictures . . . and captions enhance the brief, informative text." School Library Journal.

569.9 Humans and related genera

Deem, James M.

Bodies from the bog. James M. Deem. Houghton Mifflin, 1998. 42 p.

Grades: 4 5 6 7   **569.9**
1. Bog bodies 2. Prehistoric humans 3. Human remains (Archaeology) 4. Forensic sciences 5. Archaeology 6. Europe -- Antiquities. 7. Books for reluctant readers
ISBN 9780395857847

LC 97012010

Describes the discovery of bog bodies in northern Europe and the evidence which their remains reveal about themselves and the civilizations in which they lived.

"The text is engaging and accessible, and the starkly dramatic photos are given dignity by the spacious and understated page design." Horn Book Guide.

Includes bibliographical references (p. 39-40) and index.

Stefoff, Rebecca, 1951-

First humans. Rebecca Stefoff. Marshall Cavendish Benchmark, c2010. 112 p.: Humans: an evolutionary history

Grades: 7 8 9 10   **569.9**
1. Human evolution 2. Prehistoric humans 3. Humans -- Origin 4. Evolution 5. Anthropology
ISBN 9780761441847

LC 2008034330

Describes the search for early branches of the human family tree, including the first true humans, members of the genus Homo. Provided by publisher.

"Stefoff provides an enlightening and entertaining history of the evolution of Homo sapiens, their ancestors, and cousins, from primitive origins to today. The clear, insightful [text is] accented by intriguing sidebars and colorful photos, maps, and graphs." School Library Journal.

Includes bibliographical references and index.

Modern humans. by Rebecca Stefoff. Marshall Cavendish Benchmark, c2010. 112 p. : Humans: an evolutionary history

Grades: 7 8 9 10   **569.9**
1. Humans -- Origin 2. Prehistoric humans 3. Human evolution 4. Human population genetics
ISBN 9780761441878

LC 2009012364

Describes the rise of modern humans, Homo sapiens, including the theories about our origins and how we spread throughout the world, with information based on the latest fossil and DNA studies. Provided by publisher.

"Stefoff provides an enlightening and entertaining history of the evolution of Homo sapiens, their ancestors, and cousins, from primitive origins to today. The clear, insightful [text is] accented by intriguing sidebars and colorful photos, maps, and graphs." School Library Journal.

Includes bibliographical references and index.

Thimmesh, Catherine

Lucy long ago. by Catherine Thimmesh. Houghton Mifflin Harcourt, c2009. 63 p.

Grades: 4 5 6 7   **569.9**
1. Lucy (Fossil) 2. Prehistoric humans 3. Human evolution 4. Australopithecines 5. Australopithecus afarensis
ISBN 9780547051994

LC 2008036761

"The 1974 discovery of the fossilized partial skeleton of a small-brained primate who apparently walked upright 3.2 million years ago in what is now Ethiopia significantly changed accepted theories about human origins. Step by step, Thimmesh presents the questions the newly discovered bones raised and how they were answered. . . . Extensive research, clear organization and writing, appropriate pacing for new ideas and intriguing graphics all contribute to this exceptionally accessible introduction to the mystery of human origins." Kirkus.

569.9096822 Homo (Genus)—Paleozoology

Aronson, Marc

★ The **skull** in the rock: how a scientist, a boy, and Google Earth opened a new window on human origins. by Marc Aronson and Lee Berger. National Geographic, 2012. 64 p.

Grades: 5 6 7 8 9 10   **569.9096822**

1. Berger, Lee R. 2. Human evolution 3. Prehistoric humans 4. Excavations (Archaeology) 5. Humans -- Origin 6. Anthropology 7. Witwatersrand Region, South Africa 8. South Africa

ISBN 9781426310102

LC 2012012943

Chronicles the story behind one of the most significant archaeological discoveries of all time, explaining its significance for understanding human evolution and how it is shaping the thinking of the scientific community.

570 Biology

Kramer, Stephen P.

Hidden worlds: looking through a scientist's microscope. by Stephen Kramer; photographs by Dennis Kunkel. Houghton Mifflin, 2001. 57 p.: Scientists in the field (Houghton Mifflin)

Grades: 4 5 6 7   **570**

1. Kunkel, Dennis. 2. Microscope and microscopy 3. Microscope and microscopy -- History 4. Optical instruments 5. Scientists 6. Science -- History

ISBN 0618055460

LC 00058083

"This book takes a look at the work of a microscopist. Kunkel works with microscopes to explore science. . . . This book contains many of his photos, most taken with electron microscopes. . . . Several opening pages, along with the front and back endpapers, are visually dazzling. The heart of the book, though, is what readers learn about how Kunkel produces these images, and to what uses scientists put them. . . . This title offers a wealth of scientific information along with an insightful look at the world of an individual scientist." School Library Journal.

Includes bibliographical references (p. 54) and index.

570.28 Biology—Apparatus, equipment, procedures

Levine, Shar, 1953-

★ The **ultimate** guide to your microscope. Shar Levine & Leslie Johnstone. Sterling Pub., c2008. 143 p.

Grades: 5 6 7 8 9   **570.28**

1. Microscope and microscopy 2. Microscope and microscopy -- Technique 3. Microscope and microscopy -- Experiments

ISBN 9781435255807

LC 2006100967

An in-depth guide explains how to put bugs, water, food, plants and pollen, and even parts of the body (like fingernails) under the scope for a close-up glimpse while also explaining how to identify the microscope's different pieces and how to focus properly.

"Through this fun and inviting book, readers can begin to explore the world using a microscope. Students are encouraged to learn the basics in the two first chapters and then undertake the 41 hands-on activities in the next eight chapters. Activities are presented in manageable one or two-page uniformly formatted modules." School Library Journal.

570.78 Biology—laboratory manuals

Calhoun, Yael

Plant and animal science fair projects, revised and expanded using the scientific method. Yael Calhoun. Enslow Publishers, 2010. 160 p.: Biology science projects using the scientific method

Grades: 7 8 9 10   **570.78**

1. Natural history projects 2. Science fair experiments 3. Science projects 4. Experiments 5. Natural history

ISBN 9780766034211

LC 2009014805

Explains how to use the scientific method to conduct several science experiments about plants and animals. Includes ideas for science fair projects. Provided by publisher.

"Each volume begins with an overview of the scientific method and safety, then presents a collection of activities encouraging readers to explore central concepts in the featured fields. The activities include step-by-step instructions and helpful color diagrams, interspersed with extended coverage of scientific ideas. The Results sections ask questions rather than giving away the answers." Horn Book.

Includes bibliographical references and index.

Latham, Donna

★ **Backyard** biology: investigate habitats outside your door with 25 projects. Donna Latham; illustrated by Beth Hetland. Nomad Press, c2013. 122 p.: Build it yourself

Grades: 4 5 6 7   **570.78**

1. Nature 2. Biology -- Experiments 3. Science -- Experiments 4. Experiments

ISBN 9781619301528

LC bl2013007042

Presents basic biological facts about the plants, animals, and microorganisms that can be found in a backyard or nearby park and provides instructions for twenty-five projects that explore different aspects of this ecosystem.

VanCleave, Janice Pratt

Step-by-step science experiments in biology. Janice VanCleave. Rosen Central, 2013. 80 p.: Janice Vancleave's first-place science fair projects

Grades: 5 6 7 8   **570.78**

1. Biology -- Experiments 2. Science projects 3. Experiments

ISBN 9781448869824

LC 2012007943

Presents step-by-step experiments that introduce different biological concepts.

571.0919 Space

Turner, Pamela S.

Life on Earth---and beyond: an astrobiologist's quest. Pamela S. Turner. Charlesbridge, c2008. 109 p.

Grades: 5 6 7 8   **571.0919**

1. McKay, Christopher P. 2. Space biology 3. Life on other planets
ISBN 9781580891332

LC 2007001475

Invites readers to join NASA astrobiologist Dr. Chris McKay on a fascinating quest to better understand what factors are necessary to sustain life on both Earth and beyond.

"Astrobiologists look outward from the Earth seeking evidence of life elsewhere in the universe. But, as this fascinating book shows, they also travel to places on Earth where extreme conditions may be similar to those on distant worlds. Turner follows astrobiologist Chris McKay as he looks for life in apparently hostile environments. . . . Illustrated with many excellent color photos and other images." Booklist.

571.1 Animals

Green, Jen

Inside animals. by Jen Green. Marshall Cavendish Benchmark, 2010. 48 p. : Invisible worlds

Grades: 4 5 6 7   **571.1**

1. Anatomy 2. Physiology 3. Cells 4. Animals
ISBN 9780761441953

LC 2008037241

"The narrative is clear, well written, broken down into manageable pieces, and peppered with eye-opening facts. The numerous photographs are so phenomenal that they will inspire kids to read the text . . . so that they can wrap their minds around what they see." School Library Journal.

Includes bibliographical references and index.

571.4 Biophysics

Amstutz, Lisa J

Discover cryobiology. Lisa J. Amstutz. Lerner Publications, 2017 40 p.

Grades: 3 4 5   **571.4**

1. Cold -- Physiological effect 2. Cryobiology 3. Cryopreservation of organs, tissues, etc
ISBN 9781512412840

LC 2015047375

Discover how scientists are using extremely low temperatures to save lives. Explore the theories behind cryobiology in this high-interest book that uses simple language and striking photos to engage even the most reluctant readers. Provided by publisher.

"In four clear, concise chapters, accompanied by glossy close-up photos of technological gear and frozen organs, this explains the effects, both preservative and damaging, of cold on bodies and examines the natural reactions of animals (i.e., hibernation), before more thoroughly discussing the potential for freezing—and perhaps one day reanimating—human bodies." Booklist.

Includes bibliographical references and index.

571.6 Cell biology

Ballard, Carol

Cells and cell function. Carol Ballard. Rosen, 2010. 48 p.: Living processes

Grades: 5 6 7   **571.6**

1. Cells 2. Cytology
ISBN 9781615323425

"With colorful, quality photography, the well-organized content is divided into short chapters with bold subheadings making information easy to find. Clear and interesting writing distinguishes this . . . from older titles. The captions for pictures are used to provide identification and additional explanation for topics not included in the text." Library Media Connection.

572 Biochemistry

Haelle, Tara

Edible sunlight. Tara Haelle. Rourke Educational Media, 2016. 48 p.: Let's explore science

Grades: 5 6 7 8   **572**

1. Photosynthesis 2. Plant life cycles
ISBN 9781681913995

Describes how plants get their energy through the photosynthesis process, looks at plant reproduction, and discusses the importance of the human-plant relationship.

572.8 Biochemical genetics

Arbuthnott, Gill

What makes you you? Gill Arbuthnott; illustrated by Marc Mones. Crabtree Publishing Company, 2016, c2013. 64 p.: Drawn to science: illustrated guides to key science concepts

Grades: 5 6 7 8   **572.8**

1. DNA 2. Genetics 3. Heredity 4. Human body 5. Human physiology
ISBN 9780778722397

LC 2015042097

What Makes You You? is a mind-blowing introduction to the building blocks of life—DNA! Amazing 3D-style illustrations and diagrams help explain what it is, how it works, and what we can do with it. Breaking down complex scientific concepts and processes into bite-sized chunks, this fascinating book explains everything from the basics of evolution to the incredible achievements of modern-day genetic research—and what's in store for the future! Provided by publisher.

"While this is a lot to tackle, the book is extremely well organized and always supplies readers with page references so they can refresh on previously covered topics." Booklist.

Dorling Kindersley, Inc

The **DNA** book: discover what makes you you. DK Publishing, 2020. 72 p.

Grades: 5 6 7 8   **572.8**

1. Crick, Francis, 1916-2004 2. Watson, James D., 1928- 3. Franklin, Rosalind, 1920-1958 4. Wilkins, Maurice, 1916-2004 5. Miescher, Friedrich, 1844-1895 6. DNA 7. Genetics 8. Heredity 9. DNA research 10. Genes
ISBN 9781465492272

This book introduces children ages 7-9 to the amazing science of DNA, genetics, and what makes you you. Excerpted from publisher description.

"Excellent and appealing for readers who wish to peruse, as well as those seeking detailed information for report writing. A great resource." School Library Journal

Mooney, Carla, 1970-

Genetics: breaking the code of your DNA. Carla Mooney; illustrated by Samuel Carbaugh. Nomad Press, 2014. 128 p.: Inquire and investigate

Grades: 6 7 8 9 10 11   **572.8**
     1. Genetics 2. DNA 3. Heredity 4. Genes 5. Science
     ISBN 9781619302082

An educational introduction to the world of genetics examines such concepts as the role of chromosomes, the structure of DNA and the mechanics of genetic inheritance, profiling new discoveries and related controversies while providing suggestions for biology-based activities.

"Although the book can be used independently, it will be better appreciated with some background knowledge. A solid resource that shows life science and biology students the practicalities and marvels of genetics." Booklist.

Stewart, Whitney, 1959-

Genomics: a revolution in health and disease discovery. Whitney Stewart and Hans Andersson, MD. Twenty-First Century Books, 2021. 144 p.

Grades: 8 9 10 11 12   **572.8**
     1. Genetics 2. Genomics 3. Gene mapping 4. DNA 5. Biology
     ISBN 9781541500563

Since the completion of the Human Genome Project, genetic studies has transitioned into an era of discovery. This book explores the breakthroughs in research that inform our understanding of ancestry, inheritance, epigenetics, health, and medicine.

"This accessible introduction demystifies the complicated science. The authors strategically use scientific language and terminology paired with plainspoken explanations, and the colorful, varied physical layout enhances the reading experience. High-quality, curiosity-sparking brain fuel." Kirkus

Vaughan, Jenny, 1947-

Who discovered DNA? Jenny Vaughan. Arcturus Pub., 2010. 46 p.: Breakthroughs in science and technology

Grades: 5 6 7 8   **572.8**
     1. DNA 2. Heredity 3. Genetic engineering
     ISBN 9781848376793

                 LC 2010011021

Looking at some of the major inventions and discoveries shaping our world today, Breakthroughs in Science profiles the research leading up to the discovery (not just profiles of the one or two key "players"). Each book describes the "famous" moment and then examines the continued evolution illustrating its impact today and for the future. Provided by publisher.

"This brief well-done book presents accurate information in an interesting way, using appropriate and appealing graphics. . . . The book not only tells us that Frederick Miesche discovered DNA in 1869, but presents many relevant discoveries before that time and, especially, after it. Applications of the discoveries are also presented, as are controversies related to the genetic knowledge of our day. . . . [This] would be useful as reference and should be available to all interested students." Science Books & Films.

Includes bibliographical references (p. 45) and index.

573.7 Musculoskeletal system

Watson, Galadriel

Running wild: awesome animals in motion. written by Galadriel Watson; art by Samantha Dixon. Annick Press, 2020. 68 p.

Grades: 3 4 5 6   **573.7**
     1. Animal movement 2. Animal mechanics 3. Animals
     ISBN 9781773213705

Creatures sprint, slither, and soar in this STEM-driven dive into the extraordinary, everyday ways animals move!

"The engaging text and bright illustrations reveal how animals use their specialized abilities whether crossing land, air space, or waterways . . . An excellent choice for a book talk." School Library Journal

573.8 Nervous and sensory systems

Buchanan, Shelly C.

★ **Animal** senses. Shelly C. Buchanan. Shell Education, 2016. 32 p.

Grades: 4 5 6   **573.8**
     1. Senses and sensation 2. Animals 3. Animal behavior
     ISBN 9781480746787

"First-rate nonfiction." School Library Journal.

Grundmann, Emmanuelle

When elephants listen with their feet: discover extraordinary animal senses. by Emmanuelle Grundmann; illustrated by Clemence Dupont and translated by Erin Woods Pajama Press, 2021 39 p.

Grades: 3 4 5 6 7   **573.8**
     1. Senses and sensation in animals 2. Senses and sensation
     ISBN 9781772781236

"Negative space surrounds small blocks of intriguingly headlined text and numerous colorful, charismatic illustrations . . . . The text is graceful and often humorous. . . . [it] thoughtfully and exuberantly excites wonder in its readers." Kirkus

574.5 Ecology

Simon, Seymour

Wildfires. Seymour Simon. Morrow Junior Books, c1996. 1 v. (unpaged)

Grades: 4 5 6 7   **574.5**
     1. Wildfires 2. Fire ecology 3. Fires 4. Ecology
     ISBN 0688139353

                 LC   95012653

Presents wildfires as neither good nor bad but as part of the endless cycle of change in forests and grasslands.

"Simon lays out the evidence for the important role fires play in forest ecosystems. Featuring the 1988 Yellowstone fire, he explains its progress, the impact on plants and animals (many of which have evolved interdependence on fire events), and the use of controlled fires. In this updated edition, per usual, excellent photographs are well linked to the text." Horn Book.

575.6 Reproductive organs

Buchanan, Shelly C.
★ **Plant** reproduction. Shelly C. Buchanan. Teacher Created Materials, 2016. 32 p.: Life science (Teacher Created Materials)
Grades: 4 5 6   **575.6**
    1. Plants 2. Reproduction 3. Plant life cycles 4. Life (Biology)
ISBN 9781480746763
"The latest additions to this ongoing series deliver the same authoritative, comprehensive, and relevant information that educators have come to expect from the publisher. The high-interest subjects support inquiry-based learning and encourage readers to think critically about science, and they do so in an engaging way that holds students' attention. . . . First-rate nonfiction." School Library Journal.

576.5 Genetics

Duke, Shirley Smith
You can't wear these genes. Shirley Duke. Rourke Pub. LLC, c2011. 48 p.: Let's explore science
Grades: 4 5 6 7   **576.5**
    1. Genetics 2. Biology 3. DNA 4. Science
ISBN 9781615903245
                            LC 2010009911
"This offers a clear introduction to the complexities of genetics while inviting students to think about how their own DNA shaped who they are. In [this] title, well chosen boxed examples, abundant color photos, diagrams, and an appended glossary add interest and support the engaging [text]." Booklist.
    Includes bibliographical references and index.

Ridge, Yolanda, 1973-
CRISPR: a powerful way to change DNA. written by Yolanda Ridge; illustrated by Alex Boersma. Annick Press, 2020. 116 p.
Grades: 8 9 10 11 12   **576.5**
    1. CRISPR (Genetics) 2. Gene editing 3. Genetics 4. Genetic research 5. Genetic engineering -- Risk assessment
ISBN 9781773214245
A comprehensive introduction to CRISPR technology explains its powerful potential for eliminating disease, improving food-supply stability and promoting environmental conservation while exploring its potential risks, including consequences that have not yet been anticipated.
    "A relevant, evidence-based resource. . . . Ridge successfully demonstrates the necessity of an educated debate about the nuanced pros and cons of gene modification." School Library Journal

Simpson, Kathleen
Genetics: from DNA to designer dogs. Kathleen Simpson. National Geographic, 2008 64 p.: National Geographic investigates
Grades: 4 5 6 7   **576.5**
    1. Genetics 2. DNA 3. Human genome 4. Scientific discoveries 5. Biology
ISBN 9781426303616
Authoritative texts that include interviews with experts, useful time lines, diagrams, glossaries, and more bring readers up to date on the latest findings of specific scientific issues and discoveries in the field of genetics—from the Human Genome Project to stem cell research to the National Geographic's own Genographic Project.

"The content is fairly exciting and should grab the attention of its target audience. . . . The photographs throughout are of high quality. . . . An engaging look at a complex topic." Booklist.

576.8 Evolution

Bright, Michael
Darwin's tree of life. written by Michael Bright; illustrated by Margaux Carpentier. Crocodile Books, an imprint of Interlink Publishing Group, Inc., 2019, c2019. 48 p.
Grades: 3 4 5 6 7   **576.8**
    1. Darwin, Charles, 1809-1882. 2. Evolution 3. Natural selection 4. Adaptation (Biology)
ISBN 9781623719197
                            LC 2019000273
An illustrated exploration of the evolution of Earth's plants and animals.
    "Both an introduction to Darwinian concepts and an exploration of the Earth's life. The illustrations and layout are spectacular...The text strikes an excellent balance between upholding scientific research and noting its limits as well as its ongoing, self-correcting, nature." Kirkus.

Colson, Mary
Charles Darwin and Alfred Russel Wallace. Mary Colson. Gareth Stevens Publishing, 2015. 48 p.: Dynamic duos of science
Grades: 4 5 6   **576.8**
    1. Darwin, Charles, 1809-1882. 2. Wallace, Alfred Russel, 1823-1913. 3. Evolution 4. Natural selection 5. Scientific discoveries 6. Biologists 7. Scientists
ISBN 9781482414691
Profiles the lives and accomplishments of the two naturalists whose research on natural selection and evolution changed how the study of natural history was approached.

Gamlin, Linda
Evolution. Linda Gamlin. DK Pub., 2009. 72 p.: Eyewitness books
Grades: 4 5 6 7   **576.8**
    1. Evolution 2. Human evolution 3. Natural selection 4. Evolution -- History 5. Biology
ISBN 9780756650285
    Text about and photography of experiments, animals, plants, bones, and fossils reveal the ideas and discoveries that have changed our understanding of the natural world and how life began.

Hartman, Eve
Changing life on Earth. Eve Hartman and Wendy Meshbesher. Raintree, c2009. 48 p.: Sci-hi
Grades: 4 5 6   **576.8**
    1. Natural selection 2. Evolution 3. Mutation (Biology) 4. Zoology 5. Science
ISBN 9781410933249
                            LC 2009003459
Introduces evolution, discussing such topics as natural selection, genetics, and adaptation.

Holmes, Thom
Evolution. Thom Holmes. Chelsea House, c2010. 109 p.: Science foundations

Grades: 7 8 9 10   **576.8**
1. Evolution
ISBN 9781604133387

LC 2010015738

Explains the theory of evolution and its implications.

"A solid, competent history of the evolution of ideas and the theory of evolution itself. . . . Certainly not for browsing or easy light reading, but definitely of use to teachers or serious researchers." School Library Journal.

Includes bibliographical references (p. 100-103) and index.

Johnson, Sylvia A.

Shaking the foundation: Charles Darwin and the theory of evolution. Sylvia A. Johnson. Twenty-First Century Books, c2013. 88 p.
Grades: 6 7 8 9   **576.8**
1. Darwin, Charles, 1809-1882 2. Evolution 3. Natural selection 4. Human evolution 5. Evolution -- History 6. Evolution -- Religious aspects
ISBN 9780761354864

LC 2012018075

Examines the personal struggle of a man forced by his own observations to answer the fundamental question "Where do we come from?"

"In this thoughtful history of both Darwin and his theories of evolution, Johnson explains how the scientist lived and worked, religious and scientific challenges to his theories, and American legal challenges to evolution that continue in contemporary times. Numerous historical photographs and scientific illustrations, many from scientists of his time, greatly enhance the text." Horn Book.

Includes bibliographical references (p. 84-85) and index.

Martin, Martha

Extinction! . Martha Martin. Crabtree Publishing Company, 2013 48 p.
Grades: 4 5 6   **576.8**
1. Mass extinctions 2. Extinction (Biology) 3. Prehistoric animals 4. Dinosaurs 5. High interest-low vocabulary books
ISBN 9780778779254

Rexamines the series of events that may have caused five of Earth's great mass extinctions.

Pringle, Laurence, 1935-

★ **Billions** of years, amazing changes: the story of evolution. Laurence Pringle; illustrated by Steve Jenkins. Boyds Mills Press, 2011. 96 p.
Grades: 4 5 6 7   **576.8**
1. Evolution 2. Natural selection 3. Genetics
ISBN 9781590787236

"Pringle provides an accessible introduction to complex concepts such as natural selection and genetics, paired with Jenkins's characteristically elegant collages. . . . Compelling photographs of fossils and living creatures, as well as Jenkins's paper collages, augment the substantial text. The presentation should help children gain a confident grasp on the fundamentals of evolution." Publishers Weekly.

Solway, Andrew

Why is there life on Earth? Andrew Solway. Raintree, c2012. 48 p.: Raintree freestyle.
Grades: 5 6 7 8   **576.8**
1. Life -- Origin 2. Life on other planets 3. Earth
ISBN 9781410941602

"Delivering compact but broad summations about...life on Earth, [this] survey [is] well suited for review or reinforcement reading." School Library Journal.

Walker, Robert, 1980-

What is the theory of evolution? Robert Walker. Crabtree Pub., c2011. 64 p.: Shaping modern science
Grades: 5 6 7 8   **576.8**
1. Darwin, Charles, 1809-1882 2. Evolution 3. Human evolution 4. Evolution -- History
ISBN 9780778771982

LC 2010052628

Discusses beliefs about evolution before and after Darwin, how Darwin developed and published his theory on the subject, and reactions to his theory.

"This title is not only written and organized well, but [it is] also gorgeous in design. Full-color photographs and illustrations are set over colorful backgrounds that add depth but not distraction. [The title] includes thought-provoking quotes from famous authors and scientists and some eyebrow-raising Quick Facts throughout." School Library Journal.

Includes bibliographical references (p. 63) and index.

Winston, Robert M. L.

★ **Evolution** revolution: from Darwin to DNA. Robert Winston. DK, 2009. 96 p.
Grades: 5 6 7 8   **576.8**
1. Evolution 2. Biology
ISBN 9780756645243

Explores the history of evolution and the evolution of the future.

"The first two thirds of the book are devoted to the history of thought and research on evolution, from stories of Creation, through Darwin, to genetics. The last third looks at Evolution in Action. Information on the fetuses of related species rubs shoulders with variations within species and a time line of the Earth. Visually, the book snaps with colored backgrounds, cool graphics, topflight photos, and clever word balloons coming from vintage black-and-white reproductions." School Library Journal.

577 Ecology

Latham, Donna

Amazing biome projects you can build yourself. Donna Latham; illustrated by Farah Rizvi. Independent Pub. Group, 2009. 128 p.: Build it yourself
Grades: 4 5 6 7   **577**
1. Science projects 2. Biotic communities 3. Ecology 4. Science 5. Science -- Experiments
ISBN 9781934670408

"Although the text addresses young eco explorers directly, this book will likely be used as much by teachers, parents, and organization leaders in planning group activities. Offering an overview of eight terrestrial biomes as well as the ocean, Latham crams a lot of information about climate, plants, animals, soil, and other characteristics onto every page. . . . Instructions for hands-on activities related to different biomes include craft projects such as pictographs and a cornhusk doll. Students can learn how to make a glacier, an erupting volcano, and a tornado in a bottle." School Library Journal.

Reilly, Kathleen M

Planet Earth: finding balance on the blue marble: with environmental science activities for kids. Kathleen M. Reilly; illustrated by Tom Casteel. Nomad Press, 2019 v, 122 p.

Grades: 4 5 6 7   **577**

1. Ecology 2. Environmental sciences 3. Environmentalism 4. Science projects

ISBN 9781619307438

LC bl2019004865

Explores ecology basics, including such topics as the food web, animal habitats, and climate change.

577.078 Ecology—Science experiments

VanCleave, Janice Pratt

Step-by-step science experiments in ecology. Janice VanCleave. Rosen Central, 2013. 80 p.: Janice Vancleave's first-place science fair projects

Grades: 5 6 7 8   **577.078**

1. Ecology -- Experiments 2. Science projects 3. Experiments 4. Science -- Experiments

ISBN 9781448869800

LC 2012007781

Presents step-by-step instructions for ecological experiments.

577.0911 Frigid zones—Ecology

Buller, Laura, 1952-

Ice: chilling stories from a disappearing world. written by Laura Buller, Andrea Mills, John Woodward. DK Publishing, 2019. 160 p.

Grades: 4 5 6 7   **577.0911**

1. Ecology 2. Climate change 3. Climate and civilization 4. Polar animals 5. Prehistoric humans 6. Arctic regions 7. Polar regions

ISBN 9781465481702

LC bl2019019407

Describes how plants, animals, and humans survive in the Arctic regions, including facts on prehistoric life, sea ice, and the growing threat to the biome due to climate change.

"The effects of climate change on both the animals and the physical aspects of the regions serves as a recurring theme . . . comprehensive, beautiful, and highly useful." School Library Journal

Lynch, Wayne

Arctic. text and photographs by Wayne Lynch; assisted by Aubrey Lang. NorthWord, c2007. 64 p.: Our wild world

Grades: 4 5 6 7   **577.0911**

1. Ecology 2. Polar animals 3. Plants 4. Wildlife 5. Zoology 6. Arctic regions 7. Polar regions

ISBN 1559719605

LC 2006021920

Examines the climate, plants and animals of the Arctic regions.

"With accessible first-person writing, Lynch describes the Arctic ecosystem, discussing both the high and low Arctic. . . . Stunning photographs include close-ups and more expansive views." Horn Book Guide.

Includes bibliographical references (p. 62) and index.

577.098 Tropics--ecology--Latin America

Montgomery, Sy

Amazon adventure: how tiny fish are saving the world's largest rainforest. written by Sy Montgomery; photos by Keith Ellenbogen. Houghton Mifflin Harcourt, [2017] 96 p.: Scientists in the field (Houghton Mifflin)

Grades: 5 6 7 8 9   **577.098**

1. Fishes 2. Rain forests 3. Rain forest ecology

ISBN 9780544352995

LC 2016014693

Part science, part carnival—this winding adventure down the Amazon River with award-winning author Sy Montgomery and photographer Keith Ellenbogen explores how tiny fish, called piabas, can help preserve not only the rainforest and it's often misunderstood inhabitants, but the fate of our entire environment. Provided by publisher.

"An expansive and engaging story of biological interconnectedness and beauty." Publishers Weekly.

Includes bibliographical references.

577.27 Effects of humans on ecology

Sneideman, Joshua

Climate change: discover how it impacts spaceship Earth. Joshua Sneideman, Erin E. Tawmley; illustrated by Mike Crosier. Pgw 2015 128 p.: Build It Yourself

Grades: 4 5 6 7   **577.27**

1. Climate change 2. Global warming 3. Global environmental change 4. Green movement 5. Nature -- Effect of humans on

ISBN 9781619302693

"This installment of the well-known series encourages students to examine the timely subject of climate change. The volume is full of questions, words to know, primary sources, and fun-filled learning activities. The introductory chapter reminds readers of the importance of taking care of the planet. . . . The text and activities work together to remind students that the future is in their hands and they can be a part of the solution." School Library Journal.

Stille, Darlene R.

Nature interrupted: the science of environmental chain reactions. by Darlene Stille. Compass Point Books, c2008. 48 p.: Headline science

Grades: 5 6 7 8   **577.27**

1. Environmental chemistry 2. Nature 3. Chemical reactions 4. Chemistry 5. Science

ISBN 9780756539498

LC 2008007282

"This reviews the importance of subtle links in the environmental chain and the far-reaching consequences of its disruption. The possible harm to the food chain caused by the use of antibacterial soap is one case study. The flow of energy from one organism to the next in the food web and the unexpected results when this relationship is disrupted are shown in examinations of monarch butterflies, zebra mussels, and algal blooms. The color illustrations and charts . . . are clear and helpful, and the text, although information rich, is not overly difficult." School Library Journal.

Includes bibliographical references (p. 46-47) and index.

Zimmer, Marc

Solutions for a cleaner, greener planet: environmental chemistry. Marc Zimmer. Twenty-First Century Books, 2019. 120 p.

Grades: 8 9 10 11 12   **577.27**

    1. Environmental chemistry 2. Environmentalism 3. Pollution 4. Chemistry 5. Manufacturing processes -- Environmental aspects

    ISBN 9781541519794

                 LC 2018010574

    Many of the most toxic materials on Earth—from arsenic to plutonium—occur naturally, but manufacturers have also used them in products such as paints, plumbing, pesticides, nuclear fuel, and weaponry. Without careful management, toxins can leach into groundwater or pollute our environment. Exposure to toxins leads to various cancers, impairment of the immune and reproductive systems, as well as cognitive problems. What can be done? Solutions include a wide range of infrastructure approaches, such as better water filtration, governmental and manufacturing regulations, outright bans on certain chemicals, careful monitoring, and the use of alternative fuels. Learn more about key contaminants and their impact on health, as well as solutions on a global and individual level.

    "[T]his slim, amply illustrated book is engaging and even uplifting. Terrific for classroom use. Environmental chemistry that is eminently readable and hopeful." Kirkus.

    Includes bibliographical references and index.

577.34 Rain forest ecology

Johnson, Robin (Robin R.)

Rain forests inside out. Robin Johnson. Crabtree Publishing Company, 2015 32 p.

Grades: 4 5 6   **577.34**

    1. Rain forest ecology 2. Rain forests

    ISBN 9780778706373

                 LC 2014020968

    Explores the layers of the rainforest ecosystem; discusses climate, plant and animal life, and conservation; and describes the different types of rain forests around the world.

    "The lush photos of locations worldwide may inspire further investigation of the topic. Great selections." School Library Journal.

    Includes bibliographical references and index.

577.4 Grassland ecology

Bow, James

Grasslands inside out. James Bow. Crabtree Publishing, 2015. 32 p.: Ecosystems inside out

Grades: 4 5 6   **577.4**

    1. Grassland ecology 2. Grasslands

    ISBN 9780778706335

                 LC 2014020967

    "The lush photos of locations worldwide may inspire further investigation of the topic. Great selections." School Library Journal.

577.5 Ecology of miscellaneous environments

Bow, James

Tundras inside out. James Bow. Crabtree Publishing Company, 2015. 32 p.: Ecosystems inside out

Grades: 4 5 6   **577.5**

    1. Tundra ecology 2. Tundras

    ISBN 9780778706397

                 LC 2014020249

    "The lush photos of locations worldwide may inspire further investigation of the topic. Great selections." School Library Journal.

    Includes bibliographical references (page 31) and index.

Wicks, Maris

Coral reefs: cities of the ocean. Maris Wicks. First Second, 2016. 119 p.: Science comics

Grades: 4 5 6 7 8   **577.5**

    1. Coral reef ecology 2. Coral reefs and islands 3. Coral reef animals 4. Comics and Graphic novels

    ISBN 9781626721463

                 LC bl2016012752

    Explores coral reef ecosystems, detailing the organisms that live within the reefs, their importance in the ocean ecological system as a whole, and the scientific and medical advancements developed from coral reefs.

    "The jokes, puns, and humorous commentary will draw sea-life fans to this informative, tropical-hued introduction to coral reefs." Booklist.

    Includes bibliographical references (pages 118-119).

577.54 Desert ecology

Cohen, Marina, 1967-

Deserts inside out. Marina Cohen. Crabtree Publishing Company, 2014. 32 p.: Ecosystems inside out

Grades: 4 5 6   **577.54**

    1. Desert ecology 2. Deserts 3. Desert animals 4. Desert plants 5. Biotic communities

    ISBN 9780778706274

                 LC 2014020252

    "The even-handed tone, dynamic page layouts, extensive glossary, and concise writing make this an engaging and informative resource." Booklist.

577.68 Wetland ecology

Bow, James

Wetlands inside out. James Bow. Crabtree Publishing, 2014. 32 p.: Ecosystems inside out

Grades: 4 5 6   **577.68**

    1. Wetland ecology 2. Wetlands 3. Swamps 4. Marshes 5. Everglades, Florida

    ISBN 9780778706410

                 LC 2014020969

    "Each spread includes a few paragraphs discussing the particular wetland and one species living there. A large color photo shows the site, while a smaller close-up illustrates the featured plant or animal." Booklist.

577.7 Marine ecology

Johnson, Robin (Robin R.)

Oceans inside out. Robin Johnson. 32 p.: Ecosystems inside out

Grades: 4 5 6 **577.7**
1. Oceans 2. Marine ecology 3. Oceanography 4. Biotic communities
ISBN 9780778706359

LC 2014020250

From sunlit surface water that teems with life to the deepest, darkest depths filled with some of Earth's most unusual creatures, oceans are home to a wide array of life. Peel back the corners of the ocean to find out what fascinating life exists within this ecosystem, from Earth's biggest animal, the blue whale, to tiny organisms, such as kelp. Discover where the world's oceans are and what you can do to help protect our planet's rich waters. Provided by publisher.

"The lush photos of locations worldwide may inspire further investigation of the topic. Great selections." School Library Journal.

Includes bibliographical references (page 31) and index.

577.8 Synecology and population biology

Latham, Donna
Biomes: discover the Earth's ecosystems with environmental science activities for kids. Donna Latham; illustrated by Tom Casteel. Nomad Press, 2019 v, 122 p.
Grades: 4 5 6 7 8 **577.8**
1. Biotic communities 2. Habitat (Ecology) 3. Science -- Experiments
ISBN 9781619307360

LC bl2019006749

Explores the concept of biomes and enforces key ideas through science experiments.

"Mixing comics and thoughfully deisgned actitivies with solid information, [it] accessibly explores with precision." Booklist

Includes bibliographical references (page 119) and index.

578.769 Saltwater wetlands—Biology

Carson, Rachel, 1907-1964
The **edge** of the sea. Rachel Carson; with illustrations by Bob Hines. Houghton Mifflin, 1955. 276 p.
Grades: 7 8 9 10 11 12 Adult **578.769**
1. Seashore biology 2. Seashore animals 3. Seashore 4. Seashore ecology 5. Biology
ISBN 0395924960

LC 54010759

Introduces a world of teeming life where the sea meets the land.

Parker, Steve, 1952-
Seashore. written by Steve Parker; [special photography, Dave King]. DK Pub., 2004. 72 p.: Eyewitness books
Grades: 4 5 6 7 **578.769**
1. Ecology 2. Seashore 3. Seashore ecology 4. Seashore biology 5. Biotic communities
ISBN 0756607205

LC bl2004118720

Brief text and photos introduce the animal inhabitants of the seashore, including fish, crustaceans, snails, and shorebirds.

Wechsler, Doug
Marvels in the muck: life in the salt marshes. Doug Wechsler. Boyds Mills Press, 2008. 48 p.

Grades: 4 5 6 7 **578.769**
1. Salt marsh ecology 2. Salt marshes 3. Ecology 4. Nature 5. Marshes
ISBN 9781590785881

LC 2007052583

The salt marsh is not so friendly to humans, but it's the only place to be for many creatures and plants. Fascinating facts reveal the secrets of the salt marsh and celebrate this squishy and surprising habitat.

"A season-by-season look at the ecology of an oft-overlooked habitat. Wechsler's lucid text introduces the insects, birds, reptiles, crustaceans, and other critters that claim this salty expanse as home. . . . Clear color photos present species mentioned in the text." School Library Journal.

578.77 Oceans—Biology

Hirsch, Rebecca E.
Birds vs. blades?: offshore wind power and the race to protect seabirds. Rebecca E. Hirsch. Millbrook Press, [2017] 48 p.
Grades: 4 5 6 7 8 **578.77**
1. Sea birds 2. Coastal ecology 3. Wind power 4. Birds
ISBN 9781467795203

LC 2015044328

Shares information on how scientists are using implants in sea birds to study the impact wind farms have on the birds.

"The many illustrations include helpful, digital maps and diagrams as well as many color photos that are clearly reproduced, pertinent to the topic, and often eye-catching." Booklist

Includes bibliographical references (page 46) and index.

Kirby, Richard R.
Ocean drifters: a secret world beneath the waves. Richard R. Kirby. Firefly Books, 2011, c2010. 192 p.
Grades: 5 6 7 8 9 10 11 12 Adult **578.77**
1. Marine plankton
ISBN 9781554079827

LC 2011284690

"Kirby (Marine Inst. Research Fellow, Plymouth Univ., UK), who has published widely in scientific journals, combines in this book his area of expertise—plankton—with magnificent color photography of each species. He details the importance of the ocean's plankton layer to the health of the globe and its effects on sea and human life in the photos' descriptions...Recommended for readers interested in the smaller denizens of the natural world, the ocean, or microphotography." Library Journal.

Includes bibliographical references (p. 190-192) and index.

Somervill, Barbara A.
Marine biologist. by Barbara A. Somervill. Cherry Lake Pub., c2009. 32 p.: 21st century skills library.
Grades: 3 4 5 6 **578.77**
1. Marine biologists -- Vocational guidance 2. Marine biology 3. Scientists 4. Biologists 5. Occupations
ISBN 9781602795044

LC 2008045234

"This is highly readable. . . . Colorful photographs illustrate [the] book." School Library Journal.

579 Natural history of microorganisms, fungi, algae

Arato, Rona

Protists: algae, amoebas, plankton, and other protists. Rona Arato. Crabtree Pub. Co., 2010. 48 p. : Class of their own

Grades: 5 6 7 8   **579**
  1. Protista 2. Algae 3. Protozoa 4. Microorganisms 5. Biology
ISBN 9780778753919

LC 2009051386

"Lively section headings . . . and notes on uncommon achievements, . . . lighten the substantial load of biological terminology. Illustrated with a plethora of closeup color photos and microphotos, and closing with annotated lists of recommended Web sites, . . . [this captures] the remarkable diversity of life." School Library Journal.

Includes an index.

Eamer, Claire, 1947-

Inside your insides: a guide to the microbes that call you home. written by Claire Eamer; illustrated by Marie-Eve Tremblay. Kids Can Press, 2016. 36 p.

Grades: 3 4 5 6   **579**
  1. Microorganisms 2. Bacteria 3. Microbiology 4. Human body
ISBN 9781771383325

LC oc2016010679

A look at the good and bad microbes that live in and on the human body.

"The jazzy design and plentiful, brightly colored illustrations add appeal. Solid information presented in a sprightly manner that's sure to appeal." Kirkus.

579.3 Prokaryotes (Bacteria)

Brown, Jordan

Micro mania: a really close-up look at bacteria, bedbugs & the zillions of other gross little creatures that live in, on & all around you! Jordan D. Brown. Bookmasters Dist. Serv., 2009. 80 p.

Grades: 4 5 6   **579.3**
  1. Bacteria 2. Viruses 3. Microorganisms 4. Protozoa 5. Insects 6. Grossology 7. Trivia and miscellaneous facts
ISBN 9780982306420

"This engrossing book goes into squirm-inducing detail about the bacteria, microbes, and other assorted mini-organisms that dwell in our bodies and our homes. Each spread is well laid out with plenty of white space, large text, and colorful photos of these little critters . . . and the havoc they wreak. The writing is vivid without being breathless." School Library Journal.

Gardy, Jennifer

It's catching: the infectious world of germs and microbes. written by Jennifer Gardy, PhD; illustrated by Josh Holinaty. Owlkids Books Inc., 2014. 63 p.

Grades: 5 6 7   **579.3**
  1. Bacteria 2. Microorganisms 3. Germ theory of disease 4. Bacterial diseases 5. Diseases -- Causes
ISBN 9781771470018

LC oc2013121731

Presents general information about different types of germs, as well as the diseases they cause, and how people work to prevent them from spreading.

"An amusing but information-packed look at all things infectious. The cartoon illustrations and chatty text with terms like tummy and cooties and phrases such as a quick pit stop in the liver might lead some to assume this is a lightweight read, but there's plenty to offer in this complex but comprehensible work...This readable, slender introduction to the world of microbial life is an entertaining and informative eye-opener." School Library Journal.

579.5 Fungi

Gaya, Ester

Fungarium: welcome to the museum. Ester Gaya; illustrated by Ronda Pattison Candlewick Pr 2021 80 p.

Grades: 5 6 7 8 9   **579.5**
  1. Fungi 2. Botany 3. Mycology
ISBN 9781536217094

"The text is authoritative and informative, but the real attraction is the artwork. There are glorious spreads of ecosystems, and even the endpapers are worth a look." Booklist

580 Science—Natural history of plants and animals— Plants (Botany)

Ballard, Carol

Plant variation and classification. Carol Ballard. Rosen Central, 2010. 46 p. : Living processes

Grades: 5 6 7   **580**
  1. Plants 2. Variation (Biology) 3. Biology 4. Plants -- Variation
ISBN 9781615323456

LC 2009030568

Explains how our plant classification system works and looks at how scientists use it to identify and group plant species. The book also examines the variation between and within plants species and discusses how and why such variations have occurred.

"With colorful, quality photography, the well-organized content is divided into short chapters with bold subheadings making information easy to find. Clear and interesting writing distinguishes this . . . from older titles. The captions for pictures are used to provide identification and additional explanation for topics not included in the text." Library Media Connection.

Includes bibliographical references and index.

Willis, K. J.

Botanicum. curated by Katie Scott and Kathy Willis. Big Picture Press, an imprint of Candlewick Press, 2016. 112 p.: Welcome to the museum

Grades: 6 7 8 9   **580**
  1. Plants 2. Flowers 3. Trees 4. Botany
ISBN 9780763689230

Showcases dozens of full-color plants from around the world in a gallery format, complemented by identification information and brief descriptions.

"Visually stunning, its an engrossing overview of Earths remarkable and diverse plant life that provides opportunities for ongoing discovery on every page." Publishers Weekly.

580.75 Museum activities and services

Silvey, Anita

The **plant** hunters: true stories of their daring adventures to the far corners of the Earth. Anita Silvey. Farrar Straus Giroux, 2011. 96 p.

Grades: 6 7 8 9 10 **580.75**
    1. Plant collectors 2. Plant collecting -- History 3. Plants
ISBN 9780374309084

LC 2011005161

Documents the experiences and contributions of 18th- and 19th-century adventurers, explorers and scientists responsible for finding and cataloging many of the world's unusual plants, revealing how they often risked their lives while establishing early practices that became the science of botany.

"The slim, engaging narrative paints vivid portraits of these botanic adventurers. It is smoothly written, smartly paced and filled with exciting tales of risk taking and derring-do." Kirkus.

580.78 Plants—Science experiments

Gardner, Robert, 1929-

Ace your plant science project: great science fair ideas. Robert Gardner and Phyllis J. Perry. Enslow Publishers, c2009. 128 p. : Ace your biology science project

Grades: 5 6 7 8 **580.78**
    1. Botany -- Experiments 2. Plants -- Experiments 3. Botany projects 4. Biology -- Experiments 5. Science -- Experiments
ISBN 9780766032217

LC 2008004687

Presents several science experiments and project ideas using plants. Provided by publisher.

581.4 Adaptation

Castaldo, Nancy F. (Nancy Fusco), 1962-

The **story** of seeds: from Mendel's garden to your plate, and how there's more of less to eat around the world. Nancy Castaldo. Houghton Mifflin Harcourt, 2016. 136 p.

Grades: 6 7 8 9 **581.4**
    1. Food crops -- Seeds 2. Sustainable agriculture 3. Seeds 4. Agrobiodiversity conservation 5. Agriculture
ISBN 9780544320239

"This stellar interdisciplinary resource may need hand-selling to get readers beyond its plain packaging, but be prepared to satisfy readers' thirst for more information about, for instance, protecting Russia's international seed vaults during WWII, finding Glass Gem corn, and fighting biopiracy. A terrific, engrossing resource." Booklist.

581.6 Miscellaneous nontaxonomic kinds of plants

Richardson, Gillian

10 plants that shook the world. Gillian Richardson; art by Kim Rosen. Annick Press, c2013. 129 p.

Grades: 4 5 6 7 8 **581.6**
    1. Plants and history 2. Plants
ISBN 1554514444
Examines 10 plants that played a dramatic role in world history.

"With bold, lively caricatures from Rosen throughout, it's an intriguing and well-designed study of the ways plants have helped start wars, cure diseases, and advance technology." Publishers Weekly.

Includes bibliographical references (p. 124-125), Internet addresses, and index.

581.7 Plant ecology, plants characteristic of specific environments

Koch, Melissa

Forest talk: how trees communicate. Melissa Koch. Twenty-First Century Books, 2019 96 p.

Grades: 5 6 7 8 9 **581.7**
    1. Trees 2. Communication 3. Forest ecology 4. Forest conservation 5. Humans and trees
ISBN 9781541519770

LC 2018010569

Recently, researchers and citizen scientists made the surprising revelation that trees communicate with each other through an underground system of soil fungi and other methods. Complex social networks help trees survive and thrive by transferring resources to each other, sending defense signals, communicating with their kin, and more. Meet the tree scientists and learn more of their fascinating discoveries.

"An intriguing volume that describes the surprising hidden lives of trees and underscores their key role in our world." Booklist.

Includes bibliographical references (pages 90-93) and index.

582.13 Plants noted for their flowers

Spellenberg, Richard

National Audubon Society field guide to North American wildflowers.Western Region. Richard Spellenberg. Knopf, 2001. 862 p.

Grades: 7 8 9 10 11 12 Adult **582.13**
    1. Wild flowers -- Identification
ISBN 9780375402333

LC bl2005019525

The Western guide to identifying wildflowers in North America encompasses updated descriptions of a wide variety of species, distribution, and taxonomy and features more than seven hundred full-color photographs of flowers in their natural habitats.

Thieret, John W.

National Audubon Society field guide to North American wildflowers.. revising author, John W. Thieret; original authors, William A. Niering and Nancy C. Olmstead. Knopf, 2001. 879 p.

Grades: 7 8 9 10 11 12 Adult **582.13**
    1. Wild flowers -- Identification
ISBN 9780375402326

LC BL2001002285

Photographs, diagrams, physical descriptions, and details about habitat, season, and other characteristics facilitate the identification of eastern North America's wildflowers.

582.16 Trees

Brockman, Christian Frank, 1902-
   Trees of North America: a field guide to the major native and introduced species north of Mexico. by C. Frank Brockman; illustrated by Rebecca Merrilees; revised by Jonathan P. Latimer and Karen Stray Nolting with David Challinor. St. Martin's Press, c2001. 280 p.: A golden guide
   Grades: 8 9 10 11 12 Adult   **582.16**
      1. Trees -- Identification 2. Trees
      ISBN 9781582380926

                                    LC 2001272405
   Presents a handbook for the identification of over five hundred species of trees by illustration and text.

Galat, Joan Marie, 1963-
   Branching out: how trees are part of our world. by Joan Marie Galat; illustrated by Wendy Ding. Owlkids Books, 2014. 64 p.
   Grades: 4 5 6 7   **582.16**
      1. Trees 2. Tree ecology 3. Humans and trees 4. Botany
      ISBN 9781771470490
   Provides an in-depth introduction to trees, covering biology basics, 11 primary tree types from around the world, and the ways in which trees are an inextricable part of human society, culture and economy.
   "This short, lively introduction to the subject focuses on 11 trees from all over the world...This title is truly worldwide in its coverage; only one tree, the Red Maple, is a native of North America. Appended glossary and index are extensive and complete. A solid overview." School Library Journal.

Hirsch, Andy, 1987-
   Trees: kings of the forest. Andy Hirsch First Second, 2018. 128 p.: Science comics
   Grades: 4 5 6 7 8   **582.16**
      1. Trees 2. Plant life cycles 3. Life cycles (Biology) 4. Acorns 5. Oak 6. Comics and Graphic novels
      ISBN 9781250143112
   We follow an acorn as it learns about its future as Earth's largest, longest-living plant. Starting with the seed's germination, we learn about each stage until the tree's maturation, different types of trees, and the roles trees take on in our ecosystem.

Petrides, George A.
   A **field** guide to western trees: eastern [i.e. western] United States and Canada. George A. Petrides; illustrated by Olivia Petrides. Houghton Mifflin, 1998. xiv, 428 p.: The Peterson field guide series
   Grades: 7 8 9 10 11 12 Adult   **582.16**
      1. Trees -- Identification 2. Trees -- Pictorial works
      ISBN 9780395904541

                                    LC 98013624
   This newly designed field guide features detailed descriptions of 387 species, arranged in six major groups by visual similarity. The 47 color plates and 5 text drawings show distinctive details needed for identification. Color photographs and 295 color range maps accompany the species descriptions.—From publisher description.

Tate, Nikki, 1962-
   Deep roots: how trees sustain our planet. Nikki Tate. Orca Book Publishers, 2016. 48 p.

Grades: 4 5 6 7   **582.16**
   1. Trees 2. Ecology
   ISBN 9781459805828

                                    LC oc2015051047
   Discusses the role of trees in maintaining a vibrant ecosystem, as well as providing food, fuel and shelter.
   "Color photographs, activity suggestions, trivia bursts, sidebars, and Tates own arboreal anecdotes create an accessible and involving layout, while supplying a broad take on the global diversity and varying roles of trees." Publishers Weekly.
   Includes bibliographical references and index.

582.16078 Trees—Science experiments

Russo, Monica
   Treecology: 30 activities and observations for exploring the world of trees and forests. Monica Russo; photographs by Kevin Byron. Chicago Review Press, 2016. 114 p.: Young naturalists
   Grades: 3 4 5 6 7 8 9   **582.16078**
      1. Trees 2. Observing things 3. Creative activities for children and students 4. Nature craft 5. Tree conservation
      ISBN 9781613733967

                                    LC 2015050678
   Through 30 simple and fun activities, young readers learn how to obverse the diversity of leaf shapes, the textures of tree bark, and evidence of forest creatures. The activities promote the development of science, writing, math, arts and crafts, and observation skills.
   "A labor of love reflecting years of experience in the field as well as in writing for young readers, this offers a path to interesting explorations of the natural world." Kirkus.
   Includes bibliographical references and index.

583 Dicotyledons

Aaseng, Nathan
   Weird meat-eating plants. Nathan Aaseng. Enslow Publishers, c2011. 48 p.: Bizarre science
   Grades: 5 6 7 8   **583**
      1. Carnivorous plants 2. Plant defenses 3. Plants
      ISBN 9780766036727

                                    LC 2010016602
   Examines meat-eating plants, including the different types of carnivorous plants, how they trap their prey, why these plants eat meat, and where they are found. Provided by publisher.
   "Aimed at reluctant readers, [this title is] sure to disgust and delight in equal measure. . . . [The title] will pique interest and get kids lining up at the reference desk looking for more. The text is complemented by illustrations and magnified photos of things that you would hope never to see." School Library Journal.
   Includes bibliographical references (p. 47) and index.

590 Animals

Broom, Jenny
   Animalium. illustrated by Katie Scott; written by Jenny Broom. Big Picture Press, 2014. 112 p.: Welcome to the museum

Grades: 3 4 5 6 7 **590**
1. Animals
ISBN 9780763675080

"Each basic group includes several spreads offering examples from subgroups within the class as well as a spread with a connected habitat: coastal waters, coral reefs, rain forest, deserts, woodlands and tundra. No information sources are given, but there are good suggestions for general websites for further learning." Kirkus.

Davies, Nicola, 1958-

★ **Extreme** animals: the toughest creatures on Earth. Nicola Davies; illustrated by Neal Layton. Candlewick Press, c2006. 61 p.

Grades: 3 4 5 6 **590**
1. Adaptation (Biology) 2. Animals 3. Extreme environments
ISBN 0763630675

LC 2005043544

Animals adapt to their surroundings for survival. Learn how they survive in conditions that humans never would. Are you ready for the competition? From the persevering emperor penguins of the South Pole to the brave bacteria inside bubbling volcanoes, from the hardy reptiles of the driest deserts to the squash-proof creatures of the deepest seabeds, animals have adapted to survive in conditions that would kill a human faster than you can say "coffin." Discover how they do it in this amazing natural history book from a celebrated team—and find out who wins the title of the toughest animal of them all!

"There is life everywhere on Earth . . . and much of that life thrives in conditions that humans could not endure for five minutes or less. This funny and appealing little book describes who these amazing life-forms are and how they manage to survive. Simple and inviting cartoon drawings enliven the text and convey the types of extremes in an easy-to-understand manner." School Library Journal.

Hestermann, Josh, 1983-

Zoology for kids: understanding and working with animals: with 21 activities. Josh and Bethanie Hestermann. Chicago Review Press, Incorporated, 2015. 144 p.: For Kids

Grades: 5 6 7 8 9 **590**
1. Animals 2. Zoology -- Study and teaching -- Activity programs
3. Wildlife
ISBN 9781613749616

LC 2014042745

"Studded with fun activities and attractive animal photos, this comprehensive resource will excite those not already smitten with the animal world to enthusiastically join in the delightful exploration of what it means to study and care for animals in today's world. . . . Charming photos, hand-drawn graphics, highlighted words, and a correlative glossary enhance the clear-cut writing style." School Library Journal.

Includes bibliographical references and index.

Jenkins, Steve, 1952-

★ **Animals** by the numbers: a book of animal infographics. Steve Jenkins. Houghton Mifflin Harcourt, 2016. 48 p.

Grades: 3 4 5 6 **590**
1. Animals 2. Graphic methods
ISBN 9780544630925

An amazing look at numbers, facts, infographics, and the animals that inhabit them from the Caldecott Honor-winning author-illustrator Steve Jenkins!

"A brilliantly executed take on a perennially high-interest topic." Booklist.

Montgomery, Heather L.

Wild discoveries: wacky new animals. Heather L. Montgomery. Scholastic 2013 62 p.

Grades: 3 4 5 6 7 **590**
1. Animals 2. Biological discoveries 3. Scientific discoveries
ISBN 9780545477673

Presents some of the newly discovered species of animals from around the world, including the giant velvet worm, the psychedelic frogfish, the wattled smoky honeyeater, and the Burmese snub-nosed monkey.

Siwanowicz, Igor

Animals up close. Igor Siwanowicz. DK, 2009. 96 p.

Grades: 4 5 6 **590**
1. Animal pictures 2. Macrophotography
ISBN 9780756645137

A biologist at the Max Planck Institute of Neurobiology in Munich, Germany, brings the animal kingdom to life through cutting-edge macro-photography that zooms in on the colors, textures, and structures of the smallest of creatures.

"An eye-catching cover will attract readers to this amazing look at some of the world's insects, fish, mammals, reptiles, amphibians, and birds. The focus is on animals small enough to fit in a child's hand. Siwanowicz showcases each creature with a spread containing a full-color, high-quality, close-up photo surrounded by multiple factual asides. . . . The book is packed with interesting material that captures the author's fascination for small creatures." School Library Journal.

590.3 Zoology -- Dictionaries, encyclopedias, concordances

Buckley, James

Animals: a visual encyclopedia. writers, James Buckley, Jr., Anita Ganeri, Beth Landis Hester, Cari Jackson, Catherine Nichols, Lori Stein. Liberty Street, an imprint of Time Inc. Books, 2015. 303 p.

Grades: 3 4 5 6 7 **590.3**
1. Animals 2. Animal pictures
ISBN 9781618931535

LC 2015940344

Introducing the first encyclopedia book from Animal Planet—the leading brand for animal lovers—that tells the story of our planet's animal life and celebrates our vital and humanizing connection with the animal world.

"Gorgeous photographs of a panoply of animals are surrounded with various interesting factoids." Booklist.

Burnie, David

Kingfisher animal encyclopedia. David Burnie. Kingfisher, 2018. 319 p.

Grades: 5 6 7 8 9 **590.3**
1. Animals
ISBN 9780753474594

LC bl2018193883

A revised and updated edition of a highly visual, single-volume reference profiles 2,000 animal species from all world regions for their characteristics, behaviors and distribution and is complemented by a glossary of terms and extensive back matter.

590.72 Research

Burns, Loree Griffin

Citizen scientists: be a part of scientific discovery from your own backyard. Loree Griffin Burns; photographs by Ellen Harasimowicz. H. Holt, 2012. 80 p.

Grades: 3 4 5 6 7 8   **590.72**
   1. Suburban animals -- Research -- Citizen participation 2. Animals 3. Suburbs 4. Scientific discoveries 5. Science
ISBN 9780805090628

                               LC 2011021673
Shows young readers how a citizen scientist learns about butterflies, birds, frogs, and ladybugs.

Carson, Mary Kay

Animal watching: the definitive interactive nature guide. Mary Kay Carson; illustrated by Emily Dahl. Odd Dot 2021 448 p.

Grades: 5 6 7 8   **590.72**
   1. Nature study 2. Children and nature 3. Nature 4. Animals 5. Nature guides
ISBN 9781250230836

                               LC 2020021780
Rewild your life! With metal corners and 448 full-color, highly-illustrated pages, Outdoor School: Animal Watching is your indispensable tool for the outdoors. Make every day an adventure with the included: immersive activities to get you exploring, write-in sections to journal about experiences, next-level adventures to challenge even seasoned nature lovers. No experience is required-only curiosity and courage. This interactive field guide to animals includes: animal tracking; identifying birds by silhouette, size, and color; reading animal range maps; bird nest spotting; essential animal-watching gear; identifying mammals; bird calls and animal sounds; finding amphibians, reptiles, and fish; spotting scat; recognizing eyeshine; recording animal behavior; and so much more! Provided by publisher.

   "How to be respectful of wildlife while observing them; how animals behave and why; where to look for them; how to identify wildlife using shape, size, color, behavior, and location; and other information is presented in easily digestible segments interspersed with plenty of full-color illustrations." Kirkus

590.73 Collections and exhibits of living mammals

Halls, Kelly Milner, 1957-

Saving the Baghdad Zoo: a true story of hope and heroes. by Kelly Milner Halls and William Sumner. Greenwillow Books, c2009. 64 p.

Grades: 4 5 6 7   **590.73**
   1. Baghdad Zoo 2. Zoos 3. Zoo animals -- Conservation 4. Wildlife rescue 5. Iraq War, 2003-2011 6. Iraq 7. Baghdad, Iraq
ISBN 9780061772023

                              LC 2008052820
   "This eye-opening tale of compassion and cooperation chronicles the mission of an international team of military personnel, zoo staffers, veterinarians, and relief workers to rescue neglected animals in Baghdad. . . . Sobering and uplifting photographs—many taken by Sumner—underscore both the direness of the situation and the spirit of hope that drove the project." Publishers Weekly.

   Includes bibliographical references and index.

590.9 History, geographic treatment, biography

Johnson, Rebecca L.

Chernobyl's wild kingdom: life in the dead zone. Rebecca L. Johnson. Twenty-First Century Books, 2014. 88 p.

Grades: 7 8 9 10 11 12   **590.9**
   1. Chernobyl Nuclear Accident, 1986 2. Radiation 3. Wildlife 4. Animals 5. Plants 6. Chernobyl, Ukraine 7. Ukraine
ISBN 9781467711548

                              LC 2013039471
Looks at the events of the Chernobyl Nuclear Accident in the Ukraine, describing how scientists are monitoring the effects of radiation on the wildlife that continue to live there and what this means for the human population surrounding the area.

   "This clear presentation is supplemented with captioned photographs, explanatory boxes and a helpful map. The appropriate background and clear, easy-to-understand explanations make this one-of-a-kind title both accessible and interesting. An important story clearly and engagingly told by an experienced science writer." Kirkus.

   Includes bibliographical references (pages 59-61) and index.

Moberg, Julia

Historical animals: the dogs, cats, horses, snakes, goats, rats, dragons, bears, elephants, rabbits, and other creatures that changed the world. by Julia Moberg; illustrated by Jeff Albrecht Studios. Charlesbridge Publishing, [2015] 96 p.

Grades: 4 5 6   **590.9**
   1. Animals and history 2. Animals and civilization -- History 3. Animals 4. Illustrated books
ISBN 9781623540487

                              LC 2014018171
   "While adults might groan at the sometimes forced humor and poetry, the intended audience will eat this one up. Historical fluff? Maybe, but if nothing else, this silly yet persuasive effort will coax readers into enjoying history." School Library Journal.

590.911 Frigid zones—Zoology

Kainen, Dan

Polar: a photicular book. created by Dan Kainen; written by Carol Kaufmann. Workman Publishing, 2015.

Grades: 4 5 6 7 8   **590.911**
   1. Animals 2. Photicular books 3. Polar regions
ISBN 9780761185697

                              LC 2015026789
Offers informative essays and factual statistics on eight distinctive polar animals, each accompanied by video-like Photicular illustrations, as well as an introductory piece on the polar realms.

   "Perhaps no place on earth is more extreme than the poles, and the environmental changes occurring there take center stage in the future of all of the animals included in this intriguing, eye-catching book." Booklist.

590.92 Zoologists

Roop, Peter

Tales of famous animals. Peter and Connie Roop; illustrated by Zachary Pullen. Scholastic, 2012. 110 p.

Grades: 4 5 6 7 8   **590.92**
  1. Famous animals 2. Animals
ISBN 9780545430296
  An introduction to some of history's most noteworthy and heroic animals includes illustrated profiles of President Adams' pet alligator, Balto the sled dog and Koko the gorilla.

591 Specific topics in natural history of animals

Ambrose, Jamie
  Wildlife of the world. contributors, Jamie Ambrose, Dr. Amy-Jane Beer, Derek Harvey, Ben Hoare, Rob Hume, Tom Jackson, Steve Parker, Dr. Katie Parsons, John Woodward. DK, 2015. 480 p.
Grades: PreK K 1 2 3 4 5 6 7 8 9 10 11 12 Adult   **591**
  1. Animals
ISBN 1465438041

                        LC bl2015034492
  A sumptuously illustrated reference, produced in association with the Smithsonian Institution, combines in-depth information with portrait-style photography to profile the world's most recognized animals, detailing their behaviors, interactions and life cycles.
  "A chart at the beginning of each section indicates the number of species in each order, class, or phylum...[T]his is an important, gorgeous, accessible introduction to hundreds of species and their habitats throughout the world at a very small price." Booklist.

Yolen, Jane
  Animal stories: heartwarming true tales from the animal kingdom. by Jane Yolen, with her children Heidi E.Y. Stemple, Jason Stemple, & Adam Stemple; illustrated by Jui Ishida. National Geographic, 2014. 160 p.: National Geographic kids
Grades: 5 6 7 8   **591**
  1. Animals 2. Animal behavior
ISBN 9781426317255

                        LC 2014015729
  "In nineteen engaging short stories, Yolen and her children explore extraordinary animals from history and the connections they made with other creatures and people. Some stories will likely be familiar to readers (e.g., sled dog Balto), while others will be new discoveries. Ishida's colorful illustrations enliven the tales, and sidebars give further information." Horn Book.
  Includes bibliographical references and index.

591.3 Genetics, evolution, age characteristics

Hirsch, Rebecca E.
  Living fossils: survivors from Earth's distant past. Rebecca E. Hirsch. Millbrook Press, 2020 48 p.
Grades: 4 5 6 7 8   **591.3**
  1. Living fossils 2. Fossils 3. Evolution 4. Animals
ISBN 9781541581272
  Blue-blooded crabs? Platypus that sting? One-hundred-year old reptiles? Meet some of nature's longest-surviving species! Discover the stories of these incredible animals and find out how they help scientists piece together evolutionary history.
  "Well-organized, clearly written, nicely designed, and including new research, this will be welcomed in libraries." Kirkus

Ridley, Kimberly
  Extreme survivors: animals that time forgot. Kimberly Ridley. Tilbury House Publishers, 2017 47 p.: How nature works
Grades: 6 7 8 9   **591.3**
  1. Living fossils 2. Fossils 3. Prehistoric animals 4. Animals
ISBN 9780884485001
  Looks at animals that existed in prehistoric times and still exist today and suggests how these creatures managed to survive while other animals are now extinct.

591.47 Protective and locomotor adaptations, color

Johnson, Jinny, 1949-
  Animal tracks & signs. by Jinny Johnson; foreward by John A. Burton. National Geographic Children's Books, 2008. 192 p.
Grades: 5 6 7 8   **591.47**
  1. Animals 2. Animal tracks 3. Tracking and trailing 4. Nature 5. Animal behavior
ISBN 9781426302541
  A species-by-species guide to the clues left behind by more than four hundred animals helps readers identify what to look for when tracking animals (or imagining tracking them) in the wild or in the back yard.
  "This attractive book describes the tracks (paw prints, bird claw prints, slimy trails) and signs (molted skin, food remains, scat, tree markings) that animals leave in their wake. . . . A typical two-page layout includes a photo and short paragraph about the animal category, three or four colored boxes containing a photo or drawing of a specific animal (serval, bobcat), and a description of its size, geographic range, habitat, food, tracks and signs, and comments. . . . The beautiful photos vary from action . . . to informational. . . . The language is simple and readable." Voice of Youth Advocates.

Johnson, Rebecca L.
  ★ **When** lunch fights back: wickedly clever animal defenses. by Rebecca L. Johnson. Millbrook Press, 2014. 48 p.
Grades: 4 5 6 7   **591.47**
  1. Animal defenses 2. Animal behavior 3. Adaptation (Biology) 4. Animals
ISBN 9781467721097

                        LC 2013046646
  "Along with the ever popular hagfish (aka snot eel) and the horned lizard—which can indeed squirt blood from one or both eyes—Johnson... profiles 10 animals with particularly noxious defense mechanisms... This is an outstanding way for readers to meet scientists at work in both field and lab, as well as to learn that, for instance, fulmar chicks can project vomit up to 6 feet and, creepily, that a school of the Amazonian two-spot astyanax will attack and eject one of its own to distract an approaching predator. Thrilling reading for budding biologists." Kirkus.
  Includes bibliographical references and index.

591.5 Behavior

Castaldo, Nancy F. (Nancy Fusco), 1962-
  Beastly brains: exploring how animals think, talk, and feel. Nancy F. Castaldo. 152 p.
Grades: 7 8 9 10   **591.5**
  1. Animal intelligence 2. Cognition in animals 3. Animal behavior 4. Animals
ISBN 9780544633353

                        LC 2015045421

In this fascinating nonfiction account, author Nancy F. Castaldo reveals just what's going on inside the minds of animals, and through understanding animal intelligence we discover more about ourselves, including far more similarities than one might expect. Humans may have the biggest brains, but intelligence is not a quality exclusive to only us! Provided by publisher.

"This eye-opening, cogent, and well-structured volume will enlighten students to both the richness of the animal kingdom and the nature of intelligence." Booklist.

Includes bibliographical references (pages 141-148) and index.

Cusick, Dawn

Get the scoop on animal puke: from zombie snails to vampire bats, 251 cool facts about vomit, puke, barf, and more! Dawn Cusick. Imagine Publishing, 2014. 80 p.

Grades: 3 4 5   **591.5**
1. Vomit 2. Vomiting 3. Digestive system 4. Animals 5. Animal behavior 6. Grossology
ISBN 9781623540456

"What do hyenas, proboscis monkeys, and vampire bats have in common? Vomit. This companion to Cusick's Get the Scoop on Animal Poop! examines how and why various animals regurgitate their food... Cusick presents the material in a (very) immediate manner, providing readers with plenty of science, humor, and animal behavior facts to chew over—and even regurgitate." Publishers Weekly.

de la Bedoyere, Camilla

Creatures of the night. Camilla de la Bedoyere. Firefly Books Ltd, 2014. 80 p.

Grades: 4 5 6   **591.5**
1. Nocturnal animals 2. Bats 3. Worms 4. Animals
ISBN 9781770854598

"This detailed look at creatures that go bump in the night is a reminder of just how amazing animal adaptations are." Booklist.

Scott, Traer

Nocturne: creatures of the night. Traer Scott. Princeton Architectural Press, 2014 128 p.

Grades: 7 8 9 10 11 12 Adult   **591.5**
1. Nocturnal animals
ISBN 1616892889

LC 2014006210

Provides information about the behaviors and habitats of some of the planet's most arresting noctural animals, including the Canada lynx, spotted hyena, and barn owl, and depicts each in a series of dramatic photographs.

591.56 Behavior relating to life cycle

Allman, Toney

Animal life in groups. Toney Allman. Chelsea House, c2009. 124 p. : Animal behavior (Chelsea House)

Grades: 6 7 8 9   **591.56**
1. Animal societies 2. Social behavior in animals 3. Animal groups 4. Animal behavior
ISBN 9781604131420

LC 2008040120

Examines the societal structure among different animal species, including information on schools, flocks, herds, predator groups, and primate societies.

Downer, Ann, 1960-

The **animal** mating game: the wacky, weird world of sex in the animal kingdom. by Ann Downer. Twenty-First Century Books, [2016] 104 p.

Grades: 7 8 9 10 11 12   **591.56**
1. Courtship of animals 2. Animal behavior 3. Sexual selection in animals 4. Sex (Biology) 5. Animals -- Sexual behavior
ISBN 9781467785716

LC 2015035704

This book discusses courtship, sex, and mating habits across the animal kingdom, covering birds, reptiles, amphibians, fishes, and mammals, as well as select invertebrates. Provided by publisher.

"Downer's investigation of the myriad ways different species produce offspring is sure to enthrall researchers and browsers." School Library Journal.

Includes bibliographical references and index.

Montgomery, Sy

The **magnificent** migration: on safari with Africa's last great herds. Sy Montgomery, with photos by Roger and Logan Wood. Houghton Mifflin Harcourt, 2019 176 p.

Grades: 7 8 9 10   **591.56**
1. Animal migration 2. Wildebeest -- Migration 3. Grassland animals 4. Mammals 5. Serengeti Plain, Tanzania 6. Tanzania
ISBN 9780544761131

LC 2018034806

Follows a safari team led by Dr. Richard Estes as they track one of the largest land migrations—wildebeests crossing the Serengeti—with information on other animal migrations and the importance of protecting the African savanna ecosystem.

O'Sullivan, Joanne

Migration nation: animals on the go from coast to coast. Joanne O'Sullivan. Imagine! Publishing, 2015. 128 p.

Grades: 4 5 6 7 8   **591.56**
1. Animal behavior 2. Animal migration 3. Animals 4. North America
ISBN 9781623540500

An introduction to the migration patterns of nine very different types of animals, from gray whales and sandhill cranes to polar bears and monarch butterflies, discusses their life cycles and how to spot them.

Safina, Carl, 1955-

Beyond words: what elephants and whales think and feel. Carl Safina. Roaring Brook Press, 2019 176 p.

Grades: 4 5 6 7 8 9   **591.56**
1. Animal behavior 2. Elephants 3. Whales 4. Animal intelligence 5. Comparative psychology
ISBN 9781250144638

Follow researcher Carl Safina as he treks with a herd of elephants across the Kenyan landscape, then travel with him to the Pacific Northwest to track and monitor whales in their ocean home. Along the way, find out more about the interior lives of these giants of land and sea—how they play, how they fight, and how they communicate with one another, and sometimes with us, too.

"A profound, scientifically based appeal for recognition of the kinship of all living things." Kirkus.

591.68 Rare and endangered animals

Cotton, Katie

★ **Counting** lions: portraits from the wild. Katie Cotton; illustrated by Stephen Walton. Candlewick Press, 2015. 32 p.

Grades: 5 6 7 8   **591.68**

  1. Rare and endangered animals 2. Wildlife 3. Animal behavior 4. Counting 5. Animals

  ISBN 9780763682071

A visually striking celebration of wildlife blends a gentle counting exercise and elaborate charcoal drawings of 10 endangered creatures, including lions, elephants and pandas, complemented by poetic notes on their respective characteristics and behaviors.

"A stunning portrait of beautiful creatures in a book with a strong environmental message." School Library Journal.

Hirsch, Rebecca E.

De-extinction: the science of bringing lost species back to life. Rebecca E. Hirsch. Twenty-First Century Books, 2017. 120 p.

Grades: 5 6 7   **591.68**

  1. Clones and cloning 2. Genetics 3. Extinct animals 4. Rare and endangered animals 5. DNA, Fossil

  ISBN 9781467794909

                LC 2016019335

Explores the pros and cons of de-extinction and the new science that makes it possible.

"A staid but intellectually stimulating excursion across one of modern biology's most promising, and controversial, frontiers." Kirkus.

Includes bibliographical references and index.

591.75 Animal ecology of miscellaneous environments

Downer, Ann, 1960-

Wild animal neighbors: sharing our urban world. Ann Downer. Twenty-First Century Books, [2014] 64 p.

Grades: 5 6 7 8   **591.75**

  1. Urban animals 2. Urban ecology 3. City life 4. Suburban life 5. Human/animal relationships

  ISBN 9780761390213

                LC 2012043817

Reveals how the increase in human population is driving wild animals out of their natural habitats and into urban areas, and identifies the effects of this forced cohabitation on both species.

"Although this book's editorial stance advocates for wild animals in city habitats, it's candid about problems such animals cause humans—from messy raccoons that may carry rabies to potentially dangerous mountain lions in Los Angeles. Accurate information unhampered by a rigid template and supported by good documentation is presented in readable, balanced prose; compelling photographs illustrate the text." Horn Book.

Includes bibliographical references (page 62) and index.

Read, Nicholas, 1956-

City critters: wildlife in the urban jungle. written by Nicholas Read. Orca Book Publishers, 2012. 144 p.

Grades: 6 7 8   **591.75**

  1. Urban animals 2. Human/animal relationships 3. Urbanization -- Environmental aspects

  ISBN 9781554693948

                LC 2011942577

Discusses the lives of wild animals that live in a North American urban environment.

591.77 Marine animals

De la Bedoyere, Camilla

Monsters of the deep. Camilla de la Bedoyere. Firefly Books, 2014. 80 p.

Grades: 4 5 6   **591.77**

  1. Marine animals 2. Animals

  ISBN 9781770854659

                LC bl2014045768

Profiles some of the creepiest animals that inhabit the deep, including deep-sea anglers, flashlight fish, gulper eels, and Japanese spider crabs.

"These attractive volumes cover a wide variety of unusual animals . . . [t]he layouts are dramatic, featuring fascinating, sometimes stunning, photos and drawings set against black backgrounds . . . [c]harming looks at some odd creatures." School Library Journal.

Hoyt, Erich, 1950-

★ **Weird** sea creatures. Erich Hoyt. Firefly Books, c2013. 64 p.

Grades: 5 6 7 8 9 10   **591.77**

  1. Marine animals 2. Aquatic animals 3. Marine biology 4. Oceans

  ISBN 9781770851979

                LC oc2012649607

"Eerie, riveting eye candy for budding biologists and casual browsers alike." Kirkus.

Johnson, Rebecca L.

Journey into the deep: discovering new ocean creatures. Rebecca L. Johnson Millbrook Press, 2010. 64 p.

Grades: 4 5 6 7   **591.77**

  1. Marine animals 2. Marine ecology 3. Deep-sea sounding 4. Ocean bottom ecology 5. Scientific expeditions

  ISBN 9780761341482

"This strikingly illustrated book takes its readers on a series of research voyages exploring the ocean from its shallow edges to unfathomable depths during the recently completed ten-year International Census of Marine Life. Clearly organized text and pictures combine to introduce newly discovered marine creatures of all kinds. . . . The excitement and challenge of discovery in tangible. Scientific photographs printed on blue-to-black background . . . illustrate animals mentioned in a nicely legible text. . . . Rich, revealing and rewarding." Kirkus.

Includes filmography, bibliographical references, and index.

Rake, Matthew

Creatures of the deep. by Matthew Rake; illustrated by Simon Mendez. Lerner Publishing Group, [2016] 32 p.: Real-life monsters

Grades: 3 4 5 6   **591.77**

  1. Marine animals 2. Aquatic animals 3. Dangerous marine animals

  ISBN 9781467776431

                LC 2015014282

Reveals facts about some of the strangest creatures inhabiting the ocean, discussing their physical features, feeding habits, and behavior.

Webb, Sophie

Far from shore: chronicles of an open ocean voyage. Sophie Webb. Houghton Mifflin Books for Children, 2011. 80 p.

Grades: 4 5 6 7   **591.77**
1. Webb, Sophie Pacific Ocean 2. Dolphins 3. Sea birds 4. Marine animals 5. Oceans 6. Biologists 7. Pacific Ocean
ISBN 9780618597291

LC 2010025121

A young field biologist on a scientific sea voyage over deep water documents the variety of sea life she encounters, observing and counting such creatures as dolphins, sea birds, whales, squid, and flying fish.

"Webb returns with another richly detailed journal of her travels as a naturalist, combining scientific information, field guide-like illustrations, and a thorough account of the day-to-day experiments of a field scientist. The setting is a four-month-long research cruise on a National Ocean and Atmospheric Administration ship to study the impact of fishing on two dolphin populations that reside in the Eastern Tropical Pacific." Horn Book.

591.9 Animals by specific continents, countries, localities

Green, Jen

Barron's totally wild fact-packed, fold-out animal atlas. written by Jen Green; illustrated by Christiane Engel. Barron's Educational Series, 2015. 56 p.

Grades: 4 5 6 7   **591.9**
1. Zoogeography 2. Zoology 3. Wildlife 4. Animals 5. Pop-up books 6. Toy and movable books
ISBN 9780764168086

LC bl2015035764

Provides information on animals and where they live across the world, including prairie dogs in the United States, echidnas in Australia, and hippos in Africa.

"Green and Engel follow their 2014 atlas with an animal-themed tour of the world, and a large foldout map greets readers when they open the book." Publishers Weekly.

592 Invertebrates

Downer, Ann, 1960-

Smart and spineless: exploring invertebrate intelligence. Ann Downer. Twenty First Century Books, 2015. 88 p.

Grades: 6 7 8 9 10   **592**
1. Invertebrates 2. Cold-blooded animals 3. Marine animals 4. Animals
ISBN 9781467737395

"Lucid and well organized, the writing grips readers with a combination of facts and related narrative accounts of scientists at work. Clear color photos illustrate the main text and the many sidebars, which often highlight related research projects." Booklist.

Meinkoth, Norman August, 1913-

The **Audubon** Society field guide to North American seashore creatures. Norman A. Meinkoth. A.A. Knopf, c1981. 799 p.: The Audubon Society field guide series

Grades: 7 8 9 10 11 12 Adult   **592**
1. Marine invertebrates -- Identification
ISBN 9780394519937

LC 81080828

Presents a comprehensive guide to more than six hundred species of sea creatures living along the coasts of North America, with full-color photographs, anecdotes, identification key, and other information

592.66 Leeches

Marsico, Katie, 1980-

Leeches. Katie Marsico. Children's Press An Imprint of Scholastic Inc., 2016. 48 p.: Nature's children

Grades: 3 4 5 6   **592.66**
1. Leeches
ISBN 9780531213940

"With more than 700 species, readers will learn about blood-sucking and nonparasitic varieties and their role in human medicine." Booklist.

594 Mollusca and Molluscoidea

Arthur, Alex

Shell. written by Alex Arthur. DK Pub., 2013. 72 p.

Grades: 6 7 8   **594**
1. Shells 2. Shells (Protective body covering) 3. Shells -- Collectors and collecting
ISBN 9781465409041

LC bl2013024343

Photographs and text examine different types of shells, including seashells, eggshells, and fossil shells, focusing on such aspects as how shells camouflage themselves and how they may be collected.

Newquist, H. P. (Harvey P.)

Here there be monsters: the legendary kraken and the giant squid. H.P. Newquist. Houghton Mifflin, 2010. 73 p.

Grades: 4 5 6 7   **594**
1. Kraken 2. Giant squids 3. Monsters 4. Squids 5. Curiosities and wonders
ISBN 9780547076782

LC 2009045246

Weaves the scientific discovery of the giant squid with historical accounts of the mythological kraken to explore the nature of the giant ocean animal.

"This intriguing book offers a chronological account of giant squids, beginning with sailors' tales about krakens and leading up to the groundbreaking discoveries of the past few decades. . . . The many illustrations, in color when available, include photos, engravings, and maps. . . . An attractive, informative book on an underrepresented topic." Booklist.

Includes bibliographical references (p. 70) and index.

Rehder, Harald Alfred, 1907-

The **Audubon** Society field guide to North American seashells. Harald A. Rehder, with photographs by James H. Carmichael, Jr.; visual key by Carol Nehring and Mary Beth Brewer. Knopf, c1981. 894 p.: The Audubon Society field guide series

Grades: 7 8 9 10 11 12 Adult   **594**
1. Shells -- Identification
ISBN 9780394519135

LC 80084239

Surveys the habitat, range, behavior, biology, and reproductive habits of marine mullusks

"The more than 700 color plates are arranged according to shape and color rather than family or genus, making identification very simple for even the rankest amateur. . . . The text gives the common name, scientific name, description, habitat, range, and comments for each species. This is the most comprehensive field guide to North American seashells." Library Journal.

594.56 Octopuses

Montgomery, Sy

The **octopus** scientists. Sy Montgomery; illustrated by Keith Ellenbogen. Houghton Mifflin Harcourt 2015 80 p.: Scientists in the field (Houghton Mifflin)

Grades: 5 6 7 8 9   **594.56**

1. Octopuses 2. Marine animals 3. Marine biologists 4. Vocational guidance

ISBN 9780544232709

A latest entry in the award-winning Scientists in the Field series takes readers to the waters off of Moorea, Tahiti, to study these amazing creatures, following scientists as they uncover the secrets of the octopus's advanced intelligence to learn what these thinking, feeling animals have to teach us about the oceans and ourselves.

"Amazing photographs reveal the octopuses' remarkable shape-changing abilities and help readers visualize this experience. Science in the field at its best." Kirkus.

595.4 Chelicerata

Heos, Bridget

Stronger than steel: spider DNA and the quest for better bulletproof vests, sutures, and parachute rope. Bridget Heos; with photographs by Andy Comins. Houghton Mifflin Books for Children, 2013. 80 p. : Scientists in the field (Houghton Mifflin)

Grades: 5 6 7 8   **595.4**

1. Spiders 2. Genetic engineering 3. Spider webs 4. Nephila maculata 5. Spider webs -- Therapeutic use

ISBN 9780547681269

LC 2012010992

In The Spider Silk Scientists, readers enter Randy Lewis' lab where they come face to face with golden orb weaver spiders and genetically engineered goats, whose milk contains the proteins to spin spider silk—and to weave a nearly indestructible fiber.Learn how this amazing material might someday be used to repair or replace human ligaments and bones, improve body armor, strenghten parachute rope, and even tether an airplane to an aircraft carrier! Readers explore rapid advancements in the applicationof genetic medicine and their potential to save and improve lives while considering the crucial ethical concerns of genetic research. A timely addition to the acclaimed Scientists in the Field series. . Provided by publisher.

Hirschmann, Kris, 1967-

Deadliest spiders. Kris Hirschmann. ReferencePoint Press, [2017] 80 p.: Deadliest predators

Grades: 6 7 8 9 10   **595.4**

1. Spiders 2. Poisonous animals 3. Arachnids

ISBN 9781682820582

LC 2016020674

Profiles some of the world's deadliest spiders, including the black widow, Sydney funnel-web spider, and Chilean recluse.

"First-rate nonfiction on a high-interest topic." School Library Journal.

Includes bibliographical references (pages 68-69) and index.

Lasky, Kathryn

Silk and venom: searching for a dangerous spider. by Kathryn Lasky; photographs by Christopher Knight. Candlewick Press, 2011. 64 p.

Grades: 4 5 6 7   **595.4**

1. Binford, Greta 2. Spiders 3. Scientists 4. Arachnologists 5. Dangerous animals 6. Poisonous animals

ISBN 9780763642228

LC 2010041888

"Biology professor Greta Binford studies spiders in an Oregon lab and in the field in the Dominican Republic, where she searches for L. Taino, a Caribbean relative of the venomous brown recluse that might provide clues to how and when the recluse genus arrived in North America. . . . In leisurely, literary prose, Lasky presents the ancient class of arachnids before introducing the scientist and explaining her quest. . . . On most spreads, a full-bleed photograph is opposed by substantial text and one or two smaller pictures." Kirkus.

Markle, Sandra

Black widows: deadly biters. Sandra Markle. Lerner Publications, c2011. 48 p.: Arachnid world

Grades: 5 6 7 8   **595.4**

1. Black widow spider 2. Spiders 3. Arachnids

ISBN 9780761350385

LC 2010004274

Introduces black widow spiders, describing their physical characteristics, life cycle, behavior, and hunting skills.

"Markle presents a mix of common and less-common facts . . . and her commentary accompanies a particularly strong suite of illustrations featuring large, clear, labeled outside and inside views that display body parts. Photos go beyond the standard portraits. . . . First rate." School Library Journal.

Includes bibliographical references (p. 44) and index.

Crab spiders: phantom hunters. Sandra Markle. Lerner Publications, c2012. 48 p.: Arachnid world

Grades: 4 5 6 7   **595.4**

1. Crab spiders 2. Arachnids 3. Spiders

ISBN 9780761350453

LC 2011020443

Presents information about the crab spider, including photographs and diagrams, how they relate and differ from other spiders, and where they live.

Fishing spiders: water ninjas. Sandra Markle. Lerner Publications Company, c2012. 48 p.: Arachnid world

Grades: 4 5 6 7   **595.4**

1. Insects 2. Spiders

ISBN 9780761350446

LC 2011020442

Presents information about fishing spiders, describing their physical features, how they relate and differ from other spiders, and where they live.

Harvestmen: secret operatives. Sandra Markle. Lerner Publications, c2011. 48 p.: Arachnid world

Grades: 5 6 7 8   **595.4**

1. Daddy Longlegs 2. Spiders 3. Insects

ISBN 9780761350422

LC 2010023491

Discusses the different body parts, life cycle, diet, and natural environment of the tall spiderlike daddy longlegs.

"Markle presents a mix of common and less-common facts . . . and her commentary accompanies a particularly strong suite of illustrations featuring large, clear, labeled outside and inside views that display body parts. Photos go beyond the standard portraits. . . . First rate." School Library Journal.

Includes bibliographical references (p. 44) and index.

Jumping spiders: gold-medal stalkers. Sandra Markle. Lerner Publications, c2012. 48 p.: Arachnid world

Grades: 4 5 6 7   **595.4**
    1. Jumping spiders 2. Spiders 3. Arachnids
    ISBN 9780761350477

                     LC 2011021598

Introduces jumping spiders, describing their body parts and what they eat.

Mites: master sneaks. Sandra Markle. Lerner Publications, c2012. 48 p.: Arachnid world

Grades: 4 5 6 7   **595.4**
    1. Mites 2. Arachnids 3. Arthropods
    ISBN 9780761350460

                     LC 2011021462

Describes the anatomy and life cycle of mites, how they infest humans and animals, and the diseases they carry.

Orb weavers: hungry spinners. Sandra Markle. Lerner Publications, c2011. 48 p.: Arachnid world

Grades: 5 6 7 8   **595.4**
    1. Orb weavers 2. Spiders 3. Arachnids
    ISBN 9780761350392

                     LC 2010023490

Describes the different parts to orb weaving arachnids, their life cycle, how they spin webs, and how they use those webs to trap and eat their prey.

"Markle presents a mix of common and less-common facts . . . and her commentary accompanies a particularly strong suite of illustrations featuring large, clear, labeled outside and inside views that display body parts. Photos go beyond the standard portraits. . . . First rate." School Library Journal.

Includes bibliographical references (p. 44) and index.

Scorpions: armored stingers. Sandra Markle. Lerner, c2011. 48 p.: Arachnid world

Grades: 5 6 7 8   **595.4**
    1. Scorpions 2. Arthropods 3. Arachnids
    ISBN 9780761350378

                     LC 2010004275

Introduces scorpions, describing their physical characteristics, life cycle, behavior, and hunting skills.

"Markle presents a mix of common and less-common facts . . . and her commentary accompanies a particularly strong suite of illustrations featuring large, clear, labeled outside and inside views that display body parts. Photos go beyond the standard portraits. . . . First rate." School Library Journal.

Includes bibliographical references (p. 44) and index.

Tarantulas: supersized predators. by Sandra Markle. Lerner Publications Company, c2012. 48 p.: Arachnid world

Grades: 4 5 6 7   **595.4**
    1. Tarantulas 2. Spiders 3. Arachnids
    ISBN 9780761350439

                     LC 2011020437

Provides information about tarantulas, including anatomy, feeding habits, and behavior.

Ticks: dangerous hitchhikers. Sandra Markle. Lerner Publications, c2011. 48 p.: Arachnid world

Grades: 4 5 6 7   **595.4**
    1. Ticks 2. Bloodsucking insects 3. Tick-borne diseases 4. Ticks as carriers of disease
    ISBN 9780761350415

                     LC 2010023484

Introduces ticks, including their different body parts, life cycle, diet, and the dangers they pose to humans and pets.

"This book about ticks offers a clear, conversational text that will draw young people into the zoological facts with gripping, even gruesome examples that are well matched with unsparingly detailed photos. . . . The handsome design, featuring crisply magnified photos, and the approachable text from an experienced writer combine into a strong offering for both personal and classroom reading." Booklist.

Includes bibliographical references (p. [46]) and index.

Wind scorpions: killer jaws. Sandra Markle. Lerner Publications, c2012. 48 p.: Arachnid world

Grades: 4 5 6 7   **595.4**
    1. Scorpions 2. Arthropods 3. Arachnids 4. Poisonous animals
    ISBN 9780761350484

                     LC 2011021599

Introduces wind scorpions, describing their physical characteristics, life cycle, and behavior.

Wolf spiders: mothers on guard. Sandra Markle. Lerner Publications, c2011. 48 p.: Arachnid world

Grades: 5 6 7 8   **595.4**
    1. Wolf spiders 2. Spiders 3. Arachnids
    ISBN 9780761350408

                     LC 2010004273

Discusses the different body parts, life cycle, diet, and natural environment of wolf spiders.

"Markle presents a mix of common and less-common facts . . . and her commentary accompanies a particularly strong suite of illustrations featuring large, clear, labeled outside and inside views that display body parts. Photos go beyond the standard portraits. . . . First rate." School Library Journal.

Includes bibliographical references (p. 44-45) and index.

Montgomery, Sy

  ★ The **tarantula** scientist. by Sy Montgomery; photographs by Nic Bishop. Houghton Mifflin Co., 2004. 80 p.: Scientists in the field (Houghton Mifflin)

Grades: 4 5 6 7   **595.4**
    1. Marshall, Samuel D. 2. Arachnologists 3. Spiders 4. Tarantulas 5. Research 6. Biological research
    ISBN 0618147993

                     LC 2003020125

Describes the research that Samuel Marshall and his students are doing on tarantulas, including the largest spider on earth, the Goliath birdeating tarantula.

"Enthusiasm for the subject and respect for both Marshall and his eight-legged subjects come through on every page of the clear, informative, and even occasionally humorous text. Bishop's full-color photos . . . are amazing." Booklist.

Includes bibliographical references (p. 79) and index.

595.7 Insects

Albee, Sarah
   Bugged: how insects changed history. by Sarah Albee. Bloomsbury/Walker, 2014. 176 p.
   Grades: 4 5 6 7   **595.7**
      1. Insects -- History 2. Human-animal relationships -- History
   ISBN 9780802734228

LC 2013025968
   "Overall, this title is astonishing, disgusting, revolting, and ultimately fascinating, making it perfect for emerging entomologists, budding historians, reluctant readers, and gross-out junkies alike." School Library Journal.

Insects and spiders
   Insects and spiders.. Barron's, [2016] 32 p.: Visual explorers
   Grades: 4 5 6 7   **595.7**
      1. Insects 2. Spiders
   ISBN 9781438008271

LC bl2016014921
   Shares information on insects and spiders, including mantises, ant colonies, and butterflies.
   "Inexpensive and relatively sturdy, these large-format paperbacks make for a visually enticing series." Booklist.

Stewart, Amy
   Wicked bugs: the meanest, deadliest, grossest bugs on Earth. Amy Stewart; illustrated by Briony Morrow-Cribbs. Algonquin Young Readers, 2017. 192 p.
   Grades: 4 5 6 7 8   **595.7**
      1. Insect pests 2. Entomology 3. Insects 4. Arachnids 5. Nature 6. Grossology
   ISBN 9781616207557
   Thematically organized profiles of the world's most notorious insects includes examples ranging from predators and scavengers to destructive, stinging and poisonous species, in a younger reader's adaptation of the award-winning author's adult book by the same title.

Woodward, John, 1954-
   Super bug encyclopedia: the biggest, fastest, deadliest creepy-crawlies on the planet. author, John Woodward; Smithsonian consultant, Gary F. Hevel; general consultant, Dr. George McGavin. DK Publishing, 2016. 207 p.
   Grades: 4 5 6 7 8   **595.7**
      1. Insects
   ISBN 9781465446008

LC bl2016011037
   Macro photography and CGI artworks combine in a vibrant tour of 100 amazing insects that features engaging profiles, the latest scientific discoveries, 3-D models, cross-section insights and more.
   "This selection has high appeal for browsers and will be useful for report writers." School Library Journal.

Young, Karen Romano
   Best science fair workshops—bug science: 20 projects and experiments about arthropods: insects, arachnids, algae, worms, and other small creatures. by Karen Romano Young; illustrated by David Goldin. National Geographic, 2009. 80 p.: Science fair winners
   Grades: 6 7 8 9   **595.7**
      1. Arthropods 2. Science projects 3. Science -- Experiments 4.

Experiments
   ISBN 9781426305191

LC 2009012734
   "This book is engaging, visually stimulating, and very student friendly. . . . Includes an introduction to the topic, suggestions for how to present the findings, and an index making the information really accessible. . . . The planning steps, guidance, and tips along the way for implementing projects are very sound." Library Media Connection.

595.7097 Insects—North America

Milne, Lorus Johnson, 1910-1987
   The **Audubon** Society field guide to North American insects and spiders. Lorus and Margery Milne; visual key by Susan Rayfield. Knopf, c1980. 989 p.
   Grades: Adult   **595.7097**
      1. Insects -- Identification 2. Spiders -- Identification 3. Arachnida -- Identification
   ISBN 9780394507637

LC 80007620
   Identifies, discusses, and illustrates every important family and species in North America, providing information on the habits and characteristics of each insect and spider covered.

595.714 Insects—Physical adaptation

Beccaloni, George
   Biggest bugs life-size. George Beccaloni. Firefly Books, 2010. 86 p.
   Grades: 4 5 6 7   **595.714**
      1. Insects 2. Smallness and bigness 3. Curiosities and wonders
   ISBN 9781554076994

LC oc2010024962
   "This book presents 35 of the world's biggest, longest, and heaviest bugs. . . . Double-page spreads feature each bug's statistics, a map with its area of distribution, and straightforward text that explains its living conditions, eating habits, and life cycle. . . . The highlights, of course, are the numerous life-size and up-close full-color photographs of the bugs. . . . The visual appeal alone will entice even the most reluctant readers." Booklist.
   Includes bibliographical references and index.

595.76 Beetles

Burns, Loree Griffin
   ★ **Beetle** busters: a rogue insect and the people who track it. Loree Griffin Burns; photographs by Ellen Harasimowicz. Houghton Mifflin Harcourt, 2014. 64 p.: Scientists in the field (Houghton Mifflin)
   Grades: 5 6 7 8   **595.76**
      1. Beetles 2. Insects 3. Tracking and trailing 4. Pests 5. Asian longhorned beetle
   ISBN 9780547792675

LC 2013050160
   A fascinating nonfiction photo essay about the tree-killing Asian long-horned beetle in our very own backyards. Read about how the help of everyday people, their neighborhoods, teams of beetle-sniffing dogs,

and a nationwide effort from bug scientists to tree doctors are working to eradicate this incredibly invasive pest.

"The author lives within the quarantined area in Massachusetts and has seen firsthand areas where swatches of infested (and other) trees have been cut down. Her questions about the method employed will leave readers asking some of their own—as they should. A timely, well-told story and a call to action." School Library Journal.

Jenkins, Steve, 1952-
The **beetle** book. by Steve Jenkins. Houghton Mifflin Books for Children, 2012. 31 p.

Grades: 4 5 6 7   **595.76**
    1. Beetles 2. Insects
    ISBN 9780547680842

                  LC 2011027129
Introduces beetles, including their different parts, their life cycles, what they eat, and what makes them special in the insect world.

595.78 Moths and butterflies

Pasternak, Carol, 1954-
How to raise monarch butterflies: a step-by-step guide for kids. Carol Pasternak. Firefly Books, c2012. 48 p.

Grades: 3 4 5 6 7   **595.78**
    1. Monarch butterfly -- Life cycles 2. Butterflies
    ISBN 9781770850019
An introduction to the life cycle of monarch butterflies features dozens of close-up photographs of every stage while instructing youngsters on how to attract and raise their own butterflies, in a volume that also explains how released butterflies migrate to resume the next cycle.

Pyle, Robert Michael
The **Audubon** Society field guide to North American butterflies. Robert Michael Pyle; visual key by Carol Nehring and Jane Opper. Knopf: c1981. 916 p.

Grades: Adult   **595.78**
    1. Butterflies -- Identification 2. Insects -- Identification
    ISBN 9780394519142

                  LC 80084240
Describes the habitat, behavior, range, and developmental stages of native butterflies, native skippers, and migrating tropical butterflies

Whalley, Paul Ernest Sutton
Butterfly & moth. written by Paul Whalley. DK Pub., 2012. 72 p.: Eyewitness books

Grades: 4 5 6 7   **595.78**
    1. Butterflies 2. Moths
    ISBN 9780756692995

                  LC BL 00012911
Photographs and text explore the behavior and life cycles of butterflies and moths, examining mating rituals, camouflage, habitat, and growth from pupa to larva to adult.

595.79 Ants, bees, and wasps

Blobaum, Cindy, 1966-
Explore honey bees!: with 25 great projects. Cindy Blobaum; illustrated by Bryan Stone. Nomad Press, 2015. 96 p.: Explore your world!

Grades: 3 4 5 6   **595.79**
    1. Bees 2. Insects 3. Animal life cycles 4. Life cycles (Biology)
    ISBN 9781619302860
"A solid text that lends itself well to classroom use as well as to individual research." School Library Journal.

Chadwick, Fergus
The **bee** book. Fergus Chadwick, Steve Alton, Emma Sarah Tennant, Bill Fitzmaurice, Judy Earl. DK Publishing, 2016. 221 p.

Grades: Adult   **595.79**
    1. Bee culture 2. Bees
    ISBN 1465443835

                  LC bl2016002280
This guide to bees provides instructions for starting backyard hives, from choosing plants and creating bee "hotels" to harvesting honey and making beeswax and propolis to make home remedies, candles, and beauty treatments.

"This is a charming, information-rich book that should lead readers to appreciate bees and welcome them into their gardens and wild places and even encourage some to keep honeybees." Booklist.

Hirsch, Rebecca E.
Where have all the bees gone?: pollinators in crisis. by Rebecca E. Hirsch. Twenty-First Century Books, 2020. 104 p.

Grades: 6 7 8 9 10   **595.79**
    1. Bees 2. Insect pollinators 3. Humans and insects 4. Pollination 5. Pollinators
    ISBN 9781541534636
Bees pollinate 75 percent of the fruits, vegetables, and nuts grown in the United States. Around the world, bees pollinate $24 billion worth of crops each year. Without bees, humans would face a drastically reduced diet. We need bees to grow the foods that keep us healthy. But numbers of bees are falling, and that has scientists alarmed. What's causing the decline? Diseases, pesticides, climate change, and loss of habitat are all threatening bee populations. Some bee species teeter on the brink of extinction. Learn about the many bee species on Earth: their nests, their colonies, their life cycles, and their vital connection to flowering plants. Most importantly, find out how you can help these important pollinators.

"Accessible and concise, this volume teaches an important topic responsibly without being dry." Kirkus
Includes bibliographical references and index.

Markle, Sandra
The **case** of the vanishing honey bees: a scientific mystery. by Sandra Markle. Millbrook Press, [2014] 48 p.

Grades: 4 5 6 7 8   **595.79**
    1. Colony collapse disorder of honeybees 2. Honeybee 3. Beehives 4. Beneficial insects 5. Bees
    ISBN 9781467705929

                  LC 2012046913
Presents facts about the ongoing investigation into the decline of honey bees around the world from colony collapse disorder, as scientists look at the impact of such factors as pesticides, farmer transportation of bee hives, fungal infections, and climate change.

597 Cold-blooded vertebrates

Gilbert, Carter Rowell, 1930-
National Audubon Society field guide to fishes.. Carter R. Gilbert, James D. Williams. Alfred A. Knopf, 2002. 607 p.

Grades: 7 8 9 10 11 12 Adult **597**
  1. Fishes -- Identification
  ISBN 9780375412240

                  LC 2002020773

Covering both freshwater and saltwater species of fish, this fully revised edition brings a new level of accuracy and usefulness to the National Audubon Society's acclaimed field guides.

Turner, Pamela S.
  ★ **Project** seahorse. by Pamela S. Turner. Houghton Mifflin, 2010. 64 p.: Scientists in the field (Houghton Mifflin)
Grades: 4 5 6 7 **597**
  1. Sea horses 2. Marine animals
  ISBN 9780547207131

                  LC 2009049707

Examines the work performed by the founders of Project Seahorse, along with Filipino colleagues and fishers, to protect seahorses and the coral reefs where they live while also helping the local fishing families.

  "With striking images of coral-reef inhabitants, this photo-essay introduces Project Seahorse, an international effort to protect and rehabilitate the Danajon Bank, a double reef off a Philippine Island where seahorses once flourished . . . Tuason, a noted Asian marine photographer whose specialty is the Philippines, seems equally adept at photographing the land and people and the underwater world. This is another splendid demonstration of the work of Scientists in the Field." Kirkus.

597.17 Fishes

Page, Lawrence M.
  Peterson field guide to freshwater fishes of North America north of Mexico. Lawrence M. Page, Brooks M. Burr; illustrations by Eugene C. Beckham III ... [et al.]; maps by Griffin E. Sheehy. Houghton Mifflin Harcourt, c2011. xix, 663 p.
Grades: Adult **597.17**
  1. Freshwater fishes 2. Freshwater fishes
  ISBN 9780547242064

                  LC 2010049219

This second edition incorporates almost 150 more freshwater fish species, plus all-new maps and a collection of new and revised plates.

597.3 Sharks

Abramovitz, Melissa, 1954-
  Deadliest sharks. Melissa Abramovitz. ReferencePoint Press, [2017] 80 p.: Deadliest predators
Grades: 6 7 8 9 10 **597.3**
  1. Sharks 2. Predatory animals
  ISBN 9781682820544

                  LC 2015050838

Profiles some of the world's deadliest sharks, including the spotted wobbegong, shortfin mako, and bull shark.

  "First-rate nonfiction on a high-interest topic." School Library Journal.

  Includes bibliographical references (pages 70-71) and index.

Cerullo, Mary M.
  Journey to shark island: a shark photographer's close encounters. Mary M. Cerullo; photographs by Jeffrey L. Rotman; consultant James Sulikowski, PhD, Marine Science Department,

University of New England. Compass Point Books, a Capstone imprint, 2014. 40 p.: Shark expedition
Grades: 5 6 7 **597.3**
  1. Rotman, Jeffrey L. 2. Sharks 3. Underwater photography 4. Deep diving 5. Marine animals 6. Wildlife photographers 7. Costa Rica
  ISBN 9780756548872

                  LC 2014008678

Provides information on sharks and shares a shark diver's experiences on Coco Island, Costa Rica. Provided by publisher.

  "With their focus on more spectacular species, Seeking Giant Sharks and Great White Shark have the highest appeal, but all four books are fresh looks at an always popular subject." School Library Journal.

  Includes bibliographical references (page 39) and index.

  Searching for Great White Sharks: a shark diver's quest for Mr. Big. by Mary M. Cerullo; consultant James Sulikowski, PhD, Marine Science Department, University of New England. Compass Point Books, a Capstone imprint, 2014. 40 p.: Shark expedition
Grades: 5 6 7 **597.3**
  1. Rotman, Jeffrey L. 2. Great white shark 3. Deep diving 4. Sharks 5. Wildlife photographers 6. Underwater photography
  ISBN 9780756548841

                  LC 2014006007

Provides information on great white sharks and shares a shark diver's experiences searching for and photographing them. Provided by publisher.

  "Well-reproduced, close-up photos of sharks (and, trigger warning, one shark-attack victim) fill every dynamic, eye-catching page, and Cerullo's concise paragraphs present shark facts in a clear, engaging, and often suspenseful tone. With a high-interest topic and a graphics-heavy layout, this would be a hit with reluctant readers, as well as researchers." Booklist.

  Includes bibliographical references (page 39) and index.

  Seeking giant sharks: a shark diver's quest for whale sharks, basking sharks, and manta rays. by Mary M. Cerullo; photographs by Jeffrey L. Rotman. Compass Point Books, a Capstone imprint, [2015] 40 p.: Shark expedition
Grades: 5 6 7 **597.3**
  1. Rotman, Jeffrey L. 2. Sharks 3. Marine animals 4. Underwater photography 5. Deep diving 6. Whale shark
  ISBN 9780756548858

                  LC 2014008991

Provides information on plankton-feeders including whale sharks, basking sharks, hammerheads, and manta rays, and shares a shark diver's experiences searching for and photographing them. Provided by publisher.

  "Centered on the experiences photographer and diver Jeff Rotman, this set offers exciting insight into the world of sharks . . . With their focus on more spectacular species, Seeking Giant Sharks and Great White Shark have the highest appeal, but all four books are fresh looks at an always popular subject." School Library Journal.

  Includes bibliographical references.

  Sharks of the deep: a shark photographer's search for sharks at the bottom of the sea. Mary M. Cerullo; photographs by Jeffrey L. Rotman. Capstone Pr Inc, 2014. 40 p.: Shark expedition
Grades: 5 6 7 **597.3**
  1. Rotman, Jeffrey L. 2. Sharks 3. Deep diving 4. Wildlife

photographers 5. Marine animals 6. Aquatic animals
ISBN 9780756548865

LC 2014009112

Provides information on deep-water and ocean floor sharks and shares a shark diver's experiences searching for and photographing them. Provided by publisher.

"Centered on the experiences photographer and diver Jeff Rotman, this set offers exciting insight into the world of sharks . . . all four books are fresh looks at an always popular subject." School Library Journal.

Includes bibliographical references and index.

MacQuitty, Miranda

Shark. written by Miranda MacQuitty. DK Pub., 2004. 72 p.: Eyewitness books

Grades: 4 5 6 7   **597.3**
1. Sharks 2. Fishes 3. Predatory animals
ISBN 0756607248

LC bl2004112670

Describes, in text and photographs, the physical characteristics, behavior, and life cycle of various types of sharks.

Markle, Sandra

The **great** shark rescue: saving the whale sharks. by Sandra Markle. Millbrook Press, 2019. 48 p.

Grades: 4 5 6 7   **597.3**
1. Whale shark 2. Rare and endangered animals 3. Wildlife rescue 4. Wildlife conservation 5. Sharks
ISBN 9781541510418

LC 2018038332

Top-selling science author Sandra Markle presents the story of whale sharks—the largest fish on the planet. Facing threats from commercial fishing as well as climate change, they were categorized as endangered in 2016. Find out how scientists are working to study and protect these gentle giants of the ocean.

"Well organized, clearly written, and excitingly illustrated, this highly enlightening work is an excellent addition for any nature collection as well as for the study of the environment and endangered species." School Library Journal.

Includes bibliographical references and index.

Walker, Sally M.

Fossil fish found alive: discovering the coelacanth. Sally M. Walker. Carolrhoda Books, c2002. 72 p.

Grades: 5 6 7 8   **597.3**
1. 1930s 2. Coelacanth 3. Living fossils 4. Marine biology 5. Scientists 6. Fishers
ISBN 1575055368

LC 2001003815

Describes the 1938 discovery of the coelacanth, a fish previously believed to be extinct, and subsequent research about it.

"Walker writes well, making this relatively unknown area of science history an exciting story of exploration and discovery. Excellent, full-color photos illustrate the text." Booklist.

Includes bibliographical references (p. 69-70) and index.

597.8 Amphibians

Markle, Sandra

★ The **case** of the vanishing golden frogs: a scientific mystery. Sandra Markle. Milbrook Press, c2011. 48 p.

Grades: 4 5 6   **597.8**
1. Frogs -- Infections 2. Wildlife rescue 3. Wildlife conservation 4. Panamanian golden frog 5. Batrachochytrium dendrobatidis
ISBN 9780761351085

LC 2010042642

Looks at the Panamanian golden frog, the national symbol of Panama, which has been vanishing due to a fungus infection, and follows a team of scientists working to save these frogs and protect frog populations worldwide.

"Notable for clarity, directness, and simplicity of writing and design alike, this volume [is] both handsome and fascinating. . . . Excellent photos, microscopic views, and maps illustrate the book." Booklist.

Includes bibliographical references (p. 47) and index.

Pringle, Laurence, 1935-

Frogs!: strange and wonderful. Laurence Pringle; illustrated by Meryl Henderson. Boyds Mills Press, c2012. 30 p.

Grades: 3 4 5   **597.8**
1. Frogs 2. Toads 3. Amphibians
ISBN 9781590783719

LC bl2012005506

Provides information about frogs and toads, including different species, habitat, and life cycle.

Turner, Pamela S.

The **frog** scientist. by Pamela S. Turner. Houghton Mifflin Books for Children, 2009. 64 p. : Scientists in the field (Houghton Mifflin)

Grades: 5 6 7 8   **597.8**
1. Hayes, Tyrone 2. Frogs -- Research 3. Pesticides -- Environmental aspects 4. Scientists 5. Zoologists 6. Agricultural chemicals -- Environmental aspects
ISBN 9780618717163

LC 2008039770

Discusses the facts surrounding the depleting frog population around the world and examines the effects pesticides had on the frog population in the United States that may have resulted in fewer frogs being born.

"This volume opens with biologist Tyrone Hayes and his team collecting frogs at a pond in Wyoming. After a short chapter on Hayes' background, the discussion returns to his work: he addresses the general question of why amphibian populations world-wide are declining by studying the effects of atrizine, an agricultural pesticide, on the reproductive organs of leopard frogs from a particular pond. Well organized and clearly written. . . . Excellent color photos offer clear pictures of frogs and of this scientific team at work in the field and in the lab. . . . A vivid, realistic view of one scientist at work." Booklist.

597.9 Reptilia

Hirschmann, Kris, 1967-

Deadliest reptiles. Kris Hirschmann. ReferencePoint Press, [2017] 80 p.: Deadliest predators

Grades: 6 7 8 9 10   **597.9**
1. Reptiles 2. Predatory animals
ISBN 9781682820520

LC 2016004758

Profiles some of the world's deadliest reptiles, including the saltwater crocodile, komodo dragon, and alligator snapping turtle.

"First-rate nonfiction on a high-interest topic." School Library Journal.

Includes bibliographical references (pages 68-69) and index.

McCarthy, Colin

Reptile. written by Colin McCarthy. DK Pub., 2012. 72 p.: Eyewitness books

Grades: 4 5 6 7   **597.9**

    1. Reptiles 2. Wildlife habitats

    ISBN 9780756693053

                     LC BL 00012841

Photographs and text depict the many different kinds of reptiles, their similarities and differences, habitats, and behavior.

McGinnis, Samuel M

Peterson field guide to western reptiles and amphibians. Samuel M. McGinnis and Robert C. Stebbins; illustrations by Robert C. Stebbins; sponsored by the National Audubon Society, the National Wildlife Federation and the Roger Tory Peterson Institute. Houghton Mifflin Harcourt Company, 2018. xi, 560 p.

Grades: Adult   **597.9**

    1. Reptiles 2. Amphibians

    ISBN 9781328715500

                     LC 2017059616

This is the most comprehensive and trusted guide to reptiles and amphibians of western North America. The new edition retains the realistic and accurate paintings by Robert Stebbins and includes 160 color photographs for additional detail. All range maps are up to date and placed within their species accounts. Family, genus, species, and subspecies names have been updated to the currently accepted usage. Illustrations of eggs and larvae, which can aid in identifying salamanders and frogs, are a particularly helpful feature.—From publisher description.

Powell, Robert, 1948-

Peterson field guide to reptiles and amphibians of Eastern and Central North America. Robert Powell, Roger Conant, and Joseph T. Collins; illustrated by Isabelle Hunt Conant, Tom R. Johnson, and Errol D. Hooper Jr. Houghton Mifflin Harcourt, 2016. xiii, 494 p.

Grades: 7 8 9 10 11 12 Adult   **597.9**

    1. Amphibians 2. Reptiles

    ISBN 9780544129979

                     LC bl2016015313

Presents a reference guide to reptiles and amphibians within North America, describing the physical characteristics, habitats, and range of each species.

597.95 Lizards

Collard, Sneed B.

Sneed B. Collard III's most fun book ever about lizards. Sneed B. Collard III. Charlesbridge, 2012. 48 p.

Grades: 3 4 5 6 7   **597.95**

    1. Lizards 2. Reptiles

    ISBN 9781580893244

                     LC 2011000809

A science writer and avid lizard lover introduces readers to an impressive array of lizards—from the garden-variety Western fence lizard to the Texas horned lizard—that have faces only their mothers could love.

Somervill, Barbara A.

Monitor lizard. Barbara A. Somervill. Cherry Lake Pub., c2010. 32 p.: 21st century skills library.

Grades: 5 6 7 8   **597.95**

    1. Komodo dragon 2. Monitor lizard 3. Nonindigenous pests 4. Lizards 5. Reptiles

    ISBN 9781602796270

                     LC 2009026012

Looks at the Nile monitor lizard and examines how lizards imported as pets became an invasive species in southern Florida and other places outside of its native Africa, how it causes problems, and how Florida has attempted to deal with it.

"This offers an introduction to the problems caused by [the monitor lizard], a discussion of its physical characteristics and habits, a history of how it arrived in its new habitat, and an analysis of challenges encountered by those trying to limit its spread. . . . [It] describes the threat posed by these aggressive 7-foot reptiles, sold as babies by pet vendors and now loose in Florida. . . . [This] well-focused [book is] clearly written. The uncluttered page design features at least one color photo on each page." Booklist.

Includes bibliographical references (p. 31) and index.

597.96 Snakes

Franchino, Vicky

Black mambas. by Vicky Franchino. Children's Press, an imprint of Scholastic Inc., [2015] 48 p.: Nature's children

Grades: 3 4 5 6   **597.96**

    1. Black mamba 2. Snakes

    ISBN 9780531213926

                     LC 2014043960

This book details the life and habits of black mambas. Provided by publisher.

"Sophisticated scientific terms such as bilateral symmetry or anticoagulant are often defined in-text. Fun Fact boxes are scattered throughout." School Library Journal.

Includes bibliographical references and index.

Hirschmann, Kris, 1967-

Deadliest snakes. Kris Hirschmann. ReferencePoint Press, [2017] 80 p.: Deadliest predators

Grades: 6 7 8 9 10   **597.96**

    1. Poisonous snakes 2. Snakes 3. Poisonous animals 4. Snakebites

    ISBN 9781682820568

                     LC 2015046499

Profiles some of the world's deadliest snakes, including the black mamba, king cobra, and Dubois' sea snake.

"First-rate nonfiction on a high-interest topic." School Library Journal.

Includes bibliographical references (pages 69-70) and index.

Hofer, Charles

Snakebite!: antivenom and a global health crisis. Charles C. Hofer. Twenty-First Century Books, 2018. 104 p.

Grades: 7 8 9 10 11 12   **597.96**

    1. Poisonous snakes 2. Snakebites 3. Antivenins 4. Poisonous animals 5. Medical care

    ISBN 9781512483734

                     LC 2017046976

Examines the biology of venomous snakes, the pharmacology and biochemistry of antivenom, its use in treating disease, and the politics of bringing life-saving antivenom drugs to market.

"Readers will gain an understanding of the complexity of this issue and meet several scientists and researchers at the vanguard of antivenin program development. This thoroughly sourced text is a fascinating resource that can be used across many disciplines." Booklist.

Includes bibliographical references (pages 95-101) and index.

Messner, Kate

Tracking pythons: the quest to catch an invasive predator and save an ecosystem. Kate Messner. Millbrook Press, 2020. 64 p.

Grades: 4 5 6 7 8   **597.96**
1. Biological invasions 2. Organism introduction 3. Pythons 4. Predatory animals 5. Competition (Biology) 6. Florida
ISBN 9781541557062

Burmese pythons are native to Southeast Asia, so when one showed up dead along the side of a Florida highway in 1979, scientists wondered where it came from. No one knew the snakes had launched a full-scale invasion. Pet pythons that escaped or were released by their owners started breeding in the wild, and these enormous predators began eating every animal in their path. Today a group of scientists at the Conservancy of Southwest Florida is tracking Burmese pythons to find ways to stop their spread.

"This fascinating example of field biology holds its own against the exemplary Scientists in the Field series. Who knew that snake science could be so adventurous?" Kirkus

Includes bibliographical references (page 62) and index.

Montgomery, Sy

The **snake** scientist. Sy Montgomery; photographs by Nic Bishop. Houghton Mifflin, 1999. 48 p.

Grades: 4 5 6 7   **597.96**
1. Mason, Robert Thomas, 1959- 2. Snakes 3. Zoologists 4. Red-sided garter snake 5. Garter snakes 6. Research
ISBN 0395871697

         LC   98006124

Dr. Robert Mason, a.k.a. the Snake Scientist, studies the extraordinary mating season of snakes in Narcisse, Manitoba, where each spring, tens of thousands of snakes emerge and gather en masse to begin their courtship.

"The lively text communicates both the meticulous measurements required in this kind of work and the thrill of new discoveries. Large, full-color photos of the zoologist and young students at work, and lots of wriggly snakes, pull readers into the presentation." School Library Journal.

Includes bibliographical references (p. 46) and index.

597.98 Alligators and crocodiles

Gish, Melissa

Alligators. by Melissa Gish. Creative Education, 2017, c2010. 48 p.: Living wild

Grades: 5 6 7 8   **597.98**
1. Alligators 2. Crocodilians 3. Reptiles
ISBN 9781608188178

         LC 2009025168

A look at alligators, including their habitats, physical characteristics such as their scaly skin, behaviors, relationships with humans, and threatened status in the world today. Provided by publisher.

"The book lucidly discusses conservation and the animals' often tenuous relationships with humans. The layout is uniformly simple but effective, constructed with a nice balance of main text for the report writers, smaller chunks of esoterica for browsers, and . . . killer photos." Booklist.

Includes bibliographical references and index.

598 Birds

Burnie, David

Bird. written by David Burnie. DK Pub., 2008. 72 p.: Eyewitness books

Grades: 4 5 6 7   **598**
1. Birds
ISBN 9780756637682

         LC bl2004112674

A photo essay on the world of birds examining such topics as body construction, feathers and flight, the adaptation of beaks and feet, feeding habits, courtship, nests and eggs, and bird watching.

Latimer, Jonathan P.

Backyard birds. Jonathan P. Latimer, Karen Stray Nolting; illustrations by Roger Tory Peterson; foreword by Virginia Marie Peterson. Houghton Mifflin Co., 1999. 48 p.: Peterson field guides for young naturalists

Grades: 4 5 6 7   **598**
1. Birds 2. Birds -- Identification 3. Nature guides
ISBN 0395922763

         LC 98035509

Describes the physical characteristics, behavior, voices, and habitats of a variety of common birds, arranged by their color. Includes the Peterson System of identifying birds by their unique markings.

"This is an identification guide to birds you are likely to see where you live. . . . [It] includes a . . . selection of about 20 creatures . . . grouped by color. . . . Bright, full-color photographs and drawings clearly indicate distinguishing features. Useful, accessible." School Library Journal.

Wolf, Sallie

The **robin** makes a laughing sound: a birder's journal. Sallie Wolf; designed by Micah Bornstein. Charlesbridge, c2010 43 p.

Grades: 5 6 7 8   **598**
1. Robins 2. Birds -- Behavior 3. Bird watching 4. Seasons
ISBN 9781580893183

         LC 2008007248

Presents observations made through every season of the year of different birds and their behavior, from robins taking a bath, to cardinals searching for food in the snow, to an owl perched on a tree at night.

"The charming, eye-catching format includes short, dated nature notes written in script, some of them on glued or taped-in torn paper pieces; other paper scraps contain short, typeset poems and small, labeled watercolors. . . . Pen-and-ink sketches capture a baby house sparrow, a V-formation of geese, a downy woodpecker at a suet feeder, and more. . . . This small, instructional guide may provide the inspiration for young authors with even a bit of artistic talent to begin keeping nature journals of their own." School Library Journal.

598.072 Descriptive research

Hoose, Phillip M., 1947-
★ **Moonbird**: a year on the wind with the great survivor B95. Phillip Hoose. Farrar Straus Giroux, 2012. 176 p.
Grades: 5 6 7 8   **598.072**
1. Shore birds 2. Rare and endangered birds 3. Birds -- Migration 4. Birds 5. Bird watching
ISBN 9780374304683

LC 2011035612

Documents the survival tale of an intrepid shorebird who has endured annual migrations between Argentina and the Canadian Arctic throughout the course of a long lifetime while his species continues to decline.

598.097 Birds—North America

Alderfer, Jonathan K.
Bird guide of North America: the best birding book for kids from National Geographic's bird experts. by Jonathan Alderfer. National Geographic, 2013. 176 p.
Grades: 4 5 6 7 8   **598.097**
1. Birds 2. Bird watching
ISBN 9781426310959

LC 2012028615

Profiles one hundred bird species from coast to coast, offers information about topics ranging from bird calls to behaviors, and provides complementary sidebars, range maps, and instructions for building birdhouses and bird feeders.

Bull, John L.
The **National** Audubon Society field guide to North American birds.. John Bull and John Farrand, Jr.; revised by John Farrand; visual Key by Amanda Wilson and Lori Hogan. Knopf, 1994. 796 p.
Grades: 7 8 9 10 11 12 Adult   **598.097**
1. Birds -- Identification
ISBN 9780679428527

LC 94007768

A revised edition of the popular field guide includes hundreds of all new, full-color photographs, along with information on diverse species of eastern birds, their characteristics, habitats and ranges, identification tips, and more.

Peterson, Roger Tory, 1908-1996
★ **Peterson** field guide to birds of North America. Roger Tory Peterson; with contributions from Michael DiGiorgio ... [et al.]. Houghton Mifflin Co., 2008. xiv, 527 p.
Grades: 5 6 7 8 9 10 11 12 Adult   **598.097**
1. Birds
ISBN 9780618966141

LC 2007039803

Honoring the centennial of the acclaimed naturalist's birth, new paintings, maps, digital updates, and revised text enhance this collected edition of the popular guide to bird observation and identification.
"This field guide is of high quality and should be in millions of birders' and other nature lovers' backpacks." Science Books & Films.

Peterson field guide to birds of eastern and central North America. Roger Tory Peterson; with contributions from Michael DiGiorgio ... [et al.]. Houghton Mifflin Harcourt, 2010. xiv, 445 p.
Grades: 5 6 7 8 9 10 11 12 Adult   **598.097**
1. Birds
ISBN 9780547152462

LC 2009037681

Presents illustrations and detailed descriptions of the most common species of birds found in the eastern and central areas of North America, with advice on bird identification and maps indicating the range of each species.

Peterson field guide to birds of Western North America. Roger Tory Peterson; with contributions from Michael DiGiorgio ... [et al.] Houghton Mifflin Harcourt, 2010. xiv, 493 p.
Grades: 5 6 7 8 9 10 11 12 Adult   **598.097**
1. Birds
ISBN 0547152701

LC 2009039158

Each book in this series covers all the different species of a particular type of plant or animal, providing hundreds of color illustrations and range maps so that both nature enthusiasts and backyard observers can easily identify a particular type of flora or fauna.

598.3 Water birds

Thornhill, Jan
★ The **tragic** tale of the great auk. Jan Thornhill. House of Anansi Press, 2016. 44 p.
Grades: 2 3 4 5   **598.3**
1. Extinct animals 2. Birds 3. Extinction (Biology) 4. Extinct birds 5. Great auk
ISBN 9781554988655

LC oc2016000316

Tells the sad story of the extinction of the Great auk.
"A sobering, beautifully presented extinction story." Kirkus.

598.6 Galliformes and Columbiformes

Gish, Melissa
Peacocks. Melissa Gish. Creative Education, 2016. 48 p.: Living Wild
Grades: 5 6 7 8   **598.6**
1. Peacocks 2. Birds
ISBN 9781608187072

LC 2015026823

Looks at peacocks, describing their habitats, physical characteristics including the male's colorful plumage, behaviors, relationships with humans, and the protected status of Congo and green peacocks in the world today.
"Whether weird, beautiful, or simply adorable, this series has its animals covered." Booklist.

Hutto, Joe
When I was a turkey: based on the PBS documentary My life as a turkey. Joe Hutto and Brenda Z. Guiberson. Henry Holt and Company, 2017. 176 p.
Grades: 4 5 6 7 8   **598.6**
1. Turkeys 2. Naturalists 3. Animal rescue 4. Wild turkeys 5.

Birds
ISBN 9781627793858

LC 2017007364

After a local farmer left a bowl of wild turkey eggs on Joe Hutto?s front porch, his life was forever changed. Hutto incubated the eggs and waited for them to hatch. Deep in the wilds of Florida's Flatlands, Hutto spent each day living as a turkey mother, taking on the full-time job of raising sixteen turkey chicks. For two years, Hutto dutifully cared for his family, roosting with them, taking them foraging, and immersing himself in their world. In return, they taught him how to see the world through their eyes. Here is the remarkable true story of a man with a singular gift to connect with nature.

"An unusual, engaging choice for animal-lovers." Booklist.

598.7 Miscellaneous orders of land birds

Hoose, Phillip M., 1947-

The **race** to save the Lord God Bird. Phillip Hoose. Farrar, Straus and Giroux, c2004. 196 p.

Grades: 7 8 9 10   **598.7**
  1. Rare and endangered birds 2. Woodpeckers 3. Wildlife conservation 4. Ivory-billed woodpecker 5. Rare and endangered animals
ISBN 0374361738

LC 2003049049

Tells the story of the ivory-billed woodpecker's extinction in the United States, describing the encounters between this species and humans, and discussing what these encounters have taught us about preserving endangered creatures.

"Sharp, clear, black-and-white archival photos and reproductions appear throughout. The author's passion for his subject and high standards for excellence result in readable, compelling nonfiction." School Library Journal.

Larson, Jeanette

Hummingbirds: facts and folklore from the Americas. written by Jeanette Larson and Adrienne Yorinks; illustrations by Arienne Yorinks. Charlesbridge, c2011. 64 p.

Grades: 5 6 7 8   **598.7**
  1. Hummingbirds 2. Birds
ISBN 9781580893329

LC 2010007578

Presents information about hummingbirds, describing their physical characteristics, flight abilities, habitat, migration behavior, and life cycle, along with legends told about them from several cultures.

"In a narrative that flows easily between fact and lore, hummingbird behavior is thoroughly described and interwoven with the folktales it generated among Native American peoples. . . . All the stories show how ancient people answered the how and why questions of the behaviors they observed, and these stories beautifully echo modern-day scientific observations. The full-color photos of quilts and embroidery by Yorinks invite readers to stop and savor each one." School Library Journal.

Includes bibliographical references (p. 59-60) and index.

598.8 Perching birds (Passeriformes)

Turner, Pamela S.

Crow smarts: inside the brain of the world's brightest bird. Pamela S. Turner; photographs by Andy Comins. Houghton

Mifflin Harcourt, 2016. 80 p.: Scientists in the field (Houghton Mifflin)

Grades: 4 5 6 7 8   **598.8**
  1. Crows 2. Birds 3. Scientists 4. Wildlife conservation 5. Vocational guidance
ISBN 9780544416192

"With an approachable writing style and photos of crows festooning almost every page, this engaging volume will attract budding scientists, and the lively descriptions not only of the crows but of the scientists at work will give students plenty to ponder." Booklist.

598.9 Birds of prey

Hoena, B. A.

Everything birds of prey: swoop in for seriously fierce photos and amazing info. Blake Hoena. Natl Geographic Soc Childrens books 2015 64 p.: Everything series (Washington, D.C.)

Grades: 2 3 4 5   **598.9**
  1. Predatory animals 2. Birds of prey 3. Birds
ISBN 9781426318900

"The bold and brassy, factoid-filled text is broken into chapters that flow logically from the birds characteristics and behavior to geography and interactions with humans." Booklist.

Latimer, Jonathan P.

Birds of prey. Jonathan P. Latimer, Karen Stray Nolting; illustrations by Roger Tory Peterson; foreword by Virginia Marie Peterson. Houghton Mifflin Co., 1999. 48 p.: Peterson field guides for young naturalists

Grades: 4 5 6 7   **598.9**
  1. Birds of prey 2. Birds of prey -- Identification
ISBN 0395952115

LC 98035516

Describes the physical characteristics, behavior, voices, and habitats of a variety of eagles, hawks, falcons, and owls. Includes the Peterson System of identifying birds by their unique markings.

599 Mammalia

Brown, Martin, 1959-

Lesser spotted animals: the coolest creatures you've never heard of. Martin Brown. Scholastic Inc., 2017. 52 p.

Grades: 2 3 4 5   **599**
  1. Animals 2. Zoology
ISBN 9781338089349

"With a compulsively engaging tone, lighthearted artwork, and a meaningful kernel of education at its heart, this excellent book will entrance a wide variety of readers, who will surely be eager for more." Booklist.

Hoyt, Erich

Encyclopedia of whales, dolphins and porpoises. Erich Hoyt; principal photography by Brandon Cole; illustrations by Uko Gorter. Firefly Books, 2017 300 p.

Grades: Adult   **599**
  1. Marine mammals 2. Cetacea 3. Whales 4. Dolphins
ISBN 9781770859418

LC 2017300268

In [this book], award-winning author and whale researcher Erich Hoyt takes readers into the field for an intimate encounter with some 90 species of cetaceans that make their homes in the world's oceans. Drawing on decades of firsthand experience and a comprehensive familiarity with the current revolution in cetacean studies, Hoyt provides unique insights into the life histories of these compelling marine mammals. Here are discoveries about cetacean biology and behavior, from the physical differences and adaptations among the baleen and toothed whales to their highly intelligent hunting and feeding methods. The courtship and mating practices, family relationships and the lifelong bonds among some family members are fascinating. The symphonic composer of the whale world is the humpback whale, whose complex 30-minute songs reverberate across the liquid universe of the ocean. Some cetaceans survive deep diving and negotiate lengthy migrations across oceans. This book is a fascinating compilation of the latest data on cetaceans and an impassioned argument for the ongoing need for international protection of at-risk populations and their increasingly damaged habitat. Provided by publisher.

599.097 Mammals—North America

Whitaker, John O.
National Audubon Society field guide to North American mammals. John O. Whitaker, Jr. Knopf , c1996. 937 p.
Grades: 6 7 8 9 10 11 12 Adult   **599.097**
    1. Mammals -- Identification
    ISBN 9780679446316
                                LC 95081456
Presents information on 390 species of North American mammals, along with keys for identification, range maps, and information on tracks and anatomy

599.168 Rare mammals

Harris, Tim
Mammals of the Northern Hemisphere. edited by Tim Harris. Brown Bear Books, 2012. 64 p.: Facts at your fingertips.
Grades: 7 8 9   **599.168**
    1. Rare and endangered animals
    ISBN 9781936333349
                                LC 2010053969
Describes various mammals in the Northern Hemisphere that are endangered and at risk of becoming extinct. Data Sheet sidebars and maps accompany the text. Provided by publisher.

599.2 Marsupials and monotremes

Gish, Melissa
Kangaroos. by Melissa Gish. Creative Education, c2010. 46 p.: Living wild
Grades: 5 6 7 8   **599.2**
    1. Kangaroos 2. Marsupials
    ISBN 9781583419700
                                LC 2009025171
A look at kangaroos, including their habitats, physical characteristics such as the females' pouches, behaviors, relationships with humans, and valued status in the world today. Provided by publisher.

Montgomery, Sy
★ **Quest** for the tree kangaroo: an expedition to the Cloud Forest of New Guinea. text by Sy Montgomery; photographs by Nic Bishop. Houghton Mifflin, 2006. 79 p.: Scientists in the field (Houghton Mifflin)
Grades: 5 6 7 8   **599.2**
    1. Scientists 2. Scientific expeditions 3. Kangaroos -- Behavior 4. Women scientists 5. Tree kangaroos -- Behavior 6. New Guinea
    ISBN 0618496416
    NCTE Orbis Pictus Nonfiction Award, 2007.
"The writer and photographer of this exemplary description of science field work accompanied researcher Lisa Dabek on an expedition high in New Guinea's mountains to study tree kangaroos and promote the conservation of this elusive and endangered species. . . . Montgomery . . . paces her narrative well . . . keeping the reader engaged and concerned. . . . Bishop's photographs . . . are beautifully reproduced." Publishers Weekly.

Patent, Dorothy Hinshaw
Saving the Tasmanian devil: how science is helping the world's largest marsupial carnivore survive. Dorothy Hinshaw Patent. Houghton Mifflin Harcourt, 2019. 80 p.: Scientists in the field (Houghton Mifflin)
Grades: 5 6 7 8 9   **599.2**
    1. Mammals 2. Epidemics 3. Tasmanian devil 4. Tumors 5. Medical genetics 6. Tasmania 7. Australia
    ISBN 9780544991484
                                LC 2018034813
In this addition to the critically acclaimed Scientist in the Field series, Dorothy Patent follows the scientists trying to put a stop to a gruesome disease before it's too late. Tasmanian devils are dying at an alarming rate from a type of tumor that appears to be contagious. What scientists are learning while researching the Tasmanian devil has potential to affect all animals, and even humans, as they learn more about how to prevent and hopefully eradicate certain genetic diseases.
"Scientists from different disciplines, career stages, and parts of the world work toward saving the Tasmanian devil, an Australian carnivore threatened with extinction due to the devil facial tumor disease...A message of hope." Kirkus.

Petrie, Kristin, 1970-
Sugar gliders. Kristin Petrie. ABDO Pub. Co., c2013. 24 p.: Unique pets
Grades: 4 5 6 7   **599.2**
    1. Sugar gliders as pets 2. Sugar glider 3. Marsupials 4. Pets 5. Pet care
    ISBN 9781617834431
                                LC 2012004890
Describes the physical features, habitat, defense mechanisms, and behavior of sugar gliders and what needs to be done to care for them as pets.

599.3 Miscellaneous orders of placental mammals

Gish, Melissa
Armadillos. Melissa Gish. Creative Education, [2016] 48 p.: Living wild

Grades: 5 6 7 8   **599.3**
1. Armadillos
ISBN 9781608187034

LC 2015026813

A look at armadillos, including their habitats, physical characteristics such as their armored bodies, behaviors, relationships with humans, and threatened status of some species in the world today. Provided by publisher.

"Whether weird, beautiful, or simply adorable, this series has its animals covered." Booklist.

Sloths. Melissa Gish. Creative Education, [2016] 48 p.: Living wild
Grades: 5 6 7 8   **599.3**
1. Sloths
ISBN 9781608187096

LC 2015026882

A look at sloths, including their habitats, physical characteristics such as their long claws, behaviors, relationships with humans, and their growing popularity in the world today. Provided by publisher.

"Whether weird, beautiful, or simply adorable, this series has its animals covered." Booklist.

Gregory, Josh
Sloths. by Josh Gregory. Children's Press, an imprint of Scholastic Inc., [2016] 48 p.: Nature's children
Grades: 3 4 5 6   **599.3**
1. Sloths 2. Mammals 3. Animals
ISBN 9780531213919

LC 2014044037

This book details the life and habits of sloths. Provided by publisher.

"Sophisticated scientific terms such as bilateral symmetry or anticoagulant are often defined in-text. Fun Fact boxes are scattered throughout." School Library Journal.

Includes bibliographical references and index.

599.32 Lagomorphs

Collard, Sneed B
Hopping ahead of climate change: snowshoe hares, science, and survival. Sneed B. Collard III. Bucking Horse Books, 2016 64 p.
Grades: 4 5 6 7   **599.32**
1. Acclimatization 2. Climatic changes 3. Hares 4. Snowshoe rabbit -- Climatic factors 5. Snowshoe rabbit
ISBN 9780984446087

LC bl2018085805

Examines the effects of climate change on animals like the snowshoe hare that change their coat colors each winter.

599.33 Insectivora

Gregory, Josh
Hedgehogs. by Josh Gregory. Children's Press, an imprint of Scholastic Inc., 2016. 48 p.: Nature's children
Grades: 3 4 5 6   **599.33**
1. Hedgehogs
ISBN 9780531213902

LC 2014043978

This book details the life and habits of hedgehogs. Provided by publisher.

"Sophisticated scientific terms such as bilateral symmetry or anticoagulant are often defined in-text." School Library Journal.

Includes bibliographical references and index.

599.35 Rodentia

Marrin, Albert
Oh, rats!: the story of rats and people. Dutton Children's Books, 2006. 48 p.
Grades: 3 4 5 6   **599.35**
1. Rats -- History 2. Rodents 3. Animals 4. Human/animal relationships 5. Humans and rats
ISBN 0525477624

"This is lively and informative. . . . The nine short chapters are set in a handsome slim book with striking black-and-white scratchboard illustrations and muted red framing on many pages." School Library Journal.

Stefoff, Rebecca, 1951-
The **rodent** order. by Rebecca Stefoff. Marshall Cavendish Benchmark, c2009. 96 p.: Family trees
Grades: 6 7 8 9   **599.35**
1. Rodents 2. Habitat (Ecology) 3. Life cycles (Biology) 4. Animal behavior
ISBN 9780761430735

LC 2008017555

Explores the habitats, life cycles, and other characteristics of rodents. Provided by publisher.

599.37 Beavers

Gish, Melissa
Beavers. Melissa Gish. Creative Co., 2014. 46 p.: Living wild
Grades: 5 6 7 8   **599.37**
1. Beavers 2. Animals
ISBN 9781608184149

A scientific look at beavers, including their habitats, physical characteristics such as their gnawing teeth, behaviors, relationships with humans, and abundance of the rodents in the world today.—Provided by publisher.

"Thorough in scope and elegant in design, these stellar titles will attract the browser and the report writer alike." School Library Journal.

599.4 Bats

Carson, Mary Kay
★ The **bat** scientists. Mary Kay Carson; with photographs by Tom Uhlman. Houghton Mifflin Books for Children, 2010. 80 p.: Scientists in the field (Houghton Mifflin)
Grades: 4 5 6 7   **599.4**
1. Bats -- Research 2. Mammalogists 3. Scientists
ISBN 9780547199566

LC 2010006767

"This describes patient field work, rescue and conservation efforts to save bats. . . . Woven into particular researchers' stories is an enormous amount of information about bat biology and behavior. Uhlman's photographs are clearly identified in context and the backmatter supports further research." Kirkus.

Gish, Melissa
Bats. by Melissa Gish. Creative Education, c2010. 46 p.: Living wild
Grades: 5 6 7 8   **599.4**
   1. Bats 2. Mammals
   ISBN 9781583419663

                  LC 2009025167

A look at bats, including their habitats, physical characteristics such as their fragile wings, behaviors, relationships with humans, and persecuted status in the world today. Provided by publisher.

"The book lucidly discusses conservation and the animals' often tenuous relationship with humans. The layout is uniformly simple but effective, constructed with a nice balance of main text for the report writers, smaller chunks of esoterica for browsers, and . . . killer photos." Booklist.

Includes bibliographical references and index.

Koch, Falynn, 1985-
Bats: learning to fly. Falynn Christine Koch. First Second 2017 128 p.: Science comics
Grades: 3 4 5 6   **599.4**
   1. Bats 2. Mammals 3. Animals 4. Comics and Graphic novels
   ISBN 9781626724099

"With plenty of informative back matter, this inviting, engaging nonfiction comic is perfect for kids hungry for science." Booklist.

Markle, Sandra
The **case** of the vanishing little brown bats: a scientific mystery. Sandra Markle. Millbrook Press, 2015. 48 p.
Grades: 4 5 6   **599.4**
   1. Little brown bat 2. Bats 3. Animals as carriers of disease 4. Diseases 5. Fungi
   ISBN 9781467714631

                  LC 2013030953

"With plentiful details about the scientific work, photographs showing scientists and their tiny subjects, clear explanations, and an organization that is both topical and chronological, this title brings science to life." Kirkus.

Taschek, Karen, 1956-
Hanging with bats: ecobats, vampires, and movie stars. Karen Taschek. University of New Mexico Press, 2008. vii, 94 p.
Grades: 6 7 8 9   **599.4**
   1. Bats 2. Bats -- Behavior 3. Nocturnal animals 4. Mammals
   ISBN 9780826344038

                  LC 2008002076

"This book provides an all-inclusive look at the flying mammal many people do not understand well enough to appreciate. From the scientific discussion of where bats are found on the evolutionary tree to the whys and hows of building a bat house, there is little that cannot be learned from within these pages. . . . The text is written in a friendly style, with unusual words further defined or explained as needed, nicely allowing generous amounts of information to be absorbed without it feeling like work. The photographs and illustrations are fascinating, helping to lure in a reluctant reader. It should be noted that the photos of bats in action are particularly eye-catching. . . . It is a good choice for any Library." Voice of Youth Advocates.

599.5 Cetaceans and sea cows

Gish, Melissa
Whales. by Melissa Gish. Creative Education, 2011. 48 p.: Living wild
Grades: 5 6 7 8   **599.5**
   1. Whales 2. Marine mammals
   ISBN 9781608180844

                  LC 2010028414

A look at whales, including their habitats, physical characteristics such as their streamlined bodies, behaviors, relationships with humans, and threatened status in the world today. Provided by publisher.

Hodgkins, Fran, 1964-
★ The **whale** scientists: solving the mystery of whale strandings. by Fran Hodgkins. Houghton Mifflin Co., 2007. 63 p.: Scientists in the field (Houghton Mifflin)
Grades: 5 6 7 8   **599.5**
   1. Whales 2. Whaling 3. Whales -- Stranding 4. Marine biology
   ISBN 0618556737

                  LC 2006034634

With their numbers diminishing, scientists are trying to solve the mystery of whale strandings. Why would the world's largest mammal do something that would most likely cause it to die? Around the world, scientists are trying to find the answer.

"Hodgkins packs her text with an impressive amount of information. . . . Well-chosen color photographs amply illustrate the well-organized discussion." School Library Journal.

Lockwood, Sophie
Whales. by Sophie Lockwood. Child's World, c2008. 40 p.: The world of mammals
Grades: 4 5 6   **599.5**
   1. Whales 2. Cetacea 3. Marine animals 4. Rare and endangered marine animals
   ISBN 9781592969302

                  LC 2007020890

"This book about whales presents all the basics for reports: an introduction to the creatures' challenges, the role humans play, physical traits and behaviors, habitats, and struggles for survival. Every part of their life [cycle], including sexual maturity, birth, and family relationships, is explained. . . . Clear bright photographs pump up the content. . . . The detail that Lockwood imparts is startlingly high. The [text is] written in a dynamic and engaging style." School Library Journal.

Includes bibliographical references (p. 39) and index.

Lourie, Peter
★ The **manatee** scientists: saving vulnerable species. by Peter Lourie. Houghton Mifflin Harcourt, c2011. 80 p.: Scientists in the field (Houghton Mifflin)
Grades: 4 5 6 7   **599.5**
   1. Manatees -- Conservation 2. Marine mammalogists -- Vocational guidance 3. Marine mammals 4. Rare and endangered animals 5. Vocational guidance
   ISBN 9780547152547

                  LC 2010009739

"The manatees photographed by Lourie and others add plenty of visual appeal. . . . A sturdy addition to a standard-setting nonfiction series." Booklist.

Includes bibliographical references and index.

Whaling season: a year in the life of an arctic whale scientist. by Peter Lourie. Houghton Mifflin Harcourt, c2009. 80 p. : Scientists in the field (Houghton Mifflin)

Grades: 4 5 6 7   **599.5**
   1. Bowhead whale 2. Marine biologists 3. Nature study 4. Scientists 5. Whales
   ISBN 9780618777099

LC 2009018596

Provides middle readers with a fascinating look at how scientists conduct research on bowhead whales in remote Barrow, Alaska, and the incredible discoveries that have been made throughout the years.

"Combining exemplary color photos and simple, vivid language, the chapters detail not only George's day-today methodology but also his motivation." Booklist

O'Connell, Jennifer
The **Eye** of the Whale. Jennifer O'Connell. Tilbury House Pub, 2013. 32 p.

Grades: 5 6 7 8   **599.5**
   1. Humpback whale 2. Whales 3. Rescues 4. Fishers
   ISBN 9780884483359

Recounts the true story of the rescue of a humpback whale from fishing lines off the coast of San Francisco, describing the organized rescue efforts and the bravery of the four divers who untangled the whale to freedom.

Siebert, Charles, 1954-
The **secret** world of whales. by Charles Siebert; illustrated by Molly Baker. Chronicle Books, c2011. 108 p.

Grades: 4 5 6 7   **599.5**
   1. Whales 2. Marine biology 3. Oceans
   ISBN 9780811876414

LC 2010027355

"In this small-format volume, Siebert creates a concise introduction to whales, addressing myths and stories, the history of the whaling industry, communication and intelligence, and encounters between whales and humans. With playful, anthropomorphic cartoons, striking photographs, and a discussion of the dangers facing whales—noise pollution from boats, potentially lethal sonar—readers should gain a vivid impression of their behavior in the wild, as well as an appreciation for their majesty." Publishers Weekly.

599.53 Dolphins and porpoises

Gish, Melissa
Killer whales. by Melissa Gish. Creative Education, c2010. 46 p.: Living wild

Grades: 5 6 7 8   **599.53**
   1. Killer whale 2. Whales 3. Marine animals
   ISBN 9781583419717

LC 2009025172

A look at killer whales, including their habitats, physical characteristics such as their unique coloration, behaviors, relationships with humans, and protected status in the world today. Provided by publisher.

Swanson, Jennifer
Dolphins. Jennifer Swanson with Justine Jackson-Ricketts. Natl Geographic Soc Childrens books 2018 112 p.

Grades: 4 5 6 7   **599.53**
   1. Dolphins 2. Marine mammals 3. Marine animals 4. Mammals
   ISBN 9781426330100

"This volume describes myriad species of dolphins, their physical characteristics, echolocation, family pods, diet, and intelligence. It addresses the debate over captivity and both the positive (e.g., U.S. Navy-trained dolphins who help detect underwater mines) and negative (e.g., human pollution injuring and killing dolphins) interactions between humans and dolphins ... Lively." Booklist

Turner, Pamela S.
The **dolphins** of Shark Bay. Pamela S. Turner. Houghton Mifflin Harcourt, 2013. 76 p.: Scientists in the field (Houghton Mifflin)

Grades: 5 6 7 8   **599.53**
   1. Mann, Janet 2. Women marine biologists 3. Bottlenose dolphin 4. Women scientists 5. Marine mammals 6. Dolphins 7. Australia
   ISBN 9780547716381

LC 2012048463

A scientific journey to study the dolphins of coastal Australia considers the many potential sources of dolphin intelligence and what dolphin behavior can inform the scientific community about human intelligence, captive animals and the future of the oceans.

599.55 Sea cows

Gish, Melissa
Manatees. Melissa Gish. Creative Education, [2016] 48 p.: Living wild

Grades: 5 6 7 8   **599.55**
   1. Manatees 2. Marine mammals
   ISBN 9781608187058

LC 2015026824

A look at manatees, including their habitats, physical characteristics such as their unique respiratory system, behaviors, relationships with humans, and the protected status of these intelligent creatures in the world today. Provided by publisher.

"Whether weird, beautiful, or simply adorable, this series has its animals covered." Booklist.

599.638 Giraffe and okapi

Anderson, Tanya
Giraffe extinction: using science and technology to save the gentle giants. Tanya Anderson. Twenty-First Century Books, 2019 128 p.

Grades: 7 8 9 10 11   **599.638**
   1. Giraffes 2. Rare and endangered animals 3. Wildlife conservation 4. Animal conservation 5. Extinction (Biology)
   ISBN 9781541532380

LC 2018054714

"A fascinating and comprehensive analysis of the tragic decline of giraffes and the heroic efforts to reverse this trend." Booklist.

Includes bibliographical references and index.

599.64 Bovids

Gish, Melissa
Bison. by Melissa Gish. Creative Education, 2011. 48 p.: Living wild
Grades: 5 6 7 8   **599.64**
 1. Buffaloes 2. Hoofed mammals 3. Mammals
 ISBN 9781608180776
                LC 2010028305
 A look at bison, including their habitats, physical characteristics such as their shaggy coats, behaviors, relationships with humans, and threatened status in the world today. Provided by publisher.
 "This offers an array of interesting facts. Photography is large and beautiful—a real draw." School Library Journal.
 Includes bibliographical references and index.

599.65 Deer

Gish, Melissa
Moose. by Melissa Gish. Creative Education, c2010. 46 p.: Living wild
Grades: 5 6 7 8   **599.65**
 1. Moose 2. Hoofed mammals 3. Mammals
 ISBN 9781583419731
                LC 2009025174
 A look at moose, including their habitats, physical characteristics such as their imposing antlers, behaviors, relationships with humans, and secure status in the world today. Provided by publisher.

599.66 Odd-toed ungulates

Carson, Mary Kay
 ★ **Emi** and the rhino scientist: saving species from extinction. Mary Kay Carson; with photographs by Tom Uhlman. Houghton Mifflin, 2007. 57 p.: Scientists in the field (Houghton Mifflin)
Grades: 5 6 7 8   **599.66**
 1. Roth, Terri L. 2. Sumatran rhinoceros 3. Rhinoceros 4. Rare and endangered animals 5. Wildlife conservation
 ISBN 0618646396
                LC 2006034517
 While looking for the world's smallest rhino in the Sumatran jungle, a scientist comes upon her rare find who, to her amazement, walks out of the brush and straight up to meet her in this touching tale about one scientist's efforts to save an endangered animal from extinction through her work at the Cincinnati Zoo.
 "This describes how Terri Roth, an expert in endangered-species reproduction at the Cincinnati Zoo, helped Emi to give birth to the first Sumatran rhino born in captivity in more than 100 years. . . . The text is full of important details, and the photographs are unfailingly crisp, bright, and full of variety." School Library Journal.
 Includes bibliographical references (p. 56) and index.

Gish, Melissa
Rhinoceroses. by Melissa Gish. Creative Education, 2011. 48 p.: Living wild

Grades: 5 6 7 8   **599.66**
 1. Rhinoceros 2. Rare and endangered animals 3. Hoofed mammals
 ISBN 9781608180837
                LC 2010028316
 A look at rhinoceroses, including their habitats, physical characteristics such as their horned noses, behaviors, relationships with humans, and protected status in the world today. Provided by publisher.

Montgomery, Sy
 ★ The **tapir** scientist: saving South America's largest mammal. written by Sy Montgomery; photographed by Nic Bishop. Houghton Mifflin Harcourt, 2013. 80 p. : Scientists in the field (Houghton Mifflin)
Grades: 5 6 7 8   **599.66**
 1. Medici, Patricia, 1972- 2. Scientists 3. Tapirs 4. Rare and endangered animals 5. Mammals 6. Animals 7. South America
 ISBN 9780547815480
                LC 2012018678
 Introduces young readers to one of the strangest and most fascinating animals on the planet and recounts the extraordinary work of the dedicated scientists trying to save them. By the Sibert Medal-winning authors of Kakapo Rescue: Saving the World's Strangest Parrot.

599.665 Horse family

Farley, Terri
Wild at heart: mustangs and the young people fighting to save them. by Terri Farley; photographs by Melissa Farlow. Houghton Mifflin Harcourt, 2015. 208 p.
Grades: 5 6 7 8   **599.665**
 1. Wild horses 2. Mustangs 3. Wildlife conservation 4. Wildlife conservationists
 ISBN 9780544392946
                LC 2014041975
 Wild horses thrived for thousands of generations in the mountains, forests, and deserts of the American West. Their family herds existed in environmental harmony until man chose to "manage" them. Since then, every day more of America's wild horses disappear. But courageous people are trying very hard to reverse this, most notably, young people who feel a kinship with these often misunderstood creatures.. Provided by publisher.
 "Beginning with 'Wild Horse Annie,' the 1950s activist who secured protections for America's wild horses, this wide-ranging volume explores horses' prehistoric ancestors, herd dynamics, the horrors of government roundups, and today's young activists fighting to make a difference. Emotional language and first-person sidebars try to recruit readers to the cause, while crisp color photos depict beautiful horses in their natural habitats." Horn Book.

Frydenborg, Kay
 The **wild** horse scientists. written by Kathryn Frydenborg. Houghton Mifflin Harcourt, 2013. 80 p.: Scientists in the field (Houghton Mifflin)
Grades: 7 8 9 10   **599.665**
 1. Veterinarians 2. Wildlife conservationists 3. Wild horses 4. Assateague Island National Seashore (Md and Va)
 ISBN 9780547518312
                LC 2011039912
 Traces the dedicated work of two wildlife veterinarians who have logged countless hours in the field and laboratory to protect and chart the

lives of Assateague Island's wild horses, describing their shared efforts to balance the horses' ecosystem and raise awareness.

599.67 Elephants

Chodosh, Janie

The **elephant** doctor of India. Janie Chodosh Chicago Review Press, 2021. 208 p.

Grades: 4 5 6 7 8   **599.67**

1. Sarma, Kushal Konwar 2. Elephants 3. Veterinarians 4. Wildlife veterinarians 5. Rescues 6. Assam, India

ISBN 9781641603072

Early on a January morning in 2015, a young bull elephant touched a sagging electric line in the Paneri Tea Plantation in the Udalgari District of Assam, India. The elephant's soft-padded feet conducted the current, and the animal fell, kicking in the mud. The local veterinarian called to the scene thought the tusker was going to die. The forest department warden called the one person who could help: Dr. Kushal Konwar Sarma, India's beloved elephant doctor. The Elephant Doctor of India brings the middle-grade reader into the heart of Assam, a remote land of tea plantations, paddy fields, and ancient forests. Author Janie Chodosh spent time with Dr. Sarma and brings his incredible story—and the lives of these magnificent animals—to readers in classrooms everywhere. Provided by publisher.

"This engaging narrative, which is part biography, part veterinary science, and a full appreciation of the Asian elephant, aims to honor the wonder of the elephant and the cultures of the people that share their environment." School Library Journal

Downer, Ann, 1960-

Elephant talk: the surprising science of elephant communication. Ann Downer. Twenty-First Century Books, c2011. 112 p.

Grades: 4 5 6 7 8   **599.67**

1. Elephants -- Behavior 2. Animal communication 3. Animal behavior 4. Animal societies

ISBN 9780761357667

LC 2010024880

"The complex behavior of wild elephants is introduced in a flowing narrative accompanied by full-color photographs, diagrams and maps. Downer provides an overview of elephant evolution, places the creatures in their African and Asian contexts, and describes the lives of these intelligent social animals. Her narrative then focuses on the elephants' intricate verbal and nonverbal communication techniques. . . . The illustrations and clearly labeled diagrams and maps are well placed to amplify the text. . . . Throughout this highly readable, informative title are profiles of individuals . . . who work with these animals." School Library Journal.

Includes bibliographical references and index.

O'Connell, Caitlin, 1965-

★ The **elephant** scientist. by Caitlin O'Connell and Donna M. Jackson; photographs by Caitlin O'Connell and Timothy Rodwell. Houghton Mifflin Harcourt, 2011. 80 p.: Scientists in the field (Houghton Mifflin)

Grades: 4 5 6 7   **599.67**

1. O'Connell, Caitlin, 1965- 2. African elephant 3. Elephants 4. African elephant -- Behavior 5. Namibia

ISBN 9780547053448

LC 2010014134

"O'Connell worked with other scientists to [identify] the vibration-sensitive cells in elephants' feet and trunks that enabled to them to hear

sounds transmitted through the ground. Illustrated with many well-captioned, color photos, this eye-catching book provides a sometimes fascinating look at O'Connell's work with elephants in America and in Namibia." Booklist.

599.7 Carnivores

Allman, Toney

Deadliest mammals. Toney Allman. ReferencePoint Press, [2017] 80 p.: Deadliest predators

Grades: 6 7 8 9 10   **599.7**

1. Predatory animals 2. Mammals

ISBN 9781682820506

LC 2016023812

Profiles some of the world's deadliest mammals, including the tiger, wolverine, and honey badger.

"First-rate nonfiction on a high-interest topic." School Library Journal.

Includes bibliographical references (pages 67-69) and index.

599.74 Land carnivores

Somervill, Barbara A.

Small indian mongoose. Barbara A. Somervill. Cherry Lake Pub., c2010. 32 p.: 21st century skills library.

Grades: 5 6 7 8   **599.74**

1. Mongooses 2. Animal introduction 3. Mammals 4. Animals

ISBN 9781602796300

LC 2009028179

Looks at the small Indian mongoose and examines how it was introduced to control rats but became an invasive species on islands outside of its native South Asia, how it causes problems, and how people have attempted to deal with it.

"This offers an introduction to the problems caused by [the Small Indian Mongoose], a discussion of its physical characteristics and habits, a history of how it arrived in its new habitat, and an analysis of challenges encountered by those trying to limit its spread. . . . [This] considers the destructive effects of these mammals on islands (including several in Hawaii), where they were initially introduced to prey on rats. . . . [This] well-focused [book is] clearly written. The uncluttered page design features at least one color photo on each spread." Booklist.

Includes bibliographical references and index.

599.75 Cat family

Gish, Melissa

Jaguars. by Melissa Gish. Creative Education, 2011. 48 p.: Living wild

Grades: 5 6 7   **599.75**

1. Jaguar 2. Wild cats 3. Rare and endangered animals

ISBN 9781608180790

LC 2010028315

A look at jaguars, including their habitats, physical characteristics such as their powerful jaws, behaviors, relationships with humans, and threatened status in the world today. Provided by publisher.

"This offers an array of interesting facts. Photography is large and beautiful—a real draw." School Library Journal.

Includes bibliographical references and index.

Leopards. by Melissa Gish. Creative Education, c2010. 46 p. : Living wild

Grades: 5 6 7 8   **599.75**

   1. Leopard 2. Wild cats

   ISBN 9781583419724

                   LC 2009025173

A look at leopards, including their habitats, physical characteristics such as their spotted fur, behaviors, relationships with humans, and threatened status in the world today. Provided by publisher.

Hamilton, Sue L., 1959-

   Ambushed by a cougar. Sue Hamilton. ABDO Pub. Co., c2010. 32 p.: Close encounters of the wild kind

Grades: 4 5 6 7   **599.75**

   1. Puma 2. Animal attacks 3. Dangerous animals 4. Wild cats 5. Puma -- Behavior

   ISBN 9781604539288

                   LC 2009045521

"Students will be drawn to the realistic full-color photographs, the realistic diagrams of the creatures' bodies, the real-life stories told by victims, and the interesting, attractive formatting that includes text, diagrams, photographs, and graphics on each page. . . . [This is] exciting and attractive in a gross sort of way and will appeal particularly to boys for both leisure reading and research." Library Media Connection.

Hirsch, Andy, 1987-

   Cats: nature and nurture. Andy Hirsch. First Second, 2019 128 p.: Science comics

Grades: 4 5 6   **599.75**

   1. Cats 2. Animal behavior 3. Animals -- Adaptation 4. Comics and Graphic novels

   ISBN 9781250143136

Bean, a calico kitten abandoned on the streets, explores the history of domesticated cats, detailing how evolution and selective breeding have developed such traits in cats as retractable claws, slit pupils, and sense of balance.

Markle, Sandra

   The **great** leopard rescue: saving the Amur leopards. by Sandra Markle. Millbrook Press, [2017] 48 p.

Grades: 3 4 5 6   **599.75**

   1. Leopard 2. Wildlife rescue 3. Wildlife conservation 4. Wild cats 5. China 6. Russia

   ISBN 9781467792479

                   LC 2015044387

Amur leopards are the rarest big cats in the world. But thanks to scientists' new, innovative efforts to study them and breed a reserve population, these majestic cats have a chance to come back. Provided by publisher.

"An informative presentation showing what is being done to save this beautiful but critically endangered species." Booklist.

Includes bibliographical references and index.

Montgomery, Sy

   ★ **Chasing** cheetahs: the race to save Africa's fastest cats. written by Sy Montgomery; photographs by Nic Bishop. Houghton Mifflin Harcourt, 2014. 80 p.: Scientists in the field (Houghton Mifflin)

Grades: 5 6 7 8   **599.75**

   1. Cheetah Conservation Fund 2. Cheetah 3. Rare and endangered animals 4. Animal conservation 5. Scientists 6. Nature conservation

   ISBN 9780547815497

                   LC 2013017611

"Montgomery introduces readers to Laurie Marker and her team at the Cheetah Conservation Fund's site in Namibia. Scientific information about the cheetahs and profiles of the people who study them are interspersed with in-the-moment, journal-style accounts of activities at the site. Striking photographs capture the dedication of the scientists and the awesome power of the cheetahs." Horn Book.

   Saving the ghost of the mountain: an expedition among snow leopards in Mongolia. Sy Montgomery; photographs by Nic Bishop. Houghton Mifflin Books for Children, 2009. 80 p.: Scientists in the field (Houghton Mifflin)

Grades: 5 6 7 8   **599.75**

   1. Snow leopard 2. Animal conservation 3. Wildlife conservationists 4. Environmentalists 5. Rare and endangered animals 6. Mongolia

   ISBN 9780618916450

Provides an informative examination of the elusive snow leopards who live along the mountain ridges of Mongolia and are seldom seen by man through the studies and observations of a scientist and conservation director of the Snow Leopard Trust.

"Montgomery's enthusiasm translates well to the page and will have readers cheering for the entourage as they attempt to spot a snow leopard. This slender book abounds with information. Bishop's trademark stunning photography fills out the book with breathtaking views of the extreme environs of Central Asia and warm portraits of the charming people who live there." School Library Journal.

599.756 Tiger

Montgomery, Sy

   The **man-eating** tigers of Sundarbans. Sy Montgomery; with photographs by Eleanor Briggs. Houghton Mifflin, 2001. 57 p.

Grades: 4 5 6 7   **599.756**

   1. Tigers 2. Dangerous animals 3. Rare and endangered animals 4. Human/animal relationships 5. Sundarbans Tiger Reserve 6. Sundarbans (Bangladesh and India)

   ISBN 0618077049

                   LC 00032031

"To draw readers into this scientific puzzle, Montgomery integrates science, storytelling, anthropology, and adventure in a unique treatment, illustrated with excellent color photos and diagrams." Horn Book Guide.

Includes bibliographical references (p. 52).

599.757 Lion

Hague, Bradley

   Rise of the lioness: restoring a habitat and its pride on the Liuwa Plains. Bradley Hague. National Geographic Society Children's Books, 2016. 56 p.

Grades: 4 5 6 7   **599.757**

   1. Lion 2. Wildlife conservation 3. Zambia

   ISBN 9781426325335

"Full color photographs document the journey of Lady and her pride. This enlightening work offers in-depth information on the diverse needs of an ecosystem and offers hope for its restoration." School Library Journal.

599.769 Otters

Groc, Isabelle

Sea otters: a survival story. Isabelle Groc; foreword by Dame Judi Dench and David F. Mills. Orca Book Publishers, 2020 120 p.

Grades: 4 5 6 7   **599.769**
  1. Sea otter 2. Sea otter -- Conservation
  ISBN 9781459817371

LC bl2020011616

Presents facts about sea otters, their role in the ecosystem, and the best practices to ensure conservation of the species.

Newman, Patricia, 1958-

Sea otter heroes: the predators that saved an ecosystem. Patricia Newman. Millbrook Press, [2017] 56 p.

Grades: 6 7 8 9 10   **599.769**
  1. Sea otter 2. Marine ecology 3. Marine mammals 4. Ecology
  ISBN 9781512426311

LC 2016020573

Marine biologist Brent Hughes discovered a surprising connection between sea otters and sea grass at an estuary in northern California. Follow science in action as Hughes conducts the research that led to this major discovery. Provided by publisher.

"A very informative selection for environmental studies." School Library Journal.

Includes bibliographical references and index.

599.773 Canis lupus and Canis rufus

McAllister, Ian, 1969-

The **sea** wolves: living wild in the Great Bear Rainforest. written by Ian McAllister and Nicholas Read; photographs by Ian McAllister. Orca Book Publishers, c2010. 121 p.

Grades: 5 6 7 8   **599.773**
  1. Wolves 2. Rain forest ecology 3. Animal welfare 4. Rain forests 5. Great Bear Rainforest, British Columbia 6. British Columbia
  ISBN 9781554692064

"This extensive, informative text is illustrated with remarkable photographs taken by McAllister, who has lived in and studied the area for years. They show the lush, old-growth forest and rocky shoreline and a variety of animals that share this habitat, but the wolves are the stars: at rest, at play, on the prowl and catching fish. . . . Fascinating and useful." Kirkus.

599.78 Bears

Hamilton, Sue L., 1959-

Mauled by a bear. Sue Hamilton. ABDO, c2010. 32 p.: Close encounters of the wild kind

Grades: 4 5 6 7   **599.78**
  1. Bear attacks 2. Bears 3. Animal attacks 4. Dangerous animals
  ISBN 9781604539325

LC 2009035078

Readers learn of actual human-bear encounters, information about bears, survival strategies, and attack statistics.

"Students will be drawn to the realistic full-color photographs, the realistic diagrams of the creatures' bodies, the real-life stories told by

victims, and the interesting, attractive formatting that includes text, diagrams, photographs, and graphics on each page. . . . [This is] exciting and attractive in a gross sort of way and will appeal particularly to boys for both leisure reading and research." Library Media Connection.

Montgomery, Sy

The **golden** moon bear: science and adventure in the Asian tropics. by Sy Montgomery. Houghton Mifflin, 2004. 80 p.

Grades: 5 6 7 8   **599.78**
  1. Bears 2. Scientific expeditions 3. Rare and endangered animals 4. Asiatic black bear 5. Southeast Asia
  ISBN 0618356509

LC 2004005236

Introduces the research involved in tracking and studying a previously unknown species of bear in Southeast Asia as a scientist and her assistant go into the jungle and visit remote villages to find out all they can about this newly discovered animal.

"The exciting narrative is complemented by an array of full-color photos. . . . This attractive and informative offering is an intelligent reportage of science as it happens." School Library Journal.

Includes bibliographical references (p. 79).

599.784 Grizzly bear (Brown bear)

Gish, Melissa

Brown bears. Melissa Gish. Creative Co., 2014. 48 p.: Living wild

Grades: 5 6 7 8   **599.784**
  1. Brown bear 2. Bears 3. Animals
  ISBN 9781608184156

"Thorough in scope and elegant in design, these stellar titles will attract the browser and the report writer alike." School Library Journal.

599.786 Polar bear

Castaldo, Nancy F. (Nancy Fusco), 1962-

Polar bear rescue: all about polar bears and how to save them. by Nancy Castaldo and Karen de Seve, with National Geographic explorer Daniel Raven-Ellison. National Geographic Society Childrens Books, 2014. 128 p.: National Geographic kids mission

Grades: 4 5 6   **599.786**
  1. Polar bear -- Conservation 2. Animal conservation 3. Animal rescue 4. Wildlife
  ISBN 9781426317323

"These attractive books offer a good deal of information about endangered animals as well as encouragement for kids who want to help." Booklist.

McAllister, Ian, 1969-

★ The **salmon** bears: giants of the Great Bear Rainforest. written by Ian McAllister and Nicholas Read; photographs by Ian McAllister. Orca Book Publishers, 2010. 89 p.

Grades: 5 6 7 8   **599.786**
  1. Bears 2. Grizzly bear 3. Rain forest ecology 4. Great Bear Rainforest, British Columbia 5. British Columbia
  ISBN 9781554692057

"Read's conversational text and McAllister's excellent photos provide a perfect framework for this evocative look at the big bears of the

Great Bear Rainforest of British Columbia, and an intriguing investigation of its ecological pattern of dependency. The authors present a round of seasons from one winter to the next, touching upon such topics as the effects of fish farms on wild salmon populations, what happens during a salmon run, and what the future may hold for the fish, the bears, and the Great Bear Rainforest itself. . . . Superbly readable, informative, and attractive." School Library Journal.

599.789 Giant panda

Gish, Melissa
Pandas. by Melissa Gish. Creative Education, 2011. 48 p.: Living wild
Grades: 5 6 7 8   **599.789**
   1. Giant panda 2. Pandas
   ISBN 9781608180820
                          LC 2010028311
   A look at pandas, including their habitats, physical characteristics such as their black-and-white fur, behaviors, relationships with humans, and threatened status in the world today. Provided by publisher.

Strother, Ruth
Absolute expert: pandas. Ruth Strother; with National Geographic explorer Marc Brody. National Geographic, 2019 112 p.
Grades: 3 4 5 6 7   **599.789**
   1. Giant panda
   ISBN 9781426334320
                          LC 2018057541
   Introduces pandas, discussing what they eat, where they live, and why they are endangered.

599.79 Marine carnivores

Snyder, Eleanor
Alarming leopard seals. Eleanor Snyder. Gareth Stevens Publishing, [2017] 24 p.: Cutest animals...that could kill you!
Grades: 3 4 5   **599.79**
   1. Leopard seal 2. Seals (Animals) 3. Marine mammals
   ISBN 9781482449099
                          LC 2015046971
   "An informative, highly readable, and high-interest series." Booklist.
   Includes bibliographical references and index.

599.8 Primates

Silvey, Anita
Untamed: the wild life of Jane Goodall. Anita Silvey; foreword by Jane Goodall. National Geographic, 2015. 96 p.
Grades: 4 5 6 7 8   **599.8**
   1. Goodall, Jane, 1934- 2. Primatologists 3. Chimpanzees -- Behavior 4. Women scientists 5. Women primatologists 6. Primates -- Research
   ISBN 9781426315183
                          LC 2014017715
   This biography for children will trace Goodall's life, but each chapter will also focus on two or more of the chimpanzees that she observed, with information in sidebars about these particular animals. Along with biographical details, the book will explore the ethical issues that surround Goodall's work and show what has changed in our understanding of Great Apes. What do we know today about these animals in terms of language, speech, tool use, and DNA? How has sophisticated technology—GPS systems, Satellite imagery, portable digital microphones—been used to gain new information about animal populations? Provided by publisher.
   "Silvey (The Plant Hunters) adeptly chronicles the life of Goodall from her childhood fascination with animal behavior to her groundbreaking field research of chimpanzees in Africa and her work to preserve endangered animals habitats." Publishers Weekly.

599.884 Gorilla

Gish, Melissa
Gorillas. by Melissa Gish. Creative Education, c2010. 48 p.: Living wild
Grades: 5 6 7 8   **599.884**
   1. Gorillas 2. Primates 3. Rare and endangered animals
   ISBN 9781583419694
                          LC 2009025170
   A look at gorillas, including their habitats, physical characteristics such as their large heads, behaviors, relationships with humans, and threatened status in the world today. Provided by publisher.
   "This book lucidly discusses conservation and the animals' often tenuous relationship with humans. The layout is uniformly simple but effective, constructed with a nice balance of main text for the report writers, smaller chunks of esoterica for browsers, and . . . killer photos." Booklist.
   Includes bibliographical references and index.

Sobol, Richard
Breakfast in the rainforest: a visit with mountain gorillas. Richard Sobol; with an afterword by Leonardo DiCaprio. Candlewick Press, 2008. 40 p.
Grades: 3 4 5 6   **599.884**
   1. Gorillas -- Conservation 2. Rare and endangered animals 3. Wildlife conservation 4. Rain forests 5. Uganda
   ISBN 9780763622817
   Powerful but shy, the African mountain gorilla struggles for survival in the rainforests of Uganda's national parks. Follow wildlife photographer Richard Sobol on an arduous journey to these hidden habitats and take a hushed, close-up look at the gentle giants. Learn about the efforts being made to preserve these magnificent creatures.
   "Wildlife photographer Sobol recounts his travels to Uganda to observe gorillas living in the Virunga Mountains. In his personable text, he also touches on the creatures' habits, diet, and threats. Closeup photographs of the gorillas in addition to many pictures of the surrounding countryside and villagers help round out an understanding of the endangered animals' homeland." Horn Book Guide.

599.9 Humans

Deem, James M.
Faces from the past: forgotten people of North America. by James M. Deem. Houghton Mifflin Harcourt, c2012. 160 p.
Grades: 6 7 8 9 10   **599.9**
   1. Prehistoric humans 2. Forensic anthropology 3. Human remains (Archaeology) 4. Radiocarbon dating 5. Facial reconstruction

(Anthropology) 6. North America
ISBN 9780547370248

LC 2012006819

Traces the efforts of a scientific team to learn about the life and culture of a person whose skeletal remains are traced to prehistoric times, profiling the valuable technical achievements of artists who use special skills to reconstruct faces from archaeological remains.

"Clear prose, pleasing layout, and crisp photographs combined with subject matter rarely explored in history books make this book an excellent choice for most collections." School Library Journal.

Szpirglas, Jeff

You just can't help it!: your guide to the wild and wacky world of human behavior. Jeff Szpirglas. Owlkids, 2011. 34 p.
Grades: 4 5 6 7   **599.9**
1. Human nature 2. Human behavior 3. Instinct 4. Biology
ISBN 9781926818078

LC 2010931642

"This is a collection of curious facts and intriguing studies about human behavior. With a breezy text supported by a lively design, the author ... presents science in a way certain to attract middle-grade and middle-school readers. Chapters on the senses, emotions, communication, and interactions with other human beings cover a variety of topics.... The digital art includes bits of photographs, line drawings, the use of color and shapes to help organize the print and plenty of symbols." Kirkus.

599.9092 Physical anthropologists

Henderson, Harry, 1951-

The **Leakey** family: unearthing human ancestors. Harry Henderson. Chelsea House, c2012. xx, 127 p.
Grades: 10 11 12   **599.9092**
1. Leakey, L. S. B. (Louis Seymour Bazett), 1903-1972 2. Leakey, Mary D. (Mary Douglas), 1913-1996 3. Leakey, Richard E. 4. Physical anthropologists 5. Paleoanthropolgists 6. Fossil hominids 7. Excavations (Archaeology) 8. Olduvai Gorge (Tanzania) -- Antiquities
ISBN 9781604136746

LC 2011001972

Introduces the Leakey family, shares the advancements they made in the field of paleoanthropology, and explores their struggles, accomplishments, and failures.

600 TECHNOLOGY

600 Technology (Applied sciences)

Macaulay, David

The **way** things work now: from levers to lasers, windmills to wi-fi, a visual guide to the world of machines. David Macaulay, with Neil Ardley. Houghton Mifflin Harcourt, 2016, 1988. 400 p.
Grades: 4 5 6 7 8 9 10 11 12 Adult   **600**
1. Technology 2. Machinery 3. Mechanics 4. Science 5. Toy and movable books
ISBN 9780544824386

LC bl2016040252

The sweeping new update to the worldwide bestseller, The New Way Things Work includes all new sections on the technology that most impacts our everyday lives.

"Macaulay's brilliantly designed, engagingly informal diagrams and cutaways bring within the grasp of even casual viewers a greater understanding of the technological wonders of both past and present." Kirkus.

608 Patents

Lee, Dora, 1968-

Biomimicry: inventions inspired by nature. written by Dora Lee; illustrated by Margot Thompson. Kids Can Press, 2011. 40 p.
Grades: 4 5 6   **608**
1. Biomimicry 2. Technological innovations 3. Humans -- Effect of environment on
ISBN 9781554534678

Discusses the many human inventions that have been inspired by nature, including biodegradable plastics, Velcro, and renewable energy resources, and suggests other natural processes that can be used to benefit modern human civilization.

609 Technology—History, geographic treatment, biography

Ferris, Julie

Ideas that changed the world. authors, Julie Ferris ... [et al.]. DK Pub., 2013, c2010 256 p.
Grades: 6 7 8 9 10   **609**
1. Inventions -- History 2. Technology -- History
ISBN 9781465414236

LC bl2010015752

An in-depth reference guide to technological developments that changed the world describes each invention and explores its place in history and how it influenced civilization, discussing inventions from the wheel to computers.

"Brightly colored and packed with information, this reference volume delivers.... This book could be used in multiple subject areas. English classes might use it for general research or units on the decades, social studies for the major changes over time, and science due to the technological advancements." Library Media Connection.

Sonneborn, Liz

The **electric** light: Thomas Edison's illuminating invention. Liz Sonneborn. Chelsea House, c2007. 120 p.: Milestones in American history
Grades: 7 8 9 10   **609**
1. Edison, Thomas A. (Thomas Alva), 1847-1931. 2. Electric lighting -- History 3. Inventors 4. Electrical engineering -- History
ISBN 9780791093504

LC 2006034432

Presents the life and accomplishments of the American inventor and engineer, focusing on his development of electric light.

"This accessible [volume captures] the hard work, perseverance, and natural talent of Edison.... The [text explores] the [man's life] along with providing information about the genesis and development of [electric light]. Many photographs, reproductions, and sidebars contribute to a clean design and help clarify topics." Horn Book Guide.

Includes bibliographical references and index.

Ye, Ting-xing, 1952-

The **Chinese** thought of it: amazing inventions and innovations. Ting-Xing Ye. Firefly Books Ltd., 2009. 47 p.: We thought of it

Grades: 5 6 7 8   **609**

    1. Inventions 2. China -- Intellectual life.
    ISBN 9781554511952

"In this survey of Chinese inventions at least one double-page spread is devoted to each of the eleven topics: farming, working with metal, transportation and exploration, canals and bridges, weapons and warfare, paper and printing, silk, and everyday innovations. . . . The layout of the book is appealing and just right for quick reading or browsing. . . . The author's personal story about her childhood in Shanghai effectively draws the reader in." Voice of Youth Advocates.

609.73 Inventions — United States

Rossi, Ann

Bright ideas: the age of invention in America, 1870-1910. Ann Rossi. National Geographic, c2005. 40 p.: Crossroads America

Grades: 4 5 6   **609.73**

    1. Inventions -- History 19th century 2. Inventions -- History 20th century 3. Inventors
    ISBN 0792283562

                                 LC 2003019834

Illuminates an era marked by amazing advances in science and technology, and introduces the inventors who revolutionized the way America works, travels, and lives, including Henry Ford, Thomas Edison, and the Wright brothers.

"This solid [title] for report writers may even pull in a few curious browsers because of [its] plentiful, full-color photos and reproductions. The [layout is] inviting, and the [text is] clear, informative, and readable." School Library Journal.

610 Medicine and health

Dawson, Ian

Renaissance medicine. Ian Dawson. Enchanted Lion Books, 2005. 64 p.: History of medicine

Grades: 6 7 8 9   **610**

    1. Medicine -- History 15th century 2. Medicine -- History 16th century 3. Medicine -- History
    ISBN 1592700381

                                 LC 2004061999

Details methods of diagnosis, treatment, and prevention of disease used between 1450 and 1750, including the theory of the Four Humors, midwifery, quacks, and the plague.

"This offers a concise overview of the fascinating advancements in European medicine between 1450 and 1750. . . . Dawson carefully shows how inventions such as the printing press and microscope and the work of artists such as da Vinci influenced medical knowledge. Quotes from primary sources enhance the plainspoken language, and numerous reproductions of paintings and engravings vividly evoke the realities of surgery, leech treatments, and the horrors of the plague." Booklist.

Includes bibliographical references (p. 63) and index.

Evans, Michael, 1964-

The **adventures** of Medical Man: kids' illnesses and injuries explained: nut allergy, concussion, broken bones, strep throat, ear infection, asthma. by Michael Evans and David Wichman; art by Gareth Williams. Annick Press; c2010. 72 p.: The adventures of Medical Man

Grades: 5 6 7 8   **610**

    1. Diseases 2. Wounds and injuries 3. Food allergy 4. Diseases -- Treatment 5. Medicine
    ISBN 9781554512638

                                 LC bl2010024944

Explains the science behind five common childhood illnesses, including nut allergies, strep throat, and ear infections, and describes how doctors treat each illness and how to help prevent them before they occur.

"Using tangible experiences that kids can relate to, this book does a fantastic job of explaining common medical issues in an accessible way. A variety of heroic characters explain otherwise complicated and seemingly scary conditions and occurrences. Through the use of science fiction, adventure, and comics, the book covers nut allergies, concussions, broken bones, strep throat, ear infections, and asthma. . . . The extensive glossary is straightforward and user-friendly. The pumped-up graphic illustrations are extremely engaging and further bring these otherwise abstract concepts to life." School Library Journal.

Includes bibliographical references (p. 67) and index.

Newquist, H. P. (Harvey P.)

The **human** body. HP Newquist. Viking, published by the Penguin Group, [2015] 96 p.: Smithsonian: Invention & Impact

Grades: 4 5 6 7   **610**

    1. Medicine -- History 2. Medical innovations 3. Medical technology 4. Human physiology 5. Human anatomy
    ISBN 9780451476432

                                 LC 2015011670

An exploration of the objects that scientists and tinkerers throughout history have invented to protect, repair, or improve our bodies. Provided by publisher.

"The open page design and ample full-color photos and historical diagrams will easily draw in middle-grade readers, especially those looking for a more macabre look at history and science. A list of resources, including abundant websites, closes out this handsome volume." Booklist.

Omnigraphics, Inc

Complementary and alternative medicine information for teens: health tips about diverse medical and wellness systems including information about chiropractic medicine and other manipulative practices, movement and massage therapies, yoga and other mind-body therapies, acupuncture and other forms of energy medicine,creative arts therapies, and more.. Omnigraphics, Inc., 2018 400 p.: Teen Health

Grades: 7 8 9 10 11 12   **610**

    1. Alternative medicine 2. Teenagers -- Health
    ISBN 9780780816176

                                   LC 2017057394

Provides basic consumer health information for teens about diverse medical systems and therapies used together with or in place of conventional medicine. Includes index, resource information, and recommendations for further reading. Provided by publisher.

610.28 Auxiliary techniques and procedures; apparatus, equipment, materials

Latta, Sara L.

Body 2.0: the engineering revolution in medicine. Sara Latta. Twenty-First Century Books, 2019. 96 p.

Grades: 8 9 10 11 12   **610.28**

1. Biomedical engineering 2. Medical technology 3. Bioengineering 4. Regeneration (Biology) 5. Biotechnology

ISBN 9781541528130

LC 2018054864

Meet scientists who are on the verge of breakthroughs in biomedical engineering. From encouraging the body to regenerate damaged bone and muscle tissue to re-routing visual stimuli to the brain to help blind people see, these discoveries will change medicine radically.

"Veteran science author Latta here spotlights the fascinating convergence of medicine, engineering, and scientific discovery, offering provocative glimpses into the burgeoning fields of tissue engineering, regenerative medicine, neuroscience, microbiology, genetic engineering, and synthetic biology. Inspiring problem-solving-minded teens to explore these STEM disciplines by describing projects so cutting edge they seem like science fiction, Latta also includes brief profiles and photos of diverse researchers that enable readers to imagine themselves pursuing similar careers." Kirkus.

Includes bibliographical references and index.

Senker, Cath

The **science** of medical technology: from humble syringes to lifesaving robots. written by Cath Senker; [artists, Alexandre Affonso, Bryan Beach]. Franklin Watts', 2019. 32 p.

Grades: 4 5 6 7 8   **610.28**

1. Medical technology 2. Medical innovations

ISBN 9780531133934

LC 2018031803

Introduces the reader to the science of medical technology. Provided by publisher.

Strange, Cordelia

Medical technicians: health-care support for the 21st century. by Cordelia Strange. Mason Crest Publishers, c2011. 64 p.: New careers for the 21st century: finding your role in the global renewal

Grades: 7 8 9 10   **610.28**

1. Biomedical technicians -- Vocational guidance 2. Medical care services 3. Medical personnel 4. Occupations 5. Vocational guidance

ISBN 9781422218174

LC 2010014934

"Chapters identify and emphasize specific careers: important strengths, necessary aptitudes and interests, education and training, projected earnings, closely related occupations, type of work environment, and predictions for the future of the field. . . . Color photos have a small role amid the many statistics, figures, graphs and charts that support and supplement the . . . [text]." School Library Journal.

Includes bibliographical references (p. 60-62) and index.

610.285 Medicine—Computer applications

Nardo, Don, 1947-

The **medical** revolution: how technology is changing health care. by Don Nardo. ReferencePoint Press, 2020. 80 p.

Grades: 7 8 9 10 11 12   **610.285**

1. Medical technology 2. Medical innovations 3. Medical care 4. Medicine 5. Technology

ISBN 9781682829295

LC 2020018230

Massive breakthroughs are changing the face of medicine and healthcare. In addition to the benefits of super-smart computers that can learn, medical researchers and doctors are beginning to reap the rewards of robots that perform surgeries. There have also been advances in nanotechnology—in which doctors heal by injecting microscopic particles into the body; using 3D printing to make replacements for failing bladders and other organs; and telemedicine, in which physicians can monitor and operate on patients using remote apps.

"Compelling topics, personal stories, and the author's straightforward approach make this succeed. The relatively lengthy coverage of COVID-19 and robust notes and further-reading sections are a bonus." Booklist

Includes bibliographical references and index.

Spilsbury, Richard, 1963-

Robots in medicine. by Richard and Louise Spilsbury. Gareth Stevens Publishing, 2016. 48 p.: Amazing robots

Grades: 4 5 6 7   **610.285**

1. Robots 2. Robotics 3. Robotics in medicine

ISBN 9781482430103

"The full-color photos of robots in action and the high-interest nature of robotics may catch the interest of science-minded kids." Booklist.

610.73 Nursing and services of allied health personnel

Strange, Cordelia

Physicians assistants & nurses: new opportunities in the 21st-century health system. by Cordelia Strange. Mason Crest Publishers, c2011. 64 p. : New careers for the 21st century: finding your role in the global renewal

Grades: 7 8 9 10   **610.73**

1. Midlevel health practitioners 2. Nurses 3. Medical personnel 4. Occupations 5. Vocational guidance

ISBN 9781422218204

LC 2010017919

"Chapters identify and emphasize specific careers: important strengths, necessary aptitudes and interests, education and training, projected earnings, closely related occupations, type of work environment, and predictions for the future of the field. . . . Color photos have a small role amid the many statistics, figures, graphs and charts that support and supplement the . . . [text]." School Library Journal.

Includes bibliographical references and index.

610.9 Medicine—History

Rooney, Anne

The **history** of medicine. Anne Rooney. Rosen Pub., 2013. 208 p.: History of science (Rosen)

Grades: 7 8 9 10 11 12   **610.9**
1. Medicine -- History   2. Medical innovations -- History   3. Diseases   4. Diagnosis   5. Medical care
ISBN 9781448872282

LC 2012009971

Presents a history of medicine from the world's earliest medical minds, to the recent breakthroughs in medicine and future challenges.

"Organized thematically, this enlightening entry into the History of Science series delves into the history of disease, diagnosis, treatment, and surgery... Rooney has crafted a highly readable tome about a dense topic." Booklist.

Includes bibliographical references (p. 205) and index.

Younker, J. Marin
Bleed, blister, puke, and purge: the dirty secrets behind early American medicine. J. Marin Younker. Zest Books, 2016. 112 p.
Grades: 9 10 11 12   **610.9**
1. Medicine -- History   2. Diseases -- Treatment   3. Traditional medicine   4. Amputation   5. Physicians
ISBN 9781942186328

"An engrossing, entertaining history of medicine for those who enjoy it told with a heavy dose of blood and guts." Kirkus.

Zuchora-Walske, Christine
Your head shape reveals your personality!: science's biggest mistakes about the human body. by Christine Zuchora-Walske. Lerner Publications Company, 2014. 32 p.
Grades: 4 5 6 7   **610.9**
1. Pseudoscience   2. Human body   3. Human anatomy   4. Scientific errors   5. Human physiology
ISBN 9781467736619

LC 2013041696

What if someone told you that your liver pumped blood through your body? You'd think that person was crazy! Discover how thought about the human body has changed over the centuries. Provided by publisher.

"Although each volume [in the Science Gets It Wrong series] has its merits, Your Head Shape Reveals Your Personality! stands out due in large part to the subject matter—the human body—and its gross-out potential." School Library Journal.

Includes bibliographical references and index.

610.92 Medicine—Biography

Kidder, Tracy
Mountains beyond mountains: the quest of Dr. Paul Farmer, a man who would cure the world. by Tracy Kidder; adapted for young people by Michael French. Delacorte Press, c2013. 272 p.
Grades: 7 8 9 10   **610.92**
1. Farmer, Paul, 1959-   2. Physicians   3. Poverty   4. Right to medical care   5. Medical missionaries   6. Medical care   7. Haiti
ISBN 9780385743181

Traces the efforts of Harvard-educated Dr. Paul Farmer to transform healthcare on a global scale, documenting his visits to some of the world's most impoverished regions and the unconventional methods that enabled him to improve and save lives.

610.938 Medicine -- Greece

Gow, Mary
The **greatest** doctor of ancient times: Hippocrates and his oath. Mary Gow. Enslow Publishers, 2010. 128 p.: Great minds of ancient science and math
Grades: 5 6 7 8   **610.938**
1. Hippocrates, 460?-377? B.C.E.   2. Ancient medicine   3. Medicine -- History   4. Physicians
ISBN 9780766031180

LC 2008029630

A biography of ancient Greek physician Hippocrates, the Father of Medicine. His assumptions that diseases and cures came from nature, not the gods, and that a physician could treat a patient using knowledge obtained from experience or medical texts still form the basis of modern medicine. Provided by publisher.

"This interesting take on medicine concludes with several activities. . . . Photographs on sepia-colored pages are a good match for the subject." Booklist.

Includes bibliographical references and index.

Kelly, Kate, 1950-
Early civilizations: prehistoric times to 500 C.E.. Kate Kelly. Facts on File, c2009. xvii, 174 p.
Grades: 6 7 8 9 10 11 12   **610.938**
1. Medicine, Ancient
ISBN 9780816072057

LC 2008043441

Presents a history of medicine and the treatment of disease and injuries from prehistoric times up to the end of the Roman Empire.

611 Human anatomy, cytology, histology

Hall, Linley Erin
DNA and RNA. Linley Erin Hall. Rosen Pub., 2010. 80 p.: Understanding genetics
Grades: 7 8 9 10 11 12   **611**
1. DNA   2. R N A   3. Genetics
ISBN 9781435895324

LC 2009046612

"These hi/lo resources, with the liberal use of color illustrations, color sidebars, subsections labeled in bold color fonts, and patterns of chemical bonds as backgrounds, will appeal to less able and reluctant readers." Library Media Connection.

Includes bibliographical references and index.

Haywood, Karen
Skeletal system. by Karen Haywood. Marshall Cavendish Benchmark, c2009. 80 p.: Amazing human body
Grades: 6 7 8 9   **611**
1. Skeleton   2. Human body   3. Bones   4. Anatomy   5. Physiology
ISBN 9780761430568

LC 2008017574

Discusses the parts that make up the human skeletal system, what can go wrong, how to treat those illnesses and diseases, and how to stay healthy. Provided by publisher.

"A good choice for students beginning to research the topic." Library Media Connection.

Includes bibliographical references and index.

Roberts, Alice M.

The **complete** human body: the definitive visual guide. Alice Roberts, editor-in-chief. DK Publishing, 2010 512 p.

Grades: 8 9 10 11 12 Adult   **611**

1. Human body 2. Human anatomy 3. Human physiology
ISBN 9780756667337

Offers a complete overview of the development, form, function and disorders of the human body, from muscle structure and activity to motor pathways within the brain, completely illustrated and featuring the latest medical and microscopic imaging.

"This incorporates hundreds of stunning images and clearly written text. . . . The extraordinary detail of these pictures will give students an excellent understanding of the body's structure and organization." School Library Journal.

Includes index.

Walker, Richard, 1951-

Dr. Frankenstein's human body book. Richard Walker. Dorling Kindersley, 2008. 93 p.

Grades: 4 5 6 7   **611**

1. Human physiology 2. Human anatomy 3. Human body
ISBN 9780756640910

LC oc2008084182

The reader becomes the good doctor's trusty lab assistant as he reconstructs a human body from the skeleton out, in a title that uses bold imagery and the most recent scientific information to bring the human body to life.

"This anatomy book is as engrossing as any science fiction. Dr. Frankenstein, shown in a sepia photograph standing in a laboratory, gazing at a skull he holds in one hand, invites readers to join him as he creates a human being. . . . The story line is sustained with brief, pun-happy journal entries. . . . Gothic fonts and engraved illustrations and vignettes (in red and black and also hand-colored) blend with state-of-the-art images from MEG scans, gamma scans and other advanced technology. Clear explanations broken into easily assimilable captions and text blocks encourage the reader." Publishers Weekly.

612 Human physiology

Bennett, Howard J.

The **fantastic** body: what makes you tick & how you get sick. Dr. Howard Bennett. Rodale Kids, an imprint of Rodale-Books, 2017. 240 p.

Grades: 4 5 6 7   **612**

1. Human body 2. Human anatomy 3. Human physiology
ISBN 9781623368890

An accessible, highly visual reference guide to the human body collects fun facts, cool diagrams and gross stories as well as a range of DIY projects designed to promote further learning and less anxiety at the doctor's office.

Gardner, Robert, 1929-

Ace your human biology science project: great science fair ideas. Robert Gardner and Barbara Gardner Conklin. Enslow Publishers, 2009. 128 p.: Ace your biology science project

Grades: 5 6 7 8   **612**

1. Human biology -- Experiments 2. Science projects 3. Biology -- Experiments 4. Experiments 5. Science
ISBN 9780766032194

LC 2008030799

Presents several science projects and science project ideas about human biology. Provided by publisher.

"Dozens of . . . science activities are presented with background information, step-by-step instructions, and suggestions for extending to the science fair level. . . . Color illustrations and important safety information are included." Horn Book Guide.

Includes bibliographical references (p. 125) and index.

Goddard, Jolyon

Inside the human body. by Jolyon Goddard. Marshall Cavendish Benchmark, c2010. 48 p. : Invisible worlds

Grades: 4 5 6 7   **612**

1. Human body 2. Human physiology 3. Human biology 4. Cells
ISBN 9780761441908

LC 2008037254

Describes the fascinating details of the human body that are too small for the unaided eye to see, and how these microscopic systems work to keep the body alive and healthy. Provided by publisher.

"The narrative is clear, well written, broken down into manageable pieces, and peppered with eye-opening facts. The numerous photographs are so phenomenal that they will inspire kids to read the text . . . so that they can wrap their minds around what they see." School Library Journal.

Includes bibliographical references and index.

Green, Dan, 1975 June 20-

Human body: [a book with guts!]. [created by Basher; written by Dan Green]. Kingfisher, c2011. 128 p.: Basher science

Grades: 5 6 7 8   **612**

1. Human body 2. Human anatomy 3. Human biology
ISBN 9780753466285

LC bl2011003708

Uses cartoon-style characters and everyday situations to explain the basic elements of the human body.

"Basher brings his signature informative irreverence and smiley little cartoon icons to the world of human biology. Not a comprehensive resource, but supplemental science reading doesn't come much more fun." Booklist.

Hirsch, Rebecca E.

Microbiomes. Rebecca E. Hirsch. Twenty-First Century Books, 2016. 112 p.

Grades: 7 8 9 10   **612**

1. Medical microbiology 2. Human body -- Microbiology 3. Microbiology 4. Drug resistance in microorganisms
ISBN 9781467785686

LC 2015014264

This book explores the human microbiome—the trillions of microbes that share our bodies—and why it has become one of the hottest areas of research in human health. The book discusses the microbes that live on us and in us, how scientists study them, and how they relate to health issues such as infections, obesity, allergies, and autoimmune disorders. The book delves into the Human Microbiome Project (HMP), a US government/National Institutes of Health initiative launched in 2007, in which scientists are working to identify and study all of the microbes associated with human health and disease. The book also takes readers into stores to make informed choices about the many anti-microbial and probiotic products that line the shelves. Provided by publisher.

"Unexpectedly informative and up-to-the-minute in research, this is a nifty look through a clear window at our unsuspected personal passengers. Consider this in-depth resource for reports and students who are not easily made squeamish" School Library Journal.

Includes bibliographical references and index.

Macaulay, David

The **way** we work: getting to know the amazing human body. written and illustrated David Macaulay. Houghton Mifflin, 2008. 336 p.

Grades: 6 7 8 9 10   **612**
1. Human physiology 2. Human body 3. Anatomy 4. Organ 5. Nervous system
ISBN 9780618233786

LC 2008025109

Explores the complex inner workings of the human body in a visual study of anatomy and physiology that ranges from the cells that form the building blocks of the body, to the individual organs and systems and how they function.

"The opening chapter introduces basic concepts of biology and chemistry at the cellular level while subsequent chapters take us through the various systems of the body. . . . [Humor] occasionally leavens the information, which, though often complex and technical, is clearly and succintly presented in double-page spreads, accompanied by an illuminating array of illustrations." Horn Book.

Mooney, Carla, 1970-

Human movement: how the body walks, runs, jumps, and kicks. Carla Mooney, illustrated by Samuel Carbaugh. Nomad Press, 2017. vii, 120 p.: Inquire and investigate

Grades: 7 8 9   **612**
1. Human body 2. Human anatomy 3. Physical fitness 4. Physiology 5. Health
ISBN 9781619304819

Introduces human anatomy and physiology, explaining how different body systems work together, while promoting overall health and fitness.

Somervill, Barbara A.

★ The **human** body. Barbara Somervill. Gareth Stevens Pub., c2008. 48 p.

Grades: 5 6 7 8   **612**
1. Human body 2. Human physiology 3. Human anatomy 4. Physiology 5. Anatomy
ISBN 9780836884418

LC 2007016175

Examines the structure of the human body and how its systems work together, with information about how to keep one's body fit and healthy.

"This describes human anatomy and physiology. . . . Factoids are scattered throughout the text in a fashion that captures the reader's attention and interest. . . . [The book offers] excellent graphics, namely photos and diagrams. The artwork complements and enhances the written content." Science Books & Films.

Includes bibliographical references (p. 46) and index.

Thomas, Mindy

The **how** and wow of the human body: from your tongue to your toes and all the guts in between. by Mindy Thomas and Guy Raz; illustrated by Jack Teagle Houghton Mifflin Harcourt, 2021 160 p.: Wow in the world

Grades: 3 4 5 6 7 8   **612**
1. Human body 2. Human anatomy 3. Human physiology 4. Anatomy 5. Physiology
ISBN 9780358306634

"The hosts of NPR podcast Wow in the World lose none of their energy or comic timing in reeling off a highlights-style swing through pubescent anatomy from brain to butt." Kirkus

Walker, Richard, 1951-

Human body. Richard Walker. DK, 2014 72 p.: Eyewitness books

Grades: 4 5 6 7   **612**
1. Human body 2. Human anatomy 3. Human physiology
ISBN 9781465426208

Describes the parts and systems of the human body and discusses how they work.

Watson, Galadriel Findlay

Extreme abilities: amazing human feats and the simple science behind them. by Galadriel Watson; illustrated by Cornelia Li. Annick Press, 2019. 88 p.

Grades: 4 5 6 7   **612**
1. Superhuman abilities 2. Muscle strength 3. Memory 4. Balance 5. Meditation
ISBN 9781773212500

"This slim volume delves into nine types of extreme human abilities of the body and mind...A popular choice for libraries serving older elementary or middle school students." School Library Journal.

Wicks, Maris

★ **Human** Body Theater. a non-fiction revue by Maris Wicks. First Second, 2015. 240 p.

Grades: 4 5 6 7 8   **612**
1. Human body 2. Human anatomy 3. Human physiology 4. Anatomy 5. Physiology 6. Comics and Graphic novels 7. Books for reluctant readers
ISBN 9781626722774

A humorous and informative skeleton introduces each system of the human body, gaining a layer of her "costume" by the end of each act, becoming a fully formed human by the end of the play.

Woollcott, Tory

The **brain**: the ultimate thinking machine. written by Tory Woollcott; illustrated by Alex Graudins. First Second, 2018. 121 p.: Science comics

Grades: 4 5 6 7   **612**
1. Brain 2. Brain -- Physiology 3. Senses and sensation 4. Memory 5. Comics and Graphic novels
ISBN 9781626728004

LC 2017957416

In this volume, Fahama has been kidnapped by a mad scientist and his zombie assistant, and they are intent on stealing her brain! She'll need to learn about the brain as fast as possible in order to plan her escape! How did the brain evolve? How do our senses work in relation to the brain? How do we remember things? What makes you, YOU? Get an inside look at the human brain, the most advanced operating system in the world... if you have the nerve! Provided by publisher.

"Colorful illustrations illuminate the text. The combination of an entertaining story line (note: Fahama does escape), engaging and clear language, and bold, crisp panels makes for a highly effective introduction to the workings of the human brain." School Library Journal.

612.1 Specific functions, systems, organs

Gold, John Coopersmith

Learning about the circulatory and lymphatic systems. John C. Gold. Enslow Publishers, c2013. 48 p.

Grades: 5 6 7 8   **612.1**
1. Cardiovascular system 2. Circulatory system 3. Lymphatic system 4. Lymphatics
ISBN 9780766041561

LC 2012011099
Learn amazing facts about the Circulatory and Lymphatic Systems and discover how they work together to keep us alive. Provided by publisher.

Markle, Sandra
Faulty heart: true survival stories. Sandra Markle. Lerner Pub., c2011. 48 p.: Powerful medicine
Grades: 5 6 7 8   **612.1**
1. Heart -- Diseases 2. Cardiovascular system -- Diseases 3. Grossology
ISBN 9780822586999

LC 2009033980
"This book is extremely well done, with a number of great examples of survival stories. The examples exemplify different and important heart diseases, symptoms, and treatments. . . . That the author is a former science teacher enables her to write clearly for the intended audience. The illustrations and photographs are perfect, adding to a full understanding of the diseases described." Science Books & Films.
Includes bibliographical references (p. 46-47) and index.

Newquist, H. P. (Harvey P.)
The **book** of blood: from legends and leeches to vampires and veins. HP Newquist. Houghton Mifflin Books for Children, 2012. 208 p.
Grades: 4 5 6   **612.1**
1. Blood 2. Cardiovascular system 3. Human body 4. Bloodletting 5. Vampires 6. Grossology
ISBN 9780547315843

LC 2011025134
From ancient history to modern science, to dark and often gruesome legends of vampires and plague, this tour of the world of blood informs readers about the most important fluid in the body.

Rose, Simon, 1961-
★ **Circulatory** system. by Simon Rose. AV2 by Weigl, [2020] 32 p.
Grades: 4 5 6   **612.1**
1. Heart -- Physiology 2. Cardiovascular system 3. Science 4. Blood -- Circulation 5. Human physiology
ISBN 9781489699350

LC 2018053419
Learn about the circulatory system and how it works to support life.
"Very well done; best suited to mature, serious students rather than striving readers. Excellent for reports." School Library Journal

612.2 Respiratory system

Rose, Simon, 1961-
Respiratory system. by Simon Rose. AV2 by Weigl, 2020 32 p.
Grades: 4 5 6   **612.2**
1. Respiratory organs 2. Respiration 3. Human body 4. Human physiology
ISBN 9781489699220

LC 2018053433
Learn about the respiratory system and how it works to support life.

"Very well done; best suited to mature, serious students rather than striving readers. Excellent for reports." School Library Journal

Siy, Alexandra
Sneeze! . Alexandra Siy and Dennis Kunkel. Charlesbridge, c2007. 45 p.
Grades: 4 5 6 7   **612.2**
1. Sneezing 2. Human physiology
ISBN 1570916535

LC 2005027567
Pictures and text describe what causes sneezes and what goes on in the body during a sneeze.
"Kunkel's big, clear, beautiful color electron micrographs on every double-page spead show everything from dust mites, mildew, and pollen to the influenza A virus." Booklist.

612.3 Digestive system

Donovan, Sandra, 1967-
Hawk & drool: gross stuff in your mouth. by Sandy Donovan; illustrated by Michael Slack. Millbrook Press, c2010. 48 p.: Gross body science
Grades: 4 5 6   **612.3**
1. Saliva 2. Mouth -- Diseases 3. Bad breath 4. Dental plaque 5. Body fluids 6. Grossology
ISBN 9780822589662
"Solid information layered between sarcastic comments and kid-friendly terminology like fart, poop, barf, and puke will keep readers engaged. . . . Labeled, captioned (and graphic) photographs, cartoon-style illustrations, and micrographs add information." School Library Journal.

Rumble & spew: gross stuff in your stomach and intestines. by Sandy Donovan; illustrated by Michael Slack. Lerner Publications Company, c2010. 48 p.: Gross body science
Grades: 4 5 6   **612.3**
1. Digestive system 2. Intestines 3. Stomach 4. Human body 5. Digestive organs 6. Grossology
ISBN 9780822588993
"Solid information layered between sarcastic comments and kid-friendly terminology like fart, poop, barf, and puke will keep readers engaged. . . . Labeled, captioned (and graphic) photographs, cartoon-style illustrations, and micrographs add information." School Library Journal.

Gold, Susan Dudley
Learning about the digestive and excretory systems. Susan Dudley Gold. Enslow Publishers, c2013. 48 p.
Grades: 5 6 7 8   **612.3**
1. Digestive organs 2. Digestive system 3. Excretory system 4. Urinary organs
ISBN 9780766041578

LC 2012011100
Learn how these remarkable systems work together to bring us life-giving nutrients and rid our bodies of waste. Provided by publisher.

Montgomery, Heather L.
Who gives a poop?: Surprising Science from One End to the Other. by Heather L. Montgomery; illustrated by Iris Gottlieb. Bloomsbury Childrens Books 2020 176 p.
Grades: 5 6 7 8 9   **612.3**
1. Feces 2. Animals 3. Excretion 4. Defecation 5. Animal

behavior 6. Grossology 7. Illustrated books
ISBN 9781547603473

LC 2020020258

The author explores various scientific and medical applications of poop.

"Each entry can stand alone, making this both browsable and adaptable to classroom readalouds, but as Montgomery covers such seemingly disparate topics as the mysteries of the poorly understood cecum, fecal microbiota transplants, and the role of whale droppings in replacing ocean nutrients, readers gradually expand their scatological knowledge base." Bulletin of the Center for Children's Books

Rose, Simon, 1961-
★ **Digestive** system. by Simon Rose. AV2 by Weigl, [2020] 32 p.
Grades: 4 5 6   **612.3**
1. Digestion 2. Gastrointestinal system -- Physiology 3. Digestive system 4. Tongue 5. Stomach
ISBN 9781489699183

LC 2018053397

Learn about the digestive system and how it works to support life.

"Very well done; best suited to mature, serious students rather than striving readers. Excellent for reports." School Library Journal

Simon, Seymour
★ **Guts**: our digestive system. Seymour Simon. HarperCollins, 2019, c2005. 1 v. (unpaged)
Grades: 4 5 6 7   **612.3**
1. Digestion 2. Digestive system 3. Stomach 4. Human anatomy 5. Grossology
ISBN 9780062470423

LC 2018939988

An updated edition of an introduction to the human digestive system explains the role of major organs in processing food through the body while transforming it into energy, nutrients and waste.

"Simon's specialty of drawing in readers through large, detailed, breathtaking photos and then entertaining them with facts is again in evidence. . . . The text is enhanced with detailed colored X rays, computer-generated pictures, and microscopic photos." School Library Journal.

Viola, Jason
Digestive system: a tour through your guts. Jason Viola, Andy Ristaino. First Second 2021 128 p.: Science comics
Grades: 5 6 7 8   **612.3**
1. Digestive system 2. Gastrointestinal system 3. Stomach 4. Intestines 5. Human anatomy 6. Comics and Graphic novels
ISBN 9781250204059

A graphic-novel introduction to the human gastrointestinal tract discusses the science that underlies digestion, counseling students on subjects ranging from saliva and nutrient processing to illness and friendly bacteria.

"Magic School Bus graduates ready for a busy, heavy informational load will find this just the ticket." Kirkus

612.4 Hematopoietic, lymphatic, glandular, urinary systems

Kim, Melissa
Learning about the endocrine and reproductive systems. Melissa L. Kim. Enslow Publishers, 2013. 48 p.

Grades: 5 6 7 8   **612.4**
1. Endocrine glands 2. Generative organs
ISBN 9780766041585

LC 2012011101

Learn how these two wonderful systems work together to ensure the survival of the human race and discover some amazing facts about them both. Provided by publisher.

Klosterman, Lorrie
Excretory system. Lorrie Klosterman. Marshall Cavendish Benchmark, c2010. 77 p.
Grades: 6 7 8 9   **612.4**
1. Excretion 2. Excretory organs 3. Feces 4. Urine
ISBN 9780761440376

LC 2008037261

Discusses the parts that make up the human excretory system, what can go wrong, how to treat those illnesses and diseases, and how to stay healthy. Provided by publisher.

612.6 Human physiology—Reproduction, development, maturation

Dunham, Kelli S.
The **boy's** body book. Kelli Dunham; illustrated by Steve Bjorkman. Cider Mill Press, 2017, c2007. 111 p.
Grades: 4 5 6 7   **612.6**
1. Puberty 2. Preteen boys 3. Sex education for children 4. Sex and health 5. Health
ISBN 9781604337136

LC bl2007015811

Discusses the physical and emotional transitions that boys undergo during puberty, including growth spurts, voice changes, sexual development, peer pressure, dating, and new relationships within the family.

Gravelle, Karen
The **period** book: everything you don't want to ask (but need to know). by Karen Gravelle & Jennifer Gravelle; illustrations by Debbie Palen. Bloomsbury, 2017, c1996. 117 p.
Grades: 4 5 6 7   **612.6**
1. Menstruation 2. Reproductive system 3. Puberty 4. Girls -- Health 5. Growing up
ISBN 9781619636620

LC 95031101

Explains what happens at the onset of menstruation, discussing what to wear, going to the gynecologist, and how to handle various problems.

Holmes, Melisa
Girlology's there's something new about you: a girl's guide to growing up. Melisa Holmes & Trish Hutchison; illustrated by Lisa Perrett. Health Communications, c2010. vi, 122 p.
Grades: 6 7 8 9   **612.6**
1. Puberty 2. Menarche 3. Girls 4. Growing up 5. Health
ISBN 9780757315268

LC 2010021169

Written by physicians who are mothers of preteen and teen girls, this guide explains the changes girls will be facing as they grow up.

"The graphics are informative without being offensive, pictures of the friends are cute and appealing, giving a fresh lightheartedness to the book. This is a must-have book for all homes and libraries." Voice of Youth Advocates.

Loveless, Gina

Puberty is gross, but also really awesome. by Gina Loveless; illustrated by Lauri Johnston. Rodale Kids, 2021. 182 p.

Grades: 4 5 6 7 8   **612.6**
   1. Puberty 2. Children -- Growth 3. Breast 4. Menstruation 5. Orgasm, Male
ISBN 9781984895059

Provides readers with a humorous look at what happens to a teenager's body and mind when they reach puberty.

"A must-have puberty survival guidebook for tweens and teens, this is a perfect choice for collections in need of health titles that use gender-inclusive language." School Library Journal

Includes bibliographical references (pages 163-177) and index.

Rand, Casey

Human reproduction. Casey Rand. Raintree, c2009. 48 p.: Sci-hi

Grades: 5 6 7 8   **612.6**
   1. Human reproduction 2. Conception 3. Pregnancy 4. Puberty 5. Childbirth
ISBN 9781410933270

LC 2009003464

"In this introduction to human reproduction clear language, embedded definitions, and interesting examples illustrate abstract concepts through both text and well-chosen photographs. . . . [It] includes suggested activities to test ideas as well as a thorough glossary and a Webliography." School Library Journal.

Includes bibliographical references and index.

Stynes, Yumi, 1975-

Welcome to your period. by Yumi Stynes & Dr. Melissa Kang. Candlewick Press, 2021, 176 p.

Grades: 5 6 7 8 9   **612.6**
   1. Teenage girls -- Health and hygiene 2. Menstruation
ISBN 9781536214765

A frank, funny, age-appropriate guide for pre-teens about getting your period, from Dr Melissa Kang (a former Dolly Doctor) and Yumi Stynes (all-round excellent woman). Getting your period for the first time can be mortifying, weird and messy—and asking questions about it can feel even worse. But it doesn't have to be like that! This little book is packed with honest advice on all the things you need to know: from what cramps feel like to whether you can feel it coming out, to what you should do if your pad leaks onto your clothes. Welcome To Your Period includes case studies, first-person accounts and questions from real teens (and answers from real experts—us!) so you can manage your period like a boss.

"The straight-forward, conversational tone makes for easy reading from beginning to end, but the organization and format allow readers to easily bounce around from section to section based on what they need and want to know. . . . Latham's illustrations are colorful and fun and reflect girls from different cultural backgrounds, body shapes and sizes, skin colors, and ages." VOYA

612.7 Musculoskeletal system, integument

Brynie, Faith Hickman, 1946-

101 questions about muscles to stretch your mind and flex your brain. Faith Hickman Brynie. Twenty-First Century Books, c2008. 176 p.: 101 Questions

Grades: 8 9 10 11 12   **612.7**
   1. Muscles 2. Musculoskeletal system 3. Muscles -- Questions and answers
ISBN 0822563800

LC 2006037041

Answers various questions about muscles, including "How much of human body weight is muscle?", "How does weightlifting build muscle?", and "Why do men have bigger muscles than women?"

"This answers such questions as What do tendons do? What causes muscle cramps? . . . [This book] makes human physiology accessible, with questions everyone has always wondered about and up-to-date, detailed answers that discuss the complex science in chatty but never condescending style. Like the text, the clear diagrams and photographs deal with everything from basic information . . . to the more advanced." Booklist.

Includes bibliographical references (p. 155-171) and index.

Colligan, L. H.

Muscles. L.H. Colligan. Marshall Cavendish Benchmark, c2010. 78 p.

Grades: 6 7 8 9   **612.7**
   1. Muscles
ISBN 9780761440383

LC 2008037257

Discusses human musculature, what can go wrong, how to treat those diseases and injuries, and how to stay healthy. Provided by publisher.

Gardner, Robert, 1929-

Ace your exercise and nutrition science project: great science fair ideas. Robert Gardner, Barbara Gardner Conklin, and Salvatore Tocci. Enslow Publishers, Inc., c2010. 128 p. : Ace your biology science project

Grades: 5 6 7 8   **612.7**
   1. Exercise -- Physiological aspects -- Experiments 2. Nutrition -- Experiments 3. Biology -- Experiments 4. Science -- Experiments 5. Science projects
ISBN 9780766032187

LC 2008030798

Presents several science projects and science project ideas about exercise and nutrition. Provided by publisher.

Gold, Susan Dudley

Learning about the musculoskeletal system and the skin. Susan Dudley Gold. Enslow Publishers, Inc., c2013. 48 p.

Grades: 5 6 7 8   **612.7**
   1. Bones 2. Musculoskeletal system 3. Skin
ISBN 9780766041592

LC 2012011102

Find out how this marvelous system works and learn some interesting facts about muscles, bones and skin. Provided by publisher.

Klosterman, Lorrie

Skin. by Lorrie Klosterman. Marshall Cavendish Benchmark, c2009. 79 p.: Amazing human body

Grades: 6 7 8 9   **612.7**
   1. Skin 2. Body covering (Anatomy) 3. Human body 4. Sense organs 5. Skin -- Diseases
ISBN 9780761430575

LC 2008017580

Discusses the parts that make up human skin, what can go wrong, how to treat those illnesses and diseases, and how to stay healthy. Provided by publisher.

"A good choice for students beginning to research the topic." Library Media Connection.

Includes bibliographical references and index.

Rose, Simon, 1961-

★ **Muscular** system. by Simon Rose. AV2 by Weigl, 2020 32 p.

Grades: 4 5 6   **612.7**
    1. Musculoskeletal system 2. Science 3. Human physiology
    ISBN 9781489699268

                                            LC 2018053472

Learn about the muscular system and how it works to support life.

"Very well done; best suited to mature, serious students rather than striving readers. Excellent for reports." School Library Journal

612.75 Bones, joints, connective tissues

Rose, Simon, 1961-

★ **Skeletal** system. by Simon Rose. AV2 by Weigl, 2020 32 p.

Grades: 4 5 6   **612.75**
    1. Skeleton 2. Bones 3. Human anatomy 4. Human physiology
    ISBN 9781489699312

                                            LC 2018053422

Learn about the skeletal system and how it works to support life.

"Very well done; best suited to mature, serious students rather than striving readers. Excellent for reports." School Library Journal

612.8 Nervous system

Chudler, Eric H.

Brain lab for kids: 52 mind-blowing experiments, models, and activities to explore neuroscience. Eric H. Chudler, Ph.D. Quarry Books, 2018. 142 p.

Grades: 3 4 5 6 7 8   **612.8**
    1. Neurosciences -- Experiments 2. Brain -- Experiments 3. Senses and sensation -- Experiments 4. Science projects
    ISBN 9781631593963

                                            LC 2017054801

Brain Lab for Kids is an interactive and hands-on book that takes readers on an exciting journey into the functions of the brain through enlightening experiments and creative activities.. Provided by publisher.

Gold, Martha V.

Learning about the nervous system. Martha V. Gold. Enslow Publishers, c2013. 48 p.

Grades: 5 6 7 8   **612.8**
    1. Nervous system
    ISBN 9780766041608

                                            LC 2012011103

Discover more about how this system works and read amazing facts about the brain and nervous system. Provided by publisher.

Larsen, C. S. (Christopher Sterling), 1966-

Crust and spray: gross stuff in your eyes, ears, nose, and throat. by C.S. Larsen; illustrated by Michael Slack. Millbrook Press, 2009. 48 p.: Gross body science

Grades: 4 5 6   **612.8**
    1. Mucus 2. Body fluids 3. Human body 4. Exudates and transudates 5. Earwax 6. Grossology
    ISBN 9780822589648

                                            LC 2008033777

"Solid information layered between sarcastic comments and kid-friendly terminology like fart, poop, barf, and puke will keep readers engaged. . . . Labeled, captioned (and graphic) photographs, cartoon-style illustrations, and micrographs add information." School Library Journal.

Includes bibliographical references and index.

Mooney, Carla, 1970-

The **brain**: journey through the universe inside your head. Carla Mooney; illustrated by Tom Casteel. Nomad Press, 2015. 128 p.: Inquire and investigate

Grades: 5 6 7 8   **612.8**
    1. Brain 2. Nervous system 3. Human anatomy 4. Human body
    ISBN 9781619302747

An introduction to the world of the human brain and its effect on behavior covers such topics as brain anatomy, the science of memory, and the latest understanding about the role of lifestyle choices on brain health.

"Sidebars offer descriptions of jobs that involve the brain, links to online resources, and questions for discussion; ideas for experiments and activities appear throughout. Its an extensive introduction to the brains capability and function, with just enough humor and interactivity to keep readers engaged." Publishers Weekly.

Rau, Dana Meachen, 1971-

Freaking out!: the science of the teenage brain. by Dana Meachen Rau. Compass Point Books, c2012. 64 p.: Everyday science (Compass Point Books)

Grades: 7 8 9 10   **612.8**
    1. Brain -- Physiology 2. Nervous system 3. Human body
    ISBN 9780756544867

                                            LC 2010054302

Describes the human brain and how it functions, and discusses the nervous system, thought, memory, emotions, the sleep cycle, and brain injuries.

"This offers a solid overview of the brain. The book begins with an explanation of what the brain does, how it looks, and its various components. It then goes on to discuss more specialized topics, such as mood changes, developmental skills, and memory. The attractive format, with easy-to-read print, features bright photographs . . . and plenty of sidebars on a variety of topics." Booklist.

Includes bibliographical references (p. 63) and index.

Rose, Simon, 1961-

Nervous system. by Simon Rose. AV2 by Weigl, 2020 32 p.

Grades: 4 5 6   **612.8**
    1. Nervous system 2. Brain 3. Human physiology 4. Human body
    ISBN 9781489699145

                                            LC 2018053406

Learn about the nervous system and how it works to support life.

"Very well done; best suited to mature, serious students rather than striving readers. Excellent for reports." School Library Journal

Scott, Elaine, 1940-

All about sleep from a to zzzzzz. by Elaine Scott; illustrations by John O'Brien. Viking, c2008. 48 p.

Grades: 5 6 7 8 9 10   **612.8**
    1. Sleep 2. Dreams 3. Sleep-walking
    ISBN 9780670061884

                                            LC 2008006074

Offers a look at what happens when we sleep, the process of dreaming, the strange events that can happen during sleepwalking, and the reasons for the biological need to do this important activity about one third of one's life.

"This excellent overview is packed with interesting tidbits. . . . Scott is careful to point out which information is factual and which is theory, an important distinction. . . . The fanciful cartoon illustrations add to the book's appeal. . . . It is interesting, highly engaging, and fun to read." School Library Journal.

Simon, Seymour

Eyes and ears. Seymour Simon. Harper Collins Publishers, c2003. 1 v. (unpaged)

Grades: 4 5 6 7   **612.8**
  1. Eye 2. Ear 3. Vision 4. Hearing 5. Senses and sensation
  ISBN 9780688153038

                                                        LC 2002019060
Describes the anatomy of the eye and ear, how those organs function and some ways in which they may malfunction, and how the brain is also involved in our seeing and hearing.

"Simon is at his very best here. . . . The large, exquisitely reproduced photographs from a number of sources look like fiery planets, galaxies, and monster creatures. . . . The anatomy and physiology are detailed and accurate, with clear diagrams." Booklist.

613 Personal health and safety

Couwenhoven, Terri

The **boys'** guide to growing up: choices & changes during puberty. Terri Couwenhoven. Woodbine House, 2012. viii, 64 p.

Grades: 6 7 8   **613**
  1. Teenage boys -- Physiology 2. Sex instruction for children with mental disabilities 3. Puberty
  ISBN 9781606130896

                                                        LC 2012025776
The Boys' Guide to Growing Up gives boys with intellectual disabilities the facts they need to navigate puberty. Written at a third-grade reading level for boys aged 9-16 with Down syndrome, autism, cerebral palsy, mental retardation, fragile X, or other special needs, this book is the companion to The Girls' Guide to Growing Up (2011), also by Terri Cowenhoven.

"This book is geared to boys with 'developmental disabilities.' It explains basic information that includes body changes in growth, hair, skin, voice, and feelings. It is not a sex guide though it does not shy away from emerging sexuality. All in all, this volume will come in handy in addressing a subject area that is frequently avoided." School Library Journal

Mar, Jonathan

The **body** book for boys. by Jonathan Mar and Grace Norwich; illustrated by Ming Sun Ku. Scholastic, c2010. 128 p.

Grades: 4 5 6   **613**
  1. Teenage boys -- Health 2. Puberty 3. Family life education 4. Sex education for teenagers 5. Teenage boys -- Interpersonal relations
  ISBN 9780545237512

                                                        LC bl2010023969
Shares advice on the changing male body and the challenges of growing up, from shaving and vocal changes to acne and interpersonal relationships.

"In this reassuring title aimed at boys just entering adolescence, the authors present frank information on such topics as hygiene, the changes brought on by puberty, exercise, and dealing with girls. The tone is kept light, and the many bright illustrations also have a fun, jokey quality." Booklist.

McCoy, Kathy, 1945-

The **teenage** body book. Kathy McCoy, Ph.D., & Charles Wibbelsman, M.D.; illustrations by Bob Stover and Kelly Grady Callarman. Hatherleigh Press, 2016. xviii, 300 p.

Grades: 9 10 11 12   **613**
  1. Teenagers -- Health and hygiene 2. Adolescence 3. Health 4. Sex instruction for youth
  ISBN 9781578266432

                                                        LC bl2016037761
A handbook for teenagers discussing nutrition, health, fitness, emotions, and sexuality, including such topics as body image, drugs, STDs, fad diets, and the hazards and benefits of the Internet.

Metzger, Julie Giesy

★ **Will** puberty last my whole life?: real answers to real questions from preteens about body changes, sex, and other growing-up stuff. Julie Metzger and Robert Lehman; illustrated by Lia Cerizo. Little Bigfoot, an imprint of Sasquatch Books, 2018. 90, 90 p.

Grades: 4 5 6 7 8   **613**
  1. Puberty 2. Teenage girls -- Physiology 3. Teenage boys -- Physiology 4. Interpersonal relations 5. Reversible books 6. Toy and movable books
  ISBN 9781632171795

                                                        LC 2011038401
A flip book for boys and girls between the ages of 9 and 12. Questions asked by girls appear on one half of the book; flip it over and questions boys ask are on the other half. Contains honest, informative, and reassuring answers to questions pre-adolescents have about puberty, friends, feelings, sex, pimples, babies, body hair, menstruation, bras, and much more. Provided by publisher.

Middleman, Amy B.

American Medical Association boys' guide to becoming a teen. Amy B. Midleman, medical editor; Kate Gruenwald Pfeifer, writer. Jossey-Bass, c2006. 128 p.

Grades: 4 5 6 7   **613**
  1. Puberty 2. Teenage boys -- Growth
  ISBN 0787983438

                                                        LC 2005034809
Discusses the physical changes that occur as a teenage boy goes through puberty, covering such topics as height, skin, facial hair, the reproductive system, hormones, sex, and relationships.

"This guide addresses puberty's changes clearly. . . . The text's approach is straightforward, accessible, and nonjudgmental, whether the topic is same-sex attraction or divorcing parents. The volume closes with an extensive resource section, including hotlines." Booklist.

Includes bibliographical references and index.

Natterson, Cara Familian, 1970-

The **care** & keeping of you 2: the body book for older girls. Dr. Cara Natterson; illustrated by Josee Masse. American Girl, 2013. 96 p.

Grades: 5 6 7 8   **613**
  1. Teenage girls -- Health 2. Puberty 3. Growing up 4. Girls 5.

Menstruation
ISBN 9781609580421

LC 2012045813

This thoughtful advice book will guide you through the next steps of growing up. With illustrations and expert contributors, this book covers new questions about periods, your growing body, peer pressure, personal care, and more! Written by Dr. Cara Natterson for girls 10 and up, The Care & Keeping of You 2 follows up the original bestseller with even more in-depth details about the physical and emotional changes you're going through. Provided by publisher.

"The friendly illustrations support the overall tone and style. . . . Its neutral, matter-of-fact approach will help show readers . . . that all the changes they may be feeling are perfectly normal." School Library Journal.

Orr, Tamra

Playing safe, eating right: making healthy choices. by Tamra Orr. ABDO Pub., 2009. 112 p.

Grades: 6 7 8 9   **613**
1. Teenage girls -- Health 2. Nutrition 3. Health 4. Teenage girls -- Nutrition
ISBN 9781604531039

LC 2008017015

Brings widespread issues to life through character narratives and discussion questions to help readers develop positive ways to deal with common scenarios while also building self-esteem.

"The topics are well selected, the design is attractive, and the stories features girls from a variety of cultures." Booklist.

Pfeifer, Kate Gruenwald

Girl's guide to becoming a teen. Amy B. Middleman, medical editor; Kate Gruenwald Pfeifer, writer; [illustrations by Brie Spangler]. Jossey-Bass, c2006. 128 p.

Grades: 4 5 6 7   **613**
1. Puberty 2. Teenage girls -- Physiology
ISBN 0787983446

LC 2005034810

Discusses the physical changes that occur as a teenage girl goes through puberty, covering such topics as weight, skin, height, eating habits, the reproductive system, hormones, the menstrual cycle, sex, and body image.

"This covers the physical and emotional changes that puberty brings, along with solid tips about grooming, diet, exercise, and other health issues, such as eating disorders. . . . The clear text communicates concepts clearly . . . and girls will find plenty of useful information." Booklist.

613.2 Dietetics

Etingoff, Kim

Building a healthy diet with the 5 food groups. Kim Etingoff. Mason Crest, an imprint of National Highlights, 2014. 48 p.: On my plate

Grades: 5 6 7   **613.2**
1. Diet 2. Food habits 3. Health 4. Nutrition 5. Exercise
ISBN 9781422230954

LC 2014010544

"The sidebars and illustrations supplement the text well and the research project suggestions are especially useful for students and teachers." Voice of Youth Advocates.

Furgang, Adam

Carbonated beverages: the incredibly disgusting story. Adam Furgang. Rosen Central, 2011. 48 p.: Incredibly disgusting food

Grades: 4 5 6 7   **613.2**
1. Soft drinks 2. Beverages 3. Nonalcoholic drinks 4. Health 5. Grossology
ISBN 9781448812660

LC 2010023227

"This presents straightforward information about why [carbonated beverages] are unhealthy without resorting to extreme gross-out factors. The [book contains] a breakdown of the foods' components . . . insight into how they are processed, and both short- and long-term effects of consumption. . . . Readers may or may not be disgusted, but they will definitely learn a thing or two about smart eating habits." School Library Journal.

Includes bibliographical references and index.

Salty and sugary snacks: the incredibly disgusting story. Adam Furgang. Rosen Central, 2011. 48 p.: Incredibly disgusting food

Grades: 4 5 6 7   **613.2**
1. Snack foods -- Nutritional aspects 2. Salt -- Health aspects 3. Sugar -- Health aspects 4. Food habits
ISBN 9781448812677

LC 2010025751

This book describes how salty and sugary snacks put dangerous amounts of sugar and salt into our bodies and how these unnecessary calories can have terrible effects on the body.

"Readers may or may not be disgusted, but they will definitely learn a thing or two about smart eating habits." School Library Journal.

Includes bibliographical references (p. 44-46) and index.

Juettner, Bonnie

Diet and disease. by Bonnie Juettner. Lucent Books, c2011. 104 p.: Nutrition & health

Grades: 6 7 8 9   **613.2**
1. Nutritionally induced diseases 2. Nutrition disorders 3. Health 4. Food habits 5. Diseases
ISBN 9781420502695

LC 2010035236

Discusses the connection between poor diet and disease and what can be done to prevent illnesses using diet, exercise, and nutrition.

"This discusses the food choices that lead to the big four diseases of cancer, heart disease, stroke, and type 2 diabetes and shows how good nutrition can help prevent deadly disease. . . . [This] volume is clearly written, addressing real-life concerns with solid information and perspective, and includes color photographs, notes, and [a list] of further resources." Booklist.

Includes bibliographical references and index.

Mihaly, Christy

Diet for a changing climate: food for thought. Christy Mihaly and Sue Heavenrich. Twenty-First Century Books, 2018. 128 p.

Grades: 7 8 9 10 11 12   **613.2**
1. Food habits 2. Diet 3. Nutrition 4. Climate change 5. Pests
ISBN 9781512481211

LC 2017043702

The United Nations supports a compelling solution to world hunger: eat insects! Explore the vast world of unexpected foods that may help solve the global hunger crisis. Weeds, wild plants, invasive and feral species, and bugs are all food for thought.

Parrish, Margaret

Are you what you eat? US editor, Margaret Parrish. DK Publishing, 2015. 94 p.

Grades: 3 4 5 6   **613.2**

   1. Nutrition

ISBN 9781465429445

LC bl2015014182

Introduces nutrition, discussing how foods can affect energy, how the digestive system works, and why the human body needs nutrition.

Rau, Dana Meachen, 1971-

Going organic: a healthy guide to making the switch. by Dana Meachen Rau. Compass Point Books, c2012. 64 p.

Grades: 6 7 8 9   **613.2**

   1. Natural foods 2. Health 3. Nutrition

ISBN 9780756545239

LC 2011040704

Describes the benefits, challenges, and steps to switching to an organic diet. Provided by publisher.

"[Rau] outlines the perils of factory farms and industrial food lots, both on an environmental and personal scale; distinguishes the often interrelated terms organic, sustainable, and local; offers a rundown of potentially misleading marketing terms; and even tosses in a few recipes, charts, and other helpful sidebars." Booklist.

Includes bibliographical references and index.

Going vegetarian: a healthy guide to making the switch. by Dana Meachen Rau. Compass Point Books, c2012. 64 p.

Grades: 5 6 7 8 9   **613.2**

   1. Vegetarians 2. Vegetarianism 3. Diet 4. Health 5. Nutrition

ISBN 9780756545222

LC 2011040836

Describes the benefits, challenges, and steps to switching to a vegetarian diet. Provided by publisher.

"Whether looking to go organic, ovo-lacto vegetarian, or vegan, kids will find the information necessary to make the switch in these titles. . . . Serve these up to budding health foodies." School Library Journal.

Includes bibliographical references and index.

Waters, Rosa, 1957-

My daily diet: dairy. Rosa Waters. Mason Crest, an imprint of National Highlights, 2015. 48 p.: On my plate

Grades: 5 6 7   **613.2**

   1. Dairy products 2. Diet 3. Nutrition 4. Health

ISBN 9781422230961

LC 2014010564

"Created with help from a consultant who is a pediatrician and professor at Harvard Medical School, this series provides a thorough overview of different food groups: where they come from and what role they play in our overall health. Suggested research projects are strong and engaging." School Library Journal.

Includes bibliographical references and index.

613.2083 Personal health and safety—Dietetics—Young people

Klimecki, Zachary

Diet information for teens: health tips about nutrition fundamentals and eating plans including facts about vitamins, minerals, food additives, and weight-related concerns. edited by Zachary Klimecki and Karen Bellenir. Omnigraphics, Inc., c2012. xiii, 427 p.

Grades: 10 11 12   **613.2083**

   1. Teenagers -- Nutrition 2. Teenagers -- Health and hygiene 3. Diet 4. Health

ISBN 9780780811560

LC 2011031595

Provides basic consumer health information for teens about nutrition, healthy eating plans, and weight control, along with facts about food allergies, obesity, and related medical conditions. Includes index and resource information. Provided by publisher.

613.4 Personal cleanliness

Ashenburg, Katherine

All the dirt: a history of getting clean. Katherine Ashenburg; illustrated by Francis Blake. Annick Press, 2016. 108 p.

Grades: 5 6 7 8   **613.4**

   1. Hygiene 2. Bathing customs 3. Cleanliness 4. Health 5. Baths -- History 6. Grossology

ISBN 9781554517909

A light-hearted look at the history of personal hygiene.

"With its lively writing and presentation, this informative book makes the history of cleanliness unexpectedly fun." Booklist.

613.6 Personal safety and special topics of health

Berkenkamp, Lauri

Discover the Amazon: the world's largest rainforest. Lauri Berkenkamp; illustrated by Blair Shedd. Nomad Press, 2008. 90 p.: Discover your world

Grades: 4 5 6 7   **613.6**

   1. Rain forest ecology 2. Ecology 3. Rain forests 4. Forest ecology 5. Amazon River -- Description and travel

ISBN 9781934670279

Offering practical survival techniques based on real stories, children will learn lessons on the vital tools one would need if lost in the Amazon—tools that can be adapted to almost any outdoor situation, such as making a fire, deciphering animals tracks, and using the natural world to create necessary supplies.

"Berkenkamp's introduction to the [Amazon] river basin incorporates maps, drawings, and photos in various shades of green and brown on recycled paper. . . . The conversational style provides a you are there feeling, conveying information and anecdotes while stressing outdoor survival skills. . . . Even readers who never travel to Amazonia will appreciate the region's complexity and significance after perusing this book." School Library Journal.

Champion, Neil

Finding food and water. by Neil Champion. Amicus, c2011. 32 p.: Survive alive

Grades: 4 5 6 7 **613.6**

1. Survival skills 2. Wilderness survival 3. Survival 4. Water 5. Food
ISBN 9781607530374

LC 2009030889

Gives essential survival tips for finding food and water in the wild, including how to know what is safe to eat or drink from land, plant, and animal sources. Provided by publisher.

"This colorful [book contains] numerous photos and illustrations that effectively break the [text] into small, readable chunks. There's lots of practical, everyday information here. . . . Brief yet gripping real-life survival stories are interspersed throughout the [book]." School Library Journal.

Finding your way. Neil Champion. Amicus, c2011. 32 p.: Survive alive

Grades: 4 5 6 7 **613.6**

1. Wilderness survival 2. Survival skills 3. Orienteering 4. Wilderness living 5. Survival
ISBN 9781607530381

LC 2009030888

Gives essential survival tips for navigation in the wild, including using natural means such as the sun and stars and using technology such as compasses and GPS receivers. Provided by publisher.

"With eye-catching photographs, clear explanations, a survival skills quiz, a glossary, Web sites, and True Survival stories . . . this engaging text encourages readers to figure out where they are and where they want to go." Booklist.

In an emergency. Neil Champion. Amicus, c2011. 32 p.: Survive alive

Grades: 4 5 6 7 **613.6**

1. Survival skills 2. Wilderness survival 3. Emergencies 4. Survival
ISBN 9781607530404

LC 2010002517

Gives essential survival tips on what to do in emergency situations. Includes scenarios about fire, bad weather, accidents, injuries, extreme conditions, and more. Provided by publisher.

"This colorful [book contains] numerous photos and illustrations that effectively break the [text] into small, readable chunks. There's lots of practical, everyday information here. . . . Brief yet gripping real-life survival stories are interspersed throughout the [book]." School Library Journal.

Making shelter. Neil Champion. Amicus, c2011. 32 p.: Survive alive

Grades: 4 5 6 7 **613.6**

1. Wilderness survival 2. Survival skills 3. Alternative housing 4. Survival 5. Huts
ISBN 9781607530411

LC 2010001378

Gives essential survival tips for building shelter in the wild, including using natural means in different regions such as the desert, forest, jungle, and cold areas. Also includes information on what to bring for aid when building shelters. Provided by publisher.

Long, Denise

Survivor kid: a practical guide to wilderness survival. Denise Long. Chicago Review Press, c2011. xii, 222 p.

Grades: 4 5 6 7 **613.6**

1. Wilderness survival 2. Wilderness areas 3. Survival
ISBN 9781569767085

LC 2011004952

Presents a guide to wilderness survival in both common and unusual situations, including how to build a shelter, find water and food, deal with dangerous animals, and navigate in the wild.

"Long offers lessons on how to stay healthy and out of trouble while awaiting rescue. Her matter-of-fact, no-nonsense tone will play well with young readers, and the clear writing style is appropriate to the content. The engaging guide covers everything from building shelters to avoiding pigs and javelinas. . . . The volume invites browsing as much as studying. . . . An excellent bibliography will lead young readers to a host of fascinating websites, and 150 clipart-style line drawings complement the text." Kirkus.

Includes bibliographical references (p. 212) and index.

613.7 Physical fitness

Aikman, Louise

Pilates step-by-step. Louise Aikman and Matthew Harvey. Rosen Central, 2011. 96 p.: Skills in motion

Grades: 5 6 7 8 **613.7**

1. Pilates 2. Exercise 3. Physical fitness
ISBN 9781448815494

LC 2010007510

Presents a general guide to the Pilates exercise system using a sequence of stop-action images and text instructions to illustrate some of the most common movements.

Bellenir, Elizabeth

Fitness information for teens: health tips about exercise and active lifestyles including facts about healthy muscles and bones, starting and maintaining fitness plans, aerobic fitness, stretching and strength training, sports safety, and suggestions for team athletes and individuals. edited by Elizabeth Bellenir. Omnigraphics, c2013. xiii, 387 p.: Teen health series

Grades: 7 8 9 10 11 12 **613.7**

1. Physical fitness for teenagers 2. Teenagers -- Health 3. Exercise for teenagers 4. Health
ISBN 9780780812673

LC 2012024737

Provides basic consumer health information for teens about maintaining health through physical activity, including facts about preventing injury and overcoming obstacles to fitness. Includes index and resource information. Provided by publisher.

"In this thorough, easy-to-follow single volume, seven main sections cover information on the human body, personal fitness plans, exercise fundamentals, team activities, sports safety, obstacles to finding fitness, and resources... Highly recommended." Booklist.

Includes bibliographical references and index.

Birkemoe, Karen, 1974-

Strike a pose. written by Karen Birkemoe; illustrated by Heather Collett. Kids Can Press, c2007. 96 p.: Planet Girl

Grades: 5 6 7 8 **613.7**

1. Yoga 2. Girls -- Health 3. Hatha yoga
ISBN 155337004X

LC bl2007007250

Explains what yoga is and shows how this form of exercise can help girls focus, de-stress, and avoid sports-related injuries.

"This compact book offers a well-rounded overview of Hatha yoga. Using an easy conversational tone, Birkemoe relates the general practice and specific poses to reader's lives. The simple line drawings and color illustrations partner effectively with text to explain each move." School Library Journal.

Dicker, Katie

Exercise. Katie Dicker. Amicus, 2011 46 p.: Healthy lifestyles

Grades: 7 8 9 10   **613.7**

1. Physical fitness 2. Exercise 3. Exercise for teenagers 4. Physical fitness for teenagers 5. Health
ISBN 9781607530862

    LC 2009047566

Discusses in-depth the benefits of exercise for teenagers, including how to make exercise fun and safe and develop it into a life-long habit. Provided by publisher.

"This book is well-written and satisfyingly informative. . . . [The] magazine-like format includes numerous sidebars, color photos, and charts." School Library Journal.

Includes bibliographical references (p. 45) and index.

Gates, Mariam

This moment is your life (and so is this one): a fun and easy guide to mindfulness, meditation, and yoga. Mariam Gates; illustrated by Libby VanderPloeg. Dial Books, [2018] 241 p.

Grades: 6 7 8 9 10 11   **613.7**

1. Mindfulness (Psychology) 2. Yoga for children 3. Mediation 4. Mental health 5. Stress management
ISBN 9780399186622

    LC 2017043500

Don't just do something, be here. A hands-on introduction to mindfulness, meditation, and yoga includes quick exercises, tool kits, and five-day challenges to help implement the techniques in real life.

Jennings, Madeleine

Tai chi step-by-step. Madeleine Jennings and James Drewe. Rosen Central, 2011. 95 p.: Skills in Motion

Grades: 5 6 7 8   **613.7**

1. Tai chi 2. Exercise 3. Martial arts 4. Physical fitness
ISBN 9781448815517

    LC 2010008411

Describes the origins and meaning of the ancient Chinese art of tai chi, and provides instructions for some of the most common movements.

Kuskowski, Alex

Cool relaxing: healthy & fun ways to chill out. Alex Kuskowski. ABDO Pub. Co., c2012. 32 p.: Cool health & fitness

Grades: 4 5 6   **613.7**

1. Relaxation 2. Health 3. Personal conduct
ISBN 9781617834288

    LC 2012010345

Presents tips for relaxation and includes projects for simple yoga, stretching, and meditation.

Mason, Paul, 1967-

Improving endurance. Paul Mason. Powerkids Press, 2011. 32 p.: Training for sports

Grades: 5 6 7 8   **613.7**

1. Endurance sports -- Training 2. Physical education and training

3. Sports
ISBN 9781448833009

    LC 2010024356

Discusses endurance in sports, provides exercises for improving it, and profiles athletes known for their endurance.

"This offers detailed tips on improving . . . endurance. All-around athletes will love this and so will kids who just want to work on getting fit." Booklist.

Includes bibliographical references (p. 31) and index.

Improving flexibility. Paul Mason. Power Kids Press, 2011. 32 p.: Training for sports

Grades: 5 6 7 8   **613.7**

1. Stretching exercises 2. Physical education and training 3. Joints -- Range of motion 4. Sports
ISBN 9781448832996

    LC 2010024359

Discusses the importance of flexibility in sports, provides exercises to improve it, and profiles athletes known for their flexibility.

"All-around athletes will love this and so will kids who just want to work on getting fit." Booklist.

Includes bibliographical references (p. 31) and index.

Improving speed. Paul Mason. Powerkids Press, 2011. 32 p.: Training for Sports

Grades: 5 6 7 8   **613.7**

1. Physical education and training 2. Speed 3. Muscle strength 4. Running 5. Sports
ISBN 9781448833023

    LC 2010024354

Discusses speed in various sports, provides exercises to improve it, and profiles athletes known for their speed.

"This offers detailed tips on improving speed. . . . All-around athletes will love this and so will kids who just want to work on getting fit." Booklist.

Includes bibliographical references (p. 31) and index.

Improving strength and power. Paul Mason. Powerkids Press, 2011. 32 p.: Training for sports

Grades: 5 6 7 8   **613.7**

1. Physical education and training 2. Physical fitness 3. Muscle strength 4. Sports
ISBN 9781448833016

    LC 2010024425

Discusses strength and power in various sports, provides exercises to improve it, and profiles athletes known for strength and power.

"All-around athletes will love this and so will kids who just want to work on getting fit." Booklist.

Includes bibliographical references (p. 31) and index.

Purperhart, Helen

Yoga exercises for teens: developing a calmer mind and a stronger body. Helen Purperhart; translated by Amina Marix Evans; illustrated by Barbara van Amelsfort. Hunter House Publishers, 2008. 160 p. : Smartfun activity books

Grades: 7 8 9 10   **613.7**

1. Hatha yoga for teenagers 2. Physical fitness for teenagers 3. Yoga 4. Teenagers -- Health 5. Hatha yoga
ISBN 9780897935036

    LC 2008024262

Describes over one hundred exercises and yoga positions to help strengthen muscles and release tension for teenagers, providing guidelines for exercises to be performed alone, with others, or with music.

Rissman, Rebecca

Yoga for your mind and body: a teenage practice for a healthy, balanced life. by Rebecca Rissman. Switch Press, 2015. 208 p.

Grades: 8 9 10 11   **613.7**
1. Yoga 2. Hatha yoga for teenagers 3. Hatha yoga 4. Body awareness 5. Relaxation 6. Books for reluctant readers
ISBN 9781630790134

LC 2014048583

Presents yoga techniques and poses to promote brain power, stress relief, strength, and fitness. Provided by publisher.

"Newbies and experienced yogis alike will benefit from this easy-to-follow guide." Booklist.

Includes bibliographical references and index.

613.8 Substance abuse (Drug abuse)

Drug information for teens: health tips about the physical and mental effects of substance abuse: including information about alcohol, tobacco, marijuana, E-Cigarettes, cocaine, prescription and over-the-counter drugs, club drugs, hallucinogens, heroin, stimulants, opiates, steroids, and more.. Keith (EDT) Jones. Omnigraphics, Inc, 2016 xii, 339 p.

Grades: 10 11 12   **613.8**
1. Teenagers -- Drug use 2. Teenagers -- Alcohol use 3. Teenagers -- Health and hygiene 4. Drugs -- Physiological effect 5. Drug abuse -- Prevention
ISBN 9780780813588

LC 2015038887

Provides basic consumer health information for teens about drug use, abuse, and addiction, including facts about illegal drugs and the abuse of legally available substances found in over-the-counter medications; describes drug-related health risks and treatment for addiction. Includes index and resource information. Provided by publisher.

Gottfried, Ted

Marijuana. by Ted Gottfried with Lisa Harkrader. Marshall Cavendish Benchmark, c2010. 32 p. : Benchmark rockets.

Grades: 4 5 6 7   **613.8**
1. Marijuana 2. Cannabis 3. Hallucinogenic drugs 4. Drugs 5. Marijuana abuse
ISBN 9780761443513

LC 2008052761

Discusses the history, effects, and dangers of Marijuana as well as addiction treatment options. Provided by publisher.

"Provides clear explanations about effects, followed by diagrams of the body to clarify the specific organs/body systems that suffer the most damage. . . . An excellent starting point." School Library Journal.

LeVert, Suzanne

Ecstasy. by Suzanne LeVert with Jeff Hendricks. Marshall Cavendish Benchmark, c2010. 32 p. : Benchmark rockets.

Grades: 4 5 6 7   **613.8**
1. Ecstasy (Drug) 2. Designer drugs 3. Drug abuse -- Treatment

4. Drugs
ISBN 9780761443490

LC 2008052753

Discusses the history, effects, and dangers of Ecstasy as well as addiction treatment options. Provided by publisher.

"Provides clear explanations about effects, followed by diagrams of the body to clarify the specific organs/body systems that suffer the most damage. . . . An excellent starting point." School Library Journal.

Menhard, Francha Roffe

Inhalants. by Francha Roffe Menhard with Laura Purdie Salas. Marshall Cavendish Benchmark, c2010. 32 p. : Benchmark rockets.

Grades: 4 5 6 7   **613.8**
1. Inhalants 2. Inhalant abuse 3. Drug abuse -- Treatment 4. Drugs
ISBN 9780761443506

LC 2008052739

Discusses the history, effects, and dangers of inhalants as well as addiction treatment options. Provided by publisher.

"Provides clear explanations about effects, followed by diagrams of the body to clarify the specific organs/body systems that suffer the most damage. . . . An excellent starting point." School Library Journal.

613.81 Alcohol

Bellenir, Karen

Alcohol information for teens: health tips about alcohol use, abuse, and dependence including facts about alcohol's effects on mental and physical health, the consequences of underage drinking, and understanding alcoholic family members. edited by Karen Bellenir. Omnigraphics, Inc., 2013 xiii, 371 p.

Grades: 10 11 12   **613.81**
1. Alcohol -- Physiological effect 2. Alcoholism -- Prevention 3. Youth -- Alcohol use
ISBN 9780780813137

LC 2013000216

Provides basic consumer health information for teens about the physical and mental health effects of alcohol use, with facts about alcohol abuse and underage drinking, treatment and recovery, and coping with alcoholism in the family. Includes index and resource information. Provided by publisher.

Gilles, Renae

Understanding alcohol. Renae Gilles. Cherry Lake Publishing, 2020 32 p.

Grades: 4 5 6   **613.81**
1. Drinking 2. Teenagers -- Alcohol use 3. Alcoholism -- Prevention
ISBN 9781534147959

LC 2019008059

In Understanding Alcohol, readers will explore the social aspects and health effects of drinking and alcohol use disorder, and ways to make healthy choices. Sidebars challenge and expand readers' thinking while relating topics to 21st Century skills and themes—from creativity and innovation to financial literacy.?

"Candidly explains, without preachiness, how these issues harm body and mind, social life, and future prospects. Displaying understanding and respect, titles concede that young people may experiment—but stress caution and moderation, helping readers understand they can choose wisely." School Library Journal

613.85 Tobacco

Chandler, Matt

Understanding tobacco. Matt Chandler. Cherry Lake Publishing, [2020] 32 p.: 21st Century Skills Library: Upfront Health

Grades: 4 5 6 7 8   **613.85**

1. Tobacco 2. Smoking 3. Teenagers -- Smoking
ISBN 9781534150874

                     LC 2019008033

In Understanding Tobacco, readers will explore the social aspects and health effects of tobacco use and addiction, including e-cigarettes, and ways to make healthy choices.—Excerpted from publisher description

"Highly recommended. A well-written, intelligent empowering series covering timely topics." School Library Journal

Miller, Heather

Smoking. Heather Miller. Cherry Lake Pub., c2009. 32 p.: Health at risk

Grades: 4 5 6 7   **613.85**

1. Smoking -- Health hazards 2. Tobacco 3. Health 4. Addiction
ISBN 9781602792869

                     LC 2008017501

Discusses tobacco use, its affects, what causes addiction, and how to quit.

"Great for reports or reluctant readers." Booklist.
Includes bibliographical references (p. 31) and index.

Tobacco information for teens: health tips about the hazards of using cigarettes, smokeless tobacco, and other nicotine products: including facts about nicotine addiction, nicotine delivery systems, secondhand smoke, health consequences of tobacco use, related cancers, smoking cessation, and tobacco use statistics.. Omnigraphics (COR). Omnigraphics, 2017. xi, 361 p.

Grades: 7 8 9   **613.85**

1. Tobacco use -- Health aspects 2. Smoking -- Health aspects 3. Nicotine -- Health aspects 4. Smoking cessation 5. Teenagers -- Tobacco use -- Prevention
ISBN 9780780813878

                     LC 2016054311

Provides basic consumer health information for teens about risk factors, consequences, and prevention of various types of abuse and violence. Includes index, resource information and recommendations for further reading. Provided by publisher.

613.9 Birth control, reproductive technology, sex hygiene, sexual techniques

Bailey, Jacqui

Sex, puberty and all that stuff: a guide to growing up. Jacqui Bailey. Barron's, 2016. 112 p.

Grades: 5 6 7 8   **613.9**

1. Adolescence 2. Dating (Social customs) 3. Teenagers -- Interpersonal relations 4. Interpersonal relations 5. Life skills 6. Life skills guides
ISBN 9781438008578

                     LC bl2016007554

Describes the physical and emotional changes that occur in adolescents during puberty and discusses topics including sexual activity, pregnancy, and sexually transmitted diseases.

Madaras, Lynda

The **"what's** happening to my body?" book for boys. Lynda Madaras with Area Madaras; drawings by Simon Sullivan. Newmarket Press, c2007. xx, 233 p.: What's happening to my body?

Grades: 4 5 6 7   **613.9**

1. Teenage boys -- Growth 2. Boys -- Growth 3. Puberty 4. Sex education for children
ISBN 1557047650

                     LC 2007009874

Discusses the changes that take place in a boy's body during puberty, including information on the body's changing size and shape, the growth spurt, reproductive organs, pubic hair, beards, pimples, voice changes, wet dreams, and puberty in girls.

The **what's** happening to my body? book for girls. Lynda Madaras with Area Madaras; drawings by Simon Sullivan. Newmarket Press, c2007. xxvi, 259 p.

Grades: 4 5 6   **613.9**

1. Teenage girls -- Growth 2. Teenage girls -- Physiology 3. Puberty 4. Sex instruction for girls
ISBN 9781557047687

                     LC 2007009862

Discusses the changes that take place in a girl's body during puberty, including information on the body's changing size and shape, pubic hair, breasts, reproductive organs, the menstrual cycle, and puberty in boys.

613.9071 Birth control, reproductive technology, sex hygiene, sexual techniques—Sex education—secondary level

Harris, Robie H.

★ **It's** perfectly normal: changing bodies, growing up, sex, and sexual health. Robie H. Harris; illustrated by Michael Emberley. Candlewick Press, 2014, c1994. 112 p.

Grades: 4 5 6 7   **613.9071**

1. Sex education for children 2. Family life education 3. Puberty -- Psychological aspects 4. Childbirth 5. Sexually transmitted diseases
ISBN 9780763668716

A fully updated, 20th anniversary edition of an essential primer about puberty and sexual health incorporates new information on safe Internet use, gender identity, emergency contraception and STDs.

"This edition has been revised for a new generation, including updates in scientific and medical information about reproduction, birth control, abortion, sexual abuse, and sexually transmitted diseases." School Library Journal.

Omnigraphics, Inc

Sexual health information for teens: health tips about sexual development, reproduction, contraception, and sexually transmitted infections including facts about puberty, sexuality, birth control, HIVAIDS, human papillomavirus, chlamydia, gonorrhea, herpes, and more.. Omnigraphics (COR). Omnigraphics, Inc., 2018. xii, 382 p.

Grades: 9 10 11 12   **613.9071**

1. Teenagers -- Health and hygiene 2. Sexual health 3. Reproductive

health 4. Puberty 5. Sexually transmitted diseases -- Prevention
ISBN 9780780816442

LC 2018029168

Offers basic consumer health information for teens about puberty, development, and sexuality, maintaining sexual health, and preventing pregnancy and sexually transmitted diseases. Includes index, resource information, and online access. Provided by publisher.

614 Forensic medicine; incidence of injuries, wounds, disease; public preventive medicine

Stefoff, Rebecca, 1951-
Forensic anthropology. written by Rebecca Stefoff. Marshall Cavendish Benchmark, c2011. 95 p.: Forensic science investigated
Grades: 6 7 8 9   **614**
1. Forensic sciences 2. Forensic anthropology 3. Forensic anthropologists 4. Criminal investigation 5. Anthropology
ISBN 9780761441427

LC 2010010534

"The titles in the Forensic Science Investigated series stand out not only for their thorough overviews of how forensic science is practiced today but also for their fascinating historical perspectives. . . . Forensic Anthropology starts off with a riveting account of scientists who cracked an 1849 Harvard murder case by finding clues among the victim's remains." Booklist.
Includes bibliographical references and index.

Forensics and medicine. by Rebecca Stefoff. Marshall Cavendish Benchmark, 2011. 95 p. : Forensic science investigated
Grades: 6 7 8 9   **614**
1. Forensic medicine 2. Forensic sciences 3. Medicine 4. Forensic pathologists 5. Forensic pathology
ISBN 9780761441434

LC 2010010526

"Numerous color photos and digital illustrations . . . add further interest." Booklist.
Includes bibliographical references and index.

Walker, Sally M.
Written in bone: buried lives of Jamestown and Colonial Maryland. Sally M. Walker. Carolrhoda Books, c2009. 144 p.
Grades: 6 7 8 9 10   **614**
1. Forensic anthropology 2. Human remains (Archaeology) 3. Forensic sciences 4. Jamestown, Virginia -- History 5. Chesapeake Bay Region -- History
ISBN 9780822571353

LC 2007010768

Takes readers through the process of investigating human remains found at colonial-era sites to reveal causes of death, match remains with the names on the historical records, and determine the skeletons' gender, age at death, nationality, and even economic standing.
"Walker takes readers on an archaeological investigation of human and material remains from 17th- and 18th-century Jamestown and colonial Maryland, while addressing relevant topics in forensic anthropology, history, and archaeology. . . . The text succinctly explains complex forensic concepts. . . . Captioned, full-color photographs of skeletal, dental, and artifactual remains shed light on colonial life. Historical documents, illustrated maps, and anatomical drawings complement images of various specialists at work in the field. Photographs of reenac-

tors performing period tasks . . . provide insight into the daily life of the recovered individuals." School Library Journal.
Include bibliographical references (p. 138-139) and index.

614.4 Incidence of and public measures to prevent disease

Barnard, Bryn
★ **Outbreak**: plagues that changed history. written and illustrated by Bryn Barnard. Crown Publishers, 2005. 47 p.
Grades: 5 6 7 8   **614.4**
1. Communicable diseases -- History 2. Epidemics -- History 3. Biohistory
ISBN 037592986X

LC 2005015086

Explores how major medical events and plagues impacted society and forever changed the course of history, including a review of the black plague and its effects on the feudal system and yellow fever and its impact on the slave trade.
"This volume explores specific plagues that have impacted society. Barnard begins with an introduction to microbes and the positive and negative effects that they can have on humans. A history of the study of microorganisms follows. The bulk of the book then focuses on specific plagues with a chapter devoted to each, including the Black Death, smallpox, yellow fever, cholera, tuberculosis, and influenza. The final chapter discusses the modern struggle against disease. . . . The evocative paintings help to clarify the text. Browsers and report writers alike will find this to be a fascinating and informative resource." School Library Journal.

Gleason, Carrie, 1973-
Feasting bedbugs, mites, and ticks. Carrie Gleason. Crabtree Pub., c2011. 32 p.: Creepy crawlies
Grades: 4 5 6 7   **614.4**
1. Bedbugs 2. Ticks 3. Insects
ISBN 9780778725077

LC 2010009552

"The informational yet easy-to-read text in double-page spreads explains the classification, anatomy, life cycles, and ideal feeding and living conditions for mites, ticks, and bedbugs as well as the differences among them. . . . Children will be most interested in the long history, myths, and lore associated with these pests as well as the eye-catching layout, with numerous color photographs. . . . [This is an] equally repulsive and fascinating book." Booklist.

Goldsmith, Connie, 1945-
Pandemic: how climate, the environment, and superbugs increase the risk. Connie Goldsmith. Twenty-First Century Books, 2018 136 p.
Grades: 5 6 7 8 9   **614.4**
1. Drug resistance in microorganisms 2. Microbiology 3. Epidemics 4. Epidemiology 5. Plague
ISBN 9781512452150

Describes how scientists are studying thirty emerging diseases that have the potential to become pandemics in the future and the preventive measures that can be taken to combat them.

Hand, Carol, 1945-
Epidemiology: the fight against Ebola & other diseases. by Carol Hand; content consultant, A.R. Ruis, PhD, Fellow, Medical History and Bioethics Department, University of Wiscon-

sin-Madison. Essential Library, an imprint of Abdo Publishing, [2015] 112 p.: History of science (Essential Library (Firm))

Grades: 6 7 8 9   **614.4**

1. Epidemiology 2. Diseases 3. Communicable diseases 4. Ebola virus disease
ISBN 9781624035593

LC bl2015009067

Traces the development of the methods and technology used in epidemiology through the failures and successes of the field's scientists and innovators.

"Complex scientific principles are made accessible through meaningful, straightforward language, and in-text citations and source notes provide greater credibility and authority." School Library Journal.

Includes bibliographical references (page 104) and index.

614.5 Incidence of and public measures to prevent specific diseases and kinds of diseases

Cunningham, Kevin, 1966-

Flu. Kevin Cunningham. Morgan Reynolds Pub., c2009. 176 p.: Diseases in history

Grades: 8 9 10 11 12   **614.5**

1. Influenza 2. Influenza -- History 3. Diseases 4. Communicable diseases
ISBN 9781599351056

LC 2008051620

Describes the history of influenza and its many strains, focusing on the flu epidemics in the past century and how medical technology has evolved to combat the virus.

"This informative title reveals the continued concerns surrounding this killer disease and the possibility of a future pandemic. The text, though somewhat scientific, will help students to better understand the history of the virus, how it has mutated and jumped from animals to humans, and new concerns regarding more dangerous forms. . . . Color and black-and-white archival photos, as well as reproduction of a three-dimensional rendering of the flu virus, enhance the text." School Library Journal.

Includes bibliographical references (p. 149-170) and index.

Malaria. by Kevin Cunningham. Morgan Reynolds Pub, c2009. 144 p.: Diseases in history

Grades: 8 9 10 11 12   **614.5**

1. Malaria 2. Malaria -- History 3. Diseases
ISBN 9781599351032

LC 2008051619

"Provides fascinating information about an ongoing scourge. . . . Here readers have an accessible, well presented account of the continuing struggle against a deadly disease." Voice of Youth Advocates.

Includes bibliographical references and index.

Davis, Kenneth C.

More deadly than war: the hidden history of the Spanish flu and the First World War. Kenneth C. Davis. Henry Holt and Company, 2018 304 p.

Grades: 7 8 9 10   **614.5**

1. 1910s 2. World War I 3. Influenza -- History 20th century 4. Influenza Epidemic, 1918-1919 5. Viruses 6. Epidemics
ISBN 9781250145123

A dramatic account of the Spanish Influenza epidemic that is based on survivor accounts and archival materials to offer insight into how the outbreak catastrophically transformed the world.

"Davis lays out how the pandemic was spread, the largely ineffective efforts to curtail it, and the many ways government officials, swept up in waves of nationalism, ignored the advice of medical professionals, which ultimately made the pandemic worse. Davis lands hard on that last point: 'The story of the Spanish flu . . . is about how important it is to guard against unreasoning terror that has no basis in fact or science.'" Booklist

Jarrow, Gail

Bubonic panic: when plague invaded America. Gail Jarrow. Perseus Distribution Services, 2016. 176 p.: Deadly disease trilogy

Grades: 5 6 7 8 9   **614.5**

1. 1900s (Decade) 2. Plague 3. Diseases 4. Epidemics -- History 5. Plague -- Transmission 6. Sick persons
ISBN 9781620917381

Documents the 1900 outbreak of the bubonic plague in San Francisco's Chinatown, tracing the efforts of doctors to halt its spread, the political leaders who tried to keep the epidemic from being publicized and the scientists who unlocked the plague's secrets. Includes photographs and drawings, a glossary, a timeline, further resources, an author's note and source notes.

"The thorough, fascinating treatment is complemented by a handsome design that includes numerous primary source artifacts. An exemplary contribution to the history of science and medicine." Horn Book.

Fatal fever: tracking down Typhoid Mary. Gail Jarrow. Calkins Creek, 2015. 192 p.: Deadly disease trilogy

Grades: 6 7 8 9 10   **614.5**

1. Typhoid Mary, 1869-1938 2. 1910s 3. Typhoid fever 4. Quarantine 5. Women cooks 6. Communicable diseases 7. Diseases 8. New York City -- Social life and customs
ISBN 9781620915974

"Jarrow has written a suspenseful medical mystery for inquisitive readers. Timeline, glossary, author's note, source notes, bibliography, and index are included among the extensive back matter." Horn Book.

★ **Red** madness: how a medical mystery changed what we eat. Gail Jarrow. Calkins Creek, 2014. 192 p.: Deadly disease trilogy

Grades: 5 6 7 8 9   **614.5**

1. Epidemics -- History 2. Public health -- History 3. Malnutrition 4. Pellagra 5. Physicians 6. Southern States -- Social conditions
ISBN 9781590787328

Traces the pellagra epidemic that spread throughout the American South a century ago, drawing on real-life cases to describe its physical and cultural impact as well as related medical reports, news articles and scientific investigations.

"In 1902, a young man in Georgia displayed symptoms of a disease believed to be nonexistent in the U.S.: pellagra, a deficiency disease. Jarrow unfolds the suspenseful search for a cause of the South's epidemic, as corn fungus, insect- and bird-born parasites, and more were all blamed and rejected." Horn Book.

Jurmain, Suzanne

The **secret** of the yellow death: a true story of medical sleuthing. by Suzanne Jurmain. Houghton Mifflin, 2009. 104 p.

Grades: 6 7 8 9 10   **614.5**

1. 1900s (Decade) 2. Yellow fever -- Diagnosis 3. Scientists 4. Diseases 5. Public health 6. Medicine
ISBN 9780618965816

LC 2009022499

"This medical mystery is extremely interesting, easy to read, and well illustrated with period photos." School Library Journal.

Koch, Falynn, 1985-
Plagues: the microscopic battlefield. Falynn Koch. First Second, 2017. 122 p.: Science comics

Grades: 4 5 6 7 8   **614.5**
1. Diseases 2. Infection 3. Viruses 4. Bacteria 5. Immunity 6. Comics and Graphic novels
ISBN 9781626727533

LC bl2017035358

Combines elaborate comics-style illustrations with whimsical, engaging facts about the biology and mechanisms of infections, diseases and immunity as well as the incredible contributions of technology and medical science.

Kupperberg, Paul
The **influenza** pandemic of 1918-1919. Paul Kupperberg. Chelsea House Publishers, c2008. 120 p.: Great historic disasters

Grades: 7 8 9 10   **614.5**
1. 1910s 2. Influenza Epidemic, 1918-1919 3. Epidemics 4. Influenza -- History 20th century 5. Diseases
ISBN 9780791096406

LC 2007036552

Each book in this series begins with historical context to depict life in the time and place of the featured event, builds to a vivid description of the disaster, discusses the aftermath, and then analyzes the way the disaster changed history and impacted the future.

"This is well written and informative. . . . The inclusion of black-and-white and color photographs and drawings and sidebars help to make [this book] first-rate for reports and general browsing." School Library Journal.

Includes bibliographical references (p. 111-112) and index.

Lewis, Mark L., 1991-
Measles: how a contagious rash changed history. Mark L. Lewis; consultant, David N. Fisman, MD, Professor, Dalla Lana School of Public Health, University of Toronto. Capstone Press, a Capstone imprint, 2020 32 p.

Grades: 3 4 5 6 7 8   **614.5**
1. Measles 2. Measles -- History 3. Epidemics -- History 4. Diseases and history
ISBN 9781543572407

LC 2018061090

Explores the history and impact of measles. Provided by publisher.

Moon, Walt K.
Past pandemics and COVID-19. by Walt K. Moon. BrightPoint Press, [2021] 80 p.: COVID-19 pandemic

Grades: 6 7 8 9 10   **614.5**
1. Epidemics 2. Communicable diseases 3. COVID-19 (Disease) 4. COVID-19 Pandemic, 2019- 5. Black death
ISBN 9781678200640

COVID-19 is not the first pandemic to spread around the world. More than 500 million people became sick with the flu in 1918. The Black Death killed nearly one-third of Europe's population. Past Pandemics and COVID-19 examines how COVID-19 compares to widespread diseases of history. Provided by publisher.

"Will be useful long after the pandemic. Color photos, illustrations, and side notes beautifully support the text while still giving the book a research feel. . . . Absolutely exceptional." School Library Journal

Murphy, Jim, 1947-
★ An **American** plague: the true and terrifying story of the yellow fever epidemic of 1793. by Jim Murphy. Clarion Books, c2003. 165 p.

Grades: 5 6 7 8   **614.5**
1. Sick persons 2. Yellow fever 3. Epidemics 4. Caregivers 5. Public health 6. Pennsylvania -- History -- 1775-1865. 7. Philadelphia, Pennsylvania -- Social conditions -- 1775-1865.
ISBN 0395776082

LC 2002151355

NCTE Orbis Pictus Nonfiction Award, 2004.
Robert F. Sibert Informational Book Medal, 2004.

"Murphy culls from a number of historical records the story of the yellow fever epidemic that swept Philadelphia in 1793, skillfully drawing out from these sources the fear and drama of the time and making them immediate to modern readers. . . . Thoroughly documented, with an annotated source list, the work is both rigorous and inviting." Horn Book.

Includes bibliographical references (p. 141-153) and index.

Nardo, Don, 1947-
COVID-19 and other pandemics: a comparison. Don Nardo ReferencePoint Press, 2021 80 p.

Grades: 7 8 9 10 11 12   **614.5**
1. COVID-19 (Disease) 2. Epidemics 3. Communicable diseases -- History 4. Public health 5. Diseases -- History
ISBN 9781678200428

Similarities between human reactions to onslaughts of deadly diseases separated by millennia illustrates the morbid universality of such outbreaks. It reminds us that large attacks of lethal germs are nothing new, nor are human reactions to them. One problem inherent in such pandemics is that over time people tend to forget the lessons of past.

"A concise but thorough and cohesive overview of pandemics from ancient times to 2020. . . . Timely and worthwhile." Kirkus

Person, Stephen
Bubonic plague: the black death! by Stephen Person. Bearport Pub. Co., 2010. 32 p.: Nightmare plagues

Grades: 4 5 6 7   **614.5**
1. Plague 2. Communicable diseases 3. Black Death 4. Plague -- Transmission 5. Plague -- Prevention
ISBN 9781936088034

LC 2010008028

Looks at the disease the bubonic plague, its causes, how it affects the body, how to prevent it, and the history of its outbreaks.

"The writing is accessible and interspersed with interesting photographs and fact boxes. . . . [The book relies] on an honest discussion of [bubonic plague and is an] . . . effective, easily navigated [introduction]." School Library Journal.

Includes bibliographical references (p. 31) and index.

Malaria: super killer! by Stephen Person. Bearport Pub., c2011. 32 p.: Nightmare plagues

Grades: 4 5 6 7   **614.5**
1. Malaria 2. Communicable diseases 3. Malaria -- Transmission 4. Malaria -- Prevention
ISBN 9781936088072

LC 2010012018

Looks at the disease malaria, its causes, how it is spread, how it affects the body, how it is prevented, its history, and efforts to eradicate it.

"The writing is accessible and interspersed with interesting photographs and fact boxes. . . . [The book relies] on an honest discussion of [malaria and is an] . . . effective, easily navigated [introduction]." School Library Journal.

Includes bibliographical references (p. 31) and index.

Reingold, Adam

Smallpox: is it over? by Adam Reingold. Bearport Pub., c2011. 32 p.: Nightmare plagues

Grades: 4 5 6 7   **614.5**
1. Smallpox 2. Poxvirus diseases 3. Smallpox -- Prevention 4. Diseases 5. Communicable diseases
ISBN 9781936088027

LC 2010009371

"The writing is accessible and interspersed with interesting photographs and fact boxes. . . . [The book relies] on an honest discussion of [smallpox and is an] . . . effective, easily navigated [introduction]." School Library Journal.

Includes bibliographical references and index.

Rudolph, Jessica

The **flu** of 1918: millions dead worldwide! by Jessica Rudolph. Bearpoint Pub., 2010. 32 p.: Nightmare plagues

Grades: 4 5 6 7   **614.5**
1. Influenza Epidemic, 1918-1919 2. Influenza 3. Communicable diseases 4. Influenza -- Prevention
ISBN 9781936088058

LC 2010004684

Looks at the deadly influenza outbreak of 1918, and causes, bodily effects, and prevention measures for influenza in general.

"The writing is accessible and interspersed with interesting photographs and fact boxes. . . . [The book relies] on an honest discussion of [Influenza epidemic of 1918 and is an] . . . effective, easily navigated [introduction]." School Library Journal.

Includes bibliographical references (p. 31) and index.

Strehle Hartman, Ashley, 1986-

Teens and STDs. Ashley Strehle Hartman. ReferencePoint Press, Inc., 2019 80 p.

Grades: 7 8 9 10 11 12   **614.5**
1. Sexual health 2. Sexually transmitted diseases -- Prevention 3. Sexually transmitted diseases -- Treatment 4. Teenagers -- Health and hygiene
ISBN 9781682825136

LC 2018011553

Provides information about sexually transmitted diseases, covering their symptoms, prevention, and treatment.

"Hartman delivers a matter-of-fact, if somewhat clinical, appraisal of STDs and teen sexual health in this entry in the Teen Health and Safety series." Booklist.

Includes bibliographical references and index.

615 Pharmacology and therapeutics

Bjornlund, Lydia, 1961-

Oxycodone. by Lydia Bjornlund. ReferencePoint Press, 2012. 96 p.: Compact research series

Grades: 7 8 9 10 11 12   **615**
1. Oxycodone 2. Oxycodone abuse 3. Prescription drugs 4. Narcotics 5. Drugs
ISBN 9781601521613

LC 2011020202

Describes oxycodone abuse, including how patients can become addicted to the prescription drug, how it is currently regulated, and how further abuse may be prevented in the future.

Hyde, Natalie, 1963-

What is germ theory? Natalie Hyde. Crabtree Pub., c2011. 64 p.: Shaping modern science

Grades: 5 6 7 8   **615**
1. Germ theory of disease 2. Microorganisms 3. Diseases
ISBN 9780778772019

LC 2010052631

Discusses how the germ theory of disease came about, how it was applied to various illnesses throughout the years, and why this theory has become so important in the field of medicine.

"This title is not only written and organized well, but [it is] also gorgeous in design. Full-color photographs and illustrations are set over colorful backgrounds that add depth but not distraction. [The title] includes thought-provoking quotes from famous authors and scientists and some eyebrow-raising Quick Facts throughout." School Library Journal.

Includes bibliographical references (p. 62-63) and index.

Kidd, J. S.

Potent natural medicines: Mother Nature's pharmacy. J.S. Kidd and Renee A. Kidd. Chelsea House Publishers, c2006. xii, 212 p.: Science & society

Grades: 7 8 9 10   **615**
1. Pharmacognosy 2. Pharmacology 3. Medicinal plants
ISBN 0816056072

LC 2005041741

Discusses the use of plants as medicine, as well as the role of government in protecting public health and doing research for new medical treatments.

"This introduces plants' medicinal properties, pioneers who hunted for sources of and applications for botanical treatments, and the ways phytochemical nutrients prevent disease. . . . [Also included] are chapters about recent research, including investigation into animal sources for medicine; the impact of field research on native peoples; and the federal regulation of herb and plant supplements. . . . This [is] a good choice to support research and debate projects." Booklist.

Includes bibliographical references (p. 200-202) and index.

Winner, Cherie

Circulating life: blood transfusion from ancient superstition to modern medicine. Cherie Winner. Twenty-First Century Books, c2007. 112 p.: Discovery! (Lerner)

Grades: 6 7 8 9 10   **615**
1. Blood -- Transfusion 2. Blood 3. Surgery
ISBN 0822566060

LC 2006029921

Describes what blood is, explains why blood is important, and discusses the techniques, discoveries, and developments in transfusing blood and blood parts since the mid-1600s.

"This compendium is both a history of the art of transfusions and a scientific discourse on the chemistry of blood. From early bleeding treatments to the discovery of the circulatory system; from the earliest attempts at transfusions to Charles Drew's heroic work with plasma in World War II, Winner's clear text takes readers on an epic trip." School Library Journal.

Includes bibliographical references (p. 107-109) and index.

615.1 Pharmacology and therapeutics—Drugs

Goldsmith, Connie, 1945-
Dietary supplements: harmless, helpful, or hurtful? Connie Goldsmith. Twenty First Century Books, 2015. 96 p.

Grades: 6 7 8 9   **615.1**
  1. Food supplements 2. Vitamins 3. Drugs 4. Nutrition 5. Drug industry and trade
ISBN 9781467738484

"Excellent, detailed endmatter rounds out a balanced exploration of a timely topic. Equally apt for research projects and as a single go-to source of information." Kirkus.

615.3 Organic drugs

Brown, Don, 1949-
★ A **shot** in the arm! Big ideas that changed the world.. Don Brown Amulet Books, 2021 144 p.: Big ideas that changed the world

Grades: 4 5 6 7 8 9   **615.3**
  1. Diseases 2. Vaccines 3. Vaccination 4. Immune system 5. Scientists 6. Comics and graphic novels
ISBN 9781419750014

A Shot in the Arm! explores the history of vaccinations and the struggle to protect people from infectious diseases, from smallpox—perhaps humankind's greatest affliction to date—to the COVID-19 pandemic. Highlighting deadly diseases such as measles, polio, rabies, cholera, and influenza, Brown tackles the science behind how our immune systems work, the discovery of bacteria, the anti-vaccination movement, and major achievements.

"Through exhaustive research coupled with an understanding of human motivation and an inviting visual style, Brown investigates the development of vaccines in his insightful—and keenly relevant—graphic novel." Booklist

Haelle, Tara
Vaccination investigation: the history and science of vaccines. Tara Haelle. Twenty-First Century Books, 2018. 120 p.

Grades: 7 8 9 10 11 12   **615.3**
  1. Vaccines 2. Vaccination -- History 3. Communicable diseases 4. Anti-vaccination movement 5. Preventive medicine
ISBN 9781512425307

LC 2017005193

Presents the history of vaccines, their important role in protecting community health, and the introduction of cutting-edge research.

"This is an organized, documented, and accessible account of the history of vaccinations." Booklist.

Includes bibliographical references and index.

Hutchison, Patricia
The **debate** about vaccines. by Patricia Hutchison. Focus Readers, 2018. 48 p.: Pros and cons (Focus Readers)

Grades: 5 6 7 8   **615.3**
  1. Vaccination 2. Immunization of children 3. Anti-vaccination movement 4. Vaccines 5. Immunization
ISBN 9781635175271

Provides a thorough overview of the major pros and cons of vaccines. Readable text, interesting sidebars, and illuminating infographics invite readers to jump in and join the debate.

Nardo, Don, 1947-
How vaccines changed the world. by Don Nardo. ReferencePoint Press, Inc., 2019. 80 p.: How science changed the world

Grades: 8 9 10 11 12   **615.3**
  1. Vaccines 2. Vaccination 3. Immunization
ISBN 9781682824139

"Well-researched and engagingly written." School Library Journal

Includes bibliographical references and index.

615.7 Pharmacokinetics

Clayborne, Leigh
The **benefits** of medical marijuana: from cancer to PTSD. Leigh Clayborne. Mason Crest, 2019 80 p.

Grades: 8 9 10 11 12   **615.7**
  1. Marijuana -- Therapeutic use 2. Marijuana -- Health aspects 3. Marijuana -- Law and legislation 4. Cannabis -- Therapeutic use 5. Cannabis -- Health aspects
ISBN 9781422241080

LC bl2019026594

Explores the possible benefits of medical marijuana, providing information about how some countries handle it, what conditions it can help, and its potential side effects.

"With much talk surrounding marijuana legalization in the United States, this informative series comes at just the right time. Instead of providing answers to the debate, the authors present current, credible information from numerous studies and reputable research, allowing readers to draw their own conclusions." School Library Journal.

Includes bibliographical references (pages 79-80) and index.

Esherick, Joan
The **FDA** & psychiatric drugs: how a drug is approved. Joan Esherick. Mason Crest Publishers, Inc., 2014 128 p.

Grades: 7 8 9 10   **615.7**
  1. United States. Food and Drug Administration 2. Drug approval 3. Mental illness -- Chemotherapy 4. Psychotropic drugs -- Testing -- Law and legislation
ISBN 9781422228265

LC 2013008197

Details the FDA's approval process for psychiatric drugs and explains how the drugs work, where they come from, and adverse reactions people experience from taking them.

Szumski, Bonnie, 1958-
Is medical marijuana necessary? Bonnie Szumski and Jill Karson. ReferencePoint Press, c2013. 96 p.: In controversy

Grades: 7 8 9 10   **615.7**
  1. Medical marijuana 2. Marijuana -- Law and legislation
ISBN 9781601524584

LC 2012011561

Examines the controversy surrounding medical marijuana, including how effective it is, what the risks and benefits are, and how it should be regulated.

Walker, Ida
Sedatives and hypnotics: deadly downers. Ida Walker. Mason Crest Publishers, c2012. 128 p.

Grades: 7 8 9 10   **615.7**
1. Sedatives 2. Hypnotics
ISBN 9781422224403

LC 2011042530

Looks at some of the more common sedatives and hypnotics, discussing how they work, how they are abused and misused, and what can be done for those addicted to them.

615.9 Toxicology

Albee, Sarah
     Poison: deadly deeds, perilous professions, and murderous medicines. Sarah Albee. Crown Books for Young Readers, [2017] 192 p.
Grades: 5 6 7 8   **615.9**
1. Poisons 2. Toxicology 3. Poisoning 4. Criminal investigation 5. Forensic sciences
ISBN 9781101932247

LC 2016009205

A humorous and informative book that traces the role poisons have played in human history from antiquity to the present. Part history, part chemistry, part whodunit. Provided by publisher.
     "Albee's approach to the subject is lively, accessible, and likely to inspire many readers to delve deeper. A compelling, entertaining, and informative introduction to a sinister aspect of human history." Kirkus.

Cooper, Candy J., 1955-
     Poisoned water: how the citizens of Flint, Michigan, fought for their lives and warned the nation. Candy J. Cooper with Marc Aronson. Bloomsbury Children's Books, 2020. 304 p.
Grades: 7 8 9 10 11 12   **615.9**
1. Lead poisoning 2. Drinking water 3. Water quality management 4. Water-supply 5. Lead in drinking water -- Health hazards 6. Flint, Michigan
ISBN 9781547602322

LC 2019045874

Flint, Michigan had been built up, then abandoned, by General Motors. In 2014, as part of a plan to save money, government officials decided that Flint would temporarily switch its water supply from Lake Huron to the Flint River. Within months, many residents broke out in rashes. Children stopped growing. Some people were hospitalized with mysterious illnesses; others died. Despite the murky, foul-smelling liquid pouring from the city's faucets, officials refused to listen. Through interviews with residents and intensive research into legal records and news accounts, Cooper and Aronson show not just how the crisis unfolded, but also the history of racism and segregation that led up to it, and how the people of Flint fought— and are still fighting— for clean water and healthy lives.
     "This detailed offering, the first specifically intended for young audiences, has multiple curriculum applications (man-made disasters, ecology, racial discrimination, economics, biology, the roles of local and state government). It's also a modern-day horror story, one we can only hope will never be repeated." Booklist

Landau, Elaine
     Food poisoning and foodborne diseases. by Elaine Landau. Twenty-First Century Books, c2010. 128 p.: USA today health reports: Diseases and disorders
Grades: 7 8 9 10 11 12   **615.9**
1. Foodborne diseases 2. Food poisoning 3. Food -- Microbiology

4. Diseases
ISBN 9780822572909

LC 2009020325

"This book will draw an audience with its everyday examples of food risks as well as instructions about how to buy, prepare, cook, and store food. . . . Also included are warnings about how to keep hands and kitchen surfaces clean and what to watch out for in cafeteria and fast-food outlets. . . . [The] accessible design extends the impressive educational data." Booklist.
     Includes bibliographical references and index.

616 Diseases

Dendy, Leslie
     Guinea pig scientists: bold self-experimenters in science and medicine. Leslie Dendy and Mel Boring; with illustrations by C.B. Mordan. Henry Holt & Co., 2005. 213 p.
Grades: 5 6 7 8   **616**
1. Self-experimentation in medicine 2. Medical research 3. Medical research -- History 4. Medical researchers 5. Medical scientists
ISBN 9780805073164

LC 2004052364

Stories of ten men and women, from the 1770s to the present, who devoted their lives, and sometimes risked them, to answer some of the big questions in science and medicine.
     "The accounts are lively, compelling, and not always for the squeamish. . . . The authors cogently discuss each experiment's significance in advancing our understanding of science and medicine. Illustrated with a mix of period black-and-white photos and Mordan's nineteenth-century-style portraits." Booklist.
     Includes bibliographical references (p. 189-196) and index.

Skloot, Rebecca, 1972-
     The **immortal** life of Henrietta Lacks. Rebecca Skloot. Crown Publishers, 2009. x, 369 p., 8 p. of plates
Grades: 8 9 10 11 12 Adult   **616**
1. Lacks, Henrietta, 1920-1951 2. People with cancer 3. Cell culture 4. Medical ethics 5. Scientific discoveries 6. Medical research
ISBN 9781400052172

LC 2009031785

Documents the story of how scientists took cells from an unsuspecting descendant of freed slaves and created a human cell line that has been kept alive indefinitely, enabling discoveries in such areas as cancer research, in vitro fertilization and gene mapping.

616.07 Pathology

Murray, Elizabeth A.
     Death: corpses, cadavers, and other grave matters. by Elizabeth A. Murray. Twenty-First Century Books, c2010. 112 p.: Discovery! (Lerner)
Grades: 7 8 9 10   **616.07**
1. Death (Biology) 2. Terminal illness 3. Postmortem changes 4. People with terminal illnesses 5. Life after death
ISBN 9780761338512

LC 2009017436

"The author has written a book that deals with the scientific aspect of life and death. Her experience as a teacher of anatomy and physiology comes through as she explains the living body, what happens when systems shut down, and how postmortem remains can give evidence to solve crimes and the mysteries of diseases. . . . First-person accounts of terminally ill patients and those working in the fields of pathology, hospice, and anatomy clarify subjects presented in the chapters. Color photographs are included throughout, some of which are potentially disturbing. The glossary and bibliography are extensive and helpful. This book provides information for those who are curious about a subject that is not easy to discuss." School Library Journal.

Includes bibliographical references and index.

616.2 Diseases of respiratory system

Marcovitz, Hal

Asthma: Diseases and Disorders. Hal Marcovitz. Reference-Point Press, c2010. 96 p.

Grades: 7 8 9 10   **616.2**

  1. Asthma

  ISBN 9781601521040

              LC 2009036844

Describes the causes, symptoms, and treatments of asthma, and how people live with it.

"This title begins with an overview of [asthma], followed by chapters that define the condition, explain its causes, and discuss possible treatments. . . . The last chapter . . . is about how to live with the condition. Chapters present material in accessible language, provide report-ready, primary-source quotes from experts, and end with a Facts and Illustrations section in which information is summarized in bullet points and accompanied by colorful graphs and charts that will appeal to visual learners." School Library Journal.

Includes bibliographical references and index.

Royston, Angela, 1945-

Explaining asthma. Angela Royston. Smart Apple Media, c2010. 45 p. : Explaining--

Grades: 5 6 7 8   **616.2**

  1. Asthma 2. Lungs -- Diseases 3. People with asthma 4. Respiratory allergy 5. Diseases

  ISBN 9781599203157

              LC 2008049284

"The book provides a basic [overview] of the health concerns related to the disease; information on diagnosis and treatment; and a discussion of the challenges or complications experienced by the affected person and their family/friends, and how to manage those problems. . . . The incorporation of quotes and personal accounts in Case Notes sidebars adds to the sensitive tone found throughout [the title]." School Library Journal.

616.3 Diseases of digestive system

Giddings, Sharon

Cystic fibrosis. Sharon Giddings. Chelsea House, c2009. 128 p. : Genes and disease

Grades: 7 8 9 10   **616.3**

  1. Cystic fibrosis -- Genetic aspects 2. Birth defects

  ISBN 9780791096949

              LC 2008044771

Describes the disease, including its symptoms, causes, treatments, and current research towards finding a cure.

Goldsmith, Connie, 1945-

Hepatitis. by Connie Goldsmith. Twenty-First Century Books, c2010. 128 p.: USA today health reports: Diseases and disorders

Grades: 7 8 9 10 11 12   **616.3**

  1. Hepatitis 2. Diseases 3. Liver -- Diseases

  ISBN 9780822567875

              LC 2009020720

"This reveals that an estimated five million Americans have viral Hepatitis A, B, and C, making it a major public health problem. . . . The detailed information is combined with photos and diagrams portraying transmission, vaccines, and effective treatment. . . . [The] accessible design extends the impressive educational data." Booklist.

Includes bibliographical references and index.

Miller, Petra

Cystic fibrosis. Petra Miller. Cavendish Square, 2016. 64 p.: Genetic conditions

Grades: 8 9 10 11 12   **616.3**

  1. Cystic fibrosis 2. Medical genetics 3. Diseases

  ISBN 9781502609403

              LC 2015023055

Discusses the history, symptoms, and genetic causes of the disease, and examines current scientific research aimed at treating it.

Powell, Jillian

Explaining cystic fibrosis. Jillian Powell. Smart Apple Media, c2010. 45 p. : Explaining--

Grades: 5 6 7 8   **616.3**

  1. Cystic fibrosis 2. People with cystic fibrosis 3. Diseases

  ISBN 9781599203126

              LC 2008049288

"The book provides a basic [overview] of the health concerns related to the disease; information on diagnosis and treatment; and a discussion of the challenges or complications experienced by the affected person and their family/friends, and how to manage those problems. . . . The incorporation of quotes and personal accounts in Case Notes sidebars adds to the sensitive tone found throughout [the title]." School Library Journal.

616.4 Diseases of endocrine, hematopoietic, lymphatic, glandular systems; diseases of male breast

Ambrose, Marylou

Investigating diabetes: real facts for real lives. by Marylou Ambrose. Enslow Publishers, c2010. 160 p. : Investigating diseases

Grades: 6 7 8 9 10   **616.4**

  1. Diabetes 2. Diseases

  ISBN 9780766033382

              LC 2008030778

Provides information about diabetes, including treatment, diagnosis, history, medical advances, and true stories about people with the disease. Provided by publisher.

"The book is a comprehensive primer that can well serve patients with newly diagnosed diabetes and their families with its detailed account of diabetes, the causes of the disease, and its potential consequences." Science Books & Films.

Includes bibliographical references and index.

Brill, Marlene Targ

Diabetes. Marlene Targ Brill. Twenty-First Century Books, c2012. 128 p.: USA today health reports: diseases and disorders

Grades: 7 8 9 10 11 12   **616.4**

1. Diabetes 2. Diseases
ISBN 9780761360858

LC 2010049454

This volume explores the history of diabetes, and explains the various treatments that are available today.

"This is an important endeavor from the author [that] will be very helpful for patients and others who are looking for basic information about diabetes. The author has done a good job of helping readers understand how their bodies function and the underlying mechanism of diabetes." Science Books & Films.

Includes bibliographical references (p. 116-123) and index.

Williams, Angela L.

Diabetes information for teens: health tips about managing diabetes and preventing related complications. Angela L. Williams. Omnigraphics, c2019. 341 p.

Grades: 9 10 11 12   **616.4**

1. Diabetes 2. Diabetes in adolescence
ISBN 9780780817371

Provides updated information for teens about who is at risk, the different types of diabetes, and treatment and management options including facts about insulin and glucose meters.

616.5 Diseases of integument

Faulk, Michelle

The **case** of the flesh-eating bacteria: Annie Biotica solves skin disease crimes. Michelle Faulk. Enslow Publishers, c2013. 48 p.: Body system disease investigations

Grades: 5 6 7 8   **616.5**

1. Skin -- Infections 2. Virus diseases 3. Skin -- Diseases 4. Grossology
ISBN 9780766039452

LC 2011023985

Learn about different diseases that affect the skin, such as measles and the chicken pox. Provided by publisher.

616.6 Diseases of urogenital system

Rogers, Kara

The **kidneys** and the renal system. edited by Kara Rogers. Britannica Educational Pub. in association with Rosen Educational Services, 2012. xvii, 174 p.

Grades: 10 11 12   **616.6**

1. Kidneys -- Diseases 2. Kidneys
ISBN 9781615306794

LC 2011026615

Details the anatomy of the renal system, development and function of the kidneys, and renal diseases and disorders.

616.8 Diseases of nervous system and mental disorders

Bender, Lionel

Explaining epilepsy. Lionel Bender. Smart Apple Media, c2010. 45 p. : Explaining--

Grades: 5 6 7 8   **616.8**

1. Epilepsy 2. Children with epilepsy 3. Diseases 4. Brain -- Diseases
ISBN 9781599203096

LC 2008049292

"The book provides a basic [overview] of the health concerns related to the disease; information on diagnosis and treatment; and a discussion of the challenges or complications experienced by the affected person and their family/friends, and how to manage those problems. . . . The incorporation of quotes and personal accounts in Case Notes sidebars adds to the sensitive tone found throughout [the title]." School Library Journal.

Colligan, L. H.

Sleep disorders. by L.H. Colligan. Marshall Cavendish Benchmark, c2009. 64 p.: Health alert (New York, N.Y.)

Grades: 4 5 6 7   **616.8**

1. Sleep disorders 2. Sleep 3. Snoring 4. Neurology 5. Sleep disorders -- Treatment
ISBN 9780761429135

LC 2007034044

Provides comprehensive information on the causes, treatment, and history of sleep disorders. Provided by publisher.

"This title features a handsome format, with well-chosen illustrations, a substantial amount of information, and some practical insights." Booklist.

Dittmer, Lori

Parkinson's disease. by Lori Dittmer. Creative Education, 2011. 48 p.: Living with disease

Grades: 6 7 8 9   **616.8**

1. Parkinson's disease 2. Diseases
ISBN 9781608180769

LC 2010030366

A look at Parkinson's disease, examining the ways in which it develops, its symptoms and diagnosis, the effects it has on a person's daily life, and research toward finding better treatments. Provided by publisher.

"The text is clearly written. . . . The book's design is simple and bold. . . . A brief but informative introduction to Parkinson's disease." Booklist.

Includes bibliographical references and index.

Klosterman, Lorrie

Meningitis. Lorrie Klosterman. Marshall Cavendish Benchmark, c2007. 64 p.: Health alert (New York, N.Y.)

Grades: 4 5 6 7   **616.8**

1. Meningitis 2. Meningitis -- History 3. Meningitis -- Treatment 4. Diseases 5. Nervous system -- Diseases
ISBN 9780761422112

LC 2006015819

Explores the history, causes, symptoms, treatments, and future of different types of meningitis. Provided by publisher.

"This title features a handsome format, with well-chosen illustrations, a substantial amount of information, and some practical insights." Booklist.

Includes bibliographical references (p. 60-61) and index.

Levete, Sarah
Explaining cerebral palsy. Sarah Levete. Smart Apple Media, c2010. 45 p. : Explaining--
Grades: 5 6 7 8   **616.8**
1. Cerebral palsy 2. Developmental disabilities 3. Birth defects 4. Diseases
ISBN 9781599203119

LC 2008049287

"The book provides a basic [overview] of the health concerns related to the disease; information on diagnosis and treatment; and a discussion of the challenges or complications experienced by the affected person and their family/friends, and how to manage those problems. . . . The incorporation of quotes and personal accounts in Case Notes sidebars adds to the sensitive tone found throughout [the title]." School Library Journal.

Rawitt, Jean, 1952-
A **loved** one with dementia: insights and tips for teenagers. Jean Rawitt. Rowman & Littlefield, 2021 xii, 137 p.: Empowering you
Grades: 7 8 9 10 11 12   **616.8**
1. People with dementia -- Family relationships 2. People with dementia -- Care 3. Parent and teenager
ISBN 9781538136980

LC 2020029322

This book addresses the challenges teenagers may face when a family member has dementia. It offers valuable information and support, with stories from young adults themselves and interviews with adults who know and care for people with dementia. Provided by publisher.

"With the U.S. population growing older and people living longer, Rawitt contends that teens are increasingly likely to know and need to assist someone with dementia. . . . this comprehensive manual offers support in understanding this neurocognitive disorder." Booklist

Includes bibliographical references (pages 133-134) and index.

616.85 Miscellaneous diseases of nervous system and mental disorders

Aspromonte, John, 1977-
ADHD: the ultimate teen guide. John Aspromonte. Rowman & Littlefield, 2019 197 p.
Grades: 7 8 9   **616.85**
1. Attention-deficit disorder in adolescence 2. Attention-deficit disorder in adolescence -- Social aspects 3. Attention-deficit disorder in adolescence -- Treatment 4. Teenagers
ISBN 9781538100387

LC 2018024321

This book is for teens and their families who want to learn about Attention Deficit Hyperactivity Disorder (ADHD). The author provides information about ADHD and its effect on school, family, and social life—as well as the difficulties and successes of young people who have ADHD and what students think about ADHD.

"The book is arranged in 12 chapters that begin with background information and move into practical advice on such topics as bullying, treatment options, and schoolwork. The text is enriched with photographs, figures, tables, and stories from fellow teens." Choice.

Includes bibliographical references and index.

Barbour, Scott, 1963-
Post-traumatic stress disorder. Scott Barbour. Reference-Point Press, c2010. 104 p.

Grades: 7 8 9 10   **616.85**
1. Post-traumatic stress disorder -- Treatment 2. Post-traumatic stress disorder
ISBN 9781601521019

LC 2009033216

Describes the causes, symptoms, and treatments of post-traumatic stress disorder.

"This title begins with an overview of [post-traumatic stress disorder], followed by chapters that define the condition, explain its causes, and discuss possible treatments. . . . The final chapter discusses how society should help soldiers with the problem. . . . Chapters present material in accessible language, provide report-ready, primary-source quotes from experts, and end with a Facts and Illustrations section in which information is summarized in bullet points and accompanied by colorful graphs and charts that will appeal to visual learners." School Library Journal.

Includes bibliographical references (p. 93-94) and index.

Barton, Michael
It's raining cats and dogs: an autism spectrum guide to the confusing world of idioms, metaphors, and everyday expressions. written and illustrated by Michael Barton; foreword by Delia Barton. Jessica Kingsley Publishers, 2012. 95 p.
Grades: 3 4 5 6   **616.85**
1. Autism spectrum disorders -- Patients -- Language 2. Autistic people -- Language 3. English language -- Idioms 4. Metaphor
ISBN 9781849052832

LC 2011039514

Offers insight into an autistic person's mind through classic figures of speech that contain confusing or contradictory wording, drawings that show what he believes the expressions mean, and their actual meanings.

Currie-McGhee, L. K. (Leanne K.)
Exercise addiction. by Leanne Currie-McGhee. Lucent Books, c2011. 128 p.: Diseases and disorders series
Grades: 7 8 9 10   **616.85**
1. Exercise addiction 2. Compulsive behavior in teenagers 3. Compulsive behavior 4. Addiction
ISBN 9781420505511

LC 2010039535

"Extremely readable, with helpful illustrations and sidebars, this book includes a definition of exercise addiction (with symptoms), describes how it may be related to other psychological disorders, profiles the types of people most at risk for developing it, discusses psychological and physiological dangers, and offers treatment options. . . . Personal stories appear throughout, and there is a helpful list of questions for readers to ask themselves. This volume is interesting enough to read even if not required for an assignment." School Library Journal.

Includes bibliographical references and index.

Denkmire, Heather
The **truth** about anxiety and depression. Heather Denkmire, principal author; John Perritano, contributing author; Robert N. Golden, general editor, Fred L. Peterson, general editor. Facts on File, c2011. x, 199 p.
Grades: 10 11 12   **616.85**
1. Anxiety 2. Depression, Mental
ISBN 9780816076437

LC 2010005461

From the Publisher: In a straightforward and nonjudgmental manner, The Truth About series tackles a range of current issues that affect teens. Each A-to-Z volume delivers the information teens need to cope with pressure from a multitude of sources and to make informed choices when faced with difficult decisions. Special features such as "Q & A," "Teens Speak," and "Fact Or Fiction?" focus on critical aspects of current topics, while "Did You Know?" presents up-to-date tables and graphs. With an informative glossary and a valuable listing of hotlines and further resources, these books are essential reading for young people in search of guidance and knowledge. An estimated 26 percent of Americans age 18 and over—or one in four people in the United States—experience some type of mental disorder each year, according to the National Institute on Mental Health. The Truth About Anxiety and Depression, Second Edition presents the most up-to-date information on anxiety and depression, including the genetics of mood and anxiety disorders, gender and depression, types of treatments available, related disorders, and much more.

Earl, Rae

Your brain needs a hug: life, love, mental health, and sandwiches. Rae Earl. Imprint, 2019. 288 p.

Grades: 8 9 10 11 12   **616.85**
   1. Advice 2. Mental health 3. Teenagers with mental illnesses 4. Teenagers 5. Mental illness
   ISBN 9781250307859

Imbued with a sense of humor, understanding, and hope, Your Brain Needs a Hug is a judgment-free guide for living well with your mind.

"A validating, hopeful, and practical guide to mental health. . . . Teens struggling with mental illness will find comfort and valuable information in this superlative guide." Kirkus

Gilles, Renae

Understanding screen addiction. Renae Gilles. Cherry Lake Publishing, 2020 32 p.: 21st Century Skills Library: Upfront Health

Grades: 4 5 6 7 8   **616.85**
   1. Internet addiction 2. Internet 3. Addiction
   ISBN 9781534150836

                                    LC 2019008064
For young people, leading a healthy lifestyle requires education and empowerment. In "Understanding Screen Addiction," readers will explore the social aspects and health effects of screen use and addiction, and the ways to establish a healthy relationship with screen technology.—Excerpted from publisher description

"Candidly explains, without preachiness, how these issues harm body and mind, social life, and future prospects. Displaying understanding and respect, titles concede that young people may experiment—but stress caution and moderation, helping readers understand they can choose wisely." School Library Journal

Hudak, Heather C., 1975-

Understanding addiction. Heather C. Hudak. ReferencePoint Press, 2021. 80 p.: Mental health guides

Grades: 6 7 8 9 10 11 12   **616.85**
   1. Compulsive behavior 2. Addiction 3. Drug abuse
   ISBN 9781682829813

                                    LC 2020002444
Describes addiction, its signs, symptoms, and treatment, and its effects on society. Provided by publisher.

"Understanding Addiction considers several kinds of addiction, the stages of substance-use disorder, and how addiction affects society. A glossary and list of print and internet resources add to the research value." Booklist

Includes bibliographical references and index.

Jones, Viola

Conquering negative body image. Viola Jones and Edward Willett. Rosen Publishing, 2016. 64 p.: Conquering eating disorders

Grades: 6 7 8 9   **616.85**
   1. Body image 2. Self-acceptance in teenagers 3. Self-acceptance
   ISBN 9781499462050

                                    LC 2015019516
"Young readers will find it a useful and engaging starting point for discussions on a difficult topic." Booklist.

Includes bibliographical references and index.

McCreary, Michael, 1996-

Funny, you don't look autistic: a comedian's guide to life on the spectrum. Michael McCreary. Annick Press, 2019 176 p.

Grades: 7 8 9 10 11 12   **616.85**
   1. McCreary, Michael, 1996- 2. Comedians 3. People with autism 4. Stereotypes (Social psychology) 5. Autism 6. Men with disabilities
   ISBN 9781773212579

Diagnosed with ASD at age five, McCreary got hit with the performance bug not much later. During a difficult time in junior high, he started journaling, eventually turning his pain into something empowering—and funny. He scored his first stand-up gig at age 14, and hasn't looked back.

Mooney, Carla, 1970-

What is anxiety disorder? Carla Mooney. ReferencePoint Press, [2016] 80 p.: Understanding mental disorders

Grades: 8 9 10 11 12   **616.85**
   1. Anxiety disorders 2. Mental illness
   ISBN 9781601529206

"This explores what it is like to live with the illness as well as its causes and treatments, and the well-organized, jargon-free information allows readers not already familiar with the topic to easily understand. Graphs, color photos, and side boxes containing supplemental facts break up the text, but this volume, unlike many of its contemporaries, is ultimately more invested in providing substantive information than in creating an engaging reading experience. A list of chapter notes, organizations, and sources round up the reference credentials of the book, which will be of value to student researchers." Booklist.

Moragne, Wendy

Depression. Wendy Moragne. Twenty-First Century Books, c2011. 128 p.

Grades: 8 9 10 11 12   **616.85**
   1. Depression
   ISBN 9780761358824

                                    LC 2010034122
Examines the history, forms, and treatment options for depression, a disease that affects a person's moods.

"This book about depression will serve as solid report fodder. . . . [The] volume has an introduction, a description of the condition, chapters on what it is like to live with it, and material on research and treatments. A healthy smattering of statistics and personal stories appear throughout." School Library Journal.

Includes bibliographical references (p. 122-123) and index.

Omnigraphics, Inc

Eating disorders information for teens: health tips about anorexia, bulimia, binge eating, and body image disorders including information about risk factors, prevention, diagnosis, treatment, health consequences, and other related issues.. Omnigraphics (COR). Omnigraphics, 2017 xii, 331 p.

Grades: 7 8 9   **616.85**
   1. Eating disorders 2. Teenagers with eating disorders
   ISBN 9780780815599

           LC 2017010041

Provides consumer health information for teens about causes, prevention, and treatment of eating disorders, along with tips for healthy eating. Includes index, resource information and online access. Provided by publisher.

Petro-Roy, Jen

You are enough: your guide to body image and eating disorder recovery. Jen Petro-Roy. Feiwel and Friends, 2019. 323 p.

Grades: 5 6 7 8 9   **616.85**
   1. Anorexia nervosa 2. Eating disorders -- Treatment 3. Eating disorders -- Psychological aspects 4. Body image
   ISBN 9781250151025

           LC 2018019396

Presents a self-help guide on dealing with eating disorders, providing advice on overcoming anxiety, negative thoughts, and distorted body images and using relaxation techniques and cognitive reframing, with information about treatments and tools for recovery.

"An excellent choice for libraries needing new eating disorder resources, especially those serving middle schoolers." School Library Journal.

Includes bibliographical references.

Rodriguez, Ana Maria, 1958-

Autism spectrum disorders. Ana Maria Rodriguez. Twenty-First Century Books, c2011. 128 p.: USA today health reports: Diseases and disorders

Grades: 8 9 10 11 12   **616.85**
   1. Autism 2. Asperger's syndrome 3. Developmental disabilities 4. Autism spectrum disorders
   ISBN 9780761358831

           LC 2010034236

Introduces autism spectrum disorders, discusses the causes, describes treatment options, and provides information on support groups and other organizations.

"Back matter includes a glossary, annotated lists of resource organizations and websites, selected bibliographies, very brief lists of source notes, and recommended reading lists." Booklist.

Includes bibliographical references (p. 119-124) and index.

Scarlet, Janina

Superhero therapy: mindfulness skills to help teens and young adults deal with anxiety, depression, and trauma. Janina Scarlet, PhD; illustrated by Wellinton Alves. New Harbinger Publications, 2017, c2016. 112 p.

Grades: 7 8 9 10 11 12   **616.85**
   1. Teenagers 2. Anxiety disorders 3. Depression 4. Mindfulness (Psychology) 5. Self-help psychology for teenagers 6. Illustrated books
   ISBN 9781684030330

With this fun, outside-the-box self-help guide, teens will discover how to vanquish inner super villains such as anxiety, depression, anger, or shame; explore their unique superpowers; and become their own Superhero questing for what matters to them.

"The conceit, along with some eye-catching art and a focus on setting simple, achievable daily goals, makes this a promising alternative to more conventional self-help programs." Booklist.

Scowen, Kate

My kind of sad: what it's like to be young and depressed. Kate Scowen; illustrated by Jeff Szuc. Annick Press, 2006. 168 p.

Grades: 7 8 9 10   **616.85**
   1. Teenagers with depression 2. Teenagers -- Mental health 3. Depression 4. Mental health
   ISBN 1550379410

           LC bl2006003661

Discusses the difference between temporary difficulties and serious mental health disorders, shares the thoughts of teens who have experienced different types of depression, and offers practical guidelines for finding help.

"The book discusses the history of depression, adolescence and depression, and treatment options. Scowen's focus is on understanding the difference between simply being sad and suffering from depression. Topics such as bipolar disorder, self-mutilation, anorexia, and suicide are also discussed. . . . Scowen's book is well-written, easy to read and use, and quite informative." Voice of Youth Advocates.

Skotko, Brian

Fasten your seatbelt: a crash course on Down syndrome for brothers and sisters. Brian Skotko and Susan Levine. Woodbine House, 2009. viii, 191 p.

Grades: 4 5 6 7   **616.85**
   1. Down syndrome 2. Brothers and sisters of children with disabilities 3. People with developmental disabilities 4. People with Down syndrome -- Family relationships 5. Children with disabilities
   ISBN 9781890627867

           LC 2008049753

"Skotko and Levine address preteens and teenagers who have a sibling with Down syndrome, answering questions that have been generated through their work with this population. . . . With a wealth of information, numerous resources, and the reassurance that all siblings of people with disabilities sometimes go through periods of contradictory feelings, this is an excellent guide for young people who are trying to figure out how to negotiate an often-confusing relationship." School Library Journal.

Smith, Rita P.

Self-image and eating disorders. Rita Smith ... [et al.]. Rosen Pub., 2012. 48 p.: Teen mental health

Grades: 6 7 8 9   **616.85**
   1. Teenagers with eating disorders 2. Body image in teenagers 3. Eating disorders -- Psychological aspects 4. Eating disorders -- Treatment 5. Body image
   ISBN 9781448868940

           LC 2012003030

Provides information about body image and eating disorders, including profiles of common eating disorders, the signs and causes of these disorders, and where to go for help.

Snedden, Robert

Explaining autism. Robert Snedden. Smart Apple Media, c2010. 45 p. : Explaining--

Grades: 5 6 7 8   **616.85**
   1. Autism 2. People with autism 3. People with developmental disabilities 4. Developmental disabilities
   ISBN 9781599203072

           LC 2008049285

"The incorporation of quotes and personal accounts in Case Notes sidebars adds to the sensitive tone found throughout [the title]." School Library Journal.

Stewart, Gail B., 1949-
Bulimia. Gail B. Stewart. Cherry Lake Pub., 2009. 32 p.: Health at risk

Grades: 4 5 6 7   **616.85**
1. Bulimia 2. Eating disorders 3. Teenagers -- Health 4. Bulimia -- Treatment
ISBN 9781602792821

LC 2008017497
Describes the eating disorder known as bulimia, what is known about the causes and triggers, how it effects people, and the ways in which it is treated.
"Great for reports or reluctant readers." Booklist.
Includes bibliographical references (p. 31) and index.

Tabone, Francis, 1965-
Autism spectrum disorder: the ultimate teen guide. Francis Tabone. Rowman & Littlefield, [2016] 228 p.: It happened to me

Grades: 8 9 10 11   **616.85**
1. Autism spectrum disorders 2. Autism 3. Developmental disabilities 4. Teenagers with autism
ISBN 9781442262416

LC 2016000780
"A useful research tool and an essential resource for secondary school libraries." School Library Journal.
Includes bibliographical references and index.

Walker, Ida
Recreational ritalin: the not-so-smart drug. by Ida Walker. Mason Crest, c2013. 128 p.

Grades: 7 8 9 10   **616.85**
1. Methylphenidate hydrochloride 2. Attention-deficit hyperactivity disorder -- Chemotherapy 3. Medication abuse 4. Teenagers -- Drug use 5. Children -- Drug use
ISBN 9781422224397

LC oc2013032149
Looks at aspects of the ADHD drug, ritalin, including how it is used to treat the disorder, the ways it can be abused, and how to help those addicted to it.

616.85882 Autism

Ginsberg, Blaze, 1987-
Episodes: my life as I see it. Blaze Ginsberg. Roaring Brook, 2009. 288 p.

Grades: 6 7 8 9 10   **616.85882**
1. Ginsberg, Blaze, 1987- 2. Teenagers with autism 3. Autism 4. Interpersonal relations 5. People with autism 6. Teenage boy/girl relations
ISBN 9781596434615
Blaze Ginsberg creates titles and categories for the different periods and moments in his life, creating a list of episodes that exist in various stages of production as his life progresses and the days of his existence roll on.
"The high-functioning spectrum-disorder child portrayed in his mother Debra's Raising Blaze (2002) steps up to offer his own views of high school and after. He structures his memoir . . . as thumbnail summaries of concurrent or successive TV series. . . . He writes in a distant

but often humorous voice about feelings, fixations, and the seemingly aimless way people move in and out of his life. . . . This book provides memorable insight into the author's distinctive mind and spirit." Booklist.

616.86 Substance abuse (Drug abuse)

Allman, Toney
Drugs. Toney Allman. Cherry Lake Pub., c2009. 32 p.: Health at risk

Grades: 4 5 6 7   **616.86**
1. Drug abuse 2. Self-destructive behavior 3. Drug addiction 4. Health 5. Drug use
ISBN 9781602792838

LC 2008017503
Discusses drug use, its affects, what causes addiction, and how to overcome drug abuse and stay away from drugs.
"Great for reports or reluctant readers." Booklist.
Includes bibliographical references (p. 31) and index.

Walker, Ida
Alcohol addiction: not worth the buzz. Ida Walker. Mason Crest, c2013. 128 p.

Grades: 7 8 9 10   **616.86**
1. Alcoholism -- History 2. Alcoholism -- Treatment -- History
ISBN 9781422224281

LC oc2013032139
Looks at the issue of alcohol abuse, including its history, how it affects the body, and what can be done for alcoholics.

616.89 Diseases—Diseases of nervous system and mental disorders—Mental disorders

Hugstad, Kristi, 1957-
Beneath the surface: a teen's guide to reaching out when you or your friend is in crisis. Kristi Hugstad; foreword by Nancy Guerra, EdD. New World Library, 2019 184 p.

Grades: 7 8 9 10 11 12   **616.89**
1. Teenagers -- Mental health 2. Emotional problems of teenagers 3. Adolescent psychology 4. Self-esteem in teenagers 5. Mental health
ISBN 9781608686353
Teen-tested strategies for addressing and overcoming the overwhelm many teens feel day in and day out.

Jensen, Kelly
(Don't) call me crazy: 33 voices start the conversation about mental health. edited by Kelly Jensen. Algonquin Young Readers, 2018. 240 p.

Grades: 7 8 9 10 11 12   **616.89**
1. Mental illness 2. People with mental illnesses 3. Mental health 4. Teenagers -- Mental health 5. Anthologies 6. Essays
ISBN 9781616207816

LC 2018010861
Presents an anthology of essays that illuminate such mental health topics as autism, bipolar disorder, body dysmorphia, depression, and healing.

Kent, Deborah

Snake pits, talking cures & magic bullets: a history of mental illness. Deborah Kent. Twenty-First Century Books, c2003. 160 p.

Grades: 6 7 8 9   **616.89**

1. Mental illness -- History 2. Mental illness 3. Medicine -- History
ISBN 0761327045

     LC 2002011208

Looks at how the mentally ill have been treated throughout history, focusing on advances made in the 19th and 20th centuries regarding mental hospitals, medications, and social acceptance.

"An excellent history peppered with fascinating accounts. . . . Black-and-white archival photographs and reproductions appear throughout. . . . This is a fine treatment of a topic not heavily covered for this audience." School Library Journal.

Includes bibliographical references (p. 148-150) and index.

Siebert, Melanie

Heads up: changing minds on mental health. Melanie Siebert; illustrations by Belle Wuthrich. Orca Book Pub., 2020. 192 p.

Grades: 7 8 9 10 11 12   **616.89**

1. Mental health 2. Mental illness 3. People with mental illnesses
ISBN 9781459819115

This nonfiction book for teen readers is a guide to understanding mental health and coping with mental illness, trauma and recovery. It features real-life stories of resilient teens and highlights innovative approaches to mental health challenges.

"Informative, diverse, and highly engaging; a much-needed addition to the realm of mental health." Kirkus.

Includes bibliographical references and index.

616.8900835 Adolescent psychiatry

Omnigraphics, Inc

Mental health information for teens: health tips about mental wellness and mental illness: including facts about recognizing and treating mood, anxiety, personality, psychotic, behavioral, impulse control, and addiction disorders.. Keith (EDT) Jones. Omnigraphics, 2017 xii, 426 p.

Grades: 9 10 11 12   **616.8900835**

1. Teenagers -- Mental health 2. Adolescent psychology 3. Child mental health
ISBN 9780780815735

     LC 2017028218

Provides consumer health information about the causes, warning signs, and symptoms of mental health disorders, along with facts about treatment approaches and tips for teens on coping with stress, building self-esteem, and maintaining mental wellness. Includes a further reading list, a directory of crisis helplines and related organizations, and an index. Provided by publisher.

616.9 Other diseases

Aronin, Miriam

Tuberculosis: the white plague! by Miriam Aronin. Bearport Pub., 2010. 32 p.: Nightmare plagues

Grades: 4 5 6 7   **616.9**

1. Tuberculosis 2. Communicable diseases 3. Epidemics

4. Tuberculosis -- Prevention 5. Communicable diseases -- Transmission
ISBN 9781936088065

     LC 2010010679

Looks at the disease tuberculosis, its causes, how it is spread, how it affects the body, how it is prevented, and the history of its outbreaks.

"The writing is accessible and interspersed with interesting photographs and fact boxes. . . . [The book relies] on an honest discussion of [tuberculosis and is an] . . . effective, easily navigated [introduction]." School Library Journal.

Includes bibliographical references (p. 31) and index.

Colligan, L. H.

Tick-borne illnesses. by L.H. Colligan. Marshall Cavendish Benchmark, c2009. 64 p.: Health alert (New York, N.Y.)

Grades: 4 5 6 7   **616.9**

1. Ticks 2. Tick-borne diseases 3. Ticks as carriers of disease 4. Diseases -- Treatment
ISBN 9780761429142

     LC 2007038517

Provides comprehensive information on the causes, treatment, and history of tick-borne illnesses. Provided by publisher.

"This title features a handsome format, with well-chosen illustrations, a substantial amount of information, and some practical insights." Booklist.

Donovan, Sandra, 1967-

Keep your cool!: what you should know about stress. Sandy Donovan; illustrations by Jack Desrocher. Lerner Publications, c2009. 64 p.: Health zone

Grades: 4 5 6 7   **616.9**

1. Stress management 2. Stress management for children 3. Stress 4. Emotions 5. Health
ISBN 9780822575559

     LC 2007038858

"The format is beyond lively, with lots of color, cartoons, and an informal writing style, but it manages to present sometimes frightening material in a non-threatening and browsable way." Booklist.

Includes bibliographical references (p. 61-62) and index.

Hoffmann, Gretchen

Chickenpox. by Gretchen Hoffmann. Marshall Cavendish Benchmark, c2009. 62 p. : Health alert (New York, N.Y.)

Grades: 4 5 6 7   **616.9**

1. Chicken pox 2. Sick persons 3. Medicine 4. Chicken pox -- Treatment
ISBN 9780761429166

     LC 2007031793

Provides comprehensive information on the causes, treatment, and history of chickenpox. Provided by publisher.

"This title features a handsome format, with well-chosen illustrations, a substantial amount of information, and some practical insights." Booklist.

Lewis, Mark L., 1991-

Cholera: how the blue death changed history. Mark L. Lewis; consultant, Sean Moore, PhD, Research Assistant Professor, Biology, University of Notre Dame. Capstone Press, 2020 32 p.

Grades: 3 4 5 6 7 8   **616.9**

1. Cholera 2. Cholera -- History 3. Cholera -- Prevention 4.

Epidemics -- History 5. Diseases and history
ISBN 9781543572384

LC 2018061088

Explores the history and impact of cholera. Provided by publisher.

Murphy, Jim, 1947-

Invincible microbe: tuberculosis and the never-ending search for a cure. Jim Murphy, Alison Blank. Clarion Books, 2012. 149 p.
Grades: 5 6 7 8 9   **616.9**
1. Tuberculosis 2. Microorganisms 3. Diseases 4. Communicable diseases 5. Prejudice
ISBN 9780618535743

LC 2011025951

This is the compelling, suspenseful, down-to-earth story of a killer that has been stalking and doing away with people for thousands of years: Tuberculosis. For centuries TB in many forms was treated with everything from poultices and potions to the king's touch. The microorganism that causes the disease was eventually identified, more effective treatments were developed, and the cure for TB was thought to be within reach. But the TB germ simply will not die; drug-resistant varieties continue to plague and panic the human race. The "biography" of this deadly germ, an account of the diagnosis, treatment, and "cure" of the disease over time, and the social history of an illness that could strike anywhere but was most prevalent among the poor are woven together in an engrossing narrative supported by 70-plus archival prints and photographs. Includes bibliography, source notes, and index. Provided by publisher.

Newman, Patricia, 1958-

Ebola: fears and facts. by Patricia Newman. Millbrook Press, 2016. 48 p.
Grades: 4 5 6 7 8   **616.9**
1. Ebola virus disease 2. DIseases 3. Epidemics 4. Hemorrhagic diseases
ISBN 9781467792400

LC 2015001167

What's Ebola? Do we need to be afraid? This short book will take readers beyond the headlines to help them understand the 2014 outbreak. It will inform while helping to alleviate fears. Provided by publisher.

"Breaking new ground, Newman has written a truly excellent book for middle grade students that tackles the terrifying spector of Ebola. As the title suggests, readers will come away with more facts and [fewer] fears." School Library Journal.

Omnigraphics, Inc

Stress information for teens: health tips about the mental and physical consequences of stress including facts about the causes of stress, types of stressors, effects of stress, strategies for managing stress, and more.. Omnigraphics Omnigraphics, 2018 xii, 388 p.
Grades: 9 10 11 12   **616.9**
1. Stress management for teenagers 2. Stress (Psychology)
ISBN 9780780815896

LC 2017041421

Provides consumer health information for teens about common causes of stress, the effects of stress on the body and mind, and coping strategies. Includes index, resource information, and recommendations for further reading. Provided by publisher.

616.95 Sexually transmitted diseases, zoonose

Yancey, Diane

STDs. Diane Yancey. Twenty-First Century Books, c2012. 128 p.
Grades: 7 8 9 10 11 12   **616.95**
1. Diseases 2. Sexually transmitted diseases
ISBN 9780761354567

LC 2010036514

Explains different types of sexually transmitted diseases, how they are contracted, their symptoms, and treatment.

"Yancey writes in a straightforward manner about sexually transmitted diseases, opening with the profiles of several teens coping with an STD. . . . The causes, symptoms, and treatments of the main STDs, . . . are thoroughly covered, from the emotional side effects of genital herpes to the dangers of ordering an HIV home sample collection kit online. . . . Students, teachers, and librarians looking to supplement health textbooks with current information will find this . . . valuable." Voice of Youth Advocates.

Includes bibliographical references (p. 120-124) and index.

616.97 Diseases of immune system

Ballard, Carol

Explaining food allergies. Carol Ballard. Smart Apple Media, c2010. 42 p. : Explaining--
Grades: 5 6 7 8   **616.97**
1. Food allergy 2. Allergy 3. Food habits 4. Food
ISBN 9781599203164

LC 2008049936

"This does an excellent job of discussing complex clinical science while showing what daily life is like for kids living with food allergies, from the signs and symptoms to the tests and treatments. . . . This blend of the technical and the personal will have wide appeal." Booklist.

Sonenklar, Carol

AIDS. Carol Sonenklar. Twenty-First Century Books, c2011. 128 p.: USA today health reports: Diseases and disorders
Grades: 8 9 10 11 12   **616.97**
1. AIDS (Disease) 2. HIV (Viruses) 3. Immunologic diseases 4. Communicable diseases 5. Diseases
ISBN 9780822585817

LC 2010037633

An introduction to HIV and AIDS provides basic information about the symptoms, transmission, prevention, and treatment of the disease.

"This book about AIDS will serve as solid report fodder. . . . [The] volume has an introduction, a description of the condition, chapters on what it is like to live with it, and material on research and treatments. A healthy smattering of statistics and personal stories appear throughout." School Library Journal.

Includes bibliographical references (p. 124-125) and index.

616.99 Tumors and miscellaneous communicable diseases

Esposito, Lisa

Cancer information for teens: health tips about cancer prevention, risks, diagnosis, and treatment: including facts about cancers of most concern to teens and young adults, coping strategies, survivorship, and dealing with cancer in loved ones. edited by Lisa Esposito. Omnigraphics, [2014] xii, 410 p.: Teen health series

Grades: 7 8 9 10 11 12 **616.99**
   1. Cancer 2. People with cancer
ISBN 9780780813199

LC 2013026651

Provides basic consumer health information for teens about cancer risk factors, prevention, and treatment, along with tips for coping with cancer at home and school, and helping a friend or family member who has cancer. Includes index, resource information, and recommendations for further reading. Provided by publisher.

Markle, Sandra

Leukemia: true survival stories. by Sandra Markle. Lerner Publications, c2011. 48 p.: Powerful medicine

Grades: 5 6 7 8 **616.99**
   1. Leukemia 2. Blood -- Diseases 3. Cancer 4. People with cancer
ISBN 9780822587002

LC 2009034441

"This book about leukemia will grab the attention of middle school readers. . . . The illustrations and photos are stunning with medically accurate captions. Real-life patients, whose photos are included in the text, are highlighted, with updates on their progress at the end of . . . [the] book. . . . This . . . fills the need for up-to-date books on medical topics using vocabulary that a young teenager can understand." Voice of Youth Advocates.

Includes bibliographical references and index.

Silver, Marc, 1951-

My parent has cancer and it really sucks. Marc Silver, Maya Silver. Sourcebooks Fire, [2013] 304 p.

Grades: 6 7 8 9 10 11 12 **616.99**
   1. Children of people with cancer 2. People with cancer -- Psychology 3. Children and cancer 4. Loss (Psychology)
ISBN 9781402273070

LC 2012039095

"Drawing on their experiences, the Silvers offer advice for finding solace in people who have been there and who have found ways to cope... It's admirable that the authors don't sugarcoat the realities of cancer and will speak with an honesty that teens will identify with and find comfort in." Booklist.

617 Surgery, regional medicine, dentistry, ophthalmology, otology, audiology

Murphy, Jim, 1947-

★ **Breakthrough!**: how three people saved "blue babies" and changed medicine forever. Jim Murphy. Clarion Books, [2015] 208 p.

Grades: 4 5 6 7 8 **617**
   1. Thomas, Vivien T., 1910-1985. 2. Blalock, Alfred, 1899-1964. 3. Taussig, Helen B. (Helen Brooke), 1898-1986 4. 1940s 5. Surgeons 6. Heart -- Surgery 7. Cardiovascular system 8. Heart
ISBN 9780547821832

LC 2015013601

The story of the landmark 1944 surgical procedure that repaired the heart of a child with blue baby syndrome—lack of blood oxygen caused by a congenital defect. The team that developed the procedure included a cardiologist and a surgeon, but most of the actual work was done by Vivien Thomas, an African American lab assistant who was frequently mistaken for a janitor. Provided by publisher.

"Murphy's dramatic nonfiction narrative recounting of one of the first open heart surgeries ever performed is not to be missed—even reluctant readers will be hooked." School Library Journal.

Townsend, John, 1955-

Scalpels, stitches + scars: a history of surgery. John Townsend. Raintree, c2006. 56 p.: Raintree freestyle

Grades: 6 7 8 9 **617**
   1. Surgery -- History 2. Medicine -- History 3. Grossology
ISBN 1410913325

LC 2004014248

Discusses the procedures used by surgeons in the past, describing the dangers involved in many of them, and how surgery has improved in modern times.

"This is packed with grisly facts and gory images. . . . But the science is accurate, and many readers will be intrigued by the medical drama. . . . The design, with lots of color pictures, captions, and boxes, will grab browsers, and the cover art is a thrilling story in itself." Booklist.

Includes bibliographical references (p. 52) and index.

617.1 Injuries and wounds

Lew, Kristi

Clot & scab: gross stuff about your scrapes, bumps, and bruises. written by Kristi Lew; illustrated by Michael Slack. Millbrook Press, c2010. 48 p.: Gross body science

Grades: 4 5 6 **617.1**
   1. Skin 2. Wound healing 3. Wounds and injuries 4. Body covering (Anatomy) 5. Blood 6. Grossology
ISBN 9780822589655

LC 2008045626

"Solid information layered between sarcastic comments and kid-friendly terminology like fart, poop, barf, and puke will keep readers engaged. . . . Labeled, captioned (and graphic) photographs, cartoon-style illustrations, and micrographs add information." School Library Journal.

Includes bibliographical references and index.

Markle, Sandra

Bad burns: true survival stories. Sandra Markle. Lerner Pub., c2011. 48 p.: Powerful medicine

Grades: 5 6 7 8 **617.1**
   1. Wounds and injuries 2. Blisters 3. Burns and scalds 4. Skin -- Wounds and injuries 5. Burns and scalds -- Treatment 6. Grossology
ISBN 9780822587026

LC 2009034439

Explores how advancements in medicine and technology have helped victims of severe skin burns, and includes real-life stories of burn survivors and tips on burn prevention and treatment.

"This narrative reads like information from the Discovery Health channel, for kids: part fascinating science, part human interest story, and part Eew, gross!. . . Clear, straightforward prose is supplemented by definitions and explanations of medical techniques and jargon. The numerous color photos and medical images will satisfy readers' curiosity." School Library Journal.

Includes bibliographical references (p. 46-47) and index.

Omnigraphics, Inc

Sports injuries information for teens: health tips about acute, traumatic, and chronic injuries in adolescent athletes including facts about sprains, fractures, and overuse injuries, treatment, rehabilitation, sport-specific safety guidelines, fitness suggestions, and more.. Omnigraphics (COR). Omnigraphics, 2017 xii, 390 p.

Grades: 9 10 11 12 **617.1**
1. Sports injuries 2. Teenagers -- Wounds and injuries -- Prevention 3. Wounds and injuries
ISBN 9780780815674

LC 2017029918

Provides consumer health information for teens about sports-related injury prevention, treatment, and rehabilitation. Includes index and resource information. Provided by publisher.

617.4 Surgery by systems and regions

Goldsmith, Connie, 1945-
Traumatic brain injury: from concussion to coma. Connie Goldsmith. Twenty-First Century Books, [2014] 88 p.

Grades: 6 7 8 9 10 11 **617.4**
1. People with traumatic brain injuries 2. Brain injury 3. Neurology 4. Brain -- Diseases
ISBN 9781467713481

LC 2013001346

"Photographs, charts, and statistics are included, which expand the information. Appended are source notes, a glossary, a bibliography, and a list of websites and resources. The currency of this topic and its potential impact on teens make this a smart choice for school and public libraries." Booklist.

Includes bibliographical references and index.

Markle, Sandra
Shattered bones: true survival stories. by Sandra Markle. Lerner Publications, c2011. 48 p.: Powerful medicine

Grades: 5 6 7 8 **617.4**
1. Bones 2. Bones -- Wounds and injuries 3. Wounds and injuries 4. Grossology
ISBN 9780822587033

LC 2009034442

"This narrative reads like information from the Discovery Health channel, for kids: part fascinating science, part human interest story, and part Eew, gross!. . . Clear, straightforward prose is supplemented by definitions and explanations of medical techniques and jargon. The numerous color photos and medical images will satisfy readers' curiosity." School Library Journal.

Includes bibliographical references and index.

McClafferty, Carla Killough, 1958-
Fourth down and inches: concussions and football's make-or-break moment. by Carla Killough McClafferty. Carolrhoda Books, [2013] 96 p.

Grades: 6 7 8 9 10 11 12 **617.4**
1. Sports injuries 2. Football injuries 3. Brain -- Concussion 4. Head -- Wounds and injuries 5. Football players -- Health and hygiene
ISBN 9781467710671

LC 2013004192

Award-winning author Carla Killough McClafferty takes readers on a bone-crunching journey from football's origins to the latest research on concussion and traumatic brain injuries in the sport. Fourth Down and Inches features exclusive photography and interviews with scientists, players, and the families of athletes who have literally given everything to the game.

"A well-researched and readable informational text on sports concussions provides a strong case for greater understanding and awareness of their long-term effects...A lofty level of research is reflected in the extensive backmatter, which includes source notes, an index, a bibliography and further reading as well as a medically approved list of concussion symptoms and return-to-play recommendations." Kirkus

Includes bibliographical references and index.

Yount, Lisa
Alfred Blalock, Helen Taussig, and Vivien Thomas: mending children's hearts. Lisa Yount. Chelsea House, c2011. 127 p.: Trailblazers in science and technology

Grades: 7 8 9 10 11 12 **617.4**
1. Blalock, Alfred, 1899-1964. 2. Taussig, Helen, 1898-1986 3. Thomas, Vivien T., 1910-1985. 4. Heart surgeons 5. Pediatric cardiology -- History 6. Surgeons 7. Heart -- Surgery
ISBN 9781604136586

LC 2010035656

"Sidebars and captioned color and archival photographs round out the dense, though clearly written, texts." School Library Journal.

Includes bibliographical references and index.

617.5 Regional medicine

Rogers, Kara
Ear, nose, and throat. edited by Kara Rogers. Britannica Educational Pub., 2012. xvii, 186 p.

Grades: 10 11 12 **617.5**
1. Otolaryngology
ISBN 9781615306572

LC 2011013432

Examines the ear, nose, and throat, looking at their anatomy, physiology, and the diseases that afflict them.

617.6 Dentistry

Telgemeier, Raina
★ **Smile**. Raina Telgemeier. Graphix, 2010. 224 p.

Grades: 5 6 7 8 **617.6**
1. Telgemeier, Raina. 2. Dental care 3. Self-esteem in teenagers 4. Braces (Dentistry) 5. Self-esteem 6. Sixth-grade girls 7. Coming-of-age stories 8. Autobiographical comics 9. Comics and Graphic novels
ISBN 9780545132053

LC 2008051782

"Telgemeier has created an utterly charming graphic memoir of tooth trauma, first crushes and fickle friends, sweetly reminiscent of Judy Blume's work." Kirkus.

617.7 Ophthalmology

Bender, Lionel
Explaining blindness. Lionel Bender. Smart Apple Media, c2010. 45 p. : Explaining--

Grades: 5 6 7 8 **617.7**
1. Blindness 2. Children who are blind 3. Color-blindness 4. Eye

-- Diseases and defects 5. People with visual disabilities
ISBN 9781599203102

LC 2008049286

"The incorporation of quotes and personal accounts in Case Notes sidebars adds to the sensitive tone found throughout [the title]." School Library Journal.

Markle, Sandra

Lost sight: true survival stories. Sandra Markle. Lerner Publications, c2011. 48 p.: Powerful medicine

Grades: 5 6 7 8   **617.7**
1. Vision 2. Eye 3. Blindness 4. Medicine 5. Medical care 6. Grossology
ISBN 9780822587019

LC 2009034443

Offers true stories of people with visual impairments, along with information on the eye and its functions and treatments doctors are using to restore vision.

"This book about vision loss will grab the attention of middle school readers. . . . The illustrations and photos are stunning with medically accurate captions. Real-life patients, whose photos are included in the text, are highlighted, with updates on their progress at the end of . . . [the] book." Voice of Youth Advocates.

Includes bibliographical references (p. 46-47) and index.

617.8 Otology and audiology

Levete, Sarah

Explaining deafness. Sarah Levete. Smart Apple Media, c2010. 45 p. : Explaining--

Grades: 5 6 7 8   **617.8**
1. Deafness 2. People who are deaf 3. Ear -- Diseases 4. Physical disabilities
ISBN 9781599203133

LC 2008049289

"The incorporation of quotes and personal accounts in Case Notes sidebars adds to the sensitive tone found throughout [the title]." School Library Journal.

617.9 Operative surgery and special fields of surgery

Campbell, Andrew, 1974-

Cosmetic surgery. Andrew Campbell. Smart Apple Media, c2010. 44 p.: Science in the news

Grades: 6 7 8 9   **617.9**
1. Plastic surgery 2. Plastic surgeons 3. Surgery
ISBN 9781599203225

LC 2008049274

"This book about cosmetic surgery move[s] smoothly, occasionally pausing for the definition of a term. [The title] boast[s] plenty of attractive photos, and a clean layout allows the information to be easily consumed. . . . Provides the information that younger teens need." School Library Journal.

Schwartz, Tina P., 1969-

Organ transplants: a survival guide for the entire family: the ultimate teen guide. Tina P. Schwartz. Scarecrow Press, 2005. xii, 243 p.: It happened to me

Grades: 7 8 9 10   **617.9**
1. Transplantation of organs, tissues, etc 2. Donation of organs, tissues, etc
ISBN 0810849240

LC 2004021563

"The 13 chapters, written in a question-and-answer format, detail the steps involved from diagnosis and being placed on a waiting list to pre and post-surgery. . . .The well-written text is complemented by a comprehensive section of suggestions for additional information. . . . Texts with this breadth of coverage are rare." School Library Journal.

Includes bibliographical references and index.

617.954 Transplantation of tissue and organs

Campbell, Andrew, 1974-

Organ transplants. by Andrew Campbell. Smart Apple Media, c2010. 45 p. : Science in the news

Grades: 6 7 8 9   **617.954**
1. Transplantation of organs, tissues, etc 2. Medicine
ISBN 9781599203218

LC 2008041436

Discusses current practices of organ transplants, developments in science that make transplants possible, and the history of organ transplants as well as issues surrounding organ shortage and organ selling. Provided by publisher.

"The narrative move[s] smoothly, occasionally pausing for the definition of a term. [The title] boast[s] plenty of attractive photos, and a clean layout allows the information to be easily consumed. . . . Provides the information that younger teens need." School Library Journal.

618.200835 Young people twelve to twenty

Omnigraphics, Inc

Pregnancy information for teens: health tips about teen pregnancy and teen parenting including facts about prenatal care, pregnancy complications, labor and delivery, postpartum care, pregnancy-related lifestyle concerns, the emotional and legal issues of teen parenting, and more.. Omnigraphics (COR). Omnigraphics, 2017 xii, 424 p.

Grades: 9 10 11 12   **618.200835**
1. Teenage parents 2. Teenage pregnancy
ISBN 9780780815575

LC 2017007851

Provides consumer information for teens about maintaining health during pregnancy, preparing for childbirth, and caring for a newborn. Includes index and resource information. Provided by publisher.

618.92 Pediatrics

Chandler, Matt

Understanding obesity. Matt Chandler. Cherry Lake Publishing, 2019. 32 p.: 21st Century Skills Library: Upfront Health

Grades: 4 5 6 7 8   **618.92**
1. Obesity 2. Body weight
ISBN 9781534147997

LC 2019008063

For young people, leading a healthy lifestyle requires education and empowerment. In Understanding Obesity, readers will explore the social aspects and health effects of obesity, the fundamentals of weight gain and loss, and ways to make healthy choices. Sidebars challenge and expand readers' thinking while relating topics to 21st Century skills and themes—from creativity and innovation to financial literacy.

"Highly recommended. A well-written, intelligent empowering series covering timely topics." School Library Journal.

Crist, James J.

What to do when you're sad & lonely: a guide for kids. James J. Crist . Free Spirit Pub., c2006. 124 p.

Grades: 4 5 6 7   **618.92**

1. Children with depression 2. Teenagers with depression 3. Self-management for teenagers 4. Self-management 5. Depression
ISBN 9781575421896

LC 2005021794

Tells children and youth how to recognize and deal with sad feelings, ways to connect with other people and make new friends, and how to handle sad feelings that are too difficult to manage on one's own.

"Advising his audience to read this book and work through negative feelings with an adult, Crist describes sad and lonely feelings, distinguishes them from more serious conditions such as depression, and then suggests Blues Busters and ways to ask for help. . . . Crist's clear explanations and simple techniques . . . are relevant for both children and adults." Voice of Youth Advocates.

Includes bibliographical references and index.

Grossberg, Blythe N.

★ **Asperger's** rules!: how to make sense of school and friends. by Blythe Grossberg. Magination Press, c2012. 127 p.

Grades: 5 6 7 8   **618.92**

1. Children with autism -- Education 2. Asperger's syndrome 3. Developmental disabilities 4. Children with Asperger's syndrome 5. Autism
ISBN 9781433811289

LC 2011053483

Offers guidance to young people with Asperger's syndrome by explaining how to understand and communicate with their peers and teachers, standing up for and taking care of themselves, setting realistic goals, and making friends.

Kemper, Bitsy

Teens and phobias. Bitsy Kemper. ReferencePoint Press, [2017] 80 p.: Teen mental health (ReferencePoint)

Grades: 8 9 10 11   **618.92**

1. Phobias 2. Anxiety 3. Anxiety disorders 4. Mental health 5. Phobias in teenagers
ISBN 9781682821282

LC 2016035298

"Extremely current in its coverage, this set not only recognizes the importance of such standard topics as eating disorders and suicide but also acknowledges less-covered disorders not often associated with adolescence . . . ." School Library Journal.

Includes bibliographical references and index.

Price, Janet, 1964-

Take control of Asperger's syndrome: the official strategy guide for teens with Asperger's syndrome and nonverbal learning disorder. Janet Price and Jennifer Engel Fisher. Prufrock Press, c2010. xiv, 168 p.

Grades: 8 9 10 11 12   **618.92**

1. Asperger's syndrome in children -- Patients 2. Asperger's syndrome in adolescence -- Patients 3. Nonverbal learning disabilities -- Patients 4. Self-care, Health 5. Asperger's syndrome -- Patients
ISBN 9781593634056

LC 2009050852

Lays out strategies for success in school and social environments for those with Asperger's syndrome or a nonverbal learning disorder, covering such topics as maintaining personal hygiene, coping with bullying, and making friends.

Quinn, Patricia O.

Attention, girls!: a guide to learn all about your ADHD. by Patricia O. Quinn; illustrated by Carl Pearce. Magination Press, c2009. viii, 119 p.

Grades: 4 5 6 7   **618.92**

1. Girls with ADHD 2. Attention-deficit hyperactivity disorder 3. Learning disabilities 4. Girls with learning disabilities
ISBN 9781433804472

LC 2008054524

Introduces practical strategies for young girls suffering from attention-deficit disorder, offering tips and advice on how to manage the disorder.

"Quinn has attention deficit hyperactivity disorder and is a medical doctor; she addresses the types of AD/HD; who can help; differences between girls and boys with AD/HD; making friends; talking with adults about the condition; relaxation techniques; and medication. Her aim is to give girls a variety of ways to manage their disorders. . . . The book is attractive and inviting with colorful cartoon illustrations, sidebars, and highlighted reminders." School Library Journal.

Includes bibliographical references (p. 114-119).

Royston, Angela, 1945-

Explaining Down syndrome. Angela Royston. Smart Apple Media, c2010. 45 p. : Explaining--

Grades: 5 6 7 8   **618.92**

1. Down syndrome 2. People with Down syndrome 3. Developmental disabilities 4. People with developmental disabilities 5. Intellectual disability
ISBN 9781599203089

LC 2008049291

"This book about Down syndrome provides a basic [overview] of the health concerns related to the disease; information on diagnosis and treatment; and a discussion of the challenges or complications experienced by the affected person and their family/friends, and how to manage those problems. . . . The incorporation of quotes and personal accounts in Case Notes sidebars adds to the sensitive tone found throughout [the title]." School Library Journal.

Skrypuch, Marsha Forchuk

One step at a time: a Vietnamese child finds her way. Marsha Forchuk Skrypuch. Pajama Press, 2013, c2012. 93, vii, p.

Grades: 6 7 8   **618.92**

1. Son Thi Anh, Tuyet 2. Children with disabilities 3. Adopted children 4. Vietnamese Canadians 5. Courage 6. Orphans
ISBN 1927485010

Vietnamese-born Tuyet has escaped her war-torn homeland and found a loving family in Canada, but her dreams of running and playing with her adopted siblings, are hampered by her clubfoot and leg weakened by polio.

Stefanski, Daniel

★ **How** to talk to an autistic kid. by Daniel Stefanski; illustrated by Hazel Mitchell. Free Spirit Pub., 2011. 48 p.

Grades: 3 4 5 6 **618.92**
1. Children with autism 2. Children with developmental disabilities 3. Autism 4. Developmental disabilities 5. Interpersonal relations
ISBN 9781575423654

LC 2010043615

"Stefanski provides clear, sometimes blunt, often humorous advice for readers on how to interact with autistic classmates. An authority on this topic—he is a 14-year-old boy with autism—he begins by describing autism. . . . He describes, using a brief paragraph or two per page, some of the traits many autistic people share. . . . For each trait, he offers down-to-earth suggestions for resolving problems. . . . His insightful, matter-of-fact presentation demystifies behaviors that might confuse or disturb non-autistic classmates. Simple cartoon illustrations in black, gray and two shades of turquoise accompany the text. . . . A thought-provoking introduction to autism . . . and an essential purchase for every primary and middle-school classroom." Kirkus.

Verdick, Elizabeth
The **survival** guide for kids with autism spectrum disorders (and their parents). Elizabeth Verdick & Elizabeth Reeve; illustrated by Nick Kobyluch. Free Spirit Pub., c2012. 234 p.
Grades: 5 6 7 8 9 10 11 12 Adult **618.92**
1. Children with autism spectrum disorders 2. Children with autism -- Family relationships 3. Parents of children with autism 4. Autism
ISBN 9781575423852

LC 2011046520

This positive, straightforward book offers kids with autism spectrum disorders (ASDs) their own comprehensive resource for both understanding their condition and finding tools to cope with the challenges they face every day. Some children with ASDs are gifted; others struggle academically. Some are more introverted, while others try to be social. Some get "stuck" on things, have limited interests, or experience repeated motor movements like flapping or pacing ("stims"). The Survival Guide for Kids with Autism Spectrum Disorders covers all of these areas, with an emphasis on helping children gain new self-understanding and self-acceptance. Meant to be read with a parent, the book addresses questions ("What's an ASD?" "Why me?") and provides strategies for communicating, making and keeping friends, and succeeding in school. Body and brain basics highlight symptom management, exercise, diet, hygiene, relaxation, sleep, and toileting. Emphasis is placed on helping kids handle intense emotions and behaviors and get support from family and their team of helpers when needed. The book includes stories from real kids, fact boxes, helpful checklists, resources, and a glossary. Sections for parents offer more detailed information. Provided by publisher.

"This volume could become a treasured resource for families looking for help in successfully working through some of the problems faced by higher-functioning children with ASD." School Library Journal.

618.9297 Immune system diseases

Bellenir, Karen
Allergy information for teens: health tips about allergic reactions to food, pollen, mold, and other substances, including facts about diagnosing, treating, and preventing allergic responses and complications. edited by Karen Bellenir. Omnigraphics, 2013. xiii, 388 p.
Grades: 7 8 9 10 11 12 **618.9297**
1. Allergy 2. Allergy in children 3. Food allergy 4. Insect allergy
ISBN 9780780812888

LC 2012038514

Provides basic consumer health information for teens about allergies, including facts about treating and preventing allergic reactions and complications, and tips for coping with allergies at home and school. Includes index and resource information. Provided by publisher.

620 Engineering and allied operations

Hunt, Shannon (Shannon Chantal)
Engineered!: engineering design at work. written by Shannon Hunt; illustrated by James Gulliver Hancock. Kids Can Press, 2017. 48 p.
Grades: 5 6 7 8 9 10 **620**
1. Engineering 2. Engineers
ISBN 9781771385602

LC oc2017003548

Author Shannon Hunt explores nine feats of engineering and the step-by-step process that engineers followed to get to a winning solution.
"Eye-opening, encouraging, and attractive—a winning trifecta" Kirkus.

620.0078 Engineering—Laboratory manuals

Anderson, Maxine
Amazing Leonardo da Vinci inventions you can build yourself. Maxine Anderson. Nomad Press, c2006. 122 p.
Grades: 5 6 7 8 **620.0078**
1. Leonardo, da Vinci, 1452-1519. 2. Leonardo, da Vinci, 1452-1519 3. Inventions 4. Handicraft 5. Creative activities for children and students
ISBN 0974934429

LC bl2006005406

Provides step-by-step instructions for creating various projects that Leonardo da Vinci invented or envisioned in his notebooks using everyday household items.
"Anderson has combined biography with doable activities that mirror ideas found in Leonardo's notebooks. Using common household objects (duct tape, foil, cereal boxes, paper-towel tubes, etc.), readers can make a parachute, hydrometer, invisible ink, walk-on-water shoes, etc. Anderson introduces each project with an explanation of why Leonardo came up with the idea and whether he created just the sketch or the sketch and the object. Detailed steps and illustrations provide clarity." School Library Journal.
Includes bibliographical references (p. 119-120) and index.

Mercer, Bobby, 1961-
Junk drawer engineering: 25 construction challenges that don't cost a thing. Bobby Mercer. Chicago Review Press, 2017. 212 p.: Junk drawer science
Grades: 4 5 6 7 8 **620.0078**
1. Engineering 2. Science 3. Experiments
ISBN 9781613737163

LC 2016037089

Can children construct a "roller coaster" from recycled cardboard tubes in which the marble "car" jumps a track to land safely at its final destination? And can they create a device to safely catch a freefalling egg? These projects and more can be found in Junk Drawer Engineering, which demonstrates that you don't need high-tech equipment to make learning fun—just what you can find in your recycling bin and around the house. Provided by publisher.

VanCleave, Janice Pratt

Janice VanCleave's engineering for every kid: easy activities that make learning science fun. Janice VanCleave. Jossey-Bass, c2007. ix, 205 p.: Science for every kid

Grades: 4 5 6 7   **620.0078**

   1. Engineering -- Experiments 2. Science -- Experiments
ISBN 9780471471820

                         LC 2006010540

Presents twenty-five science experiments and projects dealing with engineering, introducing each activity with an explanation of the forces involved and the theories that will be tested.

620.1 Engineering mechanics and materials

Kassinger, Ruth, 1954-

Glass: from Cinderella's slippers to fiber optics. Ruth G. Kassinger. Twenty-First Century Books, c2003. 80 p.: Material world

Grades: 7 8 9 10   **620.1**

   1. Glass 2. Glass manufacture
ISBN 0761321098

                         LC 2002005329

Describes the physical composition and characteristics of glass, and presents glassmaking techniques and the various uses made of glass throughout history.

"This will catch the interest of a wide variety of readers. The color photographs are clear, interesting, and self-explanatory." Library Media Connection.

Includes bibliographical references (p. 76) and index.

Morris, Neil, 1946-

Metals. Neil Morris. Amicus, 2010. 48 p.: Materials that matter

Grades: 4 5 6 7   **620.1**

   1. Metals 2. Metals -- History 3. Scrap metals -- Recycling
ISBN 9781607530664

                         LC 2009029797

Discusses metals as a material, including historical uses, current uses, mining and manufacturing, and recycling. Provided by publisher.

"The clean layout includes photographs and occasional charts, graphs, and technical illustrations against a range of pastel backgrounds. Inset boxes provide further detail, interesting extras, and recycling information. . . . [This book offers] easily accessible background information for report writers." School Library Journal.

621.042 Energy engineering

Burgan, Michael

Energy. Michael Burgan. Mason Crest, [2017] 64 p.: STEM in current events

Grades: 6 7 8 9 10   **621.042**

   1. Energy 2. Energy industry and trade 3. Biomass energy 4. Renewable energy sources
ISBN 9781422235898

"A great fit for classroom or school libraries and a strong consideration for public libraries interested in the integration of STEM into everyday life." School Library Journal.

Rigsby, Mike

Doable renewables: 16 alternative energy projects for young scientists. Mike Rigsby. Chicago Review Press, c2010. xi, 195 p.

Grades: 6 7 8 9 10   **621.042**

   1. Renewable energy sources -- Experiments 2. Energy resources 3. Science -- Experiments 4. Energy conservation
ISBN 9781569763438

                         LC 2010019520

Shows readers how to create working models that generate renewable, alternative energy, including a Kelvin water drop generator, windmill, and nitinol spring wheel.

"This is a collection of science-oriented projects, focused . . . on renewable energy sources. From a windmill . . . to a human-powered LED light that relies on a hand-cranked generator, these activities range in complexity and skill, but all use simple technology to show basic and fascinating processes." Booklist.

Sobey, Edwin J. C., 1948-

Solar cell and renewable energy experiments. Ed Sobey. Enslow Publishers, c2011. 128 p.: Cool science projects with technology

Grades: 6 7 8 9   **621.042**

   1. Renewable energy sources 2. Electric power production 3. Electricity 4. Solar energy 5. Wind power
ISBN 9780766033054

                         LC 2010027430

Presents science projects on renewable energy sources, including solar, wind, and water.

621.042023 Energy engineering—Vocational guidance

Allen, John, 1957-

Careers in environmental and energy technology. by John Allen. ReferencePoint Press, Inc., 2017. 80 p.: High-tech careers

Grades: 7 8 9 10   **621.042023**

   1. Environmental engineering 2. Energy industry and trade 3. Vocational guidance for teenagers 4. Occupations 5. Vocational guidance
ISBN 9781682821107

                         LC 2016033948

"A few color photos, an interview with a renewable energy project developer, and a list of other jobs in the field round out this useful introduction for students with an interest in a career in the field." Booklist.

Includes bibliographical references and index.

621.1 Fluid-power technologies

Collier, James Lincoln, 1928-

Steam engines. James Lincoln Collier. Marshall Cavendish Benchmark, 2006. 112 p.: Great inventions (Marshall Cavendish Benchmark)

Grades: 7 8 9 10   **621.1**

   1. Steam engines 2. Engines 3. Inventions
ISBN 0761418806

                         LC 2004021816

Follows the development of the steam engine.

"This is presented thoughtfully yet conversationally. . . . [It] will reward steady reading." Horn Book Guide.

Includes bibliographical references (p. 107-108) and index.

O'Neal, Claire

How to use waste energy to heat and light your home. Claire O'Neal. Mitchell Lane Publishers, c2010. 47 p. : Robbie readers.

Grades: 4 5 6 7 **621.1**
1. Cogeneration 2. Recycling (Waste, etc) 3. Energy resource recovery 4. Environmentalism 5. Energy
ISBN 9781584157656

LC 2009004483

"This title offers numerous facts and statistics, all of which are cited. . . . Chapters cover present-day issues and . . . are interspersed with full-color photographs and short Did You Know trivia boxes. . . . Back matter includes detailed resource lists and Try This! experiments." School Library Journal.

Includes bibliographical references and index.

621.3 Electrical, magnetic, optical, communications, computer engineering; electronics, lighting

Helfand, Lewis

They changed the world: Edison - Tesla - Bell. Lewis Helfand; illustrated by Naresh Kumar. Campfire, 2014. 96 p.

Grades: 7 8 9 10 **621.3**
1. Edison, Thomas A. (Thomas Alva), 1847-1931. 2. Tesla, Nikola, 1856-1943. 3. Bell, Alexander Graham, 1847-1922. 4. Technological innovations 5. Science 6. Inventions 7. Biographical comics 8. Comics and Graphic novels
ISBN 9789380741871

"Kumar shows not only the fundamental intelligence but also the hard work and productive attitudes these three geniuses brought to their work. Helfand's solid research is a great jumping-off point for student researchers, and the inclusion of a DIY project—building a rudimentary phone—adds to the appeal." Booklist.

Swanson, Jennifer

Amazing feats of electrical engineering. by Jennifer Swanson. Essential Library, 2015. 112 p.: Great achievements in engineering

Grades: 7 8 9 **621.3**
1. Electrical engineering 2. Electrical engineers 3. Engineering
ISBN 9781624034282

LC bl2014037604

Explains what electrical engineering is, how most people get into the profession, and discusses what the future might hold for this area of engineering.

621.3092 Electrical engineers—Biography

Hardyman, Robyn

Nikola Tesla and Thomas Edison. Robyn Hardyman. Gareth Stevens Publishing, 2015. 48 p.

Grades: 4 5 6 **621.3092**
1. Edison, Thomas A. (Thomas Alva), 1847-1931 2. Tesla, Nikola, 1856-1943 3. Electrical engineers 4. Electrical engineers 5.

Inventors 6. Inventors
ISBN 9781482414738

LC bl2015005670

Discusses the lives of the two inventors, how together they changed the way the world uses electricity, and their later falling out.

"This series stands out for its attractive graphics and ability to make complex concepts accessible. The authors have done an excellent job of selecting key quotes from the scientists' writings that young readers can understand (provided in sidebars titled "In Their Own Words"). School Library Journal.

Includes bibliographical references (page 47) and index.

621.31 Generation, modification, storage, transmission of electric power

Lew, Kristi

Goodbye, gasoline: the science of fuel cells. Kristi Lew. Compass Point Books, 2009 48 p.: Headline science

Grades: 5 6 7 8 **621.31**
1. Fuel cells 2. Renewable energy sources 3. Energy resources 4. Energy production
ISBN 9780756535216

"This clearly examines the history and technology of hydrogen fuel cells, including the various types such as proton exchange membrane and alkaline cells. An excellent description of how the technology works gives readers an understanding of both the successes and problems relating to these promising energy sources. . . . The color illustrations and charts . . . are clear and helpful, and the text, although information rich, is not overly difficult." School Library Journal.

O'Neal, Claire

How to use wind power to light and heat your home. Claire O'Neal. Mitchell Lane Publishers, c2009. 47 p. : Robbie readers.

Grades: 4 5 6 7 **621.31**
1. Wind power 2. Renewable energy sources 3. Energy resources 4. Energy 5. Environmentalism
ISBN 9781584157625

LC 2009004530

"This book offers numerous facts and statistics, all of which are cited. . . . Chapters cover present-day issues and . . . are interspersed with full-color photographs and short Did You Know trivia boxes. . . . Back matter includes detailed resource lists and Try This! experiments." School Library Journal.

Includes bibliographical references and index.

Rusch, Elizabeth

The **next** wave: the quest to harness the power of the oceans. by Elizabeth Rusch. Houghton Mifflin Harcourt, 2018, 80 p.: Scientists in the field (Houghton Mifflin)

Grades: 5 6 7 8 9 **621.31**
1. Ocean energy resources 2. Tidal power 3. Renewable energy sources 4. Energy resources 5. Natural resources 6. Pacific Northwest
ISBN 9781328852328

LC 2013050150

"Rusch captures the determined, entrepreneurial spirit of the profiled engineers as well as the need for creative problem-solving and ingenuity. Photographs and illustrations feature prototypes in both small-scale laboratory and full-ocean tests." Horn Book.

Includes bibliographical references and index.

621.32 Lighting

Collier, James Lincoln, 1928-
  Electricity and the light bulb. James Lincoln Collier. Marshall Cavendish Benchmark, 2006. 112 p.: Great inventions (Marshall Cavendish Benchmark)
Grades: 7 8 9 10   **621.32**
  1. Light bulbs 2. Electric lighting 3. Electricity 4. Lighting 5. Inventions
  ISBN 0761418784

                                           LC 2004021623
  Traces the development of electric lighting.
  "This is presented thoughtfully yet conversationally. . . . [It] will reward steady reading." Horn Book Guide.
  Includes bibliographical references (p. 105-106) and index.

621.36 Optical engineering

Bow, James
  Lasers. James Bow. Gareth Stevens Publishing, 2017. 48 p.: Cutting-edge technology (Gareth Stevens Pub.)
Grades: 5 6 7 8   **621.36**
  1. Lasers
  ISBN 9781482451580
  "Rock-solid choices that will update and deepen science and technology collections." School Library Journal.

621.3815 Components and circuits

Gregory, Josh
  From butterfly wings to... display technology. Josh Gregory. Cherry Lake Publishing, 2014. 32 p.: 21st century skills innovation library.
Grades: 6 7 8 9 10   **621.3815**
  1. Digital electronics 2. Technological innovations 3. Wings 4. Electronics 5. Butterflies
  ISBN 9781624317606

                                           LC 2013030377
  Explains how the study of butterfly wings inspired innovations in display technology for digital screens.
  "These creative books use a pleasantly unusual angle to show how aspects of nature can inspire scientists and engineers. For instance, some scientists, inspired by the way a gecko's feet allow it to stick to surfaces, are attempting to create an adhesive tape using the structure of the lizard's foot. High-resolution photographs and a dark black and purple layout give the books a slick, stylish look, while the narrative is both fascinating and informative. Intriguing additions to science collections." School Library Journal.
  Includes bibliographical references (page 31) and index.

621.383 Specific communications systems

Coe, Lewis, 1911-
  The **telegraph**: a history of Morse's invention and its predecessors in the United States. by Lewis Coe. McFarland, 2003, c1993. vii, 184 p.
Grades: 7 8 9 10   **621.383**
  1. Morse, Samuel Finley Breese, 1791-1872. 2. Telegraph --

History 3. Inventors
ISBN 0786418087

                                           LC bl2007016659
  Discusses Morse's invention and its impact on communication, details the creation of the first transcontinental telegraph line, explores its effect on the Civil War, and looks at advances in telegraph technology.

621.385 Telephony

Spilsbury, Richard, 1963-
  The **telephone**. Richard and Louise Spilsbury. Heinemann Library, c2011. 32 p.: Tales of invention
Grades: 4 5 6 7   **621.385**
  1. Telephones -- History 2. Cell phones 3. Inventions 4. Telecommunication 5. Telephone systems
  ISBN 9781432938260

                                           LC 2009049027
  "Beginning with the first telegraph, the book discusses how sound travels, how speech is transmitted by wire, and how Alexander Graham Bell's first telephones worked. Then the text quickly traces later technological developments, from transatlantic cables to early cell phones to the small, light, versatile models available today. . . . The many photographs and other illustrations include excellent labeled diagrams." Booklist.
  Includes bibliographical references (p. 31) and index.

621.385092 Telephone engineers

Carson, Mary Kay
  Alexander Graham Bell for kids: his life & inventions, with 21 activities. Mary Kay Carson. Chicago Review Press, 2018. 144 p.
Grades: 4 5 6 7 8   **621.385092**
  1. Bell, Alexander Graham, 1847-1922 2. Inventors 3. Telephones -- History 4. Telecommunication 5. Inventions 6. Sign language
  ISBN 9780912777139

                                           LC 2017027641
  Alexander Graham Bell invented not only the telephone, but also early versions of the phonograph, the metal detector, airplanes, and hydrofoil boats. This Scottish immigrant was also a pioneering speech teacher and a champion of educating those with hearing impairments, work he felt was his most important contribution to society.
  "The inventor of the telephone gets extensive treatment in this book, which combines biography, history, and activities for children. . . . Many of the activities featured throughout the chapters, such as making an ear trumpet and feeling sound vibrations, use materials readers likely have at home, fairly easily giving them a taste of the devices used during Bell's time and illustrating properties of sound." Kirkus.
  Includes bibliographical references and index.

621.389 Security, sound recording, related systems

Rooney, Anne
  Audio engineering and the science of soundwaves. Anne Rooney. Crabtree Publishing Company, [2014] 32 p.: Engineering in action
Grades: 5 6 7 8   **621.389**
  1. Sound -- Recording and reproducing 2. Acoustical engineering

3. Engineering
ISBN 9780778711964

LC 2013035439

Explores how the work of audio engineers combines the science of sound with the engineering design process, including how these engineers find solutions to audio challenges.

"Books in the Engineering in Action series provide broad introductions to their respective fields in a colorfully illustrated, large-format package...Audio tackles the science of sound and hearing, the differences between analog and digital signals, and the varied work of audio engineers. Solid information for engineering-minded students." Booklist.

Includes bibliographical references (page 30) and index.

621.4 Prime movers and heat engineering

Dobson, Clive, 1949-
Wind power: 20 projects to make with paper. Clive Dobson. Firefly Books (U.S.), 2010. 96 p.
Grades: 5 6 7 8   **621.4**
    1. Wind power 2. Experiments 3. Renewable energy sources -- Experiments 4. Energy resources 5. Science -- Experiments
ISBN 9781554076598

LC bl2010030465

Surveys the history of wind power and windmills, outlines the science that makes them work, and provides instructions for increasingly difficult projects that demonstrate each principle.

"In this informative craft book, a celebration of wind and of innovative efforts to harness its energy, Dobson describes the geometric and aerodynamic principles behind windmills, sails, and wind turbines, then implements these concepts via 20 paper projects, ranging from a two-blade pinwheel to a dramatic Squirrel Cage turbine. . . . Readers should gain a more palpable understanding of the subject matter by building and watching the graceful compositions function." Publishers Weekly.

Includes bibliographical references (p. 94) and index.

Woelfle, Gretchen
The **wind** at work: an activity guide to windmills. Gretchen Woelfle. Chicago Review Press, Incorporated, [2013], ©2013. vii, 145 p.
Grades: 4 5 6   **621.4**
    1. Windmills -- History 2. Creative activities for children and students 3. Wind power 4. Winds
ISBN 1556523084

LC 96024560

Explaining how the wind works, what windmills have contributed to the past, and why they offer environmental promise today as a source of clean, renewable energy, this revised and updated edition offers a glimpse into all the current and historical uses for wind power. Featuring new information on wind energy technology and wind farms, new photographs, and 24 wind-related activities—from keeping track of household energy use and conducting science experiments to cooking traditional meals and creating arts and crafts—this handy resource offers kids interested in the science of energy and green technologies an engaging, interactive, and contemporary overview of wind power. Provided by publisher.

"The historical information is excellent, and includes Persian windmills of 1000 years ago, Dutch windmills of the 17th century, and modern wind turbines. Amusing anecdotes and intriguing facts are woven into the text, keeping it lively. . . . Black-and-white historical prints, photographs, and diagrams appear throughout." School Library Journal.

Includes bibliographical references (p. 137-138) and index.

621.43 Internal-combustion engines

Miller, Ron, 1947-
Rockets. Ron Miller. Twenty-First Century Books, c2008. 112 p.: Space innovations
Grades: 7 8 9 10   **621.43**
    1. Rockets (Aviation) 2. Rocketry
ISBN 9780822571537

LC 2006021220

Explores the history of rocketry, from the first development of rockets as toys over one thousand years ago to their modern uses in war and space exploration.

"The author describes the history of rocket science, beginning in ancient China, where saltpeter, sulfur, and charcoal were first combined to create gunpowder. . . . The stories of the development of rockets through time are complemented by short biographies of important scientists such as Robert Goddard, stories of young model rocket makers, and sidebars explaining the science that makes rockets work. . . . It is a good choice for high school libraries, as well as for boys who are interested in science and nonfiction." Voice of Youth Advocates.

Includes bibliographical references (p. 107) and index.

621.44 Geothermal engineering

Boyle, Jordan
Examining geothermal energy. Jordan Boyle. Clara House Books, 2013. 48 p.
Grades: 5 6 7   **621.44**
    1. Geothermal engineering
ISBN 9781934545416

LC 2012035244

"Each book in this series is narrated by a fictional student who travels the world and asks experts about a particular energy field. There are full-color photos or graphics, lots of white space, and brief chapters. Each presents balanced information with pros and cons of each type of energy source. This series will be a good fit for the reluctant middle school reader and will work well for Common Core research." Library Media Connection

Includes bibliographical references (pages 46-47) and index.

621.46 Electric and related motors

Gabrielson, Curt
Kinetic contraptions: build a hovercraft, airboat, and more with a hobby motor. Curt Gabrielson. Chicago Review Press, c2010. ix, 176 p.
Grades: 7 8 9 10 11 12   **621.46**
    1. Motor vehicles -- Models 2. Airplanes -- Models 3. Ground-effect machines -- Models 4. Motorboats -- Models
ISBN 9781556529573

LC 2009025695

This handy resource guide teaches you how to build two dozen contraptions using low-cost or free recycled materials, batteries, and a single motor. Some of the projects include constructing a hovercraft out of a Styrofoam plate, two corks, and binder clips; building a double-paddle wheeler out of paint stirrers, plastic bottles, and a pair of disposable knives; and, turning bamboo skewers, checkers, and a drinking straw into a three-wheeled motorcycle.

Sobey, Edwin J. C., 1948-

Electric motor experiments. Ed Sobey. Enslow Publishers, c2011. 128 p.: Cool science projects with technology

Grades: 6 7 8 9   **621.46**

   1. Electric motors 2. Motors 3. Science projects 4. Experiments
ISBN 9780766033061

            LC 2009037895

Presents several science projects dealing with electric motors. Provided by publisher.

621.47 Solar-energy engineering

Bearce, Stephanie

How to harness solar power for your home. by Stephanie Bearce. Mitchell Lane Publishers, 2009. 48 p. : Robbie readers.

Grades: 4 5 6 7   **621.47**

   1. Solar energy 2. Energy resources 3. Energy 4. Environmentalism
ISBN 9781584157618

            LC 2009004529

"This title about solar power offers numerous facts and statistics, all of which are cited. . . . Chapters cover present-day issues and . . . are interspersed with full-color photographs and short Did You Know trivia boxes. . . . Back matter includes detailed resource lists and Try This! experiments." School Library Journal.

Includes bibliographical references and index.

Bright, Sandra

Examining solar energy. Sandra Bright. Clara House Books, 2013. 48 p.

Grades: 5 6 7 8   **621.47**

   1. Solar energy
ISBN 9781934545454

            LC 2012035316

"Each book in this series is narrated by a fictional student who travels the world and asks experts about a particular energy field. There are full-color photos or graphics, lots of white space, and brief chapters. Each presents balanced information with pros and cons of each type of energy source. This series will be a good fit for the reluctant middle school reader and will work well for Common Core research." Library Media Connection

Includes bibliographical references (pages 46-47) and index.

Walker, Niki, 1972-

Harnessing power from the sun. Niki Walker. Crabtree Pub. Co., c2007. 32 p.: Energy revolution

Grades: 5 6 7 8   **621.47**

   1. Solar energy 2. Renewable energy sources 3. Energy production 4. Energy resources
ISBN 9780778729129

            LC 2006014368

Explores the different ways we use solar power known as the power of the sun.

"Vivid color photographs with informative captions extend the [text], showing diverse people and applications." School Library Journal.

621.48 Nuclear engineering

Kidd, J. S. (Jerry S.)

Nuclear power: the study of quarks and sparks. J.S. Kidd and Renee A. Kidd. Chelsea House, c2006. xiv, 208 p.: Science & society

Grades: 7 8 9 10   **621.48**

   1. Nuclear power 2. Energy resources 3. Nuclear physics
ISBN 0816056064

            LC 2005052872

Examines the people, events, and motivations leading up to modern-day discoveries and advances in nuclear physics.

"Extensive scientific explanations are kept manageable, thanks to consistent references to their historical context; and descriptions of the nuclear race during the Second World War are especially riveting." Booklist. [review of 1999 edition]

Includes bibliographical references (p. 190-196) and index.

Mahaffey, James A.

Fusion. James A. Mahaffey. Facts on File, c2012. x, 142 p.

Grades: 9 10 11 12   **621.48**

   1. Fusion
ISBN 9780816076536

            LC 2011012505

Discusses the history of fusion power, important research on the subject, and the different types of devices and equipment used in fusion reactors.

Oxlade, Chris

Nuclear power. Chris Oxlade. Smart Apple Media, c2010. 44 p. : Science in the news

Grades: 6 7 8 9   **621.48**

   1. Nuclear power 2. Nuclear power plants 3. Nuclear engineering 4. Energy resources
ISBN 9781599203201

            LC 2008049277

"This book about nuclear power move[s] smoothly, occasionally pausing for the definition of a term. [The title] boast[s] plenty of attractive photos, and a clean layout allows the information to be easily consumed. . . . Provides the information that younger teens need." School Library Journal.

621.8 Machine engineering

Eboch, Chris

Amazing feats of mechanical engineering. by Chris Eboch. Essential Library, 2015. 112 p.: Great achievements in engineering

Grades: 7 8 9   **621.8**

   1. Mechanical engineering 2. Mechanics 3. Engineers 4. Engineering
ISBN 9781624034305

            LC bl2014033233

Discusses the field of mechanical engineering, including its history, some of its most famous feats, and what the future holds for the field.

621.9 Tools

Koch, Melissa

3D printing: the revolution in personalized manufacturing. Melissa Koch. Twenty-First Century Books, 2017. 112 p.

Grades: 7 8 9 10 11 12 **621.9**

1. 3-D printing 2. Printing 3. Manufacturing processes

ISBN 9781512415704

LC 2016033030

"Student-report-friendly features and lots of color photos help to make this an attractive, timely, and popular addition to STEM collections." Booklist.

Includes bibliographical references and index.

Tomecek, Steve

Tools and machines. Stephen M. Tomecek. Chelsea House Publishers, 2010. 182 p.

Grades: 5 6 7 8 **621.9**

1. Machinery 2. Tools

ISBN 9781604131710

LC 2009022332

Describes how humans first started using tools and traces the evolution of tools from simple stone implements to the high-tech devices of today, and includes experiments illustrating the scientific concepts behind tools.

"This offers 25 easy-to-perform activities that illuminate scientific principles. . . . [This] discusses levers, pulleys, and meters and explains how people use them in their daily lives. . . . Following each experiment are additional comments on the science behind the experiment and link to the one that follows. Photographs, simple diagrams and illustrations, and sample data tables appear throughout, and the [layout is] clear and colorful." School Library Journal.

Includes bibliographical references and index.

621.988 Additive manufacturing equipment

Bow, James

3-D printers. James Bow. Gareth Stevens Publishing, 2017. 48 p.: Cutting-edge technology (Gareth Stevens Pub.)

Grades: 5 6 7 8 **621.988**

1. 3-D printing 2. Printing

ISBN 9781482451610

Explores the science behind the 3-D printing technology, explains how 3-D printers use a wide variety of materials such as plastic or wood to create an infinite amount of different creations.

"Rock-solid choices that will update and deepen science and technology collections." School Library Journal.

Includes bibliographical references (page 47) and index.

622 Mining and related operations

McDonnell, Julia, 1979-

How precious metals form. by Julia McDonnell. Gareth Stevens Publishing, 2017. 32 p.: From the Earth: how resources are made

Grades: 5 6 7 **622**

1. Precious metals 2. Mines and mineral resources

ISBN 9781482447309

LC 2016015519

Informs readers about precious metals, including why they are valuable, how they are formed, and how they can be used.

"This series would be a great addition to school or public libraries, as it makes an often dull topic really shine." School Library Journal.

Squire, Ann

Hydrofracking. by Ann O. Squire. Children's Press, an imprint of Scholastic Inc., 2013. 64 p.

Grades: 4 5 6 **622**

1. Energy resources 2. Gas well drilling 3. Shale gas 4. Hydraulic fracturing 5. Natural gas

ISBN 9780531236048

LC 2012034322

Explains how hydrofracking works, how the burning of fossil fuels contributes to global warming, and why people think the process is bad for the environment.

623.4 Ordnance

Boos, Ben, 1971-

Swords: an artist's devotion. by Ben Boos. Candlewick Press, 2008. 96 p.

Grades: 6 7 8 9 **623.4**

1. Swords -- History 2. Swords 3. Weapons 4. Books for reluctant readers

ISBN 9780763631482

LC 2007052333

Illustrated with breathtaking intricacy, a celebration of swords and swordsmen spans history and cultures to review the ancient warriors who lived by the sword, from Beowulf to medieval knights, and from stealthy ninja and samurai to legendary maidens of war.

"This absorbing, large-format collection of sketches, paintings, and historical notes on sword craft is not called an artist's devotion for nothing. Boos's treatment of his subject is reverential and his artwork is outstanding, combining meticulous attention to detail and a designer's sense for layout. The spare text provides just enough information but generally allows the illustrations to speak for themselves." School Library Journal.

Includes bibliographical references.

Collier, James Lincoln, 1928-

Gunpowder and weaponry. James Lincoln Collier. Benchmark Books, 2004. 125 p.: Great inventions (Marshall Cavendish Benchmark)

Grades: 6 7 8 9 **623.4**

1. Military art and science -- History 2. Gunpowder 3. Guns -- History 4. Ordnance 5. Weapons -- History

ISBN 0761415408

LC 2002156289

Describes the changes brought to warfare by the introduction of gunpowder, including the rise of the professional army and the industrial revolution in weapons.

Gurstelle, William

The **art** of the catapult: build Greek ballistae, Roman onagers, English trebuchets, and more ancient artillery. William Gurstelle. Chicago Review Press, 2018, c2004. xvii, 172 p.

Grades: 5 6 7 8 9 10 **623.4**

1. Catapult 2. Ballistics

ISBN 1556525265

LC 2004004866

"This collection of 10 working catapult projects offers a fascinating look at world history, military strategy, and physics, related with an engaging yet lighthearted touch. . . . Instructions are clear, with full materials lists, helpful diagrams, and no skipped steps. . . . There's excellent booktalk potential here, and lively reading even for those who never get around to constructing a catapult." School Library Journal.

Includes bibliographical references (p. 167-168) and index.

Sheinkin, Steve

★ **Bomb**: the race to build--and steal--the world's most dangerous weapon. Steve Sheinkin. Henry Holt & Co., 2012. 192 p.
Grades: 5 6 7 8 9 10 11 12 Adult   **623.4**
1. Manhattan Project (U.S.) -- History 2. Atomic bomb -- History 20th century. 3. Nuclear power research 4. Spies 5. World War II 6. United States -- History -- 1939-1945 7. United States -- History, Military -- 20th century.
ISBN 9781596434875
Robert F. Sibert Informational Book Medal, 2013.

Recounts the scientific discoveries that enabled atom splitting, the military intelligence operations that occurred in rival countries, and the work of brilliant scientists hidden at Los Alamos.

623.7 Communications, vehicles, sanitation, related topics

Jackson, Robert

101 great tanks. edited by Robert Jackson. Rosen Pub., 2010. 112 p.: 101 greatest weapons of all times
Grades: 7 8 9 10   **623.7**
1. Tanks (Military science) 2. Armored vehicles 3. Military vehicles
ISBN 9781435835955

           LC 2009032880

"Describes why and when the type of vehicle was created, its advantages and disadvantages, when and where it served, countries that may have purchased or license-built it, and when it was removed from service. . . . Contains a detailed two-dimensional color drawing and black-and-white or color photo of the featured vehicle. . . . Back matter includes a listing of memorials and museums and an excellent further-reading list. A first purchase where the subject is popular." School Library Journal.

623.74 Vehicles

Jackson, Robert

101 great bombers. Robert Jackson, editor. Rosen Pub., 2010. 112 p.: 101 greatest weapons of all times
Grades: 7 8 9 10   **623.74**
1. Bombers 2. Military aircraft 3. Military aviation 4. Airplanes
ISBN 9781435835948

           LC 2009032090

"Describes why and when the type of vehicle was created, its advantages and disadvantages, when and where it served, countries that may have purchased or license-built it, and when it was removed from service. . . . Contains a detailed two-dimensional color drawing and black-and-white or color photo of the featured vehicle. . . . Back matter includes a listing of memorials and museums and an excellent further-reading list. A first purchase where the subject is popular." School Library Journal.

101 great fighters. edited by Robert Jackson. Rosen Pub., 2010. 112 p.: 101 greatest weapons of all times
Grades: 7 8 9 10   **623.74**
1. Fighter planes 2. Military aircraft 3. Military aviation 4. Airplanes
ISBN 9781435835979

           LC 2009032122

" Describes why and when the type of vehicle was created, its advantages and disadvantages, when and where it served, countries that may have purchased or license-built it, and when it was removed from service. . . . Contains a detailed two-dimensional color drawing and black-and-white or color photo of the featured vehicle. . . . Back matter includes a listing of memorials and museums and an excellent further-reading list. A first purchase where the subject is popular." School Library Journal.

Mooney, Carla, 1970-

Pilotless planes. by Carla Mooney. Norwood House Press, c2011. 48 p.: Great idea
Grades: 3 4 5 6   **623.74**
1. Drone aircraft 2. Uninhabited combat aerial vehicles 3. Military aircraft
ISBN 9781599533810

           LC 2010008500

Pilotless planes or "drones" have become an important aspect of modern military operations. Developed for espionage and warfare, pilotless planes are also used for public safety issues and can reduce injury or death rates for pilots. Provided by publisher.

"This discusses the development and use of unmanned aerial vehicles, also called UAVs or drones, such as the Predator planes currently used by the U.S. Air Force. Looking beyond military uses, the last chapter also considers future public safety, environmental, and commercial applications. . . . Presenting specific, current information, [this book] will appeal to young people intrigued by inventions." Booklist.

Includes bibliographical references and index.

Spilsbury, Louise

Drones. Louise and Richard Spilsbury. Gareth Stevens Publishing, 2017. 48 p.: Cutting-Edge Technology
Grades: 5 6 7 8   **623.74**
1. Drone aircraft
ISBN 9781482451566

           LC bl2016049387

Introduces different types of drones; discusses their functions, from providing information and assistance to their use by the military; and considers what the future holds for drone technology.

"Rock-solid choices that will update and deepen science and technology collections." School Library Journal.

Includes bibliographical references (page 47) and index.

623.82 Nautical craft

Farndon, John

★ **Stickmen's** guide to watercraft. by John Farndon; illustrated by John Paul de Quay. Hungry Tomato, [2016] 31 p.: Stickmen's guides to how everything works
Grades: 3 4 5 6   **623.82**
1. Ships 2. Boats 3. Aircraft carriers 4. Submarines 5. Boating
ISBN 9781467793629

           LC 2015032760

Presents information about all sorts of watercraft, from sailboats and hydrofoils to submarines and hovercraft.

"Deeply informative and pleasantly approachable, this is sure to make a splash." Booklist.

Jackson, Robert

101 great warships. Robert Jackson, editor. Rosen Pub., 2010. 112 p.: 101 greatest weapons of all times

Grades: 7 8 9 10   **623.82**

1. Warships 2. Sea-power 3. Naval art and science
ISBN 9781435835962

LC 2009032929

"Describes why and when the type of vehicle was created, its advantages and disadvantages, when and where it served, countries that may have purchased or license-built it, and when it was removed from service. . . . Contains a detailed two-dimensional color drawing and black-and-white or color photo of the featured vehicle. . . . Back matter includes a listing of memorials and museums and an excellent further-reading list. A first purchase where the subject is popular." School Library Journal.

Spilsbury, Richard, 1963-

Robots underwater. by Richard and Louise Spilsbury. Gareth Stevens Publishing, 2016. 48 p.: Amazing robots

Grades: 4 5 6 7   **623.82**

1. Robots 2. Robotics 3. Remotely operated submersibles
ISBN 9781482430226

"The full-color photos of robots in action and the high-interest nature of robotics may catch the interest of science-minded kids." Booklist.

623.89 Navigation

Young, Karen Romano

Across the wide ocean: the why, how, and where of navigation for humans and animals at sea. by Karen Romano Young. Greenwillow Books, 2006. 80 p.

Grades: 4 5 6 7   **623.89**

1. Marine animals -- Behavior 2. Animal navigation 3. Navigation 4. Oceans
ISBN 0060090871

LC 2005046146

Demystifies navigation at sea by following a turtle, a whale, a shark, a submarine, a sailboat, and a container ship on their journeys across the ocean.

"Readers follow such disparate entities as a loggerhead sea turtle, a nuclear submarine, and a sailboat crew seeking scientific sightings of North Atlantic right whales as Young explores the concept of navigation. . . . Larded with photos, diagrams, and maps. . . . Deceptively simple in appearance, the informative text can push some intense mental activity." School Library Journal.

624 Civil engineering

Aaseng, Nathan

Construction: building the impossible. Nathan Aaseng. Oliver Press, 2000. 144 p.: Innovators (Oliver Press)

Grades: 6 7 8 9   **624**

1. Architects 2. Civil engineering -- History 3. Buildings 4. Civil engineering 5. Building
ISBN 1881508595

LC 98051815

Profiles eight builders and their famous construction projects, including Imhotep and the Step Pyramid, Alexandre Eiffel and the Eiffel Tower, and William Lamb and the Empire State Building.

"The prose is clear and engaging, with a layperson's approach to technical information. Sidebars feature related anecdotes, fun facts, and word definitions. Historical photos, drawings, and diagrams are fascinating and well chosen." Booklist.

Includes bibliographical references (p. 137-138) and index.

Caney, Steven

Steven Caney's ultimate building book. Steven Caney. Running Press Kids, c2006. xi, 596 p.

Grades: 4 5 6 7 8   **624**

1. Civil engineering 2. Building 3. Engineering -- Experiments 4. Experiments
ISBN 0762404094

LC bl2006025784

Presents an introduction to the concept of structure with explanations, diagrams, and examples of space frame, brick, and block structures, and provides a series of experiments which can be done to illustrate these principles.

"Caney examines building in its broadest sense, encompassing everything from skyscrapers and bridges to bird feeders and peanut-shell bricks. Opening sections investigate the history and techniques of construction, with clearly written explanations supported by black-and-white photographs and diagrams. . . . The author reinforces important concepts of design in a way that is fascinating and effective." School Library Journal.

Carmichael, L. E. (Lindsey E.)

Amazing feats of civil engineering. by L.E. Carmichael; content consultant, David A. Lange, Professor, Department of Civil & Environmental Engineering, University of Illinois at Urbana-Champaign. Essential Library, an imprint of Abdo Publishing, 2014. 112 p.: Great achievements in engineering

Grades: 7 8 9   **624**

1. Civil engineering 2. Civil engineers
ISBN 9781624034275

LC bl2014037602

Explains what civil engineering is, how most people get into the profession, and discusses notable civil engineers and their projects.

Levy, Matthys

Engineering the city: how infrastructure works: projects and principles for beginners. Matthys Levy and Richard Panchyk. Chicago Review Press, c2000. xi, 129 p.

Grades: 6 7 8 9   **624**

1. Infrastructure 2. Public works 3. Urban planning 4. Civil engineering 5. Municipal engineering
ISBN 1556524196

LC 00031774

Explains how cities obtain water, gas, and electricity and how these infrastructure systems developed along with the cities themselves; and provides experiments, games, and construction diagrams for interactive learning.

Macaulay, David

Underground. David Macaulay. Houghton Mifflin, 1976. 109 p.

Grades: 5 6 7 8 9   **624**
1. Underground utility lines 2. Underground construction 3. City life 4. Subways 5. Cities and towns
ISBN 9780395247396

LC 76013868

Text and drawings describe the subways, sewers, building foundations, telephone and power systems, columns, cables, pipes, tunnels, and other underground elements of a large modern city.

"Introduced by a visual index—a bird's eye view of a busy, hypothetical intersection with colored indicators marking the specific locations analyzed in subsequent pages—detailed illustrations are combined with a clear, precise narrative to make the subject comprehenssible and fascinating." Horn Book.

Sullivan, George, 1927-
Built to last: building America's amazing bridges, dams, tunnels, and skyscrapers. George Sullivan. Scholastic Nonfiction, c2005. 128 p.
Grades: 5 6 7 8   **624**
1. Building 2. Civil engineering -- History
ISBN 0439517370

LC 2004060996

Profiles seventeen architectural and engineering achievements spanning over two centuries, including the Brooklyn Bridge, Transcontinental Railroad, and U.S. Interstate Highway System.

"This is a survey of American building—from the Erie Canal to Boston's current Big Dig. Chronological chapters describe the historical forces that helped drive each project as well as the specific technological feats linked to each pioneering structure. . . . The wide selection of captivating illustrations includes archival photos and engravings, architectural drawings, and color photos. . . . Sullivan's skillful integration of social and economic history distinguishes this clear, well-designed title." Booklist.

Includes bibliographical references (p. 122-123) and index.

624.1 Structural engineering and underground construction

Connolly, Sean, 1956-
The **book** of massively epic engineering disasters: 33 thrilling experiments based on history's greatest blunders. Sean Connolly. Workman Publishing, 2017 xiii, 241 p.
Grades: 4 5 6 7 8   **624.1**
1. Science -- Experiments 2. Science projects 3. Engineering 4. Errors
ISBN 9780761183945

Provides step-by-step instructions for experiments using readily obtainable materials that demonstrate scientific principles related to engineering disasters.

"A new collection from an old hand at designing intriguing STEM activities that will entertain as well as enlighten." Kirkus.

Fantastic feats and failures
Fantastic feats and failures. by the editors of YES Mag. Kids Can Press, c2004. 52 p.
Grades: 4 5 6 7   **624.1**
1. Structural design 2. Structural failures 3. Structural analysis (Engineering) 4. Architecture
ISBN 1553376331

LC bl2004117431

From the Sydney Opera House to Apollo 13, this story of engineering showcases innovative designs that have positively—and negatively—impacted our world, accompanied by projects and activities for up-and-coming engineers.

"This book spotlights 20 notable highs and lows in engineering. The feats celebrated include the Sydney Opera House, the Brooklyn Bridge, and Canadarm (a huge, Canadian-built robotic arm used for repairs in space). Among the failures are the space shuttle Challenger, the Tacoma Narrows Bridge, and the Chernobyl nuclear power plant. . . . Well organized and engagingly written. . . . Excellent photos . . . illustrate the places and events discussed, while colorful drawings visually represent concepts." Booklist.

Graham, Ian, 1953-
Tremendous tunnels. Ian Graham. Amicus, c2011. 32 p.: Superstructures
Grades: 5 6 7 8   **624.1**
1. Tunnels 2. Tunneling 3. Underground construction
ISBN 9781607531340

LC 2009030865

Describes some of the longest and most famous tunnels ever built. Includes information on the tunnel designers, the challenges they faced, and statistics of the finished tunnels. Provided by publisher.

"The vivid illustrations often help clarify points made in the text. . . . [This] colorful, informative [book offers] intriguing glimpses of notable engineering feats." Booklist.

624.2 Bridges

Graham, Ian, 1953-
Fabulous bridges. by Ian Graham. Amicus, 2011. 32 p.: Superstructures
Grades: 5 6 7 8   **624.2**
1. Bridges -- Design and construction 2. Civil engineering
ISBN 9781607531326

LC 2009030864

Describes some of the longest and most famous bridges ever built. Includes information on the bridge designers, the challenges they faced, and statistics of the finished bridges. Provided by publisher.

"The vivid illustrations often help clarify points made in the text. . . . [This] colorful, informative [book offers] intriguing glimpses of notable engineering feats." Booklist.

Prentzas, G. S.
The **Brooklyn** Bridge. G.S. Prentzas. Chelsea House Publishers, c2009. 120 p.: Building America: then and now
Grades: 6 7 8 9   **624.2**
1. 19th century 2. Bridges -- Design and construction 3. Suspension bridges -- Design and construction 4. Brooklyn Bridge, New York City -- Design and construction 5. Brooklyn Bridge, New York City -- History
ISBN 9781604130737

LC 2008025543

Describes the planning, construction, and history of the Brooklyn Bridge, celebrated as one of the greatest landmarks and grandest sights of New York City.

625.26 Locomotives

Zimmermann, Karl R.

Steam locomotives: whistling, chugging, smoking iron horses of the past. Karl Zimmermann. Boyds Mills Press, 2004. 48 p.

Grades: 4 5 6 7   **625.26**

   1. Trains -- History 2. Railroads -- History 3. Transportation -- History 4. North America 5. South America

ISBN 1590781651

LC 2003111246

An overview of the development and operation of the steam locomotive, from its beginnings to when diesel-electric engines became the primary haulers for the railroads, with an emphasis on North and South America.

"In this photo-essay, Zimmermann shares his excitement for steam locomotives with young readers, tracing the development of the early engines and their impact on the history of the U.S. He includes a clear explanation . . . of how a steam engine works. The photographs, some archival and some from the present day, are excellent. . . . The engaging text clearly imparts the author's enthusiasm and love for the subject." School Library Journal.

Includes bibliographical references and index.

627 Hydraulic engineering

Aldridge, Rebecca

The **Hoover** Dam. Rebecca Aldridge. Chelsea House Publishers, c2009. 119 p.: Building America: then and now

Grades: 6 7 8 9   **627**

   1. Dams -- Design and construction -- History 2. Water-supply 3. Hoover Dam -- Design and construction. 4. Hoover Dam -- History.

ISBN 9781604130690

LC 2008025545

Describes the engineering, construction, and social and historical contexts of the Hoover Dam.

"Photos, maps, and informative sidebars supplement the densely detailed writing. American history buffs will find [this volume] useful for doing research." Horn Book Guide.

Includes bibliographical references (p. 103-110) and index.

Mann, Elizabeth, 1948-

Hoover Dam: the story of hard times, tough people and the taming of a wild river. by Elizabeth Mann; with illustrations by Alan Witschonke. Mikaya Press, c2001. 44 p.: Wonders of the world book

Grades: 4 5 6 7   **627**

   1. Dams 2. Hoover Dam 3. Hoover Dam -- History

ISBN 1931414025

LC 2001034520

Describes the engineering, construction, and social and historical contexts of the Hoover Dam.

"A wonderfully readable, well-organized book filled with fascinating detail." School Library Journal.

Nagelhout, Ryan

How do dams work? Ryan Nagelhout. PowerKids Press, 2017. 32 p.: STEM waterworks

Grades: 4 5 6   **627**

   1. Dams 2. Hydraulic engineering 3. Water-power

ISBN 9781499420012

LC 2016013444

Provides information on dams, including their history, how modern dams are constructed, and how dangerous it can be when they fail.

"The book ends with a hopeful outlook as scientists rethink ways to use dams to protect the environment. Colorful diagrams, panoramic views, and photos of dam construction not only relate the roles of these structures but show STEM in action." Booklist.

628 Sanitary engineering

Hand, Carol, 1945-

Amazing feats of environmental engineering. by Carol Hand. Essential Library, 2015. 112 p.: Great achievements in engineering

Grades: 7 8 9   **628**

   1. Environmental engineering 2. Environmental design 3. Environmental protection 4. Engineering 5. Environmental engineers

ISBN 9781624034299

LC bl2014042311

Examines how environmental engineering combines the engineering design process with scientific concepts to leave the smallest negative impact on the environment while increasing the health and comfort of people.

Harmon, Daniel E.

Jobs in environmental cleanup and emergency hazmat response. Daniel E. Harmon. Rosen Pub., 2010. 80 p.

Grades: 7 8 9   **628**

   1. Environmental sciences -- Vocational guidance 2. Hazardous waste management industry -- Vocational guidance

ISBN 9781435835702

LC 2009014946

Provides information on careers in cleaning up hazardous materials that pollute the environment, discussing working conditions, workplaces, and training.

"Written in clear, concise language, . . . [this] features color pictures and boxes with supplementary information. Chapters and sections are broken into reasonable lengths suitable for reluctant readers, but interesting enough for advanced students." Library Media Connection.

Includes bibliographical references (p. 75-76) and index.

Horn, Geoffrey

Environmental engineer. by Geoffrey M. Horn. Gareth Stevens Pub., 2010. 32 p. : Cool careers (Gareth Stevens)

Grades: 4 5 6   **628**

   1. Environmental protection 2. Sanitary engineers 3. Sanitary engineering 4. Environmental engineering 5. Occupations

ISBN 9781433919565

LC 2009004746

Introduces readers to interesting and important careers, giving children the opportunity to gain a better understanding of these cool jobs with the help of engaging sidebars, color photographs, an index, lists for further reading, and more.

"This introduction to environmental engineering careers offers clear, solid information in a large font. . . . [This] short [book is] packed with relevant, current material." School Library Journal.

Includes bibliographical references and index.

628.4 Waste technology, public toilets, street cleaning

Gardner, Robert, 1929-

Recycle: green science projects for a sustainable planet. Robert Gardner. Enslow Publishers, c2011. 128 p.: Team green science projects

Grades: 6 7 8 9 10   **628.4**

1. Recycling (Waste, etc) 2. Science projects 3. Experiments 4. Recycling (Waste, etc) -- Environmental aspects
ISBN 9780766036482

LC 2009037903

Provides environmentally friendly 'green' science projects about recycling. Provided by publisher.

"Gardner provides plenty of information, well-designed experiments, and demonstrations, and then shares brief science-fair ideas. . . . Experiments and demonstrations are presented with clear step-by-step instructions and occasional illustrations and represent a wide range of complexity." School Library Journal.

Includes bibliographical references and index.

Young, Karen Romano

Junkyard science: 20 projects and experiments about junk, garbage, waste, things we don't need any more, and ways to recycle or reuse it-- or lose it. by Karen Romano Young; illustrations by David Goldin. National Geographic, c2010. 80 p.: Science fair winners

Grades: 3 4 5 6   **628.4**

1. Salvage (Waste, etc) 2. Recycling (Waste, etc) 3. Science projects 4. Science -- Study and teaching (Elementary) -- Activity programs 5. Experiments
ISBN 9781426306907

LC 2009048212

Presents twenty science experiments involving things that are being discarded or recycled, including comparing the decomposition rate of grocery bags and finding out how much trash a person produces in a day.

"This volume provides outlines for science fair projects in the . . . environmental . . . sciences. The procedures include just enough structure to help novice experimenters get started. . . . Well-placed questions encourage creativity and further thinking. [The] volume includes humorous cartoon spot illustrations and a section on preparing presentations." Horn Book Guide.

Includes bibliographical references (p. 79) and index.

629.1 Aerospace engineering

Grove, Tim, 1967-

Milestones of flight: from hot-air balloons to SpaceShipOne. by Tim Grove. Abrams Books for Young Readers, [2016] 96 p.

Grades: 5 6 7 8   **629.1**

1. Aviation 2. Flight 3. Airplanes 4. Space exploration 5. Pilots
ISBN 9781419720031

LC 2015033040

This book is being published in association with the Smithsonian National Air and Space Museum. The museum will celebrate its 40th anniversary in July 2016. There will be a new Smithsonian exhibition, to be called "Milestones of Flight." This book is NOT a catalog of the exhibition; rather, it is a history of flight told through approximately twenty-five historical milestones. Provided by publisher.

"Period photographs, illustrations, and documents complement a crisply written and informative look at the past and present of flight, with glimpses of its future." Publishers Weekly.

Includes bibliographical references and index.

Rooney, Anne

Aerospace engineering and the principles of flight. Anne Rooney. Crabtree Pub Co, 2012. 32 p. : Engineering in action

Grades: 5 6 7 8   **629.1**

1. Aerospace engineering 2. Aerospace technology 3. Aviation 4. Engineering 5. Flight
ISBN 9780778774952

Explains how flight works, looks at the history of human attempts at flight, and describes the different roles and responsibilities of aerospace engineers.

Smibert, Angie

Amazing feats of aerospace engineering. Angie Smibert. Abdo Group, 2014. 112 p.: Great achievements in engineering

Grades: 7 8 9 10   **629.1**

1. Aerospace technology 2. Aerospace technology -- History 3. Aerospace engineers
ISBN 9781624034251

"These substantial books begin with a brief introduction and history, then validate the Amazing Feats label with remarkable projects including the International Space Station, a thought-controlled bionic leg, the Canadian Confederation Bridge, and the driverless car; challenges and problem-solving are emphasized. Illustrations include both color photos and diagrams. Career advice, facts, and a hands-on project are appended." Horn Book.

629.13 Aeronautics

Anderson, Dale

Flight and motion: the history and science of flying. Dale Anderson, Ian Graham, Brian Williams, Richard P. Hallion. M.E. Sharpe, 2008.

Grades: 6 7 8 9 10   **629.13**

1. Aeronautics 2. Aeronautics -- History 3. Flight
ISBN 9780765681003

LC 2007030815

"Report writers as well as those simply interested in browsing will find much to hold their interest in this set, which provides comprehensive coverage of the history of aviation, including spaceflight, as well as the science and technology on which it depends." Booklist.

Includes bibliographical references and indexes.

Collins, Mary, 1961-

Airborne: a photobiography of Wilbur and Orville Wright. by Mary Collins. National Geographic, 2003. 63 p.

Grades: 4 5 6 7   **629.13**

1. Wright, Orville, 1871-1948. 2. Wright, Wilbur, 1867-1912. 3. Aeronautics 4. Inventors 5. Airplanes -- History 6. Flight -- History 7. United States -- History -- 20th century.
ISBN 9780792269571

LC 2002005279

Examines the lives of the Wright brothers and discusses their experiments and triumphs in the field of flight.

"The well-chosen photos give readers a feel for Kitty Hawk: windy, sandy, solitary. This is an exceptionally well-informed picture of the

Wright brothers and what their 100-year-old achievement really meant." School Library Journal.

Includes bibliographical references and index.

Finkelstein, Norman H.

Three across: the great transatlantic air race of 1927. By Norman H. Finkelstein. Calkins Creek, 2008. 133 p.

Grades: 5 6 7 8   **629.13**

1. Lindbergh, Charles A. (Charles Augustus), 1902-1974 2. Chamberlin, Clarence. 3. Byrd, Richard Evelyn, 1888-1957. 4. 1920s 5. Aviation -- History 6. Transatlantic flights 7. Air travel 8. Pilots 9. Competition

ISBN 9781590784624

LC 2007018345

In the spring of 1927, three pilots—Clarence Chamberlin, Richard E. Byrd, and Charles Lindbergh—compete to be the first to fly across the Atlantic, in this exciting book that chronicles the daring feats of these courageous adventurers and the aftermath of their flights.

Goldstone, Lawrence, 1947-

Higher, steeper, faster: the daredevils who conquered the skies. Lawrence Goldstone. Little, Brown and Company, [2017] 208 p.

Grades: 4 5 6 7   **629.13**

1. Pilots -- History 2. Daredevils (Stunt performers) -- History 3. Aviation -- History 4. Flight -- History

ISBN 9780316350235

LC 2016016576

The pioneers of early flight performed death-defying feats and broke new technological ground as they took to the skies to thrill crowds and advance the boundaries of human innovation. Provided by publisher.

Graham, Ian, 1953-

The **science** of flight: the air-amazing truth about planes and helicopters. written by Ian Graham; [artists, Christos Skaltsas, Bryan Beach]. Franklin Watts', 2019. 32 p.

Grades: 4 5 6 7 8   **629.13**

1. Aeronautics 2. Airplanes -- Design and construction 3. Helicopters -- Design and construction 4. Flying-machines

ISBN 9780531133958

LC 2018031800

Introduces the reader to the science of flight. Provided by publisher.

Wilgus, Alison

Flying machines: how the Wright brothers soared. Alison Wilgus; Molly Brooks. First Second, 2017. 128 p.: Science comics

Grades: 5 6 7 8   **629.13**

1. Wright, Orville, 1871-1948 2. Wright, Wilbur, 1867-1912 3. Aviation 4. Airplanes -- History 5. Comics and Graphic novels

ISBN 9781626721401

An introduction to the Wright Brothers and their amazing achievements combines an engaging graphic novel format with fun facts about how the famous aviators conducted historic experiments and designed amazing machines that blazed a trail for the modern world's airplanes, jets and helicopters.

"An accessible and engaging introduction to the Wright brothers and how they ushered in the age of flight." Kirkus.

629.133 Aircraft types

White, Rowland

Cleared for takeoff: the ultimate book of flight. by Rowland White. Chronicle Books, 2016, c2013. 320 p.

Grades: 4 5 6 7 8   **629.133**

1. Airplanes 2. Aviation -- History 3. Flying-machines 4. Technological innovations 5. Transportation -- History

ISBN 9781452135502

LC 2014044858

A compendium of flight chronicles aviation's most dangerous, exciting, and courageous moments, including such topics as aircraft carriers, songs about flying, airline callsigns, and the space shuttle.

"For anybody with an interest in aviation, this will prove a fascinating resource for browsing. Wings up!" Kirkus.

629.2 Motor land vehicles, cycles

Mara, Wil

From locusts to...automobile anti-collision systems. by Wil Mara. Cherry Lake Pub., c2012. 32 p.: 21st century skills innovation library.

Grades: 4 5 6 7   **629.2**

1. Automobiles -- Collision avoidance systems 2. Locusts 3. Biomimicry 4. Nature 5. Science

ISBN 9781610805018

LC 2012011856

Introduces how some of history's most imaginative inventors were inspired by nature and how their creations continue to improve our lives today.

Smith, Miranda, 1944-

Speed machines. Miranda Smith. Kingfisher, 2009. 64 p.: Kingfisher knowledge

Grades: 5 6 7 8   **629.2**

1. Motor vehicles 2. Speed 3. Racing 4. Vehicles 5. Transportation

ISBN 9780753462874

LC oc2009002776

"This well-organized, full-color book is packed with facts, photos, and history. It covers all aspects in history dealing with humankind's quest for speed, including land, water and air. . . . There are short blocks of main text and sidebars or blurbs to add additional information. Besides the usual suspects in books that cover this topic—cars, motorcycles, and planes—this book includes boats, gliders, hot air balloons, trains, and windsurfing among other speed machines. . . . It is an essential purchase, especially where books about racing, cars, planes, trucks, motorcycles, etc. are popular." Voice of Youth Advocates.

629.22 Types of vehicles

Bearce, Stephanie

All about electric and hybrid cars and who's driving them And Who's Driving Them. Stephanie Bearce. Mitchell Lane Publishers, c2009. 47 p.: Robbie readers.

Grades: 4 5 6 7   **629.22**

1. Electric vehicles 2. Hybrid electric vehicles 3. Hybridization 4. Automobiles 5. Technological innovations

ISBN 9781584157632

LC 2009004528

Explores how hybrid cars work and new inventions in the automotive industry.

Diaz, Julio

Tesla model S. Julio Diaz. Rourke Educational Media, [2017] 32 p.: Vroom! Hot cars

Grades: 4 5 6 7 8   **629.22**
    1. Electric vehicles 2. Automobiles 3. Tesla Roadster automobile
    ISBN 9781681917498

"Some of the hottest sports car available today are highlighted in this sleek series, which delivers strong content, impressive details, and eye-popping images to young car fanatics." School Library Journal.

Rigsby, Mike

★ **Amazing** rubber band cars: easy-to-build wind-up racers, models, and toys. Mike Rigsby. Chicago Review Press, 2007. xii, 121 p.

Grades: 4 5 6 7   **629.22**
    1. Model cars 2. Toys 3. Paperboard 4. Handicraft
    ISBN 1556527365

    LC 2007013969

Provides instructions on making and modifying different types of racing cars using rubber bands, glue, and simple construction materials, with an explanation of the scientific principles behind the process.

"This offers instructions for making toy and model cars using mostly cardboard, glue, pencils, rubber bands, and a few other easily obtainable materials. . . . Readers will learn about corrugated and flat cardboard, and how to use glue and work with templates. Excellent instructions are accompanied by black-and-white photos every step of the way. . . . These projects are fun to construct, and inquisitive minds will be fascinated by the moving cars." School Library Journal.

629.222 Vehicles powered by fossil fuels and human-powered vehicles

Williams, Brian, 1943-

Who invented the automobile? Brian Williams. Arcturus Pub., 2010. 46 p.: Breakthroughs in science and technology

Grades: 5 6 7 8   **629.222**
    1. Automobiles -- History 2. Engines 3. Automobile industry and trade 4. Automobile assembly lines 5. Scientific discoveries
    ISBN 9781848376816

    LC 2010011019

Looking at some of the major inventions and discoveries shaping our world today, Breakthroughs in Science profiles the research leading up to the discovery (not just profiles of the one or two key "players"). Each book describes the "famous" moment and then examines the continued evolution illustrating its impact today and for the future. Provided by publisher.

"This book is divided into easy to read short chapters with large, colorful photographs and graphics on every page. . . . The added inserts provide additional information to engage readers and help them connect with the scientific details." Library Media Connection.

Woods, Bob

Hottest muscle cars. by Bob Woods. Enslow Publishers, c2008. 48 p.: Wild wheels! (Enslow Publishers)

Grades: 4 5 6 7   **629.222**
    1. Muscle cars -- History 2. Muscle cars
    ISBN 0766028720

    LC 2007007423

Read about the beginning of America's love for muscle cars, and see why they are still loved today. Provided by publisher.

Hottest sports cars. by Bob Woods. Enslow Publishers, c2008. 48 p.: Wild wheels! (Enslow Publishers)

Grades: 4 5 6 7   **629.222**
    1. Sports cars
    ISBN 9780766028739

    LC 2007007428

Learn about some of the world's most famous sports cars; how they began, and where they are going in the future. Provided by publisher.

629.227 Cycles

Farndon, John

Megafast motorcycles. by John Farndon; illustrated by Mat Edwards and Jeremy Pyke. Hungry Tomato, [2016] 31 p.: Megafast

Grades: 3 4 5 6   **629.227**
    1. Motorcycles 2. Motorcycles, Racing 3. Superbikes
    ISBN 9781467793643

    LC 2015031655

A look at high-speed motorcycles profiles different fast cycles and provides information on the records, stunts, and other amazing feats each has performed.

Lakin, Patricia, 1944-

Bicycles. Patricia Lakin. Aladdin, 2017. 32 p.: Made by Hand

Grades: 3 4 5 6 7   **629.227**
    1. Bicycles -- Design and construction 2. Manufacturing processes 3. Sports equipment 4. Bicycles 5. Bicycles -- Equipment and supplies
    ISBN 9781481478960

    LC 2016034643

Go behind the scenes and learn how craftsman Aaron Dykstra makes one-of-a-kind bicycles by hand with this nonfiction book that's full of photographs and illustrations about his process. Aaron Dykstra of Six-Eleven Bicycles in Roanoke, Virginia, got hisfirst job at a small local bike shop when he was fifteen and he spent the majority of his teen years riding and racing bikes. After a stint in the air force, Aaron realized his true passion was on land: making these beautiful machines. This book gives kids a detailed peek into Aaron's process making steel bike frames with his own hands. Charts, infographics, and bold photographs make this a perfect book for anyone who's curious about how a bicycle is made. This book also features a brief history of cycling, a timeline, and resources to inspire kids to make their own objects by hand. Provided by publisher.

"A must-have for school and public libraries in need of materials to support STEM curricula and maker spaces." School Library Journal.

Mulder, Michelle, 1976-

Pedal it!: how bicycles are changing the world. Michelle Mulder. Orca Book Publishers, c2013. 48 p.

Grades: 3 4 5 6 7 8   **629.227**
    1. Bicycles 2. Bicycling 3. Transportation
    ISBN 9781459802193

    LC oc2012660811

Traces the evolution of bicycles from the "walking machines" and "boneshakers" of the 19th century to the slick racing bikes of the 21st, and also shows how bikes can make the world a better place.

Smedman, Lisa

From boneshakers to choppers: the rip-roaring history of motorcycles. Lisa Smedman. Annick Press; c2007. 120 p.

Grades: 5 6 7 8 **629.227**

1. Motorcycles -- History 2. Motorcyclists 3. Books for reluctant readers

ISBN 1554510155

LC bl2007002581

A history of the motorcycle spans its beginnings as a steam-driven bicycle to its current incarnation as a racing vehicle and as a mainstream form of transportation, including the image of motorcyclists and how it has changed over the years.

"Smedman defines motorcycles broadly enough to include everything from Harleys to Vespas, and even bicycles, in this lively, wide-ranging history. . . . Illustrated with a generous array of action photos, historical shots, and period advertisements." Booklist.

Includes bibliographical references (p. 112-113) and index.

629.28 Tests, driving, maintenance, repair

Miller, Malinda, 1979-

Modern mechanics: maintaining tomorrow's green vehicles. by Malinda Miller. Mason Crest Publishers, c2011. 64 p.: New careers for the 21st century: finding your role in the global renewal

Grades: 7 8 9 10 **629.28**

1. Machinery -- Maintenance and repair 2. Automobile mechanics -- Vocational guidance 3. Occupations 4. Vocational guidance

ISBN 9781422218181

LC 2010016870

"Chapters identify and emphasize specific careers—important strengths, necessary aptitudes and interests, education and training, projected earnings, closely related occupations, type of work environment, and predictions for the future of the field. . . . Color photos have a small role amid the many statistics, figures, graphs and charts that support and supplement the . . . [text]." School Library Journal.

Includes bibliographical references and index.

Schweizer, Chris

Fix a car! Chris Schweizer. First Second, 2019. 122 p.

Grades: 5 6 7 8 9 10 **629.28**

1. Automobiles -- Maintenance and repair 2. Comics and Graphic novels

ISBN 9781250150035

LC bl2019002877

Uses a story in graphic-novel format about a group of friends who love cars to provide step-by-step instructions for how to maintain and repair a car, describing how to check fluids, maintain the battery, and change a flat tire.

"Offering challenging but realistically doable projects and specific explanations of background chemical and physical principles, these engaging guides will leave no wrench or spatula safe from middle and high school students (not to mention more intrepid grade schoolers)." School Library Journal.

629.4 Astronautics

Benoit, Peter, 1955-

The **space** race. by Peter Benoit. Children's Press, c2012. 64 p.: Cornerstones of freedom.

Grades: 4 5 6 **629.4**

1. Space programs -- International competition -- History 2. Astronautics -- History 3. Space flight -- History 4. Astronautics -- History

ISBN 9780531230657

LC 2011031454

Describes the history of the space race between the United States and the Soviet Union.

Bortz, Alfred B.

Seven wonders of space technology. Fred Bortz. Twenty-First Century Books, c2011. 80 p.

Grades: 5 6 7 8 **629.4**

1. Astronautics 2. Aerospace technology 3. Space exploration 4. Space vehicles 5. Technology

ISBN 9780761354536

LC 2010023996

Explores the science behind seven of the most remarkable space technologies, including the Great Observatories, the International Space Station, New Horizons, Moon bases and lunar water, Mars rovers, rocketry, and weather satellites.

"Highlights some of astronomy's greatest technical advancements, from land observatories to spinning satellites to moon bases. . . . [This] volume makes basic concepts clear in lively, energetic language that, along with the mesmerizing color photos and artists' renderings of space, will easily captivate a young audience, while up-to-date examples, including discoveries made in the last five years, will only increase the sense of immediacy and excitement." Booklist.

Includes bibliographical references (p. 75-77) and index.

Carlisle, Rodney P.

Exploring space. Rodney P. Carlisle; John S. Bowman and Maurice Isserman, general editors. Chelsea House Publishers, c2010. 120 p.

Grades: 6 7 8 9 10 **629.4**

1. Astronautics 2. Outer space -- Exploration

ISBN 9781604131888

LC 2009025585

Presents information on the history of human exploration of space, discussing the space race, the Moon landing, the International Space Station, and the Hubble Space Telescope.

Crompton, Samuel Willard

SputnikExplorer 1: the race to conquer space. Samuel Willard Crompton. Chelsea House, c2007. 106 p.: Milestones in American history

Grades: 7 8 9 10 **629.4**

1. Astronautics -- History 2. Astronautics -- History 3. Space programs -- International competition 4. Space exploration 5. United States -- Foreign relations -- Soviet Union. 6. Soviet Union -- Foreign relations -- United States.

ISBN 9780791093573

LC 2006034127

Provides biographical sketches, photographs, excerpts from primary source documents, and first-person narratives that detail the events surrounding the space race between the United States and the Soviet Union.

"This book begins in 1957 with Russia's successful launch of the first artificial satellite. With the Cold War as a backdrop, the text goes on to describe the space race between the United States and Russia. . . . Many photographs, quotations, and sidebars detail the roles played by key figures." Horn Book Guide.

Includes bibliographical references (p. 98-100) and index.

Harris, Joseph, 1982-

Space exploration: impact of science and technology. by Joseph Harris. Gareth Stevens Pub., 2010. 64 p. : Pros and cons (Gareth Stevens Publishing)

Grades: 5 6 7 8   **629.4**

1. Space exploration 2. Astronautics 3. Space policy 4. Astronautics -- Technology transfer
ISBN 9781433919893

         LC 2009012436

"An active layout that features color photographs, maps, graphs or charts on every spread, this . . . [book] has much to offer. . . . It conveniently outlines the range of views . . . helping students to learn how to view both sides of [the] issue[s]." School Library Journal.

Includes bibliographical references and index.

Jones, Tom, 1955 January 22-

Ask the astronaut: a galaxy of astonishing answers to your questions on spaceflight. NASA astronaut and spacewalker Tom Jones. Smithsonian Books, 2016. 224 p.

Grades: 5 6 7 8   **629.4**

1. Space exploration 2. Space flight -- Physiological aspects 3. Astronauts 4. Astronautics 5. Questions and answers 6. Space
ISBN 9781588345370

         LC 2015037850

A veteran astronaut and spacewalker introduces young science enthusiasts to what life is really like in space, answering such questions as what liftoff feels like, how astronauts navigate weightlessness and how people sleep in space.

Mara, Wil

Space exploration: science, technology, and engineering. Wil Mara. Children's Press, an imprint of Scholastic Inc., 2014. 64 p.: Calling all innovators: a career for you?

Grades: 5 6 7 8   **629.4**

1. Space flight 2. Astronautics 3. Astronauts 4. Space sciences 5. Astrophysics 6. Solar system 7. Space
ISBN 9780531206157

         LC 2014003569

"An appropriate series for middle schoolers searching for concrete career possibilities." School Library Journal.

Includes bibliographical references and index.

Ottaviani, Jim

T-minus: the race to the moon. Jim Ottaviani; illustrated by Zander Cannon, Kevin Cannon. Aladdin, 2009. 128 p.

Grades: 4 5 6 7 8 9 10 11 12 Adult   **629.4**

1. United States. National Aeronautics and Space Administration 2. Space flight to the moon 3. Space programs -- International competition 4. Astronautics -- History 5. Astronauts 6. Comics and Graphic novels
ISBN 9781416949602

         LC 2009926127

In graphic novel format, presents the story of two world superpowers racing to land a man on the moon, and the people who worked on the project.

Stott, Carole

Space exploration. Carole Stott. Dk Pub., 2009. 72 p.: Eyewitness books

Grades: 4 5 6 7   **629.4**

1. Space exploration 2. Astronomy 3. Astronautics 4. Solar system 5. Space
ISBN 9780756658281

Describes rockets, exploratory vehicles, and other technological aspects of space exploration, satellites, space stations, and the life and work of astronauts.

Young, Karen Romano

Space junk: the dangers of polluting Earth's orbit. Karen Romano Young. Twenty-First Century Books, 2016. 64 p.

Grades: 7 8 9 10   **629.4**

1. Space debris 2. Pollution 3. Waste products 4. Near-Earth objects 5. Space 6. Earth
ISBN 9781467756006

Examines the proliferation of space debris in outer space and discusses methods of retrieving and disposing of the material.

"Clearly written and concise, the book lays out the problem without sensationalizing it, while including human-interest details, such as your odds of being stuck by falling space junk (at 'one in several trillion,' decidedly low). Small, well-captioned color photos, helpful diagrams, and interesting sidebars enhance the text. A natural for booktalking to STEM-minded kids, this slender volume belongs in many libraries." Booklist.

629.4092 Astronautical engineers

Skurzynski, Gloria

This is rocket science: the true story of the risk-taking scientists who figured out ways to explore beyond Earth. by Gloria Skurzynski. National Geographic, c2010. 80 p.

Grades: 5 6 7 8   **629.4092**

1. Rocketry 2. Aerospace engineers 3. Rocketry -- History 4. Rockets (Aviation) 5. Rocket planes
ISBN 9781426305986

         LC 2009020386

"This concise book provides a historical, as well as contemporary, introduction to the field of aeronautical engineering with a decidedly human interest perspective. . . . This text will be a great introduction to many of the significant contributors to the field of rocket science." Science Books & Films.

Includes bibliographical references and index.

629.40973 United States. National Aeronautics and Space Administration

Rhuday-Perkovich, Olugbemisola

Above and beyond: NASA's journey to tomorrow. Olugbemisola Rhuday-Perkovich; with introduction from Rory Kennedy. Feiwel and Friends, 2018. 153 p.

Grades: 5 6 7 8   **629.40973**

1. United States. National Aeronautics and Space Administration 2. United States. National Aeronautics and Space Administration -- History 3. Astronautics -- History 4. Astronauts -- History
ISBN 9781250308467

         LC bl2018184634

Describes the history of NASA, detailing major contributors to the space program, its historical achievements and challenges, and how it will continue to move forward in the future.

"Space nerds will be hooked; an extensive bibliography makes this a natural for report writers, and the format and generous artwork will attract browsers." Booklist.

Includes bibliographical references (pages 146-150) and index.

629.43 Unmanned space flight

Carson, Mary Kay

Mission to Pluto: the first visit to an ice dwarf and the Kuiper belt. Mary Kay Carson; with photographs by Tom Uhlman. Houghton Mifflin Harcourt, [2016] 73 p.: Scientists in the field (Houghton Mifflin)

Grades: 5 6 7 8   **629.43**
1. New Horizons (Spacecraft) 2. Space flight 3. Space exploration 4. Pluto (Dwarf planet) 5. Kuiper Belt
ISBN 9780544416710

LC 2015037656

Follow a spacecraft the size of a piano, named New Horizons, on the first ever spacecraft mission to Pluto, the space entity formerly known as a planet, in the latest addition to the epic and authoritative Scientists in the Field series. Provided by publisher.

"This enthusiastic, accessible look at both cutting-edge scientific discovery and the dynamic work behind the scenes will be an easy sell to space-mad kids and a valuable addition to any school library." Booklist.

Includes bibliographical references (page 72) and index.

Spilsbury, Richard, 1963-

Robots in space. Richard and Louise Spilsbury. Gareth Stevens Publishing, 2016. 48 p.: Amazing robots

Grades: 4 5 6 7   **629.43**
1. Space robotics 2. Robots 3. Robotics 4. Space probes 5. Space exploration
ISBN 9781482430141

LC bl2015030053

Explains why robots play a major role in space exploration and describes probes, orbiters, landers, rovers, robotic arms, and other devices and what they have accomplished.

"The full-color photos of robots in action and the high-interest nature of robotics may catch the interest of science-minded kids." Booklist.

Includes bibliographical references (page 47) and index.

629.44 Auxiliary spacecraft

Cole, Michael D.

The **Columbia** space shuttle disaster: from first liftoff to tragic final flight. Michael D. Cole. Enslow Publishers, c2003. 48 p.

Grades: 4 5 6   **629.44**
1. Columbia (Spacecraft) 2. Columbia (Spacecraft) -- Accidents 3. Space vehicle accidents 4. Space shuttles
ISBN 9780766022959

LC 2003004823

Details the first flight of the space shuttle Columbia, as well as its tragic final flight.

"The account offers a lot of information, helping to make sense of a highly complicated subject. . . . The color and b&w photographs complement the story." Library Media Connection.

Includes bibliographical references (p. 47) and index.

Holden, Henry M.

The **coolest** job in the universe: working aboard the International Space Station. Henry M. Holden. Enslow, c2013. 48 p.: American space missions

Grades: 4 5 6 7 8   **629.44**
1. International Space Station 2. Space stations 3. Space sciences -- Research 4. Space flight
ISBN 9780766040748

LC 2012002222

Explores the International Space Station (ISS), including its construction and the missions required to build it, living and working aboard the ISS, and its importance as the future of the space program. Provided by publisher.

Miller, Ron, 1947-

Satellites. Ron Miller. Twenty-First Century Books, c2008. 112 p.: Space innovations

Grades: 7 8 9 10   **629.44**
1. Artificial satellites -- History 2. Rocketry 3. Artificial satellites 4. Sputniks -- History 5. Space probes
ISBN 0822571544

LC 2007001075

Traces the development of artificial satellites from the rise of rocketry, discussing the historical importance of Sputnik and describing what modern satellites are used for.

"This begins with the science of Newton, the history of rockets, and the vivid imaginations of nineteenth-century science-fiction writers. It traces the historical development of man-made satellites from Sputnik 1 to the Earth orbiters currently transmitting everything from Earth-based communications signals to images of the universe. . . . Illustrations include many small color photos and some paintings, diagrams, satellite images, and black-and-white photos. . . . Miller synthesizes his evident research into a well-organized discussion." Booklist.

Includes bibliographical references (p. 107-109) and index.

629.45 Manned space flight

Bodden, Valerie

To the moon. by Valerie Bodden. Creative Education, 2012. 48 p.: Great expeditions

Grades: 5 6 7 8   **629.45**
1. Project Apollo (U.S.) -- History 2. Apollo 11 (Spacecraft) -- History 3. Space flight to the moon -- History 4. Astronomy 5. Moon -- Exploration
ISBN 9781608180684

LC 2010033549

A history of America's famed Apollo 11 mission to the moon in 1969, detailing the challenges encountered, the individuals involved, the discoveries made, and how the expedition left its mark upon the world. Provided by publisher.

Brouwer, Sigmund, 1959-

★ **Moon** mission: the epic 400-year journey to Apollo 11. Sigmund Brouwer. Kids Can Press, 2019 128 p.

Grades: 4 5 6 7 8   **629.45**
1. Project Apollo (U.S.) 2. Apollo 11 (Spacecraft) 3. Space flight to the moon 4. Space exploration 5. Astronauts
ISBN 9781525300363

A narrative told from the astronauts' points of view describes the story behind Apollo 11's moon landing, linking the innovations and discoveries from the past four centuries that made the mission possible.

Chaikin, Andrew, 1956-

Mission control, this is Apollo: the story of the first voyages to the moon. by Andrew Chaikin, with Victoria Kohl; with paintings by Alan Bean Viking. Penguin Group, 2009. 128 p.

Grades: 5 6 7 8 9   **629.45**
1. Project Apollo (U.S.) -- History 2. Space flight to the moon -- History 3. Astronautics 4. Space exploration
ISBN 9780670011568

LC 2009000833

"Based on interviews with 28 astronauts, this history of the Apollo program masterfully describes the missions and personalizes them with astronauts' own words. Chaikin starts with a brief overview of its origins and of the Mercury and Gemini missions. He then highlights the significance of each manned Apollo mission in chronological chapters, with full-page sidebars on such topics as food, TV coverage, space sickness and going to the bathroom in space. The handsome design has many photographs, diagrams of the rockets and modules and more than 30 well-reproduced paintings by Apollo 12 astronaut Bean." Kirkus.

Includes bibliographical references and index.

Cherrix, Amy E.

In the shadow of the moon: America, Russia, and the hidden history of the Space Race. Amy Cherrix. Balzer + Bray, 2021 240 p.

Grades: 6 7 8 9 10   **629.45**
1. Project Apollo (U.S.) 2. Space programs -- International competition 3. Space flight to the moon 4. International competition 5. Astronautics 6. Space exploration 7. United States -- Foreign relations -- Soviet Union. 8. Soviet Union -- Foreign relations -- United States.
ISBN 9780062888754

The award-winning author chronicles the lesser-known rivalry between former Nazi-turned-U.S. Cold War scientist Wernher von Braun and Russian rocket designer Sergei Korolev, explaining how their controversial scientific achievements shaped human history.

"YA history readers frustrated by an information gap between the race for the bomb and the race to the moon will find this the essential—and thrilling—infill they've missed." Bulletin of the Center for Children's Books

Dell, Pamela

Man on the moon: how a photograph made anything seem possible. by Pamela Dell. Compass Point Books, c2011. 64 p.: Captured history

Grades: 6 7 8 9   **629.45**
1. Project Apollo (U.S.) 2. Space flight to the moon -- History 20th century 3. Photography -- Influence 4. Astronauts 5. Space flight 6. Moon
ISBN 9780756543969

LC 2010038577

Explores and analyzes the historical context and significance of Neil Armstrong's iconic photograph of Buzz Aldrin.

"Occasionally, a single photograph becomes the emblematic image that defines an era, and this quality series tells the stories of four of those iconic pictures." School Library Journal.

Edge, Laura B.

Apollo 13: a successful failure. by Laura B. Edge. Twenty-First Century Books, 2020 136 p.

Grades: 6 7 8 9 10   **629.45**
1. Project Apollo (U.S.) 2. Apollo 13 (Spacecraft) 3. Space vehicle accidents 4. Space exploration 5. Space flight 6. Space vehicles

-- Accidents
ISBN 9781541559004

LC 2019009210

This young adult book tells the story of the Apollo 13 mission in 1970. It was the seventh manned mission in the Apollo space program and the third that was meant to land on the Moon. The landing was aborted after an oxygen tank exploded, threatening all lives onboard the craft. The crew did return home safely. This book explores how the team worked together and what the space program learned from the experience.

Goodman, Susan E., 1952-

How do you burp in space?: and other tips every space tourist needs to know. by Susan Goodman; illustrated by Michael Slack. Bloomsbury Pub.: 2013. 64 p.

Grades: 4 5 6   **629.45**
1. Space flight 2. Space tourism
ISBN 9781599900681

LC 2011035303

A non-fiction travel guide to space tourism that includes information about accommodations, attractions, and more. Provided by publisher.

Ultimate field trip 5: blasting off to Space Academy. by Susan E. Goodman; photographs by Michael J. Doolittle. Atheneum Books for Young Readers, c2001. 41, 1 p.

Grades: 4 5 6 7   **629.45**
1. Space Academy (U.S. Space Camp (Huntsville, Alabama)) 2. Astronauts -- Training 3. Space flight training facilities 4. School field trips 5. Astronauts
ISBN 0689830440

LC 00038082

Describes a trip to the U.S. Space Academy where kids are able to experience weightlessness and living in space, to learn about the different parts needed to build rockets, and to participate in a simulated space mission.

"This book follows student trainees through a weeklong session at the U.S. Space Academy in Huntsville, AL, as they are exposed to what it takes to become an astronaut and to the inner workings of the entire space program. . . . Varied-colored pages, replete with outstanding full-color, captioned photos, are artistically appealing as well as informative." School Library Journal.

Includes bibliographical references (p. [42]).

Green, Carl R.

Spacewalk: the astounding Gemini 4 mission. Carl R. Green. Enslow Publishers, c2013. 48 p.: American space missions

Grades: 4 5 6 7 8   **629.45**
1. Project Gemini (U.S.) -- History 2. Astronauts 3. Space walking 4. Space vehicles
ISBN 9780766040755

LC 2011030869

Explores the Gemini 4 mission, including the astronauts and the first American spacewalk, the spacecraft and technology that made it possible, and how the Gemini mission laid the foundation for the Apollo missions to the moon. Provided by publisher.

Hartman, Eve

Mission to Mars. Eve Hartman and Wendy Meshbesher. Raintree, c2011. 56 p.: Raintree freestyle.

Grades: 5 6 7 8   **629.45**
1. Space flight to Mars 2. Mars probes 3. Space exploration 4.

Astronautics 5. Mars (Planet) -- Exploration.
ISBN 9781410938213

LC 2009053209

"Excellent black-and-white and color photos throughout are matched perfectly to the texts and well captioned. Good choices for reports and debates." School Library Journal.

Includes bibliographical references (p. 54-55) and index.

Holden, Henry M.

Danger in space: surviving the Apollo 13 disaster. Henry M. Holden. Enslow Publishers, c2013. 48 p.: American space missions

Grades: 4 5 6 7 8   **629.45**
    1. Project Apollo (U.S.) 2. Apollo 13 (Spacecraft) 3. Space vehicle accidents 4. Space vehicles 5. Astronauts
ISBN 9780766040724

LC 2011037734

Explores the Apollo 13 mission, including the causes of the disaster aboard the spacecraft, how the astronauts fixed the problems, and how the crew was saved. Provided by publisher.

Maurer, Richard, 1950-

Destination moon: the remarkable and improbable voyage of Apollo 11. Richard Maurer. Roaring Brook Press, 2019. 388 p.

Grades: 6 7 8 9 10 11   **629.45**
    1. United States. National Aeronautics and Space Administration 2. Project Apollo (U.S.) 3. Apollo 11 (Spacecraft) 4. Space flight to the moon 5. Space exploration 6. Space flight 7. Aerospace engineers 8. Moon 9. Space
ISBN 9781626727458

A dramatic account of the Apollo 11 moon landing reveals the lesser-known contributions of soldiers, engineers and world leaders while sharing contextual insights into how the space program was shaped by important historical events.

"Here's an absorbing, insightful, solidly informative resource for readers who want to understand the U.S. space program from the ground up." Booklist.

Includes bibliographical references and index.

Rocco, John

★ **How** we got to the moon: the people, technology, and daring feats of science behind humanity's greatest adventure. John Rocco. Crown Books for Young Readers, 2020. 264 p.

Grades: 5 6 7 8   **629.45**
    1. United States. National Aeronautics and Space Administration 2. Project Apollo (U.S.) 3. 1960s 4. Space flight to the moon 5. Space programs 6. Rocketry 7. Space flight 8. Space exploration 9. Moon
ISBN 9780525647416

LC 2019040738

This beautifully illustrated, oversized guide to the people and technology of the moon landing by award-winning author/illustrator John Rocco is a must-have for space fans, classrooms, and tech geeks. Provided by publisher.

"With a main narrative composed in the present tense, the result gives the insights, events, disasters, and near disasters of over a half-century ago not only visual unity, but an immediacy that will sweep readers along—and serve as a constant reminder that the participants, from well-known names like Katherine Johnson to geologist Farouk El-Baz and seamstress Ellie Foraker, weren't all White men or remote historical figures." Kirkus

Includes bibliographical references and index.

Sandler, Martin W.

Apollo 8. Martin W. Sandler. Candlewick Press, 2018. 176 p.

Grades: 6 7 8 9   **629.45**
    1. Project Apollo (U.S.). 2. 1960s 3. Space exploration 4. Apollo 8 (Spacecraft) 5. Space flight to the moon 6. Astronauts
ISBN 9780763694890

In a volume full of astonishing full-color photographs, including the iconic Earthrise photo, Martin W. Sandler unfolds an incredible chapter in U.S. history: Apollo 8 wouldn't just orbit Earth, it would take American astronauts to see the dark side of the moon.

Thimmesh, Catherine

★ **Team** moon: how 400,000 people landed Apollo 11 on the moon. Houghton Mifflin Co., 2006. 80 p.

Grades: 5 6 7 8   **629.45**
    1. Armstrong, Neil, 1930-2012 2. United States. National Aeronautics and Space Administration. 3. John F. Kennedy Space Center, Cocoa Beach, Florida 4. 1970s 5. Astronauts 6. Apollo 11 (Spacecraft) -- History 7. Space flight to the moon -- History 8. Space flight 9. Moon
ISBN 0618507574

Robert F. Sibert Informational Book Medal, 2007.

"Thimmesh retraces the course of the space mission that landed an actual man, on the actual Moon. It's an oft-told tale, but the author tells it from the point of view not of astronauts or general observers, but of some of the 17,000 behind-the-scenes workers at Kennedy Space Center, the 7500 Grumman employees who built the lunar module, the 500 designers and seamstresses who actually constructed the space suits, and other low-profile contributors who made the historic flight possible. . . . This dramatic account will mesmerize even readers already familiar with the event. . . . This stirring, authoritative tribute to the collective effort . . . belongs in every collection." School Library Journal.

629.450092 Astronauts

Stone, Tanya Lee

Almost astronauts: 13 women who dared to dream. by Tanya Lee Stone. Candlewick Press, 2009. 144 p.

Grades: 5 6 7 8 9 10   **629.450092**
    1. 1960s 2. Project Mercury 3. Women astronauts -- History 4. Space exploration 5. Women's rights -- History 20th century 6. Women astronauts
ISBN 9780763636111

LC 2008017487

Robert F. Sibert Informational Book Medal, 2010.

Presents the story of the thirteen women connected with NASA's Mercury 13 space mission, who braved prejudice and jealousy to make their mark and open the door for the female pilots and space commanders that would soon follow.

"In 1960, thirteen American women passed the physical exams required to become astronauts as surely as any of the men already involved in NASA's early space flight endeavors, but they were disqualified solely because of their gender. This book is their story. . . . Any girl with an interest in space flight or the history of women's rights will enjoy this account and applaud these courageous pioneers." Voice of Youth Advocates.

Includes bibliographical references.

629.47 Astronautical engineering

Woolf, Alex, 1964-

The **science** of spacecraft: the cosmic truth about rockets, satellites, and probes. written by Alex Woolf; artists, Ed Meyer, Bryan Beach, Jared Green, Sam Bridges, and Shutterstock. Franklin Watts, 2019. 32 p.

Grades: 4 5 6 7 8   **629.47**
1. Space vehicles 2. Space flight 3. Astronautics 4. Outer space -- Exploration
ISBN 9780531133972

LC 2018031801

Introduces the reader the science of spacecraft. Provided by publisher.

629.8 Automatic control engineering

Chaffee, Joel

How to build a prize-winning robot. Joel Chaffee. Rosen Central, 2011. 48 p.: Robotics

Grades: 5 6 7 8   **629.8**
1. Robots -- Design and construction 2. Robots -- Design and construction -- Competitions 3. Robotics
ISBN 9781448812387

LC 2010025748

Describes the steps to building robots in competitions, from the different types of robots to build and forming an effective building team to essential components, programming, and building safety tips.

"Kids who are fascinated with robots will want [this title] available." School Library Journal.

Includes bibliographical references (p. 45-46) and index.

Freedman, Jeri

Robots through history. Jeri Freedman. Rosen Central, 2011. 48 p.: Robotics

Grades: 5 6 7 8   **629.8**
1. Robotics -- History 2. Robots -- History 3. Artificial intelligence 4. Electronics 5. Cybernetics
ISBN 9781448812363

LC 2010024139

Discusses the history of robotics, from automated machines in the Middle Ages to the birth of electronics, the integration of artificial intelligence, and fully mobile, humanoid robots.

"Kids who are fascinated with robots will want [this title] available." School Library Journal.

Includes bibliographical references (p. 45-46) and index.

Gilby, Nancy Benovich

FIRST robotics. by Nancy Benovich Gilby. Cherry Lake Publishing, [2016] 32 p.: 21st century skills innovation library.

Grades: 4 5 6 7 8   **629.8**
1. Robotics 2. Robots 3. Inventions
ISBN 9781633623781

LC 2015013323

Makers of all ages are using LEGO bricks to create robots. In this book, students learn more about this recent innovation through detailed explanations built to foster creativity and critical thinking. Fun, engaging text introduces readers to new ideas and builds on maker-related concepts they may already know. Additional tools, including a glossary and an index, help students learn new vocabulary and locate information. Provided by publisher.

"Though narrowly focused, each title presents enough basic concepts that students shouldn't have much trouble expanding beyond the fundamentals." Booklist.

Includes bibliographical references and index.

Graham, Ian, 1953-

Robot technology. Ian Graham. Smart Apple Media, 2012. 46 p.: New Technology

Grades: 4 5 6 7   **629.8**
1. Robotics 2. Industrial robots 3. Robots 4. Technological innovations 5. Technology
ISBN 9781599205335

LC 2010044240

Describes current robotics technology, including the applications of robots in space, in the military, in industry, and around the house. Discusses the pros and cons of creating fully autonomous robots. Provided by publisher.

"This offers a fine overview for reports, and its attractive design may also entice middle-grade readers to learn more." Booklist.

Mercer, Bobby, 1961-

The **robot** book: build & control 20 electric gizmos, moving machines, and hacked toys. Bobby Mercer. Chicago Review Press, 2014. 208 p.: Science in motion

Grades: 4 5 6   **629.8**
1. Robots 2. Robotics 3. Personal robotics 4. Technological innovations 5. Machinery
ISBN 9781556524073

LC 2014015327

The 20 easy-to-build robots in this project book can be constructed for little or no cost using common household objects and repurposed materials. Provided by publisher.

"A solid starting point for readers with an interest in circuitry or engineering—or who simply like to take things apart to see how they work." Publishers Weekly.

Payment, Simone

Robotics careers: preparing for the future. Simone Payment. Rosen Central, 2011. 48 p.: Robotics

Grades: 5 6 7 8   **629.8**
1. Robotics -- Vocational guidance 2. Robots 3. Vocational guidance
ISBN 9781448812394

LC 2010024134

Describes how to prepare for a career in robotics, including the different jobs in the field, the education required for a position in the field, and how robotics research will be used in future applications.

"Kids who are fascinated with robots will want [this title] available." School Library Journal.

Includes bibliographical references (p. 44-46) and index.

Shea, Therese

The **robotics** club: teaming up to build robots. Therese Shea. Rosen Central, 2011. 48 p.: Robotics

Grades: 5 6 7 8   **629.8**
1. Robots -- Design and construction 2. Robotics 3. Clubs 4. Teenagers' clubs
ISBN 9781448812370

LC 2010025750

Discusses how to start a robotics club, from finding members to building a website and running a meeting, and provides such suggestions for robotics club activities as participating in robot building competitions.

"This title will provide students with the information necessary to form a club and compete at making and using robots. Kids who are fascinated with robots will want [this title] available." School Library Journal.

Includes bibliographical references (p. 44-46) and index.

Sjonger, Rebecca

Robotics engineering and our automated world. Rebecca Sjonger. 32 p.: Engineering in Action

Grades: 5 6 7 8   **629.8**
    1. Robotics 2. Technological innovations 3. Robots 4. Engineering
ISBN 9780778775379

                LC 2016027282

Robots are machines that follow a decision-making process when performing tasks. They are playing an increasing role in manufacturing, agriculture, medicine, mining, and aerospace, as well as in our everyday lives. Readers will learn how robotics engineers find new ways for robots to do work that would be dangerous, time-consuming, dull, or impossible for humans to perform. Real-life examples and a design challenge help students understand key concepts related to the engineering design process, and how robotics engineers play a vital role in expanding our knowledge of the universe. Provided by publisher.

"A fascinating and thoughtfully arranged presentation of modern engineering." Booklist.

Includes index.

Sobey, Edwin J. C., 1948-

Robot experiments. Ed Sobey. Enslow Publishers, c2011. 128 p.: Cool science projects with technology

Grades: 6 7 8 9   **629.8**
    1. Robotics 2. Robots -- Design and construction 3. Science projects 4. Experiments
ISBN 9780766033030

                LC 2009037897

Presents several science projects dealing with robots. Provided by publisher.

"While this book includes some suggestions for science-fair projects and a few experiments throughout, it also provides a detailed description of each component and step-by-step instruction for building a robot. This highly complicated process is explained using understandable terms and in a well-organized manner and includes information as detailed as computer-programming codes." School Library Journal.

Includes bibliographical references and index.

Spilsbury, Louise

Robotics. Louise and Richard Spilsbury. Gareth Stevens Publishing, 2017. 48 p.: Cutting-edge technology (Gareth Stevens Pub.)

Grades: 5 6 7 8   **629.8**
    1. Robots 2. Robotics 3. Technology
ISBN 9781482451603

"Rock-solid choices that will update and deepen science and technology collections." School Library Journal.

Spilsbury, Richard, 1963-

Robots in industry. by Richard and Louise Spilsbury. Gareth Stevens Publishing, 2016. 48 p.: Amazing robots

Grades: 4 5 6 7   **629.8**
    1. Robots 2. Industrial robots 3. Robotics
ISBN 9781482430028

"The full-color photos of robots in action and the high-interest nature of robotics may catch the interest of science-minded kids." Booklist.

Woog, Adam, 1953-

SCRATCHbot. by Adam Woog. Norwood House Press, c2010. 48 p.: Great idea

Grades: 3 4 5 6   **629.8**
    1. Robots 2. Tactile sensors 3. Animal behavior -- Research
ISBN 9781599533803

                LC 2010008502

SCRATCHbot is a robot that depends on tactile touch to process information. Using touch rather than vision, the SCRATCHbot aids scientists researching animal behavior. Provided by publisher.

"Woog introduces a small, rolling robot with prominent whiskers, used to mimic a rodent's ability to sense its surroundings through touch. Discussions include how inventors are inspired by nature and how this appealing robot might be useful. Presenting specific, current information, [this book] will appeal to young people intrigued by inventions." Booklist.

Includes bibliographical references (p. 46) and index.

630 Agriculture and related technologies

Mickelson, Trina

Free-range farming. by Trina Mickelson. Lerner Publications, [2016] 64 p.: Growing green

Grades: 5 6 7 8   **630**
    1. Sustainable agriculture 2. Agriculture 3. Organic farming 4. Agricultural systems 5. Livestock
ISBN 9781467793896

                LC 2015019694

Explains to readers what "free-range" means and what the benefits of free-range farming are.

"This series for upper-middle grades focusing on 'green' food and farming practices that have gained popularity covers what has sparked each movement, what its health and environmental benefits are, and what some of its challenges are." Horn Book.

Includes bibliographical references (pages 61-63) and index.

Perritano, John

Agriculture. John Perritano. Mason Crest, [2017] 64 p.: STEM in current events

Grades: 6 7 8 9 10   **630**
    1. Agriculture 2. Agricultural technology 3. Agricultural mathematics
ISBN 9781422235881

"A great fit for classroom or school libraries and a strong consideration for public libraries interested in the integration of STEM into everyday life." School Library Journal.

Rothman, Julia

Farm anatomy: the curious parts & pieces of country life. Julia Rothman. Storey Pub., c2011. 223 p.

Grades: Adult   **630**
    1. Farm life
ISBN 9781603429818

                LC 2012360929

Talk the talk of the country with Julia Rothman's entertaining and informative visual tour of life on the farm. Her drawings, diagrams, step-by-step sequences, and dissections reveal everything from the parts of a milking machine and the anatomy of a pig to how to plow a field and shear a sheep.—Page 4 of cover.

630.9 Agriculture—History

Rosen, Michael J., 1954-

★ **Our** farm: four seasons with five kids on one family's farm. written and photographed by Michael J. Rosen. Darby Creek Pub., 2008. 144 p.

Grades: 4 5 6 7 8　　　　　　　　**630.9**
　1. Farm life 2. Farms 3. Families 4. Farm animals 5. Ohio
ISBN 9781581960679

A journal of one year on the Bennett farm in central Ohio. Shows how one family, with the help of relatives and friends, creates a life and livelihood on a 150-acre farm.

"This engaging book is an unsentimental, appreciative look into the world of one farm family." School Library Journal.

631.4 Soil science

Graham, Ian, 1953-

You wouldn't want to live without dirt! Ian Graham. Franklin Watts, an imprint of Scholastic Inc., [2016]. 40 p.: You wouldn't want to...

Grades: 3 4 5 6　　　　　　　　**631.4**
　1. Soils
ISBN 9780531214886

"The books feature a time line and numerous ancillaries, but the myriad entertaining facts are the real hit. Who wouldn't want to read them?" Booklist.

Hirsch, Rebecca E

Soil. by Rebecca E. Hirsch; content consultant, Daniel Richter Jr., Professor of Soils and Ecology, Duke University. Core Library, an imprint of Abdo Publishing, [2015] 48 p.: Rocks and minerals (Core Library (Firm))

Grades: 5 6 7　　　　　　　　**631.4**
　1. Soils 2. Soil ecology 3. Soil erosion
ISBN 9781624033919

　　　　　　　　　　　　LC bl2014030403

Presents information on the different types of soil, discussing why soil is important and the consequences of natural erosion.

"Aligned to Common Core and state standards, the series provides ample opportunity for additional research ('Stop and Think'), hands-on experimentation ('In the Field'), and critical thinking ('Changing Minds') that will have readers looking at the world around them with a better understanding of just what exactly they're seeing. Despite a few issues, these are solid choices." School Library Journal.

Includes bibliographical references (page 47) and index.

631.5 Cultivation and harvesting

Regis, Natalie

Genetically modified crops and food. edited by Natalie Regis. Britannica Educational Publishing in association with Rosen Educational Services, 2016. 174 p.: Biotechnology revolution

Grades: 7 8 9 10 11 12　　　　　　　　**631.5**
　1. Crops -- Genetic engineering 2. Genetically engineered food 3. Food -- Biotechnology 4. Genetically engineered plants
ISBN 9781622755783

　　　　　　　　　　　　LC 2014049175

"The set up of the text is user-friendly with bold, colored fonts for the headings of each section lending to easy navigation of the text." Voice of Youth Advocates.

Includes bibliographical references and index.

633.1 Cereals

Sobol, Richard

The **life** of rice: from seedling to supper. Richard Sobol. Candlewick Press, 2010. 36 p.: Traveling photographer

Grades: 3 4 5 6　　　　　　　　**633.1**
　1. Food crops 2. Rice 3. Grain 4. Plants 5. Agriculture 6. Thailand
ISBN 9780763632526

　　　　　　　　　　　　LC 2009015138

Photographs document the farming process of one of Thailand's most valuable crops, from the beginning of the growing season at the Royal Plowing Ceremony, to the painstaking work of transplanting and harvesting rice plants, to the sharing of a delicious meal.

"Turning his lens to the rice fields of Thailand, Sobol begins this affectionate account with a description of the Royal Plowing Ceremony that kicks off the planting season and continues through cultivation and into the harvest. Brief explanations of the growing stages of rice are accompanied by beautiful color photographs of the fields in their various phases. . . . Sobol offers an interesting look at a country and its people, and their relationship to the land. The writing is accessible and lively, providing a unique, specific look at one of the world's most important staples." School Library Journal.

634.9 Forestry

Collard, Sneed B.

Fire birds: valuing natural wildfires and burned forests. written and photographed by Sneed B. Collard III. Bucking Horse Books, 2015. 48 p.

Grades: 4 5 6 7 8　　　　　　　　**634.9**
　1. Wildfires 2. Birds 3. Ecology 4. Rocky Mountains
ISBN 9780984446070

"A book that will leave readers asking questions and challenging assumptions—and with a keener appreciation of our environment." School Library Journal.

Silverstein, Alvin

★ **Wildfires**: the science behind raging infernos. Alvin and Virginia Silverstein and Laura Silverstein Nunn. Enslow Publishers, c2010. 48 p. : Science behind natural disasters

Grades: 4 5 6　　　　　　　　**634.9**
　1. Wildfires 2. Natural disasters 3. Fires
ISBN 9780766029736

　　　　　　　　　　　　LC 2008048025

Examines the science behind wildfires, including what causes them, the different types of wildfires, their devastating effects, and how to stay safe during a wildfire. Provided by publisher.

"Scientific explanations are accompanied by plentiful color diagrams that will help students to grasp causes and effects. . . . Photos . . . are effective, and are sometimes turned into helpful, lively diagrams by the addition of such features as wind-direction arrows." School Library Journal.

Includes bibliographical references and index.

635 Garden crops (Horticulture)

Cohen, Whitney

The **book** of gardening projects for kids: 101 ways to get kids outside, dirty, and having fun. Whitney Cohen and John Fisher. Timber Press, c2012. 264 p.

Grades: Adult   **635**

1. Gardening 2. Children and gardening
ISBN 9781604692457

LC 2011036778

Features gardening advice, including how to design a play-friendly garden, ideas for fun-filled theme gardens, and how to cook and preserve the garden's bounty.

635.083 Children—Gardening

Cornell, Kari A.

The **nitty-gritty** gardening book: fun projects for all seasons. Kari Cornell; photography by Jennifer Larson. Millbrook Press, 2015. 48 p.

Grades: 3 4 5 6   **635.083**

1. Children and gardening 2. Children's gardens 3. Gardening
ISBN 9781467726474

LC 2014009384

"Pleasant photographs by Larson are supplemented with clear diagrams and stock photos." Kirkus.

636 Animal husbandry

Campbell, Jeff

Daisy to the rescue: true stories of daring dogs, paramedic parrots, and other animal heroes. Jeff Campbell, Ramsey Beyer. Houghton Mifflin Harcourt, 2014. 336 p.

Grades: 6 7 8 9 10   **636**

1. Animal heroes 2. Rescues 3. Human/animal relationships
ISBN 9781936976621

Collects more than 50 true stories about animals who have saved human lives, often risking their own, in a volume that includes strikingly illustrated portraits and scientific insights into the plausibility of animal emotions.

"Inherent animal abilities are discussed alongside the accounts, as are animal traits and scientific theories in laymans terms. Individual stories of animal derring-do, illustrated with pencil portraits, make for quick, compelling reads that prompt the reader to wonder what really goes on in an animal's head and heart." Booklist.

Reed, Cristie

Ferret. Cristie Reed. Rourke Pub Group, 2015. 32 p.: You have a pet what?!

Grades: 2 3 4 5   **636**

1. Ferrets 2. Pets 3. Ferrets as pets 4. Mammals
ISBN 9781634304320

"Well written, with a clean design, these titles will be useful for educators and popular with potential pet owners." School Library Journal.

636.088 Animals for specific purposes

Keenan, Sheila

★ **Animals** in the house: a history of pets and people. Sheila Keenan. Scholastic Nonfiction, c2007. 112 p.

Grades: 4 5 6   **636.088**

1. Pets -- History 2. Human/animal relationships -- History
ISBN 0439692865

LC 2005047056

Tells the story of pets through the ages and the people who kept them, including famous pets and pet owners.

"Keenan provides an overview of pets and their people. Beginning with statistics about pet ownership, the text goes on to describe how animals and humans came together . . . and discusses how this relationship has changed and deepened. . . . Eye-catchingly designed, the format uses Photoshop to best advantage, providing interesting graphics, popping borders, and plenty of pictures featuring adorable animals." Booklist.

Includes bibliographical references (p. 109-110) and index.

Laidlaw, Rob, 1954-

On parade: the hidden world of animals in entertainment. Rob Laidlaw. Fitzhenry & Whiteside, 2010. 55 p.

Grades: 4 5 6   **636.088**

1. Animal welfare 2. Captive wild animals 3. Animals in the performing arts 4. Circus animals 5. Working animals
ISBN 9781554551439

LC oc2010013315

The author of Wild Animals in Captivity examines animals at the zoo and circus as well as animals in movies and television, and the violence toward the animals that sometimes occurs in these worlds, offering suggestions for ways to improve their conditions.

"The author's clearly argued text; crisp, captioned color photos; and appended list of organizations make this an important source for animal advocates." Booklist.

Includes bibliographical references.

Wild animals in captivity. Rob Laidlaw. Fitzhenry & Whiteside, 2008. 48 p.

Grades: 4 5 6 7 8   **636.088**

1. Captive wild animals 2. Animal welfare
ISBN 9781554550258

LC oc2007185642

A look at the lives of captive wild animals at bad zoos, good zoos, and the best wild animal sanctuaries.

"A passionate, well-written, and well-researched argument against the practices of most zoos around the world. . . . Describes the damage done when animals are unnaturally confined and moved to inhospitable climates, and compares the wild and captive lives of polar bears, orcas, elephants, and great apes—the four species most harmed by captivity. . . . The issues raised in this important and powerful book will resonate with young and old." School Library Journal.

Markle, Sandra

Animal heroes: true rescue stories. Sandra Markle. Millbrook Press, c2008. 64 p.

Grades: 4 5 6 7   **636.088**

1. Pets 2. Animals 3. Animal heroes 4. Human/animal relationships
ISBN 9780822578840

LC 2007050435

Presents true stories of animals helping humans, including animals trained to assist people with disabilities and pets that saved their families in life-threatening situations.

"Nine stories, based on interviews with the grateful survivors, describe how brave animals rescued people in catastrophic circumstances. Each edgy retelling reveals details that only the participants could know, including sounds, smells, sights, and the knowledge that at any moment they could die, deepening the tension. Mixed in are Markle's broad and perfectly attuned insights about animal behavior." School Library Journal.

Includes bibliographical references (p. 61-63) and index.

O'Connell, Caitlin, 1965-

Bridge to the wild: a day in the life of zoo curators. written by Caitlin O'Connell; with photographs by Caitlin O'Connell & Timothy Rodwell. Houghton Mifflin Harcourt, 2016. 128 p.

Grades: 4 5 6 7   **636.088**
1. O'Connell, Caitlin, 1965- 2. Atlanta Zoo. 3. Zoo keepers 4. Zoos 5. Human-animal relationships 6. Zoo animals 7. Animal behavior
ISBN 9780544277397

     LC 2015024535
With stunning photographs and exemplary narrative nonfiction, the Sibert Honor-winning creators of The Elephant Scientist, Caitlin O'Connell and Timothy Rodwell, give readers a heartwarming insider's look into a day in the life of a zoo curator and the meaningful bonds that she forms with her menagerie. Provided by publisher.

"Readers should find the book's facts and photos intriguing, and the collaborators' curiosity and passion inspiring." Publishers Weekly.

636.089 Veterinary medicine

Jackson, Donna M., 1959-

ER vets: life in an animal emergency room. by Donna M. Jackson. Houghton Mifflin, 2005. 88 p.

Grades: 5 6 7 8   **636.089**
1. Veterinarians 2. Veterinary emergencies 3. Veterinary medicine -- History 4. Animals 5. Injured animals
ISBN 0618436634

     LC 2004028231
"With plentiful, excellent-quality photographs, this highly visual book offers a behind-the-scenes look at an emergency animal hospital in Colorado. . . . A section on grief counseling for families with critically ill pets and a spread on how to put together a pet first-aid kit are included. Well-researched and well-written, ER Vets is an engaging book on a hot topic." School Library Journal.

Includes bibliographical references (p. 82) and index.

636.1 Horses

Clutton-Brock, Juliet

Horse. written by Juliet Clutton-Brock. DK Pub., 2004. 72 p.: Eyewitness books

Grades: 4 5 6 7   **636.1**
1. Horses 2. Horse breeds 3. Animal behavior 4. Hoofed mammals
ISBN 0756606861

     LC 2004558974
Examines the anatomy, history, and breeds of horses, and discusses the different ways horses have been used.

Matzke, Ann H.

★ **Mini** horse. Ann Matzke. Rourke Pub. Group, 2015 32 p.: You have a pet what?!

Grades: 3 4 5 6   **636.1**
1. Miniature horses 2. Pets 3. Horses 4. Miniature horses as pets
ISBN 9781634304344
"Well written, with a clean design, these titles will be useful for educators and popular with potential pet owners." School Library Journal.

636.2 Cattle and related animals

Freedman, Russell

★ **In** the days of the vaqueros: America's first true cowboys. by Russell Freedman. Clarion Books, c2001. 70 p.

Grades: 4 5 6 7   **636.2**
1. Cowboys -- History 2. Ranch life -- History 3. Frontier and pioneer life 4. Frontier and pioneer life 5. Southwest (United States) -- Social life and customs 6. Southwest (United States) -- History
ISBN 0395967880

     LC 2001017357
"The author tells the story with depth, clarity, and a vigor that conveys the thrilling excitement of the work and the macho swagger of the culture. . . . The book's design is beautiful, with spacious type on thick paper, and the dazzling illustrations, prints, paintings, and photos on almost every page." Booklist.

Includes bibliographical references (p. 61-62) and index.

636.4 Swine

Reed, Cristie

★ **Mini** Pig. Cristie Reed. Rourke Pub Group, 2015. 32 p.: You have a pet what?!

Grades: 3 4 5 6   **636.4**
1. Pigs 2. Pets 3. Pigs as pets 4. Animals 5. Mammals
ISBN 9781634304313
"Well written, with a clean design, these titles will be useful for educators and popular with potential pet owners." School Library Journal.

636.5 Chickens and other kinds of domestic birds

Caughey, Melissa

A **kid's** guide to keeping chickens. by Melissa Caughey. Storey Publishing, [2015] 144 p.

Grades: 4 5 6 7 8   **636.5**
1. Chickens 2. Eggs -- Production
ISBN 9781612126487

     LC 2014033788
"The book contains color photographs—including pictures of children working with chickens—and the text is broken into manageable chunks, with sidebar facts and testimonials. An index and other resources conclude. A good addition for public libraries." Booklist.

636.7 Dogs

Hirsch, Andy, 1987-

Dogs: from predator to protector. Andy Hirsch. First Second, 2017. 128 p.: Science comics

Grades: 4 5 6 7 8   **636.7**
1. Dogs 2. Dogs as pets 3. Dog breeds 4. Humans and dogs 5.

Wolves 6. Comics and Graphic novels
ISBN 9781626727670

LC 2016961597

How well do you know our favorite furry companion? Did they really descend from wolves? What's the difference between a Chihuahua and a Saint Bernard? And just how smart are they? Join one friendly mutt on a journey to discover the secret origin of dogs, how genetics and evolution shape species, and where in the world his favorite ball bounced off to.

"Thorough, clearly presented scientific information is lightened by silly asides from dog-narrator Rudy to keep readers entertained and engaged as they learn a huge amount about the science of dogs." Kirkus.

Houston, Dick

Bulu, African wonder dog. by Dick Houston. Random House, c2010. 336 p.
Grades: 5 6 7 8   **636.7**
    1. Dogs 2. Wildlife conservation 3. Wildlife refuges 4. Animal welfare 5. Terriers
ISBN 9780375947209

LC 2009015804

Traces the story of a pair of former police officers who moved to Zambia and adopted a near-feral puppy that survived dangerous situations and eventually came to nurture other animals like itself.

"In the Nyanja language, bulu means wild dog, and that's what Steve and Anna Tolan named the beloved little Jack Russell mix they adopted. Disregarding warnings about the dangers of raising a dog in the bush, the Tolans moved from England to rural Zambia to fulfill their lifelong dream of setting up an animal rescue and conservation center.... Bulu's energy, high spirits, and loyalty to his masters make the book read like a praise song to dogs. Houston's account is an animal-lovers delight, complete with the action-adventure of surviving the bush, fighting poachers, and spreading a message of conservation." Booklist.

Laidlaw, Rob, 1954-

The **dog** patrol: our canine companions and the kids who protect them. Rob Laidlaw. Ingram Pub Services, 2020. 48 p.
Grades: 3 4 5 6 7   **636.7**
    1. Dogs 2. Human-animal relationships 3. Dogs as pets 4. Dogs -- History 5. Pets
ISBN 9781772781038

Biologist and animal rights activist Rob Laidlaw explains dog biology, evolution, and behavior, and explores the dynamic relationship between humans and companion dogs. Amongst sections on dog care, training, and issues related to dog ownership are spotlight features on kids helping dogs. The book includes photographs, sidebars, a glossary, an index, and a dog anatomy gatefold. Provided by publisher.

"Topics include nutrition, the problems of confining dogs to crates, and the greater effectiveness of positive reinforcement over punishment in training, providing valuable, manageable information for young dog owners ... Perfect for dog lovers. " Kirkus

MacLeod, Elizabeth

Top dogs: canines that made history. Elizabeth MacLeod. Annick Press, 2017. 98 p.
Grades: 5 6 7   **636.7**
    1. Dogs 2. Working dogs 3. Rescue dogs 4. Working animals
ISBN 9781554519071

A collection of true stories about dogs whose actions influenced the course of history, including the first seeing-eye dog, search and rescue dogs, and military dogs.

"The chapters are well organized and chock-full of photos and other design elements to keep readers' interest." School Library Journal.

Resler, T. J

★ **Dog** breed guide: the complete reference to your best friend fur-ever. T.J. Resler & Gary Weitzman, D.V.M., president and CEO of the San Diego Humane Society. Natl Geographic Soc Childrens books 2019 288 p.
Grades: 3 4 5 6 7   **636.7**
    1. Dog breeds 2. Dogs 3. Pets 4. Animals
ISBN 9781426334450

LC bl2019024911

Presents profiles for different dog breeds that include the breed's country of origin, size, coat color and pattern, grooming difficulty, and exercise needs, along with advice on how to choose the right dog, care for it, and understand its behavior.

Sundance, Kyra

101 dog tricks: kids edition: fun & easy activities, games, and crafts. Kyra Sundance. Quarry Books, 2014. 191 p.
Grades: 3 4 5 6   **636.7**
    1. Dogs -- Training
ISBN 9781592538935

LC 2014014373

Offers instructions to teach the family dog tricks, including peekaboo, hoop jump, and handstand.

"The tricks only require common household or easily accessible items, and they include helpful tips for preparation, troubleshooting, and what to expect. Many of the tips also differentiate for differently sized and more fearful or shy dogs." Booklist.

Wadsworth, Ginger

Poop detectives: working dogs in the field. by Ginger Wadsworth. Charlesbridge, [2016] 80 p.
Grades: 3 4 5 6 7   **636.7**
    1. Working Dogs for Conservation 2. Working dogs -- Training 3. Detector dogs 4. Dogs 5. Rare and endangered animals
ISBN 9781580896504

LC 2015026876

How can dogs that sniff for excrement, urine, vomit, and mucus help protect animals from extinction? Scat-detection dogs like Wicket, Tucker, and Orbee are conservation heroes and pioneers in a cutting-edge field of science. Canine detectives use their super sense of smell to locate the scat of target animals. From loose bear dung to gooey whale poop, scat can tell scientists valuable information about an animal's sex, age, diet, and health—all without harming the animal or endangering the researcher.

"This book encourages readers to think about unconventional sources of information and the unusual methods of data collection necessary to scientific discovery." Booklist.

636.755 Terriers

Gagne, Tammy

West Highlands, Scotties, and other terriers. by Tammy Gagne. Capstone Press, [2017] 32 p.: Edge books.
Grades: 4 5 6   **636.755**
    1. Terriers 2. Dog breeds 3. Dogs
ISBN 9781515703044

LC 2015043106

Informative text and vivid photos introduce readers to various terrier dog breeds. Provided by publisher.

"While Gagne points out positive qualities in each breed discussed, readers looking for a new pet will find the carefully phrased comments in the personality, training, and care paragraphs very useful in deciding whether to choose a terrier and, if so, which one. A solid choice for libraries." Booklist.

Includes bibliographical references and index.

636.8 Cats

Clutton-Brock, Juliet

Cat. written by Juliet Clutton-Brock. DK Pub., 2004. 72 p.: Eyewitness books

Grades: 4 5 6 7   **636.8**

1. Wild cats 2. Cats

ISBN 0756606616

LC bl2005011937

Text and photographs present the anatomy, behavior, habitats, and other aspects of wild and domestic cats.

Drimmer, Stephanie Warren

★ **Cat** breed guide: a complete reference to your purr-fect best friend. Stephanie Warren Drimmer & Dr. Gary Weitzman, D.V.M., President and CEO of the San Diego Humane Society. National Geographic, [2019] 288 p.

Grades: 3 4 5 6 7   **636.8**

1. Cat breeds 2. Cats 3. Pets 4. Animals

ISBN 9781426334399

LC 2018031439

Reference book with information about all breeds of cats, for children. Provided by publisher.

"Breed descriptions, general information, and fascinating facts are combined to present highly appealing references to popular pets...First choices for pet collections." School Library Journal

Laidlaw, Rob, 1954-

Cat champions: caring for our feline friends. Rob Laidlaw. Pajama Press, 2014, c2013. 63 p.

Grades: 4 5 6 7 8   **636.8**

1. Cats -- Health 2. Cat care 3. Animal welfare 4. Animal shelters 5. Volunteers

ISBN 1927485541

This juvenile non-fiction title offers information about the many ways in which "Cat Champions" are making a difference in the lives of cats around the world. It features stories about young people who are helping at shelters, fostering kittens, volunteering with sterilization programs, and caring for abandoned cats. Informational sidebars throughout the book describe issues facing domestic and feral cats, as well as good-news feline facts, and the pages are filled with colourful photos and real-life stories that will inspire readers of all ages.

"The format is busy, but cat lovers probably won't mind so many photos, and the sidebars are all informative. The list of organizations where kids can learn about ways they can help is extensive and useful." Booklist.

636.80092 Cats — Biography

Myron, Vicki

Dewey the library cat: a true story. Vicki Myron with Bret Witter. Little, Brown, 2010. 214 p.

Grades: 4 5 6 7 8   **636.80092**

1. Dewey (Marmalade cat) 2. Abandoned cats 3. Library cats 4.

Libraries 5. Librarians 6. Cats

ISBN 9780316068710

LC 2009030867

Follows the development of an endearing kitten abandoned in an Iowa library drop-box into an affable library mascot who made many friendships with the library staff and patrons of all ages.

"From the opening chapter, when librarian Vicki Myron finds a fragile, freezing kitten in the book return, children will be hooked on her heartwarming story about Dewey Readmore Books. . . . Anecdotes such as Dewey's fascination with rubber bands, his bizarre behavior during a bat invasion, and his finicky eating habits are ideal booktalk material. So are descriptions of Dewey's tender, intuitive interactions with people of all ages and backgrounds." Booklist.

636.9 Other mammals

Matzke, Ann H.

Hedgehog. Ann Matzke. Rourke Publishing Group, 2015. 32 p.: You have a pet what?!

Grades: 3 4 5 6   **636.9**

1. Hedgehogs 2. Pets 3. Hedgehogs as pets 4. Nocturnal animals 5. Mammals

ISBN 9781634304337

"Well written, with a clean design, these titles will be useful for educators and popular with potential pet owners." School Library Journal.

636.92 Marsupials

Kenney, Karen Latchana

★ **Sugar** glider. Karen Kenney. Rourke Pub. Group, 2015 32 p.: You have a pet what?!

Grades: 3 4 5 6   **636.92**

1. Sugar gliders as pets 2. Sugar glider 3. Pets

ISBN 9781634304368

"Though most kids will be (thankfully) dissuaded by the amount of specialized care these animals require, the beautifully reproduced photos of oddball pets are undeniably appealing, and there are enough fascinating and informative facts to keep readers enthralled. Highly recommended." Booklist.

636.935 Rodents—Animal husbandry

Kenney, Karen Latchana

★ **Rat.** Karen Latchana Kenney. Rourke Pub Group 2016. 32 p.: You have a pet what?!

Grades: 3 4 5 6   **636.935**

1. Rats 2. Pets 3. Rats as pets

ISBN 9781634304351

"Well written, with a clean design, these titles will be useful for educators and popular with potential pet owners." School Library Journal.

Toor, Rachel

Misunderstood: why the humble rat may be your best pet ever. Rachel Toor. Farrar Straus Giroux Books for Young Readers, 2016. 246 p.

Grades: 6 7 8 9   **636.935**

1. Rats as pets 2. Humans and rats 3. Human/animal relationships

4. Rats 5. Rodents as pets
ISBN 9780374303082

Shares the author's experiences with her pet rat Iris, offering anecdotes of her antics and other rat owners and discussing how to care for rats, health concerns, life spans, and eating habits.

"A delightful addition to any Library or classroom's creative nonfiction section." School Library Journal.

638 Insect culture

Harkins, Susan Sales

Design your own butterfly garden. Susan Sales Harkins and William H. Harkins. Mitchell Lane Publishers, c2009. 48 p.: Robbie readers.

Grades: 3 4 5 6   **638**

1. Butterfly gardening 2. Butterflies 3. Gardening 4. Gardens 5. Children's gardens
ISBN 9781584156383

LC 2008002245

Introduces the principles of butterfly gardening, discussing how to plan the garden, what flowers to plant there, and how to maintain it in all seasons.

"All the tasks delineated are well within the scope of children's abilities, and the items needed to complete them are not hard to find. . . . [The book has] excellent full-color photography and include[s] charts and diagrams to assist in the completion of the projects." School Library Journal.

Includes bibliographical references (p. 46) and index.

639.2 Commercial fishing, whaling, sealing

Hand, Carol, 1945-

Dead zones: why earth's waters are losing oxygen. by Carol Hand. Twenty-First Century Books, 2016. 80 p.

Grades: 7 8 9 10   **639.2**

1. Oceans 2. Fish kills 3. Fishes -- Effect of water pollution on 4. Anoxic zones 5. Marine eutrophication
ISBN 9781467775731

LC 2014041304

"A significant overview for serious eco-activists or any students interested in our planet's oceans and waterways." School Library Journal.

McKissack, Pat, 1944-2017

★ **Black** hands, white sails: the story of African-American whalers. Patricia C. McKissack & Fredrick L. McKissack. Scholastic Press, c1999. 152 p.

Grades: 5 6 7 8   **639.2**

1. 18th century 2. 19th century 3. Whaling -- History 4. African-American whalers 5. African-American whalers -- History 6. Whalers 7. African Americans
ISBN 0590483137

LC 99011439

A history of African-American whalers between 1730 and 1880, describing their contributions to the whaling industry and their role in the abolitionist movement.

"A well-researched and detailed book." School Library Journal.
Includes bibliographical references (p. 144-147) and index.

639.9 Conservation of biological resources

Coey, Julia

Animal hospital: rescuing urban wildlife. Julia Coey Firefly Books, 2015. 64 p.

Grades: 4 5 6 7   **639.9**

1. Animal rescue 2. Wildlife rescue 3. Wildlife conservation 4. Animal welfare 5. Animals
ISBN 9781770855724

Text and photographs show the care that goes into the rehabilitation of sick, injured, and orphaned wild animals in Toronto and other places.

"The author's suggestions for readers' involvement include reminders about appropriate trash disposal as well as names of organizations, and a concluding chapter describes three similar rehab centers around the world. A straightforward introduction to an appealing topic for upper-elementary and middle school readers." Kirkus.

Drake, Jane, 1954-

Rewilding: giving nature a second chance. Jane Drake and Ann Love. Annick Press, 2017. 88 p.

Grades: 5 6 7 8   **639.9**

1. Wildlife reintroduction 2. Environmentalism 3. Wildlife conservation 4. Rare and endangered animals
ISBN 9781554519613

A vibrantly photographed introduction to the rewilding environmental movement shares examples from all over the world where endangered animals have been rehabilitated and returned to their natural habitats, and cities that have dedicated rooftops and disused land for nature gardens.

"Clearly organized and accessibly written, this is a welcome overview." Kirkus.

640 Home and family management

Gutman, Dan

Recycle this book: what you can do to save the world! edited by Dan Gutman. Yearling, c2009. 288 p.

Grades: 5 6 7 8   **640**

1. Environmental protection -- Citizen participation 2. Sustainable living 3. Men and nature 4. Nature -- Effect of humans on 5. Wastefulness (Ecology)
ISBN 9780385737210

LC 2008010800

"This lively collection of brief essays (and a poem) by 100 outstanding children's and young adult authors teaches through example. Each selection highlights a small step (or steps) taken by the writer toward a greener Earth. . . . The essays also provide insight into the lives and thoughts of many familiar and beloved authors such as Laurie Halse Anderson, Ralph Fletcher, Gary Schmidt, Lois Lowry, Susan Patron, and Rick Riordan. Several pages of websites offer a starting point for action and information. Highly useful for classroom and family discussions and science-project ideas." School Library Journal.

Sivertsen, Linda, 1964-

Generation green: the ultimate teen guide to living an eco-friendly life. Linda Sivertsen. Simon Pulse, 2008. 272 p.

Grades: 5 6 7 8   **640**

1. Green movement 2. Environmental protection 3. Sustainable living 4. Environmentalism 5. Global warming
ISBN 9781416961222

LC 2008922275

"A thorough yet accessible manual on green living. . . . The book's incisive voice, using teen idioms, is accessible to those who have little or no background in environmental issues, yet the standards within will likewise engage readers already committed to being green. . . . [This book is] unique, for its central focus is not to explain the science behind current environmental challenges, but rather to reveal how young people can work to solve those problems in their everyday lives." School Library Journal.

Walsh, Peter, 1956-

It's all too much, so get it together. Peter Walsh; with illustrations by John Hendrix. Simon & Schuster BFYR, c2009. 278 p.
Grades: 7 8 9 10   **640**
  1. Cleanliness 2. Organization 3. Storage in the home 4. Neatness and messiness 5. House cleaning
  ISBN 9781416995494

LC bl2009025889

Suggests ways for teens to get rid of clutter and lead more organized, less stressful lives.

"This is fun and light in tone. . . . For teens who are as overwhelmed by their lives as they are by their stuff, the quizzes and fictional scenarios will be right on point and may help them approach what they own and why in a new way. In addition to the suggestions for managing clutter (physical and mental), Walsh also offers tips for clutter-free friendships, jobs, studying, and even family fights." Voice of Youth Advocates.

641.3 Food

Llewellyn, Claire

Cooking with fruits and vegetables. by Claire Llewellyn with recipes by Clare O'Shea. Rosen Central, 2012. 48 p.: Cooking healthy
Grades: 5 6 7 8   **641.3**
  1. Cooking (Fruit) 2. Cooking (Vegetables) 3. Nutrition 4. Fruit 5. Vegetables
  ISBN 9781448848447

LC 2010039333

Presents information about fruits and vegetables and their nutritional values, as well as cooking methods and recipes for dishes featuring these foods.

"This book pairs facts about [fruits and vegetables], including where it is eaten, with eye-catching photos. . . . Each course (section) has an overview of the vegetable group . . . followed by recipes from all over the world. They vary in difficulty. . . . The cooking directions are clear and straightforward. . . . [The book is] profusely illustrated with full-color photos. Students who are learning to cook will appreciate [this] excellently organized [read]." School Library Journal.

Includes bibliographical references and index.

Thornhill, Jan

Who wants pizza?: the kids' guide to the history, science and culture of food. Jan Thornhill. Maple Tree Press, 2010. 62 p.
Grades: 4 5 6   **641.3**
  1. Food science 2. Nutrition 3. Agriculture
  ISBN 9781897349960

LC 2010920483

"This discusses where food comes from and if there's enough to go around. Amid color photographs and sidebars, Thornhill writes concisely about hunter-gatherers, agriculture, processed foods, globalization, and poverty, among numerous other topics, providing a straightforward

and balanced overview of the modern food industry, and the choices readers have when it comes to their own meals." Publishers Weekly.

Includes bibliographical references and index.

641.5 Cooking

America's Test Kitchen (Firm)

★ The **complete** cookbook for young chefs. America's Test Kitchen. Sourcebooks Jabberwocky, 2018 208 p.
Grades: 4 5 6 7 8   **641.5**
  1. Cooking 2. Recipes
  ISBN 9781492670025

LC 2018459373

Shares recipes for young cooks of all skill levels, including options for breakfasts, snacks, beverages, dinners, and desserts, along with step-by-step photographs of tips and techniques.

"The inviting, encouraging tone, which never talks down to the audience; emphasis on introducing and reinforcing basic skills; and approachable, simplified recipes make this a notable standout among cookbooks for kids." Booklist.

Carle, Megan

Teens cook: how to make what you want to eat. Megan and Jill Carle with Judi Carle; photography by Jessica Boone. Ten Speed Press, c2004. xiv, 146 p.
Grades: 7 8 9 10   **641.5**
  1. Cooking 2. Cooking and teenagers
  ISBN 1580085849

LC bl2005003408

Teaches young adults how to make great meals—and be confident and independent in the kitchen.

"This cookbook features recipes for a variety of dishes including chocolate chip scones, potato skins, broccoli cheese soup, steak fajitas, baked macaroni and cheese, and toffee bars. Because Megan is a vegetarian, there are several vegetarian recipes or vegetarian substitutes. . . . Attractive, engaging, and told from a teen perspective, this cookbook will make an excellent addition to any nonfiction collection." Voice of Youth Advocates.

Gold, Rozanne, 1954-

Eat fresh food: awesome recipes for teen chefs: more than 80 recipes! Rozanne Gold and her all-star team; photographs by Phil Mansfield. Bloomsbury Children's Books, 2009. 160 p.
Grades: 6 7 8 9 10   **641.5**
  1. Cooking 2. Food preparation 3. Recipes
  ISBN 9781599902821

LC 2008042443

Step-by-step instructions and cooking tips are compiled in this cookbook for teens that features more than eighty recipes for healthy, tasty meals, treats, and desserts.

"This joyful recipe book features fresh, healthful ingredients and encourages ambitious young chefs to collaborate on such mature dishes as Grape-and-Pignoli Breakfast Cake, Crunchy Wasabi-Lime Salmon with red cabbage and sugar snaps and orange-ginger sweet potato puree. . . . A prime pick for adventurous eaters and a potential catalyst for those in a junk food rut." Publishers Weekly.

Hughes, Meredith Sayles

Plants vs. meats: the health, history, and ethics of what we eat. Meredith Sayles Hughes. Twenty-First Century Books, [2016] 96 p.

Grades: 6 7 8 9 10   **641.5**
1. Vegetarianism 2. Diet 3. Food -- Social aspects 4. Vegetarian foods
ISBN 9781467780117

LC 2015007494

Examines the nutritional, historical, and ethical aspects of food consumption, discussing popular diets, providing facts about farming and the future of food, and encouraging readers to make informed, personal food choices.

"This solid introduction to where food comes from and the consequences of its consumption and production is a worthy addition." School Library Journal.

Includes bibliographical references (pages 90-93), filmography (page 93), and index.

Locricchio, Matthew

Teen cuisine new vegetarian. Matthew Locricchio; photography by James Peterson. Amazon Children's Pub., c2012. 207 p.
Grades: 7 8 9 10 11 12   **641.5**
1. Vegetarian cooking 2. Teenagers -- Nutrition 3. Nutrition
ISBN 9780761462583

LC 2011049502

Presents more than fifty recipes for teenagers who want to cook, with detailed instructions and advice on ingredients, kitchen equipment, and cooking techniques.

"With this useful resource, delectable dishes made with fresh ingredients are within teens' reach. Everything from breakfasts to soups, salads, entrees, and desserts are featured. Few packaged or canned shortcuts are recommended, so these recipes may involve a little extra time and care; the rewards are evident, as shown in appetizing photographs." Horn Book.

Mayhew, Maggie

How to cook: [delicious dishes perfect for teen cooks]. consultant, Maggie Mayhew. DK Pub., 2011. 127 p.
Grades: 7 8 9 10   **641.5**
1. Cooking 2. Recipes 3. Cooking and teenagers
ISBN 9780756672140

"This attractive book has dozens of recipes with an international flair. Some spreads feature a single dish, like lamb tagine, while others focus on several recipes using a single ingredient or technique. Experimentation is encouraged, and developing confidence is an unstated but obvious goal. This book is not for beginners, but teens with a bit of experience will enjoy trying the many tasty-sounding recipes for everything from jambalaya to macaroons. Vegetarian options are included throughout. Bright color photos show the finished dishes, and the pages are embellished with simple drawings showing processes and ingredients." School Library Journal.

Mooney, Carla, 1970-

Junk food junkies. Carla Mooney. Lucent Books, c2011. 104 p.: Nutrition & health
Grades: 6 7 8 9   **641.5**
1. Junk food 2. Nutrition 3. Health
ISBN 9781420502718

LC 2010016858

Discusses the health dangers of eating junk food, why it is so popular, how the food is marketed to young eaters, and provides guidelines to determine if one is addicted to junk food.

"A solid, detailed overview of the negative effects of a poor diet on health. Mooney livens up the dry subject matter with interesting nutrition facts, photographs, charts, tables, and anecdotes. She discusses health risks such as obesity and diabetes. The last chapter is particularly useful because it offers healthy alternatives for snacks and meals. It also explains how to read a nutrition label and tells readers what to avoid in terms of amounts of fat and calories. This book is useful for research and reports and as a teaching aid." School Library Journal.

Includes bibliographical references and index.

Stern, Sam, 1990-

Get cooking. Sam Stern. Candlewick Press, 2008. 144 p.
Grades: 6 7 8 9   **641.5**
1. Food 2. Cooking 3. Teenagers 4. Recipes 5. Teenagers' writings
ISBN 9780763639266

LC 2008932510

"Stern does an excellent job of introducing teens to the kitchen. . . . Every page boasts bright colors and pictures with large print and a user-friendly ingredients list in sidebar format. The recipes run from very easy to a bit challenging, but the step-by-step directions will help even the most challenged cook find a way around the kitchen." Voice of Youth Advocates.

Traugh, Susan M.

Vegetarianism. Susan M. Traugh. Lucent Books, c2011. 96 p.: Nutrition & health
Grades: 6 7 8 9   **641.5**
1. Vegetarianism 2. Diet 3. Nutrition 4. Health
ISBN 9781420502725

LC 2010014015

Discusses the vegetarian diet, examines reasons for becoming a vegetarian, and offers advice for planning a healthy meatless diet.

"The attractively designed title in the Nutrition & Health series will help middle-grade and high-school students make good decisions about the food they eat. Unlike some nutrition books, the tone remains mostly positive, informing readers about the negative effects of poor choices such as obesity and disease while also encouraging them to take control of their own decisions by reading nutrition labels. Although it uses the nutrition pyramid, recently put aside for the newer 'plate' model, the information remains very current, and each book highlights recent scientific studies." Booklist.

Includes bibliographical references and index.

Tuminelly, Nancy, 1952-

Cool meat-free recipes: delicious & fun foods without meat. Nancy Tuminelly. ABDO Publishing Company, a division of ABDO, [2013], ©2013. 32 p.: Cool recipes for your health
Grades: 3 4 5 6 7 8   **641.5**
1. Vegetarian cooking 2. Cooking and children 3. Cooking 4. Recipes
ISBN 9781617835827

LC 2012023989

Presents eight kid-friendly recipes for such meatless dishes as peanut tofu stir-fry and cheesy cha-cha chili mac, and covers basic cooking techniques, tools, and ingredients.

Warren, Rachel Meltzer

The **smart** girl's guide to going vegetarian: how to look great, feel fabulous, and be a better you. Rachel Meltzer Warren, MS, RDN. Sourcebooks Fire, [2014] 304 p.

Grades: 7 8 9 10 11 12   **641.5**
1. Vegetarianism 2. Vegetarian cooking 3. Teenagers -- Nutrition
ISBN 9781402284915

LC 2013023334

"A vegetarian herself since age 12, Warren knows the questions that teen girls ask and the arguments their parents raise when kids want to experience vegetarianism or veganism. Here, she offers sound advice for girls who are considering being or have chosen to go vegetarian or vegan and for those who waver about where they stand on the topic... The catchy, accessible text is broken up by generous topic headings and questions. Overall, a sound guide for any teenager, really, and her or his parents." Booklist.

Includes bibliographical references and index.

A **teen's** guide to gut health: the low-FODMAP way to tame IBS, Crohn's, colitis, and other digestive disorders. Rachel Meltzer Warren, MS, RDN. The Experiment, 2017 209 p.
Grades: 7 8 9 10   **641.5**
1. Gastrointestinal system -- Diseases 2. Gastrointestinal system -- Diseases -- Diet therapy 3. Teenagers -- Health and hygiene
ISBN 9781615193547

LC 2016020920

Offers a guide for young people to gut health, with advice for dealing with stomach issues through a diet low in certain types of carbs that can lurk in otherwise healthy foods and cause problems.

"There is an abundance of scientific information (plentiful but not overwhelming) as well as sound steps for managing everyday situations." School Library Journal.

Includes bibliographical references and indexes.

Webb, Lois Sinaiko
Holidays of the world cookbook for students updated and revised. by Lois Sinaiko Webb. Greenwood, 2011. 443 p.
Grades: 5 6 7 8 9 10   **641.5**
1. Holiday cooking 2. Food preparation 3. International cooking 4. Recipes 5. Holidays
ISBN 9780313397905

Presents a collection of holiday recipes from over 150 countries that include an introduction to the local holidays, customs, and foods for each country.

641.59 Cooking characteristic of specific geographic environments, ethnic cooking

D'Amico, Joan, 1957-
The **coming** to America cookbook: delicious recipes and fascinating stories from America's many cultures. Joan D'Amico, Karen Eich Drummond; illustrations by Lizzy Rockwell and Tina Cash-Walsh. Wiley, c2005. ix, 180 p.
Grades: 5 6 7 8   **641.59**
1. International cooking 2. Cooking, American 3. Recipes
ISBN 0471483354

LC 2004014947

Presents a collection of recipes from a variety of cultures, including Mexican, Chinese, Turkish, Moroccan, Nigerian, and Irish.

"The authors provide information about American immigrants from 18 nations as well as recipes representing each group. . . . Accompanied by line drawings of ethnic families choosing, preparing, and eating food, . . . chapters discuss each country's climate, history, major waves of emigration, and traditional foods. Typically, three recipes follow. . .

. Teachers and students looking for recipes from American immigrant cultures will make good use of this handy resource." Booklist.

641.594 Cooking—Europe

Wagner, Lisa, 1958-
Cool French cooking: fun and tasty recipes for kids. Lisa Wagner. ABDO Pub., c2011. 32 p.: Cool world cooking
Grades: 3 4 5 6   **641.594**
1. Cooking, French 2. Food 3. Cooking and children 4. Cooking 5. Recipes
ISBN 9781617146602

LC 2010022192

Introduces cooking terms, techniques, and utensils and offers easy-to-prepare recipes for French meals and side dishes.

Cool Italian cooking: fun and tasty recipes for kids. Lisa Wagner. ABDO Pub., c2011. 32 p.: Cool world cooking
Grades: 3 4 5 6   **641.594**
1. Cooking, Italian 2. Food habits 3. Cooking 4. Recipes
ISBN 9781617146619

LC 2010022193

Introduces cooking terms, techniques, and utensils and offers easy-to prepare recipes for Italian meals and side dishes.

641.595 Cooking—Asia

Batmanglij, Najmieh, 1947-
Happy Nowruz: cooking with children to celebrate the Persian New Year. Najmieh Batmanglij. Mage Publishers, 2008. 119 p.
Grades: 4 5 6 7 8   **641.595**
1. Cooking, Iranian 2. Nawruz (Festival) 3. Food habits 4. Holidays 5. Cooking 6. Iran -- Social life and customs
ISBN 193382316X

LC 2007036047

Offers twenty-five Nowruz recipes while introducing the history and customs surrounding the celebration of the Persian New Year.

"Combining a cookbook format with straightforward, informational text, this amply illustrated title offers a detailed introduction to the history and customs surrounding Nowruz, the Persian New Year. . . . The covered spiral binding allows pages to remain open while cooking, and the uncluttered, attractive format, featuring color photos of kids in the kitchen and whimsical illustrations, will attract interested browsers." Booklist.

Lee, Frances, 1971-
Fun with Chinese cooking. Frances Lee. PowerKids Press, 2009. 32 p. : Let's get cooking!
Grades: 4 5 6 7   **641.595**
1. Cooking, Chinese 2. Food habits 3. Cooking 4. Recipes 5. Culture
ISBN 9781435834538

LC 2009010337

"The photography is exceptional, with children engaged in the cooking process. . . . Children, and the adults who assist them, will spend hours together mastering the techniques." School Library Journal.

Wagner, Lisa, 1958-

Cool Chinese & Japanese cooking: fun and tasty recipes for kids. Lisa Wagner. ABDO Pub., c2011. 32 p.: Cool world cooking

Grades: 3 4 5 6   **641.595**

1. Cooking, Chinese 2. Cooking, Japanese 3. Cooking, Asian 4. Food habits 5. Cooking
ISBN 9781617146596

LC 2010022191

Introduces cooking terms, techniques, and utensils and offers easy-to-prepare recipes for Chinese and Japanese meals and side dishes.

641.5972 Cooking—Mexico

Wagner, Lisa, 1958-

Cool Mexican cooking: fun and tasty recipes for kids. Lisa Wagner. ABDO Pub., c2011. 32 p.: Cool world cooking

Grades: 3 4 5 6   **641.5972**

1. Cooking, Mexican 2. Food habits 3. Cooking 4. Recipes
ISBN 9781617146626

LC 2010022194

Introduces cooking terms, techniques, and utensils and offers easy-to-prepare recipes for Mexican meals and side dishes.

641.5973 United States

D'Amico, Joan, 1957-

The **United** States cookbook: fabulous foods and fascinating facts from all 50 states. Joan D'Amico and Karen Eich Drummond; illustrations by Jeff Cline and Tina Cash-Walsh. John Wiley, c2000. vi, 186 p.

Grades: 5 6 7 8   **641.5973**

1. Cooking, American
ISBN 0471358398

LC 99039548

Provides information about the fifty states along with a recipe native to each of them, such as Boston baked beans from Massachusetts, crab cakes from Maryland, Key lime pie from Florida, corn dogs from Iowa, and taco soup from New Mexico.

"There are helpful sections on the use of equipment; cooking skills, such as cutting, measuring, and mixing, and safety rules." School Library Journal.

641.8 Cooking specific kinds of dishes and preparing beverages

Carle, Megan

Teens cook dessert. Megan and Jill Carle, with Judi Carle. Ten Speed Press, 2006. 158 p.

Grades: 6 7 8 9 10   **641.8**

1. Desserts 2. Cooking
ISBN 1580087523

LC 2005024343

Presents step-by-step dessert recipes for teenagers who want to make sweets, with detailed instructions, preparation tips, cooking calculations, and ingredient advice on preparing cookies, cakes, pies, puddings, and special occasion treats.

"The authors start out with the all-around favorites, like classic chocolate chip cookies. There are holiday recipes for Halloween dirt pie, complete with cookie tombstones and gummy worms that seem to crawl out of the chocolate earth. The final chapter has fancy foods like vanilla soufflé with chocolate sauce or fresh raspberry napoleons. . . . Not only do the recipes sound delicious, they look delicious in glossy color pictures. . . . The instructions are easy to understand." Voice of Youth Advocates.

Love, Ann

Sweet!: the delicious story of candy. Ann Love & Jane Drake; illustrated by Claudia Davila. Tundra Books, 2007. 64 p.

Grades: 4 5 6 7   **641.8**

1. Candy -- History 2. Confectionery -- History 3. Food -- History
ISBN 9780887767524

"This history of things sweet and sugary is a yummy feast. The prose is chatty and inviting. Color cartoon illustrations show multiethnic people in the process of making or enjoying everything from honey to ice cream to cotton candy (called candy floss here) to jelly beans and chocolate." School Library Journal.

641.86 Desserts

Eboch, M. M

Crave-worthy candy confections with a side of science: an augmented recipe science experience: a 4d book. M.M. Eboch. Capstone Press, 2019 32 p.

Grades: 5 6 7 8 9 10 11 12   **641.86**

1. Desserts 2. Candy
ISBN 9781543510713

LC 2018011648

What makes some candy sticky? How does a spoonful of sugar turn into your favorite sweet? Budding chefs will discover the science behind making candy all while enjoying some sweet treats. Video tutorials and bonus materials offer an augmented reality experience through the free Capstone 4D app.

"Twelve recipes per book are presented in a nice tidy layout, with ingredients and supplies clearly listed in boxes at the top of the page. An excellent pick for cooking programs looking to incorporate science concepts." School Library Journal

Includes bibliographical references (pages 32).

644 Household utilities

DiPiazza, Francesca, 1961-

Remaking the john: the invention and reinvention of the toilet. Francesca Davis DiPiazza. Twenty-First Century Books, [2014. 88 p.

Grades: 6 7 8 9   **644**

1. Toilets -- History 2. Sewage 3. Sanitation 4. Eliminative behavior 5. Bathrooms 6. Grossology
ISBN 9781467726450

LC 2013040138

Explores how toilets have been invented and reinvented across history, including the ancient Roman sewer system, the world's first flush toilets, and the creation of World Toilet Day.

"This honest, fact-filled little book should attract readers and researchers (who may even begin celebrating World Toilet Day every November 19)." School Library Journal.

Includes bibliographical references (pages 58-59) and index.

646.2 Sewing and related operations

Lisle, Andria

Sewing school: hand-sewing projects kids will love to make. Andria Lisle and Amie Petronis Plumley; photography by Justin Fox Burks. Storey Pub., c2010. 143 p.

Grades: 3 4 5 6   **646.2**

1. Sewing 2. Handicraft for children 3. Needlework 4. Textile crafts
ISBN 9781603425780

LC 2010022154

"This large-format book offers appealing projects illustrated with color photos of step-by-step directions as well as kids engaged in sewing and showing off work. The opening 12 lessons begin with topics such as threading a needle, knotting the thread, and making a basic running stitch. After covering basic knowledge and skills, the presentation moves on to instructions for fun easy projects." Booklist.

646.4 Clothing and accessories construction

Kyi, Tanya Lloyd, 1973-

The **blue** jean book: the story behind the seams. by Tanya Lloyd Kyi. Annick Press, c2005. 79 p.

Grades: 6 7 8 9 10   **646.4**

1. Blue jeans -- History 2. Denim garments -- History
ISBN 1550379178

LC bl2005016384

Examines the history and America's love affair with denim jeans, from their humble origins with hardscrabble miners and cowboys, to their popularity among laborers, rebels, and the incurably hip.

"Kyi traces the history of these pants from the early life of Levi Strauss and the patented riveted pocket to the stiff competition and controversy of production in our modern world. . . . History and social issues are intertwined to show how activities, jobs, and the economy influence the development and production of clothing. . . . This is an enjoyable read for anyone wishing to know more about this fashion item and an excellent resource for an introduction to product development and economy." School Library Journal.

Includes bibliographical references (p. 74-75) and index.

Rogers, Barb, 1947-

Costumes, accessories, props, and stage illusions made easy. Barb Rogers. Meriwether Pub., 2005. 205 p.

Grades: 7 8 9 10 11 12   **646.4**

1. Costume 2. Clothing and dress -- Remaking 3. Vintage clothing
ISBN 9781566081030

LC 2005004359

A how-to book of techniques for making costumes, accessories, props, and stage illusions from cast-off clothing and second-hand items. Includes detailed instructions, illustrations, and patterns.

"Rogers transforms everyday clothing into magical costumes with simple tools such as scissors, glue guns, and paint. All are accompanied by numbered directions, line drawings, and black-and-white photos, although novice costumers may find some of the directions too brief or obtuse. Still, this is a useful volume for schools and community theaters with little or no budgets for costumes and props." School Library Journal

Warwick, Ellen

Everywear. written by Ellen Warwick; illustrated by Bernice Lum. Kids Can Press, 2008. 80 p.: Planet Girl

Grades: 5 6 7 8   **646.4**

1. Handicraft for girls 2. Dress accessories 3. Fashion design
ISBN 9781553377993

LC oc2008018124

It's never been easier (or easier on the wallet) to create frugal and fashionable accessories that embody seriously unique chic.

"After several opening pages that introduce supplies, . . . very basic stitching skills, and terminology, girls turn to the . . . issue of hair: woven-ribbon bands, jazzed-up chopsticks; fabric-flower-bedecked combs; reversible ponytail wraps. Next come body adornments . . . followed by stuff to stow it in, of clutched, dangled, and toted varieties. Each project features a list of supplies, . . . clearly numbered steps with cartoon-styled illustrations . . . and full-color photograph of the finished item. . . . [This has] genuine sleepover appeal." Bulletin of the Center for Children's Books.

646.7 Management of personal and family life

Buchholz, Rachel

How to survive anything: shark attack, lightning, embarrassing parents, pop quizzes, and other perilous situations. by Rachel Buchholz; illustrations by Chris Philpot. National Geographic, c2011. 176 p.

Grades: 5 6 7 8   **646.7**

1. Survival skills 2. Survival (after disaster) 3. Survival (after airplane accidents, shipwrecks, etc) 4. Life skills 5. Books for reluctant readers
ISBN 9781426307744

LC 2010028045

Offers teenagers advice on surviving natural disasters, embarassing moments, and social situations.

"Buchholz doles out hilarious and handy advice for suffering though both natural and manmade catastrophes. Part survival guide and part self-help book, it provides honest, tongue-in-cheek answers to questions teens may be reluctant to ask out loud, in addition to imparting disaster preparedness strategies. It's a clever, winning combination. Superb full-color digital illustrations and photographs and a lively, conversational tone will catch and keep readers' attention, and the list-heavy layout is fun to read and easy to understand." School Library Journal.

Fonseca, Christine, 1966-

The **girl** guide: finding your place in a mixed-up world. Christine Fonseca. Prufrock Press, c2013. x, 228 p.

Grades: 6 7 8 9   **646.7**

1. Teenage girls 2. Life skills 3. Teenage girls -- Personal conduct 4. Self-perception in teenagers 5. Self-confidence in teenagers
ISBN 9781618210272

LC bl2013019084

Provides advice and information for girls entering their teens on how to get to know themselves and gain the strength, confidence, and resilience to handle what life will bring them, and offers personal accounts and exercises to try.

"Sporting a sassy, appealing cover, The Girl Guide elbows its way into the already-crowded market of self-help and self-esteem-building books...There's a bit of genius at play here as the author gives the gift of time to her readers-time for reflection and for de-stressing through the act of creating. Teens should not rush through this book. No quick fixes are offered, just reasonable suggestions for maintaining true north through the turbulent teen years." School Library Journal.

Includes bibliographical references.

Heos, Bridget

A **career** as a hairstylist. Bridget Heos. Rosen Pub., 2011. 80 p.: Essential careers

Grades: 7 8 9 10 11 12   **646.7**

  1. Hairdressing 2. Barbers 3. Vocational guidance 4. Occupations

ISBN 9781435894747

LC 2009047347

Introduces the profession of hairstyling, including its history, tools, training programs, and areas of specialization.

"This title is so informative it could be subtitled Everything You Want to Know about Becoming a Hair Stylist. . . . After the basics, Heos discusses the nitty-gritty of finding a job, keeping it, and running one's own business. The history of hair-cutting careers follows, and there are even ethical discussions. . . . A must for career shelves." Booklist.

Includes bibliographical references (p. 72-76) and index.

Mayost, Eric

Amazing braids, buns & twists: a step-by-step guide to 34 beautiful styles. Eric Mayost; photography by Roee Fainburg. Imagine! Publishing, [2015] 144 p.

Grades: 8 9 10 11 12   **646.7**

  1. Braids 2. Hairstyles 3. Hairdressing 4. Fashion

ISBN 9781623540661

LC 2014033871

Presents step-by-step instructions for creating over thirty hairstyles featuring braids, buns, and twists.

"The 34 hairstyles contained in this guide will be the envy of many young women." Booklist.

Morgenstern, Julie

Organizing from the inside out for teens: the foolproof system for organizing your room, your time, and your life. Julie Morgenstern and Jessi Morgenstern-Colon; illustrations by Janet Pedersen. H. Holt, 2002. xiv, 238 p.

Grades: 7 8 9 10   **646.7**

  1. Organization 2. Teenagers 3. Time management 4. Neatness and messiness

ISBN 0805064702

LC 2002068552

Offers advice to teens on organizing bedrooms, lockers, backpacks, drawers, closets, and photographs in addition to creating realistic schedules that include time for school, activities, and fun.

"The authors offer practical advice to teenagers who want to get organized. After considering what might be holding them back and the three steps to success (analyze, strategize, attack), the discussion shifts to the two major areas of concern: managing space and managing time. . . . Useful advice in an accessible paperback format." Booklist.

649 Child rearing; home care of people with disabilities and illnesses

Chasse, Jill D.

The **babysitter's** survival guide: fun games, cool crafts, and how to be the best babysitter in town. Jill D. Chasse; illustrated by Jessica Secheret. Sterling Pub. Co., c2010. 160 p.

Grades: 5 6 7 8   **649**

  1. Babysitting 2. Handicraft for children 3. Games 4. Creative activities for children and students

ISBN 9781402746543

LC 2009002538

The ultimate babysitter's helper—a go-to guide with smart advice on everything from finding clients and getting jobs to entertaining, feeding, bathing and lulling children to sleep—includes kid-friendly recipes to tempt the picky eater, activities for all ages, suggestions for handling tantrums and emergencies, and enough practical information to make even new sitters feel confident.

"This useful, up-to-date handbook offers plenty of practical advice with a wise emphasis on safety, which makes it a good choice for new sitters as well as those with experience. Chass starts with information on starting a business, including references, advertising, and interviewing. Child development is a main focus; suggested activities and tips on interaction with children at different developmental stages will be appreciated by sitters and parents alike. . . . Occasional two-color cartoons feature diverse children and sitters." School Library Journal.

Includes bibliographical references and index.

Cole, Joanna, 1944-2020

Asking about sex & growing up: a question-and-answer book for kids. Joanna Cole; illustrated by Bill Thomas. Collins, c2009. 89 p.

Grades: 4 5 6   **649**

  1. Sex education for children 2. Family life education 3. Questions and answers

ISBN 9780061429873

LC 2008022710

Uses a question-and-answer format to present information about sex for preteens.

"This book offers straightforward information about topics such as physical changes in puberty, masturbation, birth control, pregnancy, homosexuality, and STDs. . . . Libraries . . . should consider adding it as a source of basic information for curious preteens." School Library Journal.

McIntyre, Thomas, 1952-

The **behavior** survival guide for kids: how to make good choices and stay out of trouble. Tom McIntyre; edited by Marjorie Lisovskis. Free Spirit, c2003. vii, 167 p.

Grades: 5 6 7 8   **649**

  1. Children with emotional illnesses 2. Behavior 3. Personal conduct

ISBN 1575421321

LC 2003004565

Provides information for children with behavioral problems, discussing labels for various problems and how to make better choices at school and at home when dealing with emotions and problems.

"The author provides skills and activities to learn and practice so that new behaviors can replace those that have resulted in getting students into trouble. . . . Those motivated to make better choices for how they behave in school or with friends and family will find much to help them." Voice of Youth Advocates.

Includes bibliographical references (p. 158-160) and index.

658 General management

Andrews, David

Business without borders: globalization. David Andrews. Heinemann Library, c2011. 56 p.: The global marketplace

Grades: 6 7 8 9   **658**

  1. Globalization (Economics) 2. International economic relations 3. World economy 4. International trade 5. World politics 6.

Developing countries
ISBN 9781432939335

LC 2010004097

Discusses the benefits and drawbacks of globalization, examines the history of trade and the recent economic crisis, and looks at ways citizens can work together to support economic growth.

"This title covers a wealth of material in concise paragraphs with pertinent subheadings. . . . [It has] clearly written, accessible content. It touches on currency, global trade, and purchasing power, and stresses that globalization is a process that is still going on today." School Library Journal.

Includes bibliographical references (p. 55) and index.

658.1 Organization and financial management

Rankin, Kenrya

Start it up: the complete teen business guide for turning your passions into pay. by Kenrya Rankin; [illustrators, Eriko Takada and Melissa Fiend]. Zest Books, 2011. 155 p.

Grades: 7 8 9 10 11 12   **658.1**
  1. Money-making projects 2. Entrepreneurship 3. New businesses 4. Small business 5. Money-making projects for teenagers
  ISBN 9780981973357

LC bl2011007595

Provides teens with advice on opening a business—including business types, plans, registering a business, finances, employees, marketing, customer service, doing good, and moving on—and profiles young entrepreneurs.

"Combining a conversational style with a systematic approach, [this book] walks teens through starting their own business. . . . Rankin gives a good overview of such difficult concepts as start-up and operating costs and asks readers to consider potentially overlooked topics like the pros and cons of publicizing prices and things to consider when working with family and friends." Booklist.

Includes bibliographical references and index.

658.8 Management of marketing

Weinick, Suzanne

Increasing your tweets, likes, and ratings: marketing your digital business. Suzanne Weinick. Rosen Pub., 2012. 64 p.: Digital entrepreneurship in the age of apps, the web, and mobile devices

Grades: 8 9 10 11 12   **658.8**
  1. Internet marketing 2. Electronic commerce -- Marketing 3. Social media 4. Internet
  ISBN 9781448869282

LC 2012006836

Offers strategies, tips, and techniques for marketing digital products, including software applications, games, and traditional products or services.

659.1 Management & public relations—Advertising and public relations—Advertising

Fyvie, Erica

Mad for ads: how advertising gets and stays in our heads. Erica Fyvie; illustrated by Ian Turner Kids Can Press, 2021 64 p.

Grades: 5 6 7 8   **659.1**
  1. Advertising 2. Advertising agencies 3. Marketing 4. Advertising and children 5. Mass media
  ISBN 9781525301315

"This upbeat, up-to-date look at advertising helps young readers understand just how insidious marketing can be." Booklist

660.6 Biotechnology

Abramovitz, Melissa, 1954-

Amazing feats of biological engineering. by Melissa Abramovitz; content consultant, Dan Phillips, director, Biomedical Engineering Program Rochester Institute of Technology. Essential Library, an imprint of Abdo Publishing, 2014. 112 p.: Great achievements in engineering

Grades: 7 8 9   **660.6**
  1. Bioengineering 2. Bioengineering -- History
  ISBN 9781624034268

LC bl2014033235

Discusses the field of biological engineering, including its history, some of its most famous feats, and what the future holds for the field.

Colson, Mary

GMOs. Mary Colson. Gareth Stevens Publishing, 2017. 48 p.: Cutting-edge technology (Gareth Stevens Pub.)

Grades: 5 6 7 8   **660.6**
  1. Genetically engineered organisms 2. Genetically engineered food 3. Genetic engineering 4. Biotechnology
  ISBN 9781482451573

LC bl2016040538

Explains what genetically modified organisms are, and how biotechnology could potentially be used in farming, animal breeding, and medicine.

"Useful books for updating the engineering shelves." Booklist.
Includes bibliographical references (pages 47) and index.

Lachner, Elizabeth

Bioengineering. edited by Elizabeth Lachner. Britannica Educational Publishing in association with Rosen Educational Services, 2016. 173 p.: Biotechnology revolution

Grades: 7 8 9 10 11 12   **660.6**
  1. Bioengineering 2. Biotechnology
  ISBN 9781622755806

LC 2014047675

"Each text has a table of contents, index, and full-color photographs and illustrations. The visual appeal of the books is high." Voice of Youth Advocates.

Includes bibliographical references and index.

662.6 Fuels

Steffens, Bradley, 1955-

Thinking critically: fossil fuels. by Bradley Steffens. ReferencePoint Press, Inc., 2019. 80 p.: Thinking critically

Grades: 7 8 9 10 11 12   **662.6**
  1. Fossil fuels
  ISBN 9781682825334

LC 2018040175

In the last thirty years, the industrialized nations of Europe and North America have made an effort to move away from the use of fossil fuels as a way of reducing pollution and slowing or even stopping climate change. At the same time, fossil fuels remain vital to their economies and standards of living. Controversies surround the use fossil fuels today and the role they will play in the future. Provided by publisher.

"Fossil Fuels addresses whether fossil fuels should still be used, gauges their impact on the environment, assesses their economic value, and questions if fracking is a good way to produce them. Copious and helpful back matter, including related organizations and websites and bulleted facts about key issues, conclude each title. A solid choice for analyzing today's society." Booklist

Includes bibliographical references and index.

664 Food technology

Aronson, Marc
Sugar changed the world: a story of magic, spice, slavery, freedom, and science. by Marc Aronson and Marina Budhos. Clarion Books, c2010. 176 p.
Grades: 7 8 9 10 11 12   **664**
  1. Sugar -- History 2. Sugar industry and trade -- History 3. Slavery -- History 4. Freedom -- History 5. Passive resistance -- History
  ISBN 9780618574926

                                                           LC 2009033579
"From 1600 to the 1800s, sugar drove the economies of Europe, the Americas, Asia and Africa and did more to reshape the world than any ruler, empire, or war had ever done. Millions of people were taken from Africa and enslaved to work the sugar plantations throughout the Caribbean, worked to death to supply the demand for sugar in Europe. . . . Maps, photographs and archival illustrations, all with captions that are informative in their own right, richly complement the text, and superb documentation and an essay addressed to teachers round out the fascinating volume." Kirkus.

Includes bibliographical references.

669 Metallurgy

Angliss, Sarah
Gold. Sarah Angliss. Benchmark Books, c2000. 32 p.: Elements (Benchmark Books)
Grades: 5 6 7 8   **669**
  1. Gold 2. Chemical elements
  ISBN 0761408878

                                                           LC 98046800
Explores the history of the precious metal gold and explains its chemistry, how it reacts, its uses, and its importance in our lives.

Sparrow, Giles
Iron. Giles Sparrow. Benchmark Books/Marshall Cavendish, c1999. 32 p.: Elements (Benchmark Books)
Grades: 5 6 7 8   **669**
  1. Iron 2. Chemical elements
  ISBN 0761408800

                                                           LC 97048524
Discusses the origin, discovery, special characteristics, and uses of iron.

670 Manufacturing

Slavin, Bill
Transformed: how everyday things are made. written by Bill Slavin with Jim Slavin; illustrated by Bill Slavin. Kids Can Press, c2005. 160 p.
Grades: 4 5 6 7   **670**
  1. Technology 2. Manufacturing processes 3. Mass production 4. Trivia and miscellaneous facts
  ISBN 1553371798
"This describes the manufacture of such items as baseballs, plastic dinosaurs, toothpaste, cereal, paper, and bricks. Each two-page spread covers the making of one of the 69 items in numbered paragraphs. The pictures are the best part—clear watercolor and ink images, made all the more engaging by folks in overalls directing the action." Booklist.

671.5 Joining and cutting of metals

Nelson, David Erik
Soldering. David Erik Nelson. Cherry Lake Publishing, 2014. 32 p.: 21st Century Skills Innovation Library: Makers As Innovators
Grades: 4 5 6 7 8   **671.5**
  1. Solder and soldering 2. Metal-work
  ISBN 9781631377747

                                                           LC 2014005538
Teaches readers how to solder electronic components together and build electronic devices.

"Though not the most obvious fit into the 21st Century Skills Innovation Library series, this introduction to soldering provides DIYers with basic guidelines to a skill still useful for a variety of projects, from jewelry making and plumbing to creating or repairing electronic circuits. ..Color photos depict gear, a soldered electronic board, and a young solderer at work. This quick but utilitarian guide closes with leads to several more detailed print and online resources." Booklist.

Includes bibliographical references (page 31) and index.

683.4 Small firearms

Blumenthal, Karen, 1959-2020
Tommy: the gun that changed America. Karen Blumenthal. Roaring Brook Press, 2015. 240 p.
Grades: 7 8 9 10   **683.4**
  1. Thompson, John Taliaferro, 1860-1940. 2. Dillinger, John, 1903-1934 3. Thompson submachine gun 4. Guns 5. Gangsters 6. Submachine guns 7. Weapons
  ISBN 9781626720848

                                                           LC 2014040642
"This biography of a gun traces the Thompson submachine gun (a.k.a. the Tommy) from its 1918 invention—by former Army officer John Thompson as a potential military weapon—to its use by crooks and bootleggers terrorizing people throughout the next two decades. With thorough research and impeccable documentation, Blumenthal also examines the history of American gun laws, showing the complexity of gun culture." Horn Book.

Includes bibliographical references and index.

688 Other final products, and packaging technology

Rothrock, Megan

The **LEGO** adventure book: cars, castles, dinosaurs & more!
Megan Rothrock. No Starch Press, 2012. 199 p.

Grades: 4 5 6 7 8 9   **688**
    1. LEGO toys 2. Models and modelmaking 3. Recreation 4.
Building blocks (Toys)
ISBN 9781593274429

                       LC 2012033902

Contains examples of the many things that can be built with LEGO
including step-by-step breakdowns of twenty-five different projects.

"LEGO enthusiast Megs builds an Idea Lab for creating projects
and, with its completion, travels by Transport-O-lux to see what others
are inspired to make...This one certainly won't sit on shelves. A fun read
for LEGO fans of all ages." School Library Journal.

688.7 Recreational equipment

Stone, Tanya Lee

The **good,** the bad, and the Barbie: a doll's history and her
impact on us. by Tanya Lee Stone. Viking, 2010. 130 p.

Grades: 6 7 8 9 10   **688.7**
    1. Handler, Ruth. 2. Barbie dolls -- History 3. Dolls -- Collectors
and collecting 4. Popular culture 5. Barbie dolls -- Social aspects
6. United States Popular culture -- History -- 20th century
ISBN 9780670011872

                       LC 2010007507

Golden Kite Award for Nonfiction, 2010.

Examines how the Barbie doll became the icon that she is and the
impact she has had on our culture through passionate anecdotes and
memories from a range of girls and women.

"Stone tantalizes with her brief and intriguing survey of Barbie. She
begins with the history of Mattel, started by self-made businesswoman
Ruth Handler in the 1940s, and moves onto materialism, body image,
portrayals of ethnicity, nudity, taboo and art." Kirkus.

Swanson, Jennifer

Super gear: nanotechnology and sports team up. by Jennifer
Swanson. Charlesbridge, [2016] 64 p.

Grades: 6 7 8 9   **688.7**
    1. Sports -- Technological innovations 2. Sports equipment 3.
Nanotechnology 4. Performance technology 5. Sports sciences
ISBN 9781580897204

                       LC 2015017347

"A highly engaging introduction to an exciting aspect of cutting-
edge, real-world science for STEM collections." School Library Journal.

Wulffson, Don L.

Toys!: amazing stories behind some great inventions. Don
Wulffson; with illustrations by Laurie Keller. H. Holt, 2000. 137
p.

Grades: 4 5 6 7   **688.7**
    1. Toys -- History 2. Inventions -- History 3. Toys 4. Inventions
ISBN 0805061967

                       LC 99058440

Describes the creation of a variety of toys and games, from seesaws
to Silly Putty and toy soldiers to Trivial Pursuit.

"Each of the 25 chapters is illustrated with small, humorous drawings and discusses a particular toy or game's origin and development.

The book ends with a bibliography and a list of websites. Good, readable
fare for browsing or light research." Booklist.

Includes bibliographical references (p. 135-136).

690 Construction of buildings

Macaulay, David

★ **Pyramid**. David Macaulay; illustrated by the author.
Houghton Mifflin, 1975. 80 p.

Grades: 4 5 6 7 8 9 10   **690**
    1. Pyramids -- Construction 2. Building 3. Civilization, Ancient
4. Egypt -- Civilization.
ISBN 0395214076

                       LC 75009964

Text and black-and-white illustrations follow the intricate step-by-
step process of the building of an ancient Egyptian pyramid.

"The construction of a pyramid in 25th century B.C. Egypt is described. Information about selection of the site, drawing of the plans,
calculating compass directions, clearing and leveling the ground, and
quarrying and hauling the tremendous blocks of granite and limestone is
conveyed as much by pictures as by text." Horn Book.

Unbuilding. David Macaulay. Houghton Mifflin, 1980. 78 p.

Grades: 4 5 6 7 8 9   **690**
    1. Empire State Building, New York City. 2. Wrecking 3.
Skyscrapers 4. Buildings 5. Architecture, American
ISBN 0395294576

                       LC 80015491

This fictional account of the dismantling and removal of the Empire
State Building describes the structure of a skyscraper and explains how
such an edifice would be demolished.

"Save for the fact that one particularly stunning double-page spread
is marred by tight binding, the book is a joy: accurate, informative,
handsome, and eminently readable." Bulletin of the Center for Children's Books.

Miller, Malinda, 1979-

Green construction: creating energy-efficient, low-impact
buildings. by Malinda Miller. Mason Crest Publishers, 2011. 64
p.: New careers for the 21st century: finding your role in the
global renewal

Grades: 7 8 9 10   **690**
    1. Sustainable construction 2. Building -- Vocational guidance 3.
Construction workers 4. Occupations 5. Vocational guidance
ISBN 9781422218150

                       LC 2010010013

"Chapters identify and emphasize specific careers—important
strengths, necessary aptitudes and interests, education and training, projected earnings, closely related occupations, type of work environment,
and predictions for the future of the field. . . . Color photos have a small
role amid the many statistics, figures, graphs and charts that support and
supplement the . . . [text]." School Library Journal.

Includes bibliographical references (p. 62) and index.

Weitzman, David, 1936-

Skywalkers: Mohawk ironworkers build the city. David
Weitzman. Roaring Brook Press, 2010. 124 p.

Grades: 8 9 10 11 12 Adult   **690**
    1. Construction workers 2. Mohawk Indians 3. Skyscrapers --

History 4. Iron and steel building 5. Indians of North America
ISBN 9781596431621

LC 2010284452

Narrative text and photographs examines Native American history and the development of structural engineering and architecture, focusing on Mohawk ironworkers.

"Stunning photographs complement Weitzman's comprehensive research and clear text in this memorable tribute to Mohawk ironworkers. . . . Weitzman wisely intersperses passages of construction history and technical technique with numerous personal stories. . . . Plentiful black and white archival photographs . . . are chilling or breathtaking. Throughout, Weitzman's admiration and respect for the Mohawk people shine through." Voice of Youth Advocates.

Includes bibliographical references (p. 116-119) and index.

Woolf, Alex, 1964-
Buildings. Alex Woolf. Heinemann Library, [2013], c2013. 56 p.: Design and engineering
Grades: 6 7 8 9 **690**
1. Buildings 2. Architecture 3. Nature -- Effect of humans on 4. Building 5. Engineering
ISBN 9781432970291

LC 2012013465

Presents information about the design, construction, use, maintenance, demolition, and disposal of buildings, offering an overview of what happens at each of these stages in a building's life cycle.

"Books in the Design and Engineering for STEM series offer an up-to-date introduction to an industry in a time of change..Buildings emphasizes the impact of architecture, construction, and demolition on the environment and shows how that impact can be minimized at different stages. Appearing on nearly every page, illustrations include many color photos and the occasional graph, digital drawing, or map. This attractive, informative series tackles meaningful topics and doesn't talk down to readers." Booklist.

Includes bibliographical references (page 55) and index.

696 Utilities

MacDonald, Fiona, 1958-
You wouldn't want to live without toilets. Fiona MacDonald; illustrated by David Antram. Scholastic Library Pub, 2014. 32 p.: You wouldn't want to live without...
Grades: 5 6 7 8 **696**
1. Toilets 2. Toilets -- History 3. Bathrooms -- Equipment and supplies -- History
ISBN 9780531212158

"Time lines chart the inventions' major developments and discoveries, providing a solid background for each subject, while brief yet interesting historical examples will appeal to even the most reluctant reader." School Library Journal.

700 ARTS & RECREATION

700 The arts

Stieff, Barbara
Earth, sea, sun, and sky: art in nature. Barbara Stieff. Prestel, 2011. 88 p.

Grades: 6 7 8 9 **700**
1. Nature (Aesthetics) 2. Gardens -- Styles 3. Parks 4. Earthworks (Art)
ISBN 9783791370484

LC bl2011016239

Presents an illustrated look at the ways that human culture shapes, interacts with, and represents nature for artistic effect, examining gardens, labyrinths and mazes, outdoor art installations, and representations of nature in galleries.

"A conversational writing style combines with many color photographs and drawings to convey information about art inspired by nature. In the beginning, Stieff describes the historical development of gardens and how they are an art form. She moves on to provide many examples of how art is found on land, in water, and in the air. The photographs, which range in size, further illuminate the text. Throughout the work, references are made to activities detailed in the final section. These projects, which include making daisy soup, learning some water games, forming seed balls, and creating pictures in water, encourage readers to look at or create art." School Library Journal.

700.89 Arts—Ethnic and national groups

Charleyboy, Lisa
Dreaming in Indian: contemporary Native American voices. edited by Lisa Charleyboy and Mary Beth Leatherdale. Annick Press, 2014 128 p.
Grades: 7 8 9 10 11 12 **700.89**
1. Native American artists 2. Indians of North America 3. Stereotypes (Social psychology) 4. Artists 5. North America 6. Anthologies
ISBN 9781554516872

This compelling book gives realistic insights into the experiences of growing up Indigenous in North America. Both thought provoking and honest, it challenges readers to have a more critical look at the negative stereotypes the media often portrays.

"Original and accessible, both an exuberant work of art and a uniquely valuable resource." Kirkus.

700.9 History, geographic treatment, biography of the arts

Flatt, Lizann
Arts and culture in the early Islamic world. Lizann Flatt. Crabtree Pub., c2012. 48 p.: Life in the early Islamic world
Grades: 5 6 7 **700.9**
1. Civilization, Islamic 2. Art, Islamic
ISBN 9780778721673

LC 2012000074

Traces the development of designs, styles, and crafts in the early Islamic world.

701 Philosophy and theory of fine and decorative arts

Pitamic, Maja
Fine art adventures: 36 creative, hands-on projects inspired by classic masterpieces. Maja Pitamic and Jill Laidlaw; introduction by Mike Norris, Metropolitan Museum of Art. Chicago Review Press, 2017. 143 p.

Grades: 5 6 7 8 **701**
1. Art appreciation 2. Art history 3. Handicraft for children 4. Creative activities for children and students 5. Art activities for children and students
ISBN 9780912777047

LC 2016054105
Introduces works of art in a variety of media from the 15th century to the present that represent different approaches and themes, and provides instructions for creating craft projects inspired by the featured artworks.

702 Miscellany of fine and decorative arts

Hume, Helen D., 1933-
The **art** teacher's book of lists: grades K-12. Helen D. Hume. Jossey-Bass, c2010. xiv, 402 p.
Grades: Professional **702**
1. Art
ISBN 9780470482087

LC 2010026656
A revised and updated edition of the best-selling resource for art teachers This time-tested book is written for teachers who need accurate and updated information about the world of art, artists, and art movements, including the arts of Africa, Asia,Native America and other diverse cultures. The book is filled with tools, resources, and ideas for creating art in multiple media. Written by an experienced artist and art instructor, the book is filled with vital facts, data, readings, and other references, Each of the book's lists has been updated and includes some 100 new lists. Contains new information on contemporary artists, artwork, art movements, museum holdings, art websites, and more. Offers ideas for dynamic art projects and lessons. Diverse in its content, the book covers topics such as architecture, drawing, painting, graphic arts, photography, digital arts, and much more. Provided by publisher.

702.8 Auxiliary techniques and procedures; apparatus, equipment, materials

Boldt, Claudia
Think and make like an artist: art activities for creative kids! Claudia Boldt and Eleanor Meredith. Thames & Hudson, 2017. 80 p.
Grades: 3 4 5 6 7 8 **702.8**
1. Artists 2. Art 3. Painting
ISBN 9780500650981

An engaging activity book that gives primary school children a way into how contemporary artists think and create by way of fun ideas for making their own art.
"This is an inspiring introduction to the concept of art as a vehicle to comment on or question the world." School Library Journal.

Luxbacher, Irene, 1970-
The **jumbo** book of art: an artistic adventure from the Avenue Road Arts School. written and illustrated by Irene Luxbacher. Kids Can Press, c2003. 208 p.: Jumbo books
Grades: 4 5 6 7 **702.8**
1. Art -- Technique 2. Handicraft
ISBN 1550747622

LC BL2004002157

Suggest ways for young artists to use their creative talents to make a variety of projects, including charcoal drawings, watercolors, sculptures in clay and wood, and a number of different crafts.
"Each of the four chapters is devoted to instructing readers in the basics of one technique—drawing, creating with color, sculpture, and mixed-media projects, respectively—and then inspires those readers to let loose and have fun making something beautiful. . . . The book features clear layouts, well-written definitions of terms, full-color illustrations, and more than 90 projects. . . . This practical, lively, and smart package is a must-have for every art and elementary school classroom, and a welcome addition to most Library collections." School Library Journal.

Vry, Silke
Trick of the eye: art and illusion. Silke Vry. Prestel, c2010. 89 p.
Grades: 4 5 6 **702.8**
1. Optical illusions in art 2. Visual perception 3. Stereograms 4. Optical illusions
ISBN 9783791370262

LC bl2010016554
Examines illusion in art and explores the techniques, styles, use of perspective, and composition that draw people in for repeated looks.
"From the Parthenon to the Mona Lisa to the Op-Art of the 1960s, images and text reveal the many ways our eyes play tricks on us. Perception of size and color is discussed using standard optical illusions, but this book includes much more. Anecdotes, such as the story of dueling Greek painters Zeuxis and Parrhasius, and unique reproductions, like portraits with altered facial features, lend excitement. The author has taken an interactive approach, filling the pages with questions, puzzles, and project ideas. . . . Text explains the images, which are large and clear. The broad range of styles represented and the fun of the interactive approach will no doubt appeal to young art lovers and curious kids alike." School Library Journal.

Wenzel, Angela
13 art techniques children should know. Angela Wenzel. Prestel Pub, 2013. 48 p. : Children should know
Grades: 4 5 6 **702.8**
1. Art history 2. Art -- Technique
ISBN 9783791371368

Introduces thirteen important art techniques—including modeling, watercolor, etching, and collage—as exemplified by famous works from such artists as Albrecht Dürer, Leonardo da Vinci, and Jackson Pollock.

704 Special topics in fine and decorative arts

Raczka, Bob
Before they were famous: how seven artists got their start. Bob Raczka. Millbrook Press, c2011. 32 p.: Bob Raczka's art adventures
Grades: 4 5 6 7 **704**
1. Child artists 2. Artists 3. Creativity in children 4. Art appreciation for children 5. Art appreciation
ISBN 9780761360773

LC 2009049596
"Short biographies written in conversational, jargon-free text introduce seven great artists, as young beginners and then as creators of famous works. From Dürer and Michelangelo to Picasso and Dali, the featured artists are presented chronologically on uncluttered, open spreads that include beautiful full-page reproductions. . . . Great preparation for a gallery visit, this will appeal to older readers, too, for its exciting,

704.03 Ethnic and national groups

Bolden, Tonya
Wake up our souls: a celebration of Black American artists. Tonya Bolden. H.N. Abrams; 2004. 128 p.
Grades: 6 7 8 9 10   **704.03**
  1. African American art 2. African American artists 3. African Americans -- Social conditions 4. Artists 5. Art
ISBN 0810945274

LC 2003016972

Presents a history of African American visual arts and artists from the days of slavery to the present.
  "Bolden's writing is rich and lyrical. She smoothly incorporates the historical context, explaining pivotal events and relevant artistic movements clearly and succinctly." School Library Journal.
  Includes bibliographical references (p. 123-125) and index.

Feelings, Tom
The **middle** passage: white ships/black cargo. Tom Feelings; introductions by Kadir Nelson and Kamili Feelings; historical note by Dr. Sylviane A. Diouf. Dial Books, 2018.
Grades: 7 8 9   **704.03**
  1. Feelings, Tom. 2. Africans in art 3. Slave trade in art 4. Stories without words
ISBN 9780525552444

LC 2017033256

Alex Haley's Roots awakened many Americans to the cruelty of slavery. The Middle Passage focuses attention on the torturous journey which brought slaves from Africa to the Americas, allowing readers to bear witness to the sufferings of an entire people. Provided by publisher.

January, Brendan, 1972-
Native American art & culture. Brendan January. Raintree, c2005. 56 p.: World art & culture
Grades: 5 6 7 8   **704.03**
  1. Arts, Native American 2. Indians of North America -- Material culture 3. Indians of North America -- Social life and customs
ISBN 141091108X

LC 2004008072

Describes the arts and culture of Native Americans.
  "January investigates the many art forms of the Native American tribes. . . . Chapters are dedicated to pottery, textiles, carving, and painting as well as body art, architecture, ceremonies, songs, and dances. . . . Numerous color photographs of both ancient and modern artwork are included on each spread, and they are exceptional. . . . This fresh look at Native American culture through its artwork will be a welcome alternative for reports and classroom discussion, and the popularity of the subject matter and appealing design will attract readers outside the classroom environment." School Library Journal.
  Includes bibliographical references (p. 52) and index.

704.9 Iconography

Brooks, Susie
Get into art: animals. Susie Brooks. Kingfisher: c2013. 31 p.: Get into art

Grades: 3 4 5 6 7   **704.9**
  1. Animals in art 2. Art appreciation 3. Art
ISBN 9780753470589

LC bl2013027285

Introduces readers to works of art featuring animals by such esteemed artists as M.C. Escher, Andy Warhol, Georges Braque, and Henri Matisse, and provides instruction for animal-centered art projects.

707.1 Art education

Hume, Helen D., 1933-
The **art** teacher's survival guide for elementary and middle schools. Helen D. Hume. Jossey-Bass, c2008. xvii, 494 p.: J-b Ed:survival Guides
Grades: Professional   **707.1**
  1. Art -- Study and teaching (Elementary) 2. Art -- Study and teaching (Middle school)
ISBN 9780470183021

LC 2009275495

With more than 110 creative art projects in varied types of media—from drawing to digital—plus tips, tools, and curricular resources, this work offers everything a teacher needs to know to present an effective arts education program. Authoritative, practical, and user-friendly, this comprehensive guide is an invaluable addition to every K-8 teacher's basic classroom tools.

The **art** teacher's survival guide for secondary schools: grades 7-12. Helen D. Hume. Jossey-Bass, 2014 xviii, 316 p.
Grades: Professional   **707.1**
  1. Art -- Study and teaching (Secondary)
ISBN 9781118447031

LC 2013028770

An invaluable compendium of 75 creative art projects for art educators and classroom teachers. This authoritative, practical, and comprehensive guide offers everything teachers need to know to conduct an effective arts instruction and appreciation program. It meets secondary art teacher's unique needs for creating art lessons that cover everything from the fundamentals to digital media careers for aspiring artists. The book includes ten chapters that provide detailed instructions for both teachers and students, along with creative lesson plans and practical tools such as reproducible handouts, illustrations, and photographs. Includes 75 fun and creative art projects. Fully updated to reflect the latest changes in secondary art instruction, including digital media and digital photography. Heavily illustrated with photographs and drawings. For art teachers, secondary classroom teachers, and homeschoolers, this is the ideal hands-on guide to art instruction for middle school and high school students. Provided by publisher.

708.153 Art museums—Washington (D.C.)

National Gallery of Art (U.S.)
An **eye** for art: focusing on great artists and their work.. National Gallery of Art. National Gallery of Art with Chicago Review Press, Incorporated, 2013. 180 p.
Grades: 4 5 6 7 8 9 10 11 12   **708.153**
  1. National Gallery of Art (U.S.) 2. Art appreciation for children 3. Art appreciation
ISBN 9781613748978

LC 2013009403

Combines sumptuous reproductions of famous works of art with introductions to the lives, inspirations and styles of 50 master artists, sharing corresponding activity suggestions designed to promote artistic development.

709 Arts—History, geographic treatment, biography

Langley, Andrew, 1949-
    Ancient Greece. Andrew Langley. Raintree, c2005. 48 p.: History in art
Grades: 4 5 6 7   **709**
    1. Art, Greek 2. Ancient Greece
    ISBN 1410905179
                  LC 2004007523
Examines several pieces of art from ancient Greece, and explains their history, social conditions, and culture based upon the design and depictions within the artwork.
    "The author shows how art provides primary-source information about everyday and family life, beliefs and religion, and philosophy and mythology in . . . ancient [Greece]. . . . The [book follows] a well-organized format that makes the history accessible for reports, but the [author takes the book] beyond a reports-only status. Captions for the two or three illustrations per spread are clear." School Library Journal.
    Includes bibliographical references (p. 47) and index.

Raczka, Bob
    ★ **Name** that style: all about isms in art. by Bob Raczka. Millbrook Press, c2009. 32 p.: Bob Raczka's art adventures
Grades: 5 6 7 8   **709**
    1. Art movements 2. Art history 3. Artists 4. Art appreciation for children 5. Art appreciation
    ISBN 9780822575863
                  LC 2008000312
Introduces different movements in art, including naturalism, romanticism, pointillism, and photorealism, discussing when each movement was popular, its important characteristics, and famous painters who used each style.
    "Beginning with naturalism and ending with photorealism, with many stops along the way, this compact overview documents the shifts, both in terms of technique as well as subject matter, that differentiate each style from its predecessors. Each ism gets a two-page spread, with a beautifully reproduced example. . . . This is . . . indispensible for any middle-grade classrooms introducing art history." Booklist.

709.03 Arts—Modern period, 1500-

Gunderson, Jessica
    Impressionism. Jessica Gunderson. Creative Education, 2009. 48 p.: Movements in art
Grades: 6 7 8 9   **709.03**
    1. Impressionism (Art) 2. Modern art 19th century 3. Art appreciation 4. Art
    ISBN 9781583416112
                  LC 2007008493
    "This discusses the leading Impressionist artists, their subjects, and their techniques. Quality reproductions of many paintings and occasional sepia photos of the painters and their settings illustrate the detailed, informative overview." Booklist.
    Includes bibliographical references (p. 47) and index.

Realism. Jessica Gunderson. Creative Education, c2009. 48 p.: Movements in art
Grades: 6 7 8 9   **709.03**
    1. Realism 2. Realism in art 3. Art appreciation 4. Art
    ISBN 9781583416129
                  LC 2007008494
    "Gunderson describes how art trends, politics, and inventions informed the work that was produced during [the Realism] movement. . . . [The] book provides an overview of the movement and its key players in continuous prose that is broken up by an occasional highlighted section of text. The color photographs, illustrations, and reproductions, many of them full page, are relevant and of high quality. . . . The [text delivers a] well-rounded [account] that students will find accessible." School Library Journal.
    Includes bibliographical references (p. 47) and index.

Romanticism. Jessica Gunderson. Creative Education, c2009. 48 p.: Movements in art
Grades: 6 7 8 9   **709.03**
    1. Romanticism in art 2. Art movements 3. Artists 4. Art
    ISBN 9781583416136
                  LC 2007008495
Introduces the artistic movement that flourished during the late 1700s and early 1800s and includes such famous artists as William Blake, Francisco de Goya, and Henry Fuseli.
    "Gunderson describes how art trends, politics, and inventions informed the work that was produced during [the Romantic] movement. . . . [The] book provides an overview of the movement and its key players in continuous prose that is broken up by an occasional highlighted section of text. The color photographs, illustrations, and reproductions, many of them full page, are relevant and of high quality. . . . The [text delivers a] well-rounded [account] that students will find accessible." School Library Journal.
    Includes bibliographical references (p. 47) and index.

709.04 Arts—20th century, 1900-1999

Claybourne, Anna
    Surrealism. Anna Claybourne. Heinemann Library, c2009. 48 p.: Art on the wall
Grades: 5 6 7 8 9 10   **709.04**
    1. Surrealism 2. Modern art 20th century 3. Artists 4. Art
    ISBN 9781432913670
                  LC 2008020316
    "This title succeeds in presenting a bird's-eye view of [Surrealism] without oversimplification. Information on individual artists is included in the broader context of the movement. Visually exciting, with plenty of color, [the layout is] hip and should appeal to the target audience." School Library Journal.
    Includes bibliographical references (p. 46-47) and index.

Harman, Alice
    Modern art explorer: with 30 artworks from the Centre Pompidou. Alice Harman; illustrated by Serge Bloch. Thames & Hudson Inc., 2020. 96 p.
Grades: 4 5 6 7 8   **709.04**
    1. Pompidou Arts Center, Paris, France. 2. Modern art 3. Art
    ISBN 9780500652206
                  LC bl2020046361

Featuring a diverse range of artists, Modern Art Explorer takes young readers on an undercover adventure to discover the stories behind famous modern artworks. Provided by publisher.

"In dedicated spreads, Harman presents an accessible mix of history and interpretation spiked with saucy asides." Publishers Weekly

Pitamic, Maja

Modern art adventures: 36 creative, hands-on projects inspired by artists from Monet to Banksy. Maja Pitamic and Jill Laidlaw. Chicago Review Press, 2015. 144 p.

Grades: 5 6 7 8 9   **709.04**
    1. Modern art 2. Art appreciation 3. Handicraft for children 4. Creative activities for children and students 5. Handicraft
    ISBN 9781613731772

LC 2014037521

Introduces the major movements of modern art and provides representative examples from individual artists, with thirty-six art projects that can be done in imitation of each style.

"This intriguing title introduces readers to modern art movements, from impressionism to contemporary street art, through child-friendly projects. Each movement includes examples of famous works of art, basic information (title, artist's name and nationality, and year painted) on the piece, and a brief discussion. . . . well-organized introduction to modern art concepts, perfect for classroom use." School Library Journal.

Wood, Alix

Urban 'street' art. Alix Wood. Gareth Stevens Publishing, 2015. 32 p.: But is it art?

Grades: 5 6 7 8   **709.04**
    1. Art and society 2. Street art 3. Public art 4. Art 5. Offenses against property
    ISBN 9781482422931

LC 2014033435

"Subjects include the thought-provoking, disturbing, whimsical, and unforgettable, from sidewalk 'gum art' to defaced stop signs to sunflowers planted in desolate urban areas to white 'ghost' bikes that honor fallen cyclists." School Library Journal.

Yancey, Diane

Art deco. by Diane Yancey. Lucent Books, c2011. 112 p.: Eye on art

Grades: 7 8 9 10   **709.04**
    1. Art deco 2. Art 3. Art movements
    ISBN 9781420503401

LC 2010032961

Discusses the art deco movement in fine and commercial art, architecture, and design, and describes the movement's impact on art history and society.

"Presents an in-depth look at the art deco movement and its lasting legacy. . . . [It provides] a great deal of information, so middle school readers may not read them cover to cover; however, ample cover photos and quotes from artists will make this . . . appealing to students interested in art." Voice of Youth Advocates.

Includes bibliographical references and index.

709.2 Arts—Biography

Gilberti, Fausto, 1970-

Yayoi Kusama covered everything in dots and wasn't sorry. by Fausto Gilberti Phaidon, 2020 48 p.

Grades: 4 5 6 7   **709.2**
    1. Kusama, Yayoi. 2. Artists 3. Pop artists 4. Dots (Art)
    ISBN 9781838660802

Yayoi Kusama dreamed of becoming a famous artist. Day and night she painted hundreds of dots onto large canvases. The dots soon came off her pictures and ended up on her dresses, tables, and walls. But she wasn't sorry! An inspiring story about one of the most popular contemporary artists in the world.

Greenberg, Jan, 1942-

Christo & Jeanne-Claude: through the Gates and beyond. Jan Greenberg and Sandra Jordan. Roaring Brook Press, 2008. 50 p.

Grades: 6 7 8 9   **709.2**
    1. Christo, 1935-2020 2. Jeanne-Claude, 1935-2009 3. Parks 4. Artists 5. Persistence 6. Sculpture 7. Central Park, New York City 8. New York City
    ISBN 9781596430716

LC 2007019951

Examines how artistic visionaries Christo and Jeanne-Claude persisted for more than two decades before New York City's Parks Department agreed to let them install their project "The Gates" in New York's Central Park.

"In 2005, the dull gray of a New York City winter was interrupted when two indominable artists, Christo and his partner, Jeanne-Claude, brought Central Park brilliantly to life with their outdoor work The Gates. . . . This book, chronicling both The Gates as well as the artists' other projects, is as thoughtful, eye-opening, and meticulous as the work it celebrates." Booklist.

Includes bibliographical references.

Herrera, Nicholas, 1964-

High riders, saints and death cars: a life saved by art. Nicholas Herrera; as told by Elisa Amado. Groundwood Books, 2011. 56 p.

Grades: 9 10 11 12   **709.2**
    1. Herrera, Nicholas, 1964- 2. Resistance (Psychology) in teenage boys 3. Santos (Art) 4. Folk artists 5. Santeros
    ISBN 9780888998545

LC oc2010084782

An autobiography of folk artist Nicholas Herrera who creates modern paintings and sculptures of saints and scenes from the Bible.

"The subtitle of New Mexican folk artist Herrera's autobiography (told to and written by Amado) isn't hyperbole: even Herrera's mother wasn't sure he would survive his wild and self-destructive teenage years during the 1960s. . . . After emerging from a coma following an alcohol-related car accident, Herrera devotes his life to creating art. . . . Herrera's folk art sculptures . . . [blend] religious iconography with imagery from contemporary Hispanic and biker culture, as well as social and political commentary. . . . Never minimizing the gravity of Herrera's struggles, the book makes clear the concrete impact that art can have." Publishers Weekly.

Spence, David

Michelangelo. [written by David Spence]. New Forest Press, 2010. 48 p.: Great artists and their world

Grades: 6 7 8 9   **709.2**
    1. Michelangelo Buonarroti, 1475-1564. 2. Artists 3. Painters 4. Art, Italian 5. Artists
    ISBN 9781848983090

LC bl2010026538

Explores the world, art, and life of the great Italian artist.

"Offers biographical information [of Michelangelo Buonarroti] . . . interspersed with art history and criticism in an eye-catching format. . . . [Includes] a long introductory paragraph and four-to-six images with explanatory notes. . . . Spence . . . does a good job of explaining why art that might seem ordinary today was revolutionary at the time of its creation." School Library Journal.

Includes bibliogarphical references (p. [44]) and index.

709.22 Collected biography

Herbert, Kari, 1970-
We are artists: women who made their mark on the world. stories and illustrations by Kari Herbert. Thames & Hudson, 2019. 144 p.
Grades: 5 6 7 8   **709.22**
   1. Women artists
   ISBN 9780500651964
   Wonderfully illustrated throughout, this book tells inspiring stories of fifteen women artists who made a lasting impact on art and the world through their lives and work.

709.45 Fine arts—Italy, San Marino, Vatican City, Malta

Taylor, Diane C. (Diane Carol)
   The **Renaissance** artists: with history projects for kids. Diane C. Taylor. Nomad Press, [2018] 106 p.: The Renaissance for kids
Grades: 4 5 6 7   **709.45**
   1. Art, Renaissance (Europe) 2. Painting, Renaissance (Europe) 3. European Renaissance 4. Artists 5. Artists
   ISBN 9781619306868

                                             LC bl2019012642
   Looks at the cultural legacy of Italian Renaissance art through the lives of five famous painters—Botticelli, da Vinci, Michelangelo, Raphael, and Titian.

709.73 Fine arts—United States

Finger, Brad
   13 American artists children should know. Brad Finger. Prestel, 2010. 46 p.: Children should know
Grades: 4 5 6   **709.73**
   1. Artists 2. Art 3. Art appreciation for children 4. Art appreciation 5. Art, American
   ISBN 9783791370361

                                             LC oc2010040700
   "Beginning with Winslow Homer and ending with Andy Warhol and Jasper Johns, this picture-book overview introduces 13 well-known American artists. On each double-page spread, short biographies combine with richly reproduced images of the artists' famous works. . . . Finger . . . writes with clarity and enthusiasm." Booklist.

711 Area planning (Civic art)

Macaulay, David
   ★ **City**: a story of Roman planning and construction.. David MacAulay. Houghton Mifflin, 1974. 112 p.

Grades: 4 5 6 7 8 9 10   **711**
   1. Civil engineering 2. Building 3. Urban planning 4. Cities and towns 5. Planning 6. Rome -- Antiquities.
   ISBN 039519492X

                                             LC 74004280
   Text and black and white illustrations show how the Romans planned and constructed their cities for the people who lived within them.
   "By following the inception, construction, and development of an imaginary Roman city, the account traces the evolution of Verbonia from the selection of its site under religious auspices in 26 B.C. to its completion in 100 A.D." Horn Book.

720 Architecture

Dillon, Patrick, 1962-
   The **story** of buildings: from the Pyramids to the Sydney Opera House and beyond. written by Patrick Dillon; illustrated by Stephen Biesty. Candlewick Press, 2014. 96 p.
Grades: 5 6 7 8   **720**
   1. Building 2. Architecture -- History
   ISBN 9780763669904
   "This large, handsome volume combines broad discussions of architectural history with exceptional drawings of significant buildings from ancient to modern times...Through his signature cross sections, details of interiors and construction can be seen as well. While the text, illustrations, and captions all provide information, it's the drawings of buildings that make this a valuable resource." Booklist.

Finger, Brad
   13 skyscrapers children should know. Brad Finger Prestel, [2016] 45 p.
Grades: 4 5 6 7 8   **720**
   1. Skyscrapers 2. Architecture
   ISBN 9783791372518
   "Still, fascinating anecdotes about the state of the world during each buildings inception make this an interesting read, and it provides plenty of valuable information, both at a glance and for more in-depth study." Booklist.

Hosack, Karen
   Buildings. Karen Hosack. Raintree, c2009. 32 p.: Perspectives.
Grades: 5 6 7 8   **720**
   1. Buildings 2. Architecture
   ISBN 9781410931658

                                             LC 2008009700
   "This features public spaces and private residences created from a variety of materials. Every page includes a paragraph about the structure with glossary terms in bold type. . . . [Title is] consistent in quality of design and content." School Library Journal.
   Includes bibliographical references (p. 31) and index.

Macaulay, David
   ★ **Building** big. by David Macaulay. Houghton Mifflin, 2000. 192 p.
Grades: 5 6 7 8 9 10   **720**
   1. Architecture 2. Engineering -- History 3. Building 4. Buildings 5. Engineering design
   ISBN 0395963311

                                             LC   00028116

"Macaulay combines his detailed yet vaguely whimsical illustrations with simple, straightforward prose that breaks down complex architectural and engineering accomplishments into easily digestible tidbits that don't insult the intelligence of the reader of any age." New York Times Book Review.

720.92 Architects

Heine, Florian
13 architects children should know. Florian Heine. Prestel, 2014. 45 p.
Grades: 4 5 6   **720.92**
    1. Architects 2. Architecture
ISBN 9783791371849

                           LC bl2014047141
Presents thirteen architects from various periods and styles—from Filippo Brunelleschi and Andrea Palladio to Le Corbusier, Frank Gehry, and Zaha Hadid—arranged chronologically with biographical details and comparisons to other architects.

Rubalcaba, Jill
I.M. Pei: architect of time, place, and purpose. by Jill Rubalcaba. Marshall Cavendish, c2011. 120 p.
Grades: 6 7 8 9 10 11 12   **720.92**
    1. Pei, I. M., 1917- 2. Architects 3. Chinese Americans 4. Architecture 5. Urban renewal
ISBN 9780761459736

                           LC 2011001910
A biography of the renowned architect that focuses on six of his signature buildings.
    "Rubalcaba . . . devotes one chapter each to seven architectural projects by the Chinese-born American architect I.M. Pei, adding chapters on his early life and other work; any one of them could have been the subject of its own book. Rubalcaba faithfully chronicles the trials Pei undergoes to complete each project, using color photographs and architectural plans to help tell the story." Publishers Weekly.
    Includes bibliographical references and index.

Rubin, Susan Goldman
Maya Lin: thinking with her hands. Susan Rubin. Chronicle Books, 2017. 304 p.
Grades: 5 6 7 8   **720.92**
    1. Lin, Maya Ying 2. Artists 3. Architects 4. Chinese American women 5. Chinese Americans 6. Memorials
ISBN 9781452108377

                           LC 2016058584
The Vietnam Veterans Memorial in Washington, D.C., is one of the most famous pieces of civic architecture in the world. But most people are not as familiar with the reserved college student who entered and won the design competition to build it. This accessible biography tells the story of Maya Lin, from her struggle to stick with her vision of the memorial to the wide variety of works she has created since then.
    "A finely designed, endlessly compelling examination of the life and work of one of Americas most notable architects." Booklist.

724 Architecture from 1400

Alphin, Tom
    The **LEGO** architect. Tom Alphin. No Starch Press, 2015 vi, 186 p.

Grades: 4 5 6 7 8 9   **724**
    1. Architectural models 2. LEGO toys
ISBN 9781593276133

                           LC 2015017603
Uses LEGO models to explore Neoclassical, Art Deco, Brutalist, Modernist, and other architectural styles. Each chapter includes a discussion of the architectural movement, photographs of famous real-life buildings, and a gallery of LEGO models, with step-by-step building instructions. Provided by publisher.

725 Architecture—Public structures

Roberts, Russell
    The **Eiffel** Tower. Russell Roberts. Purple Toad Publishing, Inc., [2017] 32 p.: Building on a dream
Grades: 4 5 6 7 8   **725**
    1. Eiffel Tower, Paris, France 2. Towers 3. Architecture
ISBN 9781624692031
"An enlightening look at this famous landmark." Booklist.

726 Buildings for religious and related purposes

Macaulay, David
    ★ **Mosque**. David Macaulay. Houghton Mifflin Co., c2003. 96 p.
Grades: 4 5 6 7 8 9 10   **726**
    1. Architects 2. Mosques -- Design and construction 3. Building 4. Muslims 5. Design 6. Istanbul, Turkey -- History -- 16th century.
ISBN 0618240349

                           LC 2003000177
"Once again Macaulay uses clear words and exemplary drawings to explore a majestic structure's design and construction. . . . In his respectful, straightforward explanation of the mosque's design, Macaulay offers an unusual, inspiring perspective into Islamic society." Booklist.

729 Design and decoration of structures and accessories

Macaulay, David
    ★ **Built** to last. David Macaulay. Houghton Mifflin Books for Children, 2010. 272 p.
Grades: 4 5 6 7 8 9 10   **729**
    1. Castles 2. Cathedrals 3. Mosques -- Design and construction 4. Urban planning 5. Building
ISBN 9780547342405

                           LC bl2010025805
Reveals the how and why behind some of the most fascinating and enduring structures humankind has ever created.
    "Significantly updating the Caldecott Honor-winning Castle (1977) and Cathedral (1973) with new text and full-color illustrations, this hefty volume combines them with a very lightly revised Mosque (2003) for a three-in-one architectural spree. No mere colorization of the black-and-white originals of the first two books, . . . the all-new, often breathtaking images have been drawn by hand and then digitally colored to harmonize, beautifully with the look of Mosque. . . . Take a moment to mourn the originals, then celebrate this entirely worthy revision." Kirkus.

730 Sculpture and related arts

Pitamic, Maja

Three-dimensional art adventures: 36 creative, artist-inspired projects in sculpture, ceramics, textiles, and more. Maja Pitamic and Jill Laidlaw. Chicago Review Press, 2016. 144 p.

Grades: 5 6 7 8 9   **730**

1. Sculpture 2. Handicraft for children 3. Creative activities for children and students 4. Installations (Art) 5. Ceramics

ISBN 9781613736593

     LC 2015048885

This book introduces young artists, ages 6 and up, to groundbreaking masterpieces and fresh techniques, then lets them loose. Children will: weave a tapestry using yarn and a shoebox loom, use found and recycled materials to assemble a still-life collage, tie-dye a T-shirt using several pattern-creation techniques, and more!

"Like its predecessor, it's a book that succeeds for its ambition and breadth as it helps brings art out of the museum and makes it immediate and relevant in the lives of readers." Publishers Weekly.

Wenzel, Angela

13 sculptures children should know. Angela Wenzel. Prestel Verlag, 2010. 48 p. : Children should know

Grades: 4 5 6   **730**

1. Sculpture 2. Art appreciation for children 3. Decorative arts 4. Art 5. Art appreciation

ISBN 9783791370101

"This large-format, brightly colored [survey provides a] well-oranized [introduction] to the . . . world [of sculpture]. [It] highlights a variety of works from antiquity to modern times. . . . Leading questions encourage budding artists to use the featured subjects and artworks as inspiration." Horn Book Guide.

730.92 Sculpture—Biography

Tan, Shaun

The **singing** bones: inspired by Grimms' fairy tales. Shaun Tan; foreword by Neil Gaiman; introduced by Jack Zipes. Arthur A. Levine Books, an imprint of Scholastic Inc., 2016. 192 p.

Grades: 5 6 7 8 9   **730.92**

1. Sculpture 2. Folklore in art 3. Fairy tales in art 4. Illustrated books 5. Folklore

ISBN 9780545946124

An illustrated volume of fairy tales inspired by Grimms' classics illuminates their beautiful, monstrous and macabre themes as brought to life by the Oscar-winning creator of Tales From Outer Suburbia.

"A unique addition to special and robust folktale and fairy-tale and/or art collections." School Library Journal.

Includes bibliographical references and annotated index.

736 Carving and carvings

Boursin, Didier

Easy origami. Didier Boursin. Firefly Books, 2005. 64 p.: I made it myself!

Grades: 4 5 6 7   **736**

1. Origami 2. Paper work 3. Handicraft

ISBN 1552979288

     LC 2006272864

Presents detailed instructions for how to fold paper into various shapes, ranging from an easy fish to a more challenging bird.

"Paper-folding novices in particular may be drawn to this collection by its unusually clean design and bright, inviting colors." School Library Journal.

Diehn, Gwen, 1943-

Making books that fly, fold, wrap, hide, pop up, twist, & turn: books for kids to make. Gwen Diehn. Lark Books, 2006, c1998. 96 p.

Grades: 4 5 6 7   **736**

1. Handicraft 2. Toy and movable books -- Design and construction 3. Handmade books

ISBN 1579903266

     LC bl2006005106

Presents instructions for making various kinds of books, including those that unfold like a map, hide secrets by opening in mysterious ways, tell a story on a scroll, and contain individual cards that slip into pockets.

"Clear directions and diagrams and attractive full-color photographs of completed projects will make it easy for readers to duplicate 18 different folded, wrapped, and pop-up books." Booklist.

Green, Gail

Paper artist: creations kids can fold, tear, wear, or share. by Gail D. Green, Kara L. Laughlin, and Jennifer Phillips. Capstone, 2013. 112 p.: Capstone young readers: paper creations

Grades: 4 5 6 7 8   **736**

1. Paper work 2. Art 3. Handicraft

ISBN 9781623700041

     LC 2012032454

Step-by-step instructions teach readers how to create decorations, presents, keepsakes, and accessories with paper. Provided by publisher.

"The well-organized layout is stunning, with beautiful photographs and step-by-step instructions that are appealing and simple to follow. Useful extra tips are added if needed." School Library Journal.

Kenney, Karen Latchana

Folding tech: using origami and nature to revolutionize technology. Karen Latchana Kenney. Lerner Pub Group 2020 104 p.

Grades: 8 9 10 11   **736**

1. Origami 2. Handicraft 3. Technology 4. Machinery -- Design 5. Paper work

ISBN 9781541533042

     LC 2019009069

This book discusses the history and current state of high-tech folding in the world of manufacturing and how it is informed by folding in the natural world. Readers meet the leading scientists and artists in the field, learn about the manufacturing applications of folding in aerospace and other fields, and where folding technology is going in the future.

"Effectively showcases the contemporary brilliance that can come from ancient principles." Kirkus

Includes bibliographical references (pages 95-98) and index.

Nguyen, Duy, 1960-

Zombigami: paper folding for the living dead. Duy Nguyen. Sterling, c2012. 96 p.

Grades: 5 6 7 8   **736**

1. Origami 2. Zombies in art

ISBN 9781402786464

     LC bl2012029475

Presents instructions for crafting zombie-themed origami, including a skull, a disembodied hand, and a "walking" corpse, and provides step-by-step instructions for basic origami folds and symbols.

"Featuring both a detachable photo gallery of folded ghouls placed in atmospheric settings and a package of origami paper in suitably ominous colors and patterns, this collection of 13 undead figures may not survive intact for long but offers experienced paper folders hours of creepy fun. Nguyen opens with a tutorial of creases and folding symbology then . . . goes on to show how each figure is folded with plenty of carefully drawn and clearly labeled step diagrams. Nonetheless, most of these models are challenging projects." School Library Journal.

Stern, Joel, 1953-

Jewish holiday origami. Joel Stern; photographs by David Greenfield. Dover Publications, 2006. 64 p.

Grades: 8 9 10 11 12 Adult   **736**
  1. Origami 2. Holiday decorations 3. Jewish crafts 4. Fasts and feasts -- Judaism
  ISBN 9780486450766

LC 2005056934

Clearly detailed illustrations and captions explain all the steps for an entire year's worth of Jewish holiday projects—from Chanukah dreidels and a menorah with candles to Passover pyramids and an image of the Red Sea parting. Additional projects for weekly observances include sabbath candles and kiddush cup. Great for synagogues, schools and homes, this easy-to-follow guide offers beginning paperfolders a unique, fun-filled way to celebrate Jewish culture.

736.982 Origami

Song, Sok

Origami accessories: a foldable fashion guide. by Sok Song. Capstone Press, a Capstone imprint, [2016] 48 p.: Savvy

Grades: 4 5 6 7 8   **736.982**
  1. Origami 2. Paper work 3. Dress accessories 4. Fashion 5. Handicraft
  ISBN 9781515716235

LC 2016022940

Ten original fashion origami accessories complete with written instructions and illustrated diagrams. Provided by publisher.

"Peppy printed papers and a mod-looking cover give this series lots of shelf appeal... Upgrade your origami section with these original models and excellent instructions." School Library Journal.

738.092 Ceramic arts—Biography

Greenberg, Jan, 1942-

The **mad** potter: George E. Ohr, eccentric genius. Jan Greenberg and Sandra Jordan. Roaring Brook Press, 2013. 56 p.

Grades: 4 5 6 7 8   **738.092**
  1. Ohr, George E., 1857-1918. 2. Potters 3. Art pottery, American 4. Eccentrics and eccentricities 5. Individuality 6. Biloxi, Mississippi
  ISBN 9781596438101

LC 2012047601

An account of the life of the eccentric ceramics artist traces his youth against a backdrop of the Civil War and political unrest in Biloxi, Mississippi; his creation of thousands of unconventional pots, vases and sculptures; and the remarkable trove discovered after his death that revealed the uniqueness of his talent.

740 Graphic arts

Kidd, Chip

Go: a Kidd's guide to graphic design. Chip Kidd. Workman Publishing, 2013. 150 p.

Grades: 5 6 7 8 9 10 11 12 Adult   **740**
  1. Graphic design 2. Book covers 3. Graphic arts -- Technique 4. Design 5. Books for reluctant readers
  ISBN 9780761172192

Provides an introduction to the ways in which designers communicate their ideas, whether through images, text, or placement.

"Apart from geeking out about design elements, however, Kidd's primary goal is to encourage aspiring designers to pay attention to graphics they see every day in their favorite book covers, ads, and posters and to use this newfound knowledge to create their own designs. Captivating, eye-opening, and just plain cool." Booklist.

741.2 Techniques, procedures, apparatus, equipment, materials

Temple, Kathryn, 1972-

★ **Drawing**: the only drawing book you'll ever need to be the artist you've always wanted to be. Kathryn Temple. Lark Books, c2005. 112 p.: Art for kids

Grades: 5 6 7 8   **741.2**
  1. Drawing -- Technique 2. Perspective
  ISBN 1579905870

LC 2004017909

This book's subtitle really means business! With lots of encouragement, visual examples, and step-by-step illustrations, Drawing shows how to master the basics of line drawing, light and shadow, proportion and scale, and perspective. It also includes chapters on "opening your artist's eyes"—yep, they're different from ordinary eyes—and on using the basics you learn to draw faces, bodies, and more. .

"This introduction to essential drawing techniques builds from the starting points of lines and simple shapes. . . . Eight concise chapters explore seeing with artist's eyes, line drawing, light and shadow, proportion and scale, perspective, drawing faces, drawing bodies, and using imagination. The succinct text reads smoothly and is written in a clear, understandable style. Sample sketches and crisp, color photographs extend the text." School Library Journal.

Drawing in color. Kathryn Temple. Lark Books, c2009. 112 p.: Art for kids

Grades: 5 6 7 8   **741.2**
  1. Drawing -- Technique 2. Perspective 3. Colored pencil drawing 4. Color in art 5. Color drawing
  ISBN 9781579908218

LC 2008050618

Provides hands-on activities that teach the basic elements of drawing, including shapes, shading techniques, creating perspective, and composing.

"This heavily illustrated guide encourages budding artists to learn some basic skills and decide what works for them. Before jumping into project ideas, Temple explains some drawing tools and the basics of color theory. She provides clear, step-by-step instructions while reminding children that there is no right or wrong way to draw. Then, in nine chapters that each cover a particular technique or type of subject. . . . Projects use a variety of mediums, including colored pencils, markers, and oil pastels. The balance of detailed text and color images is visually appealing. Children will enjoy honing their observation skills as they practice using color in new ways." School Library Journal.

741.5 Cartoons, graphic novels, caricatures, comics

Abadzis, Nick

Laika. by Nick Abadzis; color by Hilary Sycamore. First Second, 2007. 208 p.

Grades: 7 8 9 10 11 12　　　**741.5**

1. 1950s 2. Dogs 3. Space programs 4. Space flight 5. Animal space flight 6. Scientists 7. Soviet Union 8. Space 9. Comics and Graphic novels
ISBN 9781596431010

LC 2006051907

"Abadzis's tear-inducing and solidly researched graphic novel treatment of Laika's surpassingly tragic story is a standout." Publishers Weekly.

Allison, John, 1976-

Bad machinery. by John Allison. Oni Press, 2013. 112 p.: Bad machinery

Grades: 7 8 9 10 11 12 Adult　　　**741.5**

1. Paranormal phenomenon investigation 2. Children 3. Soccer 4. Sports 5. Ghosts 6. Yorkshire, England 7. England 8. Satirical comics 9. Comics and Graphic novels 10. Webcomics
ISBN 9781620100844

"Allison is a triple threat—he plots deftly, draws confidently, and writes dead-on adolescent dialogue. Set in a grammar school in a British working-class community, this first book in his Bad Machinery series—originally published as a webcomic—has three earnest boys vying against three sharp-tongued girls to solve mysteries." Publishers Weekly.

Anderson, M. T.

Yvain: the knight of the lion. M.T. Anderson, Andrea Offermann. Candlewick Pr., 2017. 144 p.

Grades: 7 8 9 10　　　**741.5**

1. Arthur, King 2. Medieval period (476-1492) 3. Knights and knighthood 4. King Arthur's Round Table 5. Courts and courtiers 6. Husband and wife 7. Men and animals 8. Arthurian legends 9. Comics and Graphic novels
ISBN 9780763659394

"This adaptation of Chrétien de Troyes' medieval poem beautifully ties together period art and imagery with stylish visual storytelling." Booklist.

Appignanesi, Richard

Romeo and Juliet. by William Shakespeare; adapted by Richard Appignanesi; illustrated by Sonia Leong. Amulet Books, 2007. 208 p.: Manga Shakespeare

Grades: 8 9 10 11 12　　　**741.5**

1. Teenage romance 2. Family feuds 3. Suicide 4. Romeo (Fictitious character) 5. Juliet (Fictitious character) 6. Tokyo, Japan 7. Japan 8. Romance comics 9. Comics and Graphic novels 10. Introductory classics 11. Books for reluctant readers
ISBN 9780810993259

LC 2006100362

"Although the richness of the language may be lost, the script keeps the spirit of the story intact, hitting all the major speeches." Booklist.

Arni, Samhita

Sita's Ramayana. Samhita Arni; Moyna Chitrakar, illustrator. Groundwood Books, 2011. 152 p.

Grades: 5 6 7 8　　　**741.5**

1. Valmiki 2. Rama (Hindu deity) 3. Rulers 4. Husband and wife 5. Captives 6. Exile (Punishment) 7. Comics and Graphic novels 8. Mythological fiction 9. Asian-influenced fantasy
ISBN 9781554981458

A retelling of the Ramayana told through the eyes of Sita. When Sita, Rama and his brother are banished from their kingdom, Sita is captured by the arrogant King Ravana and imprisoned in a garden across the ocean. Sita refuses to become his wife and eventually Rama comes to her rescue. But unable to trust Sita, Rama forces her to undergo an ordeal by fire to prove her loyalty.

"The Ramayana is the story of the exiled prince Rama and his beautiful wife, Sita. When she is kidnapped by a love-struck demon king, her husband's efforts to rescue her result in a war that eventually involves not only demons and mortals, but also gods, monsters, and even animals. . . . Here, a Patua scroll painter has adapted it as a fast-paced, brilliantly bold graphic novel. All of the suspense, treachery, sorcery, and pathos of this epic is depicted in homemade natural dyes layered onto paper in energetic lines, rhythmic patterns, and fields of hot, bright colors. . . . This book would be a must-purchase based on the strength of its dramatic story and arresting art, enhanced by superior design and high-quality production. Brilliant and fresh." School Library Journal.

Bertozzi, Nick

Lewis & Clark. Nick Bertozzi. First Second, 2011. 144 p.

Grades: 5 6 7 8　　　**741.5**

1. Lewis, Meriwether, 1774-1809. 2. Clark, William, 1770-1838. 3. 1800s (Decade) 4. Explorers 5. Exploration 6. Guides (Persons) 7. Women interpreters 8. Voyages and travels 9. The West (United States) -- Exploration 10. Historical comics 11. Comics and Graphic novels
ISBN 9781596434509

LC 2010036255

Presents, in graphic novel format, the adventures of explorers Lewis and Clark during their journey from St. Louis to the Pacific Ocean.

"Bertozzi brings new life to the epic westward journey of explorers Lewis and Clark in this graphic novel perfect for history buffs. . . . Lewis's . . . deteriorating mental state throughout the expedition and particularly on the return trip is eloquently drawn, with Bertozzi managing to combine both history lesson and character study in strong, gripping drawings." School Library Journal.

Black, Holly

The **Good** Neighbors. Holly Black; illustrated by Ted Naifeh. Graphix, 2008. 144 p. : Good neighbors

Grades: 7 8 9 10 11 12　　　**741.5**

1. Fairies 2. Missing persons 3. Supernatural 4. Magic 5. Mother-separated teenage girls 6. Comics and Graphic novels 7. Fantasy comics 8. Urban fantasy 9. Books for reluctant readers
ISBN 9780439855624

LC 2007049008

Sixteen-year-old Rue Silver, whose mother disappeared weeks ago, believes she is going crazy until she learns that the strange things she has been seeing are real, and that she is one of the faerie creatures, or Good Neighbors, that mortals cannot see.

"This sophisticated tale is well served by Naifeh's stylish, angular illustrations." School Library Journal.

Bowers, Rick, 1952-

Superman versus the Ku Klux Klan: the true story of how the iconic superhero battled the men of hate. by Rick Bowers. National Geographic, c2012. 160 p.

Grades: 7 8 9 10 11 12   **741.5**

  1. Ku-Klux Klan 2. 1940s 3. Superman (Comic book series) 4. Superman (Fictitious character) 5. Race relations 6. Comic books, strips, etc -- Social aspects

ISBN 9781426309151

LC 2011024660

This book tells a group of intertwining stories that culminate in the historic 1947 collision of the Superman Radio Show and the Ku Klux Klan.

Britt, Fanny

Jane, the fox and me. written by Fanny Britt; illustrated by Isabelle Arsenault; translated from the French by Christine Morelli and Susan Ouriou. Groundwood Books, 2013. 104 p.

Grades: 5 6 7 8 9   **741.5**

  1. Bronte, Charlotte, 1816-1855. Jane Eyre 2. Overweight girls 3. Books and reading 4. Social acceptance 5. Cruelty in children 6. Girls -- Friendship 7. Montreal, Quebec 8. Comics and Graphic novels 9. Translations French to English

ISBN 9781554983605

Hélène is an outcast in her grade. Her only consolation is reading Jane Eyre. Even seeing a lovely fox doesn't make her feel better, but maybe a new friendship will.

"Britt's well-constructed narrative is achieved sensitively through Arsenault's impressionistic artwork. . . . An elegant and accessible approach to an important topic." Booklist.

Brosgol, Vera

Anya's ghost. Vera Brosgol. First Second, 2011. 224 p.

Grades: 6 7 8 9 10   **741.5**

  1. Teenage girls and ghosts 2. Belonging 3. Immigrant families 4. Wells 5. Ghosts 6. Paranormal comics 7. Comics and Graphic novels 8. Books for reluctant readers

ISBN 9781596437135

LC 2010036251

Anya, embarrassed by her Russian immigrant family and self-conscious about her body, has given up on fitting in at school but falling down a well and making friends with the ghost there just may be worse.

"A moodily atmospheric spectrum of grays washes over the clean, tidy panels, setting a distinct stage before the first words appear. . . . In addition to the supernatural elements, Brosgol interweaves some savvy insights about the illusion of perfection and outward appearance." Kirkus

★ **Be** prepared. Vera Brosgol. First Second 2018 256 p.

Grades: 4 5 6 7 8   **741.5**

  1. Summer camps 2. Russian Americans 3. Russian American girls 4. Single parent families 5. Making friends 6. Connecticut 7. Autobiographical comics 8. Humorous comics 9. Comics and Graphic novels

ISBN 9781626724440

Her friends live in fancy houses and their parents can afford to send them to the best summer camps, but Vera's single mother can't afford that sort of luxury. There's only one summer camp in her price range: Russian summer camp. Nothing could prepare her for all the "cool girl" drama, endless Russian history lessons, and outhouses straight out of nightmares!

"Brosgol's artwork has immense depth, from the facial expressions and gestures to the spot-on visual gags, and she strikes a perfect balance between heartfelt honesty and uproarious, self-deprecating humor." Booklist.

Brown, Don, 1949-

In the shadow of the fallen towers: the seconds, minutes, hours, days, weeks, months, and years after the 911 attacks. Don Brown Etch/HMH Books for Young Readers 2021. 128 p.

Grades: 7 8 9 10 11 12   **741.5**

  1. World Trade Center, New York City. 2. Pentagon (Va.) 3. 21st century 4. September 11 Terrorist Attacks, 2001 5. Victims of terrorism 6. Search and rescue operations 7. Terrorism 8. War on Terrorism, 2001-2009 9. New York City 10. Arlington, Virginia 11. Comics and Graphic novels

ISBN 9780358223573

This graphic novel chronicles the immediate aftermath of the terrorist attack on the World Trade Center in New York City through moving individual stories that bear witness to our history and the ways it shapes our future.

"A succinct and impactful look at one of America's worst tragedies, skillfully rendered by one of comics journalism's best." School Library Journal

Brown, Jeffrey, 1975-

Return of the Padawan. Jeffrey Brown. Scholastic Inc., 2014. 176 p.: Jedi Academy

Grades: 3 4 5 6 7   **741.5**

  1. Jedi Knights (Fictitious characters) 2. Star Wars characters 3. Middle schools 4. Schools 5. Life on other planets 6. Star Wars fiction 7. Science fiction 8. Graphic novel hybrids

ISBN 9780545621250

Jedi Academy finds Roan Novachez entering his second year at Jedi Academy thinking it will be a breeze, but he couldn't have been more wrong when faced with alien poetry tests, menacing robots, food fights, flight simulation class, online bullies, more lightsaber duels and worst of all... a girl who is mad at him.

"Roan is a very sympathetic main character, and readers will feel his pain and laugh at his misfortune in equal measure. Roan's hand-lettered journal entries alternate with short paneled sequences and 'screenshots' of academy message boards and other ephemera." Kirkus.

★ **Star** Wars.. by Jeffery Brown. Scholastic Inc., 2013. 160 p. : Jedi Academy

Grades: 3 4 5 6 7   **741.5**

  1. Jedi Knights (Fictitious characters) 2. Star Wars characters 3. Middle schools 4. Schools 5. Novachez, Roan (Fictitious character) 6. Star Wars fiction 7. Science fiction 8. Graphic novel hybrids 9. Books for reluctant readers

ISBN 9780545505178

"While it might be disappointing for those familiar with this world to see scant representation of beloved characters, it makes the book an easy starting point for new fans. There are plenty of references to other elements (the T-16 Skyhopper and Jedi training remotes, for example) for diehards to get excited about." School Library Journal.

Cabot, Meg

Black Canary: ignite. written by Meg Cabot; illustrated by Cara McGee; colored by Caitlin Quirk; lettered by Clayton Cowles. DC Comics, [2019] 128 p.

Grades: 4 5 6 7   **741.5**

  1. Teenage girls 2. Family secrets 3. Mothers and daughters 4.

Thirteen-year-old girls 5. Superhuman abilities 6. Superhero comics 7. Comics and Graphic novels
ISBN 9781401286200

LC 2019013353

Thirteen-year-old Dinah Lance is in a rock band with her two best friends and has a good relationship with her mom, but when a mysterious figure threatens her friends and family, she learns more about herself and her mother's secret past.

Camper, Cathy

Lowriders in space. by Cathy Camper; illustrated by Raúl Gonzalez III. Chronicle Books, [2014] 112 p.: Low riders
Grades: 4 5 6 7 8   **741.5**
1. Lowriders 2. Competition 3. Mexican Americans 4. Contests 5. Friendship 6. Fantasy comics 7. Comics and Graphic novels 8. Bilingual materials English/Spanish
ISBN 9781452121550

LC 2013040709

Lupe, Flapjack, Elirio customize their car into a low rider for the Universal Car Competition to win the cash prize that will enable them to buy their own garage.

"Raúl's snazzy panels—impressively drawn in only red, blue, and black ballpoint pen on tea-stained paper—resemble an amped-up Mighty Mouse cartoon rendered in anarchic yet skillful doodles. It's a joyfully explosive style, and it perfectly matches the Latino characters and barrio setting." Booklist.

Lowriders to the center of the Earth. by Cathy Camper; illustrated by Its the Third. Chronicle Books, 2016. 128 p.: Low riders
Grades: 4 5 6 7 8   **741.5**
1. Lost cats 2. Gods and goddesses, Aztec 3. Mexican Americans 4. Lowriders 5. Friendship 6. Fantasy comics 7. Comics and Graphic novels 8. Bilingual materials English/Spanish
ISBN 9781452123431

LC 2015021996

Pura Belpré Award for Illustration, 2017.

Lupe Impala, Elirio Malaria, and El Chavo Octopus are now the proud owners of their own garage—but when a series of earthquakes hit their town and Genie, their beloved cat, disappears they find themselves traveling to the realm of Mictlantecuhtli, Aztec god of the Underworld, who is keeping Genie prisoner.

"Raúl the Third's ultradetailed crosshatched artwork more than meets the demands of this cast-of-thousands comic opus." Kirkus.

Carroll, Emily

Through the woods. Emily Carroll. Margaret K. McElderry Books, 2014. 208 p.
Grades: 8 9 10 11 12 Adult   **741.5**
1. Horror comics 2. Comics and Graphic novels 3. Fairy tale and folklore-inspired fiction 4. Books for reluctant readers
ISBN 9781442465954

LC 2013030969

Journey through the woods in this sinister, compellingly spooky collection that features four brand-new stories and one phenomenally popular tale in print for the first time. Emily Carroll brings you tales of old-school folklore and horror, presented in an illustrated style that's both unsettling and deceptively soothing.

"All the tales in Carroll's debut graphic novel are fairly standard ghost stories, but it is her eerie illustrations—popping with bold color on black, glossy pages—that masterfully build terrifying tension and a keep-the-lights-on atmosphere." Booklist.

Chanani, Nidhi

Pashmina. Nidhi Chanani. First Second 2017 176 p.
Grades: 4 5 6 7 8   **741.5**
1. Shawls 2. Identity (Psychology) 3. East Indian American teenagers 4. Culture 5. Ethnic identity 6. California 7. India 8. Comics and Graphic novels
ISBN 9781626720886

For Pri, her mother's homeland can only exist in her imagination. That is, until she find a mysterious pashmina tucked away in a forgotten suitcase. When she wraps herself in it, she is transported to a place more vivid and colorful than any guidebook or Bollywood film. But is this the real India? And what is that shadow lurking in the background?

"Contemporary reality is shown in grayscale; the past in sepia hues; and Pri's imagined India in rich colors that radiate off the pages. Priyanka is a realistically complex, sometimes moody character, with depth shown through her varied interests and inquisitive musings." Horn Book.

Chmakova, Svetlana, 1979-

Awkward. Svetlana Chmakova. Yen Press, 2015. 192 p.: Berrybrook Middle School novels
Grades: 5 6 7 8   **741.5**
1. New students 2. Embarrassment 3. Teenage boy/girl relations 4. Middle schools 5. Children's clubs 6. Comics and Graphic novels 7. Realistic fiction 8. Books for reluctant readers
ISBN 9780316381321

After shunning Jaime, the school nerd, on her first day at a new middle school, Penelope Torres tries to blend in with her new friends in the art club, until the art club goes to war with the science club, of which Jaime is a member.

Brave. Svetlana Chmakova. Yen Press, 2017. 238 p.: Berrybrook Middle School novels
Grades: 4 5 6 7   **741.5**
1. Courage 2. Middle school students 3. Bullying and bullies 4. Student organizations 5. Belonging 6. Comics and Graphic novels 7. Realistic fiction
ISBN 9780316363174

LC 2017934376

In Jenson's daydreams he is the biggest hero there ever was, in real life he is targeted by bullies and struggles in math class, and the pressure of middle school only keeps growing.

"This is a subtle, well-observed treatment of a kid who doesn't fit in. The various threads of friendship and belonging are woven masterfully and ring true, with a conclusion that brings everything together." School Library Journal.

Crush. Svetlana Chmakova. JY, 2018. 234 p.: Berrybrook Middle School novels
Grades: 5 6 7 8   **741.5**
1. Middle school students 2. Middle schools 3. Social phobia 4. Male friendship 5. Teenage boy/girl relations 6. Comics and Graphic novels 7. Realistic fiction 8. Books for reluctant readers
ISBN 9780316363235

LC 2018948318

Jorge seems to have it all together. He's big enough that nobody really messes with him, but he's also a genuinely sweet guy with a solid, reliable group of friends. The only time he ever really feels off his game is when he crosses paths with a certain girl... But when the group dynamic among the boys starts to shift, will Jorge be able to balance what his friends expect of him versus what he actually wants?

"The character development is wonderful. With each page turn, everyone becomes more complex, and the situations they experience are timely and real. The artwork tends toward colorful pastels, and the backgrounds lighten and darken to reflect characters' emotions in a lovely, subtle way." School Library Journal.

Cliff, Tony

Delilah Dirk and the Turkish Lieutenant. Tony Cliff. First Second, 2013. 176 p. : Delilah Dirk

Grades: 7 8 9 10 11 12 **741.5**
    1. 19th century 2. Women adventurers 3. Soldiers 4. Escapes 5. Turkey 6. Action and adventure comics 7. Webcomics 8. Comics and Graphic novels
    ISBN 9781596438132

Follows the adventures of Delilah Dirk and her companion, Erdemoglu Selim.

"Plenty of fight scenes will attract male readers, in addition to females looking for strong heroines. All in all, this is a carefree romp across the Ottoman Empire with an upbeat tone that is refreshing" Library Media Connection.

Colfer, Eoin

★ **Artemis** Fowl: the graphic novel. adapted by Eoin Colfer and Andrew Donkin; art by Giovanni Rigano; color by Paolo Lamanna. Hyperion Books for Children, 2007. 112 p. : Artemis Fowl (Graphic novels)

Grades: 4 5 6 7 8 9 **741.5**
    1. Gifted boys 2. Fairies 3. Ransom 4. Kidnapping 5. Criminals 6. Ireland 7. Comics and Graphic novels 8. Fantasy comics
    ISBN 9780786848812

A graphic version of the best-selling series that stars a twelve-year-old criminal mastermind named Artemis Fowl brings to life the underground fairy world, Foaly's extraordinary inventions, Fowl Manor, and Artemis's various evil exploits.

"Excellent use of color and shading gives the panels a tremendous sense of light with enchanting effect. Characters are expressively brought to life with fun, exaggerated style." School Library Journal.

Illegal. Eoin Colfer, Andrew Donkin; art by Giovanni Rigano; lettering by Chris Dickey. Sourcebooks Jabberwocky, 2018, c2017. 122 p.

Grades: 5 6 7 8 9 **741.5**
    1. Unaccompanied immigrant children 2. Child immigrants 3. Child refugees 4. Survival 5. Boy orphans 6. Africa 7. Europe 8. Comics and graphic novels 9. Books for reluctant readers
    ISBN 9781492662143

Resolved to join the siblings who left months earlier, 12-year-old Ebo ventures through the Sahara and the dangerous streets of Tripoli before embarking on a hazardous voyage from Ghana to a safe haven in Europe.

"The format allows sensitive and difficult topics such as murder, death, and horrific, traumatizing conditions to unfold for children, Ebo's reactions speaking volumes and dramatic perspectives giving a sense of scope. A creators' note provides factual context, and an appendix offers an Eritrean refugee's minimemoir in graphic form." Kirkus.

Collar, Orpheus

The **red** pyramid: the graphic novel. adapted from Rick Riordan's novel The Kane Chronicles, Book One: The Red Pyramid by Orpheus Collar; lettered by Jared Fletcher. Disney Hyperion Books, 2012. 192 p.: Kane chronicles (Graphic novels)

Grades: 4 5 6 7 8 9 **741.5**
    1. Multiracial teenagers 2. Gods and goddesses, Egyptian 3. Egyptologists 4. Quests 5. Voyages and travels 6. Egypt -- Rulers.

    7. Fantasy comics 8. Comics and Graphic novels
    ISBN 9781423150695

                    LC 2012007905

A graphic novel adaptation of the first book in the best-selling series finds separated siblings Carter and Sadie reunited by their father, a famed Egyptologist, who inadvertently unleashes the dark god Set, compelling a dangerous journey across the globe in search of their connection to a secret ancient order.

Corona, Jorge

Feathers. written & illustrated by Jorge Corona; colors by Jen Hickman; letters by Deron Bennett. Archaia, 2015. 160 p.

Grades: 5 6 7 8 **741.5**
    1. Boys with disfigurements 2. Boy orphans 3. Missing children 4. Eleven-year-old boys 5. Orphans 6. Fantasy comics 7. Comics and Graphic novels
    ISBN 9781608867530

Born covered in black feathers, abandoned as a baby in the slums of the Maze, Poe has lived his entire eleven-year-old life hidden away under the protection of his adoptive father, Gabriel. He spends his days secretly helping the Mice, bands of orphans who roam the slums, but there is a whisper of an altogether more sinister figure in the shadows, making street children disappear. When Bianca, an over-protected girl from the wealthy City beyond the Wall, escapes into the Maze in search of adventure, their worlds collide. As danger looms on all sides, a friendship grows between the city girl and the boy covered in feathers, a friendship that may just be enough to bring Bianca home, and lead Poe to his destiny.

"Poe is a true underdog hero, and Bianca's wish to be set free from her restricting life is something to which middle grades readers can relate. Stunning illustrations contrast the stark white orderly city with the dark and dangerous Maze." School Library Journal.

Craft, Jerry

★ **Class** act. Jerry Craft Quill Tree Books, an imprint of HarperCollins Publishers, 2020 256 p.

Grades: 4 5 6 7 8 **741.5**
    1. African American boys 2. Private schools 3. Interclass friendship 4. Racism 5. Friendship 6. Comics and graphic novels 7. African American fiction 8. Books for reluctant readers
    ISBN 9780062885517

Eighth grader Drew Ellis recognizes that he isn't afforded the same opportunities, no matter how hard he works, that his privileged classmates at the Riverdale Academy Day School take for granted, and to make matters worse, Drew begins to feel as if his good friend Liam might be one of those privileged kids and is finding it hard not to withdraw, even as their mutual friend Jordan tries to keep their group of friends together.

"Deftly weaving discussions of race, socioeconomics, colorism, and solidarity into an accessible narrative, Craft offers a charming cast journeying through the complicated landscapes of puberty, self-definition, and changing friendships, all while grappling with the tensions of attending an institution that structurally and culturally neglects students of color." Publishers Weekly

★ **New** kid. Jerry Craft; with color by Jim Callahan. Harper, 2019. 249 p.

Grades: 4 5 6 7 **741.5**
    1. New students 2. Belonging 3. African American boys 4. Racism 5. Boy artists 6. Comics and graphic novels 7. African American fiction 8. Books for reluctant readers
    ISBN 9780062691200

Coretta Scott King Award, Author Category, 2020.
Newbery Medal, 2020.

Perfect for fans of Raina Telgemeier and Gene Luen Yang, New Kid is a timely, honest graphic novel about starting over at a new school where diversity is low and the struggle to fit in is real, from award-winning author-illustrator Jerry Craft.

"This school story stands out as a robust, contemporary depiction of a preteen navigating sometimes hostile spaces yet staying true to himself thanks to friends, family, and art." Horn Book.

Dembicki, Matt

★ **Trickster**: Native American tales: a graphic collection. edited by Matt Dembicki. Chicago Review Press, 2021, c2010. 248 p.

Grades: 5 6 7 8   **741.5**
1. Indians of North America 2. Tricksters 3. Comics and Graphic novels
ISBN 9781682752739

LC 2009049668

Collects twenty-one short stories in graphic novel format of tricksters from a variety of Native American traditions.

"More than 40 storytellers and cartoonists have contributed to this original and provocative compendium of traditional folklore presented in authentic, colorful, and engaging sequential art. The stories are drawn from a variety of Native peoples across North America, and so the trickster character appears variously as Rabbit, a raccoon, Coyote, and in other guises; landscapes, clothing and rhythms of speech and action also vary in keeping with distinct traditions. Realistic, impressionistic, painterly, and cartoon styles of art are employed to echo and announce the tone of each tale and telling style, making this a rich visual treasure as well as cultural trove." School Library Journal.

Furudate, Haruichi, 1983-

Haikyu!! . story & art by Haruichi Furudate. Viz/Shonen Jump, 2016. 192 p.: Haikyu!!

Grades: 7 8 9 10 11 12   **741.5**
1. Volleyball 2. High school students 3. Competition 4. Teamwork (Sports) 5. Teenage boys 6. Japan 7. Manga 8. Comics and Graphic novels 9. Translations Japanese to English
ISBN 9781421587660

Playing for his idol's high school volleyball team, Shoyo loses his first and last match against Tobio, the King of the Court, and promises to get the best of this rival next season, but the new season brings him a surprising new teammate.

"With dramatic angles, typical manga-style artwork depicts scenes of thrilling action. This fast-paced, exciting manga is a story of sportsmanship, perseverance, and, above all, belief in oneself." School Library Journal.

Gillis, Peter B.

The **last** unicorn. Peter S. Beagle; adapted by Peter Gillis; illustrated by Renae de Liz and Ray Dillon. IDW, 2011. 167 p.

Grades: 6 7 8 9 10   **741.5**
1. Unicorns 2. Magicians 3. Quests 4. Extinction (Biology) 5. Magic 6. Fantasy comics 7. Comics and Graphic novels
ISBN 9781600108518

LC bl2011003536

A unicorn, alone in an enchanted wood, discovers she might be the last of her kind and sets out on a journey to find others like her.

"A beloved story is now a graphic novel in this excellent adaptation. . . . Much of the original novel's lyrical language has been included, and readers will be eager to find out if the unicorn will give up her quest for love, or if any of Schmendrick's spells will ever turn out right. . . . The illustrations are graceful and detailed, and inked in warm, glowing colors. This is a worthy successor to the classic novel and film." School Library Journal.

Grine, Chris

Animorphs.. based on the novel by K.A. Applegate & Michael Grant; adapted by Chris Grine. Graphix, 2020. 240 p.: Animorphs (Graphic novels)

Grades: 3 4 5 6 7   **741.5**
1. Imaginary wars and battles 2. Human/alien encounters 3. Aliens (Non-humanoid) 4. Metamorphosis 5. Animorphs (Fictitious characters) 6. Earth -- Invasions 7. Science fiction comics 8. Comics and graphic novels
ISBN 9781338226485

After Jake and his friends witness a strange light in the sky coming toward them and learn that the earth is under attack, a dying alien gives them the power to morph into any animal they touch, enabling them to fight against the invaders.

"This text-heavy graphic novel is full of action-packed panels and detailed, realistic illustrations." Kirkus

Gulledge, Laura Lee

Page by Paige. Laura Lee Gulledge. Amulet Books, 2011. 192 p.

Grades: 7 8 9 10 11 12   **741.5**
1. Teenage girl artists 2. Adjustment (Psychology) 3. Self-discovery in teenage girls 4. Self-discovery 5. Moving to a new state 6. New York City 7. Brooklyn, New York City 8. Realistic fiction 9. Comics and Graphic novels 10. Coming-of-age stories
ISBN 9780810997219

"Gulledge's b&w illustrations are simple but well-suited to their subject matter; the work as a whole is a good-natured, optimistic portrait of a young woman evolving toward adulthood." Publishers Weekly.

Hale, Nathan, 1976-

One trick pony: a graphic novel. Nathan Hale. Amulet Books, 2017 128 p.

Grades: 3 4 5 6   **741.5**
1. Aliens 2. Robots 3. Technology 4. Horses 5. Brothers and sisters 6. Science fiction comics 7. Comics and Graphic novels
ISBN 9781419721281

In a future where alien beings consume technology as a few humans try to preserve it, Strata, her brother, and a friend are separated from their caravan and, with a wonderful robotic horse, must fight their way back.

"A great option for fantasy and adventure fans." School Library Journal.

Hale, Shannon

★ **Rapunzel's** revenge. Shannon Hale and Dean Hale; illustrated by Nathan Hale. Bloomsbury, 2008. 144 p.

Grades: 5 6 7 8   **741.5**
1. Girl heroes 2. Self-reliance in girls 3. Imprisonment 4. Revenge in girls 5. Revenge 6. The West (United States) 7. Comics and Graphic novels 8. Fairy tale and folklore-inspired fiction
ISBN 9781599902883

LC 2007037670

Rapunzel is raised in a grand villa surrounded by towering walls. Rapunzel dreams of a different mother than Gothel, the woman she calls Mother. She climbs over the wall and finds out the truth. Her real mother, Kate, is a slave in Gothel's gold mine. In this Old West retelling, Rapunzel uses her hair as a lasso and to take on outlaws—including Gothel.

"The dialogue is witty, the story is an enticing departure from the original, and the illustrations are magically fun and expressive." School Library Journal.

Harrell, Rob

Monster on the hill.. Rob Harrell. Top Shelf, 2013. 192 p.
Grades: 4 5 6 7 8   **741.5**
 1. 1860s 2. Monsters 3. Boys and monsters 4. Quests 5. Training 6. Scientists 7. England -- Social life and customs -- 19th century 8. Fantasy comics 9. Historical comics 10. Comics and Graphic novels 11. Books for reluctant readers
ISBN 9781603090759
In a fantastical England where each small town has a monster, the people of Stoker-on-Avon have to help their own, a depressed creature named Rayburn, become the monster he was born to be.

Hart, Christopher, 1957-

The **master** guide to drawing anime: how to draw original characters from simple templates: How to Draw Original Characters from Simple Templates. Christopher Hart. Sixth&Spring Books, [2015] 144 p.: Master Guide to
Grades: 7 8 9 10 11 12   **741.5**
 1. Cartooning -- Technique 2. Drawing -- Technique
ISBN 9781936096862
                                          LC 2014030200
Provides step-by-step instructions for creating and drawing original anime characters.

Hatke, Ben

Mighty Jack.. Ben Hatke; color by Alex Campbell and Hilary Sycamore. First Second, 2016. 203 p.: Mighty Jack
Grades: 4 5 6 7   **741.5**
 1. Gardens 2. Preteens 3. Mythical creatures 4. Girls with autism 5. Children of single parents 6. Action and adventure comics 7. Fantasy comics 8. Comics and Graphic novels
ISBN 9781626722651
                                          LC bl2016024464
Prompted by his sister, Jack trades his mom's car for a box of mysterious seeds, but soon their normal garden turns into a wild jungle filled with magical creatures and, one night, changes into a dragon.

Mighty Jack.. Ben Hatke. First Second, 2017 208 p.: Mighty Jack
Grades: 4 5 6 7   **741.5**
 1. Brothers and sisters 2. Boy heroes 3. Magic 4. Giants 5. Goblins 6. Action and adventure comics 7. Fantasy comics 8. Comics and Graphic novels
ISBN 9781626722675
Jack and Lilly follow Maddy's captor to a strange floating crossroads where they encounter rats, brutal giants, and a fearsome Goblin King.

Heuvel, Eric, 1960-

A **family** secret. Eric Heuvel. Farrar, Straus, Giroux, 2009. 62 p.
Grades: 7 8 9 10 11 12   **741.5**
 1. Holocaust (1933-1945) 2. Grandmother and grandson 3. World War II -- Children 4. Families -- History 20th century. 5. Nazis 6. Amsterdam, Netherlands -- History -- German occupation, 1940-1945. 7. Historical comics 8. Comics and Graphic novels
ISBN 9780374322717
While searching his Dutch grandmother's attic for yard sale items, Jeroen finds a scrapbook which leads Gran to tell of her experiences as a girl living in Amsterdam during the Holocaust, when her father was a Nazi sympathizer and Esther, her Jewish best friend, disappeared.

"This is a moving graphic novel. . . . The art is in ink and watercolor, with very clear, highly detailed panels. . . . [A] gripping story." Booklist.

Hicks, Faith Erin

The **divided** earth. Faith Erin Hicks; color by Jordie Bellaire. First Second, 2018. 265 p.: Nameless City
Grades: 5 6 7 8 9 10   **741.5**
 1. Cities and towns 2. Imaginary wars and battles 3. Friendship 4. Social conflict 5. Adventurers 6. Fantasy comics 7. Comics and Graphic novels 8. Asian-influenced fantasy
ISBN 9781626721616
                                          LC 2017957143
Prince Erzi has taken control of the city. With the formula for napatha, a weapon of mass destruction, he has become an even bigger threat. Rat and Kai must infiltrate Erzi's palace and steal back the ancient and deadly formula for napatha, before he can use it to destroy everything Rat and Kai hold dear!

"Bold, dynamic drawings and rich, nuanced coloring heighten the drama; occasionally, the action breaks through the panel into the white space, as if the explosive force of Napatha and the energy and vitality of the heroic duo cannot be contained." Voice of Youth Advocates.

Friends with boys. Faith Erin Hicks. First Second, 2012. 224 p.
Grades: 6 7 8 9 10   **741.5**
 1. High school freshmen 2. Ghosts 3. Mother-deserted families 4. Brothers and sisters 5. Home schooled teenage girls 6. Canada 7. Webcomics 8. Comics and Graphic novels
ISBN 9781596435568
After an idyllic childhood of homeschooling with her mother and three older brothers, Maggie enrolls in public high school, where interacting with her peers is complicated by the melancholy ghost that has followed her throughout her entire life.

The **Nameless** City. Faith Erin Hicks. First Second, 2016. 240 p.: Nameless City
Grades: 5 6 7 8 9 10   **741.5**
 1. Survival 2. Friendship 3. Military occupation 4. Child heroes 5. Conspiracies 6. Fantasy comics 7. Comics and Graphic novels 8. Asian-influenced fantasy
ISBN 9781626721579
                                          LC 2015020651
Unable to share the apathetic attitude of the residents whose city has been overtaken in so many successive wars that they do not bother to name it, outsider Kaidu, a member of the latest occupying nation, clashes with native Kai before forging an unexpected friendship over their support for mutual causes.

"With comprehensive world building, well-rounded characters, and entertaining action, this expertly executed story will find a home with a wide variety of readers, all of whom will be eagerly awaiting the next installment." Booklist.

One Year at Ellsmere. Faith Erin Hicks. First Second, 2020. 208 p.
Grades: 5 6 7 8   **741.5**
 1. Children of single parents 2. Teenage girls 3. Boarding schools 4. Friendship 5. Monsters 6. Comics and graphic novels
ISBN 9781250219091
Winning a scholarship to a prestigious boarding school, Juniper endures bullying from a popular queen bee before investigating rumors

about a mythical beast in the nearby forest, in an edition that incorporates revamped and full-color art.

"Characters are expressive and cleanly drawn, complementing the straightforward text and accessible storytelling." Kirkus

The **Stone** Heart. Faith Erin Hicks; color by Jordie Bellaire. First Second, 2017. 240 p.: Nameless City

Grades: 5 6 7 8 9 10   **741.5**

1. Imaginary places 2. Power (Social sciences) 3. Imaginary wars and battles 4. Monks 5. Rulers 6. Fantasy comics 7. Comics and Graphic novels 8. Asian-influenced fantasy

ISBN 9781626721586

When diplomatic efforts fail to resolve deep conflicts within the Dao nation, Kaidu and Rat race against time to prevent a war that is complicated by Kaidu's discovery of a formula for the lost weapon of the City's mysterious founders.

"Flourishing from the strong worldbuilding and characterization of the first installment, this middle volume . . . provides a vital and enthralling closer look at those readers have already met as well as unfurling more of the Chinese-inspired city's past, as colorist Bellaire brings all to stunning emotional life." Kirkus.

Hinds, Gareth, 1971-

Beowulf. adapted and illustrated by Gareth Hinds. Candlewick Press, 2007. 1 v. (unpaged)

Grades: 8 9 10 11 12 Adult   **741.5**

1. Warriors 2. Heroes and heroines, Norse 3. Monsters 4. Northmen and Northwomen 5. Battles 6. Epic poetry 7. Comics and Graphic novels

ISBN 0763630225

LC 2006049023

A retelling in graphic format of the Anglo-Saxon epic about the heroic efforts of Beowulf, son of Edgetheow, to save the people of Heorot Hall from the terrible monster, Grendel.

"For fantasy fans both young and old, this makes an ideal introduction to a story without which the entire fantasy genre would look very different; many scenes may be too intense for very young readers." Publishers Weekly.

The **Iliad**. Gareth Hinds. Candlewick Press, 2019. 272 p.

Grades: 7 8 9 10 11 12   **741.5**

1. Ancient Aegean civilizations (3000-1000 BCE) 2. Heroes and heroines, Greek 3. Gods and goddesses, Greek 4. War 5. Battles 6. Trojan War 7. Comics and Graphic novels 8. Epic poetry

ISBN 9780763681135

"The excellent visual guides, maps, and notes aid in this task and further contextualize the epic's time, place, and significance. The most striking scenes are the battles, presented in intimate detail and in awe-inspiring, sweeping overviews. Hinds's relatively plain language retains just enough meter to hint at the cadences of the work, and, together with the dynamic art, creates an accessible entrée to an enduring classic." Publishers Weekly.

King Lear: a play. by William Shakespeare; adapted and illustrated by Gareth Hinds. Candlewick Press, 2009. 123 p.

Grades: 7 8 9 10 11 12   **741.5**

1. Rulers 2. Inheritance and succession 3. Fathers and daughters 4. Families 5. English tragedy Early modern and Elizabethan, 1500-1600 6. Great Britain -- Rulers 7. Comics and Graphic novels 8. Drama

ISBN 9780763643447

LC bl2009026732

Retells in graphic novel format Shakespeare's tragedy of a royal father and his daughters.

"Employing a range of artistic styles that convey dramatic mood, the artist begins the play almost as a fairy tale, featuring bright, softly washed drawings. Once Cordelia is cast out and things sour, the images become darker and more compact. As the king descends into madness, the art becomes downright menacing, with Lear appearing as a jagged, ghostly figure drawn with white pencil on a dark background." Kirkus.

The **merchant** of Venice. a graphic novel by Gareth Hinds; based on the play by William Shakespeare. Candlewick Press, 2008. 80 p.: Graphic Shakespeare

Grades: 8 9 10 11 12 Adult   **741.5**

1. Money lenders 2. Greed 3. Revenge 4. Shylock (Fictitious character) 5. Young men 6. Venice, Italy 7. Comics and Graphic novels 8. Introductory classics

ISBN 9780763630249

To win the love of fair Portia, young Bassanio entangles his dearest friend, Antonio, in a dangerous bargain with the moneylender Shylock, but only Bassanio's heartfelt efforts—and a clever intervention by Portia—will save Antonio, in a contemporary adaptation of a classic drama.

"Fans of the play will find this an intriguing adaptation." Publishers Weekly.

The **most** excellent and lamentable tragedy of Romeo & Juliet: a play. by William Shakespeare; adapted and illustrated by Gareth Hinds. Candlewick Press, 2013. 128 p.

Grades: 7 8 9 10   **741.5**

1. Family feuds 2. Tragedy 3. Lovers 4. Romeo (Fictitious character) 5. Juliet (Fictitious character) 6. Verona, Italy 7. Comics and Graphic novels

ISBN 9780763659486

Transports readers to the sun-washed streets and market squares of Shakespeare's Verona, vividly bringing the classic play to life through stylish artwork that offers modern touches, including a diverse cast that underscores the story's universality.

"Cleaving to Shakespeare's words and dramatic arc, Hinds (The Merchant of Venice) creates another splendid graphic novel, tracing each scene in taut, coherent dialogue. The characters, in period dress modified by a few more contemporary touches, are poignantly specific yet universal. Hinds delivers the play's essence and beauty, its glorious language, furious conflict, yearning love, and wrenching tragedy." Horn Book.

The **Odyssey**: a graphic novel. Gareth Hinds. Candlewick Press, 2010. 256 p.

Grades: 7 8 9 10 11 12 Adult   **741.5**

1. Ancient Aegean civilizations (3000-1000 BCE) 2. Heroes and heroines, Greek 3. Gods and goddesses, Greek 4. Voyages and travels 5. Odysseus (Greek mythology) 6. Cyclopes (Greek mythology) 7. Comics and Graphic novels

ISBN 9780763642662

A vivid graphic novel reinterpretation of Homer's epic poem finds the King of Ithaca cursed by the sea god Poseidon to years of shipwreck and battles against fantastical creatures.

"This is the most lavish retelling of Homer yet. . . . Hinds lets the epic story take its time, with a slow build and pages that aren't afraid to alternate packed dialogue with titanic action. The sumptuous art, produced with grain, texture, and hue, evokes a time long past while detailing every line and drop of sweat on Odysseus' face and conveying the sheer grandeur of seeing a god rise out of the ocean." Booklist.

Holm, Jennifer L.
★ **Sunny** side up. Jennifer L. Holm & Matthew Holm. Graphix, 2015 224 p.: Sunny side up
Grades: 3 4 5 6   **741.5**
    1. 1970s 2. Retirement communities 3. Family problems 4. Summer 5. Grandfathers 6. Ten-year-old girls 7. Florida 8. Comics and Graphic novels 9. Historical comics
    ISBN 9780545741651
"Woven into the Florida frolic though, through dated flashback images, is the real reason for Sunny's last-minute visit: her older brother is struggling with addiction, and Sunny thinks she got him in trouble. Though Sunny will appeal to all kinds of readers, an author's note shares Holm's hope to let kids in similar situations know that its OK to feel sad and to talk about it. Clear dialogue bubbles, plenty of wordless spreads, and Matthew's cartoons and beach-umbrella color palette keep Sunny's story an upbeat one that readers will easily stick with." Booklist.

Swing it, Sunny. Jennifer L. Holm, Matthew Holm. Scholastic 2017 224 p.: Sunny side up
Grades: 3 4 5 6   **741.5**
    1. 1970s 2. Middle school students 3. Grandfathers 4. Middle schools 5. Brothers and sisters 6. Boarding schools 7. Historical comics 8. Comics and Graphic novels
    ISBN 9780545741705
In the mid-1970s Sunny Lewin is back, star of her personal show, facing the prospect of Middle School, and dealing with the problems of her somewhat dysfunctional family—in particular her older brother, Dale, who has been sent off to a military academy because of his delinquent behavior.

Horikoshi, Kohei, 1986-
My hero academia. story & art Kohei Horikoshi; translation & English adaptation Caleb Cook. Viz Media, 2015. 187 p.: My hero academia.
Grades: 7 8 9 10 11 12   **741.5**
    1. Superheroes 2. Supervillains 3. Schools 4. Ambition in teenagers 5. Teenage boys 6. Japan 7. Manga 8. Superhero comics 9. Science fiction comics
    ISBN 9781421582696
Middle school student Izuku Midoriya wants to be a hero more than anything, but he hasn't got an ounce of power in him. With no chance of ever getting into the prestigious U.A. High School for budding heroes, his life is looking more and more like a dead end. Then an encounter with All Might, the greatest hero of them all, gives him a chance to change his destiny.
"This is a high-energy series debut with a typical cast of manga characters: the determined protagonist, the loose cannon frenemy, the narrow-minded perfectionist, and the sweet, gentle female friend. Horikoshi's artwork is solid, the characters are distinct and expressive, and readers really get a sense of the sweeping, high-octane atmosphere of Izuku's world. A slight cliff-hanger ending builds anticipation for the second volume." School Library Journal.

Horowitz, Anthony, 1955-
Stormbreaker: the graphic novel. Anthony Horowitz; adapted by Antony Johnston; illustrated by Kanako Damerum & Yuzuru Takasaki. Philomel, 2006. 144 p.: Alex Rider (Graphic novels)
Grades: 5 6 7 8   **741.5**
    1. Horowitz, Anthony, 1955- Stormbreaker 2. M I 6 3. Teenage spies 4. Teenage boy orphans 5. Computers 6. Terrorism 7. Intelligence service 8. England 9. Spy comics 10. Comics and

Graphic novels
    ISBN 0399246339
"If it's possible, this is even more rapidly paced than the novel. Alex remains an appealing hero here, and the idea of a heroic teen up against insidious adults continues to be an extremely powerful draw for readers." Booklist.

Hosler, Jay
The **way** of the hive: a honey bee's story. Jay Hosler Harper Alley, 2021 160 p.
Grades: 4 5 6 7   **741.5**
    1. Bees 2. Honeybee 3. Voyages and travels 4. Bees -- Behavior 5. Insects -- Life cycles 6. Comics and graphic novels
    ISBN 9780063007369
Nyuki is a brand-new honeybee; and she has a lot of questions. Like When does a bee go through metamorphosis? Why does a queen bee sometimes leave her hive? And where does all this honey come from, anyway? Follow Nyuki on a lifelong journey as she annoys her sisters, avoids predators, and learns to trust her inner voice as she masters the way of the hive.
"Hives may have thousands of workers, but the art and the plot create three unique personalities that will have readers invested in learning more about this all-too-important insect—a feat made even more impressive by realistic illustrations that never anthropomorphize the characters and factual details that are far from honey-coated." Kirkus

Hotta, Yumi
Hikaru no Go. story by Yumi Hotta; art by Takeshi Obata. Viz, 2004. 192 p.: Hikaru no Go
Grades: 5 6 7 8 9 10 11 12   **741.5**
    1. Sixth-grade boys 2. Seventh-grade boys 3. Middle school students 4. Spirits 5. Spirit possession 6. Japan 7. Manga 8. Comics and Graphic novels 9. Translations Japanese to English
    ISBN 159116222X
Sixth-grade Hikaru Shindo's discovery of a bloodstained game board leads to an encounter with the ghost of Go master Fujiwara-no-Sai and the formation of an unbeatable Go team.

Igarashi, Daisuke
Children of the sea. Daisuke Igarashi. Viz Signature, 2009. 320 p.: Children of the sea manga
Grades: 7 8 9 10 11 12   **741.5**
    1. Aquariums 2. Children and fish 3. Fishes 4. Disappearances (Parapsychology) 5. Action and adventure comics 6. Manga 7. Comics and Graphic novels
    ISBN 9781421529141
When Ruka was younger, she saw a ghost in the water at the aquarium where her dad works. Now she feels drawn toward the aquarium and the two mysterious boys she meets there, Umi and Sora. They were raised by dugongs and hear the same strange calls from the sea as she does. Ruka's dad and the other adults who work at the aquarium are only distantly aware of what the children are experiencing as they get caught up in the mystery of the worldwide disappearance of the oceans' fish.
"Igarashi's storytelling is quiet, thoughtful, and thought provoking, but it is his drawings that make this manga so amazing. Extremely detailed settings turn panels into mini-masterpieces." Booklist.

Jacques, Brian
Redwall: the graphic novel. by Brian Jacques; illustrated by Bret Blevins; adapted by Stuart Moore; lettering by Richard Starkings. Philomel Books, c2007. 143 p.: Redwall graphic novels

Grades: 4 5 6 7 8 9   **741.5**
1. Animals 2. Heroes and heroines 3. Good and evil 4. Mice 5. Rats 6. Animal fantasy 7. Fantasy comics 8. Comics and Graphic novels
ISBN 9780399244810

LC bl2007021765

When the peaceful life of Redwall Abbey is shattered by the arrival of the evil rat Cluny and his villainous hordes, Matthias, a young mouse, determines to find the legendary sword which will help Redwall's inhabitants destroy the enemy.

"The story is a page-turner, and the detailed black-and-white drawings capture both the passion and the pathos." School Library Journal.

Jamieson, Victoria
★ **All's** faire in middle school. Victoria Jamieson. Dial Books for Young Readers, [2017] 248 p.
Grades: 4 5 6 7 8   **741.5**
1. Middle schools 2. Eleven-year-old girls 3. Renaissance fairs 4. Schools 5. Belonging 6. Florida 7. Humorous comics 8. Comics and Graphic novels
ISBN 9780525429982

LC 2016044190

Homeschooled by Renaissance Fair enthusiasts, eleven-year-old Imogene has a hard time fitting in when her wish to enroll in public school is granted.

"Jamieson masterfully taps into the voice and concerns of middle-schoolers, and the offbeat setting of the Renaissance faire adds some lively texture." Booklist.

★ **Roller** girl. Victoria Jamieson. Dial Books for Young Readers, 2015. 239 p.
Grades: 4 5 6 7 8   **741.5**
1. Twelve-year-old girls 2. Separated friends, relatives, etc 3. Roller derby 4. Friendship 5. Persistence in girls 6. Coming-of-age stories 7. Comics and Graphic novels 8. Sports comics 9. Books for reluctant readers
ISBN 9780525429678

A graphic novel adventure about a girl who discovers roller derby right as she and her best friend are growing apart. Provided by publisher.

Johnson, Cathy G.
The **Breakaways**. Cathy G. Johnson. First Second, 2019. 224 p.
Grades: 4 5 6 7 8   **741.5**
1. Middle school students 2. Self-discovery 3. Friendship 4. Soccer 5. Popularity 6. Realistic fiction 7. Comics and Graphic novels 8. Sports comics
ISBN 9781250196941

"Vignettes show the players' varied home lives, interests, and friendship dramas. Sketchy full-color artwork features characters with exaggerated expressions." School Library Journal.

Keenan, Sheila
Dogs of war. Sheila Keenan; illustrated by Nathan Fox. Graphix, 2013. 208 p.
Grades: 4 5 6 7   **741.5**
1. Dogs -- War use 2. War 3. Human/animal relationships 4. Soldiers 5. World War I 6. War comics 7. Historical comics 8. Comics and Graphic novels 9. Books for reluctant readers
ISBN 9780545128872

LC 2011006735

Three fictional stories, told in graphic novel format, about soldiers in World War I, World War II, and the Vietnam War who were aided by combat dogs. Based on true stories.

Keplinger, Kody
Poison Ivy: thorns. written by Kody Keplinger; illustrated by Sara Kipin; colors by Jeremy Lawson; letters by Steve Wands. DC Comics, 2021. 208 p.
Grades: 7 8 9 10 11 12   **741.5**
1. Teenage girls 2. Family secrets 3. Eco-terrorism 4. Teenage girl/girl relations 5. Poison Ivy (Fictitious character) 6. Superhero comics 7. Comics and Graphic novels
ISBN 9781401298425

LC 2021001514

Even though Pamela Isley spends most of her time caring for a few small plants and does not trust other people, when cute goth girl Alice Oh comes into her life she starts to open up, but the dark secrets from home could destroy the one person who ever cared about Pamela, or as her mom called her, Ivy.

"This story explores the limits of trust and abuse, at home and in public, and considers what could bring one to a breaking point." Kirkus

Kibuishi, Kazu, 1978-
★ **Amulet.** Kazu Kibuishi Graphix, 2008. 185 p.: Amulet (Kazu Kibuishi)
Grades: 3 4 5 6 7 8   **741.5**
1. Brothers and sisters 2. Fathers -- Death 3. Amulets 4. Supernatural 5. Charms 6. Gateway fantasy 7. Comics and Graphic novels 8. Fantasy comics
ISBN 9780439846813

After the tragic death of their father, Emily and Navin move with their mother to the home of her deceased great-grandfather, but the strange house proves to be dangerous. Before long, a sinister creature lures the kids' mom through a door in the basement. Em and Navin, desperate not to lose her, follow her into an underground world inhabited by demons, robots, and talking animals....

"Filled with excitement, monsters, robots, and mysteries, this fantasy adventure will appeal to many readers." School Library Journal.

Explorer. edited by Kazu Kibuishi. Amulet Books, 2012. 126 p. : Explorer
Grades: 4 5 6 7 8   **741.5**
1. Boxes 2. Short stories 3. Comics and Graphic novels 4. Anthologies
ISBN 9781419700101

LC 2011025343

An anthology of short graphic works by such artists as Kazu Kibuishi, Dave Roman, and Raina Telgemeier, all on the theme of a mysterious box and the marvels, or mayhem, inside.

Explorer: seven graphic stories. edited by Kazu Kibuishi. Amulet, 2013. 126 p. : Explorer
Grades: 4 5 6 7 8   **741.5**
1. Islands 2. Short stories 3. Comics and Graphic novels 4. Anthologies
ISBN 9781419708817

A collection of seven new stories by an award-winning roster of comics artists centers on a theme of hidden places.

Explorer.. edited by Kazu Kibuishi. Amulet, 2014. 128 p.: Explorer

Grades: 4 5 6 7 8   **741.5**
1. Comics and Graphic novels 2. Anthologies
ISBN 9781419708824

"Readers are once again presented with an array of stories created by a cast of comics authors and illustrators smartly assembled by Kibuishi...The range in this slim volume is expansive. From funny to deep and fantastical to refined, all of the stories have a compelling narrative arc. The colors are just as varied, and are universally dynamic and nuanced. Consider this (and previous series installments) as a necessary addition to any graphic novel collection." School Library Journal.

Flight explorer. [editor/art director, Kazu Kibuishi]. Villard Books, 2008. 111 p.
Grades: 4 5 6 7   **741.5**
1. Space 2. Science fiction comics 3. Action and adventure comics 4. Comics and Graphic novels
ISBN 9780345503138

LC 2008273440

"Every story has a layout that promotes an acute sense of pacing and showcases the crisp, defined, full-color art." School Library Journal.

Kishimoto, Masashi, 1974-
Naruto. story and art by Masashi Kishimoto. Viz/Shonen Jump, 2003. 186 p. : Naruto (Manga)
Grades: 7 8 9 10 11 12   **741.5**
1. Twelve-year-old boys 2. Orphans 3. Ninja 4. Martial artists 5. Martial arts 6. Manga 7. Comics and Graphic novels 8. Translations Japanese to English
ISBN 1569319006

"Teen orphan Naruto wants to become the greatest ninja of all, despite the fact that most people in his village have despised him from birth because a terrible demon has been imprisoned in his body." Voice of Youth Advocates.

Kris, 1972-
A **bag** of marbles. based on the memoir by Joseph Joffo; adapted by Kris; illustrated by Vincent Bailly; translated by Edward Gauvin. Graphic Universe, 2013. 126 p.
Grades: 6 7 8 9 10   **741.5**
1. Joffo, Joseph, 1931-2018. 2. Joffo, Maurice. 3. Children and war 4. Brothers 5. Holocaust (1933-1945) -- Children 6. Escapes 7. Jewish boys 8. France -- History -- German occupation, 1940-1945 9. War comics 10. Historical comics 11. Biographical comics
ISBN 9781467707008

LC 2013002284

In 1941, ten-year-old Joseph Joffo and his older brother, Maurice, must hide their Jewish heritage and undertake a long and dangerous journey from Nazi-occupied Paris to reach their other brothers in the free zone.

"This graphic-novel adaptation of Joffo's 1973 memoir of the same name succeeds in melding sensitive and accurate imagery with the original narrative flow of a young secular Jewish boy's experiences in occupied France." Booklist.

Larson, Hope
All summer long. Hope Larson. Farrar Straus & Giroux 2018 176 p.: Eagle Rock trilogy
Grades: 5 6 7 8   **741.5**
1. Eighth-grade girls 2. Self-discovery 3. Friendship 4. Summer 5. Growing up 6. California 7. Realistic fiction 8. Comics and

Graphic novels 9. Coming-of-age stories
ISBN 9780374304850

A coming-of-age middle-grade graphic novel about summer and friendships.

"Larson's panels are superb at revealing emotional conflict, subtext, and humor within the deceptively simple third-person limited plot, allowing characters to grow and develop emotionally over only a few spreads." Kirkus.

All together now. Hope Larson, Farrar Straus & Giroux, 2020 192 p.: Eagle Rock trilogy
Grades: 5 6 7 8   **741.5**
1. Preteens -- Interpersonal relations 2. Crushes in boys 3. Self-acceptance in girls 4. Friendship 5. Growing up 6. California 7. Realistic fiction 8. Comics and Graphic novels 9. Coming-of-age stories
ISBN 9780374311629

A standalone follow-up to the award-winning All Summer Long finds middle school student Bina struggling with the impact a romance with one of her fellow band members is having on the group's working relationship, a situation that is further complicated by an unrequited crush.

"Heartfelt and authentic, this book tenderly captures the ebb and flow of love and friendship. Larson's artwork uses a limited palette of pinks and reds, skillfully conveying the characters' emotions as they try to untangle their new relationships." School Library Journal

Compass south. Hope Larson; illustrated by Rebecca Mock. Margaret Ferguson Books/Farrar Straus Giroux, 2016. 224 p.: Four points
Grades: 4 5 6 7   **741.5**
1. 1860s 2. Twins 3. Pirates 4. Gangs 5. Voyages and travels 6. Twelve-year-olds 7. New Orleans, Louisiana 8. New York City 9. Action and adventure comics 10. Historical comics 11. Comics and Graphic novels
ISBN 9780374300432

LC 2015039907

After escaping the Black Hook Gang in 1860 New York City, twelve-year-old twins Alexander and Cleopatra flee to New Orleans, become separated, and try to find each other in San Francisco, while being followed by pirates who think they hold the key to treasure.

"A variety of panel sizes keeps the pace brisk while allowing for the occasional pause to set the scene or linger in an emotional moment." Horn Book.

A **wrinkle** in time: the graphic novel. [Madeleine L'Engle]; adapted and illustrated by Hope Larson. Farrar Straus Giroux, 2012. 392 p.
Grades: 4 5 6 7   **741.5**
1. Space and time 2. Human/alien encounters 3. Teenage heroes and heroines 4. Genius 5. Good and evil 6. Action and adventure comics 7. Science fiction comics 8. Comics and Graphic novels
ISBN 9780374386153

A graphic novel adaptation of the classic tale in which Meg Murry and her friends become involved with unearthly strangers and a search for Meg's father, who has disappeared while engaged in secret work for the government. Provided by publisher.

Layne, Aliza
★ **Beetle** & the Hollowbones. Aliza Layne; coloring by Natalie Riess and Kristen Acampora. Atheneum Books for Young Readers, 2020. 256 p.

Grades: 3 4 5 6 7   **741.5**
1. Witches 2. Goblins 3. Ghosts 4. Haunted places 5. Shopping malls 6. Comics and graphic novels 7. Fantasy comics
ISBN 9781534441538

         LC 2020014917

Twelve-year-old goblin and witch-in-training Beetle enlists her former best friend, Kat Hollowbones, to help stop Kat's sorceress aunt from demolishing the mall where Beetle's friend Blob Ghost is trapped.

"A high-spirited debut about learning to trust one's heart and instincts." Booklist

Lee, Tony, 1970-
Outlaw: the legend of Robin Hood. written by Tony Lee; illustrated by Sam Hart; colored by Artur Fujita. Candlewick Press, 2009. 160 p.
Grades: 7 8 9 10 11 12   **741.5**
1. Outlaws 2. Robin Hood (Legendary character) 3. Sheriff of Nottingham 4. Rebels 5. Crusades 6. Sherwood Forest, England 7. Comics and Graphic novels
ISBN 9780763643997

In graphic novel format, presents the adventures of the outlaw hero Robin Hood as he and his band of Merry Men defended the poor against the cruel tyranny of the Sheriff of Nottingham in Crusades-era England.

"Lee's excellent rendition of the famed selfless hero goes hand-in-hand with Hart's expressive illustrations, featuring lots of close-ups and dramatic lighting and a beautiful jewel-toned palette. Teens will get caught up in this exciting page-turner." School Library Journal.

Leyh, Kat
Snapdragon. Kat Leyh. First Second, 2020 223 p.
Grades: 4 5 6 7 8   **741.5**
1. Middle school students 2. Witches 3. Intergenerational friendship 4. Preteen girls 5. Magic 6. Fantasy comics 7. Comics and Graphic novels 8. Books for reluctant readers
ISBN 9781250171122

         LC 2018953665

Snap's town had a witch. At least, that's how the rumor goes. But in reality, Jacks is just a crocs-wearing, internet-savvy old lady who sells roadkill skeletons online—after doing a little ritual to put their spirits to rest. It's creepy, sure, but Snap thinks it's kind of cool, too. They make a deal: Jacks will teach Snap how to take care of the baby opossums that Snap rescued, and Snap will help Jacks with her work. But as Snap starts to get to know Jacks, she realizes that Jacks may in fact have real magic—and a connection with Snap's family's past. Provided by publisher.

"Full of magic and humor, this intersectional, layered tale offers joyful and affirming depictions of social outsiders and comfortably complicated families." Publishers Weekly.

Lloyd, Megan Wagner
★ **Allergic**. Megan Wagner Lloyd; illustrated by Michelle Mee Nutter. Graphix, 2021. 240 p.
Grades: 3 4 5 6   **741.5**
1. Ten-year-old girls 2. Allergy 3. Pets 4. Families 5. Girls and pets 6. Comics and Graphic novels 7. Realistic fiction 8. Coming-of-age stories
ISBN 9781338568912

Hoping to adopt a pet to find a sense of belonging in her busy family, Maggie is disappointed to discover she is severely allergic to anything with fur and tries to find a pet to love anyway.

"In this warm and well-paced story, Lloyd (Paper Mice) shows with nuance how empathy and connection can help a person navigate circumstances outside their control, making this an encouraging tale for young readers engaging with the world of pets, family, and friendships." Publishers Weekly

Lowry, Lois
Giver quartet. Lois Lowry; adapted and illustrated by P. Craig Russell Houghton Mifflin Harcourt 2019 192 p.: Giver quartet graphic novels
Grades: 6 7 8 9   **741.5**
1. Boys 2. Dystopias 3. Memories 4. Color 5. Conformity 6. Dystopian comics 7. Comics and Graphic novels 8. Books for reluctant readers
ISBN 9780544157880

Now in graphic novel format, Lois Lowry's Newbery Medal-winning classic story of a young boy discovering the dark secrets behind his seemingly ideal world is accompanied by renowned artist P.Craig Russell's beautifully haunting illustrations.

"This striking retelling of the modern classic blends words and images to create a brilliant new representation of Lowry's dystopian conflict between the ideals of free will and security. The artwork, rendered in blue pencil and grayscale, perfectly depicts Jonas's stark, dysfunctional society, and the measured introduction and brief glimpses of color keep readers hopeful for a brighter future." School Library Journal.

Mashima, Hiro, 1977-
Fairy tail. Hiro Mashima; translated and adapted by William Flanagan. Del Rey/Ballantine Books, 2008. 198 p.: Fairy tail.
Grades: 7 8 9 10 11 12   **741.5**
1. Wizards 2. Magic 3. Disguises 4. Cats 5. Spells (Magic) 6. Fantasy comics 7. Manga 8. Comics and Graphic novels
ISBN 9780345501332

         LC 2008273355

Wizard Lucy wants to join Fairy Tail, a club for powerful wizards, but is instead grabbed by a bunch of pirates led by a devious magician, and her only hope is Natsu, a strange boy she meets on her travels.

McCann, Jim, 1974-
Return of the dapper men. written by Jim McCann; art by Janet Lee; lettered by Dave Lanphear. Top Shelf Productions, 2017, c2010. 144 p.
Grades: 4 5 6 7 8   **741.5**
1. Childhood 2. Change 3. Robots 4. Civilization, Subterranean 5. Children 6. Fantasy comics 7. Comics and Graphic novels
ISBN 9781603094139

When the Dapper men arrive in Anorev to restart time, Ayden, Zoe, and Dapper Man 41 seek to repair whatever made time stop.

McCoola, Marika
Baba Yaga's assistant. Marika McCoola; illustrated by Emily Carroll. Candlewick Pr., 2015. 136 p.
Grades: 4 5 6 7   **741.5**
1. Witches 2. Baba Yaga (Legendary character) 3. Courage in girls 4. Magic 5. Families 6. Fantasy comics 7. Fairy tale and folklore-inspired fiction 8. Comics and Graphic novels
ISBN 9780763669614

When her father announces that he is remarrying, Masha decides to leave home and become Baba Yaga's assistant. But to earn her place at the witch's house, she must first pass a series of tests.

"McCoola's offering is a well-nuanced delight, satisfyingly blending fairy tale, legend, and thrills. As a perfect complement, Carroll's evocative art enthralls, capturing both the emotion and the magic of McCoola's yarn and breathing new life into an old folk tale." Kirkus.

McGrane, Madeline

The **accursed** vampire. Madeline McGrane Quill Tree Books, 2021 176 p.

Grades: 4 5 6 7   **741.5**

1. Child vampires 2. Curses 3. Quests 4. Witches 5. Friendship 6. Middle West 7. Paranormal comics 8. Comics and Graphic novels

ISBN 9780062954350

Cursed by a witch centuries before, Dragoslava must complete every task the witch assigns to him, challenges that send him off to a sleepy midwestern town to obtain a spellbook, in what becomes a lifechanging mission that brings about friendship and a sense of belonging.

"Quirky art and characterizations balance the heavier aspects of the narrative. Queer representation within the story is prevalent and casual, and the satisfying resolution emphasizes the joy of chosen families." Kirkus

McKinney, L. L. (Leatrice L.)

Nubia: real one. written by L.L. McKinney; illustrated by Robyn Smith; cover color by Bex Glendining; interior color by Brie Henderson with Robyn Smith and Bex Glendining; lettered by Ariana Maher. DC Comics, [2021] 205 p.

Grades: 7 8 9 10 11 12   **741.5**

1. Ability 2. Identity (Psychology) 3. Teenage girls 4. African American teenage girls 5. Seventeen-year-old girls 6. Comics and Graphic novels 7. Superhero comics

ISBN 9781401296407

LC 2020040023

Nubia has always stood out because of her Amazonian strength, but even though she uses her ability for good she is seen as a threat, so when her best friend Quisha is threatened by a boy who thinks he owns the town, Nubia risks everything to become the hero society tells her she is not.

"A thrilling, timely, and thoroughly engaging full-length debut for a classic comic hero." School Library Journal

Meconis, Dylan

Queen of the sea. Dylan Meconis. Candlewick Press, 2019. 400 p.

Grades: 5 6 7 8   **741.5**

1. Tudor period (1485-1603) 2. Exiles 3. Convents 4. Women rulers 5. Girls 6. Orphans 7. Great Britain -- History -- Mary I, 1553-1558 8. Historical comics 9. Comics and Graphic novels

ISBN 9781536204988

When her sister seizes the throne, Queen Eleanor of Albion is banished to a tiny island off the coast of her kingdom. The island is also home to Margaret, a mysterious young orphan girl. Dylan Meconis paints Margaret's world in soft greens, grays, and reds, transporting readers to a quiet, windswept island at the heart of a treasonous royal plot.

"It's a stunning visual package, and the slow-burning story of Margaret's gradually opening world is made all the more captivating by the well-researched historical setting, immersive world building, and engrossing characters." Booklist

Medley, Linda

★ **Castle** waiting. Linda Medley. Fantagraphics, c2006. 457 p.

Grades: 5 6 7 8 9 10 11 12   **741.5**

1. Magic 2. Witches 3. Curses 4. Princesses 5. Household employees 6. Fantasy comics 7. Comics and Graphic novels

ISBN 9781560977476

Follows the modern fable of an abandoned castle and its eccentric inhabitants.

Melchior-Durand, Stephane

The **golden** compass: the graphic novel.. adapted and illustrated by Stephane Melchior-Durand and Clement Oubrerie; coloring by Clement Oubrerie with Philippe Bruno. Alfred A. Knopf, 2015. 80 p.: Golden compass (Graphic novels)

Grades: 6 7 8 9 10   **741.5**

1. Girl heroes 2. Familiars (Spirits) 3. Universities and colleges 4. Human experimentation in medicine 5. Missing children 6. Arctic regions 7. Fantasy comics 8. Comics and Graphic novels 9. Translations French to English.

ISBN 9780553523713

LC 2015005828

In the first of a three-volume graphic novel adaptation, Lyra Belacqua and her daemon familiar set out to prevent her best friend and other kidnapped children from becoming the subject of gruesome experiments in the Far North. Provided by publisher.

Meyer, Marissa

Wires and nerve. Marissa Meyer; art by Doug Holgate with Stephen Gilpin. Feiwel & Friends, an imprint of Macmillan Publishing Group, LLC, 2017. 238 p.: Wires and nerve

Grades: 7 8 9 10 11 12   **741.5**

1. Androids 2. Half-human hybrids 3. Imaginary wars and battles 4. Soldiers 5. Science fiction comics 6. Comics and Graphic novels

ISBN 9781250078261

When rogue packs of wolf-hybrid soldiers threaten the tenuous alliance between Earth and Luna, android Iko joins up with a handsome royal guard to hunt down the rogue leader.

"Holgate's dynamic, stylized artwork handily balances the story's action and humor while bringing Meyer's world to vivid life." Publishers Weekly.

Neri, Greg

Yummy: the last days of a Southside Shorty. by G. Neri; illustrated by Randy DuBurke. Lee & Low Books, 2008. 94 p.

Grades: 8 9 10 11 12   **741.5**

1. Sandifer, Robert. 2. Gangs 3. Child murderers 4. African American children 5. Crime 6. Violence 7. Chicago, Illinois -- Social conditions. 8. Urban fiction 9. Comics and Graphic novels 10. Books for reluctant readers

ISBN 9781584302667

LC 2006017771

A graphic novel based on the true story of Robert "Yummy" Sandifer, an eleven-year old African American gang member from Chicago who shot a young girl and was then shot by his own gang members. Provided by publisher.

"Neri's straightforward, unadorned prose is the perfect complement to DuBurke's stark black-and-white inks; great slabs of shadow and masterfully rendered faces breathe real, tragic life into the players." Publishers Weekly.

Nicholson, Hope

Moonshot: the indigenous comics collection. edited by Hope Nicholson. Alternate History Comics, [2015] 176 p.

Grades: 6 7 8 9 10 11 12 Adult   **741.5**

1. Indians of North America 2. Identity (Psychology) 3. Spirituality 4. Communities 5. Comics and Graphic novels

ISBN 9780987715258

A collection of indigenous stories exploring Native identity, culture, and spirituality in graphic format.

"This collection of folklore from a powerhouse team of Native authors, including Buffy Sainte-Marie and Richard Van Camp, will wow readers with traditional and futuristic tales based on tribal-specific cultural teachings. . . . The full-page illustrations in some selections and the bright colors in others add depth and understanding to the narratives. The artwork is as diverse as the stories collected." School Library Journal.

Nijkamp, Marieke

The **oracle** code. writer, Marieke Nijkamp; illustrator, Manuel Preitano; colorists, Jordie Bellaire with Manuel Preitano; letterer, Clayton Cowles. DC Comics, 2020 208 p.

Grades: 7 8 9 10   **741.5**
1. Gunshot victims 2. Rehabilitation 3. Self-acceptance 4. People with disabilities -- Rehabilitation 5. Paralysis 6. Mystery comics 7. Superhero comics 8. Comics and Graphic novels
ISBN 9781401290665

                     LC 2019041188

After a gunshot leaves her paralyzed, Barbara Gordon enters the Arkham Center for Independence, where Gotham's teens undergo physical and mental rehabilitation. Now using a wheelchair, Barbara must adapt to a new normal, but she cannot shake the feeling that something is dangerously amiss.

O'Neill, Kay

★ **Princess** princess ever after. Katie O'Neill. Oni Press, 2016. 56 p.

Grades: 4 5 6 7 8   **741.5**
1. Girl heroes 2. Princesses 3. Imaginary kingdoms 4. Courage 5. Unicorns 6. Fantasy comics 7. Comics and Graphic novels
ISBN 9781620103401

When the heroic princess Amira rescues the kind-hearted princess Sadie from her tower prison, the two band together to defeat a jealous sorceress with a dire grudge against Sadie.

Oseman, Alice

Heartstopper.. Alice Oseman. Graphix, 2021, c2020. 351 p.: Heartstopper

Grades: 7 8 9 10 11 12   **741.5**
1. High schools 2. Coming out (Sexual or gender identity) 3. Teenage boy/boy relations 4. Best friends 5. Friendship 6. Comics and graphic novels 7. LGBTQIA comics 8. LGBTQIA romances
ISBN 9781338617535

Charlie didn't think Nick could ever like him back, but now they're officially boyfriends. Nick has even found the courage to come out to his mom. But coming out isn't something that happens just once, and Nick and Charlie try to figure out when to tell their friends that they're dating. Not being out to their classmates gets even harder during a school trip to Paris. As Nick and Charlie's feelings get more serious, they'll need each other more than ever. Provided by publisher.

Palacio, R. J.

White bird: a Wonder story. R. J. Palacio. Alfred A. Knopf, 2019 220 p.

Grades: 4 5 6 7   **741.5**
1. Second World War era (1939-1945) 2. Jewish girls 3. Bullying and bullies 4. Boys with poliomyelitis 5. Nazis 6. Survival 7. France -- History -- German occupation, 1940-1945 8. Historical comics 9. Comics and Graphic novels
ISBN 9780525645535

                     LC 2020288121

Sydney Taylor Book Award for Older Readers, 2020.

Tells the story of Julian's Grandmere's childhood as she, a Jewish girl, was hidden by a family in a Nazi-occupied French village during World War II and how the boy she once shunned became her savior and best friend.

Pearson, Luke

★ **Hildafolk**. Luke Pearson. Nobrow Press, 2010. 48 p. : Hildafolk

Grades: 3 4 5 6   **741.5**
1. Girls 2. Rural life 3. Trolls 4. Magic 5. Adventure 6. Fantasy comics 7. Comics and Graphic novels
ISBN 9781907704048

Hilda sits in her tent listening to the thunder passing overhead when she hears a bell. As she hurtles towards the vanishing tinkling sound, Hilda unwittingly embarks on an adventure into strange worlds ruled by magical forces. Luke Pearson tells this exciting tale for kids and adults alike.

Petersen, David, 1977-

★ **Mouse** guard. written and illustrated by David Petersen. Archaia Studio Press, 2007. 192 p.: Mouse Guard

Grades: 5 6 7 8   **741.5**
1. Mice 2. Civilization, Medieval 3. Weasels 4. Knights and knighthood 5. Insurgency 6. Fantasy comics 7. Comics and Graphic novels
ISBN 9781932386578

Follows the adventures of Lieam, Saxon, and Kenzie, three mice who are part of the Mouse Guard—soldiers and guides for common mice looking to journey from one hidden mouse village to another—and their quest to uncover a traitorous plot against the Guard.

Mouse guard. written and illustrated by David Petersen. Archaia Studio Press, 2008. 192 p.: Mouse Guard

Grades: 5 6 7 8   **741.5**
1. Mice 2. Civilization, Medieval 3. Winter 4. Weasels 5. Knights and knighthood 6. Fantasy comics 7. Comics and Graphic novels
ISBN 9781932386745

In the Winter of 1152, the Mouse Guard face a food and supply shortage threatening the lives of many mouse through a cold and icy season. Some of the Guard's finest—Saxon. Kenzie, Lieam, and Sadie, led by Celanawe, the legendary Black Axe—traverse the snow-blanketed territories acting as diplomats to improve relations between the mouse cities and the Guard, and find themselves on a race against time to deliver crucial medicines. This is a winter not every Guard may survive...

"Picking up where Fall 1152 . . . left off, Winter 1152 follows the darkening adventures of the brave troops of the Mouse Guard as they battle the elements, predators, and even other mice in order to secure their way of life. The high-quality artwork found in the first volume carries over into this one. The narrative . . . is fast paced and compelling. . . . Combining a tale of action, romance, comedy, and tragedy with the graphic-novel format results in a topnotch work with wide appeal." School Library Journal.

Mouse guard. David Petersen ... [et al.]. Archaia Studio Press, 2010. 144 p.: Mouse Guard

Grades: 5 6 7 8   **741.5**
1. Mice 2. Storytelling 3. Civilization, Medieval 4. Fantasy comics 5. Comics and Graphic novels
ISBN 9781932386943

"More than just supplemental material, this book broadens Petersen's magnificently imagined miniature world and is a welcome addition for any collection that values quality, all-ages graphic novels." Booklist.

Mouse guard.. written and illustrated by David Petersen. Archaia, 2013. 192 p.: Mouse Guard

Grades: 5 6 7 8   **741.5**

1. Mice 2. Axes 3. Legends 4. Adventure 5. Adventurers 6. Fantasy comics 7. Comics and Graphic novels

ISBN 9781936393060

The arrival of distant kin takes Celanawe on an adventure that will carry him across the sea to uncharted waters and lands all while unraveling the legend of Farrer, the blacksmith who forged the mythic axe.

Mouse guard. David Petersen ... [et al.]. Archaia Studio Press, 2016. 158 p.: Mouse Guard

Grades: 5 6 7 8   **741.5**

1. Mice 2. Storytelling 3. Civilization, Medieval 4. Fantasy comics 5. Comics and Graphic novels

ISBN 9781936393268

LC 2017299433

A collection of stories about the brave, fabled Mouse Guard are told by the patrons in the June Alley Inn, whose proprietor has offered a prize to whoever can tell the greatest tale.

Phelan, Matt

Snow White: a graphic novel. Matt Phelan. Candlewick Press, 2016. 216 p.

Grades: 4 5 6 7 8   **741.5**

1. New York Stock Exchange 2. 1920s 3. Beauty 4. Jealousy 5. Stepmothers 6. Homeless children 7. Stock market 8. New York City 9. Comics and Graphic novels 10. Fairy tale and folklore-inspired fiction

ISBN 9780763672331

"With a keen historical slant, a bit of action and intrigue, high visual interest, and the fairy-tale leaning, this will awe a wide readership. Brilliant." Kirkus.

The **storm** in the barn. Matt Phelan. Candlewick Press, 2009. 208 p.

Grades: 4 5 6 7 8 9   **741.5**

1. 1930s 2. Droughts 3. Storytelling 4. Imaginary creatures 5. Courage 6. Farms 7. Dust Bowl (South Central United States) 8. Kansas 9. Historical fantasy 10. Comics and Graphic novels

ISBN 9780763636180

LC 2008938396

Scott O'Dell Historical Fiction Award, 2010.

Facing his share of ordinary challenges, from local bullies to his father's failed expectations, 11-year-old Jack Clark must also deal with the effects of the Dust Bowl in 1937 Kansas, including the rising tensions in his small town and the spread of a shadowy illness.

"Children can read this as a work of historical fiction, a piece of folklore, a scary story, a graphic novel, or all four. Written with simple, direct language, its an almost wordless book: the illustrations' shadowy grays and blurry lines eloquently depict the haze of the dust. A complex but accessible and fascinating book." School Library Journal.

Pope, Paul

Battling boy. Paul Pope; color by Hilary Sycamore. First Second, 2013. 208 p.: Battling boy

Grades: 7 8 9 10 11 12   **741.5**

1. Teenage superheroes 2. Monsters 3. Teenage heroes and heroines 4. Civil defense 5. Gods and goddesses 6. Superhero comics 7. Fantasy comics 8. Comics and Graphic novels

ISBN 9781596438057

"This is a sophisticated tale for younger readers, but Pope manages to both grant full-scale wish fulfillment and acknowledge the limitations of young boys with equal aplomb. His art, meanwhile, looks like nothing else in comics, with ropy, sinewy figures, dynamic action, and gritty urban design all captured in panels that have the rough, subversive tone of classic punk album covers." Booklist.

Renier, Aaron

★ The **unsinkable** Walker Bean. written and illustrated by Aaron Renier; colored by Alec Longstreth. First Second, 2010. 208 p. : Unsinkable Walker Bean

Grades: 5 6 7 8   **741.5**

1. Boy heroes 2. Curses 3. Skull 4. Pirate ships 5. Witches 6. Action and adventure comics 7. Fantasy comics 8. Comics and Graphic novels

ISBN 9781596434530

"The story centers around a cursed skull stolen from the lair of two deep-sea crustacean witches. Like all who look upon the skull, Walker's beloved grandpa falls deathly ill when he finds it, and the boy sets out to return the skull from whence it came. . . . The generous page size lets [the] reader dive into Renier's quavery and painstakingly detailed cartooning, and he really shows off his stuff with a bounty of full-splash dazzlers. . . . Exciting, deep, funny, and scary, with tremendous villains and valor galore." Booklist.

Roman, Dave

Astronaut Academy. Dave Roman. First Second, 2011. 192 p. : Astronaut Academy

Grades: 4 5 6 7 8   **741.5**

1. Boy heroes 2. Robots 3. Boarding schools 4. Schools 5. Friendship 6. Space 7. Comics and Graphic novels

ISBN 9781250225924

Hakata Soy, the new kid at Astronaut Academy, finds it difficult to study for classes in Fire Throwing and Anti-Gravity Gymnastics when his past as the leader of a futuristic superhero team keeps haunting him.

"Silliness is high on the agenda, aided by minimal, cartoonish art that plays on manga tropes but also manages to build character into the simple lines of a face. . . . This is one for readers looking for more involved and complex comedy than a cursory glance at the images might lead one to expect." Booklist.

Russell, P. Craig

★ **Coraline**: graphic novel. based on the novel by Neil Gaiman; adapted and illustrated by P. Craig Russell; colorist, Lovern Kindzierski; letterer, Todd Klein. HarperCollins, c2008. 186 p.

Grades: 4 5 6 7   **741.5**

1. Courage in girls 2. Child kidnapping victims 3. Parallel universes 4. Parent and child 5. Girls 6. Horror comics 7. Comics and Graphic novels

ISBN 006082543X

Looking for excitement, Coraline ventures through a mysterious door into a world that is similar, yet disturbingly different from her own, where she must challenge a gruesome entity in order to save herself, her parents, and the souls of three others.

"This version is a virtuoso adaptation. . . . A master of fantastical landscapes, Russell sharpens the realism of his imagery, perserving the humanity of the characters and heightening the horror." Booklist.

★ The **graveyard** book graphic novel. based on the novel by Neil Gaiman; adapted by P. Craig Russell; illustrated by Stephen B. Scott and Kevin Nowlan. Harper, 2014. 192 p.: Graveyard book (Graphic novels)

Grades: 5 6 7 8 9 10   **741.5**

1. Boy orphans 2. Cemeteries 3. Ghosts 4. Supernatural 5. Werewolves 6. England 7. Fantasy comics 8. Comics and Graphic novels

ISBN 9780062194817

A first volume in a two-part graphic novel adaptation of the Newbery Medal-winning tale features sumptuous illustrations by leading genre artists and follows the adventures of Bod, who is being raised by ghosts while avoiding the man who killed his family.

"Russell brings his decades of comics know-how to this lovely, lyrical adaptation of [Gaiman's] well-loved, Newbery Medal-winning book. Not content to rely exclusively on his own distinctive talents, Russell has enlisted some of the industry's greatest contemporary illustrators as contributors, who fill the panels with appropriately gothic tones. In order to give ample room to the novel's twists and turns, the adaptation has been divided into two parts." Booklist.

The **graveyard** book graphic novel. based on the novel by Neil Gaiman; adapted by P. Craig Russell; illustrated by Stephen B. Scott and Kevin Nowlan. Harpercollins Childrens Books, 2014. 176 p.: Graveyard book (Graphic novels)

Grades: 5 6 7 8 9 10   **741.5**

1. Boy orphans 2. Cemeteries 3. Ghosts 4. Supernatural 5. Werewolves 6. England 7. Fantasy comics 8. Comics and Graphic novels

ISBN 9780062194831

Nobody "Bod" Owens, who lives in a graveyard and is being raised by ghosts, leaves the safety of the graveyard to attend school and investigate his family's murder.

"Russell and his team of illustrators continue to do this amazing story justice with images that lead readers down a path into Bod's dark and magical graveyard world. Gaiman has the ability to weave beauty and intrigue into a story that has a strong potential to frighten." Voice of Youth Advocates.

Sfar, Joann

★ The **little** prince. Joann Sfar; adapted from the book by Antoine de Saint-Exupery; translated by Sarah Ardizzone; colour by Brigitte Findakly. Houghton Mifflin Harcourt, 2010. 110 p.

Grades: 5 6 7 8 9   **741.5**

1. Princes 2. Pilots 3. Purpose in life 4. Intergenerational friendship 5. Airplane accidents 6. Comics and Graphic novels 7. Translations French to English 8. Allegories

ISBN 9780547338026

"On the surface, this is a straight graphic-novel retelling of the narrator pilot getting stranded in the desert, where he meets a curious little boy who claims to be from a wee planet very far away. . . . The ultimately tricky task is to honor the source but not sound like an adaptation (otherwise, why not just read the original?) and Sfar nails it on both counts. . . . Everything is handled with both reverence and ingenuity." Booklist.

Shen, Prudence

Nothing can possibly go wrong. Prudence Shen & Faith Erin Hicks. First Second, 2013. 288 p.

Grades: 7 8 9 10   **741.5**

1. Geeks (Computer enthusiasts) 2. Competition in teenagers 3.

High school athletes 4. Teenage boy/girl relations 5. High school basketball 6. Realistic fiction 7. Comics and Graphic novels 8. Books for reluctant readers

ISBN 9781596436596

Charlie, the captain of the basketball team, and Nate, the president of the robotics club, are bestfriends. Their friendship is tested when the robotics club and the cheerleading squad—who use Charlie as their figurehead—compete for student group funding.

"Shen's plot ably balances drama, humor, angst, and robotic geekery, giving the book an immediate YA appeal, but one that's broad enough to be enjoyable to older readers, as well. Visually, Hicks's wide-eyed, inky b&w panels infuse the characters with real emotion and personality, capturing the book's heartfelt youthfulness." Publishers Weekly.

Shiga, Jason

★ **Meanwhile**. by Jason Shiga. Amulet Books, 2010. 80 col.

Grades: 4 5 6 7 8 9   **741.5**

1. Laboratories 2. Mad scientist (Concept) 3. Human experimentation in medicine 4. Boys 5. Telepathy 6. Science fiction comics 7. Plot-your-own stories 8. Comics and Graphic novels

ISBN 9780810984233

LC 2009039844

In this choose-your-own adventure graphic novel, a boy stumbles on the laboratory of a mad scientist who asks him to choose between testing a mind-reading device, a time machine, and a doomsday machine.

"In this graphic novel mind boggler . . . readers play the role of little Jimmy and on the first page make the seemingly innocuous decision of ordering a vanilla or chocolate ice-cream cone. Tubes connect panels in all directions and veer off into tabs to other pages, creating a head-spinningly tangled web of story. . . . The crux is that Jimmy stumbles into the lab of an affable mad scientist and is allowed to tinker with three inventions: a mind reader, a time machine, and the Killitron, which obliterates all life on earth aside from the user's. . . . It's maddening and challenging, all right, but that's precisely what makes it so crazy fun." Booklist.

Shimura, Takako, 1973-

Wandering son.. Shimura Takako; translated by Matt Thorn. Fantagraphics, 2011. 202 p.: Wandering son

Grades: 7 8 9 10 11 12 Adult   **741.5**

1. Gender identity 2. Transgenderism 3. Middle school students 4. Fifth graders 5. Secrets 6. Manga 7. LGBTQIA comics 8. Comics and Graphic novels

ISBN 9781606994160

"This literary manga is a lovely, sensitive portrayal of two tweens exploring their gender identity. The art has a spare, dreamy quality, while the plot focuses on the children's forthright curiosity rather than on angst." Booklist.

Smith, Jeff, 1960 February 27-

★ **Out** from Boneville. by Jeff Smith; with color by Steve Hamaker. Graphix/Scholastic, 2005, c1996. 142 p.: Bone (Jeff Smith)

Grades: 4 5 6 7 8 9 10 11 12   **741.5**

1. Separated friends, relatives, etc 2. Imaginary creatures 3. Talking animals 4. Insects 5. Wilderness areas 6. Fantasy comics 7. Comics and Graphic novels 8. Action and adventure comics

ISBN 9781417657803

LC 9683439

"The nine-volume Bone graphic novel series was the toast of the comics world when it was published by Smith's own Cartoon Books beginning in the early 1990s; in this first volume of Scholastic's new edition, the original b&w art has been beautifully converted into color." Publishers Weekly.

Rose. by Jeff Smith & Charles Vess. Graphix/Scholastic, 2009, c2000. 138 p.: Bone (Jeff Smith)

Grades: 4 5 6 7 8   **741.5**
    1. Sieges 2. Dragons 3. Princesses 4. Sisters 5. Valleys 6. Comics and Graphic novels 7. Fantasy comics
    ISBN 9780545135436

                    LC bl2004004092

A prequel to the Bone saga tells of young Princess Rose's quest to defend the small towns of the Northern Valley from dragon attacks and the impact that her actions had on the lives of both friends and foes in the years ahead.

Tall tales. by Jeff Smith with Tom Sniegoski; color by Steve Hamaker. Graphix, 2010. 108 p.: Bone (Jeff Smith)

Grades: 4 5 6 7 8   **741.5**
    1. Imaginary creatures 2. Heroes and heroines 3. Camping 4. Storytelling 5. Scouting (Youth activity) 6. Fantasy comics 7. Action and adventure comics 8. Comics and Graphic novels
    ISBN 9780545140959

Smiley entertains the Bone Scouts by telling them stories about the adventures of the mighty explorer Big Johnson Bone before his discovery of the Rolling Bone River and establishment of a famous trading post.

"This introduces Big Johnson Bone, the explorer who founded Boneville. A fearless Davey Crockett-like character, he defeats a cave bear when just a baby and grows up to best all manner of beasts, including a pack of ratlike creatures intent on taking over the forest. Big Johnson's recklessness in the face of danger results in much humor, as does the commentary of his terrified, sarcastic monkey companion. Smith's quick wit shines through in the exchanges between Johnson and his companions. The colorful art is jam-packed with action, and the characters are enhanced with exaggerated features and movements." School Library Journal.

Smith, Niki

The **deep** & dark blue. Niki Smith. Little, Brown & Co., 2020 256 p.

Grades: 4 5 6 7   **741.5**
    1. Twins 2. Self-discovery 3. Gender role 4. Disguises 5. Hiding 6. Fantasy comics 7. Comics and Graphic novels 8. LGBTQIA fiction
    ISBN 9780316485982

When a political coup usurps their noble house, Hawke and Grayson flee for their lives and assume new identities before joining an order of magical women before their quest for vengeance is compromised by Grayson's longing to remain behind and finally live as a girl.

"Smith's artwork, recalling classic manga, delivers clearly choreographed action and intense facial expressions, which capably communicate poignant emotion during the many bittersweet scenes." Booklist.

Soo, Kean

Jellaby.. by Kean Soo. Hyperion Books for Children, 2008. 143 p.: Jellaby

Grades: 4 5 6 7 8 9   **741.5**
    1. Moving to a new city 2. Loneliness in girls 3. Monsters 4. Girls 5. Mothers and daughters 6. Comics and Graphic novels
    ISBN 9781423103370

                    LC 2007930138

After moving to a new neighborhood and finding it difficult to make the adjustment to her town and school, Portia is delighted when she encounters a friendly purple monster in the backyard who is equally as eager to make a friend.

"Soo grounds the story in a fairly gritty contemporary reality, where kids deal with bullies and well-meaning adults try to help. Clear, clean lines and easy-to-follow panel layouts round out the package." Booklist.

Jellaby.. Kean Soo. Hyperion Books for Children, 2009. 176 p.: Jellaby

Grades: 4 5 6 7 8 9   **741.5**
    1. Girls 2. Friendship 3. Secrets 4. Best friends 5. Monsters 6. Comics and Graphic novels
    ISBN 9781423105657

Although she would love to keep her new best friend with her, Portia knows that she must help Jellaby get back to his own home, but while following the clues to get Jellaby where he needs to be, the friends encounter a monster with a healthy appetite for destruction and must get out of his sight before Portia becomes his next meal.

Stephens, Jay, 1971-

Heroes!: draw your own superheroes, gadget geeks & other do-gooders. Jay Stephens. Lark Books, c2007. 64 p.

Grades: 4 5 6 7   **741.5**
    1. Drawing 2. Superheroes 3. Women superheroes 4. Cartoon characters 5. Cartooning -- Technique
    ISBN 1579909345

                    LC 2006101661

From muscular bodies to action poses, from masks and capes to mutations and power effects, this guide helps budding cartoonists develop and draw new heroes.

"Stephens shows just how to draw [superheroes]. . . . Stephens does a good job organizing his material, beginning with a bit of history, then moving quickly to hero heads, . . . and on to masks, disguises, physical features, power effects, and action moves. The brightly colored illustrations offer plenty of how-to info and lots of great heroes, male and female, to use as models." Booklist.

Stevenson, Noelle

Lumberjanes.. Noelle Stevenson and Grace Ellis, writers; Shannon Watters and Brooke Allen, illustrators. Boom! Studios, 2015. 128 p.: Lumberjanes (Graphic novels)

Grades: 6 7 8 9 10 11 12 Adult   **741.5**
    1. Best friends 2. Scouting (Youth activity) 3. Summer camps 4. Girl campers 5. Imaginary creatures 6. Fantasy comics 7. Comics and Graphic novels 8. Books for reluctant readers
    ISBN 9781608866878

"Humorously riffing on everything from scout badges to the X-Men to feminist heroes . . ., it's a sharp, smart, and most of all fun celebration of sisterhood." Publishers Weekly.

Lumberjanes.. [Noelle Stevenson, Grace Ellis, Shannon Watters, Brook Allen] Boom! Studios, 2015. 112 p.: Lumberjanes (Graphic novels)

Grades: 6 7 8 9 10 11 12 Adult   **741.5**
    1. Girl campers 2. Monsters 3. Best friends 4. Friendship 5. Scouting (Youth activity) 6. Fantasy comics 7. Comics and Graphic novels
    ISBN 9781608867370

Jo, April, Mal, Molly and Ripley are not gonna let any insane quest or an array of supernatural critters get in their way, but having stumbled onto a mysterious force wreaking havoc in the camp, it's a race through the woods as the Lumberjanes work together to save not only their friends, but maybe even the whole world!

"Stevenson and Ellis' rip-roaring plot is packed with magic, mayhem, teamwork, and some fantastic jokes, and it's all riotously rendered in Allen's bold and brassy artwork, which clearly depicts even the most pell-mell scenes and perfectly complements the off-the-wall story. The series opener received broad, enthusiastic acclaim, and this follow-up should fare just as well." Booklist.

Nimona. Noelle Stevenson HarperTeen, 2015 266 p.: Nimona

Grades: 7 8 9 10 11 12   **741.5**
1. Shapeshifters 2. Supervillains 3. Good and evil 4. Quests 5. Fantasy comics 6. Webcomics 7. Comics and Graphic novels 8. Books for reluctant readers
ISBN 9780062278234

Lord Blackheart, a villain with a vendetta, and his sidekick, Nimona, an impulsive young shapeshifter, must prove to the kingdom that Sir Goldenloin and the Institution of Law Enforcement and Heroics aren't the heroes everyone thinks they are.

"This celebrated webcomic, a mash-up of medieval culture with modern science and technology, is now available in print. . . . Action scenes dominate as Nimona shifts with Hulk-like ferocity from frightful creatures such as a fire-breathing dragon to a docile cat or a timid child. Dialogue is fresh and witty with an abundance of clever lines." School Library Journal.

Stohl, Margaret
Forever red. Margaret Stohl. Marvel, [2015] 304 p.: Black Widow (Margaret Stohl)

Grades: 7 8 9 10 11 12   **741.5**
1. Women superheroes 2. Assassins 3. Secret societies 4. Teenage girls 5. Black Widow (Fictitious character) 6. Superhero stories
ISBN 9781484726433

Trained from a young age in the arts of death and deception, elite assassin Natasha reluctantly reunites with a Russian quantum physicist's daughter she once rescued in order to stop her former master's abductions of children throughout Eastern Europe.

"Great fight sequences, plenty of action, twists in the plot, and characters motivated by strong emotions will keep readers engaged and entertained." School Library Journal.

Takaya, Natsuki, 1973-
Fruits basket.. Tokyopop, 2004. 216 p. : Fruits basket

Grades: 7 8 9 10 11 12   **741.5**
1. Teenage girls 2. Teenagers 3. Teenage girl orphans 4. Orphans 5. Homeless teenage girls 6. Fantasy comics 7. Manga 8. Comics and Graphic novels
ISBN 1591826039

Tohru Honda is an orphaned teenager who comes to live with the Sohma family in exchange for housekeeping duties, but she soon comes to know the family secret.

"As Tohru and Kyo become friends, they realize that as misfits they may have a chance at understanding each other. Similar to other romance manga, this tale's illustration style is cartoonish and whimsical. Each panel-packed page conveys a melodramatic event or upturn, giving the story a fast rhythm." Publishers Weekly.

Tamaki, Mariko
Skim. words by Mariko Tamaki; drawings by Jillian Tamaki. Groundwood Books/House of Anansi Press, c2008. 141 p.

Grades: 7 8 9 10 11 12   **741.5**
1. Teenagers -- Interpersonal relations 2. Multiracial teenage girls 3. Identity (Psychology) 4. Teenage girls -- Identity 5. High school girls 6. Toronto, Ontario 7. Diary novels 8. Realistic fiction 9. Comics and Graphic novels
ISBN 9780888997531

LC bl2008006217

Presents the whole gamut of tortured teen life—friends, love, depression, suicide, and cliques—through the eyes of Skim, a.k.a. Kimberly Keiko Cameron, a would-be Wiccan goth at a girls' academy in Toronto during the 1990s.

This one summer. Mariko Tamaki; illustrated by Jillian Tamaki. First Second, 2014. 317 p.

Grades: 7 8 9 10 11 12 Adult   **741.5**
1. Growing up 2. Summer 3. Change 4. Secrets 5. Family problems 6. Comics and Graphic novels
ISBN 9781596437746

Governor General's Literary Award for English-Language Children's Literature, 2014.

"This captivating graphic novel presents a fully realized picture of a particular time in a young girl's life, an in-between summer filled with yearning and a sense of ephemerality." School Library Journal.

Tan, Shaun
The **arrival**. by Shaun Tan. Arthur A. Levine Books, 2007, c2006. 128 p.

Grades: 6 7 8 9 10   **741.5**
1. Immigration and emigration 2. Assimilation (Sociology) 3. Families 4. Voyages and travels 5. Immigrants 6. Stories without words 7. Comics and Graphic novels
ISBN 9780439895293

LC 2006021706

In this wordless graphic novel, a man leaves his homeland and sets off for a new country, where he must build a new life for himself and his family.

"Young readers will be fascinated by the strange new world the artist creates. . . . They will linger over the details in the beautiful sepia pictures and will likely pick up the book to pore over it again and again." School Library Journal.

Telgemeier, Raina
Claudia and mean Janine. by Raina Telgemeier. Graphix, 2008. 161 p.: Baby-sitters Club (Graphic novels)

Grades: 3 4 5 6   **741.5**
1. Quarreling 2. Babysitters 3. Seventh-grade girls 4. Seventh-graders 5. Girls' clubs 6. Comics and Graphic novels 7. Realistic fiction
ISBN 9780439885171

LC 2007036125

Claudia's participation in the Baby-sitters Club is curtailed when her Grandmother Mimi suffers a stroke and Claudia finds herself "Mimi-sitting" and fighting more frequently with her sister.

★ **Drama**. Raina Telgemeier; with color by Gurihiru. Graphix, 2012. 240 p.

Grades: 5 6 7 8   **741.5**
1. Crushes in girls 2. Theater 3. Musicals 4. Gay boys 5. Boy/girl relations 6. Realistic fiction 7. Comics and Graphic novels
ISBN 9780545326988

LC 2011040748

"In this realistic and sympathetic story, feelings and thoughts leap off the page, revealing Telgemeier's keen eye for young teen life." Booklist.

★ **Ghosts**. Raina Telgemeier; with color by Braden Lamb. Graphix, an imprint of Scholastic, 2016. 256 p.

Grades: 3 4 5 6 7 **741.5**

1. Sisters 2. Haunted houses 3. Moving, Household 4. Cystic fibrosis 5. Resentfulness 6. Northern California 7. California 8. Comics and Graphic novels
ISBN 9780545540612

LC 2016004672

Catrina and her family have moved to the coast of Northern California for the sake of her little sister, Maya, who has cystic fibrosis—and Cat is even less happy about the move when she is told that her new home is haunted, and Maya sets her heart on meeting a ghost.

Kristy's great idea: a graphic novel. by Raina Telgemeier; [story by] Ann M. Martin. Graphix, 2006. 192 p.: Baby-sitters Club (Graphic novels)

Grades: 3 4 5 6 **741.5**

1. Babysitters 2. Seventh-grade girls 3. Seventh-graders 4. Girls' clubs 5. Interpersonal relations 6. Comics and Graphic novels
ISBN 0439802415

LC 2005037749

Follows the adventures of Kristy and the other members of the Baby-sitters Club as they deal with crank calls, uncontrollable two-year-olds, wild pets, and parents who do not always tell the truth. A graphic novel based on the 1988 book by the same name.

"Comics artist Telgemeier's clean-lined, black-and-white art with stark black details nicely differentiates the four personable seventh-graders who parlay their babysitting experience into a business." Booklist.

TenNapel, Doug

Bad Island. Doug TenNapel. Graphix, 2011. 224 p.

Grades: 6 7 8 9 10 **741.5**

1. Islands 2. Shipwreck survivors 3. Survival (after airplane accidents, shipwrecks, etc) 4. Shipwrecks 5. Family relationships 6. Action and adventure comics 7. Comics and Graphic novels
ISBN 9780545314794

After Reese and his family are stranded on an island during a boating trip, they discover the island is not what it seems when the island's lethal inhabitants come after them.

"Though father, mother, teenage son, and tween daughter face the various dangers like a gang of Indiana Joneses, their family stresses are believable. . . . A clever, old-fashioned adventure with some modern twists and a lighthearted tone." Booklist.

Cardboard. Doug Tennapel. Scholastic, 2012. 288 p.

Grades: 5 6 7 8 **741.5**

1. Boxes 2. Paperboard 3. Bullying and bullies 4. Magic 5. Monsters 6. Fantasy comics 7. Comics and Graphic novels 8. Books for reluctant readers
ISBN 9780545418720

After Cam's father gives him a cardboard box for his birthday, they fashion it into a man that comes to life, but things spin out of control when a bully steals a scrap of the cardboard to create creatures that disobey his orders and multiply into an army.

Ghostopolis. created, written, and drawn by Doug TenNapel. Graphix/Scholastic, 2010. 272 p.

Grades: 7 8 9 10 **741.5**

1. People with terminal illnesses 2. Ghosts 3. Parallel universes 4. Life after death 5. Supernatural 6. Fantasy comics 7. Comics and Graphic novels 8. Books for reluctant readers
ISBN 9780545210270

Accidentally transported to the spirit world by a washed-out ghost wrangler, Garth Hale discovers that he wields unique powers aggressively coveted by the spirits around him and teams up with his grandfather's ghost to find a way back home.

"With a cast of characters that is sometimes one too many, in a world that includes seven kingdoms of infinite zombies, this ghost-filled graphic novel could easily overwhelm, but TenNapel reins it in by deftly illustrating each essential moment and emotion." Kirkus.

Thompson, Craig, 1975-

Space dumplins. Craig Thompson. Scholastic, 2015. 304 p.

Grades: 3 4 5 6 **741.5**

1. Girl heroes 2. Fathers and daughters 3. Space flight 4. Rescues 5. Missing men 6. Science fiction comics 7. Comics and Graphic novels
ISBN 9780545565417

"Thompson's art is wild and busy, with overcrowded, unconventional panel structures. The worldbuilding is a strikingly imaginative pastiche that seamlessly blends biblical references, poop jokes, and social satire." Kirkus.

Tolstikova, Dasha

A **year** without Mom. Dasha Tolstikova. Groundwood Books, 2015. 176 p.

Grades: 5 6 7 8 **741.5**

1. 1990s 2. Mother-separated girls 3. Moving to a new country 4. Twelve-year-old girls 5. Children and moving 6. Moscow, Russia 7. Soviet Union -- Politics and government -- 1985-1991. 8. Comics and Graphic novels 9. Autobiographical comics
ISBN 9781554986927

12-year-old Dasha experiences a year full of turmoil after her mother leaves for America and she remains in Moscow with her grandparents

"Scribbly, childlike pencil drawings are filled in with gray wash and accentuated with red and the occasional pop of blue. They are deceptively simple, but with great narrative sophistication, they capture both the specificity of Dasha's experience and the universality of her emotions." Kirkus.

Varon, Sara

Bake sale. Sara Varon. First Second, 2011. 160 p.

Grades: 3 4 5 6 7 8 **741.5**

1. Bakers 2. Cupcakes 3. Eggplant 4. Bakeries 5. Friendship 6. Stories without words 7. Comics and Graphic novels
ISBN 9781596437401

Cupcake runs a successful bakery with his best friend, Eggplant, but dreams of going abroad to meet his idol, Turkish Delight, who is the most famous pastry chef in the world.

"The book has a mellow, easygoing feel, using soft colors and showing many yummy foods. As an added bonus, recipes for how to make the various scrumptious meals readers watch Cupcake prepare are provided. . . . Varon's art is simple and cozy, making this sweet tale a confection of its own." Publishers Weekly.

Venditti, Robert

★ The **lightning** thief: the graphic novel. Rick Riordan; adapted by Robert Venditti; art by Attila Futaki. Disney/Hyperion Books, 2010. 128 p.: Percy Jackson & the Olympians (graphic novels)

Grades: 5 6 7 8   **741.5**

1. Boy adventurers 2. Demigods 3. Quests 4. Lightning 5. Camps 6. Comics and Graphic novels 7. Fantasy comics 8. Mythological fiction

ISBN 9781423116967

After learning that he is the son of a mortal woman and Poseidon, god of the sea, twelve-year-old Percy is sent to a summer camp for demigods like himself, and joins his new friends on a quest to prevent a war between the gods.

"This graphic novel adaptation of Rick Riordan's novel succeeds in spectacular fashion. . . . The book retains the excellent pacing of the original and gives a face to Riordan's vision of the mythological made modern. Futaki's artwork is exemplary but what leaves such a lasting impression is Villarrubia's coloring, which reveals both subtlety and spectacle when needed." Publishers Weekly.

Westerfeld, Scott

Shay's story. created by Scott Westerfeld; written by Scott Westerfeld and Devin Grayson; illustrations by Steven Cummings. Del Rey/Ballantine Books, c2012. 160 p.: Uglies (Manga)

Grades: 7 8 9 10   **741.5**

1. Aesthetics 2. Sixteen-year-olds 3. Conformity in teenagers 4. Teenagers 5. Individual differences 6. Science fiction comics 7. Comics and Graphic novels

ISBN 9780345527226

               LC bl2012006608

A few months shy of her sixteenth birthday, when she will be transformed into a "pretty" whose only job is to have a great time, Shay befriends the Crims, a group of teens who refuse to take anything in society at face value.

Wheeler, Andrew, 1976-

Another castle. Andrew Wheeler; Paulina Ganucheau, contributor. Oni Press, 2017. 152 p.: Another castle

Grades: 7 8 9 10 11 12 Adult   **741.5**

1. Princesses 2. Kidnapping 3. Imaginary kingdoms 4. Princes 5. Alliances 6. Fantasy comics 7. Comics and Graphic novels

ISBN 9781620103111

While awaiting a proposal from Prince Pete, Princess Artemisia of Beldora is kidnapped by the monstrous Lord Badlug, who killed her mother and now imprisons her in his castle in his kingdom, Grimoire. Rather than waiting for her prince to come, Artemisia vows to free herself and save both her own kingdom and Grimoir.

"Ganucheau contributes some thrilling and bloody action sequences, and her candy-colored palette, suffused with bright pinks and purples, is an inspired touch, just one more way this story subverts expectations." Publishers Weekly.

Whitley, Jeremy

Princeless.. Jeremy Whitley; illustrated by M. Goodwin. Action Lab Comics, 2012. 116 p.: Princeless

Grades: 4 5 6 7 8   **741.5**

1. Princesses 2. African American teenage girls 3. Self-reliance in teenage girls 4. Heroes and heroines, African American 5. Teenage girls 6. Fantasy comics 7. Action and adventure comics 8. Comics and Graphic novels

ISBN 9781450798945

Locked in a tower with her sisters and tired of waiting to be rescued by a prince, Princess Adrienne, her sidekick Bedelia, and her guardian dragon Sparky begin a quest to save themselves.

Princeless.. Jeremy Whitley; illustrated by Rosy Higgins and Ted Brandt Action Lab Entertainment, 2015. 128 p.: Princeless

Grades: 3 4 5 6 7   **741.5**

1. Princesses 2. Pirates 3. Sisters 4. Quests 5. Rescues 6. Fantasy comics 7. Action and adventure comics 8. Comics and Graphic novels

ISBN 9781632291028

When Adrienne finds Raven Xingtao, the daughter of the Pirate King, who is locked away in a tower, Adrienne decides to spring her, but it drags her into a whirlwind adventure to complete Raven's quest for revenge.

Yang, Gene Luen

American born Chinese. Gene Yang; coloring by Lark Pien. First Second, c2006. 233 p.

Grades: 7 8 9 10 11 12   **741.5**

1. Chinese Americans 2. Misfits (Persons) 3. Racism 4. Teenagers 5. Identity (Psychology) 6. Comics and Graphic novels

ISBN 9781596431522

              LC 2005058105

Michael L. Printz Award, 2007.

Alternates three interrelated stories about the problems of young Chinese Americans trying to participate in the popular culture.

"True to its origin as a Web comic, this story's clear, concise lines and expert coloring are deceptively simple yet expressive. Even when Yang slips in an occasional Chinese ideogram or myth, the sentiments he's depicting need no translation. Yang accomplishes the remarkable feat of practicing what he preaches with this book: accept who you are and you'll already have reached out to others." Publishers Weekly.

Boxers. Gene Luen Yang. First Second, 2013 336 p.: Boxers & Saints

Grades: 7 8 9 10 11 12 Adult   **741.5**

1. 19th century 2. Boxer Rebellion, 1899-1901 3. Insurgency 4. Villages 5. Gods and goddesses, Chinese 6. Kung fu 7. China -- History -- Boxer Rebellion, 1899-1901 8. Historical comics 9. Comics and Graphic novels

ISBN 9781596433595

"China's Boxer Rebellion is the unlikely backdrop for this graphic treatment of young villagers on the opposite sides of history. Bao wants to drive out the white devils that poison his country with opium and Christianity. Four-Girl is an unwanted daughter who finds purpose in the missionary life. Their stories collide in a moment of grace that could only be penned by the Printz Award-winning author of 'American Born Chinese.'" School Library Journal.

Saints. Gene Luen Yang. First Second, 2013. 176 p.: Boxers & Saints

Grades: 7 8 9 10 11 12 Adult   **741.5**

1. 19th century 2. Converts to Catholicism 3. Boxer Rebellion, 1899-1901 4. Loyalty 5. Insurgency 6. Battles 7. China -- History -- Boxer Rebellion, 1899-1901 8. Historical comics 9. Comics and Graphic novels

ISBN 9781596436893

"Yang presents a 'diptych' of graphic novels set during China's Boxer Rebellion. Boxers follows Little Bao, who learns to harness the power of ancient gods to fight the spread of Christianity; Saints centers on Four-Girl, who sits squarely on the other side of the rebellion. Yang's characteristic infusions of magical realism, bursts of humor, and distinctively drawn characters make for a compelling read." Horn Book.

Secret coders. Gene Yuen Lang & Mike Holmes. First Second Books, 2015 96 p.: Secret coders
Grades: 4 5 6 7   **741.5**
    1. Clues 2. Gifted children 3. Computer programming 4. Robots 5. Schools 6. Mystery comics 7. Comics and Graphic novels 8. STEM fiction
ISBN 9781626722767

Attending an elite school where enterprising students are challenged to solve a variety of clues and puzzles using computer programming, Hopper and her friend, Eni, resolve to crack the school founder's most elusive mystery together.

"Holmes's blocky cartoon illustrations, in black, white, and green, clearly depict basic programming concepts with tidy visual cues, such as grids of floor tiles. Yang and Holmes do such a great job explaining the concepts that even programming newbies will be likely to catch on." Booklist.

The **shadow** hero. story by Gene Luen Yang; art by Sonny Liew; lettering by Janice Chiang. First Second Books, 2014. 158 p.
Grades: 6 7 8 9 10   **741.5**
    1. 1930s 2. Superheroes 3. Chinese Americans 4. Asian Americans 5. Chinese American families 6. Mothers and sons 7. Chinatown, New York City 8. Superhero comics 9. Comics and Graphic novels 10. Books for reluctant readers
ISBN 9781596436978

In the comics boom of the 1940s, a legend was born: the Green Turtle. He solved crimes and fought injustice just like the other comics characters. But this mysterious masked crusader was hiding something more than your run-of-the-mill secret identity... The Green Turtle was the first Asian American super hero.—Publisher's description.

"Yang and Liew have crafted an origin story for the Green Turtle, a little-known . . . World War II-era comic superhero created by cartoonist Chu Hing in 1944. Much about the series remains a mystery, as Yang shares in an author's note, but according to rumors Hing wanted his star to be Chinese, and, not surprisingly for the era, his publishers balked at the idea. Now seventy years later, Yang and Liew vindicate the cartoonist by imagining the Green Turtle as 'perhaps . . . the first Asian American superhero.'" Horn Book.

Superman smashes the Klan: the graphic novel. written by Gene Luen Yang; art illustrations by Gurihiru; lettering by Janice Chiang. DC Comics, 2020 240 p.
Grades: 7 8 9 10 11 12   **741.5**
    1. Ku Klux Klan 2. 1940s 3. Chinese American families 4. Hate crimes 5. Identity (Psychology) 6. Teenagers 7. Moving to a new city 8. Superhero comics 9. Comics and Graphic novels
ISBN 9781779504210

LC 2020010185

When Dr. Lee moves his family to Metropolis, his son Tommy adjusts to the new neighborhood while daugher Roberta feels out of place, so when the evil Klan of the Fiery Cross begins a string of terrorist attacks on the city, Superman fights them, and Roberta and Superman soon learn to embrace their own unique features that set them apart.

"Clean lines, less-saturated coloring, and character designs reminiscent of vintage comics help set the tone of this period piece while the varied panel cuts and action scenes give it a more modern sensibility." Kirkus

Includes bibliographical references.

741.6 Graphic design, illustration, commercial art

Artist to artist:
★ **Artist** to artist: 23 major illustrators talk to children about their art.. Philomel Books, [2007] 105 p.
Grades: 4 5 6 7   **741.6**
    1. Illustrators 2. Children's literature illustration 3. Illustration of books 4. Illustrators
ISBN 0399246002

LC bl2007020277

Do you ever think about the artists who illustrated your favorite picture books? If you're curious about how people become professional artists and illustrators, how they think about their artwork, what inspires them, or where they work, you'll love this book. It presents letters from 23 famous artists (from Maurice Sendak and Quentin Blake to Ashley Bryan, Jane Dyer, Eric Carle, and many more) written to kids who like to paint or draw, along with samples of the artists' work, a self-portrait of each artist, and photos of the artists in their studios.

"This anthology celebrates and elucidates contemporary picture-book art. . . . Ashley Bryan, Quentin Blake, Leo Lionni, Alice Provensen, and Gennady Spirin are among the contributors, whose comments are formatted as signed letters illustrated with childhood photographs. . . . Each artist includes glorious self-portraits and a gatefold page that reveals a marvelous array of sketches, color mixes, and studio scenes. All readers will find something that piques curiosity or provides insight." Booklist.

Ellabbad, Mohieddine, 1940-
The **illustrator's** notebook. Mohieddin Ellabbad. Groundwood Books/House of Anansi Press; 2006. 30 p.
Grades: 5 6 7 8   **741.6**
    1. Ellabbad, Mohieddine, 1940- 2. Illustrators
ISBN 9780888997005

LC bl2006026236

Presents excerpts from the author's notebook that provide memories of his childhood and his views on art from an Arabic perspective.

"Part children's book, part autobiography, part design treatise, this hard-to-categorize Egyptian import is full of wonders from start to finish. Ellabbad uses excerpts from his notebooks to discuss ways of seeing art from an artist's perspective and as someone from an Arabic culture. Printed like the Egyptian edition—read right to left—the pages are magnificently and surprisingly illustrated, juxtaposing Arabic script (English translations appear in the margins), watercolor paintings, pasted-in photos and pictures from comic books, and all manner of characters from Eastern and Western cultures." School Library Journal.

Vendittelli, Marie
The **fashion** book. [written by Marie Vendittelli; illustrated by Sophie Griotto; translated by Annie Barton; edited by Jen Wainwright]. Buster Books, 2013. 127 p.
Grades: 6 7 8 9 10   **741.6**
    1. Fashion drawing 2. Fashion design 3. Fashion 4. Books for reluctant readers
ISBN 9781780551135

LC bl2013026937

Offers advice on how to begin designing clothes and accessories, through activities that begin with illustrating designs to premiering them on the catwalk.

741.64092 Books—Illustrators

Tan, Shaun
★ The **bird** king: an artist's notebook. Shaun Tan. Arthur A. Levine Books, 2013, c2010. 128 p.
Grades: 3 4 5 6 7   **741.64092**
1. Tan, Shaun. 2. Illustration of books 3. Illustration 4. Drawing 5. Illustrators
ISBN 9780545465137
A book of sketches, artwork, and personal reflections offers insight into the illustrator's creative process, his struggles with "artist's block," and the ideas that either stalled or grew into acclaimed works.

743 Drawing and drawings by subject

Butkus, Mike
How to draw zombies: discover the secrets to drawing, painting, and illustrating the undead. by Mike Butkus and Merrie Destefano. Walter Foster Pub.; 2011. 128 p.: Fantasy underground
Grades: 8 9 10 11 12   **743**
1. Monsters in art 2. Zombies 3. Drawing -- Technique 4. Zombies in art
ISBN 9781936309634
                                      LC 2010052983
"For young artists fascinated by the living dead, this sophisticated drawing book gives step-by-step instructions for creating a variety of unexpected characters. . . . Most of the drawings are done in pencil, but acrylic paints are also occasionally featured. An added bonus is the instructions for giving a final digital touch to the drawings on the computer. . . . Extra bits of zombie lore are added. Fans of the truly terrifying will appreciate the fact that the featured pictures attain a high level of creepiness. . . . Those looking for a zombie drawing book with added bite will find hours of fun with this one." Booklist.

Masiello, Ralph
Ralph Masiello's ancient Egypt drawing book. Ralph Masiello. Charlesbridge, c2008. 1 v. (unpaged)
Grades: 4 5 6 7   **743**
1. Drawing -- Technique 2. Egypt in art 3. Signs and symbols in art 4. Ancient Egypt -- Civilization -- To 332 B.C.E.
ISBN 9781570915338
                                      LC 2007027023
Easy-to-follow diagrams show young readers how to draw images from ancient Egypt, from the eye of Horus to Isis, queen of the gods, to the golden mask of Tutankhamun.
"Masiello starts by showing readers how to draw the Great Pyramid of Khafre using simple shapes and lines. His easy-to-follow instructions gradually build in complexity, as he moves to ancient symbols, then Egyptian gods, Queen Nefertiti, and King Tutankhamen. The finished pictures are colored with mixed media. Concise paragraphs tell more about each subject, including historical context." Horn Book Guide.
Includes bibliographical references.

743.6 Drawing animals

Ames, Lee J.
Draw 50 endangered animals. Lee J. Ames with Warren Budd. Broadway Books, [1993], c1992. 1 v. (unpaged)
Grades: 4 5 6 7   **743.6**
1. Animals in art 2. Rare and endangered animals 3. Drawing -- Technique
ISBN 0385469853
                                      LC BL2001008713
Offers step-by-step instructions for drawing such endangered animals as the humpback whale, giant panda, gorilla, Indian python, Galapagos penguin, peregrine falcon, and the California condor.

Bergin, Mark, 1961-
How to draw pets. by Mark Bergin. PowerKids Press, 2011. 32 p.: How to draw (PowerKids Press)
Grades: 4 5 6 7   **743.6**
1. Animals in art 2. Drawing -- Technique 3. Animal painting and illustration 4. Drawing
ISBN 9781448845118
                                      LC 2010049184
"The cover features sketches of a cat, dog, and rabbit, allowing children to see both structure as well as finished product. Inside, the book starts by showing pictures of animals drawn with different materials such as pencils, ink, charcoals, and pastels, and explains what each medium accomplishes. Next comes an introduction to perspective and looks at different parts of animals. The familiar circle method then gets kids drawing pets from head to tails. . . . The amount of information throughout is just right: thorough but not overwhelming." Booklist.

Hodges, Jared
Draw furries: how to create anthropomorphic and fantasy animals. Jared Hodges and Lindsay Cibos. IMPACT Books, 2009. 127 p.
Grades: 7 8 9 10   **743.6**
1. Fantasy in art 2. Anthropomorphism in art 3. Drawing -- Technique
ISBN 9781600614170
                                      LC 2009019609
Offers directions to draw cat-, dog-, horse-, rodent-, and bird-based human-animal hybrid characters.
"Hodges and Cibos have created a thorough guide. Describing creatures in terms of a sliding scale from human to animal, they begin with some tips on basic anatomy and style. . . . The instruction is grouped by the kind of animal portrayed. . . . Full-color spreads throughout show what can be achieved with practice, and the book concludes with chapters on color and perspective." School Library Journal.

745 Decorative arts

Major, John S., 1942-
Caravan to America: living arts of the Silk Road. John S. Major and Betty J. Belanus. Cricket Books, 2002. 130 p.
Grades: 4 5 6 7   **745**
1. Folk art, Asian 2. Handicraft 3. Expatriate artists 4. Folk artists 5. Artisans 6. Silk Road -- History
ISBN 0812626664
                                      LC 2002005477
Profiles eight artists and artisans now living in America who are originally from the "Silk Road," an ancient network of caravan trails through which trade goods, ideas, and arts pass between Asia and the Mediterranean.
"Full of colorful and informative archival and contemporary photographs and drawings. . . . Each person's story is told in an interesting manner, and information about their specialty and its history is woven

throughout the text. . . . Not only is the work informative, but it is handsome as well." School Library Journal.

Includes bibliographical references and index.

745.2 Industrial art and design

Arato, Rona

Design it: the ordinary things we use every day and the not-so-ordinary ways they came to be. Rona Arato. Tundra Books, 2009. 71 p.

Grades: 4 5 6 7   **745.2**

1. Industrial design 2. Inventions 3. Home appliances 4. Industrial designers
ISBN 9780887768460

LC oc2009081861

Introduces aspects of a career in industrial design while explaining how design principles are applied to everyday objects, sharing engaging historical information while inviting youngsters to develop awareness about how to evaluate the things they use for functionality, user-friendliness and aesthetics.

"This book opens with an explanation of what industrial designers do and with whom they work to make better products. Brief chapters then cover such topics as home, communications, lighting, and toy design and include a good-design checklist that takes function, usability, ergonomics, aesthetics, and greenness into consideration. The language is chatty and inviting, and the pages are full of cartoon illustrations and text superimposed on colorful geometric backgrounds. Sidebars offer a wealth of further information." School Library Journal.

Includes bibliographical references.

745.5 Handicrafts

Carlson, Laurie M., 1952-

Knit, hook, and spin: a kid's activity guide to fiber arts and crafts. Laurie Carlson. Chicago Review Press Incorporated, [2016] 144 p.

Grades: 4 5 6 7   **745.5**

1. Textile crafts 2. Handicraft for children 3. Handicraft
ISBN 9781613734001

LC 2015044783

"From slippers to tote bags and from friendship bracelets to comfort dolls, there is something for almost anyone wanting to learn how to create from these very tactile sources." Kirkus.

Dobson, Jolie, 1981-

The **duct** tape book: 25 projects to make with duct tape. Jolie Dobson. Firefly Books, 2012. 144 p.

Grades: 5 6 7 8   **745.5**

1. Handicraft 2. Duct tape
ISBN 9781770850989

LC 2012538483

Offers instructions for twenty five creative projects made with duct tape, beginning with basic techniques for duct tape crafting and moving on to such projects as bicycle saddle bags, handbags, smart phone holders, and board games.

Scheunemann, Pam, 1955-

Trash to treasure: fun, easy projects with paper, plastic, glass & ceramics, fabric, metal, and odds & ends. Pam Scheunemann. Scarletta Junior Readers, 2013 144 p.

Grades: 5 6 7 8   **745.5**

1. Handicraft 2. Recycling (Waste, etc) 3. Salvage (Waste, etc)
ISBN 9781938063183

LC 2013010144

With easy step-by-step instructions, this book will help kids get creative and recycle and repurpose their trash into handmade treasures. All projects feature common everyday items to reuse in a fun new way. From bottle-top pop art to felted tin-can organizers, kids will love making useful crafts and helping the environment. Great tips and advice on reusing, garage sales, and spotting treasures are also provided. So start your upcycling with these fabric, paper, metal, glass & ceramics, and odds & ends projects. Book includes: visual supply & tool lists, step-by-step instructions and photos, fun advice & tips, and safety information. Provided by publisher.

Wolf, Laurie Goldrich

Recyclo-gami: 40 crafts to make your friends green with envy! Laurie Goldrich Wolf; illustrated by Bruce Wolf. Running Press Book Pub., 2011. 112 p.

Grades: 4 5 6 7   **745.5**

1. Handicraft 2. Recycling (Waste, etc) 3. Creative activities for children and students 4. Handicraft for children 5. Salvage (Waste, etc)
ISBN 9780762440528

"Wolf's fun, resourceful projects offer straightforward ways to reuse common materials to make accessories, jewelry, household decorations, games, and gifts. Leftover tissue or wrapping paper can be used to create decoupage plates; old crayons are melted and baked into molds to make multicolored crayons; and unused CDs and DVDs are transformed into funky, freeform bowls when melted in the oven. . . . The ease of most of the activities should inspire readers to see the recycling bin as a potential treasure trove." Publishers Weekly.

745.54 Papers

Latno, Mark

The **paper** boomerang book: build them, throw them, and get them to return every time. Mark Latno. Chicago Review Press, 2010. 145 p.

Grades: 5 6 7 8   **745.54**

1. Paper work 2. Boomerangs 3. Paper toy making 4. Handicraft for children 5. Creative activities for children and students
ISBN 9781569762820

LC 2010007251

Provides instructions on how to create paper boomerangs while mastering basic and more advanced throws and catches, sharing informative historical facts and the principles of physics behind the boomerang's circuitous flight.

"In a unique . . . guide Latno . . . [explains] how to make, fine-tune, and decorate a type of paper boomerang that can be constructed with commonly available materials and thrown with (relative) safety indoors. The instructions and simply drawn diagrams are embedded in a history of boomerangs and throwing sticks, a challenging technical discussion of the physics of boomerangs and gyroscopes, and very detailed descriptions of the characteristics of railroad board (Latno's preferred paper) and alternatives, plus art-and-craft materials that can be used to dress up finished models." School Library Journal.

Includes bibliographical references.

Turnbull, Stephanie

Cool stuff to make with paper. Stephanie Turnbull. Smart Apple Media, 2015. 32 p.: Cool stuff

Grades: 4 5 6 7 8   **745.54**

1. Paper work 2. Handicraft for children 3. Party decorations 4. Handicraft

ISBN 9781625881892

LC 2013047372

Provides tips and techniques for creating crafts with paper, including origami animals, hats, snowflakes, and decorations.

745.592 Toys, models, miniatures, related objects

Kennedy, John E., 1967-

★ **Puppet** planet. John E. Kennedy. North Light Books, c2006. 79 p.

Grades: 4 5 6 7   **745.592**

1. Puppet making

ISBN 9781581807943

LC 2005033711

Presents step-by-step instructions and decorating tips for creating different styles of puppets, including marionettes and hand puppets.

Mercer, Bobby, 1961-

The **flying** machine book: build and launch 35 rockets, gliders, helicopters, boomerangs, and more. Bobby Mercer. Chicago Review Press, c2012. ix, 197 p.

Grades: 4 5 6   **745.592**

1. Paper airplanes 2. Flying-machines 3. Science fun 4. Flight

ISBN 9781613740866

LC 2011041174

Shows readers how to turn rubber bands, paper clips, straws, plastic bottles, and index cards into amazing, gravity-defying flyers. Each project contains a material list and detailed step-by-step instructions with photos. Mercer also includes explanations of the science behind each flyer, including concepts such as lift, thrust, and drag, the Bernoulli effect, and more. Provided by publisher.

745.593 Useful objects

Turnbull, Stephanie

Diaries and keepsakes: style secrets for girls. Stephanie Turnbull. Smart Apple Media, [2014] 32 p.: Girl talk

Grades: 4 5 6 7 8   **745.593**

1. Handicraft for girls 2. Book design 3. Diary writing 4. Gifts 5. Scrapbooks

ISBN 9781599209456

LC 2012051570

A book for preteen and teen girls on crafty ways to make and keep memories of events. Includes information on decorating, writing in, and hiding a private diary. Also includes idea for using photos to create scrapbooks and mugs.

745.594 Decorative objects

Trusty, Brad

The **kids'** guide to balloon twisting. by Brad and Cindy Trusty. Capstone Press, 2011. 32 p.: Edge books.

Grades: 4 5 6 7   **745.594**

1. Balloon sculpture 2. Balloon decorations 3. Creative activities for children and students 4. Balloons (Novelties)

ISBN 9781429654449

LC 2010036470

Gives kids step-by-step instructions about how to twist fun balloon animals and other shapes. Provided by publisher.

"Rare is the kid not dazzled by the squeaking, twisting balloon maestros out there, and this brightly illustrated, step-by-step guide makes it easy—well, easy-ish." Booklist.

Includes bibliographical references and index.

Turnbull, Stephanie

Cards and gifts: style secrets for girls. Stephanie Turnbull. Smart Apple Media, 2013. 32 p.: Girl talk (Smart Apple Media)

Grades: 4 5 6 7 8   **745.594**

1. Handicraft for girls 2. Greeting cards

ISBN 9781599209449

LC 2012051546

A fun magazine-like book for preteen and teen girls on crafty ways to make and present gifts. Includes information on materials that work best and step-by-step instructions to create cards, envelopes, photo frames, cookies, and other treats for girls. Provided by publisher.

745.6 Calligraphy, heraldic design, illumination

Winters, Eleanor

Calligraphy for kids. Eleanor Winters. Sterling Pub. Co., c2004. 128 p.

Grades: 6 7 8 9   **745.6**

1. Calligraphy 2. Calligraphy -- Technique

ISBN 1402706642

LC 2003023438

Introduces the art and technique of calligraphy; provides instructions for writing italic, Gothic, uncial, and Roman alphabets, punctuation, and decorative borders; and suggests projects.

"This guide to calligraphy begins with a survey of materials, a glossary, and suggestions on posture and pen and paper positions. Succinct chapters showing how to create a variety of alphabets follow. Winters . . . folds fascinating history into her expert instructions. Her clean layouts showcase beautifully rendered examples and practical exercises." Booklist.

746.46 Patchwork and quilting

Rubin, Susan Goldman

The **quilts** of Gee's Bend: piecing them up. Susan Goldman Rubin. Abrams Books for Young Readers, 2017. 56 p.

Grades: 5 6 7 8   **746.46**

1. African American quilts 2. Quilting 3. Quilts 4. African Americans 5. Patchwork quilts 6. Alabama

ISBN 9781419721311

LC 2016029253

Explores the history and culture of a group of African American quilters from Gee's Bend, Alabama, offering details on the community and their traditions.

"Combining history, memoir, and quilting, this fascinating portrait of an indomitable community will appeal to readers, artists, and crafters of all ages." School Library Journal.

Includes bibliographical references (pages 49-50) and index.

746.9 Other textile products

Beker, Jeanne

Strutting it: the grit behind the glamour. Jeanne Beker. Tundra Books, 2011. 88 p.

Grades: 6 7 8 9   **746.9**

  1. Fashion models 2. Clothing industry and trade 3. Fashion modeling 4. Model agencies 5. Professions

ISBN 9781770492240

"Beker—for 25 years a host of Canada's Fashion Television—distills the essence of her many years of experience as a model-watcher into this slim but engaging combination of advice, history and truth-telling. Each chapter showcases a different aspect of a model's career development. . . . Blessedly responsible and sane, a worthy title for any career collection for teens and a must for aspiring models." Kirkus.

Bertoletti, John C.

How fashion designers use math. by John C. Bertoletti. Chelsea Clubhouse, c2010. 32 p.: Math in the real world

Grades: 4 5 6   **746.9**

  1. Fashion design 2. Mathematics 3. Fashion

ISBN 9781604136067

LC 2009022683

Outlines the ways fashion designers use math to sketch their ideas, use symmetry appropriately, figure out how much fabric they will need for a prototype, and determine how much the tailors who make the clothes will be paid.

"Color photos of designers in action combine with diagrams that further clarify the easily digestible text." Booklist.

Includes bibliographical references (p. 31) and index.

Black, Alexandra

The **fashion** book. author, Alexandra Black. Dorling Kindersley, 2014. 160 p.

Grades: 6 7 8 9 10 11 12   **746.9**

  1. Fashion 2. Women's clothing 3. Fashion design 4. Costume -- History 5. Costume design -- History

ISBN 9781465422842

A sassy style guide for teenage girls shares insight into the fashion world and how to personalize one's appearance for best results, chronicling fashion trends throughout history while sharing practical tips from top designers and models.

Sapet, Kerrily, 1972-

Jimmy Choo. by Kerrily Sapet. Morgan Reynolds Pub., c2011. 112 p.

Grades: 7 8 9 10   **746.9**

  1. Choo, Jimmy, 1961- 2. Fashion designers 3. Shoemakers 4. Fashion 5. Malaysia

ISBN 9781599351513

LC 2010018813

"Malaysian-born Choo has shod some of the most famous feet in the world. . . . Sapet provides insider details about Choo's remarkable

career. . . . Explanations of shoe-biz terms, as well as Asian concepts such as feng shui, enliven the text, and the eye-catching design includes many color photos of both the shoes and their celebrity fans. . . . This [is an] engrossing introduction to both an exemplary designer and to the fashion business." Booklist.

Includes bibliographical references and index.

Spilsbury, Richard, 1963-

Hi-tech clothes. Richard Spilsbury. Capstone Heinemann Library, c2013. 56 p.: Design and Engineering

Grades: 5 6 7   **746.9**

  1. Fashion design 2. Clothing manufacture 3. Technological innovations 4. Product life cycle 5. Clothing industry and trade

ISBN 9781432970321

LC 2012013469

Describes recent technological advancements made in clothing and design, from high-tech materials used for sports apparel and electric lights sewn into fabric, to ecologically-conscious clothes and garments from recycled fabric.

747.7 Decoration of specific rooms of residential buildings

Weaver, Janice

★ **It's** your room!: a decorating guide for real kids. Janice Weaver and Frieda Wishinsky; illustrated by Claudia Davila. Tundra Books, c2006. 63 p.

Grades: 5 6 7 8   **747.7**

  1. Children's rooms 2. Bedrooms 3. Interior decoration

ISBN 0887767117

LC bl2006012812

You don't have to be a design star—or wealthy—to transform your room into an attractive, well-planned space that you love. If you're tired of having a messy, boring, or outdated (preschooler wallpaper, anyone?) room, check out this simple yet thorough guide to creating the decor you want. It lays out in detail how to de-clutter, organize, paint, and accessorize your personal space and introduces design concepts like proper lighting or choosing colors to create a specific mood. .

"Budding interior designers and readers who want to personalize their rooms will appreciate this title. It is filled with step-by-step guidelines for creating a budget, selecting paint colors and fabrics, organizing closets and desks, laying everything out, and adding finishing touches. The illustrations will be a hit with first-time decorators just starting to develop their own color sense." School Library Journal.

750 Painting and paintings

Raczka, Bob

★ **Unlikely** pairs: fun with famous works of art. Bob Raczka. Millbrook Press, c2006. 31 p.

Grades: 4 5 6 7   **750**

  1. Art appreciation for children 2. Painting 3. Art appreciation

ISBN 0761329366

LC 2003014078

Invites the reader to discover fourteen funny stories produced by pairing twenty-eight paintings from different eras and styles.

"Raczka deserves an A+ for cleverness. . . . Rodin's The Thinker is juxtaposed with Klee's modernistic painting of a chessboard so that the statue looks as if it is contemplating the next move. Simon-Chardin's picture of a boy blowing soap bubbles seems to be creating Kandinsky's Several Circles. Each selection takes up a page and is reproduced in crisp color. . . . This book is an amusing way to introduce children to famous works of art." School Library Journal.

751.4 Painting—Techniques and procedures

Peot, Margaret
★ **Inkblot**: drip, splat, and squish your way to creativity. Margaret Peot. Boyds Mills Press, 2011. 56 p.
Grades: 4 5 6 7   **751.4**
1. Art -- Technique 2. Creativity 3. Drawing -- Technique 4. Handicraft 5. Handicraft for children
ISBN 9781590787205
"Peot's own entrancing inkblots . . . plus a few guest blots, illustrate every step, showing how the pure blot becomes a final artwork. . . . Readers get clear directions and lively encouragement." Kirkus.

Self, Caroline, 1919-
Chinese brush painting: a hands-on introduction to the traditional art. by Caroline Self and Susan Self Tuttle Pub., 2007. 64 p.
Grades: 9 10 11 12 Adult   **751.4**
1. Ink painting, Chinese -- Technique 2. Art 3. Painting
ISBN 9780804838771
                                    LC 2006037838
"This introduces readers to the art of Chinese calligraphy and brush painting. The text is fluid and graceful . . . and the authors wrap succinct accounts of Chinese history and lore around their clear, step-by-step, illustrated instructions." Booklist.
Includes bibliographical references (p. 64).

759 Painting—History, geographic treatment, biography

D'Harcourt, Claire, 1960-
Masterpieces up close: Western painting from the 14th to 20th centuries. by Claire d'Harcourt. Chronicle Books, 2005. 64 p.
Grades: 4 5 6 7 8   **759**
1. Painting 2. Art appreciation 3. Picture interpretation 4. Picture puzzles 5. Toy and movable books 6. Lift-the-flap books 7. Translations French to English
ISBN 0811854035
                                    LC 2004016341
"As in earlier entries in this series, readers are invited to find more than one hundred details in twenty-one well-known paintings, ranging from Giotto's frescoes to Warhol's Marilyns. The details are accompanied by statements of their artistic or symbolic significance, and each group of paintings (organized chronologically) is followed by a broader discussion of the works' context and importance." Horn Book.

759.05 Painting—Periods of development—1800-1899

Heine, Florian
Impressionism: 13 artists children should know. Florian Heine. Prestel Publishing, 2015. 48 p.
Grades: 4 5 6   **759.05**
1. Impressionism (Art) 2. Impressionist artists 3. Modern art 19th century 4. Art
ISBN 9783791372068

Shares key examples of Impressionist art to demonstrate to young readers how masters including Claude Monet, John Singer Sargent and others developed Impressionist forms and influenced art history.

Sabbeth, Carol, 1957-
★ **Monet** and the Impressionists for kids: their lives and ideas, 21 activities. Carol Sabbeth. Chicago Review Press, c2002. xii, 140 p.
Grades: 5 6 7 8   **759.05**
1. Impressionism (Art) 2. Art, French 19th century 3. Artists 19th century
ISBN 1556523971
                                    LC 2001047191
Discusses the nineteenth-century French art movement known as Impressionism, focusing on the works of Monet, Renoir, Degas, Cassatt, Cezanne, Gauguin, and Seurat. Includes related projects and activities.
"A beautifully designed introduction to Impressionism. . . . Sabbeth also includes 21 appealing extension activities such as recipes, crafts, games, and writing suggestions. Quality color reproductions on glossy pages, and varied, attractive layouts add to the book." School Library Journal.
Includes bibliographical references (p. 134-135) and index.

759.06 1900-1999

Barsony, Piotr, 1946-
The **stories** of the Mona Lisa: an imaginary museum tale about the history of modern art. Piotr Barsony; translated from the French by Joanna Oseman. Skyhorse Publishing, 2012, c2010 64 p.
Grades: 5 6 7 8   **759.06**
1. Leonardo, da Vinci, 1452-1519. Mona Lisa 2. Painting, Modern 3. Art movements 4. Painting 5. European Renaissance 6. Artists 7. Translations French to English
ISBN 9781620872284
                                    LC 2012015603
A history of modern painting, presented through the story of the Mona Lisa, features an artist who serves as a museum tour guide introducing famous movements while sharing creative images of how the Mona Lisa may have appeared if painted by other master artists.

759.13 Painting—United States

Lawrence, Jacob, 1917-2000
The **great** migration: an American story. paintings by Jacob Lawrence; with a poem in appreciation by Walter Dean Myers. Museum of Modern Art; 1995, c1993. 1 v. (unpaged)
Grades: 4 5 6 7   **759.13**
1. Lawrence, Jacob, 1917-2000. 2. Painting, American 3. African Americans in art 4. Rural urban migration in art 5. African Americans -- Migrations 6. Migration, Internal
ISBN 0064434281
                                    LC BL 98000806
A series of paintings chronicles the journey of African Americans who, like the artist's family, left the rural South in the early twentieth century to find a better life in the industrial North.
"Lawrence is a storyteller with words as well as pictures: his captions and his own 1992 introduction to this book are the best commentary on his work." Booklist.

Rubin, Susan Goldman

Everybody paints!: the lives and art of the Wyeth family. by Susan Goldman Rubin. Chronicle Books, 2013. 112 p.

Grades: 6 7 8 9 10   **759.13**

1. Wyeth family 2. Artists 3. Painters 4. Art

ISBN 9780811869843

LC 2013006595

Traces three generations of the famous Wyeth art family, offering insight into the events that shaped their achievements in a volume complemented by reproductions of their most famous masterpieces.

"This small-trim book celebrates the artistic Wyeth family, mostly the work of revered illustrator N. C. Wyeth; his son Andrew, popular modern realist best-known for Christina's World; and grandson Jamie, an acclaimed painter working today. Rubin's prose is fluid, and seamlessly worked-in quotes from her subjects add to the narrative's personal feel. The handsome, clean design showcases the excellent reproductions." Horn Book.

Wideness and wonder: the life and art of Georgia O'Keeffe. by Susan Goldman Rubin. Chronicle Books, c2010. 117 p.

Grades: 6 7 8 9   **759.13**

1. O'Keeffe, Georgia, 1887-1986 2. Painters 3. Artists 4. Influence (Literary, artistic, etc) 5. New York City 6. Southwest (United States)

ISBN 9780811869836

LC 2010008256

Traces the events that shaped the artist's work and how art influenced her life in return.

"Rubin here looks at the life and work of Georgia O'Keeffe. Nicely illustrated with family photos, portrait photos by Stieglitz, and many reproductions of the artist's drawings and paintings, the book builds a convincing portrayal of O'Keeffe from her student days to her ultimate recognition as an important American artist. The book's design is striking." Booklist.

Includes bibliographical references and index.

759.4 French painting

Spence, David

Manet. [written by David Spence]. New Forest Press, c2010. 48 p.: Great artists and their world

Grades: 6 7 8 9   **759.4**

1. Manet, Edouard, 1832-1883. 2. Painters 3. Artists 4. Painting, French 5. Art, French 6. Impressionism (Art)

ISBN 9781848983137

LC bl2010026399

Presents the life and accomplishments of the French artist known for his founding of the impressionist school of painting, discusses his famous paintings, and examines how his paintings bridged the worlds of traditional and modern art.

"Offers biographical information [of Edouard Manet] . . . interspersed with art history and criticism in an eye-catching format. . . . [Includes] a long introductory paragraph and four-to-six images with explanatory notes. . . . Spence . . . does a good job of explaining why art that might seem ordinary today was revolutionary at the time of its creation." School Library Journal.

Includes bibliographical references (p. 45) and index.

759.9492 Dutch painting

Crispino, Enrica

Van Gogh. Enrica Crispino. The Oliver Press, c2008. 64 p.: Art masters

Grades: 6 7 8 9 10   **759.9492**

1. Gogh, Vincent van, 1853-1890. 2. Artists 3. Painting, Dutch 4. Painters 5. Painters 6. Expressionism (Art)

ISBN 9781934545058

"Using generous, colorful, and cleanly designed two-page spreads, Crispino situates Van Gogh among other artists within certain time periods and locations, portraying his work and life as a counterpoint to various traditions and trends. Most topics are centered by an original drawing that is surrounded by photographs, paintings, artifacts, and descriptions. . . . Consider this volume the equivalent of an unusually insightful museum tour guide." Booklist.

Whiting, Jim, 1943-

Vincent Van Gogh. Jim Whiting. Mitchell Lane Publishers, c2008. 48 p.: Art profiles for kids

Grades: 7 8 9 10   **759.9492**

1. Gogh, Vincent van, 1853-1890. 2. Artists 3. Painting, Dutch 4. Painters 5. Expressionism (Art)

ISBN 9781584155645

LC 2007000662

Profiles the famous Dutch artist known for his distinctive brushstrokes in such paintings as "Starry Night" and "Irises."

"This offers well-documented information for teens doing reports. [The] volume covers the painter's childhood, training, travels, influences, and historical context. The chronological chapters build a survey of the [artist's] oeuvres, including the style and subject matter of [his] works and past and present critical reaction." School Library Journal.

Includes bibliographical references (p. 45-46) and index.

759.972 Mexican painting

Reef, Catherine

Frida & Diego: art, love, life. Catherine Reef. Houghton Mifflin Harcourt, 2014. 176 p.

Grades: 7 8 9 10   **759.972**

1. Kahlo, Frida. 2. Rivera, Diego, 1886-1957. 3. Painters 4. Artists 5. Artist couples

ISBN 9780547821849

LC 2013021340

"Reef points out each individual's artistic development and unique qualities as a painter. Archival photos and color reproductions of artworks further enhance the narrative. Writing a dual biography is challenging, but in this case, the portrayal of each person would seem incomplete without an understanding of the other." Booklist.

Includes bibliographical references.

770 Photography, computer art, cinematography, videography

Aronson, Marc

Eyes of the world: Robert Capa, Gerda Taro, and the invention of modern photojournalism. Marc Aronson and Marina Budhos. Henry Holt and Company, 2017. 320 p.

Grades: 7 8 9 10   **770**
1. Capa, Robert, 1913-1954. 2. Taro, Gerta, 1910-1937. 3. Photojournalists 4. Photojournalism 5. War photographers 6. Spain -- History -- Civil War, 1936-1939.
ISBN 9780805098358

LC 2016020545

Presents a narrative account of the heroic achievements of photojournalism pioneers Robert Capa and Gerda Taro, describing how as young Jewish refugees they took powerful photographs throughout the Spanish Civil War to witness the tragedies and document the fight against Fascism.
"Dense but never dull, this book exposes art and humanity in history." Booklist.
Includes bibliographical references and index.

Kallen, Stuart A., 1955-
Photography. by Stuart A. Kallen. Lucent Books, c2007. 112 p.: Eye on art
Grades: 7 8 9 10 11 12   **770**
1. Artistic photography 2. Artistic photography -- History and criticism 3. Photography
ISBN 1590189868

LC 2007015978

Presents a history of artistic photography and its various techniques through the ages, from the first photograph, taken by a wealthy Frenchman called Niépce in 1826, to the modern use of digital tools.
"This volume surveys the history of photography, from the ancient camera obscura to the digital camera. . . . This title offers a clear overview of an art form that many teens both practice and appreciate." Booklist.
Includes bibliographical references and index.

Meyerowitz, Joel, 1938-
Seeing things: a kid's guide to looking at photographs. Joel Meyerowitz. Aperture, 2016. 67 p.
Grades: 6 7 8 9 10 11 12   **770**
1. Photography 2. Photographers 3. Art appreciation
ISBN 9781597113151
"Meyerowitz's informative, enthusiastic tone will be perfectly engaging for teens interested in pursuing photography." Booklist.

Proujansky, Alice
Go photo!: an activity book for kids. Alice Proujansky; with illustrations by Maggie Prendergast. Aperture, [2016] 102 p.
Grades: 4 5 6 7   **770**
1. Photography 2. Photographs 3. Cameras
ISBN 9781597113557
"Proujansky touches on technical aspects of photography, such as composition and lighting... but her emphasis is generally on playful exploration, building readers confidence behind the camera through an array of creative projects and ideas." Publishers Weekly.

Sandler, Martin W.
America through the lens: photographers who changed the nation. Martin W. Sandler. Henry Holt and Co., 2005. ix, 182 p.
Grades: 6 7 8 9   **770**
1. Photographers 2. Photography
ISBN 0805073671

LC 2004059601

From Mathew Brady's startling Civil War photographs to NASA's stunning images of the universe, a visual study of groundbreaking cin-ematographers highlights twelve photographers whose work has truly changed the nation.

Turnbull, Stephanie
Cool stuff to photograph. Stephanie Turnbull. Smart Apple Media, 2015. 32 p.: Cool stuff
Grades: 4 5 6 7 8   **770**
1. Photography 2. Photography for children 3. Digital cameras 4. Photographers
ISBN 9781625881908

LC 2013047370

Provides tips and techniques for taking photographs, with information on camera types, light, framing an image, photographing different subjects, finishing the photograph, and related topics.

770.92 Biography

Greenberg, Jan, 1942-
Meet Cindy Sherman: artist, photographer, chameleon. by Jan Greenberg & Sandra Jordan. Roaring Brook Press, [2017] 64 p.
Grades: 5 6 7 8   **770.92**
1. Sherman, Cindy 2. Photographers 3. Women photographers 4. Artistic photography
ISBN 9781626725201

LC 2016058238

Biography of legendary artist Cindy Sherman. Provided by publisher.
"This masterfully executed biography of a fascinating working artist, written in a tone ideal for its target audience, will be invaluable for libraries hoping to enliven their arts collections." Booklist.
Includes bibliographical references.

775 Digital photography

Rabbat, Suzy
Super smart information strategies.. by Suzy Rabbat. Cherry Lake Pub., c2010. 32 p.: Information explorer
Grades: 3 4 5 6   **775**
1. Photography 2. Digital images 3. Digital photography
ISBN 9781602799547

LC 2010018941

"The information on deciding between file formats and resolutions in Using Digital Images will be tremendously helpful, and some beginner techniques on taking and editing effective photos are a nice bonus." Booklist.
Includes bibliographical references and index.

778 Specific fields and special kinds of photography

Green, Julie, 1982-
Super smart information strategies. by Julie Green. Cherry Lake Pub., 2010. 32 p. : Information explorer
Grades: 3 4 5 6   **778**
1. Digital cinematography 2. Internet videos 3. Films -- Production and direction 4. Filmmaking -- Vocational guidance 5. Internet
ISBN 9781602799554

LC 2010002022

Presents tools for planning, shooting, editing, and sharing a movie.

780 Music

Earls, Irene
Young musicians in world history. Irene Earls. Greenwood Press, 2002. xiv, 139 p.
Grades: 8 9 10 11 12   **780**
    1. Musicians
ISBN 031331442X
LC 2001040559
Profiles thirteen musicians who achieved high honors and fame before the age of twenty-five, representing many different time periods and musical styles.
"A useful introduction to some of the musical giants of the last four centuries." School Library Journal.
Includes bibliographical references and index.

Hansen, Dee
The **music** and literacy connection. Dee Hansen, Elaine Bernstorf, and Gayle M. Stuber. Rowman & Littlefield, 2014. 290 p.
Grades: Professional   **780**
    1. School music -- Instruction and study 2. Interdisciplinary approach in education 3. Reading (Primary)
ISBN 9781475805987
LC 2014023926
The second edition of The Music and Literacy Connection expands our understanding of the links between reading and music by examining those skills and learning processes that are directly parallel for music learning and language arts literacy in the pre-K, elementary, and secondary levels.

Tate, Eleanora E.
African American musicians. Eleanora E. Tate; Jim Haskins, general editor. Wiley, c2000. 70 p.: Black Stars Series
Grades: 6 7 8 9   **780**
    1. African American musicians 2. African Americans
ISBN 0471253561
LC 99051360
Presents biographical profiles of African Americans, both legendary and less well-known, who have made significant contributions to music in the United States over the past 200 years.
"Many genres and skills are represented from spirituals, gospel, ragtime, blues, jazz, and soul. Scott Joplin, Marian Anderson, Duke Ellington, and Aretha Franklin are here as well as Michael Jackson and a few lesser-known individuals. Each entry includes a black-and-white photo or reproduction and sidebars on pertinent topics." School Library Journal.
Includes bibliographical references (p. 162-165) and index.

780.922 Composers—Collected biography

Rhodes, James, 1975-
Playlist: the rebels and revolutionaries of sound. James Rhodes; illustrated by Martin O'Neill. Candlewick Press, 2019 72 p.
Grades: 8 9 10 11 12   **780.922**
    1. Classical music -- History and criticism 2. Music -- History and criticism 3. Composers 4. Musicians
ISBN 9781536212143
Complemented by an online playlist of favorite classics, a celebrated concert pianist traces the links between the master composers of the past

and the music of today's world, sharing their backstories and role in shaping and defining cultural history.
"When first approaching any art, nothing enhances the experience like encouragement from a friend in love with the work, and that's the role played here by concert pianist Rhodes in this vibrant introduction to classical music." Booklist.

781.62 Folk music

Handyside, Chris
  ★ **Folk**. Christopher Handyside. Heinemann Library, c2006. 48 p.: A history of American music
Grades: 5 6 7 8   **781.62**
    1. Folk music, American -- History and criticism 2. Folk music, American 3. Folk music 4. Music, American
ISBN 1403481504
LC 2005019282
Defines folk music and traces its history and development in the United States, including its resurgence in popularity starting in the 1950s.
"This history of folk music is an excellent, clear [introduction]. . . . [It] starts with the post-Civil War era, when folklorists gathered slave songs. It describes the music's commercial success beginning with early recordings of the Carter family and Jimmie Rodgers in the 1920s and continuing with Leadbelly, Woody Guthrie, Pete Seeger, and the many musicians who became popular during the folk revival of the late 50s and early 60s. . . . It concludes with sections on folk rock, punk rock, and the future of folk music." School Library Journal.
Includes bibliographical references (p. 47) and index.

781.644 Soul

Mendelson, Aaron
American R & B: Gospel grooves, funky drummers, and soul power. Aaron Mendelson. Twenty-First Century Books, c2012. 64 p.: American music milestones
Grades: 7 8 9 10 11 12   **781.644**
    1. Soul music -- History and criticism 2. Rhythm and blues music -- History and criticism 3. Music -- History and criticism
ISBN 9780761345015
LC 2011045636
Presents a history of R&B music in the United States, profiles the genre's most notable past and present stars, and features song and album suggestions.

Pinkney, Andrea Davis
  ★ **Rhythm** ride: a road trip through the Motown sound. Andrea Davis Pinkney. Roaring Brook Press, 2015. 160 p.
Grades: 5 6 7 8 9   **781.644**
    1. Motown Record Corporation 2. Sound recording industry and trade 3. African American musicians 4. African Americans
ISBN 9781596439733
LC 2014045894
A narrative history of the Motown music label covering the historical context, personalities, and ongoing legacy of the "sound of young America." Provided by publisher.
"An ebullient, wonderfully told introduction to music that had an indelible influence on a generation and its times." Kirkus.

781.65 Jazz

Handyside, Chris
★ **Jazz.** Christopher Handyside. Heinemann Library, c2006. 48 p.: A history of American music
Grades: 5 6 7 8   **781.65**
1. Jazz music -- History and criticism 2. Jazz music 3. Music, American
ISBN 1403481490

LC 2005019305
Describes the origin and characteristics of jazz and traces its history and development in the United States.

Kallen, Stuart A., 1955-
The **history** of jazz. by Stuart A. Kallen. Lucent Books, c2012. 112 p.: Music library (Lucent)
Grades: 6 7 8 9   **781.65**
1. Jazz music -- History and criticism 2. Music
ISBN 1590181255

LC 2002002220
Covers the music, the musicians, the instruments, and music's place in cultural history. Presents a history of each musical style, from its roots to its expression along with glimpses of the lives of leading composers and musicians. This volume focuses on the music style of jazz.

"This follows jazz music's evolution from its African roots through contemporary forms. [The volume is] greatly enhanced by fascinating excerpts from primary material, including articles, letters, and diaries, often in the words of the composer or musician. . . . Students reading for reports or for personal interest will find much useful information." Booklist.

Includes bibliographical references (p. 100-104) and index.

Nelson, Marilyn, 1946-
Sweethearts of rhythm: the story of the greatest all-girl swing band in the world. written by Marilyn Nelson; illustrated by Jerry Pinkney. Dial Books, c2009. 1 v. (unpaged)
Grades: 4 5 6 7   **781.65**
1. International Sweethearts of Rhythm 2. 1940s 3. Jazz music 4. Women jazz musicians 5. Big bands 6. Women entertainers 7. Big band music 8. United States -- Social life and customs -- 20th century
ISBN 9780803731875

LC 2008046255
A look at a 1940's all-female jazz band, that originated from a boarding school in Mississippi and found its way to the most famous ballrooms in the country, offering solace during the hard years of the war.

"On all fronts, a resonant performance." Publishers Weekly.
Includes bibliographical references.

781.66 Rock (Rock 'n' Roll)

Goodmark, Robyn
Girls rock: how to get your group together and make some noise. Robyn Goodmark; illustrated by Adrienne Yan. Billboard Books, c2008. xi, 178 p.
Grades: 6 7 8 9 10   **781.66**
1. Rock music -- Vocational guidance 2. Women rock musicians -- Vocational guidance 3. Rock groups 4. Press 5. Demonstration tapes
ISBN 9780823099481

LC 2008007386

"This shows the ins, outs, and good and bad things that come with starting a band and making it successful. . . . The conversational tone and quizzes throughout give the presentation the feel of a teen magazine. . . . Clever cartoon illustrations appear throughout. . . . Not only does this book provide the technical assistance newbie musicians might need, but it also provides advice on choosing a band name and more emotional topics like how to find creative inspiration. This is a wonderful guide for any girl who wants to start a band." School Library Journal.

Witmer, Scott
Managing your band. Scott Witmer. ABDO, 2009. 32 p.: Rock band (ABDO Publishing)
Grades: 6 7 8 9   **781.66**
1. Rock music -- Vocational guidance 2. Rock groups 3. Teenage rock musicians 4. Rock musicians
ISBN 9781604536935

LC 2009006610
"Copious examples and photos of bands drawn from a wide chronological and stylistic range ensure that every reader, from metalheads (Metallica) to Linkin Park fans will find something of interest here." School Library Journal.

782.1 Operas and related dramatic vocal forms

Siberell, Anne
★ **Bravo!** brava! a night at the opera: behind the scenes with composers, cast, and crew. Anne Siberell; introduction by Frederica von Stade. Oxford University Press, c2001. 64 p.
Grades: 4 5 6 7   **782.1**
1. Operas 2. Music 3. Performing arts
ISBN 0195139666

LC 2001021206
Introduces the art of opera, and provides information on its origins, all the various types of people needed to put on a performance, and the plots of some of the best known operas.

"An excellent resource for reports, this unusual book has an exceptional range of topics for younger students and is an essential purchase for upper elementary and middle school music programs." School Library Journal.

Includes bibliographical references (p. 62) and index.

782.25 Small-scale vocal forms

Giovanni, Nikki
On my journey now: looking at African-American history through the spirituals. Nikki Giovanni; foreword by Arthur C. Jones. Candlewick Press, 2007. xi, 116 p.
Grades: 7 8 9 10   **782.25**
1. African Americans -- History 2. African American music 3. Spirituals (Songs)
ISBN 0763628859

LC 2006051695
A title that includes full lyrics to 46 songs paints compelling portraits of Africans in America through familiar songs such as "Go Down, Moses" and "Ain't Got Time to Die," celebrating a people who overcame enslavement and found a way to survive, to worship, and to build.

"Personal and passionate, Giovanni's short narrative talks about the sacred songs first sung by slaves, tracing how the people in bondage created the great spirituals to tell their stories, and what the songs still mean to us today." Booklist.

Includes discography (p. 111), bibliographical references (p. 109-110) and indexes.

782.42 Songs

Murphy, Claire Rudolf

My country, 'tis of thee: how one song reveals the history of civil rights. Claire Rudolf Murphy; illustrated by Bryan Collier. Henry Holt & Co., 2014 48 p.

Grades: 3 4 5 6   **782.42**

1. Smith, Samuel Francis, 1808-1895. America 2. Songs -- History and criticism 3. Freedom 4. History
ISBN 9780805082265

A chronicle of civil rights movements through the song's changing lyrics reveals how its words have been transformed by generations of protestors and civil rights pioneers throughout landmark historical movements.

Silverman, Jerry, 1931-

Songs and stories of the Civil War. Jerry Silverman. Twenty-First Century Books, c2002. 96 p.

Grades: 5 6 7 8   **782.42**

1. Music 19th century -- History and criticism 2. Civil war 3. United States Civil War, 1861-1865 4. United States -- History -- Civil War, 1861-1865 5. United States -- History -- Civil War, 1861-1865 -- History and criticism
ISBN 0761323058

     LC 2001035795

Provides a history of the music and lyrics of a dozen Civil War songs, describing the circumstances under which they were created and performed.

"Black-and-white reproductions of period photos, engravings, paintings, and drawings illustrate the text. A good resource offering an interesting sidelight on the times." Booklist.

Includes bibliographical references (p. 92-93), discographies, and index.

Yolen, Jane

Apple for the teacher: thirty songs for singing while you work. edited by Jane Yolen; music arranged by Adam Stemple. Harry N. Abrams, Publishers, c2005. 117 p.

Grades: 4 5 6 7   **782.42**

1. Americana 2. Occupations 3. Professions 4. Work 5. Music 6. Songs
ISBN 9780810948259

Accompanied by American folk art illustrations, a sing-along book pays tribute to the many occupations in the world, from past to present, including barbers, telephone operators, computer programmers, and astronauts.

"Yolen has brought together a collection of 30 work songs . . . which represent a wide variety of occupations. . . . She introduces each job, explaining unusual vocabulary and references in the songs. . . . The artwork . . . is elegant. Ranging from sculpture to paintings to needlework, each selection of Americana has been carefully matched to the occupation, beautifully reproduced on high-quality paper, and meticulously identified." Booklist.

782.42162 Folk songs

Cooper, Michael L., 1950-

Slave spirituals and the Jubilee Singers. by Michael L. Cooper. Clarion Books, c2001. x, 86 p.

Grades: 7 8 9 10   **782.42162**

1. Jubilee Singers. 2. Fisk University 3. African American music 4. African Americans 5. Spirituals (Songs) -- History and criticism
ISBN 0395978297

     LC 00065854

Presents the story of the Jubilee Singers, a group of African Americans who toured singing slave spirituals to raise money for their struggling school.

"The first half of this book traces the development of spirituals from African musical traditions and discusses the place of religion in the lives of the slaves. The second half focuses on Fisk University's Jubilee Singers. . . . Illustrated with many archival prints and photographs, the book includes extensive annotated source notes and the words and music to seven of the spirituals popularized by the Jubilee Singers." School Library Journal.

Includes bibliographical references (p. 72-74) and index.

Lowinger, Kathy

Give me wings: how a choir of former slaves took on the world. Kathy Lowinger. Annick Press, 2015. 146 p.

Grades: 6 7 8 9   **782.42162**

1. Jubilee Singers 2. Fisk University 3. 19th century 4. Freed people 5. African American singers 6. Singers 7. Choirs
ISBN 9781554517473

Eleven black students form a singing group and tour the world in an attempt to save Fisk University from financial ruin.

"Lowinger does not shy away from the more unpleasant aspects of that history and grounds it in the very human and relatively little-known story of Sheppard and the Jubilee Singers, which makes the struggle all the more touching and real." School Library Journal.

Stotts, Stuart, 1957-

★ **We** shall overcome: a song that changed the world. by Stuart Stotts; foreword by Pete Seeger; with illustrations by Terrance Cummings. Clarion Books, 2009. 80 p.

Grades: 5 6 7 8   **782.42162**

1. Protest songs, American -- History and criticism 2. Music -- Political aspects 3. Civil rights movement 4. Protest movements 5. Freedom Riders (Civil rights movement) 6. Songs
ISBN 9780547182100

     LC 2009022578

An accessible history of the inspiring anthem explores the influence of traditional African music and Christian hymns in shaping its lyrics and tune, offering insight into the song's role in civil rights, labor and anti-war movements in America.

"This smart, effective telling has few missteps. From the informative black-and-white photographs to the solid back matter to the CD sung by Pete Seeger, it is a complete package." Booklist.

782.42164 Western popular songs

Bieber, Justin, 1994-

Justin Bieber: first step 2 forever: my story. Justin Bieber, Robert Caplin; [edited by] Emily Brenner. HarperCollins, 2010. 236 p.

Grades: 4 5 6 7   **782.42164**

1. Bieber, Justin, 1994- 2. Teenage singers 3. Celebrities 4. Entertainers 5. Online social networks 6. Singers
ISBN 9780062039743

"Bieber, the platinum-selling singer/songwriter . . . debuts with an account of his 16-year-old life that's cheeky yet entirely in line with his safe and wholesome image. . . . The book covers his upbringing in Ontario, his early introduction to music, YouTube stardom, his love of pranks, and the stratospheric success he now enjoys—all interspersed with lyrics, tweets, and numerous full-bleed photographs of Bieber." Publishers Weekly.

Robertson, Robbie

Legends, icons & rebels: music that changed the world. written by Robbie Robertson, Jim Guerinot, Jared Levine, and Sebastian Robertson Tundra Books, 2013. 128 p.

Grades: 6 7 8 9 10 11 12   **782.42164**

1. Musicians 2. Singers
ISBN 9781770495715

LC oc2013018257

Three music industry veterans present a tribute to more than two dozen legendary music artists who significantly influenced the landscape of music for generations to come, from Ray Charles and Bob Dylan to Chuck Berry and Johnny Cash.

"In this oversize, weighty volume, music-industry-veteran authors offer collected anecdotal sketches, including personal memories, of twenty-seven music risk-takers such as Aretha Franklin, the Beatles, and Bob Dylan. Their meteoric careers, many touched by tragedy, are justly celebrated. A timeline of these artists' first recordings (1925-1968) ends the book; includes two CDs of sparkling audio quality with one iconic song by each." Horn Book.

Tsoukanelis, Erika Alexia

The **Latin** music scene: the stars, the fans, the music. Erika Alexia Tsoukanelis. Enslow, 2010. 48 p.: Music scene (Enslow Publishers)

Grades: 6 7 8 9   **782.42164**

1. Popular music -- History and criticism 2. Music, Latin American 3. Musicians 4. Music appreciation 5. Music
ISBN 9780766033993

LC 2008048013

Read about the music, stars, clothes, contracts, and world of Latin music. Provided by publisher.

782.421646 Reggae -- Songs

Manuel, Peter, 1952-

The **reggae** scene: the stars, the fans, the music. Peter Manuel and Daniel T. Neely. Enslow, 2010. 48 p.: Music scene (Enslow Publishers)

Grades: 6 7 8 9   **782.421646**

1. Reggae music -- History and criticism 2. Reggae musicians 3. Music appreciation 4. Musicians 5. Music
ISBN 9780766034006

LC 2008048014

Read about the music, stars, clothes, contracts, and world of reggae music. Provided by publisher.

"This is clearly written, well organized, and copiously illustrated with full-color photographs of noted performers." School Library Journal.

Includes bibliographical references (p. 47) and index.

782.42166 Rock (Rock 'n' roll) songs

Mead, Wendy

The **alternative** rock scene: the stars, the fans, the music. Wendy S. Mead. Enslow, 2009. 48 p. : Music scene (Enslow Publishers)

Grades: 6 7 8 9   **782.42166**

1. Alternative rock music -- History and criticism 2. Alternative rock musicians 3. Music 4. Musicians
ISBN 9780766034013

LC 2008048015

Read about the music, stars, clothes, contracts, and world of alternative rock music. Provided by publisher.

"This is clearly written, well organized, and copiously illustrated with full-color photographs of noted performers." School Library Journal.

Includes bibliographical references and index.

783 Music for single voices

Landau, Elaine

Is singing for you? Elaine Landau. Lerner Publications, 2010. 40 p.: Ready to make music

Grades: 4 5 6 7   **783**

1. Singing -- Study and teaching 2. Singing -- Vocational guidance
ISBN 9780761354277

LC 2009052350

"Landau covers all the bases so that prospective musicians have the information they need. . . . Kids thinking about taking up an instrument will find . . . [this book] helpful in their decision-making process." School Library Journal.

Includes bibliographical references and index.

784.19 Instruments

Kallen, Stuart A., 1955-

The **instruments** of music. by Stuart A. Kallen. Lucent Books, c2003. 112 p.: Music library (Lucent)

Grades: 6 7 8 9   **784.19**

1. Musical instruments 2. Music
ISBN 1590181271

LC 2001006609

Presents the history and development of various musical instruments, including percussion, woodwinds, brass, strings, and keyboards, discussing specific types of the instrument and key figures in their development.

784.4 Light orchestra

Bolden, Tonya

Take-off!: American all-girl bands during WW II. Tonya Bolden. Knopf, c2007. 76 p.

Grades: 6 7 8 9   **784.4**

1. United Service Organizations (U.S.) 2. Women entertainers 3. World War II -- Women 4. Women musicians 5. Sexism 6. Racism 7. United States
ISBN 0375927972

LC 2006024523

With the men away fighting World War II, American women were finally given a chance to showcase their musical talents and, in the process, created all-girl bands that became a celebrated staple on the USO tours as morale boosters for soldiers both home and abroad.

"To appreciate this book, readers need at least a nodding acquaintance with swing music. The accompanying CD will help, and Bolden's introduction, which features opinions from Benny Goodman, Ella Fitzgerald, and others, gets things off to a good start. Then, using fascinating archival material . . . she goes on to discuss pioneering female jazz bands. . . . Bolden [uses] a fresh style of writing, as bouncy as the music." Booklist.

785 Ensembles with only one instrument per part

Marx, Trish
  Steel drumming at the Apollo: the road to super top dog. by Trish Marx; photographs by Ellen B. Senisi. Lee & Low Books, c2007. 56 p.
  Grades: 4 5 6 7   **785**
    1. Hamilton Hill Steel Drum Band 2. Apollo Theatre 3. Musicians
    ISBN 9781600601248
                                                    LC 2007008947
Photo-essay about a high school steel drum band from upstate New York, that participated in a series of talent competitions for a chance to win Super Top Dog on Amateur Night at the Apollo Theater in Harlem. Includes a CD of the band performing. Provided by publisher.

"Marx traces the band's progress through the tiers of competition in clear evocative prose depicting the visceral experience of performing as well as the hard work of practice and composition. Senisi's color photographs enliven every page." School Library Journal.

786 Specific instruments and their music

Witmer, Scott
  Drums, keyboards, and other instruments. Scott Witmer. ABDO, 2009. 32 p. : Rock band (ABDO Publishing)
  Grades: 6 7 8 9   **786**
    1. Rock groups 2. Musical instruments 3. Rock music 4. Rock musicians
    ISBN 9781604536904
                                                    LC 2009006607
"Copious examples and photos of bands drawn from a wide chronological and stylistic range ensure that every reader, from metalheads (Metallica) to Linkin Park fans will find something of interest here." School Library Journal.

786.2 Pianos

Batten, Jack, 1932-
  Oscar Peterson: the man and his jazz. Jack Batten. Tundra Books, c2012. 165, [21] p.
  Grades: 6 7 8   **786.2**
    1. Peterson, Oscar, 1925-2007 2. Pianists 3. Jazz musicians 4. Jazz music
    ISBN 1770492690
                                                    LC 2011940582
A biography of the great Canadian jazz pianist, Oscar Peterson.

786.2092 Pianists

Lang, Lang, 1982-
  Lang Lang: playing with flying keys. by Lang Lang with Michael French; introduction by Daniel Barenboim. Delacorte Press, c2008. xv, 215 p.
  Grades: 7 8 9 10   **786.2092**
    1. Lang, Lang, 1982- 2. Musicians 3. Pianists 4. Childhood 5. Classical music 6. Music -- Study and teaching 7. China -- Social life and customs -- 20th century 8. China -- Social life and customs -- 21st century
    ISBN 9780385735780
                                                    LC 2007051597
Provides a look at the life and accomplishments of the noted pianist through his views on the differences between the cultures of the East and West, the great changes in his homeland of China, and his love for classical music.

"Although he is only 26, Chinese-born Lang is recognized as one of the world's most accomplished classical pianists. This smoothly paced, often rivetingly candid autobiography . . . follows the musician through his first encounters with the keyboard and grueling training to his triumphant debut concerts with the Chicago Symphony." Booklist.

786.9 Drums and devices used for percussive effects

Landau, Elaine
  Are the drums for you? Elaine Landau. Lerner Publications, c2011. 40 p.: Ready to make music
  Grades: 4 5 6 7   **786.9**
    1. Drum 2. Drum set 3. Percussion instruments 4. Musical instruments
    ISBN 9780761354260
                                                    LC 2009048971
Examines the drums and describes different types of drums and other percussion instruments, explains how they make music, and introduces famous drummers.

"Landau covers all the bases so that prospective musicians have the information they need. . . . Kids thinking about taking up an instrument will find . . . [this book] helpful in their decision-making process." School Library Journal.

Includes bibliographical references (p. 38) and index.

787 Stringed instruments (Chordophones)

Ellis, Rex M., 1951-
  With a banjo on my knee: a musical journey from slavery to freedom. by Rex M. Ellis. Franklin Watts, c2001. 160 p.
  Grades: 7 8 9 10   **787**
    1. Banjo players 2. African American musicians 3. Banjo 4. Banjo music 5. Banjo players
    ISBN 0531117472
                                                    LC 00033035
Traces the evolution of the banjo within the African-American community from slavery through emancipation, minstrelsy, segregation, and civil rights, and includes portraits of performers.

"This is a well-written, attractive work, which unveils a segment of social history both powerful and far reaching." Booklist.

Includes discography (p. 123-124), bibliographical references (p. 125-126), list of web sites (p. 127-129), and index.

Ganeri, Anita, 1961-

Stringed instruments. by Anita Ganeri. Smart Apple Media, c2012. 32 p.: How the world makes music

Grades: 4 5 6   **787**

1. Stringed instruments 2. Musical instruments 3. Guitar 4. Cello 5. Violin

ISBN 9781599204802

     LC 2010042418

Describes various stringed instruments from around the world including familiar instruments such as the guitar and violin, along with other traditional instruments such as the Japanese Koto and Indian lutes. Provided by publisher.

787.2 Violins

Landau, Elaine

Is the violin for you? Elaine Landau. Lerner, c2011. 40 p.: Ready to make music

Grades: 4 5 6 7   **787.2**

1. Violin 2. Stringed instruments 3. Musical instruments 4. Violinists

ISBN 9780761354239

     LC 2009045609

Examines the violin and describes its parts, explains how it makes music and the many different styles of violin music, and introduces famous violinists.

"Landau covers all the bases so that prospective musicians have the information they need. . . . Kids thinking about taking up an instrument will find . . . [this book] helpful in their decision-making process." School Library Journal.

Includes bibliographical references (p. 38) and index.

787.87 Guitars

Landau, Elaine

Is the guitar for you? Elaine Landau. Lerner Publications, 2010. 40 p.: Ready to make music

Grades: 4 5 6 7   **787.87**

1. Guitar 2. Guitarists 3. Musical instruments

ISBN 9780761354246

     LC 2009048750

"Landau covers all the bases so that prospective musicians have the information they need. . . . Kids thinking about taking up an instrument will find . . . [this book] helpful in their decision-making process." School Library Journal.

Includes bibliographical references (p. 37) and index.

Witmer, Scott

Guitars & bass. Scott Witmer. ABDO, 2009. 32 p. : Rock band (ABDO Publishing)

Grades: 6 7 8 9   **787.87**

1. Guitar 2. Rock groups 3. Bass guitar 4. Rock music 5. Rock musicians

ISBN 9781604536911

     LC 2009006608

"Copious examples and photos of bands drawn from a wide chronological and stylistic range ensure that every reader, from metalheads (Metallica) to Linkin Park fans will find something of interest here." School Library Journal.

788.3 Flute family

Landau, Elaine

Is the flute for you? Elaine Landau. Lerner Publications, 2010. 40 p.: Ready to make music

Grades: 4 5 6 7   **788.3**

1. Flute 2. Woodwind instruments 3. Musical instruments

ISBN 9780761354208

     LC 2009048970

Examines the flute and describes its parts, explains how it makes music, and introduces famous flutists.

"Landau covers all the bases so that prospective musicians have the information they need. . . . Kids thinking about taking up an instrument will find . . . [this book] helpful in their decision-making process." School Library Journal.

Includes bibliographical references (p. 38) and index.

788.9 Brass instruments (Lip-reed instruments)

Landau, Elaine

Is the trumpet for you? Elaine Landau. Lerner Publications, c2011. 40 p.: Ready to make music

Grades: 4 5 6 7   **788.9**

1. Trumpet 2. Brass instruments 3. Musical instruments 4. Trumpeters

ISBN 9780761354222

     LC 2009048280

Examines the trumpet and describes its parts, explains how it makes music and the many different styles of brass music, and introduces famous trumpeters.

"Landau covers all the bases so that prospective musicians have the information they need. . . . Kids thinking about taking up an instrument will find . . . [this book] helpful in their decision-making process." School Library Journal.

Includes bibliographical references (p. 38) and index.

790 Recreational and performing arts

Glenn, Joshua

Unbored: the essential field guide to serious fun. compiled by Joshua Glenn & Elizabeth Foy Larsen; design by Tony Leone. Bloomsbury USA, 2012. 352 p.

Grades: 5 6 7   **790**

1. Recreation 2. Amusements 3. Handicraft 4. Games

ISBN 9781608196418

     LC 2012012368

Unbored is the most original, entertaining, and instructive all-in-one book for kids ever published—jam-packed with information, ideas, and activities for children and their parents to share together. Vibrantly designed and illustrated, it's crammed with activities that are not only fun and doable, but get kids engaged in the wider world—and provides information to expand their worldviews, too, inspiring them to learn more. Right at the age where kids start to disappear into various screens, Unbored encourages them to use those tech skills in creative ways. Activities parents will remember from their childhoods are presented alongside bold new possibilities: science experiments, crafts and upcycling, board game hacking, code-cracking, geocaching, skateboard repair, yarn bombing, stop-action movie-making—plus tons of trivia, best-of lists, and forward-thinking ideas made accessible to kids. Unbored expertly walks the line between cool and constructive: parents will appreciate its wisdom and humor, its lessons in civic-mindedness and self-esteem, as well as its anti-perfectionist spirit. Kids will just think it's awesome. Provided by publisher.

790.1 General kinds of recreational activities

Ball, Jacqueline A.

Traveling green. by Jacqueline A. Ball. Bearport Pub., c2009. 32 p.: Going green

Grades: 4 5 6 7   **790.1**

   1. Voyages and travels -- Environmental aspects 2. Transportation -- Environmental aspects 3. Environmentalism 4. Nature -- Effect of humans on 5. Travelers
ISBN 9781597169646

                 LC 2009019836

"Color photographs (most full page) and a few diagrams accompany the informative text[s]. . . . Overall, the [book] . . . is user-friendly and covers topics that are not easily found elsewhere." School Library Journal.

Includes bibliographical references (p. 32) and index.

Centore, Michael, 1980-

Entertainment industry. Michael Centore. Mason Crest, [2017] 64 p.: STEM in current events

Grades: 6 7 8 9 10   **790.1**

   1. Entertainment events 2. Animal trainers 3. Computer graphics 4. Television -- Special effects 5. Circus
ISBN 9781422235904

"A great fit for classroom or school libraries and a strong consideration for public libraries interested in the integration of STEM into everyday life." School Library Journal.

Ferrer, J. J.

The **art** of stone skipping and other fun old-time games: stoopball, jacks, string games, coin flipping, line baseball, jump rope, and more. J.J. Ferrer; illustrated by Todd Dakins. Imagine! Pub., c2012. 185 p.

Grades: PreK K 1 2 3 4 5 6 7 8 9 10 11 12 Adult   **790.1**

   1. Games 2. Recreation
ISBN 9781936140749

                 LC 2012015052

Collects the rules of over fifty classic indoor and outdoor games, including dodgeball, jacks, rummy, egg toss, coin bowling, and capture the flag.

Hines-Stephens, Sarah

Show off: how to do absolutely everything one step at a time. Sarah Hines Stephens and Bethany Mann. Candlewick Press, c2009. 224 p.

Grades: 5 6 7 8   **790.1**

   1. Recreation 2. Amusements 3. Handicraft 4. Creative activities for children and students 5. Books for reluctant readers
ISBN 9780763645991

                 LC 2009015847

Featuring simple illustrated instructions, a witty and nearly word-less resource teaches kids how to do tons of cool things, from creating personalized arts and crafts to performing amazing tricks and pranks.

"This lively illustrated activity book delivers concise instructions for a variety of indoor and outdoor activities. Projects include crafts, pranks and magic tricks; ideas for nature exploration; and other purely entertain-

ing feats. . . . The instructions are heavy on graphics and light on detail, making for an eye-catching but potentially frustrating experience. But readers should enjoy the irreverence and variety." Publishers Weekly.

Schofield, Jo

Make it wild!: 101 things to make and do outdoors. Jo Schofield and Fiona Danks. Frances Lincoln, 2010. 159 p.

Grades: 4 5 6 7 8   **790.1**

   1. Outdoor recreation for children 2. Nature study -- Activity programs
ISBN 9780711228856

               LC bl2010017139

Shows how to enjoy the opportunities offered in nature, exploring the potential of raw materials such as snow, leaves and sticks demonstrating how to make anything from a cricket bat or a clay monster to ice lanterns or flaming balloons.

"Using the raw materials nature has to offer, the authors offer clear, concise instructions on how to create ephemeral art, outdoor toys, jewelry, sculptures, and dozens of other things using materials like clay, ice, leaves, sand, and wood. The instructions offer good guidance but also encourage children to use their own creativity and imagination to craft the final product. The projects range in level of difficulty and, depending on the age of the child, can be done individually or in collaboration with siblings, peers, or parents. The authors include safety instructions and recommendations for further resources on outdoor creative exercises. The activities will teach problem solving and commonsense, useful skills; instill a deeper appreciation of nature; and encourage creativity and ingenuity. An excellent choice for any library collection." Booklist.

Includes bibliographical references (p. 157) and index.

Tukey, Paul Boardway

Tag, toss & run: 40 classic lawn games. Paul Tukey & Victoria Rowell. Storey Pub., c2012. 207 p.

Grades: Adult Professional   **790.1**

   1. Games 2. Outdoor games
ISBN 9781603425605

               LC 2011049410

Presents the rules for forty classic lawn games, including ghost in the graveyard, flag football, red rover, and double ball.

790.133 Play with toys

Bedford, Allan

The **unofficial** LEGO builder's guide. Allan Bedford. No Starch Press, 2013 xvi, 221 p.

Grades: 4 5 6 7 8   **790.133**

   1. LEGO toys
ISBN 9781593274412

               LC 2013431031

Presents a guide to constructing toys, miniature buildings, and art projects with LEGO, covering topics such as scale, bonding patterns, model designs, grids, mosaics, games, tools, and techniques.

791 Public performances

Lusted, Marcia Amidon

Entertainment. by Marcia Amidon Lusted. ABDO Pub. Company, c2011. 112 p.: Inside the industry

Grades: 5 6 7 8   **791**

   1. Performing arts -- Vocational guidance 2. Entertainment industry

and trade 3. Entertainers 4. Occupations 5. Arts
ISBN 9781617147999

LC 2010041255

Provides information about many different careers, from directors to musicians, in the performing arts, and discusses education and training required, earnings potential, and career outlook.

"This well-designed [book describes] a variety of careers in [entertainment]. Because [it helps] readers assess if these positions are suitable for their personality types and backgrounds, the [title is a] good [choice] for career exploration and self-discovery. [It is] also useful for research and reports. . . . Sidebars and full-color photos appear throughout." School Library Journal.

Includes bibliographical references (p. 104-109) and index.

791.3 Circuses

Grayson, Robert, 1951-

Performers. Robert Grayson. Marshall Cavendish Benchmark, 2011. 64 p.: Working animals

Grades: 4 5 6 7   **791.3**

1. Animal training 2. Working animals 3. Animals in the performing arts 4. Animals in television 5. Animals in films
ISBN 9781608701650

LC 2010006893

Describes the role of animals in movies, sporting events, and various competitions. Provided by publisher.

791.43 Motion pictures

Bliss, John, 1958-

Art that moves: animation around the world. John Bliss. Raintree, c2011. 32 p.: Culture in action

Grades: 5 6 7 8   **791.43**

1. Animated films 2. Animation (Cinematography)
ISBN 9781410939227

LC 2009051125

Discusses various forms of animation around the world.

"This is a good choice for children interested in animated movies. Bliss looks at techniques from the early beginnings to modern times and mentions recent film releases such as Cars (2006) and Where the Wild Things Are (2010). . . . [This volume is] quick, interesting, up-to-date . . . with plenty of supportive, captioned, full-color photographs. [It] also [provides] related project suggestions." School Library Journal.

Includes bibliographical references (p. 31) and index.

Cohn, Jessica

Animator. by Jessica Cohn. Gareth Stevens Pub., 2009. 32 p. : Cool careers (Gareth Stevens)

Grades: 4 5 6   **791.43**

1. Animation (Cinematography) -- Vocational guidance 2. Special effects (Cinematography) 3. Animators 4. Filmmaking 5. Film industry and trade
ISBN 9781433919534

LC 2009002006

Introduces readers to interesting and important careers, giving children the opportunity to gain a better understanding of these cool jobs with the help of engaging sidebars, color photographs, an index, lists for further reading, and more.

"This title offers clear, solid information in a large font. . . . [This] short [book is] packed with relevant, current material." School Library Journal.

Includes bibliographical references and index.

Seba, Jaime

Gay characters in theatre, movies, and television: new roles, new attitudes: New Roles, New Attitudes. Jaime A. Seba. Mason Crest Publishers, 2011. 64 p.

Grades: 8 9 10 11 12   **791.43**

1. Gay men in mass media 2. Gays in popular culture 3. Homosexuality in literature 4. Homosexuality in motion pictures 5. Homosexuality on television
ISBN 9781422220122

LC 2010017051

Describes how theater, television, and motion pictures have become more inclusive of gay, lesbian, and transgender characters and issues throughout the years.

"This slender, accessible overview uses numerous examples, past and present, to show how the depiction of gay, lesbian, bisexual, and transgender (GLBT) characters in the entertainment industry affects popular culture and has helped push growing acceptance into the mainstream. . . . The book features an open, inviting format, and portraits, reproduced posters, and short profiles of GLTB stars . . . add to the title's browsability." Booklist.

Includes bibliographical references (p. 59-62) and index.

Woog, Adam, 1953-

Vampires in the movies. by Adam Woog. ReferencePoint Press, Inc., 2010. 80 p.: Vampire library

Grades: 7 8 9 10   **791.43**

1. Vampire films -- History and criticism 2. Vampires
ISBN 9781601521354

LC 2010017982

"Energetic and suprisingly educational, this lively [book] seizes upon a zietgeist topic and takes it as far as possible." Booklist.

Includes bibliographical references and index.

791.43092 Motion pictures—Biography

Finch, Christopher

The **art** of Walt Disney: from Mickey Mouse to the Magic Kingdoms. Christopher Finch. Abrams, 2011. 503 p.

Grades: 7 8 9 10 11 12 Adult   **791.43092**

1. Disney, Walt, 1901-1966. 2. Walt Disney Company. 3. Animators 4. Animation (Cinematography) 5. Film industry and trade 6. Cartoonists
ISBN 9780810998148

LC 2004010016

Traces the career of the beloved cartoonist while exploring the diverse artistic and cinematographic techniques used to make his animated and live action films.

791.4375 Two or more films

Reynolds, David West

Star Wars: the complete visual dictionary. written by David West Reynolds (episodes I, II and IV-VI) and James Luceno (episode III); updates and new material by Ryder Windham; special fabrications by Robert E. Barnes... [et al.]; new photography by Alex Ivanov. Lucas Books: 2006. 270 p.

Grades: 6 7 8 9 10 11 12 Adult **791.4375**

1. Star Wars films 2. Star Wars characters
ISBN 0756622387

LC 2006298949

A guide to the characters, creatures, and weapons featured in the six-film saga "Star Wars."

791.8 Animal performances

Collard, Sneed B.

The **world** famous Miles City Bucking Horse sale. written and photographed by Sneed B. Collard III. Bucking Horse Books, 2010. 64 p.

Grades: 5 6 7 8 **791.8**

1. Rodeos -- History 2. Horses 3. Rural life 4. Montana -- History
ISBN 9780984446001

LC 2010902149

Explores the drama and history of one of the West's premier rodeo and cultural events, the Miles City Bucking Horse Sale. Begun in 1951 as a way to sell "spoiled" and unruly ranch horses for use in rodeos, the sale has evolved into a four-day celebration that features horse racing, country music, a parade, and rodeo riding. Includes more than 60 photographs.

"Collard takes readers inside the Miles City [Montana] Bucking Horse Sale, a four-day event that draws visitors from across the country. Started in 1951 as a sale of wild horses, it's evolved into a jamboree of music, rodeo, food, contests, and a parade. . . . Plenty of action-filled color photographs break up the narrative. . . . Handsomely designed, . . . this is a fascinating look at a fresh topic." Booklist.

Includes bibliographical references (p. 62), filmography and index.

792 Stage presentations

Aliki

★ **William** Shakespeare & the Globe. written & illustrated by Aliki. Harper Collins Publishers, c1999. 48 p.

Grades: 4 5 6 7 8 9 **792**

1. Shakespeare, William, 1564-1616 England London 2. Shakespeare, William, 1564-1616. 3. Globe Theatre (London, England: 1599-1644) 4. 16th century 5. 17th century 6. Theater -- History 16th century 7. Dramatists, English 16th century 8. Authors, English 9. Theaters -- Reconstruction 10. Theaters 11. England -- History -- 16th century. 12. England -- History -- 17th century.
ISBN 006027820X

LC 98007903

Tells the story of the well-known playwright, William Shakespeare, and of the famous Globe Theatre in which many of his works were performed.

"A logically organized and engaging text, plenty of detailed illustrations with informative captions, and a clean design provide a fine introduction to both bard and theater." Horn Book Guide.

Currie, Stephen, 1960-

An **actor** on the Elizabethan stage. Stephen Currie. Lucent Books, c2003. 96 p.: Working life series

Grades: 6 7 8 9 **792**

1. Theater -- History 16th century 2. Great Britain -- Social life and customs -- Elizabethan period, 1558-1603
ISBN 1590181743

LC 2002009460

Discusses how Elizabethan actors rehearsed and prepared plays, including how the dramas were performed and how an acting company of the time was structured.

"This is well written and the [author draws on quotes] from many primary sources." Library Media Connection.

Includes bibliographical references (p. 83-89) and index.

Ratliff, Gerald Lee

Millennium monologs: 95 contemporary characterizations for young actors. edited by Gerald Lee Ratliff. Meriwether Pub., c2002. 261 p.

Grades: 8 9 10 11 12 **792**

1. Acting 2. Drama 20th century 3. Drama
ISBN 1566080827

LC 2002013009

An anthology of monologues by contemporary writers, divided into four categories: "Hope and Longing," "Spirit and Soul," "Fun and Fantasy," and "Doubt and Despair." Includes audition techniques.

"This fine collection of American monologues is notable for its diversity as well as for the high quality of the material." Booklist.

792.02 Miscellany

Belli, Mary Lou

Acting for young actors: the ultimate teen guide. Mary Lou Belli & Dinah Lenney. Back Stage Books, 2006. xvii, 205 p.

Grades: 7 8 9 10 11 12 **792.02**

1. Acting 2. Teenage actors and actresses
ISBN 0823049477

LC 2006007265

A guide to acting covers auditions, rehearsals, monologues, and improvisation, along with acting exercises and tips on pursuing acting as a career.

"Belli and Lenney, an Emmy-winning director of Girlfriends and a Yale-educated ER actress offer stagestruck teens trunks-full of sound advice packaged with a conversational tone and grounded experience. . . . The authors offer a series of questions for character analysis; suggested readings and viewings abound. . . . The handbook succeeds at communicating clearly without talking down to readers; engaging prose makes it an ideal text for classes and teens who want commonsense career prep and insight." Voice of Youth Advocates.

Includes bibliographical references (p. [184]-188) and index.

Kenney, Karen Latchana

Cool costumes: how to stage your very own show. Karen Latchana Kenney. Abdo Pub. Co., 2009. 32 p.: Cool performances

Grades: 4 5 6 **792.02**

1. Costume 2. Theater 3. Children's costumes 4. Creative activities for children and students
ISBN 9781604537147

"Simple language, colorful page design, and detailed step-by-step photos invite children to gather some easily available household items, apply paint and some imagination, and put on a play—or just play." School Library Journal.

Michael, Ted, 1984-

So you wanna be a superstar?: the ultimate audition guide. Ted Michael. Running Press Kids, 2012. 128 p.

Grades: 4 5 6 7 8	**792.02**
1. Musicians 2. Auditions 3. Fame
ISBN 9780762446100

The ultimate guide to unlocking and showcasing your talent includes tips, tricks and advice for nailing those singing and dancing auditions.

Schumacher, Thomas

How does the show go on?: an introduction to the theater. by Thomas Schumacher with Jeff Kurtti. Disney Editions, c2007. 128 p.

Grades: 4 5 6 7	**792.02**
1. Walt Disney Company 2. Theater 3. Musicals 4. Acting 5. Theater -- Production and direction 6. Musicals -- Production and direction
ISBN 9781423120308

LC bl2008030557

An introduction to the backstage work done in the theater uses examples from Disney musicals to show the jobs done by the cast and crew for every aspect of the show, from the playwright and set manager to the director, conductor, and actors.

"Filled with lavish color photos of Disney theater productions, this eye-catching volume has clever chapter titles, beginning with Overture, which tells about styles of theaters and kinds of shows. In Act One and Act Two, aspects of the front and back of the house are discussed, including the marquee, the box office, props, special effects, and so on. Interspersed throughout the facts and photos are Stage Notes, where bits of trivia are doled out." School Library Journal.

Includes bibliographical references (p. 120).

Skog, Jason

Acting: a practical guide to pursuing the art. by Jason Skog. Compass Point Books, 2010. 48 p.: The performing arts

Grades: 5 6 7 8	**792.02**
1. Acting -- Vocational guidance 2. Performing arts 3. Actors and actresses 4. Vocational guidance 5. Occupations
ISBN 9780756543648

LC 2010012604

"Meant for students contemplating a career in the field . . . [this book goes] beyond basic introductions and into more detail about what it takes to make it as a professional. . . . [The author maintains] . . . a frank, realistic tone, stressing the importance of hard work and dedication. Great [resource] . . . for those wanting to make their passions more than just a hobby." School Library Journal.

Includes bibliographical references and index.

Underwood, Deborah

Staging a play. Deborah Underwood. Raintree, c2010. 32 p.

Grades: 5 6 7 8	**792.02**
1. Theater -- Production and direction
ISBN 9781410934130

LC 2009000417

Discusses the various elements involved in putting together a production, including scripting, costumes, props, characters, and use of voice and movement.

"This discusses the various professionals involved in a production, such as actors, costume designers, prop masters, and stage handlers. Well organized and with bright, colorful photography, [this] introductory [title gives] readers good basic knowledge." School Library Journal.

Includes bibliographical references (p. 31) and index.

792.09 History, geographic treatment, biography

Domenico, Gino

A day at the New Amsterdam Theatre. photos by Gino Domenico; written by Dana Amendola. Disney Editions, c2004. 125 p.

Grades: 4 5 6 7	**792.09**
1. Theaters 2. Theater -- Production and direction 3. New York City -- Buildings
ISBN 0786854383

LC 2006270081

Shows the seven-day-a-week, 24-hours-a-day activity of this Broadway theater during a production of The Lion King, including highlights of the architecture and history of the New Amsterdam Theatre.

"This title covers a day in the life of Disney's The Lion King, the long-running Broadway musical. . . . A clock in a corner of each spread guides readers through the day as box-office personnel, makeup designers, dancers, actors, cleaning staff, and others do their jobs. Each spread includes several full-color photos that are often gritty, sometimes glamorous. . . . This unique volume provides an honest, realistic, eye-opening look at the behind-the-scenes work that goes into the running of a Broadway show." School Library Journal.

792.6 Musical plays

Bezdecheck, Bethany

Directing. Bethany Bezdecheck. Rosen Central, 2010. 64 p. : High school musicals

Grades: 7 8 9 10	**792.6**
1. Musicals -- Production and direction 2. Theater -- Production and direction 3. Film producers and directors 4. Filmmaking 5. Film industry and trade
ISBN 9781435852594

LC 2008041598

"Bezdecheck lays out the process of directing a musical production, from play selection to auditions to dress rehearsals. . . . There's some good, practical advice here." Booklist.

Includes bibliographical references and index.

792.7 Variety shows and theatrical dancing

Becker, Helaine

Funny business: clowning around, practical jokes, cool comedy, cartooning, and more--. written by Helaine Becker; illustrated by Claudia Davila. Maple Tree Press; c2005. 160 p.

Grades: 5 6 7 8	**792.7**
1. Stand-up comedy 2. Clowning 3. Cartooning
ISBN 1897066406

LC bl2005022316

Provides information on creating a stand-up comedy routine, becoming a clown, pulling practical jokes, and drawing comic strips.

"Becker offers funny facts, an informative diagram showing what goes on in the body when you laugh, brief discussions of different types of humor (situation comedy, parody, farce, riddles, puns), a How Funny Are You? quiz, tips and timing for standup routines, body lingo, props, six improvisation games, clowning material, and more. For kids who want to learn how to juggle, tell jokes, or use sight-gag items, it's all here. Cartooning is explained as well." School Library Journal.

792.8 Ballet and modern dance

Augustyn, Frank

★ **Footnotes**: dancing the world's best-loved ballets. Frank Augustyn and Shelley Tanaka. Millbrook Press, 2001. 94 p.

Grades: 5 6 7 8   **792.8**

1. Ballet 2. Dancing
ISBN 0761323236

LC 00050075

Describes the years of training and hard work involved in becoming a ballet dancer and the dedication and expertise needed to dance the lead roles in famous ballets such as Sleeping Beauty and Swan Lake.

"Fine photographs, most in color, add enormously to the book's appeal. A well-crafted, readable volume." Booklist.

Froman, Kyle, 1976-

In the wings: behind the scenes at the New York City Ballet. Kyle Froman. John Wiley & Sons, c2007. ix, 118 p.

Grades: 6 7 8 9 10 11 12 Adult   **792.8**

1. Froman, Kyle, 1976- 2. New York City Ballet 3. New York City Ballet
ISBN 0470173432

LC 2007024556

A dancer with the New York City Ballet presents anecdotes and behind-the-scenes photographs of what life is like within the famous company.

Lee, Laura, 1969-

A **child's** introduction to ballet: the stories, music, and magic of classical dance. Laura Lee; illustrated by Meredith Hamilton. Black Dog & Leventhal Publishers, c2007. 96 p.

Grades: 4 5 6 7 8   **792.8**

1. Ballet 2. Ballets
ISBN 9781579126995

LC 2006048867

A history of ballet provides plot synopses of famous ballets and introduces the language, steps, and costumes of the dance.

"This lively and attractive volume delves into the history of ballet from its beginnings in Italy through the 20th century. . . . Detailed and well-written descriptions of 25 of the most famous and influential ballets are provided along with colorful illustrations of scenes. A CD presents excerpts from them and the author poses some questions and gives some insights to think about as one listens to the music." School Library Journal.

Includes bibliographical references (p. 94-95).

Marsico, Katie, 1980-

Choreographer. by Katie Marsico. Cherry Lake Pub., c2012. 32 p.: Cool careers (Cherry Lake)

Grades: 4 5 6 7   **792.8**

1. Choreography 2. Choreographers -- Vocational guidance 3. Occupations 4. Dancing
ISBN 9781610801362

LC 2011001170

"Illustrated with color photos of the famous, the young, and the fabulously festooned, this is a sturdy presentation of facts and case studies that will bring the process of professional choreography home to those students considering such a competitive and demanding career." Booklist.

Includes bibliographical references and index.

Miles, Lisa

Ballet spectacular: a young ballet lover's guide and an insight into a magical world. by Lisa Miles. Barrons Educational Series, 2014. 80 p.

Grades: 4 5 6 7 8   **792.8**

1. Royal Ballet. 2. Royal Ballet. School 3. Ballet 4. Ballet dancers 5. Dancing 6. Performing arts
ISBN 9780764167454

"Combining aspects of a coffee-table book and an introductory handbook, it provides a hodgepodge of basic information about ballet history, famous ballets, life in a major company, and the elements involved in a performance, such as choreography, music, sets, and costumes, while Britain's Royal Ballet Company and School are referenced throughout the book." Booklist.

Minden, Eliza Gaynor

The **ballet** companion: a dancer's guide to the technique, traditions, and joys of ballet. Eliza Gaynor Minden. Fireside Book/ Simon & Schuster, c2005. xv, 331 p.

Grades: 6 7 8 9 10 11 12 Adult   **792.8**

1. Ballet dancing
ISBN 9780743264075

LC 2005044102

An illustrated reference for dancers at all levels shares advice about how to train safely, observe appropriate etiquette, and learn the techniques of accomplished dancers, in a volume complemented by historical information.

Nathan, Amy

Meet the dancers. Amy Nathan. Henry Holt, 2008. 176 p.

Grades: 5 6 7 8   **792.8**

1. Dancers 2. Dancing -- History 20th century.
ISBN 0805080716

Introduces young readers to dancers of all types.

"This collective biography reveals the paths that 16 diverse dancers followed to become professionals and to join prestigious companies. . . . The tone of the text is conversational. . . . The pictures dramatically capture how talented these performers are. Anyone, whether considering a career in dance or not, will be inspired and educated by these up-close-and-personal accounts." School Library Journal.

Schorer, Suki

Put your best foot forward: a young dancer's guide to life. by Suki Schorer and the School of American Ballet; illustrations by Donna Ingemanson. Workman Publishing, c2005. 96 p.

Grades: 4 5 6 7   **792.8**

1. Ballet 2. Ballet dancers
ISBN 0761137955

LC 2005051428

Presents advice for young ballet students, including practicing etiquette and grooming, finding a balance between mind and body, maintaining focus, developing patience, and fostering an attitude of generosity in dancing for audiences.

"The words of counsel proffered by the author, who was a principal dancer for the New York City Ballet and is a teacher at the School of American Ballet, are engaging, imaginative, and right on target. . . . Practical tips such as essentials that need to be in your bag and behavioral advice such as being grateful for criticism are nicely woven into the book. The photographs, mainly of female dancers, are clear and colorful. These words of wisdom will keep dancers on their toes and stretching their minds and hearts." School Library Journal.

793.3 Social, folk, national dancing

Ancona, George, 1929-2021

  ★ **¡Ole** flamenco! George Ancona. Lee & Low Books, 2010. 47 p.

Grades: 5 6 7 8   **793.3**
  1. Flamenco dancing 2. Dancing 3. Flamenco dancers 4. Flamenco music
  ISBN 9781600603617

                              LC 2010022272

Photo-essay about Flamenco, a southern Spanish art form that incorporates song, dance, and music, tracing its cultural history and focusing on a contemporary young girl and her brother as they learn the traditional style of movement and instrument playing. Includes a glossary/pronunciation guide and author's sources. Provided by publisher.

"Full-color photographs capture the excitement and dazzle. . . . All aspects of flamenco are explored, including movements, facial expressions, and sound effects." Booklist.

Garofoli, Wendy

  Hip-hop dancing. by Wendy Garofoli. Capstone Press, c2011. 4 v.

Grades: 4 5 6   **793.3**
  1. Hip-hop dance 2. Dancing 3. Dancers 4. Hip-hop culture
  ISBN 9781429654852

                              LC 2010030394

Provides instructions for joining or starting a hip-hop dance crew, and includes information about real-life crews. Provided by publisher.

"These volumes cover the basic moves as well as more detailed movements often seen on television programs. . . . Everything about the set is jazzy and current. Sentences are short and direct, with a small-sized font detailing step-by-step instructions and fact boxes extending the information." Booklist.

Includes bibliographical references and index.

Haney, Johannah

  Capoeira. Johannah Haney. Marshall Cavendish Benchmark, c2012. 47 p.: Martial arts in action

Grades: 4 5 6 7   **793.3**
  1. Capoeira (Dance) 2. Martial arts 3. Martial arts for children
  ISBN 9780761449324

                              LC 2010013829

"This treats martial arts with the dignity that serious enthusiasts bring to the sport. . . . Illustrations include not only photos of modern gear and from films but also historical images." Booklist.

793.74 Mathematical games and recreations

Ball, Johnny

  Go figure!: big questions about numbers. Johnny Ball. DK, 2016. 96 p.

Grades: 3 4 5 6 7   **793.74**
  1. Mathematics fun 2. Mathematics
  ISBN 9781465443854

                          LC bl2015053126

Presents mathematical marvels such as why daisies always have 34, 55, or 89 petals, why all the world's phone numbers appear in pi, and other paradoxes that will make readers look at numbers in a whole new way.

793.8 Magic and related activities

Carlson, Laurie M., 1952-

  Harry Houdini for kids: his life and adventures with 21 magic tricks and illusions. Laurie Carlson. Chicago Review Press, c2009. 136 p.

Grades: 4 5 6 7   **793.8**
  1. Houdini, Harry, 1874-1926 2. Magicians 3. Escape artists 4. Hungarian Americans 5. Magic tricks
  ISBN 9781556527821

                            LC 2008021404

Provides an informative review of the complex life of this magician, escape artist, actor, aviator, and possible spy for the U.S.—enhanced with instructions for numerous magic tricks, including sticking a needle into a balloon and making a coin vanish.

"Reluctant readers (as well as budding troublemakers) will flock to this biography/handbook hybrid about one of the most famous magicians who ever lived. Even for those familiar with Houdini's fascinating story, Carlson's snappy writing gives it new life. . . . Nearly every page is enlivened with period photographs, boxed sections containing biographies and definitions, and, most [importantly], 21 magic tricks that will have readers breaking out their deck of cards and practicing their sleight of hand." Booklist.

Jennings, Madeleine

  Magic step-by-step. Madeleine Jennings and Colin Francome. Rosen Central, 2010. 89 p. : Skills in motion

Grades: 5 6 7 8   **793.8**
  1. Magic tricks 2. Entertainments 3. Amusements 4. Tricks 5. Magic -- Study and teaching
  ISBN 9781435833630

                            LC 2009013221

"Colorful photographs show the entire movement of each skill presented, giving new meaning to the term step-by-step. Progression borders at the bottom of the pages highlight the salient points to notice in performing each skill from beginning to end." School Library Journal.

Noyes, Deborah

  The **magician** and the spirits: Harry Houdini and the curious pastime of communicating with the dead. Deborah Noyes. Viking Books for Young Readers, 2017. 160 p.

Grades: 6 7 8   **793.8**
  1. Houdini, Harry, 1874-1926 2. Doyle, Arthur Conan, Sir, 1859-1930 3. Psychics 4. Paranormal phenomena 5. Psychic ability 6. Seances 7. Extrasensory perception
  ISBN 9780803740181

                            LC 2016053762

Famed illusionist Harry Houdini embarks on a quest to investigate spiritual phenomena and the possibility of communication with those on the "other side." Provided by publisher.

"Noyes's attention to Houdini's outsize personality—a key component of his campaign against spiritualists—adds compelling depth. A worthwhile addition to any nonfiction section, and ideal for kids intrigued by historical oddities." Booklist.

793.93 Adventure games

Miller, John

  ★ **Unofficial** Minecraft lab for kids: family-friendly projects for exploring and teaching math, science, history, and culture through creative building. John Miller and Chris Fornell Scott. Quarry, 2016. 144 p.: Hands-on family

Grades: 4 5 6 7   **793.93**

1. Minecraft (Game) 2. Games
ISBN 9781631591174

"Family interaction is highly encouraged, although this could easily work as a library program or classroom lesson. Fans of the game will be pleased by the new skills acquired, while adults will appreciate the insight into kids' latest obsession." Booklist.

Myer, Sarah

Create a costume! Sarah Myer. First Second, 2019 128 p.

Grades: 4 5 6 7   **793.93**

1. Cosplay 2. Costume 3. Comic book fans 4. Halloween costumes 5. Fan conventions
ISBN 9781250152077

Presents a do-it-yourself guide to creating costumes for conventions, offering tips on modifying thrift store clothes, working with craft foam, using a sewing machine, and proper costume convention etiquette.

Sciandra, Mike

The **modern** nerd's guide to LARPing. Michael E. Sciandra. Gareth Stevens Publishing, 2018. 32 p.

Grades: 3 4 5 6 7 8   **793.93**

1. Fantasy games 2. Acting games 3. Role playing
ISBN 9781538212110

LC 2017033554

Introduces the hobby of LARPing, or live action role playing—dressing up and staying in character while participating in a fantasy or science fiction game—and provides advice on getting started in the field.

794.1 Chess

Basman, Michael

Chess for kids. written by Michael Basman. Dorling Kindersley Pub., 2001. 45 p.

Grades: 4 5 6 7   **794.1**

1. Chess for children 2. Chess
ISBN 078946540X

LC 00059018

Explains the rules, skills, and techniques necessary to play the game of chess.

"A solid introduction for novices and good for skilled players wanting to develop their strategies and find out about chess clubs and tournaments." Booklist.

King, Daniel

★ **Chess**: from first moves to checkmate. Daniel King. Kingfisher, 2000. 64 p.

Grades: 5 6 7 8 9 10 11 12   **794.1**

1. Chess for children 2. Chess 3. Chess -- History 4. Chess players
ISBN 0753453878

LC 00026353

Introduces the rules and strategies of chess, as well as its history and some of the great players and matches.

794.8 Electronic games

Adams, Suellen S.

Crash course in gaming. Suellen S. Adams. Libraries Unlimited, 2014. xi, 125 p.

Grades: Professional   **794.8**

1. Video games
ISBN 9781610690461

LC 2013031465

Video games aren't just for kids anymore. This book will describe the "why" and "how" to start or expand a video gaming program in the library, including some specific examples of how to target adult and female gamer patrons. Provided by publisher.

Hansen, Dustin

Game on!: video game history from Pong and Pac-man to Mario, Minecraft, and more. Dustin Hansen. Feiwel & Friends, 2019, c2016. 352 p.

Grades: 5 6 7 8 9 10 11 12   **794.8**

1. Video games -- History 2. Video games industry and trade
ISBN 9781250294456

"This satisfyingly thorough and worthy addition to any collection is sure to please hard-core gamers and newbies alike." School Library Journal.

Haugen, Hayley Mitchell, 1968-

Video games. by Hayley Mitchell Haugen. Norwood House Press, [2015] 64 p.: Matters of Opinion

Grades: 5 6 7 8 9   **794.8**

1. Video games -- Social aspects 2. Violence in video games 3. Video games industry and trade 4. Children and violence 5. Violence
ISBN 9781599536019

LC 2014003798

Examines issues related to video games, from whether they lead to violence to if they should be regulated. Aligns with Common Core Language Arts Anchor Standards for Reading Informational Text and Speaking and Listening. Text contains critical thinking components in regards to social issues and history. Includes bibliography, glossary, index, and relevant websites. Provided by publisher.

"Students will be interested in debating issues surrounding video games: whether the games lead to violence, health risks, and whether there should be regulation. In addition to pros and cons of each and a final writing assignment, three debate techniques—the author's credibility, deceptive arguments, and logical fallacies—are also analyzed. Sidebars and captioned photos support the choppy text. Reading list, timeline, websites. Glos., ind." Horn Book.

Includes bibliographical references (pages 60-61) and index.

Jozefowicz, Chris

Video game developer. by Chris Jozefowicz. Gareth Stevens Pub., 2009. 32 p. : Cool careers (Gareth Stevens)

Grades: 4 5 6   **794.8**

1. Computer games -- Programming -- Vocational guidance 2. Video games -- Design -- Vocational guidance 3. Vocational guidance 4. Occupations
ISBN 9781433919589

LC 2008053549

Introduces readers to interesting and important careers, giving children the opportunity to gain a better understanding of these cool jobs with the help of engaging sidebars, color photographs, an index, lists for further reading, and more.

"This introduction to video game developer careers offers clear, solid information in a large font. . . . [This] short [book is] packed with relevant, current material." School Library Journal.

Includes bibliographical references and index.

Oxlade, Chris

Gaming technology. Chris Oxlade. Smart Apple Media, c2012. 46 p.: New technology

Grades: 4 5 6 7   **794.8**
    1. Computer games -- Programming 2. Video games -- Technological innovations 3. Technological innovations 4. Technology
    ISBN 9781599205311

                                                  LC 2010044239

Describes the technology used for creating and playing video games. Includes information on how different platforms work and the direction video game technology may be going. Provided by publisher.

"This offers a fine overview for reports, and its attractive design may also entice middle-grade readers to learn more." Booklist.

Includes bibliographical references (p. 45) and index.

Rauf, Don

Computer game designer. by Don Rauf and Monique Vescia. Ferguson, c2008. 64 p.: Virtual apprentice

Grades: 6 7 8 9   **794.8**
    1. Computer game designers 2. Computer game design 3. Computer games -- Programming -- Vocational guidance 4. Electronic games industry and trade 5. Vocational guidance
    ISBN 0816067546

                                                  LC 2006036565

Provides a behind-the-scenes look at computer game design and the duties, training, and technology involved, discusses the history of computer games, and profiles designers and others in the industry.

"This in-depth introduction to the field of computer-game design offers specific practical advice. . . . Following a basic history of computer games and information about game types and rating levels, chapters, which are illustrated with many color photos, profile contemporary professionals and delve into current trends and the day-to-day work of game creators." Booklist.

Includes bibliographical references (p. 62) and index.

796 Athletic and outdoor sports and games

Afremow, James A.

The **young** champion's mind: how to think, train, and thrive like an elite athlete. Jim Afremow, Ph.D. Rodale Kids, 2018. 240 p.

Grades: 7 8 9 10   **796**
    1. Teenage athletes 2. Sports -- Psychological aspects 3. Mind and body 4. Student athletes 5. Athletes -- Psychology
    ISBN 9781635650563

Coach and sports psychologist Jim Afremow has helped everyone from Olympians to professional athletes train their mind, body, and spirit. Now, in this new young adult edition of his highly praised The Champion's Mind, Dr. Afremow is helping student athletes do—and feel—their best. Whether you are striving to balance your school and sports accomplishments, or just get that extra edge in your sport, his sage advice will be a much-needed guide in helping you navigate the field—or rink or court.

Berman, Len

The **greatest** moments in sports. Len Berman. Sourcebooks Inc., 2009. 136 p.

Grades: 5 6 7 8   **796**
    1. Sports 2. Athletes
    ISBN 9781402220999

"Forty years as a sportscaster gives Berman plenty of experience to choose the 25 greatest sports moments. His writing is lively, humorous, and informative—just right to sustain kids' (or adults') interest. Quality photos throughout are another plus. . . . An audio CD that includes many of the moments as they were broadcast live is part of the package." School Library Journal.

Blumenthal, Karen, 1959-2020

Let me play: the story of Title IX: the law that changed the future of girls in America. Karen Blumenthal. Atheneum Books for Young Readers, c2005. 152 p.

Grades: 6 7 8 9 10   **796**
    1. Girls and sports 2. Girl athletes -- History 3. Sexism in sports -- History 4. Women athletes -- History 5. Sex discrimination
    ISBN 0689859570

                                                  LC 2004001450

Explores the history, struggle, and passage of Title IX, the law that allowed girls the freedom to pursue sports of their choosing, and the effects this law has had on society since its inception.

"The author looks at American women's evolving rights by focusing on the history and future of Title IX, which bans sex discrimination in U.S. education. . . . The images are . . . gripping, and relevant political cartoons and fact boxes add further interest. Few books cover the last few decades of American women's history with such clarity and detail." Booklist.

Includes bibliographical references (p. 144-146) and index.

Fay, Gail

Sports: the ultimate teen guide. Gail Fay. Scarecrow Press, Inc., c2013. xv, 338 p.

Grades: 7 8 9 10 11 12   **796**
    1. High school athletes -- Training of 2. Teenage athletes -- Training of
    ISBN 9780810882171

                                                  LC 2012028320

Offers high school students information on choosing a sport to play, balancing life as a student-athlete, dealing with competition, improving performance, preventing injuries, training in the off-season, and playing in college.

Howell, Brian, 1974-

Sports. by Brian Howell. ABDO Pub. Co., c2011. 112 p.: Inside the industry

Grades: 5 6 7 8   **796**
    1. Sports -- Vocational guidance 2. Vocational guidance 3. Occupations
    ISBN 9781617148040

                                                  LC 2010042558

Provides information about many different sports industry careers, from professional athlete to sports writer, and discusses education and training required, earnings potential, and career outlook.

"This well-designed [book describes] a variety of careers in [sports]. Because [it helps] readers assess if these positions are suitable for their personality types and backgrounds, the [title is a] good [choice] for career exploration and self-discovery. [It is] also useful for research and reports. . . . Sidebars and full-color photos appear throughout." School Library Journal.

Includes bibliographical references (p. 104-109) and index.

Johnson, Rafer

Great athletes. edited by the editors of Salem Press; special consultant Rafer Johnson. Salem Press, 2010. 8 v. in 13

Grades: 9 10 11 12 **796**

1. Athletes
ISBN 9781587654732

LC 2009021905

Provides biographies of individual athletes and includes information on their career, personal history, playing style, achievements and awards.

Mattern, Joanne, 1963-

So, you want to work in sports?: the ultimate guide to exploring the sports industry. Joanne Mattern. Aladdin/Beyond Words, 2014 224 p.: Be what you want

Grades: 4 5 6 7 8 **796**

1. Sports -- Vocational guidance 2. Vocational guidance
ISBN 9781582704494

LC 2013025469

In the spirited fourth installment of the popular Be What You Want series, veteran children's author Joanne Mattern shares the secret to building a career in sports. From star athlete to sportscaster, Mattern outlines the varied positions that keep the ball rolling in the sports arena. Whatever one's skill—math, art, performance—the perfect sports job is waiting. With tips from successful athletes and professionals, inspiring biographies of young people working in sports today, games, and a huge list of resources— kids will find everything they need to get up and running in a career in sports! Learn about exciting careers such as: coach, sports writer, agent, pro athlete, sports medicine, photographer, talent scout, and more! Provided by publisher.

"Information is presented dynamically, with numerous sidebars (Did you know), graphs, lists, a career quiz, and hand-drawn illustrations. There are no photos. One of the book's strongest assets is its excellent resource section, including a six-page list of websites for professional organizations . . . and two pages of books and online documents." School Library Journal.

Includes bibliographical references and index.

Park, Louise, 1961-

The **Roman** gladiators. by Louise Park and Timothy Love. Marshall Cavendish Benchmark, 2009. 32 p. : Ancient and medieval people

Grades: 4 5 6 **796**

1. Gladiators 2. Weapons, Ancient 3. Rome -- Social life and customs. 4. Rome -- History.
ISBN 9780761444435

LC 2008055775

An introduction to the history and lifestyle of Roman gladiators. Provided by publisher.

"This title has a simple and elegant design with the proper balance of quality writing and quantity of information. . . . Handy time lines, well-chosen photos of ruins and artifacts, quality illustrations, inset Quick Facts, and What You Should Know About features will grab reluctant readers and captivate even those with short attention spans." School Library Journal.

Rand, Casey

Graphing sports. Casey Rand. Heinemann Library, c2010. 32 p.: Real world data

Grades: 5 6 7 8 **796**

1. Sports 2. Statistics -- Graphic methods 3. Graphic methods 4. Sports
ISBN 9781432926212

LC 2009001189

"The writing is spot-on for the audience. Most importantly, the statistics used are well chosen and instantly understandable, and the text clearly explains how each type of graph can be used to best display different types of data." School Library Journal.

Includes bibliographical references and index.

Zuckerman, Gregory

Rising above: inspiring women in sports. Gregory Zuckerman, with Gabriel and Elijah Zuckerman. Philomel Books, an imprint of Penguin Random House, 2018. 215 p.

Grades: 6 7 8 **796**

1. Women athletes 2. Women and sports 3. Persistence in women 4. Women 5. Sports
ISBN 9780399547478

Presents the real-life stories of female athletes who overcame adversity to rise to the top of their fields, including Simone Biles, Serena and Venus Williams, Bethany Hamilton, and Kerri Strug.

796.04 General kinds of sports and games

Hile, Lori

Surviving extreme sports. Lori Hile. Raintree, c2011. 56 p.: Raintree freestyle.

Grades: 4 5 6 7 **796.04**

1. Extreme sports 2. Survival skills 3. Survival
ISBN 9781410939685

LC 2010028689

Introduces extreme sports, offering true stories of athletes who have broken records and faced great danger while participating in them, and discussing the training and science behind their ability to survive.

"This book is fun and informative. [This] well-organized title starts with an overview [of extreme sports], offers some specific examples, and includes additional facts or tips and resources. . . . [It features] dramatic archival and full-color photos on nearly every page. . . . [This is a book] that youngsters will enjoy and talk about." School Library Journal.

Includes bibliographical references (p. 54), filmography (p. 55), and index.

796.082 Outdoor recreation — Women

Buckey, A. W.

Women and sports. A.W. Buckey. ReferencePoint Press, Inc., 2019 80 p.

Grades: 8 9 10 11 **796.082**

1. Sports for women -- History 2. Sports for women -- Social aspects 3. Sports for women -- Management 4. Women athletes -- Social conditions
ISBN 9781682825495

LC 2018038250

"Going well beyond the history of Title IX and individual athletes, the book covers gaps in wages, sponsorships, and prize winnings; inequality in media coverage, including the dearth of women in sports journalism; how objectification and expectations of femininity often beleaguer talented professional athletes in spite of their accomplishments; the discrimination inherent in gender testing, which prevents a broad range of women from being allowed to participate in sports; and many other topics." Booklist.

Includes bibliographical references and index.

Macy, Sue

Breaking through: how female athletes shattered stereotypes in the roaring twenties. Sue Macy; foreword by Muffet McGraw. National Geographic, 2020 96 p.

Grades: 5 6 7 8 9   **796.082**
    1. 1920s 2. Women athletes 3. Women and sports 4. Women's role 5. Women's sports 6. Sports -- History
    ISBN 9781426336775

Describes the achievements of women athletes in the 1920s, detailing how their defiance of social and political norms promoted women's rights, redefined femininity, and changed the course of history.

"Along with inspiring accounts of how the athletes debunked common beliefs about what women could or should be able to do, the profiles reveal the complex barriers of racism as well as sexism." Publishers Weekly

796.083 Outdoor recreation—Young people

Hewitt, Ben, 1971-

The **young** adventurer's guide to (almost) everything: build a fort, camp like a champ, poop in the woods--45 action-packed outdoor activities. Ben and Penny Hewitt; illustrations by Luke Boushee. Roost Books, 2019 208 p.

Grades: 7 8 9 10 11 12   **796.083**
    1. Outdoor recreation 2. Outdoor life 3. Exploration 4. Outdoor recreation for children 5. Wilderness living
    ISBN 9781611805949

"Outdoor-adventure activities combine wisdom and fun in this practical guide to the wild. A thoughtful introduction acknowledges the Native American origins of many of the skills introduced in the book." Kirkus.

796.086 Sports—LGBTQ athletes

Cronn-Mills, Kirstin, 1968-

LGBTQ+ athletes claim the field: striving for equality. Kirstin Cronn-Mills Twenty-First Century Books, [2016] 104 p.

Grades: 6 7 8 9 10   **796.086**
    1. LGBTQIA persons 2. Athletes 3. Homosexuality 4. Gay athletes 5. LGBTQIA rights
    ISBN 9781467780124

LC 2015036754

"Crisp color photographs, usually of athletes on or off the field, enhance the text throughout and visually reinforce the message that athletics are for everyone." School Library Journal.

Includes bibliographical references and index.

796.092 Athletes

Ignotofsky, Rachel, 1989-

Women in sports: 50 fearless athletes who played to win. written and illustrated by Rachel Ignotofsky. 128 p.

Grades: 4 5 6 7 8   **796.092**
    1. Women athletes 2. Women Olympic athletes 3. Athletes 4.

Sports 5. Illustrated books
    ISBN 9781607749783

LC 2016055531

A charmingly illustrated and inspiring book, Women in Sports highlights the achievements and stories of fifty notable women athletes—from well-known figures like tennis player Billie Jean King and gymnast Simone Biles, to lesser-known athletes like skateboarding pioneer Patti McGee and Toni Stone, the first woman to play baseball in a men's professional league. Provided by publisher.

"The writing is accessible to a wide range of readers, and the material is concise and orderly, often leaving readers wanting more. Fortunately, a thorough bibliography is appended, making it easy to dive deeper into the lives of some of these fascinating trailblazers." School Library Journal.

Includes bibliographical references and index.

796.0973 Sports—United States

Doeden, Matt

Coming up clutch: the greatest upsets, comebacks, and finishes in sports history. Matt Doeden. Millbrook Press, 2019. 64 p.

Grades: 5 6 7 8 9 10   **796.0973**
    1. Sports upsets 2. Sports 3. Comebacks 4. Books for reluctant readers
    ISBN 9781512427561

LC 2017047697

Features upsets, comebacks, and clutch performances in sports and recounts the miracle on ice, Lindsey Jacobellis's fall, and Christian Laettner's shot.

796.1 Miscellaneous games

Birmingham, Maria

Weird zone: sports. Maria Birmingham, Jamie Bennett. Owlkids, 2013. 128 p.

Grades: 4 5 6 7   **796.1**
    1. Sports 2. Curiosities and wonders 3. Sports 4. Extreme sports 5. Trivia and miscellaneous facts
    ISBN 9781926973609

A visual introduction to lesser-known sports shares historical insights, pop quizzes and other fun facts about such unconventional athletics as toe wrestling, 200-member football games and giant cheese wheel chasing.

796.15 Play with remote-control vehicles

Sobey, Edwin J. C., 1948-

Radio-controlled car experiments. Ed Sobey. Enslow Publishers, c2011. 128 p.: Cool science projects with technology

Grades: 6 7 8 9   **796.15**
    1. Model cars -- Radio control 2. Science projects 3. Experiments 4. Model cars 5. Radio-controlled models
    ISBN 9780766033047

LC 2009037896

Presents several science projects dealing with radio-controlled cars. Provided by publisher.

"This book is bursting with fast-paced experiments that have easy-to-follow instructions and are sure to interest young car enthusiasts." School Library Journal.

Includes bibliographical references (p. 123) and index.

796.2 Activities and games requiring equipment

Bell-Rehwoldt, Sheri
The **kids'** guide to jumping rope. by Sheri Bell-Rehwoldt. Capstone Press, c2011. 32 p.: Edge books.
Grades: 4 5 6 7   **796.2**
    1. Jumping rope
ISBN 9781429654432
                  LC 2010035018
Describes the sport of jumping rope, including how-to information on jumps and tricks. Provided by publisher.

"This includes plentiful photos of giddy girls (and a few guys) madly skipping rope. . . . This makes jumping rope look like the best time in the world." Booklist.

Includes bibliographical references and index.

796.22 Skateboarding

Fitzpatrick, Jim, 1948-
Skateboarding. by Jim Fitzpatrick. Cherry Lake Pub., c2009. 32 p. : 21st century skills innovation library.
Grades: 4 5 6 7   **796.22**
    1. Skateboards and skateboarding 2. Skateboarders 3. Extreme sports 4. Sports 5. Skateboards and skateboarding -- Technological innovations
ISBN 9781602792593
                  LC 2008007548
Explores how being open to different perspectives, sharing failures and successes with others, and acting on creative ideas has lead to new solutions to old problems in each of the featured sporting arenas.

"This stands out by emphasizing monumental shifts and advances in the events themselves. . . . Concise and occasionally revelatory." Booklist.

Includes bibliographical references and index.

Lakin, Patricia, 1944-
Skateboards. by Patricia Lakin. Aladdin, [2017] 32 p.: Made by Hand
Grades: 3 4 5 6 7   **796.22**
    1. Skateboards and skateboarding -- Design and construction 2. Manufacturing processes 3. Sports equipment
ISBN 9781481448338
                  LC 2016016442
Offers a look at a business owner who makes skateboards by hand, going into how he became involved in skateboards and demonstrating step-by-step how he carefully creates them.

796.323 Basketball

Bryant, Howard, 1968-
Legends: the best players, games, and teams in basketball. Howard Bryant. Philomel Books, 2016. xii, 256 p.

Grades: 6 7 8 9   **796.323**
    1. National Basketball Association 2. Professional basketball players 3. Basketball -- History
ISBN 9780399169052
                  LC 2016032754
From Magic Johnson to Michael Jordan to LeBron James to Steph Curry, ESPN's Howard Bryant presents the best from the hardwood—a collection of NBA champions and superstars for young sports fans! Provided by publisher.

"Hoops fans will find a goldmine of information guaranteed to deepen their basketball knowledge and their understanding of the game." Voice of Youth Advocates.

Coy, John, 1958-
Hoop genius: how a desperate teacher and a rowdy gym class invented basketball. John Coy; illustrations by Joe Morse. Carolrhoda Books, c2013. 1 v. (unpaged)
Grades: 2 3 4 5 6   **796.323**
    1. Naismith, James, 1861-1939 2. Basketball -- History 3. High school students 4. High schools 5. Physical education teachers 6. Sports
ISBN 9780761366171
                  LC 2011021235
Reveals how James Naismith came to invent basketball at a Springfield, Massachusetts high school in 1891 while teaching a rowdy gym class.

Doeden, Matt
The **Final** Four: the pursuit of college basketball glory. Matt Doeden. Millbrook Press, 2016 64 p.
Grades: 4 5 6 7 8   **796.323**
    1. NCAA Basketball Tournament -- History
ISBN 9781467787802
                  LC 2015025429
Describes the history of the NCAA men's basketball tournament, from the first intercollegiate basketball game in 1895 to the thrills and drama of the most recent Final Four competition.

"Though the book's appeal will be limited to serious basketball fans, the historical perspective and engaging presentation make it a solid choice." School Library Journal.

Includes bibliographical references and index.

Hoose, Phillip M., 1947-
Attucks!: Oscar Robertson and the basketball team that awakened a city. Phillip Hoose. Farrar Straus & Giroux, 2018. 160 p.
Grades: 7 8 9 10 11 12   **796.323**
    1. Robertson, Oscar, 1938- 2. 1950s 3. Segregation 4. High school basketball 5. Winning and losing 6. Basketball 7. Indiana
ISBN 9780374306120
"Acclaimed author Hoose (The Boys Who Challenged Hitler, 2015, etc.) returns to his home state with the true story of the all-black high school basketball team that broke the color barrier in segregated 1950s Indianapolis, anchored by one of the greatest players of all time." Kirkus.

Labrecque, Ellen
Basketball. by Ellen Labrecque. Cherry Lake Pub., c2009. 32 p.: 21st century skills innovation library.
Grades: 4 5 6 7   **796.323**
    1. Basketball 2. Basketball -- History 3. Sports
ISBN 9781602792562
                  LC 2008002044

Examines the history, basic rules, and terminology of basketball.

"This stands out by emphasizing monumental shifts and advances in the events themselves. . . . Concise and occasionally revelatory." Booklist.

Includes bibliographical references (p. 31) and index.

Robinson, Tom, 1964-

Girls play to win basketball. by Tom Robinson. Norwood House Press, c2010. 64 p. : Girls play to win

Grades: 4 5 6 7   **796.323**

1. Women basketball players 2. Basketball 3. Basketball for girls 4. Women athletes 5. Basketball for women
ISBN 9781599533889

      LC 2010009814

Covers the history, rules, fundamentals and significant personalities of the sport of women's basketball. Topics include: techniques, strategies, competitive events, and equipment. Glossary, Additional Resources and Index included. Provided by publisher.

"With an easy design and format, the [text is] highly accessible to even the most reluctant readers and [provides] great exposure and insight into the world of female professional sports." Horn Book Guide.

Includes bibliographical references and index.

Slade, Suzanne

Basketball: how it works. by Suzanne Slade. Capstone Press, c2010. 48 p. : Sports Illustrated kids.

Grades: 4 5 6 7   **796.323**

1. Basketball 2. Sports sciences 3. Physics
ISBN 9781429640213

      LC 2009028508

Describes the science behind the sport of basketball, including offense, defense, arenas, and trick plays. Provided by publisher.

"The book's photograph-heavy design works to engage its audience, while the easy-to-read [text explains] the science." Horn Book Guide.

Includes bibliographical references and index.

Stewart, Mark, 1960-

Swish: the quest for basketball's perfect shot. by Mark Stewart and Mike Kennedy. Millbrook Press, 2009. 64 p.: Spectacular sports

Grades: 5 6 7 8   **796.323**

1. Basketball -- History 2. Basketball players 3. Professional basketball 4. College basketball 5. Women basketball players
ISBN 9780822587521

Takes readers beyond mere statistics and explores all aspects of basketball, from how the game was invented to player profiles and stories of famous baskets.

Yancey, Diane

Basketball. by Diane Yancey. Lucent Books, c2011. 112 p.: Science behind sports

Grades: 5 6 7 8   **796.323**

1. Basketball 2. Sports sciences 3. Sports
ISBN 9781420502930

      LC 2010035239

"This explores the scientific principles such as momentum, gravity, friction, and aerodynamics, plus many more, behind [basketball]. . . . [The author discusses the sport's] origins, history, and changes, . . . the biomechanics and physiology of playing, related health and medical concerns, and the causes and treatment of sports-related injuries. Additional information tells how exercise, diet and nutrition, warming up, and training relate to peak performance and enjoyment of the sport. .

. . [The book] has features on possible side effects of anabolic steroid use; how MRIs work; and how various improvements to the courts, basketballs, shoes, and uniforms have affected the game. The action photography . . . is fantastic. . . . [A must-have] for sports fans, athletes, science students, and even anyone considering a career in sports-related medicine, coaching, or other connected fields." School Library Journal.

Includes bibliographical references and index.

796.325 Volleyball

Crisfield, Deborah

Winning volleyball for girls. Deborah W. Crisfield, John Monteleone; foreword by Maria Nolan. Chelsea House Publishers, c2010. xviii, 189 p.

Grades: 10 11 12   **796.325**

1. Volleyball for girls 2. Volleyball
ISBN 9780816077205

      LC 2009005733

Reviews rules, recommends conditioning exercises, discusses serves, and explains offensive and defensive strategies.

796.332 American football

Bryant, Howard, 1968-

Legends: the best players, games, and teams in football. Howard Bryant. Philomel Books, 2015 xiv, 305 p.

Grades: 6 7 8 9   **796.332**

1. National Football League -- History 2. Football coaches -- Rating of 3. Football players -- Rating of 4. Football teams -- Rating of 5. Football -- History
ISBN 9780399169045

      LC 2015023192

Offers highlights and entertaining facts from twenty of the greatest Super Bowls in the history of professional football.

"The top moments, games, and players are designed to be discussed and debated as only true lovers of the game can, and a thorough index and photos contribute nicely." Booklist.

Doeden, Matt

The **Super** Bowl: chasing football immortality. Matt Doeden. Millbrook Press, [2017] 64 p.: Spectacular sports

Grades: 3 4 5 6 7 8   **796.332**

1. Football 2. Football teams 3. Football players
ISBN 9781512427547

      LC 2016042224

Presents the history of the Super Bowl, covering the game's greatest moments, players, and halftime shows.

"From the beginning of the National Football League and the origins of the term Super Bowl to the transformation of the halftime show, this book provides a concise, informative history of the football's annual championship. Even better, though, are the lively descriptions of the noteworthy games and the most memorable moments in Super Bowl history, starting with the greatest upset (1969) and ending with the greatest comeback (2017)." Booklist.

Includes bibliographical references and index.

Frederick, Shane

Football: the math of the game. by Shane Frederick. Capstone Press, c2011. 48 p.: Sports Illustrated kids.

Grades: 6 7 8 9   **796.332**
    1. Football -- Mathematical models 2. Mathematics
ISBN 9781429665674

LC 2011007864

Presents the mathematical concepts involved with the sport of football. Provided by publisher.

"This offers a dazzling layout, which includes countless vivid photographs and overlays of facts and figures. . . . This takes its concept and runs all the way to the end zone with it—dense and heavy, but undoubtedly impressive." Booklist.

Includes bibliographical references (p. 47) and index.

Gigliotti, Jim

    Football. by Jim Gigliotti. Cherry Lake Pub., c2009. 32 p.: 21st century skills innovation library.

Grades: 4 5 6 7   **796.332**
    1. Football 2. Sports 3. Football equipment 4. Ball games
ISBN 9781602792579

LC 2008002305

Examines the history, basic rules, and terminology of football.

"This stands out by emphasizing monumental shifts and advances in the events themselves. . . . Concise and occasionally revelatory." Booklist.

Includes bibliographical references (p. 31) and index.

Gilbert, Sara

    The **story** of the NFL. Sara Gilbert. Creative Education, c2012. 46, 2 p.: Built for success (Creative Education, Inc. (Mankato, Minn.))

Grades: 6 7 8 9   **796.332**
    1. National Football League -- History 2. Football -- History 3. Professional football
ISBN 9781608180639

LC 2010031224

A look at the origins, leaders, growth, and management of the NFL, the professional football league that was formed in 1920 and today governs 32 teams throughout the United States. Provided by publisher.

"This book is written in a lively style, yet with a minimum of fuss. . . . The slim, gleaming format, well-chosen photos, and the effort to explore what makes a company successful today [makes this title] unique." Booklist.

Includes bibliographical references (p. [47]) and index.

Stewart, Mark, 1960-

    Touchdown: the power and precision of football's perfect play. Mark Stewart and Mike Kennedy. Millbrook Press, 2010. 64 p. : Spectacular sports

Grades: 5 6 7 8   **796.332**
    1. Football
ISBN 9780822587514

LC 2008044295

"This attractive book opens with an intriguing history of American football. . . . Next, 10 double-page spreads feature Ten Unforgettable Touchdowns in both professional and collegiate games from 1913 to 2006. After a chapter on touchdown makers, spotlighting outstanding players . . . comes a short section on notable touchdown bloopers and another on trick plays and the element of surprise. . . . Photos, period prints, and reproductions of trading cards illustrate the text while adding color to the pages. . . . This nicely designed book provides plenty of on-the-field drama as well as pertinent information in a smoothly written overview of the touchdown." Booklist.

796.334 Soccer (Association football)

Berne, Emma Carlson

    What a kick: how a clutch World Cup win propelled women's soccer. by Emma Carlson Berne. Compass Point Books, 2016. 64 p.: Captured history sports

Grades: 6 7 8 9   **796.334**
    1. Women's World Cup (Soccer) 2. Soccer for women 3. Soccer teams 4. Women and sports 5. Women soccer players
ISBN 9780756552930

LC 2015034468

Discusses the final game of the 1999 women's World Cup soccer match and iconic photograph that captured the historic event. Provided by publisher.

"The many illustrations and large photos are a fascinating visual record of events before and after the captured moment." School Library Journal.

Includes bibliographical references and index.

Crisfield, Deborah

    Winning soccer for girls. Deborah W. Crisfield; foreword by Bill Hawkey and Patrick Murphy. Checkmark Books, c2010. xx, 164 p.

Grades: 10 11 12   **796.334**
    1. Soccer for women
ISBN 9780816077144

LC 2008050595

Explains the history and rules of the sport, basic skills, offense and defense, passing and receiving, and goalkeeping, and offers a plan to improve physical conditioning for soccer.

Doeden, Matt

    The **World** Cup: soccer's global championship. Matt Doeden. Millbrook Press, 2018 64 p.: Spectacular sports

Grades: 5 6 7 8 9 10   **796.334**
    1. Professional soccer 2. Professional soccer players 3. Soccer 4. Soccer teams 5. Soccer players
ISBN 9781512427554

LC 2017009220

Explores the history of the World Cup and covers the World Cup's greatest moments, including the save of the century, Diego Maradona's hand of God goal, and the United States Women's National Team's dominance.

Hornby, Hugh

    Soccer. written by Hugh Hornby; photographed by Andy Crawford. DK Pub., 2010. 72 p.: Eyewitness books

Grades: 4 5 6 7   **796.334**
    1. Soccer 2. Soccer -- History 3. Soccer -- Training
ISBN 9780756662950

LC bl2010010658

Examines all aspects of the game of soccer: its history, rules, techniques, tactics, equipment, playing fields, competitive play, and more.

Jennings, Madeleine

    Soccer step-by-step. Madeleine Jennings and Ian Howe. Rosen Central, 2009. 95 p. : Skills in motion

Grades: 5 6 7 8   **796.334**
    1. Soccer 2. Sports
ISBN 9781435833623

LC 2009012538

"Colorful photographs show the entire movement of each skill presented, giving new meaning to the term step-by-step. Progression borders at the bottom of the pages highlight the salient points to notice in performing each skill from beginning to end." School Library Journal.

Includes bibliographical references and index.

St. John, Warren

Outcasts united: the story of a refugee soccer team that changed a town. Warren St. John. Delacorte Press, c2012. 226 p.

Grades: 6 7 8   **796.334**

1. Mufleh, Luma. 2. Soccer coaches 3. Child refugees 4. Determination (Personal quality) 5. Soccer 6. Refugees, African 7. Georgia 8. Clarkston, Georgia

ISBN 9780385741941

LC 2012001412

Shares the inspirational story of a youth soccer team comprised of refugees from around the world who, under the guidance of a formidable female coach, helped to transform their Georgia community.

Stewart, Mark, 1960-

★ **Goal!**: the fire and fury of soccer's greatest moment. Mark Stewart and Mike Kennedy. Millbrook Press, c2010. 64 p.: Spectacular sports

Grades: 5 6 7 8   **796.334**

1. Goalies (Soccer) 2. Soccer players 3. Soccer -- Goalkeeping 4. Soccer -- Defense

ISBN 9780822587545

LC 2009014098

Explains the history and role of the goalkeeper in soccer, and describes the skills and physical prowess a goalie must have.

"This well-written book explores the nuances of scoring in the world's most popular sport. A quick history of the game lays the groundwork with details that may be new to even hard-core fans. The second chapter jumps right into the good stuff with descriptions of 10 of the most famous goals. . . . Also included is a rundown of the best male and female scorers from the early twentieth century to the present and weird anomalies and amusing anecdotes from soccer lore." Booklist.

Includes bibliographical references (p. 63) and index.

Weighill, Damien

The **big** book of soccer. by Mundial Wide Eyed Editions, 2020. 112 p.

Grades: 2 3 4 5   **796.334**

1. Soccer 2. Professional soccer 3. Soccer players 4. Sports

ISBN 9780711249103

Dive into the world of soccer with this mega book of everything to do with the beautiful game. Learn all the lingo; meet the greatest players, managers, and teams from both the men's and women's games; take masterclasses with the pros; wander through the haircut hall of fame; learn the most iconic goal celebrations; and more. Excerpted from publisher description.

Zweig, Eric, 1963-

Soccer. Eric Zweig and Mark Geiger. Natl Geographic Soc Childrens books, 2018. 112 p.

Grades: 4 5 6 7   **796.334**

1. Soccer 2. Sports

ISBN 9781426330087

"Throughout the book, contributing author Geiger—a real-life professional referee—offers insights and commentary. A handful of superstar players are profiled, and vivid, well-chosen stock photographs grab attention." Horn Book

796.34 Racket games

Smolka, Bo, 1965-

Lacrosse. by Bo Smolka. Norwood House Press, c2012. 64 p.: Girls play to win

Grades: 4 5 6 7   **796.34**

1. Lacrosse 2. Sports 3. Competition 4. Lacrosse for women 5. Lacrosse for children

ISBN 9781599534633

LC 2011011050

Covers the history, rules, fundamentals, and significant personalities of the sport of women's lacrosse. Topics include: techniques, strategies, competitive events, and equipment. Glossary, Additional Resources, and Index included. Provided by publisher.

796.352 Golf

Kelley, K. C.

Golf. by K.C. Kelley. Cherry Lake Pub., c2009. 32 p.: 21st century skills innovation library.

Grades: 4 5 6 7   **796.352**

1. Golf 2. Ball games 3. Golf -- Equipment and supplies 4. Golfers 5. Sports -- History

ISBN 9781602792623

LC 2008002045

Examines the history, basic rules, and terminology of golf.

"This stands out by emphasizing monumental shifts and advances in the events themselves. . . . Concise and occasionally revelatory." Booklist.

Includes bibliographical references (p. 31) and index.

796.355 Field hockey

McKinley, Michael, 1961-

Ice time: the story of hockey. Michael McKinley. Tundra Books, 2006. 80 p.

Grades: 5 6 7 8   **796.355**

1. Hockey -- History 2. Hockey players 3. Winter Olympic medal winners 4. Sports -- History

ISBN 0887767621

LC 2005911187

A guide to the history of hockey from the Canadian perspective, from the first indoor hockey game in Montreal to the 2002 Canadian's men's team's Olympic gold medal, including biographical sketches of important players.

"This straightforward history of hockey emphasizes the professional game and Canadian players. . . . Hockey enthusiasts will find this a welcome arrival." Booklist.

796.357 Baseball

Bryant, Howard, 1968-

Legends: the best players, games, and teams in baseball. Howard Bryant. Philomel Books, 2015. 240 p.

Grades: 6 7 8 9   **796.357**

1. Baseball players 2. Baseball 3. Baseball teams 4. Athletes

5. Sports
ISBN 9780399169038

LC 2014031744

"A sports fan's delight: historical highlights (and lowlights), tributes to great players and lots of 'Top Ten' lists ripe for vigorous second guessing." Kirkus.

Gitlin, Marty

Girls play to win softball. by Marty Gitlin. Norwood House Press, c2012. 64 p.: Girls play to win

Grades: 4 5 6 7   **796.357**
    1. Softball 2. Competition 3. Softball for women 4. Softball for children 5. Sports
ISBN 9781599534657

LC 2011011051

Covers the history, rules, fundamentals, and significant personalities of the sport of women's softball. Topics include: techniques, strategies, competitive events, and equipment. Glossary, Additional Resources, and Index included. Provided by publisher.

Gola, Mark

Winning softball for girls. Mark Gola; foreword by Gretchen Cammiso. Chelsea House, c2010. xx, 220 p.

Grades: 10 11 12   **796.357**
    1. Softball for women 2. Softball
ISBN 9780816077168

LC 2008054453

Reviews rules, recommends conditioning exercises, discusses positions, and explains offensive and defensive strategies.

Thorn, John, 1947-

First pitch: how baseball began. John Thorn. Beach Ball Books, 2011 40 p.

Grades: 4 5 6 7   **796.357**
    1. Baseball 2. Baseball players 3. Sports -- History
ISBN 9781936310043

"Packed with vintage images and photographs, this history of baseball takes readers from the origins of the sport to the present day. . . . Thorn . . . writes clearly and eloquently. . . . Fans who think they know baseball may discover they have much to learn." Publishers Weekly.

796.36 Ball caught and thrown with same equipment

Luke, Andrew

Lacrosse. Andrew Luke. Mason Crest, [2016] 80 p.: Inside the world of sports

Grades: 7 8 9 10 11 12   **796.36**
    1. Lacrosse
ISBN 9781422234648

LC 2016026073

Explores the sport of lacrosse, including its history, greatest moments, notable players, and what the future of the sport holds.

"Supplemented by video clips (through QR codes), these books create an interactive learning environment teens will appreciate. Each book follows the same information-packed format. Beginning with a highlight reel of the greatest moments in the topic sport, each title goes on to explore the origin, evolution, and future of it along with portraits of contemporary and all-star players." School Library Journal.

Includes webography and index.

796.362 Lacrosse

Swissler, Becky

Winning lacrosse for girls. Becky Swissler; foreword by Katie Bergstrom. Chelsea House, c2009. xx, 212 p.

Grades: 10 11 12   **796.362**
    1. Lacrosse for girls 2. Lacrosse
ISBN 9780816077120

LC 2008051346

Explains the history and rules of the sport, basic skills, offense and defense, passing and receiving, and goalkeeping, and offers a plan to improve physical conditioning for lacrosse.

796.4 Weight lifting, track and field, gymnastics

Schwartz, Heather E.

Gymnastics. Heather E. Schwartz. Lucent Books, c2011. 96 p.: Science behind sports

Grades: 5 6 7 8   **796.4**
    1. Gymnastics 2. Gymnasts 3. Science
ISBN 9781420502770

LC 2010033544

Provides an overview of the sport's origins and evolution, presenting the scientific principles and concepts relevant to gymnastics, the biomechanics and physiology involved, and the elements of sports medicine uniquely associated with gymnasts.

"This explores the scientific principles such as momentum, gravity, friction, and aerodynamics, plus many more, behind [gymnastics]. . . . [The author discusses the sport's] origins, history, and changes, . . . the biomechanics and physiology of playing, related health and medical concerns, and the causes and treatment of sports-related injuries. Additional information tells how exercise, diet and nutrition, warming up, and training relate to peak performance and enjoyment of the sport. . . . One of the most interesting chapters . . . is The Psychology of Gymnastics, which discusses fears, force of will, honing the competitive edge, and the pressure to succeed. . . . [This volume is] jam-packed full of information. [A must-have] for sports fans, athletes, science students, and even anyone considering a career in sports-related medicine, coaching, or other connected fields." School Library Journal.

Includes bibliographical references and index.

796.42 Track and field

Burgan, Michael

Olympic gold 1936: how the image of Jesse Owens crushed Hitler's evil myth. by Michael Burgan. Compass Point Books, a Capstone imprint, [2017] 64 p.: Captured history sports

Grades: 6 7 8 9   **796.42**
    1. Owens, Jesse, 1913-1980 2. 1930s 3. Olympic games 4. Olympic athletes 5. Track and field athletes 6. African-American track and field athletes 7. Track and field 8. Berlin, Germany -- History -- 1918-1945. 9. Germany -- History -- 1933-1945.
ISBN 9780756555320

LC 2016038562

Discusses the life of the famous African American track and field star who won four gold medals at the 1936 Olympic games in Berlin.

Gifford, Clive

Track and field. Clive Gifford. PowerKids Press, 2009. 32 p.: Personal best

Grades: 4 5 6 7 8   **796.42**

1. Track and field 2. Running 3. Track and field athletes 4. Competition 5. Sports
ISBN 9781404244429

           LC 2007042984

"This guide to track and field offers well-organized and easy-to-follow instructions, focusing on rules, clothing, specific skills, and competitions. . . . Informative, readable." School Library Journal.

Housewright, Ed

Winning track and field for girls. Ed Housewright; foreword by Jason-Lamont Jackson. Chelsea House Publishers, c2010. xxi, 194 p.

Grades: 10 11 12   **796.42**

1. Track and field for women 2. Track and field
ISBN 9780816077182

           LC 2009009019

Reviews rules, recommends conditioning exercises, and discusses different events.

McDougall, Chros

Girls play to win track & field. by Chros McDougall. Norwood House Press, c2011. 64 p.: Girls play to win

Grades: 4 5 6 7   **796.42**

1. Track and field 2. Running 3. Track and field athletes 4. Competition 5. Sports
ISBN 9781599534671

           LC 2011011053

Covers the history, rules, fundamentals, and significant personalities of the sport of women's track and field. Topics include: techniques, strategies, competitive events, and equipment. Glossary, Additional Resources and Index included. Provided by publisher.

796.48 Olympic games

Macy, Sue

Swifter, higher, stronger: a photographic history of the Summer Olympics. by Sue Macy; foreword by Bob Costas. National Geographic, c2008. 96 p.

Grades: 4 5 6 7   **796.48**

1. Olympic games -- History 2. Olympic games (Ancient) 3. Athletes 4. Olympic medal winners 5. Competition
ISBN 9781426302909

           LC bl2008019743

Looks at the history of the Olympic Games, from their origins in ancient Greece, through their rebirth in nineteenth-century France, to the present, highlighting the contributions of individuals to the Games' success and popularity.

"While other books on the topic go into more depth on specific sports, athletes, or historical events, none are as enthusiastically broad or as enjoyable to read as this one. And, it's superbly illustrated with colorful, well-chosen, and enticing photographs." School Library Journal. [review of 2004 ed.]

Includes bibliographical references (p. 92-93) and index.

Maraniss, Andrew

Games of deception: the true story of the first U.S. Olympic basketball team at the 1936 Olympics in Hitler's Germany. Andrew Maraniss. Philomel Books, 2019. 240 p.

Grades: 7 8 9 10 11   **796.48**

1. 1930s 2. Olympic games -- Political aspects 3. Basketball 4. World War II 5. Nazism 6. International relations 7. Berlin, Germany -- History -- 1918-1945. 8. Germany -- History -- 1933-1945.
ISBN 9780525514633

           LC 2019034029

The true story of the birth of Olympic basketball at the 1936 Summer Games in Hitler's Germany. Provided by publisher.

"Written with the captivating voice of a color commentator and the sobriety of a historian, Maraniss peppers readers with anecdotes, statistics, and play-by-play action, shining a spotlight on names found only in the footnotes of history while making it painfully clear that racism affected both politics and sport, tarnishing, a bit, each gold medal and the five Olympic rings." Kirkus

Includes bibliographical references and index.

Smith-Llera, Danielle, 1971-

Black power salute: how a photograph captured a political protest. by Danielle Smith- Llera. Compass Point Books, a Capstone imprint, 2017. 64 p.: Captured history sports

Grades: 6 7 8 9   **796.48**

1. Smith, Tommie, 1944- 2. Carlos, John, 1945- 3. Olympic Project for Human Rights 4. African American athletes 5. Runners 6. Civil Rights Movement 7. Black power 8. Olympic games 9. Mexico (City)
ISBN 9780756555269

           LC 2016038561

Discusses the events surrounding John Carlos' and Tommie Smith's controversial silent protest at the 1968 Olympic Games, highlighting the iconic photograph that captured their raised fists, symbolizing the fight for equality and civil rights.

"These books will certainly capture the attention of kids interested in sports, civil rights history, or photography." Booklist

Includes bibliographical references and index.

796.5 Outdoor life

Paulsen, Gary

Woodsong. by Gary Paulsen. Bradbury Press, c1990. 132 p.

Grades: 7 8 9 10   **796.5**

1. Paulsen, Gary Minnesota. 2. Iditarod Trail Sled Dog Race, Alaska 3. Outdoor life 4. Dogsledding 5. Men and dogs 6. Authors, American 20th century 7. Minnesota -- Social life and customs.
ISBN 0027702219

           LC 89070835

For a rugged outdoor man and his family, life in northern Minnesota is a wild experience involving wolves, deer, and the sled dogs that make their way of life possible. Includes an account of the author's first Iditarod, a dogsled race across Alaska.

"The book is packed with vignettes that range among various shades of terror and lyrical beauty." Voice of Youth Advocates.

796.51 Walking

Davis, Jennifer Pharr

Hiking and camping: the definitive interactive nature guide. Jennifer Pharr Davis and Haley Blevins; illustrated by Aliki Karkoulia. Odd Dot, 2021. 448 p.: Outdoor school

Grades: 6 7 8 9 10 11 12 **796.51**

1. Camping 2. Hiking 3. Outdoor recreation

ISBN 9781250230843

LC 2020021773

A definitive, interactive, skill-building guide for exploring the world. Rewild your life! With metal corners and 448 full-color, highly-illustrated pages, Outdoor School is your indispensable tool for the outdoors." Provided by publisher.

"A thorough, detailed compendium of most everything readers will want and need to know about being in the outdoors." Kirkus

796.52 Walking and exploring by kind of terrain

Felix, Rebecca, 1984-

Exploring caves. Rebecca Felix; content consultant, Jason Polk, Assistant Professor of Geoscience, Western Kentucky University. ABDO Publishing Company, 2014. 144 p.

Grades: 5 6 7 8 9 10 **796.52**

1. Caving 2. Caves 3. Underground areas 4. Exploration

ISBN 9781624032493

LC bl2014005640

Documents how the caves around the world have been, and continue to be, explored, citing famous caves and reasons why these underground areas have been scouted.

Soontornvat, Christina

★ **All** thirteen: the incredible cave rescue of the Thai boys' soccer team. Christina Soontornvat. Candlewick Press, 2020. 288 p.

Grades: 5 6 7 8 **796.52**

1. Search and rescue operations 2. Caving 3. Survival 4. Caves 5. Rescues 6. Thailand 7. Books for reluctant readers

ISBN 9781536209457

Golden Kite Award for Nonfiction, 2021.

Combines firsthand interviews with scientific and cultural insights in a middle grade account of the 2018 Thai cave rescue of the Wild Boars soccer team and the critical, sophisticated engineering operation that saved the lives of 13 young people.

"Using interviews and other primary sources, [Soontornvat] keeps a tight focus on the unfolding story, with its inherent edge-of-your-seat, heart-in-your-throat drama, adroitly juggling a parade of characters." Horn Book

Includes bibliographical references (pages 271-272) and index.

796.522 Walking and exploring by kind of terrain— Mountains, hills, rocks

Athans, Sandra K., 1958-

Secrets of the sky caves: danger and discovery on Nepal's Mustang Cliffs. Sandra K. Athans. Millbrook Press, [2014] 64 p.

Grades: 4 5 6 7 **796.522**

1. Mountaineering 2. Caves 3. Antiquities 4. Nepal 5. Mustang (Nepal: District) -- Exploration

ISBN 9781467700160

LC 2013017736

Examines the mysterious caves in Nepal's Mustang cliffs, the antiquities found inside, and the climbers and archaeologists who have studied them.

"The author, sister of expedition leader Pete Athans, offers a wealth of information about this little-known archaeological wonder. Color photographs provide stunning visuals." Horn Book.

Includes bibliographical references (pages 61-62) and index.

Berne, Emma Carlson

Summiting Everest: how a photograph celebrates teamwork at the top of the world. by Emma Carlson Berne; content adviser: Olivia Sofer, Certified Guide, Association of Canadian Mountain Guides. Compass Point Books, a Capstone imprint, [2014] 64 p.: Captured history

Grades: 5 6 7 8 9 **796.522**

1. Hillary, Edmund, 1919-2008. 2. Tenzing Norkey, 1914-1986. 3. Mountaineering 4. Mountaineers 5. Portrait photography 6. Mountaineering expeditions 7. Mount Everest 8. Himalaya Mountains

ISBN 9780756547349

LC 2013027843

Discusses the events surrounding Alfred Gregory's famous photograph of Edmund Hillary and Tenzing Norgay standing on Mount Everest, which became the highest photograph anyone in human history had ever taken.

Cleare, John

Epic climbs: Eiger, K2, Everest, McKinley, Matterhorn. John Cleare. Kingfisher: 2010. 64 p.: Epic adventure

Grades: 5 6 7 8 **796.522**

1. Mountaineering 2. Mountaineers 3. Adventurers

ISBN 9780753465738

LC bl2011006281

Presents stories of epic climbs and the pioneers that found the way to high-altitude summits.

"Cleare gives the history of five of the most famous and dangerous mountains to climb: Eiger, K2, Everest, McKinley, and Matterhorn. Each section has a short, easy-to-read summary that gives the history of climbers who have conquered these peaks. Full-color photos include the view from the top and historical and contemporary climbing equipment." School Library Journal.

Olson, Tod

Into the clouds: the race to climb the world's most dangerous mountain. Tod Olson. Scholastic Focus, 2020. xviii, 265 p.

Grades: 3 4 5 6 7 **796.522**

1. Mountaineering 2. K2 (Pakistan: Mountain)

ISBN 9781338207361

LC 2019002127

Describes the expedition to the summit of the world's most deadly mountain, K2, by Charlie Houston and his fellow mountaineers, detailing their life-risking efforts to follow in the footsteps of another expedition that ended in tragedy.

Romero, Jordan, 1996-

No summit out of sight: the true story of the youngest person to climb the seven summits. Jordan Romero with Linda LeBlanc. Simon & Schuster Books for Young Readers, 2014. 288 p.

Grades: 7 8 9 10   **796.522**
1. Romero, Jordan, 1996- 2. Mountaineering 3. Teenagers 4.
Teenage boys
ISBN 9781476709628

                       LC 2013031296
The story of Jordan Romero, who at the age of 13 became the
youngest person ever to reach the summit of Mount Everest. At age 15,
he reached the summits of the world's 7 highest mountains. Provided
by publisher.

796.6 Cycling and related activities

Adamson, Thomas K., 1970-
BMX racing. by Thomas K. Adamson. Bellwether Media,
Inc., 2015. 24 p.: Extreme sports (Epic)
Grades: 3 4 5 6 7   **796.6**
1. Bicycle motocross 2. Bicycling 3. Extreme sports
ISBN 9781626172746

                       LC 2015007777
Engaging images accompany information about BMX racing. The
combination of high-interest subject matter and light text is intended for
students in grades 2 through 7. Provided by publisher.
"The book's exciting tone and dynamic illustrations will draw kids
into the world of extreme sports." Booklist.
Includes bibliographical references (page 23) and index.

Macy, Sue
★ **Wheels** of change: how women rode the bicycle to free-
dom (with a few flat tires along the way). by Sue Macy. National
Geographic, 2011. 96 p.
Grades: 4 5 6 7 8   **796.6**
1. Bicycling for women 2. Feminism -- History 3. Women's rights
-- History 4. Social change -- History 5. Bicycles -- History 6.
United States -- History -- 19th century 7. United States -- History
-- 20th century
ISBN 9781426307614
"This is an engaging look at the emancipating impact that bikes had
on late-nineteenth-century U.S. women. The eye-catching chapters,
filled with archival images . . . zero in on the profound ways that bicycles
subverted traditional notions of femininity. . . . Macy seamlessly weaves
together research, direct quotes . . . and historical overviews that put the
facts into context, while sidebars expand on related topics. . . . A strong,
high-interest choice for both classroom and personal reading." Booklist.
Includes bibliographical references and index.

Robinson, Laura
★ **Cyclist** bikelist: the book for every rider. Laura Robinson;
illustrated by Ramón K. Pérez. Tundra Books, c2010. 55 p.
Grades: 4 5 6 7   **796.6**
1. Bicycling 2. Bicycles
ISBN 9780887767845

                       LC bl2010009485
A guide to bicycles and bicycling discusses the history of bicycles,
their parts, different types, and choosing the right one; bicycling safety
and clothing; bicycle maintenance; and famous cyclists.
"The author covers a broad range of topics, from choosing and caring for a bike to differences in tires, how gear ratios work, and even
proper dress and nutrition. She also provides a quick overview of the
bicycle's history and inspiring sketches of several renowned racers. .
. . Supplemented by photos of different types of bikes, Pérez's bright,

cartoon-style pictures add both humor and . . . sharply drawn details. A
first-rate guide." Booklist.

796.72 Automobile racing

Kelley, K. C.
Hottest NASCAR machines. by K.C. Kelley. Enslow Publishers, c2008. 48 p.: Wild wheels! (Enslow Publishers)
Grades: 4 5 6 7   **796.72**
1. NASCAR (Association) -- History 2. Stock car racing -- History
3. Stock cars (Automobiles)
ISBN 0766028690

                       LC 2007007426
Experience the thrill of a NASCAR race, and learn about the cars,
personalities, and races associated with this sport. Provided by publisher.

796.72092 Automobile racing - Biography

Bascomb, Neal
The **racers**: how an outcast driver, an American heiress, and
a legendary car challenged Hitler's best. Neal Bascomb. Scholastic Focus, 2020. 320 p.
Grades: 6 7 8 9 10 11 12   **796.72092**
1. Automobile racing -- History 20th century 2. Automobile racing
drivers 20th century 3. Grand Prix racing -- History 20th century 4.
Antisemitism in sports -- History
ISBN 9781338277418

                       LC 2019059286
In the years before World War II, Adolf Hitler wanted to prove the
greatness of the Third Reich in everything from track and field to motor-
sports. The Nazis poured money into the development of new race cars,
and Mercedes-Benz came out with a stable of supercharged automobiles
called Silver Arrows. Their drivers dominated the sensational world of
European Grand Prix racing and saluted Hitler on their many returns
home with victory. As the Third Reich stripped Jews of their rights and
began their march toward war, one driver, René Dreyfus, a 32-year-old
Frenchman of Jewish heritage who had enjoyed some early successes on
the racing circuit, was barred from driving on any German or Italian race
teams, which fielded the best in class, due to the rise of Hitler and Benito
Mussolini. So it was that in 1937, Lucy Schell, an American heiress and
top Monte Carlo Rally driver, needed a racer for a new team she was creating to take on Germany's Silver Arrows. Sensing untapped potential in
Dreyfus, she funded the development of a nimble tiger of a new car built
by a little-known French manufacturer called Delahaye. As the nations
of Europe marched ever closer to war, Schell and Dreyfus faced down
Hitler's top drivers, and the world held its breath in anticipation, waiting
to see who would triumph." Provided by publisher.
"In this historical account packed with the thrill and danger of
1930s high-speed auto racing, the racetrack becomes a battleground for
Nazi might vs. independent ingenuity." Bulletin of the Center for Children's Books
Includes bibliographical references and index.

796.8 Combat sports

Hanel, Rachael
Gladiators. Rachael Hanel. Creative Education, c2008. 48
p.: Fearsome fighters

Grades: 4 5 6   **796.8**
1. Gladiators -- History 2. Weapons 3. Rome -- History
ISBN 9781583415351

LC 2006021842

Examines the history, culture, training, and fighting styles of Roman gladiators, with information about the few historical details that have survived about specific fighters.

"This recounts the brutality and cruelty of fighting for sport celebrated during Roman times. . . . [The book does] an adequate job of covering fighting techniques, weapons, and history. Photographs and archival reproductions enhance the [presentation]; sidebars provide additional information." Horn Book Guide.

Includes bibliographical references (p. 48) and index.

796.812 Wrestling

Ellis, Carol, 1945-
Wrestling. by Carol Ellis. Marshall Cavendish Benchmark, c2011. 48 p. : Martial arts in action
Grades: 4 5 6 7   **796.812**
1. Wrestling 2. Wrestlers 3. Sports 4. Athletes
ISBN 9780761449416

LC 2010013819

"This book about wrestling offers an introduction, a brief history, and expectations for students who begin taking classes. . . . [This title is] outstanding, using an approachable voice without fictionalizing and presenting the history of [wrestling] in a way that makes it feel relevant." School Library Journal.

796.815 Oriental martial arts forms

Haney-Withrow, Anna
Tae kwon do. Anna Haney-Withrow. Marshall Cavendish Benchmark, c2012. 47 p.: Martial arts in action
Grades: 4 5 6 7   **796.815**
1. Tae kwon do 2. Martial arts 3. Martial arts for children
ISBN 9780761449409

LC 2010013828

"This treats martial arts with the dignity that serious enthusiasts bring to the sport. . . . Illustrations include not only photos of modern gear and from films but also historical images." Booklist.

Inman, Roy
The **judo** handbook. Roy Inman. Rosen Pub., 2008. 256 p.: Martial arts (Rosen Publishing Group)
Grades: 7 8 9 10 11 12   **796.815**
1. Judo 2. Martial arts 3. Wrestling
ISBN 9781404213937

LC 2007037742

Introduces the sport of judo, discussing such topics as training methods, breakfalls, grips, throwing techniques, hold-downs and armlocks, and combination and counter-techniques.

"This features step-by-step descriptions of various moves, accompanied by detailed, full-color photographs. [This] volume offers a background on the history of the art and its use as a sport as well as a system for self-defense. [The] handbook features a concise description of the judo fundamentals, then begins describing the techniques: throwing techniques, combination and counter-techniques, ground techniques, and combination and counter-techniques against them. The book makes good use of the Japanese terms used in judo study, integrating their meanings seamlessly into the text." School Library Journal.

Includes bibliographical references (p. 256) and index.

Mack, Gail
Kickboxing. Gail Mack. Marshall Cavendish Benchmark, c2012. 47 p.: Martial arts in action
Grades: 4 5 6 7   **796.815**
1. Kickboxing 2. Martial arts 3. Martial arts for children
ISBN 9780761449362

LC 2010014798

"This treats martial arts with the dignity that serious enthusiasts bring to the sport. . . . Illustrations include not only photos of modern gear and from films but also historical images." Booklist.

Pawlett, Mark
The **tae** kwon do handbook. Mark Pawlett and Ray Pawlett. Rosen Pub., 2008. 256 p.: Martial arts (Rosen Publishing Group)
Grades: 7 8 9 10 11 12   **796.815**
1. Martial artists 2. Tae kwon do 3. Martial arts
ISBN 9781404213968

LC 2007031559

Discusses the history, philosophy, types, stances, and techniques of tae kwon do, presenting strikes, kicks, blocks, and sequences of moves.

"This features step-by-step descriptions of various moves, accompanied by detailed, full-color photographs. [The] volume offers a background on the history of the art and its use as a sport as well as a system for self-defense. . . . [The book] spends about 150 pages on techniques, and also covers dietary recommendations, a history of Korea, a description of the I Ching, and other concepts. . . . It [includes] an excellent section on strength training . . . and the text devoted to basic fundamentals of the sport, such as stances and stepping, gives those building blocks appropriate importance." School Library Journal.

Pawlett, Raymond
The **karate** handbook. Ray Pawlett. Rosen Pub., 2008. 256 p.: Martial arts (Rosen Publishing Group)
Grades: 7 8 9 10 11 12   **796.815**
1. Karate 2. Martial arts 3. Jiu-jitsu
ISBN 9781404213944

LC 2007032795

Introduces the sport of karate, discussing such topics as stretching and warm-up exercises, stances and stepping, punching and striking, and kicking and blocking.

"This offers a thorough introduction to karate that covers both the underlying philosophy and the physical practice. A thoughtful, sophisticated history opens the book and discusses karate's roots in Zen Buddhism, the styles of karate, and dojo etiquette. Later spreads feature lucid, step-by-step instructions." Booklist.

Includes bibliographical references (p. 256) and index.

Ritschel, John
The **kickboxing** handbook. John Ritschel. Rosen Pub., 2008. 256 p.: Martial arts (Rosen Publishing Group)
Grades: 7 8 9 10 11 12   **796.815**
1. Kickboxing 2. Martial arts
ISBN 9781404213951

LC 2007037746

Introduces the sport of kickboxing, discussing such topics as equipment, warm-up exercises and stretching, stances and footwork, punches and kicks, and the use of kickboxing as a form of self-defense.

"This volume features step-by-step descriptions of various moves and strength-building exercises, accompanied by detailed, full-color photographs. . . . [This book] does emphasize safety, showing the correct way to punch in order to avoid injuring one's hand and displaying clear photographs on striking areas of the foot in order to perform kicks properly." School Library Journal.

796.83092 Boxing—Biography

Burgan, Michael

Ali's knockout punch: how a photograph stunned the boxing world. by Michael Burgan. Compass Point Books, a Capstone imprint, 2017. 64 p.: Captured history sports

Grades: 6 7 8 9   **796.83092**

1. Ali, Muhammad, 1942-2016 2. 1960s 3. Boxers (Sports) 4. African American athletes 5. Boxing matches 6. Photographs 7. African Americans

ISBN 9780756555276

Discusses the life and career of legendary boxer Muhammad Ali, highlighting the iconic photograph of the 1965 championship bout versus Sonny Liston.

796.91 Ice skating

McDougall, Chros

Girls play to win figure skating. by Chrös McDougall. Norwood House Press, c2011. 64 p.: Girls play to win

Grades: 4 5 6 7   **796.91**

1. Women figure skaters 2. Girl figure skaters 3. Figure skating 4. Winter sports 5. Ice skating

ISBN 9781599533896

LC 2010009809

Covers the history, rules, fundamentals and significant personalities of the sport of women's figure skating. Topics include: techniques, strategies, competitive events, and equipment. Glossary, Additional Resources and Index included. Provided by publisher.

"This begins with a look back at the origin of [figure skating] and the traces the young women who played a role in skating from the olden days to today. The first of six chapters describes skating basics . . . and then the progression of stars begins. . . . Color photos, sidebars, and boxed explanations break up the text. . . . A nicely compact history." Booklist.

Includes bibliographical references and index.

796.939 Snowboarding

Schwartz, Heather E.

Snowboarding. Heather E. Schwartz. Lucent Books, c2011. 104 p.: Science behind sports

Grades: 5 6 7 8   **796.939**

1. Snowboarding 2. Snowboarders 3. Winter sports 4. Extreme sports

ISBN 9781420503227

LC 2010033274

Describes the evolution of snowboarding as a sport, the training and conditioning required, the basics of gliding and turning, intermediate and advanced jumps and tricks, and the details of competitive snowboarding.

"This explores the scientific principles such as momentum, gravity, friction, and aerodynamics, plus many more, behind [snowbarding]. .

. . [The author discusses the sport's] origins, history, and changes, . . . the biomechanics and physiology of playing, related health and medical concerns, and the causes and treatment of sports-related injuries. Additional information tells how exercise, diet and nutrition, warming up, and training relate to peak performance and enjoyment of the sport. . . . The action photography . . . is fantastic. . . . [This volume is] jam-packed full of information. [A must-have] for sports fans, athletes, science students, and even anyone considering a career in sports-related medicine, coaching, or other connected fields." School Library Journal.

Includes bibliographical references and index.

796.94 Snowmobiling

Woods, Bob

Snowmobile racers. Bob Woods. Enslow Publishers, c2010. 48 p. : Kid racers

Grades: 5 6 7 8   **796.94**

1. Snowmobile racing 2. Snowmobiles 3. Snowmobiling 4. Winter sports

ISBN 9780766034877

LC 2009020784

High interest book for reluctant readers containing action packed photos and stories of the hottest snowmobiles and races for kids, discussing which snowmobiles qualify, how they are built and raced, who the best drivers are, what to look for in a snowmobile, safety, good sportsmanship, and how racing activities can be a good part of family life. Provided by publisher.

"The easily digestible text gets more visual weight on the page, but there are plenty of captioned color photos depicting different sorts of races as well as recreational snowmobiling." Booklist.

Includes bibliographical references and index.

796.962 Ice hockey

Adams, Carly

Queens of the ice: they were fast, they were fierce, they were teenage girls. Carly Adams. J. Lorimer, c2011. 131 p.: Record books

Grades: 5 6 7 8   **796.962**

1. Preston Rivulettes (Hockey team) -- History 2. 1930s 3. Women hockey players 4. Hockey teams 5. Hockey 6. Hockey players 7. Athletes 8. Ontario -- History

ISBN 9781552777206

"Filled with exciting action, this . . . title . . . showcases the history of the Preston Rivulettes, a Canadian hockey team of teenage girls who played together for 10 seasons, from 1931 until 1940, without losing a game and at a time when many believed that girls could not play the sport and needed chaperones. . . . Adams deepens the story with the historical background of the Great Depression and the team's struggle to find money. Occasional achival photos and boxed inserts add to the clear, readable account." Booklist.

Burgan, Michael

Miracle on ice: how a stunning upset united a country. by Michael Burgan. Compass Point Books, a Capstone imprint, 2016. 64 p.: Captured history sports

Grades: 6 7 8 9   **796.962**

1. 1980s 2. Hockey -- History 3. Hockey teams -- History 4.

Olympic athletes 5. Cold War
ISBN 9780756552909

LC bl2016001567

Shares the story of the 1980 Winter Olympics hockey match known as the "Miracle on Ice," when a young team of American college players beat the Soviet hockey team.

"The many illustrations and large photos are a fascinating visual record of events before and after the captured moment. This series is certain to entice sports fans to read about history." School Library Journal.

Includes bibliographical references (pages 61-63) and index.

McMahon, Dave

Girls play to win hockey. Dave McMahon. Norwood House, 2010. 64 p.: Girls play to win

Grades: 4 5 6 7   **796.962**

1. Women hockey players 2. Hockey for girls 3. Sports 4. Women hockey players 5. Hockey -- History
ISBN 9781599533902

"With an easy design and format, the [text is] highly accessible to even the most reluctant readers and [provides] great exposure and insight into the world of female professional sports." Horn Book Guide.

Savage, Jeff, 1961-

Top 25 hockey skills, tips, and tricks. Jeff Savage. Enslow Publishers, c2012. 48 p.: Top 25 sports skills, tips and tricks

Grades: 4 5 6 7   **796.962**

1. Hockey 2. Hockey players 3. Hockey for children 4. Sports
ISBN 9780766038691

LC 2011000286

Discusses hockey skills, including the proper techniques for skating, controlling the puck, passing, shooting, and defense and provides drills, fun tricks, and tips from the pros. Provided by publisher.

Sharp, Anne Wallace

Ice hockey. Anne Wallace Sharp. Lucent Books, c2011. 112 p.: Science behind sports

Grades: 5 6 7 8   **796.962**

1. Hockey 2. Hockey players 3. Sports sciences
ISBN 9781420502817

LC 2010025670

Presents an overview of the origins and history of ice hockey; explores the scientific principles behind the sport, including speed, velocity, momentum, energy, friction, motion, and force; and looks at common injuries and treatments.

"This book about ice hockey highlights performance; chapter headings include topics such as Training and Nutrition, High-Tech Equipment, and Injuries and Treatments. Physics, biology, and psychology concepts related to the [sport] are . . . wrapped into technical discussions of moves and techniques. Many photographs of pros and novices in action add interest." Horn Book Guide.

Includes bibliographical references and index.

Stewart, Mark, 1960-

Score!: the action and artistry of hockey's magnificent moment. Mark Stewart and Mike Kennedy. Millbrook Press, c2011. 64 p.: Spectacular sports

Grades: 5 6 7 8   **796.962**

1. Hockey -- History
ISBN 9780822587538

LC 2009046981

Discusses the history of ice hockey and focuses on the rules and technique of scoring goals.

"Stewart and Kennedy take readers on a chatty, photo-studded tour of the art of scoring in the rink. This intermediate-level hockey book definitely isn't for beginners. . . . What savvy readers will get, however, is a bounty of information on the game's defining goals, goal scorers, and goal-scoring techniques. . . . This makes a worthy addition to any sports shelf." Booklist.

Includes bibliographical references (p. 63) and index.

797.12 Types of vessels

Brown, Daniel, 1951-

★ The **boys** in the boat: the true story of an American team's epic journey to win gold at the 1936 olympics. Daniel James Brown, adapted for young readers by Gregory Mone. Viking, [2015] xi, 227 p.

Grades: 5 6 7 8   **797.12**

1. University of Washington -- Rowing -- History. 2. 1930s 3. Rowing -- History 4. Working class men 5. Friendship 6. Determination in men 7. Rowers
ISBN 9780451475923

LC 2015006199

Describes the American rowing team's triumphant and unlikely win during the 1936 Olympics, and is based on The boys in the boat: Nine Americans and their epic quest for gold at the 1936 Berlin Olympics.

"Overcoming a difficult childhood, Joe Rantz made the freshman crew team at the University of Washington. There, he met equally determined boys and a coach driven to take the gold at the Olympics in Hitler's Germany. Each team member is profiled; the sport of rowing becomes comprehensible and compelling. This adaptation of the adult bestseller is liberally illustrated with black-and-white photographs." Horn Book.

797.122 Canoeing

Wurdinger, Scott D.

Kayaking. Scott Wurdinger & Leslie Rapparlie. Creative Education, c2007. 48 p.: Adventure sports

Grades: 5 6 7 8   **797.122**

1. Kayaking 2. Kayaks 3. Boats 4. Boating
ISBN 1583413979

LC 2005051057

Examines many aspects of kayaking, including equipment, fundamental skills, and ways to get started.

"Strong, full-page color photographs illustrate this overview of kayaking. . . . Tracing the use of kayaks back thousands of years, the authors touch on the history of the boats before moving on to contemporary usage for sports and recreation. . . . The exciting views . . . will instantly draw browsers and serious readers alike." Booklist.

Includes bibliographical references (p. 46) and index.

797.124 Sailing

Storey, Rita

Sailing. Rita Storey. Sea-to-Sea Publications, 2011. 30 p.: Know your sport

Grades: 4 5 6   **797.124**
   1. Sailing 2. Sailboats 3. Ocean travel
   ISBN 9781597712866

                                        LC 2010003439

Discusses the sport of sailing, and includes expert advice on equipment, techniques, and safety.

"This volume provides an introduction to the equipment, techniques, and safety measures for [sailing]. . . . Instructive photographs help illustrate such concepts as [tacking a sailboat], . . . while engaging stock images capture the excitement on the water. The [volume concludes] with racing information, profiling top racers, rules, and tactics." Horn Book Guide.

797.2 Swimming and diving

Gifford, Clive
   Swimming. Clive Gifford. PowerKids Press, 2009. 32 p.: Personal best
Grades: 4 5 6 7 8   **797.2**
   1. Swimming 2. Swimmers 3. Racing 4. Competition
   ISBN 9781404244436

                                        LC 2007043003

"This guide to swimming offers well-organized and easy-to-follow instructions, focusing on rules, clothing, specific skills, and competitions. . . . Informative, readable." School Library Journal.

797.5 Air sports

Sheinkin, Steve
   Born to fly: the first women's air race across America. Steve Sheinkin; illustrations by Bijou Karman. Roaring Brook Press, 2019. 288 p.
Grades: 6 7 8 9   **797.5**
   1. Women pilots 2. Airplane racing 3. Gender role 4. Racing pilots 5. Determination in women
   ISBN 9781626721302

                                        LC 2018051788

The gripping story of the fearless women pilots who aimed for the skies—and beyond.

"Sheinkin's storylike narration puts readers right into the action, making them gasp and cheer along with the fliers." Booklist.

Includes bibliographical references and index.

799.2 Hunting

MacRae, Sloan
   Deer hunting. Sloan MacRae. PowerKids Press, 2010. 32 p.: Open season
Grades: 4 5 6   **799.2**
   1. Deer hunting 2. Game laws 3. Accidents -- Prevention 4. Hunting 5. Deer
   ISBN 9781448807109

                                        LC 2010010700

Introduces deer hunting, including information on equipment, skills, techniques, and preparation.

Peterson, Judy Monroe
   Big game hunting. Judy Monroe Peterson. Rosen Central, 2011. 64 p.: Hunting: pursuing wild game!
Grades: 5 6 7 8   **799.2**
   1. Big game hunting 2. Hunting 3. Outdoor recreation 4. Hunters 5. Wildlife
   ISBN 9781448812400

                                        LC 2010006859

Introduces big game hunting, discusses the equipment used, and provides tips on planning a trip and preparing animals for transport.

"In this introduction to big game hunting Peterson displays an impressive grasp of the pastime by throwing in almost everything: types of guns and bows, safety laws, licenses, land access, animal behavior, clothing, methods of hunting, and preparing harvested meat. . . . [The book] is jam-packed with info. . . . A green-heavy design, bright photos of hunters . . . and prey, and above average back matter close out this solid entry." Booklist.

Includes bibliographical references (p. 59-61) and index.

800 LITERATURE

803 Literature—Dictionaries, encyclopedias, concordances

Baldick, Chris
   The **Oxford** dictionary of literary terms. Chris Baldick. x, 392 p.
Grades: Adult   **803**
   1. Literature 2. Criticism 3. English language 4. Literary form
   ISBN 9780198715443

                                        LC 2014960115

The bestselling Oxford Dictionary of Literary Terms provides clear and concise definitions of the most troublesome literary terms, from abjection to zeugma.

Lewis, Catherine
   Thrice told tales: three mice full of writing advice. Catherine Lewis; illustrated by Joost Swarte. Simon & Schuster, 2013. 128 p.
Grades: 7 8 9 10   **803**
   1. English language 2. Creative writing (Elementary education) 3. Writing
   ISBN 9781416957843

"Three blind mice. See how they run—and how they take your writing to a new level. This clever review of literary terms will delight students and experts looking for a concise way to understand exposition and point-of-view or discern an epic from a bildungsroman." Library Journal.

808 Rhetoric and collections of literary texts from more than two literatures

Anderson, Jeff, 1966-
   Everyday editing: inviting students to develop skill and craft in writer's workshop. Jeff Anderson. Stenhouse Publishers, c2007. x, 164 p.
Grades: Professional   **808**
   1. English language -- Rhetoric -- Study and teaching 2. Editing 3.

Report writing -- Study and teaching
ISBN 9781571107091

LC 2007026520

Instead of rehearsing errors and drilling students on what's wrong with a sentence, Jeff invites students to look carefully at their writing along with mentor texts, and to think about how punctuation, grammar, and style can be best used to hone and communicate meaning. Written in Jeff's characteristically witty style, this refreshing and practical guide offers an overview of his approach to editing, as well as ten detailed sets of lessons.

Daniels, Harvey, 1947-

Content-area writing: every teacher's guide. Harvey Daniels, Steven Zemelman, and Nancy Steineke. Heinemann, c2007. viii, 278 p.

Grades: Professional **808**

1. Composition (Language arts) -- Study and teaching 2. Language arts -- Correlation with content subjects 3. English language -- Composition and exercises -- Study and teaching
ISBN 9780325009728

LC 2006037120

No matter what subject [teachers] teach, Content-Area Writing is for them, especially if you're juggling broad curriculum mandates, thick textbooks, and severe time constraints. It not only shows that incorporating carefully structured writing activities into your lessons actually increases understanding and achievement, but also proves how writing can save, not consume, valuable instructional time.

Fershleiser, Rachel

I can't keep my own secrets: six-word memoirs by teens famous & obscure: from Smith magazine. edited by Rachel Fershleiser & Larry Smith. HarperTeen, c2009. 192 p.

Grades: 7 8 9 10 **808**

1. Teenagers 2. Adolescence 3. Teenagers' writings 4. Books for reluctant readers
ISBN 9780061726842

LC 2009014584

"The ruminations span from the haunting . . . to the funny . . . to the inspirational. . . . A razor focus is put on issues that hit youths the hardest. . . . It has just the right proportion of humor and heartbreak." Booklist.

Gaines, Ann

Don't steal copyrighted stuff!: avoiding plagiarism and illegal Internet downloading. Ann Graham Gaines. Enslow Publishers, c2008. 192 p.

Grades: 7 8 9 10 **808**

1. Plagiarism 2. Bibliographical citations 3. Copyright -- Law and legislation 4. Ethics 5. Intellectual property
ISBN 9780766028616

LC 2007008370

Learn how to research and write reports with proper citations and bibliographies. Also find out how to protect your own creative works. Provided by publisher.

"The first three chapters explain just what plagiarism is, the types of plagiarism, and what copyright and fair use are. Two chapters explain how to find sources, take notes properly, and construct a project or paper using proper citations in MLA format. . . . Every student should be required to read this. . . . Librarians and teachers who are looking for explanations of copyright and plagiarism and illustrative examples will find this book to be a good resource." Library Media Connection.

Includes bibliographical references and index.

Gallagher, Kelly, 1958-

Teaching adolescent writers. Kelly Gallagher. Stenhouse Publishers, c2006. viii, 200 p.

Grades: Professional **808**

1. English language -- Composition and exercises -- Study and teaching (Secondary) 2. English language -- Composition and exercises -- Study and teaching (Middle school)
ISBN 9781571104229

LC 2006023578

Describes strategies for teaching writing to adolescents, including teaching the reasons writing is important, meeting student needs in learning writing, modeling good writing by the teacher, using real-world models of writing, giving students choice, writing for authentic, real-world purposes, and assessing student writing. Provided by publisher.

Janeczko, Paul B.

Writing winning reports and essays. Paul B. Janeczko. Scholastic, 2003. 224 p.: Scholastic guides

Grades: 5 6 7 8 **808**

1. English language 2. Essay writing 3. Report writing 4. Writing
ISBN 0439287189

LC 2002030543

Provides strategies for writing successful research reports and essays, including social studies reports, book reports, persuasive essays, personal essays, and descriptive essays.

"A solid and useful resource." School Library Journal.

Turner, Kristen Hawley

Argument in the real world: teaching adolescents to read and write digital texts. Kristen Hawley Turner, Troy Hicks. Heinemann, 2017 x, 150 p.

Grades: Professional **808**

1. English language -- Composition and exercises -- Study and teaching (Secondary) -- Computer-assisted instruction 2. Persuasion (Rhetoric) -- Study and teaching (Secondary) -- Computer-assisted instruction 3. Reading (Secondary) -- Computer-assisted instruction 4. Composition (Language arts) -- Study and teaching (Secondary) -- Computer-assisted instruction 5. Computers and literacy
ISBN 9780325086750

LC 2016037593

In this book, Turner and Hicks draw from real world texts and samples of student work to share a wealth of insights and practical strategies in teaching students the logic of argument. Whether arguments are streaming in through a Twitter feed, a Facebook wall, viral videos, internet memes, or links to other blogs or websites, Turner and Hicks will guide you—and your students—in how to engage with and create digital arguments.

808.02 Authorship techniques, plagiarism, editorial techniques

Carter, Ally

Dear Ally, how do you write a book? Ally Carter. Scholastic Press, 2019 336 p.

Grades: 7 8 9 10 11 12 **808.02**

1. Writing 2. Fiction writing 3. Publishers and publishing 4. Advice 5. Authors
ISBN 9781338212266

From bestselling author Ally Carter, the definitive guide to writing a novel for the NaNoWriMo generation, including helpful tips from other YA stars.

"What Stephen King did for adult writers in On Writing (2000), popular YA novelist Carter does for aspiring teen authors in this guide to writing fiction. Chapters cover expected topics, such as getting started, world building, developing the plot, creating characters, and finding your process, while a Q&A format drives the content." Booklist.

Levine, Gail Carson

Writer to writer: from think to ink. Gail Carson Levine. HarperCollins, 2014. 176 p.

Grades: 5 6 7 8   **808.02**
   1. Writing 2. Creative writing 3. Blogs
   ISBN 9780062275301

                LC 2014005858

The Newbery Honor-winning author of Ella Enchanted presents a companion to Writing Magic that draws on advice from her popular blog to counsel aspiring writers about the creative aspects of a writing career.

"Ella Enchanted author Levine offers writing advice and prompts, primarily for fiction writers. The chapters, mostly expanded from her blog, look in-depth at aspects of writing including large-scale character and plot concerns and more specific matters of style. A lengthy section focuses on poetry and its role in fiction. Levine's second book on writing (Writing Magic) takes budding authors' craft questions seriously." Horn Book.

Myers, Walter Dean, 1937-2014

Just write: here's how! Walter Dean Myers; [afterword by Ross Workman]. Collins, c2012. 161 p.

Grades: 7 8 9   **808.02**
   1. Writing 2. Creative writing 3. Persistence
   ISBN 9780062203892

                LC bl2012011695

An award-winning author guides readers through the writing process, and includes examples from his own works, outlines for writing fiction and nonfiction, and excerpted pages from the author's writing notebooks.

808.1 Rhetoric in specific literary forms

Alexander, Kwame

★ **Out** of wonder: poems celebrating poets. Kwame Alexander with Chris Colderley and Marjory Wentworth; illustrated Ekua Holmes. Candlewick Press, 2017 40 p.

Grades: 3 4 5 6 7 8   **808.1**
   1. Poets
   ISBN 9780763680947
   Coretta Scott King Award, Illustrator Category, 2018.

"Each illustration captures not just the feeling of the poem but wakes readers up to life's excitements and small joys. Exemplary words and pictures make this a multicultural masterwork." Booklist.

Fletcher, Ralph J.

Poetry matters: writing a poem from the inside out. Ralph Fletcher. HarperTrophy, 2002. 142 p.

Grades: 4 5 6 7   **808.1**
   1. Poetry writing 2. Creative writing
   ISBN 0066235995

                LC 2001024640

Featuring interviews with published poets, a wonderful guide, drawn from a wealth of experience, demystifies the writing process, revealing how to look deep inside for emotions, image, and music, and how to revise writing to make it magical.

"Chapters deal with images; creating music, or sounds and rhythms; how to generate ideas for poems; the construction of the words on the page; and more. Tips on fine-tuning are also given. . . . Major poetic forms are defined, including haiku, ode, and free verse, and there is a section on ways to share your work. Interspersed are Fletcher's personal insights and interviews with three poets: Kristine O'Connell George, Janet S. Wong, and J. Patrick Lewis. . . . Since this thought-provoking book covers more of the internal, less-tangible aspects of poetry , it may be more suited for readers who have some experience with the genre." School Library Journal.

Includes bibliographical references.

McPhillips, Shirley

Poem central: word journeys with readers and writers. Shirley McPhillips. Stenhouse Publishers, 2014 xii, 308 p.

Grades: Professional   **808.1**
   1. Poetry -- Study and teaching 2. Poetry -- Authorship -- Study and teaching
   ISBN 9781571109637

                LC 2013044432

InPoem Central, Shirley McPhillips helps us better understand the central role poetry can play in our personal lives and in the life of our classrooms. She introduces us to professional poets, teachers, and students—people of different ages and walks of life—who are actively engaged in reading and making poems.?

Sitomer, Alan Lawrence

Hip-hop poetry and the classics: connecting our classic curriculum to hip-hop poetry through standards-based, language arts instruction. Alan Sitomer & Michael Cirelli. Milk Mug Pub., 2004. 160 p.

Grades: Professional   **808.1**
   1. Poetry -- Study and teaching (Secondary) 2. English language -- Composition and exercises -- Study and teaching (Secondary) 3. Hip-hop
   ISBN 9780972188227

                LC bl2006006930

Provides information and activities to help teachers connect the classroom poetry and language arts curriculum to hip-hop.

808.108 Rhetoric of women's poetry

Whitney, DIana

You don't have to be everything: poems for girls becoming themselves. Edited by Diana Whitney. Workman Publishing, 2021. 165 p.

Grades: 8 9 10 11 12   **808.108**
   1. Growing up 2. Young women 3. Girls
   ISBN 9781523510993

"Contributors include many established greats such as Maya Angelou, Margaret Atwood, Joy Harjo, Naomi Shihab Nye, Mary Oliver, and Elizabeth Acevedo as well as some newer voices [Amanda Gorman] who will be familiar from Instagram. . . . This collection feels like a gift, a pep talk, a shoulder to cry on, and, most of all, a mirror that will captivate its audience." Kirkus

808.2 Rhetoric of drama

Hamlett, Christina

Screenwriting for teens: the 100 principles of scriptwriting every budding writer must know. Christina Hamlett. Michael Wiese Productions, c2006. xvi, 228 p.

Grades: 8 9 10 11 12   **808.2**

    1. Screenplay writing 2. Screenplays 3. Mass media writing 4. Screenwriters 5. Creative writing
ISBN 9781932907186

LC 2006025952

A guide for budding screenwriters provides tips for how to write dialogue, plot, and characters, including specific information on genres such as horror, romance, and westerns.

808.3 Rhetoric of fiction

Anderson, Jennifer Joline

Writing fantastic fiction. by Jennifer Joline Anderson. Lerner Publications, 2016. 56 p.: Write this way

Grades: 4 5 6 7   **808.3**

    1. Fiction writing 2. Creative writing 3. Authors
ISBN 9781467779081

LC 2014044105

"Clearly presented and with a colorful design, this will work very well for middle-graders, but the advice is so good, older kids will find it extremely helpful as well. An especially inviting way to step into writing." Booklist.

Includes bibliographical references and index.

Litwin, Laura Baskes

Write horror fiction in 5 simple steps. Laura Baskes Litwin. Enslow Publishers, c2013. 48 p.: Creative writing in 5 simple steps

Grades: 4 5 6   **808.3**

    1. Horror story writing 2. Fiction writing 3. Creative writing 4. Publishers and publishing -- Vocational guidance 5. Writing
ISBN 9780766038363

LC 2010038776

Divides the creative writing process into five steps, from inspiration to publishable story, and includes in-depth treatment of the horror fiction genre with writing prompts. Provided by publisher.

Mlynowski, Sarah

See Jane write: a girl's guide to writing chick lit. by Sarah Mlynowski and Farrin Jacobs. Quirk Books, 2006. 191 p.

Grades: 8 9 10 11 12   **808.3**

    1. Fiction writing 2. Creative writing 3. Publishers and publishing 4. Book industry and trade
ISBN 9781594741159

A guide to writing chick lit novels, including developing an idea, making the characters likeable, learning the basics of plotting, pacing, and conflict, and finding an agent.

"Fun, inspiring, and organized in a clear and encouraging style, this book covers topics from what chick lit is to how to create believable characters, develop a plot, and set a tone. The authors discuss seeing a project through to the finish and getting it published. The writing style is quirky and the advice is sound." School Library Journal.

Stern, Rebecca

Brave the page: a young writer's guide to telling epic stories. by Rebecca Stern & Grant Faulkner; introduction by Jason Reynolds. Viking, an imprint of Penguin Random House, 2019 304 p.

Grades: 5 6 7 8 9 10 11 12   **808.3**

    1. Creative writing 2. Fiction writing 3. Writing 4. Child authors 5. Creativity 6. Essays
ISBN 9780451480293

A motivational guide by the National Novel Writing Month nonprofit (NaNoWriMo) shares inspiring essays by popular authors and practical advice on how to organize and commit to writing stories and novels.

808.5 Rhetoric of speech

Anderson, Chris, 1957 January 14-

Thank you for coming to my TED talk: a teen guide to great public speaking. by Chris Anderson, with Lorin Oberweger. Houghton Mifflin Harcourt 2020 256 p.

Grades: 7 8 9 10 11 12   **808.5**

    1. Public speaking 2. Speech writing
ISBN 9781328995070

LC 2019029204

A teen adaptation of the best-selling TED Talks: The Official TED Guide to Public Speaking shares tips and techniques for becoming a confident and capable speaker at school presentations, in interviews and during special occasions.

Sima, Judy

Raising voices: creating youth storytelling groups and troupes. Judy Sima, Kevin Cordi. Libraries Unlimited, 2003. xxviii, 241 p.

Grades: Professional   **808.5**

    1. Storytelling 2. Children's stories
ISBN 9781563089190

LC 2003047631

Written by two veteran storytellers, this practical handbook shows teachers how to start a youth storytelling group, taking readers through the process of planning, managing, and growing a group, and offering a wealth of games and activities as well as reproducibles and checklists.

"A unique and reliable blueprint for beginning and sustaining a successful group or troupe of storytellers from grades 4 to 12. Even though the authors work with young people in the school setting, their organizational ideas and applications are equally suitable for community groups." School Library Journal

Includes bibliographical references (p. 187-218) and index.

808.8 Collections of literary texts from more than two literatures

Jocelyn, Marthe

Scribbling women: true tales of astonishing lives. Marthe Jocelyn. Tundra Books of Northern New York, 2011. 208 p.

Grades: 6 7 8 9 10   **808.8**

    1. Women authors 2. Gender role
ISBN 9780887769528

LC 2010928788

"Liberally using each writer's own words, Jocelyn's lyrical prose takes us deep into their lives, but mostly into their spirits and courageous souls. Young readers can share the obstacles, joys, and/or sorrows each women faced," Kirkus.

808.81 Collections of poetry

Hoberman, Mary Ann

The **tree** that time built: a celebration of nature, science, and imagination. selected by Mary Ann Hoberman and Linda Winston; illustrations by Barbara Fortin. Sourcebooks Jabberwocky, 2009. xii, 209 p.

Grades: 5 6 7 8   **808.81**
    1. Nature 2. Environmentalism 3. Science
    ISBN 9781402225178

                 LC 2009032608

Celebrates the world of nature and science, with a focus on the Earth's origins and the need to protect and preserve the environment.

"Classic works by Walt Whitman, Emily Dickinson, Christina Rossetti, and the like, and selections from contemporary poets are included. . . . This handsome collection is especially appropriate for classroom use and instruction. . . . From the playful to the profound, the poems invite reflection and inspire further investigation." School Library Journal.

Janeczko, Paul B.

★ The **death** of the hat: a brief history of poetry in fifty objects. Paul B. Janeczko; illustrated by Christopher Raschka. Candlewick Pr 2015 80 p.

Grades: 3 4 5 6 7   **808.81**
    1. Poetry -- History and criticism
    ISBN 9780763669638

"Janeczko and Raschka's stellar fourth poetry collaboration, following A Poke in the I and other acclaimed titles, presents a chronological 'history' of the development of poetry, from the Middle Ages to the present. The highlighted poems are, ostensibly, about objects, but a cigar is rarely just a cigar. . . . Janeczko's substantial introduction gives an overview of poetrys evolution over the centuries, yet works like Lord Byron's 'A Riddle, on the Letter E' resonate powerfully on their own." Publishers Weekly.

Nye, Naomi Shihab

I feel a little jumpy around you: a book of her poems & his poems collected in pairs. Naomi Shihab Nye and Paul B. Janeczko, editors. Aladdin Paperbacks, 1999, c1996. xxii, 256 p.

Grades: 7 8 9 10   **808.81**
    1. Women 2. Men
    ISBN 9780689813412

                LC BL 99001326

A collection of poems, by male and female authors, presented in pairings that offer insight into how men and women look at the world, both separately and together.

"Though the gender counterpoint really plays little part in the juxtaposition, the pairings are piquant and provide a manageable way to start talking about a very large collection of poetry. An engaging marginal dialogue, taken from Nye's and Janeczko's collaborative fax correspondence, appears alongside the appendix and permits a revealing peek behind the scences. Highly readable notes from contributors are included, as is an index of poems and a gender-segregated index of poets." Bulletin of the Center for Children's Books.

What have you lost? poems selected by Naomi Shihab Nye; photographs by Michael Nye. Greenwillow Books, c1999. 205 p.

Grades: 7 8 9 10   **808.81**
    1. Loss (Psychology) 2. Letting go (Psychology) 3. Regret 4. Anthologies
    ISBN 0688161847

                 LC 98026674

A collection of poems that explore all kinds of loss.

"In her introduction, the anthologist-poet considers lossi: ts certainty, scope, and effect, and its ability to give rise to art. The topic is thoroughly explored by the one hundred and forty poets whose work is collected here in twenty-two unlabeled, thematically arranged sections. . . . The poets are all contemporary, with a dozen or so hailing from outside the United States." Horn Book.

Includes bibliographical references (p. 173-189) and index.

Stallworthy, Jon

The **new** Oxford book of war poetry. chosen and edited by Jon Stallworthy. Oxford University Press, 2014. xl, 406 p.

Grades: 8 9 10 11 12 Adult   **808.81**
    1. War and society 2. War poetry
    ISBN 019870447X

                 LC 2013497520

There can be no area of human experience that has generated a wider range of powerful feelings than war. Jon Stallworthy's classic and celebrated anthology spans centuries of human experience of war, from Homer's Iliad, through the First and Second World Wars, the Vietnam War, and the wars fought since. This new edition, published to mark the centenary of the outbreak of the First World War, includes a new introduction and additional poems from David Harsent and Peter Wyton, amongst others. The new selection provides improved coverage of the two World Wars and the Vietnam War, and new coverage of the wars of the late twentieth and early twenty-first centuries. Publisher description.

808.82 Collections of drama

Detrick, Erin

Actor's choice: monologues for teens. edited by Erin Detrick. Playscripts, c2008. xv, 131 p.

Grades: 6 7 8 9 10   **808.82**
    1. Acting 2. Drama 20th century. 3. Teenagers 4. Drama
    ISBN 9780970904669

                LC 2007050166

Collection of monologues from the Playscripts, Inc. catalog of plays, representing a variety of American playwrights. The source material for each monologue may be found on the Playscripts website, where nearly the entire text of every play can be read for free. Intended for teenage actors. Provided by publisher.

"This volume of highly entertaining monologues is gleaned from one-act and full-length plays published by Playscripts, Inc.... This is an excellent volume to help students prepare for competitions as well as to use in drama, speech, or English classes." School Library Journal.

Ellis, Roger

New audition scenes and monologs from contemporary playwrights: the best new cuttings from around the world. edited by Roger Ellis. Meriwether Pub., c2005. 177 p.

Grades: 6 7 8 9 **808.82**
  1. Acting -- Auditions 2. Drama 21st century. 3. Drama
ISBN 156608105X

LC 2004028495

"This work presents a wide variety of scenes selected especially for performers aged 12 to 24. . . . Introductions to each scene are informative and were reviewed and approved with some reshaping by the authors. . . . A good choice for students who seek new ideas for drama, forensic, and writing classes." School Library Journal.

808.83 Collections of fiction

Krok, Lisa
  Novels in verse for teens: a guidebook with activities for teachers and librarians. Lisa Krok. Libraries Unlimited, 2020. ix, 151 p.
Grades: Professional **808.83**
  1. Teenagers -- Books and reading 2. Novels in verse 3. Novels in verse -- History and criticism 4. Readers' advisory services 5. Young adults' libraries -- Activity programs
ISBN 9781440874932

LC 2019051210

A comprehensive resource for using novels in verse in classrooms and libraries. Provided by publisher.

808.88 Collections of miscellaneous writings

Bartlett, John, 1820-1905
  Bartlett's familiar quotations: a collection of passages, phrases, and proverbs traced to their sources in ancient and modern literature. John Bartlett; Geoffrey O'Brien, general editor. Little, Brown, and Co., 2012. lxi, 1438 p.
Grades: 8 9 10 11 12 Adult **808.88**
  1. Quotations, English
ISBN 0316017590

LC 2012019870

A completely revised and updated edition provides a sweeping overview of the cultural influence of inspirational language and includes new contributions by such authors as the Dalai Lama, Steve Jobs and Desmond Tutu.

809 History, description, critical appraisal of more than two literatures

Camacho, Ann
  Bookmarked: teen essays on life and literature from Tolkien to Twilight. edited by Ann Camacho. Free Spirit Pub., c2012. 215 p.
Grades: 6 7 8 **809**
  1. Literature -- Appreciation 2. Teenagers -- Books and reading 3. Books and reading 4. Literature -- Moral and ethical aspects 5. Life in literature 6. Essays
ISBN 9781575423968

LC 2011043942

In 50 compelling essays, young people from a wide range of backgrounds reflect on how words from literature connect with and influence their lives, goals, and personal philosophies. Essays explore character building topics including suffering the death of a parent, facing a life-threatening illness, letting go of perfectionism, making friends, reaching goals, and grappling with questions of identity.

Fleischman, Paul
  Alphamaniacs: builders of 26 wonders of the word. Paul Fleischman; art by Melissa Sweet. Candlewick Studio, 2020 160 p.
Grades: 6 7 8 9 10 11 12 **809**
  1. Authors 2. Language and languages 3. Writing methods and systems 4. Writing
ISBN 9780763690663

Are you a word person? A curiosity seeker? An explorer? Take a look at these twenty-six extraordinary individuals for whom love of language is an extreme sport.

"Each individual is given a brief chapter recounting their word-related exploits, interleaved with colorful, collaged illustrations by Sweet that look like stray pages from an artist's overstuffed sketchbook, incorporating relevant quotes and amplifying Fleischman's themes of abundance and possibility. A unique amalgam, one that will charm many." Publishers Weekly.

Manglik, Gauri
  ★ **Muslims** in story: expanding multicultural understanding through children's and young adult literature. Gauri Manglik and Sadaf Siddique. ALA Editions, 2018. xvi, 248 p.
Grades: Professional **809**
  1. Islam 2. Muslims 3. Children's literature 4. Children -- Books and reading
ISBN 9780838917411

LC 2018023567

One of the key causes of Islamophobia is ignorance, often fueled by negative portrayals of Muslims in media and popular culture. Counter Islamophobia through Stories is a timely and proactive approach to tackling this issue, by engendering friendships and empathy through literature. Our goal is to facilitate a systemic long term change in understanding the diversity of the Muslim experience and to build bridges of understanding and empathy. Exposing children in their formative years to positive stories about Muslims can go a long way to creating a multicultural understanding, and cementing ideas of tolerance, respect and acceptance. Books also help achieve visual diversity by showcasing different foods, dress and traditions. The proposed book will equip librarians to expose all children to Muslim children's books around different themes. Provided by publisher.

"This timely and essential purchase for public and school libraries humanizes Muslims and gives Muslim children authentic mirrors while creating important windows for non-Muslim readers." School Library Journal

Includes bibliographical references.

Sutton, Roger
  A **family** of readers: the book lover's guide to children's and young adult literature. Roger Sutton and Martha V. Parravano; foreword by Gregory Maguire. Candlewick Press, 2010. xviii, 350 p.
Grades: Adult **809**
  1. Children's literature -- History and criticism 2. Children -- Books and reading 3. Young adults -- Books and reading 4. Reading -- Parent participation
ISBN 9780763632809

LC 2009049104

Two of the most trusted reviewers in the field join with top authors, illustrators, and critics in the definitive guide to choosing books for children and young adults—and nurturing their love of reading.

809.3 Fiction—history and criticism

Sacks, Ariel

Whole novels for the whole class: a student-centered approach. Ariel Sacks. Jossey-Bass, 2014 xii, 352 p.
Grades: Professional   **809.3**
1. Fiction -- Study and teaching 2. Youth -- Books and reading 3. Critical thinking
ISBN 9781118526507

LC 2013024160

Work with students at all levels to help them read novels. Whole Novels is a practical, field-tested guide to implementing a student-centered literature program that promotes critical thinking and literary understanding through the study of novels with middle school students. Rather than using novels simply to teach basic literacy skills and comprehension strategies, Whole Novels approaches literature as art. The book is fully aligned with the Common Core ELA Standards and offers tips for implementing whole novels in various contexts, including suggestions for teachers interested in trying out small steps in their classrooms first. Includes a powerful method for teaching literature, writing, and critical thinking to middle school students. Shows how to use the Whole Novels approach in conjunction with other programs. Includes video clips of the author using the techniques in her own classroom. This resource will help teachers work with students of varying abilities in reading whole novels. Provided by publisher.

810.8 American literature (English)—Collections

Cart, Michael

911: the book of help. edited by Michael Cart; with Marc Aronson and Marianne Carus. Cricket Books, 2002. xiv, 178 p.
Grades: 8 9 10 11 12   **810.8**
1. September 11 Terrorist Attacks, 2001 2. Terrorism 3. September 11 Terrorist Attacks, 2001 -- Influence 4. Essays
ISBN 0812626761

LC 2002004707

A collection of essays, poems, short fiction, and drawings created in response to the terrorist attacks of September 11, 2001, by authors and illustrators of books for young adults.

"This stands out for its rich prose, its unusual reporting, its search for context, its reminder of wonders." New York Times Book Review.

McLaughlin, Timothy P.

Walking on Earth & touching the sky: poetry and prose by Lakota youth at Red Cloud Indian School. edited by Timothy P. McLaughlin; paintings by S.D. Nelson; foreword by Joseph M. Marshall III. Abrams Books for Young Readers, c2012. 80 p.
Grades: 6 7 8   **810.8**
1. Indians of North America 2. Lakota Indians 3. Children's writings
ISBN 9781419701795

LC 2011036454

Collects poetry written by Lakota students at Red Cloud Indian School in South Dakota on such topics as the history of oral tradition, the struggles of everyday life, and their personal connections to the natural world.

Scieszka, Jon

Guys write for Guys Read. edited by Jon Scieszka. Viking, 2005. 272 p.
Grades: 6 7 8 9 10   **810.8**
1. Boys 2. Young men 3. Men 4. Teenage boys 5. Fathers 6. Anthologies
ISBN 9780670060078

LC 2004028984

"This is a diverse and fast-paced anthology . . . that deserves a permanent place in any collection . . . . There's something undeniably grand about this collective celebration of the intellectual life of the common boy." School Library Journal.

810.9 American literature (English)—History and criticism

Hill, Laban Carrick, 1960-2021

Harlem stomp!: a cultural history of the Harlem Renaissance. by Laban Carrick Hill. Little, Brown, c2003. 151 p.
Grades: 7 8 9 10   **810.9**
1. 20th century 2. Harlem Renaissance 3. African Americans -- Intellectual life 4. African American arts -- History 20th century. 5. Intellectual life -- African Americans 6. Intellectual life 7. Harlem, New York City -- Intellectual life -- 20th century. 8. New York City -- Intellectual life -- 20th century.
ISBN 0316814113

LC 2002073067

"The vibrancy, energy, and color of the Harlem Renaissance come to life in this gem of a book packed with poetry, prose, song lyrics, art, and photography created by some of the period's most influential figures. . . . Informative and highly entertaining, it deserves to be shelved in any Library." Voice of Youth Advocates.

Includes bibliographical references (p. 137-142) and index.

Hillstrom, Kevin, 1963-

The **Harlem** Renaissance. Kevin Hillstrom. Omnigraphics, c2008. xiii, 228 p.: Defining moments (Omnigraphics)
Grades: 7 8 9 10   **810.9**
1. Harlem Renaissance 2. African American arts 20th century. 3. African American authors 4. African American artists 5. African American musicians 6. Harlem, New York City 7. New York City
ISBN 9780780810273

LC 2007051132

Provides a detailed, factual account of the emergence and development of the Harlem Renaissance and its ongoing effect on American society. Features include a narrative overview, biographical profiles, primary source documents, detailed chronology, glossary, and annotated sources for further study. Provided by publisher.

"This an insightful, highly accessible subject primer for general collections." Library Journal.

Includes bibliographical references (p. 213-217) and index.

811 American poetry

Adoff, Arnold

I am the darker brother: an anthology of modern poems by African Americans. edited and with an afterword by Arnold Adoff; drawings by Benny Andrews; introduction by Rudine Sims Bishop; foreword by Nikki Giovanni. Simon and Schuster Books for Young Readers, c1997. 208 p.

Grades: 6 7 8 9 10 **811**
1. African Americans 2. African American poetry 3. Anthologies 4. Books for reluctant readers
ISBN 0689812418

LC 97144181

"This anthology presents the African-American experience through poetry that speaks for itself. . . . Because of the historical context of many of the poems, the book will be much in demand during Black History Month, but it should be used and treasured as part of the larger canon of literature to be enjoyed by all Americans at all times of the year. An indispensable addition to library collections." School Library Journal.

Agard, John

The **young** inferno. by John Agard; illustrated by Satoshi Kitamura. Frances Lincoln Children's, 2009. 80 p.
Grades: 8 9 10 11 12 **811**
1. Hell 2. Voyages and travels 3. Sin 4. Novels in verse 5. Classics-inspired fiction 6. Illustrated books
ISBN 9781845077693

"The narrative poems in this short book are accessible and have important things to say about the state of the human race. . . . The hoodie-wearing protagonist . . . awakens in a strange and frightening forest. A dark man appears and introduces himself as the tale-teller Aesop: he is to be the teen's escort through Hell. . . . As the pair travels through the Circles of Hell, they see the sins of mankind. . . . The scribbled, heavy-lined black ink and watercolor illustrations convey exactly the right mood for a book about a modern-day expedition into Hell. This will be a great book to pair with a discussion about Dante's Inferno and/or poetic structure." School Library Journal.

Alexander, Elizabeth, 1962-

Miss Crandall's school for young ladies & little misses of color: poems. by Elizabeth Alexander & Marilyn Nelson; pictures by Floyd Cooper. Wordsong, c2007. 47 p.
Grades: 7 8 9 10 **811**
1. Crandall, Prudence, 1803-1890 2. Women educators 3. Girls' schools 4. African American students 5. African American girls 6. Discrimination in education -- History 19th century 7. Canterbury, Connecticut -- Race relations -- History -- 19th century 8. Connecticut -- Race relations -- History -- 19th century
ISBN 1590784561

LC 2006038985

Poets Elizabeth Alexander and Marilyn Nelson tell the story of Prudence Crandall's school for African American girls opened in 1833. Despite their water being poisoned and the building set afire, Miss Crandall kept her school for African-American women—several of whom were the daughters of freed slaves—running in order to give her students the education they knew they deserved.

"Twenty-four sonnets tell the story of Prudence Crandall and her efforts to educate young African-American women in Canterbury, CT, 1833-1834. . . . The sonnet format is challenging but compelling. . . . There are empty spaces in the pictures just as the language of the poetry leaves openness for readers' interpretation. A heartfelt, unusual presentation." School Library Journal.

Alexander, Kwame

Crush: love poems. Kwame Alexander. Word of Mouth Books/KA Productions, LLC, 2007. 72 p.
Grades: 8 9 10 11 12 **811**
1. Crushes (Interpersonal relations) 2. Teenage boy/girl relations

3. Love
ISBN 9781888018400

LC 2007922663

"Alexander offers a cosmopolitan menu of tanka, haiku, long titles that lead into short first lines, verbal formulas that lead to sung discoveries, French phrases, prose poems, and poems written in Spanglish. The book is divided into three sections with various speakers, and a fourth section that includes poems by Sherman Alexie, Pablo Neruda, Nikki Giovanni, and the title poem, Crush by Naomi Shihab Nye. . . . This well-crafted anthology will capture the interest of teens." School Library Journal.

Angelou, Maya

Maya Angelou. edited by Edwin Graves Wilson; illustrated by Jerome Lagarrigue. Sterling, c2007. 48 p.
Grades: 4 5 6 7 **811**
1. Children's poetry, American 2. American poetry
ISBN 9781402720239

LC 2006013803

A collection of poetry written by Maya Angelou.

"Wilson's introduction . . . addresses how Angelou's life has informed her imagination. . . . Twenty-five poems show her concern with the African-American experience. . . . Dignity, pride, and resiliancy are at this collection's core. . . . Footnotes offer definitions of colloquialisms and difficult words. Lagarrigue's painterly artwork uses golds, greens, and violets to capture the luminescent quality of the poems. . . . This [is a] distinguished work." School Library Journal.

Argueta, Jorge

Somos como las nubes = We are like the clouds. Jorge Argueta; pictures by Alfonso Ruano; translated by Amado Elisa. Groundwood Books: 2016. 36 p.
Grades: 4 5 6 7 8 **811**
1. Unaccompanied immigrant children 2. Child immigrants 3. Immigration and emigration 4. Voyages and travels 5. Poverty 6. Central America 7. Bilingual materials
ISBN 9781554988495

This bilingual (Spanish/English) collection of poems recreates the experiences of thousands of children from El Salvador, Guatemala, Honduras, and Mexico, who have been forced to abandon all they know because of poverty and violence in their home countries. The verses address the love they feel for their countries of origin, their fears about violent gangs, the loneliness that surfaces when friends leave, and their own fears about the upcoming journey.

"The scarcity of Latino children's and young-adult books that center on Central American experiences makes this poignant poetry collection extremely vital." Booklist.

Atkins, Jeannine, 1953-

Borrowed names: poems about Laura Ingalls Wilder, Madam C. J. Walker, Marie Curie, and their daughters. Jeannine Atkins. Henry Holt and Co., 2010. 224 p.
Grades: 6 7 8 9 10 **811**
1. Wilder, Laura Ingalls, 1867-1957. 2. Walker, C. J., 1867-1919. 3. Curie, Marie, 1867-1934. 4. Mothers and daughters
ISBN 9780805089349

LC 2009023446

Vivid, compelling poems tell the stories of three daughters and their remarkable mothers whose work in literature, business and science changed the world.

"In 1867, three women who achieved great success were born: writer Laura Ingalls Wilder, entrepreneur Madam C. J. Walker, and scientist

Marie Curie. All three had complicated relationships with their daughters, relationships that Atkins explores in this unusual volume of poetry. . . . In vivid scenes written with keen insight and subtle imagery, the poems offer a strong sense of each daughter's personality as well as the tensions and ties they shared with their notable mothers." Booklist.

Bryan, Ashley

★ **Ashley** Bryan's puppets. Ashley Bryan; photographs by Ken Hannon; photographs edited by Rich Entel. Atheneum Books for Young Readers, 2014. 80 p.

Grades: PreK K 1 2 3 4 5 6   **811**

    1. Puppets 2. Found objects
    ISBN 9781442487284

"Award-winning author and illustrator Bryan has combined his love of art and poetry in this captivating and beautifully designed book...Traditional African themes abound as the characters introduce themselves through their poems, and readers are invited into the world of puppets and poetry. Bryan has truly created a book for all to treasure." School Library Journal.

Burleigh, Robert

Hoops. Robert Burleigh; illustrated by Stephen T. Johnson. Silver Whistle, 1997. 32 p.

Grades: 6 7 8 9   **811**

    1. Sports 2. Basketball players 3. Basketball
    ISBN 0152014500

                      LC 96018440

Illustrations and poetic text describe the movement and feel of the game of basketball.

"Burleigh's staccato text is well matched by Johnson's dynamic pastels. Muted colors and a strong sense of motion as bodies leap and lift, pounce and poke, aptly complement the words." School Library Journal.

Carlson, Lori M.

Cool salsa: bilingual poems on growing up Latino in the United States. edited by Lori M. Carlson; introduction by Oscar Hijuelos. H. Holt and Co., 1994. xx, 123 p.

Grades: 5 6 7 8 9 10   **811**

    1. Hispanic American teenagers 2. Teenagers 3. Teenage immigrants 4. Hispanic Americans 5. Growing up 6. Bilingual materials English/Spanish
    ISBN 0805031359

                      LC 93045798

Such poets as Oscar Hijuelos and Sandra Cisneros celebrate themes and moods from Hispanic-American teenage life, from the sadness over lost lands to the passion of learning English to the pain of ethnic prejudice.

"Whether discussing the immigrant's frustration at not being able to speak English, the violence suffered both within and outside of the ethnic community, the familiar adolescent desire to belong, or celebrating the simple joys of life, these fine poems are incisive and photographic in their depiction of a moment." School Library Journal.

Clinton, Catherine

I, too, sing America: three centuries of African-American poetry. [selected and annotated by] Catherine Clinton; illustrated by Stephen Alcorn. Houghton Mifflin, 1998. 128 p.

Grades: 6 7 8 9   **811**

    1. African Americans 2. African American poetry
    ISBN 0395895995

                      LC 97046137

A collection of poems by African-American writers, including Lucy Terry, Gwendolyn Bennett, and Alice Walker.

"For each poet, Clinton provides a biography and a brief, insightful commentary on the poem(s) she has chosen, including a discussion of political as well as literary connections. Alcorn's dramatic, full-page, full-color illustrations opposite each poem evoke the quiltlike patterns and rhythmic figures of folk art." Booklist.

Crisler, Curtis L.

Tough boy sonatas. Curtis L. Crisler; illustrations by Floyd Cooper. Wordsong, 2007. 88 p.

Grades: 8 9 10 11 12   **811**

    1. African American teenage boys 2. African Americans 3. Young men 4. Gary, Indiana 5. Indiana
    ISBN 9781932425772

                      LC 2006011836

"Crisler presents a collection of potent, hard-hitting poems about growing up in Gary, Indiana. Written mostly in voices of young African American males, the poems evoke the grit and ash of crumbling, burned-out streets as well as the realities of hardscrabble life. . . . Written with skillful manipulation of sound, rhythm, and form, the poems are filled with sophisticated imagery and graphic words . . . and Cooper's illustrations extend . . . the poems' impact. Created in sooty black and gray, the powerful drawings are mostly portraits of anguished young men." Booklist.

Dunning, Stephen

Reflections on a gift of watermelon pickle ...: and other modern verse. [compiled by] Stephen Dunning, Edward Lueders [and] Hugh Smith. Design: Donald Marvine. Lothrop, Lee & Shepard, [c1966] 1967. 139 p.

Grades: 6 7 8 9 10   **811**

    ISBN 0688412319

                      LC 67029527

A selection of more than one hundred modern poems including pieces by E. E. Cummings, William Carlos Williams and Theodore Roethke.

"Although some of the [114] selections are by recognized modern writers, many are by minor or unknown poets, and few will be familiar to the reader. Nearly all are fresh in approach and contemporary in expression. . . . Striking photographs complementing or illuminating many of the poems enhance the attractiveness of the volume." Booklist.

Fleischman, Paul

Big talk: poems for four voices. Paul Fleischman; illustrated by Beppe Giacobbe. Candlewick Press, 2000. 44 p.

Grades: 4 5 6 7   **811**

    1. Oral interpretation of poetry
    ISBN 0763606367

                      LC 99046882

A collection of poems to be read aloud by four people, with color-coded text to indicate which lines are read by which readers.

"Each poem is more demanding, and more rewarding, than the last. Giacobbe highlights the humor in strips of vignettes that run along the bottom of the page. This is toe-tapping, tongue-flapping fun." Horn Book Guide.

I am Phoenix: poems for two voices. Paul Fleischman; illustrated by Ken Nutt. Harper & Row, c1985. 51 p.

Grades: 4 5 6 7   **811**

    1. Birds
    ISBN 0060218819

                      LC 85042615

A collection of poems about birds to be read aloud by two voices.

"Devotees of the almost lost art of choral reading should be among the first to appreciate this collection. . . . Printed in script form, the selections . . . have a cadenced pace and dignified flow; their combination of imaginative imagery and realistic detail is echoed by the combination of stylized fantasy and representational drawings in the black and white pictures, all soft line and strong nuance." Bulletin of the Center for Children's Books.

★ **Joyful** noise: poems for two voices. Paul Fleischman; illustrated by Eric Beddows. Harper & Row, 1988 44 p.

Grades: 4 5 6 7　　　　　　　　　　　　　　　　**811**
　1. Insects
　ISBN 0060218525

　　　　　　　　　　　　　　　　LC　87045280

Newbery Medal, 1989.

A collection of poems describing the characteristics and activities of a variety of insects.

"There are fourteen poems in the handsomely designed volume, with stylish endpapers and wonderfully interpretive black-and-white illustrations. Each selection is a gem, polished perfection." Horn Book.

Frost, Robert, 1874-1963

Poetry for kids: Robert Frost. edited by Jay Parini; illustrated by Michael Paraskevas. MoonDance Press, [2017] 48 p.: Poetry for kids

Grades: 5 6 7 8　　　　　　　　　　　　　　　　**811**
　1. Poets, American 2. Authors, American 3. Poets 4. Authors
　ISBN 9781633222205

　　　　　　　　　　　　　　　　LC　2017010647

Kids will discover the poetry of Robert Frost in this installment in the Poetry for Kids series. Professor, poet, novelist, and Frost biographer Jay Parini has carefully chosen 35 poems of interest to children and their families, including "Mending Wall," "Birches," "The Road Not Taken," "Fire and Ice," "Stopping by Woods on a Snowy Evening," and many more of Frost's favorite and most accessible works. Provided by publisher.

Robert Frost. edited by Gary D. Schmidt; illustrated by Henri Sorensen. Sterling, c1994. 48 p.: Poetry for young people

Grades: 4 5 6 7　　　　　　　　　　　　　　　　**811**
　1. Seasons 2. Nature
　ISBN 0806906332

　　　　　　　　　　　　　　　　LC　94011161

A collection of poems about the four seasons by one of the best-known American poets.

"This volume contains a three-page overview of the poet's life, 29 poems selected and arranged around the seasons of the year, brief and apt commentaries on each, and a useful index of titles and subject matter. The realistic watercolor illustrations capture the delicate beauty of a New England spring and the glory of fall while still suggesting the around-the-corner chill of winter, a disquiet echoing throughout much of Frost's poetry." School Library Journal.

George, Kristine O'Connell

Swimming upstream: middle school poems. by Kristine O'Connell George; illustrated by Debbie Tilley. Clarion Books, c2002. 79 p.

Grades: 5 6 7 8　　　　　　　　　　　　　　　　**811**
　1. Middle school students 2. Girls 3. Girls -- Interpersonal

relations 4. Middle schools 5. Schools
　ISBN 0618152504

　　　　　　　　　　　　　　　　LC　2002002746

A collection of poems capture the feelings and experiences of a girl in middle school.

"Students will relate to this voice 'navigating upstream,' while they try to find their own place in the middle-school wilderness." School Library Journal.

Giovanni, Nikki

Ego-tripping and other poems for young people. Nikki Giovanni; illustrations by George Ford; foreword by Virginia Hamilton. L. Hill Books, c1993. xi, 52 p.

Grades: 5 6 7 8　　　　　　　　　　　　　　　　**811**
　1. African Americans 2. African American poetry
　ISBN 155652188X

　　　　　　　　　　　　　　　　LC　93029578

Thirty-two poems that reflect aspects of the African American experience.

"Giovanni has added 10 new poems to her earlier collection of 23 poems for young people. Ford's illustrations in sepia shades are bold and full of character and dreaming. As Virginia Hamilton says in her foreword, Giovanni's voice is personal and warm, she celebrates ordinary folks and writes of struggle and liberation. She's upbeat and celebratory without minimizing hard times." Booklist.

Paint me like I am: teen poems. from WritersCorps; foreword by Nikki Giovanni. Harper Tempest, 2003. xi, 128 p.

Grades: 7 8 9 10　　　　　　　　　　　　　　　**811**
　1. Teenagers 2. Identity (Psychology) 3. Self-perception in teenagers 4. Creativity 5. Families 6. Teenagers' writings 7. Books for reluctant readers
　ISBN 0064472647

　　　　　　　　　　　　　　　　LC　2002005942

"The teen voices in these poems, collected from the WritersCorps youth program, are LOUD: raging, defiant, giddy, lusty, and hopeful. Grouped into arbitrary categories, the poems explore identity, creative expressions, family, neighborhood, drugs, and relationships. . . . A foreword from Nikki Giovanni rounds out this moving collection, which also includes a few thoughtful writing exercises." Booklist.

Greenberg, Jan

★ **Heart** to heart: new poems inspired by twentieth-century American art. edited by Jan Greenberg. Harry N. Abrams, 2001. 80 p.

Grades: 5 6 7 8 9 10　　　　　　　　　　　　　**811**
　1. 20th century 2. Modern art 20th century 3. Art, American
　ISBN 9780810943865

　　　　　　　　　　　　　　　　LC　99462335

A compilation of poems by Americans writing about American art in the twentieth century, including such writers as Nancy Willard, Jane Yolen, and X.J. Kennedy.

"From a tight diamante and pantoum to lyrical free verse, the range of poetic styles will speak to a wide age group. . . . Concluding with biographical notes on each poet and artist, this rich resource is an obvious choice for teachers, and the exciting interplay between art and the written word will encourage many readers to return again and again to the book." Booklist.

Grimes, Nikki

Legacy: women poets of the Harlem Renaissance. by Nikki Grimes; artwork by Cozbi A. Cabrera [and 16 others]. Bloomsbury Children's Books, 2021. 134 p.

Grades: 5 6 7 8 9   **811**

1. American poetry 2. African American poets 3. African American women poets 4. Women poets 5. Harlem Renaissance -- Influence 6. African American poetry 7. Anthologies

ISBN 9781681199443

LC 2020024833

From Children's Literature Legacy Award-winning author Nikki Grimes comes a feminist-forward new collection of poetry celebrating the little-known women poets of the Harlem Renaissance—paired with full-color, original art from today's most talented female African-American illustrators. Provided by publisher

"The eloquent and stirring voices of Grimes and her counterparts of the past resonate with passion, purpose and resilance." Horn Book

Includes bibliographical references (pages 127-129) and index.

★ **One** last word: wisdom from the Harlem Renaissance. Nikki Grimes; Illustrated by Cozbi Cabrera [and 12 others]. Bloomsbury USA Childrens, 2017. 160 p.

Grades: 5 6 7 8   **811**

1. African Americans 2. Harlem Renaissance 3. Intellectual life 4. Harlem, New York City 5. New York City

ISBN 9781619635548

LC 2016016215

The Coretta Scott King Award-winning author of What Is Goodbye? presents a collection of poetry inspired by the Harlem Renaissance and complemented by full-color artwork by such esteemed artists as Pat Cummings, Brian Pinkney and Sean Qualls.

"This anthology has plenty to offer, including effective introductions to Harlem Renaissance poets, well-expressed ideas and images, and, for young writers, a challenging way to turn admiration into inspiration." Booklist.

Hall, Donald

The **Oxford** book of children's verse in America. edited by Donald Hall. Oxford University Press, 1985. xxxviii, 319 p.

Grades: 5 6 7 8 9 10 11 12 Adult   **811**

ISBN 0195035399

LC 84020755

A collection of American poems written for children or traditionally enjoyed by children, by such authors as Longfellow, Poe, Eugene Field, Langston Hughes, Dr. Seuss, and Jack Prelutsky.

"A fine and carefully winnowed collection of American poetry is gathered in a book that will interest students of children's literature and young people who simply enjoy browsing." Horn Book.

Herrera, Juan Felipe

★ **Laughing** out loud, I fly: poems in English and Spanish. Juan Felipe Herrera; drawings by Karen Barbour. Harper Collins Publishers, c1998. 48 p.

Grades: 6 7 8 9   **811**

1. Herrera, Juan Felipe 2. Mexican Americans 3. Mexican American boys 4. Childhood 5. Bilingual materials English/ Spanish.

ISBN 0060276045

LC 96045476

A collection of poems in Spanish and English about childhood, place, and identity.

"Barbour's black-and-white drawings accompany each poem, delicately underlining its images but allowing the strong sensuality of the words to seep into readers' minds." School Library Journal.

Hovey, Kate

Ancient voices. written by Kate Hovey; illustrations by Murray Kimber. Margaret McElderry Books, c2004. 40 p.

Grades: 6 7 8 9   **811**

1. Gods and goddesses 2. Mythology, Classical 3. Mythology, Greek 4. Mythology, Roman 5. Mythology

ISBN 0689833423

LC 00028359

Twenty-three poems give voice to a variety of goddesses, gods, and mortals from Greek and Roman mythology.

"These lyrical poems and dramatic picture-book-size illustrations humanize the Greek myths with flashes of contemporary realism. . . . The poetry here is both intense and accessible, with unobtrusive rhyme that adds to the music of the lines." Booklist.

Hughes, Langston, 1902-1967

★ The **dream** keeper and other poems. Langston Hughes; illustrated by Brian Pinkney. Knopf, 1996, c1994. 83 p.

Grades: 4 5 6 7   **811**

1. African Americans 2. African American poetry

ISBN 0679883479

LC BL 99789947

A lavishly bound new edition celebrates the colloquial and complex works of one of this country's most important African-American authors and demonstrates to young people that poetry is about them.

"Black-and-white scratchboard illustrations in Pinkney's signature style express the emotion and beat of the poetry. . . . The poems are . . . colloquial and direct yet mysterious and complex." Booklist.

Langston Hughes. edited by Arnold Rampersad & David Roessel; illustrations by Benny Andrews. Sterling Pub., c2006. 48 p.: Poetry for young people

Grades: 5 6 7 8   **811**

1. Hughes, Langston, 1902-1967. 2. Poets 3. African American poets 4. African Americans 5. African Americans -- Social life and customs 20th century. 6. African American poetry

ISBN 1402718454

LC 2005025369

"This charming collection of 26 poems is vibrantly illustrated with depictions of African Americans in varied settings. . . . This will be a welcome introduction to Hughes's poetry for elementary students, and it includes sufficient detail to make it useful and enjoyable for older students." School Library Journal.

Janeczko, Paul B.

Requiem: poems of the Terezin ghetto. Paul B. Janeczko. Candlewick Press, 2011. 102 p.

Grades: 7 8 9 10   **811**

1. Theresienstadt (Concentration camp) 2. Holocaust (1933-1945)

ISBN 9780763647278

LC 2010038882

Presents a collection of poetry inspired by the history of the people in the Terezin concentration camp during the holocaust.

"Janeczko reflects on Terezin through thirty-five compact free-verse poems, most written in the voice of named (and numbered) inhabitants and guards, almost all fictional, of the camp. . . . The verses are spare and accessible, filled with crushing historical weight; the first-person approach will make the entries particularly compelling as readers theater or readalouds." Bulletin of the Center for Children's Books.

Includes bibliographical references.

Seeing the blue between: advice and inspiration for young poets. compiled by Paul B. Janeczko. Candlewick Press, 2002. 132 p.

Grades: 7 8 9 10   **811**
1. Poetry writing 2. Creative writing 3. Poetry -- Study and teaching
ISBN 9780763608811

LC 2001025882

Poets such as Jane Yolen, Nikki Grimes, and Tom Pow share a range of advice, from breaking the rules to reading Shakespeare's sonnets in the bathroom, and sample poems providing burgeoning poets with inspiration.

"Here, thirty-two established poets share their writing secrets in short letters addressed directly to the readers. Although each poet has a distinct voice . . . a familiar mantra quickly develops: read, observe, love words, write, rewrite. . . . Accompanying poems may connect directly to a letter's content, give a representative sample of an individual's body of work, or impart advice." Horn Book Guide.

Levy, Debbie

★ The **year** of goodbyes: a true story of friendship, family and farewells. Debbie Levy. Disney-Hyperion Books, 2019, c2010. 144 p.

Grades: 5 6 7 8   **811**
1. 1930s 2. Holocaust (1933-1945) 3. Jews -- Persecutions 4. Atrocities 5. Families 6. World War II -- Jews 7. Hamburg, Germany 8. Diaries
ISBN 9781368054553

LC 2009018671

The author's mother's 1938 autograph book filled with inscriptions from family and friends is the inspiration for a collection of narrative poems about life in Nazi Germany for a Jewish family trying to escape the horrors. Teacher's Guide available.

"Artfully weaving together her mother's poesiealbum (autograph/ poetry album), diary, and her own verse, Levy crafts a poignant portrait of her Jewish mother's life in 1938 Nazi Germany that crackles with adolescent vitality." Publishers Weekly.

Lewis, J. Patrick

The **brothers'** war: Civil War voices in verse. by J. Patrick Lewis; including photographs by Matthew Brady. National Geographic, 2007. 48 p.

Grades: 5 6 7 8 9 10   **811**
1. Civil war 2. United States Civil War, 1861-1865 3. United States -- History -- Civil War, 1861-1865
ISBN 1426300379

LC 2006103275

Drawn from primary-source books, articles, the speeches of Lincoln, and the letters of Grant and Lee, this powerful historical documentation of our country's Civil War uses poetry to vividly bring to life the brutal conflict that tore America apart.

"This heartrending collection of original poems paired with photographs by Civil War photographers makes real what statistics about war cannot: that the casualties of any war have human faces. Lewis . . . writes poignantly and lyrically. . . . An elegant design of gold, silver and black handsomely frames the text and photographs." Publishers Weekly.

★ The **house**. [illustrated by] Roberto Innocenti; [text by] J. Patrick Lewis. Creative Editions, 2009. 64 p.

Grades: 4 5 6 7   **811**
1. Dwellings 2. American poetry 3. Children's poetry, American
ISBN 9781568462011

LC 2008040810

A stone-and-mortar house watches a century pass and inhabitants come and go.

"The walls in a stone farmhouse literally talk in this first-person narrative that deals with the ravages of time and their effects on the structure and its inhabitants. After a brief history, the house (constructed in 1656, a plague year) fast forwards to the dawn of the 20th century, when children discover its ruins. The quatrains, one to a spread, alternate between an AABB and ABBA rhyme scheme, thus avoiding singsong predictability. . . . Children will pore over Innocenti's marvelously detailed spreads, composed in an oversize, vertical format and set in an Italian hill town. . . . In the subset of books dealing intelligently with the effects of time on a single location, this is a provocative choice." School Library Journal.

Monumental verses. J. Patrick Lewis National Geographic, 2005. 32 p.

Grades: 5 6 7 8   **811**
1. Monuments 2. Historic buildings 3. Historic sites 4. Statues 5. Buildings
ISBN 0792271351

"Lewis offers 14 poems celebrating monumental structures. From the remnants of civilizations at Stonehenge, Easter Island, and Machu Picchu to the more modern achievements of the Taj Mahal, the Eiffel Tower, and the Statue of Liberty, the subjects are varied and the accompanying photos are striking." Booklist.

Self-portrait with seven fingers: the life of Marc Chagall in verse. by J. Patrick Lewis and Jane Yolen. Creative Editions, 2011. 40 p.

Grades: 5 6 7 8   **811**
1. Chagall, Marc, 1887-1985. 2. Artists 3. Jews, Russian 4. Painters
ISBN 9781568462110

"Lewis and Yolen pair 14 poems about Marc Chagall (18871985) with reproductions of more than a dozen of his paintings (as well as vintage photographs) in this moving account of the artist's Jewish upbringing in what is now Belarus, . . . his ascent in the art world, and his loves and losses, including arrest by the Nazis while living in Paris. . . . The duo's emphatic and empathetic verse is put into context by informative biographical sidebars that appear beneath each poem. A study in resilience, dedication, and wide-ranging talent." Publishers Weekly.

Longfellow, Henry Wadsworth, 1807-1882

Henry Wadsworth Longfellow. edited by Frances Schoonmaker; illustrated by Chad Wallace. Sterling Pub., 1998. 48 p.: Poetry for young people

Grades: 4 5 6 7   **811**
ISBN 0806994177

LC 98014833

An illustrated selection of twenty-seven complete or excerpted poems by the renowned nineteenth-century New England poet. Also includes information about his life.

"A collection of 27 poems, among them, The Village Blacksmith, The Wreck of the Hesperus. The Children's Hour, Paul Revere's Ride, and Hiawatha's Childhood from The Song of Hiawatha. A several-page introduction to Longfellow's life also includes some of the stories behind the poems." Booklist.

Hiawatha and Megissogwon. Henry Wadsworth Longfellow; illustrated by Jeffrey Thompson; afterword by Joseph Bruchac. National Geographic Society, c2001. 32 p.

Grades: 5 6 7 8   **811**
1. Hiawatha, active 15th century 2. Iroquois Indians 3. Indians of North America
ISBN 0792266765

LC 00012719

Hiawatha, the son of the West Wind, slays serpents, eludes ghosts, and confronts the evil Megissogwon in an illustrated version of the classic poem.

"Readers who persevere through the no-longer-familiar poem will be rewarded for their efforts by Hiawatha's exciting adventures, ferocious battles, and victorious homecoming. The text has been capably illustrated in a complex process utilizing original drawings, black-and-white scratchboard, and a computer program for color." School Library Journal.

Marsalis, Wynton, 1961-
★ **Jazz** A-B-Z: an A to Z collection of jazz portraits. Wynton Marsalis; illustrated by Paul Rogers; with biographical sketches by Phil Schaap. Candlewick Press, 2005. 76 p.

Grades: 5 6 7 8 9 10   **811**
1. Jazz musicians 2. Jazz music 3. Music
ISBN 0763621358

LC 2005048448

"This is a witty, stunningly designed alphabet catalog. . . . The biographical sketches and notes on poetic forms by Phil Schaap are concise and genuinely informative. . . . Rogers's pastiche full-page portraits, his use of expressive typography and the smaller vignettes he sprinkles throughout are bound to heighten any reader's appreciation of both the musicians and the music. . . . [Marsalis offers] clever . . . poems, word-plays, odes and limericks." New York Times Book Review.

Mora, Pat
The **desert** is my mother = El desierto es mi madre. by Pat Mora; art by Daniel Lechon. Pinata Books, c1994. 32 p.

Grades: 4 5 6   **811**
1. Deserts 2. Desert life 3. Desert animals 4. Desert plants 5. Desert survival 6. Bilingual materials English/Spanish
ISBN 1558851216

LC 94020047

A poetic depiction of the desert as the provider of comfort, food, spirit, and life.

Myers, Walter Dean, 1937-2014
★ **Harlem**: a poem. Walter Dean Myers; pictures by Christopher Myers Scholastic Press, 1997 unpaged

Grades: 5 6 7 8 9 10   **811**
1. African Americans 2. Collage 3. Poetry of places 4. Harlem, New York City, in art 5. Harlem, New York City 6. African American poetry 7. Books for reluctant readers
ISBN 0590543407

LC 968108

Poems and collages celebrate the people, sights, and sounds of Harlem, a Black crucible of American culture.

"Myers's paean to Harlem sings, dances, and swaggers across the pages, conveying the myriad sounds on the streets. . . . Christopher My-

ers's collages add an edge to his father's words, vividly bringing to life the sights and scenes of Lenox Avenue." Horn Book Guide.

Here in Harlem: poems in many voices. Walter Dean Myers. Holiday House, 2004. 88 p.

Grades: 7 8 9 10   **811**
1. African Americans 2. Harlem, New York City
ISBN 0823418537

LC 2003067605

"In each poem here, a resident of Harlem speaks in a distinctive voice, offering a story, a thought, a reflection, or a memory. The poetic forms are varied and well chosen. . . . Expressive period photos from Myers collection accompany the text of this handsome book." Booklist.

Nelson, Marilyn, 1946-
Carver: a life in poems. Marilyn Nelson. Front Street, c2001. 103 p.

Grades: 7 8 9 10   **811**
1. Carver, George Washington, 1864?-1943 2. Botanists 3. Inventors 4. African Americans 5. Agriculturists 6. African American agriculturists
ISBN 1886910537

LC 00063624

"A series of fifty-nine poems portrays George Washington Carver as a private, scholarly man of great personal faith and social purpose. Nelson fills in the trajectory of Carver's life with details of the cultural and political contexts that shaped him even as he shaped history. As individual works, each poem stands as a finely wrought whole of . . . high caliber." Horn Book Guide.

Fortune's bones: the manumission requiem. Marilyn Nelson. Front Street, c2004. 32 p.

Grades: 7 8 9 10   **811**
1. Enslaved people 2. Slaveholders 3. African Americans 4. Slavery 5. Grief 6. Connecticut
ISBN 1932425128

LC 2004046917

"This requiem honors a slave who died in Connecticut in 1798. His owner, a doctor, dissected his body, boiling down his bones to preserve them for anatomy studies. The skeleton . . . hung in a local museum until 1970. . . . The museum . . . uncovered the skeleton's provenance, created a new exhibit, and led to the commissioning of these six poems. The selections . . . arc from grief to triumph. . . . The facts inform the verse and open up a full appreciation of its rich imagery and rhythmic, lyrical language." School Library Journal.

Includes bibliographical references (p. 32).

My Seneca village. Marilyn Nelson Namelos, 2015. 87 p.

Grades: 6 7 8 9 10   **811**
1. 19th century 2. African American neighborhoods 3. Communities 4. African Americans 5. Neighborhoods 6. New York (State)
ISBN 9781608981960

"Nelson chooses prose narrative to connect these 40-some lyric fictional portraits that include schoolchildren, a mariner, a bootblack, a hairdresser, a musician, bar owners, lovers, and a fortuneteller, among others, along with poignant snapshots of famous historical figures Frederick Douglass and Maria Stewart, the first African-American woman to lecture on politics and religion." Kirkus.

A **wreath** for Emmett Till. Marilyn Nelson; illustrated by Philippe Lardy. Houghton Mifflin, 2005. 34 p.

Grades: 8 9 10 11 12   **811**
1. Till, Emmett, 1941-1955 2. African American teenage boys
3. Murder victims 4. African Americans -- Discrimination 5.
Lynching 6. Racism 7. Mississippi
ISBN 0618397523

LC 2004009205

A sequence of fifteen interlinked sonnets pay tribute to a young man who sparked the Civil Rights Movement in 1955 Mississippi—fourteen-year-old Emmitt Till, an African-American boy who was lynched for whistling at a white woman, and whose murderers were acquitted.

"This is a poetry collection about Till's brutal, racially motivated murder. The poems form a heroic crown of sonnets—a sequence in which the last line of one poem becomes the first line of the next. . . . The rigid form distills the words' overwhelming emotion into potent, heart-stopping lines that speak from changing perspectives. . . . When matched with Lardy's gripping, spare, symbolic paintings of tree trunks, blood-red roots, and wreaths of thorns, these poems are a powerful achievement that teens and adults will want to discuss together." Booklist.

Includes bibliographical references (p. [34]).

Nye, Naomi Shihab
19 varieties of gazelle: poems of the Middle East. by Naomi Shihab Nye. Greenwillow Books, c2002. xviii, 142 p.
Grades: 7 8 9 10   **811**
1. Arab Americans 2. Palestinians 3. September 11 Terrorist Attacks, 2001 4. War 5. Peace 6. Middle East -- Social life and customs
ISBN 0060097655

LC 2002000771

"In this volume, Nye collects her poems about growing up as an Arab American (her ancestry is Palestinian), including previously published poems and newly written pieces. This rich and varied volume offers insights into the experience of childhood in two very different worlds. . . . This volume will fill a need for classroom use, for young people seeking a more personal understanding of the Middle East, and for readers seeking a connection with their own Middle Eastern background." Bulletin of the Center for Children's Books.

Cast away: poems for our time. Naomi Shihab Nye. Greenwillow Books, an imprint of HarperCollins Publishers, 2020 176 p.
Grades: 5 6 7 8 9   **811**
1. Wastefulness (Ecology) 2. Litter (Trash) 3. Sustainable living 4. Sustainability 5. Environmentalism
ISBN 9780062907691

Poet Naomi Shihab Nye shines a spotlight on the things we cast away, from plastic water bottles to refugees.

"The collection features humorous, witty, serious, and even some politically charged poems, all of which will leave readers with a consciousness of the precarious environment. Her poetic polemic on trash is truly a treasure for readers." Booklist

Honeybee: poems & short prose. by Naomi Shihab Nye. Greenwillow Books, 2008. 176 p.
Grades: 8 9 10 11 12   **811**
1. Bees
ISBN 0060853913

LC 2007036742

In eighty-two poems and paragraphs, alights on the essentials of our time, our loved ones, our dense air, our wars, our memories, our planet, and leaves us feeling curiously sweeter and profoundly soothed.

"This poetry anthology is a rallying cry, a call for us to rediscover such beelike traits as interconnectedness, strong community, and honest communication. . . . Teens at the very start of their questioning years will recognize their own angst in Nye's sense of irony, their idealistic optimism in her simple wonder." School Library Journal.

I'll ask you three times, are you ok?: tales of driving and being driven. Naomi Shihab Nye. Greenwillow Books, c2007. 242 p.
Grades: 7 8 9 10 11 12   **811**
1. Nye, Naomi Shihab 2. Women travelers 3. Misadventures 4. Voyages and travels 5. Palestinian Americans
ISBN 0060853921

LC 2006036548

Presents a collection of essays, vignettes, memories, and stories, all of which center around the author's travels across the globe where the strangest and most astonishing things happened to her while she was driving in her car.

"The author writes about sudden intimate connections with strangers, especially taxi drivers, who often yield glimpses of family and exile that can sometimes change us. . . . The prose is chatty, fast, and unpretentious, and teens will enjoy the driving stuff and the idea of her kissing in the backseat, and they'll feel her sense of control when she is behind the wheel herself." Booklist.

A **maze** me: poems for girls. Naomi Shihab Nye; illustrated by Terre Maher. Greenwillow Books, c2005. 128 p.
Grades: 7 8 9 10   **811**
1. Girls 2. Emotions in girls 3. Growth (Psychology) 4. Self-fulfillment 5. Self-fulfillment in girls
ISBN 0060581891

LC 2004003283

"These poems draw from Nye's observations about nature, home, school, and neighborhood to make connections to a girl's inner world. . . . Most poems . . . speak with a powerful immediacy. . . . A wide age range will respond to these deeply felt poems about everyday experiences." Booklist.

Time you let me in: 25 poets under 25. selected by Naomi Shihab Nye. Greenwillow Books, c2010. xix, 236 p.
Grades: 8 9 10 11 12   **811**
ISBN 9780061896378

LC 2009019387

A collection of poems from 25 poets.

"This lively collection by young contemporary writers is rooted in the strong, emotional particulars of family, friendship, childhood memories, school, dislocation, war, and more. . . . Teens will connect with the passionate, unmoderated feelings that are given clarity and shape in each poem." Booklist.

Voices in the air: poems for listeners. Naomi Shihab Nye. HarperCollins Children's Books, 2018. 208 p.
Grades: 8 9 10 11   **811**
1. Multiculturalism 2. Inspiration 3. Hope 4. Peace 5. Thought and thinking
ISBN 9780062691842

Ninety-five poems pay tribute to essential voices past and present that have the power to provoke, lead, and offer hope.

Orgill, Roxane

★ **Jazz** day: the making of a famous photograph. Roxane Orgill; illustrated by Francis Vallejo. Candlewick Press, 2016. 55 p.

Grades: 4 5 6 7 8　　　　　　　　　　**811**
　　1. Jazz musicians 2. Jazz music 3. African Americans 4. Harlem, New York City -- History -- 20th century.
　　ISBN 9780763669546

　　　　　　　　　　　　　　　　LC bl2016009218

A collection of poems recounts the efforts of Esquire magazine graphic designer Art Kane to photograph a group of famous jazz artists in front of a Harlem brownstone.

"In 21 poems, Orgill introduces Art Kane's iconic 1958 Harlem photograph to young readers, spotlighting many of the 57 jazz musicians pictured. . . . Vallejo's acrylic-and-pastel paintings vividly capture the shoot's vignettes and the skittish excitement of neighborhood kids." Kirkus.

Includes bibliographical references (pages 54-55).

Pinkney, Andrea Davis

Martin rising: requiem for a King. by Andrea Davis Pinkney; paintings by Brian Pinkney. Scholastic Press, 2017. 128 p.

Grades: 4 5 6 7 8　　　　　　　　　　**811**
　　1. King, Martin Luther, Jr., 1929-1968 2. Civil rights workers 3. African American civil rights workers 4. Civil Rights Movement 5. African Americans -- Civil rights
　　ISBN 9780545702539

　　　　　　　　　　　　　　　　LC 2016031408

"Written with an eye toward choral reading, this is a unique and remarkable resource." Publishers Weekly.

Includes bibliographical references.

Poe, Edgar Allan, 1809-1849

The **raven**. Edgar Allan Poe. Kids Can Press, 2006. 48 p.: Visions in poetry

Grades: 7 8 9 10　　　　　　　　　　**811**
　　1. Ravens 2. Mental illness 3. Guilt 4. Gothic fiction
　　ISBN 1553374738

Presents Poe's haunting poem, which explores the terrifying truths that lurk deep within the human psyche.

"Originally published in 1845, the poem is narrated by a melancholy scholar brooding over Lenore, a woman he loved who is now lost to him. One bleak December at midnight, a raven with fiery eyes visits the scholar and perches above his chamber door. Struggling to understand the meaning of the word his winged visitant repeats Nevermore! the narrator descends by stages into madness.

Prelutsky, Jack, 1940-

★ **Pizza,** pigs, and poetry: how to write a poem. Jack Prelutsky. Greenwillow Books, c2008. 191 p.

Grades: 4 5 6　　　　　　　　　　　**811**
　　1. Prelutsky, Jack, 1940- 2. Poetry writing
　　ISBN 9780061434488

　　　　　　　　　　　　　　　　LC 2007036738

Featuring personal anecdotes and an abundance of information, a humorous guide, filled with poetry exercises, ideas, projects, and pointers, teaches readers how to write poetry.

"Along with easy-to-follow tips for creating verse, haiku, and concrete poetry, the reigning Children's Poet Laureate offers insights into his own thought processes, . . . glimpses of his childhood, and personal anecdotes. . . . Prelutsky tucks in more than a dozen examples of his own work, plus 10 two-and-part-of-a-third line poem starts." Booklist.

★ The **Random** House book of poetry for children. selected and introduced by Jack Prelutsky; illustrated by Arnold Lobel. Random House, c1983. 248 p.

Grades: 3 4 5 6　　　　　　　　　　**811**
　　1. Anthologies
　　ISBN 0394850106

　　　　　　　　　　　　　　　　LC 83002990

More than 550 poems by American, English, and anonymous authors.

"In this anthology emphasis is placed on humor and light verse; but serious and thoughtful poems are also included. . . . Approximately two thirds of the selections were written within the past forty years—the splendid contributions of such writers as John Ciardi, Aileen Fisher, Dennis Lee, Myra Cohn Livingston, David McCord, Eve Merriam, and Lilian Moore. [There are] . . . samplings of earlier poets from Shakespeare and Blake to Emily Dickinson and Walter de la Mare." Horn Book.

Raczka, Bob

★ **Wet** cement: a mix of concrete poems. Bob Raczka. Roaring Brook Press, 2016. 48 p.

Grades: 3 4 5 6　　　　　　　　　　**811**
　　1. Poetry writing 2. Creative writing 3. Writing
　　ISBN 9781626722361

　　　　　　　　　　　　　　　　LC 2015027142

Who says words need to be concrete? This collection shapes poems in surprising and delightful ways.Concrete poetry is a perennially popular poetic form because they are fun to look at. But by using the arrangement of the words on the page to convey the meaning of the poem, concrete or shape poems are also easy to write! From the author of the incredibly inventive Lemonade: And Other Poems Squeezed from a Single Word comes another clever collection that shows kids how to look at words and poetry in a whole new way. Provided by publisher.

"Whether they are watching words about dominoes cascade across a two-page spread, or reading a recipe for icicles that drips down along the top edge, aspiring wordsmiths should find plenty of inspiration here." Booklist.

Reynolds, Jason

For every one. Jason Reynolds. Atheneum/Caitlyn Dlouhy Books, 2018. 112 p.

Grades: 7 8 9 10 11 12　　　　　　　**811**
　　1. Inspiration 2. Hope 3. Dreams 4. Children 5. Teenagers
　　ISBN 9781481486248

　　　　　　　　　　　　　　　　LC 2017036160

Originally performed at the Kennedy Center for the unveiling of the Martin Luther King Jr. Memorial, and later as a tribute to Walter Dean Myers, this stirring and inspirational poem is New York Times bestselling author and National Book Award finalist Jason Reynolds's rallying cry to the dreamers of the world. Provided by publisher.

"Instead of penning advice from someone who has achieved their goals, Reynolds speaks as someone still in pursuit of his dreams, ruminating on continuing to pursue your passions even when it seems as if 'making it' will never happen." VOYA

Shange, Ntozake

Freedom's a-calling me. poems by Ntozake Shange; paintings by Rod Brown. Amistad, c2012. 32 p.

Grades: 4 5 6 7　　　　　　　　　　**811**
　　1. Underground Railroad 2. Enslaved people 3. Freedom 4. African Americans 5. African American poetry
　　ISBN 9780061337437

　　　　　　　　　　　　　　　　LC 2010050515

Powerful language and stirring art bring to life the treacherous journey of the travelers on the Underground Railroad, in a universal story about the human need to be free.

"The author and illustrator present a series of poems and paintings that express the hope and frustration of enslaved people trying to navigate the Underground Railroad. Using dialect to convey a Southern cadence, Shange's poems communicate powerful emotions. . . . These poems are a cry from the heart. . . . The expressive, impressionistic paintings capture attention with their bold strokes and vivid coloring." School Library Journal.

We troubled the waters: poems. by Ntozake Shange; illustrations by Rod Brown. Collins, 2009. 29 p.

Grades: 4 5 6 7 8 9 10   **811**
1. African Americans 2. Racism 3. Civil Rights Movement 4. Discrimination 5. African Americans -- Civil rights 6. African American poetry
ISBN 9780061337352

LC 2008025360

"Each spread pairs a poem with blurred, expressive acrylic paintings, and the pages feature both well-known civil rights leaders and ordinary people who endured oppression. . . . The messages are haunting. . . . The colloquial lines, indelible images, and comparisons between then and now will keep readers talking." Booklist.

Sidman, Joyce
What the heart knows: chants, charms, and blessings. written by Joyce Sidman; illustrated by Pamela Zagarenski. Houghton Mifflin Harcourt, 2013. 80 p.

Grades: 6 7 8 9 10 11 12   **811**
1. Emotions in teenagers 2. Emotions 3. Illustrated books
ISBN 9780544106161

LC 2012047836

"Sidman and Zagarenski present Chants & Charms, Spells & Invocations, Laments & Remembrances, and Praise Songs & Blessings in a variety of poetic forms. Each poem speaks directly from Sidman's heart to the reader's, addressing subjects of deep importance: forgiveness, friendship, bravery, death, illness, moving. Zagarenski's illustrations beautifully extend the poems with her dreamy style and deft use of white space, symbolism, and images." Horn Book.

Silverstein, Shel
★ **Every** thing on it. Shel Silverstein; edited by Antonia Markiet. HarperCollins, 2011. 208 p.

Grades: 3 4 5 6   **811**
1. Nonsense verses 2. Humorous poetry
ISBN 9780061998164

"Silverstein's inspired wordplay and impish sense of humor are in abundant evidence. His signature line drawings accompany many of the poems and complete the jokes of some. . . . Adults who grew up with Uncle Shelby will find themselves wiping their eyes by the time they get to the end of this collection; children new to the master will find themselves hooked." Kirkus.

★ **Falling** up: poems and drawings. by Shel Silverstein. Harper Collins, c1996. 171 p.

Grades: 3 4 5 6   **811**
1. Boys 2. Girls 3. Children 4. Children and adults 5. Nonsense verses 6. Humorous poetry 7. Books for reluctant readers
ISBN 0060248033

LC 96075736

A collection of humorous poems and drawings.

"This collection includes more than 150 poems. . . . As always, Silverstein has a direct line to what kids like, and he gives them poems celebrating the gross, the scary, the absurd, and the comical. The drawings are much more than decoration. They often extend a poem's meaning and, in many cases, add some great comedy." Booklist.

★ **A light** in the attic. Shel Silverstein. Harper and Row, 1981 167 p.

Grades: 3 4 5 6   **811**
1. Humorous poetry
ISBN 0060256745

LC 80008453

A collection of humorous poems and drawings.

"This collection of more than one hundred poems will delight lovers of Silverstein's raucous, rollicking verse and his often tender, whimsical, philosophical advice. . . . The poems are tuned in to kids' most hidden feelings, dark wishes and enjoyment of the silly. . . . The witty line drawings are a full half of the treat of this wholly satisfying anthology by the modern successor to Edward Lear and Hilaire Belloc." School Library Journal. [review of 1981 edition]

★ **Where** the sidewalk ends: the poems & drawings of Shel Silverstein. Shel Silverstein. Harper and Row, 1974 166 p.

Grades: 3 4 5 6 7 8 9 10   **811**
1. Silliness 2. Humorous poetry
ISBN 0060256672

LC 70105486

A boy who turns into a TV set and a girl who eats a whale are only two of the characters in a collection of humorous poetry illustrated with the author's own drawings.

Smith, Charles R.
Hoop queens: poems. Charles R. Smith. Candlewick Press, 2003. 35 p.

Grades: 4 5 6 7   **811**
1. Women basketball players 2. Basketball
ISBN 076361422X

LC 2002041111

A collection of twelve poems that celebrate contemporary women basketball stars, including Yolanda Griffith, Chamique Holdsclaw, and Natalie Williams.

"Action photos of the athletes are pasted large on colorful, dynamic backgrounds that barely hold the motion-filled poems to the page. Notes about each player and poem communicate the joy Smith finds both in watching the game and writing poetry. Pure pleasure for basketball fans and inspiration for kids who doubted poetry was alive." School Library Journal.

Sneve, Virginia Driving Hawk
Dancing teepees: poems of American Indian youth. selected by Virginia Driving Hawk Sneve; with art by Stephen Gammell. Holiday House, 1989. 32 p.

Grades: 4 5 6   **811**
1. Indians of North America
ISBN 0823407241

LC 88011075

An illustrated collection of poems from the oral tradition of Native Americans.

"This is an eclectic collection, drawn from a variety of tribal traditions. Printed on heavy paper, the book is illustrated with a catalogue of marvelously rendered designs and motifs, ranging from those of the Northwest Coast to the intricate beadwork patterns of the Great Lakes and the zigzag geometric borders of Southwestern pottery." New York Times Book Review.

Soto, Gary

A **fire** in my hands: poems. Gary Soto. Harcourt, Inc., 2006. 74 p.

Grades: 6 7 8 9   **811**

1. Soto, Gary 2. Poets, American 20th century 3. Mexican American poets 4. Mexican American teenage boys 5. Mexican Americans 6. California
ISBN 0152055649

LC 2005024610

A collection of poems brings to life themes of growing up, family, friendship, and first love.

"Half the poems are new to this expanded edition of a collection first published 15 years ago, including some great ones from Soto's adult books that speak about feeling stuck at home and growing up poor, Catholic, and Mexican American. Soto's chatty introduction about writing poetry that celebrates small, common things will appeal to both readers and writers, as will the informal questions and answers at the back of the book and the brief autobiographical notes Soto includes with each poem." Booklist.

A **natural** man. Gary Soto. Chronicle Books, c1999. 71 p.

Grades: 7 8 9 10   **811**

1. Mexican Americans
ISBN 0811825183

LC 99018353

Gathers poems dealing with such topics as childhood, family, love, death, and poverty.

"This poetry anthology offers a photographic glimpse into the lives of California's Chicanos. But although the titles and use of Spanish words create a very particular setting, the characters, stories, and truths of these selections have a universal resonance." School Library Journal.

Weatherford, Carole Boston, 1956-

You can fly: the Tuskegee Airmen. Carole Boston Weatherford; art by Jeffery Boston Weatherford. Atheneum Books for Young Readers, 2016. 80 p.

Grades: 4 5 6 7   **811**

1. United States. Army Air Forces. Fighter Squadron, 99th. 2. Tuskegee Army Air Field, Alabama. 3. 1930s 4. 1940s 5. Air warfare 6. African American pilots -- History 7. World War II 8. Military campaigns 9. Western Front (World War II)
ISBN 9781481449380

LC 2015012393

Uses second-person poems to tell the story of the Tuskegee Airmen, the pioneering African-American pilots of World War II.

"This excellent treatment is enhanced with useful backmatter: author's note, timeline, and list of additional resources. Jeffery Boston Weatherford's scratchboard illustrations complement the text. A masterful, inspiring evocation of an era." Kirkus.

Includes bibliographical references.

Whipple, Laura

If the shoe fits: voices from Cinderella. by Laura Whipple; illustrations by Laura Beingessner. Margaret K. McElderry Books, c2002. 67 p.

Grades: 5 6 7 8   **811**

1. Cinderella 2. Characters and characteristics in fairy tales
ISBN 0689840705

LC 2001030778

A collection of poems recreates not only the classic fairy tale, but also the more obscure characters such as the fairy godmother known as the Magic One, Cinderella's loyal cat, and the occasionally nervous prince.

"In this version of the fairy tale the characters tell the story in blank verses. . . . The story unfolds just as it always does, but the multiple points of view—from Cinderella's to the prince's to the rat's to the queen's—enlarge and enrich the familiar tale to win a more sophisticated audience. . . . Paintings by Beingessner achieve just the right mixture of sorrow, beauty, and humor." Booklist.

Woodson, Jacqueline

★ **Locomotion**. by Jacqueline Woodson. G.P. Putnam's Sons, 2003. 128 p.

Grades: 4 5 6 7   **811**

1. African American boys 2. Brothers and sisters 3. Foster home care 4. Orphans 5. Schools
ISBN 0399231153

LC 2002069779

In a series of poems, eleven-year-old Lonnie writes about his life, after the death of his parents, separated from his younger sister, living in a foster home, and finding his poetic voice at school.

"In a masterful use of voice, Woodson allows Lonnie's poems to tell a complex story of loss and grief and to create a gritty, urban environment. Despite the spare text, Lonnie's foster mother and the other minor characters are three-dimensional, making the boy's world a convincingly real one." School Library Journal.

Worth, Valerie, 1933-1994

Pug and other animal poems. Valerie Worth; pictures by Steve Jenkins. Margaret Ferguson Books, Farrar Straus Giroux, 2013. 32 p.

Grades: 2 3 4 5   **811**

1. Animals 2. Pugs (Dogs)
ISBN 9780374350246

LC 2010034300

A collection of whimsical animal poems celebrates a range of eccentric animal behaviors and is complemented by bright collage artwork.

Yolen, Jane

The **Emily** sonnets: the life of Emily Dickinson. Jane Yolen; illustrations by Gary Kelley. Creative Editions, c2012. 40 p.

Grades: 5 6 7   **811**

1. Dickinson, Emily, 1830-1886. 2. Poets, American 19th century 3. Women recluses 4. Women poets
ISBN 9781568462158

LC 2011040841

Recounts Emily Dickinson's schooling, seclusion, and the slant rhymes for which she became famous.

Young, Ed

Beyond the great mountains: a visual poem about China. Ed Young. Chronicle Books, c2005. 36 p.

Grades: 4 5 6 7   **811**

1. Chinese characters 2. China
ISBN 0811843432

LC 2004021587

Lyrical text and illustrations featuring Chinese characters and paper collage introduce the beauty and richness of China.

"The book is comprised of 14 lines, each of which is accompanied by its own double-page illustration, done in cut-and-torn-paper collage. Young also provides the ancient characters for the images he presents. . . . Designed to be read vertically, each page is flipped up to reveal the accompanying illustration. In this way, the entire book becomes a piece of art, a visual treat of sublime colors and textures that joins with text and characters to describe the vastness and beauty of China." School Library Journal.

811.008 American poetry—Collections

Bush, Gail
Indivisible: poems for social justice. edited by Gail Bush & Randy Meyer; foreword by Common. Norwood House Press, c2013. 94 p.
Grades: 7 8 9 10 11 12   **811.008**
  1. Social problems 2. Social justice
  ISBN 9781603574174
              LC 2012021600
Anthology including over 50 works of poetry by 20th century writers on issues related to social justice in American society. Foreword by Common. Provided by publisher.

Carlson, Lori M.
Red hot salsa: bilingual poems on being young and Latino in the United States. edited by Lori Marie Carlson; introduction by Oscar Hijuelos. Henry Holt, c2005. xix, 140 p.
Grades: 7 8 9 10   **811.008**
  1. Hispanic Americans 2. Hispanic American teenagers 3. Teenagers 4. Teenage immigrants 5. Translations Spanish to English 6. Bilingual materials English/Spanish 7. Books for reluctant readers
  ISBN 0805076166
              LC 2004054005
"This is a bilingual collection of poems that appear in both Spanish and English. Included are many well-known writers, such as Gary Soto and Luis J. Rodriguez . . . as well as emerging poets. . . . The poems often speak about the complex challenges of being bicultural. . . . Most poems are translated by the poets themselves, and many are written in an inventive blend of languages, which English speakers will easily follow with help from the appended glossary. Powerful and immediate." Booklist.

Hopkins, Lee Bennett
America at war. poems selected by Lee Bennett Hopkins; illlustrated by Stephen Alcorn. Margaret K. McElderry Books, c2008. 84 p.
Grades: 5 6 7 8   **811.008**
  1. War 2. United States -- History, Military
  ISBN 9781416918325
              LC 2006008723
A collection of poems about America at war from the Revolution to the Iraq war.
"This handsome anthology, expressing Americans' varied experience during wartime, is a fine selection of poems accessible to children. . . . The poems will touch readers with their sharp poignancy and undeniable power. Throughout the well-designed book, the expressive watercolor artwork enhances the poetry." Booklist.

Lives: poems about famous Americans. selected by Lee Bennett Hopkins; illustrated by Leslie Staub. HarperCollins Publishers, c1999. 31 p.
Grades: 4 5 6 7   **811.008**
  1. Americans 2. United States 3. United States -- History 4.

Anthologies
ISBN 9780060277673
              LC 98029851
A collection of poetic portraits of sixteen famous Americans from Paul Revere to Neil Armstrong, by such authors as Jane Yolen, Nikki Grimes, and X. J. Kennedy.
"Hopkins's eloquent introduction praises the power of poetry. Concluding Notes on the Lives give readers useful biographical information. Full-page portraits feature Staub's distinctive, flat, primitive style, and their backgrounds have details particular to the subject. . . . A winning combination of poems and illustrations." School Library Journal.

★ **My** America: a poetry atlas of the United States. selected by Lee Bennett Hopkins; illustrated by Stephen Alcorn. Simon & Schuster Books for Young Readers, 2000. 83 p.
Grades: 4 5 6 7   **811.008**
  1. United States
  ISBN 0689812477
              LC 98047402
A collection of poems evocative of seven geographical regions of the United States, including the Northeast, Southeast, Great Lakes, Plains, Mountain, Southwest, and Pacific Coast States.
"Some poems are purposive, but the best . . . capture places and people in all their diversity. Stephen Alcorn's handsome, multi-textured pictures . . . avoid literal interpretation and capture the sweep of the land and the rhythm of the words." Booklist.

Janeczko, Paul B.
A **kick** in the head: an everyday guide to poetic forms. selected by Paul B. Janeczko; illustrated by Chris Raschka. Candlewick Press, 2005. 61 p.
Grades: 4 5 6 7   **811.008**
  1. Literary form
  ISBN 0763606626
              LC 2004048508
"Raschka's high-spirited, spare torn-paper-and-paint collages ingeniously broaden the poems' wide-ranging emotional tones. . . . Clear, very brief explanations of poetic forms . . . accompany each entry; a fine introduction and appended notes offer further information. . . . This is the introduction that will ignite enthusiasm." Booklist.

The **place** my words are looking for: what poets say about and through their work. selected by Paul B. Janeczko. Bradbury Press, c1990. 150 p.
Grades: 4 5 6 7   **811.008**
  1. Writing 2. Poetry writing 3. Poets, American
  ISBN 9780027476712
              LC 89039331
Thirty-nine United States poets share their poems, inspirations, thoughts, anecdotes, and memories.
"Their contributions vary widely in theme and mood and style, though the preponderance of the pieces are written in modern idiom and unrhymed meter. The accompanying comments frequently are as insightful and eloquent as the poems themselves." Horn Book.

A **poke** in the I: a collection of concrete poems. [selected by] Paul Janeczko, illustrated by Chris Raschka. Candlewick Press, 2001. 35 p.
Grades: 3 4 5 6 7 8   **811.008**
  ISBN 9780763606619
              LC 00033675

"Thirty concrete poems of all shapes and sizes are carefully laid on large white spreads, extended by Raschka's quirky watercolor and paper-collage illustrations. . . . Beautiful and playful, this title should find use in storytimes, in the classroom, and just for pleasure anywhere." School Library Journal.

Michael, Pamela

River of words: young poets and artists on the nature of things. edited by Pamela Michael; introduced by Robert Hass. Milkweed Editions, c2008. 320 p.

Grades: 4 5 6 7 8 9   **811.008**
   1. Water 2. Water in art 3. Nature (Aesthetics) 4. Nature
ISBN 9781571316806

          LC 2007046483

"In 1995 Michael and Hass . . . cofounded the River of Words project, designed to connect students' art and poetry education to the natural world immediately around them. . . . The poems and pictures in this handsomely designed volume have been culled from yearly contests. . . . The works are startling, many of them dislocating and highly complex." Publishers Weekly.

Paschen, Elise

★ **Poetry** speaks who I am: poems of discovery, inspiration, independence, and everything else.... Elise Paschen, ed. Sourcebooks, 2010. 136 p.

Grades: 5 6 7 8 9 10   **811.008**
   1. Self-discovery 2. Inspiration 3. Independence (Personal quality)
ISBN 9781402210747

From the creators of the New York Times best-sellers Poetry Speaks and Poetry Speaks to Children comes a collection filled with more than 100 remarkable selections from a wide variety of poets in an anthology featuring both classic and contemporary works. Also includes an audio CD showcasing poets reading their own work.

"This collection aims at middle-grade readers with more than 100 strikingly diverse poems by writers including Poe, Frost, Nikki Giovanni, and Sandra Cisneros. The works are slotted together in mindful thematic order, beside occasional spot art. . . . Pairing a contemporary poem like Toi Derricotte's Fears of the Eighth Grade alongside Keats's When I Have Fears That I May Cease to Be, results in a refreshing lack of literary hierarchy that enables disparate works to build and reflect upon one another. An accompanying CD features recordings of 44 of the poems. . . . A sound and rewarding introduction to the joys of poetry." Publishers Weekly.

Rochelle, Belinda

★ **Words** with wings: a treasury of African-American poetry and art. selected by Belinda Rochelle. Harper Collins, c2001. 48 p.

Grades: 4 5 6 7   **811.008**
   1. Art 2. African American art 3. African Americans 4. American poetry
ISBN 0688164153

          LC 00026864

Pairs twenty works of art by African-American artists with twenty poems by twenty African-American poets.

"Most of the combinations are stunning. . . . Short biographical paragraphs on each poet and artist round out this moving presentation." School Library Journal.

811.009 American poetry—History and criticism

Hudson, Wade

Poetry from the masters: the pioneers: an introduction to African-American poets. edited by Wade Hudson; [illustrations, Stephan J. Hudson]. Just Us Books, c2003. 88 p.

Grades: 7 8 9 10   **811.009**
   1. African-American poetry -- History and criticism 2. African American poets 3. African Americans 4. African American poetry
ISBN 0940975963

"This book focuses on a particular group of black poets, trailblazers who forged a path by overcoming almost impossible obstacles. Hudson puts these writers in perspective and provides a social and literary context. Eleven poets are profiled, starting with Phillis Wheatley and ending with Gwendolyn Brooks. . . . Each writer is introduced with a brief biographical sketch that highlights his or her literary significance and contributions, followed by the full text of two or more poems. . . . This is an excellent resource for students seeking research materials or just looking for wonderful examples of poetry to read." School Library Journal.

811.54 American poetry—1945-1999

Nelson, Marilyn, 1946-

How I discovered poetry. Marilyn Nelson; illustrated by Hadley Hooper. Dial Books, 2014. 112 p.

Grades: 7 8 9 10 11 12   **811.54**
   1. Nelson, Marilyn, 1946- 2. 1950s 3. Writing 4. Poetry writing 5. Race relations 6. Civil Rights Movement
ISBN 9780803733046

          LC 2013005289

The National Book Award, Newbery Honor and multiple Coretta Scott King Honor-winning poet reflects on her childhood in the 1950s and her development as an artist and young woman through 50 illuminating poems that consider such influences as the Civil Rights Movement, the "Red Scare" atomic bomb era and the Feminist Movement.

"In this fictionalized memoir in verse, renowned poet Nelson lyrically recounts her passage from ages 4 to 14, from numerous military base homes; through friends, schools, and dogs; and from developmental stages of initiative through industry to identity. Hooper's line-and-shade illustrations, along with Nelson's family photos, set a quiet and respectful tone and offer readers the feeling of taking an unsolicited peek behind a heavy curtain. For fans of Nelson's impressive body of children's and adult poetry, including the brilliant A Wreath for Emmett Till (2005), this insight into her modulated memories gratifies that heartfelt belief that here writes a woman of great substance." Booklist.

812 American drama in English

Black, Ann N.

Readers theatre for middle school boys: investigating the strange and mysterious. Ann N. Black; illustrated by Cody Rust. Teachers Idea Press, 2008. xiv, 190 p.

Grades: Professional   **812**
   1. Children's plays, American 2. Readers' theatre
ISBN 9781591585350

          LC 2007034923

Offers ten readers' theatre scripts along with information on the author and staging.

Brosius, Peter

Fierce & true: plays for teen audiences. Children's Theatre Company; Peter Brosius and Elissa Adams, editors. University of Minnesota Press, c2010. xiii, 219 p.

Grades: 7 8 9 10 11 12   **812**

1. Teenage drama 2. Teenage actors and actresses 3. Drama
ISBN 9780816673100

LC 2010025225

"The Children's Theatre Company located in Minneapolis, wanted to broaden its audience, so it commissioned four playwrights to create works with young people (ages 12-18) specifically in mind. The results are the full-length plays in this anthology. . . . Anon(ymous) is a contemporary retelling of Homer's Odyssey, set in a dirty North American city, and Five Fingers of Funk is a mature musical celebrating the roots of hip-hop while dealing with issues of poverty and drugs. In The Lost Boys of Sudan, three Dinka refugees flee the horrors of war and begin a harrowing yet humorous journey that takes them to Fargo, ND. And Prom is played out as a frenetic battle between students and chaperones. Each of these selections has a distinctive voice, honoring adolescents as both actor and audience capable of understanding and engaging in today's complex issues." School Library Journal.

Chanda, Justin

Acting out: six one-act plays!: six Newbery stars! edited by Justin Chanda; featuring the playwrights, Avi ... [et al.]. Atheneum Books for Young Readers, c2008. xiii, 175 p.

Grades: 5 6 7 8 9   **812**

1. One-act plays 2. Drama
ISBN 1416938486

LC 2007023613

Six original one-act plays for middle graders written by six Newbery winning authors.

"Each play was inspired by a theater-improv game in which the authors started with the selection of a single word. The pieces all include the following words: dollop, hoodwink, Justin, knuckleball, panhandle, and raven.. . . An engaging choice for literature and acting classes as well as general reading." School Library Journal.

Includes bibliographical references and index.

Fleischman, Paul

Zap. Paul Fleischman. Candlewick Press, 2005. 96 p.

Grades: 9 10 11 12   **812**

1. Drama 2. Remote control 3. Theater 4. Performance artists
ISBN 0763627747

LC 2005050790

"Framed as a performance for an imaginary audience armed with remote-control zappers, this is actually seven plays mashed into one: a turgid rendition of Shakespeare's Richard III alternating at audience's whim among six spoofs of other dramaturgical biggies, among them, The Russian Play, The English Mystery, and The Southern Play. Playgoers and actors alike . . . will relish the irreverent chaos as the boundaries between the plays gradually erode." Booklist.

Schlitz, Laura Amy

★ **Good** masters! Sweet ladies!: voices from a medieval village. Laura Amy Schlitz; illustrated by Robert Byrd Candlewick, 2007. 85 p.

Grades: 5 6 7 8   **812**

1. Medieval period (476-1492) 2. Civilization, Medieval 3. Villages 4. Children 5. Teenagers 6. England -- History -- Medieval period, 1066-1485 7. Europe -- History -- 476-1492. 8. Drama
ISBN 9780763615789

Newbery Medal, 2008.

"Designed for performance and excellent for use in interdisciplinary history classrooms, the book offers students an incredibly approachable format for learning about the Middle Ages that makes the period both realistic and relevant. . . . Byrd's illustrations evoke the era and give dramatists ideas for appropriate costuming and props." School Library Journal.

Surface, Mary Hall

Short scenes and monologues for middle school actors. by Mary Hall Surface. Smith and Kraus, 1999. viii, 183 p.: Young actors series

Grades: 6 7 8 9   **812**

1. Acting 2. Drama
ISBN 1575251795

LC 99052457

A collection of original scenes and monologues written especially for middle-school actors.

"A welcome find for young actors in search of material for auditions." School Library Journal.

Includes bibliographical references (p. 182-183).

Thoms, Annie

With their eyes: September 11th, the view from a high school at ground zero. edited by Annie Thoms; created by Taresh Batra ... [et al.]; photos by Ethan Moses. HarperTempest, c2002. xxv, 228 p.

Grades: 7 8 9 10   **812**

1. Stuyvesant High School (New York, N.Y.) 2. September 11 Terrorist Attacks, 2001 3. High school students 4. Victims of terrorism 5. Drama
ISBN 0060517182

LC 2002004552

The students of Stuyvesant High School, located a few blocks away from the World Trade Center, provide a dramatization of the events of September 11, 2001 from their perspectives.

"The speakers reveal their emotions with painful honesty. . . . The book is an obvious choice for reader's theater and for use across the curriculum; its deeply affecting contents will also make compelling personal-interest reading." Booklist.

812.008 American drama — Collections

Jennings, Coleman A.

Theatre for young audiences: 20 great plays for children. edited by Coleman A. Jennings; foreword by Maurice Sendak. St. Martin's Press, 1998. xvi, 604 p.

Grades: 4 5 6   **812.008**

1. Drama
ISBN 0312181949

LC 97036542

A collection of plays, many of which are based on favorite children's tales, including such titles as: "Charlotte's Web," "Really Rosie," "Wiley and the Hairy Man," "Wise Men of Chelm," and "The Crane Wife."

"Highly recommended for school and public libraries and anyone interested in a substantial collection of plays for children." Booklist.

813 American fiction in English

Boos, Ben, 1971-

Fantasy: an artist's realm. Ben Boos. Candlewick Press, 2010. 83 p.

Grades: 6 7 8 9   **813**
     1. Fantasy art 2. Elves 3. Dwarves (Fantasy characters) 4. Goblins
ISBN 9780763640569

                LC 2010007511

"This tour of New Perigord begins by presenting the fictional realm's geography, warriors, enemies, common weapons, and mages, including full details of their abilities and spells. . . . [Boos] reveals commonly encountered spirits, such as elves, undines, and banshees. . . . The large spreads are filled with authentically ancient-looking, digitally produced pictures of the many imagined inhabitants and elements, all described in densely packed, short blocks of text. . . . This offers plenty of entertainment for even those with a more casual interest in the fantasy genre." Booklist.

Crew, Hilary S., 1942-

Experiencing America's story through fiction: historical novels for grades 7-12. Hilary Susan Crew. ALA Editions, 2014. xii, 193 p.

Grades: Professional   **813**
     1. Historical fiction, American 2. Young adult fiction, American 3. Children's stories, American 4. Historical fiction, American 5. Young adult fiction, American 6. United States -- History 7. United States In literature
ISBN 9780838912256

                LC 2014008471

This annotated bibliography provides a list of historical novels that are appropriate for grades seven through twelve to help advise history teachers, public librarians, and school librarians in book selection. Each entry includes brief bibliographic information, suggested grade levels, a summary with connection to relevant themes and sample discussion questions.

"This annotated bibliography of more than 150 historical novels for grades 7 through 12 (published between 2000 and 2013) addresses issues that are found in the National Standards for History and Testing. This is an excellent resource guide for librarians, history teachers, and public librarians." Booklist

Includes bibliographical references (pages 183-185) and index.

Marcus, Leonard S.

Funny business: conversations with writers of comedy. compiled and edited by Leonard S. Marcus. Candlewick Press, 2009. 224 p.

Grades: 5 6 7 8 9 10   **813**
     1. Humorous writing 2. Influence (Literary, artistic, etc) 3. Humorists
ISBN 9780763632540

                LC 2008024231

In 13 fascinating interviews, one of the world's most respected writers about children's literature invites well-loved writers of humorous books for children to discuss an array of topics elucidating how they create books that not only stand the test of time but also make us laugh.

"In 12 entertaining interviews . . . Marcus's compilation explores the childhoods, writing processes and senses of humor of well-known writers for children, including Judy Blume, Beverly Cleary, Daniel Handler, Norton Juster and Jon Scieszka. Marcus's evident knowledge of his subjects' writing makes for some intriguing questions and answers.

. . . Photographs, manuscript pages and even e-mail chains between the writers and their editors add fascinating tidbits." Publishers Weekly.

Includes bibliographical references.

Noyes, Deborah

A **hopeful** heart: Louisa May Alcott before Little Women. by Deborah Noyes. Schwartz & Wade Books, 2020 304 p.

Grades: 7 8 9 10   **813**
     1. Alcott, Louisa May, 1832-1888. 2. 19th century 3. Women authors 19th century 4. Authors, American 19th century 5. Women
ISBN 9780525646242

                LC 2020014513

A middle-grade biography about literary icon Louisa May Alcott

"Noyes expertly places Alcott within the context of a chaotic and poverty-stricken family life and a confining and conventional Concord. . . . [R]eproductions of letters, magazine covers, and even a tintype of a Civil War drummer complement the text." Horn Book

Includes bibliographical references and index.

Richmond, Kia Jane

Mental illness in young adult literature: exploring real struggles through fictional characters. Kia Jane Richmond. Libraries Unlimited, 2019. x, 213 p.

Grades: Professional   **813**
     1. Mental illness in literature 2. Young adult fiction, American 21st century -- History and criticism.
ISBN 9781440857386

                LC 2018028307

This book explores how mental illness is portrayed in 21st-century young adult fiction and how selected works can help teachers, librarians, and mental health professionals to more effectively address the needs of students combating mental illness. Offers extensive analysis of contemporary young adult fiction featuring youth with mental illness to help school and youth services librarians make informed collection development and readers' advisory decisions.

"Richmond (English, Northern Michigan University) offers a somewhat dry but intriguing look at mental illness representation in teen literature...A good choice for professional development and academic collections, especially for those interested in YA literature or the representation of protagonists with mental illness." School Library Journal

Includes bibliographical references and index.

Riordan, Rick

Demigods and monsters: your favorite authors on Rick Riordan's Percy Jackson and the Olympians series. edited and original introduction by Rick Riordan; with Leah Wilson. Smart Pop an imprint of BenBella Books, Inc., [2013] x, 242 p.

Grades: 6 7 8 9   **813**
     1. Riordan, Rick. Percy Jackson & the Olympians 2. Children's stories, American -- History and criticism 3. Jackson, Percy (Fictitious character) 4. Fantasy fiction -- History and criticism 5. Essays
ISBN 9781937856366

                LC 2013007568

Presents a series of essays providing analysis on Rick Riordan's Percy Jackson series, including works by such authors as Jenny Han, Cameron Dokey, Paul Collins, and Ellen Steiber.

813.009 American fiction—History and criticism

Cart, Michael
Young adult literature: from romance to realism. Michael Cart. Neal-Schuman, 2016. xii, 310 p.
Grades: Professional   **813.009**
   1. Young adult fiction, American -- History and criticism 2. Young adult literature -- History and criticism 3. Teenagers -- Books and reading 4. Teenagers in literature
ISBN 9780838914625

                        LC 2016014835

Cart presents readers with a comprehensive examination of the emergent genre of young adult fiction in the English speaking world. He covers young adult fiction in the nineteen sixties and seventies, the eighties, the early nineties, and the mid to late nineties, YA as new literature for a new millennium, and many other topics.

"Cart presents an outstanding history and summary of young adult literature in this professional resource. This resource lays a strong foundation for anyone who is looking to learn more about YA literature. For that audience, as well as librarians and teachers, this book is a highly recommended resource." VOYA

Includes bibliographical references and index.

Marcus, Leonard S.
The **wand** in the word: conversations with writers of fantasy. compiled and edited by Leonard S. Marcus. Candlewick Press, 2006. 202 p.
Grades: 6 7 8 9   **813.009**
   1. Authors 2. Authors, American 20th century 3. Authors, English 20th century 4. Children's literature writing 5. Influence (Literary, artistic, etc)
ISBN 9780763626259

                        LC 2005046913

"Marcus presents interviews with 13 fantasy luminaries, including Lloyd Alexander, Susan Cooper, Nancy Farmer, Brian Jacques, Garth Nix, Tamora Pierce, and Philip Pullman. The writers' distinct personalities and career paths emerge, as do intriguing similarities. . . . Each profile includes a black-and-white author's photo, a reading list, and a bit of ephemera, often a handwritten manuscript page. . . . [This is] a rich resource that will be consulted as frequently by children's literature professionals as by genre fans themselves." Booklist.

815 American speeches in English

Bolden, Tonya
  ★ **Strong** voices: fifteen American speeches worth knowing. introductions by Tonya Bolden; foreword by Cokie Roberts; illustrated by Eric Velasquez. Harper, an imprint of HarperCollins Publishers, 2020 128 p.
Grades: 5 6 7 8   **815**
   1. Speeches, addresses, etc -- History and criticism 2. Speakers 3. Speech writing 4. Social movements 5. Civil rights 6. Anthologies
ISBN 9780062572042

Presents a collection of speeches, with historical context and insights, that have shaped the culture of the United States, including Abraham Lincoln's Gettysburg address, Lou Gehrig's "Farewell to Baseball," and Martin Luther King Jr.'s "I Have a Dream."

"A golden celebration of the multicultural voices who demand that the U.S. and the world do better." Kirkus.

818 American miscellaneous writings in English

Hargrave, John
  Sir John Hargrave's mischief maker's manual. by Sir John Hargrave. Grosset & Dunlap, 2009. 272 p.
Grades: 7 8 9 10   **818**
   1. Tricks 2. Jokes 3. Mischief 4. Practical jokes
ISBN 9780448449821

                        LC 2008034518

"Pranks include making a Screaming Cabinet (using the device from musical greeting cards), creating the World's Largest Butt Photo and faking an alien landing. What's most appealing, however, is the emphasis on being clever, creative and funny while making mischief." Publishers Weekly.

Kirk, Andrew
  Understanding Thoreau's Civil disobedience. Andrew Kirk. Rosen Pub., 2011. 128 p.: Words that changed the world
Grades: 7 8 9 10   **818**
   1. Thoreau, Henry David, 1817-1862. Civil disobedience. 2. Thoreau, Henry David, 1817-1862. Walden 3. Politics and literature 4. Literature -- History and criticism 5. Books and reading
ISBN 9781448816712

                        LC 2010010221

Provides background information on the circumstances that led to the writing of Thoreau's noteworthy work, and discusses its style and literary merit, its effectiveness at the time, and its subsquent influence.

"This considers Thoreau's Civil Disobedience, including its Context and Creator, Immediate Impact, Legacy, and Aftermath. . . . [Exploring] the historical context of transcendentalism and resistance to big government. . . . [The] author provides a balance of deep context, expressive writing, and pertinent information." School Library Journal.

Includes bibliographical references (p. 125-126) and index.

Rasmussen, R. Kent
  Mark Twain for kids: his life and times, 21 activities. R. Kent Rasmussen. Chicago Review Press, c2004. 146 p.
Grades: Professional   **818**
   1. Twain, Mark, 1835-1910 2. Authors, American 19th century
ISBN 9781556525278

                        LC 2004003529

Nineteenth-century America and the world of Samuel L. Clemens, better known as author Mark Twain, come to life as children journey back in time with this history and literature-laden activity book.

Scieszka, Jon
  ★ **True** stories. edited and with an introduction by Jon Scieszka; stories by Jim Murphy [and 10 others]; illustrations by Brian Floca. Walden Pond Press, 2014. 272 p.: Guys read
Grades: 4 5 6 7 8   **818**
   1. Essays 2. Anthologies
ISBN 9780061963827

Features ten stories (essays, biographies, travelogues and more) that are 100% amazing, 100% adventurous, 100% unbelievable and 100% true.

"Ten terrifically told true stories demonstrate the wide range of subjects and formats available for young readers of nonfiction. This fifth anthology in the Guys Read series stars some of the best-known names in informational writing today. . . . Selected, edited, and neatly introduced by Scieszka, National Ambassador for Young People's Literature emeritus, these appetite-whetting accounts are accompanied by occasional illustrations by Floca (not seen). You certainly don't have to be a guy to appreciate these morsels of fact-based storytelling and then beg for more." Booklist.

820 English & Old English literatures

Appleman, Deborah

Critical encounters in Secondary English: teaching literary theory to adolescents. Deborah Appleman. Teachers College Press, 2015 xvi, 255 p.

Grades: Professional   **820**

1. English literature -- Study and teaching (Secondary) 2. Literature -- History and criticism -- Theory, etc -- Study and teaching (Secondary) 3. American literature -- Study and teaching (Secondary) 4. Literature -- Study and teaching (Secondary) 5. Criticism
ISBN 9780807756232

LC 2014032415

The Third Edition of Critical Encounters in Secondary English provides an integrated approach to incorporating nonfiction and informational texts into the literature classroom. Provided by the publisher.

821 English poetry

Kipling, Rudyard, 1865-1936

If: a father's advice to his son. Rudyard Kipling; photographs by Charles R. Smith, Jr. Atheneum Books for Young Readers, [2007] 1 v. (unpaged)

Grades: 4 5 6   **821**

1. Fathers and sons 2. Advice
ISBN 9780689877995

LC 2006005312

An illustrated version of one of Kipling's famous poems about a father's advice to his son.

"Kipling's powerful poem comes to life for a contemporary audience in atmospheric photographs that use the metaphor of sports. A lovely shot of a boy heading a soccer ball accompanies the opening couplet: If you can keep your head/when all about you/are losing theirs/and blaming it on you. The mood and actions in most of the illustrations clearly invoke the verse." School Library Journal.

Myers, Christopher

Jabberwocky. [Lewis Carroll]; reimagined and illustrated by Chistopher Myers. Jump at the Sun/Hyperion Books for Children, 2007. 32 p.

Grades: 4 5 6 7   **821**

1. Basketball players 2. Basketball 3. Sports 4. Nonsense verses 5. Stories in rhyme
ISBN 9781423103721

LC 2007018337

"Myers cleverly translates Carroll's nonsense poem into a contemporary tale through sports imagery. . . . The spectacular paintings have silhouetted figures on vibrant backgrounds. . . . The jaunty text is in capital letters in an extra-large black font, with some words highlighted in color." School Library Journal.

Pockell, Leslie

100 great poems for boys. [edited by] Leslie Pockell. Grand Central Pub., 2011. xvi, 234 p.

Grades: 6 7 8 9   **821**

1. Boys
ISBN 9780446563826

LC 2010036490

In the spirit of the Dangerous Book for Boys, here are 100 essential poems for boys of all ages. Provided by publisher.

"This compilation of poems aimed at male readers provides an accessible footpath into the canon, with works from Emerson, Poe, Kipling, Dickinson, and Lear. Pockell provides insightful introductions to each topically organized section, which include Battlefields and Heroes, the more open-ended Things to Think About, . . . and several humor-focused categories, such as limericks and tongue-twisters." Publishers Weekly.

Williams, Marcia, 1945-

Chaucer's Canterbury Tales. retold and illustrated by Marcia Williams. Candlewick Press, 2006. 48 p.

Grades: 4 5 6 7   **821**

1. Medieval period (476-1492) 2. 14th century 3. Pilgrims and pilgrimages, Christian 4. Civilization, Medieval 5. England -- History -- Medieval period, 1066-1485 6. Historical comics 7. Comics and Graphic novels
ISBN 0763631973

LC 2006040619

A retelling in comic strip form of Geoffrey Chaucer's famous work in which a group of pilgrims in fourteenth-century England tell each other stories as they travel on a pilgrimage to the cathedral at Canterbury.

"Chaucer's pilgrims come to life in the energetic retelling of nine tales. . . . The watercolor-and-ink cartoon-art displayed in a comic-book format is a perfect match for the raucous and sometimes-raw humor." School Library Journal.

821.008 English poetry—Collections

Janeczko, Paul B.

★ **A foot** in the mouth: poems to speak, sing, and shout. [selected by] Paul B. Janeczko; [illustrated by] Chris Raschka. Candlewick Press, 2009. 61 p.

Grades: 4 5 6 7   **821.008**

1. Reading aloud 2. Tongue twisters 3. Bilingual materials English/Spanish.
ISBN 9780763606633

LC 2008935581

Provides middle readers with a colorful collection of playful rhymes, challenging tongue twisters, bilingual poems, and read-aloud verse.

"The poems in Janeczko and Raschka's collection . . . are not complacent, although plenty are funny and some are familiar. . . . Punchy collages flutter across airy white pages in loose visual arrangements; torn scraps of origami paper layer with fluid lines in tart color. Janeczko introduces the collection with the idea that Poetry is sound, a pleasure to vocalize and memorize. . . . Readers will be emboldened to join in the song." Publishers Weekly.

Muth, Jon J.

★ **Poems** to learn by heart. [selected by] Caroline Kennedy; paintings by Jon J Muth. Disney Hyperion Books, 2012. 191 p.

Grades: 2 3 4 5 6 7 8   **821.008**

1. Poetry and children 2. Poetry -- Memorizing 3. Memory 4. Memory in children
ISBN 9781423108054

LC 2011022651

Features one hundred readily memorizable poems that convey a wide range of feelings, meanings, and wisdom, in a volume complemented by watercolor illustrations.

Rosen, Michael

Classic poetry: an illustrated collection. selected by Michael Rosen; pictures by Paul Howard. Candlewick Press, 1998. 159 p.

Grades: 7 8 9 10 **821.008**

ISBN 9781564028907

LC 98018282

A collection of favorite poems by such writers as William Shakespeare, Emily Dickinson, Edward Lear, Walt Whitman, and Langston Hughes, with portraits of the poets, brief biographical background, and illustrations.

"This handsome edition introduces major poets through works accessible to young people. Each section begins with a portrait of the author and a short summary of his or her life, followed by one or two poems or parts of poems. Each spread includes at least one illustration evocative of the tone of the poetry as well as the times of the poet. . . . Illustrator Paul Howard's gifts are not diminished by the smaller size of some pictures, for some of his best work here is in miniature. . . . Few anthologies for this age group include such a fine selection of works from beyond the childhood classics, introduce the poets so vividly, or provide such a rich collection of haunting illustrations." Booklist.

822.3 Drama of Elizabethan period, 1558-1625

Krueger, Susan Heidi

The **tempest**. by Susan Heidi Krueger. Marshall Cavendish Benchmark, 2009. 127 p. : Shakespeare explained

Grades: 7 8 9 10 11 12 **822.3**

1. Shakespeare, William, 1564-1616. Tempest 2. Authors, English Early modern, 1500-1700 3. Literature and history 4. Drama 5. Drama -- History and criticism 6. Theater -- History 7. England -- Social life and customs -- 16th century. 8. Great Britain -- Social life and customs -- 16th century.

ISBN 9780761434238

LC 2009002587

A literary analysis of the play The Tempest. Includes information on the history and culture of Elizabethan England. Provided by publisher.

"This book offers an engaging [introduction] to the Bard's work. . . . Krueger's lively, opinionated, and knowledgeable analysis of the complex play . . . will easily draw students into further discussion." Booklist.

Includes bibliographical references and index.

Packer, Tina, 1938-

Tales from Shakespeare. retold by Tina Packer; illustrated by Gail de Marcken ... [et al.]. Scholastic Press, c2004. 192 p.

Grades: 5 6 7 8 **822.3**

1. Macbeth, King of Scotland, active 11th century 2. Hamlet (Legendary character) 3. Tragedy 4. Drama

ISBN 0439321077

LC 2003042710

A collection of prose retellings of ten familiar Shakespeare plays, each illustrated by a well-known artist or artists.

"This is a treasure trove of well-told tales. In these adaptations, Packer captures the essence of the playwright's words and ideas, placing them in concise and clearly told stories. . . . Each illustrator sets the appropriate tone for and conveys the mood of the tale, and the breadth of

artistic interpretations gives the book appeal to a wide audience." School Library Journal.

Sobran, Joseph

A **midsummer** night's dream. by Joseph Sobran. Marshall Cavendish Benchmark, 2008. 111p.: Shakespeare explained

Grades: 7 8 9 10 11 12 **822.3**

1. Shakespeare, William, 1564-1616. Midsummer night's dream 2. Authors, English Early modern, 1500-1700 3. Literature and history 4. Drama 5. Drama -- History and criticism 6. Theater -- History 7. England -- Social life and customs -- 16th century. 8. Great Britain -- Social life and customs -- 16th century.

ISBN 9780761430308

LC 2008007079

A literary analysis of the play A Midsummer Night's Dream. Includes information on the history and culture of Elizabethan England.. Provided by publisher.

"[This book] provides practical information, skillfully presented, making the complexities of Shakespearean theater accessible to present-day students. [The] author's contagious enthusiasm and attractive presentation make [it] imminently useful for high school and public libraries." Voice of Youth Advocates.

Includes bibliographical references and index.

823 English fiction

Gribbin, Mary

The **science** of Philip Pullman's His dark materials. Mary and John Gribbin; with an introduction by Philip Pullman. Knopf, [2005]. xix, 203 p.

Grades: 6 7 8 9 **823**

1. Pullman, Philip, 1946- His dark materials. 2. Pullman, Philip, 1946- 3. Subconsciousness 4. Options, alternatives, choices 5. Cosmology 6. Quantum theory 7. Life

ISBN 0375831444

LC 2004057731

"The Gribbins show how concepts are the real magic of Pullman's trilogy. Each chapter begins with a quote drawn from the books, which leads to an elegantly written explanation of the science. . . . The authors do an amazing job teasing an introduction to string theory from Will's subtle knife. . . . Naturally, fans of the series will be the best audience, but the book offers much to readers simply interested in the advanced sciences, who then may be led back to His Dark Materials." Booklist.

Includes bibliographical references (p. 187-188) and index.

Hirschmann, Kris, 1967-

Frankenstein. Kris Hirschmann. ReferencePoint Press, c2012. 80 p.: Monsters and mythical creatures

Grades: 6 7 8 9 **823**

1. Shelley, Mary Wollstonecraft, 1797-1851. Frankenstein 2. Frankenstein's monster (Fictitious character) 3. Monsters in literature 4. Monsters

ISBN 9781601521804

LC 2011002145

Describes the history of legends regarding Frankenstein's monster, from its creation in Mary Shelley's famous novel to its significance in film and popular culture.

"This is an ideal starting point for young researchers interested in the weird, mysterious, and paranormal. Using fleet, descriptive prose to communicate the impressively researched (and sourced) information, [this] medium-length [work manages] to rope in just about everything, from folklore to history to pop culture. The bulk of Frankenstein focuses upon Mary Shelley's masterpiece, not just the infamous contest for which it was written but also the reception and critical analysis, both then and now. . . . The illustrations are fine and varied, the sidebars always illuminating, and the back matter robust." Booklist.

Includes bibliographical references (p. 69-73) and index.

Jones, Diana Wynne

Reflections: on the magic of writing. Diana Wynne Jones. Greenwillow Books, 2012. xxx, 368 p.

Grades: 7 8 9 10 11 12   **823**

1. Jones, Diana Wynne 2. Children's literature writing 3. Fantasy fiction writing 4. Essays
ISBN 9780062219893

LC 2012018080

Presents a collection of essays, speeches, and biographical pieces that offer literary criticism and anecdotes about reading tours, the origins of the author's books, and thoughts in general about the life of an author and the value of writing.

860.9 Spanish literature—History and criticism

Luebering, J. E.

The **literature** of Spain and Latin America. edited by J.E. Luebering. Britannica Educational Pub. in association with Rosen Educational Services, 2011. 317 p.: Britannica guide to world literature

Grades: 8 9 10 11 12   **860.9**

1. Spanish literature -- History and criticism 2. Spanish-American literature -- History and criticism
ISBN 9781615301058

LC 2009045098

Provides an understanding of the events and cultural differences shaping these nations' texts, the lives of their writers, and the impact of Spanish and Latin American literature.

883 Classical Greek epic poetry and fiction

Homer

The **Iliad**. Homer; translated by Robert Fagles; introduction and notes by Bernard Knox. Viking, 1990. xvi, 683 p.

Grades: 8 9 10 11 12 Adult   **883**

1. Achilles (Greek mythology) 2. Trojan War 3. Classics 4. Epic poetry 5. Translations Greek to English 6. Mythology
ISBN 0670835102

LC 89070695

The centuries-old epic about the wrath of Achilles is rendered into modern English verse by a renowned translator.

"Fagles offers a new verse rendering of the Iliad. Maneuvering between the literal and the literary, he tries with varying degrees of success to suggest the vigor and manner of the original while producing readable poetry in English." Library Journal.

Includes bibliographical references (p. 635-637).

The **Odyssey**. Homer; translated by Robert Fagles; introduction and notes by Bernard Knox. Viking, c1996. x, 541 p.

Grades: 8 9 10 11 12 Adult   **883**

1. Ancient Aegean civilizations (3000-1000 BCE) 2. Heroes and heroines, Greek 3. Adventurers 4. Voyages and travels 5.

Odysseus (Greek mythology) 6. Gods and goddesses, Greek 7. Troy (Extinct city) 8. Ancient Greece 9. Epic poetry 10. Classics
ISBN 0670821624

LC 96017280

A new verse translation of the Greek classic describes the wanderings of Odysseus after the fall of Troy.

"Fagles' Odyssey is the one to put into the hands of younger, first-time readers, not least because of its paucity of notes, which, though sometimes frustrating, is a sign that translation has been used to do the work of explanation. Altogether, an outstanding piece of work." Booklist.

Includes bibliographical references.

Landmann, Bimba

★ The **fate** of Achilles. Bimba Landmann. J Paul Getty Museum, 2011. 32 p.

Grades: 4 5 6 7   **883**

1. Homer. Iliad 2. Trojan War 3. Friends' death 4. Heroes and heroines 5. Gods and goddesses, Greek 6. Achilles (Greek mythology) 7. Mythology
ISBN 9781606060858

"Landmann (The Incredible Voyage of Ulysses) continues her retelling of Homer's epics with this haunting version of the Iliad. Ghostly, Giacometti-style figures accompany the story of Achilles's life, from his baptism in the river Styx . . . to his departure for Troy, . . . the death of his dearest friend, . . . and his reconciliation with the father of the enemy he has slain. . . . Readers with the patience to sit through saga-length narratives will be fascinated by her prose, which moves easily through the sprawling epic without feeling ponderous or hurried. These kinds of retellings are few and far between, and [Landmann's] are magic." Publishers Weekly.

Lister, Robin

The **odyssey**. retold by Robin Lister; illustrated by Alan Baker. Kingfisher, 2004. 175 p.: Kingfisher epics

Grades: 5 6 7 8   **883**

1. Odysseus (Greek mythology) 2. Mythology
ISBN 0753457237

LC 2004304514

A retelling of Homer's epic that describes the wanderings of Odysseus after the fall of Troy.

895.1 Chinese literature

Liu, Siyu, 1964-

A **thousand** peaks: poems from China. by Siyu Liu and Orel Protopopescu; illustrated by Siyu Liu. Pacific View Press, c2002. 52 p.

Grades: 5 6 7 8 9 10   **895.1**

1. Translations Chinese to English
ISBN 1881896242

LC 2001034008

A collection of thirty-five poems spanning nineteen centuries, representing both famous and lesser-known poets, including both the Chinese text and a literal translation.

"This is an anthology of considerable fascination and broad utility. . . . The layout is neat, tidily fitting each poem's material on a single page and adding a line drawing featuring a relevant Chinese character. The wealth of material here provides a more stimulating entrée to

Chinese history than any dry textbook." Bulletin of the Center for Children's Books.

Includes bibliographical references (p. 51) and index.

900 HISTORY & GEOGRAPHY

901 Philosophy and theory of history

Beller, Susan Provost, 1949-

The **history** puzzle: how we know what we know about the past. Susan Provost Beller. Twenty-First Century Books, c2006. 128 p.

Grades: 7 8 9 10   **901**
   1. History -- Methodology
   ISBN 0761328777

                 LC 2005017745

Learn about the detective work that historians use to better understand our past, including the mysteries of the Stone Age, Herculaneum and Pompeii, Noah's Ark, the Great Wall of China, the legend of King Arthur, and more.

"Beller looks at more than 20 historical sites or archaeological excavations . . . in order to present the varying interpretations of history and how they have been colored by tradition, socioeconomic factors, and religious beliefs. . . . Frequent, well-placed sepia-toned photographs and period reproductions serve to enhance the text, and the source notes, further reading, and list of [websites] give students an ample list of resources for further study." School Library Journal.

Includes bibliographical references (p. 119-125) and index.

902 Miscellany of history

Hughes, Susan, 1960-

Case closed?: nine mysteries unlocked by modern science. written by Susan Hughes; illustrated by Michael Wandelmaier. Kids Can Press, 2010. 88 p.

Grades: 6 7 8 9   **902**
   1. History 2. Curiosities and wonders 3. Technological innovations
   ISBN 9781554533626

                 LC oc2010023275

Nine mysteries from the past are explained using modern science.

"The writing is clear and engaging. The full-color illustrations are a mix of photographs, maps, and flat, animation-style art." School Library Journal.

903 Dictionaries, encyclopedias, concordances of history

Znamierowski, Alfred

The **world** encyclopedia of flags: an illustrated guide to international flags, banners, standards and ensigns. Alfred Znamierowski. Lorenz Books, 2019. 256 p.

Grades: 5 6 7 8 9 10 11 12 Adult   **903**
   1. Flags
   ISBN 9780754834809

A comprehensive reference to flags including a fascinating history, with over 1400 illustrations and newly updated in a special large-format edition.

907.1 History — Education

Kirchner, Jana

Inquiry-based lessons in world history,Grades 7-10. Jana Kirchner, Ph.D., & Andrew McMichael, Ph.D. Prufrock Press, 2019 200 p.

Grades: Professional   **907.1**
   1. History -- Study and teaching (Secondary)
   ISBN 9781618218599

Spanning the time period from 15,000 BCE to 1500 CE, Inquiry-Based Lessons in World History (Vol. 1) focuses on creating global connections between people and places using primary sources in standards-based lessons. With sections on early humans, the ancient world, classical antiquity, and the world in transition, this book provides teachers with inquiry-based, ready-to-use lessons that can be adapted to any classroom and that encourage students to take part in the learning process by reading and thinking like historians.

909 World history

Adams, Simon, 1955-

★ The **Kingfisher** atlas of world history: a stunning visual journey through human history from ancient times to the present day. Simon Adams. Kingfisher, 2016. 181 p.

Grades: 4 5 6 7   **909**
   1. Historical geography 2. History
   ISBN 9780753472941

                 LC bl2015057350

Combines information from four previously published atlases into one volume, covering the history of human civilization from the ancient world to the modern era and examining religion, exploration, war, colonization, kingdoms, and technology.

"This colorful and fact-packed book is not only informative but well organized. Sections cover The Ancient World, The Medieval World, Exploration and Empire, and The Modern World, and each section contains 15 or 16 thematic maps presented in chronological order. . . . It is very useful and entertaining as well as data-filled." Booklist.

Badcott, Nicholas

Pocket timeline of Islamic civilizations. Nicholas Badcott. Interlink Books, 2009. 32 p.

Grades: 7 8 9 10 11 12   **909**
   1. Islamic civilization 2. Islamic countries -- Civilization 3. Islamic countries -- History
   ISBN 9781566567589

                 LC bl2010017703

Describes the ancient Islamic civilizations and their impact on world history and culture, including the Mughals, the Ottomans, and early Islamic Spain.

Hinds, Kathryn, 1962-

The **city**. by Kathryn Hinds. Marshall Cavendish Benchmark, 2008. 96 p. : Life in the medieval Muslim world

Grades: 6 7 8 9 10   **909**
   1. Cities and towns 2. Civilization, Medieval 3. City life 4. Muslims 5. Islamic countries 6. Islamic countries -- Social life and customs
   ISBN 9780761430896

                 LC 2008019432

A social history of the Islamic world from the eighth through the mid-thirteenth century, with a focus on life in the cities. Provided by publisher.

The **countryside**. by Kathryn Hinds. Marshall Cavendish Benchmark, 2008. 95 p. : Life in the medieval Muslim world

Grades: 6 7 8 9 10   **909**
   1. Deserts -- Social life and customs 2. Rural life 3. Civilization, Medieval 4. Muslims 5. Islamic countries
   ISBN 9780761430919

                 LC 2008019266

A social history of the Islamic world from the eighth through the mid-thirteenth century, with a focus on life in the desert and countryside. Provided by publisher.

The **palace**. by Kathryn Hinds. Marshall Cavendish Benchmark, 2009. 96 p.

Grades: 6 7 8 9 10   **909**
   1. Palaces 2. Elite (Social sciences) 3. Upper class 4. Power (Social sciences) 5. Islamic Empire -- History -- 750-1258.
   ISBN 9780761430889

                 LC 2008010734

A social history of the Islamic world from the eighth through the mid-thirteenth century, with a focus on life in the upper echelons of society. Provided by publisher.

"Richly illustrated with art reproductions, maps, photos, and ornate Islamic border designs, [this] . . . will entice visual learners." Library Media Connection.

Includes bibliographical references and index.

Huff, Toby E., 1942-

An **age** of science and revolutions, 1600-1800. Toby Huff. Oxford University Press, c2005. 173 p.: Medieval and early modern world

Grades: 7 8 9 10   **909**
   1. 17th century 2. 18th century 3. Medieval science 4. Europe -- Civilization -- 17th century 5. Europe -- Civilization -- 18th century
   ISBN 019517724X

                 LC 2004021612

Presents an overview of the seventeenth and eighteenth centuries in Europe, during which the Scientific Revolution arose, trade prospered across Europe, and political revolutions were rampant.

"This volume looks at 200 years of world history. . . . [It includes] overview chapters on China, India, and the Middle East . . . [and] discusses the Enlightenment in Europe in some depth. . . . [This is a] useful book, which may spark discussion about current controversies about connections between science and religion." Booklist.

Includes bibliographical references and index.

Hussain, Saima S.

The **Arab** world thought of it: inventions, innovations, and amazing facts. Saima S. Hussain. Annick Press, c2013. 48 p.

Grades: 6 7 8   **909**
   1. Civilization, Arabic 2. Inventions 3. Scientific discoveries 4. Curiosities and wonders
   ISBN 1554514762

Shows how peoples from the Arab world have made many significant contributions to the fields of medicine, architecture, astronomy, and more.

Lace, William W.

The **Indian** Ocean tsunami of 2004. William W. Lace. Chelsea House Publishers, c2008. 127 p.: Great historic disasters

Grades: 7 8 9 10   **909**
   1. Indian Ocean Tsunami, 2004 2. Earthquakes 3. Tsunamis 4. Disaster victims 5. Rescue work 6. Indian Ocean
   ISBN 9780791096420

                 LC 2007036950

Describes the events the occurred during the tsunami in the Indian Ocean in 2004, from the disaster itself and the damage that was caused to the rescue efforts of the international community.

"The author explains in detail the seismic activities that caused the 2004 Indian Ocean tsunami, as well as the lack of systems in place to quickly notify those in danger. Also included are many well-captioned photos . . . and short but interesting personal stories of both survivors and victims." Horn Book Guide.

Includes bibliographical references (p. 107-121) and index.

Moore, Christopher, 1950-

From then to now: a short history of the world. Christopher Moore; illustrated by Andrej Krystoforski. Tundra Books, c2011. 188 p.

Grades: 7 8 9 10   **909**
   1. Civilization -- History 2. Human settlements -- History
   ISBN 9780887765407

Governor General's Literary Award for English-Language Children's Literature, 2011.

Traces human civilization from early bands of hunter-gatherers to the multicultural world cities of the present, covering the development of agriculture, empires, law, and the major religions, the rise of Europe, colonies, and industrialization.

"Capably told and uniquely illustrated, From Then to Now explains how imaginative human cultures have produced an intellectually and socially dynamic world. The work follows the course of human history from hunter-gatherer beginnings, through expansion and contact, to a modern, tightly interconnected global world. Along the way, Moore tackles how humanity, through agricultural and industrial innovations, has shaped and been shaped by environmental obstacles. Full-color spot art appears occasionally, and color sidebars provide information on a number of subjects. . . . This exceptional history of humanity is a breath of fresh air." School Library Journal.

909.07 General historical periods

Currie, Stephen, 1960-

Medieval crusades. Stephen Currie. Lucent Books, 2009. 96 p.: World history series

Grades: 6 7 8 9   **909.07**
   1. Civilization, Medieval 2. Crusades -- History 3. War -- Religious aspects 4. Military history
   ISBN 9781420500622

Surveys the origins and events of the series of wars called crusades that lasted from 1095 to 1291.

"Each slim volume in this series covers an historical event or period from various cultures and eras... The description of this era is balanced and fair... According to the author, the Crusades' most significant impact was the creation of fear and distrust between Christians and Muslims, a legacy that continues today. The writing style of both books is clear, concise, and consistent. " VOYA.

Hinds, Kathryn, 1962-

Everyday life in medieval Europe. by Kathryn Hinds. Marshall Cavendish Benchmark, 2009. 285 p. : Everyday life (Marshall Cavendish Benchmark)

Grades: 6 7 8 9   **909.07**

   1. Civilization, Medieval 2. Culture 3. Everyday life 4. Social classes 5. History 6. Europe -- History -- 476-1492 7. Europe -- Social life and customs

ISBN 9780761439271

LC 2008012748

Describes the social and economic structure of life in the High Middle Ages (1100-1400), including the ruling classes, the peasantry, the urban dwellers, and members of the Church and the role each group played in shaping European civilization. Provided by publisher.

"Fluid, approachable, beautifully illustrated, and fascinatingly detailed." Booklist.

Includes bibliographical references and index.

Knight, Judson

Middle ages. Primary Sources. Judson Knight; edited by Judy Galens. UXL, c2001. xxxiv, 161 p.

Grades: 6 7 8 9 10   **909.07**

   1. Middle Ages

ISBN 9780787648602

LC 00059441

Presents nineteen documents written during the Middle Ages, including excerpts from Augustine's "Confessions," Dante's "Inferno," and Marco Polo's travel writings, and includes background information to place each document in context.

Langley, Andrew, 1949-

Medieval life. written by Andrew Langley; photographed by Geoff Brightling & Geoff Dann. DK Publishing, 2004. 72 p.: Eyewitness books

Grades: 4 5 6 7   **909.07**

   1. Civilization, Medieval 2. Europe -- History -- 476-1492

ISBN 0756607043

LC 2004302372

An illustrated look at various aspects of life in medieval Europe, covering everyday life, religion, royalty, and more.

Park, Louise, 1961-

The **medieval** knights. by Louise Park and Timothy Love. Marshall Cavendish Benchmark, 2009. 32 p. : Ancient and medieval people

Grades: 4 5 6   **909.07**

   1. Knights and knighthood 2. Civilization, Medieval 3. Warriors 4. Europe -- History -- 476-1492.

ISBN 9780761444442

LC 2008055777

An introduction to the history and lifestyle of medieval knights. Provided by publisher.

"This title has a simple and elegant design with the proper balance of quality writing and quantity of information. . . . Handy time lines, well-chosen photos of ruins and artifacts, quality illustrations, inset Quick Facts, and What You Should Know About features will grab reluctant readers and captivate even those with short attention spans." School Library Journal.

909.8 World history—1800

Winkler, Allan M., 1945-

The **Cold** War: a history in documents. Allan M. Winkler. Oxford University Press, c2011. ix, 160 p.

Grades: 8 9 10 11 12   **909.8**

   1. Cold War 2. Historic documents 3. World politics 1945-1990. 4. United States -- Foreign relations -- Russia 5. Russia -- Foreign relations -- United States

ISBN 9780199765997

LC 2010049111

The second edition of The Cold War: A History in Documents offers more thorough coverage of the 1970s through the 1990s.. The book features additional material on China and Africa, and several new images. There is also a revised note on sources and interpretation and updates to the lists of further reading and websites.

909.82 World history—20th century, 1900-1999

Aronson, Marc

1968: today's authors explore a year of rebellion, revolution, and change. edited by Marc Aronson and Susan Campbell Bartoletti. Candlewick Press, 2018. 208 p.

Grades: 7 8 9 10 11 12   **909.82**

   1. 1960s 2. Social advocacy 3. Culture conflict 4. Authors 5. Political violence 6. Social movements 7. United States -- History -- 1961-1969 8. Anthologies 9. Essays

ISBN 9780763689933

Essays, memoirs and other contributions by 14 award-winning authors share unique perspectives about the tumultuous changes that shaped 1968, exploring such events as the assassinations of Dr. Martin Luther King Jr. and Robert Kennedy, the mass protests all over the world and the ways the movement is being renewed in today's world.

Grant, R. G.

The **Cold** War. R. G. Grant. Arcturus Pub, c2010. 46 p.: Secret history

Grades: 4 5 6   **909.82**

   1. 20th century 2. Cold War 3. World politics 4. International relations

ISBN 9781848376960

LC 2010011765

This high-interest series, aimed at reluctant readers, looks at secret campaigns behind the major conflicts of the past 100 years. Biographical sidebars focus on heroic or notorious personalities. Highlighted fact features include special operations and their results, resistance movements, propaganda and the history of the time—as is known....and not readily known. Provided by publisher.

"The title of the Secret History series will grab readers, even reluctant ones, and they won't be disappointed by the intriguing info regarding codes and code breakers, spies, terrorists, and double agents, with profiles of heroes and traitors on all sides. . . . The readable design, with clear type on thick, high-quality paper, includes lots of sidebars, photos, screens, and quotes." Booklist.

Includes bibliographical references (p. 45) and index.

Harrison, Paul, 1969-

Why did the Cold War happen? Paul Harrison. Gareth Stevens Pub., 2011. 48 p.: Moments in history

Grades: 6 7 8 9　　　**909.82**
1. 20th century 2. Cold War 3. World politics 1945-1990
ISBN 9781433941665

LC 2010012456

Uses primary sources to document the causes behind the Cold War.

"Examines the events that served as . . . [precursors to the Cold War]. . . . Brightly colored pullout boxes highlight important turning points, the perspective of the everyday man, and further information on why specific events occurred. Numerous photographs help readers visualize concepts more fully. . . . Students should be able to easily use this resource." Library Media Connection.

Includes bibliographical references (p. 47) and index.

Kaufman, Michael T.

1968. Michael T. Kaufman. Roaring Brook Press, 2008. 160 p.

Grades: 7 8 9 10 11 12　　　**909.82**
1. King, Martin Luther, Jr., 1929-1968 2. Kennedy, Robert Francis, 1925-1968 3. Democratic Party. National Convention, Chicago, Illinois, 1968. 4. 1960s 5. Student movements -- History 20th century. 6. Protest movements 7. Modern history 1945-1989 8. Radicalism -- History 20th century. 9. Insurgency -- History 20th century.
ISBN 9781596434288

LC 2008015471

Provides a look at the major historical events that took place during this year and the impact they had on the country and the world overall, including Dr. Martin Luther King, Jr.'s assassination and man's first steps in space.

"Kaufman expertly draws young readers into the worldwide events of a single, watershed year: 1968. . . . Each chapter focuses on a different hot spot around the globe, beginning with the Tet Offensive and the Vietnam War and moving through uprisings in New York, Paris, Prague, Chicago, and Mexico City, as well as the assassinations of Martin Luther King Jr. and Robert F. Kennedy. . . . The images, drawn from the [New York] Times archives, are riveting and will easily draw young people into the fascinating, often horrifying events." Booklist.

Includes bibliographical references and index.

910 Geography and travel

Belmont, Helen

Looking at aerial photographs. Helen Belmont. Smart Apple Media, c2008. 46 p.: Geography skills

Grades: 6 7 8 9　　　**910**
1. Aerial photography 2. Geography 3. Photography
ISBN 9781599200484

LC 2006036139

Describes how aerial photography is used to help identify geographic features such as deltas, villages, and landforms.

"The text is easy to follow. . . . The examples given in the text that involve places are almost always accompanied by excellent photographs. . . . Maps, block diagrams, tables, and graphs are clearly presented and easy to interpret." Science Books & Films.

Includes bibliographical references (p. 45) and index.

Jennings, Ken, 1974-

Maps and geography. by Ken Jennings; illustrated by TK. LITTLE SIMON, an imprint of Simon & Schuster Children's Pub. Division, 2014. 160 p.: Ken Jennings' junior genius guides

Grades: 3 4 5 6　　　**910**
1. Geography 2. Maps 3. Cartography
ISBN 9781442473287

LC 2012050862

"The new line of Junior Genius Guide books kicks off with a stellar collection of facts about climate, national flags, maps, and more, all in an engaging, arch tone. Jeopardy! champ and author Jennings, making his first foray into books for children, arranges the trivia in chapters that lightly satirize a school-day schedule, including a lunch period offering an ingenious and easy recipe for an edible map, a craft project in art class, and an official certification exam before the dismissal bell... Lowery's black-and-white spot illustrations help explain concepts, such as cartographic projections, and add the overall levity, making this a successful nonfiction package as well as pure reading fun. Published simultaneously with the second in the series, Greek Mythology." Booklist.

Includes bibliographical references and index.

Kerley, Barbara

★ The **world** is waiting for you. by Barbara Kerley. National Geographic, c2013. 48 p.

Grades: 1 2 3 4 5 6　　　**910**
1. Discoveries in geography 2. Children 3. Adventurers
ISBN 9781426311147

LC 2012026526

A guidebook for young children who are unsure about what they want to be when they grow up combines evocative photographs with simple text that explains how to connect favorite interests to future careers, in a volume complemented by inspirational quotes by famous achievers.

Kirkpatrick, Katherine

Snow baby: the Arctic childhood of Admiral Robert E. Peary's daring daughter. Katherine Kirkpatrick. Holiday House, c2007. 50 p.

Grades: 5 6 7 8　　　**910**
1. Peary, Marie Ahnighito, 1893-1978 2. Peary, Robert E. (Robert Edwin), 1856-1920 3. Children 4. Explorers -- Family relationships 5. Arctic regions 6. Washington, DC
ISBN 0823419738

LC 2006002016

Profiles the life of the woman who, as a child, often accompanied her famous explorer father, Robert Peary, on many of his expeditions.

"Born north of the Arctic Circle in 1893, Marie Ahnighito Peary published her own version of her youth in 1934 (The Snowbaby's Own Story), on which this book is based. Kirkpatrick's engaging text captures the girl's adventurous spirit and the opportunities that her father's life as an explorer presented, as well as her love of the North and her Inuit friends." School Library Journal.

Includes bibliographical references (p. 48-49) and index.

Marschall, Ken

Inside the Titanic. illustrated by Ken Marschall; text by Hugh Brewster. Little, Brown, 1997. 32 p.

Grades: 4 5 6 7　　　**910**
1. Titanic (Steamship). 2. Shipwrecks 3. Books for reluctant readers
ISBN 0316557161

LC 97000382

Text and cut-away illustrations feature the stories of real-life children who sailed aboard the Titanic on the night of its disaster in the North Atlantic.

"Color cutaway paintings of the Titanic in this oversize book allow readers to view every deck as they follow two 12-year-old boys exploring the vessel, and to see how the liner struck the iceberg and sank." Booklist.

Philbrick, Nathaniel

Revenge of the whale: the true story of the whaleship Essex. Nathaniel Philbrick. G.P. Putnam, 2002. x, 164 p.

Grades: 7 8 9 10   **910**
1. Essex (Whaler) 2. 19th century 3. Shipwrecks 4. Whaling 5. Sperm whale 6. Ships 7. Whales 8. Nantucket, Massachusetts 9. South Pacific Ocean -- History.
ISBN 039923795X

LC 2002000667

Recounts the 1820 sinking of the whaleship "Essex" by an enraged sperm whale and how the crew of young men survived against impossible odds. Adapted from the author's adult book "In the Heart of the Sea."

"The story of the Essex crew is a compelling saga of desperation and survival that will appeal to young people. The grisly details of cannibalism necessary to the telling of the story may provoke shivers but should not give anyone nightmares." School Library Journal.

Includes bibliographical references (p. [161]).

Revkin, Andrew

The **North** Pole was here: puzzles and perils at the top of the world. Andrew C. Revkin. Kingfisher, 2006. 128 p.

Grades: 7 8 9 10   **910**
1. Revkin, Andrew North Pole 2. Revkin, Andrew Arctic regions 3. North Pole expeditions 4. Global warming 5. Arctic regions -- Description and travel
ISBN 0753459930

LC 2005024307

An environmental reporter recounts his expedition to the North Pole where he followed oceanographers as they drilled through nine feet of ice to dive into the frigid waters and delved into the mysteries of climate modeling and global warming, revealing how the fate of the pole will impact our world.

"The author relates his journey to the top of the world in the company of scientists studying climate changes. The informative chapters weave together accounts of his experiences and observations with details about the environment, its exploration, and scientific concepts. . . . The illustrations include full-color photographs of the author's trek, archival reproductions and photos of previous excursions, original diagrams that clarify concepts, and maps. . . . The wonderfully written narrative will pull youngsters into the book and hold them there willingly until the last page." School Library Journal.

Includes bibliographical references (p. 117-119) and index.

910.4 Accounts of travel and facilities for travelers

Bergreen, Laurence

Magellan: over the edge of the world. Laurence Bergreen. Roaring Brook Press, 2017. 144 p.

Grades: 7 8 9   **910.4**
1. Magellan, Ferdinand, 1480?-1521. 2. 16th century 3. Renaissance (1300-1600) 4. Trips around the world 5. Explorers 6. Exploration 7. Expeditions 8. Ocean travel
ISBN 9781626721203

LC 2015035814

A middle grade adaptation of Bergreen's adult title of the same name, about Magellan's historic voyage around the globe. Provided by publisher.

"Bergreen ably adapts his book for adults Over the Edge of the World: Magellan's Terrifying Circumnavigation of the Globe (2003) into a gripping and harrowing true adventure story for young readers." Kirkus.

Bristow, David (David L.)

★ The **sky** sailors: true stories of the balloon era. David L. Bristow. Farrar Straus Giroux, 2010. 134 p.

Grades: 4 5 6 7   **910.4**
1. Balloonists -- History 2. Ballooning 3. Balloons (Aeronautics) -- History 4. Airships -- History
ISBN 9780374370145

LC 2009037285

An introduction to the history of ballooning introduces the pioneers of human flight and their contraptions which were used to cross large bodies of water, sail over enemy armies, and fly into storms, from 1783 until the early twentieth century.

"This lively look at escapades of daring men—and a surprising number of women—who risked their lives flying in balloons will appeal to adventure, history and science buffs—and perhaps steampunk fans as well. Each of the nine chapters, which are chronologically arranged, focuses on an exciting story, starting with the first confirmed human balloon flight in 1783 . . . and ending with Dolly Shepherd, a young British woman in the early 1900s who parachuted out of balloons, hanging onto a trapeze. . . . Useful captions accompany many full-color illustrations of artwork and photographs." Kirkus.

Includes bibliographical references (p. 125-134).

Clifford, Barry

Real pirates: the untold story of the Whydah from slave ship to pirate ship. by Barry Clifford and Kenneth J. Kinkor, with Sharon Simpson; photography by Kenneth Garrett. National Geographic, 2007. 175 p.

Grades: 11 12 Adult   **910.4**
1. Whydah (Ship) 2. Pirates -- History 18th century. 3. Buccaneers -- History 4. Slave trade -- History 5. Shipwrecks 6. Privateering
ISBN 1426202628

LC bl2007025076

Explores the role of the Whydah in the slave trade and discusses how it came to be a pirate ship, providing evidence of what life was like for pirates in the Caribbean Area in the 18th century through artifacts found on the wrecks of pirate ships.

"Clifford, an underwater archaeological explorer, used research and the artifacts recovered from the Whydah to tell the story of its life as a slave galley and pirate ship. In the process, he dispels many myths about buccaneers. . . . Photographs of artifacts . . . and the recovery crew at work combine with large visually appealing paintings of dramatic battle, storm, and courtroom scenes. . . . The book is a fascinating blend of history, ocean-diving recovery, and archaeology, and demonstrates archaeology in action and the role artifacts play in informing us about the past." School Library Journal.

Includes bibliographical references (p. 174).

Grove, Tim

First flight around the world: the adventures of the American fliers who won the race. Tim Grove Abrams Books for Young Readers, 2015. 96 p.

Grades: 5 6 7 8   **910.4**
1. United States. Army. Air Corps. 2. Flights 3. Flights around the world 4. World records 5. Aviation
ISBN 9781419714825

"This gripping, well-designed title details the United States' 1924 successful attempt to become the first nation to circumnavigate the globe by flight. . . . Offering a look at a lesser-known historical event, this beautiful, well-written book is an essential addition for all collections." School Library Journal.

Hanel, Rachael

Pirates. Rachael Hanel. Creative Education, c2008. 48 p.: Fearsome fighters

Grades: 4 5 6   **910.4**

1. Pirates -- History 2. Buccaneers 3. Piracy 4. Treasure hunting
ISBN 9781583415375

LC 2006021844

Examines the history, culture, and fighting styles of pirates, with details about several of the most successful and infamous in history.

"This book explores the golden age of piracy from the sixteenth through the nineteenth centuries. Hanel discusses battles, types of ships and weapons, and attire and behavior. Vignettes of well-known male and female pirates are included. Archival reproductions and sidebars provide additional information." Horn Book Guide.

Includes bibliographical references (p. 48) and index.

Lavery, Brian

The **conquest** of the ocean: the illustrated history of seafaring. Brian Lavery. DK Publishing, 2019, c2013. 400 p.

Grades: 8 9 10 11 12   **910.4**

1. Ocean travel -- History 2. Seafaring life -- History 3. Discoveries in geography 4. Explorers 5. Trade routes -- History
ISBN 9780241379691

Spans five thousand years of the ocean's history to tell the stories of the courageous individuals who sailed the seas for trade, to conquer new lands, and to explore the unknown, from the early Polynesians to the first circumnavigations by the Portuguese and the British.

"Lavishly illustrating the extension of sea travel to transoceanic dimensions, Lavery's work ably serves a collection's need for a general, visually attractive chronicle of ships, sailors, and the sea." Booklist.

Mundy, Robyn

Epic voyages: Magellan, Cook, Shackleton, Heyerdahl, Chichester. Robyn Mundy, Nigel Rigby. Kingfisher; 2010. 64 p.: Epic adventure

Grades: 5 6 7 8   **910.4**

1. Adventurers 2. Seafaring life 3. Voyages and travels 4. Explorers 5. Ocean travel
ISBN 9780753465745

LC bl2011006282

Recounts the stories of five epic mariners who set off on some of the greatest ocean journeys ever undertaken and introduces the challenges of life at sea.

"The graphics will grab readers in [this] exciting, extra-large-size [title] . . . packed with high-quality color photos on every double-page spread. Just as gripping are the narratives, captions, and technical details of exploration, adventure, and survival. . . . [This] book covers Magellan, Cook, Shackleton, Heyedahl and also Chichester, who, in 1966, sailed alone around the world." Booklist.

Phelan, Matt

★ **Around** the world. Matt Phelan. Candlewick Press, 2011. 240 p.

Grades: 4 5 6 7   **910.4**

1. Stevens, Thomas, 1854-1935 2. Bly, Nellie, 1864-1922. 3. Slocum, Joshua, b. 1844 4. 19th century 5. Trips around the world

6. Adventurers 7. Voyages and travels 8. Comics and Graphic novels
ISBN 9780763636197

LC 2010043153

Challenged with circling the world at the end of the nineteenth century, three very different adventurers—avid bicyclist Thomas Stevens, fearless reporter Nellie Bly, and retired sea captain Joshua Slocum—embark on epic journeys.

"Phelan presents three true stories of around-the-world adventures inspired by Jules Verne's Around the World in Eighty Days that, even though they were undertaken in the late 1800s, would be hardly less arduous today. Thomas Stevens, Joshua Slocum, and Nellie Bly saw the world from the seat of a bicycle, aboard a 36-foot sloop, and via trains and ships, respectively. The small, specific pleasures of Phelan's work . . . are showcased in panels laid out in horizontal bands, reinforcing the linear, ever-onward nature of each narrative. The use of limited color palettes enhances the artist's characteristic delicate, expressive pen-and-ink drawings without overpowering them, allowing each traveler's character to be the dominant story element. . . . Design elements such as borders and frames lend a jaunty festivity to a graphic novel that will appeal to aficionados of the form and any reader in search of engrossing true journeys." School Library Journal.

Sandler, Martin W.

The **Whydah**: a pirate ship feared, wrecked, and found. Martin W. Sandler. Candlewick Press, 2017 170 p.

Grades: 6 7 8 9   **910.4**

1. Whidah (Ship) 2. Pirates 3. Shipwrecks 4. Piracy 5. Buccaneers 6. Slave trade -- History 18th century.
ISBN 9780763680336

Describes what happened when a slave ship that was captured by pirates in 1717, packed with plunder, was sunk by a brutal storm, and the expedition to locate the wreck and what was uncovered.

"The author weaves a fascinating story about piracy and the legendary 18th-century pirate ship Whydah, which sunk off the coast of Cape Cod on April 24, 1717, during a perfect storm." School Library Journal.

Wallace, Sandra Neil

Bound by ice: a true North Pole survival story. Sandra Neil Wallace and Rich Wallace. Calkins Creek, 2017. 192 p.

Grades: 6 7 8 9 10   **910.4**

1. De Long, George W. (George Washington), 1844-1881. 2. 1870s 3. North Pole expeditions 4. Explorers 5. Shipwrecks 6. Survival (after airplane accidents, shipwrecks, etc) 7. Adventure 8. Arctic regions 9. Polar regions
ISBN 9781629794280

Recounts George W. De Long's expedition to reach the North Pole.

"Abundant archival illustrations, bibliography, and source notes bolster this gripping, accessible account." Publishers Weekly.

Yolen, Jane

Sea queens: women pirates around the world. Jane Yolen; illustrated by Christine Joy Pratt. Charlesbridge, c2008. 112 p.

Grades: 4 5 6 7   **910.4**

1. Women pirates -- History 2. Pirates 3. Women pirates 4. Women -- History 5. Women's role
ISBN 9781580891318

LC 2007026983

"This offers 12 portraits of sword-swinging, seafaring women throughout history, from Artemisia, in 500 B.C.E. Persia, to Madame Ching, an early nineteenth-century Chinese woman and named here as the most successful pirate in the world. . . . The scratchboard illustrations work well as portraits. . . . The book is filled with fascinating, dramatically told stories and sidebars." Booklist.

Includes bibliographical references and index.

910.9 History, geographic treatment, biography

Aronson, Marc

★ The **world** made new: why the Age of Exploration happened & how it changed the world. Marc Aronson & John W. Glenn. National Geographic, c2007. 64 p.: National Geographic timelines

Grades: 4 5 6 7   **910.9**
1. Exploration 2. Explorers 3. Discoveries in geography 4. Western Hemisphere 5. Visual nonfiction
ISBN 0792269780

LC 2006022091

Describes how the discoveries made by the Europeans around the time of Columbus changed the world.

"This highly pictorial, readable overview provides significant depth of coverage. . . . The illustrations, most in full color, make ample and appropriate use of period prints as well as contemporary illustrations and photographs. The result is a visual feast that fleshes out the . . . remarkably evenhanded narrative." School Library Journal.

Includes bibliographical references (p. 60-61) and index.

Elliott, Lynne, 1968-

Exploration in the Renaissance. Lynne Elliott. Crabtree, c2009. 32 p.: Renaissance world

Grades: 6 7 8 9   **910.9**
1. Civilization, Western 2. European Renaissance 3. Exploration -- History 4. Explorers 5. Discoveries in geography -- European 6. Europe -- Civilization -- 16th century.
ISBN 9780778745938

LC 2008052601

Discusses the culture, tools, funding, and challenges of exploration during the Renaissance, with emphasis on Spain and Portugal.

"Ideal introductions to concepts, people, and events of the Renaissance... succinct and thorough." School Library Journal.

Includes bibliographical references (p. 32) and index.

Hagglund, Betty

Epic adventure: Epic treks: Lewis & Clark - Livingstone & Stanley - Burke & Wills - Amundsen & Scott. Betty Hagglund. Kingfisher, 2011. 64 p.: Epic adventures

Grades: 5 6 7 8   **910.9**
1. Explorers 2. Expeditions 3. Survival
ISBN 9780753466681

"The graphics will grab readers in [this] exciting, extra-large-size [title] . . . packed with high-quality color photos on every double-page spread. Just as gripping are the narratives, captions, and technical details of exploration, adventure, and survival. . . . Epic Treks covers Lewis and Clark, Livingston and Stanley, Burk and Wells, and Amundsen and Scott, each journey an exciting adventure filled with details about what they endured and what they found, as well as their failures and short-comings." Booklist.

Morris, Neil, 1946-

Voyages of discovery. Neil Morris. Zak Books, c2009. 48 p. : History (Zak Books (Firm))

Grades: 7 8 9 10   **910.9**
1. Discoveries in geography -- History 2. Explorers -- History 3. Explorers 4. Geography 5. Voyages and travels
ISBN 9788860981547

LC 2008008409

A detailed overview of the history of the age of exploration, including explorers from all parts of the world and how they brought knowledge of distant lands back to their people, between 1150 and 1750. Provided by publisher.

"The effectiveness lies in the combination of lush illustrations, well-chosen, captioned photographs of contemporary artifacts, and . . . [a] reasoned, concise [narrative]. Succinct time lines border most pages, and . . . the proper amount of white space, and clear dark print maintain organization and clarity. A superior choice." School Library Journal.

Ross, Stewart

Into the unknown: how great explorers found their way by land, sea, and air. Stewart Ross; illustrated by Stephen Biesty. Candlewick Press, 2011. 82 p.

Grades: 4 5 6 7   **910.9**
1. Explorers 2. Discoveries in geography 3. Exploration 4. Expeditions
ISBN 9780763649487

LC 2010038720

"Biesty's trademark amusing, informatively detailed illustrations are a highlight of this entertaining examination of several voyages of exploration. . . . Chapters cover an impressive range of exploration. In addition to the usual suspects, they include a 340 B.C.E. Greek voyage to the Arctic Circle; Chinese Admiral Zheng He to India; [and] David Livingston and Mary Kingsley into the African interior. . . . Each chapter includes a fold-out section of illustrations with a map of the journey and a cross-section of the method of transportation. . . . An altogether agreeable package for armchair explorers." Kirkus.

White. Pamela

Exploration in the world of the middle ages, 500-1500. Pamela White, John S. Bowman, and Maurice Isserman, general editors. Chelsea House Publishers, c2010. 133 p.

Grades: 7 8 9   **910.9**
1. Discoveries in geography -- History To 1500
ISBN 9781604131932

LC 2009030202

Presents information about exploration during the Middle Ages, discussing Chinese exploration, pilgrims and missionaries, Vikings, and Muslim travelers.

910.91 Geography of and travel in areas, regions, places in general

Adams, Simon, 1955-

Titanic. written by Simon Adams. DK Publishing, 2014. 72 p.

Grades: 4 5 6 7   **910.91**
1. Titanic (Steamship) 2. Shipwrecks
ISBN 9781465420992

LC 2015302651

Offers detailed descriptions of the Titanic, including its accommodations, and a retelling of its sinking in the North Atlantic in April, 1912.

Hopkinson, Deborah

★ **Titanic**: voices from the disaster. Deborah Hopkinson. Scholastic Press, 2012. 304 p.

Grades: 5 6 7 8   **910.91**

1. Titanic (Steamship) 2. Shipwrecks 3. Steamships 4. Survival 5. Disasters

ISBN 9780545116749

LC 2011006695

Tells the tale of the sinking of the Titanic using the narratives of the witnesses and survivors to the disaster.

McPherson, Stephanie Sammartino

★ **Iceberg** right ahead!: the tragedy of the Titanic. Stephanie Sammartino McPherson. Twenty-First Century Books, c2012. 112 p.

Grades: 4 5 6 7 8   **910.91**

1. Titanic (Steamship) 2. Shipwrecks

ISBN 9780761367567

LC 2011002352

Describes the ill-fated maiden voyage of the Titanic, a luxury liner claimed to be "unsinkable" that was destroyed after colliding with an iceberg, killing over one thousand passengers onboard.

"With innumerable books, movies, documentaries, novels, and biographies all telling versions of the Titanic story, it would seem that there is little more to learn, yet by providing more details and some of the most up-to-date research, McPherson's compelling, thoughtful narrative proves otherwise. . . . The layout includes plenty of period photographs, diagrams, artwork, and sidebars with interesting tangential tidbits, making for a thorough resource. . . . A comprehensive, well-written, thoroughly researched title." School Library Journal.

Includes bibliographical references (p. 107-109), filmography (p. 110), and index.

Tougias, Mike, 1955-

The **finest** hours: the true story of a heroic sea rescue. Michael J. Tougias and Casey Sherman. Christy Ottaviano Books/ Henry Holt and Company, 2014. 192 p.

Grades: 4 5 6 7 8   **910.91**

1. Pendleton (Tanker) 2. CG36500 (Lifeboat) 3. Shipwrecks -- History 4. Search and rescue operations 5. Survival (after airplane accidents, shipwrecks, etc)

ISBN 9780805097641

LC 2013030661

On the night of February 18, 1952, during one of the worst winter storms that New England has ever seen, two oil tankers just off the shore of Cape Cod were torn in half by the force of the storm. This middle-grade adaptation of an adult nonfiction book tells the story of a harrowing Coast Guard rescue when four men in a tiny lifeboat overcame insurmountable odds and saved more than 30 stranded sailors. This is a fast-paced, uplifting story that puts young readers in the middle of the action. It's a gripping story of heroism and survival with the same intensity as the bestselling book and movie The Perfect Storm. A Christy Ottaviano Book. Provided by publisher.

"The accounts of each rescue's logistics—for example, sailors trying to time their leaps from their destroyed tanker to the rescue boat amid rocking waves—are nail-biting, and they are relayed by the authors with an effectively sober, just-the-facts terseness." Booklist.

Includes bibliographical references.

910.911 Frigid zones—Travel

Nardo, Don, 1947-

Polar explorations. Don Nardo. Lucent Books, c2011. 104 p.: World history (Lucent Books)

Grades: 6 7 8 9   **910.911**

1. Explorers 2. Polar expeditions 3. Polar regions -- Exploration

ISBN 9781420503609

LC 2010039667

Describes the history of exploration of the North and South Poles, from the earliest Arctic and Antarctic explorers to exploration competitions and modern scientific voyages to both poles.

910.92 Geographers, travelers, explorers regardless of country of origin

Huang, Nellie

★ **Explorers**: amazing tales of the world's greatest adventurers. illustrated by Jessamy Hawke; written by Nellie Huang. DK Children, 2019, c2019. 144 p.

Grades: 3 4 5 6 7   **910.92**

1. Explorers 2. Discoveries (in geography) 3. Exploration -- History 4. Geography 5. Firsts (Events, inventions, etc)

ISBN 9781465481573

Detailed maps and intricate cross-section illustrations of such subjects as Spanish galleons, lost cities and space ships introduce the dangerous trials and important achievements of the world's great explorers, from Ferdinand Magellan to Barbara Hillary.

Krull, Kathleen, 1952-2021

Lives of the explorers: discoveries, disasters (and what the neighbors thought). Kathleen Krull; illustrated by Kathryn Hewitt. HMH Books for Young Readers, 2014. 96 p.: Lives of--

Grades: 4 5 6 7   **910.92**

1. Explorers 2. Adventurers 3. Discoveries in geography 4. Transportation

ISBN 9780152059101

LC 2013037697

You might know that Columbus discovered America, Lewis and Clark headed west with Sacajawea, and Sally Ride blasted into space. But what do you really know about these bold explorers? What were they like as kids? What pets or bad habits did they have? And what drove their passion to explore unknown parts of the world? With juicy tidbits about everything from favorite foods to first loves, Lives of the Explorers reveals these fascinating adventurers as both world-changers and real people. The entertaining style and solid research of the Lives Of... . series of biographies have made it a favorite with families and educators for twenty years. This new volume takes readers through the centuries and across the globe, profiling the men and women whose curiosity and courage have led them to discover our world. Provided by publisher.

"The straightforward, accessible prose makes for fast reading, and Krull doesn't shy away from some deplorable, stomach-turning facts, which kids will devour and use to spice up staid homework assignments." Kirkus.

912 Maps and plans of surface of earth and of extraterrestrial worlds

National Geographic Partners (U.S.)

National Geographic student world atlas. National Geographic Kids National Geographic, 2019. 143 p.

Grades: 7 8 9   **912**
   1. Physical geography 2. Physical geography 3. Earth (Planet)
ISBN 9781426334801

LC 2019285580

From the cartographic experts at National Geographic comes the latest edition of its award-winning student atlas, with everything kids want and need to know about our changing world. Dynamic, user-friendly content includes photos, facts, charts, graphics, and full-color political, physical, and thematic maps on important topics. Completely updated maps and statistics ensure that kids have all the latest information as they learn more about current events and become global citizens."

Taylor, Barbara, 1954-

Looking at maps. Barbara Taylor. Smart Apple Media, c2008. 46 p.: Geography skills

Grades: 6 7 8 9   **912**
   1. Maps 2. Cartography 3. Geography 4. Orientation
ISBN 1599200503

LC 2006100224

Introduces maps, telling how they are used, how the symbols and scales are used to represent real features, and how to read them.

"The text is easy to follow. . . . The examples given in the text that involve places are almost always accompanied by excellent photographs. . . . Maps, block diagrams, tables, and graphs are clearly presented and easy to interpret." Science Books & Films.

Includes bibliographical references (p. 45) and index.

914 Geography of and travel in Europe

Woods, Michael, 1946-

Seven natural wonders of Europe. Michael Woods and Mary B. Woods. Twenty-First Century Books, 2009. 80 p.

Grades: 5 6 7 8   **914**
   1. Europe -- Description and travel
ISBN 9780822590729

LC 2008027604

Looks at seven natural wonders of Europe, including the Alps, Loch Ness, and the Black Forest.

917 Geography of and travel in North America

Wallace, Mary, 1950-

Inuksuk journey: an artist at the top of the world. Mary Wallace. Maple Tree Press, 2008. 64 p.

Grades: 5 6 7 8   **917**
   1. Wallace, Mary, 1950- 2. Inuksuit 3. Painters 4. Women artists
   5. Canada, Northern -- Description and travel
ISBN 9781897349267

A unique trip to the Arctic is presented through rich portraits that capture the native people, beauty, wilderness, and unique wonders of the region through a comprehensive tour by an Inuit guide of the land she loves and respects.

"Nunavut, an Arctic territory in northern Canada, is a cold, open space where inuksuk, piles of stone in the shape of a person used to mark a family home, welcome guests, guide travelers, and ensure safe passage, are commonly found. Wallace has developed a passion for these ancient messengers, and here she presents a journal of her weeklong trek to Inuksugassait, a place where countless numbers of the stone markers stand. . . . Wallace includes personal photos, sketches, and comments that give readers an intimate portrait of life in this place. Over a dozen vibrant oil paintings depicting scenes from her journey are scattered throughout. . . . Readers will be fascinated by this firsthand account of true adventure." School Library Journal.

917.804 Geography of and travel in United States—West (U.S.)—Travel

Bodden, Valerie

Through the American West. by Valerie Bodden. Creative Education, c2012. 48 p.: Great expeditions

Grades: 5 6 7 8   **917.804**
   1. Lewis, Meriwether, 1774-1809 2. Clark, William, 1770-1838
   3. 1800s (Decade) 4. Explorers 5. Expeditions 6. Voyages and travels 7. The West (United States) -- Exploration
ISBN 9781608180653

LC 2010033413

A history of Meriwether Lewis and William Clark's famed 1804-06 journey, detailing the challenges encountered, the individuals involved, the discoveries made, and how the expedition left its mark upon the world. Provided by publisher.

Clark, William, 1770-1838

Off the map: the journals of Lewis and Clark. edited by Peter and Connie Roop; illustrations by Tim Tanner. Walker and Company, 1998, c1993. 44 p.

Grades: 5 6 7 8   **917.804**
   1. Clark, William, 1770-1838 Original journals of the Lewis and Clark Expedition Selections 2. Lewis, Meriwether, 1774-1809. Original journals of the Lewis and Clark Expedition, 1804-1806. 3. Explorers 4. Diaries
ISBN 0802775462

LC BL 98005029

A compilation of entries and excerpts from the journals of William Clark and Meriwether Lewis, describing their historic expedition.

"The full-color illustrations, mainly in warm earth tones, give the pages an attractive look, but the most vivid pictures come from the journals themselves. . . . This vivid source material would be a welcome part of any classroom study of the subject." Booklist.

919.8 Arctic islands—geography

Armstrong, Jennifer, 1961-

Shipwreck at the bottom of the world: the extraordinary true story of Shackleton and the Endurance. Jennifer Armstrong. Crown, c1998. 134 p.

Grades: 7 8 9 10 11 12   **919.8**
   1. Shackleton, Ernest Henry, Sir, 1874-1922. 2. Imperial Trans-Antarctic Expedition, 1914-1917 3. Endurance (Ship) 4. 1910s
   5. Explorers 6. Shipwrecks 7. Survival (after airplane accidents, shipwrecks, etc) 8. Wilderness survival 9. Adventure 10.

Antarctica -- Exploration
ISBN 0517800136

LC 97052063

NCTE Orbis Pictus Nonfiction Award, 1999.

Describes the events of the 1914 Shackleton Antarctic expedition when, after being trapped in a frozen sea for nine months, their ship, Endurance, was finally crushed, forcing Shackleton and his men to make a very long and perilous journey across ice and stormy seas to reach inhabited land.

"A book that will capture the attention and imagination of any reader." School Library Journal.

Includes bibliographical references (p. 129-130) and index.

Myers, Walter Dean, 1937-2014

Antarctica: journeys to the South Pole. Walter Dean Myers. Scholastic Press, 2004. 134 p.

Grades: 6 7 8 9   **919.8**

1. Explorers 2. Antarctica -- Exploration
ISBN 0439220017

LC 2004002501

Brings to life the dramatic race to the South Pole, tracking its famous explorers—including James Cook, Ernest Shackleton, and Richard Evelyn Bird—and the dangers they encountered there, as well as their contributions to science.

"This is a lucid, well-written text." School Library Journal.
Includes bibliographical references and index.

Walker, Sally M.

Frozen secrets: Antarctica revealed. by Sally M. Walker. Carolrhoda Books, c2010. 104 p.

Grades: 7 8 9 10   **919.8**

1. Continents 2. Explorers 3. Scientists 4. Wildlife researchers 5. Antarctica
ISBN 9781580136075

LC 2009034282

Introduces Antarctica, describing the history of its exploration and the current research efforts underway to investigate its geography, climate, and fossils of the past, and monitor the effects of global warming on its glaciers.

"This is an account of the rich scientific findings coming out of the planet's southernmost continent. . . . It's an excellent overview that manages to pack a lot of technical and scientific information into a small space, but it's sufficiently well structured conceptually and well laid out visually . . . that it all goes down pretty easily. The photographic images reveal the stunning beauty of the continent in shot after shot, but there are also illuminating views of the scientists at work, and diagrams and maps round out the view." Bulletin of the Center for Children's Books.

Includes bibliographical references and index.

919.89 Antarctica—Geography

Barone, Rebecca (Rebecca E.)

★ **Race** to the bottom of the Earth: surviving Antarctica. Rebecca E. F. Barone. Henry Holt and Company, 2021. 272 p.

Grades: 4 5 6 7 8   **919.89**

1. Scott, Robert Falcon, 1868-1912 Antarctica 2. Amundsen, Roald, 1872-1928 Antarctica 3. Rudd, Lou Antarctica 4. O'Brady, Colin Antarctica 5. South Pole expeditions 6. Expeditions 7. Wilderness survival 8. Exploration 9. Competition 10. Antarctica -- Exploration 11. South Pole -- Exploration
ISBN 9781250257802

LC 2020021758

In 1910, Captain Robert Scott prepared his crew for a trip that no one had ever completed: a journey to the South Pole. He vowed to get there any way he could, even if it meant looking death in the eye. Then, not long before he set out, the telegram arrived: "Proceeding to Antarctic— Roald Amundsen." What was to be an expedition had become a race. One hundred and eight years later, Captain Louis Rudd readied himself for a similarly grueling task: the first solo crossing of treacherous Antarctica. Then came the Instagram message: "On Nov. 1, I depart for the ice—Colin O'Brady." What was to be a journey had become a race.

"Readers will be caught up in the real-time action sequences and should end up rooting for everybody as these determined individuals face unimaginable physical and mental hardships. Almost every chapter ends on a cliff-hanger (sometimes literally)." Booklist

Includes bibliographical references.

Bertozzi, Nick

Shackleton: Antarctic odyssey. Nick Bertozzi. First Second, 2014. 128 p.

Grades: 5 6 7 8 9 10   **919.89**

1. Shackleton, Ernest Henry, Sir, 1874-1922 2. Imperial Trans-Antarctic Expedition, 1914-1917. 3. Endurance (Ship) 4. 1910s 5. Survival (after airplane accidents, shipwrecks, etc) 6. Explorers 7. Polar expeditions 8. Exploration 9. Rescues 10. Antarctica -- Exploration 11. Historical comics 12. Comics and Graphic novels
ISBN 9781596434516

Ernest Shackleton was one of the last great Antarctic explorers, and he led one of the most ambitious Antarctic expeditions ever undertaken. This is his story, and the story of the dozens of men who threw in their lot with him—many of whom nearly died in the unimaginably harsh conditions of the journey. It's an astonishing feat—and was unprecedented at the time—that all the men in the expedition survived.

"Bertozzi eschews all narrative explanation, relying solely on dialogue among the crew and the detailed black-and-white panels to tell the story. The snow- and ice-bound journey is the perfect match for Bertozzi's minimal style—vast stretches of white become gasp-worthy, desolate vistas." Booklist.

920 Collective biographies

Amara, Philip

Awesome Asian Americans: 20 stars who made America amazing. by Phil Amara & Oliver Chin; illustrated by Juan Calle. Immedium, Inc., 2020. 132 p.

Grades: 6 7 8 9   **920**

1. Asian Americans 2. Celebrities 3. Pacific Islander Americans
ISBN 9781597021500

LC 2020011608

This is an illustrated children's anthology of noteworthy Asian Americans: 20 groundbreaking men and women from diverse backgrounds and vocations. Provided by publisher.

"Readers will be drawn to the dynamic illustrations and lively, well-structured profiles detailing these high achievers." School Library Journal

Includes bibliographical references.

Bolden, Tonya

★ **Pathfinders**: the journeys of 16 extraordinary Black souls. Tonya Bolden. Abrams Books for Young Readers, 2017. 124 p.

Grades: 5 6 7 8 **920**
1. African Americans 2. Successful people
ISBN 9781419714559

LC 2015043356

Profiles sixteen high-achieving African Americans, including magician Richard Potter, concert singer Sissieretta Jones, and architect Paul R. Williams.

"A well-researched book introducing a varied group of African Americans who excelled in their own, individual ways." Booklist.

Includes bibliographical references (pages 111-116) and index.

Portraits of African-American heroes. Tonya Bolden; paintings by Ansel Pitcairn. Dutton Children's Books, c2003. 88 p.
Grades: 4 5 6 7 **920**
1. African Americans 2. Heroes and heroines
ISBN 0525470433

LC 2002075911

Paintings and brief accounts present the accomplishments of twenty leading African Americans from Frederick Douglass to the present, including reformers, athletes, artists, and remarkable individuals in other fields.

"Each profile lists expected biographical information, but offers even more by way of keen insights into a subject's personality based on interviews and information drawn from personal memoirs. . . . Pitcairn's beautifully rendered sepia-toned portraits make each subject jump from the page, beckoning children to come ever closer and learn." Booklist.

Includes bibliographical references (p. 88).

Bragg, Georgia
How they choked: failures, flops, and flaws of the awfully famous. Georgia Bragg; illustrated by Kevin O'Malley. Walker Books for Young Readers, 2014. 192 p.
Grades: 5 6 7 8 **920**
1. Celebrities -- Personal conduct 2. Decision making 3. Errors 4. History -- Errors, inventions, etc
ISBN 9780802734884

LC 2013039127

"On the heels of How They Croaked: The Awful Ends of the Awfully Famous (2011), Bragg seeks to reconcile what she sees as a major flaw of the biography genre—that authors ignore the human potential for error. Her compendium is unapologetically full of bad news, criticism, and belly flops...The snarkily entertaining narratives are illustrated with caricatures of each subject. For better or worse, subjects are rarely as one-dimensional as most biographies paint them, and this book proves that nobody is perfect." Booklist.

★ **How** they croaked: the awful ends of the awfully famous. by Georgia Bragg; illustrated by Kevin O'Malley. Walker & Co., 2011. 102 p.
Grades: 5 6 7 8 **920**
1. Celebrities -- Death 2. Death -- History 3. Books for reluctant readers
ISBN 9780802798176

LC 2010008659

"Bragg chronicles with ghoulish glee the chronic or fatal maladies that afflicted 19 historical figures. Nonsqueamish readers will be entranced by her riveting descriptions. . . . The author tucks quick notes on at least marginally relevant topics, such as leeching, scurvy, presidential assassins, and mummy eyes . . . between the chapters. . . . O'Malley's cartoon portraits and spot art add just the right notes of humor to keep the contents from becoming too gross." Booklist.

Buckley, Susan
Kids make history: a new look at America's story. Susan Buckley and Elspeth Leacock; Illustrations by Randy Jones. Houghton Mifflin, 2006. 48 p.
Grades: 4 5 6 7 **920**
1. Children -- Social life and customs 2. Children -- Social conditions 3. Children 4. United States -- Social life and customs 5. United States -- Social conditions
ISBN 0618223290

LC 2005036309

Hundreds of visual and verbal facts describe the experiences of children living in America from 1607 through 2001, from surviving a harsh James Towne winter to witnessing the chaos of the September 11 terrorist attacks in New York City.

"This book introduces 20 children in extraordinary times, starting in 1607 with Pocahontas and ending in 2001 with 9/11 as experienced by high school senior Jukay Hsu. Laura Ingalls Wilder; John Rankin, Jr.; and Susie Baker, a young slave celebrating her independence in 1863, are among those included. The text and the highly detailed watercolor illustrations are married with numbers in small red boxes keyed to both elements for clarification. . . . A good browsing choice for children interested in American history." School Library Journal.

Chin-Lee, Cynthia
Amelia to Zora: twenty-six women who changed the world. Cynthia Chin-Lee; illustrated by Megan Halsey and Sean Addy. Charlesbridge, c2005. 32 p.
Grades: 4 5 6 7 **920**
1. Women 2. Alphabet books
ISBN 1570915229

LC 2004003847

Profiles the lives of twenty-six women who, through their acts and deeds, helped shape and change the world during their lifetime, including pilot Amelia Earhart and anthropologist Zora Neal Hurston.

"The illustrations are done in a remarkable mix of media. . . . The text portions are short . . . but they are enticing. By choosing her subjects from every culture, the author introduces children to the scope of the struggles and achievements of women from many times and many places." Booklist.

Includes bibliographical references (p. 30-31).

Drucker, Malka
Portraits of Jewish American heroes. by Malka Drucker; illustrated by Elizabeth Rosen. Dutton Children's Books, 2008. 96 p.
Grades: 4 5 6 **920**
1. Jewish Americans 2. Jewish American women
ISBN 9780525477716

Spanning three centuries, the influence and impact on the nation by twenty Jewish artists, inventors, civil right activists, and scientists are examined and celebrated in an informative book with multimedia illustrations.

"From Albert Einstein and Bella Abzug to Ruth Bader Ginsburg, Hank Greenberg, and Steven Spielberg, this invitingly illustrated collective biography celebrates 20 Jewish American heroes in all their diversity. . . . The nicely designed volume includes full-page portraits of the subjects in various media. . . . Drucker's eloquent, chatty style opens up big issues about Judaism as a source of idealism and for a just, compassionate society." Booklist.

Includes bibliographical references.

Freedman, Russell

★ The **Wright** Brothers: how they invented the airplane. Russell Freedman; with original photographs by Wilbur and Orville Wright. Holiday House, c1991. 129 p.

Grades: 5 6 7 8 9 10   **920**
   1. Wright, Orville, 1871-1948 2. Wright, Wilbur, 1867-1912 3. Inventors 4. Pilots 5. Aviation 6. Aviation -- History 7. Airplanes -- Design and construction
   ISBN 0823408752

                      LC   90048440

Golden Kite Award for Nonfiction, 1991.

Follows the lives of the Wright brothers and describes how they developed the first airplane.

"In this combination of photography and text, Freedman reveals the frustrating, exciting, and ultimately successful journey of these two brothers from their bicycle shop in Dayton, Ohio, to their Kitty Hawk flights and beyond. . . . An essential purchase for younger YAs." Voice of Youth Advocates.

Includes bibliographical references (p. 123-124) and index.

Fritz, Jean

Around the world in a hundred years: from Henry the Navigator to Magellan. Jean Fritz; illustrated by Anthony Bacon Venti. Putnam's, c1994. 128 p.

Grades: 4 5 6 7   **920**
   1. Explorers 2. Discoveries in geography 3. Exploration 4. History
   ISBN 0399225277

                      LC 92027042

Brings to life the accomplishments of ten extraordinary explorers—including Henry the Navigator, Vasco da Gama, John Cabot, and Ferdinand Magellan—who braved the unknown to discover uncharted lands and to find their way around the world.

"Fritz examines the voyages of ten explorers, acknowledging that their contributions, though deserving of recognition, were dearly bought. Opening and closing chapters summarize the fourteenth-century world view and indicate later expansion of geographic understanding. As always, Fritz tempers scholarship with humor in this brief volume—illustrated with drawings in pencil—which reads like an adventure story." Horn Book Guide.

Includes bibliographical references (p. [123]-124) and index.

Giblin, James Cross, 1933-

Good brother, bad brother: the story of Edwin Booth and John Wilkes Booth. James Cross Giblin. Clarion Books, c2005. 244 p.

Grades: 5 6 7 8   **920**
   1. Booth, John Wilkes, 1838-1865. 2. Booth, Edwin, 1833-1893. 3. Lincoln, Abraham, 1809-1865 4. Assassins 5. Actors and actresses 6. Brothers 7. Assassination 8. Family relationships
   ISBN 0618096426

                      LC   2004021260

"Giblin frames the intertwined tale of two brothers with accounts of their families, friends, the Civil War, and nineteenth-century theater. . . . Alcoholism and depression afflicted the family, but Giblin is brilliant at showing that darkness was only one part of a life. . . . Giblin's book will engross readers until the very last footnote." Booklist.

Includes bibliographical references and index.

Halligan, Katherine

HerStory: 50 women and girls who shook up the world. Katherine Halligan; illustrated by Sarah Walsh. Simon & Schuster Books for Young Readers, 2018. 112 p.

Grades: 4 5 6 7   **920**
   1. Women
   ISBN 9781534436640

                      LC 2018016718

Presents the lives and accomplishments of fifty women, describing their childhoods, the obstacles they faced, and the impact their achievements had on the world around them, including such figures as Marie Curie, Harriet Tubman, Rachel Carson, Rosa Parks, and Indira Gandhi.

Harrison, Vashti

Little dreamers: visionary women around the world. Vashti Harrison. Little, Brown and Company, 2018. 96 p.: Little Leaders (Vashti Harrison)

Grades: 4 5 6 7 8   **920**
   1. Women 2. Women artists 3. Women scientists 4. Women inventors 5. Women social advocates
   ISBN 9780316475174

Meet the little leaders. They're brave. They're bold. They changed the world. Featuring the true stories of 40 inspirational women creators—from writers to inventors, artists to scientists—this book is as inspirational as it is educational. Readers will meet trailblazing women such as revolutionary architect, Zaha Hadid; actor/inventor Hedy Lamarr; environmental activist Wangari Maathai; modernist painter and animator Mary Blair; and physicist Chien-Shiung Wu. Some names will be familiar, some will not - but all these women had a lasting impact on their fields.

Haskins, James, 1941-

African-American religious leaders. Jim Haskins and Kathleen Benson. John Wiley & Sons, c2008. 168 p. : Black stars series

Grades: 6 7 8 9 10 11 12 Adult   **920**
   1. Religious leaders 2. African American leadership 3. African Americans 4. Christian leadership
   ISBN 0471736325

                      LC 2007027347

Explores the role and importance of African Americans as religious leaders through the profiles of significant personalities from the Revolutionary era through modern times, including Absalom Jones, Sojourner Truth, and Al Sharpton.

Herrera, Juan Felipe

★ **Portraits** of Hispanic American heroes. by Juan Felipe Herrera; pictures by Raúl Colón. Dial Books for Young Readers, 2014. 96 p.

Grades: 4 5 6 7 8   **920**
   1. Hispanic Americans 2. Portraits
   ISBN 9780803738096

                      LC   2013044661

Twenty Hispanic American artists, scientists, athletes, activists and political leaders are profiled in this stunning picture book, complete with inspirational quotes and distinctive expressionist portraits. Provided by publisher.

"Herrera packs relevant info and kid-appropriate details . . . without overwhelming the work, infusing the narratives with engaging text. Colón's portraits are luminous." School Library Journal.

Krull, Kathleen, 1952-2021

A **kids'** guide to America's first ladies. Kathleen Krull; illustrated by Anna Divito. Harpercollins Childrens Books, 2017. 240 p.: Kids' guide to American history

Grades: 4 5 6 7 8   **920**
   1. Presidents' spouses 2. Women 3. United States -- History
ISBN 9780062381071

"Gathering momentum as it rolls along chronologically through American history, this lively book profiles the women who have enjoyed, to varying degrees, the unique privileges and challenges of being first lady." Booklist.

Langley, Wanda

Women of the wind: early women aviators. Wanda Langley. Morgan Reynolds Pub., c2006. 160 p.

Grades: 6 7 8 9   **920**
   1. Women pilots 2. Pilots 3. Aviation -- History 4. Women
ISBN 1931798818

                        LC 2005022951

Biographical profiles of nine women pilots from the early years of flight, including: Harriet Quimby, the first American woman to receive a pilot's license; Bessie Coleman, the first African-American woman pilot; Anne Morrow Lindbergh, wife of Charles Lindbergh and record-setting pilot in her own right; and legendary adventurer Amelia Earhart.

"This collective biography celebrates the accomplishments of nine American women who pioneered in the field of aviation: Harriet Quimby, Katherine Stinson, Ruth Law, Bessie Coleman, Amelia Earhart, Ruth Nichols, Louise Thaden, Anne Morrow Lindbergh, and Jacqueline Cochran. . . . Well reproduced and often in color, the illustrations include a great many photos, as well as maps and period advertisements. . . . Langley . . . offers information, anecdotes, and inspiring stories." Booklist.

Includes bibliographical references.

Leon, Vicki

Outrageous women of the Middle Ages. by Vicki Leon. Wiley, c1998. ix, 118 p.: Outrageous women

Grades: 4 5 6 7 8   **920**
   1. Women 2. Women -- History 3. Civilization, Medieval
ISBN 0471170046

                        LC 97030307

Biographies of some outspoken and influential women who lived in Europe, Africa, and the Far East during the Middle Ages.

Lipsyte, Robert

Heroes of baseball: the men who made it America's favorite game. Robert Lipsyte. Atheneum Books for Young Readers, c2005. 96 p.

Grades: 4 5 6 7   **920**
   1. Baseball players 2. Baseball -- History 3. Athletes 4. Sports
ISBN 0689867417

                        LC 2005010841

Meet the men who were and remain the heroes of baseball. These are men who did more than hit home runs or pitch perfect games—they changed the way our society perceives itself, and the goals we set for ourselves and our nation.

"Using as a focus some of baseball's greats—Big Al Spalding, Babe Ruth, Mickey Mantle, Jackie Robinson, Curt Flood . . . Lipsyte offers a strong history of the game and its place in American culture. . . . Although much of this material, including the pictures, might be familiar

to young readers already absorbed in the game, it is nicely laid out and colorfully formatted. Lipsyte has a clear, vivid style." Booklist.

Includes bibliographical references (p. [96]) and index.

McCann, Michelle Roehm, 1968-

Girls who rocked the world: heroines from Joan of Arc to Mother Teresa. Michelle R. McCann and Amelie Welden; illustrated by David Hahn. Aladdin, 2012 256 p.

Grades: 5 6 7 8   **920**
   1. Girls 2. Heroes and heroines 3. Women
ISBN 9781582703022

This inspiring collection of stories provides 46 illustrated examples of strong, independent female role models, all of whom first impacted the world as teenagers or younger, from Harriet Tubman and Coco Chanel to S.E. Hinton and Maya Lin.

Orgill, Roxane

Shout, sister, shout!: ten girl singers who shaped a century. Roxane Orgill. Margaret K. McElderry Books, c2001. 148 p.

Grades: 6 7 8 9   **920**
   1. Women singers 2. Popular music (Vocal)
ISBN 0689819919

                        LC 99054374

Profiles ten celebrated singers from the past ten decades, including Ma Rainey, Judy Garland, Joan Baez, and Madonna.

"The lives of ten girl singers, representing different genres of popular music, from vaudeville to blues to jazz to country, are arranged by decade. Profiles of Sophie Tucker, Ma Rainey, Bessie Smith, Ethel Merman, Judy Garland, Anita O'Day, Joan Baez, Bette Midler, Madonna, and Lucinda Williams are included." Voice of Youth Advocates.

Includes bibliographical references (p. 139-141), discography (p. 135-138), and index.

Ottaviani, Jim

Primates: the fearless science of Jane Goodall, Dian Fossey, and Birute Galdikas. Jim Ottaviani; illustrated by Maris Wick. First Second Books, 2013. 152 p.

Grades: 5 6 7 8 9 10 11 12 Adult   **920**
   1. Goodall, Jane, 1934- 2. Fossey, Dian, 1932-1985. 3. Galdikas, Birute Marija Filomena. 4. Women primatologists 5. Women scientists 6. Women zoologists 7. Primatologists 8. Primates 9. Biographical comics 10. Comics and Graphic novels
ISBN 9781596438651

An illustrated introduction to the lives and work of three eminent primatologists shares insights into their educations under mentor Louis Leakey while exploring their pivotal contributions to 20th-century natural science.

"More story than study, the book provides an accessible introduction to Goodall's, Fossey's and Galdikas' lives and work." Kirkus.

Pinkney, Andrea Davis

★ **Let** it shine: stories of Black women freedom fighters. Andrea Davis Pinkney; illustrated by Stephen Alcorn. Harcourt, c2000. 120 p.

Grades: 4 5 6 7   **920**
   1. Truth, Sojourner, d. 1883 2. Tubman, Harriet, 1820?-1913 3. Parks, Rosa, 1913-2005. 4. Chisholm, Shirley, 1924-2005 5. African-American women civil rights workers 6. African Americans -- Civil rights -- History 7. African American women 8. Civil rights -- History 9. Women's rights -- History 10. United

States -- Race relations. 11. Antiracist literature
ISBN 015201005X

LC 99042806

Carter G. Woodson Book Awards: Middle Level, 2001.

"This collective biography tells of 10 extraordinary black women. From Sojourner Truth to Shirley Chisholm, this is also a view of African American history through individual lives. . . . Stephen Alcorn's allegorical oil portraits are dramatic and beautiful. . . . The immediacy of the text and the spacious design of the large volume make this a natural for reading aloud." Booklist.

Includes bibliographical references.

Quinn, Jason

The **Beatles**: all our yesterdays. Jason Quinn; illustrated by Lalit Kumar Sharma. Random House Inc 2017 150 p.

Grades: 7 8 9 10   920

1. Starr, Ringo, 1940- 2. McCartney, Paul 3. Lennon, John, 1940-1980 4. Harrison, George, 1943-2001 5. Beatles (Musical group) 6. Rock musicians 7. Musicians 8. Bands (Music) 9. Rock music
ISBN 9789381182222

"A lively and informal look at the young Beatles." Kirkus.

Reef, Catherine

The **Bronte** sisters: the brief lives of Charlotte, Emily and Anne. by Catherine Reef. Clarion Books, 2012. 240 p.

Grades: 7 8 9 10   920

1. Bronte, Charlotte, 1816-1855 2. Bronte, Emily, 1818-1848 3. Bronte, Anne, 1820-1849 4. Authors, English 19th century 5. Sisters 6. Women authors, English 19th century 7. Women 8. Yorkshire, England -- History -- 19th century
ISBN 9780547579665

LC 2011043559

"A solid and captivating look at these remarkable pioneers of modern fiction." Kirkus.

Includes bibliographical references.

Rhatigan, Joe

White House kids: the perks, pleasures, problems, and pratfalls of the Presidents' children. Joe Rhatigan; with illustrations by Jay Shin. Imagine! Pub., c2012. 96 p.

Grades: 5 6 7 8   920

1. White House, Washington, D.C. 2. Children of presidents 3. Presidents -- Family
ISBN 9781936140800

LC 2011045090

Shares the experiences of growing up in the White House, discusses the good and the bad, and profiles the children that have lived there.

"An inviting collection of insightful, interesting and often wacky and weird facts and stories about U.S. presidents and their families." Kirkus.

Includes bibliographical references (p. 94) and index.

Rohmer, Harriet

Heroes of the environment: true stories of people who help protect our planet. by Harriet Rohmer; illustrated by Julie McLaughlin. Chronicle Books, c2009. 110 p.

Grades: 4 5 6   920

1. Environmentalists 2. Environmentalism 3. Environmental movement
ISBN 9780811867795

LC 2009004366

Presents the true stories of twelve people from across North America who have done great things for the environment, from a teenage girl who figured out how to remove an industrial pollutant from the Ohio River to a Mexican superstar wrestler who protects turtles and whales.

"Engaging graphics and clear writing combine to provide a compelling reading experience." Science Books & Films.

Ruelle, Karen Gray

Surprising spies: unexpected heroes of World War II. Karen Gray Ruelle. Holiday House, 2020. 112 p.

Grades: 4 5 6 7 8   920

1. Spies 2. Espionage 3. Intelligence service 4. International intrigue 5. Spies -- History World War II
ISBN 9780823437573

LC 2017023913

Seven Allied spies of World War II who fooled the Nazis are profiled in this books including a Sufi princess, a major league baseball player, a magician, and others. Provided by publisher.

"Although middle-grade readers may know little about the war, the book delivers a good deal of information in concise sidebars as well as individual narratives that offer drama, varied settings, and a gradually broadening perspective." Booklist

Includes bibliographical references and index.

Schatz, Kate

Rad women worldwide: artists and athletes, pirates and punks, and other revolutionaries who shaped history. by Kate Schatz; illustrated by Miriam Klein Stahl. Ten Speed Press, 2016. 112 p.

Grades: 6 7 8 9 10 11 12 Adult   920

1. Women 2. Women's rights -- History 3. Intersectionality
ISBN 9780399578861

LC 2016012179

From the authors of the New York Times bestselling book Rad American Women A-Z, comes a bold new collection of 40 biographical profiles, each accompanied by a striking illustrated portrait, showcasing extraordinary women from around the world. Provided by publisher.

"Readers of either gender could well find a role model in the India-born U.S. astronaut Kalpana Chawla, or in Wangari Maathai, whose Green Belt Movement in Africa resulted in the planting of more than 30 million environment-reviving trees." Booklist.

Includes bibliographical references and index.

Schumann, Bettina

13 women artists children should know. Bettina Schumann; [translated from German by Jane Michael]. Prestel, 2009. 46 p.: Children should know

Grades: 5 6 7 8   920

1. Women artists 2. Artists 3. Women painters 4. Women sculptors
ISBN 9783791343334

LC bl2009030409

Introduces the lives and artistic styles of thirteen women artists from Renaissance painter Sofonisba Anguissola through such modern artists as Frida Kahlo, Niki de Saint Phalle, and Cindy Sherman.

"This large-format, brightly colored [survey proves a] solid, even inspiring [introduction] to the art world. . . . Leading questions encourage budding artists to use the featured subjects and artworks as inspiration." Horn Book Guide.

Smith-Llera, Danielle, 1971-

Serena vs. Venus: how a photograph spotlighted the fight for equality. by Danielle Smith-Llera. Compass Point Books, a Capstone imprint, [2017] 64 p.: Captured History Sports

Grades: 6 7 8 9   **920**

1. Williams, Serena, 1981- 2. Williams, Venus, 1980- 3. African American women tennis players 4. African American women 5. Tennis 6. Sisters 7. Photographs

ISBN 9780756555290

LC 2016038563

Discusses the lives and careers of tennis stars Serena and Venus Williams, highlighting the groundbreaking final match of the 2001 U.S. Open and the iconic photograph that captured the historic event.

"These books will certainly capture the attention of kids interested in sports, civil rights history, or photography." Booklist.

Includes bibliographical references and index.

Swaby, Rachel

Trailblazers: 33 women in science who changed the world. Rachel Swaby. Delacorte Press, 2016 176 p.

Grades: 5 6 7 8   **920**

1. Women scientists 2. Women inventors 3. Women

ISBN 9780399553967

LC 2016003806

Profiles thirty-three women who have made notable contributions to science, including Maria Gaetana Agnesi, Virginia Apgar, and Rachel Carson.

"Readers with scientific ambitions of their own will find much to admire in these accomplished and unconventional women." Publishers Weekly.

Swartz, Clay

Who wins?: 100 historical figures go head-to-head and you decide the winner! created by Clay Swartz; illustrated by Tom Booth. Workman Publishing Co., Inc.. [2016] 52 p.

Grades: 5 6 7 8   **920**

1. History 2. Educational games 3. Celebrities 4. Contests

ISBN 9780761185444

LC 2015040316

One can read lengthy biographies of historical figures. Or, with Who Wins?, pit them head-to-head in a Ping-Pong match, hot dog eating contest, or a pie bake-off and actually understand firsthand the strengths and weaknesses, the triumphs and losses of the people who have shaped our world. Provided by publisher.

"History with a hilarious spin and a cinch to provoke vigorous debates aplenty." Kirkus.

Vourvoulias, Sabrina

Nuestra America: 30 inspiring latinas/latinos who have shaped the United States. by Sabrina Vourvoulias; illustrated by Gloria Felix; introduction by Eduardo Diaz; reading guide by Emily Key. RP Kids, 2020. 118 p.

Grades: 3 4 5 6 7   **920**

1. Hispanic Americans 2. Hispanic American women 3. Hispanic American men

ISBN 9780762497478

Published in association with the Smithsonian Institution and the Molina Family Latino Gallery, a celebration of 30 of history's most influential Latinas and Latinos shares the uplifting stories of subjects ranging from Pura Belpré and Cesar Chavez to Jennifer Lopez and Sonia Sotomayor.

"Each entry is paired with a colorful portrait, bringing its subject and his or her accomplishments to life. While this book will educate all readers, it importantly provides Latinx American children with inspirational role models from a diverse array of professions." Booklist

Wenzel, Angela

13 artists children should know. Angela Wenzel. Prestel Pub., 2009. 48 p.: Children should know

Grades: 4 5 6   **920**

1. Artists 2. Art appreciation 3. Art history

ISBN 9783791341736

"This large-format, brightly colored [survey provides a] solid, even inspiring [introduction] to the art world. . . . Leading questions encourage budding artists to use the featured subjects and artworks as inspiration." Horn Book Guide.

Winter, Jonah, 1962-

Peaceful heroes. by Jonah Winter; illustrated by Sean Addy. Arthur A. Levine Books, 2009. 64 p.

Grades: 4 5 6 7   **920**

1. Heroes and heroines 2. Peace -- History 3. Peace activists 4. Nonviolence 5. Peace movements

ISBN 9780439623070

LC 2008048311

"Starting off with Jesus, Gandhi, King, and Sojourner Truth, this collective biography goes on to profile many less well-known peace activists across the world. . . . The detailed portraits never deny the horrifying realities that the peace-seeking leaders are fighting against. With the chatty interactive text, there are handsome full-page pictures of each activist, rendered in oil, acrylic, and collage in shades of red and brown." Booklist.

Yolen, Jane

Bad girls: sirens, Jezebels, murderesses, thieves, & other female villains. Jane Yolen, Heidi E. Y. Stemple; illustrated by Rebecca Guay. Charlesbridge, c2013. vii, 164 p.

Grades: 6 7 8 9 10 11 12   **920**

1. Women criminals 2. Femmes fatales 3. Women murderers 4. Women 5. Illustrated books 6. Books for reluctant readers

ISBN 9781580891851

LC 2012000783

An introduction to more than two dozen of history's most notorious women shares the stories of such figures as Tituba, Lizzie Borden, and Cleopatra, and allows the readers to draw their own conclusions about each woman's guilt.

Young, Jeff C., 1948-

Inspiring African-American inventors: nine extraordinary lives. Jeff C. Young. Enslow Publishers, 2009. 128 p.: Great scientists and famous inventors

Grades: 5 6 7   **920**

1. African American inventors 2. Inventors 3. African Americans

ISBN 9781598450804

"This collective biography . . . profiles nine African American inventors: Lewis Howard Latimer, Jan E. Matziliger, Granville T. Woods, George Washington Carver, Madam C. J. Walker, Garrett A. Morgan, Percy Lavon Julian, Patricia Era Bath, and Lonnie G. Johnson. . . . Clearly written and logically organized, this volume provides a useful guide to the subject." Booklist.

Includes bibliographical references and index.

920.0092 Biography—Ethnic and national groups

Davis, Kenneth C.

In the shadow of Liberty: the hidden history of slavery, four presidents, and five black lives. Kenneth C. Davis. Henry Holt and Company, 2016. 304 p.

Grades: 6 7 8 9 10   **920.0092**

1. Enslaved people 2. Slavery -- History 3. African Americans 4. Presidents -- Relations with African Americans -- History 5. United States -- Race relations -- History

ISBN 9781627793117

             LC 2015035204

An examination of American slavery through the true stories of five enslaved people who were considered the property of some of our best-known presidents. Provided by publisher.

"This well-researched book offers a chronological history of slavery in America and features five enslaved people and the four U.S. presidents who owned them. . . . Always referring to enslaved people rather than slaves, Davis organizes a great deal of factual material, personal accounts, and quotes into a very readable history book." Booklist.

Includes bibliographical references and index.

Engle, Margarita

Bravo!: poems about amazing Hispanics. Margarita Engle; illustrated by Rafael Lopez. Henry Holt and Company, 2016. 48 p.

Grades: 4 5 6 7   **920.0092**

1. Hispanic Americans 2. Latin Americans

ISBN 9780805098761

             LC 2016009015

Bold, graphic portraits and beautiful poems present famous and lesser-known Latinos from varied backgrounds who have faced life's challenges in creative ways. Provided by publisher.

920.71 Biography—Men

Peters, Stephanie True, 1965-

Groundbreaking guys: 40 men who became great by doing good. Stephanie True Peters; illustrated by Shamel Washington. Little, Brown and Company, 2019. 92 p.

Grades: 2 3 4 5 6   **920.71**

1. Men 2. Artists 3. Celebrities 4. Heroes

ISBN 9780316529419

             LC 2018053959

This illustrated survey book is a collection of forty diverse men who helped their communities. Provided by publisher.

920.72 Biography—Women

McCann, Michelle Roehm, 1968-

More girls who rocked the world: heroines from Ada Lovelace to Misty Copeland. Michelle Roehm McCann. Aladdin, 2017. 256 p.

Grades: 5 6 7 8   **920.72**

1. Girls 2. Heroes and heroines 3. Women

ISBN 9781582706412

             LC 2017006516

From the inspiring author of Girls Who Rocked the World comes another comprehensive collection of true, inspiring profiles of successful young women throughout history who made their mark on the world before turning twenty. Provided by publisher.

"A diverse compendium that will entertain, inform, and inspire." Kirkus.

Includes bibliographical references.

Schatz, Kate

Rad American women A-Z: rebels, trailblazers, and visionaries who shaped our history . . . and our future! written by Kate Schatz; illustrated by Miriam Klein Stahl. City Lights Books, 2015. 64 p.

Grades: 6 7 8 9   **920.72**

1. Women 2. Women's rights -- History 3. Intersectionality 4. Books for reluctant readers

ISBN 9780872866836

             LC 2014037930

"Colorful and hip potraitures create a visual sensation that immediately draws in readers. Profiled are 26 American women from the 18th through 21st centuries, who have made—or are still making—history as artists, writers, teachers, lawyers, or athletes...Classes across the curriculum can utilize this informative book." School Library Journal.

920.72089 Women—Specific ethnic and national groups

Sonneborn, Liz

A to Z of American Indian women. Liz Sonneborn. Facts On File, c2007. xvi, 320 p.: A to Z of women

Grades: 8 9 10 11 12   **920.72089**

1. Native American women 2. Native American women -- History 3. Indians of North America 4. Women

ISBN 9780816066940

             LC 2007008162

Offers profiles of one hundred fifty-two influential Native American women involved in social activism, literature, politics, medicine, and the arts.

"This resource is of exceptionally high quality." School Library Journal.

Includes bibliographical references (p. 291-293) and index.

929 Genealogy, names, insignia

Ollhoff, Jim, 1959-

Beginning genealogy. Jim Ollhoff. ABDO Pub. Co., c2011. 32 p.

Grades: 4 5 6 7   **929**

1. Genealogy

ISBN 9781616134600

             LC 2009050812

Introduces genealogy, explains the meaning in surnames, and provides tips on finding ancestors.

"This is great . . . for kids interested in genealogy. . . . [It does] a wonderful job of presenting the fundamentals of genealogical research in a clear and exciting manner. . . . Understanding and properly using primary documents is stressed throughout. . . . [An] attractive, spacious [layout]; full-color, sharp images; clearly labeled diagrams; and scattered maps add information and appeal." School Library Journal.

Collecting primary records. by Jim Ollhoff. ABDO Pub. Co., 2011. 32 p.: Your family tree

Grades: 4 5 6 7   **929**

  1. Research 2. Information resources 3. Genealogy
ISBN 9781616134617

               LC 2009050811

Discusses the importance of primary records and documents in genealogical research, including birth and death certificates, immigration records, and census data, and explains how to use and evaluate these documents.

"This is great . . . for kids interested in genealogy. . . . [It does] a wonderful job of presenting the fundamentals of genealogical research in a clear and exciting manner. . . . Understanding and properly using primary documents is stressed throughout. . . . [An] attractive, spacious [layout]; full-color, sharp images; clearly labeled diagrams; and scattered maps add information and appeal." School Library Journal.

DNA: window to the past. by Jim Ollhoff. ABDO Pub. Co., c2011. 32 p.: Your family tree

Grades: 4 5 6 7   **929**

  1. Genetic genealogy 2. DNA research 3. Genetics 4. Genealogy
ISBN 9781616134624

               LC 2009050808

Describes how genetic testing and DNA are being used in the field of genealogy, details famous genealogical discoveries using DNA, and explains how genetic mutations can be traced to determine ancestry.

"This is great . . . for kids interested in genealogy. . . . [It does] a wonderful job of presenting the fundamentals of genealogical research in a clear and exciting manner. . . . Understanding and properly using primary documents is stressed throughout. . . . [An] attractive, spacious [layout]; full-color, sharp images; clearly labeled diagrams; and scattered maps add information and appeal." School Library Journal.

Filling the family tree. by Jim Ollhoff. ABDO Pub. Co., c2011. 32 p.: Your family tree

Grades: 4 5 6 7   **929**

  1. Families 2. Genealogy
ISBN 9781616134648

               LC 2009050806

Introduces family trees, explains how to draw a family tree with extended family included, and provides tips on interviewing family members.

"This is great . . . for kids interested in genealogy. . . . [It does] a wonderful job of presenting the fundamentals of genealogical research in a clear and exciting manner. . . . Understanding and properly using primary documents is stressed throughout. . . . [An] attractive, spacious [layout]; full-color, sharp images; clearly labeled diagrams; and scattered maps add information and appeal." School Library Journal.

Using your research: how to check your facts and use your information. by Jim Ollhoff. ABDO Pub., c2011. 32 p.: Your family tree

Grades: 4 5 6 7   **929**

  1. Genealogy 2. Research 3. Information resources
ISBN 9781616134655

               LC 2009050805

Presents a brief guide on how to check facts and use other information in genealogical research.

"This is great . . . for kids interested in genealogy. . . . [It does] a wonderful job of presenting the fundamentals of genealogical research in a clear and exciting manner. . . . Understanding and properly using primary documents is stressed throughout. . . . [An] attractive, spacious [layout]; full-color, sharp images; clearly labeled diagrams; and scattered maps add information and appeal." School Library Journal.

929.9 Forms of insignia and identification

Bateman, Teresa

  ★ **Red,** white, blue, and Uncle who?: the stories behind some of America's patriotic symbols. by Teresa Bateman; illustrated by John O'Brien. Holiday House, c2001. 64 p.

Grades: 4 5 6 7   **929.9**

  1. National emblems 2. National monuments
ISBN 0823412857

               LC 00057258

Presents seventeen patriotic symbols, including the flag, the Liberty Bell, Uncle Sam, and the Statue of Liberty, and examines how they came to represent America.

"This volume presents 17 patriotic symbols, an umbrella term that encompasses everything from the flag to Uncle Sam, from Mount Rushmore to the Korean War Memorial. Bateman finds plenty of interesting information to share about each symbol or site, and browsers will be entertained by the many stories of origination, construction, and history." Booklist.

Bednar, Sylvie

  ★ **Flags** of the world. Sylvie Bednar. Abrams Books for Young Readers, 2009. 192 p.

Grades: 4 5 6 7   **929.9**

  1. Flags 2. Geography 3. National emblems 4. Countries 5. Signs and symbols
ISBN 9780810980105

               LC 2008045923

Each nation's flag is paired with facts and tidbits of history about that country, providing a window into the values and cultures of countries from around the globe.

"Organized by continent, this book takes a close look at the artwork and meaning of each country's flag. A large color image of the flag is accompanied by entries about the state's capital, currency, official language, area, and highest geographical point. More than 100 captioned illustrations add fascinating facts as well. . . . The consistent layout of the book and its accessible information will create an ease of both student use and comprehension." School Library Journal.

930 History of ancient world (to ca. 499)

Morris, Neil, 1946-

  Prehistory. Neil Morris. Zak Books, c2009. 48 p. : History (Zak Books (Firm))

Grades: 7 8 9 10   **930**

  1. Prehistoric humans 2. Humans -- Origin
ISBN 9788860981561

               LC 2008008399

A detailed overview of history from the beginning of the world to when humans began to record their history, including archaeological evidence for what we know about prehistory. Provided by publisher.

"The effectiveness lies in the combination of lush illustrations, well-chosen, captioned photographs of contemporary artifacts, and . . . [a] reasoned, concise [narrative]. Succinct time lines border most pages, . . . the proper amount of white space, and clear dark print maintain organization and clarity. A superior choice." School Library Journal.

930.1 Archaeology

Barber, Nicola

   Tomb explorers. Nicola Barber. Capstone Raintree, 2013. 48 p.: Ignite: treasure hunters

Grades: 5 6 7 8   **930.1**

   1. Tombs 2. Treasure troves 3. Antiquities 4. Archaeology -- History 5. Civilization, Ancient

ISBN 9781410949554

                        LC 2012012894

Looks at five ancient tombs with treasure troves, presenting information about their discoverers, how the discoveries were made, and what was found at each of them.

Hunter, Nick

   Ancient treasures. Nick Hunter; [edited by Laura Knowles ... [et al.]; illustrated by Martin Bustamante]. Raintree, c2013. 48 p.: Ignite: treasure hunters

Grades: 5 6 7 8   **930.1**

   1. Treasure troves 2. Treasure hunting 3. Civilization, Ancient 4. Archaeology -- History

ISBN 9781410949509

                        LC 2012012757

Looks at several ancient treasure troves, presenting information about their discoverers, how the discoveries were made, and what was found at each of them.

Rubalcaba, Jill

   Every bone tells a story: hominin discoveries, deductions, and debates. Jill Rubalcaba and Peter Robertshaw. Charlesbridge, c2010. 185 p.

Grades: 8 9 10 11 12   **930.1**

   1. Prehistoric humans 2. Human remains (Archaeology) 3. Excavations (Archaeology) 4. Archaeology 5. Archaeologists

ISBN 9781580891646

                        LC 2008026961

Discusses the discoveries of four hominins including Turkana Boy, Lapedo Child, Kennewick Man and Iceman, offering insight into how archaeologists analyzed the remains of each to further their understanding of ancient human behavior.

   "Archaeology and paleontology are the exciting focus in this accessible account of four hominins who lived long before recorded history. . . . The informal style never oversimplifies the engaging science and technology, and the authors raise as many questions as they answer in the detailed chapters." Booklist.

   Includes bibliographical references and index.

931 China to 420

Ball, Jacqueline A.

   ★ **National** Geographic investigates ancient China: archaeology unlocks the secrets of China's past. by Jacqueline Ball and Richard Levey; Robert Murowchick, consultant. National Geographic, c2007. 64 p.: National Geographic investigates

Grades: 5 6 7 8   **931**

   1. Excavations (Archaeology) 2. Archaeology 3. China -- Antiquities

ISBN 079227783X

                        LC bl2006029455

Discusses important archeological finds from China's past and reveals how archaeologists use the latest technology to discover clues to ancient Chinese civilization.

   "This volume spotlights archaeological finds from Ancient China. . . . While the discussions of archaeology will hold readers' interest, the accompanying illustrations steal the show." Booklist.

   Includes bibliographical references (p. 60) and index.

Liu-Perkins, Christine

   At home in her tomb: Lady Dai and the ancient Chinese treasures of Mawangdui. Christine Liu-Perkins; illustrated by Sarah Brannen. Charlesbridge, c2013. 80 p.

Grades: 5 6 7 8   **931**

   1. Excavations (Archaeology) 2. Tombs 3. Human remains (Archaeology) 4. Treasure troves 5. Material culture 6. China 7. Mawangdui Site (China)

ISBN 9781580893701

                        LC 2012024630

   "In 1971, the tomb of Lady Dai was discovered, virtually intact and of enormous archaeological significance. Here, buried in 158 BCE, was her still-soft body and more than a thousand artifacts. Liu-Perkins describes the discovery in fascinating detail; brief imagined scenes supplement the evidence. Illustrative materials include maps and well-captioned photos as well as Brannen's watercolors of the fictionalized scenes. Timeline. Bib., glos., ind." Horn Book.

   Includes bibliographical references and index.

O'Connor, Jane

   ★ The **emperor's** silent army: terracotta warriors of Ancient China. Jane O'Connor. Viking, 2002. 48 p.

Grades: 4 5 6 7   **931**

   1. Qin shi huang, Emperor of China, 259-210 B.C.E. 2. Rulers 3. Tombs 4. Archaeology 5. Terra-cotta sculpture, Chinese 6. Material culture 7. China -- History -- Qin dynasty, 221-207 B.C.E. 8. China -- Antiquities.

ISBN 0670035122

                        LC 2001046900

Describes the archaeological discovery of thousands of life-sized terracotta warrior statues in northern China in 1974, and discusses the emperor who had them created and placed near his tomb.

   "This intriguing book is enhanced by beautiful illustrations—pictures of stone engravings, colorful paintings, drawings, and maps—while numerous photographs show the clay soldiers from different perspectives. . . . The author's writing style is entertaining, yet informative. Book Rep

   Includes bibliographical references (p. 47) and index.

Rosinsky, Natalie M. (Natalie Myra)

   Ancient China. by Natalie M. Rosinsky. Compass Point Books, c2013. 48 p.: Exploring the ancient world

Grades: 6 7 8   **931**

   1. Civilization, Ancient 2. Ancient history 3. China -- Civilization 4. China -- History

ISBN 9780756545680

                        LC 2012001965

Presents information about ancient China, describing its early ruling dynasties, its art, religion, philosophy, technology, and the everyday life of its people.

932 Egypt to 640

Berger, Melvin
Mummies of the pharaohs: exploring the Valley of the Kings. Melvin Berger & Gilda Berger. National Geographic Society, c2001. 64 p.
Grades: 4 5 6 7 **932**
    1. Mummies 2. Tombs 3. Egypt -- Rulers. 4. Valley of the Kings, Egypt -- Antiquities
ISBN 0792272234

LC 00055411
Starting with the discovery of King Tutankhamun's tomb and its glorious treasures, the authors explore Egypt's entire Valley of the Kings, discussing the various tombs and their occupants.
    "This offers stunning photographs and clear, compelling text. . . . A fascinating historical resource that kids will read straight through for pleasure and also find useful for report writing." Booklist.

Croy, Anita
Ancient Egypt. edited by Anita Croy. Brown Bear Books, c2010. 64 p. : Facts at your fingertips.
Grades: 6 7 8 9 **932**
    1. Civilization, Ancient 2. Ancient history 3. Ancient Egypt -- Civilization -- To 332 B.C.E.
ISBN 9781933834542

LC 2009016802
"This begins with an introduction accompanied by a striking full-page photo, followed by a two-page time line, and a two-paged spread for each topic. This format makes information easily accessible. Beautiful color photos of ancient ruins, drawings, maps, diagrams, and re-creations create appeal and enhance the information. . . . Whether for recreational browsing or serious research, this . . . will certainly prove useful for students." Library Media Connection.

Hollar, Sherman
Ancient Egypt. edited by Sherman Hollar. Britannica Educational Pub. in association with Rosen Educational Services, 2012. 87 p.: Ancient civilizations
Grades: 5 6 7 8 **932**
    1. Civilization, Ancient 2. Ancient history 3. Ancient Egypt -- Civilization -- To 332 B.C.E. 4. Ancient Egypt -- History -- To 332 B.C.E.
ISBN 9781615305230

LC 2011004714
Presents a history of Ancient Egypt and discusses the accomplishments and culture of the people.
    "This book provides enough information about the development, way of life, accomplishments, and decline of [Ancient Egypt] without overwhelming readers. Maps; full-color illustrations and photographs, many full page; and sidebars provide additional focus. . . . The use of the Nile and its influence on the development of this civilization is emphasized. . . . The building of the great pyramids and the art of mummification are also mentioned. A detailed discussion of the everyday lives of the rich and the poor provide valuable insight." School Library Journal.
    Includes bibliographical references (p. 82) and index.

Kerrigan, Michael, 1959-
Egyptians. by Michael Kerrigan. Marshall Cavendish Benchmark, c2010. 64 p.: Ancients in their own words
Grades: 5 6 7 8 **932**
    1. Inscriptions, Egyptian 2. Ancient history 3. Quotations 4. Ancient Egypt -- Civilization -- To 332 B.C.E. 5. Ancient Egypt

-- History -- To 332 B.C.E.
ISBN 9781608700646

LC 2009033475
Offers insight into ancient times through the words of its peoples by featuring modern translations of some of the most important written records from ancient Egypt, including: the Palermo Stone; Stela of Irtysen at Abydos; the Abbott Papyrus; the Stelaat Karnak; Tiy's Wedding Scarab; and the Stela of Merneptah, with examples of hieroglyphics and hieratic scripts. Provided by publisher.
    "Features Numerous photographs provide visual interest, with text describing the images to give details and background. Translations of the writings offer primary sources to accompany the secondary material presented. . . . The text is interesting enough to read cover to cover while the table of contents' descriptive chapter titles and the comprehensive index enable the . . . [book] to be used for specific research." Library Media Connection.
    Includes bibliographical references and index.

Lace, William W.
King Tut's curse. by William W. Lace. ReferencePoint Press, Inc., 2012. 80 p.: Ancient Egyptian wonders
Grades: 8 9 10 11 12 **932**
    1. Tutankhamen, King of Egypt. 2. Tutankhamen, King of Egypt 3. Carnarvon, George Edward Stanhope Molyneux Herbert, Earl of, 1866-1923 4. Excavations (Archaeology) 5. Mummies 6. Rulers 7. Ancient history 8. Curses 9. Egypt 10. Valley of the Kings (Egypt) -- Antiquities.
ISBN 9781601522504

LC 2011048987
"This explores Egyptian history, mummy making, the discovery and opening of the tomb of Tutankhamen in 1922, and the events that happened after that. Much of the book is based on archaeologist Howard Carter's diaries and letters, and on period newspaper articles. The color photographs in [this attractive [book] are excellent, and the readable [text is] interesting." School Library Journal.
    Includes bibliographical references and index.

Mummification and death rituals of ancient Egypt. William W. Lace. ReferencePoint Press, c2013. 80 p.: Ancient Egyptian wonders
Grades: 8 9 10 11 12 **932**
    1. Mummies 2. Embalming 3. Gods and goddesses, Egyptian 4. Life after death 5. Funerals 6. Egypt -- Antiquities. 7. Ancient Egypt -- Religion -- To 332 B.C.E.
ISBN 9781601522542

LC 2012011481
Looks at the beliefs and death rituals of the ancient Egyptians, highlighting mummification.

Nardo, Don, 1947-
Cause & effect. Ancient Egypt. Don Nardo. ReferencePoint Press, 2018 80 p.: Cause & Effect: Ancient Civilizations
Grades: 6 7 8 9 10 11 12 **932**
    1. Egypt -- Civilization 2. Ancient Egypt -- History -- To 332 B.C.E.
ISBN 9781682821503

LC 2016045977
Offers a brief history of ancient Egypt and discusses the earliest civilization that developed across the Nile River Valley, the building of the pyramids, religious beliefs, and Cleopatra's role in Egypt's fall to the Romans.

Perl, Lila

Mummies, tombs, and treasure: secrets of Ancient Egypt. by Lila Perl; drawings by Erika Weihs. Clarion Books, [1990], c1987. 120 p.

Grades: 4 5 6 7   **932**

    1. Mummies 2. Tombs 3. Egypt -- Antiquities.
ISBN 0395547962

                 LC BL 99710937

Text and photographs examine the mummies and tombs of ancient Egypt.

Rubalcaba, Jill

    ★ **National** Geographic investigates ancient Egypt: archaeology unlocks the secrets of Egypt's past. by Jill Rubalcaba. National Geographic, c2007. 64 p.: National Geographic investigates

Grades: 5 6 7 8   **932**

    1. Archaeology -- Technological innovations 2. Excavations (Archaeology) 3. Egypt -- Antiquities. 4. Egypt -- History.
ISBN 0792278577

                 LC 2006032111

Learn about the discoveries that are bringing Egypt's history to light today.

    "This offers the beautiful photography and illustrations characteristic of the National Geographic Society, [a] well-written [text] and sidebars, and information on recent archaeological finds." School Library Journal.

    Includes bibliographical references (p. 60) and index.

Weitzman, David

    ★ **Pharaoh's** boat. written and illustrated by David Weitzman. Houghton Mifflin Harcourt, 2009. 32 p.

Grades: 4 5 6 7   **932**

    1. Cheops, King of Egypt 2. Rulers 3. Boat-building 4. Boats 5. Ships 6. Ships, Wooden 7. Ancient Egypt -- History -- To 332 B.C.E.
ISBN 9780547053417

                 LC 2008036081

"Weitzman recounts the construction of a boat made for the Pharaoh Cheops and discusses its rediscovery and restoration in the 20th century. He weaves the history, texts, mythology, and customs of ancient Egypt into an effective narrative. . . . The volume's stylized illustrations are inspired by the two-dimensional depictions from ancient Egyptian art. The paintings' earth tones, accentuated by bright greens and blues, are both appropriate for the subject matter and pleasing to the eye." School Library Journal.

932.01 Early history to 332 B.C.

Kallen, Stuart A., 1955-

    Pharaohs of Egypt. Stuart A. Kallen. ReferencePoint Press, c2013. 80 p.: Ancient Egyptian wonders

Grades: 8 9 10 11 12   **932.01**

    1. Rulers 2. Civilization, Ancient 3. Ancient history 4. Egypt -- Rulers. 5. Ancient Egypt -- Civilization -- To 332 B.C.E.
ISBN 9781601522566

                 LC 2012000360

Looks at the great pharaohs of Egypt, their exploits, their beliefs, and their legacies.

Whiting, Jim, 1951-

    Life along the ancient Nile. by Jim Whiting. ReferencePoint Press, 2013. 80 p.: Ancient Egyptian wonders

Grades: 8 9 10 11 12   **932.01**

    1. Material culture 2. Civilization, Ancient 3. Ancient Egypt -- Civilization -- To 332 B.C.E. 4. Ancient Egypt -- History -- To 332 B.C.E.
ISBN 9781601522528

                 LC 2012000358

Examines the everyday life, beliefs and rituals, medicine, and education of the ancient Egyptians who lived along the Nile coast.

    "This series provides a wealth of information on the ancient Egyptians, focusing on the infamous curse of King Tut, the pyramids of Giza, pharaohs, mummification and burial rites, and daily life. Even though this is oft-covered ground, these books stand out for their abundant material and the appealing presentations. The content is extensive, but it is written in a conversational style that will pull in report writers and browsers alike." School Library Journal.

    Includes bibliographical references and index.

935 Mesopotamia to 637 and Iranian Plateau to 637

Gruber, Beth

    ★ **National** Geographic investigates ancient Iraq: archaeology unlocks the secrets of Iraq's past. by Beth Gruber; Tony Wilkinson, consultant. National Geographic, 2007. 64 p.: National Geographic investigates

Grades: 5 6 7 8   **935**

    1. Excavations (Archaeology) 2. Civilization, Ancient 3. Civilization, Islamic 4. Iraq -- Antiquities. 5. Iraq -- Civilization -- To 634.
ISBN 0792253833

                 LC 2006032109

Discusses important archaeological finds from the three major historical periods of ancient Iraq and examines the insights they provide into the political and social life of that time period.

Kerrigan, Michael, 1959-

    Mesopotamians. by Michael Kerrigan. Marshall Cavendish Benchmark, c2010. 64 p.: Ancients in their own words

Grades: 5 6 7 8   **935**

    1. Civilization, Ancient 2. Ancient history 3. Quotations 4. Mesopotomia -- History. 5. Mesopotamia -- Civilization.
ISBN 9781608700660

                 LC 2009033476

Offers insight into ancient times through the words of its peoples, featuring some of the most important written records from ancient Mesopotamia, including: the Sumerian King List, the Code of Hammurabi, the Hittite-Egyptian treaty of Kadesh, and the Epic of Gilgamesh, with examples of scripts carved into clay tablets and pillars using cuneiform letters. Provided by publisher.

    "Numerous photographs provide visual interest, with text describing the images to give details and background. Translations of the writings offer primary sources to accompany the secondary material presented. . . . The text is interesting enough to read cover to cover while the table of contents' descriptive chapter titles and the comprehensive index enable the . . . [book] to be used for specific research." Library Media Connection.

    Includes bibliographical references and index.

Nardo, Don, 1947-
Cause & effect.. Don Nardo. ReferencePoint Press, 2018 80 p.: Cause & Effect: Ancient Civilizations
Grades: 6 7 8 9 10 11 12   **935**
   1. Ancient history 2. Iraq -- History -- To 634 3. Mesopotamia
ISBN 9781682821589

                         LC 2016045952
Introduces ancient Mesopotamian civilization, describing the introduction of agriculture, the rise of urban culture, the development of writing, and a brief history of the successive kingdoms that occupied the region.

936 Europe north and west of Italian Peninsula to ca. 499

Hinds, Kathryn, 1962-
Goths. Kathryn Hinds. Marshall Cavendish Benchmark, c2010. 80 p.: Barbarians!
Grades: 6 7 8 9   **936**
   1. Goths -- History 2. Warriors 3. Migrations of nations 4. Ancient history 5. Civilization, Ancient 6. Rome -- History 7. Rome -- History -- Empire, 284-476
ISBN 9780761440659

                         LC 2009014114
A history of the Goths, who rose as a power in the early third century and, under their famous leader Alaric, succeeded in sacking Rome in 410. Provided by publisher.
"This has wonderful photographs of contemporaneous and more recent artwork and sculpture, which bring the . . . [Goths] to life for the modern reader." Voice of Youth Advocates.
Includes bibliographical references (p. 71-76) and index.

Huns. Kathryn Hinds. Marshall Cavendish Benchmark, c2010. 80 p.
Grades: 6 7 8 9   **936**
   1. Attila, -453 2. Huns -- History 3. Nomads -- History 4. Nomads -- History 5. Asia, Central -- History 6. Europe -- History -- To 476
ISBN 9780761440666

                         LC 2008054828
A history of the Huns, equestrian nomads of Central Asia who pillaged Europe and Asia from the third through fifth centuries. Provided by publisher.
"This . . . devotes excellent coverage and exposure to the emergence, development, and legacy of [the Huns]." Library Media Connection.
Includes bibliographical references (p. 71-72) and index.

Millard, Anne
A **street** through time: a 12,000-year journey along the same street. written by Anne Millard; illustrated by Steve Noon. DK Publishing, 2020, c1998. 32 p.
Grades: 4 5 6 7   **936**
   1. Streets 2. Urban archaeology 3. Urban anthropology 4. Archaeological sites 5. Cities and towns 6. Europe
ISBN 9781465490636

                         LC 98003226
Traces the development of one street from the Stone Age to the present day, from dirt track to the rebuilding of inns as wine bars, showing how people lived and what they did all day.
"The time-line construct is a useful demonstration for children, and the busy vistas would make a fine spring-board for encouraging students to create scenes of local history." Horn Book Guide.

936.2 England to 410 and Wales to 410

Aronson, Marc
  ★ **If** stones could speak: unlocking the secrets of Stonehenge. by Marc Aronson; with Mike Parker Pearson and the Riverside Project. National Geographic, 2010. 64 p.
Grades: 4 5 6 7   **936.2**
   1. Megalithic monuments 2. Stonehenge, England 3. Wiltshire, England -- Antiquities
ISBN 9781426306006

                         LC 2009028870
Documents the findings of a renowned archaeologist in the wider region surrounding Stonehenge, revealing how his team has revolutionized the understanding of Stonehenge and its historical purpose, in a lavishly photographed account that also traces their discovery of a Neolithic village.
"Aronson investigates the work of archaeologist Mike Parker Pearson and his controversial theory that Stonehenge is but one end of a memorial ritual pathway that would have had an equivalent wood structure at the other end. . . . Time lines, resource lists, and photos of researchers at work add even more value to this informative, thought-provoking study. A uniquely perceptive look at how real science works." Booklist.
Includes bibliographical references and index.

936.3 Germanic regions to 481 and Pannonia

Hinds, Kathryn, 1962-
Early Germans. Kathryn Hinds. Marshall Cavendish Benchmark, c2010. 80 p.: Barbarians!
Grades: 6 7 8 9   **936.3**
   1. Ancient history 2. Civilization, Ancient 3. Germanic peoples -- History 4. Rome -- History 5. Germany -- History
ISBN 9780761440642

                         LC 2008055789
A history of the early German peoples, who lived, traded, and fought with the ancient Romans—covering the period from 230 BCE to 180 CE. Provided by publisher.
"This . . . devotes excellent coverage and exposure to the emergence, development, and legacy of [the early Germans]." Library Media Connection.
Includes bibliographical references (p. 71-76) and index.

936.4 Celtic regions to 486

Green, Jen
  ★ **Ancient** Celts: archaeology unlocks the secrets of the Celtic past. Jen Green. National Geographic, c2008. 64 p.: National Geographic investigates
Grades: 4 5 6 7   **936.4**
   1. Civilization, Celtic 2. Celts 3. Northern Europe -- History.
ISBN 1426302258
Authoritative texts that include interviews with experts, maps, useful time lines, glossaries, and more bring readers up to date on the latest findings of and current viewpoints on ancient civilizations from leading archaeologists.
"With excellent-quality photographs and a well-written text, this is a thorough presentation of the most up-to-date knowledge about this ancient European culture." School Library Journal.

Hinds, Kathryn, 1962-

Ancient Celts: Europe's tribal ancestors. Kathryn Hinds. Marshall Cavendish Benchmark, 2009. 79 p.

Grades: 6 7 8 9   **936.4**
     1. Celts
     ISBN 9780761440628

                       LC 2008035976

A history of the ancient Celts, from their Iron Age culture to their final conquest by the Romans in the first century CE. Provided by publisher.

"This book has wonderful photographs of contemporaneous and more recent artwork and sculpture, which bring the . . . [Ancient Celts] to life for the modern reader." Voice of Youth Advocates.

Includes bibliographical references (p. 69-71) and index.

937 Italian Peninsula to 476 and adjacent territories to 476

Anderson, Michael

Ancient Rome. edited by Michael Anderson. Britannica Educational Pub. in association with Rosen Educational Services, 2012. 88 p.: Ancient civilizations

Grades: 5 6 7 8   **937**
     1. Civilization, Ancient 2. Rome -- Civilization 3. Rome -- History -- Empire, 30 B.C.E.-476 C.E.
     ISBN 9781615305223

                       LC 2011004749

Presents a history of Rome and discusses the accomplishments and culture of the empire.

"This book provides enough information about the development, way of life, accomplishments, and decline of [Ancient Rome] without overwhelming readers. Maps; full-color illustrations and photographs, many full page; and sidebars provide additional focus. . . . [The book] discusses the military expertise of Caesar and Pompey and the winning of the Punic Wars that led to world domination. The Romans' genius in engineering is highlighted." School Library Journal.

Includes bibliographical references (p. 83-86) and index.

Croy, Anita

Ancient Rome. edited by Anita Croy. Brown Bear Books, c2010. 64 p. : Facts at your fingertips.

Grades: 6 7 8 9   **937**
     1. Civilization, Ancient 2. Ancient history 3. Rome -- Civilization.
     ISBN 9781933834566

                       LC 2009016805

"This begins with an introduction accompanied by a striking full-page photo, followed by a two-page time line, and a two-paged spread for each topic. This format makes information easily accessible. Beautiful color photos of ancient ruins, drawings, maps, diagrams, and recreations create appeal and enhance the information. . . . Whether for recreational browsing or serious research, this . . . will certainly prove useful for students." Library Media Connection.

Deem, James M.

★ **Bodies** from the ash. James M. Deem. Houghton Mifflin, 2005. 50 p.

Grades: 4 5 6 7   **937**
     1. Excavations (Archaeology) 2. Volcanic eruptions 3. Italy -- History. 4. Pompeii (Extinct city)
     ISBN 0618473084

                       LC 2004026553

Details the events that occurred when Mount Vesuvius erupted and buried Pompeii in 79 A.D., focusing on how this information was deduced from the skeletons found by archaeologists at the site.

"On August 24, 79 C.E., the long-silent Mt. Vesuvius erupted, and volcanic ash rained down on the 20,000 residents of Pompeii. This photo-essay explains what happened when the volcano exploded—and how the results of this disaster were discovered hundreds of years later. . . . [This offers an] enormous amount of information. . . . But the jewels here are the numerous . . . photographs, especially those featuring the plaster casts and skeletons of people in their death throes. . . . Excellent for browsers as well as researchers." Booklist.

Includes bibliographical references (p. 47-48) and index.

Hinds, Kathryn, 1962-

Everyday life in the Roman Empire. by Kathryn Hinds. Marshall Cavendish Benchmark, c2010. 320 p.

Grades: 7 8 9 10   **937**
     1. Civilization, Ancient 2. Social classes 3. Rome -- History -- Empire, 30 B.C.E.-284 C.E. 4. Rome -- Social conditions.
     ISBN 9780761444848

                       LC 2009005913

Provides a social history of life in the Roman Empire at its most powerful, from 27 B.C.E. to 200 C.E., and includes descriptions of the ruling classes, the peasantry, and the urban dwellers. Provided by publisher.

"This book combines clear, bold text with vivid reproductions of period paintings, frescoes, and sculptures, making for [a] stunning [presentation]." School Library Journal.

Kerrigan, Michael, 1959-

Romans. by Michael Kerrigan. Marshall Cavendish Benchmark, c2010. 64 p.: Ancients in their own words

Grades: 5 6 7 8   **937**
     1. Quotations 2. Civilization, Ancient 3. Ancient history 4. Romans 5. Rome -- Civilization 6. Rome -- History -- Empire, 30 B.C.E.-476 C.E.
     ISBN 9781608700677

                       LC 2009034428

Offers insight into ancient times through the words of its peoples by featuring modern translations of some of the most important written records from ancient Rome, including: Aemilius's decree; the Senatus Consultum de Bacchanalibus; Marcus Caelius's Memorial; and Lutacia Lupata's Stele, with examples of Roman writing and graffiti. Provided by publisher.

"Numerous photographs provide visual interest, with text describing the images to give details and background. Translations of the writings offer primary sources to accompany the secondary material presented. . . . The text is interesting enough to read cover to cover while the table of contents' descriptive chapter titles and the comprehensive index enable the . . . [book] to be used for specific research." Library Media Connection.

Includes bibliographical references and index.

Mann, Elizabeth, 1948-

★ The **Roman** Colosseum. by Elizabeth Mann; with illustrations by Michael Racz. Mikaya Press, 1998. 45 p.: Wonders of the world (Mikaya Press)

Grades: 4 5 6   **937**
     1. Colosseum, Rome. 2. Seven Wonders of the World 3. Theaters 4. Rome -- Buildings, structures, etc. 5. Rome -- Antiquities
     ISBN 0965049337

                       LC 98020060

Describes the building of the Colosseum in ancient Rome, and tells how it was used.

"This offers a clear, well-written text and full-color drawings and paintings." School Library Journal.

Nardo, Don, 1947-

Words of the ancient Romans: primary sources. Don Nardo, editor. Lucent Books, c2003. 128 p.: Lucent library of historical eras: Ancient Rome

Grades: 6 7 8 9   **937**

1. Rome -- History 2. Rome -- Civilization
ISBN 1590183185

LC 2003001645

Provides a historical look into the cultural, political, social, and religious aspects of ancient Roman life.

"Excerpts from historians such as Plutarch, Livy, and Suetonius, as well as the satires of Juvenal and poetry of Ovid, are included in this history of ancient Rome as told through the words of those who lived at the time. Various chapters cover the founding of the city, Julius Caesar's life, the reign of Augustus, home and family life, entertainment, leisure, and religion. . . . Each chapter . . . [begins] with an introduction that helps to put the subject in perspective for modern readers." School Library Journal.

Includes bibliographical references and index.

938 Greece to 323

Anderson, Michael

Ancient Greece. edited by Michael Anderson. Britannica Educational Pub. in association with Rosen Educational Services, 2012. 88 p.: Ancient civilizations

Grades: 5 6 7 8   **938**

1. Civilization, Ancient 2. Ancient history 3. Greek civilization 4. Greek civilization To 146 B.C.E. 5. Ancient Greece -- History -- 281-146 B.C.E. 6. Ancient Greece -- History -- To 146 B.C.E.
ISBN 9781615305131

LC 2011000086

Presents a history of ancient Greece and discusses the accomplishments and culture of the people.

"This book provides enough information about the development, way of life, accomplishments, and decline of [Ancient Greece] without overwhelming readers. Maps; full-color illustrations and photographs, many full page; and sidebars provide additional focus. . . . The system of city-states is explained. Literature, art, and architecture and their lasting influence are described in detail." School Library Journal.

Includes bibliographical references (p. 85) and index.

Croy, Anita

Ancient Greece. edited by Anita Croy. Brown Bear Books, c2010. 64 p. : Facts at your fingertips.

Grades: 6 7 8 9   **938**

1. Greek civilization 2. Civilization, Ancient 3. Ancient history 4. Greek civilization To 146 B.C.E. 5. Ancient Greece -- History -- To 146 B.C.E.
ISBN 9781933834559

LC 2009016803

"This begins with an introduction accompanied by a striking full-page photo, followed by a two-page time line, and a two-paged spread for each topic. This format makes information easily accessible. Beautiful color photos of ancient ruins, drawings, maps, diagrams, and recreations create appeal and enhance the information. . . . Whether for

recreational browsing or serious research, this . . . will certainly prove useful for students." Library Media Connection.

Kerrigan, Michael, 1959-

Greeks. by Michael Kerrigan. Marshall Cavendish Benchmark, c2010. 64 p.: Ancients in their own words

Grades: 5 6 7 8   **938**

1. Civilization, Ancient 2. Greek civilization 3. Ancient history 4. Quotations 5. Greek civilization To 146 B.C.E. 6. Ancient Greece 7. Ancient Greece -- History -- To 146 B.C.E.
ISBN 9781608700653

LC 2009034429

Offers insight into ancient times through the words of its peoples by featuring modern translations of some of the most important written records from ancient Greece, including: the Phaistos Disk; boundary stone of the Agora; the Aristotle Herma; and the Parian Marble, with examples of Greek lettering adapted from the Phoenician alphabet. Provided by publisher.

"Numerous photographs provide visual interest, with text describing the images to give details and background. Translations of the writings offer primary sources to accompany the secondary material presented. . . . The text is interesting enough to read cover to cover while the table of contents' descriptive chapter titles and the comprehensive index enable the . . . [book] to be used for specific research." Library Media Connection.

Includes bibliographical references and index.

Mann, Elizabeth, 1948-

The **Parthenon**. by Elizabeth Mann; with illustrations by Yuan Lee. Mikaya Press, c2006. 47 p.: Wonders of the world (Mikaya Press)

Grades: 4 5 6 7   **938**

1. Parthenon (Athens, Greece) 2. Athens, Greece -- History 3. Athens, Greece
ISBN 1931414157

LC 2006044981

Examines the engineering feat of the ancient Greek temple, the Parthenon, and how it reflects the civilization of Athens, from its people and its rulers to its religion and its democracy.

"This volume introduces the history of ancient Athens culminating in the building of the Parthenon. . . . [The text is] well-researched and clearly written. . . . The color illustrations include an excellent map of Greece, photos of artifacts and sculptures, and many clearly deliniated, large-scale paintings." Booklist.

Includes bibliographical references (p. 47) and index.

Marcovitz, Hal

Ancient Greece. by Hal Marcovitz. ReferencePoint Press, 2012. 96 p.: Understanding world history

Grades: 7 8 9 10   **938**

1. Civilization, Ancient 2. Ancient history 3. Greek civilization To 146 B.C.E. 4. Ancient Greece 5. Ancient Greece -- History -- To 146 B.C.E.
ISBN 9781601522849

LC 2011048991

Presents a history of ancient Greece, discussing the factors that led to its rise, its greatest achievements, the reasons for its decline, and its legacy for the modern world.

"The Understanding World History series first lays out the sequence of events in each period of history and then explains how these events shaped what happened next... These concise treatments of important historical subjects should help students get a firmer grasp on what happened when, and why we still care." Booklist.

Includes bibliographical references and index.

McGee, Marni

★ **National** Geographic investigates ancient Greece: archaeology unlocks the secrets of Greece's past. by Marni McGee; Michael Shanks, consultant. National Geographic, c2007. 64 p.: National Geographic investigates

Grades: 5 6 7 8   **938**

1. Greek civilization 2. Underwater archaeology 3. Archaeology -- Technological innovations 4. Excavations (Archaeology) 5. Greece -- Antiquities.
ISBN 0792278720

LC 2006032108

Discusses important archeological finds from Greece's past and reveals how archaeologists use the latest technology to discover clues to ancient Greek civilization.

"This offers the beautiful photography and illustrations characteristic of the National Geographic Society, [a] well-written [text] and sidebars, and information on recent archaeological finds." School Library Journal.

Includes bibliographical references (p. 62) and index.

Nardo, Don, 1947-

Classical civilization: Greece. Don Nardo. Morgan Reynolds Pub., c2012. 112 p.: World history (Morgan Reynolds)

Grades: 6 7 8 9   **938**

1. Civilization, Ancient 2. Ancient history 3. Greek civilization 4. Greek civilization To 146 B.C.E. 5. Ancient Greece -- History -- To 146 B.C.E. 6. Ancient Greece
ISBN 9781599351735

LC 2011000235

Introduces the history and culture of ancient Greece, describing the politics, sports, architecture, science, art, and writings.

Park, Louise, 1961-

The **Spartan** hoplites. by Louise Park and Timothy Love. Marshall Cavendish Benchmark, 2009. 32 p. : Ancient and medieval people

Grades: 4 5 6   **938**

1. Soldiers 2. Military campaigns 3. Warriors 4. Persian Wars, 500-449 BCE 5. Sparta (Extinct city) -- History, Military. 6. Ancient Greece -- History, Military -- To 146 B.C.E.
ISBN 9780761444497

LC 2008055779

An introduction to the history and lifestyle of Spartan hoplites. Provided by publisher.

"This title has a simple and elegant design with the proper balance of quality writing and quantity of information. . . . Handy time lines, well-chosen photos of ruins and artifacts, quality illustrations, inset Quick Facts, and What You Should Know About features will grab reluctant readers and captivate even those with short attention spans." School Library Journal.

Roberts, Jennifer Tolbert, 1947-

The **ancient** Greek world. Jennifer Roberts & Tracy Barrett. Oxford University Press, c2004. 191 p.: The world in ancient times

Grades: 7 8 9 10   **938**

1. Civilization, Ancient 2. Ancient history 3. Greek civilization To 146 B.C.E. 4. Ancient Greece -- History -- To 146 B.C.E. 5.

Ancient Greece
ISBN 019515696X

LC 2003017875

Introduces the history, culture, and people of ancient Greece and examines its many contributions to the development of Western society.

"A thoroughly researched political and cultural history. . . . Extensive quotes from primary sources, attractive page layouts, numerous good-quality color photographs of ruins and artifacts, plus the infusion of humor make for a palatable, solid resource for any collection." School Library Journal.

939 Other parts of ancient world

Podany, Amanda H.

The **ancient** Near Eastern world. Amanda H. Podany & Marni McGee. Oxford University Press, c2005. 174 p.: The world in ancient times

Grades: 7 8 9 10   **939**

1. Civilization, Ancient 2. Ancient history 3. Middle East -- History -- To 622. 4. Middle East -- Antiquities.
ISBN 0195161599

LC 2004013622

"This traces the history of the Fertile Crescent until Alexander the Great's conquest in 330 B.C.E. . . . The text is matched with a great deal of supporting matter including time lines, maps, dramatis personae, high-quality photos, and artists' renderings. [This] fine [volume is a] worthy [addition] to most libraries." School Library Journal.

Includes bibliographical references (p. 165) and index.

Rubalcaba, Jill

★ **Digging** for Troy: from Homer to Hisarlik. Jill Rubalcaba and Eric H. Cline; with illustrations by Sarah S. Brannen. Charlesbridge, c2011. 74 p.

Grades: 5 6 7 8   **939**

1. Trojan War 2. Excavations (Archaeology) 3. Archaeologists 4. Civilization, Mycenaean 5. Excavations (Archaeology) 6. Troy (Extinct city) 7. Ancient Greece -- History -- To 146 B.C.E.
ISBN 9781580893268

LC 2010007586

Presents the history of ancient Troy, covering the legend of the city and describing the excavations of Heinrich Schliemann, Carl Blegen, and Manfred Korfmann as they date the numerous layers at the site trying to find the Troy of Homer's poem.

"Rubalcaba teams up with a noted archaeologist to make sense of the complicated, controversial, contradictory history and remains of the Turkish site called Hisarlik, better known as Troy. . . . The book begins with a brief but exciting retelling of the Trojan War . . . and goes on to profile Heinrich Schliemann. . . . After Schliemann, generations of archaeologists have excavated Hisarlik: along with the history of the excavations, readers are given an overview of technological developments in the field. . . . Source notes and an impressive bibliography attest to meticulous research and guide readers to journal articles, books, and online museum exhibits. Elegant illustrations mimicking Greek red-figure pottery are lovely and appropriate. Extraordinarily readable, gracefully laid out, and speckled with lines from The Iliad, this book will inspire young people interested in solving the mysteries of the past." School Library Journal.

Includes bibliographical references (p. [68]-69) and index.

940.1 History of Europe—Early history to 1453

Biesty, Stephen
    Stephen Biesty's cross-sections: Castle. illustrated by Stephen Biesty; written by Richard Platt. Dorling Kindersley, 2019. 29 p.
Grades: 3 4 5 6 7 8   **940.1**
    1. Castles 2. Civilization, Medieval
    ISBN 9781465484703

                                    LC 2019286270
Cross-sectional drawings depict castle life and the strategies of attackers and defenders during a siege

Helget, Nicole Lea, 1976-
    Barbarians. Nicole Helget. Creative Education, c2013. 48 p.: Fearsome fighters
Grades: 5 6 7 8   **940.1**
    1. Migrations of nations 2. Weapons 3. Battles 4. Warriors 5. Goths 6. Europe -- History -- 392-814
    ISBN 9781608181827

                                    LC 2011035798
A compelling look at barbarians, including their clashes with the Greek and Roman empires, their lifestyle, their weapons, and how they remain a part of today's culture through books and film. Provided by publisher.

Malam, John, 1957-
    Early medieval times. John Malam. Zak Books, 2009. 48 p. : History (Zak Books (Firm))
Grades: 7 8 9 10   **940.1**
    1. Civilization, Medieval 2. Europe -- History -- 476-1492.
    ISBN 9788860981509

                                    LC 2008008405
A detailed overview of the history in Europe from the collapse of the Roman Empire in western Europe in the late 400s to the Norman conquest of England in 1066. Provided by publisher.
    "The effectiveness lies in the combination of lush illustrations, well-chosen, captioned photographs of contemporary artifacts, and . . . [a] reasoned, concise [narrative]. Succinct time lines border most pages, and . . . the proper amount of white space, and clear dark print maintain organization and clarity. A superior choice." School Library Journal.

Nardo, Don, 1947-
    Medieval Europe. Don Nardo. Morgan Reynolds Pub., c2012. 128 p.: World history (Morgan Reynolds)
Grades: 6 7 8 9   **940.1**
    1. Civilization, Medieval 2. Europe -- History -- 476-1492 3. Europe -- Social life and customs -- 476-1492.
    ISBN 9781599351728

                                    LC 2010054477
Presents a history of the Middle Ages, discussing such topics as the emergence of nation-states, the rise of urban life, the power of the Church, the Crusades, and the twin calamities of famine and the Black Death.

940.2 History of Europe—1453-

Claybourne, Anna
    The **Renaissance**. Anna Claybourne. Raintree, c2008. 64 p.: Time travel guides
Grades: 6 7 8 9   **940.2**
    1. European Renaissance 2. Civilization, Western 3. Europe -- History -- 1492-1648 4. Europe -- Social life and customs
    ISBN 9781410929105

                                    LC 2007006027
Presents a tour of Renaissance Europe, discussing facts about fashion, diet, houses, religion, politics, culture, transportation, crime, and illness.
    "The book is chock-full of color photographs and reproductions, maps, sidebars, and age-appropriate humor. . . . The [author has] done a commendable job of writing [text] that [measures] up to the rich visual layout." School Library Journal.
    Includes bibliographical references (p. 61) and index.

Elliott, Lynne, 1968-
    The **Renaissance** in Europe. Lynne Elliott. Crabtree Pub. Co., New York: 32 p.: Renaissance world
Grades: 6 7 8 9   **940.2**
    1. European Renaissance 2. Civilization, Western 3. Europe -- Civilization -- 16th century. 4. Europe -- History -- 1492-1648
    ISBN 9780778745914

                                    LC 2008052410
Introduces the various elements of Renaissance life, including religion, trade, education, arts, and clothes.
    "Ideal introductions to concepts, people, and events of the Renaissance... succinct and thorough." School Library Journal.
    Includes bibliographical references (p. 32) and index.

Grant, Neil, 1938-
    Renaissance Europe. Neil Grant. Zak Books, c2009. 48 p. : History (Zak Books (Firm))
Grades: 7 8 9 10   **940.2**
    1. European Renaissance 2. Civilization, Western 3. Europe -- History -- 476-1492. 4. Europe -- History -- 1492-1648
    ISBN 9788860981530

                                    LC 2008008408
A detailed overview of the history of Europe during the fourteenth and fifteenth centuries, when the cultural movement known as the Renaissance made great advances in intellectual and artistic traditions. Provided by publisher.
    "The effectiveness lies in the combination of lush illustrations, well-chosen, captioned photographs of contemporary artifacts, and . . . [a] reasoned, concise [narrative]. Succinct time lines border most pages, and . . . clear dark print maintain organization and clarity. A superior choice." School Library Journal.

Hinds, Kathryn, 1962-
    Everyday life in the Renaissance. by Kathryn Hinds. Marshall Cavendish Benchmark, c2010. 336 p.: Everyday life (Marshall Cavendish Benchmark)
Grades: 7 8 9 10   **940.2**
    1. Civilization, Western 2. European Renaissance 3. Europe -- Civilization. 4. Europe -- History -- 15th century.
    ISBN 9780761444831

                                    LC 2008054829
Describes the social and economic structure of life in the Renaissance (from roughly 1400-1600), including the ruling classes, the peasantry, the urban dwellers, and members of the Church and the role each group played in shaping European civilization. Provided by publisher.
    "This book combines clear, bold text with vivid reproductions of period paintings, frescoes, and sculptures, making for [a] stunning [presentation]." School Library Journal.

Malam, John, 1957-

The **birth** of modern nations. John Malam. Zak Books, 2009. 48 p. : History (Zak Books (Firm))

Grades: 7 8 9 10   **940.2**

1. Civilization, Western 17th century 2. Europe -- History -- 17th century.

ISBN 9788860981554

LC 2008008570

A detailed overview of the history of Europe from about 1600 to 1700, during which modern nations came into power. Provided by publisher.

"The effectiveness lies in the combination of lush illustrations, well-chosen, captioned photographs of contemporary artifacts, and . . . [a] reasoned, concise [narrative]. Succinct time lines border most pages, and . . . the proper amount of white space, and clear dark print maintain organization and clarity. A superior choice." School Library Journal.

Pederson, Charles E.

The **French** & Indian War. by Charles E. Pederson. ABDO, c2010. 112 p.: Essential events

Grades: 6 7 8 9   **940.2**

1. Indians of North America -- Wars 1750-1815. 2. United States -- History -- French and Indian War, 1754-1763

ISBN 9781604539431

LC 2009030425

Provides a history of the French and Indian War, discussing its origins, battles, key figures, and impact.

"The writing is accessible and is richer than a lot of history writing, allowing the reader to become engaged in the text as a story, and the layout provides enough white space to allow lower level readers to feel confident." Library Media Connection.

Includes bibliographical references (p. 106-109) and index.

940.3 History of Europe—World War I, 1914-1918

Adams, Simon, 1955-

World War I. written by Simon Adams; photographed by Andy Crawford. DK Publishing, 2014. 72 p.: Eyewitness books

Grades: 4 5 6 7   **940.3**

1. World War I

ISBN 9781465421005

LC 2004302371

An up-close look at World War I examines life in the trenches and the devastation of Europe by the Great War.

"The DK Eyewitness series exemplifies what the publisher does best: taking a broad topic and slicing it into two-page chapters that, while they contain no narrative thread, make for excellent museum-type browsing... Each book rounds out the guided tour with an FAQ of sorts, profiles, and plenty of places for interested readers to keep looking. Just the thing to whet appetites before trucking down to the local real-life museum." Booklist.

Barber, Nicola

World War I. Nicola Barber. Heinemann Library, c2012. 80 p.: Living through

Grades: 6 7 8 9   **940.3**

1. 1910s 2. World War I 3. War 4. Battles

ISBN 9781432960018

LC 2011015931

Explores the history of World War I, including the important players, battles, and consequences.

Batten, Jack, 1932-

The **war** to end all wars: the story of World War I. Jack Batten. Tundra Books, 2009. 154 p.

Grades: 7 8 9 10 11 12   **940.3**

1. 1910s 2. Somme, 1st Battle of the, 1916 3. Vimy Ridge, Battle of, 1917 4. Soldiers 5. World War I 6. Military campaigns 7. France 8. Europe -- History -- 1900-1945.

ISBN 9780887768798

"More than six million soldiers perished in World War I . . . and this beautifully designed, highly readable photo-essay combines a few of their personal stories with the larger picture of politics and military strategies on all sides. . . . Young people with a particular interest in the war will be enthralled." Booklist.

Bausum, Ann

Unraveling freedom: the battle for democracy on the home front during World War I. Ann Bausum. National Geographic, 2010. 88 p.

Grades: 7 8 9 10   **940.3**

1. World War I -- Social aspects 2. German Americans -- History 20th century. 3. Freedom 4. United States -- Social conditions -- 20th century.

ISBN 9781426307027

A provocative analysis of the United States' involvement in World War I examines the 1915 sinking of the Lusitania—the "9/11" of that era—and draws parallels between the administrations of Presidents Woodrow Wilson and George W. Bush, exploring the ways in which various tenets of democracy were compromised for German-American citizens.

"Bausum describes the events that would eventually lead the U.S. into the European conflict that ultimately led to World War I. She then turns her attention to describing the destruction of civil liberties by President Wilson, Congress, and those in control of political power during the country's campaign to make the world safe for democracy. . . . Black-and-white archival photos and political cartoons are arranged in an artistic manner with informative captions. Appropriate quotations by various people of the time are displayed in elegant fonts. Make this unique and timely offering a definite first purchase." School Library Journal.

Includes bibliographical references (p. 84-86) and index.

Carlisle, Rodney P.

World War I. Rodney P. Carlisle. Facts On File, Inc., c2007. x, 454 p.

Grades: 10 11 12   **940.3**

1. World War I

ISBN 9780816060610

LC 2005027236

A chronological history of World War I, including the events that led up to it and its political and social legacy, is supplemented with such primary source documents as letters, diaries, and newspaper articles.

Coetzee, Marilyn Shevin, 1955-

World War I: a history in documents. Marilyn Shevin-Coetzee and Frans Coetzee. Oxford University Press, 2011. ix, 182 p.

Grades: 10 11 12   **940.3**

1. World War I

ISBN 9780199731510

LC 2009049519

Offering a comprehensive account of the war as more than a purely military phenomenon, World War I: A History in Documents, Second Edition, also addresses its profound social, cultural, and economic implications. Authors Marilyn Shevin-Coetzee and Frans Coetzee use editorials, memoirs, newspaper articles, poems, and letters to re-create the many facets of the war.

Grant, R. G.

Why did World War I happen? R.G. Grant. Gareth Stevens Pub., 2011. 48 p.: Moments in History

Grades: 6 7 8 9   940.3
    1. World War I 2. War 3. Military history 4. World politics
ISBN 9781433941818

LC 2010012459

Uses primary sources to document the causes behind World War I.

"Examines the events that served as . . . [precursors to World War I]. . . . Brightly colored pull-out boxes highlight important turning points, the perspective of the everyday man, and further information on why specific events occurred. Numerous photographs help readers visualize concepts more fully. . . . Students should be able to easily use this resource." Library Media Connection.

Includes bibliographical references (p. 47) and index.

Osborne, Linda Barrett, 1949-

Come on in, America: the United States in World War I. Linda Barrett Osborne. Abrams Books for Young Readers, 2017. 256 p.

Grades: 5 6 7 8 9   940.3
    1. World War I 2. World War I -- American participation 3. World War I 4. World War I -- Homefront 5. World War I -- Women 6. United States -- History -- 20th century.
ISBN 9781419723780

LC 2016036830

"A study of World War I offers a context for discussing world events today, so this volume is a good bet for libraries and classrooms—a well-written treatment that can replace dry textbook accounts. A slim volume big on historical information and insight." Kirkus.

Includes bibliographical references and index.

Swain, Gwenyth, 1961-

World War I: an interactive history adventure. Gwenyth Swain. Capstone Press, 2012. 112 p. : You choose books.

Grades: 3 4 5 6   940.3
    1. 1910s 2. World War I 3. Military campaigns 4. Military history 5. War 6. Europe 7. Plot-your-own stories
ISBN 9781429660204

Describes World War I, using the reader's choices to reveal historical details from the perspectives of a Belgian resistance fighter, a British soldier, and an American Field Service volunteer.

940.4 Military history of World War I

Bascomb, Neal

The **grand** escape: the greatest prison breakout of the 20th century. by Neal Bascomb. Arthur A. Levine Books, 2018. 288 p.

Grades: 7 8 9 10   940.4
    1. First World War era (1914-1918) 2. 1910s 3. Prisoners of war 4. World War I -- Prisoners and prisons, German 5. Escaped prisoners of war 6. Soldiers 7. Airmen 8. Germany
ISBN 9781338140347

LC 2018016857

Recounts the escape from Germany's most notorious prison camp, Holzminden, by a group of Allied POWs in WWI.

Bausum, Ann

Stubby the war dog: the true story of World War I's bravest dog. Ann Bausum. National Geographic, 2014. 72 p.: National Geographic kids

Grades: 4 5 6 7   940.4
    1. United States. Army. Infantry Regiment, 102nd. 2. World War I 3. Dogs -- War use 4. Working dogs 5. Soldiers 6. Human/animal relationships
ISBN 9781426314865

Documents the heroic wartime achievements of a World War I mascot who was adopted by a soldier as an orphaned pup and who gained military honors and a display in the Smithsonian Institution for his brave service behind enemy lines.

"The popularity of tales about dogs in war stems from the inherent poignancy sweet, loyal, sad-eyed canines entered into the mad chaos of man-made destruction. But enter they occasionally do, and none more famously than Stubby... The speedy story is surrounded by evocative period photos, including plenty of the goofy-faced Stubby, and leads up to his later careers as a vaudeville star and a football mascot, and his eventual taxidermied inclusion in the Smithsonian. A triumph on three fronts: educational, emotional, and inspirational. For older teens, suggest Bausman's adult title, Sergeant Stubby." Booklist.

Murphy, Jim, 1947-

★ **Truce**: the day the soldiers stopped fighting. Jim Murphy. Scholastic Press, c2009. 116 p.

Grades: 5 6 7 8   940.4
    1. Christmas Truce, 1914 2. World War I 3. Trench warfare 4. Military campaigns 5. Christmas 6. Europe -- History, Military -- 20th century.
ISBN 9780545130493

LC 2008040500

Describes how, at Christmas, 1914, during World War I, in defiance of their officers' orders, a truce was declared by soldiers on opposing sides, who stopped fighting to engage in a spontaneous Christmas celebration with their "enemies."

"By December 1918, the western front of World War I featured two parallel trenches stretching from the North Sea to the Alps. . . . On Christmas Day, an informal peace broke out in many locations along the front. . . . Murphy's excellent telling of this unusual war story begins with an account of the events that led to WWI and follows the shift in the soldiers' mind-sets. . . . Printed in tones of sepia, the illustrations in this handsome volume include many period photos as well as paintings and maps. . . . Well organized and clearly written, this presentation vividly portrays the context and events of the Christmas Truce." Booklist.

Includes bibliographical references (p. 109-110), filmography (p. 110), and index.

940.53 World War II, 1939-1945

Altman, Linda Jacobs, 1943-

Escape, teens on the run: primary sources from the Holocaust. Linda Jacobs Altman. Enslow Pub., c2010. 128 p.: True stories of teens in the Holocaust

Grades: 7 8 9 10 11 12   940.53
    1. Holocaust (1933-1945) -- Children 2. Jewish teenagers 3. Child refugees 4. Escapes 5. Resistance to government -- History 20th century
ISBN 9780766032705

LC 2009021378

Discusses children and teens on the run during the Holocaust in Europe, including the different ways young people escaped the Nazis, places of refuge in Europe, and hiding and resistance. Provided by publisher.

"The book provides historical background, but the narratives rest upon the recollections, making the material immediate and horrifyingly real." School Library Journal.

Includes bibliographical references and index.

Hidden teens, hidden lives: primary sources from the Holocaust. Linda Jacobs Altman. Enslow, c2010. 128 p.: True stories of teens in the Holocaust

Grades: 8 9 10 11 12   **940.53**

1. Holocaust (1933-1945) -- Children 2. Holocaust (1933-1945) 3. Holocaust survivors 4. World War II -- Children 5. World War II
ISBN 9780766032712

LC 2009006504

Explores the lives of children and teens who went into hiding during the Holocaust; looks at various places used as hiding spots, such as barns and attics, and different ways to hide, like assuming false identities, and how these were used as a tool to survive. Provided by publisher.

"Altman does a great job of providing historical context and realistic commentary for the individual experiences. Photos of teens and news pictures . . . add further dimensions to the text." Booklist.

Includes bibliographical references and index.

Shattered youth in Nazi Germany: primary sources from the Holocaust. Linda Jacobs Altman. Enslow Publishers, c2010. 128 p.: True stories of teens in the Holocaust

Grades: 8 9 10 11 12   **940.53**

1. Hitler Youth 2. Nazism and children 3. Jewish children -- History 20th century. 4. Jewish teenagers -- History 20th century. 5. World War II -- Teenagers 6. Holocaust (1933-1945) -- Children 7. Germany -- Politics and government -- 1933-1945
ISBN 9780766032682

LC 2008048002

Examines the lives of children and teens living in Germany before and during the Holocaust, including the rise of Nazism, growing persecution of Jews, and the Hitler Youth. Provided by publisher.

"The book provides historical background, but the narratives rest upon the recollections, making the material immediate and horrifyingly real." School Library Journal.

Includes bibliographical references and index.

The **Warsaw** Ghetto Uprising: striking a blow against the Nazis. Linda Jacobs Altman. Enslow, c2012. 128 p.: Holocaust through primary sources

Grades: 7 8 9 10 11 12   **940.53**

1. 20th century 2. Holocaust (1933-1945) 3. Jews, Polish -- History 4. Warsaw ghetto uprising, 1943 5. Warsaw, Poland -- History
ISBN 9780766033207

LC 2010021596

Examines the Warsaw ghetto uprising, including the roots of the resistance in the Warsaw ghetto, stories from the participants in the uprising, how the battle ended, and how the small group of fighters became heroes during the Holocaust. Provided by publisher.

Ambrose, Stephen E.

★ The **good** fight: how World War II was won. by Stephen E. Ambrose. Atheneum Books for Young Readers, 2001. 96 p.

Grades: 5 6 7 8   **940.53**

1. 1940s 2. World War II 3. Soldiers 4. Battles 5. War
ISBN 0689843615

LC 00049600

A chronicle of World War II includes accounts of major events and personal anecdotes from soldiers in the field.

"An excellent balance between the big picture and the humanizing details, well supported by fact boxes, tinted photographs, and battlefield maps that are both simple and clear. . . . Ambrose's style is authoritative and warm." Booklist.

Includes bibliographical references (p. 94) and index.

Batalion, Judith

The **light** of days: the untold story of women resistance fighters in Hitler's ghettos. Judy Batalion; with Winifred Conkling. Harper, 2021. xx, 265 p.

Grades: 6 7 8 9   **940.53**

1. Second World War era (1939-1945) 2. Jewish women 3. Jewish resistance and revolts 4. Warsaw Ghetto uprising, 1943 5. Jews, Polish 6. Female friendship 7. Poland -- History -- 1918-1945.
ISBN 9780063037694

LC 2020937196

Presents the untold story of the young Jewish women who became resistance fighters against the Nazis during World War II.

"This valuable chronicle fills an important gap in Holocaust literature." Kirkus

Includes bibliographical references (pages 264-265).

Bornstein, Michael, 1940-

Survivors club: the true story of a very young prisoner of Auschwitz. Michael Bornstein, Debbie Bornstein Holinstat. Farrar Straus Giroux Books for Young Readers, [2017] 256 p.

Grades: 5 6 7 8   **940.53**

1. Bornstein, Michael, 1940- 2. Auschwitz (Concentration camp) 3. Jewish children 4. Holocaust (1933-1945) 5. Holocaust survivors 6. Concentration camps 7. Jews
ISBN 9780374305710

LC 2016028010

The incredible true story of Michael Bornstein—who at age 4 was one of the youngest children to be liberated from Auschwitz—and of his family. Provided by publisher.

Byers, Ann

Saving children from the Holocaust: the Kindertransport. Ann Byers. Enslow Publishers, c2012. 128 p.: Holocaust through primary sources

Grades: 7 8 9 10 11 12   **940.53**

1. World War II -- Jews -- Rescue 2. Kindertransports (Rescue operations) 3. Holocaust (1933-1945) -- Children 4. World War II 5. Refugees, Jewish 6. Great Britain
ISBN 9780766033238

LC 2010014215

Discusses the Kindertransport, including the people who organized the operation, how the transports worked, the children's lives who escaped on a transport, and how ten thousand children were saved from the Holocaust. Provided by publisher.

Trapped: youth in the Nazi ghettos: primary sources from the Holocaust. Ann Byers. Enslow Publishers, 2010. 128 p. : True stories of teens in the Holocaust

Grades: 8 9 10 11 12   **940.53**

1. Holocaust (1933-1945) -- Children 2. Ghettoes, Jewish 3. World

War II -- Children 4. Holocaust (1933-1945) 5. World War II
ISBN 9780766032729

LC 2009013475

Examines the lives of Jewish children and teens in the ghettos during the Holocaust, including the formation of the ghettos, the miserable conditions, hard labor, and the deportations to camps. Provided by publisher.

"The book provides historical background, but the narratives rest upon the recollections, making the material immediate and horrifyingly real." School Library Journal.

Includes bibliographical references and index.

Callery, Sean

★ **World** War II. Sean Callery. Scholastic, c2013. 105 p.: Scholastic Discover More. Expert Reader
Grades: 5 6 7 8   **940.53**
1. 1930s 2. 1940s 3. World War II -- History 4. World politics 1933-1945 5. United States -- History -- 1933-1945
ISBN 9780545479752

LC bl2013005739

Chronicles the course of the war, from the rise of Nazism to Hitler's suicide in April 1945, featuring an account that shows how individuals experienced the war, and details artworks that reveal inner workings of vehicles.

Deem, James M.

Auschwitz: voices from the death camp. James M. Deem. Enslow Publishers, c2012. 128 p.: Holocaust through primary sources
Grades: 7 8 9 10 11 12   **940.53**
1. Auschwitz (Concentration camp) 2. Holocaust (1933-1945) 3. Jews -- Persecutions 4. World War II 5. Europe -- Social conditions
ISBN 9780766033221

LC 2010003064

Examines Auschwitz, a death camp during the Holocaust, including its construction and daily workings, true accounts from prisoners of the camp and Nazi perpetrators, and how more than 1 million people were murdered there. Provided by publisher.

"Drawing on diaries, letters, and books, [this title illuminates] events by quoting at length from personal narratives, which are set apart from the main texts as sidebars. Readers will gravitate to this approachable focus, and teachers may appreciate the way that quotes from primary sources are integrated into simple texts." School Library Journal.

Includes bibliographical references (p. 125) and index.

Kristallnacht: the Nazi terror that began the Holocaust. James M. Deem. Enslow Publishers, c2011. 128 p.: Holocaust through primary sources
Grades: 7 8 9 10 11 12   **940.53**
1. 1930s 2. Jews -- Persecutions 3. Kristallnacht, 1938 4. Holocaust (1933-1945) 5. Nazis
ISBN 9780766033245

LC 2010015696

Discusses Kristallnacht, a four-day pogrom instigated by the Nazis against Germany's Jews, including stories from the victims, witnesses and perpetrators of the attack, and how it marked the beginning of the Holocaust. Provided by publisher.

"Personal testimony is a powerful way to tell history. . . . These accounts . . . are tightly edited, drawing on the memories of victims, perpetrators, and witnesses. . . . Each chapter blends an individual's testimony

with historical background and commentary as well as photos of the witness and of the brutal events." Booklist.

Includes bibliographical references and index.

The **prisoners** of Breendonk: personal histories from a World War II concentration camp. written by James M. Deem, with additional photography by Leon Nolis. Houghton Mifflin Harcourt, 2015. 352 p.
Grades: 8 9 10 11 12   **940.53**
1. Breendonk (Concentration camp). 2. Concentration camp inmates 3. Concentration camps 4. World War II 5. World War II -- Prisoners and prisons 6. Holocaust (1933-1945) 7. Belgium -- History -- German occupation, 1940-1945.
ISBN 9780544096646

LC 2015010722

This absorbing and captivating nonfiction account (with never-before-published photographs) offers readers an in-depth anthropological and historical look into the lives of those who suffered and survived Breendonk concentration camp during the Holocaust of World War II. Provided by publisher.

"The overall quality of this volume makes this title about a little-known camp a strong choice." School Library Journal.

Downing, David, 1946-

Origins of the Holocaust. David Downing. World Almanac Library, 2006. 48 p.
Grades: 7 8 9 10   **940.53**
1. Jews -- Persecutions -- History 2. Nazism -- History 3. Holocaust (1933-1945) -- Causes 4. Germany -- History -- 1918-1933.
ISBN 083685943X

LC 2005042114

Discusses the causes of the Holocaust, including the history of persecution of Jews, the fall of Germany after World War I, and the rise of the Nazi party.

"This adds essential background history to the many accounts of the Nazi genocide. Downing goes back nearly 2,000 years to show the roots of antiSemitism and the long persecution of the Jews. . . . The clear overview connects that history with the rise of the Nazi Party and Hitler's vision of the Aryan master race. . . . The book design is spacious, with many photos, clear maps, and boxed insets." Booklist.

Includes bibliographical references (p. 47) and index.

Edsel, Robert M.

The **greatest** treasure hunt in history: the story of the Monuments Men. by Robert M. Edsel. Scholastic Focus, an imprint of Scholastic Inc., [2019] 368 p.
Grades: 7 8 9 10   **940.53**
1. Allied Forces. Supreme Headquarters. Monuments, Fine Arts and Archives Section -- History. 2. 1940s 3. Art thefts 4. World War II -- Confiscations and contributions 5. Nazi plunder 6. Art and war 7. Art treasures in war 8. Germany -- History -- 20th century.
ISBN 9781338251197

LC 2018016710

Recounts the true story of eleven men and one woman who risked their lives during World War II to preserve churches, libraries, monuments, and works of art that defined the heritage of Western civilization.

Fishkin, Rebecca Love, 1972-

Heroes of the Holocaust. by Rebecca Love Fishkin. Compass Point Books, c2011. 64 p.: Holocaust
Grades: 6 7 8 9   **940.53**
1. World War II -- Jews -- Rescue 2. Righteous Gentiles in the

Holocaust 3. Holocaust (1933-1945) 4. Jewish resistance and revolts 5. Resistance to military occupation
ISBN 9780756543914

LC 2010026492

Presents information about the Jews who resisted and fought the Nazis and the heroic gentiles who provided them with false identities, hiding places, and documentation, allowing them to escape persecution.

"This volume succeeds in outlining a horrific chapter in history without oversimplifying. . . . [This] book features multiple quotes from survivors about their wartime experiences, providing voices with which young people can identify." School Library Journal.

Includes bibliographical references (p. 61-63) and index.

Fox, Anne L., 1926-

Ten thousand children: true stories told by children who escaped the Holocaust on the Kindertransport. by Anne L. Fox and Eva Abraham-Podietz. Behrman House, c1999. 128 p.

Grades: 5 6 7 8   **940.53**
1. Jewish children 2. Jews, German -- History 1933-1945 3. Refugees, Jewish 4. Jews, German 5. Great Britain 6. Germany
ISBN 0874416485

LC 98033600

Tells the true stories of children who escaped Nazi Germany on the Kindertransport, a rescue mission led by concerned British to save Jewish children from the Holocaust.

"The design is like an open scrapbook, with different size typefaces, snapshots, news photos, and marginal notes; and the combination of the general overview with personal memories will bring readers, from middle grades through adult, close to the experience." Booklist.

Frank, Anne, 1929-1945

★ The **diary** of a young girl: the definitive edition. Anne Frank; edited by Otto H. Frank and Mirjam Pressler; translated by Susan Massotty Doubleday, c1995. 340 p.

Grades: 5 6 7 8 9 10 11 12 Adult   **940.53**
1. Frank, Anne, 1929-1945 2. Holocaust (1933-1945) 3. Jewish teenage girls 4. Hidden children (Holocaust) 5. Jews -- Persecutions 6. World War II -- Jews 7. Amsterdam, Netherlands -- Interethnic relations
ISBN 9780385473781

LC 9441379

An uncut edition of Anne Frank's diary includes entries originally omitted by her father and provides insight into Anne's relationship with her mother

"This new translation of Frank's famous diary includes material about her emerging sexuality and her relationship with her mother that was originally excised by Frank's father, the only family member to survive the Holocaust." Library Journal.

Friedman, Ina R.

The **other** victims: first-person stories of non-Jews persecuted by the Nazis. Ina R. Friedman. Houghton Mifflin Co., 1990. 214 p.

Grades: 6 7 8 9   **940.53**
1. 1930s 2. 1940s 3. World War II 4. Holocaust survivors 5. Nazism 6. Religious persecution 7. Holocaust victims 8. Europe -- History
ISBN 0395502128

Personal narratives of Christians, Gypsies, deaf people, homosexuals, and blacks who suffered at the hands of the Nazis before and during World War II.

"Well organized and edited, the tales are harrowing, though they all end happily, often with escape or immigration to America and highly successful careers. Friedman points out that these were the lucky ones, and her book serves as a much-needed reminder that the Nazi nightmare extended far beyond Europe's Jewish population." Bulletin of the Center for Children's Books.

Gaddy, K. R.

Flowers in the gutter: the true story of the Edelweiss Pirates, teenagers who resisted the Nazis. K. R. Gaddy. Dutton Books, 2020 320 p.

Grades: 7 8 9 10 11 12   **940.53**
1. Edelweiss Pirates (Anti-Nazi group). 2. Resistance to government 3. Anti-Nazi movement 4. World War II 5. Teenage boys 6. Sabotage 7. Germany -- History -- 1933-1945.
ISBN 9780525555414

A photo-illustrated account documents the story of the Edelweiss Pirates, a group of working-class teens who survived the Third Reich in their Cologne neighborhoods while resisting the Hitler Youth, helping POWs and sabotaging Nazi factories.

"An eye-opening account of tenacity that brings the efforts of young anti-Nazi activists vividly to life." Kirkus.

Hodge, Deborah

Rescuing the children: the story of the Kindertransport. by Deborah Hodge. Tundra Books, 2012. 60 p.

Grades: 4 5 6   **940.53**
1. Jewish children 2. Kindertransports (Rescue operations) 3. Holocaust (1933-1945) -- Children 4. World War II -- Jews -- Rescue 5. Refugees, Jewish
ISBN 9781770492561

LC oc2012002974

Discusses the Kindertransport, which transported nearly ten thousand Jewish children out of Nazi Europe to safety in Britain in the nine months before World War II.

Hoffman, Betty N.

Liberation: stories of survival from the Holocaust. Betty N. Hoffman. Enslow Publishers, c2012. 128 p.: Holocaust through primary sources

Grades: 7 8 9 10 11 12   **940.53**
1. Holocaust (1933-1945) 2. Jews, European 3. World War II 4. Holocaust survivors 5. Refugees, Jewish
ISBN 9780766033191

LC 2010007234

Discusses the liberation of Europe and the aftermath of the Holocaust, including the displaced persons camps, primary source accounts from Holocaust survivors, and how those survivors started new lives in new countries. Provided by publisher.

Hoose, Phillip M., 1947-

The **boys** who challenged Hitler: Knud Pedersen and the Churchill Club. Phillip Hoose. Farrar Straus & Giroux 2015 192 p.

Grades: 7 8 9 10 11 12   **940.53**
1. 1940s 2. World War II 3. Anti-Nazi movement 4. Sabotage 5. Resistance to military occupation 6. Denmark -- History -- German occupation, 1940-1945.
ISBN 9780374300227

The true story of a group of boy resistance fighters in Denmark after the Nazi invasion.—From publisher description.

"Hoose brilliantly weaves Pedersen's own words into the larger narrative of Denmark's stormy social and political wartime climate, showing how the astonishing bravery of otherwise ordinary Danish teens started something extraordinary." Horn Book.

Hopkinson, Deborah

★ **We** must not forget: Holocaust stories of survival and resistance. Deborah Hopkinson. Scholastic 2021 384 p.

Grades: 5 6 7 8 **940.53**
1. Second World War era (1939-1945) 2. Holocaust (1933-1945) -- Children 3. Holocaust survivors 4. Resistance to government 5. Survival 6. Rescues 7. Europe -- History -- 20th century
ISBN 9781338255775

LC 2020014131

As World War II raged, millions of young Jewish people were caught up in the horrors of the Nazis' Final Solution. Many readers know of Adolf Hitler and the Nazi state's genocidal campaign against European Jews and others of so-called "inferior" races. Yet so many of the individual stories remain buried in time. Of those who endured the Holocaust, some were caught by the Nazis and sent to concentration camps, some hid right under Hitler's nose, some were separated from their parents, some chose to fightback. Against all odds, some survived. They all have stories that must be told. They all have stories we must keep safe in our collective memory. In this thoroughly researched and passionately written narrative nonfiction for upper middle-grade readers, critically acclaimed author Deborah Hopkinson allows the voices of Holocaust survivors to live on the page, recalling their persecution, survival, and resistance. Focusing on testimonies across Germany, the Netherlands, France, and Poland, Hopkinson paints a moving and diverse portrait of the Jewish youth experience in Europe under the shadow of the Third Reich. With archival images and myriad interviews, this compelling and beautifully told addition to Holocaust history not only honors the courage of the victims, but calls young readers to action—by reminding them that heroism begins with the ordinary, everyday feat of showing compassion toward our fellow citizens. Provided by publisher.

"The stories of Jewish children and teens who survived against all odds are told in ways that readers will never forget. The book is divided into three sections defined by geography, with stories from Germany and the Netherlands, France, and Poland. Vital and unendurably timeless." Kirkus

Includes bibliographical references and index.

Jackson, Livia E. Bitton, 1931-

I have lived a thousand years: growing up in the Holocaust. Livia Bitton-Jackson. Simon & Schuster Books for Young Readers, c1997. 224 p.

Grades: 7 8 9 10 **940.53**
1. Jackson, Livia E. Bitton, 1931- 2. Auschwitz (Concentration camp) 3. 1940s 4. Holocaust (1933-1945) 5. World War II 6. World War II 7. Jews -- Persecutions 8. Women 9. Hungary -- Interethnic relations.
ISBN 0689810229

LC 96019971

The author describes her experiences during World War II when she and her family were sent to the Nazi death camp at Auschwitz.

"This is a memorable addition to the searing accounts of Holocaust survivors." Horn Book.

Kent, Deborah

The **tragic** history of the Japanese-American internment camps. Deborah Kent. Enslow Publishers, c2008. 128 p.: From many cultures, one history

Grades: 6 7 8 9 **940.53**
1. World War II -- Japanese Americans 2. Japanese Americans -- Forced removal and incarceration, 1942-1945 3. Evacuation of civilians 4. Concentration camps 5. United States
ISBN 9780766027978

LC 2007015125

Offers a look at the impact Japanese-American internment camps had on the lives of their internees and the harsh conditions in which they had to live and raise their families after being forced from their own homes and businesses by President Roosevelt's Executive Order after the bombing of Pearl Harbor during World War II.

"This will provide clear, easy-to-understand facts with critical analysis and will be useful for reports." Library Media Connection.

Includes bibliographical references (p. 124-125) and index.

Langley, Andrew, 1949-

World War II. Andrew Langley. Heinemann Library, c2012. 80 p.

Grades: 6 7 8 9 **940.53**
1. World War II
ISBN 9781432960025

LC 2011016056

Explores the history of World War II, including the important players, battles, and consequences.

Levine, Karen, 1955-

★ **Hana's** suitcase on stage. original story by Karen Levine; play by Emil Sher. Second Story Press, 2007. 171 p.

Grades: 5 6 7 8 **940.53**
1. Brady, Hana 2. Ishioka, Fumiko 3. Theresienstadt (Concentration camp) 4. Holocaust (1933-1945) 5. Holocaust (1933-1945) -- Children 6. Drama
ISBN 189718705X

LC 2007390829

A biography of a Czech girl who died in the Holocaust, told in alternating chapters with an account of how the curator of a Japanese Holocaust center learned about her life after Hana's suitcase was sent to her, with the text of the play based on this biography.

"Set in the Tokyo Holocaust Center, the two-act play opens with the woman and two of her student helpers questioning and searching for answers to the suitcase's history. . . . Act II blends characters of Ishioka and her students with Hana and her family, each group individually recounting their stories in alternating voices. As with the original book, this title succeeds in recreating a striking representation of one child's tragic and beautiful life in a terrifying world of hate and prejudice. This volume will serve as one of the most effective teaching models for Holocaust curriculums available. Photographs and facsimiles of Nazi documents are included." School Library Journal.

Leyson, Leon, 1929-2013

The **boy** on the wooden box: how the impossible became possible . . . on Schindler's List. Leon Leyson; with Marilyn J Harran and Elisabeth B Leyson. Atheneum Books for Young Readers, [2013] 198 p.

Grades: 6 7 8 9 **940.53**
1. Leyson, Leon, 1929-2013. 2. Schindler, Oskar 1908-1974. 3. Płaszow (Concentration camp) 4. Jews, Polish 5. Holocaust (1933-1945) -- Children 6. Holocaust (1933-1945) 7. World War II -- Jews -- Rescue 8. Concentration camp inmates 9. Narewka, Poland 10. Krakow, Poland
ISBN 9781442497818

LC 2013017987

"This powerful memoir of one of the youngest boys on Schindler's list deserves to be shared...This memoir is a natural curriculum addition to WWII units for upper-elementary- and middle-school readers. Be sure to have additional materials on hand about Oskar Schindler, as readers will want to do more research into Leyson's story." Booklist.

Marrin, Albert

Uprooted: the Japanese-American experience during World War II. Albert Marrin. Alfred A. Knopf, 2016. 256 p.

Grades: 7 8 9 10 11 12   **940.53**
1. Japanese Americans -- Forced removal and incarceration, 1942-1945 2. World War II -- Japanese Americans 3. Forced relocations 4. Racism 5. Xenophobia 6. United States
ISBN 9780553509366

LC 2015025406

Uprooted takes a close look at the history of racism in America and carefully follows the treacherous path that led one of our nation's most beloved presidents to make the decision to round up over 100,000 of its own citizens based on nothing more than their ancestry and, suspicious of their loyalty, keep them in concentration camps for the better part of four years. Meanwhile, it also illuminates the history of Japan and its own struggles with racism and xenophobia, which led to the bombing of Pearl Harbor, ultimately tying the two countries together.

"A final chapter draws a connection to the treatment of Muslim Americans in the aftermath of twenty-first-century terrorist attacks and discusses the uneasy tension between liberty and security during wartime. Generous quotations and photographs are integrated throughout the text, providing the immediacy that comes with primary sources." Horn Book.

Mazzeo, Tilar J.

Irena's children: young readers edition. Tilar J. Mazzeo; adapted by Mary Cronk Farrell. Margaret K. McElderry Books, 2016. 288 p.

Grades: 7 8 9 10 11 12   **940.53**
1. Sendlerowa, Irena, 1910-2008. 2. Righteous Gentiles in the Holocaust 3. Ghettoes, Jewish 4. Holocaust (1933-1945) -- Children 5. Jews, Polish 6. Rescues 7. Warsaw, Poland -- History -- Occupation, 1939-1945. 8. Poland -- History -- 20th century.
ISBN 9781481449915

"She was short in stature but had immense courage and didn't consider herself a hero: 'What I did was not an extraordinary thing.' The children Sendler saved and the readers of this moving biography would undoubtedly disagree." Booklist.

McClafferty, Carla Killough, 1958-

In defiance of Hitler : the secret mission of Varian Fry. Carla Killough McClafferty. Farrar Straus Giroux, 2008. 208 p.

Grades: 7 8 9 10 11 12   **940.53**
1. Fry, Varian, 1908-1967 2. World War II -- Jews -- Rescue 3. Holocaust (1933-1945) 4. Righteous Gentiles in the Holocaust 5. Rescues 6. War correspondents 7. France
ISBN 9780374382049

LC 2007033271

Traveling to France in the midst of World War II, an American journalist worked to get a select group of artists and intellectuals out of Europe and was soon involved in helping many others who came to him with pleas of their own in this moving true story enhanced with maps, illustrations, and index.

"This stirring account of a young New York City journalist who secretly helped more than 2,000 refugees escape Nazi-occupied France blends exciting adventure with the grim history. . . . The author begins

with a brief overview of Hitler's rise and the threat to the Jews, and then draws heavily on Fry's autobiography and his letters home." Booklist.

Meltzer, Milton, 1915-2009

Rescue: the story of how Gentiles saved Jews in the Holocaust. Milton Meltzer. HarperTrophy, 1991, c1988. 168 p.

Grades: 6 7 8 9   **940.53**
1. World War II -- Jews -- Rescue 2. Righteous Gentiles in the Holocaust 3. Holocaust (1933-1945) 4. Jews -- Persecutions 5. Jews, European -- Relations with Gentiles
ISBN 0833551477

LC BL 99720572

A recounting drawn from historic source material of the many individual acts of heroism performed by righteous gentiles who sought to thwart the extermination of the Jews during the Holocaust.

"This is an excellent portrayal of a difficult topic. Meltzer manages to both explain without accusing, and to laud without glorifying. . . . The discussion of the complicated relations between countries are clear, but not simplistic. An impressive aspect of this book is its lack of didacticism." Voice of Youth Advocates.

Includes bibliographical references (p. 160-164) and index.

Opdyke, Irene Gut, 1921-

In my hands: memories of a Holocaust rescuer. Irene Gut Opdyke, with Jennifer Armstrong. Knopf, c1999. 276 p.

Grades: 7 8 9 10   **940.53**
1. Opdyke, Irene Gut, 1921- 2. Rescues 3. Righteous Gentiles in the Holocaust 4. World War II -- Jews -- Rescue 5. Holocaust (1933-1945) 6. Atrocities 7. Poland
ISBN 0679891811

LC 98054095

Recounts the experiences of the author who, as a young Polish girl, hid and saved Jews during the Holocaust.

"No matter how many Holocaust stories one has read, this one is a must, for its impact is so powerful. . . . Opdyke's remarkable story is simply told, with clarity and feeling." School Library Journal.

Oppenheim, Joanne

Dear Miss Breed : true stories of the Japanese American incarceration during World War II and a librarian who made a difference. by Joanne Oppenheim; foreward by Elizabeth Kikuchi Yamada; afterword by Snowden Becker. Scholastic, 2006. 287 p.

Grades: 7 8 9 10   **940.53**
1. Breed, Clara E. (Clara Estelle), 1906-1994 2. Japanese Americans -- Forced removal and incarceration, 1942-1945 3. Librarians 4. World War II 5. Children 6. Japanese American children 7. United States -- Social life and customs -- 20th century
ISBN 0439569923

LC 2004059009

Carter G. Woodson Book Awards: Secondary Level, 2007.

Provides the story of life in a Japanese internment camp during World War II through the correspondence of the children in the camp to their librarian, Miss Clara Breed, who worked on their behalf to show the injustice of their imprisonment.

"This account focuses on Clara Breed, a children's librarian at the San Diego Public Library, and the Japanese-American children she served prior to World War II and whom she continued to serve after their families were sent to an Arizona internment camp. . . . Illustrated with numerous photographs . . . and incorporating copious letters and documents, the book is . . . compelling." Horn Book.

Includes bibliographical references (p. 282) and index.

pebbles: a Holocaust story. by Lila Perl and ...menthal Lazan. Greenwillow Books, c1996. 130 p.
...: 6 7 8 9   **940.53**
1. Lazan, Marion Blumenthal, 1934- 2. Westerbork (Concentration camp) 3. Bergen-Belsen (Concentration camp) 4. Jews 5. Jews -- Persecutions 6. Holocaust (1933-1945) 7. Holocaust survivors 8. Jewish families 9. Germany 10. Books for reluctant readers
ISBN 068814294X
                                                                LC   95009752
"This book warrants attention both for the uncommon experiences it records and for the fullness of that record. . . . Quotes from Lazan's 87-year-old mother are invaluableher memories of the family's experiences afford Marion's story a precision and wholeness rarely available to child survivors." Publishers Weekly.
Includes bibliographical references (p. 129-130).

Prins, Marcel, 1962-
Hidden like Anne Frank: fourteen true stories of survival. Marcel Prins and Peter Henk Steenhuis; translated by Laura Watkinson. Arthur A. Levine Books, an imprint of Scholastic Inc., [2014] 256 p.
Grades: 7 8 9 10 11 12   **940.53**
1. Hidden children (Holocaust) 2. Jewish children 3. Holocaust (1933-1945) -- Children 4. Holocaust (1933-1945) 5. World War II 6. Netherlands 7. Translations Dutch to English
ISBN 9780545543620
                                                                LC 2013040908
A collection of eye-opening first-person accounts that share what it was like to go into hiding during World War II. Some children were only three or four years old when they were hidden; some were teenagers. Some hid with neighbors or family, while many were with complete strangers. But all know the pain of losing their homes, their families, even their own names. They describe the secret network of brave people who kept them safe. And they share the coincidences and close escapes that made all the difference. Provided by publisher.
"This volume includes compelling first-person accounts of survival during the Holocaust and WWII in Holland, including coauthor Prins's mother's experience. Readers will encounter incredible acts of courage, both from the subjects themselves and the Resistance fighters and ordinary people willing to risk their lives. Family photos and archival images appear throughout; a glossary and pictures of the survivors today are appended." Horn Book.

Rappaport, Doreen
Beyond courage: the untold story of Jewish resistance during the Holocaust.. Candlewick Press, c2012. 240 p.
Grades: 6 7 8 9 10 11 12   **940.53**
1. World War II -- Jews -- Rescue 2. Righteous Gentiles in the Holocaust 3. Jewish resistance and revolts 4. Holocaust (1933-1945) 5. Children
ISBN 9780763629762
                                                                LC 2011048116
Shares accounts of heroic Jews who organized to help others and sabotage the Nazis during the Holocaust.

Rogasky, Barbara
Smoke and ashes: the story of the Holocaust. Barbara Rogasky. Holiday House, c1988. 187 p.
Grades: 6 7 8 9   **940.53**
1. Jews, European -- History 20th century. 2. Holocaust (1933-1945) 3. Holocaust (1933-1945) -- Causes 4. Holocaust (1933-

1945) -- Influence
ISBN 0823406970
                                                                LC 87028617
Examines the causes, events, and legacies of the Holocaust which resulted in the extermination of six million Jews.
"The author details the dark horror of Nazism: from the beginning pogroms the Nazis organized against German Jews to the setting up of concentration camps and death factories. . . . In clear and simple prose, she relates how the Jews lived and died in the camps . . . and how a small number of non-Jews helped them in their struggle. She concludes with an account of the Nuremburg Trials and the many instances of contemporary anti-Semitism that have outlived Hitler." School Library Journal. [review of 1988 edition]
Bibliography: p. 181-182.

Rubin, Susan Goldman
The **cat** with the yellow star: coming of age in Terezin. by Susan Goldman Rubin with Ela Weissberger. Holiday House, c2006. 40 p.
Grades: 3 4 5 6 7   **940.53**
1. Weissberger, Ela. 2. Theresienstadt (Concentration camp) 3. 1940s 4. Holocaust survivors 5. Jewish children 6. World War II 7. War -- Moral and ethical aspects 8. Holocaust (1933-1945) -- Children 9. Sudetenland, Czech Republic 10. Czechoslovakia
ISBN 9780823418312
                                                                LC 2004057582
"In 1942, at age 11, Ela Weissberger was transported with her Czech family to the Nazi concentration camp Terezin. She survived, and now, based on extensive personal interviews, Rubin tells Weissberger's story of being a Jewish child in that camp, including how the young prisoners rehearsed and performed the opera Brundibar." Booklist.
Includes bibliographical references and index.

Samuels, Charlie, 1961-
Home front. [Charlie Samuels]. Brown Bear Books, 2011. 48 p.: World War II sourcebook
Grades: 5 6 7 8   **940.53**
1. World War II -- Social aspects 2. War 3. World War II -- Economic aspects
ISBN 9781936333226
                                                                LC 2011007054
Describes civilian life for people around the world on the home front during World War II, including stories of relocation, rations, and new jobs to support war efforts. Provided by publisher.

Life under occupation. [Charlie Samuels]. Brown Bear Books, 2011. 48 p.: World War II sourcebook
Grades: 5 6 7 8   **940.53**
1. World War II -- Occupied territories 2. Military occupation 3. War 4. Atrocities 5. Europe 6. Pacific Area
ISBN 9781936333264
                                                                LC 2011007055
Describes life for people in countries under occupation by German and Japanese soldiers during World War II. Provided by publisher.

Sandler, Martin W.
Imprisoned: the betrayal of Japanese Americans during World War II. by Martin W. Sandler. Walker Books For Young Readers, c2013. 176 p.
Grades: 7 8 9 10   **940.53**
1. Japanese Americans -- Forced removal and incarceration, 1942-1945 2. Forced relocations 3. Japanese in the United States -- Mass

internment, 1942-1945 4. World War II -- Japanese Americans 5. Japanese Americans -- History
ISBN 9780802722775

LC 2012032295

"Sandler's earnest telling is complemented by well-chosen primary sources, not just the words . . . but also the black-and-white photographs that present striking images." Horn Book.

Sender, Ruth Minsky

The **cage**. Ruth Minsky Sender. Macmillan; c1986. 245 p.
Grades: 7 8 9 10   **940.53**
1. Sender, Ruth Minsky. 2. Auschwitz (Concentration camp) 3. Holocaust (1933-1945) 4. World War II 5. Jewish women 6. Jewish teenage girls 7. Survival (in concentration camps, prisons, etc) 8. Poland
ISBN 0027818306

LC   86008562

A teenage girl recounts the suffering and persecution of her family under the Nazis, in a Polish ghetto, during deportation, and in a concentration camp.

"This Holocaust memoir presents a series of brief scenes from 1939, when the author was 12 and Hitler invaded Poland, through the Russian liberation of the Mitelsteine labor camp in 1945. . . . Older students with previous knowledge of the subject will find Sender's narrative moving and thought provoking." School Library Journal.

Senker, Cath

Why did World War II happen? Cath Senker. Gareth Stevens Pub., 2011. 48 p.: Moments in history
Grades: 6 7 8 9   **940.53**
1. World War II 2. War 3. Military history 4. World politics
ISBN 9781433941849

LC 2010015834

Uses primary sources to document the causes of World War II.

"Examines the events that served as . . . [precursors to World War II]. . . . Brightly colored pull-out boxes highlight important turning points, the perspective of the everyday man, and further information on why specific events occurred. Numerous photographs help readers visualize concepts more fully. . . . Students should be able to easily use this resource." Library Media Connection.

Includes bibliographical references and index.

Taylor, Peter Lane

The **secret** of Priest's Grotto: a Holocaust survival story. Peter Lane Taylor with Christos Nicola. Kar-Ben Pub., c2007. 64 p.
Grades: 5 6 7 8 9 10 11 12   **940.53**
1. Jews, Ukrainian -- History 2. Jewish families 3. Hiding 4. Caves 5. Holocaust (1933-1945) 6. Ukraine -- Interethnic relations.
ISBN 1580132618

LC 2006021709

Two explorers survey caves in the Western Ukraine and relate the story of how an extended Jewish family, fleeing persecution by the Nazis, lived for nearly a year in a large cave, Popowa Yama, and survived the war.

"This volume relays the tale of 38 Ukrainian Jews who sought refuge in a local cave to escape the invading Nazis in fall of 1942 and remained there for 344 days. . . . At once sobering and uplifting, this is an astounding story of survival, powerfully told." Publishers Weekly.

Thomson, Ruth, 1949-

★ **Terezin**: voices from the Holocaust. Ruth Thomson. Candlewick Press, 2011. 64 p.
Grades: 5 6 7 8   **940.53**
1. Theresienstadt (Concentration camp) 2. Jews, Czech 3. World War II 4. Concentration camps 5. Children's art 6. Children 7. Czechoslovakia
ISBN 9780763649630

LC 2010039164

"Two years after the Nazi invasion of Czechoslovakia, the small fortress village of Terezin was converted into a Jewish ghetto, and over the next four years, ten of thousands of Jews were transported there while in transit to death camps in the east. The history of Terezin is fascinating: the camp housed many noted artists. . . . Much of the art created at Terezin survived the Holocaust, and a generous sampling is included in this volume. Thomson opts to tell the story of Terezin almost entirely in the voices of those who lived there. . . . This is an accessible, carefully researched work that effectively uses primary-source material to make the experience of the Jews of Terezin come alive for today's students." Bulletin of the Center for Children's Books.

940.5308 World War II, 1939-1945—Groups of people

Mullenbach, Cheryl

Double victory: how African American women broke race and gender barriers to help win World War II. Cheryl Mullenbach. Chicago Review Press, 2012. 272 p.: Women of action
Grades: 7 8 9 10 11 12   **940.5308**
1. World War II -- African Americans 2. African American women -- History 20th century. 3. African Americans -- Employment 4. Civil rights 5. World War II -- Women 6. United States -- Race relations -- History -- 20th century.
ISBN 9781569768082

LC 2012021343

An account of the lesser-known contributions of African-American women during World War II reveals how they helped lay the foundations for the Civil Rights Movement by challenging racial and gender barriers at home and abroad.

"One of the many strengths of the book is the range of areas affected, including journalism, manufacturing, troop support, military nursing and many others. Ultimately, their unstinting efforts during World War II helped pave the way for the civil rights movement and major societal change." Kirkus.

Includes bibliographical references and index.

940.5309 World War II, 1939-1945—History, geographic treatment, biography

Silver Line (Organization)

Voices from the Second World War: stories of war as told to children of today. Candlewick Press, 2018, c2016 300 p.
Grades: 4 5 6 7 8   **940.5309**
1. World War II 2. World War II veterans
ISBN 9780763694920

LC 2018936980

The Second World War was the most devastating war in history, resulting in up to eighty million deaths and causing the map of the world to be redrawn. Now, more than seventy years after peace was declared, a variety of people who lived through the war share their memories with children so that their experiences will never be forgotten. In this compelling collection, pilots, evacuees, resistance fighters, and navy sailors, as well as survivors of the Holocaust, prisoners-of-war camps, and the Hiroshima bombing, tell their stories, passing on their personal recollections of historical events to a new generation. The stories in Voices from the Second World War were collected by children from all over the world who met with people who wanted to share experiences from the war. These stories, which take place from the outbreak of war to the Hiroshima bombing, capture the spirit and courage of a generation of people affected by World War II.

"This title will help readers understand that war affects real-life people, including children. A solid choice for collections that serve middle school students." School Library Journal.

940.54 Military history of World War II

Allen, Thomas B.

★ **Remember** Pearl Harbor: American and Japanese survivors tell their stories. by Thomas B. Allen; foreword by Robert D. Ballard. National Geographic Society, c2001. 57 p.

Grades: 5 6 7 8   **940.54**
1. 1940s 2. Pearl Harbor, Attack on, 1941 3. World War II 4. World War II 5. Pearl Harbor, Hawaii
ISBN 0792266900

LC 2001000796

"Eyewitness testimony of Japanese and American men and women from various backgrounds enriches this balanced treatment of World War II.... The first-person voices along with dozens of black-and-white photos and several full-color maps make this a draw for both browsers and World War II buffs." Booklist.

Includes bibliographical references (p. 56) and index.

Atkinson, Rick

D-Day: the invasion of Normandy, 1944. Rick Atkinson with Kate Waters. Henry Holt and Company, 2014. xviii, 202 p.

Grades: 6 7 8 9 10 11 12   **940.54**
1. 1940s 2. World War II 3. Normandy Invasion, June 6, 1944 4. Military campaigns 5. Military history 6. Military tactics 7. Normandy
ISBN 9781627791113

LC 2014005162

June 6, 1944. They came by sea and by sky to reclaim liberty from the occupying Germans. As the Allied forces stormed the beaches of Normandy, they turned the tide of World War II. In clear and accessible prose, Pulitzer Prize winner and New York Times bestselling author Rick Atkinson captures the events and the spirit of that day—the day that led to the liberation of western Europe from Nazi Germany's control.

"With Kate Waters. Adapted from Atkinson's adult book The Guns at Last Light, this young readers' edition focuses, effectively and excitingly, on the invasion of Normandy but provides enough context for WWII both before and after June 6, 1944. Copious photographs and a vibrant design will invite war buffs in; appended lists of interesting facts add appeal. Reading list, timeline, websites." Horn Book.

Includes bibliographical references (page 196) and index.

Atwood, Kathryn J.

Women heroes of World War II: 26 stories of espionage, sabotage, resistance, and rescue. Kathryn J. Atwood. Chicago Review Press, c2011. 266 p.: Women of action

Grades: 7 8 9 10   **940.54**
1. Women and war 2. Women soldiers 3. Resistance to military

occupation 4. World War II
ISBN 9781556529610

LC 2010041830

"The 26 women profiled in this collective biography served on the front lines and behind enemy lines in Europe as correspondents, couriers, propagandists, Resistance fighters, saboteurs and spies. . . . Atwood's admiration and enthusiasm for her subjects is apparent in these engaging profiles, and readers will likely be inspired to investigate these fascinating women further." Kirkus.

Includes bibliographical references and index.

Burgan, Michael

Hiroshima: birth of the nuclear age. Michael Burgan. Marshall Cavendish Benchmark, c2010. 128 p.

Grades: 8 9 10 11 12   **940.54**
1. Atomic bomb -- History 2. Hiroshima-shi (Japan) -- History -- Bombardment, 1945.
ISBN 9780761440239

LC 2008029249

Provides comprehensive information on the Manhattan Project, the bombing of Hiroshima, and its legacy. Provided by the publisher.

Raising the flag: how a photograph gave a nation hope in wartime. by Michael Burgan. Compass Point Books, c2011. 64 p. : Captured history

Grades: 6 7 8 9   **940.54**
1. Rosenthal, Joe, 1911-2006. 2. Iwo Jima, Battle of, 1945 3. World War II -- Photography 4. Photographs 5. Photography -- Influence
ISBN 9780756543952

LC 2010038572

Explores and analyzes the historical context and significance of the iconic Joe Rosenthal photograph. Provided by publisher.

"This book about the iconic Joe Rosenthal photograph of American soldiers raising the flag at Iwo Jima places the photo in historical context, profiles the photographer, describes the conditions under which it was taken, and analyzes both its immediate and its continuing impact. The [text includes] ample background information and details and [is] enhanced by large photos and sidebars." School Library Journal.

Includes bibliographical references and index.

Cornioley, Pearl Witherington, 1914-2008

Code name Pauline: memoirs of a World War II special agent. Pearl Witherington Cornioley with Herve Larroque; edited by Kathryn J. Atwood. Chicago Review Press, 2013. 208 p.: Women of Action

Grades: 8 9 10 11 12   **940.54**
1. Cornioley, Pearl Witherington, 1914-2008 2. Great Britain. Special Operations Executive -- History. 3. 1940s 4. Secret service 5. Intelligence service -- History 20th century 6. World War II 7. French Resistance (World War II)
ISBN 9781613744871

LC 2013008734

Pearl Witherington Cornioley, one of the most celebrated female World War II resistance fighters, recounts her life and experience as a special agent for the British Special Operations Executive (SOE).

"Cornioley's detailed account of her time as a British special agent in Nazi-occupied France is suited for readers already familiar with the basic events of World War II. She narrates with short sentences and a matter-of-fact tone that keeps readers at a distance from her story, but the material is well documented and thorough. Appropriate for students needing primary source material." Horn Book.

Includes bibliographical references and index.

Drez, Ronald J., 1940-

★ **Remember** D-day: the plan, the invasion, survivor stories. Ronald J. Drez. National Geographic Books, c2004. 61 p.
Grades: 5 6 7 8   **940.54**
1. Military campaigns 2. World War II 3. Normandy Invasion, June 6, 1944 4. Operation Overlord 5. War 6. Normandy 7. France -- History -- 20th century.
ISBN 0792266668

         LC 2003017733

Discusses the events and personalities involved in the momentous Allied invasion of France on June 6, 1944.

"This well-organized, clearly written account provides a solid overview for readers unfamiliar with the subject. A first-rate purchase." School Library Journal.

Includes bibliographical references (p. 60) and index.

Farrell, Mary Cronk

Standing up against hate: how black women in the Army helped change the course of WWII. Mary Cronk Farrell. Abrams Books for Young Readers, 2019. 208 p.
Grades: 5 6 7 8   **940.54**
1. Earley, Charity Adams, 1918-2002 2. United States. Army. Women's Army Auxiliary Corps -- African American officers 3. United States. Army. Women's Army Corps -- African American officers 4. Second World War era (1939-1945) 5. African American women 6. Women soldiers 7. World War II -- African Americans 8. World War II -- Women's participation 9. Racism 10. United States Armed Forces -- African Americans 11. United States Armed Forces -- Women.
ISBN 9781419731600

         LC 2018009606

Shares the story of the African American women who enlisted in the newly formed Women's Army Auxiliary Corps in World War II, centering the story around Charity Adams, the woman who commanded the only black WAAC battalion sent overseas.

Grant, R. G.

Why did Hiroshima happen? R.G. Grant. Gareth Stevens Pub., 2011. 48 p.: Moments in history
Grades: 6 7 8 9   **940.54**
1. Military capitulations 2. World War II 3. Atomic bomb -- History 4. World War II 5. Japan -- History -- 1945- 6. Hiroshima, Japan -- Atomic bombing, 1945
ISBN 9781433941634

         LC 2010012464

Uses primary sources to document the reasons why the atomic bomb was dropped on Hiroshima.

"This explains the before, during, and after of [the bombing of Hiroshima]. . . . Sidebars include meticulously cited eyewitness quotes or extra insight on particularly important events. Even more information is contained in the maps, period photographs, and well-placed captions that grace every page." School Library Journal.

Includes bibliographical references (p. 47) and index.

Haugen, David M.

The **attack** on Pearl Harbor. David Haugen and Susan Musser, book editors. Greenhaven Press, c2011. 204 p.: Perspectives on modern world history

Grades: 8 9 10 11 12   **940.54**
1. 1940s 2. Pearl Harbor, Attack on, 1941 3. Bombings 4. International relations 5. Modern history
ISBN 9780737750041

         LC 2010033590

Describes the historical background, events, and aftermath of the 1941 bombing, including firsthand accounts from veterans who survived the attack and Japanese Americans who were imprisoned because of it.

"In discussing the events of December 7, 1941. . . [this] well-organized [volume presents] a wealth of clearly written analyses from a rich variety of viewpoints. With the inclusion of historical background, firsthand experiences, and discussions of particular points of controversy, [it helps] to familiarize readers with the [attack on Pearl Harbor] and [serves] as [an exercise] in the development of analytical thinking skills." School Library Journal.

Includes bibliographical references and index.

Hillstrom, Laurie Collier, 1965-

The **attack** on Pearl Harbor. Laurie Collier Hillstrom. Omnigraphics, c2009. xiv, 237 p.
Grades: 7 8 9 10 11 12   **940.54**
1. Pearl Harbor, Attack on, 1941
ISBN 9780780810693

         LC 2009004236

Provides a detailed account of the Pearl Harbor attack and the war in the Pacific. Covers the dramatic events of December 7, 1941; chronicles America's victory over Japan; and explores the legacy of Pearl Harbor. Features include a narrative overview, biographies, primary source documents, chronology, glossary, bibliography, and index. Provided by publisher.

Holm, Tom, 1946-

Code talkers and warriors: Native Americans and World War II. Tom Holm. Chelsea House, c2007. 168 p.: Landmark events in Native American history
Grades: 7 8 9 10   **940.54**
1. Navajo code talkers 2. World War II -- Cryptography 3. World War II -- Native American troops 4. Comanche code talkers 5. Native American soldiers
ISBN 0791093409

         LC 2006102263

Presents the combatant experiences of Native Americans in World War II, discussing their unique role of using native languages to transmit secret code and their considerable bravery in battle.

"In this title about Native Americans in World War II, Holm . . . expands considerably on his specific topic to highlight significant miliary roles played by Native Americans in conflicts dating back to the sixteenth century. . . . [This is] outstanding. . . . [A] valuable resource." Booklist.

Includes bibliographical references (p. 152-161) and index.

Hopkinson, Deborah

D-Day: the World War II invasion that changed history. by Deborah Hopkinson. Scholastic Focus, 2018. 400 p.
Grades: 5 6 7 8 9 10   **940.54**
1. Normandy Invasion, June 6, 1944 2. Operation Overlord 3. World War II 4. Military campaigns 5. Battles 6. Normandy -- History. 7. France -- History.
ISBN 9780545682480

Presents a comprehensive introduction to D-Day that explains its goals and years of secret planning while discussing the important roles played by contributors such as service members, African Americans, women, and journalists.

Dive!: World War II stories of sailors & submarines in the Pacific. Deborah Hopkinson. Scholastic Press, 2016. 384 p.
Grades: 4 5 6 7 8   **940.54**
 1. Submarines 2. Submarine warfare -- History World War II 3. Naval battles 4. Submarine warfare 5. World War II 6. Pacific Ocean
ISBN 9780545425582
"With a fascinating blend of submarine mechanics and tales of courage, readers will dive in deep." Booklist.

Houston, Jeanne Wakatsuki
 Farewell to Manzanar: a true story of Japanese American experience during and after the World War II internment. Jeanne Wakatsuki Houston and James D. Houston. Houghton Mifflin, 2002, c1973. xiv, 188 p.
Grades: 7 8 9 10   **940.54**
 1. Houston, Jeanne Wakatsuki. 2. Manzanar War Relocation Center, California. 3. 1940s 4. Japanese Americans -- Forced removal and incarceration, 1942-1945 5. Concentration camps 6. Japanese Americans 7. World War II
ISBN 0618216200
                                     LC 2002727748
Jeanne Wakatsuki was seven years old in 1942 when her family was uprooted from their home and sent to live at Manzanar internment camp—with 10,000 other Japanese Americans. Along with searchlight towers and armed guards, Manzanar ludicrously featured cheerleaders, Boy Scouts, sock hops, baton twirling lessons and a dance band called the Jive Bombers who would play any popular song except the nation's #1 hit: "Don't Fence Me In." Farewell to Manzanar is the true story of one spirited Japanese-American family's attempt to survive the indignities of forced detention ... and of a native-born American child who discovered what it was like to grow up behind barbed wire in the United States.

Kuhn, Betsy
 Angels of mercy: the Army nurses of World War II. by Betsy Kuhn. Atheneum Books for Young Readers, c1999. 114 p.
Grades: 5 6 7 8   **940.54**
 1. United States. Army Nurse Corps 2. 1940s 3. Nurses 4. Medical care 5. World War II 6. North Africa 7. Europe
ISBN 0689820445
                                     LC   98036610
Relates the experiences of World War II Army nurses, who brought medical skills, courage, and cheer to hospitals throughout Europe, North Africa, and the Pacific.
"Excellent reproductions, maps and a time line accompany the clear, well-written text." School Library Journal.
Includes bibliographical references (p. 106-108) and index.

Messner, Kate
 Pearl Harbor. Kate Messner; illustrated by Dylan Meconis. Random House, 2020. 224 p.
Grades: 4 5 6 7   **940.54**
 1. Second World War era (1939-1945) 2. 1940s 3. Pearl Harbor, Attack on, 1941 4. World War II 5. Military history 6. Hawaii 7. Illustrated books
ISBN 9780593120385
A perspective-changing reanalysis of the events of the Pearl Harbor attacks investigates theories that the U.S. Navy Base was a known

possible target and that early warning signs were accidentally or deliberately ignored.
"Page-turning prose, helpful sidebars that may serve as launching points for further research, and realistic illustrations of American and Japanese leaders enhance the narrative." Booklist
Includes bibliographical references and index.

Moore, Kate, 1980-
 The **Battle** of Britain. Kate Moore. Osprey, 2010. 200 p.
Grades: 7 8 9 10 11 12   **940.54**
 1. Britain, Battle of, Great Britain, 1940
ISBN 9781846034749
                                     LC 2010281586
Published in association with the Imperial War Museum in London to celebrate the 70th anniversary of the Battle of Britain, this book brings one of the most important battles of World War II to life. Lavishly illustrated with photographs, contemporary art and propaganda posters, and accompanied by numerous first-hand accounts, The Battle of Britain captures the reality and the romance of a defining chapter in British history.
"In this spectacular oversize volume, Moore recounts with notable lucidity and depth the events and characters from both the British and German home fronts during this critical moment in world history and offers an excellent analysis of prewar preparations by both sides. The most outstanding feature of the work is without a doubt the stunning visuals." School Library Journal
Includes bibliographical references (p 195-197) and index.

Mullenbach, Cheryl
 Torpedoed!: a World War II story of a sinking passenger ship and two children's survival at sea. Cheryl Mullenbach. Chicago Review Press Incorporated, [2017] 158 p.
Grades: 4 5 6 7 8   **940.54**
 1. Steamships 2. Shipwrecks 3. Survival (after airplane accidents, shipwrecks, etc) 4. World War II 5. Children and war
ISBN 9781613738245
                                     LC 2017000468
When 14-year-old Florence Kelly and 11-year-old Russell Park left their hometowns for summer vacations in Europe in 1939, they considered themselves awfully lucky. Many of their friends' families were struggling during the Great Depression and couldn't afford fancy trips. But the young pair would soon face life-threatening troubles of their own as it became clear German dictator Adolf Hitler was intent on invading neighboring countries.
"An engaging, sometimes-harrowing account of the first casualty in what became known as the Battle of the Atlantic." Kirkus.
Includes bibliographical references and index.

Nathan, Amy
 Yankee doodle gals: women pilots of World War II. by Amy Nathan; foreword by Eileen Collins. National Geographic Society, c2001. 89 p.
Grades: 6 7 8 9   **940.54**
 1. Women Airforce Service Pilots (U.S.) 2. Women pilots 3. Military pilots 4. Women military pilots 5. Air warfare 6. World War II -- Women's participation 7. United States -- Social life and customs -- 20th century
ISBN 0792282167
                                     LC 2001000560
Describes the Women Service Airforce Pilots who fought discrimination in order to train anti-aircraft troops, tow targets, deliver planes to airbases, and test repaired planes for airworthiness during World War II.

"There's plenty of action to involve readers, and the women's perseverance in the face of obstacles is inspiring. Wonderful black-and-white photos extend the text." Booklist.

Includes bibliographical references (p. 87-88) and index.

Nelson, Peter, 1953-

Left for dead: a young man's search for justice for the USS Indianapolis. Peter Nelson; with a preface by Hunter Scott. Delacorte Press, c2002. 201 p.

Grades: 7 8 9 10   **940.54**

1. McVay, Charles Butler, d. 1968. 2. Scott, Hunter, 1985- 3. Indianapolis (Cruiser) 4. 1940s 5. Trials 6. World War II 7. Naval battles 8. Justice 9. Survival (after airplane accidents, shipwrecks, etc) 10. United States -- History -- 1933-1945.
ISBN 0385729596

LC 2001053774

Recalls the sinking of the U.S.S. Indianapolis at the end of World War II, the navy cover-up and unfair court martial of the ship's captain, and how a young boy helped the survivors set the record straight fifty-five years later.

Olson, Tod

Lost in the Pacific, 1942: not a drop to drink. Tod Olson. Scholastic Inc., 2016 176 p.: Lost (Scholastic)

Grades: 6 7 8 9   **940.54**

1. Rickenbacker, Eddie, 1890-1973 2. World War II 3. Sea survival 4. Castaways 5. Airplane accidents 6. Survival (after airplane accidents, shipwrecks, etc) 7. Pacific Ocean
ISBN 9780545928113

"A riveting, completely engrossing true survival story." Kirkus.

Pearson, P. O'Connell (Patricia O'Connell)

Fly girls: the daring American women pilots who helped win WWII. P. O'Connell Pearson. Simon & Schuster Books for Young Readers, 2018. 198 p.

Grades: 5 6 7 8 9   **940.54**

1. Women Airforce Service Pilots (U.S.) 2. Women pilots 3. Military pilots 4. World War II -- Aerial operations, American 5. World War II -- Women's participation 6. United States -- History, Military -- 20th century
ISBN 9781534404106

LC 2017011062

An introduction to women fighter pilots during World War II describes how hundreds of women proved their worth by working as civilian pilots.

Samuels, Charlie, 1961-

Propaganda. Charlie Samuels. Brown Bear Books, 2011. 48 p.: World War II sourcebook

Grades: 5 6 7 8   **940.54**

1. World War II -- Propaganda 2. Propaganda 3. War
ISBN 9781936333233

LC 2011010241

Describes the documentation published by different groups during World War II that was used to persuade civilians, soldiers, and even the enemies to support that group's cause. Provided by publisher.

Soldiers. [Charlie Samuels. Brown Bear Books, 2011. 48 p.: World War II sourcebook

Grades: 5 6 7 8   **940.54**

1. World War II 2. Soldiers -- History 20th century 3. War
ISBN 9781936333240

LC 2011007057

Describes the life of a soldier in World War II, from recruitment efforts around the world, to the daily life during the fighting. Provided by publisher.

Seiple, Samantha

Nazi saboteurs: Hitler's secret attack on America. Samantha Seiple. Scholastic Focus, 2019. 224 p.

Grades: 5 6 7 8   **940.54**

1. World War II 2. Nazis 3. Sabotage 4. Spies 5. Secret service
ISBN 9781338259148

LC 2018054402

A gripping tale of the little-known Nazi plot to attack on American soil, and the brave individuals who got in the way.

"A story that will appeal to both espionage and World War II enthusiasts." Kirkus.

Includes bibliographical references.

Sheinkin, Steve

★ The **Port** Chicago 50: disaster, mutiny, and the fight for civil rights. Steve Sheinkin. Roaring Brook Press, 2013. 208 p.

Grades: 5 6 7 8 9   **940.54**

1. United States. Navy -- African Americans -- History -- 20th century 2. World War II -- African American participation 3. Trials (Mutiny) 4. African Americans -- Civil rights -- History 20th century 5. Explosions 6. Sailors
ISBN 9781596437968

LC 2013013452

Carter G. Woodson Book Awards: Secondary Level, 2015.

Presents an account of the 1944 civil rights protest involving hundreds of African-American Navy servicemen who were unjustly charged with mutiny for refusing to work in unsafe conditions after the deadly Port Chicago explosion.

"An unusual entry point for the study of WWII and the nascent civil rights movement. Photographs are helpful, and documentation is thorough." Horn Book.

Includes bibliographical references and index.

Stone, Tanya Lee

★ **Courage** has no color: the true story of the Triple Nickles: America's first black paratroopers. Tanya Lee Stone. Candlewick Press, 2013. 147 p.

Grades: 5 6 7 8   **940.54**

1. United States. Army. Parachute Infantry Battalion, 555th 2. African American soldiers 3. World War II 4. Segregation 5. Racism 6. Stereotypes (Social psychology)
ISBN 9780763651176

Examines the role of African-Americans in the military through the history of the Triple Nickles, America's first black paratroopers, who fought against little-known attacks perpetrated on the American West by the Japanese during World War II, and "proved that the color of a man had nothing to do with his ability."

Torres, John Albert

The **Battle** of Midway. John A. Torres. Mitchell Lane Publishers, c2011. 48 p.: Technologies and strategies in battle

Grades: 6 7 8 9   **940.54**

1. 1940s 2. Midway, Battle of, 1942 3. Battles 4. World War II

5. Weapons 6. Military art and science
ISBN 9781612280783

LC 2011002746

Presents a detailed look at the World War II Battle of Midway, focusing on the weapon technologies and strategies used and how they fared in combat.

"This is an in-depth account of the 1942 Battle of Midway, detailing how it was fought by sea and air by the U.S. and Japan. . . . This useful research source packs a wealth of information into its straightforward narrative. This colorful layout intersperses abundant visuals, including maps and archival photos as well as sidebars." Booklist.

Includes bibliographical references (p. 45-46) and index.

Wukovits, John F., 1944-
The **bombing** of Pearl Harbor. by John F. Wukovits. Lucent Books, c2011. 128 p. : World history (Lucent Books)
Grades: 6 7 8 9   **940.54**
1. Pearl Harbor, Attack on, 1941 2. World War II -- Causes 3. United States -- Foreign relations -- Japan 4. United States -- History -- 1933-1945.
ISBN 9781420503302

LC 2010035993

Describes the events before, during, and after the Japanese attack on Pearl Harbor in 1941, triggering the United States' involvement in World War II.

"Archival photographs combine with dense text to provide an introduction to the 1941 attack on Pearl Harbor. The impact and aftermath of the tumultuous period in world history is also explored for readers. Sidebars featuring news headlines and personal accounts add some immediacy to the historical account." Horn Book.

Includes bibliographical references and index.

941 British Isles

Dillon, Patrick, 1962-
The **story** of Britain. Patrick Dillon; illustrations by P.J. Lynch. Candlewick Press, 2011. 341 p.
Grades: 5 6 7 8   **941**
1. Great Britain -- History 2. Ireland -- History.
ISBN 9780763651220

LC 2010038883

Presents a full account of the history of Great Britain, from the Norman conquest through nearly one thousand years of history to the end of the twentieth century.

"This well-written, thoughtfully illustrated volume [is] an indispensible tool for European history buffs." Horn Book Guide.

941.081 British Isles—Reign of Victoria, 1837-1901

Schomp, Virginia
Victoria and her court. Virginia Schomp. Marshall Cavendish Benchmark, c2010. 80 p.: Life in Victorian England
Grades: 6 7 8 9   **941.081**
1. Victoria, Queen of Great Britain, 1819-1901 2. Aristocracy -- History 19th century. 3. Change 4. Palaces 5. England -- Rulers. 6. Great Britain -- Court and courtiers -- History -- 19th century.
ISBN 9781608700288

LC 2009029688

A social history of Victorian England, focusing on life in the upper echelons of society during the reign of Queen Victoria (1837-1901). Provided by publisher.

"This is clearly written, thorough, and informative. The visually rich layout includes photographs and paintings from the time period, full-page illustrations, and attention-grabbing sidebars. Most appealing are the primary source quotations, which are plentiful and relevant.." Library Media Connection.

Includes bibliographical references (p. 73-78) and index.

941.5081 Ireland—1800-1899

Fradin, Dennis B.
The **Irish** potato famine. by Dennis Fradin. Marshall Cavendish Benchmark, 2012. 80 p.: Great escapes
Grades: 5 6 7 8   **941.5081**
1. Escapes -- History 19th century 2. Disaster victims -- History 19th century 3. Immigrants -- History 19th century 4. Ireland -- History -- Famine, 1845-1852 5. Ireland -- Great Famine, 1845-1849
ISBN 9781608704736

LC 2010018788

Provides comprehensive information on the history leading up to the Irish potato famine, presents accounts of narrow escapes, and discusses the legacy of the event. Provided by publisher.

Lyons, Mary E.
Feed the children first: Irish memories of the Great Hunger. edited by Mary E. Lyons. Atheneum Books for Young Readers, 2012, c2002. 48 p.
Grades: 5 6 7 8   **941.5081**
1. Famines 2. Hunger 3. Potatoes -- Social aspects 4. Ireland -- Great Famine, 1845-1849. 5. Ireland -- Famines -- History -- 19th century.
ISBN 9781442482920

LC 00049606

Discusses the Irish potato famine of the nineteenth century using first-person accounts, including the causes and the suffering of the people.

"Lyons compiles quotations from Irish citizens on the devastating effects of the potato famine that ravaged Ireland between 1845 and 1852." Publishers Weekly.

Includes bibliographical references (p. [48]).

941.7 Republic of Ireland (Eire)

Blashfield, Jean F.
Ireland. by Jean F. Blashfield. Children's Press; an imprint of Scholastic Inc., 2013. 144 p.: Enchantment of the World. Second Series
Grades: 5 6 7 8   **941.7**
1. Western Europe 2. Ireland
ISBN 9780531236765

LC 2013002015

"Many students turn to the Internet for writing reports, but for reliably accurate, attractively presented and well-calibrated information, the long-standing Enchantment of the World series remains a superior choice. Each volume has been completely rewritten from a previous edition—in many cases to startling effect given recent political events. Although the basic structure holds true to past versions, the updated photographs are truly eye-popping and take care to portray the countries as modern often opting for showing, say, a surgeon at work rather than a rural farmer. It might not be necessary for libraries to replace Ireland, since it hasn't changed radically, but this is a solid offering with updated statistics. Each volume in this reliable series includes extensive back matter with a detailed index." Booklist.

Includes bibliographical references and index.

Wiseman, Blaine

Republic of Ireland. Blaine Wiseman. AV2 by Weigl, 2020 32 p.

Grades: 5 6 7 8   **941.7**
   1. Ireland
   ISBN 9781791109073

LC 2019938457

"Perfect for Social Studies and World Geography classrooms and students." Booklist

942.02 England—Norman period, 1066-1154

Hamilton, Janice

The **Norman** conquest of England. Janice Hamilton. Twenty-First Century Books, c2008. 160 p.: Pivotal moments in history

Grades: 7 8 9 10   **942.02**
   1. William I, King of England, 1027 or 1028-1087 2. Normans in England 3. Great Britain -- History -- Norman period, 1066-1154 4. Normandy -- History
   ISBN 9780822559023

LC 2006102629

Examines the history of the Norman conquest of England at the hands of William the Conqueror, including an overview of pre-conquest England and Normandy, as well as a consideration of how England was affected by the conquest and subsequent Norman rule.

"This is clearly written and interesting enough for browsers as well as report writers. Maps, full-color and black-and-white photos, and reproductions of manuscripts contribute to the attractive format and make the subject matter come alive." School Library Journal.

Includes bibliographical references (p. 149-154) and index.

942.03 England—Period of House of Plantagenet, 1154-1399

Levy, Debbie

The **signing** of the Magna Carta. Debbie Levy. Twenty-First Century Books, c2008. 160 p.: Pivotal moments in history

Grades: 7 8 9 10 11 12   **942.03**
   1. 13th century 2. Constitutional history 3. Great Britain -- History -- John, 1199-1216. 4. Great Britain -- Politics and government -- 1154-1399.
   ISBN 9780822559177

LC 2005020971

Describes the events leading up to the signing of the Magna Carta and why this document is so important.

"This research source explains the intent of the treaty of 1215 that became the Magna Carta, the factors that produced it, as well as its evolution, historical significance, and relevance today. . . . The clear explanation of the Great Charter's historical context accompanied by

informative inserts and beautiful, relevant illustrations make this a book to dip into as well as to read through." Voice of Youth Advocates.

Includes bibliographical references and index.

942.05 England—Period of House of Tudor, 1485-1603

Kallen, Stuart A., 1955-

Elizabethan England. Stuart A. Kallen. ReferencePoint Press, 2012. 96 p.: Understanding world history

Grades: 7 8 9 10   **942.05**
   1. Great Britain -- History -- Elizabeth I, 1558-1603 2. England -- Social conditions -- 16th century.
   ISBN 9781601524843

LC 2012026174

Explores the Elizabethan era, discussing the pomp of the royal court, plague, poverty, religious revolution, and naval battles.

942.9 Wales

Hestler, Anna

Wales. Anna Hestler, Jo-Ann Spilling. Cavendish Square 2020 144 p.: Cultures of the World

Grades: 5 6 7 8   **942.9**
   1. Wales
   ISBN 9781502655837

Though a part of Great Britain, Wales has its own unique culture including its own language, customs, and folklore. Wales also offers stunning natural beauty, featuring valleys, mountains, rivers, lakes, and hundreds of miles of coastline. This guide utilizes vivid photographs, facts, and sidebars to showcase historic and contemporary Wales, offering an in-depth examination into the country's past, government, culture, and its relation to the United Kingdom. It highlights the country's modern operations, including its current political climate, religious affiliations, cuisine, and arts. Your readers will also learn about pressing issues related to its ecology, conservation, and school systems. Provided by publisher

943 Germany and neighboring central European countries

Walker, Ida

Germany. by Ida Walker and Shaina Carmel Indovino. Mason Crest, 2012. 64 p.: Major European Union nations

Grades: 5 6 7 8   **943**
   1. European Union 2. European Union countries 3. Germany -- History
   ISBN 9781422222430

LC 2010051291

Discusses the history, government, economy, and culture of Germany, including the unification of East and West Germany, Oktoberfest, and the famous Brothers Grimm.

943.085 Period of Weimar Republic, 1918-1933

Freeman, Charles, 1947-

Why did the rise of the Nazis happen? Charles Freeman. Gareth Stevens Pub., 2011. 48 p.: Moments in history

Grades: 6 7 8 9 **943.085**
1. Hitler, Adolf, 1889-1945 2. Nazism 3. Nazis 4. World politics 5. Germany -- Politics and government -- 1918-1933
ISBN 9781433941757

LC 2010017229

Examines the reasons for the rise of the Nazis, covering such factors as the harsh treatment of Germany by the victors of World War I, the unstable German economy, and the oratory and political ambitions of Adolf Hitler.

"Examines the events that served as . . . [precursors to the rise of the Nazis]. . . . Brightly colored pullout boxes highlight important turning points, the perspective of the everyday man, and further information on why specific events occurred. Numerous photographs help readers visualize concepts more fully. . . . Students should be able to easily use this resource." Library Media Connection.

Includes bibliographical references (p. 47) and index.

943.086 Germany—Period of the Third Reich, 1933-1945

Bartoletti, Susan Campbell
Hitler Youth: growing up in Hitler's shadow. Susan Campbell Bartoletti. Scholastic Nonfiction, 2019, c2005. 176 p.
Grades: 7 8 9 10 **943.086**
1. Hitler Youth 2. Nazism and children 3. Holocaust (1933-1945) -- Children 4. Children -- History 20th century. 5. Teenagers -- History 20th century. 6. Jewish children 7. Germany
ISBN 9781338309843

LC 2004051040

Explores the various factors which led many of Germany's young people to pledge their loyalty and support to the dictator and join the Hitler Youth during his rise to power.

"Bartoletti draws on oral histories, diaries, letters, and her own extensive interviews with Holocaust survivors, Hitler Youth, resisters, and bystanders to tell the history from the viewpoints of people who were there. . . . The stirring photos tell more of the story. . . . The extensive back matter is a part of the gripping narrative." Booklist.

Includes bibliographical references (p. 169-173) and index.

Bausum, Ann
Ensnared in the Wolf's Lair: inside the 1944 plot to kill Hitler and the ghost children of his revenge. Ann Bausum. Disney Pr 2021 144 p.
Grades: 6 7 8 9 **943.086**
1. Hitler, Adolf, 1889-1945. 2. Hofacker, Christa von, 1932- 3. Schenk von Stauffenberg, Klaus Philipp, Graf, 1907-1944 4. Anti-Nazi movement 5. Resistance to government 6. Operation Valkyrie, 1944 7. Nazism and children 8. World War II -- Children
ISBN 9781426338557

LC 2020005671

The stories of the children whose families were torn apart as a result of a failed attempt to assassinate Hitler in 1944. Provided by publisher.

"Bausum collects firsthand accounts from Christa and other survivors, their experiences lending authenticity and immediacy to the history. Few records about Sippenhaft survived so this extensively researched book offers an eye-opening look at an unforgettable historical event." Booklist

Includes bibliographical references and index.

Freedman, Russell
★ **We** will not be silent: the White Rose student resistance movement that defied Adolf Hitler. Russell Freedman. Clarion Books, 2016. 112 p.
Grades: 5 6 7 8 **943.086**
1. Scholl, Hans, 1918-1943. 2. Scholl, Sophie, 1921-1943. 3. Munich University -- Riot, 1943 4. 1940s 5. White Rose (Anti-Nazi group) 6. Anti-Nazi movement 7. World War II 8. Brothers and sisters 9. College students -- Political activity -- History 20th century. 10. Munich,Germany -- History -- 20th century.
ISBN 9780544223790

LC 2015020439

Golden Kite Award for Nonfiction, 2017.

Presents the true story of the White Rose, a group of students in Nazi Germany who were active undercover agents of the resistance movement against Hitler and his regime.

"A thorough and accessible introduction to the Holocaust and the students who dared to take a stand against evil." Kirkus.

Nardo, Don, 1947-
Hitler in Paris: how a photograph shocked a world at war. by Don Nardo. Compass Point Books, [2014] 64 p.: Captured history
Grades: 6 7 8 9 **943.086**
1. Hitler, Adolf, 1889-1945. 2. Eiffel Tower, Paris, France 3. Photographs -- Political aspects -- History 20th century 4. World War II -- Photography 5. World War II 6. Paris, France -- History, Military -- 20th century 7. France -- History -- German occupation, 1940-1945
ISBN 9780756547332

LC 2013030415

Discusses the importance of the 1940 photograph of Hitler in Paris as a warning to the rest of the world that the Nazis had to be taken seriously.

"Analyzing visual images and setting them in a larger historical and cultural context is an important skill. This volume uses Heinrich Hoffmann's 1940 photograph of Hitler in front of the Eiffel Tower to discuss the dictator's rise to power and Hoffmann's image-crafting of his subject. A spacious page design, which includes plenty of photos, enhances the presentation. Reading list, timeline." Horn Book.

Includes bibliographical references (page 63) and index.

943.8 Poland

Kadziolka, Jan
Poland. Jan Kadziolka, Tadeusz Wojciechowski. Oliver Press, 2010. 48 p. : Looking at Europe
Grades: 7 8 9 10 **943.8**
1. Poland 2. Poland -- History.
ISBN 9781881508892

LC 2009035350

"This will best suit students with good vocabularies and some knowledge of European history. . . . [It is] clearly written and well organized. . . . [It includes] many clear photos as well as colorful sidebars. . . . Attractive, informative." Booklist.

Includes bibliographical references and index.

Mara, Wil
Poland. by Wil Mara. Children's Press, an imprint of Scholastic, 2014. 144 p.: Enchantment of the world. Second series

Grades: 5 6 7 8   **943.8**
1. Countries 2. Culture 3. Poland 4. Europe
ISBN 9780531220160

LC 2013026061

Discusses the geography, culture, history, religion, economy, and community life of Poland.

944 France and Monaco

Sonneborn, Liz
France. by Liz Sonneborn. Children's Press, an imprint of Scholastic Inc., 2013. 144 p.
Grades: 5 6 7 8   **944**
1. France 2. Europe
ISBN 9780531256008

LC 2012047113

Describes the history, geography, population, wildlife, climate, economy, religion, and culture of France.

944.04 France since 1789

Riggs, Kate
The **French** Revolution. by Kate Riggs. Creative Education, 2009. 48 p.: Days of change
Grades: 5 6 7 8   **944.04**
1. War 2. Europe -- History. 3. France -- History -- Revolution, 1789-1799.
ISBN 9781583417348

LC 2008009728

Presents an overview of the French Revolution, including the causes of the conflict, the battles fought and executions held during the war, and the war's effects on French politics and society.

"With elegant design and mature prose, the Days of Change series is an ideal starting point for all manner of school projects. . . . The political pressures at the center of The French Revolution are difficult to dramatize, but Riggs carefully lays out the factions and civil disobedience that led to the Declaration of the Rights of Man and of The Citizen—and then the emperor's reign that overthrew everything." Booklist.

Includes bibliographical references and index.

945 Italy, San Marino, Vatican City, Malta

Blashfield, Jean F.
Italy. by Jean F. Blashfield. Children's Press, 2013. 144 p. : Enchantment of the world.
Grades: 5 6 7 8   **945**
1. Italy 2. Italy -- History.
ISBN 9780531236772

LC 2007052381

"Many students turn to the Internet for writing reports, but for reliably accurate, attractively presented and well-calibrated information, the long-standing Enchantment of the World series remains a superior choice. Each volume has been completely rewritten from a previous edition—in many cases to startling effect given recent political events. Although the basic structure holds true to past versions, the updated photographs are truly eye-popping and take care to portray the countries as modern often opting for showing, say, a surgeon at work rather than a rural farmer. It might not be necessary for libraries to replace [this title], since it hasn't changed radically, but this is a solid offering with updated

statistics. Each volume in this reliable series includes extensive back matter with a detailed index." Booklist.

Includes bibliographical references and index.

946.7 Eastern Spain and Andorra

Augustin, Byron
Andorra. by Byron D. Augustin. Marshall Cavendish Benchmark, c2009. 144 p. : Cultures of the world
Grades: 5 6 7 8   **946.7**
1. Andorra 2. Western Europe
ISBN 9780761431220

LC 2007040356

Provides comprehensive information on the geography, history, governmental structure, economy, cultural diversity, peoples, religion, and culture of Andorra. Provided by publisher.

946.9 Portugal

Blauer, Ettagale
Portugal. Ettagale Blauer, Jason Laure. Children's Press, an imprint of Scholastic Inc., 2019 144 p.: Enchantment of the World
Grades: 5 6 7 8   **946.9**
1. Portugal
ISBN 9780531126998

Describes the geography, wildlife, history, government, economy, religion, and culture of Portugal.

947.084 Russia—1914-1991

Lugovskaya, Nina, 1918-1993
I want to live: the diary of a young girl in Stalin's Russia. Nina Lugovskaya; translated by Andrew Bromfield. Houghton Mifflin, c2006. 280 p.
Grades: 7 8 9 10 11 12   **947.084**
1. Lugovskaya, Nina, 1918-1993 2. State-sponsored terrorism 3. Soviet Union -- Politics and government -- 1936-1953 4. Diaries
ISBN 0618605754

LC 2007298103

Offers rare insight into the life of a teenage girl in Stalin's Russia, where fear of arrest was a fact of daily life.

"Lugovskaya's diary, which was found in the NKVD archives, stands as a compelling historical artifact and Nina's story gives a moving—if relentlessly melancholy—personal account of life in Communist Russia." Publishers Weekly.

Includes bibliographical references (p. 277-279).

Streissguth, Thomas
The **rise** of the Soviet Union. Tom Streissguth, book editor. Greenhaven Press, 2002. 256 p.: Turning points in world history
Grades: 7 8 9 10   **947.084**
1. Soviet Union -- History. 2. Soviet Union -- Politics and government 1953-1985.
ISBN 0737709294

LC 2001040866

Essays by experts in the field discuss the political trends and consequences of the period, including social and economic aspects, pivotal leaders, and the long term cultural ramifications.

947.085 Russia—1953-1991

Langley, Andrew, 1949-

The **collapse** of the Soviet Union: the end of an empire. by Andrew Langley. Compass Point Books, c2007. 96 p.: Snapshots in history

Grades: 7 8 9 10   **947.085**

    1. Yeltsin, Boris Nikolayevich, 1931-2007 2. Gorbachev, Mikhail, 1931- 3. Post-communism 4. Soviet Union -- History
ISBN 0756520096

                                    LC 2006003003

Describes the events leading up to the collapse of the Soviet Union, and how it forever changed global politics.

"This describes leaders, their plans, and their ultimate downfalls, from the removal of Tsar Nicholas II to the problems of present-day Russia. [This book is] great for research . . . brief but comprehensive." School Library Journal.

Includes bibliographical references (p. 91-93) and index.

948 Scandinavia and Finland

Allan, Tony, 1946-

Exploring the life, myth, and art of the Vikings. Tony Allan. Rosen Pub., 2012. 144 p.: Civilizations of the world

Grades: 7 8 9 10 11   **948**

    1. Vikings 2. Art, Viking 3. Civilization, Viking 4. Europe -- History -- 476-1492 5. Scandinavia -- History.
ISBN 9781448848331

                                    LC 2011008856

Presents an introduction to Viking civilization, discussing its history, politics, art, religion, literature, philosophy, military, gods, and heroes.

Hinds, Kathryn, 1962-

Vikings: masters of the sea. by Kathryn Hinds. Marshall Cavendish Benchmark, c2010. 79 p.: Barbarians!

Grades: 6 7 8 9   **948**

    1. Vikings 2. Civilization, Viking 3. Scandinavia -- History
ISBN 9780761440741

                                    LC 2008039052

A history of the Viking Age, from about 793 to 1066. Provided by publisher.

"This . . . devotes excellent coverage and exposure to the emergence, development, and legacy of [the Vikings]." Library Media Connection.
Includes bibliographical references and index.

Huey, Lois Miner

American archaeology uncovers the Vikings. by Lois Miner Huey. Marshall Cavendish Benchmark, c2010. 64 p.: American archaeology

Grades: 4 5 6 7   **948**

    1. Vikings 2. Civilization, Viking 3. Archaeology and history 4. Excavations (Archaeology) 5. Northmen and Northwomen 6. Newfoundland and Labrador -- Antiquities 7. Western Hemisphere

-- Exploration
ISBN 9780761442707

                                  LC 2008050266

"This is both intriguing and engaging for young readers. . . . A welcomed addition to classroom and school libraries." Library Media Connection.

Includes bibliographical references and index.

Nardo, Don, 1947-

The **Vikings**. Don Nardo. Lucent Books/gale, Cengage Learning, c2011. 112 p.: World history (Lucent Books)

Grades: 6 7 8 9   **948**

    1. Vikings 2. Northmen and Northwomen 3. Explorers 4. Civilization, Viking 5. Western Hemisphere -- Exploration -- Norse
ISBN 9781420503166

                                    LC 2010010500

"This shines as it provides a contemporaneous writing as well as work by scholars that offer plenty of drama—and lots of facts too. . . . [It also] provides a solid time line, plenty of photographs, sourced quotes, and a list of books and websites for further investigation. Excellent for reports and research." Booklist.

Includes bibliographical references (p.105-106) and index.

948.5 Sweden

Heinrichs, Ann

Sweden. by Ann Heinrichs. Children's Press, an Imprint of Scholastic Inc., 2014. 144 p.: Enchantment of the world. Second series

Grades: 5 6 7 8   **948.5**

    1. Countries 2. Culture 3. Sweden 4. Europe
ISBN 9780531220177

                                    LC 2013022562

Introduces Sweden, describing its geography, history, animals, government, economy, food, religion, cities, culture, and family life.

949.4 Switzerland

Rogers Seavey, Lura

Switzerland. by Lura Rogers Seavey. Children's Press, 2017 144 p.: Enchantment of the world

Grades: 5 6 7 8   **949.4**

    1. Countries 2. Switzerland 3. Europe
ISBN 9780531218877

                                    LC 2016000985

Provides comprehensive information on the geography, history, wildlife, governmental structure, economy, cultural diversity, peoples, religion, and culture of Switzerland.

"With stunning, high-quality photos that reflect the richness of cultures around the globe, the Enchantment of the World series earns its name." Booklist.

Includes bibliographical references (page 134), discography (page 134), and index.

949.5 Greece

Lace, William W.
The **unholy** crusade: the ransacking of medieval Constantinople. William W. Lace. Lucent Books, c2007. 104 p.
Grades: 6 7 8 9   **949.5**
1. Crusades Fourth, 1202-1204 2. Crusades 3. Constantinople, Battle of, 1205 4. War -- Religious aspects 5. Islam -- Relations -- Christianity 6. Istanbul, Turkey -- History.
ISBN 1590188462

LC 2006002572
Discusses the reasons behind the first three Crusades and their failure, and describes how the fourth Crusade was begun, the troubles plaguing the war, and the consequences of the brutal conquering of Constantinople.
"Lace gives equal attention to the events leading up to the destruction of Constantinople and traces the planning and plotting of the Crusades. . . . [The book has] numerous color reproductions. Clear, concise writing makes [it] highly readable, while the scholarship makes [it a] valuable [resource]." School Library Journal.
Includes bibliographical references (p. 97) and index.

VanVoorst, Jennifer, 1972-
The **Byzantine** Empire. by Jenny Fretland VanVoorst. Compass Point Books, c2013. 48 p.: Exploring the ancient world
Grades: 6 7 8   **949.5**
1. Byzantine civilization 2. Civilization, Ancient 3. Ancient history 4. Byzantine Empire -- History
ISBN 9780756545659

LC 2012001994
Discusses the rise and fall of the Byzantine Empire, which preserved and protected Europe's intellectual heritage when Europe was passing through a dark age.

949.7 Serbia, Croatia, Slovenia, Bosnia and Hercegovina, Montenegro, Macedonia

King, David C.
Serbia and Montenegro. David C. King, Debbie Nevins. Cavendish Square 2020 144 p.: Cultures of the World
Grades: 5 6 7 8   **949.7**
1. Serbia 2. Montenegro
ISBN 9781502655912
For a long time, the national identities of the people of Serbia and Montenegro were shared as they lived under one country. However, in recent years, Serbia and Montenegro have become their own nations. Your readers will discover the details behind this split as they examine the similarities and differences between these neighboring nations. Using the most current information available, this volume takes readers through the complicated history of these two countries and summarizes their unique ethnic groups and cultural backgrounds. Vibrant photographs of life in Serbia and Montenegro accompany sidebars, maps, and recipes to create an engaging learning experience. Provided by publisher

949.702 Yugoslavia, 1918-1991

Filipovic, Zlata
Zlata's diary: a child's life in Sarajevo. Zlata Filipovic; with an introduction by Janine Di Giovanni; translated with notes by Christina Pibichevich-Zoric. Penguin Books, 1995, c1994. xvi, 197 p.
Grades: 6 7 8 9   **949.702**
1. Filipovic, Zlata 2. Yugoslav War, 1991-1995 -- Children 3. Children and war 4. Sarajevo (Bosnia and Hercegovina) -- History -- Siege, 1992-1996 5. Children's writings
ISBN 9780140242058

LC BL 99757296
A chronicle of the war in Sarajevo from a child's perspective details Zlata's struggle for survival and a normal life in a chaotic nation.
"Filipovic's diary personalizes the tragedy in war-torn Sarajevo." Booklist.

949.72 Croatia

Cooper, Robert, 1945 August 2-
Croatia. Robert Cooper Cavendish Square 2020 144 p.: Cultures of the World
Grades: 5 6 7 8   **949.72**
1. Croatia
ISBN 9781502650689
This book offers readers the chance to see what life in Croatia is like, including details of its history, government, lifestyle, sport, and popular foods.

949.742 Bosnia and Hercegovina

King, David C.
Bosnia and Herzegovina. David C. King, Debbie Nevins. Cavendish Square 2021 144 p.: Cultures of the World
Grades: 5 6 7 8   **949.742**
1. Bosnia and Hercegovina 2. Balkan Peninsula
ISBN 9781502655875
The story of Bosnia and Herzegovina is full of conflict and challenges, but it's also full of rich traditions and people who are proud of their heritage. This complex story is told in a comprehensive way, through detailed main text filled with the most up-to-date information, helpful maps, informative sidebars, and splendid full-color photographs. As readers discover the geographic, economic, political, religious, and even culinary identity of Bosnia and Herzegovina, they are encouraged to develop a deeper understanding and appreciation for cultural diversity. Provided by publisher

949.9 Bulgaria

Prazdny, Bronja
Bulgaria. Bronja Prazdny. Oliver Press, 2010. 48 p.: Looking at Europe
Grades: 7 8 9 10   **949.9**
1. Bulgaria 2. Bulgaria -- History.
ISBN 9781881508854

LC 2009032670
"This will best suit students with good vocabularies and some knowledge of European history. . . . [It is] clearly written and well organized. . . . [It includes] many clear photos as well as colorful sidebars. . . . Attractive, informative." Booklist.

950 History of Asia

Galloway, Priscilla, 1930-
Adventures on the ancient Silk Road. Priscilla Galloway; with Dawn Hunter. Annick Press, c2009. 164 p.
Grades: 6 7 8 9   **950**
   1. Xuanzang, ca. 596-664. 2. Polo, Marco, 1254-1323? 3. Genghis Khan, 1162-1227 4. Trade routes -- History 5. Caravans 6. Silk Road -- History 7. Silk Road -- Description and travel
   ISBN 9781554511976

"The monk Xuanzang, the conqueror Genghis Khan, and the merchant Marco Polo each traveled the Silk Road, years apart. Their journeys, by different routes and for different motives, are gripping historical narratives, sensitively and excitingly fictionalized here, in language that is lively and descriptive, clear but not oversimplified. Vibrant reproductions of art and photos of artifacts leap off every colorful page." School Library Journal.

Helget, Nicole Lea, 1976-
Mongols. Nicole Helget. Creative Education, 2013. 48 p.: Fearsome fighters
Grades: 5 6 7 8   **950**
   1. Mongols -- History 2. Conquerors 3. Military art and science -- History Medieval, 500-1500. 4. Medieval military history 5. Mongolia -- Civilization. 6. Mongol Empire -- Rulers.
   ISBN 9781608181841
                    LC 2011035800

A compelling look at the Mongols, including how they built the most widespread empire in history, their lifestyle, their weapons, and how they remain a part of today's culture through books and film. Provided by publisher.

Morris, Neil, 1946-
Asian civilisations. Neil Morris. Zak Books, c2009. 48 p. : History (Zak Books (Firm))
Grades: 7 8 9 10   **950**
   1. Asian civilization 2. Asians -- Migrations 3. Civilization, Ancient 4. Asia -- History.
   ISBN 9788860981608
                    LC 2008008403

A detailed overview of the ancient civilizations of Asia, from the empires of the Indus Valley and India and the dynasties of China, Korea, and Japan to the early civilizations of the Southeast.

"The effectiveness lies in the combination of lush illustrations, well-chosen, captioned photographs of contemporary artifacts, and . . . [a] reasoned, concise [narrative]. Succinct time lines border most pages, and . . . the proper amount of white space, and clear dark print maintain organization and clarity. A superior choice." School Library Journal.

Nardo, Don, 1947-
Genghis Khan and the Mongol Empire. by Don Nardo. Lucent Books, c2010. 96 p.: World history (Lucent Books)
Grades: 5 6 7 8 9   **950**
   1. Genghis Khan, 1162-1227. 2. Rulers 3. Mongols -- Rulers 4. Mongols -- History 5. Mongolia -- Rulers
   ISBN 9781420503265
                    LC 2010032960

"Using new scholarship, Nardo paints a more nuanced and sophisticated picture of a man who united several nomadic clans and then went on to found history's largest empire. Starting with his early childhood and ending with the death of his grandson, Kublai Khan, the book focuses on Genghis Khan's empire building and leadership, including his code of laws and justice. The book features several color photographs of present-day Mongolia period reenactments, as well as artistic representations from the era. . . . Nardo includes quotations from several scholars while still keeping the book engaging and accessible for a wide variety of readers." School Library Journal.

Includes bibliographical references and index.

951 China and adjacent areas

Mara, Wil
People's Republic of China. by Wil Mara. Children's Press, c2012. 144 p.: Enchantment of the world
Grades: 4 5 6 7 8   **951**
   1. China 2. East Asia
   ISBN 9780531253526
                    LC 2011011308

Describes the geography, plants and animals, history, economy, language, religions, culture, and people of the People's Republic of China, home of one of the world's oldest continuous civilizations.

Marx, Trish
Elephants and golden thrones: inside China's Forbidden City. written by Trish Marx; photographs ... by Ellen B. Senisi; foreword by Li Ji. Abrams Books for Young Readers, 2008. 48 p.
Grades: 4 5 6 7   **951**
   1. Forbidden City (Beijing, China) 2. Forbidden City (Beijing, China) -- History. 3. Imperialism, Chinese 4. Palaces 5. Rulers 6. China -- Rulers. 7. Beijing, China
   ISBN 9780810994850
                    LC 2007022413

Introduces Beijing's Forbidden City, recounting some of the most famous incidents from its past, and describing its rooms, their function, and some of the daily rituals of palace life.

"The author brings the Forbidden City to life by telling stories about six different royal inhabitants from Zhengde, one of the worst emperors in Chinese history, to Puyi, who became a pawn of the invading Japanese. . . . Beautiful drawings and photographs, some provided by the Palace Museum and some taken for this book, lend color and provide additional information. Of particular note are the photos of the interiors of buildings, a number of which are not regularly open to the public." Booklist.

Includes bibliographical references (p. 47).

Pelleschi, Andrea, 1962-
China. by Andrea Pelleschi. ABDO, c2012. 144 p.: Countries of the world
Grades: 6 7 8 9   **951**
   1. Countries 2. China
   ISBN 9781617831072
                    LC 2011019959

Provides information about China, with emphasis on its geography, culture, history, economy, and government.

"Chapters then cover all the expected details for report-writers... Vivid photographs and useful maps in an eye-pleasing design enliven the presentation." Horn Book.

Includes bibliographical references and index.

Qian, Jifang

Chinese history stories: Stories from the Imperial Era. translated from the original Chinese by Qian Jifang; edited by Renee Ting. Shens Books, c2009. 2 v.: Treasures of China

Grades: 6 7 8 9   **951**

1. China -- History 2. China -- Civilization
ISBN 9781885008381

LC 2009027288

Presents nineteen true stories about historical figures from China's Zhou Dynasty and Imperial Era, from 1046 B.C. to 1911 A.D., including stories about kings, generals, scholars, and princesses.

"These first two entries in a planned series of 12 volumes offer gripping introductions to China's cultural narratives. From the initial two-page condensation of 3000 years of history to the suggestions to 'Learn More' after (often more useful to read before), the well-told stories and the attractively varied illustrations are riveting. . . . Multiple illustrators provide changing art styles and historical allusions, but all are detailed, lively, and colorful." School Library Journal.

Sís, Peter, 1949-

★ **Tibet**: through the red box. Peter Sís. Farrar Straus Giroux, 1998. 1 v. (unpaged)

Grades: 4 5 6 7   **951**

1. Travelers 2. Memories 3. Fathers and sons 4. Filmmakers 5. Roads -- Design and construction 6. Tibet -- Description and travel. 7. Diaries
ISBN 0374375526

LC 97050175

The author recreates his father's visit to Tibet and the wondrous things that he found there.

"When Sís opens the red lacquered box that has sat on his father's table for decades, he finds the diary his father kept when he was lost in Tibet in the mid-1950s. The text replicates the diary's spidery handwriting, while the illustrations depict elaborate mazes and mandalas, along with dreamlike spreads that are filled with fragmented details of the father's and son's lives. . . . Impeccably designed and beautifully made, the book has a dreamlike quality that will keep readers of many ages coming back to find more in its pages." Booklist.

Sonneborn, Liz

Tibet. by Liz Sonneborn. Children's Press, 2016. 144 p.: Enchantment of the world

Grades: 5 6 7 8   **951**

1. Tibet 2. South Asia
ISBN 9780531218884

LC 2015048619

"With stunning, high-quality photos that reflect the richness of cultures around the globe, the Enchantment of the World series earns its name." Booklist.

Includes bibliographical references and index.

Yomtov, Nelson

China. Nel Yomtov. Children's Press, 2018 144 p.

Grades: 5 6 7 8   **951**

1. China
ISBN 9780531235713

LC 2016056323

This book details the history, culture, geography and government of China. Provided by publisher.

951.05 China—Period of People's Republic, 1949

Burgan, Michael

Tank man: how a photograph defined China's protest movement. Michael Burgan. Compass Point Books, 2014. 64 p.: Captured history

Grades: 6 7 8 9   **951.05**

1. Widener, Jeff, 1956- 2. Tiananmen Square Massacre, Beijing, China, June 3-4, 1989 3. Student movements 4. Students -- Political activity 5. Photography -- Influence 6. Photojournalism 7. China -- Politics and government -- 1976-2002. 8. China -- History -- 1976-2002.
ISBN 9780756547318

LC 2013031196

Discusses the iconic photo of a lone protester, Tank Man, stopping a row of tanks near Tiananmen Square during protests in 1989. Provided by publisher.

"Analyzing visual images and setting them in a larger historical and cultural context is an important skill. In this volume Burgan uses the iconic photograph of a Tiananmen Square protester facing down a tank to discuss the 1989 student protest in China and the Communist government's violent retaliation. A spacious page design, which includes plenty of photos, enhances the presentation. Reading list, timeline." Horn Book.

Includes bibliographical references (page 63) and index.

Hay, Jeff

The **Tiananmen** Square protests of 1989. Jeff Hay, book editor. Greenhaven Press, c2010. 224 p.: Perspectives on modern world history

Grades: 7 8 9 10   **951.05**

1. Tiananmen Square Massacre, Beijing, China, June 3-4, 1989 2. Student movements 3. Students -- Political activity 4. China -- History -- 20th century 5. Beijing, China
ISBN 9780737747966

LC 2009041850

"The book has numerous full-color photographs, sidebars to enhance the text, and illustrations. This is a highly readable book and would be a good addition to the Library's world history collection." Library Media Connection.

Includes bibliographical references and index.

Ma, Yan, 1987-

The **diary** of Ma Yan: the struggles and hopes of a Chinese schoolgirl. edited and introduced by Pierre Haski; translated from the French by Lisa Appignanesi. Harper Collins, 2005. 166 p.

Grades: 5 6 7 8   **951.05**

1. Ma, Yan, 1987- 2. Girls 3. Muslim girls 4. Poor people 5. Poverty 6. Farm life 7. China
ISBN 0060764961

LC 2004016136

"In 2001, while a French journalist was visiting remote Ningxia province in northwest China, a Muslim woman wearing the white headscarf of the Hui people thrust the diaries of her daughter into his hands. The three small notebooks described the girl's struggle to get an education despite extreme poverty. . . . The girl's feelings for her mother were powerful and complex, and she alternated between overwhelming love and rage at the injustices she suffered." School Library Journal.

Naden, Corinne J.

Mao Zedong and the Chinese Revolution. by Corinne J. Naden. Morgan Reynolds Pub., 2008. 128 p. : World leaders (Morgan Reynolds)

Grades: 7 8 9 10 11 12   **951.05**
    1. Mao, Zedong, 1893-1976. 2. Heads of state 3. Communism 4. China -- History -- Cultural Revolution, 1966-1976. 5. China -- History -- 20th century.
    ISBN 9781599351001

                    LC 2008027829
"This discusses Chariman Mao Zedong's rise to power and his crucial role in national and international history. . . . Naden's analysis of the significant role of young people will draw YA readers for reports and for personal interest. The readable design, with clear type and lots of historic color photos as well as screens and detailed maps, includes spacious back matter." Booklist.

Slavicek, Louise Chipley, 1956-

The **Chinese** Cultural Revolution. Louise Chipley Slavicek. Chelsea House Publishers, c2010. 128 p.: Milestones in modern world history

Grades: 8 9 10 11 12   **951.05**
    1. China -- History -- Cultural Revolution, 1966-1976 2. China -- Politics and government -- 1949-1976
    ISBN 9781604132786

                    LC 2008054885
"From the cover photo onward, young people are front and center in [this book,] . . . which focuses on the Red Guards who heard the anti-establishment call of their leader, Mao Zedong, in 1966. This political upheaval led to the deaths of up to four million Chinese over 10 years." Booklist.

Includes bibliographical references and index.

951.25 Hong Kong

Kagda, Falaq

Hong Kong. Falaq Kagda & Magdalene Koh. Marshall Cavendish Benchmark, c2009. 144 p. : Cultures of the world

Grades: 5 6 7 8   **951.25**
    1. Hong Kong 2. China
    ISBN 9780761430346

                    LC 2007048285
Provides comprehensive information on the geography, history, wildlife, governmental structure, economy, cultural diversity, peoples, religion, and culture of Hong Kong. Provided by publisher.

951.7 Mongolia

Bjorklund, Ruth

Mongolia. by Ruth Bjorklund. Children's Press, 2017. 144 p.: Enchantment of the world

Grades: 5 6 7 8   **951.7**
    1. Countries 2. Mongolia 3. Central Asia
    ISBN 9780531218846

                    LC 2015043526
"With stunning, high-quality photos that reflect the richness of cultures around the globe, the Enchantment of the World series earns its name." Booklist.

Includes bibliographical references and index.

951.9 Korea

Senker, Cath

North Korea and South Korea. Cath Senker. Rosen Central, 2013. 48 p.

Grades: 6 7 8   **951.9**
    1. North Korea 2. South Korea
    ISBN 9781448860296

                    LC 2012010617
Presents an overview of the situation between North Korea and South Korea, providing a background history of the conflict and reviewing the issues of economics, political power, human rights, and the prospects for peace.

951.904 Korea—1945-1999

Reece, Richard, 1948-

The **Korean** War. by Richard Reece. ABDO Pub., c2011. 112 p.: Essential events

Grades: 7 8 9 10 11 12   **951.904**
    1. 1950s 2. Korean War, 1950-1953 3. Korea 4. United States -- History, Military -- 20th century
    ISBN 9781617147661

                    LC 2010044661
Examines the political climate and military situation that led to the Korean War and discusses the key figures and events involved in the conflict.

951.93 North Korea (People's Democratic Republic of Korea)

Sonneborn, Liz

North Korea. by Liz Sonneborn. Children's Press, An Imprint of Scholastic Inc., 2014. 144 p. : Enchantment of the World. Second Series

Grades: 5 6 7 8   **951.93**
    1. North Korea 2. North Korea -- History
    ISBN 9780531236789

                    LC 2013003650
Describes the history, geography, population, wildlife, climate, economy, religion, and culture of North Korea.

952 Japan

Bjorklund, Ruth

Japan. Ruth Bjorklund. Children's Press, 2018 144 p.

Grades: 5 6 7 8   **952**
    1. Japan
    ISBN 9780531235690

                    LC 2016052309
This book details the history, culture, geography and government of Japan. Provided by publisher.

Blumberg, Rhoda

 ★ **Commodore** Perry in the land of the Shogun. by Rhoda Blumberg. Lothrop, Lee & Shepard Books, c1985. 144 p.

Grades: 5 6 7 8   **952**
    1. Perry, Matthew Calbraith, 1794-1858. 2. United States Naval

Expedition to Japan, 1852-1854. 3. Isolationism 4. Cultural differences 5. Art, Japanese 6. United States -- Foreign relations -- Japan. 7. Japan -- Foreign relations -- United States.
ISBN 0688037232

LC 84021800

Golden Kite Award for Nonfiction, 1985.

Details Commodore Matthew Perry's role in opening Japan's closed society to world trade in the 1850s, one of history's most significant diplomatic achievements.

"This is a well-written story of Matthew Perry's expedition to open Japan to American trade and whaling ports. The account is sensitive to the extreme cultural differences that both the Japanese and Americans had to overcome. Especially good are the chapters and paragraphs explaining Japanese feudal society and culture. The text is marvelously complemented by the illustrations, almost all reproductions of contemporary Japanese art." School Library Journal.

Bibliography: p. 139-140.

Moore, Willamarie

All about Japan: stories, songs, crafts, and more. Willamarie Moore; illustrated by Kazumi Wilds. Tuttle Pub., c2011. 63 p.
Grades: 3 4 5 6   **952**
1. National characteristics, Japanese 2. Culture 3. Countries 4. Japan -- Social life and customs
ISBN 9784805310779

LC 2010040843

Introduces Japan, describing its history, culture, everyday life, food, sports, and holidays, as well as providing examples of Japanese poems, songs, handicrafts, writing, legends, and folkore.

"In this treasure-trove of information, two children, one a Tokyo urbanite and the other from a rural village, introduce readers to their country and its culture, including geography, language, traditional arts, costume, etiquette, sports, and festivals. The dual narrators' conversational descriptions of their homes and daily routines will engage young readers while highlighting the differences between the Westernized big-city existence and the traditional way of life in Japan's countryside, deftly demonstrating the rich variety of lifestyles within this island nation. The scope of this book is remarkably comprehensive, covering almost anything a child would want to know." School Library Journal.

Includes bibliographical references (p. 62) and index.

Niz, Xavier

Samurai: a guide to the feudal knights. by Xavier W. Niz. Capstone Press, c2012. 48 p.: History's greatest warriors (Minneapolis, Minn.)
Grades: 6 7 8   **952**
1. Samurai -- History 2. Honor 3. Weapons 4. Samurai -- Social life and customs 5. Japan -- History.
ISBN 9781429666015

LC 2011004956

"...Focuses [more] on relaying facts about the four groups of exceptional fighters than on a narrative... [and has] extensive modern cultural references to which students will relate." School Library Journal.

Somervill, Barbara A.

Japan. by Barbara A. Somervill. Children's Press, 2012. 144 p.: Enchantment of the world
Grades: 5 6 7 8   **952**
1. Japan 2. East Asia
ISBN 9780531253540

LC 2011009503

Explores the history, geography, wildlife, government, economy, religion, culture, and people of Japan, including the most current facts and statistics that relate to Japan.

Turnbull, Stephen R.

The **most** daring raid of the samurai. Stephen Turnbull. Rosen Pub., 2011, c2009. 64 p.: Most daring raids in history
Grades: 7 8 9 10   **952**
1. 17th century 2. Samurai -- History 17th century 3. Raids (Military science) 4. Military history 5. Samurai -- History 6. Japan -- History -- Tokugawa period, 1600-1868 7. Ryukyu Islands -- History, Military -- 17th century
ISBN 9781448818723

LC 2010030843

Describes the 1609 raid from Satsuma against Ryukyu, detailing the events leading up to the raid, the strategic plans over both land and sea, and the aftermath of the successful raid.

"This book is packed with facts, covering the details of the action, the people involved, and the tools used, in engaging prose. The authors cite their sources thoroughly. . . . Diagrams, . . . and maps make the action easy to follow and provide visual context for the raids. . . . This . . . is sure to find a large readership." School Library Journal.

Includes bibliographical references (p. 62-63) and index.

953.3 Yemen

O'Neal, Claire

We visit Yemen. by Claire O'Neal. Mitchell Lane Publishers, 2011. 64 p.: Your land and my land: the Middle East
Grades: 4 5 6 7 8   **953.3**
1. Yemen (Republic) 2. Yemen (Republic) -- History.
ISBN 9781584159612

LC 2011016773

Discusses the history of Yemen, including ancient monuments, its government, the land, sports, festivals, food, crafts, and everyday life.

953.53 Oman

Ejaz, Khadija

We visit Oman. Khadija Ejaz. Mitchell Lane Publishers, c2012. 63 p.: Your land and my land: The Middle East
Grades: 4 5 6 7 8   **953.53**
1. Oman 2. Islamic countries
ISBN 9781584159629

LC 2011000724

Discusses the history of Oman, including ancient monuments, its government, the land, sports, festivals, food, crafts, and everyday life.

953.57 United Arab Emirates

King, David C.

United Arab Emirates. David C. King. Marshall Cavendish Benchmark, c2008. 144 p.: Cultures of the world
Grades: 5 6 7 8   **953.57**
1. United Arab Emirates 2. Arab countries
ISBN 9780761425656

LC 2006030237

Provides comprehensive information on the geography, history, governmental structure, economy, cultural diversity, peoples, religion, and culture of the United Arab Emirates. Provided by publisher.

953.65 Bahrain

Cooper, Robert, 1945 August 2-
Bahrain. Robert Cooper and Jo-Ann Spilling. Marshall Cavendish Benchmark, c2011. 144 p.: Cultures of the world
Grades: 5 6 7 8   **953.65**
1. Islands 2. Bahrain 3. Middle East
ISBN 9781608702138

LC 2010019621
Describes the history, geography, culture, government, and people of the Persian Gulf state of Bahrain.

953.67 Kuwait

O'Shea, Maria
Kuwait. Maria O'Shea, Michael Spilling, Debbie Nevins. Cavendish Square, 2018, c2009. 128 p.: Cultures of the world
Grades: 5 6 7 8   **953.67**
1. Kuwait 2. Arab countries
ISBN 9781502636409
Provides comprehensive information on the geography, history, wildlife, governmental structure, economy, cultural diversity, peoples, religion, and culture of Kuwait. Provided by publisher.

Sonneborn, Liz
Kuwait. by Liz Sonneborn. Children's Press, An Imprint of Scholastic Inc., 2014. 144 p.: Enchantment of the World. Second Series
Grades: 5 6 7 8   **953.67**
1. Countries 2. Culture 3. Kuwait 4. Middle East
ISBN 9780531220153

LC 2013026062
"Many students turn to the Internet for writing reports, but for reliably accurate, attractively presented and well-calibrated information, the long-standing Enchantment of the World series remains a superior choice. Each volume has been completely rewritten from a previous edition—in many cases to startling effect given recent political events. Although the basic structure holds true to past versions, the updated photographs are truly eye-popping and take care to portray the countries as modern often opting for showing, say, a surgeon at work rather than a rural farmer. It might not be necessary for libraries to replace [this title], since it hasn't changed radically, but this is a solid offering with updated statistics. Each volume in this reliable series includes extensive back matter with a detailed index." Booklist.
Includes bibliographical references and index.

Tracy, Kathleen
We visit Kuwait. by Kathleen Tracy. Mitchell Lane Publishers, c2011. 64 p.: Your land and my land: the Middle East
Grades: 4 5 6 7 8   **953.67**
1. Kuwait 2. Kuwait -- History.
ISBN 9781584159582

LC 2011002756
An intoduction to the land and people of Kuwait.

953.8 Saudi Arabia

Tracy, Kathleen
We visit Saudi Arabia. by Kathleen Tracy. Mitchell Lane Publishers, c2011. 64 p.: Your land and my land: the Middle East
Grades: 4 5 6 7 8   **953.8**
1. Saudi Arabia -- History. 2. Saudi Arabia -- Politics and government.
ISBN 9781584159636

LC 2011000728
Discusses the history of Saudi Arabia, including ancient monuments, its government, the land, sports, festivals, food, crafts, and everyday life.

954 India and neighboring south Asian countries

Gibson, Karen Bush
The **Taj** Mahal. Karen Bush Gibson. Purple Toad Publishing, Inc., 2017. 32 p.: Building on a dream
Grades: 4 5 6 7 8   **954**
1. Taj Mahal (Agra, India) 2. Mausoleums 3. Architecture
ISBN 9781624692116
"Clearly written narratives and informative graphics tell the stories of the conception, construction, and symbolic importance of some of the world's most magnificent structures." School Library Journal.

NgCheong-Lum, Roseline, 1962-
Maldives. Roseline NgCheong-Lum. Marshall Cavendish Benchmark, 2011. 144 p.: Cultures of the world
Grades: 5 6 7 8   **954**
1. Maldives 2. South Asia
ISBN 9781608702176

LC 2010019746
Describes the history, geography, culture, government, and people of Maldives, an archipelago in the Indian Ocean.

954.02 India and neighboring south Asian countries—647-1785

Mann, Elizabeth, 1948-
Taj Mahal. by Elizabeth Mann; with illustrations by Alan Witschonke. Mikaya Press, c2008. 47 p. : Wonders of the world (Mikaya Press)
Grades: 4 5 6 7   **954.02**
1. Taj Mahal (Agra, India) 2. Mughal Empire -- History 3. Agra, India -- Buildings
ISBN 9781931414203

LC 2008060054
"This is a dramatic retelling of the construction of the Taj Mahal. Mann begins with two pages of prose that relay the commonly told legend, but then proceeds to explode that legend with descriptive writing, colorful illustrations, ancient paintings, maps, and photographs." Booklist.
Includes bibliographical references and index.

954.91 Pakistan

Hinman, Bonnie
We visit Pakistan. Bonnie Hinman. Mitchell Lane Publishers, 2011. 64 p.: Your land and my land: the Middle East
Grades: 4 5 6 7 8   **954.91**
1. Pakistan 2. Pakistan -- History
ISBN 9781584159605
Discusses the history of Pakistan, including ancient monuments, its government, the land, sports, festivals, food, crafts, and everyday life.

Sonneborn, Liz
Pakistan. by Liz Sonneborn. Children's Press, c2013. 144 p.: Cornerstones of freedom.
Grades: 5 6 7 8   **954.91**
1. Pakistan 2. Islamic countries
ISBN 9780531275443
LC 2012000505
Explores the geography, climate, history, wildlife, economy, government, people, religion, and culture of Pakistan.

954.96 Nepal

Taylor-Butler, Christine
Sacred mountain: Everest. by Christine Taylor-Butler. Lee & Low Books, c2009. 48 p.
Grades: 5 6 7 8   **954.96**
1. Mountaineering -- History 2. Sherpa (Nepalese people) 3. Mount Everest 4. Nepal -- Description and travel.
ISBN 9781600602559
LC 2008030423
A cultural, geological, and ecological history of Mount Everest focusing on the indigenous Sherpa and their spiritual connection to the mountain, record-setting multinational climbing expeditions, and the effects of tourism on the environment. Illustrated with photographs, maps, diagrams, and timelines. Provided by publisher.
"The informative text is amply illustrated with well-chosen black-and-white and color photographs." School Library Journal.
Includes bibliographical references (p. 48).

955 Iran

DiPrimio, Pete
We visit Iran. by Pete DiPrimio. Mitchell Lane Publishers, 2011. 64 p.: Your land and my land: the Middle East
Grades: 4 5 6 7 8   **955**
1. Recreation 2. Oil industry and trade 3. Iran -- Religion. 4. Iran -- History.
ISBN 9781584159544
LC 2011016765
Discusses the history of Iran, including ancient monuments, its government, the land, sports, festivals, food, crafts, and everyday life.

955.05 Iran—1906-2005

Wagner, Heather Lehr
The Iranian Revolution. Heather Lehr Wagner. Chelsea House, c2010. 112 p.

Grades: 7 8 9 10 11 12   **955.05**
1. Iran -- History -- Revolution, 1979
ISBN 9781604134902
LC 2009022336
Examines the history of the Iranian Revolution, starting with information about Iran prior to the revolution, through the events of the revolution itself, and finally touching on life in Iran after the overthrow of the shah.
"Chapters cover the origin of the Pahlavi dynasty, [Ayatollah] Khomeini's early life and how he came to symbolize opposition to the shah's regime, and the shah's aggressive campaigns of reform and Westernization. . . . A solid addition to the series." School Library Journal.
Includes bibliographical references and index.

955.06 Iran—2005-

Steele, Philip, 1948-
Iran and the West. Philip Steele. Rosen Central, 2013. 48 p.: Our world divided
Grades: 6 7 8   **955.06**
1. International relations 2. Iran -- History 3. Iran -- Foreign relations
ISBN 9781448860319
LC 2012010613
Looks at the current situation of Iran and its complicated relationship with the West, providing a background history and reviewing issues of religion, human rights, oil, nuclear power, the position of women, and free speech.

956.04 Middle East—1945-1980

Immell, Myra
Israel. Myra Immell, editor. Greenhaven Press, 2010. 240 p.: Opposing viewpoints series
Grades: 8 9 10 11 12   **956.04**
1. Arab-Israeli conflict 2. Palestinians -- History 20th century 3. Arab-Israeli conflict 1993- 4. Pacific settlement of international disputes 5. Arab countries -- History -- 20th century 6. Israel -- Politics and government -- 1993-
ISBN 9780737749748
Provides essays offering varying viewpoints on Israel and the Israeli-Palestinian conflict.

Woolf, Alex, 1964-
The Arab-Israeli War since 1948. Alex Woolf. Heinemann Library, c2012. 80 p.: Living through
Grades: 6 7 8 9   **956.04**
1. Arab-Israeli conflict 2. World politics 3. War 4. Middle East
ISBN 9781432959951
LC 2011015920
Provides information about the Arab-Israeli conflict, including which leaders were involved, how the wars have affected the world, and why the wars have lasted for so long.

956.1 Turkey

Laroche, Amelia
We visit Turkey. Amelia Laroche. Mitchell Lane Publishers, 2011. 64 p.: Your land and my land: the Middle East
Grades: 4 5 6 7 8   **956.1**
1. Turkey 2. Turkey -- History.
ISBN 9781584159568
Discusses the history of Turkey, including ancient monuments, its government, the land, sports, festivals, food, crafts, and everyday life.

956.7 Iraq

O'Neal, Claire
We visit Iraq. by Claire O'Neal. Mitchell Lane Publishers, 2011. 64 p.: Your land and my land: the Middle East
Grades: 4 5 6 7 8   **956.7**
1. Recreation 2. Oil industry and trade 3. Iraq -- History. 4. Mesopotamia -- History.
ISBN 9781584159551
                                          LC 2011016771
Discusses the history of Iraq, including ancient monuments, its government, the land, sports, festivals, food, crafts, and everyday life.

Samuels, Charlie, 1961-
★ **Iraq**. Charlie Samuels. National Geographic, c2007. 64 p.: National Geographic countries of the world
Grades: 4 5 6 7   **956.7**
1. Iraq 2. Middle East
ISBN 1426300611
                                          LC 2007024675
A basic overview of the history, geography, climate, and culture of Iraq.

Yomtov, Nelson
Iraq. Nel Yomtov. Children's Press, 2018. 144 p.
Grades: 5 6 7 8   **956.7**
1. Iraq
ISBN 9780531235904
                                          LC 2017025777
Describes the geography, plants, animals, history, economy, language, sports, arts, religions, culture, and people of Iraq.

956.7044 Iraq—1979-

Adams, Simon, 1955-
The **Iraq** War. Simon Adams. Arcturus Pub., 2010. 46 p.: Secret history
Grades: 7 8 9 10   **956.7044**
1. Iraq War, 2003-2011 2. Espionage -- History 3. Special operations (Military science) 4. Propaganda 5. Iraq 6. Middle East 7. High interest-low vocabulary books
ISBN 9781848376984
                                          LC 2010011764
This high-interest series, aimed at reluctant readers, looks at secret campaigns behind the major conflicts of the past 100 years. Biographical sidebars focus on heroic or notorious personalities. Highlighted fact features include special operations and their results, resistance movements, propaganda and the history of the time—as is known....and not readily known. Provided by publisher.

"This examines the Iraq War, including from propaganda and intelligence to technology and sacrifice. . . . Archival photographs combine with a busy but well-organized design to present an engaging perspective. . . . Both reluctant readers and history buffs in need of a fresh approach to events will appreciate this [book]." Horn Book Guide.

Includes bibliographical references (p. 45) and index.

Bingham, Jane
The **Gulf** Wars with Iraq. Jane Bingham. Heinemann Library, c2012. 80 p.: Living through
Grades: 6 7 8 9   **956.7044**
1. Persian Gulf War, 1991 2. Iraq War, 2003-2011 3. Iraq -- History -- 2003-
ISBN 9781432959975
                                          LC 2011015922
Discusses what it was like to live through the Gulf Wars with Iraq, and how these conflicts have changed lives on both sides.

Mason, Paul, 1967-
The **Iraq** War. Paul Mason. Arcturus Publishing, c2010. 48 p.: Timelines
Grades: 7 8 9 10   **956.7044**
1. Iraq War, 2003-2011 2. Military occupation 3. War 4. Iraq -- History -- 2003- 5. United States -- Politics and government -- 2001-2009
ISBN 9781848376397
                                          LC 2009051266
Discusses events in Iraq that lead up to the current war in Iraq, beginning with the end of the Persian Gulf War and continuing through the planned withdrawal for all coalition forces from the country. Provided by publisher.

"Each date and accompanying fact is explained, illustrated, and connected to previous and future events by a chronology and notes referencing related topics. This is a useful format to help students see the relationships between single events and their causes and effects in history." School Library Journal.

Includes bibliographical references and index.

Smithson, Ryan
Ghosts of war: the true story of a 19-year-old GI. Ryan Smithson. HarperTeen, 2009. 321 p., [8] p. of plates
Grades: 8 9 10 11 12   **956.7044**
1. Smithson, Ryan 2. Soldiers 3. War 4. Iraq War, 2003-2011 5. Nineteen-year-old men 6. Post-traumatic stress disorder
ISBN 9780061664687
                                          LC 2008035420
"Ryan Smithson was a typical 16-year-old high-school student until 9/11. . . . Smithson enlisted in the Army Reserve the following year and, a year into the Iraq war, was deployed to an Army engineer unit as a heavy-equipment operator. His poignant, often harrowing account, especially vivid in sensory details, chronicles his experiences in basic training and in Iraq. . . . This memoir is a remarkable, deeply penetrating read that will compel teens to reflect on their own thoughts about duty, patriotism and sacrifice." Kirkus.

Includes bibliographical references and index.

956.91 Syria

Yomtov, Nelson

Syria. Nel Yomtov. Children's Press, an imprint of Scholastic Inc., 2013. 144 p.: Enchantment of the World. Second Series

Grades: 5 6 7 8   **956.91**

1. Syria 2. Middle East
ISBN 9780531236796

LC 2013000088

"Many students turn to the Internet for writing reports, but for reliably accurate, attractively presented and well-calibrated information, the long-standing Enchantment of the World series remains a superior choice. Each volume has been completely rewritten from a previous edition—in many cases to startling effect given recent political events. Although the basic structure holds true to past versions, the updated photographs are truly eye-popping and take care to portray the countries as modernoften opting for showing, say, a surgeon at work rather than a rural farmer. Syria obviously can't be completely up-to-date because of the ongoing rebellion, but it does a good job of explaining the roots of the unrest, along with the usual topics of food, religion, and customs. Each volume in this reliable series includes extensive back matter with a detailed index." Booklist.

Includes bibliographical references and index.

956.94 Palestine; Israel

Owings, Lisa

Israel. Lisa Owings. ABDO Publishing Company, [2013] 144 p.

Grades: 8 9 10 11 12   **956.94**

1. Israel 2. Middle East
ISBN 9781617836305

Provides information about Israel, with emphasis on its geography, culture, history, economy, and government.

Saul, Laya

We visit Israel. by Laya Saul. Mitchell Lane, 2011. 64 p.: Your land and my land: the Middle East

Grades: 4 5 6 7 8   **956.94**

1. Israel -- History. 2. Israel -- Social life and customs.
ISBN 9781584159575

LC 2011024706

Explores Israel, highlighting its history, people, and customs.

956.9405 Israel—1948-

Ellis, Deborah, 1960-

Three wishes: Palestinian and Israeli children speak. Deborah Ellis. Groundwood Books, c2004. 110 p.

Grades: 5 6 7 8   **956.9405**

1. Arab-Israeli conflict 2. Children 3. Teenagers 4. Interethnic conflict 5. Social conflict 6. Israel -- Foreign relations -- Palestine. 7. Palestine -- Foreign relations -- Israel.
ISBN 0888995547

LC 2006386925

Through in-depth interviews with young adults living in the midst of the Israeli-Palestinian conflict, the experiences, dreams, and sorrows of a diverse group of children from both sides are presented.

"An excellent presentation of a confusing historic struggle, told within a palpable, perceptive and empathetic format." School Library Journal.

Tolan, Sandy

The lemon tree: An Arab, a Jew, and the Heart of the Middle East Young Readers' Edition. by Sandy Tolan. Bloomsbury Childrens Books 2020 192 p.

Grades: 5 6 7 8   **956.9405**

1. Khayri, Bashir 2. Landau, Dalia Eshkenazi, 1947- 3. Palestinians 4. Israelis 5. Friendship 6. Arab-Israeli conflict 7. Israeli-Palestinian relations 8. Israel
ISBN 9781547603947

LC 2020020277

In 1967, Bashir Khairi, a twenty-five-year-old Palestinian, journeyed to Israel with the goal of seeing the beloved stone house with the lemon tree behind it that he and his family had fled nineteen years earlier. To his surprise, when he found the house he was greeted by Dalia Eshkenazi Landau, a nineteen-year-old Israeli college student, whose family left Europe for Israel following the Holocaust. On the stoop of their shared home, Dalia and Bashir began a rare friendship, forged in the aftermathof war and tested over the next half century in ways that neither could imagine on that summer day in 1967. Sandy Tolan brings the Israeli-Palestinian conflict down to its most human level, demonstrating that even amid the bleakest political realities there exist stories of hope and transformation. Provided by publisher.

"Tolan seamlessly weaves in the modern history of Palestine/Israel—including dates, roles played by leaders, and details from both Bashir's and Dalia's experiences. The writing is rich, especially when describing the house—it and its lemon tree form the center of this moving story. Captivating and complicated." Kirkus

956.95 Jordan and West Bank

Robinson, Anthony, 1949 September 8-

Young Palestinians speak: living under occupation. by Anthony Robinson and Annemarie Young. Interlink Books, an imprint of Interlink Publishing Group, Inc., 2017. 118 p.

Grades: 6 7 8 9 10 11 12   **956.95**

1. Arab-Israeli conflict 2. Palestinians -- History 20th century 3. Children 4. Arab countries -- History -- 20th century 5. Middle East -- History -- 20th century
ISBN 9781566560153

LC 2016042874

An overview of the history of the Israel-Palestine conflict and interviews with Palestinian children living under occupation, presented as an educational resource for children ages 9 and up.

"A poignant, powerful, and insightful collection of voices seldom heard." Kirkus.

Includes bibliographical references.

Sonneborn, Liz

Jordan. Liz Sonneborn. Children's Press, 2019 144 p.: Enchantment of the World

Grades: 5 6 7 8   **956.95**

1. Jordan
ISBN 9780531126981

Describes the geography, wildlife, history, government, economy, religion, and culture of Jordan.

958.1 Afghanistan

Bjorklund, Ruth
Afghanistan. by Ruth Bjorklund. Children's Press, c2012. 144 p.: Enchantment of the world
Grades: 5 6 7 8   **958.1**
    1. Afghanistan 2. South Asia
    ISBN 9780531253502
                                            LC 2011013627
Describes the geography, history, government, economy, people, religion, and daily life of Afghanistan.

Gerszak, Rafal
Beyond bullets: a photo journal of Afghanistan. by Rafal Gerszak; with Dawn Hunter; photographs by Rafal Gerszak. Annick Press, 2011. 128 p.
Grades: 7 8 9 10 11 12   **958.1**
    1. Afghan War, 2001- 2. Photojournalism 3. Culture 4. Afghanistan -- Social conditions. 5. Afghanistan 6. Diaries
    ISBN 9781554512935
Photographer Rafal Gerszak presents a collection of stunning photographs and vivid journal entries from Afghanistan.
    "Author/photographer Gerszak first went to Afghanistan to spend a year embedded with an American military unit documenting house searches, disputes with village elders and the aftermath of battles. He returned as an unaffiliated photographer without a military escort, determined to document civilian life. This photo journal features images from both trips to Afghanistan, accompanied by diary-like accounts of his travels. Gerszak's frank and descriptive observations effectively convey the ugliness, monotony and tragedy of war." Kirkus.

Steele, Philip, 1948-
Afghanistan: from war to peace? Philip Steele. Rosen Central, 2013. 48 p.: Our world divided
Grades: 6 7 8   **958.1**
    1. Afghanistan 2. Afghanistan -- History
    ISBN 9781448860302
                                            LC 2012010616
Looks at the current situation of Afghanistan in the twenty-first century, providing a background history of previous conflicts and reviewing the current war and the issues of religion, economics, political power, and human rights, and the prospects for peace.

Whitfield, Susan
Afghanistan. Susan Whitfield. National Geographic, c2008. 64 p.: National Geographic countries of the world
Grades: 4 5 6 7   **958.1**
    1. Afghanistan 2. South Asia
    ISBN 1426302568
A basic overview of the history, geography, climate, and culture of Afghanistan.

958.45 Kazakhstan

Pang, Guek-Cheng, 1950-
Kazakhstan. Guek Cheng Pang, Bethany Bryan. Cavendish Square 2020 144 p.: Cultures of the World
Grades: 5 6 7 8   **958.45**
    1. Kazakhstan 2. Central Asia
    ISBN 9781502655790

Kazakhstan is the ninth-largest country in the world, a landlocked nation that borders both China and Russia. Kazakhstan has long struggled to find its own identity. Since declaring independence in 1991 after the breakup of the Soviet Union, Kazakhs have struggled to regain their unique culture. This volume takes readers through its past and current events, across mountains and valleys, and into the everyday lives of its citizens, using vivid photographs, engaging sidebars, and accessible maps. Readers explore Kazakhstan's culture, geography, government, and people. They'll be encouraged to develop an interest in global exploration, history, and current events. Provided by publisher

959.604 Cambodia—1949-

Sonneborn, Liz
The **Khmer** Rouge. Liz Sonneborn. Marshall Cavendish Benchmark, c2012. 80 p.: Great escapes
Grades: 5 6 7 8   **959.604**
    1. Dith Pran, 1942-2008 2. Parti communiste du Kampuchea 3. 1970s 4. Political refugees 5. Atrocities 6. Journalists 7. State-sponsored terrorism 8. Genocide 9. Cambodia -- History -- 1975-1979
    ISBN 9781608704743
                                            LC 2011005595
Presents accounts of narrow escapes executed by oppressed individuals and groups while illuminating social issues and the historical background that led to the atrocities committed in Cambodia's "killing fields" by the Khmer Rouge. Provided by publisher.

959.7 Vietnam

Yasuda, Anita
Vietnam. Anita Yasuda. AV2 by Weigl, 2017 32 p.
Grades: 5 6 7 8   **959.7**
    1. Vietnam
    ISBN 9781489650290
                                            LC 2015049792
Introduces Vietnam, describing its geography and climate, industries, history, resources and wildlife, culture, politics, and sports.
    "Perfect for social studies and world geography classrooms and students, the Exploring Countires series provides informative and well-written titles on individual countries." Booklist

959.704 Vietnam—1945-

Caputo, Philip, 1941-
10,000 days of thunder: a history of the Vietnam War. Philip Caputo. Atheneum Books for Young Readers, 2005. 128 p.
Grades: 6 7 8 9   **959.704**
    1. Vietnam War, 1961-1975
    ISBN 0689862318
                                            LC 2004015468
Author Philip Caputo, a Vietnam veteran and Pulitzer Prize-winning journalist, provides an in-depth examination of the significant events and battles of the Vietnam War in 10,000 Days of Thunder.
    "In this history of the Vietnam War Caputo has produced what is at once an overview and a sensitive, resonant picture of the war as seen and experienced by American soldiers, the Viet Cong, North Vietnamese guerrillas, and the citizens of both South Vietnam and the United States. . . . Caputo's prose is clear and direct, and the award-winning photos . . .

add an immediacy that sets this title apart from more conventional treatments." School Library Journal.

Includes bibliographical references (p. 122-123) and index.

DiConsiglio, John

Vietnam: the bloodbath at Hamburger Hill. John DiConsiglio. Franklin Watts, c2010. 64 p.: 24/7: goes to war
Grades: 6 7 8 9   **959.704**
1. War 2. Military campaigns 3. Vietnam War, 1961-1975 4. Hamburger Hill, Vietnam, Battle of, 1969 5. Vietnam
ISBN 9780531255261

         LC 2009014912

"This will appeal to these readers, because . . . [it tells] a story while presenting the facts. . . . The first chapter gives the historic details concerning the war up to the particular battle, with the story of the battle told from a first-person perspective. A mixture of news photos and photos taken by the men involved appear throughout the book." Library Media Connection.

Includes bibliographical references (p. 59) and index.

Gifford, Clive

Why did the Vietnam War happen? Clive Gifford. Gareth Stevens, 2011. 48 p.: Moments in history
Grades: 6 7 8 9   **959.704**
1. Vietnam War, 1961-1975 2. War 3. World politics
ISBN 9781433941788

         LC 2010015835

Describes American entry into the Vietnam War and the events of the war, describing the perceived Communist threat, the purported attack on American warships in the Gulf of Tonkin, the failed progress to win the war, and the eventual waning of American support.

"Brightly colored pull-out boxes highlight important turning points, the perspective of the everyday man, and further information on why specific events occurred. Numerous photographs help readers visualize concepts more fully. . . . Students should be able to easily use this resource." Library Media Connection.

Includes bibliographical references (p. 47) and index.

Gitlin, Marty

U.S. involvement in Vietnam. Martin Gitlin; content consultant Clarence R. Wyatt. ABDO Pub. Co., c2010. 112 p.
Grades: 7 8 9   **959.704**
1. Vietnam War, 1961-1975 2. United States -- History -- 1961-1969 3. United States -- History -- 1969-
ISBN 9781604539493

         LC 2009031071

Chronicles America's involvment in Vietnam, covering battles, key figures, the antiwar movement at home, peace talks, and the aftermath.

McNab, Chris, 1970-

50 things you should know about the Vietnam War. Chris McNab. QED Publishing, 2016. 80 p.: 50 things you should know about
Grades: 4 5 6 7 8   **959.704**
1. Vietnam War, 1961-1975 2. War 3. Military history 20th century. 4. United States -- History -- 1961-1975 5. Vietnam -- History -- 1945-1975
ISBN 9781609929619

"An excellent starting point for understanding the Vietnam War, presented as a conflict that commenced with French colonial occupation and continues even today." Kirkus.

Partridge, Elizabeth

Boots on the ground: America's war in Vietnam. Elizabeth Partridge. Viking Books for Young Readers, 2018. 224 p.
Grades: 7 8 9 10 11 12   **959.704**
1. 1960s 2. 1970s 3. Vietnam War, 1961-1975 -- Causes 4. War 5. Soldiers 6. Refugees 7. Veterans 8. Vietnam -- History
ISBN 9780670785063
Golden Kite Award for Nonfiction, 2019.

America's war in Vietnam. In over a decade of bitter fighting, it claimed the lives of more than 58,000 American soldiers and beleaguered four US presidents. More than forty years after America left Vietnam in defeat in 1975, the war remains controversial and divisive both in the United States and abroad.

"With an impressive amount of well-chosen photographs, this is a necessary, conscientious look at a factious time in American and world history." Booklist.

Senker, Cath

The **Vietnam** War. Cath Senker. Heinemann Library, c2012. 80 p.: Living through
Grades: 6 7 8 9   **959.704**
1. Vietnam War, 1961-1975 2. War 3. Soldiers
ISBN 9781432960001

         LC 2011015928

Explores what it was like to live through the Vietnam War, and discusses the consequences of the war for both countries.

Sheinkin, Steve

Most dangerous: Daniel Ellsberg and the secret history of the Vietnam War. Steve Sheinkin. Square Fish, 2019. 208 p.
Grades: 7 8 9 10 11 12   **959.704**
1. Ellsberg, Daniel 2. Pentagon Papers Case 3. Vietnam War, 1961-1975 4. Whistle blowing 5. United States -- Politics and government -- 1969-1974
ISBN 9781250180834

         LC 2014040761

The story of Daniel Ellsberg and his decision to steal and publish secret documents about America's involvement in the Vietnam War. Provided by publisher.

"In this thoroughly researched, thoughtfully produced, and beautifully written book, Sheinkin delves into the life of Daniel Ellsberg, former Pentagon consultant and a self-described 'cold warrior,' who gradually made an about-face with regard to America's presence in Vietnam. . . . A timely and extraordinary addition to every library." School Library Journal.

Includes bibliographical references and index.

Skrypuch, Marsha Forchuk

Last airlift: a Vietnamese orphan's rescue from war. Marsha Forchuk Skrypuch. Pajama Press, c2011. 99, vii p.
Grades: 3 4 5 6   **959.704**
1. Orphans 2. Orphanages 3. Vietnam War, 1961-1975 -- Children 4. Adopted children 5. Vietnamese Canadians 6. Ho Chi Minh City, Vietnam
ISBN 098694954X
The story of the last Canadian airlift rescue operation that left Saigon and arrived in Toronto on April 13, 1975. Son Thi Anh Tuyet was one of the 57 babies and children on that flight. Based on personal interviews and enhanced with archival photographs.

Warren, Andrea

Escape from Saigon: how a Vietnam War orphan became an American boy. Andrea Warren. Farrar, Straus and Giroux, 2004. 110 p.

Grades: 6 7 8 9 10 **959.704**

1. Steiner, Matt. 2. Vietnamese Americans 3. Vietnamese American boys 4. Adopted children 5. Orphans 6. Vietnam War, 1961-1975 -- Children 7. Ho Chi Minh City, Vietnam
ISBN 0374322244

LC 2003060672

Chronicles the experiences of an orphaned Amerasian boy from his birth and early childhood in Saigon through his departure from Vietnam in the 1975 Operation Babylift and his subsequent life as the adopted son of an American family in Ohio.

"The child-at-war story and the facts about the Operation Babylift rescue are tense and exciting. Just as gripping is the boy's personal conflict." Booklist.

Young, Marilyn B.

The **Vietnam** War: a history in documents. Marilyn B. Young, John J. Fitzgerald, A. Tom Grunfeld. Oxford University Press, c2002. 175 p.: Pages from history

Grades: 7 8 9 10 **959.704**

1. Vietnam War, 1961-1975
ISBN 019512278X

LC 2001052338

Explores the Vietnam War through the eyes of those who were most impacted by its consequences.

"The documents are skillfully tied together by brief text that gives good background information. . . . The book is well balanced in showing both sides. . . . Good-quality, black-and-white photos and illustrations are plentiful and informative." School Library Journal.

Includes bibliographical references (p. 165-166) and index.

960 History of Africa

Habeeb, William Mark, 1955-

Africa: facts and figures. William Mark Habeeb. Mason Crest Publishers, c2013. 87 p.

Grades: 7 8 9 10 **960**

1. Africa
ISBN 9781422221761

LC 2004010186

"This is an excellent, detailed overview. . . . The attractive, open design, with clear type, beautiful photos, maps, and lots of extras in lists and insets, manages to pack in an extraordinary amount of information." Booklist.

Includes bibliographical references and index.

Mitchell, Peter

Peoples and cultures of Africa. edited by Peter Mitchell. Chelsea House, c2006. 6 v.

Grades: 5 6 7 8 **960**

1. Ethnology 2. African civilization 3. Africa -- Social life and customs.
ISBN 9780816062607

LC 2006040011

A six-volume set arranged by large geographical regions contains an introduction to the countries of the African continent, including coverage of ethnic groups, material cultures, performing arts, literature, religions, and social life and customs.

"This attractive and informative set provides well-written, well-researched introductory information about African geography and culture. Each of the first five volumes covers a region within the continent . . . and opens with introductory information on that area's physical features, biomes, religions, languages, and cultures, and includes an extensive time line. It is followed by color-coded, alphabetically arranged entries examining the region's tribal and ethnic groups; art, sculpture, and textiles; performing arts and literature; and religion and individual cultures in further detail. . . . The final volume is devoted to single-page geographic and economic profiles of Africa's nations. . . . This quality set will give report writers a solid introduction to the diversity of Africa." School Library Journal.

Includes bibliographical references and index.

Opini, Bathseba

Africans thought of it: amazing innovations. Bathseba Opini, Richard B. Lee. Annick Press, 2011. 48 p.: We thought of it

Grades: 3 4 5 6 **960**

1. Inventions 2. African civilization 3. Africa
ISBN 9781554512775

"Vivid photographs feature authentic objects used . . . while people engaged in activities capture an enthusiastic look at the reliance on community. Colored backgrounds and borders present a busy, though uncluttered, dynamic portrayal of nuanced cultures. . . . Succinct definitions and compact descriptions provide a brief and interesting blend of the contemporary with the traditional." School Library Journal.

Sherrow, Victoria

★ **National** Geographic investigates ancient Africa: archaeology unlocks the secrets of Africa's past. by Victoria Sherrow; James Denbow, consultant. National Geographic Society, 2007. 64 p.: National Geographic investigates

Grades: 4 5 6 7 **960**

1. Excavations (Archaeology) 2. Civilization, Ancient 3. African civilization 4. Africa -- History. 5. Africa -- Antiquities.
ISBN 079225399X

LC 2007277594

Discusses important archeological finds from Africa's past and reveals how archaeologists use the latest technology to discover clues to ancient African civilization.

Woods, Michael, 1946-

Seven natural wonders of Africa. by Michael Woods and Mary B. Woods. Twenty-First Century Books, 2009. 80 p.

Grades: 5 6 7 8 **960**

1. Natural history 2. Landforms 3. Animals 4. Mountains 5. Deserts 6. Africa 7. Sahara
ISBN 9780822590712

"This book takes seven noteworthy wonders in [Africa] and spotlights them in separate chapters. The text introduces each one from a historical perspective, and beautiful color photographs offer inviting views, while maps, sidebars, and featured quotes add variety to the pages. [This book] looks at mountain gorillas, the Nile, Victoria Falls, the Sahara Desert, Mount Kilimanjaro, the Seychelles Islands and the Serengeti Plain." Booklist.

Includes bibliographical references and index.

961.1 Tunisia

Brown, Roslind Varghese

Tunisia. by Roslind Varghese Brown & Michael Spilling. Marshall Cavendish Benchmark, 2008. 144 p. : Cultures of the world

Grades: 5 6 7 8   **961.1**
    1. Tunisia 2. North Africa
    ISBN 9780761430377
                                        LC 2007050798

Provides comprehensive information on the geography, history, wildlife, governmental structure, economy, cultural diversity, peoples, religion, and culture of Tunisia. Provided by publisher.

962 Egypt, Sudan, South Sudan

Heinrichs, Ann

The **Nile**. by Ann Heinrichs. Marshall Cavendish Benchmark, 2008. 96 p. : Nature's wonders

Grades: 5 6 7 8   **962**
    1. Rivers 2. Natural history 3. Ecology 4. Wildlife 5. Nile Valley 6. Nile River
    ISBN 9780761428541
                                        LC 2007019187

Provides comprehensive information on the geography, history, wildlife, peoples, and environmental issues of the Nile River Basin. Provided by publisher.

"It's tough to make a river interesting, but this . . . does an admirable job of it. . . . Crisp, full-color photos and original artwork decorate nearly every page. . . . [This is a] well-thought-out natural history." Booklist.

Includes bibliographical references and index.

962.4 Sudan and South Sudan

Steele, Philip, 1948-

Sudan, Darfur, and the nomadic conflicts. Philip Steele. Rosen Central, 2012. 48 p.: Our world divided

Grades: 6 7 8   **962.4**
    1. Interethnic relations 2. Sudan -- History 3. Sudan -- Interethnic relations
    ISBN 9781448860289
                                        LC 2012010639

Discusses the Sudan, including its history, ethnic conflicts, and natural resources.

962.404 Sudan—1956-

Brownlie Bojang, Ali, 1949-

Sudan in our world. by Ali Brownlie Bojang. Smart Apple Media, c2011. 32 p.: Countries in our world

Grades: 5 6 7 8   **962.404**
    1. Sudan 2. Arab countries
    ISBN 9781599204345
                                        LC 2009052421

Describes the economy, government, and culture of Sudan today and discusses Sudan's influence of and relations with the rest of the world. Provided by publisher.

"Issues such as Civil War, fighting in Darfur, the government, and millions of displaced refugees continue to cripple the country and impede its advancement. While Sudan is rich in resources, its future remains uncertain. [This title] will appeal to children interested in learning more about Africa and those needing factual information for reports." School Library Journal.

Includes bibliographical references (p. 31) and index.

963.5 Eritrea

Ngcheong-Lum, Roseline

Eritrea. Roseline Ngcheong-Lum, Tamra Orr. Cavendish Square 2020 144 p.: Cultures of the World

Grades: 5 6 7 8   **963.5**
    1. Eritrea 2. Northeast Africa
    ISBN 9781502655776

Eritrea lies along the coast of the Red Sea in northeastern Africa. Its people are resilient and determined. When the border war between Eritrea and Ethiopia ended in 2018, hope surged for a better future for the country. The country still has significant obstacles to overcome, including religious persecution and strict censorship, but Eritreans will keep fighting for a brighter tomorrow. This guidebook explores these aspects and other key elements such as geography, government, religion, and art, through detailed photographs, maps, and sidebars, giving a comprehensive view of this distinct African nation. Provided by publisher

965 Algeria

Wagner, Heather Lehr

The **Algerian** war. Heather Lehr Wagner. Chelsea House, c2012. 120 p.

Grades: 10 11 12   **965**
    1. National liberation movements 2. Algeria -- History Revolution, 1954-1962 3. France -- Colonies -- Africa -- History
    ISBN 9781604139235
                                        LC 2011023060

Many different factors led to the French invasion of Algeria in June 1830, but the result was the establishment of a French colony in North Africa that would last 132 years. For more than a century, Algeria was marked by sharp divisions between its European colonizers and the mainly Muslim people who had occupied the land prior to the arrival of French troops. Discrimination, prejudice, and injustice separated these two groups until a war for independence began on November 1, 1954. After nearly eight years of violence, Algeria became an independent nation in 1962, but a half century later, it remains a country haunted by violence and struggling to achieve stability and prosperity for its people. Read about this conflict in The Algerian War. Provided by publisher.

966 West Africa and offshore islands

Haywood, John, 1956-

West African kingdoms. John Haywood. Raintree, c2008. 64 p.: Time travel guides

Grades: 6 7 8 9   **966**
    1. West Africa -- History 2. West Africa -- Civilization
    ISBN 9781410929129
                                        LC 2007006053

Presents a tour of West African kingdoms between 1200 and 1600, discussing facts about religion, war, slavery, diet, houses, politics, culture, transportation, crime, and illness.

966.1 Mauritania

Blauer, Ettagale
Mauritania. by Ettagale Blauer and Jason Laure. Marshall Cavendish Benchmark, c2009. 144 p. : Cultures of the world
Grades: 5 6 7 8   **966.1**
   1. Mauritania 2. West Africa
   ISBN 9780761431169
                                             LC 2007043897
Provides comprehensive information on the geography, history, governmental structure, economy, cultural diversity, peoples, religion, and culture of Mauritania. Provided by publisher.

966.2 Mali, Burkina Faso, Niger

McKissack, Pat, 1944-2017
The **royal** kingdoms of Ghana, Mali, and Songhay: life in medieval Africa. Patricia and Fredrick McKissack. H. Holt, 1995, c1994. xviii, 142 p.
Grades: 5 6 7 8   **966.2**
   1. Ghana Empire 2. Mali Empire
   ISBN 0805042598
                                             LC BL 99770144
Examines the civilizations of the Western Sudan which flourished from 700 to 1700 A.D., acquiring such vast wealth that they became centers of trade and culture for a continent.
"The McKissacks are careful to distinguish what is known from what is surmised; they draw on the oral tradition, eyewitness accounts, and contemporary scholarship; and chapter source notes discuss various conflicting views of events." Booklist.
Includes bibliographical references (p. 131-135) and index.

966.23 Mali

Blauer, Ettagale
Mali. Ettagale Blauer and Jason Laure. Marshall Cavendish Benchmark, c2008. 144 p.: Cultures of the world
Grades: 5 6 7 8   **966.23**
   1. Mali 2. West Africa
   ISBN 9780761425687
                                             LC 2006101933
Provides comprehensive information on the geography, history, governmental structure, economy, cultural diversity, peoples, religion, and culture of Mali. Provided by publisher.

966.26 Niger

Seffal, Rabah
Niger. Rabah Seffal, Jo-Ann Spilling, and Debbie Nevins. Cavendish Square Publishing, 2019. 144 p.: Cultures of the World

Grades: 5 6 7 8   **966.26**
   1. Niger
   ISBN 9781502647528
                                             LC 2019013494
A book for middle and high schoolers about the history and culture of the African nation Niger. Provided by publisher.

966.3 Senegal

Bjorklund, Ruth
Senegal. Ruth Bjorklund. Children's Press 2019 144 p.: Enchantment of the World
Grades: 5 6 7 8   **966.3**
   1. Senegal
   ISBN 9780531126950
Jutting westward into the Atlantic Ocean, Senegal is continental Africa's westernmost country. Readers will cross the dry desert sands of the Sahara, walk the streets of Dakar, and make their way through dense tropical rainforests as they explore this amazing country and learn about its history, government, and economy. They will also learn about life in Senegal, from what the average school day is like to which kinds of foods are likely to be served at dinner. Features include maps and photos; sidebars that highlight individuals, places and events; fun facts and statistics; a timeline; economic information; flags and more.

966.4 Sierra Leone

Fowler, Will, 1947-
Counterterrorism in West Africa: the most dangerous SAS assault. Will Fowler. Rosen Pub., 2011, c2010. 64 p.: Most daring raids in history
Grades: 7 8 9 10   **966.4**
   1. Great Britain. Army. Special Air Service 2. Search and rescue operations 3. Rescue work 4. Terrorism -- Prevention 5. Operation Barras, 2000 6. Sierra Leone -- History -- Civil War, 1991-2002
   ISBN 9781448818716
                                             LC 2010029621
Describes the 2000 raid by members of the British Special Air Service to rescue British soldiers held hostage and other captives in the hands of one side in the Sierra Leone Civil War, the strategic plans, and the aftermath of the raid.
"This book is packed with facts, covering the details of the action, the people involved, and the tools used, in engaging prose. The authors cite their sources thoroughly. . . . Diagrams, photos, . . . and maps make the action easy to follow and provide visual context for the raids. . . . This . . . is sure to find a large readership." School Library Journal.
Includes bibliographical references (p. 62-63) and index.

LeVert, Suzanne
Sierra Leone. Suzanne LeVert. Marshall Cavendish Benchmark, c2007. 144 p.: Cultures of the world
Grades: 5 6 7 8   **966.4**
   1. Sierra Leone 2. West Africa
   ISBN 0761423346
                                             LC 2005035964
Provides comprehensive information on the geography, history, governmental structure, economy, cultural diversity, peoples, religion, and culture of Sierra Leone.

966.68 Côte d'Ivoire (Ivory Coast)

Bjorklund, Ruth
  Côte d'Ivoire (Ivory Coast). Ruth Bjorklund. Children's Press, 2019 144 p.
Grades: 5 6 7 8   **966.68**
  1. Côte d'Ivoire
  ISBN 9780531126974

LC 2018019517
  This book details the history, culture, geography and government of Ivory Coast. Provided by publisher.

966.9 Nigeria

Walker, Ida
  Nigeria. Ida Walker. Mason Crest Publishers, c2013. 79 p.
Grades: 5 6 7 8 9 10 11   **966.9**
  1. Nigeria 2. Africa
  ISBN 9781422222003

LC 2010047767
  "This series is a needed collection for high school media centers. It fills a void by supplying up-to-date books on African countries that incorporates both an historical and modern perspective. Each book covers the land, government, economy, culture, people, religion, holidays, and festivals...These books will be useful for researchers and browsers alike." Library Media Connection.
  Includes bibliographical references and index.

967.11 Cameroon

Sheehan, Sean, 1951-
  Cameroon. Sean Sheehan and Josie Elias. Marshall Cavendish Benchmark, 2020. 144 p.: Cultures of the world
Grades: 5 6 7 8   **967.11**
  1. Cameroon 2. Africa
  ISBN 9781502650702

LC 2010019623
  Describes the history, geography, culture, government, and people of the African nation of Cameroon.

967.571 Rwanda

Koopmans, Andy
  Rwanda. Andy Koopmans. Mason Crest Publishers, c2013. 87 p.
Grades: 5 6 7 8   **967.571**
  1. Rwanda 2. Central Africa
  ISBN 9781422221839

LC 2004004826
  Presents facts about the East African nation, including geography, history, politics, and economy.

967.57104 Rwanda—1962-

Nardo, Don, 1947-
  The **Rwandan** genocide. by Don Nardo. Lucent Books, c2011. 104 p.: World history (Lucent Books)

Grades: 6 7 8 9   **967.57104**
  1. Genocide -- History 20th century 2. Tutsi (African people) -- History 3. Hutu (African people) -- History 4. Crimes against humanity 5. Interethnic conflict -- History 20th century 6. Rwanda -- History -- Civil War, 1994 -- Atrocities. 7. Rwanda -- Interethnic relations -- History -- 20th century
  ISBN 9781420505672

LC 2010039533
  Outlines the circumstances that led to the genocide in Rwanda, where nearly one million people of an ethnic minority were exterminated in one hundred days, and discusses international reactions and the aftermath.

967.6104 Uganda—1962-

Dunstan, Simon
  Entebbe: the most daring raid of Israel's special forces. Simon Dunstan. Rosen Pub., 2011. 64 p.: Most daring raids in history
Grades: 7 8 9 10   **967.6104**
  1. 1970s 2. Entebbe Airport Raid, 1976 3. Terrorists 4. Hijacking of aircraft 5. Hostages 6. Raids (Military science)
  ISBN 9781448818686

LC 2010029622
  Describes the dramatic Israeli raid on Entebbe Airport in Uganda in 1976, including the events that led to the hijacking of an airplane by Palestinian terrorists, the aftermath of the raid, and its legacy in hostage negotiations training.
  "This book is packed with facts, covering the details of the action, the people involved, and the tools used, in engaging prose. The authors cite their sources thoroughly. . . . Diagrams, photos (where available), and maps make the action easy to follow and provide visual context for the raids. . . . This . . . is sure to find a large readership." School Library Journal.
  Includes bibliographical references (p. 62-63) and index.

967.62 Kenya

Broberg, Catherine
  Kenya in pictures. by Catherine Broberg. Lerner Publications Co., 2003. 80 p.: Visual geography series
Grades: 5 6 7 8   **967.62**
  1. Kenya
  ISBN 0822519577

LC 2001003829
  A brief overview of Kenya's land, history, government, people, and culture.
  "The book is visually appealing with photos and sidebars that complement the text." Library Media Connection.
  Includes bibliographical references (p. 74-75) and index.

967.73 Somalia

Hassig, Susan M., 1969-
  Somalia. by Susan M. Hassig, Zawiah Abdul Latif, and Ruth Bjorklund. Cavendish Square Publishing, 2017. 144 p.: Cultures of the world

Grades: 5 6 7 8 **967.73**
1. Somalia 2. Africa
ISBN 9781502626073

LC 2006102270

Provides comprehensive information on the geography, history, wildlife, governmental structure, economy, cultural diversity, peoples, religion, and culture of Somalia. Provided by publisher.

967.8 Tanzania

MacDonald, Joan Vos
Tanzania. Joan Vos MacDonald. Mason Crest Publishers, c2013. 87 p.
Grades: 5 6 7 8 **967.8**
1. Tanzania 2. Africa
ISBN 9781422221860

LC 2010048002

Presents facts about the East African nation, including geography, history, politics, and economy.

967.9 Mozambique

Mulroy, Tanya
Mozambique. Tanya Mulroy. Mason Crest Publishers, c2013. 87 p.
Grades: 5 6 7 8 **967.9**
1. Mozambique 2. Africa
ISBN 9781422221822

LC 2011018504

Presents facts about the East African nation, including its geography, history, politics, and economy.

968.06 South Africa—Period as Republic, 1961

Brownlie Bojang, Ali, 1949-
South Africa in our world. Ali Brownlie Bojang. Smart Apple Media, c2011. 32 p.: Countries in our world
Grades: 5 6 7 8 **968.06**
1. Countries 2. South Africa
ISBN 9781599204444

LC 2009043163

Describes the economy, government, and culture of South Africa today and discusses South Africa's influence of and relations with the rest of the world. Provided by publisher.

"This contains relevant information presented in a visually appealing layout. Large colorful photographs inform readers about the past, present, and future of the country. . . . The book gives an honest view of apartheid, poverty, and government conflicts. At the same time, it is hopeful about recent changes, such as the hosting of the World Cup and the growing economy." School Library Journal.

Sonneborn, Liz
The **end** of apartheid in South Africa. Liz Sonneborn. Chelsea House, c2010. 120 p.: Milestones in modern world history
Grades: 8 9 10 11 12 **968.06**
1. Anti-apartheid Movement 2. Apartheid 3. South Africa -- Race

relations -- History.
ISBN 9781604134094

LC 2008054805

"This is an excellent in-depth overview, one of the best on the subject, with chapters on the early history before the establishment of the apartheid regime and with profiles of many important leaders (not just Nelson Mandela), as well as clear discussion of present-day politics, the role of the Truth and Reconciliation Commission, and the ongoing inequality. Never simplistic, it is an outstanding overview for teens new to the subject; for those who know something of the history, it fills in the big picture with depth and detail about both leaders and ordinary people, what has changed, and how much still needs to be done." Booklist.

Includes bibliographical references and index.

968.4 KwaZulu-Natal

Weltig, Matthew Scott
The **aftermath** of the Anglo-Zulu war. Matthew S. Weltig. Twenty-First Century Books, c2009. 160 p.: Aftermath of history
Grades: 6 7 8 9 10 **968.4**
1. 1870s 2. Zulu War, 1879 -- Influence 3. Zulu (African people) -- History 4. South Africa -- History. 5. Zululand -- History
ISBN 9780822575993

LC 2007050826

Discusses the history and culture of the South African Zulus, whose warriors astonished the British with their skill and fierceness during the 1879 Zulu War.

"The well written text provides a detailed account of the devastation and ruin brought to Zululand by the British government and by Boer settlers, replete with text boxes that provide clarification and further explanation of what are often complex and confusing issues and events. Illustrations consist of both period photographs and paintings of the fierce fighting. Reckless bravery, treachery, cruelty, betrayal, and greed are all here, resulting in an absorbing, but tragic story." School Library Journal.

Includes bibliographical references (p. 147-151), filmography (p. 153-154), and index.

968.83 Botswana

Wittmann, Kelly
Botswana. Kelly Wittmann. Mason Crest Publishers, c2013. 79 p.
Grades: 5 6 7 8 **968.83**
1. Botswana 2. Africa
ISBN 9781422221938

LC 2011018530

Introduces Botswana, describing its geography, animals, plants, recent history, government, economy, and major cities.

968.91 Zimbabwe

Hall, Martin, 1952-
Great Zimbabwe: digging for the past. Martin Hall and Rebecca Stefoff. Oxford University Press, c2006. 47 p.: Digging for the past
Grades: 7 8 9 10 **968.91**
1. African civilization 2. Archaeological sites 3. Racism 4. Shona

(African people) 5. Extinct cities 6. Great Zimbabwe (City) 7. Mozambique -- History.
ISBN 0195157737

LC 2005014607

"This explores a ruined fourteenth-century stone city in Zimbabwe and covers controversies over its origin, its artifacts, and theories about its former inhabitants. The well-written text will spur readers' curiosity, while archival and modern photos, ancient maps, and European explorers' notes add a fascinating variety to the book's visual presentation." Horn Book Guide.

Includes bibliographical references (p. [46]) and index.

968.94 Zambia

Holmes, Timothy, 1936-
Zambia. by Timothy Holmes & Winnie Wong. Marshall Cavendish Benchmark, 2008. 144 p.: Cultures of the world
Grades: 5 6 7 8   **968.94**
  1. Zambia 2. Southern Africa
ISBN 9780761430391

Provides comprehensive information on the geography, history, wildlife, governmental structure, economy, cultural diversity, peoples, religion, and culture of Zambia.

969.1 Madagascar

Heale, Jay
Madagascar. by Jay Heale & Zawiah Abdul Latif. Marshall Cavendish Benchmark, 2008. 144 p.: Cultures of the world
Grades: 5 6 7 8   **969.1**
  1. Islands 2. Madagascar 3. Madagascar -- Social life and customs.
ISBN 9780761430360

LC 2007048288

Provides comprehensive information on the geography, history, wildlife, governmental structure, economy, cultural diversity, peoples, religion, and culture of Madagascar. Provided by publisher.

970 History of North America

Katz, William Loren
Black Indians: a hidden heritage. William Loren Katz. Aladdin Paperbacks, 1997. 198 p.
Grades: 8 9 10 11 12   **970**
  1. African Americans -- Relations with Indians 2. Indians of North America -- Relations with African Americans 3. African Americans 4. Multiracial persons 5. United States -- Race relations -- History.
ISBN 0689809018

LC 97133375

Traces the history of relations between blacks and American Indians, and the existence of Black Indians, from the earliest foreign landings through pioneer days.

Lepore, Jill
Encounters in the New World: a history in documents. [edited by] Jill Lepore. Oxford University Press, c2000. 175 p.: Pages from history
Grades: 7 8 9 10 11 12   **970**
  1. Indians of North America -- History 2. First contact of indigenous

peoples with Europeans 3. First contact (Anthropology)
ISBN 0195105133

LC 99045335

A collection of documents illustrating encounters between Native American peoples and a variety of European newcomers from the fifteenth to the eighteenth centuries. Includes maps, journals, advertisements, and letters.

970.004 Ethnic and national groups

Connolly, Sean, 1956-
The **Americas** and the Pacific. Sean Connolly. Zak Books, c2009. 48 p. : History (Zak Books (Firm))
Grades: 4 5 6 7 8   **970.004**
  1. Indians of North America -- History 2. Paleo-Indians 3. Aboriginal Australians -- History 4. Maori (New Zealand people) -- History 5. History
ISBN 9788860981615

LC 2008008404

A detailed overview of the early history of American and Pacific peoples, including Native Americans, Maya, Aztecs, Inca, Aborigines, and the Maori, up to 1200 CE. Provided by publisher.

"Artists' renderings show groups of people engaged in representative activities, but it's the reproductions of artifacts . . . that will pull readers and browsers most. . . . [This is an] engaging overview." Booklist.

Includes bibliographical references and index.

Ehrlich, Amy, 1942-
Wounded Knee: an Indian history of the American West. Dee Brown; adapted for young readers by Amy Ehrlich from Dee Brown's Bury my heart at Wounded Knee. Henry Holt, 1993, c1974. xix, 202 p.
Grades: 6 7 8 9   **970.004**
  1. Indians of North America -- Wars 2. The West (United States) -- History.
ISBN 0805027009

LC BL 99741890

Traces the white man's conquest of the Indians of the American West, emphasizing the causes, events, and effects of the major Indian Wars leading to the symbolic end of Indian freedom at Wounded Knee.

"Some chapters [of the original] have been deleted, others condensed, and in some instances sentence structure and language have been simplified. The editing is good, and this version is interesting, readable, and smooth." School Library Journal.

Includes bibliographical references (p. 187-196) and index.

Ellis, Deborah, 1960-
Looks like daylight: voices of indigenous kids. Deborah Ellis. Groundwood Books/House of Anansi Press, 2018. 256 p.
Grades: 6 7 8 9 10 11 12   **970.004**
  1. Indians of North America 2. Native American children 3. Everyday life
ISBN 9781554981212

Deborah Ellis, a champion of children's rights, enlightens readers with her honest portrayal of the lives of several First Nations youth. Their honest and personal stories will resonate with many readers as they get a glimpse and better understanding of their lives.

"In this cultural undertaking, Ellis interviews Native American and aboriginal children and teens, ages nine to eighteen. Whether heartwrenching or uplifting, each first-person narrative is compelling, insightful, and incredibly moving. Introductory matter sheds painful light on the historically horrific treatment of North America's indigenous peoples, as well as the challenges they face still. An extensive list of charitable and informational organizations is appended." Horn Book.

Gibson, Karen Bush

Native American history for kids: with 21 activities. Karen Bush Gibson. Chicago Review Press, c2010. xiv, 127 p.

Grades: 6 7 8 9 10   **970.004**

1. Indians of North America -- History 2. Indians of North America -- Social life and customs 3. United States -- History.
ISBN 9781569762806

LC 2010005695

"This gripping, highly readable overview will draw teens and even some adults into the history of Native Americans, from early times and the arrival of European settlers up to the present. The examples of racism are horrifying. . . . Also horrifying are the accounts of forced assimilation." Booklist.

Includes bibliographical references.

Jastrzembski, Joseph C.

The **Apache** wars: the final resistance. Joseph C. Jastrzembski. Chelsea House, c2007. 133 p.

Grades: 8 9 10 11 12   **970.004**

1. Apache Indians -- Wars 2. Apache Indians -- Government relations 3. Apache Indians -- Social conditions 4. San Carlos Indian Reservation (Ariz) -- History
ISBN 9780791093436

LC 2007000990

Describes the resistance of the Apache Indians to the rule of the United States government after the Treaty of Guadalupe Hidalgo, discussing the restrictions placed upon the tribes and resulting battles until the defeat of Geronimo in 1886.

Mendoza, Jean

An **indigenous** peoples' history of the United States for young people. Roxanne Dunbar-Ortiz; adapted by Jean Mendoza and Debbie Reese. Beacon Press, 2019 272 p.

Grades: 7 8 9 10 11 12   **970.004**

1. Indians of North America -- Colonization 2. Indians of North America, Treatment of 3. Intersectionality 4. North America -- Colonization 5. Antiracist literature
ISBN 9780807049396

LC 2019004266

Going beyond the story of America as a country "discovered" by a few brave men in the "New World," Indigenous human rights advocate Roxanne Dunbar-Ortiz reveals the roles that settler colonialism and policies of American Indian genocide played in forming our national identity. The original academic text is fully adapted by renowned curriculum experts Debbie Reese and Jean Mendoza, for middle-grade and young adult readers to include discussion topics, archival images, original maps, recommendations for further reading, and other materials to encourage students, teachers, and general readers to think critically about their own place in history. Provided by publisher.

National Museum of the American Indian

Do all Indians live in tipis?: 101 questions and answers. from the National Museum of the American Indian. Collins, in association with the National Museum of the American Indian, Smithsonian Institution, c2007. 239 p.

Grades: 8 9 10 11 12   **970.004**

1. Native American Studies 2. Indians of North America -- Public opinion 3. Indians of North America -- Social life and customs 4. Native Americans in popular culture 5. Public opinion
ISBN 9780061153013

LC 2007060874

Answers questions about Native Americans, including those related to identity, origins and history, animals and land, language and education, love and marriage, and culture.

"This highly accessible and informative book aims to dispel some of the major myths and stereotypes still surrounding Native people in the United States and Canada. . . . The straightforward questions were compiled from actual phone calls, emails, letters, and in-person visits to the George Gustav Heye Center in New York, a major branch of the National Museum of the American Indian. The Native American writers who answered them did so concisely with hints of humor and an abundance of research and experience. . . . This is a topnotch resource for both people just learning about Native American cultures and those who think they know the facts." School Library Journal.

Zimmerman, Larry J., 1947-

Exploring the life, myth, and art of Native Americans. Larry J. Zimmerman. Rosen Pub., 2010. 144 p.: Civilizations of the world

Grades: 7 8 9 10 11 12   **970.004**

1. Indians of North America -- Social life and customs 2. Indians of North America -- Religion 3. Art, Native American 4. North America -- Civilization 5. Mythology
ISBN 9781435856141

LC 2009009268

"This beautifully illustrated and well-written [title] . . . is perfect for those assignments where students must look at the culture of a civilization. Artwork and pictures blend seamlessly with the information and the reader is taken on a journey of discovery. Myths are used as the story of how the people view themselves, blended with the discussion of the reality of life. Everyday life is tied to the belief systems and is explained in light of those beliefs. The pictures are beautifully done and there is almost as much information in the captions as there is in the text." Library Media Connection.

Includes bibliographical references (p. 136) and index.

970.00497 American native peoples

King, David C.

First people. David C. King; consultant, Peter M. Whiteley. DK Publishing, 2008. 192 p.

Grades: 5 6 7 8   **970.00497**

1. Indians of North America 2. Culture 3. Indians of North America -- Social life and customs
ISBN 9780756640927

With the help of modern and historic images, innovative page layouts, and compelling first-person accounts, an eye-opening look at the richness and variety of North American natives presents each tribe as an individual, evolving culture, with its own history, artwork, and traditions.

"This rich pictorial work serves as an entertaining, informative, and visually appealing introduction to American Indian culture and history. Each of the seven chapters covers a different time period in chronological order. . . . The glossy photographs, colorful drawings, and easily accessible paragraphs . . . make for an easy-to-use overall package." School Library Journal.

970.01 North America—Early history to 1599

Freedman, Russell

Who was first?: discovering the Americas. by Russell Freedman. Clarion Books, c2007. vii, 88 p.

Grades: 6 7 8 9   **970.01**

1. Barr, Linda, 1944- Biography 2. Explorers 3. Discoveries (in geography) 4. Western Hemisphere -- Exploration. 5. Western Hemisphere -- Exploration -- Pre-Columbian.
ISBN 0618663916

LC 2006102485

An intriguing look at America's past weaves together colorful legends and first-person accounts into a narrative that explores the evidence that explorers came to America long before Columbus.

"This looks at various ideas about the discovery of the Americas. . . . Beyond the very readable presentation of facts and theories, the book's main accomplishment is in showing that history is . . . an evolving process of logically interpreted evidence continually questioned, disputed, and revised. . . . The illustrations, many in color, include many excellent maps as well as reproductions of period drawings, paintings, engravings, and photos. . . . A well-researched, intelligent account." Booklist.

Includes bibliographical references (p. 83-85) and index.

Gunderson, Jessica

Conquistadors. Jessica Gunderson. Creative Education, c2013. 48 p.: Fearsome fighters

Grades: 5 6 7 8   **970.01**

1. Conquistadors 2. Soldiers 3. Military art and science -- History 4. Explorers 5. North America -- Exploration -- Spanish
ISBN 9781608181834

LC 2011035799

A compelling look at conquistadors, including how and why they sailed to the New World, their lifestyle, their weapons, and how they remain a part of today's culture through books and film. Provided by publisher.

Harrison, David L.

Mammoth bones and broken stones: the mystery of North America's first people. David L. Harrison; with illustrations by Richard Hilliard and archaeological photographs. Boyds Mills Press, c2010. 48 p.

Grades: 4 5 6 7   **970.01**

1. Paleo-Indians 2. Prehistoric humans 3. Indians of North America -- History 4. United States -- History
ISBN 9781590785614

LC 2009020247

Introduces the history of the prehistoric peoples of North America, discussing their possible routes to the continent and describing what the archaeological evidence shows about when they arrived and how they lived.

"How and when the Western Hemisphere . . . came to be populated continues to be both mysterious and controversial for scientists. . . . Harrison does a good job setting the issue in context. He describes the earliest efforts to identify the original inhabitants of the continents, exploring the Clovis culture. . . . After clearly explaining how scholars decided that they were the first, he then lists the arguments against this hypothesis. . . . The narrative is aided by both photographs and original illustrations that imagine scenes from both the distant past and the field experiences." Kirkus.

Includes bibliographical references (p. 47) and index.

Mann, Charles C.

★ **Before** Columbus: the Americas of 1491. Charles C. Mann; adapted by Rebecca Stefoff. Atheneum Books for Young Readers, c2009. 128 p.

Grades: 5 6 7 8 9 10   **970.01**

1. Indians of North America -- History 2. Indians of Central America -- History 3. Indians of South America -- History 4. Civilization, Native American 5. North America -- History. 6. Central America -- History.
ISBN 9781416949008

LC 2009007691

"Mann paints a superb picture of pre-Columbian America. In the process, he overturns the misconceived image of Natives as simple, widely scattered savages with minimal impact on their surroundings. Well-chosen, vividly colored graphics and photographs of mummies, pyramids, artifacts, and landscapes as well as the author's skillful storytelling will command the attention of even the most reluctant readers." School Library Journal.

Mooney, Carla, 1970-

Explorers of the new world: discover the golden age of exploration. Carla Mooney; illustrated by Tom Casteel. Nomad Press, c2011. vii, 120 p.: Build it yourself

Grades: 3 4 5 6 7   **970.01**

1. Explorers -- History 2. Exploration 3. Creative activities for children and students 4. Handicraft for children 5. Handicraft 6. North America -- Exploration -- Spanish 7. Spain -- Colonies -- History
ISBN 9781936313440

LC 2011278155

Provides twenty-two step-by-step projects to help readers learn about the explorers that discovered America and their voyages.

"This informative, entertaining activity book takes readers on a fascinating voyage of their own. . . . Each chapter concludes with Make Your Own activities that bring life to the history with instructions for the construction of a logbook, clay activities, recipes, games, etc. Some may require the assistance of an adult but are not complicated or time consuming." School Library Journal.

Includes bibliographical references (p. 116) and index.

Peterson, Cris

Birchbark brigade: a fur trade history. Cris Peterson. Calkins Creek, c2009. 135 p.

Grades: 7 8 9 10   **970.01**

1. Frontier and pioneer life 2. Fur industry and trade -- History 3. Fur traders -- History 4. Birchbark canoes -- History 5. Indians of North America -- Relations with Europeans 6. North America -- Exploration 7. North America -- History
ISBN 9781590784266

LC 2008055109

Drawing on primary sources, gives readers a glimpse into how the North American fur trade influenced every aspect of life in the New World, from how European settlers related to the Native Americans to how and where settlements were built.

"Peterson first provides a history of the military, political and economic development of the [fur] trade and then gives readers a snapshot of the lives of the Indians and voyageurs who did the actual work. She relies on a wealth of primary-source material, from archival illustrations to quotes from players both large and small. . . . The author's enthusiasm for her subject will communicate itself to readers, even those who never dreamed they'd be interested, making this the best kind of discovery." Kirkus.

Includes bibliographical references and index.

Walker, Sally M.

Their skeletons speak: Kennewick man and the Paleoamerican world. by Sally M. Walker and Douglas W. Owsley. Carolrhoda Books, c2012. 136 p.

Grades: 8 9 10 11 12 **970.01**
1. Kennewick Man 2. Human remains (Archaeology) 3. Prehistoric humans 4. Cultural property 5. Indians of North America -- Origin 6. Washington (State) -- Antiquities
ISBN 9780761374572

LC 2011051329

Discusses the processes used by scientists to discern the identity of the Kennewick Man and what this nine thousand-year-old skeleton revealed about the arrival of humans in North America.

"Along with introducing other North American finds of similar age, such as the Spirit Cave Mummy, the authors show how interpretations of evidence can change or be refined over time and also cover current theories about the migratory origins of the earliest Americans. Enhanced by maps and diagrams as well as photos of discovery sites, remains, and scientists at work, this account imparts a clear sense of how hard and subtle that work is—and how exciting, too." Booklist.

Includes bibliographical references and index.

Wulffson, Don L.

Before Columbus: early voyages to the Americas. by Don Wulffson. Twenty-First Century Books, c2008. 128 p.

Grades: 6 7 8 9 **970.01**
1. Archaeology 2. Explorers 3. Western Hemisphere -- Exploration -- Pre-Columbian 4. Western Hemisphere -- Antiquities
ISBN 9780822559788

LC 2005024487

Presents the archaeological evidence for and historical theories of the exploration of North America by numerous civilizations long before Columbus, discussing seven groups spanning 146 B.C. to 1492.

"This engaging presentation of early exploration of the Americas offers both fact and speculation on who, when, and why voyagers came; how they traveled; and what evidence they left behind. . . . Citing legends and sagas, oral and written histories, and archaeological discoveries, Wulffson presents an intriguing array of possibilities. . . . The stories and unanswered questions about pre-Columbian voyagers will capture the imaginations of many readers, offer fascinating glimpses of different cultural groups, [and] stimulate further research." School Library Journal.

Includes bibliographical references (p. 114-122) and index.

970.1 North American native peoples

Treuer, Anton

Everything you wanted to know about Indians but were afraid to ask: young readers edition. Anton Treuer Levine Querido, 2021 400 p.

Grades: 7 8 9 10 11 12 **970.1**
1. Indians of North America -- History 2. Ojibwa Indians 3. Race relations 4. Interethnic relations 5. Native Americans in popular culture
ISBN 9781646140459

An Ojibwe scholar and cultural preservationist answers the most commonly asked questions about Native Americans, both historical and modern.

"Academic and Ojibwe author Treuer here adapts his 2012 adult title for young readers. . . . He doesn't sugarcoat the often-difficult history of Indigenous-settler relations, but neither does he scold." Booklist

Yellowhorn, Eldon, 1956-

Turtle Island: the story of North America's first people. Eldon Yellowhorn and Kathy Lowinger. Annick Press, 2017. 116 p.

Grades: 4 5 6 7 **970.1**
1. Indians of North America 2. Indigenous peoples
ISBN 9781554519446

Based on archeological finds and scientific research, goes back to the Ice Age to give young readers a glimpse of what life was like in the Americas before Europeans arrived.

"The multifaceted history of the Indigenous peoples of North American before and after European contact is made accessible in a well-written, fluid narrative complemented by appealing graphics." School Library Journal.

971 Canada

Mara, Wil

Canada. Wil Mara. Children's Press, 2018 144 p.

Grades: 5 6 7 8 **971**
1. Canada
ISBN 9780531235720

LC 2016050354

Describes the geography, plants, animals, history, economy, language, sports, arts, religions, culture, and people of Canada.

Sonneborn, Liz

Canada. by Liz Sonneborn. Children's Press, c2012. 144 p.: Enchantment of the world

Grades: 5 6 7 8 **971**
1. Canada 2. North America
ISBN 9780531253519

LC 2011011970

Explores the history, geography, wildlife, government, economy, religion, culture, and people of Canada.

Weaver, Janice

Mirror with a memory: a nation's story in photographs. Janice Weaver. Tundra Books, c2007. 159 p.

Grades: 6 7 8 9 **971**
1. Canada -- Social life and customs. 2. Canada -- History
ISBN 0887767478

LC bl2007025030

A photographic journey through the history of Canada, which came into existence along with the art of photography in the middle of the nineteenth century, features famous shots as well as the faces of ordinary Canadians.

"Defining moments in Canadian history are thematically presented in this photography collection. . . . In the conversational commentary that accompanies each image, Weaver provides historical context. Thought-provoking media literacy issues are also raised. . . . A great visual retrospective of a nation's people, places, and events." School Library Journal.

Williams, Brian, 1943-

★ **Canada**. Brian Williams; Tom Carter and Ben Cecil, consultants. National Geographic, c2007. 64 p.: National Geographic countries of the world

Grades: 4 5 6 7   **971**

    1. Canada 2. North America

    ISBN 1426300255

                LC 2007296572

A basic overview of the history, geography, climate, and culture of Canada.

"This clear, succinct [overview] will support assignments without overwhelming casual readers. . . . A good selection of recent, high-quality color photographs gives the [book] visual appeal." School Library Journal.

Includes bibliographical references (p. 61) and index.

971.004 Canada – First Nations

Gray Smith, Monique, 1968-

Speaking our truth: a journey of reconciliation. Monique Gray Smith. Orca Book Publishers, 2017. 160 p.

Grades: 6 7 8 9 10   **971.004**

    1. Reconciliation 2. Indigenous peoples 3. Indians of North America 4. Race relations 5. Schools 6. Canada -- Race relations

    ISBN 9781459815834

                LC oc2017010132

Looks at ways to heal and repair the relationship between Canada and its Indigenous people which has suffered as a result of both the residential school system and the lack of understanding of the impact of those schools.

"A sensitive and extensive insight into the experiences of Indigenous people in Canada. Smith traces the historical events, movements, and laws affecting people of the First Nations and connects this history to the impact still resonating generations later." School Library Journal.

971.01 Early history to 1763

Worth, Richard

New France 1534-1763: featuring the region that now includes all or parts of Michigan, Minnesota, Wisconsin, Illinois, Indiana, Ohio, Pennsylvania, Vermont, Maine, and Canada from Manitoba to Newfoundland. Richard Worth with Jose Antonio Brandao. National Geographic Society, 2007. 109 p.: Voices from colonial America

Grades: 5 6 7 8   **971.01**

    1. French in North America -- History 2. New France 3. France -- Colonies -- North America -- History.

    ISBN 9781426301476

                LC 2007029544

Explores the everyday lives of the people who inhabited what was called New France during North America's colonial history.

"Worth presents the history of the vast French colony known as New France. Clearly written, the book is studded with quotes from people living in the colony and illustrated with colorful paintings, prints, and maps from a variety of periods. . . . This nicely designed introduction to a historically significant area fills a gap in many colonial history series and library collections." Booklist.

Includes bibliographical references (p. 105-106) and index.

971.1 British Columbia

Palana, Brett J.

British Columbia. by Brett J. Palana. Lucent Books, c2003. 112 p.: Exploring Canada

Grades: 6 7 8 9   **971.1**

    1. Canadian provinces 2. British Columbia 3. Pacific Northwest

    ISBN 1590180461

                LC 2002004112

Examines the history, geography, climate, industries, people, and culture of Canada's westernmost province.

971.23 Alberta

Laws, Gordon D.

Alberta. by Gordon D. Laws and Lauren M. Laws. Lucent Books, c2003. 112 p.: Exploring Canada

Grades: 6 7 8 9   **971.23**

    1. Canadian provinces 2. Alberta 3. Canada

    ISBN 1590180453

                LC 2002009880

Explains the history, geography, climate, industry, people, and culture of Canada's princess province, having been named after the daughter of Queen Victoria.

971.27 Manitoba

Laws, Gordon D.

Manitoba. by Gordon D. Laws and Lauren M. Laws. Lucent Books, c2003. 112 p.: Exploring Canada

Grades: 6 7 8 9   **971.27**

    1. Canadian provinces 2. Manitoba 3. Canada

    ISBN 159018047X

                LC 2002014364

Examines the history, geography, climate, industries, people, and culture of one of the most diverse of Canada's provinces.

971.3 Ontario

Ferry, Steven, 1953-

Ontario. by Steven Ferry. Lucent Books, c2003. 112 p.: Exploring Canada

Grades: 6 7 8 9   **971.3**

    1. Canadian provinces 2. Ontario 3. Canada

    ISBN 159018050X

                LC 2002014351

Examines the history, geography, climate, industries, people, and culture of what is by far the most populous of Canada's provinces.

971.4 Quebec

Ferry, Steven, 1953-

Quebec. by Steven Ferry. Lucent Books, c2003. 112 p.: Exploring Canada

Grades: 6 7 8 9   **971.4**
   1. Canadian provinces 2. Quebec (Province) 3. Canada
   ISBN 1590180518

                     LC 2002004111
Examines the history, geography, climate, industries, people, culture, and ongoing separatist struggle of Canada's largest province.

971.5 Atlantic Provinces

Laws, Gordon D.
   The **Maritime** provinces. by Gordon D. Laws and Lauren M. Laws. Lucent Books, c2004. 112 p.: Exploring Canada
Grades: 6 7 8 9   **971.5**
   1. Canadian provinces 2. Canada 3. New Brunswick
   ISBN 1590183355

                     LC 2003005440
Examines the history, geography, climate, industries, people, and culture of Canada's Maritime Provinces.

971.6 Nova Scotia

Walker, Sally M.
   ★ **Blizzard** of glass: the Halifax explosion of 1917. Sally M. Walker. Henry Holt, 2011. 160 p.
Grades: 5 6 7 8   **971.6**
   1. 1910s 2. Halifax Explosion, December 6, 1917 3. Explosions -- History 20th century 4. Ships 5. Halifax, Nova Scotia -- History -- 20th century
   ISBN 9780805089455

                     LC 2011005914
When two ships collided in Halifax Harbour, on December 6, 1917, one of them was full of munitions for World War I. The ensuing explosion, aftershocks, and tsunami wreaked unbelievable devastation. It was the largest explosion in the world until the atomic bomb was detonated in World War II in 1945.

"The text reads smoothly with unfamiliar words defined in the text. Illustrations consist of two full-page maps and numerous black-and-white photos. The final chapter revisits the featured families and their descendants, thus tying up the loose ends. . . . This tragic, but well-told story belongs in most collections." School Library Journal.

Includes bibliographical references.

971.8 Newfoundland and Labrador, Saint Pierre and Miquelon

Mayell, Mark
   Newfoundland. by Mark Mayell. Lucent Books, 2003. 112 p.: Exploring Canada
Grades: 6 7 8 9   **971.8**
   1. Canadian provinces 2. Newfoundland and Labrador 3. Canada
   ISBN 1590180488

                     LC 2003002060
Examines the history, geography, climate, industries, people, and culture of Canada's Newfoundland.

971.9 Northern territories

Baker, Stuart (Stuart Neil)
   Climate change in the Arctic. by Stuart Baker. Marshall Cavendish Benchmark, 2010. 32 p. : Climate change (Marshall Cavendish Benchmark)
Grades: 5 6 7 8   **971.9**
   1. Climate change -- Environmental aspects 2. Global warming 3. Global temperature changes 4. Nature -- Effect of humans on 5. Arctic regions
   ISBN 9780761444374

                     LC 2009005767
"The book about climate change in the Arctic is perfectly organized for students. . . . Unique layout features serve as signposts and will help focus readers' attention. . . . [The book] features an outstanding chart of possible effects of global warming on the area in question, listing Possible Event, Predicted Result, and Impact in short, bulleted statements." School Library Journal.

Ferry, Steven, 1953-
   Yukon Territory. Steven Ferry, Blake Harris, Liz Szynkowski. Lucent Books, c2003. 112 p.: Exploring Canada
Grades: 6 7 8 9   **971.9**
   1. Yukon Territory 2. Canada
   ISBN 1590180534

                     LC 2002004110
Examines the history, geography, climate, industries, people, and culture of Canada's most remote and untamed region.

Meissner, David
   Call of the Klondike: a true gold rush adventure. David Meissner, Kim Richardson. Calkins Creek,, [2013] 168 p.
Grades: 6 7 8   **971.9**
   1. Pearce, Stanley 2. Bond, Marshall, 1867-1941 3. Frontier and pioneer life 4. Gold mines and mining 5. Gold rush 6. Prospecting 7. Prospectors
   ISBN 9781590788233

                     LC 2013931060
Golden Kite Award for Nonfiction, 2014.
Traces the true story of prospectors Stanley Pearce and Marshall Bond, who joined thousands of men along the dangerous Chilkoot and White Passes to seek their fortunes in the gold fields of Canada.

972 Mexico, Central America, West Indies, Bermuda

Bingham, Jane
   The **Aztec** empire. Jane Bingham. Raintree, c2007. 64 p.: Time travel guides
Grades: 6 7 8 9   **972**
   1. Aztecs 2. Mexico (City)
   ISBN 141092730X

                     LC 2006033875
A description of life in the Aztec empire written in the form of a travel guide.

Cooke, Tim (Tim A.)
   ★ **National** Geographic investigates ancient Aztec: archaeology unlock the secrets of Mexico's past. by Tim Cooke. National Geographic, c2007. 64 p.: National geographic investigates

Grades: 4 5 6 7   **972**
1. Aztecs -- Antiquities 2. Aztecs -- Material culture 3. Civilization, Ancient 4. Excavations (Archaeology) 5. Mexico -- Antiquities.
ISBN 9781426300721

"Pithy and appealing. . . . Aerial photos, time [line], informative sidebars, an interview with an archaeologist, and excellent maps augment rigorously supported [text] that [asks] and [answers] interesting questions." School Library Journal.

Croy, Anita

Ancient Aztec and Maya. edited by Anita Croy. Brown Bear Books, c2010. 64 p. : Facts at your fingertips.
Grades: 6 7 8 9   **972**
1. Aztecs 2. Mayas 3. Civilization, Native American 4. Indians of Central America 5. Civilization, Ancient 6. Central America -- Civilization.
ISBN 9781933834580

LC 2009017295
"This begins with an introduction accompanied by a striking full-page photo, followed by a two-page time line, and a two-paged spread for each topic. This format makes information easily accessible. Beautiful color photos of ancient ruins, drawings, maps, diagrams, and recreations create appeal and enhance the information. . . . Whether for recreational browsing or serious research, this . . . will certainly prove useful for students." Library Media Connection.

Heinrichs, Ann

The **Aztecs**. Ann Heinrichs. Mashall Cavendish Benchmark, c2012. 64 p.: Technology of the ancients
Grades: 4 5 6 7   **972**
1. Aztecs 2. Ancient technology 3. Technological innovations -- History
ISBN 9781608707652

LC 2011018348
Focuses on the discoveries and inventions of the ancient Aztec civilization in the areas of transportation, agriculture, architecture, science, and technology. Provided by publisher.

Kops, Deborah

Palenque. by Deborah Kops. Twenty-First Century Books, c2008. 80 p.: Unearthing ancient worlds
Grades: 5 6 7 8   **972**
1. Mayas -- Antiquities 2. Excavations (Archaeology) 3. Indians of Central America 4. Palenque, Chiapas, Mexico -- Antiquities 5. Mexico -- Antiquities.
ISBN 9780822575047

LC 2007021323
Chronicles the discovery of the ancient Maya ruins of Palenque in Mexico, and discusses what archaeologists have learned about Mayan pyramids, writing, and architecture from their excavations of the site.

"This clearly written [title is] illustrated with large photographs and period artwork, and the pages are broken up with text boxes featuring quotes and interesting anecdotes." School Library Journal.
Includes bibliographical references (p. 76-77) and index.

Lourie, Peter

Hidden world of the Aztec. by Peter Lourie. Boyds Mills Press, c2006. 48 p.
Grades: 4 5 6 7   **972**
1. Templo Mayor (Mexico City, Mexico) 2. Aztecs -- History 3. Aztec architecture 4. Aztecs -- Religion 5. Temples 6. Excavations

(Archaeology) 7. Mexico (City) -- Antiquities.
ISBN 1590780698

LC 2005037353
Tours the excavation site of the Great Temple of the Aztec civilization in Mexico City, providing an overview of Aztec culture, history, and religion.

"The author takes a look at the Aztecs from the perspective of archaeological digs at the Great Temple in modern-day Mexico City and at the Pyramid of the Moon in Teotihuacan. . . . The writing style is clear, informative, and interesting." School Library Journal.
Includes bibliographical references (p. 48) and index.

Nardo, Don, 1947-

Aztec civilization. Don Nardo. Lucent Books, c2010. 104 p.: World history series
Grades: 6 7 8 9   **972**
1. Indians of Mexico 2. Civilization, Ancient 3. Aztecs -- History 4. Aztecs -- Social life and customs 5. Aztecs
ISBN 9781420502428

LC 2009040802
"This shines as it provides a contemporaneous writing as well as work by scholars that offer plenty of drama—and lots of facts too. . . . [It also] provides a solid time line, plenty of photographs, sourced quotes, and a list of books and websites for further investigation. Excellent for reports and research." Booklist.
Includes bibliographical references and index.

Schomp, Virginia

The **Aztecs**. by Virginia Schomp. Marshall Cavendish Benchmark, c2009. 96 p. : Myths of the world
Grades: 6 7 8 9   **972**
1. Aztecs 2. Civilization, Ancient 3. Culture 4. Characters and characteristics in mythology 5. Central America -- History. 6. Mythology
ISBN 9780761430964

LC 2008007082
A retelling of several key Aztec myths, with background information describing the history, geography, belief systems, and customs of the Aztecs. Provided by publisher.

Stein, R. Conrad

Ancient Mexico. R. Conrad Stein. Morgan Reynolds Pub., c2011. 144 p.: Story of Mexico
Grades: 6 7 8 9   **972**
1. Indians of Mexico -- History 2. Culture 3. Ancient history 4. Mexico -- History -- To 1519
ISBN 9781599351612

LC 2010041379
Describes the history of ancient Mexico, from the land's first inhabitants to the many Native American societies flourishing in the area until the Spanish conquest, including the Olmecs, the Maya, and the Aztecs.

"Stein organizes and clearly presents a great deal of information. . . . The . . . format features a chonological text supplemented with useful sidebars and brightened with color illustrations, including many photos, artifacts, and period artworks. . . . [The book] provides a historical survey of Mexico's early inhabitants, from the arrival of Paleo-Indians through civilizations such as the Olmecs, the Maya, and Toltecs, and the Aztecs." Booklist.
Includes bibliographical references (p. 138) and index.

The **story** of Mexico: Cortés and the Spanish Conquest. R. Conrad Stein. Morgan Reynolds Pub., c2008. 160 p.

Grades: 6 7 8 9 10   **972**
1. Mexico -- History -- Conquest, 1519-1540
ISBN 159935053X

LC 2007016004

Describes the Aztec civilization and how it was conquered by Hernando Cortés and his Spanish army.

"This identifies the encounter between the Spanish and Aztecs as one that would put the human character itself on trial. The author provides a look at both societies, tracing the Aztecs' rise to power and the Spaniards' interest in exploration. The Spanish conquest of the Aztecs, led by Hernando Cortés, is related in great depth, and the book ends with a discussion of its legacy. [An] excellent [introduction] to Mexican history." School Library Journal.

Includes bibliographical references (p. 149-157) and index.

The **story** of Mexico: the Mexican War of Independence. R. Conrad Stein. Morgan Reynolds Pub., c2008. 144 p.

Grades: 6 7 8 9 10   **972**
1. Mexico -- History -- Wars of Independence, 1810-1821. 2. Mexico -- History -- 1821-1867
ISBN 9781599350547

LC 2007022137

Discusses the causes, key personalities, and important battles of Mexico's eleven-year war for independence from Spain and describes the following war against the United States over the state of Texas.

"This covers the years between 1521, when Hernando Cortés completed his conquest of the Aztec empire, and 1855, when Antonio Lopez Santa Anna was overthrown. The book provides excellent background information about three centuries of Spain's rule over Mexico. . . . [The book has] a lively narrative style. . . . Pertinent illustrations, including photographs, historical paintings, and maps are sprinkled throughout. . . . Well-written and well-researched." School Library Journal.

Includes bibliographical references (p. 141-142) and index.

972.08 Mexico since 1867

Stein, R. Conrad
Modern Mexico. R. Conrad Stein. Morgan Reynolds Pub., c2011. 144 p.: Story of Mexico

Grades: 6 7 8 9   **972.08**
1. Modern history 2. Culture 3. Mexico -- History -- 1910-1946 4. Mexico -- History -- 1946-
ISBN 9781599351629

LC 2010053630

Describes the history of Mexico after the Mexican Revolution in 1920, including the political and social changes and transition into stability, the renaissance of the arts, and current economic and social problems.

"Stein organizes and clearly presents a great deal of information. . . . The . . . format features a chronological text supplemented with useful sidebars and brightened with color illustrations, including many photos, artifacts, and period artworks. . . . [The book] looks at events in Mexico since 1920, focusing primarily on presidential administrations, economic problems, political unrest, and emigration." Booklist.

Includes bibliographical references (p. 138-139) and index.

The **story** of Mexico: the Mexican Revolution R. Conrad Stein.. Morgan Reynolds Pub., c2008. 160 p.

Grades: 6 7 8 9 10   **972.08**
1. Revolutions 2. Mexico -- History -- Revolution, 1910-1920. 3.

Mexico -- History -- 1910-1946.
ISBN 9781599350516

LC 2007022136

Discusses the social conditions that led to the coup against Porfirio Diaz in 1910, the following ten years of shifting political power and revolutions, and the political and social legacy of this time of unrest in Mexico's history.

"Opening with Porfirio Daz's presidency (beginning in 1876), [this book] explains how Indian land was expropriated and allotted to rich hacienda owners, describes resistance movements led by Emiliano Zapata and Pancho Villa, and details 10 years of political upheaval and violent uprisings (1910-1920), ending with Alvaro Obreg's election as president of Mexico. . . . [The book has] a lively narrative style. . . . Pertinent illustrations, including photographs, historical paintings, and maps are sprinkled throughout. . . . Well-written and well-researched." School Library Journal.

Includes bibliographical references (p. 156-157) and index.

972.8 Central America

Harris, Nathaniel, 1937-
★ **Ancient** Maya: archaeology unlocks the secrets to the Maya's past. by Nathaniel Harris; Elizabeth Graham, consultant. National Geographic, 2008. 64 p. : National Geographic investigates

Grades: 4 5 6 7   **972.8**
1. Mayas -- Antiquities 2. Excavations (Archaeology) 3. Excavations (Archaeology) 4. Central America -- Antiquities. 5. Mexico -- Antiquities.
ISBN 1426302282

LC 2007047837

Authoritative texts that include interviews with experts, maps, useful time lines, glossaries, and more bring readers up to date on the latest findings of and current viewpoints on ancient civilizations from leading archaeologists.

972.81 Guatemala

Laughton, Timothy
Exploring the life, myth, and art of the Maya. Timothy Laughton. Rosen Pub., 2012. 144 p.: Civilizations of the world

Grades: 7 8 9 10 11   **972.81**
1. Mayas -- History 2. Mayas -- Social life and customs 3. Civilization, Ancient 4. Mayas 5. Art, Maya
ISBN 9781448848324

LC 2011009790

Presents an introduction to Mayan civilization, discussing its history, politics, art, religion, literature, philosophy, military, gods, and heroes.

VanVoorst, Jennifer, 1972-
The **ancient** Maya. by Jenny Fretland VanVoorst. Compass Point Books, c2013. 48 p.: Exploring the ancient world

Grades: 4 5 6 7 8   **972.81**
1. Mayas 2. Indians of Central America 3. Civilization, Ancient 4. Mayas -- History 5. Mayas -- Social life and customs 6. Mexico -- Civilization 7. Central America -- Civilization
ISBN 9780756545642

LC 2012001966

Describes the Ancient Mayan civilization, including their religious views, intellectual achievements, and everyday life.

972.82 Belize

Jermyn, Leslie
   Belize. Leslie Jermyn, Jui Lin Yong. Cavendish Square 2020
144 p.: Cultures of the World
Grades: 5 6 7 8   **972.82**
   1. Belize 2. Central America
   ISBN 9781502655738
If Belize is known for one thing, it's diversity. The only country in
continental Central America to use English as its official language, this
former British colony is host to a rich culture shaped by its Garinagu,
Creole, Maya, Mestizo, and Mennonite population. Today, tourists flock
to Belize to experience some of the greatest biodiversity on the planet.
This travel volume utilizes helpful maps, intriguing sidebars, and colorful photographs to highlight the history, geography, wildlife, and traditions of this unique nation. Readers can even try making foods from
Belize with simple recipes. Provided by publisher

972.84 El Salvador

Foley, Erin, 1967-
   El Salvador. Erin Foley, Rafiz Hapipi. Marshall Cavendish
Benchmark, 2005. 144 p.: Cultures of the world
Grades: 5 6 7 8   **972.84**
   1. Culture 2. Central America 3. El Salvador -- History.
   ISBN 0761419675
                                               LC 2005009360
Explores the geography, history, government, economy, people, and
culture of El Salvador. Provided by publisher.

972.85 Nicaragua

Kott, Jennifer, 1971-
   ★ **Nicaragua**. Jennifer Kott, Kristi Streiffert. Marshall Cav-
endish Benchmark, 2005. 144 p.: Cultures of the world
Grades: 5 6 7 8   **972.85**
   1. Nicaragua 2. Nicaragua -- Social life and customs.
   ISBN 0761419691
   Geography—History—Government—Economy—Environment—
Nicaraguans—Lifestyle—Religion—Language—Arts—Leisure—Fes-
tivals—Food—Map of Nicaragua.
   Explores the geography, history, government, economy, people, and
culture of Nicaragua.

972.8505 Nicaragua—1893-

Kallen, Stuart A., 1955-
   The **aftermath** of the Sandinista Revolution. Stuart A. Kallen. Twenty-First Century Books, c2009. 160 p.: Aftermath of
history
Grades: 8 9 10 11 12   **972.8505**
   1. Sandinista National Liberation Front -- History 2. Revolutions
3. Social change 4. Nicaragua -- Politics and government -- 1979-
1990 5. Nicaragua -- Politics and government -- 1990-
   ISBN 9780822590910
                                               LC 2008025356
Examines the causes, events, and consequences of the Sandinista
Revolution in Nicaragua.

"The 1979 overthrow of the corrupt Nicaraguan government by the
Marxist Sandinistas brought change to one of the poorest countries in
the Americas and instilled in the U.S. new fears about the spread of
Communism. . . . Kallen offers a good overview of one of the Latin
American theaters of the Cold War." School Library Journal.
   Includes bibliographical references (p. 141-152) and index.

972.86 Costa Rica

Yomtov, Nelson
   ★ **Costa** Rica. by Nel Yomtov. Children's Press, An Imprint
of Scholastic Inc., 2014. 144 p.: Enchantment of the World. Second Series
Grades: 5 6 7 8   **972.86**
   1. Countries 2. Culture 3. Costa Rica
   ISBN 9780531220146
                                               LC 2013022563
Discusses the geography, culture, history, religion, economy, and
community life of Costa Rica.

972.87 Panama

Hassig, Susan M., 1969-
   Panama. Susan Hassig & Lynette Quek. Marshall Cavendish Benchmark, c2007. 144 p.: Cultures of the world
Grades: 5 6 7 8   **972.87**
   1. Panama 2. Panama -- Social life and customs
   ISBN 9780761420286
                                               LC 2006020824
Provides comprehesive information on the geography, history, wildlife, governmental structure, economy, cultural diversity, peoples, religion, and culture of Panama. Provided by publisher.

Vander Hook, Sue, 1949-
   Building the Panama Canal. by Sue Vander Hook. ABDO
Pub. Co., 2010. 112 p.: Essential events
Grades: 6 7 8 9   **972.87**
   1. Canals -- Design and construction 2. Canals -- History 3.
Panama Canal
   ISBN 9781604539424
                                               LC 2009030373
Provides a history of the building of the Panama Canal, discuss-
ing the project's construction, challenges along the way, the people in-
volved, and its current status.
   "The writing is accessible and is richer than a lot of history writing,
allowing the reader to become engaged in the text as a story, and the
layout provides enough white space to allow lower level readers to feel
confident." Library Media Connection.
   Includes bibliographical references (p. 106-109) and index.

972.91 Cuba

Tracy, Kathleen
   We visit Cuba. Kathleen Tracy. Mitchell Lane Publishers,
c2011. 63 p.: Your land and my land

Grades: 4 5 6 7   **972.91**
  1. Cuba 2. Caribbean Area
  ISBN 9781584158905

                        LC 2010006558
Describes the history, natural features, geography, government, people, and culture of Cuba.

"With an inviting format that includes bright color photos on every spread, this title . . . offers an appealing overview of Cuba's history, geography, culture and lifestyle, politics, economics, and more. . . . A good starting point for research as well as for personal interest." Booklist.

Includes bibliographical references (p. 61) and index.

Wright, David K.
  Cuba. by David K. Wright. Children's Press, 2008. 144 p. : Enchantment of the world
Grades: 5 6 7 8   **972.91**
  1. Cuba 2. Caribbean Area
  ISBN 9780531120965

                        LC 2008008423
Presents the geography, climate, wildlife, history, culture, economy, government, and people of Cuba.

972.9106 Cuba—1899-

Smith-Llera, Danielle, 1971-
  Che Guevara's face: how a Cuban photographer's image became a cultural icon. by Danielle Smith-Llera. Compass Point Books, a Capstone imprint, [2017] 64 p.: Captured world history
Grades: 6 7 8 9   **972.9106**
  1. Korda, Alberto, 1928-2001. Guerillero heroico 2. Guevara, Che, 1928-1967 3. Mass media 4. Guerrillas 5. Photography 6. Cuba -- History -- 1959-1990
  ISBN 9780756554408

                        LC 2016008219
Discusses the iconic photograph of revolutionary Che Guevara taken in 1960 by Cuban photographer Alberto Korda. Provided by publisher.

"The books in the series are handsomely designed and visually do their subjects justice. The fact-filled texts are inviting but never talk down to the audience. Mark this series as a great way to discuss history, photography, and the way both shape public perception." Booklist.

Includes bibliographical references (page 63) and index.

Stein, R. Conrad
  Cuban Missile Crisis: in the shadow of nuclear war. R. Conrad Stein. Enslow Publishers, c2009. 128 p.: America's living history
Grades: 5 6 7 8   **972.9106**
  1. 1960s 2. Cuban Missile Crisis, 1962 3. Ballistic missiles 4. Missiles 5. United States -- Foreign relations -- Cuba 6. Soviet Union -- Foreign relations -- United States
  ISBN 9780766029057

                        LC 2008004703
Discusses the Cuban missile crisis, a thirteen-day struggle between the United States and the Soviet Union, including the causes of the conflict, the leaders faced with important decisions, and the final resolution to avoid nuclear war. Provided by publisher.

"This engaging account provides a thorough discussion of events. . . . Archival photographs, maps, sidebars, and many primary sources effectively depict key figures, political posturing, and the nation's anxiety." Horn Book Guide.

Includes bibliographical references and index.

972.93 Dominican Republic

Rogers, Barbara Radcliffe
  Dominican Republic: enchantment of the world. by Barbara Radcliffe Rogers and Lura Rogers Seavey. Children's Press, an imprint of Scholastic Inc., 2019. 144 p.: Enchantment of the World
Grades: 5 6 7 8   **972.93**
  1. Dominican Republic
  ISBN 9780531126967

                        LC 2018019486
This book details the history, culture, geography and government of the Dominican Republic. Provided by publisher.

972.94 Haiti

Aronin, Miriam
  Earthquake in Haiti. by Miriam Aronin. Bearport Pub., c2011. 32 p.: Code red
Grades: 4 5 6 7   **972.94**
  1. Haiti Earthquake, Haiti, 2010 2. Earthquakes 3. Natural disasters 4. Disaster relief 5. Disaster victims 6. Haiti -- Social conditions 7. Haiti -- Economic conditions
  ISBN 9781936088669

                        LC 2010011126
Describes the devastating earthquake that occurred in Haiti on January 12, 2010.

"The text is written from the points of view of some of the people involved, including primary source direct quotes. Some of the pictures are necessarily graphic, which adds to the authenticity. . . . This title will be used for browsing as well as for reports." Library Media Connection.

Includes bibliographical references (p. 31) and index.

Hale, Nathan
  Blades of freedom: a Louisiana Purchase tale. Nathan Hale. Amulet Books, 2020 128 p.: Nathan Hale's hazardous tales
Grades: 3 4 5 6 7   **972.94**
  1. 1790s 2. 18th century 3. Louisiana Purchase 4. Haiti -- History -- Revolution, 1791-1804. 5. United States -- History -- 1801-1809 6. Comics and Graphic novels 7. Historical comics
  ISBN 9781419746918

Presents, in graphic novel format, the story of the Haitian Revolution and its role in Napoleon's decision to sell Thomas Jefferson and James Monroe the whole Louisiana Territory, when they sought to buy only New Orleans.

Yomtov, Nelson
  Haiti. Nel Yomtov. Children's Press, 2012. 144 p.: Enchantment of the world
Grades: 5 6 7 8   **972.94**
  1. Haiti 2. Caribbean Area
  ISBN 9780531253533

                        LC 2011010048
Explores the history, geography, wildlife, government, economy, religion, culture, and people of Haiti.

972.95 Puerto Rico

Worth, Richard
   Puerto Rico in American history. Richard Worth. Enslow Publishers, c2008. 128 p.: From many cultures, one history
Grades: 6 7 8 9 10   **972.95**
   1. Colonies 2. Puerto Rico -- History 3. United States -- Colonies.
   ISBN 9780766028364
                    LC 2006037087
   Explores the history of Puerto Rico, from its time as a Spanish colony to its acceptance as a commonwealth of the United States.
   "This is a book about the ties between Puerto Rico and the U.S. . . . Worth's overview will help to acclimate readers new to the island's history. . . . Writing in short, plain sentences, the author touches upon the commonwealth's ongoing struggle with poverty, migration, and language and the current conflicts about statehood and independence. The book's clean design is inviting, with lots of color-screened boxes, full-color photos, archival artwork, and maps." Booklist.
   Includes bibliographical references (p. 124) and index.

972.96 Bahama Islands

Nevins, Debbie
   Bahamas. Debbie Nevins, Robert Barlas, Jui Lin Yong. Cavendish Square 2020 144 p.: Cultures of the World
Grades: 5 6 7 8   **972.96**
   1. Bahamas
   ISBN 9781502647429
   For centuries, the Bahamas was under colonial rule. As such, today the country still has a strong European influence on its traditions, culture, and celebrations. However, it also has a distinct island identity that citizens share every year with the thousands of tourists that flock to it. This book examines the distant past of the Bahamas and the nation's buildup to independence from Britain in 1973. It explores the country today, especially its foods, beliefs, economy, government, and unique festivities. Using compelling sidebars and photographs, this book ultimately gives readers a comprehensive view of the island nation in the twenty-first century.—Publisher's description

972.974 Antigua and Barbuda

Kras, Sara Louise
   Antigua and Barbuda. by Sara Louise Kras. Marshall Cavendish Benchmark, c2008. 144 p.: Cultures of the world
Grades: 5 6 7 8   **972.974**
   1. Antigua and Barbuda 2. West Indies
   ISBN 9780761425700
                    LC 2006031537
   Provides comprehensive information on the geography, history, governmental structure, economy, cultural diversity, peoples, religion, and culture of the Antigua and Barbuda. Provided by publisher.

972.981 Barbados

Elias, Marie Louise
   Barbados. Marie Louise Elias, Josie Elias, and Bethany Bryan. Cavendish Square, 2019. 144 p.: Cultures of the World

Grades: 5 6 7 8   **972.981**
   1. Barbados
   ISBN 9781502647306
   Provides comprehensive information on the geography, history, wildlife, governmental structure, economy, cultural diversity, peoples, religion, and culture of Barbados. Provided by publisher

972.983 Trinidad and Tobago

Sheehan, Sean
   Trinidad and Tobago. Sean Sheehan, Jui Lin Yong. Cavendish Square 2020 144 p.: Cultures of the World
Grades: 5 6 7 8   **972.983**
   1. Trinidad and Tobago
   ISBN 9781502655813
   Trinidad and Tobago are two tropical islands located off the northern coast of Venezuela in the Caribbean Sea, but together they make one nation. Both are home to a vibrant culture. Through this detailed book, readers explore many aspects of this country, such as its history, geography, lifestyle, language, festivals, and food. Informative sidebars, comprehensive maps, a detailed glossary, and eye-catching, full-color photographs bring extra insight to this social studies curriculum topic. Readers will gain useful knowledge as they learn about the customs of this unique nation. Provided by publisher

972.9843 Saint Lucia

Orr, Tamra
   Saint Lucia. Tamra Orr. Marshall Cavendish Benchmark, 2008. 144 p.: Cultures of the world
Grades: 5 6 7 8   **972.9843**
   1. St Lucia 2. West Indies
   ISBN 9780761425694
                    LC 2006038625
   Provides comprehensive information on the geography, history, governmental structure, economy, cultural diversity, peoples, religion, and culture of the St. Lucia. Provided by publisher.

972.9845 Grenada and Carriacou

Pang, Guek-Cheng, 1950-
   Grenada. Guek-Cheng Pang. Marshall Cavendish Benchmark, c2011. 144 p.: Cultures of the world
Grades: 5 6 7 8   **972.9845**
   1. Grenada 2. Caribbean Basin Initiative countries
   ISBN 9781608702169
                    LC 2010019807
   Provides comprehensive information on the geography, history, wildlife, governmental structure, economy, cultural diversity, peoples, religion, and culture of Grenada. Provided by publisher.

973 United States

Armstrong, Jennifer, 1961-
   ★ The **American** story: 100 true tales from American history. by Jennifer Armstrong; illustrated by Roger Roth. Alfred A. Knopf, 2006. 368 p.

Grades: 4 5 6 7 **973**
1. Americans 2. Immigrants 3. Inventors 4. Human settlements 5. Sports 6. United States -- History 7. United States -- Social life and customs
ISBN 0375812563

LC 2005034822

"This large, fully illustrated compendium features 100 stories, familiar and lesser known, drawn from America's past and arranged in chronological order. . . . Thanks to writing that is consistently good and sometimes excellent, the tales will certainly hold readers' attention, and brightening nearly every page are lively drawings enhanced by watercolor washes." Booklist.

Includes bibliographical references and index.

Bolden, Tonya

★ **How** to build a museum: Smithsonian's National Museum of African American History and Culture. Tonya Bolden. Viking Childrens Books, [2016] 64 p.: Smithsonian
Grades: 5 6 7 8 **973**
1. National Museum of African American History and Culture (U.S.) 2. African Americans -- Museums 3. Historical museums -- Design and construction 4. Museums
ISBN 9780451476371

LC 2016011612

"A well-organized and informative book introducing this significant new historical center." Booklist.

Buckley, Susan

★ **Journeys** for freedom: a new look at America's story. Susan Buckley and Elspeth Leacock; illustrations by Rodica Prato. Houghton Mifflin, 2006. 48 p.
Grades: 4 5 6 7 **973**
1. Freedom -- History 2. United States -- History 3. United States
ISBN 0618223231

LC 2004000974

Depicts and recounts the experiences of individuals from history pursuing freedom, from a Delaware Indian chief negotiating a peace treaty to an African child surviving the Amistad slave ship rebellion.

"This history focuses on 20 individuals' quest for freedom across U.S. history. Some . . . will be familiar, but most will not. The stories, both varied and fascinating, often go beyond the personal. . . . Running along the bottom of each double-page spread is a pictorial map keyed to the text. . . . The authors make excellent use of primary sources. . . . As powerful as it is useful." Booklist.

Croy, Elden

United States. Elden Croy. National Geographic, c2010. 64 p.: National Geographic countries of the world
Grades: 4 5 6 7 **973**
1. United States 2. North America
ISBN 9781426306327

LC oc2010003038

"The information is substantial but not overwhelming. The [text is] clear, and the discussion points are well chosen. . . . [The text is] complemented with stunning photographs." School Library Journal.

Includes bibliographical references (p. 61) and index.

Dennis, Yvonne Wakim

A **kid's** guide to Arab American history: more than 50 activities. Yvonne Wakim Dennis and Maha Addasi. Chicago Review Press, 2013. 160 p.: Kid's guide

Grades: 4 5 6 7 **973**
1. Arab Americans -- History 2. Immigrants, Arab 3. Immigrants -- Social conditions 4. United States -- Immigration and emigration 5. Arab countries -- Immigration and emigration
ISBN 9781613740170

LC 2012035758

Presents step-by-step instructions for crafts based on Arab American customs along with a brief history of why the craft is important to Arab American culture.

Eggers, Dave

★ **Her** right foot. story by Dave Eggers; art by Shawn Harris. Chronicle Books, 2017. 104 p.
Grades: 3 4 5 6 7 8 **973**
1. Statue of Liberty (New York, NY) -- History 2. National monuments 3. Signs and symbols, American 4. Monuments 5. Historic sites 6. New York City
ISBN 9781452162812

LC 2016057953

In this fascinating, fun take on nonfiction, Dave Eggers and Shawn Harris investigate a seemingly small trait of America's most emblematic statue. What they find is about more than history, more than art. What they find in the Statue of Liberty's right foot is the powerful message of acceptance that is essential to an entire country's creation.

"This beautifully designed and conversational yet sophisticated book about the history of the iconic statue is also filled with humor and interesting trivia." School Library Journal.

Elish, Dan

The **Trail** of Tears: the story of the Cherokee removal. by Dan Elish. Benchmark Books, c2002. 96 p.: Great journeys
Grades: 5 6 7 8 **973**
1. Trail of Tears, 1838-1839 2. Cherokee Indians -- Relocation 3. Cherokee Indians -- History 4. Indians of North America -- History 5. Indian Removal, 1813-1903
ISBN 076141228X

LC 00052902

Describes the journey of thousands of Cherokee Indians from Georgia to Oklahoma; forced from their land during the winter without proper food, clothing, or shelter.

Hoose, Phillip M., 1947-

★ **We** were there, too!: young people in U.S. history. Phillip Hoose. Farrar Straus Giroux, 2001. vii, 264 p.
Grades: 5 6 7 8 **973**
1. Children 2. Teenagers 3. United States -- History 4. United States
ISBN 0374382522

LC 99089052

Biographies of dozens of young people who made a mark in American history, including explorers, planters, spies, cowpunchers, sweatshop workers, and civil rights workers.

"A treasure chest of history come to life, this is an inspired collection. . . . Because the book is packed with historical documents, evocatively illustrated . . . and full of eyewitness quotations, it should prove valuable to young historians and researchers." School Library Journal.

Includes bibliographical references (p. 253-256) and index.

Johnston, Robert D.

★ The **making** of America: the history of the United States from 1492 to the present. Robert D. Johnston; with a foreword by Douglas Brinkley. National Geographic, c2010. 240 p.

Grades: 5 6 7 8 **973**
1. United States -- History. 2. United States -- Politics and government.
ISBN 9781426306631

LC bl2010012368

Discusses each major era in the history of the United States and includes biographies of key people, summaries of social movements and issues, time lines, historic documents and speeches, and a guide to historic sites.

"This energetically written and profusely illustrated history remains one of the top-drawer single-volume accounts of the founding and growth of the U.S. for middle grade students. The previous edition ended with 9/11; here, into the same page count, Johnston fits Hurricane Katrina, the wars in Iraq and Afghanistan, Barack Obama's election, and other major events." Booklist.

Includes bibliographical references (p. 226-234) and index.

King, David C.

★ **Children's** encyclopedia of American history. by David C. King. DK in association with the Smithsonian Institution, 2014, c2003. 320 p.
Grades: 4 5 6 **973**
1. History 2. United States -- History.
ISBN 9781465428431

LC 2002073388

Full-color maps, photographs, and paintings illustrate a comprehensive reference guide to American history.

"This revised edition takes a look at U.S. history, from the exploration of the New World in the 1400s to the present day. . . . New content includes the Boston bombing of 2013, the War on Terror, the death of Osama Bin Laden, and a focus on globalization and sports. Natural disasters, such as Hurricane Katrina, and additional environmental concerns are detailed. Presidential coverage is expanded to incorporate the election of Barack Obama, while other new topics include the growth of the Tea Party Movement and controversy regarding guns." School Library Journal.

Krasner, Barbara

Russian immigrants: in their shoes. Barbara Krasner. Child's World, 2019 32 p.
Grades: 4 5 6 7 **973**
1. Emigration and immigration -- Social aspects 2. Immigrants -- History 3. Immigrants 4. Russian Americans
ISBN 9781503828018

LC bl2019003443

Looks into the lives, challenges, and successes of Russian immigrants.

Lake, Matthew

Weird U.S.: a freaky field trip through the 50 states. by Matt Lake and Randy Fairbanks. Sterling Children's Books, c2011. 128 p.
Grades: 6 7 8 9 **973**
1. Curiosities and wonders 2. United States 3. United States -- Description and travel
ISBN 9781402754623

LC 2010027019

Introduces young readers to bizarre objects, oddities, and strange sites throughout the United States.

"Imagine the kitsch of a field trip to the world's largest ball of twine and multiple it by about a thousand and you'll begin to appreciate the imaginative and colorful romp through the United States' weirdest roadside attractions. Each site . . . is described in detail with full-color photo-graphs. . . . Sure to be a hit with students that pore over the Guiness Book of World Records and Ripley's Believe It or Not!." Booklist.

Lesh, Bruce A.

"Why won't you just tell us the answer?": teaching historical thinking in grades 7-12. Bruce A. Lesh; foreword by Ed Ayres. Stenhouse Publishers, c2011. x, 230 p.
Grades: Professional **973**
1. History -- Study and teaching (Secondary) 2. United States -- History -- Study and teaching (Secondary)
ISBN 9781571108128

LC 2010050306

Over the last fifteen years, Bruce has refined a method of teaching history that mirrors the process used by historians, where students are taught to ask questions of evidence and develop historical explanations. By the end of the book, teachers will have learned how to teach history via a lens of interpretive questions and interrogative evidence that allows both student and teacher to develop evidence-based answers to history's greatest questions.

Panchyk, Richard

The **keys** to American history: understanding our most important historic documents. Richard Panchyk. Chicago Review Press, c2008. vi, 241 p.
Grades: 7 8 9 10 11 12 **973**
1. United States. Declaration of Independence 2. Monroe doctrine 3. Presidents 4. United States -- History
ISBN 9781556527166

LC 2008010662

Organizes American history primary sources chronologically with analysis and explanations.

"This impressive collection is a valuable resource for gaining a greater appreciation for and understanding of our nation's dynamic history." School Library Journal.

Includes bibliographical references and index.

Percoco, James A.

Take the journey: teaching American history through place-based learning. James A. Percoco; foreword by Milton Chen; afterword by Cathy Gorn. Stenhouse Publishers, 2017 xiv, 252 p.
Grades: Professional **973**
1. Place-based education 2. United States -- History -- Study and teaching.
ISBN 9781625311436

LC 2016047552

In Take the Journey, author, historian, and educator James Percoco invites you and your students to the places where many events in American history happened. Though it might prove difficult to visit these particular sites with your students, Percoco argues that every community has a story that can be connected to larger themes in American history and that placed-based history education can be made a part of every classroom, from Nevada to Washington to Pennsylvania.

Petrillo, Valerie

★ A **kid's** guide to Latino history: more than 70 activities. Valerie Petrillo. Chicago Review Press, 2009. 208 p.
Grades: 4 5 6 7 **973**
1. Hispanic Americans -- History 2. Immigrants, Hispanic American 3. Creative activities for children and students 4. United states -- History
ISBN 9781556527715

LC 2008040433

"This big, lively overview examines the history of Latinos in the U.S. . . . The chatty, informative text, presented in readable, spacious layouts, will draw kids with lots of fun, illustrated instructions for related activities. . . . The accessible facts and the individual portraits of notable authors, athletes, entertainers, and politicians portray Latinos' rich contribution to U.S. heritage, and kids will want to talk about the well-presented issues." Booklist.

Includes bibliographical references.

Pinkney, Andrea Davis

Hand in hand: ten Black men who changed America. by Andrea Davis Pinkney; paintings by Brian Pinkney. Disney/Jump at the Sun Books, c2012. 243 p.

Grades: 4 5 6 7   **973**
    1. African American men 2. African Americans 3. Social change -- History 4. Antiracist literature
    ISBN 9781423142577

LC 2011051348

Coretta Scott King Award, Author Category, 2013.

Presents the stories of 10 African-American men from different eras in American history, organized chronologically to provide a scope from slavery to the modern day. Backmatter includes a Civil Rights timeline, sources and further reading. Illustrated by a two-time Caldecott Honor winner and multiple Coretta Scott King Book Award recipient.

Tarrant-Reid, Linda

★ **Discovering** Black America: from the age of exploration to the twenty-first century. Linda Tarrant-Reid. Abrams Books for Young Readers, 2012. xi, 244 p.

Grades: 5 6 7 8 9 10   **973**
    1. African Americans -- History 2. African Americans 3. United States -- History.
    ISBN 9780810970984

LC 2011052201

Traces over four centuries of African American history, drawing on personal journals, interviews, and archival materials to document times ranging from the Colonial period and slavery through the Civil War and the Civil Rights era.

Tunis, Edwin, 1897-1973

Frontier living. written and illustrated by Edwin Tunis. Lyons Press, 2000, c1961. 165 p.

Grades: 5 6 7 8 9 10   **973**
    1. Frontier and pioneer life 2. Pioneers 3. The West (United States) -- Social life and customs -- 19th century.
    ISBN 158574137X

LC 00710694

Describes the daily lives of American pioneers who explored and settled the territories west of the Appalachians.

Williams, Yohuru R.

Teaching U.S. history beyond the textbook: six investigative strategies grades 5-12. Yohuru Rashied Williams; forword by James Percoco. Corwin Press, c2009. xv, 138 p.

Grades: Professional   **973**
    1. Teaching -- Methodology 2. Teaching -- Philosophy 3. Education -- Study and teaching 4. United States -- History -- Study and teaching.
    ISBN 9781412966214

LC 2008026480

Aligned with national standards, these strategies and sample lessons turn learners into history detectives as they solve historical mysteries, prepare arguments for famous cases, and more.

Yue, Charlotte

The **wigwam** and the longhouse. Charlotte and David Yue. Houghton Mifflin, 2000. 118 p.

Grades: 4 5 6 7   **973**
    1. Woodland Indians 2. Indians of North America
    ISBN 0395841690

LC 98028971

Describes the history, customs, religion, government, homes, and present-day status of the various native peoples that inhabited the eastern woodlands since before the coming of the Europeans.

973.03 United States – Encyclopedias

Edgar, Kathleen J.

★ **Junior** worldmark encyclopedia of the states. Drew Johnson and Cynthia Johnson, editors; Kathleen J. Edgar, project editor. U.X.L, 2013 4 vols., 1,260 p.

Grades: 5 6 7 8 9 10   **973.03**
    1. US states 2. United States
    ISBN 9781414498591

LC 2012050641

Provides geographic, demographic, economic, and social information about each state in the Union, the District of Columbia, and other United States territories and dependencies.

973.04 United States—Ethnic and national groups

Dolan, Edward F., 1924-

The **American** Indian wars. Edward F. Dolan. Millbrook Press, c2003. 112 p.

Grades: 5 6 7 8   **973.04**
    1. Battles 2. Land claims 3. Indians of North America -- Wars 4. Indians of North America -- Relations with European-Americans
    ISBN 0761319689

LC 2002153012

Examines the battles and treaties between native peoples and early European settlers of what was to become the United States, as conflicts arose primarily over land, but also over food and other issues.

"Period drawings, paintings, and photographs effectively illustrate a text packed with history." Booklist.

Includes bibliographical references (p. 105-107) and index.

Marsico, Katie, 1980-

The **trail** of tears: the tragedy of the American Indians. Katie Marsico. Marshall Cavendish Benchmark, c2010. 128 p.

Grades: 8 9 10   **973.04**
    1. Trail of Tears, 1838-1839 2. Cherokee Indians -- Relocation 3. Cherokee Indians -- Government relations 4. Cherokee Indians -- Social conditions
    ISBN 9780761440291

LC 2008041217

Provides comprehensive information on the forced removal of American Indians from their homes to the Oklahoma Territory and its legacy. Provided by publisher.

Philip, Neil

The **great** circle: a history of the First Nations. Neil Philip; foreword by Dennis Hastings. Clarion Books, c2006. 153 p.

Grades: 7 8 9 10 11 12 Adult   **973.04**

1. Indians of North America -- History 2. Government relations with indigenous peoples 3. Indians of North America -- Social life and customs 4. Indians of North America -- Relations with European-Americans 5. Indians of North America -- Relations with missionaries, traders, etc 6. United States -- Race relations. 7. United States -- Interethnic relations.

ISBN 9780618159413

LC 2005032743

Offers a look at the long history of the Native American tribes in North America, the culture, their struggles against the white immigrants, and the resurgence of their customs, enhanced with source notes, index, and archival photographs.

"Philip takes on a huge challenge here: to present a unified narrative that explains the complex and confrontational relationships between Native Americans and white settlers. . . . He pulls it off, however, thanks to solid research, an engaging writing style, and a talent for making individual stories serve the whole. . . . Top marks, too, for the volume's photographs and historical renderings, which so intensely illustrate the pages." Booklist.

Includes bibliographical references (p. 143-146) and index.

Stewart, Mark, 1960-

The **Indian** Removal Act: forced relocation. by Mark Stewart. Compass Point Books, c2007. 96 p.: Snapshots in history

Grades: 6 7 8 9   **973.04**

1. Jefferson, Thomas, 1743-1826 2. Indian Removal, 1813-1903 3. Indians of North America 4. Government relations with indigenous peoples 5. Forced relocations -- History 6. Land tenure -- Government policy 7. United States -- Territorial expansion 8. United States -- Race relations

ISBN 0756524520

LC 2006027084

Profiles the "Trail of Tears," the forced removal of five Southeastern Native American tribes to land west of the Mississippi River during the winter of 1838 and 1839.

"The book organizes a good deal of historical information into a cogent presentation. . . . Illustrations, many in color, include photos and maps as well as period engravings, portraits, and documents." Booklist.

Includes bibliographical references (p. 93) and index.

973.09 United States—History, geographic treatment, biography

Bausum, Ann

Our country's first ladies. Ann Bausum; with a foreword by First Lady Laura Bush. National Geographic, 2007. 127 p.

Grades: 5 6 7 8   **973.09**

1. Presidents' spouses 2. Women

ISBN 9781426300066

LC 2006021284

"A well-researched, thoughtfully written, attractive account. Fact boxes provide basic information such as birth and death dates, marriage dates, and children's names; a Did You Know section shares interesting personal tidbits. Periodic time lines help to place the women's lives within the broader events of history. There is enough information here for simple reports. Interesting facts and anecdotes will hold readers' at-

tention. . . . An excellent layout and clear, colorful photographs and reproductions will further entice readers." School Library Journal.

Includes bibliographical references (p. 124-125) and index.

Kane, Joseph Nathan, born 1899

Facts about the presidents: a compilation of biographical and historical information. Joseph Nathan Kane, Janet Podell. H.W. Wilson Co., 2009. vii, 801 p.

Grades: 8 9 10 11 12 Adult   **973.09**

1. Presidents -- History 2. United States -- Politics and government

ISBN 9780824210878

LC 2008056016

"The eighth edition offers one-stop access to consistently formatted text, facts, and comparative data, and it remains a staple of the ready-reference shelf." Booklist.

973.099 Presidents—United States—Collected biography

Bausum, Ann

★ **Our** country's presidents: a complete encyclopedia of the U.S. presidency. written by Ann Bausum. National Geographic Partners, 2021. 224 p.

Grades: 4 5 6 7   **973.099**

1. Presidents 2. United States -- History

ISBN 9781426371998

Revised and updated to include the winner of the 2020 presidential election, this photo-filled and fact-packed book is a timely must-have reference. National Geographic presents the 45 individuals who have led the U.S. in this up-to-date, authoritative, and lavishly illustrated family, school, and library reference. Provided by publisher

"A clear, colorful design; a variety of sidebars; and rich historical material make this a solid, go-to resource for information on the presidents." School Library Journal.

Includes bibliographical references and index.

Krull, Kathleen, 1952-2021

★ **Lives** of the presidents: fame, shame, (and what the neighbors thought). written by Kathleen Krull; illustrated by Kathryn Hewitt. Harcourt Children's Books, 2011. 104 p.: Lives of--

Grades: 4 5 6 7   **973.099**

1. Presidents 2. Presidents' spouses 3. Politicians

ISBN 9780547498096

LC 2011453117

Focuses on the lives of presidents as parents, husbands, pet-owners, and neighbors while also including humorous anecdotes about hairstyles, attitudes, diets, fears, and sleep patterns.

"This new edition is sure to be even more popular than the original title (Harcourt, 1998) as it includes Presidents George W. Bush and Barack Obama, who are given the same cheeky-but-respectful treatment as their predecessors. . . . [Krull] provides further information on ex-Presidential activity since 1998, such as Jimmy Carter's Nobel Prize, Ronald Reagan's passing, and the Clintons' post-White House work. All other entries and art are virtually unaltered. Guaranteed to inject some levity into the ubiquitous presidential biography assignment, the 2011 Lives of the Presidents is a must-have for elementary schools and public libraries." School Library Journal.

Includes bibliographical references (p. 104).

973.1 Early history to 1607

Smith, Tom, 1953-
Discovery of the Americas, 1492-1800. Tom Smith; John S. Bowman and Maurice Isserman, general editors. Chelsea House, c2010. 134 p.
Grades: 7 8 9   **973.1**
   1. Explorers -- History 2. Explorers 3. America -- Discovery and exploration
ISBN 9781604131956

                          LC 2009022330
Describes the exploration of the Americas, including the discoveries of Christopher Columbus, Hernan Cortes, Amerigo Vespucci, Vasco Nunez de Balboa, Hernando de Soto, and George Vancouver.

973.2 United States—Colonial period, 1607-1775

Capaccio, George
   The **countryside** in colonial America. George Capaccio. Cavendish Square, 2015. 80 p.: Life in Colonial America
Grades: 6 7 8   **973.2**
   1. Rural life 2. Indians of North America -- History Colonial period, 1600-1775 3. United States -- Social conditions -- Colonial period, 1600-1775. 4. United States -- Social life and customs -- Colonial period, 1600-1775.
ISBN 9781627128858

                          LC 2014006063
Presents a history of settlement during the colonial period, describing what life was like in the early colonies of Jamestown and Plymouth, the relationship of the settlers with Indian tribes who lived in the region, and the skills the colonists needed to survive.
   "Thoroughly researched and expertly executed, this series describes in rich detail the lives of Native Americans, African Americans, and white settlers, including children, women, and criminals. The introductory material that prefaces each title is of particular value, as it demonstrates that the colonists were part of a larger world picture...Content in each title incorporates quotes from period letters and journals as well as a plethora of well-chosen, colorful illustrations. Strong, attractive titles for those looking for more coverage of Colonial America." School Library Journal.
   Includes bibliographical references (pages 72-77) and index.

Huey, Lois Miner
   American archaeology uncovers the earliest English colonies. by Lois Miner Huey. Marshall Cavendish Benchmark, c2010. 64 p.: American archaeology
Grades: 4 5 6 7   **973.2**
   1. Archaeology and history 2. Colonies 3. Archaeology 4. Excavations (Archaeology) 5. Virginia -- Antiquities 6. Jamestown, Virginia -- History
ISBN 9780761442646

                          LC 2008050259
   "Huey enthusiastically brings . . . [this era] to life through artifacts and field research. . . . [The volume begins with an] introduction that defines historical archaeology and explains its value in terms simple enough for lower-elementary readers to comprehend, yet detailed enough for older children to enjoy, an approach followed in the remaining chapters. . . . Huey's focus on American history, which is broken down into small, manageable chunks, is sure to entice budding historians." School Library Journal.
   Includes bibliographical references and index.

Mandell, Daniel R., 1956-
   King Philip's war: the conflict over New England. Daniel R. Mandell. Chelsea House, c2007. 144 p.: Landmark events in Native American history
Grades: 7 8 9 10   **973.2**
   1. 17th century 2. King Philip's War, 1675-1676 3. Wampanoag Indians -- History 4. Indians of North America -- History 5. Government relations with indigenous peoples 6. New England -- History -- Colonial period, 1600-1775
ISBN 9780791093467

                          LC 2006102258
Describes the war between the Native Americans and the New England colonists that took place from 1675 to 1676, discussing the events that led to it, what happened during it, and its results for both groups.
   "This account features lively writing and direct quotes, and [is] enhanced by many color and black-and-white photos, drawings, and illustrations." School Library Journal.
   Includes bibliographical references (p. [135]-136) and index.

McNeese, Tim
   Colonial America, 1543-1763. Tim McNeese; consulting editor, Richard Jensen. Chelsea House, c2010. 136 p.
Grades: 5 6 7 8   **973.2**
   1. United States -- History -- Colonial period, ca. 1600-1775 2. United States -- History -- Revolution, 1775-1783
ISBN 9781604133493

                          LC 2008055170
A series that spans the complex and varied history of the United States from prehistoric times to the present day, offering clear and entertaining narrative, interesting boxed insets and lively illustrations that bring to life the people and events that have shaped the nation.
   "This history of Colonial America begins with a chapter on Rivals for North America and ends with The Fight for the Ohio Country. . . . [The] book has an excellent chronology; rich sidebars; and numerous well-captioned illustrations, maps, and photos that enhance the texts. [This book provides a] satisfying [introduction] to American history for students." School Library Journal.
   Includes bibliographical references and index.

Nardo, Don, 1947-
   Daily life in colonial America. Don Nardo. Lucent Books, c2010. 96 p.: Lucent library of historical eras.
Grades: 6 7 8 9   **973.2**
   1. Colonists 2. Marriage 3. Education 4. Crime 5. Medicine 6. United States -- Social life and customs -- To 1775. 7. United States -- History -- Colonial period, 1600-1775
ISBN 9781420502640

                          LC 2009045636
Presents an introduction to life in colonial America, discussing family and home life, occupations, education, recreation, medicine, and laws.

   The **establishment** of the thirteen colonies. Don Nardo. Lucent Books, c2010. 96 p.: Lucent library of historical eras.
Grades: 6 7 8 9   **973.2**
   1. Colonies 2. Colonists 3. United States -- History -- Colonial period, 1600-1775
ISBN 9781420502671

                          LC 2009045055
Discusses the colonization of America by Europeans, including why they moved to the new country, and how the Native Americans reacted to and were treated by the colonists.

"In this history of the establishment of the thirteen colonies in North America, the detailed text is interspersed with sidebars of primary and secondary quotations and historical color illustrations that add both substance and visual interest. With its long paragraphs and dutiful citations, this is a fairy advanced take on the topic." Booklist.

Includes bibliographical references and index.

Government and social class in colonial America. Don Nardo. Lucent Books, c2010. 96 p.: Lucent library of historical eras

Grades: 6 7 8 9   **973.2**

1. Social classes -- History 2. United States -- History -- Colonial period, 1600-1775

ISBN 9781420502657

LC 2009043640

Discusses the social and political organization of colonial America, including information on fashion and social rank, elections, slavery, and the influence of the Enlightenment.

"The detailed text is interspersed with sidebars of primary and secondary quotations and historical color illustrations that add both substance and visual interest. With its long paragraphs and dutiful citations, this is a fairly advanced take on the topic." Booklist.

Includes bibliographical references and index.

Philbrick, Nathaniel

The **Mayflower** and the Pilgrims' new world. by Nathaniel Philbrick. G.P. Putnam's Sons, 2008. xii, 338 p.

Grades: 7 8 9 10 11 12   **973.2**

1. Mayflower (Ship) 2. 17th century 3. Pilgrims (New England settlers) 4. Indians of North America -- Wars 1600-1750 5. Colonists 6. Indians of North America -- Relations with European-Americans -- History 7. Massachusetts -- History -- New Plymouth, 1620-1691 8. United States -- History -- 17th century

ISBN 9780399247958

LC 2007030669

Offers the true story of the pioneers who crossed the Atlantic to establish a new world in Massachusetts, the challenges they faced upon their arrival, and their relationship with the local Native Americans.

"This volume highlights both the Pilgrims' determination to find and settle a home where they could worship freely and the perilous journey that it took to make that happen. In accessible prose, the author shatters the American myth of the landing at Plymouth Rock and the first Thanksgiving. . . . The various maps, reproductions of historical documents, photographs of significant locations, and illustrations all come together with the text to help separate fact from legend and create a realistic, readable portrayal of the Pilgrims and their first 50 years in America." School Library Journal.

Saari, Peggy

Colonial America: primary sources. Peggy Saari; Julie Carnagie, editor. U·X·L, c2000. xvi, 297, [6] p.: U-X-L colonial America reference library

Grades: 8 9 10 11 12   **973.2**

1. 17th century 2. 18th century 3. United States -- History -- Colonial period, 1600-1775

ISBN 0787637661

LC 99034460

Presents the historical events and social issues of colonial America through twenty-four primary documents, including diary entries, poems, and personal narratives.

"Each chapter adds helpful material before and after the excerpt to explain its importance. Illustrations and sidebars are used in this volume also, and difficult words are defined." Booklist.

Includes bibliographical references and index.

Stefoff, Rebecca, 1951-

Colonial life. Rebecca Stefoff. Benchmark Books, c2003. xxi, 119 p.: American voices from--

Grades: 6 7 8 9   **973.2**

1. United States -- History -- Colonial period, 1600-1775 2. United States -- History -- Colonial period, 1600-1775

ISBN 0761412050

LC 2002003223

Presents the history of the British colonies in North America, beginning with the Jamestown settlement, through excerpts from letters, pamphlets, journal entries, and other documents of the time.

973.3 United States—Periods of Revolution and Confederation, 1775-1789

Aronson, Marc

The **real** revolution: the global story of American independence. by Marc Aronson. Clarion Books, c2005. 238 p.

Grades: 7 8 9 10   **973.3**

1. World politics 18th century. 2. Globalization (Economics) 3. Revolutions 4. American Revolution, 1775-1783 5. United States -- History -- Revolution, 1775-1783 Causes. 6. United States -- Politics and government -- 1600-1775.

ISBN 9780618181797

LC 2005001088

"In this volume, Aronson investigates the origins of the American Revolution and discovers some startling global connections. The colonies' quest for independence is tied to such seemingly unrelated incidents as Robert Clive's triumph over the French in India in 1750 and John Wilkes's accusations against the king in his newspaper, The North Briton, in the 1760s. . . . This outstanding work is highly compelling reading and belongs in every Library." School Library Journal.

Includes bibliographical references (p. 215-221) and index.

Driver, Stephanie Schwartz

Understanding the Declaration of Independence. Stephanie Schwartz Driver. Rosen Pub., 2010. 128 p.: Words that changed the world

Grades: 7 8 9 10   **973.3**

1. United States. Declaration of Independence 2. United States -- Politics and government -- 1775-1783.

ISBN 9781448816699

LC 2010010371

Provides background information on the circumstances that led to the writing of the Declaration of Independence, and discusses its style and literary merit, its effectiveness at the time, and its subsequent influence.

"This surveys The Declaration of Independence, considering the document's Context and Creator, Immediate Impact, Legacy, and Aftermath. . . . Exploring the colonial crisis leading to America's formal separation from the British Empire, . . . [the] author provides a balance of deep context, expressive writing, and pertinent information. Scattered throughout the [text] are a good number of well-captioned, color illustrations and photos. [This book is a] valuable [resource] for teachers and students doing research projects across the curriculum." School Library Journal.

Includes bibliographical references (p. 123-125) and index.

Hale, Nathan, 1976-

One dead spy. Nathan Hale. Amulet Books, 2012. 127 p.: Nathan Hale's hazardous tales

Grades: 3 4 5 6 7   **973.3**

1. Hale, Nathan, 1755-1776. 2. Spies 3. Military intelligence officers 4. Soldiers 5. Revolutions 6. American Revolution, 1775-1783 7. United States -- History -- Revolution, 1775-1783 -- Secret service 8. Comics and Graphic novels
ISBN 9781419703966

Nathan Hale, the author's historical namesake, was America's first spy, a Revolutionary War hero who famously said "I only regret that I have but one life to lose for my country" before being hanged by the British. In the Nathan Hale's Hazardous Tales series, author Nathan Hale channels his namesake to present history's roughest, toughest, and craziest stories in the graphic novel format.

Kiernan, Denise

Signing their rights away: the fame and misfortune of the men who signed the U.S. Constitution. Denise Kiernan, Joseph D'Agnese. Quirk Books, 2011. 256 p.

Grades: 8 9 10 11 12 Adult   **973.3**

1. United States. Constitution. 2. 18th century 3. 1770s 4. Political leadership 5. Politicians 6. United States -- History.
ISBN 9781594745201

"For readers of American history, this is both educational and entertaining." Booklist.

McNeese, Tim

Early national America, 1790-1850. written by Tim Mc-Neese. Chelsea House, c2010. 136 p.

Grades: 5 6 7 8   **973.3**

1. United States -- History -- 1783-1865
ISBN 9781604133516

LC 2009003679

A series that spans the complex and varied history of the United States from prehistoric times to the present day, offering clear and entertaining narrative, interesting boxed insets and lively illustrations that bring to life the people and events that have shaped the nation.

"McNeese discusses the people, politics, economic conditions, and foreign affairs of [the U.S. from 1790 to 1850], objectively explaining how the attitudes, perceptions, and expectations of the American people and their leaders shaped the development of the country. . . . Color period art and photos, maps, and cutaway drawings supplement the [text]." School Library Journal.

Includes bibliographical references and index.

Roberts, Cokie, 1943-2019

Founding mothers: remembering the ladies. Cokie Roberts, Diane Goode; [edited by] Alyson Day. HarperCollins, 2014. 40 p.

Grades: 3 4 5 6 7   **973.3**

1. 18th century 2. Women 3. Revolutions 4. Women -- Political activity -- History 5. American Revolution, 1775-1783 6. United States -- History -- Revolution, 1775-1783 -- Women.
ISBN 9780060780029

LC 2013936887

"Most children know that the Founding Fathers are the men who helped the 13 colonies develop into the United States. What about the women of the time period?...Grammarians may not appreciate the author's colloquial style, but the conversational tone is appealing. Beautifully intricate illustrations, rendered with antique pens, sepia ink, and watercolors, suit the text well. Thoughtful design, well-chosen facts, and an approachable format combine to make a book readers will enjoy and appreciate." School Library Journal.

973.4 United States—Constitutional period, 1789-1809

St. George, Judith, 1931-

The **duel**: the parallel lives of Alexander Hamilton and Aaron Burr. by Judith St. George. Viking, c2009. 112 p.

Grades: 6 7 8 9 10   **973.4**

1. Burr, Aaron, 1756-1836 2. Hamilton, Alexander, 1757-1804 3. 1800s (Decade) 4. Burr-Hamilton Duel, Weehawken, NJ, 1804 5. Dueling -- History 19th century.
ISBN 9780670011247

LC 2009005660

Examines the events that led up to the deadly duel between Alexander Hamilton and Aaron Burr by reviewing both their lives and the similarities that they shared, including serving as staff officers under George Washington.

"After a prologue following the steps of Alexander Hamilton and Aaron Burr on the morning of their famous duel, St. George backtracks to trace the parallel lives mentioned in the subtitle. . . . Well researched and organized, the book offers insights into the personalities, lives, and times of Burr and Hamilton." Booklist.

Stefoff, Rebecca, 1951-

The **new** republic: 1783-1830. Rebecca Stefoff. Benchmark Books, c2005. 116 p.: American voices from--

Grades: 6 7 8 9 10   **973.4**

1. United States -- Politics and government -- 1783-1865 2. United States -- Civilization -- 1783-1865
ISBN 0761416951

LC 2004011391

Describes events and beliefs from the early history of the United States, including the Monroe Doctrine, antislavery crusades, and the invention of the cotton gin, and provides primary sources from the eighteenth and nineteenth centuries.

973.5 United States—1809-1845

MacLeod, D. Peter, 1955-

Four wars of 1812: One war, four perspectives. D. Peter MacLeod; with the Canadian War Museum 1812 team, Eric Fernberg ... [et al.]. Douglas & McIntyre, c2012. 95 p.

Grades: 6 7 8   **973.5**

1. Indians of North America -- Wars 1812-1815 2. United States -- History -- War of 1812. 3. Great Britain -- History -- 1800-1837.
ISBN 9781771000505

LC bl2013008374

Examines the War of 1812 from the diverse perspectives of American, British, Canadian, and Native American participants.

973.6 United States—1845-1861

Carey, Charles W.

The **Mexican** War: "Mr. Polk's War". Charles W. Carey, Jr. Enslow Publishers, c2002. 128 p.: American war series

Grades: 6 7 8 9   **973.6**

1. Mexican-American War, 1845-1848 2. Mexico -- Foreign relations -- United States. 3. United States -- Foreign relations -- Mexico
ISBN 0766018539

LC 2001000817

Examines the people and events involved on one of the most controversial wars in history, between Mexico and the United States.

"This account of the 1846-1848 war addresses the origins, strategies, battles, and people involved in the conflict. The ramifications of the war for each country are discussed in separate chapters. . . . [This volume has] numerous black-and-white illustrations, a time line, solid footnotes, and chapters that begin with relevant quotes." School Library Journal.

Includes bibliographical references (p. 125) and index.

DiConsiglio, John

The **Mexican-American** War. John DiConsiglio. Heinemann Library, c2012. 80 p.: Living through

Grades: 6 7 8 9   **973.6**
1. 19th century 2. 1840s 3. Mexican-American War, 1845-1848 4. Battles 5. War
ISBN 9781432959982

LC 2011016817

Explores the history of the Mexican-American War, including the important players, battles, and consequences.

973.7 Administration of Abraham Lincoln, 1861-1865

Allen, Thomas B.

Mr. Lincoln's high-tech war: how the North used the telegraph, railroads, surveillance balloons, ironclads, high-powered weapons, and more to win the Civil War. by Thomas B. Allen and Roger MacBride Allen. National Geographic, 2008. 144 p.

Grades: 5 6 7 8 9 10   **973.7**
1. Lincoln, Abraham, 1809-1865 2. United States. Army -- History -- Civil War, 1861-1865 3. Technology -- History 19th century 4. Weapons -- History 19th century 5. Military history 19th century 6. Technological innovations 7. Civil war 8. United States -- History -- Civil War, 1861-1865 -- Technology
ISBN 9781426303807

LC 2008024546

Reveals how President Lincoln's appreciation for the power of technology played a critical role in the North's Civil War victory over the less developed South, and discusses the specific technologies used by the North in the war.

"Well researched and clearly written, the book discusses the course of the Civil War in terms of new technology, from the ironclad and the submarine to the rapid-fire, repeating rifle and the use of railroads to carry troops and supplies. . . . The many illustrations include captioned black-and-white reproductions of period prints, paintings, and photos as well as clearly labeled drawings. . . . [Readers] will gain a fascinating perspective on why the war progressed as it did and how it was ultimately won." Booklist.

Includes bibliographical references and index.

Anderson, Maxine

Great Civil War projects: you can build yourself. Maxine Anderson. Nomad Press , [c2012] viii, 120 p.

Grades: 7 8 9 10   **973.7**
1. Handicraft 2. United States -- History -- Civil War, 1861-1865 3. United States -- History -- Civil War, 1861-1865 -- Study and teaching -- Activity programs
ISBN 9781936749461

LC 2012454636

Explores the history and inventions of the Civil War by providing building projects and activities.

Beller, Susan Provost, 1949-

Billy Yank & Johnny Reb: soldiering in the Civil War. Susan Provost Beller. Twenty-First Century Books, 2007. 112 p.

Grades: 5 6 7 8   **973.7**
1. United States. Army -- Military life -- History -- Civil War, 1861-1865. 2. Confederate States of America. Army -- History. 3. Union soldiers 4. United States Civil War, 1861-1865 5. Confederate soldiers 6. Civil war 7. United States -- History -- Civil War, 1861-1865.
ISBN 9780822568032

"The author presents a good deal of solid information in an interesting manner. . . . Good black-and-white reproductions, mainly of photographs from the 1860s, appear throughout the book." Booklist. [review of 2000 ed]

Benoit, Peter, 1955-

The **surrender** at Appomattox. by Peter Benoit. Scholastic, 2012. 64 p.: Cornerstones of freedom.

Grades: 4 5 6   **973.7**
1. Lee, Robert E. (Robert Edward), 1807-1870. 2. Grant, Ulysses S., 1822-1885. 3. Appomattox Campaign, 1865 4. Military capitulations 5. Civil war 6. United States Civil War, 1861-1865 7. United States -- History -- Civil War, 1861-1865 -- Peace. 8. United States -- History -- Civil War, 1861-1865.
ISBN 9780531250419

LC 2011011967

Discusses the major battles and events leading up to Lee's surrender at Appomattox.

Bolden, Tonya

Emancipation Proclamation: Lincoln and the dawn of liberty. Tonya Bolden. Abrams Books for Young Readers, 2012. 128 p.

Grades: 6 7 8 9   **973.7**
1. Lincoln, Abraham, 1809-1865 2. Historic documents 3. Enslaved people -- Emancipation 4. African Americans -- History 1863-1877 5. Slavery -- History 6. Civil war 7. United States -- Politics and government -- 1861-1865 8. United States -- History -- Civil War, 1861-1865.
ISBN 9781419703904

LC 2012000845

Carter G. Woodson Book Awards: Middle Level, 2014.

A sesquicentennial anniversary commemorative introduction to the Emancipation Proclamation provides excerpts from historical sources, reproductions of archival images and lesser-known facts that challenge popular beliefs.

"Bolden succeeds in taking a complicated story and a dry document (possessing "all the moral grandeur of a bill of lading" as historian Richard Hofstadter wrote) and making the narrative interesting, lively, and personal, if sometimes overly casual in tone." Horn Book.

Includes bibliographical references and index.

DK Publishing, Inc

★ The **Civil** War: a visual history. [produced in association with the Smithsonian Institution]. DK Pub., c2011. 360 p.

Grades: 11 12 Adult   **973.7**
1. Confederate States of America 2. Confederate States of America -- History, Military
ISBN 9780756671853

LC 2011281338

Presents a pictorial history of the Civil War that includes artifacts, maps, personal narratives, and historical timelines for each year of the war.

"Espionage, the home front, and politics get a nod, but this book is for those wanting to smell the sulfur and hear the thunder of guns." Library Journal.

Includes bibliographical references and index.

Gourley, Catherine, 1950-

The **horrors** of Andersonville: life and death inside a civil war prison. by Catherine Gourley. Twenty-First Century Books, c2010. 192 p.

Grades: 8 9 10 11 12   **973.7**

1. Wirz, Henry, 1823-1865 2. Andersonville Prison 3. Confederate States of America. Army -- Officers 4. Trials 5. Courts-martial and courts of inquiry 6. Prisoners of war -- History 7. Prisoner abuse 8. Prisons 9. United States -- History -- Civil War, 1861-1865 -- Prisoners and prisons
ISBN 9780761342120

LC 2008046595

Details the conditions at Andersonville Prison in Georgia—including overcrowding, lack of supplies, harsh rules, and prison gangs—that led to the deaths of 13,000 Union prisoners, and recounts the trial of the camp's commandant, Henry Wirz.

"This well-researched book describes the notorious Confederate prison camp known as Andersonville, where more than 45,000 Union soldiers lived in deplorable conditions and some 13,000 died, beginning in 1864.... Illustrated with many captioned photos and prints and enlivened with quotes from firsthand accounts, this book provides a balanced, informative introduction to Andersonville." Booklist.

Includes bibliographical references and index.

Gregory, Josh

Gettysburg. Josh Gregory. Scholastic Library Pub., 2011. 64 p. : Cornerstones of freedom.

Grades: 4 5 6   **973.7**

1. Gettysburg Campaign, 1863 2. Gettysburg, Battle of, 1863 3. Civil war 4. United States Civil War, 1861-1865 5. United States -- History -- Civil War, 1861-1865 -- Campaigns 6. Pennsylvania -- History -- Civil War, 1861-1865
ISBN 9780531250341

Examines the famous battle, its importance during the war, and its results.

Hernandez, Roger E.

The **Civil** War, 1840s-1890s. by Roger E. Hernandez. Marshall Cavendish Benchmark, 2008. 80 p. : Hispanic America

Grades: 4 5 6 7   **973.7**

1. Hispanic Americans -- History 19th century 2. Civil war 3. Hispanic Americans 4. United States Civil War, 1861-1865 5. United States -- Interethnic relations -- History -- 19th century 6. United States -- History -- Civil War, 1861-1865 -- Participation, Hispanic American
ISBN 9780761429395

LC 2007049525

Describes Hispanic American participation in the United States Civil War and how Hispanics in New Mexico and other acquired territories transitioned to becoming a part of the nation.

Jarrow, Gail

Lincoln's flying spies: Thaddeus Lowe and the Civil War balloon corps. Gail Jarrow. Calkins Creek, c2010. 109 p.

Grades: 7 8 9 10   **973.7**

1. Lowe, T. S. C. (Thaddeus Sobieski Coulincourt), 1832-1913 2. Military aviation -- History 19th century 3. Ballooning -- History 19th century 4. Military aviation -- History 5. Ballooning -- History 6. Civil war 7. United States -- History -- Civil War, 1861-1865 -- Balloons 8. United States -- History -- Civil War, 1861-1865 -- Aerial operations
ISBN 9781590787199

LC bl2010017017

Describes the contributions made to the Union's efforts in the Civil War by Thaddeus Lowe and a corps of hot air balloonists who helped spy on the Confederate army, despite becoming targets in the war themselves.

"This well-researched volume introduces American aeronaut and showman Thaddeus Lowe, who convinced President Lincoln that hydrogen-filled balloons, rising high above the countryside, could provide Union generals with useful information about the position, strength, and movements of Confederate troops and artillery.... The text offers a detailed account of [Lowe's] contribution to the Union war effort. Many period photos, prints, and drawings illustrate the book in black and white.... Jarrow provides a solid introduction to an intriguing aspect of Civil War history." Booklist.

Includes bibliographical references (p. 97-103) and index.

Marrin, Albert

A **volcano** beneath the snow: John Brown's war against slavery. Albert Marrin. Alfred A. Knopf, 2014. 272 p.

Grades: 8 9 10 11 12   **973.7**

1. Brown, John, 1800-1859 2. Abolitionists 3. Anti-slavery movements -- History 19th century. 4. Harper's Ferry, West Virginia -- History -- John Brown's Raid, 1859
ISBN 9780307981523

LC 2012043231

A discussion-provoking assessment of the character and historical influence of the 19th-century radical abolitionist includes coverage of the fanatical religious beliefs that prompted his use of terrorism to combat slavery while assessing his role in the Harper's Ferry arsenal seizure that helped trigger the American Civil War. By the National Book Award finalist author of Flesh & Blood So Cheap.

"Chapters present the history of the 'peculiar institution' (slavery) both here and abroad, details of Brown's life and family, his relationship with the abolitionists, his radicalization leading to the killings at Pottawatomie, Kansas, and, eventually, the uprising at Harper's Ferry and his trial and hanging.... black-and-white illustrations include period photos, portraits, artwork, maps, fliers, and posters. Extensive notes and further-reading suggestions are included." School Library Journal.

Includes bibliographical references.

McNeese, Tim

Civil War battles. Tim McNeese. Chelsea House Publishers, c2009. 140 p.

Grades: 6 7 8 9   **973.7**

1. United States -- History -- Civil War, 1861-1865 -- Campaigns.
ISBN 9781604130348

LC 2008026561

Examines the key battles of the Civil War, describing the military maneuvers and mishaps in each battle and how they played pivotal roles for both the Union and the Confederacy.

O'Connor, Jim

What was the Battle of Gettysburg? by Jim O'Connor; illustrated by John Mantha. Grosset & Dunlap, 2013. 128 p.: What was--?

Grades: 3 4 5 6   **973.7**

1. Gettysburg, Battle of, 1863 2. Gettysburg Campaign, 1863 3. Civil war 4. United States Civil War, 1861-1865 5. United States -- History -- Civil War, 1861-1865 -- Campaigns 6. Pennsylvania -- History -- Civil War, 1861-1865

ISBN 9780448465753

         LC 2012027557

A new series presented in the same format and designed for the same audience as the phenomenally successful Who Was...? series offers compelling, easy-to-read accounts of historical events that changed our world and includes 16 pages of photos and reproductions as well as illustrations.

Osborne, Linda Barrett, 1949-

Traveling the freedom road: from slavery & the Civil War through Reconstruction. Linda Barrett Osborne; published in association with the Library of Congress. Abrams Books for Young Readers, 2009. 128 p.

Grades: 6 7 8 9 10   **973.7**

1. African Americans -- History 2. Enslaved people 3. Slavery -- History 19th century 4. Reconstruction (United States history) 5. U S states -- Politics and government 19th century 6. United States -- History -- Civil War, 1861-1865 -- African Americans 7. United States -- Politics and government -- 1783-1865

ISBN 9780810983380

         LC 2008022298

Presents a history of slavery in the United States, from the early establishment of the slave trade prior to the American Revolution, to the abolitionist movement, emancipation, and the upheavals of the Reconstructive period of the late nineteenth century.

"This fascinating, well-designed volume offers an essential introduction to the experiences of African Americans between 1800 and 1877. . . . Osborne moves from . . . personal stories to broader historical milestones, and in highly accessible language, she provides basic background even as she challenges readers with philosophical questions. . . . This fluid exchange between political events and intimate, human stories creates a highly absorbing whole." Booklist.

Includes bibliographical references (p. 120-122) and index.

Otfinoski, Steven

The **Civil** War. by Steven Otfinoski. Children's Press, an imprint of Scholastic Inc., 2017. 144 p.: Step into history (Scholastic)

Grades: 6 7 8 9   **973.7**

1. 1860s 2. Civil war 3. United States Civil War, 1861-1865 4. United States -- History -- Civil War, 1861-1865.

ISBN 9780531225691

         LC 2016031160

This book details major events of the U.S. Civil War, as well as the war's cultural impact. Provided by publisher.

"Maps, a list of the Union and Confederate states, and useful back matter make this well-designed and thorough historical account one that kids will actually enjoy reading." Booklist.

Includes bibliographical references and index.

Raatma, Lucia

The **Underground** Railroad. Lucia Raatma. Scholastic Library Pub., 2011. 64 p. : Cornerstones of freedom.

Grades: 4 5 6   **973.7**

1. Underground railroad 2. Freedom seekers 3. Slavery -- History 4. Enslaved people 5. African Americans -- History 6. United States -- History -- 19th century

ISBN 9780531250433

Describes life under slavery, highlighting the Underground Railroad and the antislavery movement as a whole.

Rees, Bob

The **Civil** War. Bob Rees. Heinemann Library, c2012. 80 p.: Living through

Grades: 6 7 8 9   **973.7**

1. 1860s 2. Civil war 3. Battles 4. War 5. United States Civil War, 1861-1865 6. United States -- History -- Civil War, 1861-1865

ISBN 9781432959968

         LC 2011018258

Explores the history of the Civil War, including the important players, battles, and consequences.

Reis, Ronald A.

African Americans and the Civil War. by Ronald A. Reis and Tim McNeese. Chelsea House Publishers, 2009. 133 p.

Grades: 6 7 8 9   **973.7**

1. Civil war 2. African Americans -- History Civil War, 1861-1865. 3. African American soldiers -- History Civil War, 1861-1865. 4. Slavery 5. Racism 6. United States -- History -- Civil War, 1861-1865 -- African-Americans.

ISBN 9781604130386

The role African Americans played in the Civil War.

Rottman, Gordon L.

The **most** daring raid of the Civil War: the great locomotive chase. Gordon L. Rottman. Rosen Pub., 2011. 64 p.: Most daring raids in history

Grades: 7 8 9 10   **973.7**

1. Chattanooga Railroad Expedition, 1862 2. Civil war 3. Raids (Military science) 4. Military history 5. United States Civil War, 1861-1865 6. United States -- History -- Civil War, 1861-1865.

ISBN 9781448818709

         LC 2010030195

Describes the Union military raid of a locomotive, riding it from Georgia to Tennessee and destroying the railways as they traveled, and details what happened to the raiders and the impact the raid had on the Civil War.

"This book is packed with facts, covering the details of the action, the people involved, and the tools used, in engaging prose. The authors cite their sources thoroughly. . . . Diagrams, . . . and maps make the action easy to follow and provide visual context for the raids. . . . This . . . is sure to find a large readership." School Library Journal.

Includes bibliographical references (p. 62-63) and index.

Shepard, Ray

Now or never!: 54th Massachusetts Infantry's war to end slavery. Ray Shepard. Calkins Creek Books, 2017. 144 p.

Grades: 6 7 8 9 10 11 12   **973.7**

1. United States. Army. Massachusetts Infantry Regiment, 54th (1863-1865) 2. United States. Army -- Officers 3. African American soldiers 4. United States Civil War, 1861-1865 5. Union soldiers 6. Civil war 7. African Americans

ISBN 9781629793405

Here are the life stories of George E. Stephens and James Henry Gooding, African American soldiers who fought in the Massachusetts

54th Infantry, the famous black regiment of the Civil War, and who were also the first African American war correspondents to report from the battlefield.

"This is a powerful use of primary resources, one that illuminates the lives of its subjects but never gets in the way of their remarkable stories." Kirkus.

Wagner, Heather Lehr

Spies in the Civil War. Heather Lehr Wagner. Chelsea House Publishers, c2009. 112 p.

Grades: 10 11 12   **973.7**

1. Spies -- History 19th century 2. Spies 3. United States -- History -- Civil War, 1861-1865 -- Secret service. 4. United States -- History -- Civil War, 1861-1865 -- Underground movements.
ISBN 9781604130393

LC 2008026568

The stories of the men and women who served as spies in the Civil War offer a fascinating glimpse into the strong passions that divided a nation.

Walker, Sally M.

Deadly aim: the Civil War story of Michigan's Anishinaabe sharpshooters. Sally M. Walker. Henry Holt & Co 2019 304 p.

Grades: 6 7 8 9   **973.7**

1. American Civil War era (1861-1865) 2. Native American soldiers 3. Indians of North America 4. United States Civil War, 1861-1865 5. Civil war 6. Sharpshooters 7. United States -- History -- Civil War, 1861-1865 -- Native American participation.
ISBN 9781250125255

LC 2018038286

Sibert Award winner Sally M. Walker crafts an engaging, middle-grade nonfiction narrative of the American Indian soldiers who bravely fought in the Civil War. Provided by publisher.

"Students researching the role of Native Americans in the Civil War will find this a thoroughly researched, meticulously documented, and richly informative resource. " Kirkus.

Includes bibliographical references and index.

Warren, Andrea

Under siege!: three children at the Civil War battle for Vicksburg. by Andrea Warren. Melanie Kroupa Books, c2009. 176 p.

Grades: 7 8 9 10   **973.7**

1. 1860s 2. Children -- History 19th century 3. Civil war 4. Battles 5. Sieges 6. United States Civil War, 1861-1865 7. Vicksburg, Mississippi -- History -- Siege, 1863 8. United States -- History -- Civil War, 1861-1865 -- Children
ISBN 9780374312558

LC 2008001136

Period photographs, engravings, and maps extend the dramatic story of the siege of Vicksburg in 1863—recreating one of the most important Civil War battles through the eyes of ordinary townspeople, officers and enlisted men from both sides, and above all, three brave children who were there.

"Warren creates a compelling account of the 1863 siege at Vicksburg that follows three young people from December 1862 through the aftermath of the surrender on July 4, 1863. . . . The author uses primary sources throughout, including scores of quotes, many attributed to the children themselves, period photographs, maps, and paintings. . . . The back matter is extensive, including an annotated list of recommended Civil War books, a longer bibliography of sources, and extensive endnotes and illustration credits." Voice of Youth Advocates.

Includes bibliographical references and index.

Williams, Carla, 1965-

The **Underground** Railroad. Carla Williams. Child's World, 2009. 32 p.

Grades: 4 5 6   **973.7**

1. Freedom seekers 2. Underground Railroad 3. United States -- History -- 19th century
ISBN 9781602531390

LC 2008031946

Describes the Underground Railroad, where escaped slaves traveled in secret from the South to the North of the United States in the nineteenth century in order to gain their freedom.

"Underground Railroad describes how this secret system worked and introduces key figures. Williams discusses relevant laws and amendments as well as the advent and conclusion of the Civil War. The facts, presented through stories, historical news accounts, and biographical sketches of Harriet Tubman and Levi Weeks, capture the desperation of the enslaved as well as the abolitionists commitment to them. The [book is] concise and direct, yet the writing remains sophisticated. Vibrant personal stories accompanied by striking photographs of historical figures and artifacts provide a sense of the subjects hopes and dreams." School Library Journal.

Includes bibliographical references and index.

973.7092 United States—1861-1865—Biography

Freedman, Russell

★ **Abraham** Lincoln and Frederick Douglass: the story behind an American friendship. by Russell Freedman. Houghton Mifflin Harcourt, 2012. 119 p.

Grades: 4 5 6 7 8   **973.7092**

1. Lincoln, Abraham, 1809-1865 2. Douglass, Frederick, 1818-1895 3. Presidents 4. African American abolitionists 5. Friendship
ISBN 9780547385624

LC 2011025953

Recounts Abraham Lincoln's brief friendship with African-American leader Frederick Douglass before and during the Civil War, narrated against the backdrop of the race relations and politics of the time. Includes 70 archival photographs.

Jurmain, Suzanne

Murder on the Baltimore Express: the plot to keep Abraham Lincoln from becoming president. Suzanne Jurmain. Yellow Jacket, 2021. 240 p.

Grades: 4 5 6 7   **973.7092**

1. Lincoln, Abraham, 1809-1865 2. Pinkerton, Allan, 1819-1884. 3. Pinkerton's National Detective Agency 4. 1860s 5. Presidents -- Attempted assassination 6. Proslavery movements 7. Assassination plots 8. Conspiracies 9. Political crimes and offenses 10. United States -- History -- Civil War, 1861-1865 11. Baltimore, Maryland -- History -- 19th century
ISBN 9781499810448

LC 2020047219

A chapter-book account of the assassination plot against a newly elected 16th President describes the activities of pro-slave organization Knights of the Golden Circle and the role of Allen Pinkerton detectives in securing Lincoln's safety.

"Basing her narrative on numerous primary sources, Jurmain's nonfiction thriller resonates by touching upon contemporary concerns, particularly deep-seated political prejudice and racial division." Publishers Weekly

Includes bibliographical references and index.

Sheinkin, Steve

Lincoln's grave robbers. Steve Sheinkin. Scholastic, 2018, c2013 224 p.

Grades: 5 6 7 8   **973.7092**

1. Lincoln, Abraham, 1809-1865 2. 19th century 3. 1870s 4. Grave robbing 5. Counterfeits and counterfeiting 6. Ransom 7. Criminals 8. Undercover operations

ISBN 9780545405720

A dramatic account of the 1875 attempt to steal the 16th president's body describes how a counterfeiting ring plotted to ransom Lincoln's body to secure the release of their imprisoned ringleader and how a fledgling Secret Service and an undercover agent conducted a daring election-night sting operation.

Swanson, James L., 1959-

Bloody times: the funeral of Abraham Lincoln and the manhunt for Jefferson Davis. James L. Swanson. HarperCollins Children's Books, 2010. 196 p.

Grades: 6 7 8 9   **973.7092**

1. Lincoln, Abraham, 1809-1865 2. Davis, Jefferson, 1808-1889 3. Presidents 4. Civil war 5. United States Civil War, 1861-1865 6. United States -- History -- Civil War, 1861-1865 -- Peace.

ISBN 9780061560897

LC 2010045611

Based on the author's adult title, Bloody Crimes, a teen adaption brings to light the end of the Civil War, which includes President Lincoln's assassination and funeral, and the manhunt for Confederate President Jefferson Davis.

"This tells the story of Lincoln's assassination, detailing the funeral and the return of the body for burial in Springfield, IL. Juxtaposed with this compelling drama is that of Jefferson Davis, president of the Confederate States of America, as he learned of Lee's surrender and traveled across the South trying to keep the Confederacy alive while being pursued by Federal forces bent on his arrest. . . . Lincoln's body was placed aboard a train that retraced the route taken by Lincoln as he traveled to the capital as president-elect. Readers will be fascinated by the details needed to plan this trip and the people involved. . . . Just as riveting is Davis's fruitless effort to avoid arrest. . . . A brilliant book that is sure to be hit with history aficionados." School Library Journal.

Zeller, Bob, 1952-

Lincoln in 3-D. By Bob Zeller and John Richter. Chronicle Books, c2010. 223 p.

Grades: 6 7 8 9   **973.7092**

1. Lincoln, Abraham, 1809-1865 2. Photography, Stereoscopic

ISBN 9780811872317

LC 2010013792

Offers text and three-dimensional photographs of Abraham Lincoln and the Civil War, covering such topics as Lincoln's path to presidency, factors leading to the war, key battles, and the war's aftermath.

"This visually striking volume is built around 185 stereoscopic photographs from the Civil War era. Glasses included in the back give the full three-dimensional effect. . . . The introduction offers fascinating background on stereoscopic pictures, followed by a narrative text tracing Lincoln's life and the stages of the war. All of the photos include informative captions that give context even for images not mentioned in the text. . . . The striking images make this a powerful visual depiction of Lincoln and his times." School Library Journal.

Includes bibliographical references.

973.8 United States—Reconstruction period, 1865-1901

Hillstrom, Kevin, 1963-

American Indian removal and the trail to Wounded Knee. Kevin Hillstrom and Laurie Collier Hillstrom. Omnigraphics, c2010. xvi, 250 p.

Grades: 8 9 10 11 12   **973.8**

1. Indians of North America -- Relocation 2. Indians of North America -- Government relations -- History 19th century 3. Indians, Treatment of -- History 19th century 4. Wounded Knee Massacre, SD, 1890

ISBN 9780780811294

LC 2010004676

Analyzes the development of Indian removal policies and the tragedy at Wounded Knee, the 1890 massacre of American Indians by U.S. Cavalry troops. Examines the wider context of Indian-white relations in America. Features include a narrative overview, biographies, primary sources, chronology, glossary, bibliography, and index. Provided by publisher.

"This well-written volume effectively explores a topic of intense historical debate. Fascinating sidebars add significantly to the text." School Library Journal.

Includes bibliographical references and index.

Ruggiero, Adriane

Reconstruction. Adriane Ruggiero. Marshall Cavendish Benchmark, c2007. 103 p.: American voices from--

Grades: 6 7 8 9 10 11 12   **973.8**

1. Reconstruction (United States history) 2. United States -- History -- 1865-1898 3. United States -- History -- 1865-1921

ISBN 0761421688

LC 2005024949

Presents the history of the era of Reconstruction, 1865-1877, through a variety of primary source documents, such as diary entries, newspaper accounts, political speeches, laws, popular songs, and personal letters. Provided by publisher.

"This does an excellent job of bringing history close. . . . The spacious design . . . is very approachable, and the combination of voices and commentary will readers think critically." Booklist.

Includes bibliographical references and index.

Telgen, Diane

The **Gilded** Age. Diane Telgen. Omnigraphics, c2012. xvi, 252 p.: Defining moments (Omnigraphics)

Grades: 7 8 9 10 11 12   **973.8**

1. United States -- History -- 1865-1898 2. United States -- History -- 19th century

ISBN 9780780812383

LC 2011048642

Provides a comprehensive overview of the political and economic forces that transformed the United States during the nineteenth century from a farming society to an urban, industrial one dominated by powerful industrialists and their vast corporate empires. Includes a narrative overview, biographies, primary sources, chronology, glossary, bibliography, and index. Provided by publisher.

Walker, Paul Robert

Remember Little Bighorn: Indians, soldiers, and scouts tell their stories. written by Paul Robert Walker; foreword by John A. Doerner. National Geographic Society, 2006. 61 p.

Grades: 5 6 7 8   **973.8**

1. Little Big Horn, Battle of the, 1876 2. Cheyenne Indians -- Wars,

1876 3. Dakota Indians -- Wars, 1876 4. Indians of North America 5. War -- Moral and ethical aspects
ISBN 0792255216

LC 2005030929

"This volume gives an almost blow-by-blow account of the famous battle that came to be known as Custer's Last Stand. Walker concentrates on the battle itself, fought on the Great Plains in 1876, and the book includes diagrams of each side's tactics. . . . Walker's exhaustive research . . . [brings] together the conflicting viewpoints of the whites and the Lakota Sioux, Cheyenne, and Arapaho fighters, documenting everything in source notes. The handsome book design, with thick paper, clear type, maps, stirring photos, and archival images, will attract readers to the battle story and then start them thinking about lasting historical issues." Booklist.

Includes bibliographical references (p. 60) and index.

973.91 United States—1901-1953

Sandler, Martin W.
1919: the year that changed America. by Martin W. Sandler. Bloomsbury Children's Books, 2019. 192 p.

Grades: 7 8 9 10 11 12 **973.91**
1. 1910s 2. 20th century 3. Social movements 4. Social history 5. Social change 6. Prohibition 7. Women -- suffrage 8. United States
ISBN 9781681198019

LC 2018012754

National Book Award for Young People's Literature, 2019.

1919 was a world-shaking year. America was recovering from World War I and black soldiers returned to racism so violent that that summer would become known as the Red Summer. The suffrage movement had a long-fought win when women gained the right to vote. Laborers took to the streets to protest working conditions; nationalistic fervor led to a communism scare; and temperance gained such traction that prohibition went into effect. Each of these movements reached a tipping point that year.

"Even so, Sandler's narrative skill and eye for detail, and the abundant archival photos throughout, make for an engrossing resource." Publishers Weekly.

Includes bibliographical references and index.

973.917 Administration of Franklin Delano Roosevelt, 1933-1945

Bolden, Tonya
FDR's Alphabet soup: New Deal America, 1932-1939. Tonya Bolden. Alfred A. Knopf, c2010. 144 p.

Grades: 5 6 7 8 **973.917**
1. 1940s 2. 1930s 3. New Deal, 1933-1939 4. Depressions 1929-1941 5. Economic policy 1933-1945 6. United States -- Economic conditions -- 1918-1945 7. United States -- Politics and government -- 1933-1945
ISBN 9780375952142

LC 2009028727

Counsels students on how to better understand present-day economic dilemmas against a backdrop of the Great Depression and the 32nd president's famous "First 100 Days," evaluating key reforms in such areas as labor, finance and the arts.

"Retracing the course of New Deal intiatives from the newly elected Roosevelt's famous First Hundred Days of action! action! action! to

his creation of the powerful Executive Office of the President in 1939, [Bolden] presents a coherent account of how FDR and his adminstration successfully (mostly) battled political, ideological, and legal challenges to create a sweeping recovery agenda. . . . Generally illustrated with period photos . . . this lively look back both invites and equips readers to ponder the pros and cons of gumptious government in any era." Booklist.

Includes bibliographical references and index.

Nardo, Don, 1947-
Migrant mother: how a photograph defined the Great Depression. by Don Nardo. Compass Point Books, c2011. 64 p. : Captured history

Grades: 6 7 8 9 **973.917**
1. Lange, Dorothea, 1895-1965. 2. Depressions 1929-1941 3. Migrant workers 4. Photographs 5. Photography -- Influence 6. United States -- History -- 1919-1933 7. United States -- History -- 1933-1945
ISBN 9780756543976

LC 2010038578

Explores and analyzes the historical context and significance of the iconic Dorothea Lange photograph. Provided by publisher.

"This describes the significance of the iconic Dorothea Lange photograph of a migrant mother during the Great Depression and places it in historical context, profiles the photographer, describes the conditions under which it was taken, and analyzes both its immediate and continuing impact. The [text includes] ample background information and details and [is] enhanced by large photos and sidebars." School Library Journal.

Includes bibliographical references and index.

Sandler, Martin W.
★ The **Dust** Bowl through the lens: how photography revealed and helped remedy a national disaster. Martin W. Sandler. Walker & Co., 2009. 96 p.

Grades: 5 6 7 8 **973.917**
1. Dust Bowl Era, 1931-1939 2. Droughts 3. Documentary photography -- History 20th century. 4. Photography 5. Farmers -- History 20th century. 6. Dust Bowl (South Central United States) 7. Great Plains (United States) -- History -- 20th century
ISBN 9780802795472

LC 2008055979

"This excellent photo-essay traces the history of the Dust Bowl from its causes to its resolution. In tandem, Sandler treats the role of the budding field of photojournalism. Forty-four spreads feature a page of clear, direct text with a large, well-reproduced image, many of which are set on color pages. . . . Seldom has the connection between the arts and the general quality of life been made so clear. The text deals equally with those who fled the decimated Bread Basket for California and those who waited out the devastation and dust. Throughout, the use of primary sources is superb, with quotations from affected citizens, the photojournalists themselves, political and entertainment figures, and writers, giving a multifaceted picture of a seminal time in United States history." School Library Journal.

973.921 Administration of Dwight David Eisenhower, 1953-1961

Fitzgerald, Brian, 1972-
McCarthyism: the Red Scare. by Brian Fitzgerald. Compass Point Books, c2007. 96 p.: Snapshots in history

Grades: 7 8 9 10   **973.921**
1. McCarthy, Joseph, 1908-1957 2. United States. Congress. Senate 3. Anti-communist movements -- History 20th century 4. Legislators 5. Cold War 6. Anti-communist movements -- History 20th century 7. Legislators
ISBN 075652007X

     LC 2006003005

Discusses the "Red Scare" of the 1950s, in which Senator Joseph McCarthy led investigations for communist spies, adding to the hysteria in the United States created by Soviet nuclear testing and the expansion of Soviet influence.

"This vividly portrays the fear of Communism in the U.S., beginning after the Russian Revolution. This book shows, in clear language, how McCarthy spread paranoia throughout the country and ruined many lives and careers." School Library Journal.

Includes bibliographical references (p. 91-93) and index.

973.922092 United States—1961-1963—Biography

Nardo, Don, 1947-

Assassination and its aftermath: how a photograph reassured a shocked nation. by Don Nardo; content adviser: Shelia Blackford, managing editor, American President, Miller Center, University of Virginia. Compass Point Books, a Capstone imprint, [2014] 64 p.: Captured history
Grades: 6 7 8 9   **973.922092**
1. Kennedy, John F. (John Fitzgerald), 1917-1963 2. Johnson, Lyndon B., 1908-1973 3. Stoughton, Cecil 4. Presidents -- Succession -- History 20th century 5. Assassination 6. Photojournalists
ISBN 9780756546922

     LC 2012051716

Analyzes the historical context and significance of the photograph of Jacqueline Kennedy standing beside Lyndon Johnson as he took the presidential oath of office just hours after John Kennedy's assassination in 1963.

O'Reilly, Bill

Kennedy's last days: the assassination that defined a generation. Bill O'Reilly. Henry Holt and Company, 2013. 336 p.
Grades: 6 7 8 9   **973.922092**
1. Kennedy, John F. (John Fitzgerald), 1917-1963 2. 1960s 3. Presidents -- Assassination 4. Assassination 5. Modern history
ISBN 9780805098020

     LC 2013009026

A historical narrative of the events surrounding the death of the 35th president is set against the backdrop of an escalating Cold War and describes the many political challenges Kennedy was facing before his assassination, in an account that also describes Lee Harvey Oswald's story and the events surrounding his death.

Swanson, James L., 1959-

"The president has been shot!": the assassination of President John F. Kennedy. by James L. Swanson. Scholastic, 2013. 336 p.
Grades: 6 7 8 9 10 11 12   **973.922092**
1. Kennedy, John F. (John Fitzgerald), 1917-1963 2. 1960s 3. Presidents -- Assassination 4. Assassination 5. Modern history
ISBN 9780545490078

     LC 2012041167

Recounts the 35th president's assassination and details key events while sharing informative back matter and archival photographs.

"Swanson's clear, concisely written, and riveting narrative highlights the key events of the Kennedy administration before focusing on the moment-by-moment details of JFK's assassination. Also included are an exploration of Lee Harvey Oswald's background, an aerial-view photograph of Dealey Plaza in Dallas, a detailed map of the motorcade route, and images of the Texas School Book Depository, where Oswald perched, rifle in hand." Horn Book.

Includes bibliographical references and index.

973.923 Administration of Lyndon Baines Johnson, 1963-1969

Lindop, Edmund

America in the 1960s. Edmund Lindop; with Margaret J. Goldstein. Twenty-First Century Books, c2010. 144 p.: The decades of twentieth-century America
Grades: 7 8 9 10   **973.923**
1. 1960s 2. United States -- History -- 1960-1969
ISBN 9780761334538

     LC 2007038028

"The text is enlivened with quotes and excerpts from primary sources, period photos, and two sets of sidebars. Profiles provides biographical sketches of important people and Turning Points explains the significance of important events. . . . A solid choice for readers and researchers." School Library Journal.

Includes bibliographical references (p. 135-140) and index.

973.924 Administration of Richard Milhous Nixon, 1969-1974

Pearson, P. O'Connell (Patricia O'Connell)

Conspiracy: Nixon, Watergate, and democracy's defenders. P. O'Connell Pearson. Simon & Schuster 2020 176 p.
Grades: 5 6 7 8   **973.924**
1. Nixon, Richard M. (Richard Milhous), 1913-1994 2. 1970s 3. Watergate Scandal 4. Scandals 5. Political corruption 6. Government cover-ups 7. Abuse of administrative power 8. United States -- Politics and government -- 1969-1974
ISBN 9781534480032

     LC 2020010059

An exploration of President Nixon's contentious time in office, the Watergate scandal, and the people who helped protect our Constitution. Provided by publisher.

"This is a multi-tentacled beast of a story, but Pearson skillfully tames it for middle grade accessibility—paring down the list of named players in the drama, using bracketed in-text definitions of legal terms to keep vocabulary under control, providing themed dramatis personae lists, and maintaining effective pacing via short sentences and fragments." Bulletin of the Center for Children's Books

Includes bibliographical references and index.

973.93 United States—2001-

Corrigan, Jim

The **2000s** decade in photos: a new millennium. by Jim Corrigan. Enslow Publishers, 2009. 64 p.: Amazing decades in photos

Grades: 4 5 6 7   **973.93**
1. 21st century 2. United States -- History -- 21st century 3. United States -- Social conditions -- 21st century
ISBN 9780766031395

       LC 2008054644

Middle school readers will find out about the important world, national, and cultural developments of the first decade of the new millennium. Provided by publisher.

Sutherland, James, 1974-

The **ten-year** century: explaining the first decade of the new millennium. by James Sutherland. Penguin Group, c2010. 151 p.

Grades: 7 8 9 10   **973.93**
1. Modern history 21st century. 2. War 3. United States -- History -- 21st century. 4. United States -- Politics and government -- 2001-2009 5. Essays
ISBN 9780670012237

       LC 2010007314

"This overview of the first 10 years of the new millennium focuses on significant developments that have shaped life in the United States today.... The lucid, balanced narration results in a nuanced representation of a rapidly changing era." Publishers Weekly.

Includes bibliographical references and index.

973.931 Administration of George W. Bush, 2001-2009

Brown, Don, 1949-

In the shadow of the fallen towers: the seconds, minutes, hours, days, weeks, months, and years after the 911 attacks. Don Brown Etch/HMH Books for Young Readers, 2021. 128 p.

Grades: 7 8 9 10 11 12   **973.931**
1. World Trade Center, New York City. 2. Pentagon (Va.) 3. 21st century 4. September 11 Terrorist Attacks, 2001 5. Victims of terrorism 6. Search and rescue operations 7. Terrorism 8. War on Terrorism, 2001-2009 9. New York City 10. Arlington, Virginia 11. Comics and Graphic novels
ISBN 9780358223573

This graphic novel chronicles the immediate aftermath of the terrorist attack on the World Trade Center in New York City through moving individual stories that bear witness to our history and the ways it shapes our future.

"A succinct and impactful look at one of America's worst tragedies, skillfully rendered by one of comics journalism's best." School Library Journal

Hillstrom, Kevin, 1963-

The **September** 11 terrorist attacks. Kevin Hillstrom. Omnigraphics, c2012. xv, 268 p.

Grades: 8 9 10 11 12   **973.931**
1. Qaida (Organization) 2. September 11 Terrorist Attacks, 2001 3. Terrorism
ISBN 9780780812406

       LC 2011050673

Provides a comprehensive account of the origins of Islamic radicalism; the development of Osama bin Laden and al-Qaeda into a deadly force; the horrible events of September 11; the post-9/11 investigations; and the legacy of the 9/11 attacks. Includes anarrative overview, biographies, primary sources, chronology, glossary, bibliography, and index. Provided by publisher.

Murray, Laura K., 1989-

The **911** attacks. by Laura K. Murray. Creative Education, Creative Paperbacks, [2017] 48 p.: Turning points (Creative Education)

Grades: 5 6 7 8   **973.931**
1. September 11 Terrorist Attacks, 2001 2. Terrorism 3. War on Terrorism, 2001-2009
ISBN 9781608187508

       LC 2016002146

A historical account of the 9/11 terrorist attacks, including the events leading up to that day, the people involved, the monumental rescue and recovery efforts, and the lingering aftermath. Provided by publisher.

"This highly readable and balanced account places events in a global context while handling the tragedy with respect." Booklist.

Includes bibliographical references (pages 46-47) and index.

Wachtel, Alan

September 11: a primary source history. Alan Wachtel. Gareth Stevens Pub., 2009. 48 p.: In their own words (Gareth Stevens)

Grades: 5 6 7 8   **973.931**
1. World Trade Center, New York City. 2. September 11 Terrorist Attacks, 2001 3. Terrorism 4. War on Terrorism, 2001-2009 5. Victims of terrorism 6. New York City -- History -- 21st century. 7. United States -- History -- 21st century.
ISBN 9781433900488

       LC 2008045132

"The horror of September 11 feels very immediate, and uses both quotes from those who lived through it and stills from the attacks. The book does a fine job of chronicling the events, up to and including the controversies surrounding the New York memorial. The use of transcripts of phone conversations that took place aboard the doomed planes gives the book's beginning an almost you-are-there effect. Later chapters feature such diverse sources as text from the Patriot Act and lyrics from Neil Young's song Let's Roll to amplify the mood of the country." Booklist.

Includes bibliographical references and index.

973.932 Administration of Barack Obama, 2009-2017

Dillon, Molly

Yes she can: 10 stories of hope & change from young female staffers of the Obama White House. compiled by Molly Dillon. Schwartz & Wade Books, [2019] 272 p.

Grades: 8 9 10 11 12   **973.932**
1. Obama, Barack. 2. Presidents -- Staff 3. Young women 4. Women -- Political activity 5. United States -- Politics and government -- 2009-2017. 6. Essays 7. Anthologies
ISBN 9781984848451

       LC 2018053010

An anthology for young women by young women, featuring stories from ten inspiring young staffers who joined the Obama administration in their 20s with the hope of making a difference. Provided by publisher.

Moss, Caroline, 1987-

★ **Become** a leader like Michelle Obama. written by Caroline Moss; illustrated by Sinem Erkas. Frances Lincoln Children's Books, 2020. 56 p.: Work it, girl

Grades: 4 5 6 7   **973.932**
1. Obama, Michelle, 1964- 2. Leadership 3. Presidents' spouses

4. Women world leaders
ISBN 9780711245181

A new series of empowering biographies featuring modern women in the world of work. Michelle Obama grew up on the South Side of Chicago in a little bungalow with a close-knit family. She loved going to school, and she knew that, one day, she would use her voice to empower other young girls, just like her. Discover how Michelle became an inspirational leader, FLOTUS, lawyer and role model in this true story of her life. Then, learn 10 key lessons from her work you can apply to your own life. Featuring inspiring quotes and mantras, this is a book for all kids wanting to forge their own career path.

"[T]he design, with its cut-paper illustrations and highlighted quotes, is excellent and engrossing. Life lessons, essay questions, and extensive further reading round out the detailed text." Booklist

Includes bibliographical references.

974 Northeastern United States (New England and Middle Atlantic states)

Johnson, Claudia Durst, 1938-

Daily life in colonial New England. Claudia Durst Johnson. Greenwood Press, 2002. xxvii, 215 p.: Daily life through history
Grades: 7 8 9 10   **974**
   1. New England -- History -- Colonial period, 1600-1775 2. New England -- Social life and customs -- 1600-1775
ISBN 0313314586

               LC 00061721

"In this excellent volume, Johnson draws a remarkably clear and complete picture of the day-to-day existence of the first European settlers in New England." Voice of Youth Advocates.

Includes bibliographical references and index.

Rylant, Cynthia

Appalachia: the voices of sleeping birds. by Cynthia Rylant; illustrated by Barry Moser. Harcourt Brace Jovanovich, 1991. 21 p.
Grades: 4 5 6 7   **974**
   1. Rural life 2. Small town life 3. Appalachian Region -- Description and travel. 4. Appalachian Region, Southern -- Social life and customs.
ISBN 0152016058

               LC 90036798

Text and illustrations explore the countryside and people of Appalachia.

"Taking her subtitle from a passage by James Agee, the author conveys with a marvelous economy of words the essence of the very special part of America where she was raised. A poetic text projects emotion as well as information. . . . Moser's watercolors capture the scene perfectly. . . . The book is a treasure—simply a beautiful combination of text and art." Horn Book.

974.1 Maine

Heinrichs, Ann

Maine. by Ann Heinrichs. Children's Press, 2014. 144 p. : America the beautiful
Grades: 4 5 6 7   **974.1**
   1. US states 2. Maine 3. United States
ISBN 9780531248874

               LC 2007000302

Describes the history, geography, ecology, people, economy, cities, and sights of the state of Maine.

974.2 New Hampshire

Kent, Deborah

New Hampshire. Deborah Kent. Children's Press, 2009. 144 p. : America the beautiful
Grades: 4 5 6 7   **974.2**
   1. US states 2. Geography 3. New Hampshire 4. United States
ISBN 9780531185018

               LC 2008048940

Takes readers on a tour of New Hampshire, describing the state's history, culture, land, economy, government, and sights, and including unique facts, color maps and photos, the state song, suggested activities, lists of famous people, cultural institutions, and annual events, and other resources.

974.4 Massachusetts

Messner, Kate

The **Mayflower**. Kate Messner; illustrated by Dylan Meconis. Random House Children's Books, 2020. 224 p.
Grades: 4 5 6 7   **974.4**
   1. Mayflower (Ship) 2. 17th century 3. Pilgrims (New England settlers) 4. Voyages and travels 5. Colonies 6. Puritans 7. Wampanoag Indians 8. Massachusetts -- History -- New Plymouth, 1620-1691 9. Illustrated books
ISBN 9780593120323

Through illustrations, graphic panels, photographs, sidebars, and more, acclaimed author Kate Messner smashes history by exploring the little-known details behind the legends of the Mayflower and the first Thanksgiving.

Trueit, Trudi Strain

Massachusetts. Trudi Strain Trueit. Children's Press, 2014 144 p.: America the Beautiful. Third Series
Grades: 4 5 6 7   **974.4**
   1. US states 2. Massachusetts 3. United States
ISBN 9780531248898

Describes the history, geography, ecology, people, economy, cities, and sights of the Bay State, Massachusetts.

974.6 Connecticut

Kent, Zachary

Connecticut. by Zachary Kent. Children's Press, c2014. 144 p. : America the beautiful
Grades: 4 5 6 7   **974.6**
   1. US states 2. Connecticut 3. United States
ISBN 9780531248799

               LC 2007002328

Describes the history, geography, ecology, people, economy, cities, and sights of the state of Connecticut.

974.7 New York

Bolden, Tonya
★ **Maritcha**: a nineteenth-century American girl. Tonya Bolden. Harry N. Abrams, 2005. 47 p.

Grades: 4 5 6 7 8   **974.7**

    1. Lyons, Maritcha Remond, 1848-1929. 2. 19th century 3. African American girls 4. Free African Americans 5. African Americans -- Social conditions 19th century. 6. African Americans -- Social life and customs 19th century. 7. Race relations 19th century. 8. New York (State) -- Social life and customs -- 19th century. 9. New York (State) -- Social conditions -- 19th century.

    ISBN 0810950456

The story of Maritcha Raemond Lyons, born and raised in New York City, tells what it was like to be a black child born free during the days of slavery, and her fight to attend a whites-only high school in Providence, Rhode Island.

"The high quality of writing and the excellent documentation make this a first choice for all collections." School Library Journal.

Includes bibliographical references (p. 46).

Huey, Lois Miner
American archeology uncovers the Dutch colonies. Lois Miner Huey. Marshall Cavendish Corp., 2009. 64 p.: American archaeology

Grades: 4 5 6 7   **974.7**

    1. Archaeology and history 2. Dutch in North America -- History 3. Archaeology 4. Netherlands -- Colonies 5. New Netherland -- History.

    ISBN 9780761442639

"The text is quite chatty in this attractive title. . . . An inviting design with clear type includes several paintings of the period by a modern artist as well as maps and photos of excavation sites." Booklist.

Marrin, Albert
★ **Flesh** & blood so cheap: the Triangle fire and its legacy. Albert Marrin. Alfred A. Knopf, c2011. 192 p.

Grades: 5 6 7 8   **974.7**

    1. Triangle Shirtwaist Company, Inc., New York City -- Fire, 1911 2. 1910s 3. Sweatshops -- History 4. Industrial accidents 5. Factories -- History 6. Labor laws and legislation 7. Occupational health and safety -- History 20th century 8. New York City -- History -- 1898-1951

    ISBN 9780375868894

          LC 2010021533

Describes the conditions in the textile industry in the early twentieth century behind the fire at the Triangle Shirtwaist Company that led to the death of many young women, and explains its impact on the labor movement and on society.

"Published to coincide with the centennial anniversary of the 1911 fire that erupted in the Triangle Shirtwaist Factory, this powerful chronicle examines the circumstances surrounding the disaster, which resulted in the deaths of 146 workers, mostly young Italian and Jewish women. . . . B&W photographs and illustrations reveal immigrant families' impoverished living environments, while testimonials describe the humiliating work rules and unsafe conditions of factories like Triangle. . . . A concluding description of a Bangladeshi garment factory fire in 2010 offers contemporary parallels. Marrin's message that protecting human dignity is our shared responsibility is vitally resonant." Publishers Weekly.

Includes bibliographical references.

Marsico, Katie, 1980-
The **Triangle** Shirtwaist Factory fire: its legacy of labor rights. Katie Marsico. Marshall Cavendish Benchmark, c2010. 112 p.

Grades: 7 8 9 10   **974.7**

    1. Triangle Shirtwaist Company -- Fire, 1911 2. Clothing factories -- Safety measures -- History 20th century 3. Fires -- History 20th century 4. Labor laws and legislation -- History 20th century 5. New York City -- History -- 1898-1951

    ISBN 9780761440277

          LC 2008023267

Provides comprehensive information on industry and immigration, the Triangle Shirtwaist Factory Fire, its aftermath, and labor rights. Provided by publisher.

"This well-written title examines many of the details preceding the 1911 disaster, the conditions that caused it, and the impact the incident continues to have on labor and businesses today. Historical accounts of the event, told through numerous direct quotes and shown in black-and-white photos of sweatshops and descriptions of tenement living conditions, reveal that poor labor laws and factory regulations were to blame. . . . Color photos and full-page sidebars provide additional information." School Library Journal.

Includes bibliographical references (p. 104-106) and index.

Somervill, Barbara A.
New York. by Barbara A. Somervill. Children's Press, c2014. 144 p. : America the beautiful

Grades: 4 5 6 7   **974.7**

    1. US states 2. New York (State)

    ISBN 9780531248959

          LC 2006101742

Describes the geography, plants, animals, history, economy, religions, culture, sports, arts, and people of New York.

974.8 Pennsylvania

Koestler-Grack, Rachel A., 1973-
Johnstown flood of 1889. Rachel A. Koestler-Grack. Chelsea House, 2008. 101 p. : Great historic disasters

Grades: 6 7 8 9   **974.8**

    1. 19th century 2. 1880s 3. Floods 4. Natural disasters 5. Dam failures 6. Johnstown, Pennsylvania Flood, 1889 7. Pennsylvania -- History -- 19th century.

    ISBN 9780791097632

          LC 2008004894

Each book in this series begins with historical context to depict life in the time and place of the featured event, builds to a vivid description of the disaster, discusses the aftermath, and then analyzes the way the disaster changed history and impacted the future.

"Combining first-hand accounts, photographs, and other primary sources with a detailed and lively text, [this] fact-packed [resource offers] much to both report writers and history buffs." Horn Book Guide.

Includes bibliographical references and index.

Walker, Sally M.
Boundaries: how the Mason-Dixon line settled a family feud & divided a nation. Sally M. Walker. Candlewick Press, 2014. 202 p.

Grades: 7 8 9 10 11 12   **974.8**

    1. Mason, Charles, 1728-1786 2. Dixon, Jeremiah, 1733-1779 3. Surveying -- History 18th century 4. Family feuds 5. Mason-

Dixon Line 6. Pennsylvania -- Boundaries -- Maryland
ISBN 9780763656126

Traces the history of the Mason-Dixon Line as reflected by family feuds, exploration, scientific advancement and the cultural conflicts between America's northern and southern states.

"This thoroughly researched account of the Mason-Dixon Line encompasses a broad span of time and place, from sixteenth-century England to twentieth-century America... Walker's latest book offers a good deal of pertinent information on the subject at hand, as well as some interesting sidelights on American history." Booklist.

974.9 New Jersey

Doak, Robin S. (Robin Santos), 1963-
New Jersey, 1609-1776. Robin Doak with Brendan McConville. National Geographic, c2005. 108 p.: Voices from colonial America
Grades: 5 6 7 8   **974.9**
1. Revolutions 2. American Revolution, 1775-1783 3. New Jersey -- History -- Colonial period, 1600-1775. 4. New Jersey -- History -- Revolution, 1775-1783.
ISBN 0792266803

LC 2004026242

Provides a history of the state, discussing the attempts by the Dutch and the Swedes to settle there, the colonization by the British, relations with the Lenni-Lanape tribe, and the use of indentured servants and slaves in the colony. Eye-catching graphics and engaging narrative create a compelling picture of life in colonial New Jersey. Originally settled by the Dutch as part of their "New Netherland," New Jersey did not flourish as a colony until it came under British control in 1664. Readers will learn how the promise of political and religious freedom led to its becoming the first Quaker colony in America and one of the most ethnically diverse. They'll learn how for a while it was divided into East and West Jersey, how it had its own version of the Boston Tea Party, and how its location between New York City and Philadelphia made it the site of nearly 100 battles during the struggle for independence that eventually led to its becoming the nation's third state.

"This book gives detailed descriptions of family life and working in a Colonial village and the fight for independence. It also includes information about the Native people, early settlers, and first developments. . . . Paintings, maps, woodcuts, portraits, and reproductions accompany the well-written text. . . . An excellent resource." School Library Journal.

Includes bibliographical references (p. 105-106) and index.

Kent, Deborah
New Jersey. Deborah Kent. Children's Press, c2014. 144 p.: America the beautiful
Grades: 4 5 6 7   **974.9**
1. US states 2. New Jersey
ISBN 9780531248942

Describes the geography, plants, animals, history, economy, religions, culture, sports, arts, and people of the Garden State.

Moragne, Wendy
New Jersey. Wendy Moragne, Tamra B. Orr. Marshall Cavendish Corp., 2008. 144 p.: Celebrate the states
Grades: 4 5 6 7   **974.9**
1. Multiculturalism 2. US states 3. Culture 4. Religion 5. New Jersey
ISBN 9780761430063

Provides comprehensive information on the geography, history, wildlife, governmental structure, economy, cultural diversity, peoples, religion, and landmarks of New Jersey. Provided by publisher.

975.004 Southeastern United States—Ethnic and national groups

Vander Hook, Sue, 1949-
Trail of Tears. by Sue Vander Hook. ABDO Pub. Co., c2010. 112 p.: Essential events
Grades: 6 7 8 9   **975.004**
1. 19th century 2. Trail of Tears, 1838-1839 3. Cherokee Indians -- Relocation 4. Cherokee Indians -- History 5. Indians of North America -- History 6. United States -- History -- 19th century.
ISBN 9781604539462

LC 2009031066

Presents a brief history of the Cherokee Indians and describes their forced migration, which came to be known as the Trail of Tears, following the Indian Removal Act of 1830.

"The writing is accessible and is richer than a lot of history writing, allowing the reader to become engaged in the text as a story, and the layout provides enough white space to allow lower level readers to feel confident." Library Media Connection.

Includes bibliographical references and index.

975.2 Maryland

Blashfield, Jean F.
Maryland. by Jean F. Blashfield. Children's Press, 2014. 144 p. : America the beautiful
Grades: 4 5 6 7   **975.2**
1. US states 2. Maryland 3. United States
ISBN 9780531248881

LC 2007012699

Describes the history, geography, ecology, people, economy, cities, and sights of the state of Maryland.

Pietrzyk, Leslie, 1961-
Maryland. by Leslie Rauth and Martha Kneib. Marshall Cavendish Benchmark, 2008. 144 p. : Celebrate the states
Grades: 4 5 6 7   **975.2**
1. US states 2. Geography 3. Culture 4. Maryland 5. United States
ISBN 9780761430049

LC 2007029497

Provides comprehensive information on the geography, history, wildlife, governmental structure, economy, cultural diversity, peoples, religion, and landmarks of Maryland. Provided by publisher.

975.3 District of Columbia (Washington)

Aretha, David
The **story** of the civil rights March on Washington for Jobs and Freedom in photographs. David Aretha. Enslow Publishers, Inc., 2014 48 p.
Grades: 5 6 7 8   **975.3**
1. March on Washington for Jobs and Freedom (1963: Washington, D.C.) 2. Civil rights demonstrations -- History 20th century 3.

African Americans -- Civil rights -- History 20th century
ISBN 9780766042384

LC 2013004860

Discusses the March on Washington for Jobs and Freedom in 1963, including the causes for the march, how the march was organized and its leaders, the important speeches, and the impact it had on the Civil Rights Movement. Provided by publisher.

House, Katherine L. (Katherine Lucille)

The **White** House for kids: a history of a home, office, and national symbol: with 21 activities. Katherine L. House. Chicago Review Press, 2014. 144 p.: For kids series

Grades: 4 5 6 7   **975.3**
    1. White House (Washington, D.C.) 2. Buildings 3. Presidents 4. Washington, DC -- Buildings
ISBN 9781613744611

LC 2013038108

An in-depth introduction to the White House blends facts from numerous primary sources with engaging anecdotes about the first families, details about the many changes and renovations that have occurred throughout the years and descriptions of everyday activities of residents and their staffs.

"Chapter organization enhances interest by covering seven subjects and including examples from multiple historical periods. From the purposes and architecture of the building to the nature of multiple jobs performed, this book shows the varied functions of the White House." Voice of Youth Advocates.

Includes bibliographical references and index.

Kent, Deborah

Washington, D.C., by Deborah Kent. Children's Press, an Imprint of Scholastic Inc., [2014] 144 p.: America the beautiful

Grades: 4 5 6 7   **975.3**
    1. Washington, DC
ISBN 9780531282984

LC 98054910

Surveys the history, geography, and economy of the District of Columbia, as well as the diverse ways of life of its people.

National Children's Book and Literacy Alliance

★ **Our** White House: looking in, looking out. The National Children's Book and Literacy Alliance. Candlewick Press, 2008. 256 p.

Grades: 5 6 7 8   **975.3**
    1. White House, Washington, D.C. 2. Washington, DC 3. United States -- History 4. Anthologies
ISBN 9780763620677

More than one hundred leading authors and illustrators donate their talents to a collection of essays, personal accounts, historical fiction, and poetry which looks at America's history through the prism of the White House.

"The White House is the focus of this handsome, large-format compendium of writings, both factual and fictional, and illustrations. . . . Poems and essays, stories and memoirs all combine to create a mosaic of impressions of the house's residents and visitors and of the important events that occurred there. . . . The often-spectacular artwork, beautifully reproduced on glossy paper, is particularly striking." Booklist.

975.5 Virginia

Gillette, Robert H.

Escape to Virginia: fom Nazi Germany to Thalhimer's farm. Robert H. Gillette. History Press, 2016 252 p.

Grades: 7 8 9 10   **975.5**
    1. 1930s 2. Jews, German 3. Escapes 4. Farms 5. Farmers
ISBN 9781626199125

Jewish teenagers Eva and Topper desperately searched for an escape from the stranglehold of 1930s Nazi Germany. They studied agriculture at the Gross Breesen Institute and hoped to secure visas to gain freedom from the tyranny around them. Richmond department store owner William B. Thalhimer created a safe haven on a rural Virginia farm where Eva and Topper would find refuge

"Gillette calls his narrative 'creative history' though his account is not fictionalized, he nonetheless strives to make it read like a novel. Mostly, he succeeds: Gillette is an excellent storyteller, and the details he uses so illustratively are from primary sources, such as letters, diaries, photos, and other personal narratives. Although Eva sometimes seems too good to be true, overall, this is an engrossing and informative study of a less familiar corner of a much-covered period. Ample source notes make this a solid choice for student research." Booklist.

Includes bibliographical references and index.

Kent, Deborah

Virginia. by Deborah Kent. Children's Press, 2014. 144 p. : America the beautiful

Grades: 4 5 6 7   **975.5**
    1. US states 2. Virginia
ISBN 9780531248997

LC 2007028463

Describes the history, geography, ecology, people, economy, cities, and sights of the state of Virginia.

975.6 North Carolina

Heinrichs, Ann

North Carolina. by Ann Heinrichs. Children's Press, 2014. 144 p. : America the beautiful

Grades: 4 5 6 7   **975.6**
    1. US states 2. North Carolina
ISBN 9780531248966

LC 2007039773

Describes the geography, history, economy, culture, and people of the state of North Carolina.

975.8 Georgia

Prentzas, G. S.

Georgia. by G.S. Prentzas. Children's Press, 2014. 144 p. : America the beautiful

Grades: 4 5 6 7   **975.8**
    1. US states 2. United States 3. Georgia
ISBN 9780531248812

LC 2007008256

Describes the history, geography, ecology, people, economy, cities, and sights of the state of Georgia.

975.9 Florida

Orr, Tamra

    Florida. Tamra B. Orr. Children's Press, 2014 144 p.: America the Beautiful. Third Series

Grades: 4 5 6 7   **975.9**

    1. US states 2. Florida 3. United States

    ISBN 9780531248805

Describes the geography, plants, animals, history, economy, language, religions, culture, sports, art, and people of this southern state.

Turner, Glennette Tilley

    ★ **Fort** Mose: and the story of the man who built the first free black settlement in colonial America. Glennette Tilley Turner. Abrams Books for Young Readers, 2010. 42 p.

Grades: 5 6 7 8   **975.9**

    1. Menendez, Francisco, b. ca. 1700 2. Freed people 3. Slavery -- History 18th century. 4. Florida -- History -- Spanish colony, 1565-1763. 5. Fort Mose Site, Florida

    ISBN 9780810940567

Follows the history of slavery from West Africa to America, recounts what daily life was like, and describes the founding of the Spanish colonies.

    "In the 18th century, some Africans escaped slavery in England's southern colonies to find freedom in the Spanish colony of Florida. As a leader of St. Augustine's community, African-born Francisco Menendez helped establish Fort Mose, the first free black community on North American soil. Turner does an excellent job of explaining how the residents of Fort Mose probably blended African, English, and Spanish traditions to create a uniqueand uniquely American culture." School Library Journal.

    Includes bibliographical references (p. 38-40) and index.

976 South central United States

Pietras, Jamie

    Hurricane Katrina. Jamie Pietras. Chelsea House, c2008. 128 p.: Great historic disasters

Grades: 7 8 9 10   **976**

    1. Hurricane Katrina, 2005 2. Hurricanes 3. Disaster victims 4. Disaster relief 5. New Orleans, Louisiana

    ISBN 9780791096390

        LC 2007036551

Describes the events that occurred after Hurricane Katrina hit New Orleans, Louisiana, in 2005, including the relief effort and work done to help rebuild the city.

    "This book details the meteorological, political, and social circumstances that came together so fatally during 2005's Hurricane Katrina. Mostly objective, the writing is occasionally peppered with commentary on the local and federal governments' missteps and inaction following the storm and ensuing floods. Gripping photographs support the text." Horn Book Guide.

    Includes bibliographical references (p. 112-119) and index.

976.1 Alabama

Somervill, Barbara A.

    Alabama. Barbara A. Somervill. Children's Press, 2014. 144 p.

Grades: 4 5 6 7   **976.1**

    1. US states 2. Alabama

    ISBN 9780531248751

Describes the geography, plants, animals, history, economy, language, religions, culture, sports, art, and people of this southern state, whose first European settlers were Spanish and French rather than British.

976.2 Mississippi

Dell, Pamela

    Mississippi. Pamela Dell. Children's Press, c2014. 144 p.: America the beautiful

Grades: 4 5 6 7   **976.2**

    1. US states 2. Mississippi

    ISBN 9780531248911

Describes the geography, plants and animals, history, economy, language, religions, culture, and people of the state of Mississippi.

Ribeiro, Myra

    The **assassination** of Medgar Evers. Myra Ribeiro. Rosen Pub. Group, 2002. 64 p.: The library of political assassinations

Grades: 5 6 7 8   **976.2**

    1. Evers, Medgar Wiley, 1925-1963 2. Beckwith, Byron De La, 1920-2001 3. African American civil rights workers 4. African Americans -- History 5. Assassination 6. Jackson, Mississippi -- History -- 20th century. 7. Mississippi -- Race relations

    ISBN 0823935442

        LC 2001002389

Discusses the lives of civil rights leader Medgar Evers and his assassin Byron De La Beckwith.

    "There are numerous photos, and each book has a glossary, a chronology, and a bibliography, but no footnotes." Booklist.

    Includes bibliographical references (p. 58-59), filmography (p. 57) and index.

976.3 Louisiana

Goldstone, Lawrence, 1947-

    Unpunished murder: massacre at Colfax and the quest for justice. Lawrence Goldstone; foreword by Angela Onwuachi-Willig. Scholastic Focus, 2018. 288 p.

Grades: 7 8 9 10 11 12   **976.3**

    1. United States. Supreme Court 2. 1870s 3. Racism in criminology 4. Massacres 5. White supremacists 6. Discrimination 7. Racism 8. Louisiana 9. United States -- History -- 1865-1898

    ISBN 9781338239454

Describes the 1873 Easter Sunday massacre of unarmed African Americans in Louisiana and the subsequent court case that ushered in the age of Jim Crow in the United States.

Lassieur, Allison

    Louisiana. by Allison Lassieur. Children's Press, 2014. 144 p. : America the beautiful

Grades: 4 5 6 7   **976.3**

    1. US states 2. Louisiana

    ISBN 9780531248867

        LC 2007000300

Describes the history, geography, ecology, people, economy, cities, and sights of the Pelican State of Louisiana.

976.4 Texas

Hale, Nathan, 1976-
   Alamo all-stars. Nathan Hale. Harry N Abrams Inc, 2016. 128 p.: Nathan Hale's hazardous tales
Grades: 3 4 5 6   **976.4**
   1. Alamo -- Siege, 1836. 2. Forts 3. Alamo 4. Texas -- History -- To 1846. 5. Comics and Graphic novels
   ISBN 9781419719028
   "The irreverent tone, interjections by the narrators, and often humorous backstories of the major players lighten the mood and break up battle scenes in digestible pieces, and Hale's dynamic cartoon art renders each character uniquely enough that they're easy to tell apart—no small feat, given the large cast." Booklist.

Lourie, Peter
   On the Texas trail of Cabeza de Vaca. Peter Lourie. Boyds Mills Press, 2008. 48 p.
Grades: 4 5 6 7   **976.4**
   1. Cabeza de Vaca, Alvar Nunez, 1490?-1557. 2. Conquistadors 3. Explorers 4. Exploration 5. Spaniards in North America 6. North America -- Exploration -- Spanish 7. Texas -- Description and travel.
   ISBN 9781590784921
                                                       LC 2007049180
   Join conquistador Cabeza de Vaca, the first European to live amongst the native people of Texas, as he sets sail for the Spanish territory of La Florida in 1527—a journey that became one of history's greatest adventures.
   "In 1527, Governor Pnfilo de Narvez sailed westward from Spain to explore the land that stretched between present-day Florida and Mexico, colonizing and conquering. With him, as his treasurer and sheriff, was Cabeza de Vaca. . . . He [returned] with a wealth of information, codified in La Relacin, his account of his experience. Then, 475 years later, Lourie set out to follow Cabeza de Vaca's trail through Texas. . . . This well-researched, beautifully composed book is the result. Using primary sources and period reproductions as well as the author's experiences and contemporary pictures, it highlights historical information within the context of current circumstances. Beautifully placed photos, reproductions, maps, and sidebars enhance the fluid text." School Library Journal.

Newton, Michael, 1951-
   The **Texas** Rangers. Michael Newton. Chelsea House, 2010. 128 p. : Law enforcement agencies
Grades: 6 7 8 9   **976.4**
   1. Texas Rangers -- History. 2. Law enforcement -- History 3. Law enforcement agencies 4. Vocational guidance 5. Occupations 6. Texas
   ISBN 9781604136265
                                                       LC 2010028274
   "Solidly and comprehensively researched. . . . In The Texas Rangers, a group that has long excited the country's imagination gets a full treatment, including its appearances on screen. An attractive design, plenty of photos, and solid back matter complete [the] package. Extremely useful for students and appealing for browsers." Booklist.
   Includes bibliographical references and index.

Somervill, Barbara A.
   Texas. by Barbara A. Somervill. Children's Press, 2014. 144 p. : America the beautiful
Grades: 4 5 6 7   **976.4**
   1. US states 2. Texas
   ISBN 9780531248980
                                                       LC 2007017787
   Describes the history, geography, ecology, people, economy, cities, and sights of the state of Texas.

Walker, Paul Robert
   ★ **Remember** the Alamo: Texians, Tejanos, and Mexicans tell their stories. Paul Robert Walker. National Geographic, c2007. 61 p.
Grades: 5 6 7 8   **976.4**
   1. Alamo -- Siege, 1836. 2. 19th century 3. Battles 4. Texas -- History -- Revolution, 1835-1836.
   ISBN 1426300115
                                                       LC 2006034497
   An account of the famous battle of the Alamo which presents different points of view of the event.
   "Opening with clear context about why tensions between Texas residents and the Mexican government were brought to a head, the book then chronicles events directly leading to the siege of the Alamo and its immediate aftermath, following up with an epilogue on the decisive battle of San Jacinto 10 months later. Bringing the history to life is a healthy selection of dramatic, modern paintings along with plenty of archival drawings, maps, and old photos." Booklist.
   Includes bibliographical references (p. 60) and index.

976.6 Oklahoma

Madigan, Tim
   The **burning**: Black Wall Street and the Tulsa race massacre of 1921. Tim Madigan; adapted for young people by Hilary Beard Henry Holt & Co 2021 302 p.
Grades: 6 7 8 9 10   **976.6**
   1. African Americans -- History 20th century. 2. Neighborhoods -- History 20th century. 3. Riots -- History 20th century. 4. Violence -- History 20th century. 5. Racism -- History 20th century. 6. Tulsa, Oklahoma -- Race relations. 7. United States -- Race relations -- History -- 20th century
   ISBN 9781250787699
   A powerful adaptation of The Burning recounts the true story of Black Wall Street and the 1921 Tulsa Race Massacre, when a white mob murdered hundreds of citizens and decimated the thriving Black community of Greenwood in Tulsa, Oklahoma.
   "Because the original text, published in 2001, had a predominantly white focus, adaptor Beard integrates here more perspectives of Black Tulsans who bravely fought for their community. . . . Beard also concludes with a new section that relates the Tulsa massacre to more recent racial injustices and the BLM movement." Booklist.

Orr, Tamra
   Oklahoma. Tamra B. Orr. Children's Press, c2014. 144 p. : America the beautiful
Grades: 4 5 6 7   **976.6**
   1. US states 2. Oklahoma
   ISBN 9780531248973
                                                       LC 2007004774

Describes the geography, plants, animals, history, economy, religions, culture, sports, arts, and people of Oklahoma.

976.7 Arkansas

Wallace, Sandra Neil

Race against time: the untold story of Scipio Jones and the battle to save twelve innocent men. Sandra Neil Wallace, Rich Wallace. Calkins Creek, 2021 144 p.

Grades: 6 7 8 9   **976.7**

1. Jones, Scipio Africanus, 1863-1943. 2. Elaine Race Riot, Elaine, Ark, 1919 3. African American lawyers 4. Riots -- History 5. African Americans -- History 6. Trials (Murder) -- History 20th century. 7. Phillips County, Arkansas -- Race relations -- History -- 20th century. 8. Phillips County, Arkansas -- History.
ISBN 9781629798165

In October 1919, a group of black sharecroppers met at a church in an Arkansas village to organize a union. Bullets rained down on the meeting from outside. Many were killed by a white mob, and others were rounded up and arrested. Twelve of the sharecroppers were hastily tried and sentenced to death. Up stepped Scipio Africanus Jones, a self-taught lawyer who'd been born enslaved. Could he save the men's lives and set them free?

"The action takes place at breakneck speed, accompanied by ample background information, period photographs, and appearances by the nascent NAACP, journalist Ida Tarbell, and a young Thurgood Marshall. . . . an often-overlooked landmark event in the early history of civil rights." Booklist

976.9 Kentucky

Santella, Andrew

Kentucky. by Andrew Santella. Children's Press, 2014. 144 p. : America the beautiful

Grades: 4 5 6 7   **976.9**

1. US states 2. Kentucky 3. Kentucky -- History
ISBN 9780531248850

LC 2007004803

Describes the history, geography, ecology, people, economy, cities, and sights of the state of Kentucky.

977.2 Indiana

Stille, Darlene R.

Indiana. by Darlene R. Stille. Children's Press, 2014. 144 p. : America the beautiful

Grades: 4 5 6 7   **977.2**

1. US states 2. Indiana
ISBN 9780531248843

LC 2007043670

Describes the geography, history, economy, culture, and people of the state of Indiana.

977.3 Illinois

Bennie, Paul

The **Great** Chicago Fire of 1871. Paul Bennie. Chelsea House Publishers, c2008. 128 p.: Great historic disasters

Grades: 7 8 9 10   **977.3**

1. Fires -- History 19th century. 2. Great Fire, Chicago, Ill, 1871 3. Illinois -- History -- 19th century. 4. Chicago, Illinois -- History -- 19th century.
ISBN 9780791096383

LC 2007036550

Recreates the events of the thirty dramatic hours in which the city of Chicago was destroyed by fire.

"On October 8, 1871, a fire started in the O'Learys' barn in Chicago. . . . [This occurence] brought about lasting changes in fire prevention and building codes. . . . [This book], which [describes] the [disaster] and [its] aftermath in detail, [is] well written and informative. . . . [This is] first-rate for reports and general browsing." School Library Journal.

Includes bibliographical references (p. 117-119) and index.

Burgan, Michael

Illinois. by Michael Burgan. Children's Press, 2014. 144 p. : America the beautiful

Grades: 4 5 6 7   **977.3**

1. US states 2. Illinois
ISBN 9780531248836

LC 2006036020

Describes the history, geography, ecology, people, economy, cities, and sights of Illinois.

Hannigan, Kate

The **Great** Chicago Fire: rising from the ashes. written by Kate Hannigan; art by Alex Graudins First Second, 2020 128 p.

Grades: 4 5 6 7 8   **977.3**

1. Great Fire, Chicago, Ill, 1871 2. Fires -- History 19th century 3. Disasters 4. Chicago, Illinois -- History -- To 1875 5. Comics and Graphic novels
ISBN 9781250174253

A graphic novel introduction to the events surrounding the Great Chicago Fire of 1871, describing how dry prairie winds ignited a blaze that engulfed Chicago for two days, trapping two siblings and their pup in a race to escape and reunite with their family.

"Graudins' bright, evocative illustrations neatly fit together with the text and bring the ferociousness of the fire amid vignettes sprinkled throughout that add context to local and national decisions." Booklist

977.4 Michigan

Raatma, Lucia

Michigan. by Lucia Raatma. Children's Press, c2014. 144 p. : America the beautiful

Grades: 4 5 6 7   **977.4**

1. US states 2. Michigan
ISBN 9780531248904

LC 2006100708

Describes the geography, plants, animals, history, economy, language, religions, culture, sports, art, and people of the state of Michigan.

977.5 Wisconsin

Blashfield, Jean F.
Wisconsin. Jean F. Blashfield. Children's Press, 2014. 144 p.: America the beautiful
Grades: 4 5 6 7   **977.5**
   1. US states 2. Wisconsin
ISBN 9780531248744
                  LC 97049198
An introduction to the geography, history, natural resources, economy, culture, and people of Wisconsin.

977.7 Iowa

Blashfield, Jean F.
Iowa. Jean F. Blashfield. Children's Press, an Imprint of Scholastic Inc., [2014] 144 p.: America the beautiful
Grades: 4 5 6 7   **977.7**
   1. US states 2. Iowa 3. Middle West
ISBN 9780531282793
Surveys the history, geography, and economy of the Hawkeye State, as well as the diverse ways of life of its people.

978 Western United States

Bial, Raymond
The **Shoshone**. Raymond Bial. Benchmark Books, c2002. 128 p.: Lifeways
Grades: 5 6 7 8   **978**
   1. Shoshoni Indians -- History 2. Shoshoni Indians -- Social life and customs 3. Shoshoni Indians 4. Indians of North America -- History
ISBN 0761412115
                  LC 2001018496
Describes the history, culture, everday life, social structure, beliefs, and customs of the Shoshoni people, and the struggles they face to adapt to modern life and keep traditions alive.

Brown, Dee, 1908-2002
Bury my heart at Wounded Knee: an Indian history of the American West. by Dee Brown. H. Holt, 2001, c1971. xix, 487 p.
Grades: 8 9 10 11 12 Adult   **978**
   1. 19th century 2. Indians of North America -- Wars 3. Battles 4. Indians of North America -- History 5. The West (United States) -- History -- 19th century.
ISBN 0805066349
                LC   00040958
The systematic destruction of the American Indians, told in the words of those who were there.

Brown, Don, 1949-
The **great** American Dust Bowl. Don Brown. Houghton Mifflin Harcourt, 2013. 80 p.
Grades: 5 6 7 8 9   **978**
   1. 1930s 2. Dust Bowl Era, 1931-1939 3. Depressions 1929-1941 4. Weather 5. Dust storms 6. Economics -- Social aspects 7. Dust Bowl (South Central United States) 8. Historical comics 9. Comics and Graphic novels
ISBN 9780547815503
A graphic novel account of the giant dust storms in the Midwest in the 1930s discusses the ecological and agricultural damage caused by the storms.
"In this bleak yet compelling graphic-novel-style glimpse at the Dirty Thirties, Brown crisply paces the narrative with fascinating glimpses of the sociological and geological causes of the Dust Bowl. The color brown is a recurring theme here, as Brown relies, aptly, almost entirely on shades of brown throughout. Primary source material is used liberally, as characters speak directly to the reader, documentary-style." Horn Book.

Countryman, Edward
The **Old** West: history and heritage. editor, Edward Countryman. Marshall Cavendish, 2008. 11 v.
Grades: 6 7 8 9 10 11 12   **978**
   1. Popular culture 2. West (US) -- History 3. West (US) -- Social life and customs
ISBN 9780761478294
                LC 2008062302
Articles discuss the people, places, events, technology, and society of the American West, including neighboring Canada and Mexico, from 1787 to 1912, and the ways in which the West has been incorporated in popular culture.

Fleming, Candace
Presenting Buffalo Bill: the man who invented the Wild West. Candace Fleming. Roaring Brook Press, 2016. 128 p.
Grades: 6 7 8 9 10   **978**
   1. Buffalo Bill, 1846-1917 2. Entertainers 3. Pioneers 4. The West (United States)
ISBN 9781596437630
                LC 2015035540
The award-winning author of The Family Romanov presents an introduction to the life of the American West hero that separates fact from myth to illuminate his actual contributions to the Pony Express, the Battle of Little Big Horn and Native American rights, in a portrait complemented by archival images.
"Illustrated with archival material and supplemented with extensive backmatter, this is a thoroughly engaging portrait of a fascinating, larger-than-life figure." Kirkus.
Includes bibliographical references.

Marrin, Albert
Years of dust: the story of the Dust Bowl. Albert Marrin. Dutton Children's Books, 2009. 128 p.
Grades: 6 7 8 9 10   **978**
   1. Depressions 1929-1941 2. Dust storms -- History 20th century. 3. Droughts -- History 20th century. 4. Ecology 5. Natural disasters -- History 6. Dust Bowl (South Central United States) 7. Great Plains (United States) -- History -- 20th century.
ISBN 9780525420774
                LC 2008013898
Offers a review of the events that led up to and took place during this natural disaster in the Great Plains during the 1930s, and discusses the changes that were instituted in farming and land conservation as a result of it.
"The engaging narrative includes quotes from a variety of primary sources, and it is abundantly illustrated throughout with photographs and other archival material, making this a reader-friendly, insightful work of history." Kirkus.
Includes bibliographical references.

Miller, Brandon Marie

Women of the frontier: 16 tales of trailblazing homesteaders, entrepreneurs, and rabble-rousers. Brandon Marie Miller. Chicago Review Press, 2013. 272 p.: Women of action

Grades: 7 8 9 10 11 12   **978**

1. Pioneer women 2. Frontier and pioneer life 3. The West (United States) -- History -- 19th century.
ISBN 9781883052973

                         LC 2012035756

Drawing on journal entries, letters and song lyrics to evoke the courage and spirit of female pioneers and early activists, a collection of portraits traces the heroic lives of such individuals as Amelia Stewart Knight, Miriam Colt and Clara Brown.

"The trials and tribulations of each woman show courage, perseverance, and an enduring spirit. Recounting the impact pioneers had on those who were already living in the region as well as how they adapted to their new lives and the rugged, often dangerous landscape, this exploration reveals how these influential women tamed the Wild West." Library Media Connection.

Includes bibliographical references and index.

Sheinkin, Steve

★ **Which** way to the wild west?: everything your schoolbooks didn't tell you about America's westward expansion. Steve Sheinkin; illustrated by Tim Robinson. Roaring Brook Press, 2009. 260 p.

Grades: 5 6 7 8   **978**

1. Frontier and pioneer life 2. Overland journeys to the Pacific 3. Indians of North America 4. Gold rush 5. The West (United States) 6. United States -- Territorial expansion
ISBN 9781596433212

"An engaging storyteller, the author uses humor and little-known anecdotes to make such subjects as Manifest Destiny, the Mexican-American War, the Gold Rush and Custer's Last Stand entertaining for readers. His chatty, informal style . . . will appeal to young readers turned off to history by stale textbooks. Robinson's cartoons complement the text. . . . An accessible and engaging historical overview." Kirkus.

Stefoff, Rebecca, 1951-

The **Wild** West. Rebecca Stefoff. Marshall Cavendish Benchmark, c2007. 111 p.: American voices from--

Grades: 6 7 8 9   **978**

1. Frontier and pioneer life 2. The West (United States) -- History -- 19th century
ISBN 9780761421702

                         LC 2005028192

Presents the history of the Wild West through a variety of primary source images and documents, such as diary entries, newspaper accounts, public speeches, popular literature, and personal letters. Provided by publisher.

978.004 Western United States—Ethnic and national groups

Langley, Andrew, 1949-

The **Plains** Indian wars 1864-1890. Andrew Langley. Heinemann Library, c2012. 80 p.: Living through

Grades: 6 7 8 9   **978.004**

1. 19th century 2. Indians of North America -- Wars 1866-1895 3. Battles 4. War 5. Indians of North America -- Wars 6. Indians of

North America -- History 19th century
ISBN 9781432959999

                         LC 2011015925

Explores the history of the wars against the Plains Indians, including the important players, battles, and consequences.

Patent, Dorothy Hinshaw

The **horse** and the Plains Indians: a powerful partnership. Dorothy Hinshaw Patent; photographs by William Munoz. Clarion Books, 2012. 98 p.

Grades: 4 5 6 7 8   **978.004**

1. Indians of North America -- Horses 2. Horses 3. Human/animal relationships 4. Humans and horses
ISBN 9780547125510

The award-winning team of The Buffalo and the Indians documents the transformative period in the early 16th century when the Spaniards introduced horses to the Great Plains and how hoses became an integral part of the Plains Indians' culture.

978.2 Nebraska

Heinrichs, Ann

Nebraska. by Ann Heinrichs. Children's Press, c2014. 144 p. : America the beautiful

Grades: 4 5 6 7   **978.2**

1. US states 2. Nebraska 3. United States
ISBN 9780531248928

                         LC 2007006720

Describes the history, geography, ecology, people, economy, cities, and sights of the state of Nebraska.

978.7 Wyoming

Prentzas, G. S.

Wyoming. by G.S. Prentzas. Children's Press, 2009. 144 p.: America the beautiful

Grades: 4 5 6 7   **978.7**

1. US states 2. Wyoming 3. Mountain States
ISBN 9780531185087

Describes the geography, plants, animals, history, economy, language, religions, culture, sports, art, and people of the state of Wyoming.

978.9 New Mexico

Vivian, R. Gwinn

Chaco Canyon. R. Gwinn Vivian and Margaret Anderson. Oxford University Press, c2002. 47 p.: Digging for the past

Grades: 5 6 7 8   **978.9**

1. Excavations (Archaeology) 2. Anasazi Culture 3. Archaeologists 4. Indians of North America 5. Cliff dwellings 6. Southwest (United States) 7. Chaco Canyon, New Mexico -- Antiquities.
ISBN 0195142802

                         LC 2001054855

Relates the nineteenth-century discovery of cliff dwellings in the Chaco Canyon of northwest New Mexico, the excavations of the ancient ruins, and what the artifacts reveal about the civilization of the ancient Pueblo Indians.

"This brings young readers up close to the field of archaeology. . . . Sharp color photos show the sites, artifacts, and the scientists at work." Booklist.

Includes bibliographical references (p. 45) and index.

979.1 Arizona

McDaniel, Melissa, 1964-
Arizona. by Melissa McDaniel and Wendy Mead. Marshall Cavendish Benchmark, 2009. 144 p. : Celebrate the states
Grades: 4 5 6 7   **979.1**
   1. US states 2. Arizona
ISBN 9780761433989
                          LC 2008006212
Provides comprehensive information on the geography, history, wildlife, governmental structure, economy, cultural diversity, peoples, religion, and landmarks of Arizona. Provided by publisher.

979.3 Nevada

Heinrichs, Ann
Nevada. Ann Heinrichs. Children's Press, 2014. 144 p. : America the beautiful
Grades: 4 5 6 7   **979.3**
   1. US states 2. Nevada
ISBN 9780531248935
                          LC 2006039526
Describes the geography, plants, animals, history, economy, religions, culture, sports, arts, and people of Nevada.

979.4 California

Brimner, Larry Dane
The **rain** wizard: the amazing, mysterious, true life of Charles Mallory Hatfield. Larry Dane Brimner. Calkins Creek Books, 2015. 80 p.
Grades: 5 6 7 8 9   **979.4**
   1. Hatfield, Charles Mallory, 1875-1958 2. 20th century 3. Rain and rainfall 4. Chemicals 5. Floods 6. Weather 7. San Diego, California
ISBN 9781590789902
"The generously leaded text is set within wide margins and accompanied by copious archival illustrations; both decisions keep the relatively complex text accessible. An engaging, intriguing story of a fascinating man." Kirkus.

Calabro, Marian
★ The **perilous** journey of the Donner Party. by Marian Calabro. Clarion Books, c1999. 192 p.
Grades: 5 6 7 8   **979.4**
   1. Pioneer children 2. Wagon trains 3. Survival 4. Frontier and pioneer life 5. Overland journeys to the Pacific
ISBN 0395866103
                          LC 98029610
Uses materials from letters and diaries written by survivors of the Donner Party to relate the experiences of that ill-fated group as they endured horrific circumstances on their way to California in 1846-47.

"Calabro's offering is a fine addition to the Donner Party canon and particularly well suited to its young audience, for whom the story of hardship and survival will be nothing short of riveting. . . . From the haunting cover with its lonely campfire to the recounting of a survivors' reunion, this is a page-turner." Booklist.

Includes bibliographical references and index.

Doak, Robin S. (Robin Santos), 1963-
California, 1542-1850. Robin Doak with Andres Resendez, consultant. National Geographic Society, c2006. 109 p.: Voices from colonial America
Grades: 5 6 7 8   **979.4**
   1. California -- History -- To 1846 2. California -- History -- 1846-1850
ISBN 079226391X
                          LC 2005030920
Traces California's history from its origins as a sparsely populated outpost of the Spanish empire in the sixteenth century to the frenzied westward migration of the 1850s.

"The text is not written in sound bites but in full paragraphs, making up chronological chapters. These are divided into topical sections, which are clearly marked by large headings. This lovely, calm layout is liberally sprinkled with primary source illustrations, including reproductions of period maps, pamphlets, paintings, and drawings. . . . An essential purchase for schools with a colonies research project . . . and for the public libraries that support their communities." Voice of Youth Advocates.

Includes bibliograhical references (p. 105-106) and index.

Hale, Nathan, 1976-
Donner dinner party. Nathan Hale. Harry N Abrams Inc, 2013. 128 p. : Nathan Hale's hazardous tales
Grades: 4 5 6 7   **979.4**
   1. Donner Party 2. Overland journeys to the Pacific 3. Pioneers 4. Pioneers 5. Frontier and pioneer life 6. The West (United States) 7. Comics and Graphic novels
ISBN 9781419708565
"This informative graphic novel capitalizes on enticingly gross history to great effect, balancing raw facts with strong storytelling." Booklist.

Markham, Lauren
The **far** away brothers: two teenage immigrants making a life in America. Lauren Markham. Delacorte Press, 2019. xv, 265 p.
Grades: 6 7 8 9   **979.4**
   1. Flores, Ernesto, 1997- 2. Flores, Raul, 1997- 3. Twin brothers 4. Undocumented immigrants 5. Teenagers 6. Immigration policy 7. Immigration and emigration law 8. El Salvador 9. Oakland, California
ISBN 9781984829771
                          LC 2018025469
Identical twins Ernesto and Raul Flores, seventeen, must flee El Salvador, make a harrowing journey across the Rio Grande and the Texas desert, face capture by immigration authorities, and struggle to navigate life in America.

McNeese, Tim
The **Donner** Party: a doomed journey. Tim McNeese. Chelsea House, 2009. 146 p. : Milestones in American history
Grades: 6 7 8 9 10   **979.4**
   1. 19th century 2. Donner Party 3. Overland journeys to the Pacific 4. Pioneers -- History 19th century. 5. Cannibalism 6. The

West (United States) -- Description and travel. 9. Sierra Nevada
Mountains -- History -- 19th century.
ISBN 9781604130256

LC 2008029652

Recounts the journey of the Donner Party which, in 1846, sought
to travel from Independence, Missouri, to California but took an un-
tried shortcut that trapped them in the Sierra Nevada mountains during
a terrible winter.

"McNeese presents a thoroughly researched, clearly written account
of the ill-fated Donner Party and the events and decisions that conspired
against this early wagon train headed from Springfield, IL, to California.
. . . Photos, reproductions, drawings, and primary-source documents as
well as a detailed chronology make this an excellent resource." School
Library Journal.

Includes bibliographical references and index.

Olson, Tod

★ **How** to get rich in the California Gold Rush: an adventurer's guide to the fabulous riches discovered in 1848. Thomas
Hartley, Tod Olson; illustrations by Scott Allred; afterword by
Marc Aronson. National Geographic, c2008. 47 p.: How to get
rich

Grades: 4 5 6 7   **979.4**
1. 1840s 2. Frontier and pioneer life 3. Gold mines and mining
-- History 19th century 4. Prospecting 5. Gold rush 6. Money-
making projects 7. California -- History -- 1846-1850
ISBN 9781426303159

LC 2008019601

The fictional Thomas Hartley gives readers a historical portrait of
life in the California gold fields, offering a unique and witty snapshot of
a key period in the economic development of the United States.

"This deftly blends story with history to not only give readers an
understanding of a gold rush but also to provide a lighthearted and engaging entry point into frontier life. . . . Period lithographs are reproduced alongside original illustrations. . . . A ledger on each page tracks
the young men's finances in a genuinely exciting way, adding a sly element of math to this well-conceived and compulsively appealing book."
Booklist.

Includes bibliographical references (p. 45).

Orr, Tamra

California. Tamra B. Orr. Children's Press, 2014 144 p.:
America the Beautiful. Third Series
Grades: 4 5 6 7   **979.4**
1. US states 2. California 3. United States
ISBN 9780531248775

Explores the geography, history, economy, people, government, and
landmarks of California.

Slavicek, Louise Chipley, 1956-

The **San** Francisco earthquake and fire of 1906. Louise Chi-
pley Slavicek. Chelsea House, 2008. 128 p. : Great historic di-
sasters
Grades: 5 6 7 8   **979.4**
1. 1900s (Decade) 2. Earthquakes -- History 20th century 3. Fires
-- History 20th century 4. Natural disasters 5. San Francisco
Earthquake and Fire, Calif, 1906 6. San Francisco, California --
History -- 20th century
ISBN 9780791096505

LC 2008004896

Each book in this series begins with historical context to depict life
in the time and place of the featured event, builds to a vivid description

of the disaster, discusses the aftermath, and then analyzes the way the
disaster changed history and impacted the future.

"Combining first-hand accounts, photographs, and other primary
sources with a detailed and lively text, [this] fact-packed [resource of-
fers] much to both report writers and history buffs." Horn Book Guide.

Includes bibliographical references and index.

979.5 Oregon

Kent, Deborah

Oregon. Deborah Kent. Children's Press, 2008. 144 p. :
America the beautiful
Grades: 4 5 6 7   **979.5**
1. US states 2. Oregon
ISBN 9780531185872

LC 2007038691

Describes the geography, history, economy, culture, and people of
the state of Oregon.

979.6 Idaho

Kent, Deborah

Idaho. Deborah Kent. Children's Press, 2009. 144 p.: America the beautiful
Grades: 4 5 6 7   **979.6**
1. US states 2. Idaho 3. The West (United States)
ISBN 9780531185988

Takes readers on a tour of Idaho, describing the state's history,
culture, land, economy, government, and sights, and including unique
facts, color maps and photos, the state song, suggested activities,
lists of famous people, cultural institutions, and annual events, and
other resources.

Stefoff, Rebecca, 1951-

Idaho. by Rebecca Stefoff. Marshall Cavendish Benchmark,
2008. 144 p. : Celebrate the states
Grades: 4 5 6 7   **979.6**
1. US states 2. Culture 3. Geography 4. Civilization 5. Idaho
ISBN 9780761430032

LC 2007029496

Provides comprehensive information on the geography, history,
wildlife, governmental structure, economy, cultural diversity, peoples,
religion, and landmarks of Idaho. Provided by publisher.

979.7 Washington

Kirkpatrick, Katherine

Mysterious bones: the story of Kennewick Man. by Kath-
erine Kirkpatrick; illustrated by Emma Stevenson. Holiday
House, c2011. 60 p.
Grades: 6 7 8 9   **979.7**
1. Kennewick Man 2. Human remains (Archaeology) 3. Cultural
property 4. Indians of North America -- Origin 5. Indians of North
America -- Antiquities 6. Washington (State) -- Antiquities
ISBN 9780823421879

LC 2009025575

"Kennewick Man was found in remarkable condition near the Columbia River in Washington . . . in 1996—one of the oldest and most

complete skeletons found in America. Kirkpatrick addresses the controversy surrounding the treatment of his remains. . . . Excellent illustrations accompany the story, with crisp line-drawings of tools, skeletons, maps and possible facial reconstructions." Kirkus.

Stefoff, Rebecca, 1951-

Washington. Rebecca Stefoff. Marshall Cavendish Benchmark, c2008. 144 p.: Celebrate the states

Grades: 4 5 6 7   **979.7**
    1. US states 2. Geography 3. Culture 4. Washington (State) 5. United States
    ISBN 9780761425618

                          LC 2006032436

Provides comprehensive information on the geography, history, wildlife, governmental structure, economy, cultural diversity, peoples, religion, and landmarks of Washington. Provided by publisher.

979.8 Alaska

Orr, Tamra

Alaska. Tamra B. Orr. Children's Press, 2014 144 p.: America the Beautiful. Third Series

Grades: 4 5 6 7   **979.8**
    1. US states 2. Alaska 3. United States
    ISBN 9780531248768

Describes the history, geography, ecology, people, economy, cities, and sights of the state of Alaska.

980 History of South America

Gorrell, Gena K. (Gena Kinton), 1946-

★ **In** the Land of the Jaguar: South America and its people. Gena K. Gorrell; illustrated by Andrej Krystoforski. Tundra Books, c2007. vii, 149 p.

Grades: 5 6 7 8 9   **980**
    1. South America 2. South America -- History
    ISBN 0887767567

                          LC bl2007016421

Presents a historical review of South America, its people, and its natural wonders for middle readers.

"This beautifully designed volume, with an engaging narrative, combines a highly informative overview of the continent with country-by-country detail. . . . The spacious design includes big maps, clear type on thick paper, and small, beautiful, fully captioned illustrations." Booklist.

Includes bibliographical references (p. 140-141) and index.

982 Argentina

Blashfield, Jean F.

Argentina. by Jean F. Blashfield. Children's Press, an imprint of Scholastic Inc., 2015. 144 p.: Enchantment of the World. Second Series

Grades: 4 5 6 7   **982**
    1. Countries 2. Argentina 3. South America
    ISBN 9780531212509

                          LC 2014031836

Introduces Argentina, describing the country's food, people, culture, and geography.

Fearns, Les

Argentina. Les and Daisy Fearns. Facts on File, c2005. 61 p.: Countries of the world (Facts on File)

Grades: 7 8 9 10   **982**
    1. Argentina 2. South America
    ISBN 0816060088

                          LC 2005040675

Provides information on the geography, climate, people, resources, culture, and future of Argentina.

"This is an introduction to Argentina's culture, history, geography, government, and economy. [It is] competently written and [contains] current information. [The text is] clear but the level of vocabulary is quite high, which might prove challenging for less competent readers. Visually, the [book is] quite impressive, with full-color photographs, maps, tables, and graphs distributed throughout." School Library Journal.

Includes bibliographical references (p. 59) and index.

983 Chile

Burgan, Michael

Chile. by Michael Burgan. Children's Press, 2017. 144 p.: Enchantment of the world

Grades: 5 6 7 8   **983**
    1. Chile 2. South America
    ISBN 9780531218853

                          LC 2015048543

"With stunning, high-quality photos that reflect the richness of cultures around the globe, the Enchantment of the World series earns its name." Booklist.

Includes bibliographical references and index.

984 Bolivia

Yomtov, Nelson

Bolivia. Nel Yomtov. Children's Press, 2019. 144 p.

Grades: 5 6 7 8   **984**
    1. Bolivia
    ISBN 9780531126943

                          LC 2018019516

This book details the history, culture, geography and government of Bolivia." Provided by publisher.

985 Peru

Calvert, Patricia

★ The **ancient** Inca. written by Patricia Calvert. Franklin Watts, c2004. 128 p.: People of the ancient world

Grades: 5 6 7 8   **985**
    1. Incas -- History 2. Incas -- Social life and customs 3. Indians of South America 4. Civilization, Native American
    ISBN 0531123588

                          LC 2004001956

Looks at the ancient Inca civilization, discussing daily life, social structure, and contibutions made to later civilizations.

"This well-written, attractive [title has] extensive collections of quality color photographs of ruins and artifacts." School Library Journal.

Includes bibliographical references (119-120) and index.

Gruber, Beth

★ **National** Geographic investigates ancient Inca: archaeology unlocks the secrets of the Inca's past. by Beth Gruber; Johan Reinhard, consultant. National Geographic, c2007. 64 p. : National Geographic investigates

Grades: 5 6 7 8   **985**

   1. Incas -- Antiquities 2. Excavations (Archaeology) 3. Archaeology 4. Andes Region -- Antiquities. 5. Peru -- Antiquities.
ISBN 0792278739

"This offers the beautiful photography and illustrations characteristic of the National Geographic Society, [a] well-written [text] and sidebars, and information on recent archaeological finds." School Library Journal.

986.1 Colombia

Yomtov, Nelson

★ **Colombia**. by Nel Yomtov. Children's Press, An Imprint of Scholastic Inc., 2014 144 p.: Enchantment of the World. Second Series

Grades: 5 6 7 8   **986.1**

   1. Countries 2. Culture 3. Colombia
ISBN 9780531220139

                      LC 2013026060

Discusses the geography, culture, history, religion, economy, and community life of Colombia.

986.6 Ecuador

Foley, Erin, 1967-

Ecuador. writers: Erin Foley, Leslie Jermyn, and Caitlyn Paley. Cavendish Square, 2016. 144 p.: Cultures of the world

Grades: 5 6 7 8   **986.6**

   1. Ecuador 2. South America
ISBN 9781502617019

                      LC 2015046630

Provides comprehensive information on the geography, history, governmental structure, economy, peoples, religion, and culture of Ecuador.

Kras, Sara Louise

The **Galapagos** Islands. by Sara Louise Kras. Marshall Cavendish Benchmark, c2009. 96 p. : Nature's wonders

Grades: 5 6 7 8   **986.6**

   1. Natural history 2. Botany 3. Wildlife 4. Zoology 5. Galapagos Islands 6. Ecuador
ISBN 9780761428565

                      LC 2007020416

Provides comprehensive information on the geography, history, wildlife, peoples, and environmental issues of the Galapagos Islands. Provided by publisher.

Lourie, Peter

Lost treasure of the Inca. Peter Lourie. Boyds Mills Press, 1999. 48 p.

Grades: 4 5 6 7   **986.6**

   1. Inca metal-work 2. Treasure hunting 3. Incas -- Antiquities 4. Gold
ISBN 1563977435

                      LC 98088216

Chronicle of an expedition into the Llanganati Mountains of Ecuador in search of 750 tons of worked gold, which the Incas hid from the Spanish conquistadors after Pizarro executed the Sun King, Atahualpa.

"Lourie succumbed to altitude sickness and had to descend without discovering a glimmer of the gold. But he did return with a ripping good yarn to tell . . . and some breathtaking photographs of the mist-shrouded volcanic peaks. This should be a hot pick for armchair travelers." Bulletin of the Center for Children's Books.

988.1 Guyana

Jermyn, Leslie

Guyana. Leslie Jermyn, Winnie Wong, and Debbie Nevins. Cavendish Square 2019 144 p.: Cultures of the World

Grades: 5 6 7 8   **988.1**

   1. Guyana
ISBN 9781502647467

A book for middle and high school students about the history and culture of the South American nation Guyana.. Provided by publisher.

989.5 Uruguay

Jermyn, Leslie

Uruguay. Leslie Jermyn, Winnie Wong, Debbie Nevins. Cavendish Square Publishing, 2019, c2010. 128 p. : Cultures of the world

Grades: 5 6 7 8   **989.5**

   1. Countries 2. Uruguay 3. South America
ISBN 9781502636447

                      LC 2009007127

Describes the geography, history, government, economy, people, lifestyle, religion, language, arts, leisure, festivals, and food of the smallest country in South America.

993 New Zealand

Gillespie, Carol Ann

New Zealand. Carol Ann Gillespie. Chelsea House Publishers, c2006. 100 p.: Modern world nations

Grades: 7 8 9 10   **993**

   1. New Zealand 2. Islands of the Pacific
ISBN 0791087085

                      LC 2005045445

Introduces the history, wildlife, economy, politics, and people of New Zealand.

Jackson, Barbara

★ **New** Zealand. Barbara Jackson. National Geographic, 2008. 64 p.: National Geographic countries of the world

Grades: 4 5 6 7   **993**

   1. Maori (New Zealand people) 2. New Zealand -- Description and travel. 3. New Zealand -- Social life and customs.
ISBN 9781426303012

Draws readers into some of the world's most interesting and important countries with current, detailed information on virtually everything that defines life in a particular place, from economy and the environment to geography and social trends.

Smelt, Roselynn

New Zealand. Roselynn Smelt. Marshall Cavendish Corp., 2008. 144 p.: Cultures of the world

Grades: 5 6 7 8 **993**

1. Ethnology 2. Geography 3. Culture 4. Wildlife 5. Multiculturalism 6. New Zealand
ISBN 9780761434153

Provides comprehensive information on the geography, history, wildlife, governmental structure, economy, cultural diversity, peoples, religion, and culture of New Zealand. Provided by publisher.

994 Australia

Einfeld, Jann

Life in the Australian Outback. by Jann Einfeld. Lucent Books, c2003. 112 p.: The way people live

Grades: 6 7 8 9 **994**

1. Wilderness areas 2. Australia -- Social life and customs 3. Australia
ISBN 1590180143

LC 2001007504

Describes the variety of people, careers, and lifestyles found in Australia's Outback.

"An in-depth look at a unique culture that exists in Australia's remote interior. Well detailed and meticulously documented, this book does an excellent job of illustrating the diversity of the outback population as well as the challenges faced by its inhabitants." School Library Journal.

Includes bibliographical references (p. 101-106) and index.

Leppman, Elizabeth J.

Australia and the Pacific. Elizabeth J. Leppman. Chelsea House Publishers, 2006. vii, 118 p.: Modern world cultures

Grades: 7 8 9 10 **994**

1. Australia 2. Oceania
ISBN 0791081508

LC 2005010040

Describes the history, culture, politics, economy, and physical geography of Australia and the Pacific Islands.

Turner, Kate, 1967-

★ **Australia**. Kate Turner. National Geographic, c2007. 64 p.: National Geographic countries of the world

Grades: 4 5 6 7 **994**

1. Australia
ISBN 1426300557

LC 2007027848

A basic overview of the history, geography, climate, and culture of Australia.

"This appealing [title has] wonderful photographs and maps. . . . [This book is a] reliable [source] for country research, and the interesting current material hold browsing potential as well." School Library Journal.

Includes bibliographical references (p. 61) and index.

994.01 Australia—Early history to 1788

Arnold, Caroline

★ **Uluru,** Australia's Aboriginal heart. by Caroline Arnold; photographs by Arthur Arnold. Clarion Books, c2003. 64 p.

Grades: 5 6 7 8 **994.01**

1. Aboriginal Australians 2. Aboriginal Australians -- Religion 3. Sacred space 4. National parks and reserves 5. Uluru-Kata Tjuta National Park, Northern Territory 6. Uluru/Ayers Rock, Northern Territory
ISBN 0618181814

LC 2002015542

Describes Uluru, formerly known as Ayers Rock, in Australia's Uluru-Kata Tjuta National Park, its plant and animal life, and the country's Aboriginal people for whom the site is sacred.

"The book's greatest accomplishment . . . is to give readers a sense of the ongoing spiritual importance of Uluru to the Anangu, who have lived around it for 10,000 years. Clear, colorful photos of Uluru and its surroundings appear on nearly every page, illustrating the text with beauty and finesse." Booklist.

995.3 Papua New Guinea

Gascoigne, Ingrid

Papua New Guinea. Ingrid Gascoigne. Marshall Cavendish, 2008. 144 p.: Cultures of the world

Grades: 5 6 7 8 **995.3**

1. Wildlife 2. Behavior and culture 3. Economics 4. Geography 5. Papua New Guinea Peoples 6. Papua New Guinea -- Social life and customs
ISBN 9780761434160

Provides comprehensive information on the geography, history, wildlife, governmental structure, economy, cultural diversity, peoples, religion, and culture of Papua New Guinea. Provided by publisher.

996.1 Southwest central Pacific, and isolated islands of southeast Pacific

Kraske, Robert

Marooned: the strange but true adventures of Alexander Selkirk, the real Robinson Crusoe. by Robert Kraske; illustrated by Robert Andrew Parker. Clarion Books, c2005. 120 p.

Grades: 5 6 7 8 **996.1**

1. Selkirk, Alexander, 1676-1721. 2. Defoe, Daniel, 1661?-1731. Robinson Crusoe. 3. Castaways 4. Survival (After airplane accidents, shipwrecks, etc) 5. Survival skills 6. Island life
ISBN 9780618568437

LC 2004028769

Marooned on a South Pacific island, Alexander Selkirk survived in complete solitude for more than four years. After his rescue in 1709 he became the real-life model for Daniel Defoe's novel Robinson Crusoe.

"In 1704, English sailing master Alexander Selkirk was marooned on Juan Fernandez, an isolated Pacific island. . . . In 1709, two English ships rescued him, hired him as a second mate, and later captured a Spanish treasure ship. . . . Kraske offers a well-focused look at life in several quite different settings during the early eighteenth century as well as an absorbing telling of Selkirk's story." Booklist.

Includes bibliographical references (p. 117-118) and index.

Pelta, Kathy

Rediscovering Easter Island: how history is invented. Kathy Pelta. Lerner, c2001. 112 p.: How history is invented

Grades: 5 6 7 8   **996.1**
1. Easter Island -- History 2. Easter Island -- Antiquities
ISBN 0822548909

LC 00009163

Discusses the many visits made by explorers, missionaries, businessmen, scientists, and others to Easter Island since the late 1600s and what they revealed about life on this remote Pacific island.

"Coverage is serious, generally evenhanded, and smoothly presented, making this a fine foundation for readers who enjoy digging up the past." Bulletin of the Center for Children's Books.

Includes bibliographical references (p. 104-108) and index.

996.11 Fiji

Ngcheong-Lum, Roseline
Fiji. Debbie Nevins, Roseline Ngcheong-Lum. Cavendish Square 2020 144 p.: Cultures of the World
Grades: 5 6 7 8   **996.11**
1. Fiji
ISBN 9781502647443

A book for middle and high schoolers about the history and culture of the island nation Fiji. Provided by publisher.

996.2 South central Pacific Ocean islands

NgCheong-Lum, Roseline, 1962-
Tahiti. by Roseline NgCheong-Lum. Marshall Cavendish Benchmark, 2008. 144 p.: Cultures of the world
Grades: 5 6 7 8   **996.2**
1. Tahiti 2. Polynesia
ISBN 9780761420897

LC 2007014901

Provides comprehensive information on the geography, history, wildlife, governmental structure, economy, cultural diversity, peoples, religion, and culture of Tahiti. Provided by publisher.

996.9 Hawaii and neighboring north central Pacific Ocean islands

Kent, Deborah
Hawaii. by Deborah Kent. Children's Press, 2014. 144 p. : America the beautiful
Grades: 4 5 6 7   **996.9**
1. US states 2. Hawaii 3. United States
ISBN 9780531248829

LC 2007005705

Describes the history, geography, ecology, people, economy, cities, and sights of the state of Hawaii.

BIOGRAPHY

Abbott, Berenice, 1898-1991
Sullivan, George, 1927-. **Berenice** Abbott, photographer: an independent vision. by George Sullivan. Clarion Books, c2006. 170 p.

Grades: 7 8 9 10   **B**
1. Photographers 2. Women photographers 3. Women
ISBN 0618440267

LC 2005030736

A biography of Berenice Abbott, who was a pioneer in the field of professional photography and is particularly acclaimed for her photographs of the streets and buildings of New York City before they were replaced by skyscrapers during a building boom in the 1920s and early 1930s.

"Sullivan brings together an enormous amount of information about Abbott and presents it in a clear, thoughtful manner. . . . Large, clear reproductions of Abbott's photos appear throughout the book." Booklist.

Includes bibliographical references (p. 161-166) and index.

Abu al-Qasim Khalaf ibn Abbas al-Zahrawi, d. 1013?
Ramen, Fred. **Albucasis** (Abu al-Qasim al-Zahrawi): renowned Muslim surgeon of the tenth century. Fred Ramen. Rosen Central, 2006. 112 p.
Grades: 5 6 7 8   **B**
1. Physicians 2. Surgeons 3. Arabic medicine -- History
ISBN 1404205101

LC 2005015786

Describes the life and accomplishments of the Muslim surgeon who perfected surgical techniques for bladder, kidney, and gallstone procedures, and developed several surgical instruments that are used today, including the tongue depressor.

"Acknowledging the skimpy historical record on his subject, Ramen fleshes out this profile of an influential Spanish physician with sweeping histories of ancient Mediterranean civilizations, early medicine, the rise of Islam, and the rise and fall of Muslim culture in Spain. Readers will come away impressed by the surgeon's contributions to medicine, which ranged from an encyclopedic surgical text to the invention of the forceps to the pioneering use of sutures. The information is buttressed by color photos of architectural remains and manuscript pages." Booklist.

Includes bibliographical references (p. 107-108) and index.

Addams, Jane, 1860-1935
Fradin, Judith Bloom. **Jane** Addams: champion of democracy. Judith & Dennis Fradin. Clarion Books, 2006. 216 p.
Grades: 7 8 9 10   **B**
1. Hull House (Chicago, Illinois) 2. 19th century 3. 20th century 4. Women social reformers 5. Women social workers 6. Peace activists 7. Social advocacy 8. Political reform 9. Chicago, Illinois 10. Illinois
ISBN 0618504362

A look at the life of the "pacifist" Jane Addams.

"A fascinating and rich life is related in strong, unfussy prose." Booklist.

Alcott, Louisa May, 1832-1888
Meigs, Cornelia, 1884-1973. **Invincible** Louisa: the story of the author of Little women. by Cornelia Meigs. Little, Brown, [1995], c1933. 210 p.
Grades: 7 8 9   **B**
1. Authors, American 19th century 2. Women authors
ISBN 0316565946

LC BL 99768354

Newbery Medal, 1934.

Profiles the life of the noted nineteenth-century writer, detailing her early, happy childhood in Pennsylvania and Boston, and her later success as author of the classic Little Women.

"This biography is to be praised still for its straightforward account of a life of struggle and success. . . . If you want to know about Louisa's external life, and trace there the events which gave rise to the internal urges and passions that produced Little Women, this book will serve well." New York Times Book Review.

Alexander, the Great, 356-323 B.C.E.

Adams, Simon, 1955-.Marshall Editions Limited. **Alexander**: the boy soldier who conquered the world. Simon Adams; conceived, edited and designed by Marshall Editions. National Geographic Society, 2005. 64 p.: National Geographic world history biographies

Grades: 4 5 6 7 **B**
    1. Generals 2. Ancient Greece -- History -- Macedonian expansion, 359-323 B.C.E. 3. Ancient Greece -- Rulers
    ISBN 0792236610

LC 2005001360

Presents the life of the king of Macedonia, discussing his childhood, his education under Aristotle, his military conquests and rule over the largest empire of the known world, and his untimely death at the age of thirty-three.

"This is a handsomely designed [book]. . . . illustrated with maps and many color photographs of art and sculpture that give substance to [the era]. . . . Adams does not downplay Alexander's brutality or all-consuming ambition and includes examples of both." School Library Journal.

Includes bibliographical references (p. 62) and index.

Ali, Muhammad, 1942-2016

Myers, Walter Dean, 1937-2014. The **greatest**: Muhammad Ali. Walter Dean Myers. Scholastic Press, 2001. 192 p.

Grades: 7 8 9 10 **B**
    1. African American boxers 2. African American athletes 3. Political activists 4. Boxing -- History 20th century. 5. Boxers (Sports)
    ISBN 0590543423

LC 00130210

"In this biography Myers combines reportage of Ali's major fights (especially against Sonny Liston, Joe Frazier, and George Foreman) with his own reflections about the sport's destructiveness and about Ali's unpopular views." Horn Book.

Includes bibliographical references (p. 164) and index.

★ Smith, Charles R.. **Twelve** rounds to glory: the story of Muhammad Ali. Charles R. Smith, Bryan Collier, ill. Candlewick Press, 2007. 80 p.

Grades: 5 6 7 8 **B**
    1. Athletes 2. Professional athletes 3. Olympic athletes 4. People with Parkinson's disease 5. Boxers (Sports)
    ISBN 0763616923

"Rap-style cadences perfectly capture the drama that has always surrounded the boxer's life. . . . Collier's compelling watercolor collages with their brown overtones beautifully portray Ali's determination and strength." School Library Journal.

Amundsen, Roald, 1872-1928

Bodden, Valerie. **To** the South Pole. by Valerie Bodden. Creative Education, c2011. 48 p.: Great expeditions

Grades: 5 6 7 8 **B**
    1. Explorers 2. Exploration 3. South Pole expeditions 4. South Pole
    ISBN 9781608180691

LC 2010033552

A history of Roald Amundsen's successful 1911 trip to the South Pole, detailing the challenges encountered, the individuals involved, the discoveries made, and how the expedition left its mark upon the world. Provided by publisher.

Andersen, H. C. (Hans Christian), 1805-1875

★ Varmer, Hjørdis. **Hans** Christian Andersen: his fairy tale life. Groundwood, 2006. 111 p.

Grades: 5 6 7 8 **B**
    1. Authors, Danish 19th century 2. Children's authors 3. Misfits (Persons) 4. Poverty 5. Inspiration 6. Denmark -- History -- 19th century.
    ISBN 088899690X

"Most of this book describes Andersen's childhood and belated schooling, showing his poverty and the grief he experienced over the death of his beloved father, as well as several horrifying events such as being forced by a teacher to witness the beheading of three young people. . . . The biography is divided into 11 chapters, set up as if they were stories. . . . The writing flows smoothly, with many details provided to help students picture the places and events. Brøgger's haunting, mixed-media illustrations add to the somber and at times surreal feeling of the text." School Library Journal.

Anderson, Laurie Halse

Anderson, Laurie Halse. **Shout**: a poetry memoir. Laurie Halse Anderson. Viking, 2019 291 p.

Grades: 7 8 9 10 11 12 **B**
    1. Women authors 2. Rape victims 3. Healing 4. Adult child sexual abuse victims 5. Sexually abused girls 6. First-person narratives
    ISBN 9780670012107

LC 2019286089

A poetic memoir and urgent call-to-action by the award-winning author of Speak blends free-verse reflections with deeply personal stories from her life to rally today's young people to stand up and fight the abuses, censorship and hatred of today's world.

"But more than that, it is a captivating, powerful read about clawing your way out of trauma, reclaiming your body, and undoing lifetimes of lessons in order to use your voice as the weapon it is. Fervent and deafening." Booklist.

Anderson, Marian, 1897-1993

★ Freedman, Russell. The **voice** that challenged a nation: Marian Anderson and the struggle for equal rights. by Russell Freedman. Clarion Books, c2004. 114 p.

Grades: 5 6 7 8 **B**
    1. African American singers 2. African Americans 3. Women 4. African Americans -- Civil rights 5. Singers
    ISBN 0618159762

LC 2003019558

Carter G. Woodson Book Awards: Middle Level, 2005.
Robert F. Sibert Informational Book Medal, 2005.

"In his signature prose, plain yet eloquent, Freedman tells Anderson's triumphant story, with numerous black-and-white photos and prints that convey her personal struggle, professional artistry, and landmark civil rights role." Booklist.

Includes bibliographical references (p. 101-103), discography (p. 105-106), and index.

Appleseed, Johnny, 1774-1845

Worth, Richard. **Johnny** Appleseed: "select good seeds and plant them in good ground". Richard Worth. Enslow Publishers, c2010. 128 p.: Americans: the spirit of a nation

Grades: 4 5 6 7   **B**

1. Apple growers 2. Nurseries (Horticulture) 3. Pioneers 4. Frontier and pioneer life
ISBN 9780766033528

LC 2008048701

Discusses the life of Johnny Appleseed, including his childhood in colonial America, his moveable nursery, the real stories behind his folk legend, and the legacy he left on American history. Provided by publisher.

"This nicely illustrated and sourced [biography] . . . includes full-page sidebars." Booklist.

Includes bibliographical references and index.

Armstrong, Louis, 1901-1971

Orr, Tamra. **Louis** Armstrong. Tamra Orr. Mitchell Lane Publishers, [2012], ©2013. 47 p.: American jazz

Grades: 6 7 8 9   **B**

1. Jazz musicians 2. African American jazz musicians 3. Musicians 4. Jazz music 5. African Americans
ISBN 9781612282640

LC 2012008631

Introduces the famous jazz trumpeter who was nicknamed Satchmo.

Partridge, Kenneth, 1980-. **Louis** Armstrong: musician. by Kenneth Partridge. Chelsea House, 2011. 110 p.: Black Americans of achievement

Grades: 6 7 8 9   **B**

1. Jazz musicians 2. African American jazz musicians 3. Musicians 4. Jazz music 5. African Americans
ISBN 9781604138337

"This is a sweet, touching biography that looks at the extraordinary life of a musical genius. The writing is clear and engaging, with a light, humorous touch. . . . Readers are treated to an overview of a unique personality." School Library Journal.

Includes bibliographical references and index.

Arnold, Benedict, 1741-1801

Murphy, Jim, 1947-. The **real** Benedict Arnold. by Jim Murphy. Clarion Books, 2007. 272 p.

Grades: 7 8 9 10   **B**

1. United States. Continental Army 2. American loyalists 3. Generals 4. Traitors 5. Revolutions 6. American Revolution, 1775-1783 7. United States -- History -- Revolution, 1775-1783
ISBN 0395776090

LC 2007005700

Provides a comprehensive look at the life of this American army officer and hero who turned traitor and the motives that led him to do what he did through letters, memoirs, and political documents from that period in history.

"Using Arnold's surviving military journals and political documents, Murphy carefully contrasts popular myth with historical fact. . . . As far as possible, he meticulously traces Arnold's life, revealing a complex man who was actually as much admired as he was loathed." Booklist.

Includes bibliographical references and index.

Sheinkin, Steve. The **notorious** Benedict Arnold: a true story of adventure, heroism, & treachery. Steve Sheinkin. Roaring Brook Press, c2010. 337 p.

Grades: 7 8 9 10   **B**

1. United States. Continental Army 2. Generals 3. Loyalists (United States history) 4. Traitors 5. Revolutions 6. American Revolution, 1775-1783 7. United States -- History -- Revolution, 1775-1783
ISBN 9781596434868

LC 2010034797

Provides a biography of America's first traitor—Benedict Arnold—that reads like an adventure tale, full of heroism, treachery, battle scenes, and surprising twists.

"Sheinkin sees Arnold as America's original action hero and succeeds in writing a brilliant, fast-paced biography that reads like an adventure novel. . . . The author's obvious mastery of his material, lively prose and abundant use of eyewitness accounts make this one of the most exciting biographies young readers will find." Kirkus.

Attila, 406?-453

Price, Sean. **Attila** the Hun: leader of the barbarian hordes. Sean Stewart Price. Franklin Watts, c2009. 128 p.: Wicked history

Grades: 6 7 8 9   **B**

1. Huns 2. Rulers 3. Rome -- History -- Empire, 30 B.C.E.-476 C.E.
ISBN 9780531218013

LC 2008040520

"In fascinating detail, the book not only introduces Attila, but gives the backstory on what made the rise of the Huns possible. The exciting yet concise writing brings readers close to the battlefield, but the fighting and intrigue are neatly set against the sweep of history." Booklist.

Includes bibliographical references and index.

Audubon, John James, 1785-1851

Plain, Nancy. **This** strange wilderness: the life and art of John James Audubon. Nancy Plain. University of Nebraska Press, 2015. 136 p.

Grades: 5 6 7 8 9 10   **B**

1. Ornithologists 2. Animal painting and illustration 3. Naturalists 4. Painters 5. Artists
ISBN 9780803248847

LC 2014020552

"This narrative of the life of a dedicated and hard-working figure is the story of an amazing individual and a glimpse into the natural history of the early United States." School Library Journal.

Includes bibliographical references and index.

Aung San Suu Kyi

O'Keefe, Sherry. **Champion** of freedom: Aung San Suu Kyi. Sherry O'Keefe. Morgan Reynolds Pub., c2012. 160 p.: Champion of freedom

Grades: 7 8 9 10 11 12   **B**

1. Women political prisoners 2. Women political activists 3. Political activists 4. Democracy 5. Women Nobel Prize winners 6. Burma -- Politics and government -- 1945-
ISBN 9781599351681

LC 2011035740

Chronicles the life of the Burmese opposition figure who has spent much of her recent life under house arrest imposed by the country's military junta.

Rose, Simon, 1961-. **Aung** San Suu Kyi. Simon Rose. AV2 by Weigl, 2011 24 p.: Remarkable people

Grades: 4 5 6 7 **B**
1. Women political activists 2. Political activists 3. Women political prisoners 4. Democracy 5. Burma -- Politics and government -- 1945-
ISBN 9781616908331

LC 2011011584

A biography of the Burmese leader who won the Nobel Peace Prize in 1991 while under house arrest.

"This looks at Aung San Suu Kyi's life, accomplishments, and challenges while including a page of quotes, an annotated list of contemporaries and influences, starter suggestions for writing a paper, and a time line and glossary. [The book] looks into the Nobel Peace Prize winning Myanmar activist, whose struggle for democracy has landed her under house arrest multiple times." Booklist.

Austen, Jane, 1775-1817

Reef, Catherine. **Jane** Austen: a life revealed. by Catherine Reef. Clarion Books, 2011. 208 p.

Grades: 6 7 8 9 10 **B**
1. Authors, English 19th century 2. Women authors 19th century 3. Women authors, English 19th century 4. Women
ISBN 9780547370217

LC 2011008146

"Reef combines firsthand accounts of Austen written by relatives and friends, historical information about Britain in the late 1700s, the basic facts of Austen's life that are readily known, and Austen's own novels and surviving letters, presented in a chronological format. . . . Reef's account also focuses on Austen's large family and many friends, highlighting the connections between Austen's novels and her life. . . . For devout Janeites it's fascinating to see all this information combined, and for others it's a worthwhile introduction to a masterful writer's life." Horn Book.

Includes bibliographical references and index.

Barakat, Ibtisam

Barakat, Ibtisam. **Tasting** the sky: a Palestinian childhood. Ibtisam Barakat Farrar, Straus and Giroux, 2007. 192 p.

Grades: 6 7 8 9 10 **B**
1. Palestinians 2. Detention of persons 3. Palestinian children 4. Arab-Israeli conflict 5. War
ISBN 9780374357337

LC 2006041265

The author remembers her childhood in Ramallah and as a Palestinian refugee in the late 1960s.

"In 1981 the author, then in high school, boarded a bus bound for Ramallah. The bus was detained by Israeli soldiers at a checkpoint on the West Bank, and she was taken to a detention center before being released. The episode triggers sometimes heart-wrenching memories of herself as a young child, at the start of the 1967 Six Days' War, as Israeli soldiers conducted raids, their planes bombed her home, and she fled with her family across the border to Jordan. . . . What makes the memoir so compelling is the immediacy of the child's viewpoint, which depicts both conflict and daily life without exploitation or sentimentality." Booklist.

Barnum, P. T. (Phineas Taylor), 1810-1891

★ Fleming, Candace. The **great** and only Barnum: the tremendous, stupendous life of showman P.T. Barnum. Candace Fleming. Schwartz & Wade Books, c2009. 106 p.

Grades: 5 6 7 8 **B**
1. 19th century 2. Circus owners 3. Popular culture -- History 19th century. 4. Circus
ISBN 9780375945977

LC 2008045847

"In this sweeping yet cohesive biography, Fleming so finely tunes Barnum's legendary ballyhoo that you can practically hear the hucksterism and smell the sawdust. . . . The material is inherently juicy, but credit Fleming's vivacious prose, bountiful period illustrations, and copious source notes for fashioning a full picture on one of the forebearers of modern celebrity." Booklist.

Includes bibliographical references and index.

Barton, Clara, 1821-1912

Hamen, Susan E.. **Clara** Barton: Civil War hero & American Red Cross founder. Susan E. Hamen. ABDO Pub., 2010. 112 p.: Military heroes

Grades: 7 8 9 **B**
1. American National Red Cross 2. Nurses 3. Women 4. Civil war 5. United States Civil War, 1861-1865 6. United States -- History -- Civil War, 1861-1865.
ISBN 9781604539608

"The rush of literary adrenalin will hook readers immediately and keep them enthralled until the end. . . . Given the dynamic topic [and] . . . appealing layout . . . [this is] likely to attract reluctant readers. In addition, sources are plentiful and well documented." School Library Journal.

Includes bibliographical references and index.

Krensky, Stephen. **Clara** Barton. Stephen Krensky. DK Pub., 2011. 128 p.: DK biography

Grades: 5 6 7 8 **B**
1. American National Red Cross 2. Nurses 3. Women 4. Civil war 5. United States Civil War, 1861-1865 6. United States -- History -- Civil War, 1861-1865 -- Medical care
ISBN 9780756672799

"Barton is placed in historical context, and key concepts, such as the causes of the Civil War, the struggle for women's suffrage, and the importance of the Geneva Convention, are explained. Compact in form, the text is complemented by full-color and archival photographs and reproductions on every spread. . . . An excellent resource for reports that will also appeal to fans of biography." School Library Journal.

Behan, Teju

Behan, Teju. **Drawing** from the city. Teju Behan. Tara Books, 2012. 28 p.

Grades: 3 4 5 6 7 8 **B**
1. Folk artists 2. Folk art, Indic 3. Artists 4. Women singers 5. Poor girls
ISBN 9789380340173

Teju Behan is a singer and self taught urban folk artist from Ahmedabad in western India who describes her life of poverty until a job working as a singer with a fellow artist led her to discover her own artistic talent.

Bell, Alexander Graham, 1847-1922

Carson, Mary Kay. **Alexander** Graham Bell: giving voice to the world. Mary Kay Carson. Sterling, c2007. 124 p.: Sterling biographies

Grades: 6 7 8 9 **B**
1. Inventors 2. Telephones -- History
ISBN 1402749511

LC 2007003502

Profiles the inventor of the telephone, who was also a teacher of the deaf, co-founder of the National Geographic Society, and creator of the metal detector.

"Carson introduces Bell's life, giving readers an excellent picture of why this man became so famous. . . . [The book provides] clear, concise information in an easy-to-follow format with captioned photographs and illustrations on most pages." School Library Journal.

Includes bibliographical references (p. 121) and index.

Bell, Cece

★ Bell, Cece. **El** Deafo. Cece Bell; illustrated by David Lasky. Abrams Books, 2014. 248 p.

Grades: 3 4 5 6 7   **B**
1. Girls who are deaf 2. Hearing 3. Cartoonists 4. Girls with disabilities 5. Deafness 6. Autobiographical comics 7. Comics and Graphic novels
ISBN 9781419710209

"Bell's bold and blocky full-color cartoons perfectly complement her childhood stories—she often struggles to fit in and sometimes experiences bullying, but the cheerful illustrations promise a sunny future." Booklist.

Bernhardt, Sarah, 1844-1923

Reef, Catherine. **Sarah** Bernhardt: the divine and dazzling life of the world's first superstar. Catherine Reef. Clarion Books/ Houghton Mifflin Harcourt, 2020 192 p.

Grades: 6 7 8 9 10   **B**
1. Actors and actresses 2. Silent film actors and actresses
ISBN 9781328557506

LC 2019017244

A tantalizing biography for teens on Sarah Bernhardt, the first international celebrity and one of the greatest actors of all time, who lived a highly unconventional, utterly fascinating life. Illustrated with more than sixty-five photos of Bernhardt onstage, in film, and in real life. Provided by publisher.

Bernstein, Leonard, 1918-1990

★ Rubin, Susan Goldman. **Music** was it: young Leonard Bernstein. Susan Goldman Rubin. Charlesbridge, c2011. xi, 178 p.

Grades: 5 6 7 8   **B**
1. Musicians 2. Classical music 3. Composers
ISBN 9781580893442

LC 2010007584

Carter G. Woodson Book Awards: Middle Level, 2012.

Sydney Taylor Book Award for Older Readers, 2012.

Describes the musician's childhood and education, his relationship with his family, and his career as a composer and conductor.

"An impeccably researched and told biography of Leonard Bernstein's musical apprenticeship, from toddlerhood to his conducting debut with the New York Philharmonic at age 25. . . . Drawn from interviews, family memoirs and other print resources, quotations are well-integrated and assiduously attributed. Photos, concert programs, early doodles and letters, excerpts from musical scores and other primary documentation enhance the text. Excellent bookmaking—from type to trim size—complements a remarkable celebration of a uniquely American musical genius." Kirkus.

Includes bibliographical references (p. 155-156), discography (p. 152-154), videography (p. 154), and index.

Bhutto, Benazir, 1953-2007

Naden, Corinne J.. **Benazir** Bhutto. Corinne J. Naden. Marshall Cavendish Benchmark, c2011. 96 p.: Leading women

Grades: 5 6 7 8   **B**
1. Prime ministers 2. Women politicians 3. Women 4. Pakistan -- Politics and government.
ISBN 9780761449522

LC 2009029654

Presents the biography of Benazir Bhutto against the backdrop of her political, historical, and cultural environment. Provided by publisher.

"In this biography readers learn about Bhutto's student years at Radcliffe College and her rise to prime minister of Pakistan, the first woman to lead a Muslim state. . . . The [woman's life is] revealed within the political and historical context of [her] times and [includes] quotes from autobiographical material. . . . Color and black-and-white photos are included. . . . The compact size, chronological organization, and accessible writing [style makes this biography a] good [resource] for reports." School Library Journal.

Includes bibliographical references (p. 92-93) and index.

Price, Sean. **Benazir** Bhutto. Sean Stewart Price. Heinemann Library, 2010. 112 p.: Front-page lives

Grades: 6 7 8 9 10   **B**
1. Prime ministers 2. Women politicians 3. Women 4. Pakistan -- Politics and government. 5. Pakistan
ISBN 9781432932220

LC 2009018315

"This volume, on the assassinated leader of Pakistan, is particularly well done, thanks to Price's clear and compelling text. . . . The many color photographs are particularly crisp and colorful, and the sidebars briefly but effectively deal with important topics." Booklist.

Includes bibliographical references (p. 106) and index.

Biden, Joseph R., 1942-

Gormley, Beatrice. **Joe** Biden: our 46th President. Beatrice Gormley. Simon & Schuster 2021 176 p.

Grades: 6 7 8 9   **B**
1. United States. Congress. Senate 2. Presidents 3. Legislators 4. United States -- Politics and government
ISBN 9781534479326

A student biography of the respected Democratic veteran and former vice president traces Joe Biden's life from his childhood and his decades in the Senate through his service during Barack Obama's administration and beyond.

"Gormley's personal angles shine strongest, and interspersed essays about topics such as civil and voting rights and the Supreme Court contextualize events and underscore complicated issues." Publishers Weekly

Biles, Simone, 1997-

Biles, Simone, 1997-. **Courage** to soar: a body in motion, a life in balance. Simone Biles; with Michelle Burford; [foreword by Mary Lou Retton]. Zondervan, [2016] 250 p.

Grades: 5 6 7 8 9   **B**
1. Gymnasts 2. Olympic athletes 3. African American athletes 4. Adopted teenage girls
ISBN 9780310759669

In Courage to Soar, the official autobiography from US Olympic gymnast Simone Biles, Simone presents the story of how she overcame early childhood challenges to become the most decorated US female gymnast and the only female gymnast to ever win three consecutive World Championship titles.

"Biles's narration is effervescent, showing her to be, as her brother says, 'a goofy and down-to-earth kid.' . . . Essential for libraries serving tween and teen gymnastics fans." School Library Journal

Bin Laden, Osama, 1957-2011

Elish, Dan. **Inside** the situation room: how a photograph showed America defeating Osama bin Laden. by Dan Elish. Compass Point Books, 2019. 64 p.

Grades: 4 5 6   **B**
    1. United States. Navy. SEALs 2. Special operations (Military science) 3. Terrorism -- Prevention 4. War on Terrorism, 2001-2009 5. Middle East -- Politics and government -- 21st century
    ISBN 9780756558796

                LC 2018018480

On-point historical photographs combined with strong narration bring the story of the raid that captured bin Laden to life. Kids will feel as though they are in the room with President Barack Obama, Secretary of State Hillary Clinton, and the others in the cabinet who called for and monitored the raid. Primary source quotations make the event feel immediate, and photographs by the White House photographer add to the immediacy, and the understanding of the risks and dangers posed by the ultimately successful mission.

Lunis, Natalie. The **takedown** of Osama bin Laden. by Natalie Lunis; consultant, Fred Pushies. Bearport Pub., c2012. 32 p.: Special ops (Bearport Pub.)

Grades: 4 5 6 7   **B**
    1. United States. Navy. SEALs 2. Terrorists 3. Terrorism 4. Navy SEALs
    ISBN 9781617724596

                LC 2011040472

Large action photos, fact boxes and colorful maps enrich real-life narratives from United States military heroes who defend their nation and save lives while performing the most dangerous missions in the world.

Black Elk, 1863-1950

★ Nelson, S. D.. **Black** Elk's vision: a Lakota story. S.D. Nelson. Abrams Books for Young Readers, 2010. 47 p.

Grades: 5 6 7 8   **B**
    1. Oglala Indians 2. Indians of North America 3. United States -- History -- 19th century 4. United States -- History -- 20th century
    ISBN 9780810983991

                LC 2009009392

Narrates the life of the Lakota Native American, providing first-person perspectives on such topics as his childhood visions, involvement in the battles of Little Bighorn and Wounded Knee, and contributions to Buffalo Bill's Wild West Show.

"This handsomely designed, large-format book tells the story of Black Elk (1863-1950), a Lakota man who saw many changes come to his people. . . . Often quoting from Black Elk Speaks (1932), Nelson makes vivid the painful ways life changed for the Lakotain in the 1800s. . . . Colorful, imaginative artwork, created using pencils and acrylic paints, is interspersed with nineteenth-century photos, underscoring that this dramatic account reflects the experiences of a man who witnessed history." Booklist.

Includes bibliographical references (p. 46) and index.

Bledsoe, Lucy Jane

★ Bledsoe, Lucy Jane. **How** to survive in Antarctica. written and photographed by Lucy Jane Bledsoe. Holiday House, c2006. ix, 101 p.

Grades: 5 6 7 8   **B**
    1. Women adventurers 2. Adventurers 3. Antarctica -- Description and travel
    ISBN 0823418901

                LC 2004060639

During her exploratory sojourns to Antarctica, Lucy Jane Bledsoe witnessed many amazing sights, such as mummified seals, and picked up more than a few survival tactics; for example, if you should find yourself in danger of falling into a cravasse, you should stretch out your body to avoid dropping farther. Part memoir, part survival tips, part curiosities, Lucy Jane Bledsoe's book lets readers vicariously experience the author's adventures while on exploration in Antarctica.

"Bledsoe, who made three trips to study Antarctica, bases her informal, chatty narrative on her thrilling adventure, bringing close the amazing science and geography as well as the gritty facts of human survival in the frigid environment. . . . Bledsoe's own black-and-white photos . . . will grab students across the curriculum." Booklist.

Bly, Nellie, 1864-1922

Bankston, John, 1974-. **Nellie** Bly: journalist. by John Bankston. Chelsea House, 2011. 128 p.: Women of achievement

Grades: 7 8 9 10   **B**
    1. Journalists 2. Women journalists 3. Women
    ISBN 9781604139082

                LC 2011000040

Tells the story of a young woman from Pennsylvania who overcame social barriers and other challenges to become the successful and respected investigative reporter she had always dreamed of becoming.

"Interspersed photos and sidebars relate prominent people and events throughout her life, while extensive back matter and a brief look at Bly's legacy conclude this engaging biography." Booklist.

Includes bibliographical references and index.

Macy, Sue. **Bylines**: a photobiography of Nellie Bly. by Sue Macy. National Geographic Society, 2009. 64 p.: Photobiographies

Grades: 5 6 7 8   **B**
    1. Women journalists 2. Women investigative journalists 3. Investigative journalism 4. Women business owners 5. Industrialists
    ISBN 9781426305146

                LC 2008052329

Examines the heroic life of Elizabeth Jane Cochran, a pioneering American journalist who, at the turn of the 20th century, not only made news herself for her very public life, but reported on the news makers of her time, exposing corruption and providing a travelogue of the many exotic locales she visited.

"This detailed biography of the trailblazing 19th-century journalist incorporates photographs of Bly and her subjects. The extensive text explores the details of a life spent seeking justice. . . . A thorough introduction to the life of a fascinating figure." Publishers Weekly.

Includes bibliographical references and index.

Bolivar, Simon, 1783-1830

Reis, Ronald A.. **Simon** Bolivar. Ronald A. Reis. Chelsea House, c2010. 120 p.: The great Hispanic heritage

Grades: 6 7 8 9   **B**
    1. Heads of state 2. Revolutionaries 3. South America -- History -- Wars of Independence, 1806-1830.
    ISBN 9781604137316

                LC 2010009485

"This offers a balanced view of El Liberator, who shed his privileged youth in a wealthy Creole Venezuelan family and became a military strategist determined to create independent Latin American states. . . . A selection of well-chosen images, a chronology, chapter notes, and [a] suggested reading [list] round out [this] engaging [title] in a sure-to-be popular [book] for reports and personal interest." Booklist.

Includes bibliographical references and index.

Bonhoeffer, Dietrich, 1906-1945

Hendrix, John, 1976-. The **faithful** spy: Dietrich Bonhoeffer and the plot to kill Hitler. John Hendrix. Amulet, 2018 176 p.

Grades: 6 7 8 9 10 11 12   **B**

1. 1940s 2. Theologians 3. Clergy 4. Anti-Nazi movement 5. World War II 6. Martyrs 7. Germany -- History -- 1933-1945. 8. Comics and Graphic novels 9. Biographical comics
ISBN 9781419732652

Adolf Hitler's Nazi party is gaining strength and becoming more menacing every day. Dietrich Bonhoeffer, a pastor upset by the complacency of the German church toward the suffering around it, forms a breakaway church to speak out against the established political and religious authorities. When the Nazis outlaw the church, he escapes as a fugitive. Struggling to reconcile his faith and the teachings of the Bible with the Nazi Party's evil agenda, Bonhoeffer decides that Hitler must be stopped by any means possible!

"Biographies of key figures from WWII are plentiful in kids' books, but Hendrix's captivating account of the life of Dietrich Bonhoeffer is a standout." Booklist.

Martin, Michael, 1948-. **Champion** of freedom: Dietrich Bonhoeffer. by Michael J. Martin. Morgan Reynolds Pub., c2012. 144 p.: Champion of freedom

Grades: 7 8 9 10 11 12   **B**

1. 1940s 2. Anti-Nazi movement 3. World War II 4. Nazism 5. Clergy 6. Theologians 7. Germany -- History -- 1933-1945. 8. Germany -- History -- 20th century.
ISBN 9781599353135

LC 2010049095

Chronicles the life of the German pastor who opposed Nazi anti-Christian policies and, after being exposed as a conspirator in the plot to assassinate Hitler, died at the Flossenburg concentration camp in 1945.

McCormick, Patricia, 1956-. The **plot** to kill Hitler: Dietrich Bonhoeffer: pastor, spy, unlikely hero. Patricia A. McCormick. Balzer + Bray, 2016. 174 p.

Grades: 6 7 8 9   **B**

1. Clergy 2. Pacifists 3. Anti-Nazi movement
ISBN 9780062411082

Traces the life of the German theologian and pacifist, whose faith led him to speak out against the Nazis and participate in an assassination plot that targeted Adolf Hitler.

Bourgeois, Louise, 1911-

Greenberg, Jan, 1942-. **Runaway** girl: the artist Louise Bourgeois. Jan Greenberg and Sandra Jordan. Harry N. Abrams, 2003. 80 p.

Grades: 7 8 9 10   **B**

1. Artists 2. Women
ISBN 0810942372

LC 2002011922

Introduces the life of renowned modern artist Louise Bourgeois, who is known primarily for her sculptures.

"In clear, elegant prose, bolstered with numerous quotes from the artist, the authors seamlessly juxtapose stories of Bourgeois' life with relevant artworks. . . . Beautifully reproduced photographs, printed on well-designed pages, offer an excellent mix of the artist's personal life and her art." Booklist.

Includes bibliographical references (p. 72) and index.

Bradbury, Ray, 1920-2012

Bankston, John, 1974-. **Ray** Bradbury. by John Bankston. Chelsea House, 2011. 120 p.: Who wrote that?

Grades: 6 7 8 9 10   **B**

1. Authors, American 20th century 2. Science fiction authors 3. Fantasy fiction authors
ISBN 9781604137781

LC 2010029477

Presents the life and career of the science fiction author, discussing his major works, awards, and personal life.

"Students who want to know more about the authors of their popular (and/or required) reading can begin with the Who Wrote That? series. Opening with an attention-grabbing anecdote, each title focuses on how the author's childhood and environment shaped the content and style of his or her writing. The books also explain how the authors' writing progressed throughout their careers and offer a brief overview and literary criticism of seminal works." Booklist.

Includes bibliographical references and index.

Brady, Hana

Levine, Karen, 1955-. **Hana's** suitcase: a true story. by Karen Levine. Albert Whitman, 2003. vii, 111 p.

Grades: 4 5 6 7   **B**

1. Horokosuto Kyoiku Shiryo Senta. 2. Tokyo Holocaust Education Resource Center. 3. 1940s 4. Separated friends, relatives, etc 5. War -- Psychological aspects 6. Hiding 7. War and society 8. Culture conflict 9. Nove Mesto nad Metuji, Czech Republic 10. Czech Republic -- History -- 20th century.
ISBN 0807531480

LC 2002027439

Sydney Taylor Book Award for Older Readers, 2002.

A biography of a Czech girl who died in the Holocaust, told in alternating chapters with an account of how the curator of a Japanese Holocaust center learned about her life after Hana's suitcase was sent to her.

"The account, based on a radio documentary Levine did in Canada . . . is part history, part suspenseful mystery, and always anguished family drama, with an incredible climactic revelation." Booklist.

Braille, Louis, 1809-1852

Freedman, Russell. **Out** of darkness: the story of Louis Braille. by Russell Freedman; illustrated by Kate Kiesler. Clarion Books, c1997. 81 p.

Grades: 4 5 6 7   **B**

1. Braille 2. Men who are blind 3. Teachers 4. People who are blind 5. People with disabilities
ISBN 9780395775165

LC 95052353

A biography of the nineteenth-century Frenchman who, having been blinded himself at the age of three, went on to develop a system of raised dots on paper that enabled blind people to read and write.

"Without melodrama, Freedman tells the momentous story in quiet chapters in his best plain style, making the facts immediate and personal. . . . A diagram explains how the Braille alphabet works, and Kate Kessler's full-page shaded pencil illustrations are part of the understated poignant drama." Booklist.

Brave Bird, Mary

Brave Bird, Mary. **Lakota** woman. by Mary Crow Dog and Richard Erdoes. Grove Weidenfeld, 1990. 263 p., [16] p. of plates

Grades: 8 9 10 11 12 Adult   **B**

  1. American Indian Movement 2. Lakota Indians 3. Dakota Indians -- Social conditions 4. Social advocates 5. Indians of North America 6. Rosebud Indian Reservation (SD)

ISBN 0802111017

          LC   89024862

Relates the experiences of an Indian woman who grew up on a reservation and joined in the revolution for Indian rights in the sixties and seventies

Bridgman, Laura Dewey, 1829-1889

Alexander, Sally Hobart. **She** touched the world: Laura Bridgman, deaf-blind pioneer. by Sally Hobart Alexander and Robert Alexander. Clarion Books, c2008. 100 p.

Grades: 5 6 7 8   **B**

  1. 19th century 2. Women who are blind and deaf 3. Children with disabilities -- Education 4. Education 5. People who are blind and deaf 6. Women with disabilities 7. United States -- Social life and customs -- 19th century.

ISBN 0618852999

When she was just two years old, Laura Bridgman lost her sight, her hearing, and most of her senses of smell and taste. But then a progressive doctor, who had just opened the country's first school for the blind in Boston, took her in. Laura learned to communicate, read, and write—and eventually even to teach.

"At the age of three, in 1832, Laura Bridgman contracted scarlet fever and lost her sight, her hearing, her sense of smell, and much of her sense of taste. Her family sent her to Dr. Samuel [Gridley] Howe at the New England Institute for the Education of the Blind, and by the age of 10, Laura was world-famous for her accomplishments. . . . Alexander . . . presents a well-written and thoroughly researched biography of this remarkable woman, with numerous black-and-white photos." Booklist.

Brin, Sergey, 1973-

Sapet, Kerrily, 1972-. **Google** founders: Larry Page and Sergey Brin. by Kerrily Sapet. Morgan Reynolds Pub., 2012. 112 p.: Business leaders

Grades: 7 8 9 10 11 12   **B**

  1. Google (Firm) 2. Computer programmers 3. Businesspeople 4. Internet programming 5. Web search engines 6. Internet industry and trade executives

ISBN 9781599351773

          LC 2011014665

Highlights the life and accomplishments of Larry Page and Sergey Brin, the two founders of Google and describes the company's success.

"This biography of Google founders Larry Page and Sergey Bring will grab YAs. . . . The design is browsable, with clear type and lots of color screens and informal photos of young people at work." Booklist.

Includes bibliographical references (p. 105-106) and index.

Brown, Henry Box, b. 1816

★ Weatherford, Carole Boston, 1956-. **Box**: Henry Brown mails himself to freedom. Carole Boston Weatherford; illustrated by Michele Wood Candlewick Press, 2020. 56 p.

Grades: 4 5 6 7 8   **B**

  1. 19th century 2. Freedom seekers 3. African American men 4. Escapes 5. Enslaved people 6. African Americans 7. United States -- History -- 19th century. 8. Novels in verse

ISBN 9780763691561

Retells in verse form the story of Henry Brown, an enslaved man who escaped from Virginia by having himself enclosed in a wooden box and shipped to freedom in Philadelphia.

"Weatherford's moving, poetic verse gives the story a very personal tone as the reader becomes immersed in Brown's harrowing tale of loss and sorrow and his determination to be free." Horn Book.

Includes bibliographical references.

Bruchac, Joseph, 1942-

Bruchac, Joseph, 1942-. **Bowman's** store: a journey to myself. Joseph Bruchac. Lee & Low Books, 2001, c1997. 315 p.

Grades: 7 8 9 10   **B**

  1. Abenaki Indians 2. Native American authors 3. Indians of North America 4. Multiracial persons 5. New York (State) -- Social life and customs -- 20th century 6. Adirondack Mountains, New York

ISBN 1584300272

          LC 2001016435

"Each episode is constructed with a true storyteller's attention to language and plot development. Students of modern Native American cultures will find plenty of food for thought." Booklist.

Bryan, Ashley

Bryan, Ashley. **Infinite** hope: a black artist's journey from World War II to peace. Ashley Bryan. Atheneum Books for Young Readers, 2019. 112 p.

Grades: 6 7 8 9   **B**

  1. 1940s 2. Soldiers 3. Racism in the military 4. African American artists 5. Racism 6. Segregation

ISBN 9781534404908

          LC 2019015826

Carter G. Woodson Book Awards: Middle/Secondary Level, 2020.

From celebrated author and illustrator Ashley Bryan comes a deeply moving picture book memoir about serving in the segregated army during World War II, and how love and the pursuit of art sustained him.

"Watching Bryan generously transform the bittersweet into beauty is watching the meaning of art." Kirkus.

Buffalo Bill, 1846-1917

Sanford, William R. (William Reynolds), 1927-. **Buffalo** Bill Cody: courageous wild west showman. William R. Sanford and Carl R. Green. Enslow Publishers, c2013. 48 p.

Grades: 5 6 7 8   **B**

  1. Buffalo Bill's Wild West Show -- History 2. Pioneers 3. Entertainers 4. Entertainers 5. West (US)

ISBN 9780766040076

          LC 2011031052

Explores Buffalo Bill Cody, including his childhood; working as a scout, buffalo hunter, and Pony Express rider; the creation and performances of his Wild West Show and his legacy in American history. Provided by publisher.

Bullard, Eugene Jacques, 1894-1961

Greenly, Larry W.. **Eugene** Bullard: world's first black fighter pilot. Larry W. Greenly. NewSouth Books, [2013] xii, 147 p.

Grades: 8 9 10 11 12   **B**

  1. Fighter pilots 2. African Americans 3. Racism -- History 20th century 4. African American fighter pilots 5. World War I -- Aerial operations, French 6. France

ISBN 9781588382801

          LC 2012036425

Presents the life of the African American pilot who flew missions for France during World War I, experienced racial discrimination in the United States, was beaten in the Peekskill Riots of 1949, and became a member of the French Legion of Honor.

"The incredible story of Eugene Bullard—an African American honored by the French, yet shunned by the Americans—is one too long neglected. . . . Though his heroic deeds brought recognition from the French, a white American doctor in Paris became a constant stumbling block for further progress in Eugene's life and career. . . . Using Bullard's memoirs and other sparse information about him, Greenly crafts a moving, novelistic biography that portrays Bullard's courage throughout his life. Meanwhile, the black-and-white photos, of everything from a teenage Bullard boxing to wartime aircrafts, add plenty of historical flavor." Booklist.

Includes bibliographical references (page 142) and index.

Burke, Glenn

Maraniss, Andrew. **Singled** out: the true story of Glenn Burke. Andrew Maraniss. Philomel Books, 2021 320 p.

Grades: 8 9 10 11 12   **B**
1. Professional baseball 2. Professional baseball players 3. Gay professional baseball players 4. Gay athletes 5. Gay men
ISBN 9780593116722

A photograph-complemented early biography documents the remarkable life of the lesser-known Los Angeles Dodgers outfielder, sharing insight into how Glenn Burke navigated painful obstacles to break barriers for LGBTQ+ athletes, inventing the "high five" along the way.

"Maraniss does an extraordinary job of recording this memorable life in black-and-white photographs and fluid, compelling writing that is both biography and de facto history of gay rights and the depredations of homophobia." Booklist

Burns, Anthony, 1834-1862

Hamilton, Virginia, 1936-2002. **Anthony** Burns: the defeat and triumph of a fugitive slave. by Virginia Hamilton. A.A. Knopf, c1988. xiii, 193 p.

Grades: 5 6 7 8   **B**
1. Freedom seekers 2. African American defendants 3. Trials 4. Abolitionists 5. African Americans 6. United States -- History -- 19th century
ISBN 0394881850

LC 87038063

A biography of the slave who escaped to Boston in 1854, was arrested at the instigation of his owner, and whose trial caused a furor between abolitionists and those determined to enforce the Fugitive Slave Acts.

"This book does exactly what good biography for children ought to do: takes readers directly into the life of the subject and makes them feel what it was like to be that person in those times." Horn Book.

Bibliography: p. 187-189.

Busby, Cylin

Busby, Cylin. The **year** we disappeared: a father - daughter memoir. by Cylin Busby & John Busby. Bloomsbury, 2008. 329 p.

Grades: 8 9 10 11 12   **B**
1. 1970s 2. Police shootings 3. Hiding 4. Fathers and daughters 5. Police 6. Men with disfigurements 7. Massachusetts
ISBN 9781599901411

LC 2008017215

After her police officer father is shot one night and barely gets away with his life, everything changes for Cylin's family when they are forced to move from their home and cut off ties with everyone they know in order to maintain their safety while the search for the attempted murderer continues.

"No one with even a marginal interest in true crime writing should miss this page-turner, by turns shocking and almost unbearably sad. In 1979, in an underworld-style hit, a gunman shot John Busby, a policeman in Cape Cod; a fluke saved John's life, but he was permanently disfigured and disabled, and the family placed under 24-hour protection. Eventually the family went into hiding in Tennessee, but arguably their disappearance takes place long before they moveas John and his daughter, Cylin, alternately narrate, readers can see how the shooting erased the family's sense of themselves. . . . Where John's chapters provide the grim facts, it is Cylin's authentically childlike perspective that, in revealing the cost to her innocence, renders the tragic experience most searingly." Publishers Weekly.

Includes bibliographical references and index.

Caesar, Julius, 100-44 B.C.E

Galford, Ellen.National Geographic Society . **Julius** Caesar: the boy who conquered an empire. Ellen Galford. National Geographic, 2007. 64 p.: National Geographic world history biographies

Grades: 5 6 7 8   **B**
1. Heads of state 2. Generals 3. Politicians 4. Rome -- History -- Republic, 265-30 B.C.E.
ISBN 9781426300646

LC 2006020777

"This visually appealing [title is] packed with excellent photographs and reproductions, interesting sidebars, and [has] a time line running along the bottom of every page. . . . [This book is] useful, well-written." School Library Journal.

Includes bibliographical references (p. 62) and index.

Calamity Jane, 1856-1903

Sanford, William R. (William Reynolds), 1927-. **Calamity** Jane: courageous wild west woman. William R. Sanford and Carl R. Green. Enslow Publishers, c2013. 47 p.

Grades: 5 6 7 8   **B**
1. Pioneers 2. Women 3. Women pioneers 5. The West (United States)
ISBN 9780766040106

LC 2011033840

Separates the myth from the truth in the life of Calamity Jane, including her early life, her many different occupations, her travels throughout the Wild West, and how she became a legendary figure. Provided by publisher.

Calcines, Eduardo F.

Calcines, Eduardo F.. **Leaving** Glorytown: one boy's struggle under Castro. Eduardo F. Calcines. Farrar Straus Giroux, 2009. 221 p.

Grades: 7 8 9 10   **B**
1. Cubans 2. Refugees 3. Cuba -- History -- 1959-1990
ISBN 9780374343941

LC 2008007506

The author, a child of Fidel Castro's Cuba, recounts his boyhood and chronicles the conditions that led him to leave behind his beloved extended family and his home for a chance at a better life in the United States.

"Calcines's spirited memoir captures the political tension, economic hardship, family stress, and personal anxiety of growing up during the early years of the Castro regime in Cuba. . . . The author shares startling, clear memories about his life in the Glorytown barrio of Cienfuegos. .

. . Calcines writes about Cuba with immediacy, nostalgia, and passion. This personal account will acquaint readers with the oppressive and ironic effects of communism." School Library Journal.

Carson, Rachel, 1907-1964

Rae, Rowena. **Rachel** Carson and ecology for kids: her life and ideas, with 21 activities and experiments. Rowena Rae. Independent Pub Group 2020 144 p.

Grades: 5 6 7 8 **B**
    1. Women biologists 2. Women environmentalists 3. Women scientists 4. Biologists 5. Environmentalists
    ISBN 9780897339339
                        LC 2019035062

Rachel Carson and Ecology for Kids explores the life and ideas of American biologist, conservationist, and science writer Rachel Carson, who served as the catalyst of the modern environmental movement. Provided by publisher.

"The book does a masterful job of intertwining entertaining and poignant stories about Carson with significant detail on topics that interested the scientist." Booklist

Includes bibliographical references and index.

Carver, George Washington, 1864?-1943

Harness, Cheryl. The **groundbreaking,** chance-taking life of George Washington Carver and science & invention in America. painstakingly written and illustrated by Cheryl Harness. National Geographic, c2008. 143 p.: Cheryl Harness histories

Grades: 4 5 6 7 **B**
    1. Agriculturists 2. African American agriculturists 3. African Americans
    ISBN 1426301979
                        LC 2007029316

A look at the life of America's Plant Doctor, who rose from slavery to international fame, details his childhood, his thirst for knowledge, and his revolutionary innovations that profoundly impacted American agriculture.

"Harness presents Carver as a man who, regardless of constant hardship and racial prejudice, persevered to become a beloved teacher and devoted scientist. . . . The author raises challenging questions throughout. . . . The lively prose style conveys his sense of passion and adventure about the man and his intellectual pursuits, and the simple black-and-white drawings add a further sense of drama." School Library Journal.

Includes bibliographical references (p. 139) and index.

MacLeod, Elizabeth. **George** Washington Carver: an innovative life. written by Elizabeth MacLeod. Kids Can Press, c2007. 32 p.: Snapshots: images of people and places in history

Grades: 4 5 6 7 **B**
    1. African American agriculturists 2. Agriculturists 3. Scientists 4. African Americans
    ISBN 1553379063
                        LC bl2007000973

Presents the life of the African American scientist who was born a slave and overcame racial discrimination to become a college professor famous for numerous discoveries in the field of agriculture.

"MacLeod chronicles Carver's life from childhood to the end of his career, and the recognition he received posthumously. Each spread has a page of text with a quote from Carver in the margin and a page filled with many graphics in black and white and color, including photographs, illustrations, and reproductions of artifacts, all with captions. . . . With the richness of detail presented, even reluctant readers will find something of interest about this exceptional individual." School Library Journal.

Cash, Johnny, 1932-2003

Willett, Edward, 1959-. **Johnny** Cash: "the man in black". Edward Willett. Enslow Publishers, c2011. 160 p.: American rebels

Grades: 6 7 8 9 **B**
    1. Musicians 2. Country music 3. Country musicians
    ISBN 9780766033863
                        LC 2009017346

A biography of country singer Johnny Cash, discussing his early struggles with poverty, rise to fame, personal hardships, and legacy. Provided by publisher.

"This fascinating, well-organized [portrait of the country music singer] . . . opens with the infamous 1968 live-album recording at California's Folsom State Prison. . . . Skillfully chosen photos, chapter notes, and [a] suggested-reading [list completes this] well-researched, wholly engaging [introduction]." Booklist.

Includes bibliographical references (p. 142-156), discography (p. 138-139), and index.

Castle, James, 1900-1977

★ Say, Allen. **Silent** days, silent dreams. Allen Say. Arthur A. Levine Books, An Imprint of Scholastic Inc., [2017] 64 p.

Grades: 3 4 5 6 7 8 **B**
    1. People who are deaf 2. People with autism 3. Artists 4. People with disabilities 5. Painters
    ISBN 9780545927611
                        LC 2017017323

Schneider Family Book Award for Young Children, 2018.

A fictional biography of James Castle, a deaf, autistic artist whose drawings hang in major museums throughout the world.

"With sensitive text and powerful illustrations, Say brings this remarkable, inspiring life to poignant reality." Kirkus.

Includes bibliographical references.

Catherine the Great

Vincent, Zu, 1952-. **Catherine** the Great: Empress of Russia. Zu Vincent. Franklin Watts, c2009. 128 p.: Wicked history

Grades: 6 7 8 9 **B**
    1. 18th century 2. Women rulers 3. Monarchy 4. Russia -- History -- Catherine II, 1762-1796
    ISBN 9780531218020
                        LC 2008041543

"Catherine the Great might be . . . known as a cruel dictator with lots of lovers, but author Vincent shows how the Empress of Russia actually took on her position (well, after she had her husband murdered) with some good intentions. . . . Young readers will find the manipulation of Catherine's early days particularly interesting." Booklist.

Includes bibliographical references and index.

Catlin, George, 1796-1872

Reich, Susanna. **Painting** the wild frontier: the art and adventures of George Catlin. Susanna Reich. Clarion Books, c2008. xiv, 160 p.

Grades: 7 8 9 10 11 12 **B**
    1. 19th century 2. Painters 19th century 3. Indians of North America in art 4. The West (United States) in art 5. Artists 19th century 6. The West (United States)
    ISBN 9780618714704
                        LC 2007038847

Generously illustrated with archival prints and photos of Catlin's own paintings, an accessible biography of one of America's best-known painters weaves a well-researched history with stories of Catlin's travels and adventures.

"This is a biography of nineteenth-century painter George Catlin, famous for his portraits of Native American life. . . . A great introduction to Catlin's work as well as an excellent title to use in social studies, history, and art classes." Booklist.

Includes bibliographical references (p. 152-155) and index.

Cézanne, Paul, 1839-1906

Burleigh, Robert. **Paul** Cézanne: a painter's journey. by Robert Burleigh. H.N. Abrams, 2006. 32 p.

Grades: 4 5 6 7   **B**

1. Painters 2. Families 3. Fathers and sons 4. Impressionism (Art) 5. Art, French
ISBN 0810957841

LC 2005011779

"Burleigh offers brief insights into Cézanne's personal life, such as his relationship with his father, who did not support his son's interest in art. However, the emphasis is on interpreting some individual paintings and understanding the artist's various styles, including the impact of the Impressionists and his evolution to a freer and simpler manner of expression in his later years. . . . The high-quality reproductions demonstrate Burleigh's points. . . . A solid, lively introduction." School Library Journal.

Spence, David. **Cézanne**. David Spence. NewForest Press, 2011. 48 p.: Great artists and their world

Grades: 6 7 8 9   **B**

1. Painters 2. Artists 3. Art, French 4. Impressionism (Art)
ISBN 9781848983151

LC 2010925202

"Offers biographical information [of Paul Cézanne] . . . interspersed with art history and criticism in an eye-catching format. . . . [Includes] a long introductory paragraph and four-to-six images with explanatory notes. . . . Spence . . . does a good job of explaining why art that might seem ordinary today was revolutionary at the time of its creation." School Library Journal.

Chaplin, Charlie, 1889-1977

Fleischman, Sid, 1920-2010. **Sir** Charlie Chaplin: the funniest man in the world. by Sid Fleischman. Greenwillow Books, c2010. 288 p.

Grades: 5 6 7 8 9   **B**

1. Comedians 2. Film actors and actresses 3. Silent films
ISBN 9780061896408

LC 2009019689

"This lively and engaging account of a poor Cockney boy who became the world's greatest silent-movie comedian is a must for biography collections. . . . Brief, easily digestible chapters, an extensive time line, and plenty of photos make the book's well-researched content accessible and appealing." School Library Journal.

Charles, Ray, 1930-2004

Woog, Adam, 1953-. **Ray** Charles and the birth of soul. Adam Woog. Lucent Books, c2006. 112 p.: Lucent library of Black history

Grades: 7 8 9 10   **B**

1. African American singers 2. African American pianists 3. African Americans 4. Men who are blind 5. Musicians
ISBN 1590188446

LC 2005022586

Describes the life of world-renowned musician Ray Charles and the impact he had upon music.

"Woog does an excellent job of describing Charles's rare talent and the trajectory of his long and legendary career. . . . The text is clearly written and well organized. Black-and-white photographs illustrate and inform." School Library Journal.

Includes bibliographical references (p. 101-106) and index.

Chikwanine, Michel

Humphreys, Jessica Dee. **Child** soldier: when boys and girls are used in war. written by Jessica Dee Humphreys & Michel Chikwanine; illustrated by Claudia Davila. Kids Can Press, [2015] 47 p.: CitizenKid

Grades: 5 6 7 8   **B**

1. Child soldiers 2. Children and war 3. War 4. Children's rights 5. Congo (Democratic Republic) -- History -- 1997- 6. Comics and Graphic novels
ISBN 9781771381260

Michel Chikwanine was five years old when he was abducted from his schoolyard soccer game in the Democratic Republic of Congo and forced to become a soldier for a brutal rebel militia. Against the odds, Michel managed to escape and find his way back to his family, but he was never the same again.

Chisholm, Shirley, 1924-2005

Raatma, Lucia. **Shirley** Chisholm. Lucia Raatma. Marshall Cavendish Benchmark, c2011. 96 p.: Leading women

Grades: 4 5 6 7   **B**

1. United States. Congress. House 2. African American women legislators 3. African Americans 4. African American legislators 5. Women legislators 6. Legislators
ISBN 9780761449539

LC 2009029673

Presents the biography of Shirley Chisholm against the backdrop of her political, historical, and cultural environment. Provided by publisher.

"The arresting portrait on the cover will guide readers right into this well-written [biography of] . . . the first African American woman to enter Congress. . . . Raatma vividly explains what was happening in the country at the time and uses those events effectively as a backdrop. The many photos, both black and white and color, are good choices for the well-designed book." Booklist.

Includes bibliographical references (p. 92-93) and index.

Cleary, Beverly, 1916-2021

Cleary, Beverly, 1916-2021. A **girl** from Yamhill: a memoir. Beverly Cleary. Morrow, 1988. 279 p., 29 p. of plates

Grades: 6 7 8 9   **B**

1. Authors, American 20th century 2. Women authors 3. Women 4. Authors, American 5. Oregon -- Social life and customs.
ISBN 9780688078003

LC 87031554

Follows the popular children's author from her childhood years in Oregon through high school and into young adulthood, highlighting her family life and her growing interest in writing.

"The author sees her child self with the same clarity and objectivity as she has seen her fictional characters, and her reminiscences have a resultant integrity and candor." Bulletin of the Center for Children's Books.

Cleopatra, Queen of Egypt, 69-30 B.C.E.

Blackaby, Susan. **Cleopatra**: Egypt's last and greatest queen. by Susan Blackaby. Sterling Pub., 2009. 128 p.: Sterling biographies

Grades: 5 6 7 8   **B**
    1. Women 2. Egypt -- Rulers. 3. Ancient Egypt -- History -- 332-30 B.C.E.
ISBN 9781402765407

Profiles the last queen of Egypt, who gained and maintained power over her kingdom through her alliance with Julius Caesar and later Marc Antony.

"Villainess or goddess, a great queen or a selfish and overly ambitious woman—readers get to decide. They will be drawn into this biography by a description of a legendary magnificent banquet given by Mark Antony for Cleopatra. The lively narrative maintains interest from her birth in 69 BCE to her death in 31 BCE. . . . Sidebars, color photographs, and reproductions appear throughout. . . . This book leaves readers fascinated and eager to learn more about her time in history." School Library Journal.

Includes bibliographical references and index.

Shecter, Vicky. **Cleopatra** rules!: the amazing life of the original teen queen. Vicky Alvear Shecter. Boyds Mills Press, c2010. 128 p.

Grades: 5 6 7 8   **B**
    1. Women rulers 2. Ancient Egypt -- History -- 332-30 B.C.E.
ISBN 9781590787182

LC 2009026737

Presents the life of the last Egyptian queen, who survived internal politics to became the powerful ruler of her country and was linked to two famous Roman leaders, Julius Caesar and Marc Antony.

"This attractive book presents Cleopatra's story through an unusual text, informative sidebars, and excellent color illustrations. . . . Calling attention to the writing as much as its story, the text includes puns, informal language, and contemporary metaphors. . . . Shecter's solid research is evident." Booklist.

Includes bibliographical references (p. 119-121) and index.

Clinton, Hillary Rodham

Blumenthal, Karen, 1959-2020. **Hillary** Rodham Clinton: a woman living history. Karen Blumenthal. Feiwel and Friends, 2016. 320 p.

Grades: 7 8 9 10 11 12   **B**
    1. United States. Department of State 2. United States. Congress. Senate 3. Women legislators 4. Cabinet officers 5. Presidents' spouses 6. Legislators 7. Women cabinet officers
ISBN 9781250060143

LC 2015026916

"As astounding as Clinton's many accomplishments are, readers receive a balanced, wholly human portrait with all the flaws it entails. A richly detailed study that is as perceptive as it is engaging." Kirkus.

Levinson, Cynthia. **Hillary** Rodham Clinton: do all the good you can. Cynthia Levinson. Balzer & Bray, 2016. 240 p.

Grades: 5 6 7 8   **B**
    1. United States. Secretary of State. 2. Women legislators 3. Presidential candidates 4. Women politicians 5. Legislators 6. Presidents' spouses
ISBN 9780062387301

A portrait of the former First Lady, Secretary of State, and presidential candidate includes coverage of her childhood in Illinois, rise to political prominence, struggles with personal setbacks, and achievements as a Senator and beyond.

"A respectful, insightful, and inspiring portrait of a fiercely ambitious, remarkably successful woman who has changed the face of American politics." Kirkus.

Includes bibliographical references (pages 293-322) and index.

Collard, Sneed B.

Collard, Sneed B.. **Snakes,** alligators, and broken hearts: journeys of a biologist's son. Sneed B. Collard. Bucking Horse Books, 2015. 174 p.

Grades: 5 6 7 8   **B**
    1. Authors, American 20th century 2. Fathers and sons
ISBN 9780984446063

"Collard proceeds to lay the groundwork for his future as a writer and observer of the natural world, describing similarly vivid animal encounters alongside otherwise fairly typical accounts of schooling, Scouting, brushes with girls, and growing up in the increasingly troubled 1960s." Booklist.

Collins, Michael, 1930-

Collins, Michael, 1930-. **Flying** to the moon: an astronaut's story. Michael Collins. Farrar, Straus and Giroux, c1994. 162 p.

Grades: 5 6 7 8   **B**
    1. Space flight to the moon 2. Astronauts
ISBN 0374423563

LC 93042001

The astronaut discusses his early career, his training for space flight, his trips into space including the first lunar landing, and the possibilities for life and flight in space in the future

Schyffert, Bea Uusma. The **man** who went to the far side of the moon: the story of Apollo 11 astronaut Michael Collins. by Bea Uusma Schyffert; [translated by Emi Guner]. Chronicle Books, 2003. 77 p.

Grades: 5 6 7 8   **B**
    1. United States. National Aeronautics and Space Administration. 2. Project Apollo (U.S.) 3. 1970s 4. Astronauts 5. Apollo 11 (Spacecraft) -- History 6. Space flight to the moon 7. Moon 8. Translations Swedish to English
ISBN 0811840077

LC 2002151912

A biography of the astronaut, Michael Collins, who circled the moon in the Apollo 11 space capsule while his colleagues Neil Armstrong and Buzz Aldrin landed the lunar module and walked on the moon.

"This excellent book—illustrated scrapbook-style with a cleverly presented mix of photographs, illustrations, and charts—communicates the excitement of space travel." Booklist.

Coltrane, John, 1926-1967

Golio, Gary. **Spirit** seeker: John Coltrane's musical journey. by Gary Golio; paintings by Rudy Gutierrez. Clarion Books, 2012. 48 p.

Grades: 3 4 5 6 7   **B**
    1. Jazz musicians 2. African American musicians 3. Saxophonists 4. African American jazz musicians 5. African Americans
ISBN 9780547239941

LC 2011045948

Tells the story of the legendary jazz musician, from his deeply religious childhood to his career as a boundary-breaking musician who found inspiration in his own unique approach to both spirituality and music.

Colvin, Claudette, 1939-

Hoose, Phillip M., 1947-. **Claudette** Colvin: twice toward justice. by Phillip Hoose. Melanie Kroupa Books, 2009. 144 p.

Grades: 6 7 8 9 10   **B**

1. African American teenage girls 2. Segregation in transportation -- History 3. Civil rights movement 4. African American civil rights workers 5. Segregation 6. Montgomery, Alabama 7. Montgomery, Alabama -- Race relations -- History -- 20th century.
ISBN 9780374313227

LC 2008005435

Carter G. Woodson Book Awards: Middle Level, 2010.
National Book Award for Young People's Literature, 2009.
"Teenager Claudette Colvin's significant contribution to the struggle for equal accommodation is presented in this biography that smoothly weaves excerpts from Hoose's extensive interviews with Colvin and his own supplementary commentary. . . . [Readers learn] why her arrest for refusing to give up her bus seat to a white passenger never became the crucial incident to spark the Montgomery Bus Boycott. . . . Plenty of black-and-white photographs and well-deployed sidebars enhance the text." Bulletin of the Center for Children's Books.
Includes bibliographical references and index.

Copeland, Misty

Copeland, Misty. **Life** in motion: an unlikely ballerina: young readers edition. by Misty Copeland with Brandy Colbert Aladdin. Aladdin, 2016 192 p.

Grades: 5 6 7 8 9   **B**

1. Ballet dancers 2. African American dancers 3. Women dancers 4. African American women
ISBN 9781481479806

LC 2016036841

"In this young readers' edition of her 2014 memoir of the same name and with Colbert's assistance, Copeland writes in a conversational tone. She devotes much space to her innate abilities, her ABT career, and her overwhelming desire to succeed and be an inspiration." Kirkus.
Includes bibliographical references and index.

Crandall, Prudence, 1803-1890

★ Jurmain, Suzanne. The **forbidden** schoolhouse: the true and dramatic story of Prudence Crandall and her students. Suzanne Jurmain. Houghton Mifflin, 2005. 150 p.

Grades: 5 6 7 8   **B**

1. 19th century 2. Women educators 3. African American women -- Education -- History 4. African American women teachers 5. Racism 6. Race relations 7. Connecticut -- History -- 19th century.
ISBN 9780618473021

LC 2004026554

"A compelling, highly readable book. . . . Writing with a sense of drama that propels readers forward . . . Jurmain makes painfully clear what Crandall and her students faced. . . . Including a number of sepia-toned and color photographs as well as historical engravings, the book's look will draw in readers." Booklist.
Includes bibliographical references (p. 138-144) and index.

Crazy Horse, approximately 1842-1877

Sanford, William R., (William Reynolds), 1927-. **Oglala** Sioux Chief Crazy Horse. William R. Sanford. Enslow Publishers, c2013. 48 p.: Native American chiefs and warriors

Grades: 6 7 8 9   **B**

1. Chiefs (Political anthropology) 2. Little Big Horn, Battle of the,

1876 3. Rulers 4. Oglala Indians 5. Indians of North America
ISBN 9780766040946

LC 2011048758

Read about one of the greatest chiefs of the Oglala Sioux, and his victory at the Battle of Little Bighorn. Provided by publisher.

Crockett, Davy, 1786-1836

Sanford, William R. (William Reynolds), 1927-. **Davy** Crockett: courageous hero of the Alamo. William R. Sanford and Carl R. Green. Enslow Publishers, c2013. 48 p.

Grades: 5 6 7 8   **B**

1. United States. Congress. House 2. Frontier and pioneer life 3. Legislators 4. Alamo (San Antonio, Tex) -- Siege, 1836.
ISBN 9780766040052

LC 2011037749

Explores the life of Davy Crockett, including his childhood on the frontier, his time as a scout and soldier, his political career, and his last heroic moments defending the Alamo. Provided by publisher.

Curie family

Hardyman, Robyn. **Pierre** and Marie Curie. Robyn Hardyman. Gareth Stevens Publishing, 2015. 48 p.: Dynamic duos of science

Grades: 4 5 6   **B**

1. Chemists 2. Women chemists 3. Women scientists 4. Nobel Prize winners 5. Radioactivity
ISBN 9781482414745

LC bl2014040527

Chronicles the life and work of the couple who toiled together to better understand radioactivity.
"This series stands out for its attractive graphics and ability to make complex concepts accessible. The authors have done an excellent job of selecting key quotes from the scientists' writings that young readers can understand (provided in sidebars titled "In Their Own Words")." School Library Journal.
Includes bibliographical references (page 47) and index.

Curie, Marie, 1867-1934

Krull, Kathleen, 1952-2021. **Marie** Curie. by Kathleen Krull; illustrations by Boris Kulikov. Viking Children's Book, 2007. 144 p.: Giants of science (Viking)

Grades: 5 6 7 8   **B**

1. Women scientists 2. Chemists 3. Physicists 4. Women chemists 20th century. 5. Women
ISBN 0670058947

LC 2007024251

This latest installment in the "Giants of Science" series traces the life of this reclusive scientist who coined the term radioactivity, and won two Nobel prizes in physics and chemistry.
"The compelling and conversational narrative (ably assisted by Kulikov's black-and-white drawings) portrays a brilliant . . . woman with plenty of idiosyncrasies, and the story of her discovery of radium . . . is as engaging as any of her personal dramas and challenges." Horn Book.

Dahl, Roald

Dahl, Roald. **Boy**: tales of childhood. Roald Dahl. Farrar, Straus, Giroux, 1984. 160 p.

Grades: 4 5 6 7 8 9   **B**

1. Authors, English 20th century 2. Children's literature authors 20th century. 3. Boarding school students 4. Children of immigrants 5. Immigrants, Norwegian 6. Great Britain -- Social

life and customs -- 20th century 7. Wales
ISBN 0374373744

LC   84048462

Presents humorous anecdotes from the author's childhood which includes summer vacations in Norway and an English boarding school.

"In these memoirs, Dahl reminisces about growing up in a large Norwegian family living in Wales during the 1920s and 1930s. The text is illustrated with sketches, old photographs and excerpts of letters he wrote as a boy." School Library Journal.

Dalai Lama

Kimmel, Elizabeth Cody. **Boy** on the Lion Throne: the childhood of the 14th Dalai Lama. by Elizabeth Cody Kimmel; with a foreword by the Dalai Lama. Flash Point, 2009, c2008. 146, 3 p.
Grades: 4 5 6 7 **B**
  1. Dalai lamas 2. Religious leaders 3. Buddhism
ISBN 9781596433946

LC   bl2009005822

Follows the childhood of Lhamo Thondup, who was identified at the age of two as the fourteenth reincarnation of the Dalai Lama, describing the humble life he was born into and how his life changed after he was recognized.

"Kimmel is reverent without being adulatory, and her explanation of the Dalai Lama's relationship with Maoist China is presented in simple, clear language. This is a strange and fascinating story told in an engaging style, and young readers will find lots to keep them turning the pages." Bulletin of the Center for Children's Books.

Includes bibliographical references (p. [148-149]) and index.

Daniels, Jonathan Myrick, 1939-1965

Wallace, Rich. **Blood** Brother: Jonathan Daniels and his sacrifice for civil rights. Rich Wallace + Sandra Neil Wallace. Calkins Creek, 2016 352 p.
Grades: 6 7 8 9 10 **B**
  1. Civil rights workers 2. Civil Rights Movement 3. Social justice 4. African Americans -- Civil rights 5. Murder -- History 20th century. 6. Alabama
ISBN 9781629790947

LC   2016932211

A biography of civil rights worker Jonathan Daniels who was ultimately murdered in Hayneville, Alabama.

"An unusually inspiring story skillfully told." Kirkus.

Includes bibliographical references (pages 328-337) and index.

Darwin, Charles, 1809-1882

★ Krull, Kathleen, 1952-2021. **Charles** Darwin. by Kathleen Krull; illustrated by Boris Kulikov. Penguin Group, c2010. 128 p.: Giants of Science (Viking)
Grades: 5 6 7 8 **B**
  1. Naturalists 19th century 2. Naturalists 3. Evolution
ISBN 9780670063352

LC   2010007315

"Krull once again offers an illuminating, humanizing portrait of a famous scientist. . . . Krull . . . writes in easily paced, lively, conversational prose, knitting together interesting facts, anecdotes, and historical overviews into a fascinating whole. She offers clear definitions of not only Darwin's theories but also how his discoveries built on previous scientists' work. . . . Kulikov's whimsical ink drawings and well-culled list of resources round out this strong entry in the series." Booklist.

Wood, A. J., 1960-. **Charles** Darwin and the Beagle adventure. written by A.J. Wood & Clint Twist. Candlewick Press, 2009. 30 p.
Grades: 4 5 6 7 8 **B**
  1. Beagle (Ship) 2. Naturalists 3. Evolution 4. Voyages and travels 5. Adaptation (Biology)
ISBN 9780763645380

LC   2009921214

"This beautifully illustrated large-format book immediately appeals to both the eye and the mind. Imitating a 19th-century scrapbook to a certain extent, including various pullouts . . . the book draws the young reader in. . . . Included are copious quotes from Darwin's journals and other writings, as well as reproductions . . . of numerous 19th-century engravings, drawings, and watercolors, some from the Beagle voyage itself. . . . Integrated into the 19th-century material are modern illustrations and well-written narratives relating background information, the story of the Beagle's voyage . . . and notes on Darwin's life and work. . . . This volume provides an excellent introduction to Darwin and his accomplishments." Science Books & Films.

Dau, John Bul

Dau, John Bul. **Lost** boy, lost girl: escaping civil war in Sudan. by John Bul Dau and Martha Arual Akech; with Michael Sweeney and Karen Kostyal. National Geographic, 2010. 160 p.
Grades: 7 8 9 10 **B**
  1. Refugees, Sudanese 2. War 3. Survival 4. Dinka (African people) 5. Sudan -- History -- Civil War, 1983-2005.
ISBN 9781426307089

LC   2010017960

"The tragic story of Sudan's Lost Boys and Lost [Girls] is told in simple language by two survivors. . . . In 1987, when Dau was 13 and Akech was 6, war came to their village. Both traveled hundreds of miles to a UN refugee camp in Ethiopia. After a few years of safety, the refugees were forced to move again. . . . Teens who know little about Sudan and its problems will be drawn into this moving, inspiration story." School Library Journal.

Dave, fl. 1834-1864

Cheng, Andrea. **Etched** in clay: the life of Dave, enslaved potter and poet. Andrea Cheng; with woodcuts by the author. Lee & Low Books, c2012. 144 p.
Grades: 4 5 6 **B**
  1. African-American potters 2. African American poets 3. Enslaved people 4. Potters 5. Poets 6. South Carolina -- History -- 19th century.
ISBN 9781600604515

LC   2012027280

The life of Dave, an enslaved potter who inscribed his works with sayings and poems in spite of South Carolina's slave anti-literacy laws in the years leading up to the Civil War. Includes afterword, author's note, and sources. Provided by publisher.

Davis, Benjamin O., Jr., 1912-2002

Earl, Sari. **Benjamin** O. Davis, Jr.: Air Force general & Tuskegee Airmen leader. Sari Earl. ABDO Pub. Co., c2010. 111 p.
Grades: 7 8 9 **B**
  1. United States. Air Force 2. African American generals 3. Generals
ISBN 9781604539615

LC   2009032339

Examines the life of Benjamin Davis, Jr., the first black man to graduate from West Point in the twentieth century, who pursued his chosen course of a military career despite the prejudice against him.

"The rush of literary adrenaline will hook readers immediately and keep them enthralled until the end. . . . Given the dynamic topic [and] . . . appealing layout . . . [this is] likely to attract reluctant readers. In addition, sources are plentiful and well documented." School Library Journal.

Includes bibliographical references (p. 106-108).

Davis, Miles

Orr, Tamra. **Miles** Davis. Tamra Orr. Mitchell Lane Publishers, [2012], ©2013. 47 p.: American jazz

Grades: 6 7 8 9 **B**

1. Jazz music 2. Jazz musicians 3. African American musicians 4. Trumpeters 5. Rock music 6. United States Popular culture -- History -- 20th century.
ISBN 9781612282657

LC 2012008632

Profiles the noted jazz trumpeter who got his start with Charlie Parker's quintet and gained fame performing at the first Newport Jazz Festival in 1955.

De la Renta, Oscar

Darraj, Susan Muaddi. **Oscar** de la Renta. Susan Muaddi Darraj. Chelsea House, c2010. 116 p.: The great Hispanic heritage

Grades: 6 7 8 9 **B**

1. Dominican Americans 2. Fashion designers 3. Fashion design 4. Clothing industry and trade 5. Hispanic Americans
ISBN 9781604137330

LC 2010009488

Narrates the story of the Dominican American who had studied art in Spain but gave up painting in order to pursue a career as a fashion designer.

"This presents a warm, almost fawning account of the wildly successful fashion designer, who maintains a home in and close ties to his native Dominican Republic. . . . A selection of well-chosen images, a chronology, chapter notes, and [a] suggested reading [list] round out [this] engaging [title] in a sure-to-be-popular [book] for reports and personal interest." Booklist.

Includes bibliographical references (p. 103-110) and index.

De Soto, Hernando, 1500?-1542

Young, Jeff C., 1948-. **Hernando** de Soto: Spanish conquistador in the Americas. Jeff C. Young. Enslow Publishers, c2009. 128 p.: Great explorers of the world

Grades: 6 7 8 9 **B**

1. Explorers 2. Spaniards in North America 3. North America -- Exploration -- Spanish 4. Mississippi Valley -- Exploration -- Spanish
ISBN 9781598451047

LC 2008030753

Discusses the life of Spanish explorer Hernando de Soto, including his travels in the Americas, the claim of Florida for Spain, and his eventual discovery of the Mississippi River. Provided by publisher.

Degas, Edgar, 1834-1917

Spence, David. **Degas**. David Spence. NewForest Press, 2011. 48 p.: Great artists and their world

Grades: 6 7 8 9 **B**

1. Painters 2. Artists 3. Painting, French 4. Impressionism (Art)
ISBN 9781848983182

LC 2010925208

"Offers biographical information [of Edgar Degas] . . . interspersed with art history and criticism in an eye-catching format. . . . [Includes] a long introductory paragraph and four-to-six images with explanatory notes. . . . Spence . . . does a good job of explaining why art that might seem ordinary today was revolutionary at the time of its creation." School Library Journal.

Diakite, Baba Wague

Diakite, Baba Wague. A **gift** from childhood: memories of an African boyhood. Baba Wague Diakite. Groundwood Books, 2010. 134 p.

Grades: 5 6 7 8 **B**

1. Parenting by grandparents 2. Grandparents 3. Childhood 4. Rural life 5. Children's book illustrators 6. Mali
ISBN 9780888999313

A beautiful memoir of a young boy growing up in a village in Mali.

"Diakite's . . . illustrated memoir focuses on his childhood in a small Malian village. . . . Interspersed with Diakite's recounting of his youth . . . are stories about his grandfather's brokering peaceful relations with the French, a blacksmith who stymies Death, and others. . . . Diakite's precise language and vibrant illustrations, created on earthenware tiles, form an engrossing story of community life. Studded with Malian proverbs, metaphors, and morals . . . it's a memoir alive with far more voices than just that of the author." Publishers Weekly.

Dickens, Charles, 1812-1870

Rosen, Michael, 1946-. **Dickens**: his work and his world. Michael Rosen; illustrated by Robert Ingpen. Candlewick Press, 2005. 95 p.

Grades: 5 6 7 8 **B**

1. Authors, English 19th century.
ISBN 0763627526

LC 2004061847

Presents the life and accomplishments of the English author, with discussions on some of his most popular works, including "A Christmas Carol" and "David Copperfield."

"The art adds to the richness of a volume designed and written with care." Booklist.

Warren, Andrea. **Charles** Dickens and the street children of London. by Andrea Warren. Houghton Mifflin Books for Children/Houghton Mifflin Harcourt, 2011. 144 p.

Grades: 6 7 8 9 10 **B**

1. Authors, English 19th century 2. Homeless children in literature 3. Poor people in literature 4. London, England in literature
ISBN 9780547395746

LC 2011003450

"This absorbing book introduces Dickens within the context of his times. . . . Chapters about his life and his novels alternate with related chapters describing the plight of the poor (especially children) in Victorian England (especially London). . . . Glimpses of his world are offered in reproductions of illustrations from Dickens' novels as well as period portraits and photos of people and places that appear throughout the book. . . . Warren writes in a clear, direct, vivid manner that brings it all to life." Booklist.

Wells, Catherine, 1955-. **Charles** Dickens: England's most captivating storyteller. Catherine Wells-Cole. Candlewick Press, 2012. 28 p.

Grades: 7 8 9 10 11 12   **B**

   1. 19th century 2. Authors, English 3. Authors, English 19th century 4. England -- Social life and customs -- 19th century

ISBN 9780763655679

                  LC 2011013677

"In this scrapbook homage to Dickens, each page teems with images and reproductions, from letters to book excerpts to maps, all pertaining to a different area of Dickens's life and work. The topics range widely, skimming the surface of both the esteemed author's life and the subjects that interested him most. . . . The gorgeous, high-quality reproductions make a strong visual impact, and while the flaps, folds, and envelopes make readers work to uncover information, most will be quickly drawn into the hunt for more treasured tidbits about Dickens and his time." School Library Journal.

Douglas, Gabrielle, 1995-

Douglas, Gabrielle, 1995-. **Grace,** gold and glory: my leap of faith: the Gabrielle Douglas story. Gabrielle Douglas; with Michelle Burford. Zondervan, 2012. 224 p.

Grades: 4 5 6 7 8 9   **B**

   1. Women gymnasts 2. Gymnastics 3. Women Olympic medal winners 4. Women Olympic athletes 5. Gymnasts

ISBN 9780310740612

                  LC 2012042389

The Olympic gold medalist shares the story of her life and how her faith allowed her to persevere and reach her dreams.

Douglass, Frederick, 1818-1895

Adler, David A.. **Frederick** Douglass: a noble life. by David A. Adler. Holiday House, c2010. 144 p.

Grades: 7 8 9 10   **B**

   1. Abolitionists 2. African American abolitionists 3. Anti-slavery movements 4. African Americans 5. United States -- Race relations -- History.

ISBN 9780823420568

                  LC 2009029970

Follows the life of the famous orator, journalist, author and adviser to U.S. presidents who, against all odds, rose above a brutal life of slavery on a Maryland plantation to become an inspiration to many.

"This is a thoroughly researched, lucidly written biography. . . . Adler does an excellent job of exploring the atrocities and dehumanizing indignities . . . visited on those who lived in slavery." Booklist.

Includes bibliographical references.

Cline-Ransome, Lesa. **Words** set me free: the story of young Frederick Douglass. Lesa Cline-Ransome; illustrated by James E. Ransome. Simon & Schuster Books for Young Readers, 2012. 40 p.

Grades: 6 7 8   **B**

   1. 19th century 2. Enslaved people 3. Abolitionists 4. African American abolitionists 5. Anti-slavery movements -- History 19th century 6. African Americans 7. United States -- History -- 19th century

ISBN 9781416959038

                  LC 2011013323

Words Set Me Free is the inspiring story of young Frederick Douglass's path to freedom through reading. Provided by publisher.

Esty, Amos. **Unbound** and unbroken: the story of Frederick Douglass. Amos Esty. Morgan Reynolds Pub., c2011. 143 p.

Grades: 7 8 9 10   **B**

   1. Abolitionists 2. African American abolitionists 3. Anti-slavery movements 4. African Americans 5. United States -- Race relations -- History.

ISBN 9781599351360

                  LC 2009054287

Traces the life and historical impact of the noted abolitionist, detailing his birth into slavery and harsh upbringing, his subsequent escape, and his emergence as a leader.

"Multiple biographies have been written about Douglass; however, few capture the depth of his intellect as an orator and writer. Through interwoven quotes from his autobiography, speeches, and pictures, this story also serves as prime research material. Douglass's ingenious case for the Constitution and fifth of July speech make the biography accessible from cover to cover." Voice of Youth Advocates.

Includes bibliographical references (p. 136-139) and index.

Sanders, Nancy I.. **Frederick** Douglass for kids: his life and times with 21 activities. Nancy I. Sanders. Chicago Review Press, c2012. ix, 145

Grades: 5 6 7   **B**

   1. Abolitionists -- History 19th century 2. African American abolitionists 3. Anti-slavery movements 4. African Americans 5. Creative activities for children and students 6. United States -- Race relations -- History. 7. United States -- History -- 19th century

ISBN 9781569767177

                  LC 2011050092

An interactive biography of the life of former slave and abolitionist Frederick Douglass.

Doyle, Arthur Conan, Sir, 1859-1930

Pascal, Janet B.. **Arthur** Conan Doyle: beyond Baker Street. Janet B. Pascal. Oxford University Press, c2000. 158 p.: Oxford portraits

Grades: 7 8 9 10   **B**

   1. Mystery story writers 2. Authors, Scottish 19th century 3. Holmes, Sherlock (Fictitious character) 4. Spiritualists 5. Physicians

ISBN 0195122623

                  LC 99036643

Reveals the author's life through historical photographs and narratives devoted to his literary career, adventurous travels, and major accomplishments.

"Pascal does a fine job of conveying the era in which her object lived." School Library Journal.

Includes bibliographical references (p. 151-154) and index.

Duncan, Tim, 1976-

Thornley, Stew. **Tim** Duncan: champion basketball star. Stew Thornley. Enslow Publishers, c2013. 48 p.: Sports star champions

Grades: 4 5 6 7   **B**

   1. National Basketball Association 2. San Antonio Spurs (Basketball team) 3. Basketball players 4. Professional basketball players 5. Caribbean-Americans 6. Professional athletes 7. Basketball

ISBN 9780766040304

                  LC 2011050440

Explores the life of San Antonio Spurs power forward Tim Duncan, including his childhood and college career, his rise to stardom in the NBA, and his championship seasons with the Spurs. Provided by publisher.

Earhart, Amelia, 1897-1937

Brown, Jeremy K.. **Amelia** Earhart: aviator. by Jeremy K. Brown. Chelsea House, c2011. 132 p.: Women of achievement

Grades: 6 7 8   **B**

1. Women pilots 2. Pilots 3. Cross-country flying -- History 20th century 4. Flights around the world -- History 20th century
ISBN 9781604139105

"This supplies an evenhanded account of Earhart's personal life, her challenges as a woman in aviation, and her many achievements in flight. . . . Solid fare for the biography collection." Booklist.

Includes bibliographical references and index.

Fleming, Candace. **Amelia** lost: the life and disappearance of Amelia Earhart. by Candace Fleming. Schwartz & Wade Books, c2011. 128 p.

Grades: 4 5 6 7   **B**

1. Women pilots 2. Pilots 3. Women
ISBN 9780375945984

LC 2010005279

Golden Kite Award for Nonfiction, 2011.

"Fleming offers a fresh look at this famous aviatrix. Employing dual narratives—straightforward biographical chapters alternating with a chilling recounting of Earhart's final flight and the search that followed—Fleming seeks to uncover the history of the hype, pointing out numerous examples in which Earhart took an active role in mythologizing her own life. . . . Frequent sidebars, well-chosen maps, archival documents, and photos further clarify textual references without disturbing the overall narrative flow." Booklist.

Includes bibliographical references.

Tanaka, Shelley. **Amelia** Earhart: the legend of the lost aviator. by Shelley Tanaka; illustrated by David Craig. Abrams Books for Young Readers, 2008. 48 p.

Grades: 3 4 5 6   **B**

1. Women pilots 2. Pilots 3. Women 4. Pilots
ISBN 9780810970953

LC 2007039749

NCTE Orbis Pictus Nonfiction Award, 2009.

Describes the life of aviator Amelia Earhart from age eleven, when someone points out a plane to her, to the day she disappears on an airplane, accompanied by illustrations, photographs, and quotes.

"This title is notable . . . for its smooth, powerful storytelling, ample gallery of well-chosen photographs, and nicely placed sidebar information on such topics as flight delays, navigation, and around-the-world flight records." Bulletin of the Center for Children's Books.

Includes bibliographical references (p. 46) and index.

Edison, Thomas A. (Thomas Alva), 1847-1931

Krieg, Katherine. **Thomas** Edison: world-changing inventor. Katherine Krieg Core Library, an imprint of Abdo Publishing, 2015. 48 p.: Great minds of science (Core Library (Firm))

Grades: 4 5 6   **B**

1. Electrical engineers 2. Inventors
ISBN 9781624033780

LC bl2014030376

Chronicles the life and career of the genius inventor, from his time inventing for Western Union to his creation of the lightbulb and phonograph.

"Students will learn about the different accomplishments of each scientist while joining them on the often tumultuous journey to success. A staple for libraries." School Library Journal.

Includes bibliographical references (page 47) and index.

Woodside, Martin. **Thomas** A. Edison: the man who lit up the world. Martin Woodside. Sterling, c2007. 124 p.: Sterling biographies

Grades: 5 6 7 8   **B**

1. Inventors 2. Electrical engineers 3. Inventors
ISBN 1402749554

LC 2007003509

Profiles the inventor best known for his work with the incandescent lightbulb and the phonograph, as well as his rivalry with Nikola Tesla.

"Woodside presents the life, struggles, failures, and successes of a man whose motto was the most important way to succeed is always to try one more time. [The book provides] clear, concise information in an easy-to-read format with captioned photographs and illustrations on most pages." School Library Journal.

Includes bibliographical references (p. 121) and index.

Einstein, Albert, 1879-1955

Delano, Marfe Ferguson. **Genius**: a photobiography of Albert Einstein. by Marfe Ferguson Delano. National Geographic Society, c2005. 63 p.

Grades: 5 6 7 8   **B**

1. Physicists 2. Scientists 3. Science -- History 20th century. 4. General relativity (Physics)
ISBN 9780792295440

LC 2004015001

Presents the life of the renowned physicist, from his privileged childhood to his early struggles to develop the theory of relativity, to his eventual recognition as one of the greatest scientists of the twentieth century.

"This combines a solid text with a particularly attractive format. . . . Delano offers just enough information about Einstein's theories to give a sense of his work. . . . Oversize and filled with well-selected photographs, the book is very handsome." Booklist.

Krull, Kathleen, 1952-2021. **Albert** Einstein. by Kathleen Krull; illustrated by Boris Kulikov. Viking, c2009. 128 p.: Giants of science (Viking)

Grades: 5 6 7 8   **B**

1. Physicists 2. Scientists
ISBN 9780670063321

LC 2009016037

"Krull delivers a splendidly humane biography of that gold standard of brilliance, Albert Einstein. . . . Drawing extensively on Einstein's writings, she presents a fully rounded portrait of a man whose genius combined with a bad temper and arrogance, to the detriment of his own professional advancement, not to mention his relationships with women and his children. Using concrete examples, the author brings such mind-bending notions as his General Theory of Relativity within the grasp of child readers." Kirkus.

Eleanor, of Aquitaine, Queen, consort of Henry II, King of England, 1122?-1204

Kramer, Ann, 1946-. **Eleanor** of Aquitaine: the queen who rode off to battle. Ann Kramer. National Geographic, 2006. 64 p.: National Geographic world history biographies

Grades: 5 6 7 8   **B**

1. Rulers 2. Rulers 3. Women rulers 4. Women 5. Great Britain

-- History -- Henry II, 1154-1189 6. France -- History -- Louis VII, 1137-1180
ISBN 0792258967

LC 2006299190

Presents the life of the twelfth-century ruler, who became the queen of France and then England, who was an active participant in many of the rivalries between the royal houses of the period, and was the mother of ten children, including Richard the Lionhearted.

Elizabeth I, Queen of England, 1533-1603

★ Adams, Simon, 1955-. **Elizabeth** I: the outcast who became England's queen. Simon Adams. National Geographic, 2005. 64 p.: National Geographic world history biographies

Grades: 4 5 6 7   **B**
1. Women rulers 2. Great Britain -- History -- Elizabeth I, 1558-1603
ISBN 0792236548

LC 2005001359

Discusses the life of Queen Elizabeth I, from her birth to Henry VIII and Anne Boleyn in 1533, her imprisonment by her half-sister, through her reign as one of England's more respected monarchs, to her death in 1603.

"Accomplishments and hardships are clearly explained with supporting quotes and facts. . . . Beautifully illustrated and visually appealing." School Library Journal.

Includes bibliographical references (p. 62) and index.

Hollihan, Kerrie Logan. **Elizabeth** I--the people's queen: her life and times: 21 activities. Kerrie Logan Hollihan. Chicago Review Press, 2011. 144 p.

Grades: 4 5 6 7 8   **B**
1. 16th century 2. Women rulers 3. Royal houses 4. Creative activities for children and students 5. Great Britain -- History -- Elizabeth I, 1558-1603 6. Great Britain -- Social life and customs -- 16th century
ISBN 9781569763490

LC 2010047647

"The writing is clear and suited to readers with no previous knowledge of the topic. The activities vary in difficulty, from reading The Faerie Queen, to creating a family coat of arms, to growing a knot garden. The book is well illustrated with black-and-white reproductions of portraits, engravings, and paintings depicting major events in the Tudors' lives. . . . This well-organized book succeeds at being interesting and scholarly at the same time." School Library Journal.

Includes bibliographical references and index.

Ellington, Duke, 1899-1974

Stein Crease, Stephanie. **Duke** Ellington: his life in jazz with 21 activities. Stephanie Stein Crease. Chicago Review Press: c2009. 148 p.

Grades: 5 6 7 8   **B**
1. Jazz musicians 2. African Americans 3. African American jazz musicians 4. Jazz pianists 5. Jazz music
ISBN 9781556527241

LC 2008023742

Offers a look at the life, times, and accomplishments of this celebrated musician of jazz with tips for how to make a ragtime rhythm, create a washtub bass, do a piano roll, and more through a number of fun activities for middle readers.

"This large-format book combines an illustrated biography of Duke Ellington with activities designed to offer insights into Ellington's era

and his music. An informative account in an attractive...format." Booklist.

Includes bibliographical references, discography, filmography, and index.

Emerson, Ralph Waldo, 1803-1882

Caravantes, Peggy, 1935-. **Self** reliance: the story of Ralph Waldo Emerson. Peggy Caravantes. Morgan Reynolds Pub., c2011. 143 p.: World writers

Grades: 7 8 9 10   **B**
1. 19th century 2. Authors, American 19th century 3. Transcendentalists (New England) 4. New England -- History
ISBN 9781599351247

LC 2010008143

Presents the life and career of the eighteenth century New England essayist, poet, and lecturer who advocated a philosophy of self-reliance and individualism and was an important figure in the American Transcendental Movement.

"This volume treats young adult readers with respect and . . . [works] to ease them into scholarly research and writing in an engaging manner." Voice of Youth Advocates.

Includes bibliographical references (p. 123-137) and index.

Engle, Margarita

Engle, Margarita . **Soaring** earth: a companion memoir to Enchanted air. Margarita Engle. Atheneum Books for Young Readers, 2019. 157 p.

Grades: 8 9 10 11 12   **B**
1. 1960s 2. 1970s 3. Cuban Americans 4. Social change 5. Teenage girls -- Identity 6. War and society 7. Civil rights 8. Los Angeles, California 9. New York City
ISBN 9781534429536

LC 2018003603

In this follow-up to her award-winning memoir Enchanted Air, Margarita Engle details her teenage years in Los Angeles against the turbulent backdrop of the Vietnam War. In vulnerable verse, she addresses the notions of peace, civil rights, freedom of expression, and environmental protection that are once again under threat. Despite these circumstances, young Margarita was able to find solace and empowerment through her education.

"The author's evocative language, vivid imagery, and authentic portrayal will engage teens. Her bumpy and circuitous road filled with failures, homelessness, and eventual resolution and academic success will encourage young adults on their own paths." School Library Journal..

Eratosthenes

Gow, Mary. **Measuring** the Earth: Eratosthenes and his celestial geometry. Mary Gow. Enslow Publishers, c2010. 128 p.: Great minds of ancient science and math

Grades: 5 6 7 8   **B**
1. Mathematicians 2. Arc measures 3. Ancient mathematics 4. Mathematics, Greek 5. Astronomers 6. Earth Figure Measurement.
ISBN 9780766031203

LC 2008038523

A biography of ancient Greek mathematician Eratosthenes, who used geometry to calculate the circumference of the earth. He is also known as the Father of Geography. Provided by publisher.

"This biography is a solid [choice], as . . . [it provides] a good overview of the cultural and political landscape of the times, as well as pictures." School Library Journal.

Includes bibliographical references and index.

Ericsson, Aprille, 1963-

Waxman, Laura Hamilton. **Aerospace** engineer Aprille Ericsson. by Laura Hamilton Waxman. Lerner Publications, [2015] 32 p.: STEM Trailblazer Bios

Grades: 4 5 6 7   **B**
   1. United States. National Aeronautics and Space Administration 2. Women engineers 3. Aerospace engineers 4. Astronautics 5. African American women aerospace engineers
ISBN 9781467757935

LC 2014013767

"Highly recommended, especially where current biographies, particularly of those involved in STEM careers, are needed and requested; strong supplemental reading for science classes, too." School Library Journal.

Includes bibliographical references and index.

Fitzgerald, Ella, 1918-1996

Stone, Tanya Lee. **Ella** Fitzgerald. by Tanya Lee Stone. Viking, 2008. 208 p.: Up close (Viking)

Grades: 7 8 9 10   **B**
   1. African-American women jazz singers 2. Singers 3. African American women 4. Women
ISBN 0670061492

LC 2007023117

Presents the life and accomplishments of the world-revered jazz singer who won thirteen Grammys, toured for more than fifty years, and became known as the First Lady of Song.

"This is a strong biography [of the African American singer]. . . . Stone's smooth, straightforward narrative draws from authoritative sources. . . . The abundant quotes from Fitzgerald and her musician peers greatly develop the narrative." Booklist.

Fleischman, Sid, 1920-2010

Fleischman, Sid, 1920-2010. The **abracadabra** kid: a writer's life. Sid Fleischman. Greenwillow Books, c1996. 198 p.

Grades: 5 6 7 8   **B**
   1. Authors, American 20th century 2. Children's literature authors 20th century. 3. Authors 4. Magicians 5. Depressions 1929-1941.
ISBN 9780688148591

LC 95047382

The autobiography of the Newbery award-winning children's author who set out from childhood to be a magician.

"This autobiography, turns real life into a story complete with cliffhangers. And it's a classic boy's story, from card tricks and traveling magic shows to World War II naval experiences and screen-writing gigs for John Wayne movies. En route, we learn how Fleischman learned the craft of writing." Bulletin of the Center for Children's Books.

Fossey, Dian, 1932-1985

Kushner, Jill Menkes. **Who** on earth is Dian Fossey?: defender of the mountain gorillas. Jill Menkes Kushner. Enslow Publishers, c2010. 112 p.: Scientists saving the earth

Grades: 5 6 7 8   **B**
   1. Primatologists 2. Zoologists 3. Gorillas 4. Women 5. Women scientists
ISBN 9781598451177

LC 2008029376

Details Dian Fossey's life, with chapters devoted to her early years, life, work, writings, and legacy, as well as how children can follow in her footsteps. Provided by publisher.

"The book is filled with factual information, yet is written in a manner that makes both Fossey and her gorillas come to life for the reader." Science Books & Films.

Includes bibliographical references (p. 106-108) and index.

France, Diane L.

Hopping, Lorraine Jean. **Bone** detective: the story of forensic anthropologist Diane France. by Lorraine Jean Hopping. Franklin Watts; c2005. 118 p.: Women's adventures in science

Grades: 7 8 9 10   **B**
   1. Women scientists 2. Forensic anthropologists 3. Dead -- Identification 4. Women forensic anthropologists
ISBN 0531167763

LC 2005000784

Discusses the life and many specific achievements of forensic anthropologist Diane France.

"This introduces the life and work of a contemporary forensic anthropologist, from her rural childhood to her work identifying the victims of the 9/11 tragedies. . . . The extensive detail gives readers a vivid sense of the daily work of a bone detective, and clear explanations of the science will intrigue and inspire readers." Booklist.

Includes bibliographical references (p. 110-111) and index.

Frank, Anne, 1929-1945

Folman, Ari. **Anne** Frank's diary: the graphic adaptation. adapted by Ari Folman; illustrations by David Polonsky. Pantheon Books, 2018 160 p.

Grades: 8 9 10 11 12   **B**
   1. Holocaust (1933-1945) 2. Jewish teenage girls 3. Hidden children (Holocaust) 4. World War II -- Jews 5. Jews -- Persecutions 6. Amsterdam, Netherlands -- Interethnic relations. 7. Biographical comics 8. Comics and Graphic novels
ISBN 9781101871799

LC 2017034415

Offers a graphic version of Anne Frank's diary authorized by the Anne Frank Foundation and using text from the diary.

"The classic, original text of Frank's diary is, as Folman writes in his adapter's note, impossible to improve upon; instead, he and Polonsky (cocreators of the film Waltz with Bashir) focus on illuminating its humor, insight, and supporting cast in this spirited graphic adaptation, authorized by the Anne Frank Foundation." Publishers Weekly.

Lee, Carol Ann. **Anne** Frank and the children of the Holocaust. by Carol Ann Lee. Viking, 2006. 242 p.

Grades: 6 7 8 9 10   **B**
   1. Jewish children 2. Jews 3. Holocaust (1933-1945) 4. Jewish girls 5. Girls 6. Amsterdam, Netherlands
ISBN 0670061077

LC 2006009610

Combing historical information with narratives from survivors and excerpts from other victims' journals, this companion to the diary tells the life story of Anne Frank set chronologically against the significant events of the Holocaust.

"This book will still serve as an excellent overview in the classroom and for personal reading." Booklist.

Muller, Melissa, 1967-. **Anne** Frank: the biography. Melissa Muller; translated from the German by Rita and Robert Kimber. Metropolitan Books/Henry Holt and Company, 2013. 458 p.

Grades: 7 8 9 10 11 12 Adult   **B**
   1. Jewish children 2. Jews 3. Holocaust (1933-1945) 4. Jewish

girls 5. Girls 6. Translations German to English
ISBN 9780805087314

LC 00266940

Moves beyond the girl's internationally beloved biography of life in hiding during the Holocaust to fill in the gaps—where did Anne come from, what was her relationship with her mother, and who betrayed the family to the Nazis.

★ Metselaar, Menno. Anne Frank House. **Anne** Frank: her life in words and pictures: from the archives of the Anne Frank House. Menno Metselaar & Ruud van der Rol; translated by Arnold J. Pomerans. Flash Point, 2009. 215 p.

Grades: 5 6 7 8 **B**
    1. Jewish girls 2. Holocaust (1933-1945) 3. Hidden children (Holocaust) 4. Jews 5. Teenage girls 6. Amsterdam, Netherlands
ISBN 9781596435469

LC bl2009023240

Highlights the life and trials of the Jewish girl who spent two years hiding from the Nazis in a secret apartment in the Netherlands, and includes photos of the famous diary and her hiding place, as well as school pictures.

"Beginning with a single photograph of the cover of Anne Frank's diary and the quote, 'One of my nicest presents, this small, beautifully formatted book,' is accessible, compelling, and richly pictorial. . . . The book immediately immerses readers in the girl's life via a series of family photographs, many previously unpublished. Divided chronologically, the accompanying text is enhanced by diary entries, resulting in a historically succinct yet descriptive presentation. . . . Even for those collections where Anne Frank is well represented, this is a moving and valuable book." School Library Journal.

Rol, Ruud van der. **Anne** Frank, beyond the diary: a photographic remembrance. by Ruud van der Rol and Rian Verhoeven in association with the Anne Frank House; translated by Tony Langham and Plym Peters; with an introduction by Anna Quindlen. Viking, 1993. 113 p.

Grades: 5 6 7 8 **B**
    1. Jews, Dutch 2. Holocaust (1933-1945) 3. Jewish teenage girls 4. Antisemitism 5. Nazism 6. Amsterdam, Netherlands 7. Translations Dutch to English
ISBN 0670849324

LC 92041528

Photographs, illustrations, and maps accompany historical essays, diary excerpts, and interviews, providing an insight to Anne Frank and the massive upheaval which tore apart her world.

"Readers will become absorbed in the richness of the detail and careful explanation which revisit and expand the familiar, well-loved story." Horn Book.

Franklin, Benjamin, 1706-1790

Dash, Joan. A **dangerous** engine: Benjamin Franklin, from scientist to diplomat. Joan Dash; pictures by Dusan Petricic. Frances Foster Books, 2006. 246 p.

Grades: 7 8 9 10 **B**
    1. Inventors 2. Diplomats 3. Printers 4. United States -- Foreign relations -- 1775-1783.
ISBN 0374306699

LC 2004063204

At the time of his famous kite experiment, Benjamin Franklin was unaware that his theories about electricity had already made him a celebrity all over Europe, especially in France, where fashionable circles loved to discuss scientific discovery. Admired by the French court and beloved by French citizens, Franklin effectively became America's first foreign diplomat, later helping to enlist France's military and financial support for the American Revolution. A father of the revolution and a signer of the Constitution, Franklin was a lightning rod in political circles—"a dangerous Engine," according to a critic. And although he devoted the last twenty-five years of his life to affairs of state, his first love was always science. Handsome pen-and-ink drawings highlight moments in this revolutionary thinker's life.

"Franklin's long, productive, and interesting life is vividly recounted in a lively manner. Familiar aspects are covered, from his days as a printer in Philadelphia to his diplomatic service and his role in the development of the fledgling United States democracy. What may be new to some readers is Franklin's dedication to, and life-long love of, science and invention. . . . Witty pen-and-ink illustrations appear throughout." School Library Journal.

Includes bibliographical references (p. [227]-240) and index.

Franklin, Rosalind, 1920-1958

Polcovar, Jane. **Rosalind** Franklin and the structure of life. Jane Polcovar. Morgan Reynolds Pub., c2006. 144 p.: Profiles in science

Grades: 7 8 9 10 **B**
    1. Molecular biologists 2. Molecular biology 3. DNA -- History 4. Women scientists 5. Women
ISBN 159935022X

LC 2006016864

A biography of the scientist whose unpublished research led to the discovery of the structure of DNA.

"Polcovar writes a rattling good story on two fronts: a woman becoming a scientist in an age when that was still unusual and the complex dynamics of personalities in a field sometimes thought of as impersonal." Booklist.

Includes bibliographical references (p. 139-141) and index.

Yount, Lisa. **Rosalind** Franklin: photographing biomolecules. Lisa Yount. Chelsea House, c2011. 125 p.: Trailblazers in science and technology

Grades: 7 8 9 10 11 12 **B**
    1. Molecular biologists 2. Women molecular biologists 3. DNA -- History 4. Women
ISBN 9781604136609

LC 2010048229

Examines the life and career of Rosalind Franklin, a scientist whose X-ray knowledge led to her imaging of molecules, including carbon, viruses, and human DNA.

"This series, which defines a "trailblazer" as a person who exhibits imagination, determination, and courage, gives a look into the lives of some of the most influential people in the world of science and technology." School Library Journal.

Includes bibliographical references and index.

Friedman, Cory

Patterson, James, 1947-. **Med** head: my knock-down, dragout, drugged up battle with my brain. James Patterson and Hal Friedman. Little, Brown & Co., 2010. 302 p.

Grades: 6 7 8 9 10 **B**
    1. Obsessive-compulsive disorder in men 2. Tourette syndrome 3. Tic disorders 4. Prescription drugs 5. Obsessive-compulsive disorder
ISBN 9780316076173

"Based on detailed notes on medications, physician appointments, and school visits, this is a page-turning examination of what could have been a wasted, despairing life. . . . While nonfiction resources can provide the facts on mental disorders, this excellent biography puts them into a context that promotes compassion." Voice of Youth Advocates.

Frost, Robert, 1874-1963

Caravantes, Peggy, 1935-. **Deep** woods: the story of Robert Frost. Peggy Caravantes. Morgan Reynolds Pub., c2006. 176 p.: World writers

Grades: 7 8 9 10   **B**

1. Poets, American 20th century
ISBN 1931798923

LC 2005037514

Presents the life and accomplishments of the poet known for such works as "Mending Wall," "The Road Not Taken," and "Birches."

"This introduces poet Robert Frost. . . . Though focused on the man, Caravantes' presentation includes a few short selections from Frost's verse and, in sidebars, a bit of information about poetic forms. . . . Well organized and clearly written, the book offers a very readable account of Frost's often troubled life as an individual, a family man, a poet, and a public figure." Booklist.

Includes bibliographical references (p. 169-170) and index.

Gage, Phineas

★ Fleischman, John, 1948-. **Phineas** Gage: a gruesome but true story about brain science. by John Fleischman. Houghton Mifflin, c2002. 86 p.

Grades: 5 6 7 8 9   **B**

1. 1840s 2. 19th century 3. People with brain injuries 4. Brain damage -- Case studies 5. Personality disorders 6. Railroad workers
ISBN 0618052526

LC 2001039253

"The author deftly introduces readers to a diverse range of relevant scientific history as well as more specific beliefs that influenced the medical establishment's understanding of Gage, then goes on to examine subsequent neurological discoveries that have changed and enhanced our understanding of Gage's fate. The book's present-tense narrative is inviting and intimate, and the text is crisp and lucid." Bulletin of the Center for Children's Books.

Includes bibliographical references and index.

Galen

Yount, Lisa. The **father** of anatomy: Galen and his dissections. Lisa Yount. Enslow Publishers, c2010. 128 p.: Great minds of ancient science and math

Grades: 6 7 8 9   **B**

1. Human dissection 2. Human anatomy 3. Medical research 4. Physicians 5. Animal anatomy
ISBN 9780766033801

LC 2008029633

A biography of ancient Greek physician Galen, whose dissections of animals led to discoveries about human anatomy. He was the authority on medical knowledge in the Western world for more than fifteen hundred years. Provided by publisher.

Galilei, Galileo, 1564-1642

Panchyk, Richard. **Galileo** for kids: his life and ideas. Richard Panchyk; foreword by Buzz Aldrin. Chicago Review Press, c2005. xv, 166 p.

Grades: 5 6 7 8   **B**

1. Astronomers 2. Physicists 3. Astronomy -- Experiments 4.

Physics -- Experiments 5. Experiments
ISBN 1556525664

LC 2004022936

Biography of the man who invented the telescope and proved the earth revolves around the sun. Includes activities.

"Clear . . . writing places Galileo squarely within the historical context of the turbulent Italian Renaissance. . . . Panchyk's title is a good choice for those interested in integrating history and science curriculums." School Library Journal.

Includes bibliographical references (p. 163) and index.

Steele, Philip, 1948-. **Galileo**: the genius who faced the inquisition. Philip Steele. National Geographic, 2005. 64 p.: National Geographic world history biographies

Grades: 4 5 6 7   **B**

1. Astronomers 2. Physicists 3. Scientists 4. Astronomy -- History 16th century. 5. Astronomy -- History 17th century.
ISBN 0792236572

LC 2005001357

Chronicles the life and times of the Tuscan astronomer and physicist, focusing on his defense of the Copernican theory and his struggles with the Catholic Church.

"Accompliments and hardships are clearly explained with supporting quotes and facts. . . . Beautifully illustrated and visually appealing." School Library Journal.

Includes bibliographical references and index.

Gama, Vasco da, 1469-1524

Calvert, Patricia. **Vasco** da Gama: so strong a spirit. Patricia Calvert. Benchmark Books, c2005. 96 p.: Great explorations

Grades: 5 6 7 8   **B**

1. Explorers 2. Discoveries in geography -- Portuguese 3. Discoveries in geography
ISBN 0761416110

LC 2003022946

Recounts the voyages undertaken by fifteenth-century Portuguese explorer Vasco da Gama to strengthen his nation's power by establishing a sea trade route to India.

Gandhi, Indira, 1917-1984

Schupack, Sara. **Indira** Gandhi. Sara Schupack. Cavendish Square, 2014. 96 p.: Leading women

Grades: 6 7 8 9   **B**

1. Prime ministers 2. Women prime ministers 3. India -- Politics and government -- 1947-
ISBN 9780761449553

LC 2011009224

Presents the biography of Indira Gandhi against the backdrop of her political, historical, and cultural environment. Provided by publisher.

Gandhi, Mahatma, 1869-1948

Ebine, Kazuki. **Gandhi**: a manga biography. Kazuki Ebine. Penguin, 2011, c2010. 192 p.

Grades: 7 8 9 10   **B**

1. Peace activists 2. Political activists 3. Politicians 4. National liberation movements 5. Resistance to government 6. India -- Politics and government -- 1919-1947. 7. Biographical comics 8. Manga 9. Translations Japanese to English
ISBN 9780143120247

Depicts the life of Mahatma Gandhi and his nonviolent struggle against the British Raj.

"Ebine's nicely drawn manga biography is a clear and concise introduction to Gandhi's life. The biography not only touches upon Gandhi's major accomplishements . . . but also humanizes Gandhi by showing his struggles with insecurity as a young man. . . . This title is a great addition to social studies curricula, and it will have special appeal to budding young activists and idealists." Booklist.

Includes bibliographical references.

Lambilly-Bresson, Elisabeth de. **Gandhi**: his life, his struggles, his words. written by Elisabeth de Lambilly; illustrated by Severine Cordier. Enchanted Lion Books, 2010. 67 p.: Great spiritual leaders of modern times

Grades: 6 7 8 9 **B**
    1. Spiritual leaders 2. Pacifists 3. Politicians 4. National liberation movements 5. World leaders 6. India -- Politics and government -- 1919-1947
    ISBN 9781592700943

    LC 2010025235

An engaging biography of the great Indian leader consists of an 11-page graphic narrative about Gandhi's life; a chronology; 12 two-page chapters about his early years in London, Hinduism, nonviolence and Indian independence; a section of referenced quotes both from Gandhi and about him; a list of recommended books; and an index.

"The historical facts are as compelling as the biographical story, and the message of nonviolence will spark intense debate about political action, then and now." Booklist.

Includes bibliographical references and index.

Sawyer, Kem Knapp. **Champion** of freedom: Mohandas Gandhi. by Kem Knapp Sawyer. Morgan Reynolds Pub., c2011. 144 p.

Grades: 6 7 8 9 10 **B**
    1. Nationalists 2. Politicians 3. Political activists 4. India -- Politics and government -- 1919-1947.
    ISBN 9781599351667

    LC 2010047904

Profiles the life and work of the political activist who helped bring an end to British rule in India.

"This title starts with an overview of the British Raj at the time of Mohandas Gandhi's birth and what life was like for those living under it. The thorough biography then goes on to trace the key events, philosophical influences, and personal relationships that shaped the life of a man who spread the doctrine of nonviolence. Interesting anecdotes, explanations of Indian culture, and an engaging, well-organized narrative make this a solid resource." Booklist.

Includes bibliographical references (p. 138-139) and index.

Wilkinson, Philip, 1955-. **Gandhi**: the young protester who founded a nation. Philip Wilkinson. National Geographic Society, 2005. 64 p.: National Geographic world history biographies
Grades: 4 5 6 7 **B**
    1. Spiritual leaders 2. Politicians 3. National liberation movements
    ISBN 9780792236481

    LC 2005001351

A biography of Mahatma Gandhi, the Indian political and spiritual leader who led his country to freedom from British rule through his policy of nonviolent resistance.

"Double-page spreads describe phases in Gandhi's life, from childhood to his tragic death, detailed in Wilkinson's straightforward, succinct language and in anecdotes, which will capture young people's attention and also humanize the great leader." Booklist.

Includes bibliographical references (p. 62) and index.

Gansworth, Eric L.

Gansworth, Eric L.. **Apple**: skin to the core. Eric Gansworth. Levine Querido, 2020. 352 p.

Grades: 8 9 10 11 12 **B**
    1. Authors 2. Native American men 3. Indians of North America 4. Indian reservations 5. Racism
    ISBN 9781646140138

    LC 2019957000

The term "Apple" is a slur in Native communities across the country. It's for someone supposedly "red on the outside, white on the inside." Eric Gansworth tells the story of his family, of Onondaga among Tuscaroras, of Native folks everywhere. From the horrible legacy of the government boarding schools, to a boy watching his siblings leave and return and leave again, to a young man fighting to be an artist who balances multiple worlds.

"Playing off the derogatory term apple (red on the outside; white on the inside), often used in Native communities, [Gansworth] explores the realities of growing up on the rez, being subjected to racism and poverty, and learning to navigate the white world. . . . With language rich in metaphor, this is a timely and important work that begs for multiple readings." Booklist

Gantos, Jack

Gantos, Jack. **Hole** in my life. Jack Gantos. Farrar, Straus and Giroux, 2002. 199 p.

Grades: 7 8 9 10 **B**
    1. Former convicts 2. Authors, American 20th century 3. Former convicts 4. Drug smuggling 5. Teenage prisoners
    ISBN 9780374399887

    LC 2001040957

The author relates how, as a young adult, he became a drug user and smuggler, was arrested, did time in prison, and eventually got out and went to college, all the while hoping to become a writer.

"Gantos' spare narrative style and straightforward revelation of the truth have, together, a cumulative power that will capture not only a reader's attention but also empathy and imagination." Booklist.

Gautama Buddha

★ Demi. **Buddha**. Demi. Henry Holt and Co., 1996. 1 v. (unpaged)

Grades: 4 5 6 **B**
    1. Buddhism -- History 2. Spiritual journeys 3. Enlightenment (Buddhism) 4. Spiritual leaders
    ISBN 0805042032

    LC 95016906

An introduction to the Buddha follows Prince Siddhartha's privileged childhood, his decision to leave his easy life, his quest for the truth about human suffering, and his spiritual journey that culminated in his enlightenment

"Demi uses clear, uncomplicated storytelling to present complex philosophical concepts. . . . The gilded illustrations (based, according to the jacket, on Indian, Chinese, Japanese, Burmese, and Indonesian paintings, sculptures, and sutra illustrations) are delicate, yet the colors and composition are bold, with central figures and action cascading beyond the careful borders." Bulletin of the Center for Children's Books.

Gehrig, Lou, 1903-1941

Buckley, James. **Lou** Gehrig: iron horse of baseball. James, Buckley, Jr. Sterling Publishing, 2010. 128 p.: Sterling biographies

Grades: 6 7 8 9 **B**
    1. Professional baseball players 2. Baseball 3. Professional

athletes 4. Baseball players 5. Athletes
ISBN 9781402771514

Loads of information is packed into each title of this series about world inventors, innovative thinkers and great athletes, including timelines, sidebars, a glossary, maps, rare photographs and world-class writing that make these books accessible and dramatic.

"This biography of Lou Gehrig is studded with quotes and illustrated with photos. . . . Lou Gehrig is today inextricably linked with ALS, the progressive nerve disease that ended his baseball career and ultimately his life, but he is also remembered as the Iron Horse of baseball, the legendary slugger who played a phenomenal 2,130 consecutive games for the Yankees. Written in a straightforward, journalistic style, [this biography presents a] very readable [account] of the [life] of [an athlete] who made [his mark] on American culture." Booklist.

Geronimo, Apache chief, 1829-1909

Sullivan, George, 1927-. **Geronimo**: Apache renegade. by George Sullivan. Sterling, 2010. 128 p.: Sterling biographies
Grades: 7 8 9 10   **B**
1. 19th century 2. Apache Indians 3. Indians of North America 4. Chiefs (Political anthropology) 5. Apache Indians -- Wars
ISBN 9781402768439

LC 2009024135

"Geronimo describes how the Apache leader was feared and hated as he led violent clashes with whites, pursuing bloody vengeance for the massacre of his family and all that his people had lost, an identity far from the romanticized image that glorified him. . . . [The] spacious design is highly scannable, with color background screens, photos, maps, and historic prints throughout." Booklist.

Includes bibliographical references and index.

Gillespie, Dizzy, 1917-1993

Boone, Mary, 1963-. **Dizzy** Gillespie. Mary Boone. Mitchell Lane Publishers, c2013. 47 p.: American jazz
Grades: 6 7 8 9   **B**
1. Jazz musicians 2. Bebop music 3. African American musicians 4. Trumpeters 5. Jazz music
ISBN 9781612282725

LC 2012008630

A biography of the Afro-American musician and "ambassador of jazz" who introduced the world to "bebop."

Goh, Chan Hon

Goh, Chan Hon. **Beyond** the dance: a ballerina's life. Chan Han Go with Cary Fagan. Tundra Books, c2002. 151 p.
Grades: 6 7 8 9   **B**
1. Dancers 2. Women dancers 3. Chinese Canadians 4. Canadians
ISBN 0887765963

LC 2002101724

The ballet dancer tells the story of her life, from her early childhood in China to her family's flight to Canada, describing her training and achievements as the first Chinese-born prima ballerina for the National Ballet of Canada.

"This autobiography introduces a prima ballerina with the National Ballet of Canada. Goh was born in Beijing but raised in Vancouver by her dancer parents. She discusses the events in her homeland that led her family to emigrate, their adjustment to life in Vancouver, and her parents' struggles to build the Goh Ballet Company. . . . The book is lavishly illustrated with black-and-white photographs, and balletomanes will enjoy poring over every detail." School Library Journal.

Goodall, Jane, 1934-

Anniss, Matt. **Jane** Goodall and Mary Leakey. Matt Anniss. Gareth Stevens Publishing, 2015. 48 p.
Grades: 4 5 6   **B**
1. Chimpanzees 2. Fossil hominids 3. Primatologists 4. Wildlife conservation 5. Women 6. Olduvai Gorge (Tanzania) -- Antiquities
ISBN 9781482414721

LC bl2014051921

Chronicles the life and work of two women scientists who, although they did not have university educations, worked long years in Tanzania and made major contributions to the study of human origins and of chimpanzees, humans' nearest relatives.

"Reading their parallel stories will let children see how different people solve the same problems. Original takes on science biographies." School Library Journal.

Includes bibliographical references (page 47) and index.

Goodman, Benny, 1909-1986

Mattern, Joanne, 1963-. **Benny** Goodman. Joanne Mattern. Mitchell Lane Publishers, c2013. 47 p.: American jazz
Grades: 6 7 8 9   **B**
1. Clarinetists 2. Jazz musicians 3. Jazz music -- Influence 4. Swing music -- History and criticism 5. United States -- Social life and customs -- 20th century
ISBN 9781612282695

LC 2012008483

A biography of the great jazz musician, describing how his extraordinary musical ability was originally encouraged by his immigrant father.

Gownley, Jimmy

Gownley, Jimmy. The **dumbest** idea ever! Jimmy Gownley. Scholastic Press, 2014. 236 p.
Grades: 5 6 7   **B**
1. Cartoonists 2. Chicken pox 3. Catholic schools 4. Schools 5. Teenage boys 6. Comics and Graphic novels 7. Coming-of-age stories
ISBN 9780545453462

A renowned comics creator recounts his adventures as he grows from an eager-to-please boy into a teenage comic book artist, sharing the real-life story of how the DUMBEST idea ever became the BEST thing that ever happened to him.

"[Gownley] recounts his beginnings as a cartoonist. . . . Humble, endearing and utterly easy to relate to." Kirkus.

Graham, Martha

Freedman, Russell. **Martha** Graham: a dancer's life. by Russell Freedman. Clarion Books, c1998. 175 p.
Grades: 7 8 9 10   **B**
1. Women dancers 2. Choreographers 3. Modern dance 4. Dancers 5. Dance teachers
ISBN 0395746558

LC 97015832

Golden Kite Award for Nonfiction, 1998.

A photo-biography of the American dancer, teacher, and choreographer who was born in Pittsburgh in 1895 and who became a leading figure in the world of modern dance.

"A showstopping biography that captures its dynamic subject's personality, vision, and artistry." School Library Journal.

Includes bibliographical references (p. 165-168) and index.

Grandin, Temple

Montgomery, Sy. **Temple** Grandin: how the girl who loved cows embraced autism and changed the world. by Sy Montgomery. Houghton Mifflin Books for Children/Houghton Mifflin Harcourt, 2012. 160 p.

Grades: 4 5 6 7 8   **B**

    1. People with autism 2. Livestock -- Handling 3. Women scientists 4. Animal scientists 5. Animal specialists

    ISBN 9780547443157

               LC 2011039911

An authorized portrait about the co-author's life with autism and her groundbreaking work as a scientist and designer of cruelty-free livestock facilities includes photographs from Gradin's personal collection and describes how she overcame key disabilities through education and the support of her mother.

Sepahban, Lois. **Temple** Grandin: inspiring animal-behavior scientist. by Lois Sepahban. Core Library, an imprint of Abdo Publishing, 2015. 48 p.: Great minds of science (Core Library (Firm))

Grades: 4 5 6   **B**

    1. People with autism 2. Women scientists 3. Livestock 4. Animal scientists 5. Animal welfare

    ISBN 9781624033803

               LC bl2014030384

Chronicles the life and career of the animal scientist, from her work to help others with autism to her lobbying for animal welfare.

"Students will learn about the different accomplishments of each scientist while joining them on the often tumultuous journey to success. A staple for libraries." School Library Journal.

Includes bibliographical references (page 47) and index.

Greenberg, Hank

Sommer, Shelley. **Hammerin'** Hank Greenberg: baseball pioneer. Shelley Sommer. Calkins Creek, c2011. 135 p.

Grades: 5 6 7 8   **B**

    1. Detroit Tigers (Baseball team) -- History 2. Baseball players 3. Jewish American men 4. Athletes 5. Jewish Americans 6. Antisemitism

    ISBN 9781590784525

"Greenberg grew up in an Orthodox Jewish family in New York and went on to be a Hall-of-Fame first baseman and left fielder, playing most of his career with the Detroit Tigers in the 1930s and 1940s. . . . Sommer presents a fast-moving, straightforward biography. . . . Numerous black-and-white photos enhance the text. . . . An excellent choice for kids who enjoy delving into baseball history." Booklist.

Grimberg, Tina

Grimberg, Tina. **Out** of line: growing up Soviet. Tina Grimberg. Tundra Books, c2007. viii, 117 p.

Grades: 7 8 9 10   **B**

    1. Jewish children 2. Jewish childhood 3. Growing up 4. Jews 5. Jews, Ukrainian 6. Ukraine -- Social conditions -- 1945-1991 7. Kiev, Ukraine -- Social life and customs.

    ISBN 0887768032

               LC bl2007028023

A rabbi remembers her life as a child in Kiev, Ukraine, where her family lived under Soviet rule until they moved to the United States when she was fifteen.

"In this warm memoir, Grimberg recalls her childhood in Kiev during the '60s and '70s. She shares the difficulties of Soviet life and explains how members of her family coped with challenges such as short-ages. . . . Interwoven with her own experience of growing up in a Jewish family are the stories of her maternal and paternal grandparents. . . . The book is an exemplar of clear, graceful writing and fine storytelling skills." School Library Journal.

Grimes, Nikki

Grimes, Nikki. **Ordinary** hazards: a memoir. Nikki Grimes. WordSong, 2019. 336 p.

Grades: 10 11 12   **B**

    1. Women authors, American 2. African American children 3. Children of people with mental illnesses 4. Creative writing 5. Child abuse victims

    ISBN 9781629798813

The author recounts her traumatic childhood, with a mother suffering from mental illness, unfortunate experiences in a series of foster homes, and her discovery of her love of writing, which eventually helped her overcome the hazards of her life.

Guevara, Che, 1928-1967

Abrams, Dennis, 1960-. **Ernesto** "Che" Guevara. Dennis Abrams. Chelsea House, c2010. 128 p.: The great Hispanic heritage

Grades: 6 7 8 9   **B**

    1. Guerrillas 2. Revolutions 3. Cuba -- History -- 20th century 4. Latin America -- History -- 1948-1980

    ISBN 9781604137323

               LC 2010007514

Examines the life of Ernesto "Che" Guevara, who was a trained doctor, writer, military leader and radical activist.

"This begins with Guevara's childhood as the son of Argentinean aristocrats and gives a balanced portrait of the controversial figure, from his famous worldwide revolutionary efforts to his assassination at the age of 39. . . . A selection of well-chosen images, a chronology, chapter notes, and [a] suggested reading [list] round out [this] engaging [title] in a sure-to-be popular [book] for reports and personal interest." Booklist.

Includes bibliographical references (p. 119-120) and index.

Kallen, Stuart A., 1955-. **Che** Guevara. by Stuart A. Kallen. Twenty-First Century Books, 2012. 88 p.

Grades: 8 9 10 11 12   **B**

    1. Guerrillas 2. Revolutionaries 3. Cuba -- History -- 1959-1990. 4. Latin America -- History -- 1948-1980.

    ISBN 9780822590354

               LC 2011045480

Examines the life of Che Guevara, including his family's background, childhood, education, and groundbreaking work as a revolutionary fighting against poverty.

"Sidebars, photographs, and primary sources add depth to the engaging narrative, providing insight into a man at the center of Cold War history and controversy." Horn Book.

Includes bibliographical references and index.

Miller, Calvin Craig, 1954-. **Che** Guevara: in search of revolution. Calvin Craig Miller. Morgan Reynolds Pub., c2006. 192 p.: World leaders (Morgan Reynolds)

Grades: 7 8 9 10   **B**

    1. Guerrillas 2. Revolutionaries 3. Cuba -- History -- 1959-1990 4. Latin America -- History -- 1948-1980

    ISBN 1931798931

               LC 2006005975

Chronicles the life and accomplishments of the internationally famous Argentinian guerrilla fighter.

"This biography of the guerilla leader is woven into . . . [an] account of the global politics of his day, including his role in the Cuban revolution and the showdown with the U.S. The design is appealing, with clear type, occasional photos, and maps, and teens will be drawn to the account of the young leader who made a difference in spite of an inglorious defeat." Booklist.

Includes bibliographical references (p. 184-189) and index.

Guthrie, Woody, 1912-1967

Partridge, Elizabeth. **This** land was made for you and me: the life and songs of Woody Guthrie. Elizabeth Partridge. Viking, 2002. 217 p.

Grades: 7 8 9 10   **B**
  1. Singers 2. Folk singers 3. People with Huntington's disease
  4. Folk music
  ISBN 0670035351

                                               LC 2001046770

Golden Kite Award for Nonfiction, 2002.

A biography of Woody Guthrie, a singer who wrote over 3,000 folk songs and ballads as he traveled around the United States, including "This Land is Your Land" and "So Long It's Been Good to Know Yuh."

"This presents an unflinchingly accurate portrait of a rambling and unpredictable man. . . . In addition to a panoply of archival photographs, which add realism to this engrossing story of a life, the book includes carefully selected quotes from songs, acquaintances, and documents to punctuate the story with authenticating detail without detracting from the momentum of the narrative." Bulletin of the Center for Children's Books.

Includes bibliographical references (p. 211) and index.

Halilbegovic, Nadja, 1979-

Halilbegovic, Nadja, 1979-. **My** childhood under fire: a Sarajevo diary. Nadja Halilbegovich. Kids Can Press, c2006. 120 p.

Grades: 5 6 7 8   **B**
  1. Teenagers 2. Children and war 3. Teenagers and war 4.
  Yugoslav War, 1991-1995 5. Sarajevo (Bosnia and Hercegovina) --
  History -- Siege, 1992-1996 6. Bosnia and Hercegovina -- History
  ISBN 1553377974

                                               LC bl2006006772

Presents the author's diary written during the siege of Sarajevo, describing how she survived the constant bombings, sniper attacks, and a critical lack of basic supplies for three long years.

"In 1992, when the bombing started in Sarajevo, Halilbegovich, 12, kept a diary of her terrifying daily life under siege. Her terse vignettes replay the horror of her comfortable home torn apart." Booklist.

Halvorsen, Gail S.

★ Tunnell, Michael O.. **Candy** bomber: the story of the Berlin Airlift's "Chocolate Pilot". Michael O. Tunnell. Charlesbridge, c2010. ix, 110 p.

Grades: 4 5 6 7   **B**
  1. United States. Air Force. Military Airlift Command -- History 2.
  Children and war 3. Military pilots 4. World War II 5. Candy 6.
  Berlin, Germany -- Blockade, 1948-1949. 7. Germany -- History
  -- 1945-1955.
  ISBN 9781580893367

                                               LC 2009026648

Presents the life of the American Air Force pilot responsible for setting up the airlift of candy to the children of Berlin in 1948 and 1949 after the end of World War II and describes the gratitude of the German people for his efforts.

"Curious about the city into which he ferried goods during the Berlin Airlift in 1948, pilot Gail Halvorsen stayed over to visit, met some children, and offered to drop candy and gum when he next flew over. This simple idea grew into a massive project with reverberations today. Tunnell tells this appealing story . . . clearly and chronologically, weaving just enough background for twenty-first century readers and illustrating almost every page with black-and-white photographs, many from Halvorsen's own collection." Booklist.

Includes bibliographical references (p. [105]-106) and index.

Hamilton, Alexander, 1757-1804

Kanefield, Teri, 1960-. **Alexander** Hamilton: the making of America. by Teri Kanefield. Abrams Books for Young Readers, 2017. 208 p.: Making of America (Abrams)

Grades: 5 6 7 8   **B**
  1. Politicians 2. Founding Fathers of the United States 3. American
  Revolution, 1775-1783 4. United States -- Politics and government
  -- 1783-1809. 5. United States -- History -- 18th century.
  ISBN 9781419725784

                                               LC 2016046103

Chronicles the life of the Founding Father, from his impoverished childhood in the West Indies and journey to New York City to his role in developing the Constitution and untimely death in a duel with Aaron Burr.

"A great addition to upper elementary and middle school libraries." Kirkus.

Hammel, Heidi

Bortz, Alfred B.. **Beyond** Jupiter: the story of planetary astronomer Heidi Hammel. by Fred Bortz. Franklin Watts; c2005. ix, 110 p.: Women's adventures in science

Grades: 7 8 9 10   **B**
  1. Women researchers 2. Women scientists 3. Women astronomers
  4. Women
  ISBN 0531167755

                                               LC 2005000778

Details the life and major accomplishments of planetary astronomer Heidi Hammel, who studies both Jupiter and Neptune.

"The author has captured some of the engaging qualities of Heidi Hammel's personality through extensive work with her and with the cooperation of her friends and family." Science Books & Films.

Includes bibliographical references (p. 101-102) and index.

Hannibal, 247-182 B.C.E.

Mills, Cliff, 1947-. **Hannibal**. Clifford W. Mills. Chelsea House, c2008. 120 p.: Ancient world leaders

Grades: 6 7 8 9   **B**
  1. Generals 2. Punic War, 2nd, 218-201, BCE 3. Ancient history
  4. Civilization, Ancient 5. Carthage (Extinct city) -- History. 6.
  Rome -- History -- Republic, 265-30 B.C.E.
  ISBN 9780791095805

                                               LC 2007050493

Takes a historical look at the charismatic and powerful figures of the ancient world who led armies to victory and ruled over vast domains in a time when the world was still young.

"Mills's informative biography starts with Hannibal preparing to attack the Romans and then goes back in time to explain the founding of Carthage and the history of its conflict with Rome, mainly focusing on the Second Punic War and the subject's journey and battles during that time. . . . Frequent inserts add extra information . . . without distracting readers from the narrative. Colorful reproductions are also interspersed throughout. . . . [This offers] clear, descriptive writing." School Library Journal.

Includes bibliographical references and index.

Hatshepsut, Queen of Egypt 1503-1482 B.C.E.

★ Galford, Ellen. **Hatshepsut**: the princess who became king. Ellen Galford. National Geographic, 2005. 64 p.: National Geographic world history biographies

Grades: 4 5 6 7   **B**

   1. Women rulers 2. Egypt -- Rulers. 3. Ancient Egypt -- History -- To 332 B.C.E.

ISBN 0792236467

LC 2004024634

Chronicles the ancient Egyptian female pharaoh's life, and describes the civilization's social customs and culture during the fifteenth century B.C.

"This presents the life of Queen Hatshepsut, who ruled Egypt as pharaoh during the New Kingdom, around 3500 years ago. Illustrated with clear, color photos of artifacts and sites as well as colorful maps, the text discusses aspects of Egyptian life such as education and religion in Hatshepsut's life. . . . With a clearly written text and many handsome photos, this provides an accessible introduction to Hatshepsut and her times." Booklist.

Includes bibliographical references (p. 62) and index.

Hawking, Stephen, 1942-2018

Bankston, John, 1974-. **Stephen** Hawking: breaking the boundaries of time and space. John Bankston. Enslow Publishers, c2005. 128 p.: Great minds of science

Grades: 5 6 7 8   **B**

   1. Physicists 2. Big Bang Theory (Astronomy) 3. Cosmology 4. People with disabilities

ISBN 0766022811

LC 2004009193

Discusses the life and work of the brilliant physicist who has overcome the challenges of ALS to become one of the foremost scientists of the twentieth century.

"This excellent book features large font size and double spacing that makes it easy for any one to read. . . . The activities part of the book is outstanding." Science Books & Films.

Includes bibliographical references and index.

Kenney, Karen Latchana. **Stephen** Hawking: extraordinary theoretical physicist. by Karen Latchana Kenney; content consultant, Scott Watson, Assistant Physics Professor, Syracuse University. Core Library, an imprint of Abdo Publishing, [2015] 48 p.: Great minds of science (Core Library (Firm))

Grades: 4 5 6   **B**

   1. Scientists 2. Physicists 3. People with disabilities 4. People with amyotrophic lateral sclerosis

ISBN 9781624033810

LC bl2014030379

Chronicles the life and career of the theoretical physicist, from his battle with ALS to his work on black holes.

"Students will learn about the different accomplishments of each scientist while joining them on the often tumultuous journey to success. A staple for libraries." School Library Journal.

Includes bibliographical references (page 47) and index.

Hendrix, Jimi, 1942-1970

Willett, Edward, 1959-. **Jimi** Hendrix: "Kiss the sky". Edward Willett. Enslow Publishers, c2006. 160 p.: American rebels

Grades: 7 8 9 10   **B**

   1. African American guitarists 2. African-American rock musicians 3. Rock musicians

ISBN 0766024490

LC 2005033751

Willett pens a biography covering all the high and low points in the short life of the man "Rolling Stone" magazine called the greatest rock guitarist of all time: Jimi Hendrix.

"This biography introduces electric-guitar virtuouso Jimi Hendrix. . . . [This is a] good, basic introduction to Hendrix's life and the reasons for his enduring fame." Booklist.

Includes bibliographical references, discography (p. 155-156) and index.

Henson, Matthew Alexander, 1866-1955

★ Johnson, Dolores, 1949-. **Onward**: a photobiography of African-American polar explorer Matthew Henson. by Dolores Johnson. National Geographic, c2006. 64 p.

Grades: 5 6 7 8   **B**

   1. 1900s (Decade) 2. African American explorers 3. Indians of North America 4. Inuit 5. Peary expeditions 6. Polar expeditions 7. North Pole

ISBN 0792279158

LC 2005005837

"The quest to be the first to reach the North Pole is an exciting adventure story, and Henson got there first, as part of the ninth expedition led by Robert Peary in 1909. But Henson was African American, labeled as Peary's Negro manservant, and he did not get full recognition until 2001. This . . . focuses on the physical details of the dangerous Arctic journeys . . . the repeated failures and the teamwork, as well as Henson's skills, stamina, and essential role in forging relationships with the Inuit. . . . The book design is beautiful: thick paper, spacious type, and stirring photos that capture the icy storms as well as the people involved in the history." Booklist.

Includes bibliographical references (p. 63).

Hernandez, Daniel, 1990-

Hernandez, Daniel, 1990-. **They** call me a hero: a memoir of my youth. Daniel Hernandez and Susan Goldman Rubin. Simon & Schuster Books for Young Readers, c2013. 256 p.

Grades: 7 8 9 10 11 12   **B**

   1. Heroes and heroines 2. Courage 3. LGBTQIA persons 4. Growing up 5. Interns 6. Tucson, Arizona -- History -- 21st century.

ISBN 9781442462281

LC 2012019829

A University of Arizona student and political intern credited with saving the life of Congresswoman Gabrielle Giffords during the Tucson shooting in January 2011 shares the story of his young life while exploring the character qualities that have helped him rise above adversity and pursue remarkable goals.

Hickam, Homer H., 1943-

Hickam, Homer H., 1943-. **Rocket** boys: a memoir. Homer H. Hickam, Jr. Delacorte Press, 1998. xii, 368 p.

Grades: 7 8 9 10 11 12 Adult   **B**

   1. United States. National Aeronautics and Space Administration 2. Coal mining towns 3. Small town life 4. High school boys 5. Aerospace engineers 6. Childhood 7. United States -- Social life and customs -- 20th century

ISBN 038533320X

LC 98019304

The author traces the boyhood enthusiasm for rockets that eventually led to a career at NASA, describing how he built model rockets in the family garage in West Virginia, inspired by the launch of the Soviet satellite "Sputnik."

"Even if Hickam stretched the strict truth to metamorphose his memories into Stand By Me-like material for Hollywood . . . the embellishing only converts what is a good story into an absorbing, rapidly readable one that is unsentimental but artful about adolescence, high school, and family life." Booklist.

Hillary, Edmund, 1919-2008

Coburn, Broughton, 1951-. **Triumph** on Everest: a photobiography of Sir Edmund Hillary. by Broughton Coburn. National Geographic Society, c2000. 64 p.

Grades: 4 5 6 7 **B**
1. Mountaineering -- History 2. Extreme sports 3. New Zealanders 4. Mount Everest -- Description and travel.
ISBN 0792271149

LC 00027009

A biography of Edmund Hillary, whose love of snow, mountains, and the outdoor life culminated in his conquering the highest peak in the world.

"Threaded with quotes from Hillary's own writings, and full of fine, blue-toned photographs, the engrossing text presents the life of a reticent but world-renowned mountaineer, adventurer, and philanthropist." School Library Journal.

Includes bibliographical references (p. 63) and index.

Crompton, Samuel Willard. **Sir** Edmund Hillary. Samuel Willard Crompton. Chelsea House, c2009. 112 p.: Great explorers (Chelsea House Publishers)

Grades: 6 7 8 9 10 11 12 **B**
1. Explorers 2. Mountaineers 3. Mountaineering 4. Mount Everest
ISBN 9781604134209

LC 2009008688

"The information . . . is presented in such a way as to attract and maintain readers' interest. . . . With a full complement of maps, photographs (where available), illustrations, time lines, and document reproductions, a full story is told. Well-written and throughly researched, this . . . will make a solid addition." School Library Journal.

Includes bibliographical references and index.

Hillman, Laura

Hillman, Laura. **I** will plant you a lilac tree: a memoir of a Schindler's list survivor. Laura Hillman. Atheneum Books for Young Readers, c2005. 243 p.

Grades: 7 8 9 10 **B**
1. Auschwitz (Concentration camp) 2. Jews 3. Holocaust (1933-1945) -- Children 4. Holocaust survivors 5. Survival (in concentration camps, prisons, etc) 6. Concentration camps
ISBN 0689869800

LC 2004010534

"In 1942 Berlin, Hannelore, 16, bravely volunteers to be deported with her mother and two younger brothers to Poland. . . . They are soon separated, and during the next three years Hannelore is moved through eight concentration camps. In clipped, first-person narrative, she remembers the worst. . . . She tells it as she endured it, quietly relaying the facts without sensationalism or sentimentality." Booklist.

Hine, Lewis Wickes, 1874-1940

Freedman, Russell. **Kids** at work: Lewis Hine and the crusade against child labor. by Russell Freedman; with photographs by Lewis Hine. Clarion Books, c1994. 104 p.

Grades: 5 6 7 8 **B**
1. Photographers 2. Child labor exploitation 3. Social reformers 4. Teachers 5. Investigative journalists
ISBN 0395587034

LC 93005989

Golden Kite Award for Nonfiction, 1994.

"Freedman does an outstanding job of integrating historical photographs with meticulously researched and highly readable prose." Publishers Weekly.

Includes bibliographical references (p. 99-100) and index.

Hitler, Adolf, 1889-1945

Giblin, James Cross, 1933-. The **life** and death of Adolf Hitler. by James Cross Giblin. Clarion Books, 2002. 246 p.

Grades: 7 8 9 10 **B**
1. Heads of state 2. Nazism 3. Germany -- History -- 1918-1933. 4. Germany -- History -- 1933-1945.
ISBN 0395903718

LC 2001047091

Robert F. Sibert Informational Book Medal, 2003.

"In a time when people, young and old, are unaware or have forgotten that people like Hitler, his nation of followers, and his high command existed, Giblin's carefully researched account is more important than ever. It is so readable that it should hold younger readers and educate older ones who may need their brains refilled with the facts of history. An essential purchase." Kirkus.

Includes bibliographical references and index.

Hodgman, Ann

Hodgman, Ann. **How** to die of embarrassment every day. Ann Hodgman. Henry Holt and Co., 2011. 240 p.

Grades: 5 6 7 8 **B**
1. Authors, American 20th century 2. Embarrassment in children 3. Growing up
ISBN 9780805087055

LC 2010049004

"Hodgman offers a chatty personal narrative . . . focusing on her childhood years and her tendency to land herself into humiliating situations. . . . The generous supply of spot art and relevant images from Hodgman's childhood adds to the browsibility. . . . There's . . . plenty of humor . . . but more importantly there's a tacit message about the survivability of embarrassment and the fact that we all, even seemingly perfect and polished adults, spend our lives goofing up." Bulletin of the Center for Children's Books.

Honnold, Alex

Synnott, Hampton. The **impossible** climb: Alex Honnold, El Capitan, and a climber's life. by Mark Synnott; adapted for young readers by Hampton Synnott. Viking, 2021. vii, 215 p.

Grades: 6 7 8 9 10 **B**
1. Mountaineers 2. Free solo climbing 3. Rock climbing 4. Free climbing 5. El Capitan (Mountain) 6. California
ISBN 9780593203927

Recounts Alex Honnold's unprecedented solo climb of Yosemite's El Capitan, describing the feat along with the other climbing expeditions that populated his amateur and professional experiences.

"A heart-pounding adventure that will pull in any reader who is looking to live life to its fullest. A beautiful, unique addition to most nonfiction sports collections." School Library Journal

Hopper, Edward, 1882-1967

Rubin, Susan Goldman. **Edward** Hopper: painter of light and shadow. Susan Goldman Rubin. Abrams Books for Young Readers, 2007. 47 p.

Grades: 5 6 7 8 **B**

1. Painters 2. Painting, American
ISBN 0810993473

LC 2006031978

Examines the life of the realist painter, describing his long years of struggle as an unknown artist, and his final recognition as one of the masters of twentieth century American art.

"On every page of this beautifully designed biography, readers will find a reproduction of Hopper's work, matched to clear, eloquent commentary. . . . Readers . . . will come back to read about the man and look at his art again and again." Booklist.

Includes bibliographical references (p. 46).

Houdini, Harry, 1874-1926

★ Fleischman, Sid, 1920-2010. **Escape!**: the story of the great Houdini. by Sid Fleischman. Greenwillow Books, 2006. 224 p.

Grades: 5 6 7 8 **B**

1. Magicians 2. Escape artists 3. Hungarian Americans 4. American dream 5. Jewish men
ISBN 0060850949

LC 2005052631

"Fleischman looks at Houdini's life through his own eyes, as a fellow magician. . . . Fleischman's tone is lively and he develops a relationship with readers by revealing just enough truth behind Houdini's razzle-dazzle to keep the legend alive. . . . Engaging and fascinating." School Library Journal.

Includes bibliographical references.

Lutes, Jason. **Houdini**: the handcuff king. Jason Lutes and Nick Bertozzi. Hyperion, 2007. 81 p.

Grades: 4 5 6 7 8 9 10 **B**

1. 1900s (Decade) 2. Stunts 3. Magicians 4. Training 5. Magic tricks 6. Antisemitism 7. Boston, Massachusetts 8. Biographical comics 9. Comics and Graphic novels
ISBN 0786839023

Offers a portrait of the legendary escape artist in graphic novel format, and reveals the secret behind his most amazing trick.

"This is a fascinating graphic novel. . . . The format will instantly draw a lot of attention from readers and then hold on to it. Lutes and Bertozzi use grayscale comic panels to share their story about the life of Harry Houdini in a unique way. . . . The book resembles a hybrid between fiction and nonfiction, and the ingenious choice of format will appeal to a broad age range of readers" Voice of Youth Advocates.

Houston, Sam, 1793-1863

Bodden, Valerie. **Samuel** Houston: Army leader & historic politician. Valerie Bodden. ABDO Pub. Co., c2010. 112 p.: Military heroes

Grades: 7 8 9 **B**

1. United States. Congress. Senate 2. Governors 3. Legislators 4. Texas -- History -- To 1846.
ISBN 9781604539622

LC 2009032373

"The rush of literary adrenaline will hook readers immediately and keep them enthralled until the end. . . . Given the dynamic topic [and] . . . appealing layout . . . [this is] likely to attract reluctant readers. In addition, sources are plentiful and well documented." School Library Journal.

Includes bibliographical references (p. 106-109) and index.

Sanford, William R. (William Reynolds), 1927-. **Sam** Houston: courageous Texas hero. William R. Sanford and Carl R. Green. Enslow Publishers, c2013. 48 p.

Grades: 5 6 7 8 **B**

1. United States. Congress. Senate 2. Governors 3. Legislators
ISBN 9781464400926

LC 2011051265

Examines the life of Sam Houston, including his early life on the Western frontier, his time as a soldier, leading the fight for Texas' independence, and his political career in Texas. Provided by publisher.

Howland, John, 1592?-1672

★ Lynch, P. J., 1962-. The **boy** who fell off the Mayflower: or John Howland's good fortune. P. J. Lynch. Candlewick Press, 2015. 64 p.

Grades: 2 3 4 5 6 **B**

1. Mayflower (Ship). 2. Indentured servants 3. Pilgrims (New England settlers) 4. Ocean travel 5. Survival 6. Good luck 7. United States -- History -- Colonial period, 1600-1775.
ISBN 9780763665845

An illustrated account of the life of John Howland, the young servant who was indentured to Pilgrim John Carver, describes how he embarked on the Mayflower and survived a fall off the ship before helping his ill shipmates by scouting out a safe harbor.

Hudson, Henry, died 1611

Otfinoski, Steven. **Henry** Hudson: in search of the Northwest Passage. by Steven Otfinoski. Marshall Cavendish Benchmark, c2007. 80 p.: Great explorations

Grades: 5 6 7 8 **B**

1. Explorers 17th century 2. North America -- History -- Colonial period, 1600-1775. 3. United States -- History -- Colonial period, 1600-1775.
ISBN 0761422250

LC 2005027927

An examination of the life and accomplishments of the famed explorer who lent his name to several geographic locations in North America. Provided by publisher.

Weaver, Janice. **Hudson**. Janice Weaver; David Craig, illustrator. Tundra Books, c2009. 48 p.

Grades: 3 4 5 6 **B**

1. Explorers 2. Western Hemisphere -- Exploration -- British
ISBN 9780887768149

"This dramatic picture-book biography about Henry Hudson, who discovered neither the new land nor the passage to Asia he sought, makes the explorer's lack of success a gripping read. . . . Weaver is clear about what is fact and what is supposition, and the tumultuous early-seventeenth-century history is meticulously documented. . . . Craig's glowing period portraits, landscapes, and watercolors of the ship in dangerous seas intensify the drama, and archival prints and maps add interest." Booklist.

Hunter, Clementine, 1886-1988

★ Whitehead, Kathy, 1957-. **Art** from her heart: folk artist Clementine Hunter. Kathy Whitehead; illustrated by Shane Evans. G.P. Putnam's Sons, 2008. 32 p.

Grades: 4 5 6 7 **B**
    1. African American painters 2. African American folk artists 3. Plantations in art 4. African Americans 5. Women
ISBN 9780399242199

LC 2006034458

Lyrical writing introduces readers to a self-taught artist whose paintings captured scenes of backbreaking work and joyous celebrations of southern farm life, but because of the color of her skin, she was not allowed into the museums or galleries where her art was shown.

"Whitehead's lyrical text speaks of Hunter's perseverance and talent as well as of the simplicity, love of nature, and caring of friends and family that informed her work. Evans bolsters Whitehead's words with bold mixed-media illustrations that portray Hunter in hard times and in good." School Library Journal.

Hunter-Gault, Charlayne

Hunter-Gault, Charlayne. **To** the mountaintop!: my journey through the civil rights movement. Charlayne Hunter-Gault. Roaring Brook Press, 2012. 144 p.: New York Times

Grades: 6 7 8 9 10 11 12 **B**
    1. African American journalists 2. Civil Rights Movement 3. African Americans -- Civil rights -- History 20th century 4. Journalists 5. Southern States -- Race relations
ISBN 9781596436053

LC 2011020894

A personal history of the Civil Rights Movement from an activist and acclaimed journalist begins at the 2009 presidential inauguration of Barak Obama and journeys back through the decades, offering witness to the events of the social movement that changed the course of United States history and honoring the men and women on whose shoulders Obama stands.

"This very personal account (shorter than her 1992 memoir about the same period, In My Place) offers a unique witness to the events of the Civil Rights Era, as an accomplished woman looks back on her younger self, making history." Library Journal.

Includes bibliographical references and index.

Hurston, Zora Neale

Lyons, Mary E.. **Sorrow's** kitchen: the life and folklore of Zora Neale Hurston. Mary E. Lyons. Collier Books; 1993. xiii, 144 p.

Grades: 7 8 9 10 **B**
    1. Authors, American 20th century 2. Folklorists, African American 3. African American women authors 4. Authors, American 5. African American women
ISBN 0020444451

LC 92030600

Carter G. Woodson Book Awards: Secondary Level, 1991.

Describes the life and work of the prolific black author who wrote stories, plays, essays, and articles, recorded black folklore, and was involved in the Harlem Renaissance.

"This biography details Hurston's migration from Florida to Baltimore, Washington, D.C., and finally Harlem as well as her travels through the West Indies to collect folklore. The text contains eleven excerpts from Hurston's books. . . . Lyons has created a prime example of biography—fascinating, enlightening, stimulating, and satisfying." Horn Book.

Includes bibliographical references (p. 135-139) and index.

Iturbide, Graciela, 1942-

Quintero, Isabel.J. Paul Getty Museum. **Photographic**: the life of Graciela Iturbide. Isabel Quintero and Zeke Pena. The J. Paul Getty Museum, Getty Publications, [2018] 95 p.

Grades: 7 8 9 10 11 12 **B**
    1. Women photographers 2. Artistic photography 3. Women artists 4. Women 5. Photographers 6. Biographical comics 7. Comics and graphic novels
ISBN 9781947440005

LC 2017023891

A blending of photographs and illustrations trace the life and work of Mexican photographer Graciela Iturbide, who embarked on a journey across Mexico and the world.

"Teens will come away with an evolved sense of how to look at a creator's life and work and how to think critically about art as a process." School Library Journal.

Includes bibliographical references.

Jackson, Livia E. Bitton, 1931-

Jackson, Livia E. Bitton, 1931-. **My** bridges of hope: searching for life and love after Auschwitz. Livia Bitton-Jackson. Aladdin Paperbacks, 2001, c1999. 258 p.

Grades: 7 8 9 10 **B**
    1. Holocaust survivors 2. Jewish teenagers 3. Holocaust survivors 4. Jews 5. Women 6. Slovakia
ISBN 0606208151

LC BL2001001719

In 1945, after surviving a harrowing year in Auschwitz, fourteen-year-old Elli returns, along with her mother and brother, to the family home, now part of Slovakia, where they try to find a way to rebuild their shattered lives.

"The author's story is utterly involving, and adds an important chapter to the ongoing attempt to understand the Holocaust and its consequences." Publishers Weekly.

Jacobs, Jane, 1916-2006

Lang, Glenna. **Genius** of common sense: Jane Jacobs and the story of The death and life of great American cities. Glenna Lang & Marjory Wunsch. David R. Godine, Publisher, 2009. 127 p.

Grades: 7 8 9 10 11 12 **B**
    1. Urban planners 2. Urban planning -- History 20th century 3. Urban sociology -- History 20th century 4. Women urban planners
ISBN 9781567923841

LC 2009008304

A biography of Jane Jacobs, heroine of New York, which covers her views on the value of cities and the influence she had on New York and America. This book is written for children but is interesting and inspiring for all ages.

"This is the story of a remarkable woman, brought up during the Depression and with no college education, who single-handedly changed the way America viewed its cities. . . . At 18, she moved to New York to pursue her career as a writer and fell in love with the city. It was there that she had her infamous battles with Robert Moses over urban renewal and did the research for her most famous book, The Death and Life of Great American Cities. Black-and-white photographs, maps, and political cartoons and other reproductions appear on most pages. . . . Lang and Wunsch are to be commended for introducing a fascinating female role model." School Library Journal.

Includes bibliographical references (p. 118-121) and index.

James, LeBron

Wetzel, Dan. **LeBron** James. Dan Wetzel. Henry Holt & Co 2019 160 p.

Grades: 4 5 6 7　　　　　　　　　　　　　　　**B**
　　1. Basketball players 2. African American basketball players 3. Professional basketball players 4. Basketball 5. African Americans
　　ISBN 9781250295804

　　　　　　　　　　　　　　　LC 2019002042

The fifth book in a middle-grade nonfiction sports series that focuses on today's superstars and up-and-comers. Provided by publisher.

Yasuda, Anita. **LeBron** James. Anita Yasuda. AV2 by Weigl, c2011. 24 p.: Remarkable people

Grades: 4 5 6 7　　　　　　　　　　　　　　　**B**
　　1. Basketball players 2. African American basketball players 3. Professional basketball players 4. African Americans
　　ISBN 9781616906696

　　　　　　　　　　　　　　　LC 2010051003

An overview of the life of basketball player LeBron James. Best known for his speed and skill, he rarely allows other players to take the ball away.

"This looks at Lebron James' life, accomplishments, and challenges while including a page of quotes, an annotated list of contemporaries and influences, starter suggestions for writing a paper, and a time line and glossary.... [This book] follows basketball's King James from his early life with a single teen mother to his splashy entry into the NBA at age 19." Booklist.

Jemison, Mae, 1956-

Jemison, Mae, 1956-. **Find** where the wind goes: moments from my life. by Mae Jemison. Scholastic, 2001. 196 p.

Grades: 5 6 7 8　　　　　　　　　　　　　　　**B**
　　1. African American women astronauts 2. Astronauts 3. African Americans 4. Women
　　ISBN 0439131952

　　　　　　　　　　　　　　　LC 00041008

The first African American woman to travel to space shares her special memories from her childhood in Chicago, to her college career at Stanford University, to her work in West Africa as the Peace Corps' youngest medical officer.

Jiang, Ji-li, 1954-

Jiang, Ji-li. **Red** scarf girl: a memoir of the Cultural Revolution. Ji-li Jiang; foreword by David Henry Hwang. Harper Collins, c1997. xvii, 285 p.

Grades: 6 7 8 9 10　　　　　　　　　　　　　**B**
　　1. Chinese Cultural Revolution (1966-1976) 2. Teenage girls 3. Atrocities 4. State-sponsored terrorism 5. Power (Social sciences) 6. Revolutions 7. China
　　ISBN 0060275855

　　　　　　　　　　　　　　　LC 97005089

"This is an autobiographical account of growing up during Mao's Cultural Revolution in China in 1966.... Jiang describes in terrifying detail the ordeals of her family and those like them, including unauthorized search and seizure, persecution, arrest and torture, hunger, and public humiliation.... Her voice is that of an intelligent, confused adolescent, and her focus on the effects of the revolution on herself, her family, and her friends provides an emotional focal point for the book, and will allow even those with limited knowledge of Chinese history to access the text." Bulletin of the Center for Children's Books.

Jobs, Steve, 1955-2011

Blumenthal, Karen, 1959-2020. **Steve** Jobs: the man who thought different. Karen Blumenthal Feiwel & Friends, 2012. 310 p.

Grades: 7 8 9 10　　　　　　　　　　　　　　**B**
　　1. Apple Computer, Inc. -- History 2. Computer industry and trade 3. Computer engineers 4. Computers -- History 5. Adopted children 6. College dropouts
　　ISBN 9781250015570

Traces the inspiring life and career of the late founder of Apple, covering topics ranging from his struggles as an adopted child and a college dropout to his Buddhist faith and friendship with Steve Wozniack, in a portrait framed around his inspirational Stanford University commencement speech.

Johnson, Katherine G. 1918-2020

Johnson, Katherine G., 1918-2020. **Reaching** for the Moon: the autobiography of NASA mathematician Katherine Johnson. Katherine Johnson. Atheneum Books for Young Readers, 2019. 256 p.

Grades: 4 5 6 7 8　　　　　　　　　　　　　**B**
　　1. United States. National Aeronautics and Space Administration -- Officials and employees 2. Project Apollo (U.S.) 3. Apollo 11 (Spacecraft) 4. Women mathematicians 5. African American women 6. Determination in women 7. Mathematicians
　　ISBN 9781534440838

　　　　　　　　　　　　　　　LC 2019003873

The inspiring autobiography of NASA mathematician Katherine Johnson, who helped launch Apollo 11.. Provided by publisher.

"Much has been written about the black women mathematicians who worked behind the scenes at NASA; now young readers can hear Katherine Johnson's story in her own words." Kirkus.

Johnson, Magic, 1958-

Roselius, J. Chris. **Magic** Johnson: basketball star & entrepreneur. J. Chris Roselius. ABDO Pub. Co., c2011. 112 p.: Legendary athletes

Grades: 6 7 8 9　　　　　　　　　　　　　　　**B**
　　1. Basketball players 2. African American basketball players 3. Businesspeople 4. African American businesspeople 5. Basketball
　　ISBN 9781617147562

　　　　　　　　　　　　　　　LC 2010046696

A biography of the basketball superstar, from his childhood in Michigan through his record-breaking career with the Los Angeles Lakers to his off-court work promoting HIV/AIDS awareness.

"This biography of basketball star Magic Johnson goes beyond merely discussing [his] accomplishments.... [It] also [explores] the social and political [influence he] had on society as a whole. In addition, [it introduces] historical events in the context of [his life].... This ... is teeming with information and is a must-purchase for sports fans and readers interested in social activism." School Library Journal.

Includes bibliographical references (p. 104) and index.

Johnson, Mamie

Green, Michelle Y.. A **strong** right arm: the story of Mamie "Peanut" Johnson. Michelle Y. Green; introduction by Mamie Johnson. Dial Books for Young Readers, c2002. xiv, 111 p.

Grades: 4 5 6 7　　　　　　　　　　　　　　　**B**
　　1. Baseball players 2. African American baseball players 3.

Women baseball players 4. Women 5. African Americans
ISBN 0803726619

LC 2001028616

Presents a biography of Mamie Johnson, one of three women to play in the professional Negro League, discussing the challenges she faced as a black woman to make her way into professional baseball.

"Johnson was a pitcher with the Negro Leagues' Indianapolis Clowns from 1953 to 1955. In the introduction, Johnson speaks directly and movingly to the reader about her meeting with author Green, who then lets the famous ballplayer tell her own story in a lively first-person narrative. Johnson's ebullient personality and determination fairly leap off the page." Booklist.

Includes bibliographical references (p. 107).

Johnson, Robert, 1911-1938

Lewis, J. Patrick. **Black** cat bone: the life of blues legend Robert Johnson. by J. Patrick Lewis; illustrated by Gary Kelley. Creative Editions, 2006. 48 p.

Grades: 6 7 8 9 10 **B**
1. African American men 2. African American musicians 3. African American blues musicians 4. Blues musicians 5. Blues guitarists 6. Mississippi 7. Delta Region, Mississippi
ISBN 1568461941

LC 2005052298

"Robert Johnson, the celebrated blues musician, is said to have sold his soul to the devil for his skills on the guitar. . . . Lewis's verse echoes Johnson's music. . . . A single line of text parades ghostlike across the bottom of each page, explaining the aspect of the man's life that the poem sings of, and becoming a cumulative mini-bio in itself. A couple of Johnson's own lyrics appear with the sequence of Lewis's poems where they add to the narrative tension. Kelley's mixed-media illustrations in blues and browns add to the mood and enliven the layout." School Library Journal.

Jordan, Barbara, 1936-1996

Raatma, Lucia. **Barbara** Jordan. Lucia Raatma. Cavendish Square, 2014. 96 p.: Leading women

Grades: 7 8 9 **B**
1. United States. Congress. House 2. Legislators 3. African American women legislators 4. Legislators 5. African Americans 6. Texas -- Politics and government -- 1951-
ISBN 9780761449560

LC 2011003470

Presents the biography of Barbara Jordan against the backdrop of her political, historical, and cultural environment. Provided by publisher.

Joseph, (Nez Perce Chief), 1840-1904

Hopping, Lorraine Jean. **Chief** Joseph: the voice for peace. by Lorraine Hopping Egan. Sterling, c2009. 128 p.: Sterling biographies

Grades: 7 8 9 10 **B**
1. Native American leadership 2. Chiefs (Political anthropology) 3. Nez Perce Indians -- Wars, 1877 4. Forced relocations 5. Nez Perce Indians
ISBN 9781402768422

LC 2009024132

"This biography is packed with fast action and detailed analysis. . . . Hopping tells of Joseph's painful decision to leave his land to save Nez Perc lives, choosing peace because he knew they could not win against the U.S. . . . [The] spacious design is highly scannable, with color background screens, photos, maps, and historic prints throughout." Booklist.

Includes bibliographical references and index.

Juarez, Benito Pablo, 1806-1872

Stein, R. Conrad. The **story** of Mexico: Benito Juarez and the French Intervention. R. Conrad Stein. Morgan Reynolds Pub., c2008. 160 p.

Grades: 6 7 8 9 **B**
1. Mexico -- History -- 1821-1867 2. Mexico -- History -- European intervention, 1861-1867
ISBN 1599350521

LC 2007016005

Profiles the man who is considered the father of the modern Republic of Mexico, describing his rise to the presidency, resistance to Napoleon's invasion, and coup of the French regime a few years later.

"The book provides detailed information in a readable format, and [a] lively writing style. . . . Colorful reproductions and photographs help to maintain interest. [This] title tells the story of Jurez, a Zapotec Indian, and his rise to political leadership. Born into poverty in 1806, he became Mexico's first Indian president, presiding over a country in turmoil." School Library Journal.

Includes bibliographical references (p. 149-156) and index.

Kahlo, Frida

Bernier-Grand, Carmen T.. **Frida**: viva la vida! = long live life! by Carmen T. Bernier-Grand. Marshall Cavendish Children, c2007. 64 p.

Grades: 8 9 10 11 12 **B**
1. Artists 2. Painters 3. Women
ISBN 0761453369

LC 2006014479

Biographical poems about the life and work of Mexican artist Frida Kahlo.

"Bernier-Grand introduces a famous life with lyrical free-verse poems. Nearly every double-page spread pairs a well-reproduced painting by Frida Kahlo with an original poem that defines turning points in the artist's life. Bernier-Grand's words expertly extend the autobiographical imagery so evident in the art." Booklist.

Includes bibliographical references (p. 61-63).

Kamkwamba, William, 1987-

Kamkwamba, William, 1987-. The **boy** who harnessed the wind. William Kamkwamba and Bryan Mealer; illustrated by Anna Hymas. Dial Books for Young Readers, 2015. 304 p.

Grades: 4 5 6 7 **B**
1. Inventors 2. Windmills 3. Electric power production 4. Irrigation 5. Rural electrification 6. Malawi 7. Africa
ISBN 9780803740808

An adaptation for young readers of a best-selling memoir follows the experiences of 14-year-old William Kamkwamba, who built a windmill out of junkyard scraps to bring electricity to his famine-stricken Malawi village.

"This youth edition of the original adult book of the same title has been skillfully adapted for middle grade readers." School Library Journal.

Kazerooni, Abbas, 1978-

Kazerooni, Abbas, 1978-. **On** two feet and wings: one boy's amazing story of survival. Abbas Kazerooni. Skyscape, 2014 238 p.

Grades: 5 6 7 8 **B**
1. Refugees, Iranian 2. Iran-Iraq War, 1980-1988 3. Child refugees 4. Iran -- History -- Islamic revolution, 1979-1997.
ISBN 9781477847831

Recounts the author's experiences fleeing Iran as a young boy during the Iran-Iraq war, and making his way on his own in the unfamiliar city of Istanbul in hopes of attaining a visa in England.

"Young readers will understand [Kazerooni's] overwhelming loneliness and fear as well as his satisfaction at managing on his own. With child immigrants so much in the news, Kazerooni's unusual, compelling story is especially timely." Booklist.

Keat, Nawuth, 1964-

Keat, Nawuth, 1964-. **Alive** in the killing fields: the true story of Nawuth Keat, a Khmer Rouge survivor. by Nawuth Keat and Martha Kendall. National Geographic, 2009. 112 p.

Grades: 7 8 9 10 11 **B**
1. Khmer Rouge. 2. 1970s 3. Child refugees 4. Political refugees 5. Children and war 6. Voyages and travels 7. Atrocities 8. Cambodia -- History -- Civil War, 1970-1975. 9. Cambodia -- History -- 1975-
ISBN 9781426305160

LC 2008039805

A survivor of the horrors of war-torn Cambodia breaks his longtime silence to share his family's story of death, enslavement, and torture in the hands of Pol Pot's Khmer Rouge fighters, providing an inspirational story of hope to children whose worlds have been devastated by catastrophe.

"Told with stark simplicity, Nawuth's narrative is memorable yet accessible to young readers." Voice of Youth Advocates.

Includes bibliographical references and index.

Kellar, Harry, 1849-1922

Jarrow, Gail. The **amazing** Harry Kellar: great American magician. Gail Jarrow. Calkins Creek, c2012. 96 p.

Grades: 3 4 5 6 7 8 **B**
1. Magicians
ISBN 9781590788653

LC bl2012005509

Chronicles the life of the American magician, including his famous tricks and colorful posters.

Keller, Helen, 1880-1968

Keller, Helen, 1880-1968. The **story** of my life. Helen Keller. Modern Library, 2003. xlvi, 343 p.

Grades: 8 9 10 11 12 Adult **B**
1. Women who are blind and deaf 2. Women who are blind 3. Women who are deaf 4. Women with disabilities 5. Women
ISBN 0679642870

LC 2002040971

A serious illness destroyed Helen Keller's sight and hearing at the age of two. At seven, she was helped by Anne Sullivan, her beloved teacher and friend. Through sheer determination and resolve, she learned to speak and prepared herself for entry into prep school by age sixteen. Later she enrolled at Radcliffe and graduated with honors. Her motto: "There are no handicaps, only challenges."

Lambert, Joseph, 1984-. **Annie** Sullivan and the trials of Helen Keller. by Joseph Lambert. Disney/Hyperion Books, 2012. 92 p.

Grades: 5 6 7 **B**
1. Teacher-student relationships 2. Women who are blind and deaf 3. Women teachers 4. Teaching 5. Students 6. Biographical comics 7. Comics and Graphic novels
ISBN 9781423113362

LC 2011036324

Using abstract imagery to convey how Helen experienced her world, an introduction to Helen Keller's tutelage under Annie Sullivan's determined care shares lesser-known aspects of their lives, from Annie's troubled upbringing to the plagiarism charge that threatened to destroy their reputations.

Lawlor, Laurie. **Helen** Keller: rebellious spirit. Laurie Lawlor. Holiday House, c2001. 198 p.

Grades: 5 6 7 8 **B**
1. People who are blind and deaf 2. Teachers of children who are blind and deaf 3. People with disabilities 4. Women 5. Teacher-student relationships
ISBN 0823415880

LC 00036950

"A biography of the most famous deaf and blind person in history. Drawing on social and scientific studies of deafness and blindness as well as on American history texts, Lawlor puts Keller's experiences in context. . . . At the same time, readers get a strong feel for Keller's personality and for the personalities of Annie Sullivan, Alexander Graham Bell, and other major figures in her life. Aided by numerous well-chosen photographs and excerpts from Keller's writings." Horn Book.

Includes bibliographical references (p. 161-165) and index.

Kennedy, John F. (John Fitzgerald), 1917-1963

Cooper, Ilene. **Jack**: the early years of John F. Kennedy. Ilene Cooper. Dutton Children's Books, 2003. 168 p.

Grades: 5 6 7 8 9 10 11 12 **B**
1. Presidents 2. Family relationships 3. Brothers 4. Competition 5. Competition in boys 6. United States -- History -- 20th century.
ISBN 0525469230

LC 2002075912

A description of the childhood and youth of John Fitzgerald Kennedy, the thirty-fifth president of the United States.

"Intelligent design and numerous fabulous, well-placed, and well-captioned black-and-white photographs enrich Cooper's clear prose. . . . This sensitive, well-researched biography will enhance any collection." Voice of Youth Advocates.

Includes bibliographical references and index.

Kennedy, Robert Francis, 1925-1968

Aronson, Marc. **Robert** F. Kennedy: a twentieth-century life. Marc Aronson. Viking, 2007. 204 p.: Up close (Viking)

Grades: 8 9 10 11 12 **B**
1. United States. Congress. Senate 2. Legislators
ISBN 9780670060665

LC 2006102150

Presents the life of Robert F. Kennedy, discussing his childhood in an environment of immense wealth and privilege, his political career, his role as mentor to the poor and powerless, and his personal charisma.

King, Billie Jean, 1943-

Gitlin, Marty. **Billie** Jean King: tennis star & social activist. by Marty Gitlin. ABDO Pub. Co., c2011. 112 p.: Legendary athletes

Grades: 6 7 8 9 **B**
1. Tennis players 2. Women tennis players 3. Women athletes 4. Women
ISBN 9781617147579

LC 2010046584

Highlights the life and accomplishments of one of the first women to play professional tennis.

"This biography of tennis champion Billie Jean King goes beyond merely discussing [her] accomplishments. . . . [It] also [explores] the social and political [influence she] had on society as a whole. In addition, [it introduces] historical events in the context of [her life]. . . . This . . . is teeming with information and is a must-purchase for sports fans and readers interested in social activism." School Library Journal.

Includes bibliographical references (p. 104-109) and index.

King, Henrietta Chamberlain, 1832-1925

Wade, Mary Dodson. **Henrietta** King, la patrona. Mary Dodson Wade; illustrations by Bill Farnsworth. Bright Sky Press, c2012. 64 p.: Texas heroes for young readers

Grades: 4 5 6 7 **B**

1. Women ranchers 2. Philanthropists 3. Women philanthropists 4. Ranchers 5. King Ranch (Tex) 6. Texas

ISBN 9781933979632

LC 2011052721

Presents the life story of Henrietta King who had humble beginnings, but went on to became the owner of one of the largest ranches in Texas.

King, Martin Luther, Jr., 1929-1968

Bodden, Valerie. The **assassination** of Martin Luther King Jr.. by Valerie Bodden. Creative Education, Creative Paperbacks, [2017] 48 p.: Turning points (Creative Education)

Grades: 5 6 7 8 **B**

1. Assassination

ISBN 9781608187478

LC 2016000993

A historical account of Martin Luther King's assassination, including the events leading up to it, the people involved, the conditions of racial tension, and the lingering aftermath. Provided by publisher.

"Large glossy photographs are included throughout, along with sidebars providing background or expanding on information." Horn Book.

Includes bibliographical references and index.

Bolden, Tonya. **M.L.K.**: journey of a King. by Tonya Bolden; photo editor, Bob Adelman. Abrams Books for Young Readers, c2007. 128 p.

Grades: 7 8 9 10 **B**

1. African American civil rights workers 2. Baptists -- Clergy 3. Civil Rights Movement 4. Civil disobedience 5. Civil rights workers

ISBN 0810954761

LC 2006013332

NCTE Orbis Pictus Nonfiction Award, 2008.

Profiles the life and accomplishments of Baptist minister and civil rights leader Dr. Martin Luther King, Jr.

"Do libraries need another biography of King? Yes, if it's as good as this one, which will reach a wide audience. . . . Stirring, beautifully reproduced, well-captioned photos . . . accompany the text." Booklist.

Includes bibliographical references (p. 116-120) and index.

Swanson, James L., 1959-. **Chasing** King's killer: the hunt for Martin Luther King, Jr.'s assassin. by James L. Swanson; foreword by Congressman John Lewis Scholastic Press, [2018] 373 p.

Grades: 7 8 9 10 11 12 **B**

1. Civil rights workers 2. Murderers 3. African Americans 4. Clergy 5. Escaped convicts

ISBN 9780545723336

LC 2017008562

Offers an inside look into the lives of Martin Luther King, Jr. and his assassin, James Earl Ray, discussing the history of the time and systematically examining the assassination and its aftermath.

"Page-turning nonfiction that captures the tenor of the times with meticulous research and a trove of photographs. . . . An important contribution to the understanding of a complex period in United States history that still reverberates today." Kirkus

Includes bibliographical references and index.

Kor, Eva Mozes

Kor, Eva Mozes. **Surviving** the angel of death: the true story of a Mengele twin in Auschwitz. by Eva Mozes Kor and Lisa Rojany Buccieri. Tanglewood, 2020, c2009. iv, 141 p.

Grades: 7 8 9 10 **B**

1. Auschwitz (Concentration camp) 2. Jewish children 3. Holocaust (1933-1945) -- Children 4. Jews -- Persecutions 5. Twins 6. World War II 7. Germany

ISBN 9781939100450

LC 2009009494

Describes the life of Eva Mozes and her twin sister Miriam as they were interred at the Auschwitz concentration camp during the Holocaust, where Dr. Josef Mengele performed sadistic medical experiments on them until their release.

"In straightforward language the book relates the twins' daily routines, including lab experiments and occasions on which they suffered serious brushes with death as the result of injections they were given. Many of the memories related come across as rough sketches, though some graphic details are included." Kirkus

Korematsu, Fred, 1919-2005

Atkins, Laura. **Fred** Korematsu speaks up. by Laura Atkins and Stan Yogi; illustrations by Yutaka Houlette. Heyday, [2016] 112 p.: Fighting for justice

Grades: 4 5 6 7 8 **B**

1. Japanese Americans -- Forced removal and incarceration, 1942-1945 2. Injustice 3. Imprisonment 4. Japanese Americans -- Civil rights -- History 20th century.

ISBN 9781597143684

LC 2016008098

Carter G. Woodson Book Awards: Middle Level, 2018.

Highlights the life and accomplishments of the man who challenged the legality of imprisoning Japanese Americans during World War II, describing the prejudice he and other Japanese Americans experienced and his long struggle for justice.

Krosoczka, Jarrett

Krosoczka, Jarrett. **Hey,** kiddo: how I lost my mother, found my father, and dealt with family addiction. Jarrett J. Krosoczka. Graphix, 2018. 294 p., 20 unnumbered p.

Grades: 7 8 9 10 11 12 **B**

1. Family relationships 2. Nontraditional families 3. Parent-separated boys 4. Children of drug abusers 5. Grandparents 6. Autobiographical comics 7. Comics and graphic novels

ISBN 9780545902472

LC 2019300454

A powerful graphic memoir by the award-winning author traces the author's unconventional coming of age with a drug-addict mother, an absent father and two lovingly opinionated grandparents.

"Krosoczka as an author generously and lovingly shows his flawed family members striving to do the best they can even as Krosoczka the character clearly aches for more. Honest, important, and timely." Kirkus.

Lafayette, Marie Joseph Paul Yves Roch Gilbert Du Motier, marquis de, 1757-1834

Freedman, Russell. **Lafayette** and the American Revolution. Russell Freedman. Holiday House, c2010. 88 p.

Grades: 5 6 7 8   **B**
1. United States. Army 2. France. Army 3. Diplomats 4. Generals 5. Revolutions 6. American Revolution, 1775-1783 7. United States -- History -- Revolution, 1775-1783 -- French participation 8. France -- History -- 1789-1815.
ISBN 9780823421824

LC 2009052342

An account of Marquis de Lafayette, a young French nobleman, who helped bring victory at Yorktown and became a lifelong friend of George Washington.

Hale, Nathan, 1976-. **Lafayette!**: a Revolutionary War tale. by Nathan Hale. Amulet Books, 2018. 128 p.: Nathan Hale's hazardous tales

Grades: 3 4 5 6   **B**
1. United States. Army 2. France. Army 3. Generals 4. Diplomats 5. Revolutions 6. American Revolution, 1775-1783 7. United States -- History -- Revolution, 1775-1783 -- French participation 8. Biographical comics 9. Comics and Graphic novels
ISBN 9781419731488

LC 2018023605

Tells the story of the Marquis de Lafayette, both what happened before and during the American Revolution, including all the Frenchman's escapades across France and the colonies.

"Hale does a tremendous job of telling the complicated story of one of the most celebrated men in history with facts and figures interspersed throughout the often humorous and informative narrative. His intricately drawn panels are beautifully colored, with pastels of grey and pink, and although a multitude of people from across the globe feature in his story, Hale does an extraordinary job of differentiating characters throughout." Booklist.

Lat

Lat. **Kampung** boy. by Lat. First Second, 2006, c1979. 141 p.

Grades: 7 8 9 10 11 12 Adult   **B**
1. 1950s 2. Boys 3. Rubber plantations 4. Cartoonists -- Biography 5. Muslims 6. Mischief in boys 7. Malaysia -- Social life and customs -- 20th century. 8. Autobiographical comics 9. Comics and Graphic novels
ISBN 1596431210

LC 2005034135

Relates the life experiences, from birth to beginning boarding school, of a boy growing up on a rubber plantation in rural Malaysia.

"Malaysian cartoonist Lat uses the graphic novel format to share the story of his childhood in a small village, or kampung. From his birth and adventures as a toddler to the enlargement of his world as he attends classes in the village, makes friends, and, finally, departs for a prestigious city boarding school, this autobiography is warm, authentic, and wholly engaging." Booklist.

Lauren, Ralph

Mattern, Joanne, 1963-. **Ralph** Lauren. Joanne Mattern. Chelsea House, c2011. 101 p.: Famous fashion designers

Grades: 6 7 8 9 10   **B**
1. Fashion designers 2. Fashion design 3. Clothing industry and trade 4. Fashion
ISBN 9781604139785

LC 2010036192

Profiles the life and career of the famed designer, including his childhood in New York, fashion empire, and health scares.

Lawrence, Jacob, 1917-2000

★ Duggleby, John, 1952-. **Story** painter: the life of Jacob Lawrence. by John Duggleby. Chronicle Books, c1998. 55 p.

Grades: 4 5 6 7   **B**
1. African American painters 2. African Americans in art 3. Artists 4. African Americans 5. Art appreciation
ISBN 0811820823

LC 98004513

Carter G. Woodson Book Awards: Elementary Level, 1999.

A biography of the African American artist who grew up in the midst of the Harlem Renaissance and became one of the most renowned painters of the life of his people.

"Lawrence's expressionistic, stark paintings, in excellent full-page color reproduction . . . nicely complement Duggleby's measured account of a materially poor but culturally rich childhood and Lawrence's subsequent struggles and successes." Publishers Weekly.

Includes bibliographical references (p. 54).

Layson, Annelex Hofstra

Layson, Annelex Hofstra. **Lost** childhood: my life in a Japanese prison camp during World War II. Annelex Hofstra Layson; with Herman Viola. National Geographic, 2008. 128 p.

Grades: 5 6 7 8 9   **B**
1. World War II -- Prisoners and prisons, Japanese 2. Children and war 3. World War II -- Children 4. World War II 5. Concentration camps 6. Indonesia -- History -- Japanese occupation, 1942-1945. 7. Java
ISBN 9781426303227

LC 2008011671

In a shockingly honest narrative, a former prisoner-of-war tells how her family, along with ten thousand other Dutch residents living in the Dutch East Indies were shipped off to interment camps where food rationing, terrible sanitary conditions, and an uncertain future were the norms for more than three years.

"The author's narrative is warm and enthralling. . . . Layson's voice captivates and engages." Library Media Connection.

Includes bibliographical references and index.

Lee, Harper

Don, Katherine. **Real** courage: the story of Harper Lee. by Katherine Don. Morgan Reynolds Pub., c2013. 128 p.: World writers

Grades: 7 8 9 10   **B**
1. Authors, American 20th century 2. Authors
ISBN 9781599353487

LC 2012016871

"Students and teachers looking for a solid, accessible biography will find this to be a fine choice as the writing is straightforward and engaging." School Library Journal.

Includes bibliographical references and index.

Madden, Kerry. **Harper** Lee. Kerry Madden. Viking Children's Books, 2009. 208 p.: Up close (Viking)

Grades: 7 8 9 10   **B**
1. Authors, American 20th century 2. Women authors 3. Women
ISBN 9780670010950

LC 2008053911

Highlights the life and accomplishments of the Southern writer known for her book "To Kill a Mockingbird."

"A narrative both well paced and richly detailed . . . this biography will appeal to fans of the novel and to newcomers. . . . Extensive source notes and an excellent bibliography round out this superb biography." Kirkus.

Includes bibliographical references and index.

Shields, Charles J., 1951-. **I** am Scout: a biography of Harper Lee. Charles Shields. Henry Holt, 2008. 256 p.
Grades: 7 8 9 10   **B**
1. Authors, American 20th century 2. Women authors 20th century 3. Women
ISBN 0805083340

The author of Mockingbird: A Portrait of Harper Lee adapts his bestselling title to bring to young readers the life of the unconventional, high-spirited woman who wrote one of the greatest novels of all time, To Kill a Mockingbird.

"Shields offers a fascinating look at the unconventional Lee, which captures his elusive subject and her lifelong friend, Truman Capote. . . . Shields' formidable research . . . will impress any student who has ever written a term paper." Booklist.

Includes bibliographical references and index.

Lee, Robert E. (Robert Edward), 1807-1870

Robertson, James I.. **Robert** E. Lee: Virginian soldier, American citizen. James I. Robertson, Jr. Atheneum Books for Young Readers, 2005. 159 p.
Grades: 7 8 9 10   **B**
1. Confederate States of America. Army. 2. Generals 3. Civil war 4. United States Civil War, 1861-1865 5. Confederate soldiers 6. United States -- History -- Civil War, 1861-1865 -- Campaigns 7. Confederate States of America
ISBN 0689857314

LC 2003022108

"This portrait of the Confederate general puts particular emphasis on his life during the Civil War years but provides plenty of information on his youth, his early military career, and his postwar years. . . . Useful for reports and interesting in its own right, this well-researched biography will be a solid addition to Library collections." Booklist.

Leiv Eiriksson, -approximately 1020

DeFries, Cheryl L.. **Leif** Eriksson: Viking explorer of the New World. Cheryl DeFries. Enslow Publishers, c2010. 112 p.: Great explorers of the world
Grades: 6 7 8 9   **B**
1. Vikings 2. Explorers 3. Northmen and Northwomen 4. Civilization, Viking 5. Western Hemisphere -- Exploration -- Norse
ISBN 9781598451269

LC 2009044205

Examines the life of Viking explorer Leif Eriksson, including his explorations, his discovery of North America, and his legacy in American history. Provided by publisher.

"This provides some interesting stories from the Vikings' family history. Readers will be intrigued by the folklore and legends. The mystery behind [Ericksson's] discovery of America is explored briefly, as well as its impact on navigation, law, and culture. Photographs of Viking artifacts bring provide an interesting glimpse into the past. . . . This . . .

would serve as a useful resource for middle and elementary school students and may inspire them to read further." Voice of Youth Advocates.

Includes bibliographical references and index.

Lennon, John, 1940-1980

Behnke, Alison. **Death** of a dreamer: the assassination of John Lennon. Alison Marie Behnke. Twenty-First Century Books, c2012. 96 p.
Grades: 5 6 7 8   **B**
1. Rock musicians 2. Rock music 3. Assassination 4. Assassins
ISBN 9780822590361

LC 2010005550

Presents the life, accomplishments, and assassination of John Lennon and the troubled history of his assassin, Mark David Chapman.

Burlingame, Jeff. **John** Lennon: "Imagine". Jeff Burlingame. Enslow, c2011. 160 p.: American rebels
Grades: 6 7 8 9   **B**
1. Beatles (Musical group) 2. Rock musicians
ISBN 9780766036758

LC 2009040045

A biography of British-born rock-and-roll legend John Lennon, who lived and died in New York City. This book discusses his early life, rise and fall of the Beatles, personal hardships, and legacy. Provided by publisher.

"This attractive biography includes sidebars, wide margins, large type, and many photographs throughout. Burlingame maintains readers' interest." School Library Journal.

Includes bibliographical references and index.

Partridge, Elizabeth. **John** Lennon: all I want is the truth: a biography. by Elizabeth Partridge. Viking, 2005. 232 p.
Grades: 8 9 10 11 12   **B**
1. Beatles (Musical group) 2. Rock musicians 3. Sexuality 4. Drug use 5. Musicians 6. Singers
ISBN 0670059544

LC 2005011850

"This handsome book will be eagerly received by both Beatles fans, who are legion, and their elders, who will enjoy reliving the glory days of the Fab Four and exploring the inner workings of a creative talent." School Library Journal.

Includes bibliographical references (p. 215-219) and index.

Rappaport, Doreen. **John's** secret dreams: the life of John Lennon. written by Doreen Rappaport; illustrated by Bryan Collier. Hyperion Books for Children, c2004. 1 v. (unpaged): Big Words
Grades: 4 5 6 7   **B**
1. Beatles (Musical group) 2. Rock musicians 3. Musicians
ISBN 0786808179

LC 2003057116

Introduces the life of John Lennon who, as a member of the Beatles and as a solo artist, sought to make the world a better and more peaceful place than the one in which he was raised.

"Using a combination of simple prose, song lyrics, and illustration, this heartfelt picture-book biography traces Lennon's life from his childhood to his death. Striking in both its simplicity and complexity, it captures this enigmatic singer, artist, songwriter, and folk hero in a way that will move and fascinate those too young to remember the man but are surrounded by his music and myth." School Library Journal.

Lewis, C. S. (Clive Staples), 1898-1963

Hamilton, Janet. **C.S.** Lewis: twentieth century pilgrim. Janet Hamilton. Morgan Reynolds Pub., c2011. 128 p.: World writers

Grades: 7 8 9 10 **B**

    1. Church of England. 2. Authors, English 20th century 3. Anglicans 4. Christian authors 5. Authors, Irish 20th century 6. Fantasy fiction authors

ISBN 9781599351124

LC 2009007134

Presents the life of the English author, describing the early loss of his beloved mother, his life as an Oxford don, his conversion to Christianity, and his composition of the classic children's series "The Chronicles of Narnia."

"In this biography of the British author, Lewis' childhood is well-documented, as is his love of literature as an escape from the real world. Hamilton clearly shows the importance religion played in Lewis's life. The impact that war, and the resulting loss of the imaginative worlds he could find in literature, and his struggle with religious belief are tied directly to his writing." Voice of Youth Advocates.

Includes bibliographical references (p. 122-126) and index.

Lewis, John, 1940-2020

Bausum, Ann. **Freedom** Riders: John Lewis and Jim Zwerg on the front lines of the civil rights movement. by Ann Bausum; forewords by Freedom Riders Congressman John Lewis and Jim Zwerg. National Geographic, c2006. 79 p.

Grades: 5 6 7 8 **B**

    1. 1960s 2. 20th century 3. Freedom Rides (Civil rights movement) 4. Determination (Personal quality) 5. Civil Rights Movement 6. Civil rights workers 7. African Americans -- Civil rights -- History 20th century. 8. Southern States -- Race relations.

ISBN 0792241738

LC 2005012947

"Bausum's narrative style, fresh, engrossing, and at times heart-stopping, brings the story of the turbulent and often violent dismantling of segregated travel alive in vivid detail. The language, presentation of material, and pacing will draw readers in and keep them captivated." School Library Journal.

Includes bibliographical references and index.

Lewis, John, 1940-2020. **March.** John Lewis, Andrew Aydin, and Nate Powell. Top Shelf Productions, 2013. 121 p.: March

Grades: 8 9 10 11 12 Adult **B**

    1. Civil Rights Movement 2. Politicians 3. Racism 4. Protests, demonstrations, vigils, etc 5. African Americans -- Civil rights 6. Alabama -- Race relations. 7. United States -- Social conditions -- 20th century. 8. Autobiographical comics 9. Comics and Graphic novels

ISBN 9781603093002

Carter G. Woodson Book Awards: Secondary Level, 2017.

A first-hand account of the author's lifelong struggle for civil and human rights spans his youth in rural Alabama, his life-changing meeting with Martin Luther King, Jr., and the birth of the Nashville Student Movement.

"This is superb visual storytelling that establishes a convincing, definitive record of a key eyewitness to significant social change." School Library Journal.

Lewis, John, 1940-2020. **March.** John Lewis, Andrew Aydin, and Nate Powell. Top Shelf Productions, 2015. 160 p.: March

Grades: 8 9 10 11 12 Adult **B**

    1. Student Nonviolent Coordinating Committee (U.S.) 2. 1960s 3.

Civil Rights Movement 4. Protests, demonstrations, vigils, etc 5. Politicians 6. Racism 7. Race relations 8. United States -- Social conditions -- 20th century. 9. Autobiographical comics 10. Comics and Graphic novels

ISBN 9781603094009

Carter G. Woodson Book Awards: Secondary Level, 2017.

The award-winning, best-selling series returns, as John Lewis' story continues through Freedom Rides and the legendary 1963 March on Washington.

"Heroism and steadiness of purpose continue to light up Lewis' frank, harrowing account of the civil rights movement's climactic days. . . . The contrast between the dignified marchers and the vicious, hate-filled actions and expressions of their tormentors will leave a deep impression on readers." Kirkus.

Lewis, John, 1940-2020. **March..** John Lewis with Andrew Aydin; art by Nate Powell. Top Shelf Productions, 2016. 246 p.: March

Grades: 8 9 10 11 12 Adult **B**

    1. Student Nonviolent Coordinating Committee (U.S.) 2. 1960s 3. Civil Rights Movement 4. Protests, demonstrations, vigils, etc 5. Politicians 6. Racism 7. Race relations 8. United States -- Social conditions -- 20th century. 9. Autobiographical comics 10. Comics and Graphic novels

ISBN 9781603094023

Carter G. Woodson Book Awards: Secondary Level, 2017.

Coretta Scott King Award, Author Category, 2017.

Michael L. Printz Award, 2017.

National Book Award for Young People's Literature, 2016.

Robert F. Sibert Informational Book Medal, 2017.

Congressman John Lewis, one of the key figures of the civil rights movement, joins co-writer Andrew Aydin and artist Nate Powell to bring the lessons of history to vivid life for a new generation, urgently relevant for today's world.

"Though Lewis and Aydin throw a lot at readers in this volume, their message, helped along seamlessly and splendidly by Powell's fantastic, cinematic artwork, is abundantly clear: the victories of the civil rights movement, symbolized in particular by Barack Obama's inauguration, are hard-won and only succeeded through the dogged dedication of a wide variety of people." Booklist.

Lewis, John, 1940-2020. **Run..** written by John Lewis and Andrew Aydin; art by L. Fury with Nate Powell. Abrams ComicArts, 2018. 128 p.: Run (John Lewis)

Grades: 7 8 9 10 11 12 Adult **B**

    1. African American legislators 2. Legislators 3. Politicians 4. African Americans -- Civil rights 5. Political campaigns 6. Georgia -- Politics and government -- 1951- 7. United States -- Politics and government -- 1981- 8. Autobiographical comics 9. Comics and Graphic novels

ISBN 9781419730696

LC 2018024127

Tells the true story of John Lewis and his colleagues in the movement following the historic success of the Selma campaign and the Voting Rights Act.

"This living history gives faces and voices to the legends of the civil rights era and connects their struggles to the present." Publishers Weekly

Li, Moying, 1954-

Li, Moying, 1954-. **Snow** falling in spring: coming of age in China during the cultural revolution. Moying Li. Farrar, Straus and Giroux, 2008. 192 p.

Grades: 7 8 9 10 11 12   **B**
1. China -- History -- Cultural Revolution, 1966-1976
ISBN 0374399220

LC 2006038356

Bringing to life a dark time in China's history, this powerful memoir follows the author, who, during the summer of 1966 when student Red Guards launched brutal assaults and forced confessions, finds solace in a world of imagination and learning when her father smuggles a reading list of banned books to her from labor camp.

"This memoir . . . offers a highly personal look at China's Cultural Revolution. The author is four years old when Mao initiates the Great Leap Forward in 1958. . . . Li effectively builds the climate of fear that accompanies the rise of the Red Guard, while accounts of her headmaster's suicide and the pulping of her father's book collection give a harrowing, closeup view of the persecution. Sketches about her grandparents root the narrative within a broader context of Chinese traditions as well as her own family's values." Publishers Weekly.

Li, Zhongmei, 1966-
Bernstein, Richard, 1944-. A **girl** named Faithful Plum: a true story of a dancer from China and how she achieved her dream. by Richard Bernstein. Alfred A. Knopf Books for Young Readers, 2011. 288 p.
Grades: 7 8 9 10 11 12   **B**
1. Dancers 2. Poverty 3. Persistence in girls 4. Dancing -- Auditions 5. Girl dancers 6. China -- History -- 20th century.
ISBN 9780375869600

LC 2010048722

Narrates the story of how a young dancer from rural China was admitted to the prestigious Beijing Dance Academy and through hard work and perserverance went on to become one of the most famous dancers in China.

Lichtenstein, Roy, 1923-1997
Rubin, Susan Goldman. **Whaam!**: the art & life of Roy Lichtenstein. by Susan Goldman Rubin. Abrams Books for Young Readers, 2008. 48 p.
Grades: 4 5 6 7   **B**
1. Artists 2. Pop art 3. Art 4. Art teachers 5. Painters
ISBN 9780810994928

LC 2007042048

"Rubin presents an overview of a modern master with clear writing and an abundance of his eye-popping works, all framed on pages that mirror the artist's signature use of primary colors and Benday dots." Booklist.

Lincoln, Abraham, 1809-1865
Aronson, Billy. **Abraham** Lincoln. by Billy Aronson. Marshall Cavendish Benchmark, 2008. 96 p.: Presidents and their times
Grades: 5 6 7 8   **B**
1. Presidents 2. Political leadership 3. Civil war 4. United States Civil War, 1861-1865 5. United States -- History -- Civil War, 1861-1865
ISBN 9780761428398

LC 2007019190

Provides comprehensive information on President Abraham Lincoln and places him within his historical and cultural context. Also explored are the formative events of his times and how he responded. Provided by publisher.

Fleming, Candace. The **Lincolns**: a scrapbook look at Abraham and Mary. Candace Fleming. Schwartz & Wade Books, c2008. 200 p.
Grades: 7 8 9 10 11 12   **B**
1. Presidents 2. Married people 3. Presidents' spouses 4. Presidents -- History 19th century 5. Presidents' spouses -- History 19th century 6. Washington, DC -- History -- Civil War, 1861-1865 7. United States -- History -- Civil War, 1861-1865
ISBN 9780375836183

LC 2007044113

Period photographs, illustrations, letters, and engravings are compiled in a moving biography of the enduring relationship between this celebrated president and his devoted wife through a review of their childhoods, the way they met, the struggles they endured together, and the tragic end to their long journey together upon President Lincoln's assassination.

"Fleming twines accounts of two lives—Abraham and Mary Todd Lincoln—into one fascinating whole. On spreads that combine well-chosen visuals with blocks of headlined text, Fleming gives a full, birth-to-death view of the inextricably bound Lincolns." Booklist.

Freedman, Russell. **Lincoln**: a photobiography. Russell Freedman. Clarion Books, 1987. 150 p.
Grades: 5 6 7 8 9 10   **B**
1. 19th century 2. Presidents 3. Political leadership 4. United States -- Politics and government.
ISBN 0899193803

LC 86033379

Newbery Medal, 1988.
Photographs and text trace the life of the Civil War President.

"This is a balanced work, elegantly designed and enhanced by dozens of period photographs and drawings, some familiar, some refreshingly unfamiliar." Publishers Weekly.

Includes bibliographical references (p. 142-143) and index.

Holzer, Harold. **Father** Abraham: Lincoln and his sons. Harold Holzer. Calkins Creek, 2010. 232 p.
Grades: 6 7 8 9   **B**
1. Fathers and sons 2. Presidents' spouses 3. Family relationships 4. Presidents -- Family 5. Boys 6. United States -- Social life and customs -- 19th century.
ISBN 9781590783030

"This profile of the clan that might have become America's royal family but instead became America's cursed family offers both a wagonload of fascinating period photos and a case study in domestic tragedy and dysfunction. . . . If the author sometimes hobbles his narrative with fussy details, he also tucks in such intimate touches as samples of homely verse from both parents and children and finishes off with quick looks at all of the direct descendants." Kirkus.

Lincoln, Abraham, 1809-1865. **Abraham** Lincoln, the writer: a treasury of his greatest speeches and letters. compiled and edited by Harold Holzer. Boyds Mills Press, 2000. 106 p.
Grades: 7 8 9 10   **B**
1. Presidents 2. United States -- Politics and government -- 1815-1861. 3. United States -- Politics and government -- 1861-1865.
ISBN 1563977729

LC 99066551

Gathers a collection of letters, poetry, and speeches written throughout the life of America's sixteenth President, providing detailed background information and a timeline.

"Lincoln's writings include personal letters, notes on the law, excerpts from speeches, debates, and inaugural addresses, letters to parents of fallen soldiers, and telegrams to his family. Reproductions of period photos, portraits, and documents illustrate the text effectively. . . . Highly interesting and a fine resource for students seeking quotations or for those wanting to meet Lincoln through his own words." Booklist.

Sandler, Martin W.. **Lincoln** through the lens: how photography revealed and shaped an extraordinary life. Martin W. Sandler. Walker Pub. Co., c2008. 97 p.

Grades: 6 7 8 9 10   **B**
1. Presidents 2. Photography -- History 19th century. 3. Presidents
ISBN 9780802796660

LC 2008000219

Offers a complete portrait of this celebrated president through a review of his childhood upbringing, political views and goals, and historic legacy through an examination of his speeches, including the Gettysburg Address, period photographs, personal statements, and more.

"When Lincoln became president, photography was new and he joined the very first generation of human beings ever to be photographed. . . . This extraordinary book is a tribute to the way contemporary and future generations came to view Lincoln. . . . Part biography, part history of of the Civil War, the book touches on many interesting topics. . . . Every step of the way there are fascinating photographs. . . . Although it's the pictures that provide the wow factor, Sandler's perceptive words have their own elegance." Booklist.

Lindbergh, Charles A. (Charles Augustus), 1902-1974
Fleming, Candace. The **rise** and fall of Charles Lindbergh. Candace Fleming. Schwartz & Wade Books, 2020 384 p.

Grades: 7 8 9 10 11 12   **B**
1. 20th century 2. Pilots 3. Parents of murder victims 4. Kidnapping 5. Millionaires 6. Eugenics
ISBN 9780525646549

A biography of one of America's most celebrated heroes, and most complicated, troubled men, Charles Lindbergh.

"In riveting detail and frequently quoting from Lindbergh's diaries and his wife's, Fleming relates his planning and execution of the solo transatlantic flight that made him the most famous man in the world, his marriage and the tragic kidnapping of his firstborn child, his obsession with engineering humankind's immortality, and the existence of his multiple secret families." Publishers Weekly.

Giblin, James Cross, 1933-. **Charles** A. Lindbergh: a human hero. James Cross Giblin. Clarion Books, c1997. 212 p.

Grades: 6 7 8 9   **B**
1. Pilots 2. Transatlantic flights 3. Aviation 4. Kidnapping 5. United States -- History -- 20th century.
ISBN 0395633893

LC 96009501

A biography of the pilot whose life was full of controversy and tragedy, but also fulfilling achievements.

"This sympathetic and informed account (beautifully illustrated with contemporary photographs) is an excellent introduction to Lindbergh and also to the early years of the celebrity society in which we live now." New York Times Book Review.

Includes bibliographical references (p. 201-205) and index.

Liu, Na, 1973-
Liu, Na, 1973-. **Little** White Duck: a childhood in China. by Andres Vera Martinez and Na Liu; illustrated by Andres Vera Martinez. Graphic Universe, 2012. 108 p.

Grades: 4 5 6   **B**
1. 1970s 2. Growing up 3. Girls 4. Sisters 5. Change 6. Social change 7. China -- History -- 1976-2002 8. Autobiographical comics 9. Comics and Graphic novels
ISBN 9780761365877

LC 2011005347

A young girl describes her experiences growing up in China, beginning with the death of Chairman Mao in 1976.

"This picturesque treasure introduces Chinese culture through a personal perspective that is both delightful and thought-provoking." School Library Journal.

London, Jack, 1876-1916
Lourie, Peter. **Jack** London and the Klondike gold rush. Peter Lourie; illustrated by Wendell Minor. Henry Holt and Company, 2017. 192 p.

Grades: 4 5 6 7 8   **B**
1. Authors, American 19th century 2. Adventurers 3. Authors, American 20th century
ISBN 9780805097573

LC 2016012053

A middle grade biography of Jack London that sheds light on how he drew upon adventure and life experience to create works of literature. Provided by publisher.

Love, Nat, 1854-1921
Bloom, Barbara Lee, 1943-. **Nat** Love. Barbara Lee Bloom. Chelsea House, c2010. 103 p.: Legends of the Wild West

Grades: 6 7 8 9   **B**
1. Freed people 2. African American cowboys 3. Cowboys 4. The West (United States)
ISBN 9781604135992

LC 2009034814

"Bloom does a fine job chronicling [Love's] exploits as a black cowboy and beyond. . . . Weaving historical context throughout in related sidebars and lengthy captions, the book features black-and-white and color photos, paintings, and other illustrations." Booklist.

Includes bibliographical references and index.

Lovelace, Ada King, Countess of, 1815-1852
McCully, Emily Arnold. **Dreaming** in code: Ada Byron Lovelace, computer pioneer. Emily Arnold McCully. Candlewick Press, 2019. 176 p.

Grades: 5 6 7 8 9 10   **B**
1. 19th century 2. Women mathematicians 3. Computer algorithms 4. Women computer programmers 5. Women intellectuals 6. Determination in girls 7. Great Britain
ISBN 9780763693565

An award-winning author presents an illuminating biography of Ada Lovelace, the brilliant daughter of Lord Byron, Britain's most infamous Romantic poet, who is now recognized as a pioneer and prophet of the information age for her ideas and concepts, formulated in collaboration with inventor Charles Babbage, that presaged computer programming by almost 200 years.

"Interest in Ada Byron Lovelace and other female pioneers of science has soared of late. This young adult biography is a particularly exemplary example of the burgeoning genre and should find a home in all libraries." Booklist.

Includes bibliographical references (pages 154-157) and index.

Low, Juliette Gordon, 1860-1927

★ Wadsworth, Ginger. **First** Girl Scout: the life of Juliette Gordon Low. Ginger Wadsworth. Clarion Books, 2012. 224 p.

Grades: 7 8 9 10 11 12   **B**
    1. Girl Scouts of the United States of America 2. Girl Scouts 3. Scouting (Youth activity) 4. People with hearing impairments 5. Women 6. Divorce
    ISBN 9780547243948

LC 2011009642

Juliette (Daisy) Gordon Low was a remarkable woman with ideas that were ahead of her time. She witnessed important eras in U.S. history, from the Civil War and Reconstruction to westward expansion to post-World War I. And she made history by founding the first national organization to bring girls from all backgrounds into the out-of-doors. Daisy created controversy by encouraging them to prepare not only for traditional homemaking but also for roles as professional women—in the arts, sciences, and business—and for active citizenship outside the home. Her group also welcomed girls with disabilities at a time when they were usually excluded. Includes author's note, source notes, bibliography, timeline, places to visit, recipes, The Girl Scout Promise and Law, and sheet music for the favorite scout song "Make New Friends.". Provided by publisher.

"Low's personality really comes to life through the details in the narrative. Wadsworth shows readers that this remarkable woman was a skilled leader and hostess in spite of having suffered severe hearing loss that made conversation difficult. . . . The attractive book design features chapter headings that look like Girl Scout badges, and most spreads include period photos or reproductions of primary-source documents." School Library Journal.

Lowry, Lois

Lowry, Lois. **Looking** back: a book of memories. Lois Lowry. Houghton Mifflin Harcourt, [2016] 259 p.

Grades: 4 5 6 7 8   **B**
    1. Authors, American 20th century 2. Women authors, American 3. Children's literature authors, American 20th century 4. Women
    ISBN 9780544807969

LC 98011376

In this updated and refreshed photographic memoir, two-time Newbery Medalist Lois Lowry offers an intimate look at pivotal moments that affected her life, inspired her writing, and often evolved into her rich and wonderful novels beloved the world over.

Malcolm X, 1925-1965

Sharp, Anne Wallace. **Malcolm** X and black pride. by Anne Wallace Sharp. Lucent Books, c2010. 128 p.: Lucent library of black history

Grades: 6 7 8 9   **B**
    1. Black Muslims 2. Race awareness 3. Afrocentricity 4. African Americans -- Identity
    ISBN 9781420501230

"This book takes a frank, balanced, and compelling look at the man who was born Malcolm Little and whose furious insistence on equality for African Americans continues to both inspire and provoke controversy. . . . Supported by well-selected photos, extensive chapter notes, and further-reading suggestions, this is a strong choice for student research." Booklist.

Includes bibliographical references and index.

Mandela, Nelson, 1918-2013

Gormley, Beatrice. **Nelson** Mandela: South African revolutionary. by Beatrice Gormley. Aladdin, 2014. 192 p.: A Real-life Story

Grades: 5 6 7 8   **B**
    1. Presidents 2. Nobel Prize winners 3. Anti-apartheid activists 4. Apartheid -- History 5. South Africa -- History -- 20th century.
    ISBN 9781481420594

LC 2014019020

From Nelson Mandela's childhood to his monumental impact on race relations and nonviolent activism, this comprehensive biography shares the truth about the man behind the iconic smile: his struggles, his triumphs, and the sacrifices along the way.

"More than a year after his death, the influence of Nelson Mandela is still felt keenly by people around the world. This timely biography provides a complete picture of a complex man...This book is an understandable and multifaceted tribute to an icon of defiance and optimism in the face of tribulation." Booklist.

Includes bibliographical references and index.

Mandelbaum, Jack

★ Warren, Andrea. **Surviving** Hitler: a boy in the Nazi death camps. by Andrea Warren. Harper Collins Publishers, c2001. 146 p.

Grades: 5 6 7 8   **B**
    1. Jewish children 2. Holocaust (1933-1945) 3. Jews, Polish 4. Holocaust survivors 5. Concentration camps 6. Poland
    ISBN 0688174973

LC 00038899

Provides the story of the Holocaust survivor who at fifteen was placed in a Nazi concentration camp and was forced to overcome intolerable conditions in order to not become a victim of Hitler's Final Solution.

"Simply told, Warren's powerful story blends the personal testimony of Holocaust survivor Jack Mandelbaum with the history of his time, documented by stirring photos from the archives of the U.S. Holocaust Memorial Museum. . . . An excellent introduction for readers who don't know much about the history." Booklist.

Includes bibliographical references and index.

Manzano, Sonia

Manzano, Sonia. **Becoming** Maria: love and chaos in the South Bronx. Sonia Manzano. Scholastic Press, 2015. 272 p.

Grades: 9 10 11 12   **B**
    1. 1950s 2. Television actors and actresses 3. Hispanic American women 4. Childhood 5. Hispanic American actors and actresses 6. Puerto Ricans in the United States 7. Bronx, New York City
    ISBN 9780545621847

LC 2015007490

"This beautifully rendered coming-of-age story calls to mind Betty Smith's classic A Tree Grows in Brooklyn. Though it's a bit slow moving at times and would have benefited from a time line to help ground readers, this is nevertheless an inspiring portrait of resiliency and a time capsule for a New York that now feels like a distant memory." Booklist.

Mao, Zedong, 1893-1976

Heuston, Kimberley Burton, 1960-. **Mao** Zedong. Kimberley Heuston. Franklin Watts, c2010. 128 p.: Wicked history

Grades: 5 6 7 8   **B**
    1. Heads of state 2. China -- History -- 20th century.
    ISBN 9780531207567

LC 2009034157

Traces the life of the peasant who rose to the position of "chairman" of China's communist party and absolute ruler of the country, overseeing both reform and terrible butchery during his long reign.

"...short enough not to intimidate yet long enough to impart the enormity of the tyrant's atrocities. Opening with a description of Zedong's ruthlessness as an early revolutionary, Heuston follows him through the 82 years of his life, describing his devastating impact on China. Black-and-white photos, maps of Uganda and of China, time lines of the men's lives, and labeled webs showing their allies and enemies... make the books accessible." School Library Journal.

Includes bibliographical references and index.

Slavicek, Louise Chipley, 1956-. **Mao** Zedong. Louise Chipley Slavicek; introduction by Casper W. Weinberger. Chelsea House Publishers, c2004. 116 p.

Grades: 6 7 8 9   **B**
    1. 1930s 2. Heads of state 3. Communists 4. Ideology 5. Communism 6. China -- History -- 1949-1976 7. China -- History -- Long March, 1934-1935
    ISBN 0791074072

       LC 2003006929

A biography of Chinese leader Mao Zedong, discussing the battles that helped shape him and reasons behind his popularity among his countrymen.

"Slavicek blends personal, philosophical, and historical information to trace Mao's journey to power. Clear accounts of the communist movement, the Long March, and the eventual battle with the Nationalists and Japanese are included." School Library Journal.

Includes bibliographical references (p. 108) and index.

Marley, Bob

Medina, Tony. **I** and I: Bob Marley. by Tony Medina; illustrated by Jesse Joshua Watson. Lee & Low Books, c2009. 48 p.

Grades: 4 5 6   **B**
    1. Singers 2. Reggae musicians 3. Reggae music 4. Multiracial persons 5. Rastafarians 6. Jamaica -- Social life and customs -- 20th century
    ISBN 9781600602573

       LC 2008033485

A biography in verse about the Jamaican reggae musician Bob Marley, offering an overview of key events and themes in his life, including his biracial heritage, Rastafarian beliefs, and love of music. End notes on poems provide further biographical information. Provided by publisher.

"In the words and rhythms of Jamaican patois, Medina's lyrical, direct lines make the most sense when read in tandem with the extensive appended notes. . . . Like the words, Watson's beautifully expressive acrylic paintings evoke a strong sense of Marley's remarkable life and his Caribbean homeland." Booklist.

Includes bibliographical references.

Paprocki, Sherry. **Bob** Marley: musician. Sherry Beck Paprocki. Chelsea House, c2006. 111 p.: Black Americans of achievement

Grades: 6 7 8 9   **B**
    1. Reggae musicians 2. Jamaica
    ISBN 0791092135

       LC 2006004578

Profiles the Jamaican musician who earned a following as a Rastafarian prophet even as he refined the genre of reggae.

"The book goes beyond the typical personal information to provide some social history revelant to the subject's time. Captioned photo-

graphs and boxed inserts enhance the conversational [text]." Horn Book Guide.

Includes discography (p. 101), bibliographical references (p. 104), and index.

Martin, Joseph Plumb, 1760-1850

★ Murphy, Jim, 1947-. A **young** patriot: the American Revolution as experienced by one boy. by Jim Murphy. Clarion Books, c1996. 101 p.

Grades: 5 6 7 8   **B**
    1. War 2. Teenage soldiers 3. Teenagers and war 4. Soldiers 5. Revolutions 6. United States -- History -- Revolution, 1775-1783 -- Campaigns. 7. Connecticut -- History -- Revolution, 1775-1783.
    ISBN 0395605237

       LC 93038789

"Using Joseph Plumb Martin's first person account of his participation in the Revolutionary War as primary source material, Murphy intertwines this story of one teenager's life as a soldier with broader information about the Revolution, to put Martin's story in context. The handsome, informative, and fascinating look at American history is illustrated with many period reproductions." Horn Book Guide.

Includes bibliographical references (p. 91-93) and index.

Marx, Karl, 1818-1883

Rossig, Wolfgang. **Karl** Marx. by Wolfgang Rossig. Morgan Reynolds Pub., 2009. 112 p.: Profiles in economics

Grades: 8 9 10   **B**
    1. Communists 2. Philosophers 3. Intellectuals
    ISBN 9781599351322

"This book presents the life of Karl Marx and places his social and economic theories within the useful context of his youth in a prosperous German family. . . . [The author] provides a well-researched account of Marx's life and his work." Booklist.

Includes bibliographical references and index.

Mason, Biddy, 1818-1891

White, Arisa. **Biddy** Mason speaks up. by Arisa White and Laura Atkins; illustrations by Laura Freeman. Heyday, 2019. 112 p.: Fighting for justice

Grades: 5 6 7 8 9   **B**
    1. African American women 2. Nurses 3. Enslaved women 4. Enslaved people 5. Rape
    ISBN 9781597144032

       LC 2018010807

Presents the life of a California ex-slave, nurse, and midwife, who started many philanthropic projects.

McCartney, Stella, 1971-

Aldridge, Rebecca. **Stella** McCartney. Rebecca Aldridge. Chelsea House, c2011. 112 p.: Famous fashion designers

Grades: 6 7 8 9 10   **B**
    1. Fashion designers 2. Women fashion designers 3. Clothing industry and trade
    ISBN 9781604139822

       LC 2010033972

Profiles the life and career of the fashion designer, including her famous parents, work in fashion, activism, and family life.

"Biography collections in need of a bit of sprucing up should find [this title] helpful." School Library Journal.

Includes bibliographical references (p. 100-107) and index.

McClintock, Barbara, 1902-1992

Spangenburg, Ray, 1939-. **Barbara** McClintock: pioneering geneticist. Ray Spangenburg and Diane Kit Moser. Chelsea House Publishers, c2008. xxi, 136 p.: Makers of modern science

Grades: 8 9 10 11 12 **B**
1. Geneticists 2. Women scientists 3. Nobel Prize winners 4. Scientists 5. Women
ISBN 9780816061723

LC 2006032356

Highlights the life and achievements of the geneticist who in 1983 was awarded the Nobel Prize for her study of maize cells.

McMullan, James, 1934-

McMullan, James, 1934-. **Leaving** China: an artist paints his World War II childhood. James McMullan. Algonquin Young Readers, 2014. 128 p.

Grades: 7 8 9 10 11 12 **B**
1. Illustrators 2. Children of missionaries 3. World War II 4. China -- History -- 1937-1945 5. Illustrated books
ISBN 9781616202552

LC 2013035241

The award-winning artist of I Stink! recounts in more than 50 short essays and evocative illustrations how his early childhood in China and wartime journeys with his mother influenced his life and career.

Meir, Golda Mabovitz, 1898-1978

Blashfield, Jean F.. **Golda** Meir. Jean F. Blashfield. Marshall Cavendish Benchmark, c2011. 112 p.: Leading women

Grades: 5 6 7 8 **B**
1. Women prime ministers 2. Prime ministers 3. Zionists 4. Women 5. Israel
ISBN 9780761449607

LC 2009030630

Presents the biography of Golda Meir against the backdrop of her political, historical, and cultural environment. Provided by publisher.

"Meir survived pogroms in Russia as a child and became prime minister of Israel. . . . The [woman's life is] revealed within the political and historical context of [her] times and [includes] quotes from autobiographical material. . . . Color and black-and-white photos are included. . . . The compact size, chronological organization, and accessible writing [style makes this biography a] good [resource] for reports." School Library Journal.

Includes bibliographical references (p. 108-109) and index.

Meltzer, Milton, 1915-2009

Meltzer, Milton, 1915-2009. **Milton** Meltzer: writing matters. by Milton Meltzer. Franklin Watts, c2004. 160 p.

Grades: 7 8 9 10 **B**
1. Historians 2. Historiography 3. Authors 4. Essay writing 5. Children of immigrants
ISBN 0531122573

LC 2004002947

A nonfiction author explores his personal evolution as an author, from his early inspirations to his life as a full-time writer, offering his own firsthand experiences during the Depression, World War II, and other historic eras.

"The author includes clear, interesting explanations about the American historical and economic events that influenced his life. While this book is a pleasure to read for general interest, it would also supplement units on American history." School Library Journal.

Includes bibliographical references (p. 147-149) and index.

Mercado, Yehudi

Mercado, Yehudi. **Chunky**. Yehudi Mercado Harpercollins Childrens Books 2021 208 p.

Grades: 4 5 6 7 **B**
1. Imaginary companions 2. Overweight boys 3. Baseball 4. Sick boys 5. Misfits (Persons) 6. Autobiographical comics 7. Comics and Graphic novels
ISBN 9780062972798

"Mercado offers relatable insights into the life of a child who is eager to fit in but also coming into his sense of self, sometimes with the help of adults and sometimes in spite of them." School Library Journal

Merian, Maria Sibylla, 1647-1717

Sidman, Joyce. The **girl** who drew butterflies: how Maria Merian's art changed science. written by Joyce Sidman. Houghton Mifflin Harcourt, 2018. 217 p.

Grades: 4 5 6 7 **B**
1. 17th century 2. Naturalists 3. Entomologists 4. Women scientists 5. Entomology 6. Women naturalists 7. Germany
ISBN 9780544717138

LC 2016057731

Robert F. Sibert Informational Book Medal, 2019.

Newbery-Honor winning author Joyce Sidman explores the extraordinary life and scientific discoveries of Maria Merian, who discovered the truth about metamorphosis and documented the science behind the mystery in this visual biography that features many original paintings by Maria herself. Provided by publisher.

"An exceptionally crafted visual biography of a pioneering entomologist and naturalist who lived a life devoted to discovery." Kirkus.

Includes bibliographical references.

Mexia, Ynes, 1870-1938

Anema, Durlynn. **Ynes** Mexia: botanist and adventurer. Durlynn Anema. Morgan Reynolds Pub., c2005. 144 p.

Grades: 6 7 8 9 **B**
1. Women botanists 2. Botanists 3. Scientists 4. Women scientists 5. Mexican American women
ISBN 1931798672

LC 2005010694

Details the life and accomplishments of the amateur botanist and adventurer.

"An interesting and colorful look at a Mexican-American scientist. The easy-to-read narrative draws on the woman's correspondences." School Library Journal.

Includes bibliographical references (p. 132-141) and index.

Milk, Harvey, 1930-1978

Aretha, David. **No** compromise: the story of Harvey Milk. David Aretha. Morgan Reynolds Pub., 2010. 128 p.

Grades: 7 8 9 10 11 12 **B**
1. 1970s 2. Gay politicians 3. Assassination 4. Political culture -- History 20th century 5. Politicians 6. Gay communities 7. San Francisco, California -- History -- 20th century 8. United States -- History -- 20th century
ISBN 9781599351292

LC 2009025708

Chronicles the life and career of the California activist and politician, including his crusade for gay rights, his successful city supervisor campaign in 1977, and the legacy he left after his murder.

"This is written with simple and engaging prose. . . . Full-color and black-and-white photos are interspersed thoughout, giving a sense of the time period." School Library Journal.

Includes bibliographical references (p. 124-125) and index.

Minamoto, Yoshitsune, 1159-1189

Turner, Pamela S.. **Samurai** rising: the epic life of Minamoto Yoshitsune. Pamela S. Turner; with illustrations by Gareth Hinds. Charlesbridge, 2015. 240 p.

Grades: 7 8 9 10   **B**
    1. Generals 2. Samurai 3. Japan -- History -- Heian period, 794-1185
ISBN 9781580895842

               LC 2014049179

"The back cover warns: 'Very few people in this story die of natural causes.' Turner delivers on the promise of that hook, and it will leave lovers of military history clamoring for more of this type." Horn Book.

Mineta, Norman Yoshio, 1931-

Warren, Andrea. **Enemy** child: the story of Norman Mineta, a boy imprisoned in a Japanese American internment camp during World War II. Andrea Warren. Margaret Ferguson Books/ Holiday House, 2019. 224 p.

Grades: 5 6 7 8 9   **B**
    1. Heart Mountain War Relocation Center, Wyoming 2. 1940s 3. Japanese American boys 4. World War II -- Japanese Americans 5. Forced relocations 6. Japanese Americans -- Forced removal and incarceration, 1942-1945 7. Concentration camps
ISBN 9780823441518

               LC 2018009814

Presents a biography of Norman Mineta, from his internment as a child in Heart Mountain Internment Camp during World War II, through his political career in Congress where he was instrumental in getting the Civil Liberties Act of 1988 passed.

Mizrahi, Isaac

Petrillo, Lisa. **Isaac** Mizrahi. Lisa Petrillo. Morgan Reynolds Pub., c2011. 111 p.: Profiles in fashion

Grades: 7 8 9 10   **B**
    1. Fashion designers 2. Clothing industry and trade 3. Fashion
ISBN 9781599351520

               LC 2010018312

Presents the life and career of the Egyptian American designer, describing his interest in fashion as a child, early work with top designers, the success of his first collection, and his emergence as an international fashion celebrity.

"This biography of Isaac Mizrahi discusses the designer's cultural background, childhood, family, work history and education. The [author describes] the early influences that inspired the [designer] to pursue this career and [provides] details of the philosophy [the] designer uses to make [his] clothing unique. . . . The writing is clear and well organized. Color photos are included and give readers a feel for the time period and the types of clothing and accessories the [designer] created." Voice of Youth Advocates.

Includes bibliographical references (p. 99-108) and index.

Mohamed, Omar (Social worker)

★ Jamieson, Victoria. **When** stars are scattered. Victoria Jamieson and Omar Mohamed; color by Iman Geddy. Dial Books for Young Readers, 2020. 264 p.

Grades: 4 5 6 7   **B**
    1. Child refugees 2. Refugee camps 3. Children -- Nonverbal communication 4. Nonverbal communication 5. Refugees, Somali 6. Autobiographical comics 7. Comics and Graphic novels
ISBN 9780525553915

               LC 2019047886

Omar and his younger brother Hassan live in a refugee camp, and when an opportunity for Omar to get an education comes along, he must decide between going to school every day or caring for his nonverbal brother in this intimate and touching portrayal of family and daily life in a refugee camp.

"The authors highlight moments of levity and sweetness as the children and their families do their best to carve out meaningful lives in the bleakest of circumstances." School Library Journal

Monaque, Mathilda

Monaque, Mathilda. **Trouble** in my head: a young girl's fight with depression. Mathilde Monaque. Trafalgar Square, 2009. 176 p.

Grades: 7 8 9 10   **B**
    1. Fourteen-year-old girls 2. Teenagers with depression 3. Teenagers with mental illnesses 4. Depression 5. Anorexia nervosa
ISBN 9780091917234

Mathilde Monaque developed severe depression when she was just 14. The eldest in a family of six and an exceptionally bright and gifted little girl, the discovery shook her family to the core. This work is Mathilde's tender and illuminating account of her struggle to surface from a disease that could have taken her life.

"Monaque tells her own story of depression, which began at age 14. Recounting her experience from memory, the teen attempts to discern what caused the illness as well as to explain the process she went through to overcome it. . . . She is bright and articulate and paints a vivid picture of what depression feels like from the inside." School Library Journal.

Monet, Claude, 1840-1926

Spence, David. **Monet**. [written by David Spence]. New Forest Press, c2010. 48 p.: Great artists and their world

Grades: 6 7 8 9   **B**
    1. Painters 2. Impressionism (Art) 3. Artists 4. Art, French
ISBN 9781848983120

               LC bl2010026393

Presents a biography of the artist who practiced plein air painting and transformed the landscape genre, and whose vision led to the start of a new art movement called impressionism.

"This slender title offers a thorough introduction to Oscar Claude Monet, who, before helping to found the French Impressionist movement, was known for his sharp-eyed, witty caricature drawings. . . . The spreads cover a wide range of topics, all presented in short paragraphs and long captions that accompany the multiple, mostly well-reproduced artwork and archival photos on every page." Booklist.

Monroe, James, 1758-1831

Naden, Corinne J.. **James** Monroe. by Corinne J. Naden and Rose Blue. Marshall Cavendish Benchmark, 2008. 96 p.: Presidents and their times

Grades: 5 6 7 8   **B**
    1. 19th century 2. Presidents 3. Political leadership 4. United States -- Politics and government -- 1817-1825
ISBN 9780761428381

               LC 2007029480

Provides comprehensive information on President James Monroe and places him within his historical and cultural context. Also explored are the formative events of his times and how he responded. Provided by publisher.

Montgomery, L. M. (Lucy Maud), 1874-1942

Rosenberg, Liz. **House** of dreams: the life of L. M. Montgomery. Liz Rosenberg; illustrated by Julie Morstad. Candlewick Press, 2018 352 p.

Grades: 6 7 8 9 10   **B**

1. Authors, Canadian 20th century 2. Authors, Canadian 3. Children's literature writing

ISBN 9780763660574

An affecting portrait of the author of Anne of Green Gables is a first biography for young readers that shares revelations about Montgomery's final days as well as the complexities of her brilliant but often troubled life.

Moore, Wes, 1978-

Moore, Wes, 1978-. **Discovering** Wes Moore: chances, choices, changes. by Wes Moore. Delacorte Press, c2012. 192 p.

Grades: 7 8 9 10 11 12   **B**

1. African American teenagers 2. Criminals 3. Soldiers 4. African American men 5. Teenagers -- Personal conduct 6. Baltimore, Maryland -- Social conditions -- 20th century. 7. Bronx, New York City -- Social conditions -- 20th century.

ISBN 9780385741675

LC 2011049135

A military paratrooper and White House fellow presents a younger reader's adaptation of the best-selling The Other Wes Moore, which contrasts events from his life with those of a fatherless friend to explore the issues that separate the outcomes of success and failure.

"The story concludes with Moore's questions and ruminations about how, regardless of limitations and societal expectations, the decisions an individual makes determine who he or she will become. Moore wisely opens the door for teens to contemplate their own answers and beliefs, while laying out his own experiences honestly and openly." Publishers Weekly.

Morrison, Toni 1931-2019

Kramer, Barbara. **Toni** Morrison: a biography of a Nobel Prize-winning writer. by Barbara Kramer. Enslow Publishers, c2013. 104 p.: African-American icons

Grades: 7 8 9 10   **B**

1. Authors, American 20th century 2. African American authors 3. Women 4. African Americans

ISBN 9780766039896

LC 2011024344

Read about Toni Morrison's life and writings. Provided by publisher.

Mozart, Wolfgang Amadeus, 1756-1791

Weeks, Marcus. **Mozart**: the boy who changed the world with his music. Marcus Weeks. National Geographic, 2007. 64 p.: National Geographic world history biographies

Grades: 5 6 7 8   **B**

1. Composers 2. Child prodigies 3. Classical musicians

ISBN 1426300034

LC 2006020783

An introduction to the life and music of the composer and musician Mozart.

"This visually appealing [title is] packed with excellent photographs and reproductions, interesting sidebars, and have a time line running along the bottom of every page. . . . [The book is] useful, well-written." School Library Journal.

Includes bibliographical references (p. 62) and index.

Muhammad, Ibtihaj, 1985-

Muhammad, Ibtihaj, 1985-. **Proud**: living my American dream. Olympic medalist Ibtihaj Muhammad. Little, Brown and Company, 2018 304 p.

Grades: 6 7 8 9 10 11 12   **B**

1. Muslim women 2. Women Olympic athletes 3. Fencing 4. Determination (Personal quality) 5. Black Muslims

ISBN 9780316477000

Shares the life story of the Olympic fencer, including how she overcame feeling out of place in her sport and how she became the first American woman to compete in the Olympics wearing a hijab.

"Muhammad describes her struggles with classmates, teammates, referees, and even the public at large, who only saw her as an outsider. She also relates how finding a community of fencers of color, supportive family and trainers, perseverance, and, above all, her faith helped her overcome adversity." Booklist.

Myers, Walter Dean, 1937-2014

Myers, Walter Dean, 1937-2014. **Bad** boy: a memoir. by Walter Dean Myers. Harper Collins Publishers, 2001. 214 p.

Grades: 7 8 9 10   **B**

1. Authors, American 20th century 2. African American authors 3. Children's literature writing 4. Authors, American 5. African Americans 6. Harlem, New York City

ISBN 0060295236

LC 00052978

The author relates his experiences growing up in Harlem, the home of Sugar Ray Robinson and Langston Hughes, in the 1940s and 1950s.

"This is a story full of funny anecdotes, lofty ideals, and tender moments." School Library Journal.

Nailling, Lee, 1917-

Warren, Andrea. **Orphan** train rider: one boy's true story. by Andrea Warren. Houghton Mifflin, 1996. 80 p.

Grades: 4 5 6 7   **B**

1. Children's Aid Society. 2. Orphan trains 3. Orphans 4. Abandoned children 5. Homeless children

ISBN 0395698227

LC 94043688

Discusses the placement of over 200,000 orphaned or abandoned children in homes throughout the Midwest from 1854 to 1929 by recounting the story of one boy and his brothers.

"An excellent introduction to researching or discussing children-at-risk in an earlier generation. The book is clearly written and illustrated with numerous black-and-white photographs and reproductions." School Library Journal.

Includes bibliographical references (p. 73-74) and index.

Nakahama, Manjiro, 1827-1898

★ Blumberg, Rhoda. **Shipwrecked!**: the true adventures of a Japanese boy. Rhoda Blumberg. Harper Collins, c2001. 80 p.

Grades: 5 6 7 8   **B**

1. 1840s 2. 19th century 3. Fourteen-year-old boys 4. Teenage boys 5. Shipwreck survivors 6. Castaways 7. Shipwrecks 8. Japan -- History -- 19th century. 9. Japan -- Relations -- United States.

ISBN 0688174841

LC 99086664

In 1841, rescued by an American whaler after a terrible shipwreck leaves him and his four companions castaways on a remote island, fourteen-year-old Manjiro learns new laws and customs as he becomes the first Japanese person to set foot in the United States.

"Exemplary in both her research and writing, Blumberg hooks readers with anecdotes that astonish without sensationalizing, and she uses language that's elegant and challenging, yet always clear. Particularly notable is the well-chosen reproductions of original artwork." Booklist.

Nefertiti, Queen of Egypt, 14th cent. B.C.E.

Lange, Brenda. **Nefertiti**. Brenda Lange. Chelsea House, 2008. 108 p.: Ancient world leaders

Grades: 6 7 8 9   **B**
> 1. Women rulers 2. Ancient Egypt -- History -- Eighteenth dynasty, ca. 1570-1320 B.C.E.
> ISBN 9780791095812

     LC 2008004869

"This biography of Nefertiti deals less with the specifics of the [ancient Egyptian queen] and more with [her world] and times, including religious and political issues. The [author uses] speculation, derived from both tradition and scholarship, as to who [this] ancient [leader] may have been and how [she] might have governed." School Library Journal.

Includes bibliographical references and index.

Newton, Isaac, 1642-1727

Krull, Kathleen, 1952-2021. **Isaac** Newton. by Kathleen Krull; [Boris Kulikov, illustrator]. Viking, 2006. 128 p.: Giants of science (Viking)

Grades: 5 6 7 8   **B**
> 1. Physicists 2. Inventors 3. Telescopes 4. Jealousy 5. Gifted men
> ISBN 9780670059218

     LC 2005017741

Isaac Newton was not only briiliant, but secretive, vindictive and obsessive. Here is a portrait of the man, contradictions and all, than places him against the backdrop of seventeenth-century England, a time of plague, the Great Fire of London, and two revolutions.

"This profiles Sir Isaac Newton, the secretive, obsessive, and brilliant English scientist who invented calculus, built the first reflecting telescope, developed the modern scientific method, and discerned many of our laws of physics and optics. . . . The lively, conversational style will appeal to readers. . . . Kulikov's humorous pen-and-ink drawings complement the lighthearted text of this fascinating introduction." Booklist.

Includes bibliographical references and index.

Losure, Mary. **Isaac** the alchemist: secrets of Isaac Newton, reveal'd. Mary Losure. Candlewick Press, 2017. 176 p.

Grades: 5 6 7 8 9   **B**
> 1. Physicists 2. Mathematicians 3. Alchemy 4. Physics 5. Scientists
> ISBN 9780763670634

"Narrative nonfiction at its best and most convincing." Kirkus.

Nezahualcoyotl, King of Texcoco, 1402-1472

★ Serrano, Francisco, 1949-. The **poet** king of Texcoco: a great leader of ancient Mexico. by Francisco Serrano; ilustrated by Pablo Serrano; biography translated and adapted by Trudy Balch; poetry translated by Jo Anne Engelbert. Groundwood Books/House of Anansi Press , 2007. 35 p.

Grades: 4 5 6 7   **B**
> 1. Tezcucan Indians 2. Indians of Mexico 3. Rulers 4. Poets, Mexican 5. Translations Spanish to English
> ISBN 0888997876

     LC bl2007011687

Presents a biography of Nezahualcoyotl, the monarch of Tezcoco, poet, astronomer, statesman, philosopher, legislator, engineer, and architect who is considered the most important figure of pre-Hispanic Mexico.

"In the fifteenth century, the land where Mexico City now sprawls was a vast, green kingdom called Tezcoco. This . . . introduces one of Tezcoco's greatest rulers, a Toltec royal named Nezahualcoyotl. . . . The folk-art inspired illustrations echo the area's artistic traditions with beautiful patterning and symbolic imagery and flat, simplified characters reminiscent of hieroglyphics. Groundbreaking in its coverage of exciting history, this book offers details that are rarely presented to young people." Booklist.

Includes bibliographical references (p. 35).

Nightingale, Florence, 1820-1910

Reef, Catherine. **Florence** Nightingale: the courageous life of the legendary nurse. Catherine Reef. Clarion Books, [2017] 176 p.

Grades: 7 8 9 10 11 12   **B**
> 1. Nurses 2. Medical care 3. Crimean War, 1853-1856
> ISBN 9780544535800

     LC 2015045606

A biography for young adult readers on Florence Nightingale, the pioneering nurse best known for her work during the Crimean War, where she rectified horrifying conditions and made nightly rounds to check on patients, saving hundreds of lives and sparking worldwide healthcare reform. Provided by publisher.

"A captivating and inspiring study of one woman's perseverance and the good that came from it." Booklist.

Includes bibliographical references and index.

Noguchi, Isamu, 1904-1988

Tiger, Caroline. **Isamu** Noguchi. Caroline Tiger. Chelsea House, c2007. 112 p.: Asian-Americans of achievement

Grades: 6 7 8 9   **B**
> 1. Japanese Americans 2. Sculptors
> ISBN 0791092763

     LC 2006026230

"This engaging account of the prolific and diverse artist will add depth to any biography collection." School Library Journal.

Includes bibliographical references and index.

Northup, Solomon, b. 1808

Fradin, Judith Bloom. **Stolen** into slavery: the true story of Solomon Northup, free black man. by Judy and Dennis Fradin. National Geographic Society, 2012. 128 p.

Grades: 6 7 8   **B**
> 1. Slavery 2. Enslaved people 3. African Americans 4. Plantation life -- History 19th century. 5. Louisiana 6. United States -- History -- 19th century
> ISBN 9781426309373

     LC 2011024664

Carter G. Woodson Book Awards: Secondary Level, 2013.

Follows the story of Solomon Northup—a free black man who was kidnapped and forced into slavery—through his twelve years of bondage in Louisiana until friends from New York rescued him from a cotton plantation.

O'Brien, Soledad, 1966-

Robson, David, 1966-. **Soledad** O'Brien: television journalist. David Robson. Mason Crest Publishers, c2010. 64 p.: Transcending race in America: biographies of biracial achievers

Grades: 5 6 7 8   **B**
1. Television newscasters and commentators 2. Multiracial persons 3. Journalists 4. Women journalists 5. Broadcast journalists
ISBN 9781422216170

LC 2009024024

Presents the life and career of the Harvard educated television journalist, from her childhood and early career with at NBC, to her high profile job as CNN's Special Correspondent.

Oakley, Annie, 1860-1926

Koestler-Grack, Rachel A., 1973-. **Annie** Oakley. Rachel A. Koestler-Grack. Chelsea House, c2010. 104 p.: Legends of the Wild West
Grades: 6 7 8 9   **B**
1. Shooters of firearms 2. Women sharpshooters 3. Women entertainers 4. Entertainers
ISBN 9781604135947

LC 2009041338

Describes the life and accomplishments of the woman whose natural talent for shooting led her to become the star of Buffalo Bill's Wild West Show.

Obama, Barack

Abramson, Jill, 1954-. **Obama**: the historic journey. text by Jill Abramson; design by Krupa Jhaveri. New York Times/Callaway, 2009. 94 p.
Grades: 5 6 7 8   **B**
1. Presidents 2. Multiracial persons
ISBN 9780670012084

LC 2009005051

Photographs and text adapted from "New York Times" articles trace Barack Obama's journey from his birth in Hawaii, through his political career in Chicago and his primary and presidential campaigns, to his inauguration in 2009.

"This scaled down, teen-friendly version of The New York Times's adult biography is geared for middle school students. Containing many of the same photos, it provides a brief overview of the President's life, information that has been revealed over the election year and during his administration. . . . Its' allure is in the many photographs with captions, sidebars, speech quotes, and charts. The book is nicely organized. The writing is direct and simple, explaining things such as convention delegates. . . . The book should entice young readers to explore his life further." Voice of Youth Advocates.

Obama, Barack. **Dreams** from my father: a story of race and inheritance. Barack Obama. Crown Publishers, 2007, c1995. xvii, 442 p.
Grades: 7 8 9 10 11 12 Adult   **B**
1. African American legislators 2. African Americans 3. Multiracial persons 4. Racism 5. Community organizers 6. Chicago, Illinois -- Race relations. 7. United States -- Race relations.
ISBN 9780307383419

LC 2007271892

The son of an African father and white American mother discusses his childhood in Hawaii, his struggle to find his identity as an African American, and his life accomplishments.

"The author offers an account of his life's journey that reflects brilliantly on the power of race consciousness in America. . . . Obama writes well; his account is sensitive, probing, and compelling." Choice. [review of 1995 edition]

Shaffer, Jody Jensen. **Barack** Obama: first African-American President. Jody Jensen Shaffer. The Child's World, 2021. 32 p.: Black American Journey
Grades: 5 6 7   **B**
1. Presidents 2. Multiracial persons 3. Nobel Prize winners 4. Politicians 5. African Americans
ISBN 9781503853775

Briefly, examines the childhood, education, adulthood, and presidency of the first African-American president in U.S. history. Additional features include detailed captions and sidebars, critical-thinking questions, a phonetic glossary, an index, and sources for further research. Provided by publisher.

"This is true Black American history everyone should know about. Highly recommended." School Library Journal

Obama, Michelle, 1964-

Obama, Michelle, 1964-. **Becoming**: adapted for young readers. Michelle Obama. Delacorte Press, 2021. 432 p.
Grades: 5 6 7 8 9 10   **B**
1. Presidents' spouses 2. African American women lawyers 3. African American lawyers 4. African American women 5. Work-life balance 6. United States -- Politics and government -- 2009-2017.
ISBN 9780593303740

LC 2021931956

Michelle Obama's worldwide bestselling memoir, Becoming, adapted for young readers.—Provided by publisher.

"Anecdotes about her coming-of-age, experiences on the campaign trail, and life in the White House are compelling. Throughout the lively narrative, she expresses an encouraging tone as she tells her story with accessibility and intimacy." Kirkus

Ogle, Rex

Ogle, Rex. **Free** lunch. Rex Ogle. Norton Young Readers, 2019 208 p.
Grades: 5 6 7 8 9   **B**
1. Middle school students 2. Poor families 3. Shame 4. School lunch programs 5. Poor boys
ISBN 9781324003601

A sixth grader from an economically disadvantaged family struggles in a new school where he is forced to endure humiliation over his secondhand clothing and public daily requests for his school's free lunch program.

"Middle school can be daunting, even under ideal conditions. But if, like Rex, you are also dealing with a father who abandoned you, a mother and her boyfriend who beat you, food and housing insecurity, and the stigma of free lunch, the results can be overwhelming." Booklist.

Osceola, Seminole chief, 1804-1838

Sanford, William R., (William Reynolds), 1927-. **Seminole** chief Osceola. William R. Sanford. Enslow Publishers, c2013. 48 p.: Native American chiefs and warriors
Grades: 6 7 8 9   **B**
1. Chiefs (Political anthropology) 2. Rulers 3. Indians of North America 4. Seminole Indians
ISBN 9780766041172

LC 2011050996

Describes the life of the Seminole chief and warrior who struggled to prevent the removal of his people from their land in Florida.

Owens, Jesse, 1913-1980

Burlingame, Jeff. **Jesse** Owens: "I always loved running". Jeff Burlingame. Enslow Publishers, 2010. 128 p.: African-American biography library

Grades: 6 7 8 9   **B**

  1. African-American track and field athletes 2. Athletes 3. Olympic athletes 4. Track and field athletes 5. African Americans

ISBN 9780766034976

LC 2010015697

Explores the life of Jesse Owens, including his childhood and family, his rise to excellence in track and field, his 1936 Olympic triumph, and his death and legacy. Provided by publisher.

"This book opens with Jesse Owens' celebrated victory in the 1936 Olympics in Berlin, when he triumphed in the 100-meter dash and Hitler refused to congratulate him. In a more nuanced historical account than many books offer, Burlingame looks at different interpretations of the day's events and comments on how Owens' own account changed over time. . . . After the dramatic opening chapter, the book offers a chronological account of Owens' life. . . . On every page, color brightens the headings, backgrounds, bordered photos, sidebars, and boxed quotes." Booklist.

Includes bibliographical references and index.

Gigliotti, Jim. **Jesse** Owens: gold medal hero. Jim Gigliotti. Sterling Pub Co Inc 2010 128 p.: Sterling biographies

Grades: 6 7 8 9   **B**

  1. Olympic athletes 2. Athletes 3. Runners

ISBN 9781402771491

Loads of information is packed into each title of this series about world inventors, innovative thinkers and great athletes, including timelines, sidebars, a glossary, maps, rare photographs and world-class writing that make these books accessible and dramatic.

"Opinionated yet informative, . . . [this blends] anecdotes, quotations, and facts to create [an] engaging [portrait]. . . . Photographs and sidebars are incorporated into [a] reader-friendly [design]." Horn Book Guide.

McDougall, Chros. **Jesse** Owens: trailblazing sprinter. by Chros McDougall. ABDO Pub. Co., c2011. 112 p.: Legendary athletes

Grades: 6 7 8 9   **B**

  1. Track and field athletes 2. African-American track and field athletes 3. Track and field 4. African Americans

ISBN 9781617147586

LC 2010046697

Highlights the life and accomplishments of the famous African American track and field star who won four gold medals at the 1936 Olympic games in Berlin.

"This biography of track star Jesse Owens goes beyond merely discussing [his] accomplishments. . . . [It] also [explores] the social and political [influence he] had on society as a whole. In addition, [it introduces] historical events in the context of [his life]. . . . This . . . is teeming with information and is a must-purchase for sports fans and readers interested in social activism." School Library Journal.

Includes bibliographical references (p. 104) and index.

Paige, Satchel, 1906-1982

Sturm, James, 1965-. **Satchel** Paige: striking out Jim Crow. by James Sturm & Rich Tommaso; with an introduction by Gerald Early. Jump at the Sun, 2007. 89 p.

Grades: 4 5 6 7 8 9 10   **B**

  1. Racism in sports 2. Racism in baseball 3. African American baseball players 4. Baseball -- History 5. African Americans 6. Southern States -- History -- 20th century. 7. Comics and Graphic novels

ISBN 9781368022323

LC 2007061362

Baseball Hall-of-Famer Leroy "Satchel" Paige changed the face of the game in a career that spanned five decades. In stark prose and powerful graphics, author and artist share the story of a sports hero, role model, consummate showman, and era-defining American.

"This graphic novel is about fictional Emmet Wilson, a black farmer whose moment of glory as a player in the Negro Leagues came when he scored a run off the great pitcher, Satchel Paige. . . . This visually powerful, suspenseful, even profound story makes an excellent choice for readers interested in baseball or in the history of race relations." Booklist.

Parker, Charlie, 1920-1955

Rice, Earle. **Charlie** Parker. Earle Rice Jr. Mitchell Lane Publishers, c2012. 47 p.: American jazz

Grades: 6 7 8 9   **B**

  1. Jazz musicians 2. African American musicians 3. Jazz music 4. African Americans

ISBN 9781612282664

LC 2012008628

Introduces the famous jazz saxophonist and his style of jazz known as bebop.

Parker, Quanah, Comanche chief, 1847-1911

Sanford, William R., (William Reynolds), 1927-. **Comanche** Chief Quanah Parker. William R. Sanford. Enslow Publishers, c2013. 48 p.: Native American chiefs and warriors

Grades: 6 7 8 9   **B**

  1. Rulers 2. Comanche Indians -- Wars 3. Comanche Indians 4. Chiefs (Political anthropology) 5. Indians of North America

ISBN 9780766040953

LC 2011048762

Read about how this great chief of the Comanche led his people into a war for survival. Provided by publisher.

Parks, Rosa, 1913-2005

★ Parks, Rosa, 1913-2005. **Rosa** Parks: my story. by Rosa Parks; with Jim Haskins. Dial Books, c1992. 192 p.

Grades: 5 6 7 8   **B**

  1. 1950s 2. African Americans 3. Civil rights workers 4. Segregation in transportation -- History 20th century. 5. African Americans -- Civil rights -- History 20th century. 6. Segregation 7. Montgomery, Alabama -- History -- 20th century. 8. Montgomery, Alabama -- Race relations.

ISBN 0803706731

LC 89001124

Discusses Parks' role in the Montgomery NAACP, her refusal to give up her bus seat to a white man, the Montgomery bus boycott, and Dr. Martin Luther King, Jr

"A remarkable story, a record of quiet bravery and modesty, a document of social significance, a taut drama told with candor." Bulletin of the Center for Children's Books.

Theoharis, Jeanne. The **rebellious** life of Mrs. Rosa Parks: adapted for young people. Jeanne Theoharis; adapted by Brandy Colbert and Jeanne Theoharis. Beacon Press, 2021 296 p.

Grades: 7 8 9 10 11 12   **B**

  1. African American women civil rights workers 2. Civil rights

workers 3. African American women 4. Women 5. Segregation in transportation 6. Montgomery, Alabama -- Race relations
ISBN 9780807067574

LC 2020011430

This definitive biography of Rosa Parks accessibly examines her six decades of activism, challenging young readers' perceptions of her as an accidental actor in the civil rights movement. Provided by publisher.

"This detailed, readable narrative refutes the myth of the accidentally significant historical figure, focusing on the totality of Parks' life as a champion of full citizenship for African Americans as well as the complexities of struggles against White resistance." Kirkus

Includes bibliographical references (pages 274-278) and index.

Paterson, Katherine

Paterson, Katherine. **Stories** of my life. Katherine Paterson. Dial Books for Young Readers, 2014. 288 p.
Grades: 9 10 11 12 Adult Professional   **B**
1. Authors, American 20th century 2. Children's literature writing
ISBN 9780803740433

LC 2013042628

An uplifting personal account by the Newbery Medal- and National Book Award-winning author shares intimate stories about the experiences that inspired her novels, from her early childhood in China to her marriage to a minister and relationships with four children.

"Written in a conversational style, these 'kitchen sink stories' will perhaps be received best by professional adults and readers who grew up with her books; much of what she recounts is about the distant past, courtship, and motherhood. What absolutely shines through is Paterson's warm, self-effacing humor, and the extraordinary humility of a writer who has won two National Book Awards, two Newbery Medals, and the Hans Christian Andersen Medal." Publishers Weekly.

Paul, Alice, 1885-1977

Kops, Deborah. **Alice** Paul and the fight for women's rights: from the vote to the Equal Rights Amendment. Deborah Kops. Calkins Creek Books, 2017. 220 p.
Grades: 7 8 9 10 11 12   **B**
1. United States. Constitution. 19th Amendment. 2. Suffragists 3. Women -- Suffrage 4. Protests, demonstrations, vigils, etc 5. Suffragist movement 6. Women's rights
ISBN 9781629793238

LC 2016951184

Here is the story of extraordinary leader Alice Paul, from the woman suffrage movement—the long struggle for votes for women—to the "second wave," when women demanded full equality with men. Paul made a significant impact on both.

"A rich, fascinating, and inspiring account of a tireless champion for women's rights." Kirkus.

Includes bibliographical references (pages 200-206) and index.

Paulsen, Gary

Paulsen, Gary. **Gone** to the woods: surviving a lost childhood. Gary Paulsen. Farrar Straus & Giroux, 2021 288 p.
Grades: 6 7 8 9   **B**
1. United States. Army. 2. Survival 3. Books and reading 4. Psychic trauma in children 5. Storytelling 6. Resilience in children 7. United States 8. Manila, Philippines
ISBN 9780374314156

From the author of the bestselling Hatchet comes a true story of high-stakes wilderness survival! At the age of five Gary Paulsen escaped from a shocking Chicago upbringing to a North Woods homestead, find-

ing a powerful respect for nature that would stay with him throughout his life. At the age of thirteen a librarian handed him his first book, and there he found a lasting love of reading. As a teenager he desperately enlisted in the Army, and there amazingly discovered his true calling as a storyteller. A moving and enthralling story of grit and growing up, Gone to the Woods is perfect for newcomers to the voice and lifelong fans alike, from the acclaimed author at his rawest and realest.

"Beautifully written, Paulsen's memoir demonstrates that good can triumph over bad beginnings." Booklist

Paulsen, Gary. **Guts**: the true stories behind Hatchet and the Brian books. Gary Paulsen. Delacorte Press, c2001. 148 p.
Grades: 6 7 8 9   **B**
1. Authors, American 20th century 2. Children's stories -- Authorship 3. Authors, American
ISBN 9780385326506

LC 00034061

The author relates incidents in his life and how they inspired parts of his books about the character, Brian Robeson.

"Readers squeamish about hunting or the death of animals will find many of the stories disturbing . . . but those who embrace the sport or have enjoyed the novels will see in Paulsen a responsible role model—a man who respects life and death as equal partners." Booklist.

Paulsen, Gary. **My** life in dog years. Gary Paulsen; with drawings by Ruth Wright Paulsen. Delacorte Press, c1998. 137 p.
Grades: 4 5 6 7   **B**
1. Sled dogs 2. Humans and dogs 3. Dog owners 4. Authors, American 20th century 5. Children's literature authors 20th century.
ISBN 0385325703

LC 97040254

The author describes some of the dogs that have had special places in his life, including his first dog, Snowball, in the Philippines; Dirk, who protected him from bullies; and Cookie, who saved his life.

"Paulsen differentiates his canine friends beautifully, as only a keen observer and lover of dogs can. At the same time, he presents an intimate glimpse of himself, a lonely child of alcoholic parents, who drew strength and solace from his four-legged companions and a love of the great outdoors. Poignant but never saccharine, honest, and open." Booklist.

Paulsen, Gary. **This** side of wild: mutts, mares, and laughing dinosaurs. Gary Paulsen. Simon & Schuster Books for Young Readers, [2015] 176 p.
Grades: 4 5 6 7 8   **B**
1. Authors, American 20th century 2. Human-animal relationships 3. Animals
ISBN 9781481451505

LC 2015004132

The Newbery Honor-winning author of Hatchet and Dogsong shares surprising true stories about his relationship with animals, highlighting their compassion, intellect, intuition, and sense of adventure.

"For anyone who loves the natural world and excellent writing, this is a must-read." Booklist.

Pei, I. M., 1917-

Slavicek, Louise Chipley, 1956-. **I.M.** Pei. Louise Chipley Slavicek. Chelsea House, 2009. 120 p.: Asian-Americans of achievement

Grades: 6 7 8 9   **B**

1. Chinese Americans 2. Asian Americans 3. Architects
ISBN 9781604135671

LC 2009014609

"A fascinating look at the world-renowned architect. . . . Slavecek deftly covers Pei's life, including his childhood and political events that were going on in China at the time. . . . The narrative is easy to read, the sidebars are informative, and the chronology and glossary are very helpful. A solid choice for most libraries." School Library Journal.

Includes bibliographical references and index.

Pele, 1940-

Buckley, James. **Pelé.** James Buckley, Jr. DK Pub., 2007. 128 p.: DK biography
Grades: 6 7 8 9   **B**

1. Soccer players
ISBN 0756629969

LC bl2007016789

Presents the life and accomplishments of Pelé, the Brazillian who has been called the king of soccer.

"This introduces Edson Arantes do Nascimento, know to the world as soccer legend Pelé. The chapters stretch from Pelé's Brazilian youth . . . through his astonishing career and his current retirement. . . . Buckley grounds his enthusiasm with well-integrated facts and quotes. . . . Crisply reproduced photographs appear on every page." Booklist.

Includes bibliographical references (p. 124-125) and index.

Simon, Eddy, 1968-. **Pelé**: the king of soccer. written by Eddy Simon; illustrated by Vincent Brascaglia; translated by Joe Johnson. First Second, 2017, c2016. 144 p.
Grades: 4 5 6 7 8 9   **B**

1. Soccer players 2. Professional athletes 3. Fame 4. Poor boys 5. Competition 6. Brazil -- History -- 20th century 7. Brazil -- Politics and government 8. Biographical comics 9. Comics and Graphic novels 10. Translations French to English
ISBN 9781626727557

A middle-grade biographical tribute to the world's most distinguished soccer player describes the formidable economic challenges that marked his early life, his rapid ascent to the professional leagues and the World Cup victories that have made him a celebrated, boundary-breaking star.

Peron, Eva Duarte, 1919-1952

Favor, Lesli J.. **Eva** Peron. Lesli J.Favor. Marshall Cavendish Benchmark, c2011. 112 p.: Leading women
Grades: 5 6 7 8   **B**

1. Women politicians 2. Presidents' spouses 3. Argentina -- History -- 1943-1955
ISBN 9780761449621

LC 2009029671

Presents the biography of Eva Peron against the backdrop of her political, historical, and cultural environment. Provided by publisher.

Picasso, Pablo, 1881-1973

Spence, David. **Picasso.** [written by David Spence]. New Forest Press, c2010. 48 p.
Grades: 6 7 8 9   **B**

1. Artists
ISBN 9781848983144

LC bl2010026394

Explores the world, art, and inspiration of the innovative artist who was born in Spain and lived most of his life in France.

"Offers biographical information [of Pablo Picasso] . . . interspersed with art history and criticism in an eye-catching format. . . . [Includes] a long introductory paragraph and four-to-six images with explanatory notes. . . . Spence . . . does a good job of explaining why art that might seem ordinary today was revolutionary at the time of its creation." School Library Journal.

Includes bibliographical references (p. 45) and index.

Pike, Zebulon Montgomery, 1779-1813

Sanford, William R. (William Reynolds), 1927-. **Zebulon** Pike: courageous Rocky Mountain explorer. William R. Sanford and Carl R. Green. Enslow Publishers, c2013. 48 p.
Grades: 5 6 7 8   **B**

1. Explorers 2. West (US) 3. West (US) -- Discovery and exploration
ISBN 9780766040120

LC 2011051629

Examines the life of Zebulon Pike, including his childhood on the frontier, his days as a soldier, exploring the Rocky Mountains and the Southwest, and his legacy in American history. Provided by publisher.

Plato, 428-347 B.C.E.

Gow, Mary. The **great** philosopher: Plato and his pursuit of knowledge. Mary Gow. Enslow Publishers, c2011. 128 p.: Great minds of ancient science and math
Grades: 6 7 8 9   **B**

1. Philosophers 2. Ancient philosophers 3. Intellectual life 4. Ancient Greece -- History.
ISBN 9780766031197

LC 2009044566

Introduces the life and works of the Greek philosopher, covering his writings on Socrates, his later books, and the influence he has had on philosophic thought up to the present day.

Poe, Edgar Allan, 1809-1849

Lange, Karen E.. **Nevermore**: a photobiography of Edgar Allan Poe. Karen E. Lange. National Geographic, c2009. 64 p.: Photobiographies
Grades: 6 7 8 9   **B**

1. 19th century 2. Authors, American 19th century 3. Gothic fiction writers 4. Mystery story writers 5. Short story writers
ISBN 9781426303982

LC 2008039833

Examines the life and times of the author and poet who pioneered the psychological horror story and whose work had a huge influence on future generations of writers, poets, artists, and even songwriters.

"The drama of Poe's tortured life unfolds in accessible prose. Textual information is interspersed with photos, artistic interpretations, and revealing quotations presented in script. . . . This volume offers a fairly complete and thoroughly readable description of Poe's life and his importance to literature." School Library Journal.

Includes bibliographical references (p. 63) and index.

Polo, Marco, 1254-1323?

Twist, Clint. **Marco** Polo: history's great adventurer: being an account of his travels, 1270-1295. written by Clint Twist. Templar Books, 2011. 1 v. (unpaged): Historical notebooks
Grades: 5 6 7 8   **B**

1. Travelers 2. Merchants 3. Voyages and travels -- History To 1500 4. Voyages and travels 5. Travelers 6. China -- Description

and travel 7. Silk Road -- Description and travel
ISBN 9780763652869

LC 2010040131

Presents the travels of Marco Polo as he travels along the Silk Road to medieval China, in a book that includes booklets, foldouts, and maps.

"In this sumptuous scrapbook, excerpts from Marco Polo's own account of his travels are paired with beautiful maps, drawings, and illustrations. . . . This volume is well suited to browsing, and many readers will want to spend time poring over the many details." School Library Journal.

Powell, Barbara Johns, 1935-1991

Kanefield, Teri, 1960-. The **girl** from the tar paper school: Barbara Rose Johns and the advent of the civil rights movement. Teri Kanefield. Abrams Books for Young Readers, 2014. 56 p.
Grades: 5 6 7 8   B
1. Segregation in education -- History 20th century 2. Civil Rights Movement 3. Civil rights workers 4. African American civil rights workers 5. African Americans 6. Virginia -- Race relations -- History -- 20th century
ISBN 9781419707964

LC 2012040990

Carter G. Woodson Book Awards: Middle Level, 2015.

Describes the peaceful protest organized by teenager Barbara Rose Johns in order to secure a permanent building for her segregated high school in Virginia in 1951, and explains how her actions helped fuel the civil rights movement.

"A heartfelt tribute to Barbara Rose Johns, a lesser-known heroine of the early civil rights movement. In 1951 Virginia, black Robert R. Moton High School and white Farmville High were separate but definitely not equal, and quiet Barbara and her classmates decided to strike. Profuse details, some extraneous, threaten to overtake the inspiring story of bravery." Horn Book.

Includes bibliographical references (pages 50-51) and index.

Powell, John Wesley, 1834-1902

Hale, Nathan, 1976-. **Major** Impossible. Nathan Hale. Amulet Books, 2019. 127 p.: Nathan Hale's hazardous tales
Grades: 4 5 6 7   B
1. Explorers 2. Grand Canyon -- Exploration 3. Grand Canyon region -- Exploration 4. Comics and Graphic novels
ISBN 9781419737084

Traces the story of the heralded explorer who after losing an arm during the American Civil War joined the 1869 Colorado River Exploring Expedition on a dangerous journey through the Grand Canyon.

Prince, Liz, 1981-

Prince, Liz, 1981-. **Tomboy**: a graphic memoir. Liz Prince. Zest Books, 2014. 272 p.
Grades: 7 8 9 10 11 12 Adult   B
1. Gender identity 2. Tomboys 3. Gender role 4. Teenage girls 5. Comics and Graphic novels 6. Autobiographical comics
ISBN 9781936976553

Eschewing female stereotypes throughout her early years and failing to gain acceptance on the boys' baseball team, Liz learns to embrace her own views on gender as she comes of age, in an anecdotal graphic novel memoir. By the award-winning author of Will You Love Me If I Wet the Bed?

"Prince's honest voice and self-deprecating humor help make young Liz a sympathetic and relatable character. The simply rendered black-and-white panel drawings have an unpretentious quality, in keeping with the narrative tone." Horn Book.

Puente, Tito, 1923-2000

McNeese, Tim. **Tito** Puente. Tim McNeese. Chelsea House, c2008. 118 p.: The great Hispanic heritage
Grades: 6 7 8 9   B
1. Salsa musicians 2. Musicians 3. Hispanic Americans
ISBN 9780791096666

LC 2007031984

A biography of the band leader and recording artist who grew up in Spanish Harlem and gained worldwide popularity as the "King of Latin Music."

"This biography provides a substantive [portrait], including background information and historical context of . . . charismatic band leader Puente. . . . The well-documented [text] effectively [combines] anecdotes, quotations, and historical details. Many photographs and sidebars are also included." Horn Book Guide.

Includes bibliographical references (p. 108-111) and index.

Pythagoras

Karamanides, Dimitra. **Pythagoras**: pioneering mathematician and musical theorist of Ancient Greece. Dimitra Karamanides. Rosen Pub. Group, 2006. 112 p.
Grades: 9 10 11 12   B
1. Philosophers 2. Mathematicians 3. Musicians 4. Mathematics -- History 5. Ancient Greece
ISBN 1404205004

LC 2005011968

Describes the life and ideas of the influential Greek mathematician and musician, including how Pythagorean thought influenced later scientists.

"This series introduces students to the great philosophers and mathematicians who helped shape the intellectual world in modern times. More in depth than many text books for middle school students, the lives and teachings of these men come alive with the aid of colorful maps and illustrations, as well as examples of the kinds of knowledge these men taught to their students." Library Media Connection.

Includes bibliographical references (p. 107-108) and index.

Raisman, Aly, 1994-

Raisman, Aly, 1994-. **Fierce**: how competing for myself changed everything. Aly Raisman with Blythe Lawrence. Little, Brown and Company, 2017. 358 p.
Grades: 7 8 9 10 11 12   B
1. Women gymnasts 2. Gymnasts 3. Women Olympic athletes 4. Determination in women 5. Women Olympic medal winners
ISBN 9780316472708

LC bl2017046405

Shares the author's journey to Olympic gold, including when she began her gymnastics training, how she dealt with naysayers who said she would never make it, and how she surrounded herself with a strong support system.

Ramses

Fitzgerald, Stephanie. **Ramses** II: Egyptian pharaoh, warrior, and builder. by Stephanie Fitzgerald. Compass Point Books, c2008. 112 p.: Signature lives
Grades: 6 7 8 9   B
1. Rulers 2. Ancient history 3. Civilization, Ancient 4. Ancient Egypt -- History -- Nineteenth dynasty, ca. 1320-1200 B.C.E.
ISBN 9780756538361

LC 2008005726

"This biography of the pharaoh Ramses II offers details about the history and daily life of Egypt's New Kingdom era. . . . [The texts is] accompanied by high-quality photographs of artifacts, maps, and floor plans. [The] book's detailed time line, comparing events in Egypt to those throughout the world, is helpful for placing the lives of the pharaohs in context." School Library Journal.

Includes bibliographical references (p. 103, 107-108) and index.

Rankin, Jeannette, 1880-1973

Naden, Corinne J.. **Jeannette** Rankin. Corinne J. Naden. Cavendish Square, 2014. 96 p.: Leading women

Grades: 7 8 9   **B**

    1. Women legislators 2. Women pacifists 3. Suffragists 4. Women
ISBN 9780761449638

                                        LC 2010047559

Presents the biography of Jeannette Rankin against the backdrop of her political, historical, and cultural environment. Provided by publisher.

Rasputin, Grigori Efimovich, 1869-1916

Goldberg, Enid A.. **Grigory** Rasputin: holy man or mad monk? Enid A. Goldberg & Norman Itzkowitz. Scholastic, C2008. 128 p.: Wicked history

Grades: 6 7 8 9   **B**

    1. Mystics 2. Monks 3. Murder victims 4. Russia -- Court and courtiers 5. Russia -- History -- Nicholas II, 1894-1917
ISBN 9780531125946

                                   LC 2007001692

Traces the life of the a poor peasant who became one of the most powerful men in Russia by claiming to have mystical powers.

"This engaging, thought-provoking book provides a chronological account of Rasputin's life as well as the historical background necessary to understand it in context. Was Rasputin a holy man, or was he simply a philandering charlatan who rose to power because of his unique relationship with Tsar Nicholas and Tsarina Alexandra? . . . Captioned, black-and-white period photographs enhance the text. Recommended for both curricular pursuits and pleasure reading." School Library Journal.

Includes bibliographical references (p. 125) and index.

Rector, Sarah, 1902-

Bolden, Tonya. **Searching** for Sarah Rector: the richest black girl in America. Tonya Bolden. Abrams Books for Young Readers, 2014. 76 p.

Grades: 4 5 6 7 8   **B**

    1. African American women 2. Millionaires 3. Oil industry and trade -- History 20th century 4. Creek Indians 5. African Americans 6. Oklahoma 7. Creek County, Oklahoma
ISBN 9781419708466

                                   LC 2012039254

Recounts the story of the 1914 disappearance of eleven-year-old Sarah Rector, an African American who was part of the Creek Indian people and whose land had made her wealthy, and what it reveals about race, money, and American society.

Red Cloud, 1822-1909

★ Nelson, S. D.. **Red** Cloud: a Lakota story of war and surrender. S. D. Nelson. Abrams Books for Young Readers, [2017] 56 p.

Grades: 4 5 6 7   **B**

    1. American Westward Expansion (1803-1899) 2. Oglala Indians 3. Warriors 4. Lakota Indians 5. Indians of North America 6. Red Cloud's War, 1866-1867 7. The West (United States)
ISBN 9781419723131

                                   LC 2016048744

A leader among the Lakota during the 1860s, Chief Red Cloud deeply opposed white expansion into Native American territory. He rejected treaties from the U.S. government and instead united the warriors of the Lakota and nearby tribes, becoming the only Native American to win a war against the U.S. Army.

"An impressive amount of information movingly and handsomely conveyed." Kirkus.

Sanford, William R., (William Reynolds), 1927-. **Oglala** Lakota Chief Red Cloud. William R. Sanford. Enslow Publishers, c2013. 48 p.: Native American chiefs and warriors

Grades: 6 7 8 9   **B**

    1. Chiefs (Political anthropology) 2. Rulers 3. Indians of North America 4. Oglala Indians -- Wars 5. Oglala Indians
ISBN 9780766040960

                                   LC 2011048760

Read about how this fearless Native American Chief of the Oglala Sioux led his people into a war for survival against the United States Army. Provided by publisher.

Rembrandt Harmenszoon van Rijn, 1606-1669

Roberts, Russell, 1953-. **Rembrandt**. Russell Roberts. Mitchell Lane Publishers, c2009. 48 p.: Art profiles for kids

Grades: 7 8 9 10   **B**

    1. Painters 2. Artists 3. Painting, Dutch 4. Netherlands -- Civilization -- 17th century. 5. Netherlands -- Social life and customs.
ISBN 9781584157106

                                   LC 2008002241

Presents the life and accomplishments of the Dutch painter known for his portraits, biblical scenes, and use of chiaroscuro, discussing his childhood, art education, and famous paintings.

"Tracks the artist's rise to fame and the bitter years and bankruptcy that followed. . . . [Goes] beyond basic facts, providing historical context and significance of the art and the artist. . . . Provide[s] plenty of information for reports in a reader-friendly format." School Library Journal.

Includes bibliographical references (p. 45-46) and index.

Rhodes-Courter, Ashley, 1985-

Rhodes-Courter, Ashley, 1985-. **Three** little words: a memoir. Ashley Rhodes-Courter. Atheneum, c2008. 304 p.

Grades: 8 9 10 11 12 Adult   **B**

    1. Adopted children 2. Foster children 3. Foster home care
ISBN 1416948066

                                   LC 2007021629

Traces the author's painful childhood in a series of foster homes, her deteriorating relationship with her emotionally unstable mother, abuse at the hands of a foster family, and her subsequent efforts to advocate for an improved foster care system.

"This memoir lends a powerful voice to thousands of boomerang kids who repeatedly wind up back in foster care." School Library Journal.

Ride, Sally

Macy, Sue. **Sally** Ride: life on a mission. by Sue Macy. Aladdin, 2014. 160 p.: Real-life story

Grades: 4 5 6 7 8   **B**

    1. United States. National Aeronautics and Space Administration 2. Women astronauts 3. Astronauts 4. Physicists 5. Women 6. Women physicists
ISBN 9781442488540

                                   LC 2014016685

Details the lesser-known achievements of the first woman in space, from her national tennis rankings and work as a physicist to her Presidential Medal of Freedom award and her contributions as a founder of a company for girls interested in science and math.

"The extensive backmatter provides scholarly data, while the writing imparts the drive and character of this famous woman. Macy's slim, empathetic account makes readers see the woman behind the achievement." Kirkus.

Includes bibliographical references and index.

O'Shaughnessy, Tam E.. **Sally** Ride: a photobiography of America's pioneering woman in space. Tam O'Shaughnessy. Roaring Brook Press, 2015. 128 p.

Grades: 4 5 6 7 8   **B**
1. Women astronauts 2. Astronauts
ISBN 9781596439948

LC 2015004913

A biography of the famous astronaut drawing on personal and family photographs from her childhood, school days, college, life in the astronaut corps, and afterward. Provided by publisher.

"Ride was notoriously private, and this glimpse into her life and background will be both eye-opening and inspiring for many young readers. The irresistible photos and appealing page layouts make it an especially good pick for reluctant readers." Booklist.

Rivera, Diego, 1886-1957

Bernier-Grand, Carmen T.. **Diego:** bigger than life. by Carmen T. Bernier-Grand; illustrated by David Diaz. Marshall Cavendish, 2009. 64 p.

Grades: 8 9 10 11 12   **B**
1. Painters 2. Artists
ISBN 9780761453833

LC 2007013761

The life and work of the artist Diego Rivera is told through chronological poems that capture salient points in his life. Provided by publisher.

"This is a well written and beautifully illustrated volume. . . . Almost all written in first-person from the artist's point of view, the poems convey information succinctly within a context of colorful narrative and clearly expressed emotion. . . . Apart from four reproductions of Rivera's paintings and one photo of the artist, the illustrations are mixed-media pictures by Diaz. Depicting Rivera and his world, these iconic images glow with warmth, light, and color." Booklist.

Includes bibliographical references.

Hillstrom, Kevin, 1963-. **Diego** Rivera: muralist. By Kevin Hillstrom. Lucent Books, 2007. 104 p.: Twentieth century's most influential Hispanics

Grades: 6 7 8 9 10   **B**
1. Painters 2. Artists 3. Latin Americans 4. Mexico -- Social life and customs -- 20th century.
ISBN 142050018X

LC 2007032104

"Rivera's life, beginnning with his childhood, is placed in the context of the artistic, political, and economic influences on family and his career. . . . The layout draws the eye with colorful headings and highlighted quotes." Library Media Connection.

Includes bibliographical references and index.

★ Rubin, Susan Goldman. **Diego** Rivera: an artist for the people. Susan Goldman Rubin. Harry N Abrams, 2013. 56 p.

Grades: 5 6 7 8   **B**
1. Painters 2. Muralists 3. Artists
ISBN 9780810984110

Offers insight into the life and artwork of the famous Mexican painter and muralist and follows his career, looking at his influences, and tracing the evolution of his style.

Rizal, Jose, 1861-1896

Arruda, Suzanne Middendorf, 1954-. **Freedom's** martyr: the story of Jose Rizal, national hero of the Philippines. Suzanne Middendorf Arruda. Avisson Press, c2003. 106 p.: Avisson young adult series

Grades: 7 8 9 10   **B**
1. Philippine-American War, 1896-1902 2. Martyrs 3. Heroes and heroines, Philippine 4. Revolutionaries 5. Philippines -- History
ISBN 1888105550

LC 2003045320

"Born in the Philippines on June 19, 1861, Rizal was executed by the Spanish for treason on December 30, 1896. . . . Rizal wanted representation for native peoples in the Spanish government and wrote three novels and several poems detailing their plight. . . . This well-written, readable biography will prove useful for reports and background information on the history of the Philippines." School Library Journal.

Includes bibliographical references (p. 103-104) and index.

Robeson, Paul, 1898-1976

Duberman, Martin B.. **Paul** Robeson: no one can silence me: the life of the legendary artist and activist, adapted for young adults. by Martin Duberman; foreword by Jason Reynolds The New Press, 2021. xxii, 259 p.

Grades: 7 8 9 10 11 12   **B**
1. Singers 2. Civil rights workers 3. African American men 4. African American singers 5. African American political activists
ISBN 9781620976494

"Duberman balances Robeson's tireless civil rights work with his marital troubles and later mental-health problems. Numerous photographs throughout help document Robeson's robust life. A powerful tribute to this #BlackLivesMatter predecessor." Booklist

Includes bibliographical references (pages 229-243) and index.

Rubin, Susan Goldman. **Sing** and shout: the mighty voice of Paul Robeson. Susan Goldman Rubin. Calkins Creek, 2020 288 p.

Grades: 6 7 8 9   **B**
1. African Americans 2. Singers 3. Political activists 4. African American political activists 5. African American singers
ISBN 9781629798578

When faced with the decision to remain silent or be ostracized, Paul Robeson chose to sing, shout, and speak out. Excerpted from publisher description.

Slavicek, Louise Chipley, 1956-. **Paul** Robeson: entertainer and activist. by Louise Chipley Slavicek. Chelsea House, 2011. 120 p.: Black Americans of achievement

Grades: 6 7 8 9 10   **B**
1. African Americans 2. Actors and actresses 3. Singers
ISBN 9781604138436

LC 2010026879

"This biography of the African American singer, actor, and activist chronicles Robeson's struggles to overcome racial prejudice, leading to his staunch support of communism—a stand that caused him to lose favor in Hollywood and contributed to his eventual reclusion. Slavicek delves deeply into Robeson's story, giving readers a strong sense of the challenges Robeson faced, as well as the complex, courageous individual behind the legend. Archival black-and-white photos further lend a sense of intimacy, while did you know sidebars expand on related topics." Booklist.

Includes bibliographical references and index.

Robinson, Jackie, 1919-1972

★ Robinson, Sharon, 1950-. **Promises** to keep: how Jackie Robinson changed America. Sharon Robinson. Scholastic Press, c2004. 64 p.

Grades: 4 5 6 7 **B**

    1. African American baseball players 2. African Americans 3. Baseball players 4. Personal conduct 5. Baseball players 6. United States -- Race relations

    ISBN 0439425921

                    LC 2003042709

A biography of baseball legend Jackie Robinson, the first African American to play in the major leagues, as told by his daughter.

"Robinson's daughter, Sharon, describes her father's youth, his rise to become major-league baseball's first African American player, and his involvement in the civil rights movement. . . . Her private view of her father's accomplishments, placed within the context of American sports and social history, makes for absorbing reading. An excellent selection of family and team photographs and other materials . . . illustrate this fine tribute." Booklist.

Roosevelt, Franklin D. (Franklin Delano), 1882-1945

Kanefield, Teri, 1960-. **Franklin** D. Roosevelt. Teri Kanefield. Abrams Books for Young Readers, 2019. 250 p.: Making of America (Abrams)

Grades: 4 5 6 **B**

    1. Presidents 2. Politicians 3. United States -- Politics and government -- 1933-1945

    ISBN 9781419734021

                    LC 2019011547

Examines the life of America's 32nd president: his birth into one of America's elite families, his domineering mother, his marriage to Eleanor Roosevelt, his struggle with polio, and his political career. A Democrat, Roosevelt (1882-1945) won a record four presidential elections and is the longest-serving US President. During his time in office, he led the country through the Great Depression and World War II. He helped to redefine the role of the US government with the New Deal. Scholars often rated him as one of the three greatest US presidents along with George Washington and Abraham Lincoln.

Tobin, James, 1956-. **Master** of his fate: Roosevelt's rise from polio to the presidency. James Tobin. Christy Ottaviano Books, Henry Holt and Company, 2021. 256 p.

Grades: 6 7 8 **B**

    1. Presidents 2. Poliomyelitis -- Patients 3. People with disabilities 4. Politicians 5. Life change events 6. United States -- Politics and government -- 1933-1945

    ISBN 9781627795203

                    LC 2020020580

A biography of FDR, focusing on his battle with polio and how his disease set him on the course to become president; for fans of Steve Sheinkin's political biographies. Provided by publisher.

"A nuanced, engaging, and thought-provoking blend of biography and disability history." Kirkus

Includes bibliographical references.

Roosevelt, Theodore, 1858-1919

Adler, David A.. **Colonel** Theodore Roosevelt. David A. Adler. Holiday House, 2014 144 p.

Grades: 4 5 6 **B**

    1. Presidents 2. Politicians 3. Political leadership

    ISBN 9780823429509

Presents a portrait of the man who grew from a sickly child into a passionate conservationist, skilled outdoorsman, Nobel Peace Prize-winning mediator and one of the most colorful and energetic U.S. presidents in history.

Cooper, Michael L., 1950-. **Theodore** Roosevelt: a twentieth-century life. by Michael L. Cooper. Viking, 2009. 208 p.: Up close (Viking)

Grades: 7 8 9 10 **B**

    1. Presidents 2. United States -- Politics and government -- 1901-1909.

    ISBN 9780670011346

                    LC bl2009016900

Highlights the life and accomplishments of the twenty-sixth president of the United States, whose presidency included programs in conservation and the beginning of the Panama Canal.

"This biography presents an evenhanded account of the life and presidency of Theodore Roosevelt. . . . This clearly written biography includes many anecdotes and well-chosen quotes that help bring Roosevelt to life. . . . Cooper offers a solid portrayal of this noteworthy American president." Booklist.

Includes bibliographical references (p. 200-202) and index.

Fitzpatrick, Brad. **Theodore** Roosevelt. Brad Fitzpatrick. Chelsea House, c2011. 142 p.: Conservation heroes

Grades: 6 7 8 9 10 **B**

    1. Presidents 2. Environmentalists 3. Nature conservation -- History 4. Conservation of natural resources -- History 5. Environmentalism

    ISBN 9781604139488

                    LC 2010026475

Examines the life of President Theodore Roosevelt, emphasizing his love of nature and his efforts to protect the environment.

"Captivating, richly informative. . . . The scope of [this book] is comprehensive. . . . [The book is] engaging as [it is] educational and will be ideal for research and reports." School Library Journal.

Includes bibliographical references (p. 132-133) and index.

★ Rappaport, Doreen. **To** dare mighty things: the life of Theodore Roosevelt. written by Doreen Rappaport; illustrated by C. F. Payne. Disney*Hyperion, 2013. 48 p.: Big Words

Grades: 2 3 4 5 6 **B**

    1. Presidents 2. Environmentalists 3. Naturalists

    ISBN 9781423124887

This picture book biography explores the life of Theodore Roosevelt through vivid prose and the president's own words. Provided by publisher.

Rowling, J. K.

Peterson-Hilleque, Victoria, 1971-. **J.K.** Rowling: extraordinary author. by Victoria Peterson-Hilleque. ABDO Pub., c2011. 112 p.: Essential lives

Grades: 5 6 7 8 **B**

    1. Authors, English 20th century 2. Children's literature writing 3.

Authors, English 4. Women 5. Potter, Harry (Fictitious character)
ISBN 9781616135171

LC 2010000503

Describes the life of the British author whose blockbuster "Harry Potter" series catapulted her from poverty into worldwide fame.

"This biography of author J. K. Rowling toggles between the subject's personal and professional life. . . . [The book] offers sidebar . . . definitions of particular characters or events in the Harry Potter series. The writing is accessible, the format is open, and full-color photos appear throughout." School Library Journal.

Includes bibliographical references (p. 102-103) and index.

Rudolph, Wilma, 1940-1994

Anderson, Jennifer Joline. **Wilma** Rudolph: track and field inspiration. by Jennifer Joline Anderson. ABDO Pub. Co., c2011. 112 p.: Legendary athletes
Grades: 6 7 8 9   **B**
    1. African American women athletes 2. Women runners 3. Runners 4. African American women runners 5. African American women
ISBN 9781617147593

LC 2010046698

Profiles Wilma Rudolph, who overcame childhood polio to become an Olympic medal-winning runner.

"This biography of track star Wilma Rudolph goes beyond merely discussing [her] accomplishments. . . . [It] also [explores] the social and political [influence she] had on society as a whole. In addition, [it introduces] historical events in the context of [her life]. . . . This . . . is teeming with information and is a must-purchase for sports fans and readers interested in social activism." School Library Journal.

Includes bibliographical references (p. 104) and index.

Ruffu, Gail

Neri, Greg. **Grand** theft horse: a graphic novel. by G. Neri; illustrated by Corban Wilkin. Tu Books, an imprint of Lee & Low Books, 2018 240 p.
Grades: 7 8 9 10 11 12   **B**
    1. Race horse trainers 2. Horse racing 3. Animal welfare 4. Race horses 5. Horse training 6. Biographical comics 7. Comics and Graphic novels
ISBN 9781620148556

Author G. Neri returns to graphic novels with the powerful story of his cousin Gail Ruffu, who stole a racehorse in order to save it, and ended up taking on the whole racing industry to fight for the humane treatment of animals.

"The pen-and-ink illustrations vividly capture the drama of this riveting tale that will provoke readers to ponder the ethics of our treatment of animals who suffer for human entertainment as well as the actions of a woman who broke the law to stand up for her principles and the horse she loved." Kirkus.

Runyon, Brent

Runyon, Brent. The **burn** journals. Brent Runyon. Alfred A. Knopf, c2004. 374 p.
Grades: 7 8 9 10   **B**
    1. Teenage boys 2. Teenage burn victims 3. Guilt in teenage boys 4. Coping in teenage boys 5. Family and suicide 6. Virginia 7. Diaries
ISBN 0375826211

LC 2004005643

"One February day in 1991, Runyon came home from eighth grade . . . and set himself on fire. . . . The dialogue between Runyon and his nurses, parents, and especially his hapless psychotherapists is natural and believable, and his inner dialogue is flip, often funny, and sometimes raw. . . . The authentically adolescent voice of the journals will engage even those reluctant to read such a dark story." School Library Journal.

Rustin, Bayard, 1912-1987

★ Brimner, Larry Dane. **We** are one: the story of Bayard Rustin. Larry Dane Brimner. Calkins Creek, 2007. 48 p.
Grades: 5 6 7 8   **B**
    1. African Americans 2. Civil Rights Movement
ISBN 1590784987

Accompanied by archival photographs, this powerful biography traces the life of nonviolent activist Bayard Rustin who, working alongside many African American leaders, fought against injustice and discrimination.

"Brimner sets Rustin's personal story against the history of segregation in his time and focuses on his leadership role . . . in the struggle for civil rights. On each page, the clearly written, informal text is accompanied by eloquently captioned archival photos." Booklist.

Houtman, Jacqueline. **Trouble** maker for justice: the story of Bayard Rustin, the man behind the march on Washington. Jacqueline Houtman, Walter Naegl, Michael G. Long. City Lights Books, 2019, 172 p.
Grades: 7 8 9 10 11 12   **B**
    1. African American civil rights workers 2. March on Washington for Jobs and Freedom, 1963 3. Social action 4. Pacifism 5. Civil rights workers 6. United States -- Race relations -- History -- 20th century
ISBN 9780872867659

LC 2019018987

Recounts the life and accomplishments of Bayard Rustin, focusing on his nonviolent protest methods and his organization of the March on Washington in 1963.

"An excellent biography that belongs in every young adult library. Readers will find Rustin's story captivating; his story could encourage young people to fight for change." School Library Journal

Includes bibliographical references.

Miller, Calvin Craig, 1954-. **No** easy answers: Bayard Rustin and the civil rights movement. Calvin Craig Miller. Morgan Reynolds Pub., c2005. 160 p.
Grades: 7 8 9 10   **B**
    1. African American civil rights workers 2. Civil rights workers 3. Civil Rights Movement 4. African Americans -- Civil rights 5. African Americans
ISBN 1931798435

LC 2004018518

Carter G. Woodson Book Awards: Secondary Level, 2006.

Looks at the life of Bayard Rustin, an organizer behind the scenes of the civil rights movement whose ideas influenced Martin Luther King, Jr.

"Miller combines the life story of a great social activist with the history of the struggle for civil rights in the U.S. The politics are exciting, with details of the radical campaigns in the 1940s and 1950s, Rustin's impassioned call for nonviolent protest, and his role in organizing both the Montgomery Bus Boycott and the 1963 March on Washington." Booklist.

Includes bibliographical references (p. 150-156) and index.

Sabic-El-Rayess, Amra

Sabic-El-Rayess, Amra. The **cat** I never named: a true story of love, war, and survival. Amra Sabic-El-Rayess and Laura L. Sullivan. Bloomsbury Children's Books, 2020. 384 p.

Grades: 8 9 10 11 12 **B**
> 1. Muslim teenagers 2. Yugoslav War, 1991-1995 3. Abandoned cats 4. Girls and cats 5. Survival 6. Bosnia and Hercegovina -- Interethnic relations 7. Yugoslavia
> ISBN 9781547604531

LC 2020021991

In Bihac, Bosnia, in 1992, sixteen-year-old Amra and her family face starvation and the threat of brutal ethnic violence as Serbs and Bosnians clash, while a stray cat, Maci, provides solace.

"At once a story of an individual surviving horrifying circumstances and an unflinching exploration of the political and societal forces that breed ethnic hate and discrimination, Sabic-El-Rayess's memoir is as timely as it is effective." Publishers Weekly

Sacagawea

Berne, Emma Carlson. **Sacagawea**: crossing the continent with Lewis & Clark. by Emma Carlson Berne. Sterling, c2010. 128 p.: Sterling biographies

Grades: 7 8 9 10 **B**
> 1. Guides (Persons) 2. Women interpreters 3. Shoshoni women 4. Shoshoni Indians 5. Women
> ISBN 9781402768453

"Contrary to myth, Sacagawea explains that the Shoshone teen was not a princess, her relationship with Clark was platonic, and she was a peace symbol rather than a guide until they finally reached the Shoshone tribe. . . . [The] spacious design is highly scannable, with color background screens, photos, maps, and historic prints throughout." Booklist.

Sanford, William R. (William Reynolds), 1927-. **Sacagawea**: courageous American Indian guide. William R. Sanford and Carl R. Green. Enslow Publishers, c2013. 48 p.

Grades: 5 6 7 8 **B**
> 1. Indians of North America 2. Shoshoni Indians 3. Shoshoni women 4. Women
> ISBN 9780766040069

LC 2011048291

Discusses the life of Sacagawea, including her Shoshone childhood, her kidnapping by the Hidatsa, her journey with the Lewis and Clark expedition, and her legacy in American history. Provided by publisher.

Saint-Georges, Joseph Bologne, chevalier de, 1745-1799

Brewster, Hugh. The **other** Mozart: the life of the famous Chevalier de Saint George. by Hugh Brewster; illustrated by Eric Velasquez. Abrams Books for Young Readers, 2006. 48 p.

Grades: 4 5 6 7 **B**
> 1. Children of enslaved people 2. Musicians 3. African French men 4. Multiracial men 5. Fencers 6. France -- History -- 18th century.
> ISBN 0810957205

LC 2006007488

"Born to a white plantation owner and a black slave in eighteenth-century Guadeloupe, Joseph Bologne grew up to become the Chevalier de Saint-George, one of France's most accomplished composers. In this picture-book biography for middle-graders, Brewster introduces his subject's fascinating life. . . . Archival images and Velasquez's arresting full-page portraits will captivate many young readers." Booklist.

Salk, Jonas, 1914-1995

Sherrow, Victoria. **Jonas** Salk: beyond the microscope. Victoria Sherrow. Chelsea House Publishers, c2008. xiv, 146 p.: Makers of modern science

Grades: 7 8 9 10 **B**
> 1. Virologists 2. Poliomyelitis vaccine 3. Physicians 4. Poliomyelitis
> ISBN 9780816061808

LC 2006033429

Highlights the life and achievements of the American doctor and medical researcher who helped to develop successful influenza and polio vaccines, then turned his attention to vaccines for cancer and AIDS prevention.

Samanci, Özge, 1975-

Samanci, Özge, 1975-. **Dare** to disappoint: growing up in Turkey. Özge Samanci. Farrar, Straus and Giroux, 2015. 190 p.

Grades: 6 7 8 9 10 **B**
> 1. Women artists 2. Childhood 3. Interethnic conflict 4. Memories 5. Military government 6. Turkey -- History -- 1960- 7. Autobiographical comics 8. Comics and Graphic novels
> ISBN 9780374316983

LC 2015000704

In her unpredictable and funny graphic memoir, Özge recounts her story using inventive collages, weaving together images of the sea, politics, science, and friendship.

"In the growing body of graphic novel memoirs, this one is a standout." School Library Journal.

Santa Anna, Antonio Lopez de, 1794?-1876

Lange, Brenda. **Antonio** Lopez de Santa Anna. Chelsea House, c2010. 102 p.: The great Hispanic heritage

Grades: 6 7 8 9 **B**
> 1. Alamo -- Siege, 1836. 2. Presidents 3. Generals 4. Mexico -- History -- 1821-1861 5. Texas -- History -- To 1846
> ISBN 9781604137347

LC 2010007515

Describes the life of the soldier, general, and president of Mexico who defeated Texas troops at the Battle of the Alamo.

Say, Allen

Say, Allen. The **inker's** shadow. Allen Say. Scholastic Press, 2015. 80 p.

Grades: 5 6 7 8 **B**
> 1. Growing up 2. Military academies 3. Fathers and sons 4. Cartoonists 5. Fifteen-year-old boys 6. California 7. Autobiographical comics 8. Comics and Graphic novels
> ISBN 9780545437769

"A deceptively simple story, given depth by technically excellent illustrations that require a sophisticated level of visual and cultural literacy to successfully interpret." School Library Journal.

Schaller, George B.

Turner, Pamela S. A **life** in the wild: George Schaller's struggle to save the last great beasts. Pamela S. Turner. Farrar, Straus, and Giroux, 2008. 112 p.

Grades: 5 6 7 8 **B**
> 1. Zoologists 2. Wildlife conservation 3. Wildlife conservationists
> ISBN 9780374345785

LC 2007042844

Golden Kite Award for Nonfiction, 2008.

For more than fifty years, explorer-naturalist George Schaller has been on a mission: to save the world's great wild beasts and their environments. This biography examines the amazing life and groundbreaking work of the man International Wildlife calls "the world's foremost field biologist."

"The author interviewed Schaller and had access to his photos, which allowed her to capture beautifully the spirit of Schaller's work. The book is organized chronologically, and each chapter covers a geographic area and the principal animals that Schaller studied there. . . . Animal lovers and conservation-minded students will enjoy this excellent introduction to Schaller and his ideals." Voice of Youth Advocates.

Schiaparelli, Elsa, 1890-1973

Rubin, Susan Goldman. **Hot** pink: the life & fashions of Elsa Schiaparelli. Susan Goldman Rubin. Abrams Books For Young Readers, 2015. 56 p.

Grades: 5 6 7 8 9 **B**
1. Women fashion designers 2. Fashion design -- History 20th century. 3. Fashion -- History 20th century. 4. Fashion designers
ISBN 9781419716423

LC 2014032527

Presents the life and accomplishments of the fashion designer, from her early life of poverty, to her successes in the Paris fashion world, her collaboration with well-known artists of her day, and the influence of her innovative designs on later fashion.

"With accessible text, an inviting format, and a comprehensive list of multimedia resources in the back matter, this concise biography is well suited to classroom use, particularly for students who prefer to approach history through art." Booklist.

Includes bibliographical references (pages 48-53) and index.

Schliemann, Heinrich, 1822-1890

★ Schlitz, Laura Amy. The **hero** Schliemann: the dreamer who dug for Troy. Laura Amy Schlitz; illustrated by Robert Byrd. Candlewick Press, c2006. 72 p.

Grades: 4 5 6 **B**
1. Businesspeople 2. Archaeologists 3. Excavations (Archaeology) -- History 19th century. 4. Ancient cities and towns 5. Mycenae (Extinct city) 6. Troy (Extinct city)
ISBN 0763622834

LC 2005046916

A biography of Heinrich Schliemann—a nineteenth-century German romantic who most believe found the ancient city of Troy—reveals him to be a fascinating mixture of archaeologist, mythmaker, and crook.

"In this slim biography, Schlitz introduces Heinrich Schliemann, a nineteenth-century storyteller, archaeologist, and crook, who led a search for the lost cities of Homer's epic poems." Booklist.

Includes bibliographical references.

Schumann, Clara, 1819-1896

★ Reich, Susanna. **Clara** Schumann: piano virtuoso. by Susanna Reich. Clarion Books, c1999. 118 p.

Grades: 5 6 7 8 **B**
1. 19th century 2. Pianists 3. Women pianists 4. Women 5. Women composers 6. Men with mental illnesses 7. Germany
ISBN 0395891191

LC 98024510

Describes the life of the German pianist and composer who made her professional debut at age nine and who devoted her life to music and to her family.

"This thoroughly researched book draws on primary sources, both Clara's own diaries and her voluminous correspondence with her hus-

band. . . . Reich's lucid, quietly passionate biography is liberally illustrated with photographs and reproductions." Horn Book Guide.

Schutz, Samantha

Schutz, Samantha. **I** don't want to be crazy. Samantha Schutz. Scholastic, c2006. 280 p.

Grades: 8 9 10 11 12 **B**
1. Anxiety in women 2. Young women 3. College students 4. Women -- Interpersonal relations 5. Men/women relations
ISBN 9780439805186

After going away to college and finding the independence she desired difficult to handle, the author begins to suffer from incapacitating anxiety attacks that change everything she had planned.

"In this moving memoir, Schutz details her struggle with anxiety disorder. . . . Written in verse, this memoir successfully conveys what it is like to suffer from panic attacks." Voice of Youth Advocates.

Schwalb, Edith

Kacer, Kathy, 1954-. **Hiding** Edith: a true story. Second Story, 2006. 151 p.

Grades: 4 5 6 7 **B**
1. 1930s 2. 1940s 3. Righteous Gentiles in the Holocaust 4. Holocaust (1933-1945) -- Children 5. World War II -- Children 6. Jewish girls 7. Refugees, Jewish 8. Moissac, France 9. France
ISBN 1897187068

Describes the wartime experiences of Edith Schwalb, a young Jewish girl who was sent to live in the French town of Moissac after the Nazi invasion.

"Kacer recounts some extraordinary history: in Moissac, France, under Nazi occupation, a French Jewish couple hid 100 Jewish refugee children with the support of the townspeople. Kacer, who based her account on interviews, tells the story of one child, Edith Schwalb. Captioned black-and-white photos on almost every page show Edith at home in Vienna before the war, then in Belgium, and then, separated from her parents, living with the rescuers." Booklist.

Seeger, Pete, 1919-2014

Silvey, Anita. **Let** your voice be heard: the life and times of Pete Seeger. Anita Silvey. Clarion Books, [2016] 144 p.

Grades: 5 6 7 8 **B**
1. Folk singers 2. Folk music 3. Folk music, American 4. Social action
ISBN 9780547330129

LC 2015034787

"A lively, unique contribution to the biography shelves." Booklist.
Includes bibliographical references and index.

Seguin, Juan Nepomuceno, 1806-1890

Chemerka, William R.. **Juan** Seguin: Tejano leader. William R. Chemerka; illustrations by Don Collins. Bright Sky Press, [2012], ©2012. 64 p.: Texas heros for young readers

Grades: 3 4 5 6 **B**
1. Alamo -- Siege, 1836. 2. 1830s 3. 19th century 4. Soldiers 5. Politicians 6. Texas -- History -- Revolution, 1835-1836 7. Texas -- History -- Republic, 1836-1846
ISBN 9781933979793

LC 2011052720

Presents the life and accomplishments of Juan Seguin, who was a prominent leader during the fight for Texas' independence.

Sellins, Fannie, 1870 or 1872-1919

Farrell, Mary Cronk. **Fannie** never flinched: one woman's courage in the struggle for American labor union rights. Mary Cronk Farrell. Abrams books for Young Readers, 2016. 56 p.

Grades: 4 5 6 7 8   **B**

1. Women labor leaders 2. Labor unions 3. Human rights activists 4. Labor rights 5. Employee rights 6. United States -- Social conditions -- 20th century

ISBN 9781419718847

"A cogent, well-documented, handsomely designed treatment of a heretofore forgotten hero of labor." Kirkus.

Seuss, Dr

Anderson, Tanya. **Dr.** Seuss (Theodor Geisel). by Tanya Anderson. Chelsea House, 2011. 112 p.: Who wrote that?

Grades: 6 7 8 9   **B**

1. Authors, American 20th century 2. Children's literature authors, American 20th century 3. Children's book illustrators 20th century 4. Illustrators 5. Children's literature writing

ISBN 9781604137507

LC 2010030589

Presents the life and career of the children's author and illustrator Theodor Geisel, better known as Dr. Seuss, famous for timeless children's books, including "The Cat in the Hat" and "How the Grinch stole Christmas."

Shakespeare, William, 1564-1616

Stanley, Diane. **Bard** of Avon: the story of William Shakespeare. Diane Stanley and Peter Vennema; illustrated by Diane Stanley. Mulberry Paperback Book, 1998, c1992. 1 v. (unpaged)

Grades: 4 5 6 7   **B**

1. Dramatists, English Early modern, 1500-1700 2. Theater -- History 16th century. 3. Authors, English 4. Theater -- History 17th century.

ISBN 0688162940

LC BL 98008442

A brief biography of the world's most famous playwright, using only historically correct information.

"A remarkably rounded picture of Shakespeare's life and the period in which he lived is presented . . . together with a thoughtful attempt to relate circumstances in his personal life to the content of his plays. . . . The text is splendidly supported by the illustrations, which are stylized, yet recognizable, and present a clear view of life in the late sixteenth century. A discerning, knowledgeable biography, rising far above the ordinary." Horn Book.

Includes bibliographical references.

Shakur, Tupac, 1971-1996

Harris, Ashley Rae. **Tupac** Shakur: multi-platinum rapper. Ashley Rae Harris. ABDO Pub. Co., c2010. 112 p.: Lives cut short

Grades: 5 6 7 8   **B**

1. Rap musicians 2. Rap music industry and trade 3. African Americans

ISBN 9781604537918

LC 2009034356

"This discusses Tupac Shakur's early life, providing details that give insight into later success and troubles and maintaining a laudatory tone that focuses on the individual's artistic achievements and hard work to achieve fame. Details [such as] explaining . . . that Tupac Shakur was a standout student in high school are bound to resonate with readers.

Numerous photos and sidebars appear throughout. [A] worthwhile [resource] for reports as well as popular reading." School Library Journal.

Includes bibliographical references and index.

Sharp, Tori

Sharp, Tori. **Just** pretend. Tori Sharp Little Brown & Co 2021 320 p.

Grades: 4 5 6 7   **B**

1. Children of divorced parents 2. Middle school students 3. Seventh grade girls 4. Interpersonal relations 5. Bullying and bullies 6. Allentown, New Jersey 7. New Jersey 8. Autobiographical comics 9. Comics and Graphic novels

ISBN 9780316538893

Shuffling between the homes of parents who still treat her like a kid, Tori turns to her writing to make sense of the complexities of her fractured family and its impact on her friendships.

"A rich and deeply felt slice of life." Kirkus

Sheba, Queen of

Lucks, Naomi. **Queen** of Sheba. Naomi Lucks. Chelsea House, 2008. 128 p.: Ancient world leaders

Grades: 6 7 8 9   **B**

1. Rulers 2. Women rulers 3. Sabaeans -- Rulers 4. Yemen (Republic) -- History.

ISBN 9780791095799

LC 2008004872

"This biography of the Queen of Sheba references various oral traditions from Europe, the Middle East, and Ethiopia to reveal aspects of the woman's personality. Classical paintings and full-color photographs of sculptures, landscapes, and archaeological finds complement the text. . . . The [text is] easily digestible and appropriate for the intended age group." School Library Journal.

Includes bibliographical references and index.

Shelley, Mary Wollstonecraft, 1797-1851

Judge, Lita. **Mary's** monster: love, madness, and how Mary Shelley created Frankenstein. Lita Judge. Roaring Brook Press, 2018. 320 p.

Grades: 8 9 10 11 12   **B**

1. Authors, English 19th century 2. Authors, English 3. Women

ISBN 9781626725003

A free verse biography of Mary Shelley, the author of Frankenstein, featuring over 300 pages of black-and-white watercolor illustrations.

Wells, Catherine, 1955-. **Strange** creatures: the story of Mary Shelley. by Catherine Wells. Morgan Reynolds, c2009. 160 p.: World writers

Grades: 7 8 9 10   **B**

1. Authors, English 19th century 2. Women authors 3. Authors, English 4. Women

ISBN 9781599350929

LC 2008039042

"This engaging biography limns [Mary Shelley's] unconventional life, focusing on her love affair (and later marriage) with poet Percy Bysshe Shelley, the writing of Frankenstein when she was still a teenager, and the novel's infamy and lasting influence. Period illustrations and photographs appear throughout." Horn Book Guide.

Includes bibliographical references and index.

Shiner, Michael, 1805-1880

Bolden, Tonya. **Capital** days: Michael Shiner's journal and the growth of our nation's capital. by Tonya Bolden. Abrams Books for Young Readers, 2015. 56 p.

Grades: 4 5 6   **B**
1. African Americans 2. Freed people 3. Enslaved people 4. Washington (DC) -- History -- 19th century. 5. Washington, DC -- Race relations 6. Diaries
ISBN 9781419707339

LC 2014024668

This book for young readers tells the story of Washington, D.C., through the story of an African American man, Michael Shiner, who lived there from approximately 1804 to 1880 and who kept a journal, excerpts of which are interspersed throughout the heavily illustrated text. Provided by publisher.

Shivack, Nadia

Shivack, Nadia. **Inside** out: portrait of an eating disorder. written and illustrated by Nadia Shivack. Atheneum Books for Young Readers, c2005. 64 p.

Grades: 7 8 9 10 11 12   **B**
1. Teenagers 2. Teenage girls -- Body image 3. Teenage girls -- Health 4. Young women -- Health 5. Young women -- Body image 6. Comics and Graphic novels
ISBN 0689852169

LC 2004016096

"In this heartfelt, honest memoir, the author uses a graphic novel format to reveal her anguished, ongoing struggle with bulimia. . . . Though intensely personal and—perhaps of necessity—repetitious, this harrowing chronicle may well provide support and solace to teens facing a similar crisis." Publishers Weekly.

Siegal, Aranka, 1930-

Siegal, Aranka, 1930-. **Memories** of Babi. Aranka Siegal. Farrar Straus Giroux, 2008. 128 p.

Grades: 4 5 6 7   **B**
1. Jewish children 2. Grandparent and child
ISBN 0374399786

LC 2007007002

"Siegal's Upon the Head of the Goat (1981) is about her childhood in Hungary as Hitler comes to power. In this follow-up, written in nine wry sketches, she remembers the years before that—especially her close relationship with her Jewish grandmother, who lived on a small farm just across the Hungarian border in Ukraine." Booklist.

Siegal, Aranka, 1930-. **Upon** the head of the goat: a childhood in Hungary, 1939-1944. Aranka Siegal. Farrar, Straus and Giroux, 2003, c1981. 213 p.

Grades: 6 7 8 9   **B**
1. Jews, Ukrainian 2. Holocaust (1933-1945) 3. Ukraine
ISBN 0374480796

LC BL2003005080

Nine-year-old Piri describes the bewilderment of being a Jewish child during the 1939-1944 German occupation of her hometown (then in Hungary and now in Ukraine) and relates the ordeal of trying to survive in the ghetto.

"The story is familiar . . . but a few pages into Aranka Siegal's fine memoir . . . you feel the power and interest of her particular experience and remember that this story cannot be told too often." Newsweek.

Sís, Peter, 1949-

★ Sís, Peter, 1949-. The **wall**: growing up behind the Iron Curtain. Peter Sís. Farrar, Straus and Giroux, 2007. 56 p.

Grades: 4 5 6 7 8 9 10   **B**
1. Illustrators 2. Authors, American 20th century 3. Cold War 4. Czech Americans 5. Czechoslovakia -- Social conditions -- 1945-1992. 6. Czechoslovakia -- History -- 1945-1992.
ISBN 0374347018

LC 2006049149

Robert F. Sibert Informational Book Medal, 2008.

Annotated illustrations, journals, maps, and dreamscapes take readers on an extraordinary journey of how the artist-author's life was shaped while growing up in Czechoslovakia during the Cold War, as well as the influence of western culture through the influx of banned books, music, and news, in a powerful graphic memoir.

"The author pairs his remarkable artistry with journal entries, historical context and period photography to create a powerful account of his childhood in Cold War-era Prague." Publishers Weekly.

Sitting Bull, 1831-1890

★ Nelson, S. D.. **Sitting** Bull: Lakota warrior and defender of his people. S.D. Nelson. Abrams Books for Young Readers, 2015. 55 p.

Grades: 4 5 6   **B**
1. Dakota Indians 2. Hunkpapa Indians -- History 3. Indians of North America 4. Hunkpapa Indians -- Rulers
ISBN 9781419707315

LC 2014045761

Describes the life and accomplishments of the leader of the Sioux nation, detailing his resistance against the United States government, particularly at the Battles of Killdeer Mountain and Little Bighorn, and highlighting his legacy.

"A tragic true story told in powerfully subdued tones." Booklist.
Includes bibliographical references (page 54) and index.

Stanley, George Edward. **Sitting** Bull: great Sioux hero. by George Edward Stanley. Sterling, c2010. 128 p.: Sterling biographies

Grades: 7 8 9 10   **B**
1. Dakota Indians 2. Chiefs (Political anthropology) 3. Hunkpapa Indians 4. Indians of North America 5. Little Big Horn, Battle of the, 1876
ISBN 9781402768460

LC 2009024141

Presents the life of the famous Sioux chief, from his youth and participation in the Battle of the Little Bighorn to his involvement in many of the Native American conflicts of his time.

Skomal, Gregory

Montgomery, Sy. The **great** white shark scientist. Sy Montgomery. Houghton Mifflin Harcourt, [2016] 80 p.: Scientists in the field (Houghton Mifflin)

Grades: 5 6 7 8 9   **B**
1. Great white shark 2. Marine animals 3. Marine biologists 4. Vocational guidance 5. Sharks
ISBN 9780544352988

LC oc2015050630

The Great White Shark Scientist is the latest ocean adventure from the venerable team of Sy Montgomery and Keith Ellenbogen. In it, they follow Dr. Greg Skomal, biologist and head of the Massachusetts Shark Research Program, as he strives to better understand the habits and habitats of Great Whites in order to save this amazing, if maligned, creature of the deep."

"This appreciative introduction to a much-maligned species will thrill readers while it encourages them to see great white sharks in a new way." Kirkus.

Includes bibliographical references.

Sotomayor, Sonia, 1954-

Sotomayor, Sonia, 1954-. The **beloved** world of Sonia Sotomayor. written by Sonia Sotomayor. Delacorte Books for Young Readers, 2018. 352 p.

Grades: 6 7 8 9   **B**
   1. United States. Supreme Court -- Officials and employees 2. Hispanic American women 3. Judges 4. Children of immigrants 5. Determination (Personal quality) 6. Families
ISBN 9781524771157

LC 2018014386

An adaptation for middle graders based on the bestselling adult memoir, My Beloved World, in which the Associate Justice of the Supreme Court, Sonia Sotomayor, details her achievements, which serve as a true testament to the fact that no matter the obstacles, dreams can come true. Includes an 8-page photo insert. Provided by publisher.

Spiegelman, Art

Spiegelman, Art. **Maus**: a survivor's tale. Art Spiegelman. Pantheon Books, 1997. 295 p.

Grades: 7 8 9 10 11 12 Adult   **B**
   1. Auschwitz (Concentration camp) 2. Children of Holocaust survivors 3. Fathers and sons 4. Holocaust (1933-1945) 5. Holocaust survivors 6. Jewish American men 7. Comics and Graphic novels
ISBN 0679406417

LC 96032796

A son struggles to come to terms with the horrific story of his parents and their experiences during the Holocaust and in postwar America, in an omnibus edition of Spiegelman's two-part, Pulitzer Prize-winning best-seller.

"An undisputed classic and award-winning title (including a Pulitzer Prize in 1992) in which renowned cartoonist Spiegelman depicts his father's experiences as a World War II Nazi concentration camp survivor." Library Journal.

Spinelli, Jerry

Spinelli, Jerry. **Knots** in my yo-yo string: the autobiography of a kid. by Jerry Spinelli. Knopf, c1998. 148 p.

Grades: 4 5 6 7   **B**
   1. Authors, American 20th century 2. Children's literature authors, American 20th century 3. Italian Americans 4. Pennsylvania -- Social life and customs -- 20th century 5. Norristown, Pennsylvania -- Social life and customs -- 20th century
ISBN 9780679887911

LC 97030827

This Italian-American author and illustrator presents a humorous account of his childhood and youth in Norristown, Pennsylvania.

"There is an everyboy universality to Spinelli's experiences, but his keen powers of observation and recall turn the story into a richly rewarding personal history." Horn Book Guide.

Starr, Ringo, 1940-

Roberts, Jeremy, 1956-. The **Beatles**: music revolutionaries. by Jeremy Roberts.s Twenty-First Century Books, c2011. 112 p.: Lifeline biographies

Grades: 6 7 8 9 10   **B**
   1. Beatles (Musical group) 2. Rock musicians 3. Bands (Music) 4. Musicians 5. Rock music
ISBN 9780761364214

LC 2010031041

Tells the story of the Beatles, describing how the group began, their phenomenal success and influence, the breakup of the group, and their separate musical careers.

"This takes readers on an accessible tour of the band's rollicking run from Liverpool's underground scene to its nearly decade-long perch atop the charts. Written in a straightforward, reportorial style, . . . the book offers a fine dissection of the Beatle phenomenon. . . . As easy on the eyes as it is fun to read." Booklist.

Includes bibliographical references, discography (p. 106-107), filmography(p. 108), and index.

Steinem, Gloria, 1934-

Conkling, Winifred. **Ms.** Gloria Steinem: A Life. Winifred Conkling. Feiwel & Friends, 2020. 320 p.

Grades: 8 9 10 11 12   **B**
   1. Feminism 2. Women political activists 3. Women's movement 4. Feminists 5. Gender role
ISBN 9781250244574

Documenting everything from her boundary-pushing journalistic career to the foundation of Ms. magazine to being awarded the 2013 Presidential Medal of Freedom, Winifred Conkling's Ms. Gloria Steinem: A Life is a meticulously researched YA biography that is sure to satisfy even the most voracious of aspiring glass-ceiling smashers.

"Conkling's biography describes the life of feminist icon Gloria Steinem. An enlightening, high-quality narrative history of a woman and her work as a leader of American feminism." School Library Journal

Stewart, Kimberly

Swinburne, Stephen R.. **Sea** turtle scientist. by Stephen R. Swinburne. Houghton Mifflin Books for Children, Houghton Mifflin Harcourt, 2013. 80 p.: Scientists in the field (Houghton Mifflin)

Grades: 5 6 7 8 9   **B**
   1. Sea turtles 2. Leatherback turtle -- Research 3. Rare and endangered animals 4. Scientists 5. Wildlife conservation
ISBN 9780547367552

LC 2012034045

This compelling addition to the award-winning Scientists in the Field series explores the leatherback sea turtle's remarkable natural history and recounts the extraordinary efforts being made by scientists trying to save them.

"This refreshing journey with a dedicated woman hard at work in her chosen field will resonate with readers." School Library Journal.

Su, Shi, 1037-1101

Demi. **Su** Dongpo: Chinese genius. by Demi. Lee & Low Books, 2006. 56 p.

Grades: 4 5 6 7   **B**
   1. 11th century 2. Authors, Chinese 3. Nature 4. Politicians 5. Civil engineers 6. Poets, Chinese 7. China -- History -- 11th century.
ISBN 1584302569

LC 2005030437

A biography of Su Dongpo, Chinese poet, civil engineer, and statesman, whose appreciation for nature and justice were evident in his works and led him to experience both triumph and adversity in 11th century China. Provided by publisher.

"Beautifully designed and produced, the book features delicately limned, brilliantly colored paintings of scenes from Su Dongpo's life, outlined in scarlet and bordered with thin bands of gold. A visually striking introduction to the man sometimes referred to as Su Shi or Su Tung-po." Booklist.

Sullivan, Annie, 1866-1936

Delano, Marfe Ferguson. **Helen's** eyes: a photobiography of Annie Sullivan, Helen Keller's teacher. by Marfe Ferguson Delano. National Geographic, 2008. 64 p.

Grades: 4 5 6 7   **B**
1. Children who are blind 2. Teachers
ISBN 1426302096

A photobiography of Annie Sullivan.

"There are many biographies of Helen Keller and Annie Sullivan, but this one is very nicely done. . . . The book is honest in its portrayals, especially of Sullivan. . . . What makes this oversize book so appealing is the clean design, with large typeface. The many fascinating photographs are sometimes placed over historical documents." Booklist.

Tarbell, Ida M. (Ida Minerva), 1857-1944

McCully, Emily Arnold. **Ida** M. Tarbell: the woman who challenged big business--and won! by Emily Arnold McCully. Clarion Books/Houghton Mifflin Harcourt, [2014] 336 p.

Grades: 7 8 9 10   **B**
1. Journalists 2. Investigative journalism 3. Gender role 4. Corruption 5. Women
ISBN 9780547290928

                                        LC 2012039650

"McCully expertly brings to life the story of a unique and determined woman in this well-written and thoroughly researched biography, filled with numerous and pertinent photographs." School Library Journal.

Includes bibliographical references and index.

Tecumseh, Shawnee Chief, 1768-1813

Zimmerman, Dwight Jon. **Tecumseh**: Shooting Star of the Shawnee. by Dwight Jon Zimmerman. Sterling, c2010. 128 p.: Sterling biographies

Grades: 7 8 9 10   **B**
1. Chiefs (Political anthropology) 2. Native American leadership 3. Shawnee Indians -- Wars 1750-1815. 4. Shawnee Indians 5. Indians of North America
ISBN 9781402768477

"Lots of detailed physical battles dominate Tecumseh, with a strong focus on the Shawnee's brutal displacement by white settlers and the Indians caught up in the tensions between the U.S. and Great Britain. . . . [The] spacious design is highly scannable, with color background screens, photos, maps, and historic prints throughout." Booklist.

Tesla, Nikola, 1856-1943

Yount, Lisa. **Nikola** Tesla: harnessing electricity. Lisa Yount. Chelsea House, c2011. 128 p.: Trailblazers in science and technology

Grades: 7 8 9 10 11 12   **B**
1. Electrical engineers 2. Inventors
ISBN 9781604136708

                                        LC 2010052627

Chronicles the life and career of Nikola Tesla, world-reknowned inventor and engineer, and the legend behind alternating current.

Thomas, George Henry, 1816-1870

Bobrick, Benson, 1947-. The **Battle** of Nashville: General George H. Thomas & the most decisive battle of the Civil War. Benson Bobrick. Alfred A. Knopf Books for Young Readers, c2010. 132 p.

Grades: 7 8 9 10   **B**
1. Nashville, Battle of, 1864 2. Military campaigns 3. Battles 4. Civil war 5. United States Civil War, 1861-1865 6. United States -- History -- Civil War, 1861-1865 7. Tennessee -- History -- Civil War, 1861-1865
ISBN 9780375848872

                                        LC 2009054072

This volume profiles the career of General George H. Thomas, and his role in winning the Civil War. While the book focuses on the Battle of Nashville, it also examines his other experiences during the Civil War.

"Background, strategies, and key individuals involved in the 1864 battle of Nashville come to life in this engaging piece of history. Starting on the eve of the fighting, the narrative then shifts back to examine the complex series of events leading to that moment, outlining the causes of the Civil War, key developments, and major figures. . . . Battle scenes are vivid, capturing the chaos and emotion involved, and military strategies, such as the innovative use of cavalry, are explained clearly. Plentiful illustrations from the period, including many portraits and several dramatic two-page paintings, help bring the period to life." School Library Journal.

Includes bibliographical references (p. 127-130) and index.

Thoreau, Henry David, 1817-1862

McCurdy, Michael. **Walden** then & now: an alphabetical tour of Henry Thoreau's pond. Michael McCurdy. Charlesbridge, 2010. 32 p.

Grades: 4 5 6 7   **B**
1. Natural history 2. Walden Woods, Massachusetts 3. Alphabet books
ISBN 9781580892537

                                        LC 2009026645

An alphabet book contains rhymes featuring items from A to Z that symbolize Thoreau's Walden retreat, with paragraphs explaining their connection to the pond and Thoreau's sojourn there.

"Elegiac woodcarvings evoke the setting of Henry Thoreau's Walden Pond as the text weaves past and present in this lengthy alphabet poem. On each spread, consecutive letters face one another, making a couplet of the lines. A dark, but not somber, woodcarving illustrates each letter, and an explanatory paragraph expands upon the information in the verse. . . . The book ends with entries from Thoreau's diary and McCurdy's inspiration and starting point for this book. Purchase as an introduction to Thoreau and for poetry shelves." School Library Journal.

Thorpe, Jim, 1887-1953

Labrecque, Ellen. **Jim** Thorpe: an athlete for the ages. by Ellen Labrecque. Sterling, c2010. 124 p.: Sterling biographies

Grades: 7 8 9 10   **B**
1. Athletes 2. Native American athletes 3. Sports
ISBN 9781402771507

                                        LC 2009024231

Loads of information is packed into each title of this series about world inventors, innovative thinkers and great athletes, including timelines, sidebars, a glossary, maps, rare photographs and world-class writing that make these books accessible and dramatic.

"This biography of Native American athlete Jim Thorpe is studded with quotes and illustrated with photos. . . . [It] details his taking of Olympic gold in the 1912 decathlon and pentathlon events, though he was forced to return the medals the following year amid charges of professionalism, a matter resolved in his favor 70 years later. Written in a straightforward, journalistic style, [this biography presents a] very readable [account] of the [life] of [an athlete] who made [his mark] on American culture." Booklist.

Includes bibliographical references and index.

Thrash, Maggie

Thrash, Maggie. **Honor** girl: a graphic memoir. Maggie Thrash. Candlewick Press, 2015. 272 p.

Grades: 7 8 9 10 11 12　　　　　　　　　　**B**
1. Self-discovery in teenage girls 2. Teenage girl/girl relations 3. Summer camps 4. First loves 5. Fifteen-year-old girls 6. Appalachian Region, Southern 7. Kentucky 8. LGBTQIA comics 9. Autobiographical comics 10. Comics and Graphic novels
ISBN 9780763673826

LC 2014951805

"Thrash finds both heartwarming support from her friends and smarmy disapproval from adults in the southern camp, and although she doesn't deny her burgeoning feelings, her revelation doesn't result in easy confidence, either. Though the understated artwork might not appeal to all readers, this honest, raw, and touching graphic memoir will resonate with teens coming to terms with identities of all stripes." Booklist.

Thrash, Maggie. **Lost** soul, be at peace. Maggie Thrash Candlewick Press, 2018. 187 p.

Grades: 7 8 9 10 11 12　　　　　　　　　　**B**
1. Teenage girls 2. Depression 3. Mental illness 4. Self-discovery in teenage girls 5. Lost cats 6. Autobiographical comics 7. Comics and Graphic novels
ISBN 9780763694197

A graphic memoir follow-up to Honor Girl revisits the author's baffling struggles with teen depression and how a search for her cat, who went missing somewhere in the walls of her cavernous home, became a metaphor for her poignant search for herself.

Thumb, Tom, 1838-1883

Sullivan, George, 1927-. **Tom** Thumb: the remarkable true story of a man in miniature. by George Sullivan. Clarion Books, c2010. 208 p.

Grades: 6 7 8 9　　　　　　　　　　　　　**B**
1. 19th century 2. Little people 3. Exploitation 4. Social acceptance 5. Freaks (Entertainers) 6. Dwarfism
ISBN 9780547182032

LC 2009052910

When Charles S. Stratton was born in 1838, he seemed perfect in every way. But then he stopped growing. At age four, though a happy and mischievous child, he was just over two feet tall and weighed fifteen pounds—the exact size he had been as a seven-month-old baby. It was then that P. T. Barnum persuaded Charley's family to allow him to exhibit their son in his museum and tour him around the world as a curiosity.

"Insets on dwarfism appear early in the text, elucidating Tom Thumb's condition for readers without seriously interrupting the genial flow of the narration. Generous leading and a large stock of photographs and period reproductions will entice readers who shy away from longer works of nonfiction." Bulletin of the Center for Children's Books.

Thunberg, Greta, 2003-

Marcovitz, Hal. **Greta** Thunberg: climate activist. Hal Marcovitz. ReferencePoint Press, 2021. 80 p.

Grades: 6 7 8 9 10 11 12　　　　　　　　　**B**
1. Child environmentalists 2. Environmentalists 3. Climate change
ISBN 9781682829233

LC 2020005613

Scientists have been warning about the catastrophes that could be caused by climate change for several decades, but governmental leaders have done relatively little to address the problem. Many governmental leaders fear that reigning in the industries and lifestyles responsible for warming the planet's atmosphere would severely impact the economies of their nations, leading to job loss, poverty and other ills. In the face of this inaction, Thunberg's activism to combat global warming has ignited a spark-particularly among teens and other young people. Provided by publisher.

"The straightforward, accessibly written text includes short pullout sections on a variety of topics and occasional photographs. Informative and well-sourced, this holds appeal for young activists." Kirkus

Includes bibliographical references (pages 62-67) and index.

Tillage, Leon Walter, 1936-

★ Tillage, Leon Walter, 1936-. **Leon's** story. Leon Tillage, with pictures by Susan L. Roth. Farrar Straus Giroux, 1997. 107 p.

Grades: 4 5 6 7 8　　　　　　　　　　　　**B**
1. African Americans 2. Civil Rights Movement 3. Civil rights 4. Race relations 5. Prejudice 6. North Carolina -- Race relations. 7. Fuquay-Varina, North Carolina
ISBN 0374343799

LC 96043544

Carter G. Woodson Book Awards: Elementary Level, 1998.

The son of a North Carolina sharecropper recalls the hard times faced by his family and other African Americans in the first half of the twentieth century and the changes that the civil rights movement helped bring about.

"The author's voice is direct, the words are simple. There is no rhetoric, no commentary, no bitterness. . . . This quiet drama will move readers of all ages . . . and may encourage them to record their own family stories." Booklist.

Tolkien, J. R. R. (John Ronald Reuel), 1892-1973

Neimark, Anne E.. **Mythmaker**: the life of J.R.R. Tolkien, creator of The hobbit and The lord of the rings. Anne E. Neimark. Harcourt Children's Books, 2012, c1996. vii, 126 p.

Grades: 4 5 6　　　　　　　　　　　　　　**B**
1. Authors, English 20th century 2. Fantasy fiction writing 3. Authors 4. Middle Earth (Imaginary place) 5. Authors, English
ISBN 9780547997346

LC bl2012030753

Follows the life and work of the renowned fantasy writer, creator of hobbits and Middle Earth and "The Lord of the Rings."

Toussaint L'Ouverture, 1743-1803

★ Rockwell, Anne F.. **Open** the door to liberty!: a biography of Toussaint L'Ouverture. by Anne Rockwell; illustrated by R. Gregory Christie. Houghton Mifflin Co., 2009. 80 p.

Grades: 5 6 7 8　　　　　　　　　　　　　**B**
1. Revolutionaries 2. Generals 3. Slavery -- History 18th century. 4. Enslaved people's resistance and revolts 5. Courage in men 6. Haiti -- History -- Revolution, 1791-1804 7. West Indies
ISBN 9780618605705

Describes how an African slave, Toussaint L'Ouverture, led his fellow slaves of the island of St. Domingue (now Haiti) to revolt against the white plantation owners to gain their freedom and influence the course of world history.

"In this eye-opening biography, Rockwell makes a strong case that Toussaint L'Ouverture is one of the most overlooked heroes of the eighteenth century. A freed slave of the French colony of St. Domingue (what we now know as Haiti), L'Ouverture was 48 when he was so inspired by his people's uprising against the French that he joined them and, through his oratory and strategical skills, became their leader. In 1793, he led history's first triumphant slave rebellion, but the resulting freedom would not last long. . . . Evocative paintings in primary colors help tell the story." Booklist.

Tubman, Harriet, 1820?-1913

Adler, David A.. **Harriet** Tubman and the Underground Railroad. by David A. Adler. Holiday House, 2013. 144 p.
Grades: 5 6 7 8   **B**
> 1. Enslaved people 2. African American women 3. Underground Railroad 4. African Americans 5. United States -- History -- 19th century
ISBN 9780823423651

LC 2012006582

A comprehensive introduction to the life and achievements of the heroic former slave details how after managing her own escape, Harriet Tubman returned 13 times to guide other slaves to freedom along the Underground Railroad, in a portrait that also relates her subsequent contributions as a wartime cook, nurse, spy and suffragist.

Allen, Thomas B.. **Harriet** Tubman, secret agent: how daring slaves and free Blacks spied for the Union during the Civil War. written by Thomas B. Allen; with illustrations by Carla Bauer. National Geographic Society, 2006. 191 p.
Grades: 6 7 8 9   **B**
> 1. Enslaved people 2. Women abolitionists 3. Spies 4. African-American spies -- History Civil War, 1861-1865. 5. Enslaved people's resistance and revolts 6. United States -- History -- Civil War, 1861-1865.
ISBN 0792278895

LC 2005030927

"Allen brings readers much more than the usual biography of the brave rescuer on the Underground Railroad. This small, packed volume tells of Harriet Tubman's astonishing roles as spy, secret agent, and military leader, and it combines her personal story with a history of the abolitionist movement and the Civil War, focusing on how ex-slaves and free blacks served the Union cause. . . . The dense history is illustrated with numerous archival images, maps, and woodcuts, and the documentation is meticulous." Booklist.

Includes bibliographical references and index.

Hale, Nathan, 1976-. The **underground** abductor: an abolitionist tale. Nathan Hale. Harry N Abrams Inc., 2015 128 p.: Nathan Hale's hazardous tales
Grades: 3 4 5 6 7   **B**
> 1. African American women 2. Underground Railroad 3. Antislavery movements -- History 19th century. 4. African Americans 5. Enslaved people 6. Comics and Graphic novels
ISBN 9781419715365

"Although several children's books about Tubman exist (all conveniently listed in a bibliography), the author injects danger, espionage, and slapstick humor into his work, as he peels back the layers of this courageous woman's rebellion." School Library Journal.

Twain, Mark, 1835-1910

Caravantes, Peggy, 1935-. A **great** and sublime fool: the story of Mark Twain. Peggy Caravantes. Morgan Reynolds Pub., c2009. 176 p.: World writers
Grades: 7 8 9 10   **B**
> 1. Authors, American 19th century 2. Humorists 19th century 3. Journalists
ISBN 9781599350882

LC 2008034139

Presents the life of Mark Twain, a steamboat pilot who became the great American humorist and writer of the 19th century.

"This offers a workmanlike but readable account of one of America's first great writers. . . . A nice selection of photographs and artwork complement the narrative. . . . Detailed source notes and an in-depth time line round out this even and reliable . . . biography." Booklist.

Includes bibliographical references (p. 170-173) and index.

★ Fleischman, Sid, 1920-2010. The **trouble** begins at 8: a life of Mark Twain in the wild, wild West. Sid Fleischman. Greenwillow Books, c2008. 220 p.
Grades: 5 6 7 8   **B**
> 1. 19th century 2. Authors, American 19th century 3. Humorists 19th century 4. Journalists 19th century 5. Boys 6. The West (United States)
ISBN 9780061344329

A biography of Mark Twain.

"Fleischman writes a charming biography of Samuel Clemens before he became Mark Twain, the great American novelist. . . . Written with a sense of humor and wit that honors Twain, this book is sprinkled with famous Twain quotes, excerpts of his writing, and pictures of Twain and other primary documents from the era Clemens spent both on the Mississippi River and in the West." Voice of Youth Advocates.

Includes bibliographical references.

Sonneborn, Liz. **Mark** Twain. Liz Sonneborn. Chelsea House, 2010. 125 p.: Who wrote that?
Grades: 6 7 8 9 10   **B**
> 1. Authors, American 19th century 2. Humorists 19th century 3. Children's literature writing
ISBN 9781604137286

LC 2010006601

"This biography of Mark Twain begins with the writer's memorable visit to his Missouri hometown in 1902, then tracks back to his early days and his well-known transformation from Sam Clemens to Mark Twain. Sonneborn deals with her material well, hitting all the highlights and keeping the narrative moving along. Good use of details adds interest. . . . A solid purchase." School Library Journal.

Includes bibliographical references and index.

Typhoid Mary, 1869-1938

Bartoletti, Susan Campbell. **Terrible** Typhoid Mary: a true story of the deadliest cook in America. by Susan Campbell Bartoletti. Houghton Mifflin Harcourt, [2015] 240 p.
Grades: 6 7 8 9 10   **B**
> 1. 1910s 2. Typhoid fever 3. Quarantine 4. Women cooks 5. Communicable diseases 6. Diseases 7. New York City -- Social life and customs.
ISBN 9780544313675

LC 2014023057

What happens when a person's reputation has been forever damaged? With archival photographs and text among other primary sources, this riveting biography of Mary Mallon by the Sibert medalist and Newbery Honor winner Susan Bartoletti looks beyond the tabloid scandal of Mary's controversial life.

"This well-researched biography of Mary Mallon, also known as Typhoid Mary, begins in 1906, when Mallon was hired as a cook for a wealthy family vacationing in Oyster Bay, Long Island. The outbreak of typhoid that swept through the household a few weeks later turned out to be a pivotal event that forever changed her life. . . . Middle grade biography lovers will gravitate toward this compelling title." School Library Journal.

Includes bibliographical references.

Valentino, 1932-

Reis, Ronald A.. **Valentino**. by Ronald A. Reis. Chelsea House, 2011. 120 p.: Famous fashion designers

Grades: 6 7 8 9 10   B

1. Fashion designers 2. Fashion design 3. Clothing industry and trade 4. Fashion
ISBN 9781604139839

LC 2010034101

Profiles the life and career of the famed designer, from his childhood in Italy, the opening of his fashion house, and his recent retirement.

Vedder, Amy

Ebersole, Rene, 1974-. **Gorilla** mountain: the story of wildlife biologist, Amy Vedder. by Rene Ebersole. F. Watts; c2005. ix, 118 p.: Women's Adventures in Science

Grades: 7 8 9 10   B

1. Women scientists 2. Women wildlife biologists 3. Wildlife biologists 4. Gorillas 5. Wildlife conservationists
ISBN 0531167798

LC 2005000823

Describes the life of wildlife biologist Amy Vedder as she earned her graduate degrees, studied and worked in Africa, and raised a family.

"This is interesting, substantive, and eminently readable." School Library Journal.

Includes bibliographical references (p. 109-110) and index.

Verdi, Giuseppe, 1813-1901

Bauer, Helen, 1943-. **Verdi** for kids: his life and music: with 21 activities. Helen Bauer; foreword by Deborah Voigt. Chicago Review Press, [2013], c2013. xvii, 121 p.

Grades: 4 5 6 7   B

1. Composers
ISBN 9781613745007

LC 2012042742

Chronicles the life and career of the renowned Italian composer and includes such activities as making pasta, learning bocce, and crafting a carnival mask.

"This introduction to the towering classical composer sets the story of his life and work in the context of the revolutionary events of early-19th-century Europe. . . . The author's own extensive musical experience contributes to the breadth of this title. Sidebars and historical prints add further information about musical forms and instruments, historical events and people mentioned. . . . This will be particularly useful for parents and classroom teachers hoping to make the study of great music more interesting." Kirkus.

Includes bibliographical references (page 113) and index.

Verne, Jules, 1828-1905

Schoell, William. **Remarkable** journeys: the story of Jules Verne. William Schoell. Morgan Reynolds Pub., c2002. 112 p.: World writers

Grades: 4 5 6 7 8   B

1. Authors, French 19th century 2. Science fiction authors
ISBN 1883846927

LC 2002002016

A biography of the nineteenth-century Frenchman whose childhood love of literature, science, and adventure, along with his vivid imagination, led him to become a highly successful science fiction author.

"Thanks to Schoell's smooth, crisp writing, this fascinating, approachable biography, which lends insight into Verne's eccentric characters and relatives, proves nearly as exciting as the writer's best stories." Booklist.

Includes bibliographical references (p. 107-109) and index.

Versace, Gianni, 1946-1997

Davis, Daniel K.. **Versace**. Daniel K. Davis. Chelsea House, 2011. 112 p.: Famous fashion designers

Grades: 6 7 8 9 10   B

1. Fashion designers 2. Fashion design 3. Clothing industry and trade 4. Fashion
ISBN 9781604139808

LC 2010034103

"Biography collections in need of a bit of sprucing up should find [this title] helpful." School Library Journal.

Includes bibliographical references and index.

Victoria, Queen of Great Britain, 1819-1901

Reef, Catherine. **Victoria**: portrait of a queen. Catherine Reef. Clarion Books, 2017. 208 p.

Grades: 7 8 9   B

1. Victorian era (1837-1901) 2. Rulers 3. Women rulers 4. Political leadership 5. Great Britain -- History -- Victoria, 1837-1901
ISBN 9780544716148

LC 2016050621

A biography for teens on Queen Victoria (1819-1901). Her long reign was filled with drama, death, intrigue, and passion, and took place during a time of great transformation, an era that bears the imprint of her personality and values as well as that ofher name—the Victorian period. Provided by publisher.

"Victoria's personality comes through in the lively narrative, though Reef never shies from the public and personal controversies that Victoria brought on herself. All the necessary context for understanding her life and times is woven through without ever getting in the way." Kirkus.

Includes bibliographical references and index.

Vincent, Erin

Vincent, Erin. **Grief** girl: my true story. Erin Vincent. Delacorte Press, c2007. 306 p.

Grades: 8 9 10 11 12   B

1. Grief in teenagers 2. Bereavement in teenagers 3. Parents -- Death -- Psychological aspects 4. Teenagers and death
ISBN 0385733534

LC 2006011650

The author describes how her parents were killed in a car accident when she was a teenager, and how she and her seventeen-year-old sister and three-year-old brother were left to deal with the pain and hardship while they struggled to survive on their own.

"In 1983, Vincent, then 14, lost both her parents in a road accident. In this poignant memoir, she chronicles her rocky journey through adolescence as she, her 17-year-old sister, Tracy, and their brother, Trent, learn to cope on their own." Booklist.

Wald, Lillian D., 1867-1940

Kaplan, Paul M.. **Lillian** Wald: America's great social and healthcare reformer. Paul M. Kaplan. Pelican Publishing Company, [2018] 112 p.

Grades: 7 8 9 10 11 12   **B**
>   1. Henry Street Settlement (New York, N.Y.). 2. Nurses 3. Social reformers 4. Public health 5. Women social advocates
>   ISBN 9781455623495

                                        LC 2017033545

In this immensely significant biography, Paul Kaplan follows powerful activist Lillian Wald, a social and education reformer dedicated to helping less fortunate citizens in New York. This biography is brilliant for children looking for a strong female role model from the past, for today.

"The book employs sidebars where necessary and is illustrated with archival photographs; all is presented in a conversational, greatly admiring tone. A fascinating introduction to the 'angel of Henry Street' for a new generation." Kirkus

Includes bibliographical references and index.

Walden, Tillie, 1996-

Walden, Tillie, 1996-. **Spinning**. Tillie Walden. First Second, 2017. 395 p.

Grades: 7 8 9 10 11 12   **B**
>   1. Figure skaters 2. Coming out (Sexual or gender identity) 3. Lesbians 4. Cartoonists 5. Figure skating 6. Autobiographical comics 7. Comics and Graphic novels 8. Sports comics
>   ISBN 9781626729407

                                        LC bl2017025193

A graphic memoir recounts the years Walden spent competitively figure skating, before her developing love of art and first girlfriend causes her to question the insular world of figure skating.

"Walden's cumulative growth and courage to speak up for what she actually wants are unmistakable and deeply satisfying. A stirring, gorgeously illustrated story of finding the strength to follow ones own path." Booklist.

Waldman, Neil

Waldman, Neil. **Out** of the shadows: an artist's journey. Neil Waldman. Boyds Mills Press, c2006. 144 p.

Grades: 5 6 7 8   **B**
>   1. Illustrators 2. Jewish artists
>   ISBN 9781590784112

                                        LC 2005021139

Neil Waldman reveals how his passion for art emerged in the kitchen of his family's apartment, where he discovered the work of Van Gogh and the ability to use illustration as a means to escape the sadness that plagued his home.

"Young artists, as well as readers who wonder about the person behind the pictures they have seen, will appreciate every element of this book: well-constructed story, visual richness, and uncompromising honesty." Booklist.

Walker, C. J., 1867-1919

Hobkirk, Lori. **Madam** C.J. Walker: entrepreneur. by Lori Hobkirk. The Child's World, 2021 32 p.: Black American Journey

Grades: 4 5 6 7   **B**
>   1. African American women executives 2. African Americans 3. Hair care products 4. African American businesspeople 5. Women
>   ISBN 9781503853768

Starting a successful business is not an easy task. It was even more difficult for a Black woman to accomplish this in the 1900s. Yet, this is what Madam C.J. Walker did.—Page 5.

"The writing is approachable and the texts are evenhanded. Period photos, drawings, and maps are generous. . . . This is true Black American history everyone should know about." School Library Journal

Includes bibliographical references and index.

Wallace, Alfred Russel, 1823-1913

Dorion, Christiane. **Darwin's** rival: Alfred Russel Wallace and the search for evolution. Christiane Dorion; illustrated by Harry Tennant. Candlewick Studio, an imprint of Candlewick Press, 2020. 64 p.

Grades: 5 6 7 8   **B**
>   1. Naturalists 2. Explorers 3. Evolution -- History 19th century
>   ISBN 9781536209327

Everyone knows Charles Darwin, the famous naturalist who proposed a theory of evolution. But not everyone knows the story of Alfred Russel Wallace, Darwin's friend and rival who simultaneously discovered the process of natural selection. This sumptuously illustrated book tells Wallace's story, from his humble beginnings to his adventures in the Amazon rain forest and Malay Archipelago, and demonstrates the great contribution he made to one of the most important scientific discoveries of all time. Provided by publisher.

"This large, wide-format book offers informative text describing Wallace's adventurous life and evocative illustrations depicting his travels." Booklist

Wallace, Perry

Maraniss, Andrew. **Strong** inside: the true story of how Perry Wallace broke college basketball's color line: young readers edition. Andrew Maraniss. Philomel Books, [2017] 262 p.

Grades: 7 8 9 10   **B**
>   1. Vanderbilt University -- Basketball -- History 2. Vanderbilt Commodores (Basketball team) -- History 3. African American basketball players 4. Racism in sports -- History 20 century 5. Basketball players 6. Civil rights -- History 20th century 7. African Americans 8. Southern States -- Race relations
>   ISBN 9780399548345

                                        LC bl2016054917

A biography of the first African American basketball player in the Southeastern Conference details his struggles against racism, persistence of will, and role as a civil rights trailblazer.

"This moving biography is thought-provoking, riveting and heart-wrenching, though it remains hopeful as it takes readers into the midst of the basketball and civil rights action." Booklist..

Includes bibliographical references (pages 248-251) and index.

Wallenberg, Raoul, 1912-1947

Borden, Louise. **His** name was Raoul Wallenberg. by Louise Borden. Houghton Mifflin Company, 2012. 128 p.

Grades: 7 8 9 10 11 12   **B**
>   1. Righteous Gentiles in the Holocaust 2. Holocaust (1933-1945) 3. World War II -- Jews -- Rescue
>   ISBN 9780618507559

                                        LC 2011003451

Sydney Taylor Book Award for Older Readers, 2013.

"Based on Borden's years of intensive personal research, including interviews and archival sources, this account written in rapid-reading free verse . . . is presented in a spacious, accessible format that includes lots of historic and personal photos, documents, and profiles of victims and heroes. Borden skillfully places the biographical story in historical context. . . . This is an important addition to the Holocaust curriculum." Booklist.

Wang, Vera

Petrillo, Lisa. **Vera** Wang. by Lisa Petrillo. Morgan Reynolds Pub., c2011. 112 p.: Profiles in fashion

Grades: 7 8 9 10 **B**

1. Women fashion designers 2. Fashion designers 3. Women 4. Asian Americans 5. Clothing industry and trade
ISBN 9781599351506

LC 2010017978

"This discusses the fashion designer's cultural background, childhood, family, work history and education. . . . The writing is clear and well organized. Color photos are included and give readers a feel for the time period and the types of clothing and accessories the [designer] created." Voice of Youth Advocates.

Includes bibliographical references (p. 103-105) and index.

Warhol, Andy, 1928-1987

Rubin, Susan Goldman. **Andy** Warhol: pop art painter. by Susan Goldman Rubin. Abrams Books for Young Readers, 2006. 48 p.

Grades: 4 5 6 7 **B**

1. Artists 2. Pop art 3. Pop artists 4. Nonconformists 5. Creativity
ISBN 081095477X

LC 2005013238

"Andy Warhol was a colorful figure who revolutionized how the world looks at art. Rubin's coherent and interesting narrative is filled with quotes by the artist and people who knew him. . . . Excellent-quality black-and-white and full-color photographs of Warhol and his family and reproductions of his paintings and those of others who influenced him appear throughout." School Library Journal.

Includes bibliographical references.

Wasdin, Howard E.

Wasdin, Howard E.. **I** am a SEAL Team Six warrior: memoirs of an American soldier. Howard E. Wasdin and Stephen Templin. St. Martin's Griffin, 2012. vi, 182 p.

Grades: 8 9 10 11 12 **B**

1. United States. Navy. SEALs 2. United States. Navy -- Commando troops 3. Snipers 4. Soldiers 5. Undercover operations 6. Military strategy 7. Military education
ISBN 9781250016430

LC 2012376658

Recounts the story of how the author overcame a tough and abusive childhood to fulfill his dream of joining the exciting and dangerous world of the Navy SEALs by becoming a Special Forces sniper.

Washington, Booker T., 1856-1915

Washington, Booker T., 1856-1915. **Up** from slavery. Booker T. Washington. Penguin Books, 1986, c1901. liii, 332 p.

Grades: 7 8 9 10 11 12 Adult **B**

1. Tuskegee Institute. 2. 19th century 3. African Americans 4. Educators 5. Social advocates 6. Race relations 7. Freed people
ISBN 9780140390513

LC 8516712

The African-American educator documents his struggle for freedom and self-respect and his fight to establish industrial training and educational programs for black Americans.

Washington, George, 1732-1799

Earl, Sari. **George** Washington: revolutionary leader & founding father. by Sari K. Earl. ABDO Pub., c2010. 112 p.: Military heroes

Grades: 7 8 9 **B**

1. United States. Continental Army 2. Generals 3. Presidents 4. Revolutions 5. American Revolution, 1775-1783 6. United States -- History -- Revolution, 1775-1783.
ISBN 9781604539677

LC 2009032372

"The rush of literary adrenaline will hook readers immediately and keep them enthralled until the end. . . . Given the dynamic topic [and] . . . appealing layout . . . [this is] likely to attract reluctant readers. In addition, sources are plentiful and well documented." School Library Journal.

Includes bibliographical references (p. 102, 106-108) and index.

McClafferty, Carla Killough, 1958-. The **many** faces of George Washington: remaking a presidential icon. Carla Killough McClafferty. Carolrhoda Books, c2011. 120 p.: Exceptional social studies titles for intermediate grades

Grades: 6 7 8 9 **B**

1. Statues 2. Presidents 3. Revolutions 4. American Revolution, 1775-1783 5. United States -- History -- Revolution, 1775-1783. 6. United States -- Politics and government -- 1775-1783.
ISBN 9780761356080

LC 2010028178

"With the goal of boosting interest in George Washington, in 2005 Mount Vernon commissioned three life-size reproductions of him at ages 19, 45 and 57. Enthusiastic prose and informative photographs convey in considerable detail the work on this project by a variety of experts, including sculptors, archaeologists, historians, dentists, painters, taxidermists and more. . . . Quotations from Washington and his contemporaries add a personal note, while reproductions of portraits, statues and artifacts supply visual interest. Color photographs show some of the steps in the reconstruction." Kirkus.

Includes bibliographical references and index.

Mooney, Carla, 1970-. **George** Washington: 25 great projects you can build yourself. Carla Mooney; illustrated by Samuel Carbaugh. Nomad Press, 2010. 121 p.: ill., maps; 27 cm.: Build it yourself

Grades: 4 5 6 7 **B**

1. Presidents 2. Handicraft for children 3. Creative activities for children and students
ISBN 9781934670637

"The life of George Washington lends itself remarkably well to a variety of kid-friendly crafts that don't require old-fashioned materials or 18th-century skills. . . . The projects separate biographical chapters that are thorough and clear. . . . Sidebars with vocabulary words, quotes, interesting facts about the man and his time, and What if? questions regarding pivotal moments in Washington's life add to the text. These sidebars, as well as amusing cartoon illustrations, make the subject light and approachable." School Library Journal.

Weber, EdNah New Rider

Weber, EdNah New Rider. **Rattlesnake** Mesa: stories from a native American childhood. by EdNah New Rider Weber; photographs by Richela Renkun. Lee & Low Books, c2004. 132 p.

Grades: 4 5 6 7 **B**

1. Phoenix Indian School -- History. 2. Indians of North America

3. Indian reservations 4. Native American girls 5. Pawnee girls 6. Pawnee Indians 7. Phoenix, Arizona
ISBN 1584302313

LC 2004002385

"Weber describes her experiences with warmth and affection in this unusually compelling memoir. Striking black-and-white photos . . . add to the book's appeal." Horn Book Guide.

Webster, Noah, 1758-1843
Reef, Catherine. **Noah** Webster: man of many words. Catherine Reef. Clarion Books, 2015. 160 p.
Grades: 7 8 9   **B**
1. Lexicographers 2. Educators 3. Teachers
ISBN 9780544129832

LC 2014027803

A biography on Noah Webster, a controversial political activist, the primary shaper of the American language, and author of the Blue-Backed Spellers and the famous dictionary that bears his name. Illustrated with black-and-white archival images. Provided by publisher.

"Though the narrative is occasionally dry, the abundance of information and accessible writing are undeniable, and with a helpful time line, photos and reproductions of primary documents, and a list of additional resources, this volume will be very useful for students working on American history reports." Booklist.

Wharton, Edith, 1862-1937
Wooldridge, Connie Nordhielm. The **brave** escape of Edith Wharton: a biography. by Connie Nordhielm Wooldridge. Clarion Books, 2010. 184 p.
Grades: 7 8 9 10   **B**
1. Authors, American 20th century. 2. Women 3. Women intellectuals 4. Authors, American 5. Gender role
ISBN 9780547236308

LC 2009033574

Reviews the life of the author of "Ethan Frome," a woman well ahead of her time who sought ways to escape her privileged upbringing, surrounded herself with male friends, and was recognized for her generosity during World War I.

"In this thoroughly researched, humanizing biography, Wooldridge writes with lively specifics about both the author and her time. . . . Frequent, well-woven quotes from Wharton's family and friends contribute to a strong sense of an energetic, groundbreaking, and ferociously intelligent writer, but it's the many quotes in Wharton's own voice that leave the most indelible impact." Booklist.

Includes bibliographical references (p. 168-170) and index.

Whitman, Walt, 1819-1892
★ Kerley, Barbara. **Walt** Whitman: words for America. by Barbara Kerley; illustrated by Brian Selznick. Scholastic Press, 2004. 56 p.
Grades: 4 5 6 7   **B**
1. Poets, American 19th century 2. War 3. Nurses 4. Union soldiers 5. Civil war 6. United States -- History -- Civil War, 1861-1865 -- Medical care.
ISBN 9780439357913

LC 2003020085

A biography of the American poet whose compassion led him to nurse soldiers during the Civil War, to give voice to the nation's grief at Lincoln's assassination, and to capture the true American spirit in verse.

"Delightfully old-fashioned in design, [the book's] oversized pages are replete with graceful illustrations and snippets of poetry. The bril-

liantly inventive paintings add vibrant testimonial to the nuanced text." School Library Journal.

Wiesel, Elie, 1928-2016
Koestler-Grack, Rachel A., 1973-. **Elie** Wiesel: witness for humanity. by Rachel Koestler-Grack. Gareth Stevens Pub., 2009. 112 p.: Life portraits
Grades: 7 8 9 10   **B**
1. Holocaust survivors 2. Authors, Jewish 3. Holocaust (1933-1945) 4. Concentration camp survivors 5. Jews, Romanian
ISBN 9781433900549

LC 2008031630

Each title in this series takes an in-depth and critical look at a leading contemporary or historical figure, examining his or her early life, rise to prominence, accomplishments, and lasting influence with the help of time lines, index, and glossary.

"Recounts the struggles . . . [Wiesel] experienced as a Holocaust survivor and as someone who still works to end all violence against humanity. . . . Many photos, images, and sidebars, as well as the expected back matter contribute . . . without being didactic and educate without preaching." Voice of Youth Advocates.

Includes bibliographical references and index.

Wiesenthal, Simon
★ Rubin, Susan Goldman. The **Anne** Frank Case: Simon Wiesenthal's search for the truth. by Susan Goldman Rubin; illustrated by Bill Farnsworth. Holiday House, c2009. 40 p.
Grades: 4 5 6 7   **B**
1. Jews, Austrian 2. Holocaust survivors 3. Nazi hunters 4. Holocaust (1933-1945) 5. Austria
ISBN 9780823421091

LC 2007028396

In 1958, in Linz, Austria, demonstrators interrupted a performance of The Diary of Anne Frank, claiming that Anne Frank never existed. Determined to prove otherwise, Simon Wiesenthal, a Holocaust survivor, set out to find the Gestapo officer who arrested the Franks years before.

Woodson, Jacqueline
★ Woodson, Jacqueline. **Brown** girl dreaming. Jacqueline Woodson. Nancy Paulsen Books, 2014. 240 p.
Grades: 4 5 6 7 8   **B**
1. Women authors, American 2. African American children 3. Growing up 4. Civil Rights Movement 5. African American women 6. South Carolina -- History -- 20th century
ISBN 9780399252518
Coretta Scott King Award, Author Category, 2015.
National Book Award for Young People's Literature, 2014.

In vivid poems that reflect the joy of finding her voice through writing stories, an award-winning author shares what it was like to grow up in the 1960s and 1970s in both the North and the South.

"Here is a memoir-in-verse so immediate that readers will feel they are experiencing the author's childhood right along with her." Horn Book.

Wright, Richard, 1908-1960
Hart, Joyce, 1954-. **Native** son: the story of Richard Wright. Joyce Hart. Morgan Reynolds Pub., c2003. 128 p.: World writers
Grades: 7 8 9 10   **B**
1. Authors, American 20th century 2. African American authors 3.

African Americans
ISBN 1931798060

LC 2002013686

Traces the life and achievements of the twentieth-century African American novelist, whose early life was shaped by a strict grandmother who had been a slave, an illiterate father, and a mother educated as a schoolteacher.

"The writing is accessible and flows smoothly." School Library Journal.

Includes bibliographical references (p. 122-123) and index.

Yasui, Sachiko

★ Stelson, Caren Barzelay. **Sachiko**: a Nagasaki bomb survivor's story. Caren Stelson. Carolrhoda Books, 2016. 144 p.

Grades: 5 6 7 8   **B**

1. Hibakusha 2. Survival (after nuclear warfare) 3. Resilience (Personal quality) 4. Atomic bomb 5. World War II 6. Nagasaki, Japan -- Atomic bombing, 1945. 7. Japan -- History -- 1945-
ISBN 9781467789035

LC 2015043908

Tells the story of the atomic bombing of Nagasaki through the eyes of Sachiko Yasui, who was six when the devastation was wrought, describing her experiences in the aftermath of the attack as well as her long journey to find peace.

"This powerful narrative account of one person finding her voice after insufferable trauma encapsulates a grim era in global history." Publishers Weekly.

Includes bibliographical references and index.

Yep, Laurence, 1948-

Yep, Laurence, 1948-. The **lost** garden. Laurence Yep. Beech Tree Books, 1996, c1991. xi, 116 p.

Grades: 5 6 7 8   **B**

1. Authors, American 20th century 2. Chinese Americans 3. Authors, American 4. San Francisco, California
ISBN 9780688137014

LC 95053801

The author describes how he grew up as a Chinese American in San Francisco and how he came to use his writing to celebrate his family and his ethnic heritage.

"The writing is warm, wry, and humorous. . . . The Lost Garden will be welcomed as a literary autobiography for children and, more, a thoughtful probing into what it means to be an American." School Library Journal.

Yousafzai, Malala, 1997-

Aretha, David. **Malala** Yousafzai and the girls of Pakistan. by David Aretha. Morgan Reynolds Publishing, 2014. 34 p.: Out in front

Grades: 5 6 7 8   **B**

1. Taliban 2. Social reformers 3. Sex discrimination in education 4. Violence against girls 5. Girls -- Education 6. Pakistan -- Social conditions
ISBN 9781599354545

"This biography of the Pakistani girl who survived an assassination attempt by the Taliban provides geographical, historical, and sociopolitical context for Yousafzai's dedication to education activism. Captioned color photographs pair well with the concise and factual text. Important quotes are printed in red, which is difficult to read on some backgrounds. Significant terms are defined in the text. Websites. Bib., ind." Horn Book.

Yousafzai, Malala, 1997-. **I** am Malala: how one girl stood up for education and changed the world. Malala Yousafzai with Patricia McCormick. Little, Brown and Company, 2014. 230 p.

Grades: 5 6 7 8   **B**

1. Taliban 2. Girls -- Education 3. Education 4. Schools 5. Children's rights 6. Victims of crimes 7. Pakistan
ISBN 9780316327930

LC 2014015881

Documents the educational pursuits of the Nobel Peace Prize nominee who became an international symbol of hope and inspiration when she challenged the traditions of her Pakistan community, offering insight into the influential role of her courageous father.

"Young education activist and Taliban victim Malala Yousafzai recounts her Pakistani childhood in this deftly adapted memoir. Domestic and academic tales illustrate her unusual maturity and resilience in the face of increasing Taliban threats. Yousafzai's moving narrative and engaging, sincere voice may provide an entryway to international awareness for middle-grade readers; a map and a thorough timeline provide additional political context." Horn Book.

Zaharias, Babe Didrikson, 1911-1956

Freedman, Russell. **Babe** Didrikson Zaharias: the making of a champion. by Russell Freedman. Clarion Books, c1999. 192 p.

Grades: 5 6 7 8 9 10   **B**

1. Women athletes 2. Olympic athletes 3. Gender role 4. Athletes 5. Women Olympic athletes
ISBN 0395633672

LC 98050208

A biography of Babe Didrikson, who broke records in golf, track and field, and other sports, at a time when there were few opportunities for female athletes.

"Freedman's measured yet lively style captures the spirit of the great athlete. . . . Plenty of black-and-white photos capture Babe's spirit and dashing good looks; the documentation . . . is impeccable." Horn Book.

Includes bibliographical references (p. 179-183) and index.

Lobby, Mackenzie, 1982-. **Babe** Didrikson Zaharias: groundbreaking all-around athlete. by Mackenzie Lobby. ABDO Pub. Co., c2011. 112 p.: Legendary athletes

Grades: 6 7 8 9   **B**

1. Athletes 2. Women athletes 3. Women 4. Olympic athletes 5. Sports
ISBN 9781617147555

LC 2010041158

Tells the story of this athlete's early life, All-Star basketball career, and winning of three medals in track and field at the 1932 Olympics.

"This biography of athlete Babe Didrikson Zaharias goes beyond merely discussing [her] accomplishments. . . . [It] also [explores] the social and political [influence she] had on society as a whole. In addition, [it introduces] historical events in the context of [her life]. . . . This . . . is teeming with information and is a must-purchase for sports fans and readers interested in social activism." School Library Journal.

Includes bibliographical references and index.

Van Natta, Don, 1964-. **Wonder** girl: the magnificent sporting life of Babe Didrikson Zaharias. Don Van Natta Jr. Little, Brown and Co., c2011. 416 p.

Grades: 5 6 7 8   **B**

1. Ladies Professional Golf Association -- History 2. Women athletes 3. Women and sports 4. Women golfers 5. Women

Olympic medal winners 6. United States -- History -- 20th century
ISBN 9780316056991

LC 2010041794

Describes the exceptional life and times of LPGA founder Babe Didrikson, the Texas woman who achieved All-American status in basketball, won gold medals in track and field in the 1932 Olympics, and became the first woman to play against men in a PGA tournament.

"This is an engaging biography.... Van Natta marvelously narrates the forgotten life of the greatest all-around athlete of all time, a story that every American sport fan should relish." Publishers Weekly.

Includes bibliographical references and index.

Wallace, Rich. **Babe** conquers the world: the legendary life of Babe Didrikson Zaharias. Rich Wallace and Sandra Neil Wallace. Calkins Creek Books, 2014 272 p.

Grades: 4 5 6 7 8 **B**

1. Women athletes 2. Children of immigrants 3. Olympic athletes 4. Women 5. Success (Concept)
ISBN 9781590789810

"Babe Didrikson Zaharias is perhaps the most accomplished athlete that young people have never heard of. She was an Olympic track star in the 1932 games, a noted professional basketball player, and a formative member of the LPGA...This is part sports journalism, part narrative nonfiction, and part proof that professional athletes can be exemplary role models for young people." Booklist.

Zapata, Emiliano, 1879-1919

Stein, R. Conrad. **Emiliano** Zapata and the Mexican Revolution. R. Conrad Stein. Morgan Reynolds Pub., c2011. 144 p.: Story of Mexico

Grades: 6 7 8 9 **B**

1. 1910s 2. Generals 3. Revolutionaries 4. Revolutions 5. Mexico -- History -- Revolution, 1910-1920
ISBN 9781599351636

LC 2010041616

Describes the Mexican Revolution in the early twentieth century, focusing on the general Emiliano Zapata, who was considered a leader of the Mexican poor, and discusses his legacy after his death.

"Stein organizes and clearly presents a great deal of information... . The ... format features a chronological text supplemented with useful sidebars and brightened with color illustrations, including many photos, artifacts, and period artworks." Booklist.

Includes bibliographical references (p. 136-140) and index.

Zenatti, Valerie, 1970-

Zenatti, Valerie, 1970-. **When** I was a soldier: a memoir. Valerie Zenatti; translated from the French by Adriana Hunter. Bloomsbury Children's Books, 2005. 235 p.

Grades: 7 8 9 10 **B**

1. Israel. Army 2. 1980s 3. Women soldiers 4. Soldiers 5. Jews, French 6. Jewish women 7. Young women 8. Israel -- History, Military 9. Israel -- History -- 20th century 10. Translations French to English
ISBN 1582349789

LC 2004060888

"A fast, wry, present-tense memoir.... Readers on all sides of the war-peace continuum, here and there, will find much to talk about." Booklist.

FICTION

50 Cent

Playground. 50 Cent, with Laura Moser; illustrations by Lizzi Akana. Razorbill, c2011. 314 p.

Grades: 7 8 9 10 **Fic**

1. African American teenage boys 2. Bullying and bullies 3. Psychotherapy 4. Overweight teenage boys 5. Friendship 6. Long Island, New York 7. Realistic fiction 8. African American fiction
ISBN 9781595144348

"Readers who were ever confused about having a gay parent, or being overweight, or going through a parental breakup, or just wanting to fit in and be accepted by their peers, will relate to Butterball. 50 Cent's debut young adult novel is a quick read that will be great for discussions on a variety of important and timely topics." Voice of Youth Advocates.

Abbott, Tony, 1952-

The **forbidden** stone. by Tony Abbott. Katherine Tegen Books, an imprint of HarperCollinsPublishers, 2014. 304 p.: Copernicus legacy

Grades: 4 5 6 7 **Fic**

1. Copernicus, Nicolaus, 1473-1543. 2. Relics 3. Clues 4. Scientists 5. Quests 6. Secrets 7. Fantasy fiction
ISBN 9780062194473

LC 2013038560

Wade, Lily, Darrell, and Becca fly from Texas to Germany for the funeral of an old family friend. But instead of just paying their respects, they wind up on a dangerous, mind-blowing quest to unlock an ancient, guarded secret that could destroy the fate of the world.

"Four precocious preteens and a distracted astrophysicist travel to Europe to unravel a mystery that has already claimed several lives... . Filled with riddles and ciphers, this first of 12 installments will keep readers intellectually stimulated as well as entertained. The stepbrothers' bond, a budding crush and a mystery that plays off of real historical figures and facts make this more than a pedestrian whodunit. With engaging characters, a globe-trotting plot and dangerous villains, it is hard to find something not to like. Equal parts edge-of-your-seat suspense and heartfelt coming-of-age." Kirkus.

The **summer** of Owen Todd. Tony Abbott. Farrar Straus Giroux, 2017. 224 p.

Grades: 5 6 7 8 **Fic**

1. Child sexual abuse 2. Sexually abused boys 3. Best friends 4. Summer 5. Eleven-year-old boys 6. Cape Cod, Massachusetts 7. Massachusetts 8. Realistic fiction
ISBN 9780374305505

In the touristy town of Cape Cod, eleven-year-old Owen faces a dilemma when his best friend Sean is sexually abused by a trusted adult, but warns Owen not tell anyone what is happening.

"Abbott has done a fine job of dramatizing the books central problem. Books about abuse, especially of boys, are rare for this age group, so happily, this is a good example, and one hopes that it will spark much-needed discussion." Booklist.

Wade and the scorpion's claw. by Tony Abbott. Katherine Tegen Books, an imprint of HarperCollinsPublishers, 2014. 224 p.: Copernicus archives

Grades: 4 5 6 7 **Fic**

1. Relics 2. Kidnapping 3. Secret societies 4. Riddles 5. Blended families 6. Adventure stories
ISBN 9780062314727

LC 2014010026

In this first in a series of six novellas in the Copernicus Legacy series, Wade travels to Hawaii and San Francisco in a race to find one of the twelve ancient relics. Provided by publisher.

"This first in a string of novellas is intended to link each of the six full-length novels in the Copernicus Legacy series. . . . This fast-paced adventure features vivid settings, difficult brainteasers and likable characters." Kirkus.

Abdel-Fattah, Randa

Does my head look big in this? Randa Abdel-Fattah. Orchard Books, 2007. 368 p.
Grades: 7 8 9 10 11 12   **Fic**
    1. Sixteen-year-old girls 2. Teenage girls 3. Teenage boys 4. Muslims 5. Identity (Psychology) 6. Melbourne, Victoria 7. Australia 8. Realistic fiction 9. Teen chick lit
ISBN 9780439919470
    LC 2006029117
Year Eleven at an exclusive prep school in the suburbs of Melbourne, Australia, would be tough enough, but it is further complicated for Amal when she decides to wear the hijab, the Muslim head scarf, full-time as a badge of her faith—without losing her identity or sense of style.

"While the novel deals with a number of serious issues, it is extremely funny and entertaining." School Library Journal.

Ten things I hate about me. Randa Abdel-Fattah. Orchard Books, 2009, c2006. 304 p.
Grades: 7 8 9 10   **Fic**
    1. Muslim teenagers 2. Secret identity 3. Culture conflict 4. Identity (Psychology) 5. Self-acceptance 6. Sydney, New South Wales 7. Realistic fiction 8. Teen chick lit
ISBN 9780545050555
Have you ever hidden something about yourself because of what people might think? Sixteen-year-old Jamilah does it every day. She goes by "Jamie," wears blue-tinted contacts, and bleaches her hair so that no one at her Australian high school will guess her Lebanese heritage, or that she is Muslim. Why? Mostly because the popular students are hateful to anyone they see as different, and they make crazy assumptions—as if all Muslims "fly planes into buildings as a hobby." But living a double life is stressful, and "Jamie" isn't sure how much longer she can keep it up.

"A message of the importance of self-disclosure to maintain loving relationships of all kinds plays itself out as Jamie learns to negotiate her roles as daughter, sister, and friend. Readers will also get an enlightening look at post-9/11 racial tensions outside the U.S. and the problems they pose for Muslim teens." Bulletin of the Center for Children's Books.

★ **Where** the streets had a name. Randa Abdel-Fattah. Scholastic Press, 2010. 313 p.
Grades: 5 6 7 8   **Fic**
    1. Palestinians 2. Arab-Israeli conflict 1993- 3. Soils 4. Best friends 5. Friendship 6. West Bank (Jordan River) 7. Jerusalem, Israel 8. Realistic fiction
ISBN 9780545172929
Thirteen-year-old Hayaat of Bethlehem faces check points, curfews, and the travel permit system designed to keep people on the West Bank when she attempts to go to her grandmother's ancestral home in Jerusalem with her best friend.

"Hayaat chronicles this life-altering journey in the first-person, present tense, giving readers an intimate glimpse into the life of her warm, eccentric Muslim family, who survive despite the volatile political environment. A refreshing and hopeful teen perspective on the Israeli-Palestinian dilemma." Kirkus.

Abdul-Jabbar, Kareem, 1947-

Stealing the game. Kareem Abdul-Jabbar and Raymond Obstfeld. Disney * Hyperion Books, 2015. 304 p.: Streetball crew
Grades: 4 5 6 7   **Fic**
    1. African American boys 2. Brothers 3. Basketball 4. Criminal investigation 5. Middle schools 6. Realistic fiction 7. Mysteries
ISBN 9781423178712
"The shifting structure of the story and a clever series of blind alleys keep readers on tenterhooks. A deft, understated sports thriller with a solid moral compass." Kirkus.

Acampora, Paul

Rachel Spinelli punched me in the face. Paul Acampora. Roaring Brook Press, 2011. 176 p.
Grades: 5 6 7 8   **Fic**
    1. Mother-deserted children 2. Brothers and sisters of children with disabilities 3. Neighbors 4. Friendship 5. Moving to a new state 6. Connecticut 7. Realistic fiction
ISBN 9781596435483
    LC 2010027436
When fourteen-year-old Zachary and his father move to Falls, Connecticut, he spends a summer falling in love, coming to terms with his mother's absence, and forming eclectic friendships.

"Realistic dialogue and poignantly amusing situations . . . all come together to gently flesh out a few months in the lives of people readers will savor getting to know. . . . An outstanding, humane coming-of-age tale of loss, yearning and forgiveness." Kirkus.

Ada, Alma Flor

Yes! We are Latinos. Alma Flor Ada and F. Isabel Campoy; pictures by David Diaz. Charlesbridge, c2013. 96 p.
Grades: 7 8 9 10   **Fic**
    1. Latin Americans 2. Immigrants 3. Immigration and emigration 4. Short stories
ISBN 9781580893831
    LC 2012027214
A collection of stories about young Latinos' immigrant experiences in the United States.

Adams, Douglas, 1952-2001

The **hitchhiker's** guide to the galaxy. Douglas Adams. Harmony Books, 1980, c1979. 215 p.: Hitchhiker series
Grades: 7 8 9 10 11 12 Adult   **Fic**
    1. Misadventures 2. Meaning (Psychology) 3. Life on other planets 4. Aliens (Humanoid) 5. Space flight 6. Science fiction classics 7. Science fiction 8. Humorous stories
ISBN 9780517542095
    LC 80014572
Chronicles the off-beat and occasionally extraterrestrial journeys, notions, and acquaintances of galactic traveler Arthur Dent.

Adams, Richard, 1920-2016

Watership Down. Richard Adams. Macmillan, 1974, c1972. 448 p.: Rabbit tales
Grades: 6 7 8 9 10 11 12 Adult   **Fic**
    1. Rabbits 2. Survival 3. Safety 4. Peace 5. Nature 6. Fantasy fiction 7. Classics
ISBN 0027000303
    LC 73006044
Carnegie Medal, 1972.
In a constant struggle against oppression, a group of rabbits search for peaceful co-existence. Chronicles the adventures of a group of rab-

bits searching for a safe place to establish a new warren where they can live in peace.

Adams, S. J., 1980-

Sparks: the epic, completely true blue, (almost) holy quest of Debbie. S.J. Adams. Flux, 2011. 264 p.

Grades: 8 9 10 11 12   **Fic**

1. Lesbian teenagers 2. Religion 3. Secrets 4. Best friends 5. Crushes (Interpersonal relations) 6. Des Moines, Iowa 7. Humorous stories 8. Realistic fiction 9. Coming-of-age stories

ISBN 9780738726762

LC 2011022913

A sixteen-year-old lesbian tries to get over a crush on her religious best friend by embarking on a "holy quest" with a couple of misfits who have invented a wacky, made-up faith called the Church of Blue.

"Adams has an easy sense of humor . . . and Debbie and her offbeat cohorts are nuanced and authentic as they follow a circuitous path to greater self-awareness and self-reliance." Publishers Weekly.

Adlington, L. J. (Lucy J.), 1970-

The **diary** of Pelly D. by L.J. Adlington. Greenwillow Books, 2005. 282 p.

Grades: 7 8 9 10   **Fic**

1. Construction workers 2. Fourteen-year-old boys 3. Fifteen-year-old girls 4. Teenagers 5. Diarists 6. Dystopian fiction 7. Science fiction

ISBN 0060766158

LC 2004052258

When Toni V, a construction worker on a futuristic colony, finds the diary of a teenage girl whose life has been turned upside-down by holocaust-like events, he begins to question his own beliefs.

"Adlington has crafted an original and disturbing dystopian fantasy told in a smart and sympathetic teen voice." Booklist.

Agosin, Marjorie

I lived on Butterfly Hill. Marjorie Agosin; translated by E.M. O'Connor; illustrated by Lee White. Atheneum Books for Young Readers, 2014. 400 p.: Butterfly Hill

Grades: 5 6 7 8   **Fic**

1. Refugees 2. Parent-separated girls 3. Homesickness 4. Children of physicians 5. Girl refugees 6. Chile 7. Maine 8. Historical fiction 9. Translations

ISBN 9781416953449

Pura Belpre Award for Narrative, 2015.

A tale inspired by the Pinochet takeover of Chile follows the experiences of young dreamer Celeste Marconi, who becomes increasingly alarmed by the disappearances of her neighbors in the wake of political unrest and then is sent away to safety by her loving parents.

"The language is poetic and full of imagery and, while the book is long, it moves at a smooth pace. Occasional illustrations reflect the mood of each phase of the story." School Library Journal.

Aguirre, Ann

Enclave. Ann Aguirre. Feiwel and Friends, 2011. 272 p.: Razorland

Grades: 8 9 10   **Fic**

1. Hunters 2. Zombies 3. Dystopias 4. Corruption 5. Post-apocalypse 6. Dystopian fiction 7. Science fiction

ISBN 9780312650087

LC 2010031039

In the aftermath of war and plague, most of New York City's survivors have moved underground, establishing enclaves where they eke out an existence and hide from zombie-like Freaks. After 15-year-old Deuce, an enclave-dweller, earns the rank of Huntress, she is paired with a mysterious outsider named Fade...and the two of them discover a secret that could destroy their precarious society. .

"Aguirre has created a gritty and highly competent heroine, an equally deadly sidekick/love interest, and a fascinating if unpleasant civilization." Publishers Weekly.

Ahdieh, Renee

Flame in the mist. Renee Ahdieh. G.P. Putnam's Sons, an imprint of Penguin Random House LLC, 2017. 392 p.: Flame in the mist

Grades: 7 8 9 10 11 12   **Fic**

1. Tokugawa period (1600-1868) 2. Disguises 3. Samurai 4. Political intrigue 5. Revenge 6. Arranged marriage 7. Japan 8. Historical fantasy 9. Asian-influenced fantasy

ISBN 9780399171635

The daughter of a prominent samurai in feudal Japan is targeted by a dangerous gang of bandits who want to prevent her political marriage, a situation that compels her to disguise herself as a boy and infiltrate the gang's ranks in order to stop the individual behind the plot.

"Ahdieh delivers an elaborate fantasy set in feudal Japan, where a resilient young woman defies class conventions and gender roles in a quest for vengeance and autonomy." Publishers Weekly.

Ahmed, Samira

Internment. Samira Ahmed. Little, Brown and Company, 2019. 400 p.

Grades: 7 8 9 10 11   **Fic**

1. Muslim teenagers 2. Resistance to government 3. Near future 4. Xenophobia 5. Islamophobia 6. Dystopian fiction

ISBN 9780316522694

Forced into an interment camp for Muslim-American citizens in a near-future United States, 17-year-old Layla Amin helps forge an alliance of new friends and outside sympathizers before becoming the leader of a revolution against the camp's corrupt guards.

"Set shortly after the 2016 presidential election, Ahmed's novel presents a chilling depiction of America, in which U.S. citizens allow themselves to be controlled by prejudice and fear and succumb to the hateful rhetoric of a populist leader." Booklist.

Love, hate & other filters. Samira Ahmed. Soho Teen, [2018] 288 p.

Grades: 8 9 10 11   **Fic**

1. Muslims 2. East Indian Americans 3. Terrorism 4. Dating (Social customs) 5. Teenage boy/girl relations 6. Chicago, Illinois 7. Realistic fiction

ISBN 9781616958473

LC 2017021616

Maya Aziz, seventeen, is caught between her India-born parents' world of college and marrying a suitable Muslim boy and her dream world of film school and dating her classmate, Phil, when a terrorist attack changes her life forever.

"A well-crafted plot with interesting revelations about living as a secular Muslim teen in today's climate." Kirkus.

Al-Mansour, Haifaa, 1974-

The **green** bicycle. Haifaa Al Mansour. Dial Books for Young Readers, [2015] 352 p.

Grades: 5 6 7 8   **Fic**

1. Gender role 2. Bicycles 3. Competition 4. Eleven-year-old

girls 5. Preteen girls 6. Saudi Arabia 7. Coming-of-age stories
ISBN 9780525428060

LC 2015014551

Since girls do not ride bikes in Riyadh, Saudi Arabia, eleven year old Wadjda has to scheme to get her own. Provided by publisher.

"Young readers will easily sympathize with Wadjda's wish for a bike, and they will come away with a deeper understanding of a faraway culture." Booklist.

Alban, Andrea

Anya's war. Andrea Alban. Feiwel and Friends, 2011. 208 p.

Grades: 7 8 9 10 **Fic**

1. 1930s 2. Jewish teenage girls 3. Abandoned infants 4. Immigration and emigration 5. Immigrants, Russian 6. Refugees 7. Shanghai, China 8. China 9. Historical fiction
ISBN 9780312370930

LC 2010037089

In 1937, the privileged and relatively carefee life of a fourteen-year-old Jewish girl, whose family emigrated from Odessa, Ukraine, to Shanghai, China, comes to an end when she finds an abandoned baby, her hero, Amelia Earhart, goes missing, and war breaks out with Japan. Based on the author's family history.

"Most moving are the scenes with the full cast of family characters, who are irritating, irritable, funny, surprising, mean, and prejudiced. Alban also explores the complexities of Anya's Jewish community. . . . An important addition to literature about WWII refugees." Booklist.

Aldredge, Betsy

Sasquatch, love, and other imaginary things. Betsy Aldredge and Carrie DuBois-Shaw. Merit Press, 2017 272 p.

Grades: 7 8 9 10 **Fic**

1. Reality television programs 2. Competition 3. Jewish teenage girls 4. Social classes 5. Sasquatch 6. Realistic fiction
ISBN 9781507202807

Dragged around her whole life by her obsessed yeti-hunting parents, Samantha is humiliated when her parents participate in a reality show under the watch of a contemptuous prep-school crew, including a boy who scorns Samantha's humble Ohio roots.

"Samantha's first-person narration is marked by her sarcastic, wry, and delightfully snarky humor. 'Squatching' doesn't get any funnier than this." Kirkus.

Alegria, Malin

Estrella's quinceanera. Malin Alegria. Simon & Schuster Books for Young Readers, 2006. 272 p.

Grades: 7 8 9 10 **Fic**

1. Mexican Americans 2. Mexican American women 3. Mexican American teenage girls 4. Fourteen-year-old girls 5. Rich girls 6. Realistic fiction
ISBN 0689878095

LC 2005014540

Estrella's mother and aunt are planning a gaudy, traditional quinceanera for her, even though it is the last thing she wants.

"Alegria writes about Mexican American culture, first love, family, and of moving between worlds with poignant, sharp-sighted humor and authentic dialogue." Booklist.

Alender, Katie

The **dead** girls of Hysteria Hall. Katie Alender. Point, an imprint of Scholastic Inc., 2015. 304 p.

Grades: 7 8 9 10 11 12 **Fic**

1. Haunted houses 2. Psychiatric hospitals 3. Ghosts 4. Families

5. Secrets 6. Horror 7. Ghost stories
ISBN 9780545639996

LC 2014046681

Murdered by a spirit in her house, which was previously an insane asylum, sixteen-year-old Cordelia wanders the house, meeting other trapped ghosts and learning the house's dark secrets, searching for a way to save her family, and perhaps herself.

"Alender creates a fascinating, eerie world that turns on a nicely original use of time and features constantly interesting characters." Kirkus.

Alexander, Jill (Jill Shurbet)

The **sweetheart** of Prosper County. Jill Alexander. Feiwel and Friends, 2009. 224 p.

Grades: 7 8 9 10 **Fic**

1. Future Farmers of America 2. Teenage girls 3. Self-confidence 4. Mothers and daughters 5. Fourteen-year-old girls 6. Bullying and bullies 7. Texas
ISBN 9780312548568

LC 2008034757

In a small East Texas town largely ruled by prejudices and bullies, fourteen-year-old Austin sets out to win a ride in the next parade and, in the process, grows in her understanding of friendship and helps her widowed mother through her mourning.

"This is a warm, humorous story. . . . A refreshing picture of teen angst, with realistic dialogue and memorable characters." School Library Journal.

Alexander, Kwame

★ **Booked.** Kwame Alexander Houghton Mifflin Harcourt, 2016. 320 p.: Crossover (Kwame Alexander)

Grades: 5 6 7 8 9 **Fic**

1. Children of divorced parents 2. Boy soccer players 3. Bullying and bullies 4. Soccer 5. Appendectomy 6. Realistic fiction 7. Novels in verse 8. African American fiction
ISBN 9780544570986

Twelve-year-old Nick loves soccer and hates books, but soon learns the power of words as he wrestles with problems at home, stands up to a bully, and tries to impress the girl of his dreams.

"Alexander scores again with this sports-themed verse novel, a companion to his Newbery Medal-winning The Crossover. . . . Emotionally resonant and with a pace like a player on a breakaway." Publishers Weekly.

★ The **crossover**: a basketball novel. Kwame Alexander. Houghton Mifflin Harcourt, 2014. 240 p.: Crossover (Kwame Alexander)

Grades: 6 7 8 9 10 **Fic**

1. Twin brothers 2. Boy basketball players 3. African Americans 4. Coping 5. Fathers and sons 6. Sports fiction 7. Realistic fiction 8. Basketball stories
ISBN 9780544107717
Newbery Medal, 2015.

Fourteen-year-old twin basketball stars Josh and Jordan wrestle with highs and lows on and off the court as their father ignores his declining health.

"Despite his immaturity, Josh is a likable, funny, and authentic character. Underscoring the sports and the fraternal tension is a portrait of a family that truly loves and supports one another. Alexander has crafted a story that vibrates with energy and heart and begs to be read aloud." School Library Journal.

Alexander, Lloyd

The **black** cauldron. Lloyd Alexander. Holt, 1965. 224 p.: Prydain chronicles

Grades: 5 6 7 8   **Fic**

1. Good and evil 2. Wizards 3. Quests 4. Imaginary kingdoms 5. Prydain (Imaginary place) 6. High fantasy 7. Fantasy fiction 8. Classics
ISBN 0805009922

LC 65013868

Trouble again bestirs Prydain as the kingdom must conquer the threat of Arawn, Lord of the Land of Death

The **book** of three. Lloyd Alexander. Holt, 1964. 217 p.: Prydain chronicles

Grades: 5 6 7 8   **Fic**

1. Good and evil 2. Heroes and heroines 3. Quests 4. Pig farming 5. Pigs 6. High fantasy 7. Fantasy fiction 8. Classics
ISBN 0805008748

LC 64018250

"Related in a simple, direct style, this fast-paced tale of high adventure has a well-balanced blend of fantasy, realism, and humor." School Library Journal.

The **foundling,** and other tales of Prydain. Lloyd Alexander; pictures by Margot Zemach. Holt, 1973. 87 p..: Prydain chronicles

Grades: 5 6 7 8   **Fic**

1. Good and evil 2. Magic 3. Imaginary kingdoms 4. Prydain (Imaginary place) 5. High fantasy 6. Fantasy fiction
ISBN 9780030074318

LC 73005964

"The stories are written with vivid grace and humor." Chicago. Children's Book Center [review of 1973 edition]

The **golden** dream of Carlo Chuchio. Lloyd Alexander. H. Holt, 2007. 320 p.

Grades: 5 6 7 8 9   **Fic**

1. Adventurers 2. Treasure hunting 3. Voyages and travels 4. Treasure hunters 5. Love 6. Fantasy fiction 7. Middle Eastern-influenced fantasy
ISBN 9780805083330

LC 2006049710

Naive and bumbling Carlo, his shady camel-puller Baksheesh, and Shira, a girl determined to return home, follow a treasure map through the deserts and cities of the infamous Golden Road, as mysterious strangers try in vain to point them toward real treasures.

"This is an exuberant and compassionate tale of adventure." Publishers Weekly.

The **iron** ring. Lloyd Alexander Dutton Children's Books, 1997. 283 p.

Grades: 5 6 7 8   **Fic**

1. Rulers 2. Quests 3. Voyages and travels 4. Good and evil 5. Fantasy fiction 6. Asian-influenced fantasy
ISBN 0525455973

LC 96-29730

Driven by his sense of dharma, or honor, young King Tamar sets off on a perilous journey, with a significance greater than he can imagine, during which he meets talking animals, villainous and noble kings, demons, and the love of his life. Includes glossary.

"Young Tamar, ruler of a small Indian kingdom, wagers with a visiting king and loses his kingdom and his freedom. Traveling to the king's land to make good on his debt, he collects quite an entourage and eventually overcomes his enemies with his friends' help. This tale offers delightful characters, a philosophical interest in the meaning of life, a thoughtful look at the caste system, and a clever use of Indian animal folktales." Horn Book Guide.

The **remarkable** journey of Prince Jen. Lloyd Alexander. Dutton Children's Books, 1991. 273 p.

Grades: 5 6 7 8   **Fic**

1. Princes 2. Voyages and travels 3. Leadership 4. Legends 5. Resourcefulness 6. Coming-of-age stories 7. Fantasy fiction 8. Asian-influenced fantasy
ISBN 9780525448266

LC 91013720

Carrying six unusual gifts, Young Lord Prince Jen embarks on a perilous journey to the marvelous realm of T'ien-kuo.

"Alexander satisfies the taste for excitement, but his vivid characters and the food for thought he offers will nourish long after the last page is turned." School Library Journal.

Taran Wanderer. Lloyd Alexander. H. Holt, 1999, c1967. ix, 222 p.: Prydain chronicles

Grades: 5 6 7 8   **Fic**

1. Good and evil 2. Identity (Psychology) 3. Quests 4. Heroes and heroines 5. Magic 6. High fantasy 7. Fantasy fiction 8. Classics
ISBN 9780805061345

Tells of the adventures that befell Taran when he went in search of his birthright and the truth about himself.

Westmark. Lloyd Alexander. E. P. Dutton, 1981. 184 p.: Westmark trilogy

Grades: 5 6 7 8   **Fic**

1. Apprentices 2. Fugitives 3. Rulers 4. Magicians 5. Ventriloquists 6. Fantasy fiction
ISBN 0525423354

LC 80022242

National Book Award for Children's Books, 1982.

A boy fleeing from criminal charges falls in with a charlatan, his dwarf attendant, and an urchin girl, travels with them about the kingdom of Westmark, and ultimately arrives at the palace where the king is grieving over the loss of his daughter.

"The author peoples his tale with a marvelous cast of individuals, and weaves an intricate story of high adventure that climaxes in a superbly conceived conclusion, which, though predictable, is reached through carefully built tension and subtly added comic relief." Booklist.

Alexander, William (William Joseph), 1976-

Ambassador. William Alexander. Margaret K. McElderry Books, 2014. 240 p.: Ambassador (William Alexander)

Grades: 5 6 7 8   **Fic**

1. Human-alien encounters 2. Mexican Americans 3. Undocumented immigrants 4. Ambassadors 5. Aliens (Non-humanoid) 6. Science fiction
ISBN 9781442497641

Recruited by a sock-puppet alien to become Earth's ambassador to the galaxy, 11-year-old Gabe Fuentes journeys into space and discovers that Earth is in the path of a destructive alien force that wants to assassinate him.

"A shape-shifting creature called 'the Envoy' informs eleven-year-old Gabe that it has appointed him Earth's ambassador to 'everyone else.' Gabe travels across space (while he's asleep) to the Embassy.

When he wakes up back home, he discovers his father is to be deported to Mexico the next day—and one of the other ambassadors is trying to kill Gabe. A meaty and entertaining novel." Horn Book.

Nomad. William Alexander. Margaret K. McElderry Books, 2015. 256 p.: Ambassador (William Alexander)
Grades: 5 6 7 8   **Fic**
    1. Human-alien encounters 2. Mexican Americans 3. Ambassadors 4. Undocumented immigrants 5. Aliens (Non-humanoid) 6. Science fiction
ISBN 9781442497672
"Alexander is clearly passionate about science, space exploration, and social justice, but he never allows that passion to shortchange the crackerjack adventure." Kirkus.

Ali, S. K.

Love from A to Z. S. K. Ali. Salaam Reads, 2019 352 p.
Grades: 8 9 10 11 12   **Fic**
    1. Muslim teenagers 2. Prejudice 3. Grief 4. Islamophobia 5. Families 6. Qatar 7. Indiana 8. Contemporary romances 9. Epistolary novels
ISBN 9781534442726
                         LC 2018056836
Eighteen-year-old Muslims Adam and Zayneb meet in Doha, Qatar, during spring break and fall in love as both struggle to find a way to live their own truths.
"Heartfelt, honest, and featuring characters readers will fall in love with, this is sure to become a beloved book for many." School Library Journal.

Allison, Jennifer

Gilda Joyce, psychic investigator. by Jennifer Allison. Dutton Children's Books, 2005. 336 p.: Gilda Joyce mysteries
Grades: 5 6 7 8   **Fic**
    1. Joyce, Gilda (Fictitious character) 2. Thirteen-year-old girls 3. Teenage girls 4. Teenage detectives 5. Teenage psychics 6. San Francisco, California 7. Supernatural mysteries
ISBN 0525473750
                         LC 2004010834
During the summer before ninth grade, intrepid Gilda Joyce invites herself to the San Francisco mansion of distant cousin Lester Splinter and his thirteen-year-old daughter, where she uses her purported psychic abilities and detective skills to solve the mystery of the mansion's boarded-up tower.
"Allison pulls off something special here. She not only offers a credible mystery . . . but also . . . provides particularly strong characterizations." Booklist.

Almond, David, 1951-

The **boy** who swam with piranhas. David Almond; illustrated by Oliver Jeffers. Candlewick Press, 2013. 230 p.
Grades: 4 5 6 7   **Fic**
    1. Boy orphans 2. Carnivals 3. Runaway boys 4. Piranhas 5. Uncles
ISBN 9780763661694
                         LC 2012947721
"After his parents' deaths, Stanley Potts runs away with a carnival. He meets Pancho Pirelli, who performs the death-defying act of swimming with piranhas. Pirelli takes Stan under his wing, grooming him to become his sidekick and successor. Almond offers up some lighthearted fare, complete with old-fashioned intrusive narrator and numerous spot illustrations. The silliness is tempered by unsentimental, clear-eyed wisdom." Horn Book.

Clay. David Almond. Delacorte Press, c2006. 256 p.
Grades: 7 8 9 10   **Fic**
    1. Supernatural 2. Monsters 3. Fourteen-year-old boys 4. Acolytes 5. Sculpture 6. England 7. Horror 8. Fantasy fiction
ISBN 038573171X
                         LC 2005022681
The developing relationship between teenager Davie and a mysterious new boy in town morphs into something darker and more sinister when Davie learns firsthand of the boy's supernatural powers.
"Rooted in the ordinariness of a community and in one boy's chance to play God, this story will grab readers with its gripping action and its important ideas." Booklist.

The **fire-eaters**. David Almond. Delacorte Press, 2004. 224 p.
Grades: 7 8 9 10   **Fic**
    1. Boys 2. Sick fathers 3. Hope 4. Magicians 5. Schools 6. Great Britain
ISBN 0385731701
                         LC 2003055709
In 1962 England, despite observing his father's illness and the suffering of the fire-eating Mr. McNulty, as well as enduring abuse at school and the stress of the Cuban Missile Crisis, Bobby Burns and his family and friends still find reasons to rejoice in their lives and to have hope for the future.
"The author's trademark themes . . . are here in full, and resonate long after the last page is turned." School Library Journal.

Half a creature from the sea: a life in stories. David Almond; illustrated by Eleanor Taylor. Candlewick Press, 2015. 222 p.
Grades: 7 8 9 10   **Fic**
    1. England 2. Magical realism 3. Short stories 4. Illustrated books
ISBN 9780763678777
A master storyteller presents a beautiful collection of short fiction, interwoven with pieces that illuminate the inspiration behind the stories.
"Taylor's illustrations help add depth, as do the interstitial author's notes offering glimpses into each story's autobiographical roots and other inspirations. Likely to appeal to aspiring writers and fans of The Tightrope Walkers." Horn Book.

Kit's wilderness. David Almond. Delacorte Press, 2000, c1999. 229 p.
Grades: 6 7 8 9 10   **Fic**
    1. Teenage boys 2. Ghosts 3. Coal mining towns 4. Child ghosts 5. Grandfather and child 6. England 7. Ghost stories
ISBN 0385326653
                         LC 99034332
Michael L. Printz Award, 2001.
Thirteen-year-old Kit goes to live with his grandfather in the decaying coal mining town of Stoneygate, England, and finds both the old man and the town haunted by ghosts of the past.
"The author explores the power of friendship and family, the importance of memory, and the role of magic in our lives. This is a highly satisfying literary experience." School Library Journal.

Mouse, bird, snake, wolf. David Almond; illustrated by Dave McKean. Candlewick Press, 2013. 80 p.
Grades: 4 5 6 7   **Fic**
    1. Gods and goddesses 2. Creativity 3. Imagination 4. Courage

5. Mythological fiction
ISBN 9780763659127

When the gods create a safe, calm world and settle into a lazy routine of self-contentment and admiration, young Harry, Sue and little Ben struggle with feelings of emptiness and begin building imaginative innovations from everyday materials, sparking the fears of their creators.

My name is Mina. David Almond. Delacorte Press, 2011. 272 p.

Grades: 5 6 7 8   **Fic**
  1. Gifted girls 2. Girl misfits 3. Loneliness in girls 4. Loneliness 5. Widows 6. Realistic fiction
  ISBN 9780385740739

"This intimate prequel to Skellig is built around Mina McKee, the curious and brilliant home-schooled child who eventually befriends that book's protagonist, Michael. Mina, a budding writer, reveals her love of words in her journal; most of the book unfolds in a handwritten-looking font, with Mina's more emphatic entries exploding onto the pages in massive display type. Her lyrical, nonlinear prose records her reflections on her past, existential musings . . . and self-directed writing exercises . . . . Almond gives readers a vivid picture of the joyfully freeform workings of Mina's mind and her mixed emotions about being an isolated child. Her gradual emergence from the protective shell of home is beautifully portrayed. . . . This novel will inspire children to let their imaginations soar." Publishers Weekly.

Raven summer. David Almond. Delacorte Press, 2009. 198 p.

Grades: 7 8 9 10 11 12   **Fic**
  1. Abandoned children 2. Foster children 3. Secrets 4. War 5. Fourteen-year-old boys 6. England 7. Northumberland, England 8. Realistic fiction
  ISBN 9780385738064

Discovering an abandoned baby, events unfold that lead Liam's family to seek her adoption, yet while visiting his soon-to-be sibling at her foster home, he meets Oliver, a young boy who relates stories of his dark past and fears he has for his future if he is ever forced to return to his native land.

"The tension builds to a shocking and totally believable ending. . . . A haunting story, perfect for group discussion." Booklist.

The **savage**. David Almond, illustrated by Dave McKean. Candlewick Press, 2008. 80 p.

Grades: 5 6 7 8   **Fic**
  1. Fathers -- Death 2. Grief in boys 3. Wild children 4. Imagination in boys 5. Emotions in boys 6. England 7. Fantasy fiction
  ISBN 9780763639327

After his dad's death, Blue Baker finds comfort in writing about a savage living alone in the woods near his home, but when the savage pays a night-time visit to the local bully, boundaries become blurred and Blue begins to wonder where he ends and the savage begins.

"This illustrated novella, a graphic novel within a novel, will satisfy Almond's fans and newcomers alike. McKean's illustrations—ink and watercolor in black, blues, and greens—add an appropriately eerie touch." Horn Book Guide.

Skellig. David Almond. Delacorte Press, c1998. 182 p.

Grades: 5 6 7 8 9 10   **Fic**
  1. Angels 2. Sick children 3. Moving, Household 4. Strangers 5. Families 6. England 7. Fantasy fiction 8. Classics
  ISBN 038532653X

                                              LC 98-23121

Carnegie Medal, 1998.

Unhappy about his baby sister's illness and the chaos of moving into a dilapidated old house, Michael retreats to the garage and finds a mysterious stranger who is something like a bird and something like an angel.

"The plot is beautifully paced and the characters are drawn with a graceful, careful hand. . . . A lovingly done, thought-provoking novel." School Library Journal.

Slog's dad. David Almond; illustrated by Dave McKean. Candlewick Press, 2011. 52 p.

Grades: 5 6 7 8   **Fic**
  1. Fathers and sons 2. Life after death 3. Grief in boys 4. Grief 5. Promises 6. England 7. Realistic fiction
  ISBN 9780763649401

                                           LC 2010038700

When Slog's father died he promised to return for one last visit in the spring, but when Slog spots a scruffy man on a bench outside the butcher shop and identifies him as his father, his best friend Davie is skeptical.

"This grief-strafed wonder tale is brilliantly matched by some of McKean's most moving artwork yet. Text pages, featuring a voice steeped on Northern English flavor, are counterpoised against wordless illustration sequences that move readers from heaven to earth and back again, beginning with a celestial descent from the sky to a park bench by a man trailing clouds of watercolor glory." Bulletin of the Center for Children's Books.

Alonzo, Sandra

Riding invisible: an adventure journal. Sandra Alonzo, Nathan Huang. Disney Press, 2010. 240 p.

Grades: 7 8 9 10   **Fic**
  1. Runaway teenage boys 2. Frustration in teenage boys 3. Brothers and sisters of people with mental illnesses 4. Teenage boys 5. Fifteen-year-old boys 6. Diary novels 7. Adventure stories
  ISBN 9781423118985

Tormented and abused by his older brother Will, 15-year-old Yancy Aparicio runs away from home on the night that his brother viciously attacks his horse, Shy, taking to the California desert on a journey of self-discovery.

"Written in a journal style and punctuated with sketches depicting Yancy's experiences, there's a lot here to engage readers." Horn Book Guide.

Alsaid, Adi

We didn't ask for this. Adi Alsaid. Inkyard Press, 2020. 352 p.

Grades: 8 9 10 11 12   **Fic**
  1. High school students 2. Protests, demonstrations, vigils, etc 3. Environmentalism 4. Teenagers -- Political activity 5. High schools 6. Realistic fiction
  ISBN 9781335146762

Every year, lock-in night changes lives. This year, when a group of students stages an eco-protest, it might just change the world. Adapted from publisher description.

"Through multiple points of view, Alsaid movingly examines characters' home lives, their dreams and crushes, and their changing attitudes, leaving readers to decide whether the protest is a success." Publishers Weekly.

Alston, B.B

★ **Amari** and the night brothers. B.B Alston. Balzer + Bray, 2021. 416 p.: Amari

Grades: 3 4 5 6 7   **Fic**
  1. Supernatural 2. Preteen girls 3. Missing persons 4. African

Americans 5. Good and evil 6. Magical realism 7. Illustrated books
ISBN 9780062975164

Thirteen-year-old Amari, a poor Black girl from the projects, gets an invitation from her missing brother to join the Bureau of Supernatural Affairs and join in the fight against an evil magician.

"Amari, a Black girl with limited means, confronts privilege and prejudice even while delving into a world of wonder, humor, and adventure, making this a sure-to-please winner." Publishers Weekly

Alvarez, Julia

Before we were free. Julia Alvarez. A. Knopf, c2002. 167 p.

Grades: 7 8 9 10   **Fic**
1. Trujillo Molina, Rafael Leonidas, 1891-1961 2. 1960s 3. Political prisoners 4. Separated friends, relatives, etc 5. Attempted assassination 6. Girls 7. Families 8. Dominican Republic -- History -- 1930-1961. 9. Diary novels 10. Historical fiction
ISBN 0375815449

LC 2001050520

Pura Belpré Award for Narrative, 2004.

In the Dominican Republic of 1960, Anita de la Torre is baffled when her "best-friend cousins" suddenly leave the country for the U.S. and the secret police show up at her extended family's compound. When her uncle disappears and her parents seem increasingly nervous and secretive, Anita begins keeping a diary to sort things out. This novel describes—from a young girl's perspective—the bloody rule of the dictator General Trujillo and the attempts to overthrow his regime.

"This is a realistic and compelling account of a girl growing up too quickly while coming to terms with the cost of freedom." Horn Book.

How Tia Lola came to (visit) stay. Julia Alvarez. Alfred A. Knopf c2001. 147 p.: Tia Lola stories

Grades: 4 5 6 7   **Fic**
1. Aunts 2. Dominican Americans 3. Divorce 4. Hispanic American women 5. Families 6. Vermont 7. Realistic fiction
ISBN 0375902155

LC 00062932

Although ten-year-old Miguel is at first embarrassed by his colorful aunt, Tia Lola, when she comes to Vermont from the Dominican Republic to stay with his mother, his sister, and him after his parents' divorce, he learns to love her.

"Readers will enjoy the funny situations, identify with the developing relationships and conflicting feelings of the characters, and will get a spicy taste of Caribbean culture in the bargain." School Library Journal.

Return to sender. Julia Alvarez. Alfred A. Knopf, 2009. 240 p.

Grades: 4 5 6 7   **Fic**
1. Farm life 2. Mexican American migrant agricultural laborers 3. Mexican American girls 4. Migrant agricultural laborers 5. Friendship 6. Vermont 7. Realistic fiction
ISBN 9780375958380

LC 2008023520

Pura Belpre Award for Narrative, 2010.

After his family hires migrant Mexican workers to help save their Vermont farm from foreclosure, eleven-year-old Tyler befriends the oldest daughter, but when he discovers they may not be in the country legally, he realizes that real friendship knows no borders.

"Readers will be moved by small moments. . . . A tender, well-constructed book." Publishers Weekly.

Anderson, Jodi Lynn

My diary from the edge of the world. Jodi Lynn Anderson. Aladdin, 2015. 432 p.

Grades: 4 5 6 7   **Fic**
1. Automobile travel 2. Imaginary creatures 3. Sasquatch 4. Guardian angels 5. Death 6. Fantasy fiction 7. Diary novels
ISBN 9781442483873

Spirited, restless Gracie Lockwood has lived in Cliffden, Maine, her whole life. She's a typical girl in an atypical world: one where sasquatches helped to win the Civil War, where dragons glide over Route 1 on their way south for the winter (sometimes burning down a T.J. Maxx or an Applebee's along the way), where giants hide in caves near LA and mermaids hunt along the beaches, and where Dark Clouds come for people when they die.

"An endearing narrator, a beguiling world that accommodates both mermaids and Pixy Stix, and a genuinely moving family story propel this adventure." Kirkus.

Tiger Lily. Jodi Lynn Anderson. HarperTeen, 2012. 256 p.

Grades: 8 9 10 11   **Fic**
1. Unrequited love 2. Native American teenage girls 3. Fairies 4. Magic 5. Peter Pan (Fictitious character) 6. Fantasy fiction 7. Classics-inspired fiction
ISBN 9780062003256

LC 2011032659

Fifteen-year-old Tiger Lily receives special protections from the spiritual forces of Neverland, but then she meets her tribe's most dangerous enemy—Peter Pan—and falls in love with him.

Anderson, John David, 1975-

Minion. John David Anderson. Walden Pond Press, an imprint of HarperCollinsPublishers, [2014] 288 p.

Grades: 4 5 6 7   **Fic**
1. Supervillains 2. Mind control 3. Adopted boys 4. Criminals 5. Superheroes 6. Superhero stories
ISBN 9780062133113

LC 2013043188

Michael Morn is a supervillain-in-training and the adoptive son of the brilliant criminal mastermind whose sense of right and wrong is thrown into question when a new superhero arrives in town. Provided by publisher.

"Michael is as complex as the best Marvel and DC characters, and his dialogue is just as funny. The author trusts his readers enough to keep the characters ambiguous and to leave some mysteries unexplained at the end of the book." Kirkus.

Ms. Bixby's last day. John David Anderson. Walden Pond Press, an imprint of HarperCollinsPublishers, 2016 300 p.

Grades: 4 5 6 7   **Fic**
1. Teachers 2. People with cancer 3. Altruism 4. Hospital patients 5. Schools 6. Realistic fiction
ISBN 9780062338174

Loving their gifted teacher, who makes them feel like the indignity of school is somehow worthwhile, three boys are dismayed when the teacher falls ill and leaves for the rest of the school year, a situation that compels them to share their stories while cutting class and journeying across town together on a fateful day.

"Through their individual, interwoven narratives, these well-developed characters become the most intriguing elements of the story. A smart, funny, ultimately moving novel." Booklist.

One last shot. John David Anderson. Walden Pond Press, 2020. 336 p.

Grades: 4 5 6 7 **Fic**

1. Fathers and sons 2. Miniature golf 3. Family problems 4. Competition 5. Shyness in boys 6. Realistic fiction 7. Sports fiction

ISBN 9780062643926

For as long as he can remember, Malcolm has never felt like he was good enough. Not for his parents, who have always seemed at odds with each other, with Malcolm caught in between. And especially not for his dad, whose competitive drive and love for sports Malcolm has never shared. That is, until Malcolm discovers miniature golf, the one sport he actually enjoys. Maybe it's the way in which every hole is a puzzle to be solved. Or the whimsy of the windmills and waterfalls that decorate the course. Or maybe it's the slushies at the snack bar. But whatever the reason, something about mini golf just clicks for Malcolm. And best of all, it's a sport his dad can't possibly obsess over. Or so Malcolm thinks.

★ **Posted**. John David Anderson. Walden Pond Press, an imprint of HarperCollinsPublishers, 2017. 369 p.

Grades: 5 6 7 8 **Fic**

1. Bullying and bullies 2. New students 3. Middle school students 4. Friendship 5. Written communication 6. Michigan 7. Realistic fiction

ISBN 9780062338204

When cell phones are banned at their school, Frost and his friends start communicating through sticky notes left all over the school before other kids start following their example, triggering a wave of bullying activities in the wake of a new girl's arrival.

"A forceful book that focuses on bullying and the development of friendships in middle school amid exploration of the power of words." School Library Journal.

Sidekicked. John David Anderson. Walden Pond Press, an imprint of HarperCollinsPublishers, 2013. 320 p.

Grades: 4 5 6 7 **Fic**

1. Superheroes 2. Self-confidence 3. Mentors 4. Identity (Psychology) 5. Loyalty 6. Superhero stories

ISBN 9780062133144

LC 2012025495

Thirteen-year-old superhero sidekick-in-training Drew "The Sensationalist" Bean must overcome his not-so-superpowers and become the hero everyone needs when a supervillain, The Dealer, returns to Justicia.

Standard hero behavior. John David Anderson. Clarion Books, 2007. 288 p.

Grades: 6 7 8 **Fic**

1. Heroes and heroines 2. Orcs 3. Goblins 4. Quests 5. Fathers 6. Fantasy fiction

ISBN 0618759204

LC 2007013059

When fifteen-year-old Mason Quayle finds out that their town of Darlington is about to be attacked by orcs, goblins, ogres, and trolls, he goes in search of some heroes to save the day.

"Mason is thoroughly believable. . . . Using imaginative details, witty language with a scattering of modern idiom, and lots of allusions, Anderson manages the difficult task of constructing a satisfying story while poking large fun at all genre traditions. Fantasy fans are ensured a good laugh." Booklist.

Anderson, Laurie Halse

Ashes. Laurie Halse Anderson Atheneum Books for Young Readers, 2016. 304 p.: Seeds of America trilogy

Grades: 6 7 8 9 10 **Fic**

1. United States. Continental Army 2. Revolutionary America (1775-1783) 3. 18th century 4. Enslaved teenagers 5. Teenage soldiers 6. Runaways 7. Teenagers and war 8. Slavery 9. United States. 10. Historical fiction

ISBN 9781416961468

"It's a gripping finish to an epic journey that speaks resoundingly to the human capacity to persevere." Publishers Weekly.

★ **Chains**. Laurie Halse Anderson. Simon & Schuster Books for Young Readers, 2008. 304 p.: Seeds of America trilogy

Grades: 6 7 8 9 10 **Fic**

1. Revolutionary America (1775-1783) 2. 18th century 3. Slavery 4. Enslaved teenagers 5. Spies 6. Loyalists (United States history) 7. Sisters 8. New York City 9. United States 10. Historical fiction

ISBN 9781416905851

LC 2007052139

Scott O'Dell Historical Fiction Award, 2009.

After being sold to a cruel couple in New York City, a slave named Isabel spies for the rebels during the Revolutionary War.

"This gripping novel offers readers a startlingly provocative view of the Revolutionary War. . . . [Anderson's] solidly researched exploration of British and Patriot treatment of slaves during a war for freedom is nuanced and evenhanded, presented in service of a fast-moving, emotionally involving plot." Publishers Weekly.

Fever, 1793. Laurie Halse Anderson. Simon & Schuster Books for Young Readers, 2000. 251 p.

Grades: 5 6 7 8 9 **Fic**

1. Early America (1784-1819) 2. 1790s 3. 18th century 4. Survival 5. Epidemics 6. Yellow fever 7. Teenage girls 8. Sixteen-year-old girls 9. Pennsylvania 10. Philadelphia, Pennsylvania 11. Historical fiction 12. Classics

ISBN 9780689838583

LC 00032238

In 1793 Philadelphia, sixteen-year-old Matilda Cook, separated from her sick mother, learns about perseverance and self-reliance when she is forced to cope with the horrors of a yellow fever epidemic.

"A vivid work, rich with well-drawn and believable characters. Unexpected events pepper the top-flight novel that combines accurate historical detail with a spellbinding story line." Voice of Youth Advocates.

★ **Forge**. Laurie Halse Anderson. Atheneum Books for Young Readers, c2010. 272 p.: Seeds of America trilogy

Grades: 6 7 8 9 10 **Fic**

1. United States. Continental Army 2. Revolutionary America (1775-1783) 3. 18th century 4. Enslaved teenagers 5. Teenage soldiers 6. Teenagers and war 7. Slavery 8. African American teenage boys 9. Pennsylvania. 10. Valley Forge, Pennsylvania. 11. Historical fiction

ISBN 9781416961444

LC 2010015971

Separated from his friend Isabel after their daring escape from slavery, fifteen-year-old Curzon serves as a free man in the Continental Army at Valley Forge until he and Isabel are thrown together again, as slaves once more.

"Weaving a huge amount of historical detail seamlessly into the story, Anderson creates a vivid setting, believable characters both good and despicable and a clear portrayal of the moral ambiguity of the Revolutionary age. Not only can this sequel stand alone, for many readers it will be one of the best novels they have ever read." Kirkus.

Speak. Laurie Halse Anderson. Farrar Straus Giroux, 1999. 197 p.

Grades: 7 8 9 10 **Fic**

1. Misfits (Persons) 2. High school students 3. Teenage rape victims 4. Teenage girls 5. Emotional problems 6. Realistic fiction 7. Classics

ISBN 0374371520

Golden Kite Award for Fiction, 1999.

A traumatic event in the summer has a devastating effect on Melinda's freshman year of high school.

"The novel is keenly aware of the corrosive details of outsiderhood and the gap between home and daily life at high school; kids whose exclusion may have less concrete cause than Melinda's will nonetheless find the picture recognizable. This is a gripping account of personal wounding and recovery." Bulletin of the Center for Children's Books.

Wintergirls. by Laurie Halse Anderson. Viking, 2009. 288 p.

Grades: 8 9 10 11 12 **Fic**

1. Anorexia nervosa 2. Best friends -- Death 3. Eating disorders 4. Teenage girls with eating disorders 5. Self-harm 6. Realistic fiction

ISBN 9780670011100

LC 2008037452

Eighteen-year-old Lia comes to terms with her best friend's death from anorexia as she struggles with the same disorder.

"As events play out, Lia's guilt, her need to be thin, and her fight for acceptance unravel in an almost poetic stream of consciousness in this startlingly crisp and pitch-perfect first-person narrative." School Library Journal.

Anderson, M. T.

Feed. M.T. Anderson. Candlewick Press, 2002. 237 p.

Grades: 8 9 10 11 12 **Fic**

1. Computers and civilization 2. Consumerism 3. Environmental degradation 4. Consumers 5. Teenagers 6. Science fiction 7. Dystopian fiction

ISBN 0763617261

LC 2002023738

In a future where most people have computer implants in their heads to control their environment, a boy meets an unusual girl who is in serious trouble.

"An ingenious satire of corporate America and our present-day value system." Horn Book Guide.

He laughed with his other mouths. M.T. Anderson; illustrations by Kurt Cyrus. Beach Lane Books, 2014. 304 p.: Pals in peril tales

Grades: 4 5 6 7 **Fic**

1. Father-separated boys 2. Aliens 3. Missing persons 4. Adventure 5. Space 6. Science fiction 7. Humorous stories 8. Metafiction

ISBN 9781442451100

LC 2013034710

In this sixth Pals in Peril adventure, Jasper Dash is off into the universe to search for his long lost father! Provided by publisher.

"The novel doesn't transcend the wacky sci-fi of old that inspired it but rather embraces it and dissects it, celebrating it and exploring why

so many people fell in love with these silly worlds and gee-whiz heroes in the first place." Kirkus.

Whales on stilts! M.T. Anderson; illustrations by Kurt Cyrus. Harcourt Children's Books/Harcourt, Inc., 2005. 192 p.: Pals in peril tales

Grades: 4 5 6 7 **Fic**

1. Child heroes 2. Whales 3. Mad scientist (Concept) 4. Friendship 5. Best friends 6. Science fiction 7. Humorous stories 8. Metafiction

ISBN 0152053409

LC 2004017754

Racing against the clock, shy middle-school student Lily and her best friends, Katie and Jasper, must foil the plot of her father's conniving boss to conquer the world using an army of whales.

"A story written with the author's tongue shoved firmly into his cheek. . . . It's full of witty pokes at other series novels and Jasper's nutty inventions." School Library Journal.

Anderson, Natalie C.

City of saints & thieves. Natalie C. Anderson. G.P. Putnam's Sons, 2017. 432 p.

Grades: 7 8 9 10 **Fic**

1. Refugees 2. Revenge 3. Gangs 4. Thieves 5. Sisters 6. Congo (Democratic Republic) 7. Kenya 8. Thrillers and suspense

ISBN 9780399547584

Sixteen-year-old Tina and two friends leave Kenya and slip into the Congo, from where she and her mother fled years before, seeking revenge for her mother's murder but uncovering startling secrets.

"The novel is peppered with Swahili words and phrases, and Anderson makes an effort to paint a picture of the country. A story full of twists and turns, proving nothing is ever as black and white as it may seem." Kirkus.

Anderson, Sophie

★ The **girl** who speaks bear. Sophie Anderson. Scholastic Press, 2020. 272 p.

Grades: 3 4 5 6 7 **Fic**

1. Twelve-year-old girls 2. Curses 3. Bears 4. Superhuman abilities 5. Secrets 6. Fairy tale and folklore-inspired fiction 7. Fantasy fiction

ISBN 9781338580839

Discovered in a bear cave as a baby, 12-year-old Yanka dreams of knowing who she really is. Although Yanka is happy at home with her loving foster mother, she feels out of place in the village where the other children mock her for her unusual size and strength. So when Yanka wakes up one morning to find her legs have become bear legs, she knows she has no choice but to leave her village. She has to find somewhere she truly belongs, so she ventures into the Snow Forest with her pet weasel, Mousetrap, in search of the truth about her past.

"Anderson's tale draws themes and inspiration from Russian fairy tales, deftly weaving the threads of these magical stories into Yanka's adventure and evoking the folklore, music, art, and customs of the Eastern European north...Charmed and charming." Kirkus

Andrews, Christiane M.

Spindlefish and stars. Christiane M. Andrews. Little, Brown and Company, 2020. 384 p.

Grades: 5 6 7 8 **Fic**

1. Missing persons 2. Voyages and travels 3. Islands 4. Tapestry

5. Thieves 6. Fantasy fiction
ISBN 9780316496018

LC 2020012167

When Clo's father goes missing, she takes the mysterious items he left behind and journeys across the sea to find him, but is stranded on a strange island and must learn to spin fish into yarn to unravel the secret of all that has happened.

"A lyrical debut exploring the nature of destiny and sacrifice. . . . The narrative voice . . . makes this enchanting story feel like an all-new myth built from classic material." Publishers Weekly

Andrews, Jesse

Me and Earl and the dying girl. by Jesse Andrews. Amulet Books, 2012. 288 p.

Grades: 8 9 10   **Fic**

1. Jewish teenagers 2. Teenage girls with leukemia 3. Teenage filmmakers 4. Alienation (Social psychology) 5. Leukemia 6. Pittsburgh, Pennsylvania 7. Pennsylvania 8. Realistic fiction
ISBN 9781419701764

LC 2011031796

Seventeen-year-old Greg has managed to become part of every social group at his Pittsburgh high school without having any friends, but his life changes when his mother forces him to befriend Rachel, a girl he once knew in Hebrew school who has leukemia.

Angleberger, Tom

Darth Paper strikes back: an Origami Yoda book. Tom Angleberger. Amulet Books, 2011. 176 p.: Origami Yoda books

Grades: 4 5 6 7   **Fic**

1. Boy misfits 2. Origami 3. Seventh-graders 4. Finger puppets 5. Yoda (Fictitious character) 6. Realistic fiction 7. Illustrated books
ISBN 9781419700279

LC 2011010388

Harvey, upset when his Darth Paper finger puppet brings humiliation, gets Dwight suspended, but Origami Yoda asks Tommy and Kellan, now in seventh grade, to make a new casefile to persuade the School Board to reinstate Dwight.

"This is a satisfying tale of friendship and just resistance to authority. Pitch-perfect middle-school milieu and enough Star Wars references (and laughs) to satisfy fans and win new ones." Kirkus.

Emperor Pickletine rides the bus: an Origami Yoda Book. Tom Angleberger. Amulet Books, 2014. 224 p.: Origami Yoda books

Grades: 4 5 6 7   **Fic**

1. Origami 2. School field trips 3. Bus travel 4. Interpersonal relations 5. Middle school students 6. Washington (DC) 7. Realistic fiction 8. Illustrated books
ISBN 9781419709333

LC 2014012574

The seventh graders of McQuarrie Middle School and their Star Wars-inspired origami finger puppets go on a field trip to Washington, D.C., on what proves to be a very long trip full of shifting alliances, betrayals, carsickness, and sugar rushes.

"The seventh grade of McQuarrie Middle School hits Washington, D.C., in this final installment of the popular Origami Yoda series. Exciting as a field trip is, the Rebel Alliance is reeling because Principal Rabbski has banned origami for the entire trip! . . . Origami Yoda has an earth-shattering revelation or two to impart before the book's end, making for a fitting series conclusion." Booklist.

Fuzzy. by Tom Angleberger and Paul Dellinger. Amulet Books, 2016 224 p.

Grades: 4 5 6 7   **Fic**

1. Robots 2. Middle schools 3. Artificial intelligence 4. Schools 5. Middle school students 6. Science fiction
ISBN 9781419721229

"The result is a smart, sci-fi page-turner that will grab kids imagination and appeal to their conscience and sense of humor." Booklist.

Horton Halfpott, or, The fiendish mystery of Smugwick Manor, or, The loosening of M'Lady Luggertuck's corset. Tom Angleberger. Amulet Books, 2011. 176 p.

Grades: 4 5 6 7   **Fic**

1. Victorian era (1837-1901) 2. 19th century 3. Household employees 4. Jewelry theft 5. Castles 6. Social classes 7. Eccentrics and eccentricities 8. England 9. Great Britain 10. Historical mysteries 11. Mysteries
ISBN 9780810997158

LC 2010038096

Horton, an upstanding kitchen boy in a castle in nineteenth-century England, becomes embroiled in a mystery surrounding a series of thefts, which is also connected to the pursuit of a very eligible and wealthy young lady's affections.

"Readers will enjoy Angleberger's . . . penchant for the absurd as well as his many droll asides. . . . The ending satisfies, and with Angleberger's many eclectic characters, his wild-and-witty storytelling, and a lighthearted but perplexing mystery . . . readers are in for a treat." Publishers Weekly.

Princess Labelmaker to the rescue!: an Origami Yoda book. by Tom Angleberger. Amulet Books, 2014. 208 p.: Origami Yoda books

Grades: 4 5 6 7   **Fic**

1. Standardized tests 2. Origami 3. Middle school students 4. Finger puppets 5. Middle schools 6. Realistic fiction 7. Illustrated books
ISBN 9781419710520

LC 2013047291

One month before the state standards test are to take place, the Origami Rebel Alliance has found powerful allies in unexpected places in their fight against the FunTime test preparation program, but Principal Rabbski has not yet declared her allegiance.

"Angleberger continues to develop authentic and engaging voices in these 'case files.'" Horn Book.

The **strange** case of Origami Yoda. Tom Angleberger; [illustrations by Tom Angleberger and Jason Rosenstock]. Amulet Books, c2010. 141 p.: Origami Yoda books

Grades: 4 5 6 7   **Fic**

1. Boy misfits 2. Origami 3. Sixth-graders 4. Interpersonal relations 5. Yoda (Fictitious character) 6. Realistic fiction 7. Illustrated books
ISBN 9780810984257

LC 2009039748

Sixth-grader Tommy and his friends describe their interactions with a paper finger puppet of Yoda, worn by their weird classmate Dwight, as they try to figure out whether or not the puppet can really predict the future. Includes instructions for making Origami Yoda.

"The situations that Yoda has a hand in are pretty authentic, and the setting is broad enough to be any school. The plot is age-old but with the twist of being presented on crumpled pages with cartoon sketches, supposed hand printing, and varying typefaces. Kids should love it." School Library Journal.

Ansari, Rebecca K. S.

★ The **in-between**. Rebecca K. S. Ansari. Walden Pond Press, 2021. 304 p.

Grades: 5 6 7 8   **Fic**

   1. Brothers and sisters 2. Railroad accidents 3. Investigations 4. Ghosts 5. Space and time 6. Chicago, Illinois 7. Supernatural mysteries 8. Ghost stories
   ISBN 9780062916099

Cooper is lost. Ever since his father left their family three years ago, he has become distant from his friends, constantly annoyed by his little sister, Jess, and completely fed up with the pale, creepy rich girl who moved in next door and won't stop staring at him. So when Cooper learns of an unsolved mystery his sister has discovered online, he welcomes the distraction. It's the tale of a deadly train crash that occurred a hundred years ago, in which one young boy among the dead was never identified. The only distinguishing mark on him was a strange insignia on his suit coat, a symbol no one had seen before or since. Jess is fascinated by the mystery of the unknown child because she's seen the insignia. It's the symbol of the jacket of the girl next door. As they uncover more information, and mounting evidence of the girl's seemingly impossible connection to the tragedy, Cooper and Jess begin to wonder if a similar disaster could be heading to their hometown.

"The increasingly dangerous supernatural mystery (with an exceptionally well-described climax) is intriguing enough to make this a page-turner, but the characters and their powerfully thematic emotional journeys are what will make the book linger." Kirkus

The **missing** piece of Charlie O'Reilly. Rebecca K. S. Ansari. Walden Pond Press, an imprint of HarperCollinsPublishers, 2019. 400 p.

Grades: 4 5 6 7 8   **Fic**

   1. Missing persons 2. Brothers 3. Best friends 4. Family relationships 5. Forgiveness 6. Fantasy fiction
   ISBN 9780062679666

Charlie O'Reilly is an only child. Which is why it makes everyone uncomfortable when he talks about his brother, Liam. His eight-year-old kid brother, who, up until a year ago, slept in the bunk above Charlie, took pride in being as annoying as possible, and was the only person who could make Charlie laugh until it hurt. Then came the morning when the bunk, and Liam, disappeared forever. No one even remembers him—not Charlie's mother, who has been lost in her own troubles; and not Charlie's father, who is gone frequently on business trips. The only person who believes Charlie is his best friend, Ana—even if she has no memory of Liam, she is as determined as Charlie is to figure out what happened to him.

"Ansari trusts her audience with a complex narrative that traverses the breadth of time and the depths of self. The weave of guilt, family struggle, and forgiveness both complicates and complements questions of love and self-acceptance." Kirkus.

Antieau, Kim

Ruby's imagine. written by Kim Antieau. Houghton Mifflin Co., 2008. 201 p.

Grades: 6 7 8 9   **Fic**

   1. Hurricane Katrina, 2005 2. Grandmother and granddaughter 3. Memories 4. African American girls 5. Secrets 6. New Orleans, Louisiana 7. Coming-of-age stories 8. Realistic fiction
   ISBN 9780618997671

                             LC 2007047736

Tells the story of Hurricane Katrina from the point of view of Ruby, an unusually intuitive girl who lives with her grandmother in New Orleans but has powerful memories of an earlier life in the swamps.

"Antieau offers a complex, personal account of Katrina and its aftermath. . . . Ruby's atmospheric narrative is as dense and pungent as the bayou." Booklist.

Apelfeld, Aharon

Adam and Thomas. by Aharon Appelfeld; translated from Hebrew by Jeffrey Green; illustrated by Philippe Dumas. Seven Stories Press, [2015] 160 p.

Grades: 4 5 6 7 8   **Fic**

   1. Jewish boys 2. Wilderness survival 3. Holocaust (1933-1945) 4. Nine-year-old boys 5. Fugitives 6. Historical fiction 7. Translations
   ISBN 9781609806347

                             LC 2015010371

Sydney Taylor Book Award for Older Readers, 2016.

Adam and Thomas, two nine-year-old Jewish boys who survive World War II, take refuge in the forest where they learn to forage and survive, soon meeting and helping other fugitives fleeing for their lives.

"Translated from the original Hebrew text and accompanied by Dumas' moving illustrations, the story is one of quiet perseverance and growing friendship between two very different boys experiencing the world together in a horrific time and place." Booklist.

Appelt, Kathi, 1954-

Keeper. Kathi Appelt; illustrated by August Hall. Atheneum Books for Young Readers, 2010. 399 p.

Grades: 5 6 7 8   **Fic**

   1. Mother-separated girls 2. Mermaids 3. Determination in girls 4. Determination (Personal quality) 5. Sailing 6. Gulf of Mexico 7. Fantasy fiction
   ISBN 9781416950608

                             LC 2010000795

Ten-year-old Keeper lives a happy, simple life on the Gulf Coast of Texas with patient and loving Signe, her guardian. But Keeper is afraid that she's ruined everything, and she needs to find her mom—who Keeper truly believes is a mermaid—in order to make things right. Giving away too many details would ruin this moving and magical story of family, love, secrets, and taking chances...this book will hold you spellbound.

"Deftly spinning together mermaid lore, local legend and natural history, this stunning tale proves every landscape has its magical beings, and the most unlikely ones can form a perfect family. Hall's black-and-white illustrations lend perspective and immediacy. Beautiful and evocativean absolute keeper." Kirkus.

Kissing Tennessee and other stories from the Stardust Dance. Harcourt, 2000. 118 p.

Grades: 6 7 8 9   **Fic**

   1. Junior high schools 2. Dancing 3. Eighth-graders 4. School dances 5. Teenagers -- Interpersonal relations
   ISBN 015202249X

                           LC 99050505

Graduating eighth graders relate their stories of love and heartbreak that have brought them to Dogwood Junior High's magical Stardust Dance.

"This collection will spark conversation in contemporary literature discussions, will quietly unsettle readers, and will elevate the quality of short-story collections." School Library Journal.

Maybe a fox. Kathi Appelt and Alison McGhee. Atheneum Books for Young Readers, 2016. 272 p.

Grades: 4 5 6 7 8   **Fic**
1. Grief 2. Loss (Psychology) 3. Foxes 4. Sisters 5. Missing girls 6. Vermont 7. Fantasy fiction
ISBN 9781442482425

"A good cry can be cathartic, and this book about nourishing one's soul during times of great sadness does the trick." Horn Book.

★ The **true** blue scouts of Sugar Man Swamp. Kathi Appelt. Atheneum Books for Young Readers, 2013. 336 p.

Grades: 5 6 7 8   **Fic**
1. Bayous 2. Land developers 3. Swamp animals 4. Swamps 5. Raccoons 6. Texas 7. Animal fantasy
ISBN 9781442421059

LC 2012023723

Twelve-year-old Chap Brayburn, ancient Sugar Man, and his raccoon-brother Swamp Scouts Bingo and J'miah try to save Bayou Tourterelle from feral pigs Clydine and Buzzie, greedy Sunny Boy Beaucoup, and world-class alligator wrestler and would-be land developer Jaeger Stitch.

The **underneath**. by Kathi Appelt; illustrated by David Small. Atheneum Books for Young Readers, c2008. 313 p.

Grades: 3 4 5 6   **Fic**
1. Survival 2. Dogs 3. Cats 4. Kittens 5. Abandoned animals 6. Texas 7. Animal fantasy 8. Fantasy fiction
ISBN 9781416950585

LC 2007031969

An old hound that has been chained up at his hateful owner's run-down shack and two kittens born underneath the house endure separation, danger, and many other tribulations in their quest to be reunited and free.

"Well realized in Small's excellent full-page drawings, this fine book is most of all distinguished by the originality of the story and the fresh beauty of its author's voice." Horn Book.

Applegate, Katherine

Home of the brave. Katherine Applegate. Feiwel & Friends, 2007. 249 p.

Grades: 5 6 7 8   **Fic**
1. Mother-separated boys 2. Boy refugees 3. Cows 4. Refugees, Sudanese 5. Assimilation (Sociology) 6. Minneapolis, Minnesota 7. Minnesota 8. Realistic fiction 9. Novels in verse
ISBN 9780312367657
Golden Kite Award for Fiction, 2007.

Kek, an African refugee, is confronted by many strange things at the Minneapolis home of his aunt and cousin, as well as in his fifth grade classroom, and longs for his missing mother, but finds comfort in the company of a cow and her owner.

"This beautiful story of hope and resilience is written in free verse." Voice of Youth Advocates.

★ The **one** and only Ivan. by Katherine Applegate. Harper, 2011. 272 p.

Grades: 3 4 5 6   **Fic**
1. Gorillas 2. Elephant babies 3. Captive wild animals 4. Elephants 5. Animal welfare 6. Stories told by animals
ISBN 9780061992254

LC 2011010034

Newbery Medal, 2013.

When Ivan, a gorilla who has lived for years in a down-and-out circus-themed mall, meets Ruby, a baby elephant that has been added to the mall, he decides that he must find her a better life.

"Ivan narrates his tale in short, image-rich sentences and acute, sometimes humorous, observations that are all the more heartbreaking for their simple delivery. . . . Spot art captures poignant moments throughout. Utterly believable, this bittersweet story, complete with an author's note identifying the real Ivan, will inspire a new generation of advocates." Kirkus.

★ **Wishtree**. Katherine Applegate. Feiwel and Friends 2017 208 p.

Grades: 4 5 6 7 8   **Fic**
1. Prejudice 2. Toleration 3. Immigrant families 4. Refugees 5. Muslims 6. Low fantasy
ISBN 9781250043221

An old red oak tree tells how he and his crow friend, Bongo, help their human neighbors get along after a threat against an immigrant family is carved into the tree's trunk.

"Even those who shy away from books with talking animals will find this believable fantasy elegant and poignant. Widening the appeal is a sparse word count, making this a great choice for a family or classroom read-aloud and an inviting option for reluctant readers." School Library Journal.

Arden, Katherine

★ **Dead** voices. Katherine Arden. G.P. Putnam's Sons, 2019 256 p.: Small spaces quartet

Grades: 4 5 6 7 8   **Fic**
1. Haunted places 2. Vacations 3. Paranormal phenomena 4. Best friends 5. Families 6. Vermont 7. Horror 8. Ghost stories
ISBN 9780525515050

LC 2019014459

Best friends Ollie, Coco and Brian spend winter break at a down-on-its-heels ski resort before the ghost of the resort's late co-owner reaches out for help solving his murder.

"Arden is fantastic at cultivating atmosphere, and she uses that to great effect in this novel, particularly when it comes to describing the sensory experience of the lodge and the appearance of the many ghastly ghosts and creatures." Booklist.

Argueta, Jorge

Caravan to the North: Misael's long walk. Jorge Argueta; illustrated by Manuel Monroy. Groundwood Books, 2019. 111 p.

Grades: 4 5 6 7 8   **Fic**
1. Caravans 2. Child refugees 3. Voyages and travels 4. Central American boys 5. Families 6. El Salvador 7. Mexican-American border region 8. Novels in verse 9. Realistic fiction
ISBN 9781773063294

A novel in verse about a Salvadorian boy and his family as they join a caravan heading to the United States.

"Argueta's spare text is given emotional potency through Misael's observations of the members of the caravan, whose stories mirror his own fears of undertaking the arduous journey, as well as the hopes that drive them." Booklist.

Armstrong, Alan W., 1939-

Looking for Marco Polo. by Alan Armstrong; illustrated by Tim Jessell. Random House, 2009. 304 p.

Grades: 4 5 6 7   **Fic**
1. Polo, Marco, 1254-1323? 2. Voyages and travels 3. Storytelling 4. Eleven-year-old boys 5. Father-separated boys 6. Adventure 7.

Venice, Italy 8. Gobi Desert Exploring expeditions
ISBN 9780375933219

LC 2008008815

When they lose touch with his father's Gobi Desert expedition, eleven-year-old Mark accompanies his mother to Venice, Italy, and there, while waiting for news of his father, learns about the legendary Marco Polo and his adventures in the Far East.

"Armstrong ably conjures up the atmosphere of damp, foggy Venice in late December while blowing some dust off of the accounts of Marco Polo's travels with his lively storytelling. . . . Whether or not readers know the specifics of Marco Polo's voyages, they will enjoy this entertaining blend of contemporary and historical adventure." Booklist.

Whittington. by Alan Armstrong; illustrated by S.D. Schindler. Random House, c2005. 191 p.

Grades: 4 5 6 **Fic**
1. Whittington, Richard, 1358?-1423 2. Cats 3. Storytelling 4. Boys with dyslexia 5. Ancestors 6. Winter 7. New England 8. Historical fantasy
ISBN 0375828648

LC 2004005789

Whittington, a feline descendant of Dick Whittington's famous cat of English folklore, appears at a rundown barnyard plagued by rats and restores harmony while telling his ancestor's story.

"The story works beautifully, both as historical fiction about medieval street life and commerce and as a witty, engaging tale of barnyard camaraderie and survival." Booklist.

Armstrong, Kelley

Loki's wolves. by K.L. Armstrong and M.A. Marr. Little, Brown and Company, 2013. 368 p.: Blackwell pages

Grades: 4 5 6 7 8 **Fic**
1. Monsters 2. Gods and goddesses, Norse 3. Shapeshifters 4. Prophecies 5. Supernatural 6. South Dakota 7. Mythological fiction 8. Fantasy fiction
ISBN 9780316204965

LC 2012029851

Matt Thorsen is a direct descendent of the order-keeping god Thor, and his classmates Fen and Laurie Brekke are descendents of the trickster god Loki. When Ragnarok—the apocalypse—threatens, the human descendents of the gods must fight monsters to stop the end of the world.

"It is so methodically constructed that readers will welcome the action Ragnark will offer. . . . Norse mythology brought to life with engaging contemporary characters and future volumes that promise explosive action; ideal for Percy Jackson fans who want to branch out." Kirkus.

Odin's ravens. K.L. Armstrong; M.A. Marr. Little, Brown and Company, 2014. 342 p.: Blackwell pages

Grades: 4 5 6 7 8 **Fic**
1. Monsters 2. Gods and goddesses, Norse 3. Shapeshifters 4. Valhalla 5. Prophecies 6. Mythological fiction 7. Fantasy fiction
ISBN 9780316204989

LC 2013018519

When Ragnarok—the apocalypse—threatens, the human descendants of the gods band together to fight monsters, and Matt Thorsen and his friends must journey to the underworld to save a descendant.

"This sequel stands by itself, as essential details of the first are neatly woven throughout. Intense action, well-crafted scenes and humor-laced dialogue add up to a sure winner. Just enough black-and-white illustrations add a visual dimension to the vivid text." Kirkus.

A **royal** guide to monster slaying. Kelley Armstrong; illustrated by Xaviere Daumarie. Puffin Canada, 2019. 288 p.: Royal guide to monster slaying

Grades: 4 5 6 7 **Fic**
1. Princesses 2. Twin brothers and sisters 3. Mythical creatures 4. Inheritance and succession 5. Twelve-year-old girls 6. Fantasy fiction
ISBN 9780735265356

Twelve-year-old Rowan is destined to be Queen; her twin brother, Rhydd, to be Royal Monster Hunter. Rowan would give anything to switch places, but the oldest child is always next in line, even if she is only older by two minutes. She resigns herself to admiring her monster hunting aunt's glorious sword and joining her queen mother for boring diplomatic teas. But tragedy shatters the longstanding rule, and Rowan finds herself hunting the most dangerous monster of all: a gryphon.

"Twelve-year-old Rowan is a princess destined for political life on the throne, despite being better suited to the role of monster hunter. Hers is an Arthurian world where several brown-skinned clans are united under the protection of Rowan's mother, the queen. It's also a world populated by a menagerie of fantastical beasts, the most fearsome being the gryphon." Booklist.

Armstrong, William H. (William Howard), 1914-1999

★ **Sounder**. Illustrations by James Barkley. Harper, 1969. 116 p.

Grades: 5 6 7 8 **Fic**
1. Dogs 2. African American sharecroppers 3. African American families 4. Depressions 1929-1941 5. Poor families 6. Coming-of-age stories 7. Classics
ISBN 0060201436

LC 70085030

Newbery Medal, 1970.

Angry and humiliated when his sharecropper father is jailed for stealing food for his family, a young black boy grows in courage and understanding by learning to read and with the help of his devoted dog Sounder.

"Set in the South in the era of sharecropping and segregation, this succinctly told tale poignantly describes the courage of a father who steals a ham in order to feed his undernourished family; the determination of the eldest son, who searches for his father despite the apathy of prison authorities; and the devotion of a coon dog named Sounder." Shapiro. Fic for Youth. 3d edition

Arnold, Elana K.

Far from fair. Elana K. Arnold. 229 p.

Grades: 5 6 7 **Fic**
1. Moving, Household 2. Family problems 3. Anger in girls 4. Anger 5. Grandmothers 6. Realistic fiction
ISBN 9780544602274

LC 2015013893

As far as twelve-year-old Odette Zyskowski is concerned, her parents have ruined her life by selling the house she and her younger brother have grown up in, getting an RV, and giving her some little mutt instead of the Labrador Retriever she wanted—but as they travel north to see her grandmother, Odette becomes aware of an even more frightening problem: her parents may be on the verge of a divorce.

"Arnold deals with the many bumps in the road honestly, yet maintains an onward-and-upward outlook on life." Booklist.

The **question** of miracles. by Elana K. Arnold. 208 p.

Grades: 4 5 6 7 **Fic**
1. Grief in girls 2. Friends' death 3. Friendship 4. Boy misfits

5. Miracles 6. Oregon 7. Corvallis, Oregon 8. Realistic fiction
ISBN 9780544334649

LC 2014000738

Unhappy about moving from sunny California to rainy Corvallis, Oregon, and grieving over the death of her best friend, sixth-grader Iris looks for a miracle and may find one in new friend Boris.

"This is a realistic view of grief, with particular emphasis on the agonizing longing to know if a lost loved one is truly out there somewhere." School Library Journal.

Arntson, Steven, 1973-

The **wikkeling**. Steven Arnston. Running Press Kids, 2011. 224 p.

Grades: 4 5 6   **Fic**
    1. Attics 2. Cats 3. Dystopias 4. Headache 5. Imaginary creatures 6. Fantasy fiction
ISBN 9780762439034

"In Henrietta's world, every part of life is monitored and regulated by computers. House cats are considered wild and dangerous animals. Old houses and old books can make children sick. The girl's orderly and safe life is disrupted the day she discovers a secret attic above her bedroom. . . . Soon after this discovery, she starts seeing the Wikkeling, a menacing yellow creature that gives children headaches with the touch of a finger. . . . Arntson has created a detailed and fascinating dystopian world that seems eerily similar to our own, and Terrazzini's illustrations strike just the right note." School Library Journal.

Asher, Jay, 1975-

The **future** of us. Jay Asher and Carolyn Mackler. Razorbill, c2011. 368 p.

Grades: 8 9 10 11 12   **Fic**
    1. 1990s 2. Internet 3. Consequences 4. Computers 5. Friendship 6. Teenage boy/girl relations
ISBN 9781595144911

"It's 1996, and Emma Nelson has just received her first computer. . . . When Emma powers up the computer, she discovers her own Facebook page (even though Facebook doesn't exist yet) and herself in an unhappy marriage 15 years in the future. Alternating chapters from Josh and Emma over the course of five days propel this riveting read, as Emma discovers she can alter her future by adjusting her present actions and intentions." Booklist.

Thirteen reasons why: a novel. by Jay Asher. Razorbill, 2008. 288 p.

Grades: 8 9 10 11 12   **Fic**
    1. Suicide victims 2. Rape 3. Emotions in teenagers 4. Guilt 5. Suicide 6. Realistic fiction
ISBN 9781595141712

LC 2007003097

When high school student Clay Jenkins receives a box in the mail containing thirteen cassette tapes recorded by his classmate Hannah, who committed suicide, he spends a bewildering and heartbreaking night crisscrossing their town, listening to Hannah's voice recounting the events leading up to her death.

"Clay's pain is palpable and exquisitely drawn in gripping casually poetic prose. The complex and soulful characters expose astoundingly rich and singularly teenage inner lives." School Library Journal.

Asimov, Isaac, 1920-1992

I, robot. Isaac Asimov. Bantam Books, 2004, c1950. 224 p.
Grades: 7 8 9 10 11 12 Adult   **Fic**
    1. Robots 2. Androids 3. Robotics 4. Artificial intelligence 5.

Robots -- Behavior 6. Short stories 7. Hard science fiction 8. Science fiction classics
ISBN 0553803700

LC 2003069139

Asimov chronicles the development of the robot through a series of interlinked stories: from its primitive origins in the present to its ultimate perfection in the not-so-distant future—a future in which humanity itself may be rendered obsolete. Here are stories of robots gone mad, of mind-reading robots, and robots with a sense of humor. Of robot politicians, and robots who secretly run the world.

Aster, Alex

Curse of the forgotten city. Alex Aster. Sourcebooks Inc 2021 352 p.: Emblem Island
Grades: 4 5 6 7 8   **Fic**
    1. Fate and fatalism 2. Curses 3. Characters and characteristics in mythology 4. Preteen boys 5. Ability 6. Fantasy fiction
ISBN 9781492697237

LC 2021001021

Tor, Engle, and Melda must stop a band of cursed pirates from taking over their home.

"Aster's brisk, lyrical prose weaves rich, intriguing worldbuilding details and wrinkles into this engrossing series that encompasses tales indebted to Latin American myths. . . . A mightily marvelous sequel." Kirkus

Curse of the Night Witch. Alex Aster. Sourcebooks Young Readers, 2020. 306 p.: Emblem Island
Grades: 4 5 6 7 8   **Fic**
    1. Fate and fatalism 2. Curses 3. Characters and characteristics in mythology 4. Preteen boys 5. Quests 6. Fantasy fiction
ISBN 9781492697206

LC 2019052808

After changing the fate he has known since birth, twelve-year-old Tor Luna, accompanied by his friends Engle and Melda, must visit the notorious Night Witch to break the curse he now faces.

"Despite some flat characterization, Aster balances a fast-paced plot rife with hair-raising action and snippets of Emblem Island folklore, offering a story about sacrifice and risk-taking that's great for young mythology fans, and ending with the promise of a thrilling sequel." Booklist

Atkins, Jeannine, 1953-

Finding wonders: three girls who changed science. Jeannine Atkins. Atheneum Books for Young Readers, [2016] 208 p.
Grades: 5 6 7 8   **Fic**
    1. Merian, Maria Sibylla, 1647-1717 2. Anning, Mary, 1799-1847 3. Mitchell, Maria, 1818-1889 4. Naturalists 5. Paleontologists 6. Astronomers 7. Women scientists 8. Scientists 9. Novels in verse 10. Biographical fiction 11. Historical fiction
ISBN 9781481465656

LC 2015036450

A biographical novel in verse of three different girls in three different time periods who grew up to become groundbreaking scientists. Provided by publisher.

"Science is woven through the narratives, but within the fabric of the characters' daily lives and family struggles. While the Mary Anning narrative is the most haunting, each of these three perceptive portrayals is original and memorable." Booklist.

Includes bibliographical references.

Atkinson, E. J. (Elizabeth Jane), 1961-

I, Emma Freke. Elizabeth Atkinson. Carolrhoda Books, c2010. 234 p.

Grades: 4 5 6 7 **Fic**

    1. Eccentrics and eccentricities 2. Family reunions 3. Twelve-year-old girls 4. Single-parent families 5. Families 6. Massachusetts 7. Wisconsin 8. Coming-of-age stories

ISBN 9780761356042

LC 2009038923

Growing up near Boston with her free-spirited mother and old-world grandfather, twelve-year-old Emma has always felt out of place but when she attends the family reunion her father's family holds annually in Wisconsin, she is in for some surprises.

"This rich story of self-acceptance offers readers much to think about. . . . The first-person narrative moves along briskly, with believable dialogue and plenty of humor." Booklist.

Austen, Catherine, 1965-

Walking backward. Catherine Austen. Orca Book Publishers, 2009. 176 p.

Grades: 6 7 8 9 **Fic**

    1. Twelve-year-old boys 2. Children of widowers 3. Grief in families 4. Mothers -- Death 5. Women traffic accident victims 6. Realistic fiction 7. Diary novels

ISBN 9781554691470

LC 2009928210

"In this impressive debut novel, Josh keeps a journal to chart his feelings and thoughts, allowing readers to follow his journey from sadness to acceptance and the eventual return of cohesion in his family. Given the subject matter, the story is never maudlin, and Josh's voice rings natural and true. An elegantly crafted volume of lasting power." Kirkus.

Auxier, Jonathan

The **night** gardener. Jonathan Auxier. Amulet Books, 2014. 400 p.

Grades: 4 5 6 7 **Fic**

    1. Orphans 2. Household employees 3. Storytelling 4. Ghosts 5. Trees 6. England 7. Horror 8. Ghost stories 9. Historical fiction

ISBN 9781419711442

LC 2013047655

When orphaned Irish siblings Molly and Kip arrive to work as servants at a creepy, crumbling English manor house, they discover that the house and its inhabitants are not what they seem. Soon the siblings are confronted by a mysterious stranger and the secrets of the cursed house will change their lives forever.

"Molly's whimsical tales illustrate life's essential lessons even as they entertain. As the characters face the unhealthy pull of the tree's allurements, they grow and change, revealing unexpected personality traits. Storytelling as a force to cope with life's challenges is subtly expressed and adds complexity to the fast-paced plot." School Library Journal.

Peter Nimble and his fantastic eyes: a story. by Jonathan Auxier. Amulet Books, 2011. 400 p.: Peter Nimble adventures

Grades: 4 5 6 7 **Fic**

    1. Boys who are blind 2. Boy thieves 3. Eye 4. Magic 5. Adventure 6. Gateway fantasy 7. Fantasy fiction

ISBN 9781419700255

LC 2010048692

When 10-year-old Peter Nimble, a blind orphan, discovers a magical pair of eyes, he is magically transported to a hidden island where he is asked to travel beyond the known world and rescue a lost kingdom from its evil ruler.

"The fast-paced, episodic story, accompanied by Auxier's occasional pen-and-ink drawings, is inventive, unpredictable, and—like its hero—nimble." Publishers Weekly.

★ **Sophie** Quire and the last Storyguard. by Jonathan Auxier. Amulet Books, 2016. 400 p.: Peter Nimble adventures

Grades: 4 5 6 7 **Fic**

    1. Books 2. Boy orphans 3. Adventure 4. Magic 5. Boys who are blind 6. Fantasy fiction

ISBN 9781419717475

LC 2015039272

It's been two years since Peter Nimble and Sir Tode rescued the kingdom of HazelPort. In that time, they have traveled far and wide in search of adventure. Now they have been summoned by Professor Cake for a new mission: To find a twelve-year-old bookmender named Sophie Quire. Sophie knows little beyond the four walls of her father's bookshop, where she repairs old books and dreams of escaping the confines of her dull life. But when a strange boy and his talking cat/horse companion show up with a rare and mysterious book, she finds herself pulled into an adventure beyond anything she has ever read.

"Ultimately, this affecting, compelling story stands on its own, embodying and highlighting the power and impact of tales well told—and why they endure." Booklist.

Avery, Tom

Not as we know it. Tom Avery. Schwartz & Wade Books, [2016] 176 p.

Grades: 5 6 7 8 9 **Fic**

    1. 1980s 2. Twin brothers 3. Cystic fibrosis 4. Mermen 5. Imaginary creatures 6. Coastal towns 7. England 8. Low fantasy

ISBN 9780553535099

LC oc2015054847

Can a mysterious sea creature save eleven-year-old Jamie's very sick twin brother?

"Through Jamies thoughtful narration, readers are treated to a hauntingly beautiful story about brotherly bonds, wrenching grief, and the untethered hope that everything will somehow work out." Publishers Weekly.

Aveyard, Victoria

Red queen. Victoria Aveyard. HarperTeen, 2015. 416 p.: Red queen (Victoria Aveyard)

Grades: 8 9 10 11 **Fic**

    1. Thieves 2. Revolutions 3. Superhuman abilities 4. Princesses 5. Blood 6. Fantasy fiction 7. Dystopian fiction

ISBN 9780062310637

When her latent supernatural powers manifest in front of a noble court, Mare, a thief in a world divided between commoners and superhumans, is forced to assume the role of lost princess before risking everything to help a growing rebellion.

"First-time author Aveyard has created a volatile world with a dynamic heroine, and while there are moments of romance, they refreshingly take a backseat to the action. Anticipation is already high for this debut, and with the movie rights already acquired and two sequels to come, it will likely only grow." Booklist.

Avi, 1937-

The **button** war: a tale of the Great War. Avi. Candlewick Press, 2018 240 p.

Grades: 5 6 7 8   **Fic**

1. 1910s 2. Soldiers 3. Stealing 4. Competition in boys 5. Twelve-year-old boys 6. Friendship 7. Poland 8. Historical fiction
ISBN 9780763690533

Running with friends who entertain themselves by coming up with risky dares, Patryk watches as their village is occupied by hostile nations throughout the Great War, before his friends begin looting the dead soldiers as part of their competition.

Catch you later, traitor: a novel. by Avi. Algonquin Young Readers, [2015] 304 p.

Grades: 4 5 6 7   **Fic**

1. 1950s 2. Communism 3. Suspicion 4. Baseball teams 5. Families 6. Twelve-year-old boys 7. Brooklyn, New York City 8. Historical fiction
ISBN 9781616203597

LC 2014031983

It's 1951, and twelve-year-old Pete Collison is a regular kid in Brooklyn, New York, who loves Sam Spade detective books and radio crime dramas. But when an FBI agent shows up at Pete's doorstep, accusing Pete's father of being a Communist, Pete is caught in a real-life mystery. Could there really be Commies in Pete's family? Provided by publisher.

City of orphans. Avi; illustrated by Greg Ruth. Atheneum Books for Young Readers, 2011. 288 p.

Grades: 5 6 7 8   **Fic**

1. Waldorf-Astoria Hotel, New York. 2. 1890s 3. Newspaper vendors 4. Malicious accusation 5. Homeless girls 6. Lawyers 7. Gangs 8. New York City 9. Historical fiction
ISBN 9781416971023

LC 2010049229

In 1893 New York, thirteen-year-old Maks, a newsboy, teams up with Willa, a homeless girl, to clear his older sister, Emma, from charges that she stole from the brand new Waldorf Hotel, where she works. Includes historical notes.

"Avi's vivid recreation of the sights and sounds of that time and place is spot on, masterfully weaving accurate historical details with Maks' experiences." Kirkus.

Includes bibliographical references.

Crispin: the cross of lead. Avi. Hyperion Books for Children, 2002. 256 p.: Crispin

Grades: 5 6 7 8   **Fic**

1. Medieval period (476-1492) 2. Plantagenet period (1154-1485) 3. 14th century 4. Malicious accusation 5. Orphans 6. Secrets 7. Boys 8. Identity (Psychology) 9. Great Britain 10. Historical fiction
ISBN 0786808284

LC 2001051829

Newbery Medal, 2003.

Falsely accused of theft and murder, an orphaned peasant boy in fourteenth-century England flees his village and meets a larger-than-life juggler who holds a dangerous secret.

"This book is a page-turner from beginning to end.... A meticulously crafted story, full of adventure, mystery, and action." School Library Journal.

The **end** of the world and beyond: continues The unexpected life of Oliver Cromwell Pitts: being an absolutely accurate autobiographical account of my follies, fortune & fate written by himself. Avi. Algonquin Young Readers, 2019. 304 p.

Grades: 4 5 6 7   **Fic**

1. Colonial America (1600-1775) 2. Georgian era (1714-1837) 3. Indentured servants 4. Separated friends, relatives, etc 5. Male friendship 6. Prisoners 7. Slavery 8. United States 9. Great Britain 10. Historical fiction
ISBN 9781616205652

LC 2018014555

After his thievery conviction in 1724, Oliver Cromwell Pitts is sent from England across the Atlantic to America where he is enslaved on a tobacco farm, never giving up on finding his sister, Charity, brought to the colonies on a different ship.

The **fighting** ground. by Avi. HarperTropy, 1987, c1984. 157 p.

Grades: 5 6 7 8   **Fic**

1. Revolutionary America (1775-1783) 2. 18th century 3. Teenage soldiers 4. Thirteen-year-old boys 5. Revolutions 6. American Revolution, 1775-1783 7. United States 8. War stories 9. Historical fiction
ISBN 9780064401852

LC 880141037

Scott O'Dell Historical Fiction Award, 1985.

Thirteen-year-old Jonathan goes off to fight in the Revolutionary War and discovers the real war is being fought within himself.

"It's April 1776, and the fighting ground is both the farm country of Pennsylvania and the heart of a boy which is wonderful ripe for war. Twenty-four hours transform Jonathan from a cocky 13-year-old, eager to take on the British, into a young man who now knows the horror, the pathos, the ambiguities of war." Voice of Youth Advocates.

Gold rush girl. Avi. Candlewick Press, 2020. 320 p.

Grades: 5 6 7 8   **Fic**

1. 1840s 2. Independence in girls 3. Gold rush 4. Kidnapping 5. Gender role 6. Rescues 7. San Francisco, California 8. Historical fiction 9. Adventure stories
ISBN 9781536206791

Finding freedom and friendship in 1848 San Francisco while her father searches for gold, Tory embarks on a mud-caked search for her kidnapped brother throughout San Francisco Bay's treacherous Rotten Row area and its hundreds of abandoned ships.

"Tory's first-person narration further connects readers to the gold rush-era story, which concludes with room for future exploits. One of Avi's best." Booklist

Iron thunder: the battle between the Monitor & the Merrimac: a Civil War novel. Avi. Hyperion, 2007. 224 p.: I witness

Grades: 4 5 6   **Fic**

1. Ericsson, John, 1803-1889 2. Monitor (Ironclad) 3. Merrimack (Frigate) 4. American Civil War era (1861-1865) 5. Thirteen-year-old boys 6. Responsibility 7. Spies 8. Spies -- History 19th century 9. New York City 10. Historical fiction
ISBN 1423104463

After his father is killed during the Civil War, thirteen-year-old Tom takes on a job to at the ironworks to support his family, and finds himself a target of ruthless spies when he begins assisting with the ironclad ship the "Monitor."

"This fascinating adventure taken from U.S. history begins in Brooklyn in 1862, when Tom Carroll, 13, is hired at the Iron Works in Greenpoint for a secret project, derisively known around the borough as Ericsson's Folly. John Ericsson, a Swedish inventor, is trying to build an ironclad ship that can battle the Merrimac, a Confederate ship being outfitted with metal plates in Virginia.... Illustrated with period engravings, this is gripping historical fiction from a keenly imagined perspective." Publishers Weekly.

The **most** important thing: stories about sons, fathers, and grandfathers. Avi. Candlewick Press, 2016 215 p.

Grades: 5 6 7 8 **Fic**

1. Fathers and sons 2. Grandfather and grandson 3. Family relationships 4. Families 5. Realistic fiction 6. Short stories
ISBN 9780763681111

"Avi's deft incorporation of humor, heartache, and the occasional touch of the supernatural will draw readers in as they ponder how family ties bind in both positive and negative ways." Publishers Weekly.

Nothing but the truth: a documentary novel. Avi. Orchard Books, 1991. 177 p.

Grades: 6 7 8 9 10 **Fic**

1. Journalism 2. Student suspension 3. Patriotism 4. Teacher-student relationships 5. Women high school principals
ISBN 9780545174152

LC   91009200

A ninth-grader's suspension for singing "The Star-Spangled Banner" during homeroom becomes a national news story.

Old wolf. Avi; illustrated by Brian Floca. Atheneum Books for Young Readers, 2015 160 p.

Grades: 5 6 7 8 **Fic**

1. Wolves 2. Ravens 3. Hunting 4. Video games 5. Thirteen-year-old boys 6. Animal fantasy
ISBN 9781442499218

A wolf teams up with a remarkable raven to survive a period of winter privation in the Colorado Mountains, where they cross paths with a 13-year-old computer gamer.

The **seer** of shadows. by Avi. HarperCollins Publishers, 2008. 202 p.

Grades: 4 5 6 7 **Fic**

1. 1870s 2. Fourteen-year-old boys 3. Ghosts 4. Fourteen-year-olds 5. Swindlers and swindling 6. Photographers 7. New York City 8. Horror
ISBN 9780060000158

LC   2007010891

In New York City in 1872, fourteen-year-old Horace, a photographer's apprentice, becomes entangled in a plot to create fraudulent spirit photographs, but when Horace accidentally frees the real ghost of a dead girl bent on revenge, his life takes a frightening turn.

"Fast-paced yet haunting. . . . This engaging novel has great immediacy and strong narrative drive." Booklist.

★ **Sophia's** war: a tale of the Revolution. Avi. Beach Lane Books, 2012. 288 p.

Grades: 5 6 7 8 **Fic**

1. Revolutionary America (1775-1783) 2. 18th century 3. Spies 4. Courage 5. Espionage 6. Teenage girls 7. American Revolution, 1775-1783 8. New York City. 9. United States. 10. Historical fiction
ISBN 9781442414419

LC   2012007962

In 1776, after witnessing the execution of Nathan Hale in New York City, newly occupied by the British army, young Sophia Calderwood resolves to do all she can to help the American cause, including becoming a spy.

The **true** confessions of Charlotte Doyle. Avi; decorations by Ruth E. Murray. Orchard Books, 1990. 215 p.

Grades: 5 6 7 **Fic**

1. 1830s 2. 19th century 3. Thirteen-year-old girls 4. Travelers 5. Mutiny 6. Conspiracies 7. Independence in girls 8. Atlantic Ocean 9. Adventure stories 10. Historical fiction 11. Sea stories
ISBN 9780545477116

LC   90030624

Golden Kite Award for Fiction, 1990.

As the lone "young lady" on a transatlantic voyage in 1832, Charlotte learns that the captain is murderous and the crew rebellious. Includes ship illustrations in an appendix.

"The author has fashioned an intriguing, suspenseful, carefully crafted tale, with nonstop action on the high seas." Booklist.

The **unexpected** life of Oliver Cromwell Pitts. Avi. Algonquin Young Readers, 2017. 240 p.

Grades: 4 5 6 7 **Fic**

1. Georgian era (1714-1837) 2. Runaway boys 3. Criminals 4. Separated friends, relatives, etc 5. Institutions (for debtors, the poor, homeless, etc) 6. Voyages and travels 7. England 8. Great Britain 9. Historical fiction
ISBN 9781616205645

LC   2016042923

In 1724 England, twelve-year-old Oliver Cromwell Pitts embarks on a journey from his seaside home in Melcombe Regis to London to find his father and his older sister, a journey filled with thieves, adventurers, and treachery.

"An ingeniously plotted Dickensian story filled with suspense, surprises, and ultimately satisfaction." Booklist.

Axelrod, Amy

Your friend in fashion, Abby Shapiro. Amy Axelrod. Holiday House, 2011. 261 p.

Grades: 4 5 6 **Fic**

1. Onassis, Jacqueline Kennedy, 1929-1994. 2. 1950s 3. Jewish girls 4. Fashion design 5. Bras 6. Barbie dolls 7. Letter writing 8. Massachusetts 9. Historical fiction
ISBN 9780823423408

LC   2010024185

Beginning in 1959, Abby, nearly eleven, writes a series of letters to Jackie Kennedy, each with sketches of outfits she has designed, as she faces family problems, concerns about neighbors, and her own desperate desire for both her first bra and a Barbie doll.

"Abby is an especially memorable protagonist, but all [Axelrod's] characters vibrate with life. . . . Funny, lively, sensitivea real winner." Kirkus.

Azad, Nafiza

The **candle** and the flame. Nafiza Azad. Scholastic Press, 2019. 391 p.

Grades: 8 9 10 11 **Fic**

1. Genies 2. Transformations (Magic) 3. Political intrigue 4. Civil war 5. Magic 6. Silk Road 7. Middle East 8. Middle Eastern-influenced fantasy 9. Mythological fiction 10. Fantasy fiction
ISBN 9781338306040

LC   2018041274

Fatima lives in the city of Noor, on the Silk Road, which is currently protected by the Ifrit, djinn of order and reason, from attacks by the violent and ruthless Shayateen djinn—but Fatima was infused with the fire of the Ifrit who died saving her when she was four years old, and when one of the most important Ifrit dies she finds herself drawn into the intrigues of the court, the affairs of the djinn, and the very real dangers of a magical battlefield.

"Azad combines Islamic concepts and Middle Eastern mythology with a variety of other traditions to create a magical treatise on identity, community, friendship, and love. Readers will identify with female characters who struggle against limiting societal expectations. The themes of trauma and grief are treated with care. Azad's vivid depiction of the details of Noor's sights and sounds make the city come alive." School Library Journal.

Babbitt, Natalie

★ **Tuck** everlasting. Natalie Babbitt. Farrar, Straus, Giroux, 1975. 139 p.

Grades: 5 6 7 8   **Fic**
1. Fountains of youth (Legendary springs) 2. Immortality 3. Secrets 4. Aging 5. Boy/girl relations 6. Low fantasy 7. Fantasy fiction 8. Classics
ISBN 0374378487

LC   75033306

A family accidentally stumbles upon a spring with water endowing them with the gift of eternal life. Seventy years later, without having grown a day older, a young girl discovers them and learns their secret.

"The story is macabre and moral, exciting and excellently written." New York Times Book Review.

Bacigalupi, Paolo

The **Drowned** Cities. by Paolo Bacigalupi. Little, Brown and Co., 2012. 448 p.

Grades: 9 10 11 12   **Fic**
1. Dystopias 2. Post-apocalypse 3. Orphans 4. Genetic engineering 5. Rescues 6. Science fiction
ISBN 9780316056243

LC   2011031762

In a dark future America that has devolved into unending civil wars, orphans Mahlia and Mouse barely escape the war-torn lands of the Drowned Cities, but their fragile safety is soon threatened and Mahlia will have to risk everything if she is to save Mouse, as he once saved her.

Ship breaker: a novel. by Paolo Bacigalupi. Little, Brown and Co., 2010. 326 p.

Grades: 8 9 10 11 12   **Fic**
1. Post-apocalypse 2. Shipwreck survivors 3. Dystopias 4. Scavenging 5. Clipper-ships 6. Gulf Coast (United States) 7. Dystopian fiction 8. Science fiction
ISBN 9780316056212

LC   2009034424

Michael L. Printz Award, 2011.

A tale set in a Gulf Coast shanty town 100 years in the future finds teen Nailer dreaming of a better life on the sea before discovering a beached clipper ship and lone survivor.

"Bacigalupi's cast is ethnically and morally diverse, and the book's message never overshadows the storytelling, action-packed pacing, or intricate world-building. At its core, the novel is an exploration of Nailer's discovery of the nature of the world around him and his ability to transcend that world's expectations." Publishers Weekly.

Tool of war. Paolo Bacigalupi. Little, Brown and Company, 2017. 384 p.

Grades: 8 9 10 11 12   **Fic**
1. Genetically engineered men 2. Resistance to government 3.

Revenge 4. Dystopias 5. Soldiers 6. Science fiction
ISBN 9780316220835

LC 2016051846

In a future beset with rising seas, corporate government, and constant civil war, a bioengineered half-man/half-beast super-soldier who calls himself Tool breaks his conditioning to overcome his genetically enhanced sense of loyalty to the corporation that created him and seeks revenge against his old masters.

"Tool is at center stage at last as readers move through Bacigalupi's exploration of the intricate relationships connecting hunter and prey, master and enslaved, human and monster. Masterful." Kirkus.

Baker, Matthew, 1985-

If you find this. by Matthew Baker. 368 p.

Grades: 4 5 6 7   **Fic**
1. Heirlooms 2. Boy prodigies 3. Child misfits 4. Grandfathers 5. Haunted houses 6. Adventure stories
ISBN 9780316240086

LC 2013044749

When the grandfather he never knew is released from prison suffering from dementia, eleven-year-old Nicholas, a mathematical and musical genius, tries to save the family's home by helping search for heirlooms Grandpa claims to have buried.

"The vivid setting, complex characters, and original writing style result in a story with lasting impact. Reminiscent of Louis Sachars Holes (1998), this is a rich, captivating tale about family and redemption that redefines the meaning of treasure." Booklist.

Baldwin, James, 1924-1987

Go tell it on the mountain. James Baldwin. Dial Press Trade Paperbacks, 2005, c1953. 226 p.

Grades: 8 9 10 11 12 Adult   **Fic**
1. 1930s 2. African American men 3. Identity (Psychology) 4. Culture conflict 5. Racism 6. Children of clergy 7. Harlem, New York City 8. New York City 9. Modern classics 10. Literary fiction 11. Coming-of-age stories
ISBN 0385334575

LC 2005280211

While his family struggles with guilt, bitterness, and spiritual issues, John Grimes experiences a religious conversion in the Temple of the Fire Baptised.

"Though the religious experiences of these characters may seem sectarian, they are really universal. All of the major characters are trying to build and sustain community in the face of dehumanizing oppression. Their particular version of Christianity is an effective response to being captives in a racist culture." Magill Book Review.

Balliett, Blue, 1955-

Chasing Vermeer. by Blue Balliett; with artwork by Brett Helquist. Scholastic Press, 2004. 272 p.: Chasing Vermeer

Grades: 5 6 7 8   **Fic**
1. Vermeer, Johannes, 1632-1675 2. Child detectives 3. Art thefts 4. International intrigue 5. Sixth-graders 6. Friendship 7. Chicago, Illinois 8. Mysteries
ISBN 0439372941

LC 2002152106

When seemingly unrelated and strange events start to happen and a precious Vermeer painting disappears, eleven-year-olds Petra and Calder combine their talents to solve an international art scandal.

"Balliett's purpose seems to be to get children to think about relationships, connections, coincidences, and the subtle language of artwork. . . . [This is] a book that offers children something new upon each reading. . . . Helquist . . . outdoes himself here, providing an interactive mystery in his pictures." Booklist.

The danger box. Blue Balliett. Scholastic Press, 2010. 306 p.
Grades: 5 6 7 8 **Fic**
    1. Darwin, Charles, 1809-1882 2. Children of alcoholic fathers 3. Diaries 4. Stealing 5. Nearsightedness 6. Grandparents 7. Michigan 8. Mysteries
ISBN 9780439852098

                     LC 2010016622
In small-town Michigan, twelve-year-old Zoomy and his new friend Lorrol investigate the journal found inside a mysterious box and find family secrets and a more valuable treasure, while a dangerous stranger watches and waits.
    "This highly satisfying story will enlighten readers even as it inspires them to think about their own danger boxes." School Library Journal.

Hold fast. by Blue Balliett. Scholastic Press, 2013. 288 p.
Grades: 3 4 5 6 **Fic**
    1. Homelessness 2. Missing persons 3. Library employees 4. Kidnapping 5. Father-separated children 6. Chicago, Illinois 7. Mysteries 8. Realistic fiction
ISBN 9780545299886

                     LC 2012041035
On a cold winter day in Chicago, Early's father disappeared, and now she, her mother and her brother have been forced to flee their apartment and join the ranks of the homeless—and it is up to Early to hold her family together and solve the mystery surrounding her father.

Pieces and players. Blue Balliett. Scholastic Press, 2015 306 p.: Chasing Vermeer
Grades: 5 6 7 8 **Fic**
    1. Art thefts 2. Museum thefts 3. Teenage detectives 4. Ghosts 5. Thirteen-year-olds 6. Chicago, Illinois 7. Mysteries
ISBN 9780545299909

"This time it's a small family museum and 13 missing pieces of art providing the mystery that brings back characters met in previous titles. Tommy, Petra, and Calder are joined by Early Pearl and Zoomy Chamberlain. With all five kids led by their teacher Mrs. Hussey, each of the detective's special skills add to their understanding and help them arrive at the solution. Fans of the previous books will be delighted as these characters continue with their familiar predilections such as Calder's pentominoes clacking in his pockets. . . . Fun and engaging; a fitting addition for readers addicted to these art mysteries." School Library Journal.

Bannen, Megan

The bird and the blade. Megan Bannen. Balzer + Bray, 2018 432 p.
Grades: 7 8 9 10 11 12 **Fic**
    1. 13th century 2. Enslaved women 3. Exiles 4. Princes 5. Rulers 6. Marriage 7. Mongol Empire 8. Historical fiction
ISBN 9780062674159

A slave with a secret past is forced to serve the exiled prince she loves as he risks his life in a desperate effort to forge a political marriage with a powerful and deadly princess.

Baptiste, Tracey

The jumbie god's revenge. Tracey Baptiste. Algonquin Young Readers, 2019. 272 p.: The jumbies (Tracey Baptiste)
Grades: 4 5 6 7 **Fic**
    1. Spirits 2. Half-human hybrids 3. Hurricanes 4. Quests 5.

Gods and goddesses, African Caribbean 6. Caribbean Area 7. Fantasy fiction 8. Fairy tale and folklore-inspired fiction
ISBN 9781616208912

                     LC 2019006071
After two out-of-season hurricanes nearly destroy her island home, Corinne discovers that the god Huracan is angry and she, aided by friends and enemies alike, races to calm him.
    "Baptiste continues to successfully blend fantastical and realistic elements, punctuating the plot with true and terrifying details, such as the speed and level of a hurricane's physical destruction, without impeding the Caribbean folktale motifs that underscore the series." Horn Book.

The jumbies. Tracey Baptiste. Algonquin Young Readers, an imprint of Algonquin Books, 2015. 240 p.: The jumbies (Tracey Baptiste)
Grades: 4 5 6 7 **Fic**
    1. Spirits 2. Revenge 3. Forests 4. Magic 5. Single-parent families 6. Caribbean Area 7. Horror 8. Fantasy fiction 9. Fairy tale and folklore-inspired fiction
ISBN 9781616204143

                     LC 2014038605
Eleven-year-old Corinne must call on her courage and an ancient magic to stop an evil spirit and save her island home.

Rise of the jumbies. by Tracey Baptiste. Algonquin Young Readers, 2017. 256 p.: The jumbies (Tracey Baptiste)
Grades: 4 5 6 7 **Fic**
    1. Spirits 2. Half-human hybrids 3. Mermaids 4. Missing children 5. Quests 6. Caribbean Area 7. Fantasy fiction 8. Horror 9. Fairy tale and folklore-inspired fiction
ISBN 9781616206659

                     LC 2017020557
Suspicion falls on half-jumbie Corinne when local children from her Caribbean island home begin to disappear, and she is forced to go deep into the ocean to seek the help of a dangerous jumbie who rules the waves.
    "Baptiste allows her characters to find and create ways to grapple with uncomfortable truths. A stirring and mystical tale sure to keep readers thinking past the final page." Kirkus.

Baratz-Logsted, Lauren

Crazy beautiful. by Lauren Baratz-Logsted. Houghton Mifflin Harcourt, 2009. 208 p.
Grades: 7 8 9 10 **Fic**
    1. People who have had amputations 2. Teenage boys with disabilities 3. Friendship 4. Interpersonal relations 5. High school students 6. Realistic fiction 7. Fairy tale and folklore-inspired fiction
ISBN 9780547223070

                     LC 2008040463
In this contemporary retelling of "Beauty and the Beast," a teenaged boy whose hands were amputated in an explosion and a gorgeous girl whose mother has recently died form an instant connection when they meet on their first day as new students.
    "This romance transcends all of its potential pitfalls to create a powerful story about recovery and friendship." Kirkus.

Bardugo, Leigh

King of scars. Leigh Bardugo. Imprint, a part of Macmillan Publishing Group, LLC, 2019. 527 p.: King of Scars duology
Grades: 8 9 10 11 12 **Fic**
    1. Rulers 2. Transformations (Magic) 3. Imaginary kingdoms 4.

Demonic possession 5. Demons 6. High fantasy 7. Fantasy fiction
ISBN 9781250142283

When the dark magical force within him challenges his effort to forge new alliances and build a defense against a new threat, Nikolai Lantsov, the young king of Ravka, embarks on a journey to his country's most magical places to vanquish it.

"Deadly clever political intrigue, heart-stopping adventure, memorable characters, and several understated, hinted-at romances (how will we wait?!) come together in one glorious, Slavic-folklore-infused package." Booklist.

Ruin and rising. Leigh Bardugo. Henry Holt and Company, 2014. 448 p.: Grisha trilogy
Grades: 8 9 10 11 12   **Fic**
    1. Quests 2. Orphans 3. Power (Social sciences) 4. Firebird (Mythical bird) 5. Good and evil 6. High fantasy 7. Fantasy fiction
ISBN 9780805094619
                        LC 2013049306

The Darkling rules Ravka from his shadow throne. Alina forges new alliances as she and Mal search for Morozova's last amplifier. But as she begins to unravel the Darkling's secrets, she reveals a past that alters her understanding of the bond they share and the power she wields" Provided by publisher.

"Alina and company have only one hope: if they can kill the Firebird, its magical bones can be used to break the Darkling's chokehold on Ravka. In this concluding volume, Alina must rely on her childhood friend Mal's preternatural tracking ability. Bardugo's longstanding theme of power corrupts is developed organically; the magic she invents will surprise and delight readers." Horn Book.

Siege and storm. Leigh Bardugo. Henry Holt and Company, 2013. 384 p.: Grisha trilogy
Grades: 8 9 10 11 12   **Fic**
    1. Orphans 2. Power (Social sciences) 3. Monsters 4. Visions 5. Magic 6. High fantasy 7. Fantasy fiction
ISBN 9780805094602
                        LC 2012046361

Hunted across the True Sea and haunted by the lives she took on the Fold, Alina must try to make a life with Mal in an unfamiliar land, all while keeping her identity as the Sun Summoner a secret.

Wonder Woman: Warbringer. Leigh Bardugo. Random House, [2017] 304 p.: DC icons
Grades: 6 7 8 9 10   **Fic**
    1. Women superheroes 2. Women warriors 3. Teenage girl orphans 4. Wonder Woman (Fictitious character) 5. Rescues 6. Superhero stories 7. Franchise books
ISBN 9780399549731
                        LC 2016044698

Diana, Princess of the Amazons, journeys to the World of Man in this coming-of-age young adult story. Provided by publisher.

"Bardugo breathes zippy new life into the story with a twisty plot, whip-smart characters, and her trademark masterful writing." Booklist.

Barker, M. P. (Michele P.), 1960-
Mending horses. M.P. Barker. Holiday House, [2014] viii, 309 p.
Grades: 5 6 7 8   **Fic**
    1. 19th century 2. 1830s 3. Irish Americans 4. Horses 5. Peddlers 6. Gender role 7. Prejudice 8. New England -- History.

9. Historical fiction
ISBN 9780823429486
                        LC bl2014005100

Daniel and his horse, Ivy, make their way in the world along with a group of unlikely friends.

Barnes, Jennifer (Jennifer Lynn)
Perfect cover. Jennifer Lynn Barnes. Delacorte Press, 2008. 288 p.: Squad
Grades: 7 8 9 10   **Fic**
    1. Teenage spies 2. Cheerleading 3. High schools 4. Teenage girls 5. Hackers 6. Spy fiction 7. Humorous stories 8. Teenagers' writings
ISBN 9780385734547
                        LC 2007009352

High school sophomore Toby Klein enjoys computer hacking and wearing combat boots, so she thinks it is a joke when she is invited to join the cheerleading squad but soon learns cheering is just a cover for an elite group of government operatives known as the Squad.

"In addition to offering crafty plotting and time-honored, typical teen conflicts and rivalries, Barnes maintains a sharp sense of humor in this action-adventure series." Bulletin of the Center for Children's Books.

Barnett, Mac
The **terrible** two. by Mac Barnett & Jory John; illustrated by Kevin Cornell. Amulet Books, 2015. 240 p.: Terrible two
Grades: 4 5 6 7 8   **Fic**
    1. Practical jokers 2. Practical jokes 3. New students 4. Schools 5. Moving, Household 6. Realistic fiction 7. Humorous stories 8. Illustrated books
ISBN 9781419714917
                        LC 2014027503

When master prankster Miles Murphy moves to sleepy Yawnee Valley, he challenges the local, mystery prankster in an epic battle of tricks but soon the two join forces to pull off the biggest prank ever seen.

"Cornell's (The Chicken Squad) b&w cartoons layer on the laughs, especially when portraying the megalomaniacal Principal Barkin, and Barnett and John's deadpan writing lets Yawnee Valleys absurdity shine." Publishers Weekly.

The **terrible** two get worse. Mac Barnett, Jory John; illustrated by Kevin Cornell. Amulet Books, 2016. 224 p.: Terrible two
Grades: 4 5 6 7 8   **Fic**
    1. Practical jokers 2. Practical jokes 3. School principals 4. Schools 5. Friendship 6. Realistic fiction 7. Humorous stories 8. Illustrated books
ISBN 9781419716805
                        LC 2015011114

Friends and pranking partners Miles and Niles face a tough challenge when their favorite goat and nemesis, Principal Barkin, is replaced by his stern, no-nonsense father, Former Principal Barkin, who turns the school into boot camp. Provided by publisher.

"This humorous sequel makes for engaging, fast-paced reading that again highlights the meaning of friendship, and animated, amusing cartoon illustrations enhance and extend the story." Booklist.

Barnhill, Kelly Regan
★ The **girl** who drank the moon. Kelly Barnhill. Algonquin Young Readers, 2016. 368 p.
Grades: 5 6 7 8   **Fic**
    1. Witches 2. Human sacrifice 3. Adopted girls 4. Forests 5.

Magic 6. Fantasy fiction
ISBN 9781616205676

LC 2016006542

Newbery Medal, 2017.

An epic fantasy about a young girl raised by a witch, a swamp monster, and a Perfectly Tiny Dragon, who must unlock the powerful magic buried deep inside her.

"The swiftly paced, highly imaginative plot draws a myriad of threads together to form a web of characters, magic, and integrated lives. Spiritual overtones encompass much of the storytelling with love as the glue that holds it all together." School Library Journal.

The **mostly** true story of Jack. by Kelly Barnhill. Little, Brown, 2011. 336 p.

Grades: 5 6 7 8 **Fic**
1. Children of divorced parents 2. Missing children 3. Bullying and bullies 4. Magic 5. Friendship 6. Iowa 7. Fantasy fiction
ISBN 9780316056700

LC 2010044934

Jack is practically invisible at home, but when his parents send him to Hazelwood, Iowa, to spend a summer with his odd aunt and uncle, he suddenly makes friends, is beaten up by the town bully, and is plotted against by the richest man in town.

"A truly splendid amalgamation of mystery, magic and creeping horror will spellbind the middle-grade set. . . . The mystery deepens with each chapter, revealing exactly the right amount with each step. Answers are doled out so meticulously that readers will be continually intrigued rather than frustrated. The result is the ultime page-turner." Kirkus.

★ The **witch's** boy. Kelly Barnhill. Algonquin Young Readers, 2014. 384 p.

Grades: 5 6 7 8 **Fic**
1. Witches 2. Outlaws 3. Twin brothers 4. Magic 5. Soul 6. Fantasy fiction
ISBN 9781616203511

LC 2014014704

When a Bandit King comes to take the magic that Ned's mother, a witch, is meant to protect, the stuttering, weak boy villagers think should have drowned rather than his twin summons the strength to protect his family and community, while in the woods, the bandit's daughter puzzles over a mystery that ties her to Ned.

"The writing is beautiful and lyrical, but keeps pace with an action-packed story. Powerful themes of grief, redemption, forgiveness, sacrifice, and generosity are all present." Voice of Youth Advocates.

Barnholdt, Lauren

Sometimes it happens. by Lauren Barnholdt. Simon Pulse, 2011. 320 p.

Grades: 7 8 9 10 **Fic**
1. Breaking up (Interpersonal relations) 2. Betrayal 3. Insecurity in teenage girls 4. Insecurity (Psychology) 5. Interpersonal relations 6. Teen chick lit
ISBN 9781442413146

With help from her best friend Ava and Ava's boyfriend Noah, Hannah is recovering from being dumped by her boyfriend Sebastian, but on the first day of their senior year in high school, Ava learns that Hannah and Noah betrayed her while she was away.

"The writing style is smooth, featuring believable dialogue and first-person narration from Hannah's perspective. Hannah is a sympathetic character struggling with a relatable dilemma of liking your friend's significant other, yet wanting to be a faithful friend. The underlying message is captured by the title, Sometimes It Happens, as Hannah grows to understand that part of being human is hurting people without meaning to and then needing to ask for forgiveness." Voice of Youth Advocates.

Barratt, Mark

Joe Rat. by Mark Barratt. Eerdmans Books for Young Readers, 2009. 307 p.

Grades: 7 8 9 10 **Fic**
1. Victorian era (1837-1901) 2. Homeless children 3. Sewers 4. Crime 5. Runaways 6. Boy orphans 7. London, England 8. Great Britain 9. Historical fiction
ISBN 9780802853561

LC 2008055972

In the dark, dank sewers of Victorian London, a boy known as Joe Rat scrounges for valuables which he gives to "Mother," a criminal mastermind who considers him a favorite, but a chance meeting with a runaway girl and "the Madman" transforms all their lives.

"The unraveling of the Madman's identity is but one of the pleasures of Barratt's leisurely and convincing historical fiction." Booklist.

Barrett, Tracy, 1955-

The **stepsister's** tale. Tracy Barrett. Harlequin Teen, [2014] 304 p.

Grades: 7 8 9 10 **Fic**
1. Stepsisters 2. Poverty 3. Blended families 4. Balls (Parties) 5. Poor families 6. Fairy tale and folklore-inspired fiction
ISBN 9780373211210

LC bl2014023484

Jane cares for her mother and sister until her stepfather dies, leaving nothing but debts and Jane's spoiled stepsister behind, but a mysterious boy from the woods and an invitation to a royal ball are certain to change her fate.

"Sometimes it feels like fairy-tale retellings are a dime a dozen, and this is certainly not the first or the last account of a misunderstood antagonist. But, Barrett's comparably quiet account of a household of women working to survive together as a family, sometimes in spite of one another, shines with soft, bucolic realism...Overall, this is an enjoyable read. The inclusion of discussion questions in the back makes it a solid choice for book clubs." Voice of Youth Advocates.

Barron, Rena

Maya and the rising dark. Rena Barron. Houghton Mifflin Harcourt, 2020. 304 p.: Maya and the rising dark

Grades: 5 6 7 **Fic**
1. Missing persons 2. Demigods 3. African American girls 4. Good and evil 5. Characters and characteristics in mythology 6. Chicago, Illinois 7. Afrofuturism and Afrofantasy 8. Fantasy fiction 9. Mythological fiction
ISBN 9781328635181

Struggling to understand why nobody else in her South Side Chicago neighborhood can see strange phenomena, 12-year-old Maya discovers that her missing father has been protecting a supernatural boundary between worlds.

"This opening installment of what will be a much-anticipated series is fast-paced and adventurous, offering a fresh blend of culture, community, and folklore rooted broadly in the African diaspora." Booklist

Barron, T. A.

The **lost** years of Merlin. T.A. Barron. Philomel Books, 1996. 326 p.: Lost years of Merlin

Grades: 5 6 7 8 **Fic**
1. Wizards 2. Child wizards 3. Magic 4. Merlin (Legendary

character) 5. Arthurian fantasy 6. Historical fantasy
ISBN 0399230181

LC 96-33920

A young boy who has no identity nor memory of his past washes ashore on the coast of Wales and finds his true name after a series of fantastic adventures.

"A boy, hurled on the rocks by the sea, regains consciousness unable to remember anything—not his parents, not his own name. He is sure that the secretive Branwen is not his mother, despite her claims, and that Emrys is not his real name. The two soon find themselves feared because of Branwen's healing abilities and Emrys' growing powers. . . . Barron has created not only a magical land populated by remarkable beings but also a completely magical tale, filled with ancient Celtic and Druidic lore, that will enchant readers." Booklist.

Bartlett, Claire Eliza

We rule the night. Claire Eliza Bartlett. Little, Brown and Company, 2019. 400 p.

Grades: 8 9 10 11 12   **Fic**

1. Fighter pilots 2. Women soldiers 3. War and society 4. Magic 5. Interpersonal conflict 6. Historical fantasy
ISBN 9780316417273

LC 2018022805

Seventeen-year-olds Revna, the daughter of a traitor, and Linne, the daughter of a general, must use forbidden magic to fly planes in wartime despite their deep dislike of each other.

"Rich characterizations and an enemy that, while it looms in the background, never feels quite as threatening as the country the girls are fighting for complete a story set against the bright, brutal backdrop of war. A breathless series starter from a new voice to watch." Booklist.

Bartoletti, Susan Campbell

★ The **boy** who dared. by Susan Campbell Bartoletti. Scholastic Press, 2008. 202 p.

Grades: 5 6 7 8   **Fic**

1. Hubener, Helmuth, 1925-1942. 2. 1940s 3. Seventeen-year-old boys 4. Courage in teenage boys 5. Nazism 6. Anti-Nazi movement 7. Mormon teenage boys 8. Germany 9. Biographical fiction 10. Historical fiction
ISBN 9780439680134

LC 2007014166

In October, 1942, seventeen-year-old Helmuth Hubener, imprisoned for distributing anti-Nazi leaflets, recalls his past life and how he came to dedicate himself to bring the truth about Hitler and the war to the German people.

"Bartoletti does an excellent job of conveying the political climate surrounding Hitler's ascent to power, seamlessly integrating a complex range of socioeconomic conditions into her absorbing drama." Publishers Weekly.

Barzak, Christopher

The **gone** away place. Christopher Barzak. Alfred A. Knopf, 2018 304 p.

Grades: 7 8 9 10   **Fic**

1. Tornadoes 2. Survivor guilt 3. Grief in teenage girls 4. Friends' death 5. Seventeen-year-old girls 6. Ohio 7. Middle West 8. Ghost stories
ISBN 9780399556098

LC 2017044047

After tornadoes demolish Newfoundland, Ohio, Ellie, seventeen, is haunted by ghosts of the dead, as well as survivors struggling to cope, but a chance encounter shows her how to free the lingering spirits.

Bashardoust, Melissa

Girls made of snow and glass. Melissa Bashardoust. Flatiron Books, 2017. 400 p.

Grades: 7 8 9 10   **Fic**

1. Stepmothers 2. Princesses 3. Rulers 4. Fathers 5. Inheritance and succession 6. Fairy tale and folklore-inspired fiction 7. Fantasy fiction
ISBN 9781250077738

A feminist fantasy reimagining of "Snow White" relates the past and present experiences of a magician's daughter-turned-heartless queen and her beautiful rival stepdaughter.

"Compellingly flawed characters, vivid world building, and pitch-perfect pacing make this utterly superb." Booklist.

Baskin, Nora Raleigh

All we know of love. Nora Raleigh Baskin. Candlewick Press, 2008. 201 p.

Grades: 6 7 8 9 10   **Fic**

1. Mother-deserted children 2. Bus travel 3. Love 4. Dating (Social customs) 5. Obsession 6. Connecticut 7. Florida 8. Realistic fiction 9. Coming-of-age stories
ISBN 9780763636234

LC 2007022396

Natalie, almost sixteen, sneaks away from her Connecticut home and takes the bus to Florida, looking for the mother who abandoned her father and her when she was ten years old.

"Baskin takes a familiar story line and examines it in a new and interesting way that will engage readers." Voice of Youth Advocates.

★ **Anything** but typical. Nora Raleigh Baskin. Simon & Schuster Books for Young Readers, 2009. 176 p.

Grades: 4 5 6 7   **Fic**

1. Boys with autism 2. Creative writing 3. Autism 4. Online friendship 5. Internet -- Social aspects 6. Realistic fiction
ISBN 9781416963783

LC 2008020994

Schneider Family Book Award for Middle School, 2010.

Jason, a twelve-year-old autistic boy who wants to become a writer, relates what his life is like as he tries to make sense of his world.

"This is an enormously difficult subject, but Baskin, without dramatics or sentimentality, makes it universal." Booklist.

Nine, ten: a September 11 story. Nora Raleigh Baskin. Atheneum Books for Young Readers, [2016] 208 p.

Grades: 4 5 6 7 8   **Fic**

1. September 11 Terrorist Attacks, 2001 2. African American boys 3. Muslim girls 4. Jewish girls 5. Terrorism 6. Historical fiction
ISBN 9781442485068

LC 2015011934

Relates how the lives of four children living in different parts of the country intersect and are affected by the events of September 11, 2001.

"Adults may be chilled by key names and places and what they portend, but children may gain a small sense of the magnitude of the changes that day wrought on our world. Tense, disturbing, and thought-provoking." Kirkus.

Ruby on the outside. Nora Raleigh Baskin. Simon & Schuster Books for Young Readers, 2015. 176 p.

Grades: 4 5 6 7 8   **Fic**

1. Children of prisoners 2. Friendship 3. Mothers and daughters

4. Best friends 5. Aunts 6. Realistic fiction
ISBN 9781442485037

LC 2014018268

Eleven-year-old Ruby Danes has a real best friend for the first time ever, but agonizes over whether or not to tell her a secret she has never shared with anyone—that her mother has been in prison since Ruby was five—and over whether to express her anger to her mother.

"This lyrical novel explores multiple aspects of the effects of incarceration on family: guilt, fear, anger, loneliness, and heavy responsibility. Baskin's plot structure, which flows from the present to periodic flashbacks, keeps the story from being unbearably dark. Margalit may be too good to be true, but she is just what the doctor ordered for Ruby's healing." Booklist.

The **summer** before boys. Nora Raleigh Baskin. Simon & Schuster Books for Young Readers, c2011. 224 p.

Grades: 6 7 8 **Fic**
1. Children of military personnel 2. Girl cousins 3. Crushes in girls 4. Boy/girl relations 5. First loves 6. Realistic fiction
ISBN 9781416986737

LC 2010045688

Twelve-year-old best friends and relatives, Julia and Eliza are happy to spend the summer together while Julia's mother is serving in the National Guard in Iraq but when they meet a neighborhood boy, their close relationship begins to change.

"A poignant story of children on the homefront and the ways that a first love can break up longtime friendships and change things forever." Booklist.

Bass, Karen, 1962-

Graffiti knight. Karen Bass. Pajama Press Inc., c2013. 288 p.

Grades: 7 8 9 10 **Fic**
1. Anger in teenage boys 2. Graffiti 3. World War II -- Post-war aspects 4. Teenage boys 5. Courage in teenage boys 6. Germany 7. Historical fiction
ISBN 9781927485538

In post-war Leipzig, teen Wilm feels justified in spray painting messages at night on police buildings in order to voice his displeasure, until one night his actions go too far.

"Just as Ruta Sepetys revealed a different perspective of the Holocaust in Between Shades of Gray (2011), Bass introduces another view of history unknown to many American readers...This eye-opening story shows that war's end is never tidy." Booklist.

Bateson, Catherine, 1960-

Being Bee. Catherine Bateson. Holiday House, 2007. 126 p.
Grades: 4 5 6 **Fic**
1. Children of widowers 2. Emotions in girls 3. Letters 4. Guinea pigs 5. Single-parent families 6. Australia 7. Realistic fiction
ISBN 9780823421046

LC 2006101561

Bee faces friction at home and at school when her widowed father begins seriously dating Jazzi, who seems to take over the house and their lives, but as shared secrets and common interests finally begin to draw them together, Jazzi accidentally makes a terrible mistake.

"Bee's emotions are perspectives are honest and clearly presented. . . . She is a likable, believable character." School Library Journal.

Bauer, A. C. E.

Come Fall. A. C. E. Bauer. Random House Childrens Books, 2010. 240 p.

Grades: 4 5 6 7 **Fic**
1. Middle school students 2. Friendship 3. Supernatural 4. Fairies 5. New students 6. Fantasy fiction 7. Shakespeare-inspired fiction
ISBN 9780375958557

Foster kid Salman Page is starting seventh grade in yet another new school when he's assigned a "designated buddy," eighth-grader Lu-Ellen Zimmer. Past experience has made him distrustful, so he tries to avoid Lu at first, but Salman eventually becomes friends with her and another kid on the fringes, Blos Pease. The three of them deal with the ups and downs at Riverfalls Junior High together, little suspecting that the fairy Puck (who narrates many chapters of the book) is meddling in their affairs.

"Weaving in magic, dreams, doubles, contrasts, and other elements from the original play, Bauer spins an enticing variant." Booklist.

No castles here. A.C.E. Bauer. Random House, c2007. 270 p.
Grades: 4 5 6 7 **Fic**
1. Sixth-grade boys 2. Eleven-year-old boys 3. Preteen boys 4. Misfits (Persons) 5. Booksellers 6. Camden, New Jersey 7. Fantasy fiction
ISBN 9780375839214

Eleven-year-old Augie Boretski dreams of escaping his run-down Camden, New Jersey, neighborhood, but things start to turn around with help from a Big Brother, a music teacher, and a mysterious bookstore owner, so when his school is in trouble, he pulls the community together to save it.

"This is a heartwarming novel." Booklist.

Bauer, Joan, 1951-

Almost home. Joan Bauer. Viking, 2012. 240 p.
Grades: 5 6 7 8 **Fic**
1. Poor girls 2. Homelessness 3. Resilience in girls 4. Resilience (Personal quality) 5. Girls and dogs 6. Realistic fiction
ISBN 9780670012893

LC 2011050483

Sixth-grader Sugar and her mother lose their beloved house and experience the harsh world of homelessness.

Close to famous. by Joan Bauer. Viking Childrens Books, 2011. 240 p.

Grades: 5 6 7 8 **Fic**
1. Girl bakers 2. Cupcakes 3. Literacy 4. Baking 5. Rural life 6. West Virginia 7. Realistic fiction
ISBN 9780670012824

LC 2010030022

Schneider Family Book Award for Middle School, 2012.

Twelve-year-old Foster McFee and her mother escape from her mother's abusive boyfriend and end up in the small town of Culpepper, West Virginia, where they use their strengths and challenge themselves to build a new life, with the help of the friends they make there.

"Bauer skillfully brings readers to the heart of Culpepper with rich depictions of a contemporary small town and its residents and rhythms." Publishers Weekly.

Peeled. Joan Bauer. G.P. Putnam's Sons, 2008. 256 p.
Grades: 6 7 8 9 10 **Fic**
1. Teenage journalists 2. Haunted houses 3. Independence (Personal quality) 4. Supernatural 5. Journalism 6. New York (State) 7. Mysteries
ISBN 9780399234750

LC 2007042835

In an upstate New York farming community, high school reporter Hildy Biddle investigates a series of strange occurrences at a house rumored to be haunted.

"This is a warm and funny story full of likable, offbeat characters led by a strongly voiced, independently minded female protagonist on her way to genuine, well-earned maturity." School Library Journal.

Soar. Joan Bauer. Viking, published by Penguin Group, 2016. 256 p.

Grades: 5 6 7 8   **Fic**

    1. Adopted boys 2. Transplantation of organs, tissues, etc 3. Baseball 4. Small towns 5. Heart -- Transplantation 6. Ohio 7. Realistic fiction 8. Sports fiction 9. Baseball stories

ISBN 9780451470348

Moving to Hillcrest, Ohio, when his adoptive father accepts a temporary job, twelve-year-old Jeremiah, a heart transplant recipient, has sixty days to find a baseball team to coach.

"An outstanding, tender exploration of courage and the true nature of heroism and, for good measure, a fine homage to America's game, as well." Kirkus.

Bauer, Marion Dane

Little dog, lost. Marion Dane Bauer; illustrated by Jennifer Bell. Atheneum Books for Young Readers, 2012. 240 p.

Grades: 4 5 6 7   **Fic**

    1. Loneliness 2. Dogs 3. Human/animal relationships 4. Pets 5. Senior men 6. Novels in verse

ISBN 9781442434233

                            LC 2011034024

A boy, a dog, and an old man are lonely before the boy plans a rally, the dog looks for a boy, and all the townspeople run to the old man's aid when lightning strikes his home and something miraculous happens.

On my honor. Marion Dane Bauer. Clarion Books, 1986. 90 p.

Grades: 4 5 6 7   **Fic**

    1. Guilt in children 2. Accidents 3. Friends' death 4. Teenagers and death 5. Boys -- Friendship 6. Realistic fiction

ISBN 0899194397

                            LC 86002679

When his best friend drowns while they are both swimming in a treacherous river that they had promised never to go near, Joel is devastated and terrified at having to tell both sets of parents the terrible consequences of their disobedience.

"Bauer's association of Joel's guilt with the smell of the polluted river on his skin is particularly noteworthy. Its miasma almost rises off the pages. Descriptions are vivid, characterization and dialogue natural, and the style taut but unforced. A powerful, moving book." School Library Journal.

Bayard, Louis

Lucky strikes. Louis Bayard. Henry Holt and Company, 2016. 288 p.

Grades: 6 7 8 9   **Fic**

    1. Depression era (1929-1941) 2. Orphans 3. Poverty 4. Service stations 5. Brothers and sisters 6. Drifters 7. Virginia 8. Historical fiction

ISBN 9781627793902

                            LC 2015023829

Set in Depression Era Virginia, this is the story of orphaned Amelia and her struggle to keep her siblings together. Provided by publisher.

"Her foible-ridden supporting cast features more adults than kids, and in an interesting twist, they give young readers insight into grown-up issues that transcend those usually found in youth books. Most of all, though, this is a darn good yarn with plenty of room for rooting and more than a few laughs." Booklist.

Bayerl, Katie

A **psalm** for lost girls. Katie Bayerl. G.P. Putnam's Sons, [2017]. 368 p.

Grades: 8 9 10 11 12   **Fic**

    1. Grief in teenage girls 2. Kidnapping 3. Sisters -- Death 4. Saints 5. Death 6. Massachusetts 7. Mysteries

ISBN 9780399545252

                            LC 2016027798

Determined to protect her sister Tess's memory, Callie da Costa sets out to prove Tess wasn't really a saint and finds herself pulled into a kidnapping investigation. Provided by publisher.

Bean, Lexie

The **ship** we built. Lexie Bean; illustrated by Noah Grigni. Dial Books, 2020. 288 p.

Grades: 5 6 7 8   **Fic**

    1. Transgender children 2. Misfits (Persons) 3. Letters 4. Friendship 5. Secrecy 6. Realistic fiction 7. LGBTQIA fiction

ISBN 9780525554837

                            LC 2019051654

Ostracized at school and abused at home for being different, a trans teen writes his secrets in letters that he attaches to balloons and releases into the skies before making a trustworthy friend who understands how it feels to be lonely and scared.

"This heartfelt, emotionally raw narrative delicately and respectfully covers incredibly complex issues (homophobia, substance abuse, sexual abuse, racism) that many young people around the world face, compounded by Rowan's status as a trans boy." Booklist

Beasley, Cassie

Circus Mirandus. by Cassie Beasley. Dial Books for Young Readers, an imprint of Penguin Group (USA) Inc., 2015. 304 p.: Circus Mirandus

Grades: 4 5 6   **Fic**

    1. Circus 2. Grandfather and grandson 3. Boy orphans 4. Sick persons 5. Magic 6. Fantasy fiction

ISBN 9780525428435

                            LC 2014031463

When he realizes that his grandfather's stories of an enchanted circus are true, Micah Tuttle sets out to find the mysterious Circus Mirandus— and to use its magic to save his grandfather's life. Provided by publisher.

Beatty, Robert, 1963-

Serafina and the twisted staff. Robert Beatty. 304 p.: Serafina (Robert Beatty)

Grades: 5 6 7   **Fic**

    1. Biltmore Estate (Asheville, N.C.) 2. 1890s 3. Shapeshifting 4. Fate and fatalism 5. Supernatural 6. Identity (Psychology) 7. Twelve-year-old girls 8. Asheville, North Carolina 9. Historical fantasy 10. Horror

ISBN 9781484775035

                            LC 2016006654

In 1899, when an evil threatens all the humans and animals of the Blue Ridge Mountains, twelve-year-old Serafina, rat catcher for the Biltmore estate and the daughter of a shapeshifting mountain lion, must search deep inside herself and embrace the destiny that awaits her.

"Even better than its predecessor, a sequel that delivers nonstop thrills from beginning to end." Kirkus.

Willa of Dark Hollow. Robert Beatty. Disney-Hyperion, 2021. 384 p.: Willa of the Wood

Grades: 4 5 6 7 **Fic**
> 1. 19th century 2. Spirits 3. Options, alternatives, choices 4. Forest conservation 5. Home (Concept) 6. Forests 7. Great Smoky Mountains (NC and Tenn) 8. Mysteries 9. Historical fantasy
> ISBN 9781368007603

Willa and her clan are the last of the Faeran, an ancient race of forest people who have lived in the Great Smoky Mountains for as long as the trees have grown there. But as crews of newly arrived humans start cutting down great swaths of the forest she loves, she is helpless to stop them. How can she fight the destroyers of the forest and their powerful machines?

"The gorgeous prose and imagery of the mountains will inspire in readers a deep admiration for nature and support for Willa's fight. A fantastic, heartbreaking crescendo that echoes beyond the final page." Kirkus

Beaty, Andrea
Cicada summer. Andrea Beaty. Amulet Books, 2008. 167 p.

Grades: 4 5 6 7 **Fic**
> 1. Brothers and sisters 2. Elective mutism 3. Secrets 4. Death 5. Grief 6. Illinois 7. Realistic fiction 8. Mysteries
> ISBN 9780810994720

LC 2007022266

Twelve-year-old Lily mourns her brother, and has not spoken since the accident she feels she could of prevented, but the summer Tinny comes to town she is the only one who realizes Lily's secret.

"This is compelling fiction that will be a hit with young readers. . . . Rich and thought-provoking and yet . . . accessible." Horn Book.

Beaufrand, Mary Jane
Useless Bay. M. J. Beaufrand. Amulet Books, 2016. 336 p.

Grades: 8 9 10 11 **Fic**
> 1. Quintuplets 2. Missing children 3. Family secrets 4. Islands 5. Brothers and sisters 6. Washington (State) 7. Mysteries
> ISBN 9781419721380

LC 2016007659

On Whidbey Island, north of Seattle, the Gray family's quintuplets join the search for a young boy gone missing and soon discover deep family secrets and that crimes have been committed.

"Short in length but long on atmosphere, it's a gripping mystery with a supernatural overlay that makes its setting all the more haunting. But it's the irresistible Gray quints, subject to their own rumors and local mythos, who steal the show." Publishers Weekly.

Beckhorn, Susan Williams, 1953-
The **wolf's** boy. Susan Williams Beckhorn. Disney Hyperion, 2016. 240 p.

Grades: 4 5 6 7 **Fic**
> 1. Boys and wolves 2. Prehistoric boys 3. Survival 4. Wild children 5. Prehistoric humans 6. Animal fantasy
> ISBN 9781484725535

LC 2015016834

Shunned because of a birth defect, Paleolithic youth Kai is nurtured by a pack of yellow wolves and risks everything to save a young cub with whom he embarks on a treacherous journey north during the course of a dangerous Ice Age winter.

"The bond between boy and canine—even one that's just learning to be a dog—is timeless, and animal-lovers in particular will be touched by this telling." Booklist.

Bedford, Martyn
Flip. Martyn Bedford. Wendy Lamb Books, 2011. 272 p.

Grades: 8 9 10 11 12 **Fic**
> 1. Teenagers with asthma 2. Identity (Psychology) 3. Soul 4. Body swapping 5. Supernatural 6. England 7. Psychological suspense 8. Paranormal fiction
> ISBN 9780385739900

A teenager wakes up inside another boy's body and faces a life-or-death quest to return to his true self or be trapped forever in the wrong existence.

"Bedford packs so much exhilarating action and cleanly cut characterizations into his teen debut that readers will be catapulted head-first into Alex's strange new world." Kirkus.

Behar, Ruth, 1956-
Lucky broken girl. Ruth Behar. Nancy Paulsen Books, 2017 256 p.

Grades: 5 6 7 8 **Fic**
> 1. 1960s 2. Traffic accident victims 3. Cuban Americans 4. Immigrants 5. Fractures 6. Jewish girls 7. New York City 8. Queens, New York City 9. Historical fiction 10. Autobiographical fiction
> ISBN 9780399546440

Pura Belpré Award for Narrative, 2018.

A semi-autobiographical story about a multicultural girl's coming-of-age in the 1960s describes how Cuban-Jewish Ruthie Mizrahi emigrates with her family from Castro's Cuba to New York, where a devastating accident challenges her perceptions about mortality and strength.

Beil, Michael D.
The **ring** of Rocamadour. Michael D. Beil. Alfred A. Knopf, 2009. 299 p.: Red Blazer Girls

Grades: 5 6 7 8 **Fic**
> 1. Girl detectives 2. Rings 3. Seventh-grade girls 4. Friendship 5. Catholic schools 6. New York City 7. Upper East Side, New York City 8. Mysteries
> ISBN 9780375948145

LC 2008025254

Catholic-schooled seventh-graders Sophie, Margaret, Rebecca, and Leigh Ann help an elderly neighbor solve a puzzle her father left for her estranged daughter twenty years ago.

"The dialogue is fast and funny, the clues are often solvable." Booklist.

The **vanishing** violin. Michael D. Beil. Alfred A. Knopf, c2010. 329 p.: Red Blazer Girls

Grades: 5 6 7 8 **Fic**
> 1. Girl detectives 2. Violin 3. Seventh-grade girls 4. Stealing 5. Clues 6. New York City 7. Upper East Side, New York City 8. Mysteries
> ISBN 9780375861031

Their reputation established by the discovery of the Ring of Rocamadour, the Red Blazer Girls receive sundry job requests and unwanted criminal attention before investigating a missing violin, a case that involves clues from myriad sources and an unexpected victim.

"Sophie, Margaret, Rebecca, and Leigh Ann . . . find themselves in the midst of several interlocking mysteries, mostly involving violins. . . . Beil has lost none of his edge when it comes to setting up sleuthing scenarios and offering kids codes and clues that will intrigue (or drive them crazy). Smartly plotted, smartly played." Booklist.

Bell, Hilari

Traitor's son. Hilari Bell. Houghton Mifflin, 2012. 288 p.: Raven duet

Grades: 7 8 9 10 11 12   **Fic**
1. Native American teenage boys 2. Shapeshifters 3. Plague 4. Family feuds 5. Indians of North America 6. Alaska 7. Fantasy fiction
ISBN 9780547196213

In Alaska in the middle of the twenty-first century, Jase is drafted by a Native American trickster spirit to help stop a bio-plague caused by disruptions in the earth's flow of magic, and finds himself in the middle of a shapeshifter war.

"The juxtaposition of magic with science is fascinating, and the waking dreams into the spirit world will keep readers riveted. It does help to have read Trickster's Girl first." School Library Journal

Bell, Juliet

Kepler's Dream. Juliet Bell. G. P. Putnam's Sons, 2012. 256 p.

Grades: 5 6 7 8   **Fic**
1. Kepler, Johannes, 1571-1630. Somnium. 2. Children of people with cancer 3. Rare books 4. Swindlers and swindling 5. Grandmothers 6. Families 7. New Mexico 8. Albuquerque, New Mexico 9. Mysteries
ISBN 9780399256455

                                        LC 2011024136
While her mother undergoes radical cancer treatment, eleven-year-old Ella stays with her father's mother in Albuquerque, New Mexico, where she learns about grammar and family history, and helps investigate the theft of an extremely rare book from her grandmother's library.

Benjamin, Ali

The **thing** about jellyfish. by Ali Benjamin. Little, Brown and Company, 2015. 352 p.

Grades: 4 5 6 7   **Fic**
1. Grief in girls 2. Girls and death 3. Loss (Psychology) 4. Best friends -- Death 5. Guilt 6. Realistic fiction
ISBN 9780316380867

                                        LC 2014044025
Twelve-year-old Suzy Swanson wades through her intense grief over the loss of her best friend by investigating the rare jellyfish she is convinced was responsible for her friend's death.

"Benjamin's inverse approach to tragedy, placing the death at the beginning of the novel and storytelling through the grieving process, transcends the trope, as the story triumphs in the affecting realities of emotional response and resilience." School Library Journal.

Benoit, Charles

You. Charles Benoit. HarperTeen, 2010. 208 p.

Grades: 8 9 10 11 12   **Fic**
1. Teenage boy misfits 2. Consequences 3. Crushes in teenage boys 4. Crushes (Interpersonal relations) 5. Personal conduct 6. Realistic fiction
ISBN 9780061947049

                                        LC 2009043990
Fifteen-year-old Kyle discovers the shattering ramifications of the decisions he makes, and does not make, about school, the girl he likes, and his future.

"The rapid pace is well suited to the narrative. . . . In the end, Benoit creates a fully realized world where choices have impact and the consequences of both action and inaction can be severe." School Library Journal.

Benway, Robin

Also known as. by Robin Benway. Walker Books For Young Readers, 2013. 320 p.: Also known as novels

Grades: 7 8 9 10   **Fic**
1. Teenage spies 2. Safecrackers 3. High schools 4. Sixteen-year-old girls 5. Teenage girls 6. New York City 7. Spy fiction
ISBN 9780802733900

                                        LC 2012026254
As the active-duty daughter of international spies, sixteen-year-old safecracker Maggie Silver never attended high school so when she and her parents are sent to New York for her first solo assignment, Maggie is introduced to cliques, school lunches, and maybe even a boyfriend.

"While the framework requires more than a little suspension of disbelief, the absolutely delightful cast of characters and snappy dialogue transform this book into a huge success." School Library Journal.

Far from the tree. Robin Benway. HarperTeen, 2017. 256 p.

Grades: 7 8 9 10 11 12   **Fic**
1. Adoption 2. Brothers and sisters 3. Families 4. Teenage pregnancy 5. Love 6. Realistic fiction
ISBN 9780062330628

National Book Award for Young People's Literature, 2017.

Feeling incomplete as an adopted child after placing her own baby up for adoption, teen Grace tracks down her biological siblings and finds herself struggling with the dynamics of being a middle child between an embittered older brother and an outspoken younger sister.

"Benway delves into the souls of these characters as they wrestle to overcome feelings of inadequacy, abandonment, and betrayal, gradually coming to understand themselves and each other." Publishers Weekly.

Benwell, Fox

The **last** leaves falling. Sarah Benwell. Simon & Schuster, 2015. 352 p.

Grades: 7 8 9 10 11 12   **Fic**
1. Amyotrophic lateral sclerosis 2. Teenagers with terminal illnesses 3. Assisted suicide 4. Internet 5. Friendship 6. Japan 7. Realistic fiction
ISBN 9781481430654

"References to samurai culture and snippets of poetry will leave readers at peace with the drifting ending. Benwell's gentle treatment of friendship and death with dignity will touch fans of John Green's The Fault in Our Stars (2012)." Kirkus.

Berk, Josh

The **dark** days of Hamburger Halpin. by Josh Berk. Alfred A. Knopf, 2010 208 p.

Grades: 8 9 10 11 12   **Fic**
1. Teenagers who are deaf 2. Overweight teenage boys 3. Murder investigation 4. Teenage boys with disabilities 5. Sixteen-year-old boys 6. Pennsylvania 7. Mysteries
ISBN 9780375956997

When Will Halpin transfers from his all-deaf school into a mainstream Pennsylvania high school, he faces discrimination and bullying, but still manages to solve a mystery surrounding the death of a popular football player in his class.

"A coming-of-age mash-up of satire, realistic fiction, mystery, and ill-fated teen romance, The Dark Days of Hamburger Halpin is a genre-bending breakthrough that teens are going to love." School Library Journal.

Berlin, Eric

The **puzzling** world of Winston Breen: the secret in the box. Eric Berlin. G. P. Putnam's Sons, 2007. 224 p.: Puzzling world of Winston Breen

Grades: 4 5 6 7   **Fic**
   1. Brothers and sisters 2. Twelve-year-old boys 3. Ten-year-old girls 4. Librarians 5. Former police 6. Mysteries
ISBN 9780399246937

                      LC 2006020531

Puzzle-crazy, twelve-year-old Winston and his ten-year-old sister Katie find themselves involved in a dangerous mystery involving a hidden ring. Puzzles for the reader to solve are included throughout the text.

   "A delightfully clever mystery. . . . There is plenty of suspense to engage readers." School Library Journal.

Bernard, Romily

Find me. Romily Bernard. HarperTeen, an imprint of HarperCollinsPublishers, 2013. 288 p.: Wick Tate series

Grades: 7 8 9 10 11 12   **Fic**
   1. Teenage hackers 2. Foster teenagers 3. Children of criminals 4. Sisters 5. Teenage romance 6. Thrillers and suspense
ISBN 9780062229038

                      LC 2013021519

When teen hacker and foster child Wick Tate finds a dead classmate's diary on her front step, with a note reading "Find me," she sets off on a perverse game of hide-and-seek to catch the killer.

Berry, Julie, 1974-

All the truth that's in me. by Julie Berry. Viking, [2013] 288 p.

Grades: 7 8 9 10 11 12   **Fic**
   1. Teenage girls who are mute 2. Teenage girl kidnapping victims 3. Teenage girl misfits 4. Crushes in teenage girls 5. Community life 6. Historical fiction
ISBN 9780670786152

                      LC 2012043218

Rendered an outsider by a horrifying trauma that killed her best friend and left her unable to speak, Judith spends her days longing for the boy she loves until an attack on the community reveals long-buried secrets and compels Judith to reclaim her voice, even if it means changing her world, and the lives around her, forever.

   "Berry's novel is set in a claustrophobic village that seems to resemble an early American colonial settlement. Readers gradually learn all the truth from eighteen-year-old narrator Judith, who speaks directly (though only in her head) to her love, Lucas. Berry keeps readers on edge, tantalizing us with pieces of the puzzle right up until the gripping conclusion." Horn Book.

The **Amaranth** enchantment. Julie Berry. Bloomsbury U.S.A. Children's Books, 2009. 288 p.

Grades: 6 7 8 9   **Fic**
   1. Magic 2. Fifteen-year-old girls 3. Princes 4. Orphans 5. Teenage girls 6. Fantasy fiction
ISBN 9781599903347

                      LC 2008022354

Orphaned at age five, Lucinda, now fifteen, stands with courage against the man who took everything from her, aided by a thief, a clever goat, and a mysterious woman called the Witch of Amaranth, while the prince she knew as a child prepares to marry, unaware that he, too, is in danger.

   "A lively, quick, stylish, engaging first novel with some lovely, familiar fairy-tale elements." Publishers Weekly.

The **passion** of Dolssa. by Julie Berry. Penguin Group, [2016] 480 p.

Grades: 7 8 9 10   **Fic**
   1. Medieval period (476-1492) 2. 13th century 3. Inquisition 4. Faith 5. Albigenses 6. Christian heresies 7. Teenage girls 8. France 9. Provence, France 10. Historical fiction 11. Magical realism
ISBN 9780451469922

                      LC 2015020814

In mid-thirteenth century Provence, Dolssa de Stigata is a fervently religious girl who feels the call to preach, condemned by the Inquisition as an "unnatural woman," and hunted by the Dominican Friar Lucien who fears a resurgence of the Albigensian heresy; Botille is a matchmaker trying to protect her sisters from being branded as gypsies or witches—but when she finds the hunted Dolssa dying on a hillside, she feels compelled to protect her, a decision that may cost her everything.

   "A (fictional) Catholic mystic, Dolssa de Stigata, escapes being burned as a heretic in 1241 France; mostly, this is the story of Botille, an enterprising young matchmaker from a tiny fishing village who rescues Dolssa. Botille's spirited character, the heart-rending suspense of events, and the terrifying context of the Inquisition in medieval Europe all render the novel irresistibly compelling." Horn Book.

   Includes bibliographical references.

Bertagna, Julie

Exodus. Julie Bertagna. Walker: 2008, c2002. 352 p.: Exodus (Julie Bertagna)

Grades: 6 7 8 9 10   **Fic**
   1. 22nd century 2. Survival 3. Global warming 4. Near future 5. Refugees 6. Climate change 7. Apocalyptic fiction 8. Science fiction
ISBN 9780802797452

                      LC 2007023116

In the year 2100, as the island of Wing is about to be covered by water, fifteen-year-old Mara discovers the existence of New World sky cities that are safe from the storms and rising waters, and convinces her people to travel to one of these cities in order to save themselves.

   "Astonishing in its scope and exhilarating in both its action and its philosophical inquiry." Booklist.

Bick, Ilsa J.

Ashes. Ilsa J. Bick. Egmont USA, 2011. 465 p.: Ashes trilogy (Ilsa J. Bick)

Grades: 8 9 10 11 12   **Fic**
   1. Teenage girl orphans 2. Zombies 3. Survival 4. Electromagnetic waves 5. Soldiers 6. Science fiction 7. Horror 8. Apocalyptic fiction
ISBN 9781606841754

                      LC 2010051825

Seventeen-year-old Alex is on a solo camping trip in the woods (and playing hooky from her seemingly pointless chemo treatments) when a series of electromagnetic pulses renders all technology useless, kills most of Earth's population, and turns many of those left alive into ravenous, bloodthirsty cannibals. But Alex isn't entirely alone; she teams up with an eight-year-old girl and a young soldier on leave who, like her, weren't transformed by the pulses, and the three of them fight together for survival.

"Bick delivers an action-packed tale of an apocalypse unfolding. . . . [She] doesn't shy away from gore—one woman's guts boiled out in a dusky, desiccated tangle, like limp spaghetti—but it doesn't derail the story's progress." Publishers Weekly.

Bigelow, Lisa Jenn

Hazel's theory of evolution. Lisa Jenn Bigelow. Harpercollins Childrens Books, 2019. 325 p.

Grades: 5 6 7 8   **Fic**
1. Eighth grade girls 2. New students 3. Middle schools 4. Family farms 5. Reading 6. Michigan 7. Coming-of-age stories
ISBN 9780062791177

Hazel knows a lot about the world. That's because when she's not hanging with her best friend, taking care of her dog, or helping care for the goats on her family's farm, she loves reading through dusty encyclopedias. But even Hazel doesn't have answers for the questions awaiting her as she enters eighth grade. What if no one at her new school gets her, and she doesn't make any friends? What's going to happen to one of her moms, who's pregnant again after having two miscarriages? Why does everything have to change when life was already perfectly fine?

"Drawing parallels between Hazel and the misunderstood creatures she reads about in her beloved set of animal encyclopedias, Bigelow celebrates intersectional diversity with her cast of well-drawn characters." Publishers Weekly.

Starting from here. Lisa Jenn Bigelow. Amazon Children's Pub., c2012. 282 p.

Grades: 8 9 10 11 12   **Fic**
1. Lesbian teenagers 2. Teenagers and dogs 3. Loneliness 4. Dating (Social customs) 5. Dogs 6. Realistic fiction 7. LGBTQIA fiction
ISBN 9780761462330

LC 2011040129

Sixteen-year-old Colby is barely hanging on with her mother dead, her long-haul trucker father often away, her almost-girlfriend dumping her for a boy, and her failing grades, when a stray dog appears and helps her find hope.

Bildner, Phil

A **high** five for Glenn Burke. Phil Bildner. Farrar Straus Giroux, 2020. 288 p.

Grades: 4 5 6 7 8   **Fic**
1. Boy baseball players 2. Coming out (Sexual or gender identity) 3. Gay boys 4. Baseball players 5. Baseball 6. LGBTQIA fiction 7. Realistic fiction
ISBN 9780374312732

LC 2019009796

After researching Glenn Burke, the first major league baseball player to come out as gay, sixth-grader Silas Wade slowly comes out to his best friend Zoey, then his coach, with unexpected consequences.

"Silas is an engaging narrator, slipping easily and honestly between accounts of his public bravado, his understandable trepidation of worst-case scenario fallout, and his private adoption of a role model in Burke, who both represents Silas' dilemma and cries out for vindication." Bulletin of the Center for Children's Books

Billingsley, Franny, 1954-

Chime. by Franny Billingsley. Dial Books for Young Readers, 2011. 320 p.

Grades: 7 8 9 10 11 12   **Fic**
1. Twin sisters 2. Guilt in teenage girls 3. Swamps 4. Guilt 5.

Supernatural 6. England 7. Historical fantasy
ISBN 9780803735521

LC 2010012140

Plagued by guilt for harm that she believes she brought on her family, 17-year-old Briony Larkin is convinced that she's a witch. But there are many dark secrets in Briony's village of Swampsea, and when a London engineer and his handsome son arrive to drain the marshes—causing the supernatural Old Ones who live in the swamp to retaliate—those secrets begin bubbling to the surface.

"Filled with eccentric characters—self-hating Briony foremost—and oddly beautiful language, this is a darkly beguiling fantasy." Publishers Weekly.

Bingham, Kelly L., 1967-

Shark girl. Kelly Bingham. Candlewick Press, 2007. 288 p.

Grades: 7 8 9 10   **Fic**
1. People who have had amputations 2. Coping in teenage girls 3. Teenage girl artists 4. Artists 5. Coping 6. Realistic fiction 7. Novels in verse
ISBN 9780763632076

LC 2006049120

After a shark attack causes the amputation of her right arm, fifteen-year-old Jane, an aspiring artist, struggles to come to terms with her loss and the changes it imposes on her day-to-day life and her plans for the future.

"In carefully constructed, sparsely crafted free verse, Bingham's debut novel offers a strong view of a teenager struggling to survive and learn to live again." Booklist.

Bird, James

The **brave**. James Bird. Feiwel & Friends, 2020 320 p.

Grades: 5 6 7 8 9   **Fic**
1. Mothers and sons 2. Obsessive-compulsive disorder 3. Belonging 4. Friendship 5. Sick persons 6. Minnesota 7. Coming-of-age stories 8. Realistic fiction
ISBN 9781250247759

Targeted by bullies for his escalating OCD, Collin is sent to live with his biological mother on an Ojibwe reservation where his differences are accepted and where he finds companionship in a physically challenged girl whose circumstances inspire Collin to make a difficult choice. Atlas Publishing

"This is an amazing debut full of heart, authenticity, and courage." School Library Journal

Birdsall, Jeanne

★ The **Penderwicks**: a summer tale of four sisters, two rabbits, and a very interesting boy. Jeanne Birdsall. Knopf, 2005. 192 p.: The Penderwicks

Grades: 3 4 5 6   **Fic**
1. Sisters 2. Family vacations 3. Rich people 4. Cottages 5. Girls 6. Humorous stories 7. Realistic fiction
ISBN 0375831436

LC 2004020364

National Book Award for Young People's Literature, 2005.

While vacationing with their widowed father in the Berkshire Mountains, four lovable sisters, ages four through twelve, share adventures with a local boy, much to the dismay of his snobbish mother.

"This comforting family story . . . [offers] . . . four marvelously appealing sisters, true childhood behavior . . . , and a writing style that will draw readers close." Booklist.

The **Penderwicks** at last. Jeanne Birdsall. Random House Childrens Books, 2018. 256 p.: The Penderwicks

Grades: 4 5 6 7   **Fic**

   1. Blended families 2. Families 3. Family secrets 4. Eleven-year-old girls 5. Massachusetts 6. Maine 7. Realistic fiction

ISBN 9780385755672

Nine years, five older siblings, a few beloved dogs, and an endless array of adventures—these are the things that have shaped Lydia's journey since readers first met her in The Penderwicks in Spring.

The **Penderwicks** at Point Mouette. Jeanne Birdsall. Alfred A. Knopf, 2011. 304 p.: The Penderwicks

Grades: 4 5 6 7   **Fic**

   1. Sisters 2. Vacations 3. Neighbors 4. Musicians 5. Single-parent families 6. Maine 7. Humorous stories 8. Realistic fiction

ISBN 9780375858512

                         LC 2011005806

The three youngest Penderwick sisters join their Aunt Claire and their friend/honorary brother, Jeffrey, for summer vacation at a cottage in a tiny, seaside Maine town. Mr. Penderwick is honeymooning in England with his new bride, and eldest daughter Rosalind is vacationing with a friend in New Jersey, so next-eldest sister Skye is taking her first turn as Oldest Available Penderwick (OAP)—meaning that she's in charge (ulp).

"Balancing the novel's comedy is an affecting, neatly crafted subplot that builds up to the emotionally charged revelation involving Jeffrey. From start to finish, this is a summer holiday to savor." Publishers Weekly.

The **Penderwicks** in spring. Jeanne Birdsall. Knopf Books for Young Readers, 2015. 256 p.: The Penderwicks

Grades: 4 5 6 7   **Fic**

   1. Blended families 2. Singing 3. Money-making projects 4. Birthdays 5. Families 6. Massachusetts 7. Maine 8. Realistic fiction

ISBN 9780375870774

                         LC 2014023537

As spring arrives on Gardam Street, there are surprises in store for each Penderwick, from neighbor Nick Geiger's expected return from the war to Batty's new dog-walking business, but her plans to use her profits to surprise her family on her eleventh birthday go astray.

"[T]he compelling story line examines the guilt that Batty feels over both the death of her mother and her inability to keep the family dog, Hound, alive—and it does so in touching ways. Batty is the narrator most of the time, but younger Ben takes over on occasion, and 2-year-old Lydia is an eccentric presence." Booklist.

The **Penderwicks** on Gardam Street. Jeanne Birdsall; illustrations by David Frankland. Alfred A. Knopf, 2008. 320 p.: The Penderwicks

Grades: 3 4 5 6 7   **Fic**

   1. Sisters 2. Children and single parent dating 3. Families 4. Widowers 5. Single-parent families 6. Massachusetts 7. Humorous stories 8. Realistic fiction

ISBN 9780375840906

                         LC 2007049232

The four Penderwick sisters are faced with the unimaginable prospect of their widowed father dating, and they hatch a plot to stop him.

"Laugh-out-loud moments abound and the humor comes naturally from the characters and situations. . . . This is a book to cherish." School Library Journal.

Black, Holly

  Black heart. Holly Black. Margaret K. McElderry Books, 2012. 320 p.: Curse workers

Grades: 7 8 9 10   **Fic**

   1. Teenage boys 2. Civil service workers 3. Love 4. Crime 5. Seventeen-year-old boys 6. Urban fantasy

ISBN 9781442403468

                         LC 2011028143

Cassel Sharpe, a powerful transformation worker, is torn between his decision to work for the federal government and his love for Lila, who has joined her father's criminal organization.

The **bronze** key. Holly Black and Cassandra Clare; with illustrations by Scott Fischer. Scholastic Press, 2016 264 p.: Magisterium

Grades: 4 5 6 7 8   **Fic**

   1. Child wizards 2. Schools 3. Good and evil 4. Magic 5. Preteen boys 6. Fantasy fiction

ISBN 9780545522311

Following the death of one of their classmates, Callum, Tamara, and Aaron set out to find and stop the killer before he can use his magical powers to commit further evils.

The **copper** gauntlet. Holly Black and Cassandra Clare Scholastic Press, 2015. 304 p.: Magisterium

Grades: 5 6 7 8   **Fic**

   1. Child wizards 2. Schools 3. Friendship 4. Good and evil 5. Children of widowers 6. Virginia 7. Fantasy fiction

ISBN 9780545522281

                         LC 2015015713

Callum Hunt's life has been difficult ever since he was admitted to the Magisterium, since his father suspects him of being evil, and his closest companion is a Chaos-ridden wolf—but when he discovers that his father may be trying to destroy both him and Havoc, he escapes back to the magical world and he and his friends Aaron and Tamara, become involved in the search for the stolen Alkahest, a copper gauntlet with dangerous powers.

"The third-person narration, filtered through Callum's delightfully insecure-and-overcompensating-with-snarky-bravado perspective, carries a tone that will likely have readers chortling in recognition. A promising beginning to a complex exploration of good and evil, as well as friendship's loyalty." Kirkus.

★ **Doll** bones. Holly Black. Margaret K. McElderry Books, 2013. 256 p.

Grades: 5 6 7 8   **Fic**

   1. Growing up 2. Dolls 3. Ghosts 4. Bus travel 5. Friendship 6. Pennsylvania 7. Ohio 8. Horror

ISBN 9781416963981

                         LC 2012018299

Zach, Alice, and Poppy, friends from a Pennsylvania middle school who have long enjoyed acting out imaginary adventures with dolls and action figures, embark on a real-life quest to Ohio to bury a doll made from the ashes of a dead girl.

"Veteran Black packs both heft and depth into a deceptively simple (and convincingly uncanny) narrative. . . . A few rich metaphors . . . are woven throughout the story, as every encounter redraws the blurry lines between childishness and maturity, truth and lies, secrecy and honesty, magic and madness. Spooky, melancholy, elegiac and ultimately hopeful; a small gem." Kirkus.

The **iron** trial. Holly Black & Cassandra Clare. Scholastic, 2014. 320 p.: Magisterium

Grades: 4 5 6 7 8   **Fic**
> 1. Child wizards 2. Schools 3. Friendship 4. Good and evil 5. Children of widowers 6. Virginia 7. Fantasy fiction
> ISBN 9780545522250

Warned away from magic all of his life, Callum endeavors to fail the trials that would admit him to the Magisterium only to be drawn into its ranks against his will and forced to confront dark elements from his past.

"The third-person narration, filtered through Callum's delightfully insecure-and-overcompensating-with-snarky-bravado perspective, carries a tone that will likely have readers chortling in recognition. A promising beginning to a complex exploration of good and evil, as well as friendship's loyalty." Kirkus.

Red glove. Holly Black. Margaret K. McElderry Books, 2011. 320 p.: Curse workers

Grades: 7 8 9 10   **Fic**
> 1. Criminals 2. Gangsters 3. Curses 4. Swindlers and swindling 5. Magic 6. Urban fantasy
> ISBN 9781442403390

LC 2010031884

When federal agents learn that seventeen-year-old Cassel Sharpe, a powerful transformation worker, may be of use to them, they offer him a deal to join them rather than the mobsters for whom his brothers work.

"This offers a sleek a stylish blend of urban fantasy and crime noir." Booklist.

The **silver** mask. Holly Black and Cassandra Clare; with illustrations by Scott Fischer. Scholastic Press, 2017 240 p.: Magisterium

Grades: 5 6 7 8   **Fic**
> 1. Child wizards 2. Schools 3. Good and evil 4. Magic 5. Preteen boys 6. Fantasy fiction
> ISBN 9780545522366

As one of the most feared and reviled students in Magisterium, Callum Hunt has been imprisoned and interrogated to reveal Constantine's plans and how Constantine lives on within him, information that Call doesn't know until he is broken out of prison.

"Calls struggles with his magic, his morals, and, yes, even everyday teenage boy problems are compelling." Booklist.

The **white** cat. Holly Black. Margaret K. McElderry Books, 2010. 320 p.: Curse workers

Grades: 7 8 9 10   **Fic**
> 1. Dreams 2. Brothers 3. Swindlers and swindling 4. Memory 5. Sleep-walking 6. Urban fantasy
> ISBN 9781416963967

LC 2009033979

Cassel Sharpe comes from a family of criminals and "curse workers," people who practice magic illegally and can alter others' luck or memories with a single touch. Cassel, who doesn't seem to have inherited his family's talents, tries very hard to convince his private-school classmates that he's just a regular guy. But he's haunted by a dirty secret from his past, and a white cat that keeps appearing in his nightmares. .

"This starts out with spine-tingling terror, and information is initially dispensed so sparingly, readers will be hooked." Booklist.

Black, Peter Jay

Urban outlaws. Peter Jay Black. Bloomsbury USA Childrens, 2014. 320 p.: Urban Outlaws

Grades: 5 6 7 8   **Fic**
> 1. Supercomputers 2. Orphans 3. Hackers 4. Computers 5. Ability 6. London, England 7. Science fiction
> ISBN 9781619634008

LC 2014005604

Deep beneath London, five extraordinary youths, orphans who bonded over their shared sense of justice, have formed the Urban Outlaws and dedicated themselves to outsmarting criminals and performing Random Acts of Kindness (R.A.K.s), but they are in serious trouble when the face a genius super-computer, Proteus.

"Five orphans—Jack, Charlie, Wren, Obi, and Slink—have made a home for themselves in a WWII bunker under the London subway. They are skilled in various ways—technological savvy, surveillance, and physical prowess in particular—and work together as the Urban Outlaws, using their knowledge to play Robin Hood against local criminals and sharing the benefits of their activities with those less fortunate than themselves...The characters are warm and well developed and will appeal to reluctant readers across middle school. This new series will be an excellent choice for younger fans of Alex Rider." Booklist.

Blackburne, Livia

Midnight thief. Livia Blackburne. Hyperion, 2014. 384 p.: Midnight thief novels

Grades: 7 8 9 10 11 12   **Fic**
> 1. Knights and knighthood 2. Teenage girl orphans 3. Assassins 4. Thieves 5. Revenge 6. High fantasy 7. Fantasy fiction
> ISBN 9781423176381

LC 2013021230

Kyra, a highly skilled seventeen-year-old thief, joins a guild of assassins with questionable motives. Tristam, a young knight, fights against the vicious Demon Riders that are ravaging the city. Provided by publisher.

Rosemarked. Livia Blackburne. Hyperion, 2017. 400 p.: Rosemarked

Grades: 7 8 9 10 11 12   **Fic**
> 1. Plague 2. Healers 3. Spies 4. Soldiers 5. Revenge 6. Fantasy fiction
> ISBN 9781484788554

Embarking on a high-stakes mission to spy on the capital, Zivah, a healer, and Dineas, a warrior, grow closer amidst the fear of discovery.

Blackstone, Matt

Sorry you're lost. Matt Blackstone. Farrar, Straus and Giroux, 2014. 272 p.

Grades: 6 7 8 9   **Fic**
> 1. Grief 2. Fathers and sons 3. School dances 4. Loss (Psychology) 5. Mothers -- Death 6. Realistic fiction
> ISBN 9780374380656

LC 2013021215

New Jersey seventh grader and class clown Denny Murphy has just lost his mother, his father is uncommunicative, he is in trouble with his teachers, and to top it all off, his best friend has a scheme to get dates for the end-of-year school dance.

"Ever since his mother died, seventh grader Denny 'Donuts' Murphy has felt alone and small. So he intentionally develops a big persona, making everything into a joke. With the help of friends and a budding romance, Donuts sheds his manic showman exterior. The first-person narrative is a perfect vehicle to reveal Donuts's inner self in this story of substance and hope." Horn Book.

Blackwood, Gary L.

★ The **Shakespeare** stealer. Gary Blackwood. Dutton Children's Books, 1998. 216 p.: Shakespeare stealer

Grades: 5 6 7 8 **Fic**

1. Shakespeare, William, 1564-1616 2. Globe Theatre (London, England: 1599-1644) 3. Elizabethan era (1558-1603) 4. Tudor period (1485-1603) 5. Boy orphans 6. Theater 7. Stealing 8. Actors and actresses 9. Drama 10. England 11. Great Britain 12. Historical fiction

ISBN 0525458638

LC 97042987

A young orphan boy is ordered by his master to infiltrate Shakespeare's acting troupe in order to steal the script of "Hamlet," but he discovers instead the meaning of friendship and loyalty.

"Wry humor, cliffhanger chapter endings, and a plucky protagonist make this a fitting introduction to Shakespeare's world." Horn Book.

The **year** of the hangman. by Gary Blackwood. Dutton Children's Books, 2002. 196 p.

Grades: 8 9 10 11 12 **Fic**

1. 1770s 2. 18th century 3. Fifteen-year-old boys 4. Kidnapping 5. Revolutions 6. American Revolution, 1775-1783 7. United States 8. Alternate histories

ISBN 0525469214

LC 2002067498

In 1777, having been kidnapped and taken forcibly from England to the American colonies, fifteen-year-old Creighton becomes part of developments in the political unrest there that may spell defeat for the patriots and change the course of history.

"Packed with action, convincing historical speculation, and compelling portrayals of real-life and fictional characters, this page-turner will appeal to fans of both history and fantasy." School Library Journal.

Blackwood, Sage

★ **Jinx**. Sage Blackwood. Harper, 2013. 368 p.: Jinx trilogy (Sage Blackwood)

Grades: 4 5 6 7 **Fic**

1. Wizards 2. Abandoned boys 3. Adventure 4. Magic 5. Forests 6. Fantasy fiction

ISBN 9780062129901

LC 2012005249

A young boy named Jinx encounters magic and danger as he grows up in the deep, dark forest known as the Urwald and discovers that the world beyond—and within—the Urwald is more complex than he could imagine.

Jinx's fire. Sage Blackwood. Katherine Tegen Books, an imprint of HarperCollinsPublishers, 2015. 400 p.: Jinx trilogy (Sage Blackwood)

Grades: 4 5 6 7 **Fic**

1. Boy orphans 2. Wizards 3. Forests 4. Magic 5. Prophecies 6. Fantasy fiction

ISBN 9780062129963

LC 2014022688

Jinx travels throughout the Urwald to unite its people and creatures against encroaching threats. Provided by publisher.

"In this concluding volume of Blackwood's critically acclaimed series, Jinx is nearly 15, and he finally rescues his mentor, Simon, from the fate the evil Bonemaster wrought in Jinx's Magic (2014). . . . Series fans will be elated to have another outing with the sweetly sardonic hero,

whose conscience is almost as troublesome as his grasp of spells. Fans of Cornelia Funke should add this to their stacks." Booklist.

Jinx's magic. Sage Blackwood. Katherine Tegen Books, an imprint of HarperCollinsPublishers, 2014. 300 p.: Jinx trilogy (Sage Blackwood)

Grades: 4 5 6 7 **Fic**

1. Boy orphans 2. Wizards 3. Forests 4. Quests 5. Wizards' apprentices 6. Fantasy fiction

ISBN 9780062129932

Searching for answers about his alleged connection to the evil Bonemaster and magical uprisings, Jinx travels to the desert land of Samara, where his search for ancient magic ensnares him in a centuries-old conspiracy that threatens the Urwald.

"The plot is a little convoluted, wrapping up loose ends from the first volume and setting up elements for the next before finally establishing its own internal tension, but the unique setting, smart pace, likable characters, and sprightly voice hold the narrative together." Horn Book.

★ **Miss** Ellicott's school for the magically minded. Sage Blackwood. Katherine Tegen Books, 2017. 361 p.

Grades: 4 5 6 7 8 **Fic**

1. Boarding schools 2. Witches 3. Missing persons 4. Dragons 5. Gender role 6. Fantasy fiction

ISBN 9780062402639

Repeatedly landing in trouble at her finishing school because of her preference for practicing magic instead of manners, Chantel enlists her friends to protect the kingdom when her teacher goes missing along with the city's protective magic.

"This clever fantasy is a strong purchase for most middle grade collections." School Library Journal.

Blake, Ashley Herring

Hazel Bly and the deep blue sea. Ashley Herring Blake. Little, Brown and Company, 2021. 320 p.

Grades: 4 5 6 7 **Fic**

1. Preteen girls 2. Mothers -- Death 3. Lesbian mothers 4. Grief in children 5. Making friends 6. Maine 7. Realistic fiction

ISBN 9780316535458

Traumatized and facially scarred by the accident that ended a parent's life, young Hazel joins other family members traveling for two years before settling in a Maine community, where an unlikely friend informs her about a local mermaid legend.

"An undercurrent of mermaid folklore adds memorable mystery and a hint of hopeful magic to this portrait of profound grief, worn-thin coping mechanisms, and the power of friendship." Bulletin of the Center for Children's Books

Blake, Kendare

Anna dressed in blood. Kendare Blake. Tor Teen, 2011. 320 p.: Anna Korlov series

Grades: 8 9 10 11 12 **Fic**

1. Girl ghosts 2. Ghosts 3. Psychics 4. Detectives 5. Knives 6. Horror 7. Ghost stories

ISBN 9780765328656

For three years, seventeen-year-old Cas Lowood has carried on his father's work of dispatching the murderous dead, traveling with his kitchen-witch mother and their spirit-sniffing cat, but everything changes when he meets Anna, a girl unlike any ghost he has faced before.

"Blake populates the story with a nice mixture of personalities, including Anna, and spices it with plenty of gallows humor, all the while keeping the suspense pounding. . . . Abundantly original, marvelously inventive and enormous fun, this can stand alongside the best horror fiction out there. We demand sequels." Kirkus.

Two dark reigns. Kendare Blake. Harper Teen, an imprint of HarperCollins Publishers, 2018 447 p.: Three dark crowns

Grades: 8 9 10 11 12 **Fic**
1. Inheritance and succession 2. Triplets 3. Rulers 4. Heirs and heiresses 5. Sisters 6. High fantasy 7. Fantasy fiction
ISBN 9780062686145

LC bl2018181567

When she finally gets the crown, Queen Elizabeth faces murmurs of dissent among her people and the threat of her sisters returning to Fennbirn to usurp her throne.

Blakemore, Megan Frazer

The **friendship** riddle. by Megan Frazer Blakemore. Bloomsbury, 2015. 256 p.

Grades: 4 5 6 7 **Fic**
1. Riddles 2. Spelling bees 3. Friendship 4. Former friends 5. Small towns 6. Maine 7. Realistic fiction
ISBN 9781619636309

LC 2014030036

When her former best friend gets popular and leaves her behind, sixth-grader Ruth prefers to be alone, studying for the school spelling bee, until she finds a riddle in an old book.

Blankman, Anne

★ The **blackbird** girls. Anne Blankman. Viking Childrens Books, 2020. 352 p.

Grades: 4 5 6 7 **Fic**
1. 1940s 2. 1980s 3. Grief in girls 4. Disasters 5. Life change events 6. Chernobyl Nuclear Accident, 1986 7. Nuclear power plants -- Accidents 8. Soviet Union 9. Ukraine 10. Historical fiction
ISBN 9781984837356

Told in alternating perspectives among three girls—Valentina and Oksana in 1986 and Rifka in 1941—this story shows that hatred, intolerance, and oppression are no match for the power of true friendship.— Excerpted from publisher description.

Block, Francesca Lia

Love in the time of global warming. Francesca Lia Block. Henry Holt and Company, 2013. 224 p.

Grades: 8 9 10 11 12 **Fic**
1. Survival 2. Earthquakes 3. Voyages and travels 4. Teenage romance 5. Post-apocalypse 6. Los Angeles, California 7. Magical realism 8. Apocalyptic fiction
ISBN 9780805096279

LC 2012047808

After a devastating earthquake destroys the West Coast, causing seventeen-year-old Penelope to lose her home, her parents, and her ten-year-old brother, she navigates a dark world, holding hope and love in her hands and refusing to be defeated.

"In this Odyssey-inspired story, after the devastating Earth Shaker, Penelope sets out into the brutal Los Angeles landscape in search of her family. She meets an intriguing boy named Hex who joins her on her journey. Block's imagery is remarkable in this sophisticated melding of post-apocalyptic setting, re-imagined classic, and her signature magical realism." Horn Book.

Bloor, Edward, 1950-

Taken. Edward Bloor. Alfred A. Knopf, 2007. 256 p.

Grades: 6 7 8 9 10 **Fic**
1. Near future 2. Kidnapping 3. Kidnapping victims 4. Social classes 5. Gated communities 6. Florida 7. Science fiction
ISBN 9780375836367

LC 2006035561

In 2036 kidnapping rich children has become an industry, but when thirteen-year-old Charity Meyers is taken and held for ransom, she soon discovers that this particular kidnapping is not what it seems.

"Deftly constructed, this is as riveting as it is thought-provoking." Publishers Weekly.

Blume, Judy

★ **Are** you there God? It's me, Margaret. Judy Blume. Bradbury Press, 1970. 149 p.

Grades: 4 5 6 7 **Fic**
1. Change 2. Children and religion 3. Puberty 4. Anxiety in girls 5. Moving to a new state 6. Realistic fiction 7. Classics
ISBN 9780130458568

LC 79122741

Faced with the difficulties of growing up and choosing a religion, an eleven-year-old girl talks over her problems with her own private God.

"A story about the emotional, physical, and spiritual ups and downs experienced by 12-year-old Margaret, child of a Jewish-Protestant union. Natl Counc of Teach of Engl. Adventuring with Books. 2d edition

Tiger eyes: a novel. Judy Blume. Bradbury Press, 1981. 206 p.

Grades: 7 8 9 10 **Fic**
1. Teenagers and death 2. Fathers -- Death 3. Grief in teenagers 4. Anger in teenagers 5. Fifteen-year-old girls 6. Los Alamos, New Mexico 7. Realistic fiction
ISBN 0878881859

LC 81006152

Resettled in Los Alamos, New Mexico with her mother and brother, Davey Wexler recovers from the shock of her father's death during a holdup of his 7-Eleven store in Atlantic City.

"The plot is strong, interesting and believable. . . . The story though intense and complicated flows smoothly and easily." Voice of Youth Advocates.

Blumenthal, Deborah

Mafia girl. Deborah Blumenthal. Albert Whitman & Company, 2014. 256 p.

Grades: 8 9 10 11 **Fic**
1. Mafia 2. Private schools 3. Identity (Psychology) 4. Police 5. Schools 6. Manhattan, New York City 7. Realistic fiction
ISBN 9780807549117

LC 2013028440

As the daughter of an infamous mob boss, seventeen-year-old Gia struggles to come out of the shadow of her family's notorious reputation and be her own person.

"Gia, the prized daughter of a New York Mafia boss, enjoys the carefree lifestyle her father's money and connections afford her. When the feds begin to close in on the family business, Gia must find an identity outside of Don's Daughter. Gia's voice is an entertaining, effervescent stream-of-consciousness, but the book's frantic pace muddles too many competing plot lines." Horn Book.

Blundell, Judy

A **city** tossed and broken: the diary of Minnie Bonner. Judy Blundell. Scholastic Inc., 2013. 224 p.: Dear America

Grades: 4 5 6 7   **Fic**
1. 1900s (Decade) 2. Earthquakes 3. Household employees 4. Families 5. Teenage girls 6. San Francisco Earthquake and Fire, Calif, 1906 7. San Francisco, California 8. Historical fiction 9. Diary novels
ISBN 9780545310222

It is 1906, and when her family is cheated out of their tavern, fourteen-year-old Minnie Bonner is forced to become a maid to the Sump family, who are moving to San Francisco—three weeks before the great earthquake.

"The author deftly incorporates true events, circumstances and key historical figures into the rapidly unfolding fictional plot... Exciting, suspenseful, absorbing and informative." Kirkus.

Strings attached. Judy Blundell. Scholastic Press, 2011. 320 p.
Grades: 7 8 9 10   **Fic**
1. 1950s 2. Teenage girl dancers 3. Mafia 4. High school dropouts 5. Former boyfriends 6. Italian Americans 7. New York City 8. Historical fiction
ISBN 9780545221269

LC 2010041078

When she drops out of school and struggles to start a career on Broadway in the fall of 1950, seventeen-year-old Kit Corrigan accepts help from an old family friend, a lawyer said to have ties with the mob, who then asks her to do some favors for him.

"Blundell successfully constructs a complex web of intrigue that connects characters in unexpected ways. History and theater buffs will especially appreciate her attention to detail—Blundell again demonstrates she can turn out first-rate historical fiction." Publishers Weekly.

What I saw and how I lied. Judy Blundell. Scholastic Press, 2008. 288 p.
Grades: 8 9 10 11 12   **Fic**
1. 1940s 2. Family problems 3. Secrets 4. Stepfathers 5. Teenage girls 6. Fifteen-year-old girls 7. Florida 8. Historical fiction
ISBN 9780439903462

LC 2008008503

National Book Award for Young People's Literature, 2008.

In 1947, with her jovial stepfather Joe back from the war and family life returning to normal, teenage Evie, smitten by the handsome young ex-GI who seems to have a secret hold on Joe, finds herself caught in a complicated web of lies whose devastating outcome change her life and that of her family forever.

"Using pitch-perfect dialogue and short sentences filled with meaning, Blundell has crafted a suspenseful, historical mystery." Booklist.

Bock, Caroline
Lie. Caroline Bock. St. Martin's Griffin, 2011. 224 p.
Grades: 8 9 10 11 12   **Fic**
1. Hate crimes 2. Right and wrong 3. Racism 4. Personal conduct 5. Bullying and bullies 6. Long Island, New York 7. Psychological suspense
ISBN 9780312668327

LC 2011019824

Told in several voices, a group of Long Island high school seniors conspire to protect eighteen-year-old Jimmy after he brutally assaults two Salvadoran immigrants, until they begin to see the moral implications of Jimmy's actions and the consequences of being loyal to a violent bully.

"This effective, character-driven, episodic story examines the consequences of a hate crime on the teens involved in it. . . . Realistic and devastatingly insightful, this novel can serve as a springboard to classroom and family discussions. Unusual and important." Kirkus.

Bodeen, S. A. (Stephanie A.), 1965-
The **compound**. S.A. Bodeen. Feiwel and Friends, 2008. 248 p.
Grades: 7 8 9 10   **Fic**
1. Deception 2. Psychopaths 3. Fallout shelters 4. Survival 5. Fathers 6. Thrillers and suspense
ISBN 9780312370152

LC 2007036148

After his parents, two sisters, and he have spent six years in a vast underground compound built by his wealthy father to protect them from a nuclear holocaust, fifteen-year-old Eli, whose twin brother and grandmother were left behind, discovers that his father has perpetrated a monstrous hoax on them all.

"The audience will feel the pressure closing in on them as they, like the characters, race through hairpin turns in the plot toward a breathless climax." Publishers Weekly.

The **raft**. S. A. Bodeen. Feiwel & Friends, 2012. 240 p.
Grades: 7 8 9 10   **Fic**
1. Airplane accidents 2. Castaways 3. Survival (after airplane accidents, shipwrecks, etc) 4. Rafts 5. FIfteen-year-old girls 6. Survival stories 7. Adventure stories
ISBN 9780312650100

When her last-minute cargo flight to the Pacific Islands Midway Atoll is brought down by a catastrophic storm, lone passenger Robie finds herself drifting in the middle of the ocean on a raft with the co-pilot, Max, with whom she struggles to survive without supplies.

"There is an odd lack of panic to much of the proceedings, but if you can get beyond that, this is tight, engaging, cleverly constructed fiction, with a late-in-the-game twist that makes perfect, if heartbreaking, sense." Booklist.

Boecker, Virginia
An **assassin's** guide to love and treason. Virginia Boecker. Little Brown & Company, 2018 384 p.
Grades: 7 8 9 10 11 12   **Fic**
1. Elizabethan era (1558-1603) 2. Tudor period (1485-1603) 3. Assassination plots 4. Theater 5. Teenage spies 6. Assassins 7. Political intrigue 8. London, England 9. Great Britain 10. Historical fiction
ISBN 9780316327343

In the early sixteen-hundreds, two star-crossed assassins, nineteen-year-old Toby and seventeen-year-old Kit, go undercover as actors in a Shakespeare play in a plot to kill Queen Elizabeth.

Bolden, Tonya
Crossing Ebenezer Creek. by Tonya Bolden. Bloomsbury, 2017. 240 p.: Crossing Ebenezer Creek
Grades: 7 8 9 10 11 12   **Fic**
1. American Civil War era (1861-1865) 2. African Americans 3. Freed people 4. Resilience (Personal quality) 5. Sherman's March to the Sea 6. Brothers and sisters 7. Georgia 8. United States 9. Historical fiction 10. African American fiction
ISBN 9781599903194

LC 2016037742

Freed from slavery, Mariah and her young brother Zeke join Sherman's march through Georgia, where Mariah meets a free Black named Caleb and dares to imagine the possibility of true love, but hope can come at a cost.

"A poetic, raw, and extraordinary imagining of a little-known, shameful chapter in American history." Kirkus.

Inventing Victoria. by Tonya Bolden. Bloomsbury, 2019. 272 p.: Crossing Ebenezer Creek

Grades: 8 9 10 11 12   **Fic**
   1. 1880s 2. Gilded Age (1865-1898) 3. 19th century 4. Social classes 5. African American women 6. Ambition 7. Upward mobility 8. Young women 9. Savannah, Georgia 10. Washington, DC 11. Historical fiction 12. Coming-of-age stories 13. African American fiction
ISBN 9781681198071

                    LC 2018024642

Essie, a young Black woman in 1880s Savannah, is offered the opportunity to leave her shameful past and be transformed into an educated, high-society woman in Washington, D.C.

Saving Savannah. by Tonya Bolden. Bloomsbury, 2020. 240 p.

Grades: 8 9 10 11 12   **Fic**
   1. 1900s (Decade) 2. African Americans 3. Suffragists 4. Social change 5. Socialism 6. Postwar life 7. Washington (DC) 8. Historical fiction
ISBN 9781681198040

                  LC 2019019792

Savannah Riddle feels suffocated by her life as the daughter of an upper class African American family in Washington, D.C., until she meets a working-class girl named Nella who introduces her to the suffragette and socialist movements and to her politically active cousin Lloyd.

"While Savannah's characterization lacks some nuance, the story is richly complex in its historical detail, and it builds to a revelatory climax. Enhanced by a comprehensive author's note, this is a valuable portrayal of affluent African-American society and of post-WWI life." Publishers Weekly

Bond, Victoria, 1979-

Zora and me: the song of Ivory. by Victoria Bond and T.R. Simon. Candlewick Press, 2010. 192 p.: Zora and me

Grades: 4 5 6 7   **Fic**
   1. Hurston, Zora Neale 2. African American girls 3. Truthfulness and falsehood 4. Race relations 5. African Americans 6. Pretending 7. Florida 8. Eatonville (Fla) 9. Coming-of-age stories 10. African American fiction
ISBN 9780763643003

A fictionalized account of Zora Neale Hurston's childhood with her best friend Carrie, in Eatonville, Florida, as they learn about life, death, and the differences between truth, lies, and pretending. Includes an annotated bibliography of the works of Zora Neale Hurston, a short biography of the author, and information about Eatonville, Florida.

"The brilliance of this novel is its rendering of African-American child life during the Jim Crow era as a time of wonder and imagination, while also attending to its harsh realities. Absolutely outstanding." Kirkus.

Includes bibliographical references.

Boniface, William

The **great** powers outage. William Boniface. Harpercollins Childrens Books, 2008. 320 p.: Extraordinary adventures of Ordinary Boy

Grades: 4 5 6 7   **Fic**
   1. Boys 2. Villains 3. Good and evil 4. Superheroes 5. Heroes and heroines 6. Humorous stories 7. Superhero stories
ISBN 9780060774707

When the citizens of Superopolis begin to mysteriously lose their superpowers, Ordinary Boy and his friends investigate the world of master villains.

"Boniface has cleverly interlaced bits and pieces of story lines from past novels with this one to expand his wacky world with enough history and political overtones to appeal to those readers savvy enough to understand the satire behind the silliness. Reluctant readers can enjoy the comic graphic-novel essence of the text as well as Gilpin's humorous sketches." School Library Journal.

The **hero** revealed. by William Boniface; illustrations by Stephen Gilpin. Harper Collins, c2006. 294 p.: Extraordinary adventures of Ordinary Boy

Grades: 4 5 6 7   **Fic**
   1. Boys 2. Heroes and heroines 3. Superheroes 4. Boy superheroes 5. Villains 6. Humorous stories 7. Superhero stories
ISBN 0060774649

                  LC 2005018676

Ordinary Boy, the only resident of Superopolis without a superpower, uncovers and foils a sinister plot to destroy the town.

"This first book in a new series is great fun. . . . Boniface wields a cynical, but definitely kid-friendly, sense of humor, and Gilpin's illustrations are sharp and witty." School Library Journal.

The **return** of Meteor Boy? William Boniface. Harper Collins Children's Books, 2007. 352 p.: Extraordinary adventures of Ordinary Boy

Grades: 4 5 6 7   **Fic**
   1. Boys 2. Superheroes 3. Boy superheroes 4. Villains 5. Heroes and heroines 6. Humorous stories 7. Superhero stories
ISBN 9780060774677

                  LC 2006029877

While working on a time machine for the Spring Science Fair, Ordinary Boy discovers the true identity of long-lost Superopolis hero Meteor Boy.

"This second book in the series will appeal to superhero and comic-book readers. . . . The conversational style and full black-and-white cartoon illustrations . . . add to the silly mood." Booklist.

Booraem, Ellen

River magic. Ellen Booraem Penguin Group USA 2021 256 p.

Grades: 5 6 7 8   **Fic**
   1. Wizards 2. Teenage girls 3. Good and evil 4. Imaginary creatures 5. Senior women 6. Fantasy fiction
ISBN 9780525428046

When her humble circumstances are complicated by a family member's passing, a young river girl takes a cleaning job for an elderly new neighbor who turns out to be an ancient thunder wizard with a vindictive temper.

"A dense emotional core, resonant voice, and themes of grief, shifting friendships, and family enliven Booraem's contemporary fantasy, reminding readers that 'hope is everywhere.'" Publishers Weekly

Small persons with wings. Ellen Booraem. Dial Books for Young Readers, 2011. 304 p.

Grades: 4 5 6 7   **Fic**
   1. Fairies 2. Rings 3. Inns 4. Magic 5. Spells (Magic) 6.

Fantasy fiction
ISBN 9780803734715

LC 2010008400

When Mellie Turpin's grandfather dies and leaves her family his run-down inn and bar, she learns that for generations her family members have been fairy guardians, and now that the fairies want an important ring returned, the Turpins become involved in a series of magical adventures as they try to locate the missing ring.

"In a fairy story that's wistful, humorous, and clever, Booraem . . . suggests that the real world—with its disappointments and failings—is still better than living with illusions. . . . The theme of making progress, rather than ignoring problems, is a strong one, gently presented." Publishers Weekly.

The **unnameables**. Ellen Booraem. Harcourt, c2008. xii, 317 p.

Grades: 6 7 8 9   **Fic**

1. Teenage boy orphans 2. Names, Personal 3. Change 4. Dystopias 5. Satyrs 6. Fantasy fiction
ISBN 9780152063689

LC 2007048844

On an island in whose strict society only useful objects are named and the unnamed are ignored or forbidden, thirteen-year-old Medford encounters an unusual and powerful creature, half-man, half-goat, and together they attempt to bring some changes to the community.

Booth, Coe

Kinda like brothers. Coe Booth. Scholastic Press, 2014. 248 p.

Grades: 4 5 6 7 8   **Fic**

1. Inner city 2. African American boys 3. Summer schools 4. Foster home care 5. Inner city children 6. Realistic fiction 7. African American fiction
ISBN 9780545224963

Accustomed to the foster care babies and toddlers that briefly stay in his home, Jarrett initially feels threatened by a foster boy, Kevon, who is his age and whose story leads to an unexpected bond.

Booth, Molly

Saving Hamlet. Molly Booth. 352 p.

Grades: 7 8 9 10   **Fic**

1. Shakespeare, William, 1564-1616 Hamlet. 2. Globe Theatre (London, England: 1599-1644) 3. Elizabethan era (1558-1603) 4. Theater 5. Time travel (Past) 6. Actors and actresses 7. Crushes in teenage girls 8. Fifteen-year-old girls 9. England 10. Fantasy fiction
ISBN 9781484752746

LC 2015045426

Fifteen-year-old Emma is acting as stage manager for her school's production of Hamlet when she finds herself transported to the original staging of Hamlet in Shakespearean England. Provided by publisher.

"Emma is an easy-to-root-for heroine whose struggles will resonate with teens, drama geeks or otherwise, and her forays into Shakespeare's London add insight into gender identity in the theater. A fun, imaginative debut." Booklist.

Bosch, Pseudonymous

If you're reading this, it's too late. Pseudonymous Bosch; illustrations by Gilbert Ford. Little, Brown, 2008. 400 p.: Secret series

Grades: 4 5 6   **Fic**

1. Child misfits 2. Immortality 3. Codes (Communication) 4.

Secret societies 5. Villains 6. Fantasy mysteries
ISBN 9780316113670

LC 2008012405

Cass and Max-Ernest discover the Museum of Magic, unscramble more coded messages, and solve new mysteries in their attempt to thwart the Terces Society's ambitions of discovering immortality.

"This combines mystery, adventure, and fantasy. . . . The numerous parenthetical comments and footnotes are often laugh-out-loud funny. . . . The dark illustrations, descending chapter numbers, and playful fonts will catch readers' attention." School Library Journal.

The **name** of this book is secret. by Pseudonymous Bosch; illustrations by Gilbert Ford. Little, Brown, 2007. 360 p.: Secret series

Grades: 4 5 6   **Fic**

1. Child misfits 2. Immortality 3. Magicians 4. Synesthesia 5. Secrets 6. Fantasy mysteries 7. Metafiction
ISBN 9780316113663

This book begins with a warning: "Do not read beyond this page!" Though the brain teasers and coded messages in this supernatural mystery will make you curious about what happens next, beware! As you read, you (like Max-Ernst and Cass, the book's eccentric 11-year-old heroes) might learn secrets that put you in mortal danger at the hands of a covert, immortality-obsessed cult. .

"This is equal parts supernatural whodunit, suspense-filled adventure and evocative coming-of-age tale." Publishers Weekly.

This book is not good for you. chef de cuisine, Pseudonymous Bosch; illustrations by Gilbert Ford. Little, Brown, 2009. 394 p.: Secret series

Grades: 4 5 6   **Fic**

1. Child misfits 2. Cooks 3. Immortality 4. Ransom 5. Chocolate 6. Fantasy mysteries
ISBN 9780316040860

LC bl2009023174

As an evil dessert chef concocts a recipe for disaster in the form of a tempting chocolate bar, Cass and Max-Ernest attempt to stop an evil organization from carrying out its plot to gain immortality and wreak havoc on the world.

"Twists and turns in the ordering of the chapters give the author time for commentary and a choose-your-own adventure for readers who will still be on the edges of their seats at the end for the Secret to be revealed." Voice of Youth Advocates.

This isn't what it looks like. Pseudonymous Bosch; illustrations by Gilbert Ford. Little, Brown, 2010. 423 p.: Secret series

Grades: 4 5 6   **Fic**

1. Child misfits 2. Time travel (Past) 3. Children in comas 4. Chocolate 5. Secrets 6. Fantasy mysteries
ISBN 9780316076258

"The book's blend of mystery, fantasy, puzzles, puns, and puckish, sometimes snarky sense of humor will keep readers engaged." Horn Book Guide.

Boteju, Tanya

Kings, queens, and in-betweens. Tanya Boteju. Simon & Schuster, 2019. 368 p.

Grades: 8 9 10 11 12   **Fic**

1. Lesbian teenagers 2. Identity (Psychology) 3. Drag shows 4. Self-esteem in teenagers 5. Abandonment (Psychology) 6. Realistic fiction
ISBN 9781534430655

After a bewildering encounter at her small town's annual summer festival, seventeen-year-old biracial, queer Nima plunges into the world of drag, where she has the chance to explore questions of identity, acceptance, self-expression, and love.

Bourne, Shakirah

Josephine against the sea. Shakirah Bourne. Scholastic Press, 2021. 304 p.

Grades: 4 5 6 7   **Fic**
1. Preteen girls 2. Fathers and daughters 3. Mythical creatures 4. Girlfriends 5. Cricket players 6. Barbados 7. Fantasy fiction
ISBN 9781338642087

When she discovers her father's new girlfriend, Mariss, is actually a sea creature eager to take her place as his first love, Josephine must convince her friends to help her and use her cricket skills to save her dad from Mariss' clutches.

"Twining fantastical elements with a steady pace and a contemporary setting, Bourne nets a relatable story of processing grief, trust in one's family and community, and Black girl magic." Publishers Weekly

Bowling, Dusti

The **canyon's** edge. Dusti Bowling. Little, Brown and Company, 2020. 240 p.

Grades: 5 6 7 8   **Fic**
1. Fathers and daughters 2. Survival 3. Deserts 4. People with post-traumatic stress disorder 5. Grief 6. Arizona 7. Survival stories 8. Adventure stories 9. Novels in verse
ISBN 9780316494694

A year after the death of her mother in a restaurant shooting, Nora is left struggling to stay alive when a climbing trip with her father goes terribly wrong.

"As Nora fights waves of panic, her harrowing tale of survival unfolds through a mix of free-verse and concrete poetry. Flashbacks and nightmares fill in details about her mother's death and the PTSD it imprinted on the lives of Nora and her father. . . . A triumphant story of healing and bravery." Booklist

★ **Insignificant** events in the life of a cactus. Dusti Bowling. Sterling Pub. Co. Inc., 2017 272 p.: Life of a cactus

Grades: 5 6 7 8   **Fic**
1. Girls with disabilities 2. Moving to a new state 3. Amusement parks 4. Adopted girls 5. Tourette syndrome 6. Arizona 7. Realistic fiction
ISBN 9781454923459

Aven Green was born without arms, so when her dad takes a job running a dying western theme park in Arizona, she knows she'll become the center of unwanted attention at her new school. But she bonds with Connor, a classmate with his own disability to conquer. Then they discover a room at the park that holds bigger secrets than Aven ever could have imagined. Can Aven face her fears, solve a mystery, and help her friend, too?

"The tale of Stagecoach Pass is just as compelling as the story of Aven, and the setting, like the many colorful characters who people this novel, is so vivid and quirky that it's practically cinematic." School Library Journal.

Momentous events in the life of a cactus. by Dusti Bowling. Sterling Children's Books, [2019] 320 p.: Life of a cactus

Grades: 5 6 7 8   **Fic**
1. Teenage girls with disabilities 2. High school freshmen 3. Bullying and bullies 4. Self-confidence 5. High schools 6.

Arizona 7. Realistic fiction
ISBN 9781454933298

LC 2019011133

After navigating middle school, ninth-grader Aven, born without arms, struggles with the challenges of high school, which test her confidence, strength, and sense of self.

Bowling, Nicholas

Witch born. Nicholas Bowling. Chicken House, 2018, c2017. 320 p.

Grades: 6 7 8 9 10 11   **Fic**
1. Dee, John, 1527-1608 2. Mary, Queen of Scots, 1542-1587 3. Elizabeth I, Queen of England, 1533-1603 4. Elizabethan era (1558-1603) 5. 16th century 6. Witches 7. Women rulers 8. Witchcraft 9. Black magic 10. Innkeepers 11. Great Britain 12. Europe 13. Historical fantasy
ISBN 9781338277531

When her mother is cruelly burned at the stake for practicing witchcraft, Alyce receives help from an innkeeper and a boy with his own troubles when she is targeted by a witch hunter at the same time her fledgling powers ensnare her in a web of secrets, lies and dark magic.

Bowman, Akemi Dawn

Starfish. Akemi Dawn Bowman. Simon Pulse, 2017. 352 p.

Grades: 7 8 9 10   **Fic**
1. Multiracial teenage girls 2. Artists 3. Self-perception in teenage girls 4. Self-perception 5. Family problems 6. Nebraska 7. California 8. Realistic fiction
ISBN 9781481487726

LC 2016045829

Kiko Himura yearns to escape the toxic relationship with her mother by getting into her dream art school, but when things do not work out as she hoped Kiko jumps at the opportunity to tour art schools with her childhood friend, learning life-changing truths about herself and her past along the way.

"The story will resonate deeply with readers who have experienced abuse of any kind, or who have been held back by social anxiety. This is a stunningly beautiful, highly nuanced debut." Booklist.

Summer bird blue. Akemi Dawn Bowman. Simon Pulse, 2018 384 p.

Grades: 7 8 9 10 11 12   **Fic**
1. Parent-separated teenage girls 2. Survivor guilt 3. Sisters -- Death 4. Intergenerational friendship 5. Grief in teenagers 6. Hawaii 7. Coming-of-age stories 8. Realistic fiction
ISBN 9781481487757

Rumi Seto plans to spend her life writing music with her younger sister, Lea. When Lea dies in a car accident, her mother sends Rumi to live with her aunt in Hawaii while she deals with her own grief. Struggling with the loss of her sister, abandoned by her mother, and without music in her life, Rumi turns to the friendship of a teenage surfer named Kai, and an eighty-year-old named George Watanabe. And Rumi is determined to write the song she and Lea never had the chance to finish.— adapted from jacket.

Boyne, John, 1971-

The **boy** in the striped pajamas: a fable. by John Boyne. David Fickling Books, 2006. 224 p.

Grades: 7 8 9 10 11   **Fic**
1. Auschwitz (Concentration camp) 2. Second World War era (1939-1945) 3. 1940s 4. Children of Nazis 5. Jewish boys 6. Secret friends 7. Child Holocaust victims 8. Holocaust (1933-

1945) -- Children 9. Poland 10. Historical fiction
ISBN 0385751079

LC 2005033596

Bored and lonely after his family moves from Berlin to a place called "Out-With" in 1942, Bruno, the son of a Nazi officer, befriends a boy in striped pajamas who lives behind a wire fence.

"Some of the most thought-provoking Holocaust books are about bystanders, including those who say they did not know what was happening. This first novel tells the bystander story from the viewpoint of an innocent child. . . . It's all part of a poignant construct: Shmuel is Bruno's alternative self, and as the story builds to a horrifying climax, the innocent's experience brings home the unimaginable horror. Pair this with Anne Frank's classic diary and Anita Lobel's No Pretty Pictures: A Child of War (1998)." Booklist.

Bracken, Alexandra

The **darkest** minds. Alexandra Bracken. Hyperion, 2012. 496 p.: Darkest minds novels

Grades: 8 9 10   **Fic**

1. Dystopias 2. Psychic ability 3. Runaway teenagers 4. Escapes 5. Interpersonal relations 6. Dystopian fiction 7. Science fiction
ISBN 9781423157373

LC 2012008661

Sixteen-year-old Ruby breaks out of a government-run "rehabilitation camp" for teens who acquired dangerous powers after surviving a virus that wiped out most American children.

Never fade. Alexandra Bracken. Hyperion, [2013] 400 p.: Darkest minds novels

Grades: 8 9 10   **Fic**

1. Dystopias 2. Psychic ability 3. Epidemics 4. Teenage girls 5. Dystopian fiction 6. Science fiction
ISBN 9781423157519

LC 2013012607

Believing herself to be a monster in spite of powerful abilities that enable her to lead dangerous psychic missions against a corrupt government, Ruby is entrusted with an explosive secret about the disease that killed most of America's youth and embarks on a search in a lawless country to find Liam Stewart.

Bradbury, Jennifer. (Jennifer A.)

Shift. Jennifer Bradbury. Atheneum Books for Young Readers, c2008. 245 p.

Grades: 7 8 9 10 11 12   **Fic**

1. Missing teenage boys 2. Transcontinental journeys 3. Children of rich people 4. Family problems 5. Bicycling 6. Realistic fiction 7. Coming-of-age stories
ISBN 9781416947325

LC 2007023558

After graduating from high school, best friends Win and Chris take a cross-country bicycle trek from West Virginia to Washington state, during which they discover amazingly beautiful places, meet fascinating people...and have a nasty fight. Win abandons Chris in Montana with no explanation, so Chris finishes the trip solo and returns home to start college...and until an FBI agent shows up to question him about the details of their trip, Chris has no idea that Win never made it back. Outdoor types, armchair travelers, and mystery fans won't be able to flip these pages fast enough. .

"Bradbury's keen details . . . add wonderful texture to this exciting [novel.] . . . Best of all is the friendship story." Booklist.

Bradbury, Ray, 1920-2012

The **Halloween** tree. Ray Bradbury; illustrated by Joseph Mugnaini. Knopf; [distributed by Random House, 1972] 145 p.

Grades: 6 7 8 9   **Fic**

1. Halloween 2. Time travel 3. Spirits 4. Boys 5. Sick children 6. Fantasy fiction 7. Classics
ISBN 0394824091

LC 72002433

A group of children and a "spirit" go back through time to discover the beginnings of Halloween. Meet the mysterious Mr. Moonshroud, who leads eight boys on a journey back through the centuries to discover the real meaning of Halloween. Prose of exquisite beauty will send shivers of delight—and terror—through readers, who will want to take this trip over and over again, long after the last jack-o'-lantern has gone dark.

"This is fast-moving, genuinely eerie." Booklist.

Something wicked this way comes. Ray Bradbury. Avon Books, 1998. 304 p.

Grades: 7 8 9 10 11 12 Adult   **Fic**

1. Carnivals 2. Good and evil 3. Thirteen-year-old boys 4. Boys -- Friendship 5. Best friends 6. Illinois 7. Horror 8. Coming-of-age stories 9. Fantasy classics
ISBN 0380729407

Story of two young boys who begin to encounter evil secrets when a lightning rod salesman gives them one of his contraptions covered with mystical symbols.

Bradley, Alex

24 girls in 7 days. Alex Bradley. Dutton, 2005. 265 p.

Grades: 7 8 9 10   **Fic**

1. Teenagers 2. Teenage boys 3. High school seniors 4. Personal ads 5. Teenage boy/girl relations 6. Humorous stories
ISBN 0525473696

"When the love of his life rejects his invitation to the senior prom, Jack Grammar's so-called best friends pose as Jack and run a personal ad in the online school newspaper soliciting a date. . . . The result is a hilarious adventure as Jack tries to speed-date 24 girls in 7 days. . . . This entertaining guy's eye view on dating, friendship, and understanding one's self is one that most libraries will want to own." School Library Journal.

Bradley, Kimberly Brubaker

★ **Fighting** words. Kimberly Brubaker Bradley. Dial Books, 2020 272 p.

Grades: 4 5 6 7 8   **Fic**

1. Sisters 2. Suicidal behavior 3. Child sexual abuse 4. Protectiveness 5. Foster home care 6. Realistic fiction
ISBN 9781984815682

Depending on an older sister who protected her when their mother went to prison and their mother's boyfriend committed a terrible act, 10-year-old Della tries to figure out what to do when her older sister attempts suicide.

"Believable and immensely appealing, Suki, Francine, and especially Della light up what might have been an unremittingly bleak story. . . . Refusing to soft-pedal hard issues, the novel speaks with an astringent honesty, at once heartbreaking and hopeful." Kirkus

★ **Jefferson's** sons: a founding father's secret children. by Kimberly Brubaker Bradley. Dial Books for Young Readers, 2011. 368 p.

Grades: 5 6 7 8   **Fic**

1. Jefferson, Thomas, 1743-1826. 2. Hemings, Sally, 1773-1835?

3. Monticello (Va.) 4. 19th century 5. Slavery 6. Multiracial children 7. Enslaved people 8. Illegitimacy 9. African Americans 10. Virginia 11. Historical fiction

ISBN 9780803734999

LC 2010049650

A fictionalized look at the last twenty years of Thomas Jefferson's life at Monticello through the eyes of three of his slaves, two of whom were his sons by his slave, Sally Hemings.

"The characters spring to life. . . . [This is a] fascinating story of an American family that represents so many of the contradictions of our history. The afterword is as fascinating as the novel." Kirkus.

★ The **war** that saved my life. by Kimberly Brubaker Bradley. Dial Books for Young Readers, 2015. 320 p.

Grades: 4 5 6 7   **Fic**

1. Second World War era (1939-1945) 2. 1940s 3. People with disabilities 4. Brothers and sisters 5. World War II 6. Evacuation of civilians 7. War 8. Great Britain 9. Historical fiction

ISBN 9780803740815

LC 2014002168

Schneider Family Book Award for Middle School, 2016.

A young disabled girl and her brother are evacuated from London to the English countryside during World War II, where they find life to be much sweeter away from their abusive mother.

"The home-front realities of WWII, as well as Ada's realistic anger and fear, come to life in Bradley's affecting and austerely told story, and readers will cheer for steadfast Ada as she triumphs over despair." Booklist.

Brahmachari, Sita, 1966-

Jasmine skies. Sita Brahmachari. Albert Whitman & Company, 2014. 330 p.

Grades: 6 7 8 9   **Fic**

1. East Indian British teenagers 2. Family visits 3. British in India 4. Families 5. Teenage boy/girl relations 6. India 7. London, England 8. Realistic fiction

ISBN 9780807537824

LC 2014013302

Fourteen-year-old Mira Levenson travels from London to Kolkata to meet her aunt and her cousin and to find out why the families haven't spoken in years. Provided by publisher.

"Vivid descriptions of the exotic setting, an emotionally honest (if naive and stubborn) narrator, and a sweet romance should captivate readers." Booklist.

Brant, Wendy

Zenn diagram. Wendy Brant. KCP Loft, 2017 328 p.

Grades: 8 9 10 11 12   **Fic**

1. Genius 2. Teenage artists 3. Visions 4. Teenage romance 5. New students 6. Paranormal romances

ISBN 9781771387927

A teen math genius who secretly possesses the ability to read the emotions, fears and dreams of anyone she touches is drawn to an artistic newcomer with a troubled home life only to discover their shattering common history.

"Though the plot coincidences stretch belief at times, they are forgiven in light of the strengths of the story, which include a unique premise, natural dialogue, and complex characters." Booklist.

Brashares, Ann

3 willows: the sisterhood grows. Ann Brashares. Delacorte Press, 2009. 336 p.

Grades: 6 7 8 9 10   **Fic**

1. Summer 2. Best friends 3. Friendship 4. Growing up 5. Interpersonal relations 6. Maryland 7. Bethesda, Maryland 8. Realistic fiction 9. Teen chick lit

ISBN 9780385736763

Ama, Jo, and Polly, three close friends from Bethesda, Maryland, spend the summer before ninth grade learning about themselves, their families, and the changing nature of their friendship.

"Brashares gets her characters' emotions and interactions just right." Publishers Weekly.

The **sisterhood** of the traveling pants. Ann Brashares. Delacorte Press, 2001. 294 p.: Sisterhood of the Traveling Pants series

Grades: 8 9 10   **Fic**

1. Best friends 2. Blue jeans 3. Teenage girls -- Friendship 4. Teenage girls -- Personal conduct 5. Teenagers 6. Coming-of-age stories 7. Realistic fiction 8. Teen chick lit

ISBN 0385729332

Four best girlfriends spend the biggest summer of their lives enchanted by a magical pair of pants.

"Four lifelong high-school friends and a magical pair of jeans take summer journeys to discover love, disappointment, and self-realization." Booklist.

Brashear, Amy

The **incredible** true story of the making of the Eve of Destruction. Amy Brashear. Soho Teen, 2018. 320 p.

Grades: 8 9 10 11 12   **Fic**

1. 1980s 2. Cold War 3. Filmmaking 4. Nuclear weapons 5. Stepbrothers and stepsisters 6. Teenagers 7. Arkansas 8. Historical fiction

ISBN 9781616959036

LC 2018027722

In 1984, while grappling with her parents' divorce and her mother's remarriage to an African-American man, sixteen-year-old Laura wins a walk-on role in the nuclear holocaust movie being filmed in her Arkansas town.

Braswell, Liz

Part of your world: a twisted tale. Liz Braswell Disney Press, 2018. 480 p.: Twisted tales (Liz Braswell)

Grades: 6 7 8 9 10   **Fic**

1. Curses 2. Transformations (Magic) 3. Mermaids 4. Magic 5. Father-separated teenage girls 6. Fantasy fiction 7. Fairy tale and folklore-inspired fiction

ISBN 9781368013819

In a reimagining of what would have happened if Ariel had never defeated Ursula, 5 years have elapsed and Ariel is now the voiceless queen of Atlantica while Ursula runs Prince Eric's kingdom on land, but when Ariel discovers that her father, King Triton, might still be alive, she finds herself returning to a world—and a prince—she never imagined she would see again.

A **whole** new world. Liz Braswell. Disney Press, 2015. 304 p.: Twisted tales (Liz Braswell)

Grades: 6 7 8 9   **Fic**

1. Genies 2. Magic lamps 3. Poor boys 4. Princesses 5. Fantasy fiction 6. Fairy tale and folklore-inspired fiction 7. Middle Eastern-influenced fantasy

ISBN 9781484707296

In an alternate take on the Disney film, Jafar, not Aladdin finds the lamp and uses it to attain power while a poor Aladdin and displaced Jasmine must unite the common people in rebellion against the evil usurper.

Bray, Libba

Beauty queens. Libba Bray. Scholastic Press, 2011. 400 p.
Grades: 8 9 10 11 12   **Fic**
1. Castaways 2. Beauty contestants 3. Survival (after airplane accidents, shipwrecks, etc) 4. Beauty contests 5. Survival 6. Humorous stories
ISBN 9780439895972
LC 2011002321

When a plane crash strands thirteen teen beauty contestants on a mysterious island, they struggle to survive, to get along with one another, to combat the island's other diabolical occupants, and to learn their dance numbers in case they are rescued in time for the competition.

"A full-scale send-up of consumer culture, beauty pageants, and reality television: . . . it makes readers really examine their own values while they are laughing, and shaking their heads at the hyperbolic absurdity of those values gone seriously awry." Bulletin of the Center for Children's Books.

A **great** and terrible beauty. Libba Bray. Delacorte Press, 2004. 416 p.: Gemma Doyle trilogy
Grades: 9 10 11 12   **Fic**
1. Victorian era (1837-1901) 2. 19th century 3. Sixteen-year-old girls 4. Boarding schools 5. Teenage girls 6. Women -- History 19th century. 7. Friendship 8. Great Britain 9. England 10. Historical fantasy
ISBN 0385730284
LC 2003009472

After the suspicious death of her mother in 1895, sixteen-year-old Gemma returns to England, after many years in India, to attend a finishing school where she becomes aware of her magical powers and ability to see into the spirit world.

"The reader will race to the end to discover the mysterious and realistic challenges of an exciting teenage gothic mystery." Library Media Connection.

Brewer, Zac, 1973-

Eighth grade bites. Heather Brewer. Dutton Children's Books, 2007. 182 p.: Chronicles of Vladimir Tod
Grades: 6 7 8 9   **Fic**
1. Teenage vampires 2. Teenage boy orphans 3. Substitute teachers 4. Vampires 5. Supernatural 6. Urban fantasy
ISBN 9780525478119
LC 2006030455

For thirteen years, Vlad, aided by his aunt and best friend, has kept secret that he is half-vampire, but when his missing teacher is replaced by a sinister substitute, he learns that there is more to being a vampire, and to his parents' deaths, than he could have guessed.

"This is an exceptional current-day vampire story. The mix of typical teen angst and dealing with growing vampiric urges make for a fast-moving, engaging story." Voice of Youth Advocates.

Brezenoff, Steven

Brooklyn, burning. by Steve Brezenoff. Carolrhoda Lab, 2011. 202 p.
Grades: 8 9 10 11   **Fic**
1. Teenage musicians 2. Drummers 3. Crushes in teenagers 4. Crushes (Interpersonal relations) 5. Interpersonal relations 6. Brooklyn, New York City 7. New York City 8. Realistic fiction 9.

LGBTQIA fiction
ISBN 9780761375265
LC 2010051447

Sixteen-year-old Kid, who lives on the streets of Brooklyn, loves Felix, a guitarist and junkie who disappears, leaving Kid the prime suspect in an arson investigation, but a year later Scout arrives, giving Kid a second chance to be in a band and find true love.

"Homelessness, queerness and the rougher sides of living on the street are handled without a whiff of sensationalism, and the moments between Kid, the first-person narrator, and Scout, addressed as you, are described in language so natural and vibrant that readers may not even notice that neither character's gender is ever specified. . . . Overall, the tone is as raw, down-to-earth and transcendent as the music Scout and Kid ultimately make together." Kirkus.

Brignull, Irena

The **hawkweed** prophecy. Irena Brignull. Weinstein Books, 2016. 362 p.: Hawkweed prophecy
Grades: 7 8 9 10   **Fic**
1. Witches 2. Prophecies 3. Love triangles 4. Family secrets 5. Identity (Psychology) 6. Paranormal fiction 7. Coming-of-age stories
ISBN 9781602863002

"The third-person narration switches focus from character to character as they make frustrating, heart-rending, totally believable choices. Fantasy and nonfantasy readers alike will appreciate this gritty and intriguing coming-of-age story." Kirkus.

Broach, Elise

Shakespeare's secret. Elise Broach. Henry Holt, 2005. 250 p.
Grades: 5 6 7 8   **Fic**
1. Shakespeare, William, 1564-1616 2. De Vere, Edward, 17th Earl of Oxford, 1550-1604 3. Moving, Household 4. New students 5. Misfits (Persons) 6. Secrets 7. Sixth-grade girls 8. Great Britain 9. Mysteries
ISBN 0805073876
LC 2004054020

Named after a character in a Shakespeare play, misfit sixth-grader Hero becomes interested in exploring this unusual connection because of a valuable diamond supposedly hidden in her new house, an intriguing neighbor, and the unexpected attention of the most popular boy in school.

"The mystery alone will engage readers. . . . The main characters are all well developed, and the dialogue is both realistic and well planned." School Library Journal.

The **wolf** keepers. Elise Broach; with illustrations by Alice Ratterree. Henry Holt and Company, 2016. 272 p.
Grades: 4 5 6 7 8   **Fic**
1. Zoos 2. Wolves 3. Runaway boys 4. African American boys 5. Friendship 6. Mysteries
ISBN 9780805098990
LC 2015049899

Twelve-year-old Lizzie Durango lives in a zoo, spending her days taking note of the animals' behaviors, then she meets runaway Tyler Briggs and together they investigate the wolves who are suddenly dying.

"Tyler's wry comments about his race add further dimensions to a thoughtful, well-told tale, as do the pencil drawings. John Muir's spirit hums along under a well-developed plot with likable characters." Kirkus.

Brody, Jessica

The **geography** of lost things. Jessica Brody. Simon & Schuster, 2018. 320 p.

Grades: 8 9 10 11 12　　　　　　　　　　**Fic**

1. Former boyfriends 2. Self-fulfillment 3. Fathers and daughters 4. Teenage boy/girl relations 5. High school graduates 6. Contemporary romances

ISBN 9781481499217

Ali and her ex-boyfriend, Nico, both eighteen, rehash their ill-fated romance during a road trip to sell the 1968 Firebird convertible she just inherited from her estranged father.

Sky without stars. by Jessica Brody and Joanne Rendell. Simon Pulse, 2019. 624 p.: System Divine

Grades: 8 9 10 11 12　　　　　　　　　　**Fic**

1. Social classes 2. Power (Social sciences) 3. Revolutions 4. Space colonies 5. Elite (Social sciences) 6. Space 7. Space opera 8. Science fiction 9. Coming-of-age stories

ISBN 9781534410633

　　　　　　　　　　　　　LC 2018030021

This sweeping reimagining of Les Miserables tells the story of three teens from very different backgrounds who are thrown together amidst the looming threat of revolution on the French planet-colony of Laterre. Provided by publisher.

Brooks, Martha, 1944-

Mistik Lake. Martha Brooks. Farrar, Straus and Giroux, 2007. 206 p.

Grades: 8 9 10　　　　　　　　　　　　**Fic**

1. Mother-separated teenage girls 2. Loss (Psychology) 3. Family secrets 4. Seventeen-year-old girls 5. Teenage girls 6. Manitoba

ISBN 9780374349851

　　　　　　　　　　　　　LC 2006037391

After Odella's mother leaves her, her sisters, and their father in Manitoba and moves to Iceland with another man, she then dies there, and the family finally learns some of the many secrets that have haunted them for two generations.

"All of the characters seem distinct and real, thanks to the author's exceptional skill with details." Publishers Weekly.

Queen of hearts. Martha Brooks. Groundwood Books, c2010. 208 p.

Grades: 7 8 9 10　　　　　　　　　　　**Fic**

1. Second World War era (1939-1945) 2. People with tuberculosis 3. Hospitals 4. Loneliness in teenagers 5. Teenage girls -- Friendship 6. Family relationships 7. Manitoba 8. Historical fiction

ISBN 9780888998286

"Readers will be held by the story's heartbreaking truths, right to the end." Booklist.

Brouwer, Sigmund, 1959-

Devil's pass. Sigmund Brouwer. Orca Book Pub., 2012. 256 p.: Seven

Grades: 6 7 8 9 10　　　　　　　　　　**Fic**

1. Seventeen-year-old boys 2. Wills 3. Grandfathers 4. Wilderness areas 5. Teenage boys 6. Toronto, Ontario 7. Canada 8. Realistic fiction

ISBN 9781554699384

Seventeen-year-old Webb, a street musician from Toronto, faces grizzly bears and a madman when he travels to the Canol Trail in Canada's Far North in order to fulfill a request made in his grandfather's will.

Brown, Gavin, 1983-

Josh Baxter levels up. written by Gavin Brown. Scholastic Press, 2016. 192 p.

Grades: 4 5 6 7 8　　　　　　　　　　　**Fic**

1. Video games and boys 2. Video gamers 3. New students 4. Middle school students 5. Middle schools 6. Realistic fiction

ISBN 9780545772945

Starting at a new school for the third time in two years, video game enthusiast and disgruntled new kid Josh Baxter becomes an accidental enemy to his middle school's football star before his poor grades cause him to lose his gaming privileges.

"Smartly paced and emotionally engaging, a book even those who have never held a controller will enjoy." Kirkus.

Brown, Skila

Caminar. Skila Brown. Candlewick Press, 2014. 192 p.

Grades: 6 7 8 9　　　　　　　　　　　　**Fic**

1. 1980s 2. Self-esteem in boys 3. War 4. Loss (Psychology) 5. Violence 6. Civil war 7. Guatemala 8. Novels in verse 9. Coming-of-age stories 10. Historical fiction

ISBN 9780763665166

Longing to assume a defensive adult role but dissuaded by his mother from confronting soldiers who have murdered a neighbor in his 1981 Guatemalan village, young Carlos joins a band of guerillas in the hope of carrying a warning to his grandmother's mountaintop home.

"Unlike many novels in verse, which can read like conventional narratives with line breaks, Caminar contributes poetry that elevates the genre. In this story of a decimated Guatemalan village in 1981, readers will encounter a range of imagery, repetition, rhythms, and visual effects that bring to life the psychological experience of Carlos, a young boy caught in the violent clash between the government's army and the people's rebels...This is a much-needed addition to Latin American-themed middle grade fiction." School Library Journal.

To stay alive: Mary Ann Graves and the tragic journey of the Donner Party. Skila Brown. Candlewick Press, 2016. 275 p.

Grades: 6 7 8 9 10　　　　　　　　　　**Fic**

1. Graves, Mary Ann, 1826-1891 2. American Westward Expansion (1803-1899) 3. 1840s 4. Donner Party 5. Overland journeys to the Pacific 6. Survival 7. Cannibalism 8. Blizzards 9. Historical fiction 10. Novels in verse

ISBN 9780763678111

A young survivor of the tragic Donner Party of 1846 describes how her family and others became victims of freezing temperatures and starvation.

"The strong novel in verse uses beautiful, descriptive words to depict the vastness of the landscape and the emotional and mental toll of perpetual suffering. This is a well-crafted narrative in which readers get to know and empathize with Mary Ann as her adventure shifts to survival. However, it might be difficult to stomach the travelers' desperate choices: the book does not shy away from the Donner Party's well-known resort to cannibalism." School Library Journal.

Bruchac, Joseph, 1942-

Code Talker. Joseph Bruchac. Dial Books, c2005. 240 p.

Grades: 6 7 8 9 10　　　　　　　　　　**Fic**

1. United States. Marine Corps -- Indian troops 2. Second World War era (1939-1945) 3. Native American teenage boys 4. Codes (Communication) 5. War 6. Cryptography 7. Sixteen-year-old boys 8. Historical fiction

ISBN 0803729219

　　　　　　　　　　　　　LC 2003022792

After being taught in a boarding school run by whites that Navajo is a useless language, Ned Begay and other Navajo men are recruited by the Marines to become Code Talkers, sending messages during World War II in their native tongue.

"Bruchac's gentle prose presents a clear historical picture of young men in wartime. . . . Nonsensational and accurate, Bruchac's tale is quietly inspiring." School Library Journal.

Includes bibliographical references.

Dragon castle. by Joseph Bruchac. Dial Books for Young Readers, 2011. 352 p.

Grades: 4 5 6 7   **Fic**
1. Princes 2. Dragons 3. Barons and baronesses 4. Good and evil 5. Rulers 6. Fantasy fiction
ISBN 9780803733763

LC 2010028798

Young Prince Rashko believes that his parents and his older brother Paulek, while loveable, are utter fools. He's even more convinced of this after the King and Queen depart castle Hladka Hvorka unexpectedly, the hostile Baron Temny gathers his army outside the castle walls, and Paulek invites Temny and his troops inside. Now it's up to Prince Rashko to stop the baron and save the kingdom—but, smart as he is, is he up to the challenge?

"Bruchac spins a good-natured and humorous fairy tale. . . . With its subtle focus on peaceful resistance and use of classic folk-tale elements, this story exudes a gentle sense of fun." Publishers Weekly.

Killer of enemies. Joseph Bruchac. Tu Books, 2013. 400 p.: Killer of enemies

Grades: 7 8 9 10 11 12   **Fic**
1. Native American teenage girls 2. Dystopias 3. Monsters 4. Near future 5. Genetic engineering 6. Southwest (United States) 7. Science fiction 8. Apocalyptic fiction
ISBN 9781620141434

LC 2013023567

In a world that has barely survived an apocalypse that leaves it with pre-twentieth century technology, Lozen is a monster hunter for four tyrants who are holding her family hostage.

"A deadly assassin with extrasensory powers, Lozen (named for an Apache-Chiricahua warrior-woman forebear) takes out genetically modified superbeasts; her family is being held hostage to ensure her continued service. Bruchac devises ever-more-dangerous battles for his protagonist in the increasingly suspenseful story. What really makes the narrative vibrate is Lozen's sardonic voice, capturing both gallows humor and a very human vulnerability." Horn Book.

Walking two worlds. Joseph Bruchac; illustrated by David Fadden. 7th Generation, 2015 120 p.

Grades: 5 6 7 8 9   **Fic**
1. Parker, Ely Samuel, 1828-1895 2. 1840s 3. Native American teenage boys 4. Seneca Indians 5. Prejudice 6. Racism 7. Boarding schools 8. New York (State) 9. Historical fiction
ISBN 9781939053107

"Though the book lacks formal resources and references, and the time frame of events, including Ely's birth date, is occasionally unclear, Ely's challenges and successes are supportively portrayed, and may inspire readers to learn more about his life and times. An afterword provides some information on his later years." Booklist.

Bruton, Catherine

I predict a riot. Catherine Bruton. Electric Monkey, 2014. 291 p.

Grades: 7 8 9 10   **Fic**
1. Gangs 2. Riots 3. Filmmakers 4. Neighborhoods 5. Children of politicians 6. Realistic fiction
ISBN 9781405267199

"Maggie's video camera seems to represent all the stories that aren't told in the media, making this searing tale one that will get readers talking." Booklist.

Bryant, Jennifer

Kaleidoscope eyes. Jen Bryant. Alfred A. Knopf, 2009. 272 p.

Grades: 5 6 7 8   **Fic**
1. 1960s 2. Thirteen-year-olds 3. Treasure hunting 4. Grandfathers 5. Teenagers 6. Single-parent families 7. New Jersey 8. Novels in verse 9. Realistic fiction 10. Historical mysteries
ISBN 9780375940484

LC 2008027345

In 1968, with the Vietnam War raging, thirteen-year-old Lyza inherits a project from her deceased grandfather, who had been using his knowledge of maps and the geography of Lyza's New Jersey hometown to locate the lost treasure of Captain Kidd.

"Bryant weaves an emotional novel in poems based on a true story of buried treasure. Tensions among families are drawn with heart-wrenching prose, and her depiction of segregation is flawless. . . . The characters are witty and well developed." Voice of Youth Advocates.

Ringside, 1925: views from the Scopes trial. Jen Bryant. Alfred A. Knopf, 2008. 240 p.

Grades: 8 9 10 11 12   **Fic**
1. Scopes, John Thomas 2. 1920s 3. Scopes Trial, 1925 4. Evolution -- Study and teaching -- Law and legislation 5. Community life 6. Trials 7. Small towns 8. Dayton, Tennessee 9. Tennessee 10. Novels in verse 11. Historical fiction
ISBN 9780375840470

LC 2007007177

Visitors, spectators, and residents of Dayton, Tennessee, in 1925 describe, in a series of free-verse poems, the Scopes "monkey trial" and its effects on that small town and its citizens.

"Bryant offers readers a ringside seat in this compelling and well-researched novel. It is fast-paced, interesting, and relevant to many current first-amendment challenges." School Library Journal.

Bryce, Celia

Anthem for Jackson Dawes. by Celia Bryce. Bloomsbury USA Childrens, 2013. 272 p.

Grades: 7 8 9 10   **Fic**
1. Teenagers with cancer 2. Teenage boy/girl relations 3. Hospital patients 4. Cancer 5. Brain cancer 6. Realistic fiction
ISBN 9781599909752

LC 2012024989

When Megan, thirteen, arrives for her first cancer treatment, she is frustrated to be on the pediatric unit where the only other teen is Jackson Dawes, who is as cute and charming as he is rebellious and annoying, and who helps when her friends are frightened away by her illness.

"Sensitive and honest, this novel addresses meaningful questions concerning mortality and soul searching, and its content is appropriate for younger teens." School Library Journal.

Buckley-Archer, Linda

The **many** lives of John Stone. Linda Buckley-Archer. Simon & Schuster Books for Young Readers, 2015. 464 p.

Grades: 8 9 10 11   **Fic**
  1. Diaries 2. Longevity 3. Courts and courtiers 4. Supernatural 5. Summer employment 6. England 7. Paranormal fiction
  ISBN 9781481426374

"Spark's contemporary coming-of-age story is brilliantly heightened by the reader's understanding of her secret connection to John Stone. Exceptionally well orchestrated and a simply magnificent story." Booklist.

Budhos, Marina Tamar

Ask me no questions. Marina Budhos. Atheneum Books for Young Readers, 2006. 176 p.

Grades: 7 8 9 10   **Fic**
  1. Muslim families 2. Undocumented immigrants 3. Teenage girls 4. Fourteen-year-old girls 5. Immigrants 6. New York City 7. Family sagas
  ISBN 1416903518

                                                  LC 2005001831

Fourteen-year-old Nadira, her sister, and their parents leave Bangladesh for New York City, but the expiration of their visas and the events of September 11, 2001, bring frustration, sorrow, and terror for the whole family.

"Nadira and Aisha's strategies for surviving and succeeding in high school offer sharp insight into the narrow margins between belonging and not belonging." Horn Book Guide.

The **long** ride. Marina Budhos. Wendy Lamb Books, an imprint of Random House Children's Books, 2019 208 p.

Grades: 5 6 7 8   **Fic**
  1. 1970s 2. Multiracial girls 3. School integration 4. Social change 5. Multiculturalism 6. Identity (Psychology) 7. New York City 8. Coming-of-age stories 9. Historical fiction
  ISBN 9780553534238

In New York in 1971, Jamila and Josie are bused across Queens where they try to fit in at a new, integrated junior high school while their best friend, Francesca, tests the limits at a private school.

"Save for descriptions of Peter Pan collars and landlines, many of the sentiments and scenarios feel almost entirely contemporary, and they'll resonate with a wide audience while adding context to still-contentious debates about the legacy of integration policies." Booklist

Tell us we're home. Marina Budhos. Atheneum Books for Young Readers, 2010. 304 p.

Grades: 6 7 8 9 10   **Fic**
  1. Teenage immigrants 2. Interethnic friendship 3. Interpersonal conflict 4. Best friends 5. Immigrants 6. New Jersey 7. Realistic fiction
  ISBN 9781416903529

                                                  LC 2009027386

Three immigrant girls from different parts of the world meet and become close friends in a small New Jersey town where their mothers have found domestic work, but their relationships are tested when one girl's mother is accused of stealing a precious heirloom.

"These fully realized heroines are full of heart, and their passionate struggles against systemic injustice only make them more inspiring. Keenly necessary." Kirkus.

Watched. Marina Budhos. Wendy Lamb Books, 2016. 272 p.

Grades: 9 10 11 12   **Fic**
  1. Muslim teenagers 2. Informers 3. Police surveillance 4. Ethnic identity 5. Immigrants 6. Queens, New York City 7. Realistic fiction
  ISBN 9780553534184

Moving quickly throughout his Queens immigrant neighborhood to avoid the watchful eyes of his hardworking Bangladeshi parents, their gossipy neighbors and surveillance cameras mounted everywhere, charismatic but troubled youth Naeem is offered a deal by the cops to become a community protector in ways that challenge his sense of identity.

"Action takes second place to a deeper message, and room is left for readers to speculate on the fates of certain characters. While the absence of certainty may frustrate some readers, it also speaks to the underlying takeaway: you can never be sure what others' intentions are, even if you have made it your job to study them." Kirkus.

Bullen, Alexandra

Wish: a novel. by Alexandra Bullen. Point, 2010. 323 p.: Wish series (Alexandra Bullen)

Grades: 8 9 10 11 12   **Fic**
  1. Twin sisters 2. Wishing and wishes 3. Shyness in teenage girls 4. Shyness 5. Grief 6. California 7. San Francisco, California 8. Fantasy fiction
  ISBN 9780545139052

"The detailed descriptions of San Francisco and above all the sisters' relationship provide solid grounding for a touching, enjoyable read." Kirkus.

Bunce, Elizabeth C.

Premeditated Myrtle. Elizabeth C. Bunce. Algonquin Young Readers, 2020. 304 p.: Myrtle Hardcastle mystery

Grades: 5 6 7 8   **Fic**
  1. Victorian era (1837-1901) 2. Girl detectives 3. Murder investigation 4. Murder 5. Governesses 6. Neighbors 7. England 8. Great Britain 9. Historical mysteries
  ISBN 9781616209186

                                                  LC 2019030590

When twelve-year-old aspiring detective Myrtle Hardcastle learns her neighor in quiet Swinburne, England, a breeder of rare flowers, has died she is certain it was murder and that she must find the killer.

"Bunce does an excellent job of making Myrtle the lead actor but gives her a strong set of (mostly female) supporters, including her beloved governess, Miss Judson; the family cook; a surprise-twist-at-the-end ally; and one very vocal cat." Horn Book

Starcrossed. Elizabeth Bunce. Arthur A. Levine Books, 2010. 368 p.: Thief errant

Grades: 8 9 10 11 12   **Fic**
  1. Teenage spies 2. Thieves 3. Insurgency 4. Freedom of religion 5. Nobility 6. High fantasy 7. Fantasy fiction
  ISBN 9780545136051

"Couching her characters and setting in top-notch writing, Bunce . . . hooks readers into an intelligent page-turner with strong themes of growth, determination, and friendship." Publishers Weekly.

Bunker, Lisa

Felix Yz. Lisa Bunker. Viking, [2017]. 304 p.

Grades: 5 6 7 8 9   **Fic**
  1. Aliens 2. Family secrets 3. Crushes in teenage boys 4. Bullying and bullies 5. Schools 6. Maine 7. Science fiction
  ISBN 9780425288504

                                                  LC 2016029068

Thirteen-year-old Felix Yz chronicles the final month before an experimental procedure meant to separate him from the fourth-dimensional creature, Zyx, with whom he was accidentally fused as a young child.

"Joyful, heartbreaking, completely bonkers, and exuberantly alive." Kirkus.

Zenobia July. Lisa Bunker. Penguin Group USA, 2019. 320 p.

Grades: 5 6 7 8   **Fic**

1. Transgender persons 2. Belonging 3. Hacking 4. Online hate speech 5. Prejudice 6. Realistic fiction 7. LGBTQIA fiction
ISBN 9780451479402

Moving from her father's home in Arizona to live with her aunts in Maine, a transgender girl uses her elite coding and hacking skills to identify the anonymous poster of hateful memes on her new school's website, a mystery that helps her find the courage to live openly.

"A young trans girl solves a mystery and finds her people...a fun read that manages to feel solidly traditional while breaking new ground." Kirkus.

Bunting, Eve, 1928-

Blackwater. Joanna Cotler Books, 1999. 146 p.

Grades: 5 6 7 8   **Fic**

1. Secrets 2. Teenagers and death 3. Drowning 4. Children -- Death 5. Guilt in boys 6. Realistic fiction
ISBN 0060278382

LC 99024895

When a boy and girl are drowned in the Blackwater River, thirteen-year-old Brodie must decide whether to confess that he may have caused the accident.

"Bunting's thought-provoking theme, solid characterization and skillful juggling of suspense and pathos make this a top-notch choice." Publishers Weekly.

Burg, Ann E.

All the broken pieces: a novel in verse. by Ann E. Burg. Scholastic Press, 2009. 218 p.

Grades: 7 8 9 10   **Fic**

1. 1970s 2. Vietnam War, 1961-1975 -- Psychological aspects 3. Children and war 4. Adoption 5. Vietnamese Americans 6. Adopted children 7. Novels in verse 8. Historical fiction
ISBN 9780545080927

LC 2008012381

Two years after being airlifted out of Vietnam in 1975, Matt Pin is haunted by the terrible secret he left behind and, now, in a loving adoptive home in the United States, a series of profound events forces him to confront his past.

"This is written in rapid, simple free verse. . . . The intensity of the simple words . . . will make readers want to rush to the end and then return to the beginning again to make connections between past and present, friends and enemies." Booklist.

Serafina's promise: a novel in verse. by Ann E. Burg. Scholastic Press, 2013. 304 p.

Grades: 5 6 7 8   **Fic**

1. Rural girls 2. Earthquakes 3. Ambition 4. Children of pregnant women 5. Families 6. Haiti 7. Port-au-Prince (Haiti) 8. Novels in verse
ISBN 9780545535649

LC 2012045609

In a poor village outside of Port-au-Prince, Haiti, Serafina works hard to help her family, but dreams of going to school and becoming a doctor—then the earthquake hits and Serafina must summon all her courage to find her father and still get medicine for her sick baby brother as she promised.

Unbound: a novel in verse. Ann E. Burg. Scholastic Press, 2016. 352 p.

Grades: 4 5 6 7   **Fic**

1. Freedom seekers 2. Enslaved people 3. African American families 4. Slavery 5. Enslaved girls 6. Southern States 7. Dismal Swamp (North Carolina and Virginia) 8. Novels in verse 9. Historical fiction
ISBN 9780545934275

LC 2016022923

The day nine-year-old Grace is called to work in the kitchen in the Big House, everyone warns her to to keep her head down and her thoughts to herself, but the more she sees of the oppressive Master and his hateful wife, the more she questions things until one day her thoughts escape—and to avoid being separated she and her family flee into the Dismal Swamp, to join the other escaped slaves who live there.

"Grace's story of familial love, community, and hope is a moving, sensitive read." Publishers Weekly.

Burgis, Stephanie

The **princess** who flew with dragons. by Stephanie Burgis. Bloomsbury Childrens Books, 2019. 240 p.

Grades: 4 5 6 7   **Fic**

1. Princesses 2. Disguises 3. Girls and dragons 4. Dragons 5. Exiles 6. Fantasy fiction
ISBN 9781547602070

Twelve-year-old Princess Sofia of Drachenheim enjoys freedom from her sister's manipulations during a diplomatic mission to far-off Villenne, until she and her dragon friend, Jasper, are forced to face ice giants.

"As in the other books in the series, Burgis deals with issues as serious as privilege, immigration, and identity in a manner that is both honest and free of didacticism." Kirkus.

Burnett, Frances Hodgson, 1849-1924

★ The **secret** garden [Moore, ill.]. Frances Hodgson Burnett; illustrated by Inga Moore. Candlewick Press, 2008. 278 p.

Grades: 3 4 5 6   **Fic**

1. Edwardian era (1901-1914) 2. Gardens 3. Orphans 4. Children with disabilities 5. Ten-year-old girls 6. Mansions 7. Yorkshire, England 8. Great Britain 9. Classics
ISBN 9780763631611

A ten-year-old orphan comes to live in a lonely house on the Yorkshire moors where she discovers an invalid cousin and the mysteries of a locked garden.

"Burnett's tale . . . is presented in an elegant, oversize volume and handsomely illustrated with Moore's detailed ink and watercolor paintings. Cleanly laid-out text pages are balanced by artwork ranging from delicate spot images to full-page renderings." School Library Journal.

Burt, Jake

Greetings from witness protection! Jake Burt. Feiwel and Friends, 2017 368 p.

Grades: 5 6 7 8   **Fic**

1. Witnesses -- Protection 2. Foster children 3. Families 4. Kleptomania 5. Schools 6. North Carolina 7. Realistic fiction
ISBN 9781250107114

Thirteen-year-old Nikki Demere is an orphan and a kleptomaniac, making her the perfect girl to portray the Trevors' daughter in witness protection, but she soon learns that the biggest threat to her new family's security comes from her own past.

"Nicki, sassy but lonely, is an endearing, easy-to-root-for heroine, and the bonds she forms with the Trevor family as well as her numerous escapades charm as easily as they entertain. A delightful, sometimes touching balance of action, humor, and heart." Booklist.

Bushnell, Candace

Rules for being a girl. Candace Bushnell and Katie Cotugno. Balzer + Bray, 2020 304 p.

Grades: 7 8 9 10 11 12   **Fic**
   1. Teenage girls 2. High school teachers 3. Sexism in education 4. Sexual harassment 5. High schools 6. Realistic fiction
   ISBN 9780062803382

A girl fights to expose sexism at her school after a run-in with a predatory teacher.

"Rife with references to pop culture, this fast-paced narrative introduces the complexities of intersectionality, identifies the insidious impact of rape culture, and encourages readers to take a stand against everyday injustices." School Library Journal

Buyea, Rob

Because of Mr. Terupt. Rob Buyea. Delacorte Press, 2010. 269 p.: Mr. Terupt

Grades: 4 5 6   **Fic**
   1. Fifth-graders 2. People in comas 3. Teacher-student relationships 4. Elementary school teachers 5. Responsibility 6. Connecticut 7. Realistic fiction
   ISBN 9780385738828

An energetic new teacher brings order and fun to a fifth-grade class where he also helps seven troubled students work through respective challenges until a fateful accident on a snowy winter day changes everything they believe.

"Introducing characters and conflicts that will be familiar to any middle-school student, this powerful and emotional story is likely to spur discussion." Publishers Weekly.

Byars, Betsy Cromer, 1928-2020

Cracker Jackson. Betsy Cromer Byars. Viking Kestrel, 1985. viii, 147 p.

Grades: 5 6 7 8   **Fic**
   1. Baby sitters 2. Eleven-year-old boys 3. Violence against women 4. Abused women 5. Partner abuse 6. Realistic fiction
   ISBN 9780670805464

                   LC   84024684

After attempting to save his ex-babysitter from wife abuse, Cracker Jackson gains an adult insight into the sadness of failed heroics.

"Suspense, danger, near-tragedy, heartbreak and tension-relieving, unwittingly comic efforts at seriously heroic action mark this as the best of middle-grade fiction to highlight the problems of wife-battering and child abuse." School Library Journal.

The **dark** stairs. Betsy Cromer Byars. Viking, 1994. 130 p.: Herculeah Jones mysteries

Grades: 4 5 6   **Fic**
   1. Girl detectives 2. Curiosity in girls 3. Murder investigation 4. Mansions 5. Cold cases (Criminal investigation) 6. Mysteries 7. Humorous stories
   ISBN 0670854875

                LC   94014012 /AC

The intrepid Herculeah Jones helps her mother, a private investigator, solve a puzzling and frightening case.

"There is plenty to laugh at in this book, including classic chapter headings guaranteed to cause shivers for the uninitiated; practiced mystery readers may feel that they are in on a bit of a joke and appreciate the hint of parody. This is a page-turner that is sure to entice the most reluctant readers." School Library Journal.

The **keeper** of the doves. by Betsy Byars. Viking, 2002. 121 p.

Grades: 4 5 6 7   **Fic**
   1. 19th century 2. Recluses 3. Sisters 4. Families 5. Doves 6. Kentucky 7. Historical fiction
   ISBN 0670035769

                LC 2002009283

In the late 1800s in Kentucky, Amie McBee and her four sisters both fear and torment the reclusive and seemingly sinister Mr. Tominski, but their father continues to provide for his needs.

"This is Byars at her best-witty, appealing, thought-provoking." Horn Book.

Byng, Georgia

Molly Moon's incredible book of hypnotism. Georgia Byng. Harper Collins Publishers, c2002. 371 p.: Molly Moon

Grades: 4 5 6   **Fic**
   1. Girl orphans 2. Hypnotism 3. Orphanages 4. Orphans 5. Moon, Molly (Fictitious character) 6. England 7. New York City 8. Fantasy fiction
   ISBN 006051406X

                LC 2002010274

Unlucky and unloved, Molly Moon, living in a dreary orphanage in a small English town, discovers a hidden talent for hypnotism and hypnotizes her way to stardom in New York City.

Cabot, Meg

All-American girl. Meg Cabot. Harper Collins Publishers, c2002. 247 p.

Grades: 7 8 9 10   **Fic**
   1. Presidents -- Assassination attempts 2. Heroes and heroines 3. Attempted assassination 4. Teenage romance 5. Interpersonal relations 6. Washington, DC 7. Teen chick lit
   ISBN 0060294698

                LC 2002019049

A sophomore girl stops a presidential assassination attempt, is appointed Teen Ambassador to the United Nations, and catches the eye of the very cute First Son.

"There's surprising depth in the characters and plenty of authenticity in the cultural details and the teenage voices—particularly in Sam's poignant, laugh-out-loud narration." Booklist.

★ **From** the notebooks of a middle school princess. written & illustrated by Meg Cabot. Feiwel & Friends, 2015. 192 p.: From the notebooks of a middle school princess

Grades: 4 5 6 7   **Fic**
   1. Princesses 2. Multiracial girls 3. Families 4. Middle schools 5. Schools 6. Realistic fiction 7. Diary novels
   ISBN 9781250066022

                LC 2014043845

A middle-grade spinoff of The Princess Diaries, about the long-lost sister of Mia Thermopolis, Princess of Genovia. Provided by publisher.

"Cabot manages to combine wit and lavish details to positive effect, as evidenced by a royal grandmother who manages to be both familiar and surprising. While readers who already know the Princess Diaries might find this fairy tale a bit too retold, young newcomers to the Cabot magic will be charmed. A sweet fantasy, both funny and highly satisfying." Kirkus.

The **princess** diaries: Princess diaries, vol. I. Meg Cabot. Harper, an imprint of HarperCollinsPublishers, 2020, 238 p.: Princess diaries

Grades: 6 7 8 9 **Fic**
1. Princesses 2. Identity (Psychology) 3. Fathers and daughters 4. Fourteen-year-old girls 5. Teenage girls -- Identity 6. New York City 7. Diary novels 8. Romantic comedies 9. Teen chick lit
ISBN 9780062998453

LC 99046479

Fourteen-year-old Mia, who is trying to lead a normal life as a teenage girl in New York City, is shocked to learn that her father is the Prince of Genovia, a small European principality, and that she is a princess and the heir to the throne.

"Readers will relate to Mia's bubbly, chatty voice and enjoy the humor of this unlikely fairy tale." School Library Journal.

Caine, Rachel, 1962-2020
Ink and bone. Rachel Caine. New American Library, [2015] 352 p.: Great library

Grades: 8 9 10 11 12 **Fic**
1. Alexandrian Library. 2. Near future 3. Libraries 4. Dystopias 5. Smugglers 6. Sixteen-year-old boys 7. Alternate histories 8. Dystopian fiction 9. Fantasy fiction
ISBN 9780451472397

LC 2015001509

"Caine has created a Dickensian future with an odd mix of technologies and elements of sorcery. A strong cast of characters and nail-biting intensity make for a promising start to this new series." School Library Journal.

Calejo, Ryan
Charlie Hernandez & the castle of bones. Ryan Calejo. Aladdin, 2019. 608 p.: Charlie Hernandez

Grades: 5 6 7 8 **Fic**
1. Transformations (Magic) 2. Mexican American boys 3. Kidnapping 4. Secret societies 5. Characters and characteristics in mythology 6. Miami, Florida 7. Mythological fiction 8. Fantasy fiction
ISBN 9781534426610

LC 2019011849

When Queen Joanna is kidnapped Charlie and Violet set out across South America to find her and discover a conspiracy to raise the dead. Provided by publisher.

"Through brief, fast-paced chapters, this ongoing adventure introduces more vibrant culture and legends, all while developing Charlie, Violet, and the other members of La Liga." Booklist.

Caletti, Deb
The **last** forever. Deb Caletti. Simon Pulse, 2014. 320 p.

Grades: 8 9 10 11 12 **Fic**
1. Grief in teenage girls 2. Automobile travel 3. Loss (Psychology) 4. Plants 5. Fathers and daughters 6. Realistic fiction
ISBN 9781442450004

LC 2013031010

After her mother's death, it's all Tessa can do to keep her friends, her boyfriend, her happiness from slipping away. Even the rare plant her mother entrusted to her care starts to wilt. Then she meets Henry. Though secrets stand between them, each has a chance at healing...if first, Tessa can find the courage to believe in forever. Provided by publisher.

"Featuring sharp-witted first-person narration, some fascinating facts about plants and seeds, relatable characters, and evocative settings, Caletti's (The Story of Us) inspiring novel eloquently depicts the nature of mutability. As with her previous books, this love story reverberates with honesty and emotion." Publishers Weekly.

Callender, Kacen
Hurricane child. by Kheryn Callender. Scholastic Press, 2018. 224 p.

Grades: 4 5 6 7 **Fic**
1. Lesbian girls 2. Emotions in children 3. Searching 4. Grief 5. Love 6. Virgin Islands of the United States 7. St Thomas, Virgin Islands 8. Coming-of-age stories 9. LGBTQIA fiction
ISBN 9781338129304

LC 2017032545

Born on Water Island in the Virgin Islands during a hurricane, which is considered bad luck, twelve-year-old Caroline falls in love with another girl—and together they set out in a hurricane to find Caroline's missing mother.

"An excellent and nuanced coming-of-age tale with a dash of magical realism for readers who enjoy character-driven novels, especially those with middle grade LGBTQ+ characterizations." School Library Journal.

King and the dragonflies. Kacen Callender. Scholastic Press, 2020. 272 p.

Grades: 5 6 7 8 9 **Fic**
1. Preteen boys 2. Best friends 3. Coming out (Sexual or gender identity) 4. Small town life 5. Self-acceptance 6. Louisiana 7. Realistic fiction 8. African American fiction
ISBN 9781338129335

LC 2019006158

National Book Award for Young People's Literature, 2020.

In a small but turbulent Louisiana town, one boy's grief takes him beyond the bayous of his backyard, to learn that there is no right way to be yourself.

"This quiet novel movingly addresses toxic masculinity, homophobia in the black community—especially related to men—fear, and memory. Elegiac and hopeful." Kirkus

Cameron, Sharon, 1970-
The **Forgetting**. Sharon Cameron. Scholastic Press, 2016. 416 p.: The Forgetting (Sharon Cameron)

Grades: 8 9 10 11 12 **Fic**
1. Memory 2. Amnesia 3. Conspiracies 4. Dystopias 5. Books 6. Dystopian fiction 7. Science fiction
ISBN 9780545945219

LC 2016007978

Canaan is a quiet city on an idyllic world, hemmed in by high walls, but every twelve years the town breaks out in a chaos of bloody violence, after which all the people undergo the Forgetting, in which they are left without any trace of memory of themselves, their families, or their lives—but somehow seventeen-year-old Nadia has never forgotten, and she is determined to find out what causes it and how to put a stop to the Forgetting forever.

"Effective worldbuilding and strong characterization (even minor players have emotional depth) add substance to the fast-paced plot. A cosmetic resemblance to blockbuster teen dystopias allows Cameron to toy slyly with readers' expectations, but this is no retread." Kirkus.

The **light** in hidden places. Sharon Cameron. Scholastic 2020 400 p.

Grades: 8 9 10 11 12   **Fic**
   1. Second World War era (1939-1945) 2. Resistance to military
occupation 3. Holocaust (1933-1945) 4. Catholic girls 5. Hiding
6. Nazis 7. Poland 8. Historical fiction 9. Biographical fiction
10. First-person narratives
ISBN 9781338355932

                             LC 2019025341

Sixteen-year-old Catholic Stefania Podgorska has worked in the
Diamant family's grocery store for four years, even falling in love with
one of their sons, Izio; but when the Nazis came to Przemyl, Poland,
the Jewish Diamants are forced into the ghetto (and worse) but Izio's
brother Max manages to escape, and Stefania embarks on a dangerous
course—protecting thirteen Jews in her attic, caring for her younger sister, Helena, and keeping everything secret from the two Nazi officers
who are living in her house.

Cameron, Sophie

   Last bus to Everland. Sophie Cameron. Roaring Brook
Press, 2019 336 p.
Grades: 7 8 9 10 11 12   **Fic**
   1. Gay teenagers 2. Alienation (Social psychology) 3. Parallel
universes 4. Misfits (Persons) 5. Options, alternatives, choices
6. Gateway fantasy 7. Magical realism 8. Coming-of-age stories
ISBN 9781250149930

Forging a bond with a compassionate artist, a youth in the projects
joins a band of misfits and miscreants who meet weekly for adventures
in a Narnia-inspired world, before dwindling magic forces him to choose
between those he loves.— Atlas Publishing

"Everland is a lovely conceit amid beautifully realized worlds and
wonderfully individual, empathetic characters." Booklist.

Cao, Wenxuan, 1954-

   Bronze and Sunflower. by Wenxuan Cao; illustrated by Mei-
lo So; and translated by Helen Wang. Candlewick Press, 2017.
400 p.
Grades: 4 5 6 7 8   **Fic**
   1. Chinese Cultural Revolution (1966-1976) 2. 1960s 3. 1970s 4.
Orphans 5. Friendship 6. Poor families 7. Poverty 8. Farm life
9. China 10. Historical fiction 11. Translations
ISBN 9780763688165

Taken in by a poor family in a rural village after the death of her
father, Sunflower bonds with the family's only child, Bronze, who has
not spoken since being traumatized by a terrible fire.

Card, Orson Scott

   Ender's game. Orson Scott Card. T. Doherty Associates,
1985. 357 p.: Ender Wiggin
Grades: 7 8 9 10 11 12 Adult   **Fic**
   1. Gifted children 2. Space warfare 3. Aliens (Humanoid) 4.
Wiggin, Ender (Fictitious character) 5. Brothers and sisters 6.
Hard science fiction 7. Science fiction classics 8. Science fiction
ISBN 0312932081

Six-year-old Ender Wiggin and his fellow students at Battle School
are being tested and trained to determine whether they possess the abilities to remake the world—if the world survives an all-out war with an
alien enemy.

"The key, of course, is Ender Wiggin himself. Mr. Card never makes
the mistake of patronizing or sentimentalizing his hero. Alternately likable and insufferable, he is a convincing little Napoleon in short pants."
New York Times Book Review.

The **lost** gate. Orson Scott Card. Tor, 2011. 384 p.: Mither-
mages
Grades: 7 8 9 10 11 12   **Fic**
   1. Teenage wizards 2. Teenage kidnapping victims 3. Gates 4.
Family secrets 5. Kidnapping 6. Virginia 7. Urban fantasy
ISBN 9780765326577

Danny grew up in a family compound in Virginia, believing that he
alone of his family had no magical power. But he was wrong. Kidnapped
from his high school by a rival family, he learns that he has the power to
reopen the gates between Earth and the world of Westil.

   Pathfinder. Orson Scott Card. Simon Pulse, 2010. 432 p.:
Pathfinder (Orson Scott Card)
Grades: 6 7 8 9 10   **Fic**
   1. Teenage boy psychics 2. Space and time 3. Space colonies 4.
Psychic ability 5. Time travel (Past) 6. Science fiction
ISBN 9781416991762

                             LC 2010023243

Thirteen-year-old Rigg has a secret ability to see the paths of others'
pasts, but revelations after his father's death set him on a dangerous
quest that brings new threats from those who would either control his
destiny or kill him.

"While Card delves deeply into his story's knotted twists and turns,
readers should have no trouble following the philosophical and scientific
mysteries, which the characters are parsing right along with them. An
epic in the best sense, and not simply because the twin stories stretch
across centuries." Publishers Weekly.

Carey, Edward, 1970-

   Heap House. written and illustrated by Edward Carey. The
Overlook Press, 2014, ©2013 416 p.: Iremonger
Grades: 5 6 7 8 9 10   **Fic**
   1. Victorian era (1837-1901) 2. 1870s 3. Mansions 4. Family
secrets 5. Orphans 6. Household employees 7. Solid waste
disposal 8. London, England 9. England 10. Historical fantasy
11. Gothic fiction 12. Illustrated books
ISBN 9781468309539

Young Clod, living in his family's mansion amongst a mass of shifting forgotten items, becomes aware of the items whispering to him and
senses a growing storm ahead, needing the help of an orphan servant to
unravel the mystery.

"Living among sentient trash heaps, Clod Iremonger has always
been able to hear the voices of the objects that his family members carry,
but the arrival of serving girl Lucy imbues the objects with a new and
dangerous energy. Descriptive prose and black-and-white portraits create a unique cast of characters in a bleak, dilapidated home. Fans of Joan
Aiken will flock to this dark mystery." Horn Book.

Carey, Janet Lee

   Dragon's keep. Janet Lee Carey. Harcourt, 2007. 320 p.:
Wilde Island chronicles
Grades: 7 8 9 10   **Fic**
   1. 12th century 2. Dragons 3. Prophecies 4. Inheritance and
succession 5. Princesses 6. Teenage girls 7. British Isles 8.
Historical fantasy
ISBN 0152059261

                             LC 2006024669

Long ago, it was prophesied that Princess Rosalind would restore
glory to her dragon-infested home of Wilde Island. But Rosalind isn't
sure how she's supposed to achieve her destiny when her hands are constantly hidden to conceal the dragon's talon that grows in place of her

left ring finger. It isn't until she's kidnapped by the formidable dragon Lord Faul that Rosalind discovers the secret behind her dragon claw. .

"This is told in stunning, lyrical prose. . . . Carey smoothly blends many traditional fantasy tropes here, but her telling is fresh as well as thoroughly compelling." Booklist.

Carlton, Susan Kaplan

In the neighborhood of true. Susan Kaplan Carlton. Algonquin, 2019. 314 p.

Grades: 7 8 9 10   **Fic**

  1. 1950s 2. Belonging 3. Secrets 4. Bombings 5. Synagogues 6. Secrecy 7. Atlanta, Georgia 8. Historical fiction

  ISBN 9781616208608

         LC 2018028820

In the very white, very Christian world of Atlanta society in 1958, New York transplant Ruth decides not to tell her new high school friends and boyfriend that she is Jewish, but when a violent act rocks the city, Ruth must figure out where her loyalties lie.

Carman, Patrick

The **Crossbones**. [by Patrick Carman; illustrated by Joshua Pease and Squire Broel]. Scholastic/PC Studio, 2010. 209 p.: Skeleton Creek

Grades: 5 6 7 8   **Fic**

  1. Teenage detectives 2. Secret societies 3. Investigations 4. Haunted places 5. Ghosts 6. Oregon 7. Supernatural mysteries 8. Horror 9. Diary novels

  ISBN 9780545249942

The Crossbones have a long history of destroying people who get in their way and now Ryan and Sarah find themselves in their crosshairs.

The **Dark** Hills divide. Patrick Carman. Orchard Books, 2005. 253 p.: Land of Elyon

Grades: 4 5 6 7   **Fic**

  1. Talking animals 2. Walls 3. Human/animal communication 4. Forest animals 5. Forests 6. Fantasy fiction 7. High fantasy

  ISBN 0439700930

         LC 2004016312

When she finds the key to a secret passageway leading out of the walled city of Bridewell, twelve-year-old Alexa realizes her lifelong wish to explore the mysterious forests and mountains that lie beyond the wall.

"Narrator Aasne Vigesaa clearly portrays Alexa's thoughtful, inquisitive nature and unsettled feelings. . . . Vigesaa's excellent use of pace, pitch, and tone help differentiate each character." School Library Journal.

Skeleton Creek. Patrick Carman. Scholastic Press, 2009. 185 p.: Skeleton Creek

Grades: 5 6 7 8   **Fic**

  1. Teenage detectives 2. Ghosts 3. Investigations 4. Supernatural 5. Fractures 6. Oregon 7. Supernatural mysteries 8. Horror 9. Diary novels

  ISBN 9780545075664

         LC 2008014312

Although housebound following an eerie accident, teenaged Ryan continues to investigate the strange occurences in his hometown of Skeleton Creek, recording his findings in a journal and viewing email video clips sent by fellow detective Sarah. The reader may view Sarah's videos on a website by using links and passwords found in the text.

Carriger, Gail

Curtsies & conspiracies. Gail Carriger. Little, Brown and Company, 2013. 320 p.: Finishing school

Grades: 7 8 9 10 11 12   **Fic**

  1. Victorian era (1837-1901) 2. 19th century 3. 1850s 4. Boarding schools 5. Espionage 6. Schools 7. Etiquette 8. Robots 9. Great Britain 10. Steampunk 11. Historical fantasy

  ISBN 9780316190114

         LC 2012048520

In her alternate England of 1851, fifteen-year-old Sophronia tries to uncover who is behind a plot to control a prototype that has the potential to alter human and supernatural travel, and to learn what role Mademoiselle Geraldine's academy for young spies plays in the affair.

"With the school's dirigible heading toward London for a liaison with an inventor studying aetherospheric travel, Sophronia (Etiquette & Espionage) is convinced that her professors are Up To Something. Is the academy affiliated with vampire hives, werewolf packs, the anti-supernatural Picklemen, or the Crown—all of whom would benefit from controlling aether technology? A witty and suspenseful steampunk romp." Horn Book.

Etiquette & espionage. by Gail Carriger. Little, Brown, 2013. 320 p.: Finishing school

Grades: 7 8 9 10 11 12   **Fic**

  1. Victorian era (1837-1901) 2. 19th century 3. 1850s 4. Boarding schools 5. Espionage 6. Schools 7. Etiquette 8. Robots 9. Great Britain 10. Steampunk 11. Historical fantasy

  ISBN 9780316190084

         LC 2012005498

In an alternate England of 1851, spirited fourteen-year-old Sophronia is enrolled in a finishing school where, she is suprised to learn, lessons include not only the fine arts of dance, dress, and etiquette, but also diversion, deceit, and espionage.

Waistcoats & weaponry. Gail Carriger. Little Brown & Co 2014 298 p.: Finishing school

Grades: 6 7 8 9 10 11 12   **Fic**

  1. Victorian era (1837-1901) 2. 19th century 3. 1850s 4. Werewolves 5. Espionage 6. Boarding schools 7. Schools 8. Etiquette 9. Great Britain 10. Steampunk 11. Historical fantasy

  ISBN 9780316190275

         LC 2014002829

In her alternate England of 1851, while taking her friend Sidheag by train to her werewolf pack in Scotland, sixteen-year-old Sophronia uncovers a plot that threatens to dissolve all of London into chaos and must decide where her loyalties lie once and for all.

Carroll, Emma, 1970-

In darkling wood. Emma Carroll. Delacorte Press, [2016] 240 p.

Grades: 5 6 7 8 9   **Fic**

  1. Fairies 2. Forests 3. Magic 4. Letters 5. Brothers and sisters 6. England 7. Fantasy fiction 8. Gothic fiction

  ISBN 9780399556012

         LC 2015049623

When Alice goes to stay with her grandmother she discovers the magical Darkling Wood, where she meets a strange friend and discovers letters written between a brother and sister during WWI.

"A haunting and poignant exploration of family, loss, and redemption." Booklist..

Carson, Rae

The **bitter** kingdom. Rae Carson. Greenwillow Books, 2013. 400 p.: Fire and thorns trilogy

Grades: 8 9 10 11 12   **Fic**

1. Teenage rulers 2. Prophecies 3. Rescues 4. Civil war 5. Magic 6. High fantasy 7. Fantasy fiction

ISBN 9780062026545

        LC 2013011912

Elisa, a fugitive in her own kingdom, faces great challenges to rescue the man she loves from her enemies, prevent a civil war, and take back her throne, but as her magic grows, Elisa discovers the shocking truth about her enemy's ultimate goal.

The **crown** of embers. by Rae Carson. Greenwillow Books, 2012. 416 p.: Fire and thorns trilogy

Grades: 8 9 10 11 12   **Fic**

1. Teenage rulers 2. Attempted assassination 3. Crushes in teenage girls 4. Magic 5. Teenage romance 6. High fantasy 7. Fantasy fiction

ISBN 9780062026514

Elisa, struggling to master the power of the Godstone, takes a leap of faith and crosses an ocean accompanied by a one-eyed warrior, an enemy defector, and the man she is falling in love with in search of the source of its power.

"Caron's world building and character development do not lag in this middle part of a trilogy, and the heat of the love story makes this accessible even for those who have yet to read the first volume (although they will then race for it). Both religion and politics play roles that invite discussion, and Elisa, not only brave but brilliant, tracks her own growing awareness with a self-consciousness credible for her age." Booklist.

The **girl** of fire and thorns. Rae Carson. Greenwillow Books, 2011. 448 p.: Fire and thorns trilogy

Grades: 8 9 10 11 12   **Fic**

1. Princesses 2. Self-hate in teenage girls 3. Self-fulfillment in teenage girls 4. Sixteen-year-old girls 5. Overweight girls 6. High fantasy 7. Fantasy fiction

ISBN 9780062026484

"This fast-moving and exciting novel is rife with political conspiracies and machinations." School Library Journal.

Walk on Earth a stranger. Rae Carson. Harpercollins Childrens Books, 2015. 432 p.: Gold seer trilogy

Grades: 7 8 9 10   **Fic**

1. American Westward Expansion (1803-1899) 2. Gold 3. Superhuman abilities 4. Gold Rush 5. Magic 6. Voyages and travels 7. Georgia 8. California 9. Historical fantasy

ISBN 9780062242914

"Carson's story is simply terrific—tense and exciting, while gently and honestly addressing the brutal hardships of the westward migration. Even minor characters are fully three-dimensional, but it's Leah who rightfully takes center stage as a smart, resourceful, determined, and realistic heroine who embodies the age-old philosophy that it isn't what happens to you, but how you react to it that matters." Publishers Weekly.

Cartaya, Pablo

★ The **epic** fail of Arturo Zamora. Pablo Cartaya. Viking, 2017 236 p.

Grades: 5 6 7   **Fic**

1. Cuban Americans 2. Restaurants 3. Resistance to land development 4. Family businesses 5. Communities 6. Miami, Florida 7. Florida 8. Realistic fiction

ISBN 9781101997239

Arturo's Miami summer is marked by the arrival of poetry enthusiast Carmen, who helps him use the power of protest to fight the plans of a land developer who wants to demolish his Abuela's restaurant.

"At turns funny, beautiful, and heartbreaking, this engrossing story will get kids cheering for triumphant, relatable Arturo and his powerful connections to family, tradition, and community." Booklist.

Carter, Ally

All fall down. Ally Carter Scholastic, 2015. 320 p.: Embassy Row novels

Grades: 7 8 9 10   **Fic**

1. Diplomatic and consular service 2. Ambassadors 3. Intrigue 4. Murder 5. Mothers -- Death 6. Thrillers and suspense

ISBN 9780545654746

Daredevil Army brat Grace, the granddaughter of the world's most powerful ambassador, returns to the Embassy Row of her childhood summers to solve the mystery of her mother's death.

"This exciting first book in the Embassy Row series features sixteen-year-old Grace, who has moved into the United States Embassy on the coast of Adria with her ambassador grandfather. It is the first time in three years that she has been back to Adria, since her mothers tragic death in a fire... Her quest to find the truth is one that readers will love to follow, through the twists and turns of Embassy Row and with a diverse array of characters. Some help her, and some stand in her way . . . but Grace is a fighter, and she will stop at nothing to find out what happened to her mother. Readers will love this first book in what promises to be an exciting, thrilling mystery series from best-selling author Carter." Voice of Youth Advocates.

Cross my heart and hope to spy. by Ally Carter. Hyperion Books for Children, 2007. 240 p.: Gallagher girls

Grades: 6 7 8 9   **Fic**

1. Teenage spies 2. Boarding schools 3. Teenage boy/girl relations 4. Fifteen-year-old girls 5. Teenage girls 6. Spy fiction

ISBN 1423100050

"Narrator Renee Raudman provides a well-paced narration . . . and gives the teens believable voices. Chick lit? You bet, but it's well written and well plotted." School Library Journal.

Don't judge a girl by her cover. by Ally Carter. Hyperion Books for Children, 2009. 240 p.: Gallagher girls

Grades: 6 7 8 9   **Fic**

1. Teenage spies 2. Kidnapping 3. Boarding school students 4. Boarding schools 5. Fifteen-year-old girls 6. Spy fiction

ISBN 9781423116387

"These girls remain the most awesome, kick-butt teens ever, but now readers are also getting a glimpse at what makes them vulnerable." Voice of Youth Advocates.

Heist society. Ally Carter. Disney/Hyperion, 2010. 304 p.: Heist society novels

Grades: 7 8 9 10   **Fic**

1. Art thefts 2. Thieves 3. Revenge 4. Families 5. Friendship 6. New York (State) 7. Europe 8. Teen chick lit

ISBN 9781423116394

        LC 2009040377

A group of teenagers uses their combined talents to re-steal several priceless paintings and save fifteen-year-old Kat Bishop's father, himself an international art thief, from a vengeful collector.

"Carter skillfully maintains suspense. . . . This is a thoroughly enjoyable, cinema-ready adventure." Booklist.

I'd tell you I love you, but then I'd have to kill you. Ally Carter. Hyperion Books for Children, 2006. 288 p.: Gallagher girls

Grades: 6 7 8 9   **Fic**
    1. Teenage spies 2. Teenage boy/girl relations 3. Boarding schools 4. Spies 5. Mothers and daughters 6. Spy fiction
    ISBN 9781423100034

                               LC   2005055144
Cammie Morgan, who attends the spy school The Gallagher Academy for Exceptional Young Women, can speak fourteen different languages, hack CIA computer codes, and kill a man seven different ways, but she is ill-prepared when she falls in love with an ordinary boy who thinks she's an ordinary girl.

Only the good spy young. Ally Carter. Disney/Hyperion Books, c2010. 265 p.: Gallagher girls

Grades: 6 7 8 9   **Fic**
    1. Teenage spies 2. Double agents 3. Trust in teenage girls 4. Trust 5. Interpersonal relations 6. London, England 7. Spy fiction
    ISBN 9781423128205

                               LC   bl2010013618
When danger follows Cammie "The Chameleon" Morgan to London, she must again face off with the Circle of Cavan to find the rogue operative who may have infiltrated the halls of the Gallagher Academy for Exceptional Young Women.
    "Humorous fast-paced fun." School Library Journal.

Out of sight, out of time. Ally Carter. Disney/Hyperion Books, c2012. 272 p.: Gallagher girls

Grades: 6 7 8 9   **Fic**
    1. Teenage spies 2. Torture victims 3. Terrorists 4. Amnesia 5. Teenage girl boarding school students 6. Spy fiction
    ISBN 9781423147947

When seventeen-year-old Cammie wakes up in a convent high in the Alps, she slowly comes to realize that she's been tortured, the last four months have been erased from her mind, and an ancient terrorist organization is hunting for her.

Uncommon criminals: a Heist society novel. Ally Carter. Disney/Hyperion, 2011. 304 p.: Heist society novels

Grades: 7 8 9 10   **Fic**
    1. Thieves 2. Gem theft 3. Swindlers and swindling 4. Emeralds 5. Crime 6. New York (State) 7. Europe 8. Teen chick lit
    ISBN 9781423147954

Fifteen-year-old Kat Bishop and her fellow talented teenagers work together to find and steal the "Cleopatra Emerald" from an unscrupulous dealer and return it to its rightful owner, while a former love of her Uncle Eddie tries to get the gem for herself.
    "This is an exciting, entertaining read with a fast-moving plot, a spot of romance, and a strong and smart female protagonist." School Library Journal.

Carter, Caela

Forever, or a long, long time. Caela Carter. Harper, an imprint of HarperCollinsPublishers, 2017 309 p.

Grades: 5 6 7   **Fic**
    1. Adopted children 2. Former foster children 3. Interracial families 4. Brothers and sisters 5. Families 6. Realistic fiction
    ISBN 9780062385680

Having shared so many foster homes that they are unable to trust that the family that has adopted them will last, Flora and her brother, Julian, are assisted by their new mother on a journey to resolve their past so that they can build a future.
    "Poetic and meditative, this emotionally enthralling novel undresses assumptions with purpose and hope." Kirkus.

How to be a girl in the world. Caela Carter. Quill Tree Books, 2020 304 p.

Grades: 5 6 7 8   **Fic**
    1. Mothers and daughters 2. Moving, Household 3. Spells (Magic) 4. Objectification (Social psychology) 5. Body image 6. Coming-of-age stories
    ISBN 9780062672704

Struggling to come to terms with adolescent body changes that have attracted unwanted attention, a tween begins wearing layers and escaping into horror novels before moving to a dilapidated new home, where she discovers a book of spells.
    "This ambitious novel covers significant, rarely explored ground. Do manspreading, unchecked sexualized teasing, and sexual predation share a continuum of exploitation? Who gets to define each? . . . Sure to ignite mother-daughter book club debates." Kirkus

Carvell, Marlene

Sweetgrass basket. Marlene Carvell. Dutton Childrens Books, 2005. 243 p.

Grades: 7 8 9 10   **Fic**
    1. United States Indian School (Carlisle, Pa.) 2. Native American girls 3. Mohawk girls 4. Sisters 5. Native American children 6. Mohawk Indians 7. Pennsylvania
    ISBN 0525475478

                                 LC   2004024374
    In alternating passages, two Mohawk sisters describe their lives at the Carlisle Indian Industrial School, established in 1879 to educate Native Americans, as they try to assimilate into white culture and one of them is falsely accused of stealing.
    "Carvell has put together a compelling, authentic, and sensitive portrayal of a part of our history that is still not made accurately available to young readers." School Library Journal.

Cashore, Kristin

Fire. Kristin Cashore. Dial Books, c2009. 461 p.: Graceling realm

Grades: 9 10 11 12   **Fic**
    1. Teenage girl psychics 2. Mind control 3. Beauty 4. Political corruption 5. Monsters 6. High fantasy 7. Fantasy fiction
    ISBN 9780803734616

                                 LC   2009005187
    In a kingdom called the Dells, Fire is the last human-shaped monster, with unimaginable beauty and the ability to control the minds of those around her, but even with these gifts she cannot escape the strife that overcomes her world.
    "Many twists propel the action . . . [and] Cashore's conclusion satisfies, but readers will clamor for a sequel to the prequel—a book bridging the gap between this one and Graceling." Publishers Weekly.

Graceling. Kristin Cashore. Harcourt, 2008. 480 p.: Graceling Realm

Grades: 8 9 10 11 12   **Fic**
    1. Girl warriors 2. Political corruption 3. Princes 4. Rulers 5.

Uncles 6. High fantasy 7. Fantasy fiction
ISBN 9780152063962

LC 2007045436

In a world where some people are born with extreme and often-feared skills called Graces, Katsa struggles for redemption from her own horrifying Grace, and teams up with another young fighter to save their land from a corrupt king.

"This is gorgeous storytelling: exciting, stirring, and accessible. Fantasy and romance readers will be thrilled." School Library Journal.

Jane, unlimited. Kristin Cashore. Kathy Dawson Books, 2017. 464 p.

Grades: 8 9 10 11 12 **Fic**
1. Teenage girl orphans 2. Bisexual teenage girls 3. Mansions 4. Rich people 5. Teenage romance 6. Fantasy fiction
ISBN 9780803741492

"Creation, compassion, and choice repeatedly emerge as themes in this ambitious, mind-expanding novel." Booklist.

Castellucci, Cecil, 1969-

Boy proof. Cecil Castellucci. Candlewick Press, 2005. 208 p.

Grades: 7 8 9 10 **Fic**
1. Teenage misfits 2. New students 3. Film industry and trade 4. Teenage girls 5. Teenagers 6. Los Angeles, California 7. Realistic fiction
ISBN 0763623334

LC 2004050256

Feeling alienated from everyone around her, Los Angeles high school senior and cinephile Victoria Denton hides behind the identity of a favorite movie character until an interesting new boy arrives at school and helps her realize that there is more to life than just the movies.

"This novel's clipped, funny, first-person, present-tense narrative will grab teens . . . with its romance and the screwball special effects, and with the story of an outsider's struggle both to belong and to be true to herself." Booklist.

Don't cosplay with my heart. Cecil Castellucci. Scholastic Press, 2018. 288 p.

Grades: 7 8 9 10 **Fic**
1. Cosplay 2. Teenage girls 3. Family problems 4. Clubs 5. Coping 6. Los Angeles, California 7. Realistic fiction 8. Coming-of-age stories
ISBN 9781338125498

LC 2017032550

Cosplaying under the guise of outspoken bad girl in order to navigate the challenges of a stressful family life, her best friend's summertime absence and her crush's confusing behavior, Edan connects with her dream boy at a costume competition where she struggles to find the strength to be a hero in real life.

Catmull, Katherine

The **radiant** road: a novel. by Katherine Catmull. Dutton Books, an imprint of Penguin Random House LLC, [2016] 336 p.

Grades: 7 8 9 10 **Fic**
1. Fairies 2. Half-human hybrids 3. Parallel universes 4. Magic 5. Identity (Psychology) 6. Ireland 7. Urban fantasy
ISBN 9780525953470

LC 2015020678

After nine years Clare Macleod and her father are finally returning to their old home in Ireland, a house by the sea, with a yew tree growing inside it, a tree with its roots in both the human and fairy world—and

soon Clare, who has always been able to sense the "Strange," meets the boy Finn, and discovers that she must battle against the forces of evil in to restore order to both worlds.

"Catmull has created an eerily lovely story, writing with an old-fashioned style that at times sings like a lullaby. An excellent addition to either teen or juvenile collections of all sizes." Booklist.

Cavanaugh, Nancy J.

★ **This** journal belongs to Ratchet. by Nancy J. Cavanaugh. Sourcebooks Jabberwocky, [2013] 224 p.

Grades: 4 5 6 7 **Fic**
1. Eleven-year-old girls 2. Home schooling 3. Self-acceptance in girls 4. Belonging 5. Fathers and daughters 6. Realistic fiction
ISBN 9781402281068

LC 2012041339

Homeschooled by her mechanic-environmentalist father, eleven-year-old Rachel "Ratchet" Vance records her efforts to make friends, save a park, remember her mother, and find her own definition of "normal."

"At first it seems artificial, with observations that are too on-the-nose. But as the novel's unexpectedly multifaceted plot comes together, it becomes increasingly compelling, suspenseful and moving. Triumphant enough to make readers cheer; touching enough to make them cry." Kirkus.

Cervantes, Angela

Gaby, lost and found. Angela Cervantes. Scholastic Press, 2013. 224 p.: Furry Friends Animal Shelter

Grades: 5 6 7 **Fic**
1. Hispanic American girls 2. Mother-separated girls 3. Animal shelters 4. Girl volunteers 5. Undocumented immigrants 6. Realistic fiction
ISBN 9780545489454

Gaby enjoys working at the local animal shelter and wants to adopt a cat but is unsure of her own living situation when her mother is deported back to Honduras.

Chabon, Michael

Summerland. by Michael Chabon and illustrated by William Joyce. Talk Miramax Books/Hyperion Books for Children, 2002 512 p.

Grades: 5 6 7 8 **Fic**
1. Baseball players 2. Kidnapping victims 3. Time travel 4. Fairies 5. Magic 6. Fantasy fiction
ISBN 0786808772

LC 2002027497

Ethan Feld, the worst baseball player in the history of the game, finds himself recruited by a 100-year-old scout to help a band of fairies triumph over an ancient enemy.

"Much of the prose is beautifully descriptive as Chabon navigates vividly imagined other worlds and offers up some timeless themes." Horn Book.

Chadda, Sarwat

City of the plague god. Sarwat Chadda. Disney-Hyperion, 2021. 400 p.

Grades: 4 5 6 7 **Fic**
1. Heroes and heroines 2. Muslim American teenagers 3. Gods and goddesses, Sumerian 4. Diseases 5. Gilgamesh (Legendary character) 6. New York City 7. Fantasy fiction 8. Mythological fiction
ISBN 9781368051507

Thirteen-year-old Sikander Aziz has to team up with the hero Gilgamesh in order to stop Nergal, the ancient god of plagues, from wiping out the population of Manhattan in this adventure based on Mesopotamian mythology. Provided by publisher.

"Chadda brings attention to the less well-recognized mythology of ancient Mesopotamia with engaging humor and wit." Kirkus

Chaltas, Thalia

Because I am furniture. by Thalia Chaltas. Viking, c2009. 352 p.

Grades: 8 9 10 11 **Fic**
1. Child abuse 2. Child sexual abuse 3. Guilt in teenage girls 4. Guilt 5. Violence in men 6. Novels in verse 7. Realistic fiction
ISBN 9780670062980

LC 2008023235

The youngest of three siblings, fourteen-year-old Anke feels both relieved and neglected that her father abuses her brother and sister but ignores her, but when she catches him with one of her friends, she finally becomes angry enough to take action.

"Incendiary, devastating, yet—in total—offering empowerment and hope, Chaltas's poems leave an indelible mark." Publishers Weekly.

Chambliss Bertman, Jennifer

★ **Book** scavenger. Jennifer Chambliss Bertman. Christy Ottaviano Books, Henry Holt and Company, 2015. 272 p.: Book scavenger

Grades: 4 5 6 7 **Fic**
1. Codes (Communication) 2. Books 3. Treasure hunts (Games) 4. Publishers and publishing 5. Moving, Household 6. San Francisco, California 7. Mysteries
ISBN 9781627791151

LC 2014045884

Just after twelve-year-old Emily and her family move to San Francisco, she teams up with new friend James to follow clues in an odd book they find, hoping to figure out its secrets before the men who attacked Emily's hero, publisher Garrison Griswold, solve the mystery or come after the friends.

★ The **unbreakable** code. Jennifer Chambliss Bertman; with illustrations by Sarah Watts. Christy Ottaviano Books, Henry Holt and Company, 2017. 353 p.: Book scavenger

Grades: 4 5 6 7 **Fic**
1. Codes (Communication) 2. Arson 3. Books 4. Publishers and publishing 5. Child detectives 6. San Francisco, California 7. Mysteries
ISBN 9781627791168

Uncovering a trail of encrypted messages in books by Mark Twain when Mr. Quisling's behavior turns mysterious, Emily and James are alarmed when each hidden book triggers an arson fire, compelling them to race against time to crack the code before more disasters occur.

"Brisk, bookish good fun for puzzle and code lovers." Kirkus.

Chan, Gillian

The **disappearance**. Gillian Chan. Annick Press, 2017. 208 p.

Grades: 8 9 10 11 12 **Fic**
1. Missing teenage boys 2. Group homes 3. Psychic ability 4. Supernatural 5. Bullying and bullies 6. Paranormal fiction
ISBN 9781554519835

Scarred physically and emotionally after the murder of his younger brother, Mike, a teenager, ends up in a group home, where he encounters Jacob, a strange young boy who seems to be from another place and time, and seems to know everything about Mike, including what happened to his brother.

"Reluctant highly capable readers will be enticed, as will fans of R. L. Stine, Ripleys Believe It or Not, and ghost stories." Voice of Youth Advocates.

Chanani, Nidhi

Jukebox. Nidhi Chanani First Second 2021. 224 p.

Grades: 4 5 6 7 8 **Fic**
1. Cousins 2. Time travel (Past) 3. Jukeboxes 4. Missing persons 5. Fathers and daughters 6. San Francisco, California 7. Fantasy comics 8. Comics and Graphic novels
ISBN 9781250156365

A mysterious jukebox, old vinyl records, and cryptic notes on music history, are Shaheen's only clues to her father's abrupt disappearance. She looks to her cousin, Tannaz, who seems just as perplexed, before they both turn to the jukebox which starts glowing. Suddenly, the girls are pulled from their era and transported to another time! Keyed to the music on the record, the jukebox sends them through decade after decade of music history, from political marches, to landmark concerts. But can they find Shaheen's dad before the music stops? This time-bending magical mystery tour invites readers to take the ride of their lives for a coming-of-age adventure.

"Exquisite attention to detail—fashion, architecture, dialect—brings each era to life, providing a treasure trove for young history buffs and a launchpad for those interested in music history." Booklist

Chao, Gloria, 1986-

American panda. by Gloria Chao. Simon Pulse, 2018. 320 p.

Grades: 9 10 11 12 **Fic**
1. Massachusetts Institute of Technology 2. College freshmen 3. Expectation (Psychology) 4. Tradition (Philosophy) 5. Secrets 6. Taiwanese American teenagers 7. Boston, Massachusetts 8. Realistic fiction 9. Humorous stories
ISBN 9781481499101

LC 2017014314

A freshman at MIT, seventeen-year-old Mei Lu tries to live up to her Taiwanese parents' expectations, but no amount of tradition, obligation, or guilt prevent her from hiding several truths: that she is a germaphobe who cannot become a doctor, she prefers dancing to biology, she decides to reconnect with her estranged older brother, and she is dating a Japanese boy.

Our wayward fate. by Gloria Chao. Simon Pulse, 2019. 320 p.

Grades: 8 9 10 11 12 **Fic**
1. Expectation (Psychology) 2. Teenage boy/girl relations 3. Asian Americans 4. Family secrets 5. Small towns 6. Indiana 7. Realistic fiction 8. Love stories
ISBN 9781534427617

LC 2019028306

Forging a bond with the only other Taiwanese kid in her school, 17-year-old Ali Chu finds a sense of belonging and the courage to push back against discrimination before her mother's disapproval of the relationship reveals astonishing family secrets.

Chapman, Elsie

Caster. Elsie Chapman. Scholastic Press, 2019. 336 p.: Caster (Elsie Chapman)

Grades: 8 9 10 11 12 **Fic**
1. Superhuman abilities 2. Tournaments 3. Debt 4. Magic 5.

Competition 6. Asian-influenced fantasy 7. Dystopian fiction
ISBN 9781338332629

LC 2018060381

Aza Wu knows that casting magic can kill—it killed her sister—but she needs money desperately to pay off Saint Willow, who controls her sector of Lotusland, and save the family teahouse, so she secretly enters an underground casting tournament—and finds herself competing against other castors with "full magic," and where even victory could cause her to lose her freedom, her magic, and her life.

"Chapman ... has created compelling young adult novels before, but this is a cut above; the fully realized and atmospheric dystopia is crafted at a level not seen often. This stunning fantasy will fly off the shelves." Booklist.

Charbonneau, Joelle

Graduation day. Joelle Charbonneau. Houghton Mifflin, Houghton Mifflin Harcourt , 2014. 320 p.: The Testing trilogy
Grades: 7 8 9 10 11 12   **Fic**
   1. Dystopias 2. Loyalty 3. Resistance to government 4. Survival 5. Love 6. Dystopian fiction 7. Science fiction
ISBN 9780547959214

LC 2013034743

The United Commonwealth wants to eliminate the rebel alliance fighting to destroy The Testing for good. Cia is ready to lead the charge, but will her lethal classmates follow her into battle? Provided by publisher.

"Charbonneau concludes her dystopian Testing trilogy with this action-packed finale, which sees Cia Vale secretly tasked by the President of the United Commonwealth to remove the officials behind the lethal Testing process that has claimed so many young lives...As in the previous books, Charbonneau remains focused on philosophical worries and moral tests over spectacle and bloodshed, with multiple layers and twists to keep readers forever guessing. Enough potential threads are left dangling to leave room for future stories." Publishers Weekly.

Independent study. Joelle Charbonneau. Houghton Mifflin, Houghton Mifflin Harcourt , 2014. 320 p.: The Testing trilogy
Grades: 7 8 9 10 11 12   **Fic**
   1. Dystopias 2. Examinations 3. Universities and colleges 4. Survival 5. Resistance to government 6. Dystopian fiction 7. Science fiction
ISBN 9780547959207

LC 2013004815

Now a freshman at the University in Tosu City with her hometown sweetheart, Tomas, Cia Vale attempts to expose the ugly truth behind the government's grueling and deadly Testing put her and her loved ones in great danger.

"In this sequel to The Testing (Houghton Harcourt, 2013), Cia is drawn deeper into the political machinations of Tosu City as she enters the University...Fans of The Testing will be thrilled with this new installment and will be anxiously waiting for the story's conclusion." School Library Journal.

The **Testing**. by Joelle Charbonneau. Houghton Mifflin Harcourt, 2013. 336 p.: The Testing trilogy
Grades: 7 8 9 10 11 12   **Fic**
   1. Dystopias 2. Examinations 3. Survival 4. Schools 5. Universities and colleges 6. Dystopian fiction 7. Science fiction
ISBN 9780547959108

LC 2012018090

Sixteen-year-old Malencia (Cia) Vale is chosen to participate in The Testing to attend the University; however, Cia is fearful when she figures out her friends who do not pass The Testing are disappearing.

Charles, Tami

Becoming Beatriz. by Tami Charles. Charlesbridge, 2019. 272 p.
Grades: 7 8 9 10   **Fic**
   1. 1980s 2. Teenage girl dancers 3. Puerto Ricans 4. Gangs 5. Gang members 6. Brothers -- Death 7. Newark, New Jersey 8. Historical fiction 9. African American fiction
ISBN 9781580897785

LC 2018031378

In 1984 Newark, Beatriz Mendez navigates romance, gang culture, and her family's past. After her gang-leader brother is killed, Beatriz gives up her dreams of dancing in order to run the gang. But her eyes are reopened to her dream of a career in dance when the school brainiac asks her to compete in a dance competition with him—but will the gang let her go? Provided by publisher.

"Readers with diverse backgrounds will feel at home with Beatriz's identities as Latina, Black, and American, and everyone will be cheering her on, right up until the satisfying, heartwarming end." Booklist.

Like Vanessa. Tami Charles. Charlesbridge, 2018 288 p.
Grades: 5 6 7 8   **Fic**
   1. Williams, Vanessa 2. 1980s 3. African American teenage girls 4. Beauty contests 5. Self-acceptance 6. Thirteen-year-old girls 7. Inner city schools 8. Newark, New Jersey 9. Realistic fiction 10. Historical fiction 11. African American fiction
ISBN 9781580897778

LC 2016053961

It is 1983 and Vanessa Martin, a thirteen-year-old African American girl in Newark's public housing, dreams of following in the footsteps of the first black Miss America, Vanessa Williams; but the odds are against her until a new teacher at school organizes a beauty pageant and encourages Vanessa to enter.

Chase, Paula Jeanne, 1966-

Dough boys. Paula Chase. Harpercollins Childrens Books 2019 336 p.
Grades: 5 6 7 8   **Fic**
   1. African American teenage boys 2. Gangs 3. Options, alternatives, choices 4. Best friends 5. Street life 6. Realistic fiction 7. African American fiction
ISBN 9780062691811

LC 2018052590

Told in two voices, thirteen-year-old best friends Simp and Rollie play on a basketball team in their housing project, but Rollie dreams of being a drummer and Simp, to impress the gang leader, Coach Tez.

"A thoughtful exploration of the soul-fulfilling heaviness of life in black urban communities." Kirkus

So done. Paula Chase. Harpercollins Childrens Books 2018 240 p.
Grades: 5 6 7 8   **Fic**
   1. Thirteen-year-old girls 2. Secrets 3. Friendship 4. Reunions 5. Summer 6. Realistic fiction 7. African American fiction
ISBN 9780062691781

When best friends Metai and Jamila are reunited after a summer apart, their friendship threatens to combust from the pressure of secrets, middle school, and looming auditions for a potentially life-changing new talented-and-gifted program. Provided by publisher.

Turning point. Paula Chase. Harpercollins Childrens Books 2020 304 p.

Grades: 5 6 7 8 9 **Fic**

1. Friendship 2. African American girls 3. Self-discovery 4. Best friends 5. Ballet 6. Realistic fiction 7. African American fiction 8. Coming-of-age stories
ISBN 9780062965660

LC 2020024445

Best friends Rasheeda and Monique navigate the ups and downs of a teenager's summer, Mo at home in the Cove; Sheeda at a sleepaway ballet intensive. Provided by publisher.

"[Chase] delves into the unique pressures of ballet and church cultures with empathetic understanding while also referencing difficulties faced by the Black working-class communities to which the main characters belong. An insightful look at unintentional pressures placed upon children." Kirkus

Chee, Traci

The **reader**. Traci Chee. G.P. Putnam's Sons, [2016] 464 p.: Sea of ink and gold
Grades: 8 9 10 11 12 **Fic**

1. Books 2. Orphans 3. Pirates 4. Reading 5. Kidnapping 6. Fantasy fiction
ISBN 9780399176777

LC 2015039924

Set in a world where reading is unheard-of, Sefia makes use of a mysterious object to track down who kidnapped her aunt Nin and what really happened the day her father was murdered.

"This cleverly layered fantasy leaves more questions than it answers, but fortunately, it's only the first of what promises to be an enchanting series." Kirkus.

The **speaker**. Traci Chee; map and interior illustrations by Ian Schoenherr. G.P. Putnam's Sons, 2017. 512 p.: Sea of ink and gold
Grades: 8 9 10 11 12 **Fic**

1. Books 2. Orphans 3. Pirates 4. Reading 5. Kidnapping 6. Fantasy fiction
ISBN 9780399176784

"Filled with even more magic and intrigue than its predecessor, this is a gripping follow-up that will leave readers speculating and wanting more." Kirkus.

The **storyteller**. Traci Chee. G.P. Putnam's Sons, 2018 544 p.: Sea of ink and gold
Grades: 8 9 10 11 12 **Fic**

1. Teenage orphans 2. Fate and fatalism 3. Protectiveness in teenagers 4. Imaginary wars and battles 5. Books 6. Fantasy fiction
ISBN 9780399176791

LC 2018028167

As Sefia and Archer watch Kelanna start to crumble to the Guard's will, they will have to choose between their love and joining a war that just might tear them apart. Provided by publisher.

We are not free. Traci Chee. Houghton Mifflin Harcourt, 2020 400 p.
Grades: 7 8 9 10 11 12 **Fic**

1. Japanese in the United States -- Mass internment, 1942-1945 2. Japanese Americans -- Forced removal and incarceration, 1942-1945 3. World War II -- Japanese Americans 4. Teenagers 5. Friendship 6. Japantown, San Francisco, California 7. San Francisco, California 8. Historical fiction
ISBN 9780358131434

LC 2019029407

Growing up together in the community of Japantown, San Francisco, four second-generation Japanese American teens find their bond tested by widespread discrimination and the mass incarcerations of people of Japanese ancestry during World War II.

"Ambitious in scope and complexity, this is an essential contribution to the understanding of the wide-ranging experiences impacting people of Japanese ancestry in the U.S. during WWII." Publishers Weekly

Cheng, Jack

★ **See** you in the cosmos. Jack Cheng. Dial, 2017. 288 p.
Grades: 5 6 7 8 **Fic**

1. Boys and dogs 2. Cross-country automobile trips 3. Families 4. Father-separated boys 5. iPod (Digital music player) 6. Realistic fiction
ISBN 9780399186370

Golden Kite Award for Middle Grade/Young Reader Fiction, 2018.

Eleven-year-old Alex Petroski is determined to launch his golden iPod into space, just like his hero Carl Sagan launched the Golden Record into space ages and ages ago. Instead, Alex and his dog, aptly named Carl Sagan, wind up on a road trip with some unexpected (and awesome) traveling companions and more than one eye-opening detour.

"Riveting, inspiring, and sometimes hilarious." Kirkus.

Chibbaro, Julie

Deadly. Julie Chibbaro; illustrated by Jean-Marc Superville Sovak. Atheneum Books for Young Readers, 2011. 304 p.
Grades: 6 7 8 9 10 **Fic**

1. Typhoid Mary, 1869-1938 2. 1900s (Decade) 3. Epidemiology 4. Epidemics 5. Father-separated teenage girls 6. Gender role 7. Typhoid fever 8. New York City 9. Diary novels 10. Historical fiction
ISBN 9780689857386

LC 2010002291

In the early 1900s, sixteen-year-old Prudence Galewski leaves school to take a job assisting the head epidemiologist at New York's Department of Health and Sanitation, investigating the intriguing case of "Typhoid Mary," a seemingly healthy woman who is infecting others with typhoid fever.

"A deeply personal coming-of-age story set in an era of tumultuous social change, this is top-notch historical fiction that highlights the struggle between rational science and popular opinion as shaped by a sensational, reactionary press." School Library Journal.

Chilton, Andrew S.

The **goblin's** puzzle: being the adventures of a boy with no name and two girls called Alice. by Andrew S. Chilton; illustrations by Jensine Eckwall. Alfred A. Knopf, 2016. 288 p.
Grades: 4 5 6 7 8 **Fic**

1. Goblins 2. Enslaved boys 3. Quests 4. Voyages and travels 5. Scholars and academics 6. High fantasy 7. Fantasy fiction 8. Humorous stories
ISBN 9780553520705

LC 2015013261

A boy, a goblin, a scholar, and a princess join forces to defeat a dragon, outwit a scheming duke, and solve a logic puzzle.

"An emphasis on questioning fate, societal rules, and traditions as well as the importance of wit and logic rather than brawn renders this lighthearted adventure fresh." Kirkus.

Chima, Cinda Williams

The **Demon** King: a Seven Realms novel. Cinda Williams Chima. Disney/Hyperion Books, c2009. 506 p.: Seven Realms novels

Grades: 7 8 9 10 11 12   **Fic**
   1. Princesses 2. Former gang members 3. Amulets 4. Good and evil 5. Wizards 6. High fantasy 7. Fantasy fiction
ISBN 9781423118237

                      LC 2008046178

Relates the intertwining fates of former street gang leader Han Alister and headstrong Princess Raisa, as Han takes possession of an amulet that once belonged to an evil wizard and Raisa uncovers a conspiracy in the Grey Wolf Court.

"With full-blooded, endearing heroes, a well-developed supporting cast and a detail-rich setting, Chima explores the lives of two young adults, one at the top of the world and the other at the bottom, struggling to find their place and protect those they love." Publishers Weekly.

The **warrior** heir. Cinda Williams Chima. Hyperion Books for Children, c2006. 426 p.: Heir chronicles

Grades: 7 8 9 10 11 12   **Fic**
   1. Warriors 2. Magic swords 3. Dueling 4. Wizards 5. Magic 6. Ohio 7. Great Britain 8. Fantasy fiction
ISBN 0786839163

                      LC 2005052720

After learning about his magical ancestry and his own warrior powers, sixteen-year-old Jack embarks on a training program to fight enemy wizards.

"Twists and turns abound in this remarkable, nearly flawless debut novel that mixes a young man's coming-of-age with fantasy and adventure. Fast paced and brilliantly plotted." Voice of Youth Advocates.

Choldenko, Gennifer, 1957-

★ **Al** Capone does my shirts. Gennifer Choldenko. G.P. Putnam's Sons, c2004. 228 p.: Al Capone at Alcatraz

Grades: 5 6 7 8   **Fic**
   1. Capone, Al, 1899-1947 2. United States Penitentiary, Alcatraz Island, California 3. 1930s 4. Boys and moving 5. Money-making projects for children 6. Girls with autism 7. Brothers and sisters of children with autism 8. Prison guards 9. Alcatraz Island, California 10. Historical fiction 11. Coming-of-age stories
ISBN 0399238611

                      LC 2002031766

A twelve-year-old boy named Moose moves to Alcatraz Island in 1935 when guards' families were housed there, and has to contend with his extraordinary new environment in addition to life with his autistic sister.

"With its unique setting and well-developed characters, this warm, engaging coming-of-age story has plenty of appeal, and Choldenko offers some fascinating historical background on Alcatraz Island in an afterword." Booklist.

Chasing secrets. Gennifer Choldenko. Wendy Lamb Books, an imprint of Random House Children's Books, [2015] 228 p.

Grades: 5 6 7 8   **Fic**
   1. 1900s (Decade) 2. Thirteen-year-old girls 3. Plague 4. Friendship 5. Quarantine 6. Hiding 7. Chinatown, San Francisco, California 8. San Francisco, California 9. Historical mysteries
ISBN 9780385742535

                      LC 2014040329

Thirteen-year-old Lizzie and her secret friend Noah, who is hiding in her house, plan to rescue Noah's father from the quarantined Chinatown, and save everyone they love from contracting the plague that is spreading in 1900 San Francisco.

"Thirteen-year-old Lizzie is a smart, scientifically-minded girl, out of place in a San Francisco finishing school in 1900. Applying the scientific method to rumors of the bubonic plague in Chinatown, Lizzie faces the power of the media and racist political schemes as she attempts to rescue her Chinese housekeeper from quarantine. Appealing, convincing characters and a detail-rich setting keep the light mystery afloat." Horn Book.

Chupeco, Rin

Wicked as you wish. Rin Chupeco. Sourcebooks Fire, 2020. 432 p.: Hundred names for magic

Grades: 8 9 10 11 12   **Fic**
   1. Filipino Americans 2. Princes 3. Characters and characteristics in fairy tales 4. Imaginary kingdoms 5. Magic 6. Arizona 7. Fairy tale and folklore-inspired fiction 8. Urban fantasy 9. Fantasy fiction
ISBN 9781492672661

                      LC 2019032045

Years after the evil Snow Queen desolated the magical kingdom of Avalon, Prince Alexei, his friend Tala, and a ragtag band, inspired by the appearance of the Firebird, try to reclaim their land.

"Readers looking for a vibrant, Harry Potteresque fantasy full of secrets, spies, magic, monsters, and mayhem need look no further." Booklist

Cisneros, Ernesto

★ **Efren** divided: a novel. by Ernesto Cisneros. Quill Tree Books, 2020. 272 p.

Grades: 3 4 5 6 7   **Fic**
   1. Mexican American families 2. Separated friends, relatives, etc 3. Deportation 4. Undocumented immigrants 5. Mexican American boys 6. Realistic fiction
ISBN 9780062881687

                      LC 2019027332

While his father works two jobs, seventh-grader Efren Nava must take care of his twin siblings, kindergartners Max and Mia, after their mother is deported to Mexico. Includes glossary of Spanish words.

Cisneros, Sandra

The **house** on Mango Street. Sandra Cisneros. Alfred A. Knopf, 1984, c1991. 134 p.

Grades: 7 8 9 10 11 12 Adult   **Fic**
   1. Home (Concept) 2. Mexican American girls 3. Growing up 4. Friendship 5. Family relationships 6. Chicago, Illinois 7. Illinois 8. Coming-of-age stories 9. Novels in verse 10. Classics
ISBN 9780679433354

                      LC 93043564

For Esperanza, a young girl growing up in the Hispanic quarter of Chicago, life is an endless landscape of concrete and run-down tenements, and she tries to rise above the hopelessness.

"This is a composite of evocative snapshots that manages to passionately recreate the milieu of the poor quarters of Chicago." Commonwealth.

Clark, Henry, 1952-

What we found in the sofa (and how it saved the world). Henry Clark; illustrated by Jeremy Holmes. Little, Brown and Company, 2013. 355 p.

Grades: 3 4 5 6 7   **Fic**
   1. Mind control 2. Sofas 3. Flash mobs 4. Aliens 5. Mansions

6. Earth 7. Humorous stories
ISBN 9780316206662

Discovering a rare crayon between the cushions of a mysterious sofa found at their bus stop, River, Freak and Fiona unwittingly embark on a quest to save the world from an alien invasion unleashed by a criminal mastermind.

Cleary, Beverly, 1916-2021

★ **Dear** Mr. Henshaw. Beverly Cleary; illustrated by Paul O. Zelinsky. W. Morrow, 1983. 133 p.

Grades: 4 5 6 7 **Fic**
1. New students 2. Children of divorced parents 3. Sixth-graders 4. Father-separated children 5. Ten-year-old boys 6. Realistic fiction 7. Epistolary novels 8. Classics
ISBN 9780688024055

LC 83005372

Newbery Medal, 1984.

In his letters to his favorite author, ten-year-old Leigh reveals his problems coping with his parents' divorce, being the new boy in school, and generally finding his own place in the world.

Strider. Beverly Cleary; illustrated by Paul O. Zelinsky. Morrow Junior Books, 1991. 179 p.

Grades: 4 5 6 7 **Fic**
1. Abandoned dogs 2. Teenagers and dogs 3. Children of divorced parents 4. High school track and field athletics 5. Diary writing 6. Diary novels
ISBN 9780688099008

LC 90006608

In a series of diary entries, Leigh tells how he comes to terms with his parents' divorce, acquires joint custody of an abandoned dog, and joins the track team at school.

"The development of the narrative is vintage Beverly Cleary, an inimitable blend of comic and poignant moments." Horn Book.

Clements, Andrew, 1949-2019

★ **Extra** credit. Andrew Clements; illustrations by Mark Elliott. Atheneum Books for Young Readers, c2009. 183 p.

Grades: 4 5 6 **Fic**
1. Pen pals 2. Interethnic friendship 3. Letters 4. Intercultural communication 5. Schools 6. Afghanistan 7. Illinois 8. Realistic fiction
ISBN 9781416949299

As letters flow back and forth—between the prairies of Illinois and the mountains of Afghanistan, across cultural and religious divides—sixth-grader Abby, ten-year-old Amira, and eleven-year-old Sadeed begin to speak and listen to each other.

"Clements successfully bridges two cultures in this timely and insightful dual-perspective story." Publishers Weekly.

Cline-Ransome, Lesa

★ **Being** Clem. Lesa Cline-Ransome. Holiday House, 2021. 256 p.: Finding Langston

Grades: 4 5 6 7 **Fic**
1. 1940s 2. African American boys 3. Grief in children 4. Single-parent families 5. Fathers -- Death 6. Courage in children 7. South Side, Chicago, Illinois 8. Chicago, Illinois 9. Historical fiction 10. African American fiction
ISBN 9780823446049

When nine-year-old Clem's father dies in the Port Chicago Disaster he is forced to navigate his family's losses and struggles in 1940's Chicago.

"Cline-Ransome's mastery of first-person narration and her gift for dialogue present a close-up look at Chicago's African American community in the 1940s." Horn Book

Leaving Lymon. Lesa Cline-Ransome. Holiday House, 2020. 224 p.: Finding Langston

Grades: 4 5 6 7 **Fic**
1. 1940s 2. African American boys 3. Family problems 4. Rural-urban migration 5. Personal conduct 6. Boy musicians 7. Milwaukee, Wisconsin 8. Chicago, Illinois 9. Historical fiction 10. African American fiction
ISBN 9780823444427

In a companion to the award-winning Finding Langston, young Lymon is uprooted by tragedy from his life in the Deep South of 1946 before the limits of his talents and resilience are tested in two Northern cities.

"Balancing rich history and timeless themes of race, instability, and the importance of music and the arts, this title is another must-have from Cline-Ransome." School Library Journal

Coats, J. Anderson (Jillian Anderson)

The **wicked** and the just. by Jillian Anderson Coats. Harcourt, 2012. 384 p.

Grades: 7 8 9 10 11 12 **Fic**
1. Medieval period (476-1492) 2. 13th century 3. Teenage household employees 4. Resentfulness in teenagers 5. Civilization, Medieval 6. Resentfulness 7. Prejudice 8. Wales 9. Historical fiction
ISBN 9780547688374

LC 2011027315

In medieval Wales, follows Cecily whose family is lured by cheap land and the duty of all Englishman to help keep down the "vicious" Welshmen, and Gwenhwyfar, a Welsh girl who must wait hand and foot on her new English mistress.

Cody, Matthew

Powerless. Matthew Cody. Alfred A. Knopf, 2009. 279 p.: Supers of Noble's Green

Grades: 5 6 7 8 **Fic**
1. Child superheroes 2. Boy detectives 3. Bullying and bullies 4. Supernatural 5. Superheroes 6. Pennsylvania 7. Superhero stories
ISBN 9780375855955

LC 2008040885

Daniel Corrigan and his parents have just moved to Noble's Green, Pennsylvania, when Daniel (who's a big fan of Sherlock Holmes and therefore a careful observer) notices something odd about his neighbor Mollie and her friends. While they may look like ordinary kids, all of them have super-human abilities that they use to keep the town safe. After confessing their secret to Daniel, Mollie and the other super-kids reveal the catch—like similarly gifted kids from the town's past, they'll all lose their special abilities and their memories of ever being heroes as soon as they turn 13. That is, unless Daniel can solve the mystery behind the loss of their powers first! .

"This first novel has an intriguing premise, appealing characters, and a straightforward narrative arc with plenty of action as well as some serious moments." Booklist.

Cohen, Marina, 1967-

The **Inn** Between. by Marina Cohen; illustrations by Sarah Watts. Roaring Brook Press, [2016] 208 p.

Grades: 5 6 7 8 **Fic**
1. Haunted hotels 2. Haunted places 3. Missing persons 4. Best

friends 5. Friendship 6. Nevada 7. Horror 8. Illustrated books
ISBN 9781626722026

LC 2015004042

During a long car trip, best friends Quinn and Kara explore the strange and creepy goings-on at a remote Nevada inn when Kara's family stops for the night.

"Readers looking for a mystery with heart, humor, and hairy moments will be captivated." Kirkus.

Colbert, Brandy

The **revolution** of Birdie Randolph. Brandy Colbert. Little, Brown and Company, 2019 325 p.

Grades: 8 9 10 11 12   **Fic**

1. African American teenage girls 2. Expectation (Psychology) 3. Family secrets 4. Family relationships 5. African American families 6. Chicago, Illinois 7. Coming-of-age stories 8. African American fiction
ISBN 9780316448567

LC 2018022809

Sixteen-year-old Dove "Birdie" Randolph's close bond with her parents is threatened by a family secret, and by hiding her relationship with Booker, who has been in juvenile detention.

"Heavier topics like addiction, trauma, and the ills of juvenile justice system for teens of color are also explored in a refreshingly nuanced way that is handled with intelligence and care." Booklist

Colfer, Chris, 1990-

A **tale** of magic.... Chris Colfer; illustrated by Brandon Dorman. 496 p.: Tale of magic

Grades: 4 5 6 7   **Fic**

1. Fairies 2. Books and reading 3. Gender role 4. Magic 5. Quests 6. Fantasy fiction
ISBN 9780316523479

LC 2019012140

Fourteen-year-old Brystal Evergreen risks everything by opposing her kingdom's repression of women, but Madame Weatherberry, seeing her potential, invites her to a school where she hopes to change the world's perception of magic.

"Strong characters and an engaging story line make this a thoroughly satisfying adventure that can stand alone for Colfer newcomers." Publishers Weekly.

Colfer, Eoin

Airman. Eoin Colfer. Disney-Hyperion, 2020, 416 p.

Grades: 5 6 7 8 9   **Fic**

1. 19th century 2. Teenage prisoners 3. Flying machines 4. Escapes 5. Adventurers 6. Inventors 7. Ireland 8. Saltee Islands (Ireland) 9. Steampunk 10. Historical fantasy
ISBN 9781368068666

LC 2007038415

In the late nineteenth century, when Conor Broekhart discovers a conspiracy to overthrow the king, he is branded a traitor, imprisoned, and forced to mine for diamonds under brutal conditions while he plans a daring escape from Little Saltee prison by way of a flying machine that he must design, build, and, hardest of all, trust to carry him to safety.

"This is polished, sophisticated storytelling. . . . A tour de force." Publishers Weekly.

★ **Artemis** Fowl. Eoin Colfer. Talk Miramax Books/Hyperion Books For Children, c2001. 277 p.: Artemis Fowl series

Grades: 5 6 7 8   **Fic**

1. Gifted boys 2. Fairies 3. Ransom 4. Kidnapping 5. Criminals

6. Ireland 7. Fantasy fiction
ISBN 0786808012

LC 2001016632

When a twelve-year-old evil genius tries to restore his family fortune by capturing a fairy and demanding a ransom in gold, the fairies fight back with magic, technology, and a particularly nasty troll.

"Colfer's antihero, techno fantasy is cleverly written and filled to the brim with action, suspense, and humor." School Library Journal.

The **Fowl** twins. Eoin Colfer. Disney-Hyperion, 2019 368 p.: Fowl twins

Grades: 5 6 7 8   **Fic**

1. Twin brothers 2. Trolls 3. Chases 4. Escapes 5. Fairies 6. Ireland 7. Fantasy fiction
ISBN 9781368043755

Eleven-year-old twins Miles and Beckett Fowl enjoy adventure and mayhem while helping a troll escape nefarious forces that want his magic.

"Colfer's clever spin-off of the Artemis Fowl series focuses on Artemis Fowl's twin younger brothers, hyperintelligent Myles and near-feral Beckett, both 11. Accessible and entertaining." Publishers Weekly.

The **reluctant** assassin. Eoin Colfer. Hyperion, [2013] 304 p.: W.A.R.P.

Grades: 5 6 7 8   **Fic**

1. Assassins 2. Time travel 3. Wormholes (Astrophysics) 4. FBI agents 5. Orphans 6. London, England 7. Science fiction
ISBN 9781423161622

LC 2012048160

In Victorian London, Albert Garrick, an assassin-for-hire, and his reluctant young apprentice, Riley, are transported via wormhole to modern London, where Riley teams up with a young FBI agent to stop Garrick from returning to his own time and using his newly acquired scientific knowledge and power to change the world forever.

Collins, Suzanne

Catching fire. Suzanne Collins. Scholastic Press, 2009. 400 p.: Hunger Games trilogy

Grades: 7 8 9 10   **Fic**

1. Dystopias 2. Survival 3. Contests 4. Insurgency 5. Revenge 6. North America 7. Science fiction 8. Dystopian fiction
ISBN 9780439023498

LC 2008050493

By winning the annual Hunger Games, District 12 tributes Katniss Everdeen and Peeta Mellark have secured a life of safety and plenty for themselves and their families, but because they won by defying the rules, they unwittingly become the faces of an impending rebellion.

"Beyond the expert world building, the acute social commentary and the large cast of fully realized characters, there's action, intrigue, romance and some amount of hope in a story readers will find completely engrossing." Kirkus.

★ **Gregor** the Overlander. Suzanne Collins. Scholastic Press, 2003. 311 p.: Underland chronicles

Grades: 4 5 6 7   **Fic**

1. Brothers and sisters 2. Prophecies 3. Underground areas 4. Voyages and travels 5. Quests 6. Gateway fantasy 7. Fantasy fiction
ISBN 0439435366

LC 2002155865

When eleven-year-old Gregor and his two-year-old sister are pulled into a strange underground world, they trigger an epic battle involving men, bats, rats, cockroaches, and spiders while on a quest foretold by ancient prophecy.

"Collins creates a fascinating, vivid, highly original world and a superb story to go along with it." Booklist.

The **Hunger** Games. by Suzanne Collins. Scholastic Press, 2008. 374 p.: Hunger Games trilogy

Grades: 7 8 9 10 **Fic**
1. Survival 2. Contests 3. Dystopias 4. Television programs 5. Competition 6. North America 7. Science fiction 8. Dystopian fiction
ISBN 9780439023481

LC 2007039987

In a future North America, where the rulers of Panem maintain control through an annual televised survival competition pitting young people from each of the twelve districts against one another, sixteen-year-old Katniss's skills are put to the test when she voluntarily takes her younger sister's place.

"Collins's characters are completely realistic and sympathetic. . . . The plot is tense, dramatic, and engrossing." School Library Journal.

Mockingjay. Suzanne Collins. Scholastic Press, 2010. 400 p.: Hunger Games trilogy

Grades: 7 8 9 10 **Fic**
1. Survival 2. Contests 3. Dystopias 4. Television programs 5. Competition 6. North America 7. Science fiction 8. Dystopian fiction
ISBN 9780439023511

In a final installment in the trilogy, two-time Hunger Games survivor Katniss Everdeen is targeted by a vengeful Capitol that vows to make Katniss and all of District 12 pay for the ensuing unrest.

"This concluding volume in Collins's Hunger Games trilogy accomplishes a rare feat, the last installment being the best yet, a beautifully orchestrated and intelligent novel that succeeds on every level." Publishers Weekly.

Compestine, Ying Chang

A **banquet** for hungry ghosts. Ying Chang Compestine; illustrated by Coleman Polhemus. Henry Holt and Co., 2009. 192 p.

Grades: 6 7 8 9 10 **Fic**
1. Ghosts 2. Cooking, Chinese 3. Families 4. Recipes 5. China 6. Ghost stories 7. Short stories
ISBN 9780805082081

LC 2008050273

Presents an eight-course banquet of ghost stories centering around Chinese cooking and culture. Each story is followed by a recipe and historical notes.

"The stories are laced with beautiful (as well as lurid) images and chilling illustrations of the ghosts and their victims. Like the ghosts themselves, Compestine's memorable stories should prove difficult to shake." Publishers Weekly.

Revolution is not a dinner party. Ying Chang Compestine. Henry Holt and Company, 2007. 256 p.

Grades: 5 6 7 8 **Fic**
1. Chinese Cultural Revolution (1966-1976) 2. 1970s 3. Nine-year-old girls 4. State-sponsored terrorism 5. Families 6. Physicians 7. Communism 8. China
ISBN 0805082077

LC 2006035465

Starting in 1972 when she is nine years old, Ling, the daughter of two doctors, struggles to make sense of the communists' Cultural Revolution, which empties stores of food, homes of appliances deemed "bourgeois," and people of laughter.

"Readers should remain rapt by Compestine's storytelling throughout this gripping account of life during China's Cultural Revolution." Publishers Weekly.

Condie, Allyson Braithwaite

The **Beast**. by Ally Condie and Brendan Reichs. Bloomsbury Children's Books, 2019. 272 p.: Darkdeep

Grades: 4 5 6 7 **Fic**
1. Supernatural 2. Middle school students 3. Monsters 4. Secrets 5. Small towns 6. Pacific Northwest 7. Thrillers and suspense 8. Paranormal fiction
ISBN 9781547602032

LC 2019004264

Middle-schoolers Nico, Opal, Tyler, and Emma face a more dangerous threat and must uncover the whirlpool's origins, as well as those of that freaky "Thing in a Jar," while fending off paranormal investigators.

The **Darkdeep**. by Ally Condie and Brendan Reichs. Bloomsbury, 2018. 272 p.: Darkdeep

Grades: 4 5 6 7 **Fic**
1. Doorways 2. Supernatural 3. Friendship 4. Houseboats 5. Islands 6. Pacific Northwest 7. Thrillers and suspense 8. Paranormal fiction
ISBN 9781547600465

LC 2018024232

Middle-schoolers Nico, Tyler, Ella, and Opal discover a hidden island in a forbidden cove that appears uninhabited, but something ancient has awakened knowing their wishes, dreams, and darkest secrets.

The **last** voyage of Poe Blythe. Ally Condie. Dutton Books for Young Readers, 2019. 336 p.

Grades: 7 8 9 10 11 12 **Fic**
1. Ship captains 2. Revenge in teenage girls 3. Gold mines and mining 4. Grief 5. Revenge 6. Dystopian fiction 7. Steampunk
ISBN 9780525426455

LC 2018042052

Seeking to avenge the murder of her true love while on a dredge ship searching for gold, fifteen-year-old captain Poe Blythe becomes the architect of new defenses designed to destroy her enemies.

"The plot moves across a well-thought-out dystopian backdrop, offering enough surprises to both intrigue and excite. Fans of Condie's Matched should find this a welcome and satisfying return to the author's YA roots." Publishers Weekly.

Matched. Ally Condie. Dutton Childrens Books, 2010. 369 p.: Matched trilogy

Grades: 7 8 9 10 **Fic**
1. Matchmaking 2. Dystopias 3. Free will and determinism 4. Mate selection 5. Teenage boy/girl relations 6. Dystopian fiction 7. Science fiction
ISBN 9780525423645

Cassia has always trusted the Society to make the right choices for her, so when Xander appears on-screen at her Matching ceremony, Cassia knows he is her ideal mate—until Ky Markham's face appears for an instant before the screen fades to black.

"Condie's enthralling and twisty dystopian plot is well served by her intriguing characters and fine writing. While the ending is unresolved . . . , Cassia's metamorphosis is gripping and satisfying." Publishers Weekly.

Connis, Dave

Suggested reading. Dave Connis. Katherine Tegen Books, 2019. 400 p.

Grades: 8 9 10 11 12   **Fic**

1. Teenage rebels 2. Books and reading 3. Censorship 4. Banned books 5. Protest movements 6. Chattanooga, Tennessee 7. Tennessee 8. Realistic fiction

ISBN 9780062685254

A bookworm finds a way to fight back when her school bans dozens of classic and meaningful books. Publisher description

Connolly, MarcyKate

Comet rising. MarcyKate Connolly. Sourcebooks Jabberwocky, [2019] 304 p.: Shadow weaver

Grades: 4 5 6 7 8   **Fic**

1. Shadows 2. Spells (Magic) 3. Escapes 4. Magic 5. Good and evil 6. Fantasy fiction

ISBN 9781492649984

LC 2018010652

Shadow weaver Emmeline and her best friend Lucas, a light singer, must try to use their powers to stop evil Lady Aisling, the magic eater, once and for all.

Hollow dolls. MarcyKate Connolly. Sourcebooks Jabberwocky, 2020. 336 p.

Grades: 4 5 6 7 8   **Fic**

1. Preteen girls 2. Telepathy 3. Supernatural 4. Girls with amnesia 5. Magic 6. Fantasy fiction

ISBN 9781492688198

Freed after Lady Aisling is destroyed, mind-reader Simone sets off to find her family but as she delves deeper into her history, she learns truths she never could have imagined.

"While retaining the familiar fantasy setting and some characters from the Shadow Weaver duology, Connolly deftly answers the questions left dangling at the end of Comet Rising (2019), even as she introduces new characters and a gripping plot with a twist all sure to captivate readers who devoured the first set." Booklist.

Shadow weaver. MarcyKate Connolly. Sourcebooks Jabberwocky, [2018] 320 p.: Shadow weaver

Grades: 4 5 6 7 8   **Fic**

1. Shadows 2. Magic 3. Good and evil 4. Preteen girls 5. Friendship 6. Fantasy fiction

ISBN 9781492649953

LC 2017015540

Twelve-year-old Emmeline possesses the unique ability to manipulate shadows, but when her magical powers are threatened by a noble family she desperately turns to Dar, her shadow friend, who offers to save her if Emmeline makes Dar flesh again, but this bargain only puts Emmeline's life in further jeopardy.

Connor, Leslie

All rise for the honorable Perry T. Cook. Leslie Connor. 2016. 381 p.

Grades: 4 5 6 7 8   **Fic**

1. Children of prisoners 2. Foster children 3. District attorneys 4. Prisons 5. Mothers and sons 6. Nebraska 7. Realistic fiction

ISBN 9780062333469

"With complex, memorable characters, a situation that demands sympathy, and a story that's shown, not just told, this is fresh and affecting. Well-crafted, warm, and wonderful." Kirkus.

Waiting for normal. Leslie Connor. Katherine Tegen Books, c2008. 290 p.

Grades: 5 6 7 8   **Fic**

1. Child neglect 2. Children of divorced parents 3. Self-reliance in girls 4. Resilience (Personal quality) 5. Mothers and daughters 6. New York (State) 7. Realistic fiction

ISBN 0060890886

Schneider Family Book Award for Middle School, 2009.

Twelve-year-old Addie tries to cope with her mother's erratic behavior and being separated from her beloved stepfather and half-sisters when she and her mother go to live in a small trailer by the railroad tracks on the outskirts of Schenectady, New York.

"Connor . . . treats the subject of child neglect with honesty and grace in this poignant story. . . . Characters as persuasively optimistic as Addie are rare, and readers will gravitate to her." Publishers Weekly.

Constable, Kate, 1966-

The **singer** of all songs. Kate Constable. Arthur A. Levine Books, 2004. 297 p.: Chanters of Tremaris trilogy

Grades: 7 8 9 10   **Fic**

1. Young women 2. Women rulers 3. Women priests 4. Wizards 5. Singers 6. Fantasy fiction

ISBN 0439554780

LC 2003009034

Calwyn, a young priestess of ice magic, or "chantment," joins with other chanters who have different magical skills to fight a sorcerer who wants to claim all powers for his own.

"An impressive debut by an author who clearly has much to contribute to the fantasy genre." Booklist.

Cooney, Caroline B.

The **face** on the milk carton. Caroline Cooney. Bantam Books, 1990. 184 p.: Janie Johnson

Grades: 7 8 9 10   **Fic**

1. Missing children 2. Child kidnapping victims 3. Fifteen-year-old girls 4. Teenage girls -- Identity 5. Classics

ISBN 9780440220657

LC   89018311

A photograph of a missing girl on a milk carton leads Janie on a search for her real identity.

"Cooney demonstrates an excellent ear for dialogue and a gift for portraying responsible middle-class teenagers trying to come to terms with very real concerns." School Library Journal.

Janie face to face. Caroline B. Cooney. Delacorte Press, 2013. 192 p.: Janie Johnson

Grades: 7 8 9 10   **Fic**

1. Women college students 2. Child kidnapping victims 3. Authors 4. Kidnappers 5. Dating (Social customs) 6. New York City 7. Realistic fiction

ISBN 9780385742061

LC 2012006145

At college in New York City, Janie Johnson, aka Jennie Spring, seems to have successfully left behind her past as "The face on the milk carton," but soon she, her families, and friends are pursued by a true-crime writer who wants their help in telling her kidnapper's tale.

Cooper, Michelle, 1969-

A **brief** history of Montmaray. Michelle Cooper. Alfred A. Knopf, 2009, c2008. 286 p.: Montmaray journals

Grades: 7 8 9 10   **Fic**

1. Imaginary kingdoms 2. Teenage girls 3. Royal houses 4.

FitzOsborne, Sophia (Fictitious character) 5. Europe 6. Diary novels 7. Historical fiction
ISBN 9780375858642

On her sixteenth birthday in 1936, Sophia begins a diary of life in a fictional island country off the coast of Spain, where she is among the last descendants of an impoverished royal family trying to hold their nation together on the eve of the second World War.

"Cooper has crafted a sort of updated Gothic romance where sweeping adventure play equal with fluttering hearts." Booklist.

Cooper, Susan, 1935-

King of shadows. Susan Cooper. Margaret K. McElderry Books, 1999. 186 p.

Grades: 5 6 7 8   **Fic**
  1. Shakespeare, William 1564-1616 2. Globe Theatre (London, England: 1599-1644) 3. Boy actors 4. Grief in boys 5. Time travel (Past) 6. Grief 7. Children of suicide victims 8. London, England 9. Fantasy fiction
ISBN 9780689828171

While in London as part of an all-boy acting company preparing to perform in a replica of the famous Globe Theatre, Nat Field suddenly finds himself transported back to 1599 and performing in the original theater under the tutelage of Shakespeare himself.

"Cleverly explicating old and new acting and performance techniques, Susan Cooper entertains her contemporary readers while giving them a first-rate theatrical education." New York Times Book Review.

Cornwell, Betsy

Venturess. Betsy Cornwell. 320 p.: Mechanica

Grades: 5 6 7 8 9 10   **Fic**
  1. Inventors 2. Princes 3. Automata 4. Imaginary wars and battles 5. Magic 6. Steampunk 7. Fantasy fiction 8. Fairy tale and folklore-inspired fiction
ISBN 9780544319271

          LC 2016032623

An indomitable inventor and her loyal (and royal) friends cross the ocean to the lush world of Faerie, where they join a rising rebellion.

"This unexpected sequel hits a sweet spot for fairy tale and steampunk lovers alike." Booklist.

Cottrell Boyce, Frank

Sputnik's guide to life on earth. Frank Cottrell Boyce. Walden Pond Press, 2017. 321 p.

Grades: 4 5 6 7   **Fic**
  1. Children who are mute 2. Quests 3. End of the world 4. Foster children 5. Boys 6. Scotland 7. Science fiction
ISBN 9780062643629

Separated from his grandfather and placed in a foster home, Prez forges a friendship with an alien who appears as a dog to everyone else and entreats Prez to help compile a list of Earth's redeeming qualities.

"A stellar exploration of the meaning of home and the earthly wonders all around us." Booklist.

Coulthurst, Audrey

Of fire and stars. Audrey Coulthurst. Balzer + Bray, an imprint of HarperCollins Publishers, 2016 389 p.: Of fire and stars

Grades: 8 9 10 11   **Fic**
  1. Princesses 2. Teenage girl/girl relations 3. Assassination 4. Superhuman abilities 5. Magic 6. High fantasy 7. Fantasy fiction
ISBN 9780062433251

"A worthy debut that succeeds as both an adventure and a romance." Booklist.

Courtney, Nadine Jolie, 1980-

All-American Muslim girl. Nadine Jolie Courtney. Farrar, Straus and Giroux, 2019. 256 p.

Grades: 8 9 10 11 12   **Fic**
  1. Muslim teenagers 2. Teenage romance 3. Islamophobia 4. Self-acceptance 5. Small towns 6. Georgia 7. Southern States 8. Coming-of-age stories 9. Realistic fiction
ISBN 9780374309527

          LC 2018056246

Sixteen-year-old Allie, aged seven when she knew her family was different and feared, struggles to claim her Muslim and Arabic heritage while finding her place as an American teenager.

"Religion is rarely handled with such wisdom and depth in YA, or discussed so lovingly. A rich and memorable exploration of faith and family that is a first purchase for all collections." School Library Journal.

Coville, Bruce

William Shakespeare's A midsummer night's dream. adapted by Bruce Coville. Dial Books, 1996. unpaged.

Grades: 5 6 7 8 9   **Fic**
  1. Men/women relations 2. Fairies 3. Transformations (Magic)
ISBN 0803717857

          LC 94-12600

A simplified prose retelling of Shakespeare's play about the strange events that take place in a forest inhabited by fairies who magically transform the romantic fate of two young couples.

"Coville introduces the story and also conveys something of the poetry and drama. Nolan's framed graphite and watercolor paintings express the dreaminess and absurdity of the play, and the pictures have a theatrical flair." Booklist.

Creech, Sharon

★ **Absolutely** normal chaos. Sharon Creech. Harper Collins Publishers, 1995. 230 p.

Grades: 5 6 7 8   **Fic**
  1. Thirteen-year-old girls 2. Cousins 3. Birthfathers -- Identification 4. Girls 5. Homesickness 6. Ohio 7. Diary novels 8. Realistic fiction
ISBN 0060269898

          LC 95022448 /AC

Thirteen-year-old Mary Lou grows up considerably during the summer while learning about romance, homesickness, death, and her cousin's search for his biological father.

"Those in search of a light, humorous read will find it; those in search of something a little deeper will also be rewarded." School Library Journal.

Hate that cat. Sharon Creech. Joanna Cotler Books, 2008. 176 p.

Grades: 4 5 6 7   **Fic**
  1. Boy poets 2. Fifth-grade boys 3. Boys and cats 4. Emotions in boys 5. Cats 6. Novels in verse 7. Realistic fiction
ISBN 9780061430923

Jack is studying poetry again in school, and he continues to write poems reflecting his understanding of famous poems and how they relate to his life.

"Creech employs sensitivity and spare verse to carve an indelible portrait of a boy who discovers the power of self-expression." Booklist.

★ **Love** that dog. Sharon Creech. Harper Collins, 2001. 86 p.

Grades: 4 5 6 7   **Fic**
  1. Myers, Walter Dean, 1937-2014. 2. Boys and dogs 3. Teacher-

student relationships 4. Poetry writing 5. Boy poets 6. Boys 7. Novels in verse 8. Realistic fiction
ISBN 0060292873

LC   00054233

A young student, who comes to love poetry through a personal understanding of what different famous poems mean to him, and an appearance at his school by Walter Dean Myers, surprises himself by writing his own inspired poem.

"Creech has created a poignant, funny picture of a child's encounter with the power of poetry. . . . This book is a tiny treasure." School Library Journal.

The **unfinished** angel. Sharon Creech. Joanna Cotler Books, 2009. 176 p.

Grades: 4 5 6   **Fic**
1. Angels 2. Orphans 3. Private schools 4. Peace 5. Communities 6. Switzerland 7. Fantasy fiction
ISBN 9780061430961

LC 2009002796

In a tiny village in the Swiss Alps, an angel meets an American girl named Zola who has come with her father to open a school, and together Zola and the angel rescue a group of homeless orphans, who gradually change everything.

"Some books are absolute magic, and this is one of them. . . . Creech's protagonist is hugely likable. . . . Creech's offering deserves to be read out loud and more than once to truly enjoy the angel's hilarious malapropisms and outright invented words, and to appreciate the book's tender, comical celebration of the human spirit." School Library Journal.

★ **Walk** two moons. Sharon Creech. Harper Collins, c1994. 280 p.

Grades: 6 7 8 9   **Fic**
1. Native American teenage girls 2. Automobile travel 3. Storytelling 4. Mother-separated children 5. Mothers -- Death 6. Realistic fiction 7. Classics
ISBN 0060233346

LC   93031277 /AC

Newbery Medal, 1995.

After her mother leaves home suddenly, thirteen-year-old Sal and her grandparents take a car trip retracing her mother's route. Along the way, Sal recounts the story of her friend Phoebe, whose mother also left.

"An engaging story of love and loss, told with humor and suspense. . . . A richly layered novel about real and metaphorical journeys." School Library Journal.

Croggon, Alison, 1962-

The **threads** of magic. by Alison Croggon; art by Matt Saunders. Candlewick Press, 2021, 384 p.

Grades: 5 6 7 8   **Fic**
1. Pickpockets 2. Immortality 3. Heart 4. Spells (Magic) 5. Magic 6. Fantasy fiction
ISBN 9781536207194

An atmospheric and riveting fantasy adventure, perfect for fans of Frances Hardinge and Cornelia Funke. Pip lives on his wits in the city of Clarel. When he pickpockets the wrong man, he finds himself in possession of a strange object, a heart in a silver casket. What's more, the heart seems to be trying to communicate with Pip, and the royal officials who lost it will stop at nothing to get it back. Pip has unwittingly broken an ancient spell, and his theft will have far-reaching consequences for the whole city. As the ancient war between the Spectres and witches of Clarel reignites, the heart prepares to seek revenge for all it has suffered. Alison Croggon conjures a rich, immersive world with brilliant

and memorable characters in this captivating story of loyalty, courage and friendship.

"The premise and the power-squabbling . . . are intriguing, but the distinct characters and a vein of humor that ensures the story never takes itself too seriously are really where this novel shines." Bulletin of the Center for Children's Books

Cross, Gillian

The **Iliad**. retold by Gillian Cross; illustrated by Neil Packer. Candlewick Press, 2015. 151 p.

Grades: 6 7 8 9   **Fic**
1. Trojan War 2. Heroes and heroines, Greek 3. Gods and goddesses, Greek 4. Rulers 5. Troy (Extinct city) 6. Illustrated books
ISBN 9780763678326

LC bl2015037202

An illustrated adaptation of Homer's classic traces the rivalry between two powerful Greek leaders for the hand of a beautiful woman against the backdrop of the Trojan War.

"The striking mixed-media artwork varies from large, richly colored scenes to others using a minimum of color very effectively. Packer uses forms, particularly human forms, in expressive, inventive ways. An eye-catching introduction to the classic story." Booklist.

Crossan, Sarah

Being Toffee. by Sarah Crossan. Bloomsbury Childrens Books 2020 416 p.

Grades: 8 9 10 11 12   **Fic**
1. Runaways 2. Senior women 3. Intergenerational friendship 4. Child abuse 5. Elder abuse 6. Novels in verse 7. Realistic fiction
ISBN 9781547603299

LC 2020014880

Allison runs away and, in what she thinks is an abandoned house, finds a home with Marla, an elderly woman with dementia who believes her to be an old friend named Toffee.

One. by Sarah Crossan. Greenwillow Books, an imprint of HarperCollinsPublishers, [2015] 400 p.

Grades: 8 9 10 11 12   **Fic**
1. Conjoined twins 2. Twin sisters 3. Private schools 4. High schools 5. Schools 6. Realistic fiction 7. Novels in verse
ISBN 9780062118752

LC 2015004714

Carnegie Medal, 2016.

Despite problems at home, sixteen-year-old conjoined twins Tippi and Grace are loving going to school for the first time and making real friends when they learn that a cardiac problem will force them to have separation surgery, which they have never before considered.

"Crossan trusts her characters and her readers to find their better selves through her gently paced story." Booklist.

Crowder, Melanie

An **uninterrupted** view of the sky. Melanie Crowder. Philomel Books, 2017. 304 p.

Grades: 7 8 9 10 11 12   **Fic**
1. 1990s 2. Prisons 3. Political corruption 4. Indians of South America 5. Aymara Indians 6. Poverty 7. Bolivia 8. Historical fiction
ISBN 9780399169007

When his father is sent to jail after being falsely convicted of a crime in 1999 Bolivia, teen Francisco is forced to choose between living with his father in prison and relocating to the mountains, where people have lived for centuries without education or modern conveniences.

Crowley, Cath

Words in deep blue. Cath Crowley. Alfred A. Knopf, 2017, c2016. 288 p.

Grades: 8 9 10 11   **Fic**

1. Love 2. Best friends 3. Bookstores 4. Grief in teenagers 5. Self-discovery in teenagers 6. Melbourne, Victoria 7. Australia 8. Love stories
ISBN 9781101937648

Teenagers Rachel and Henry find their way back to each other while working in an old bookstore full of secrets and crushes, love letters and memories, grief and hope.

"This journey is original, wise, and essential . . . This love story is an ode to words and life." Kirkus.

Crutcher, Chris

Deadline. Chris Crutcher. Greenwillow Books, 2007. 316 p.

Grades: 8 9 10 11 12   **Fic**

1. High school athletes 2. Teenagers with terminal illnesses 3. Crushes in teenage boys 4. Teenagers with leukemia 5. Leukemia 6. Idaho 7. Humorous stories 8. Realistic fiction
ISBN 9780060850890

LC 2006031526

Given the medical diagnosis of one year to live, high school senior Ben Wolf decides to fulfill his greatest fantasies, ponders his life's purpose and legacy, and converses through dreams with a spiritual guide known as "Hey-Soos."

"Ben's sensitive voice uses self-deprecating humor, philosophical pondering, and effective dramatic irony." Voice of Youth Advocates.

Cuevas, Adrianna

The **total** eclipse of Nestor Lopez. Adrianna Cuevas. Farrar Straus Giroux Books for Young Readers, 2020 288 p.

Grades: 4 5 6 7   **Fic**

1. Hispanic American boys 2. Human/animal communication 3. Transformations, Magic 4. Witches 5. Magic 6. Texas 7. Fantasy fiction 8. Fairy tale and folklore-inspired fiction
ISBN 9780374313609

A Cuban American boy must use his secret ability to communicate with animals to save the inhabitants of his town when they are threatened by a tule vieja, a witch that transforms into animals. Excerpted from publisher description.

Curato, Mike

Flamer. Mike Curato Henry Holt and Company, 2020 368 p.

Grades: 7 8 9 10 11 12   **Fic**

1. 1990s 2. Bullying and bullies 3. Summer camps 4. Questioning (Sexual or gender identity) 5. Self-discovery in teenage boys 6. Sexual orientation 7. Realistic fiction 8. Comics and Graphic novels
ISBN 9781627796415

In the summer between middle school and high school, Aiden Navarro navigates friendships, deals with bullies, and finds himself drawn to Elias, a boy he can't stop thinking about.

"The monochromatic illustrations, sometimes highlighted with red, orange, and yellow, are timeless moments of a remembered childhood. . . . But the true star of this book is the writing, which describes a boy who could live in any decade on his journey of self-discovery." Kirkus

Currier, Katrina Saltonstall, 1969-

Kai's journey to Gold Mountain: an Angel Island story. by Katrina Saltonstall Currier. Angel Island Association, 2004. 44 p.

Grades: 4 5 6 7   **Fic**

1. Angel Island Immigration Station, California -- History -- 20th century 2. 1930s 3. Twelve-year-old boys 4. Boy immigrants 5. Chinese Americans 6. Chinese American boys 7. Immigration and emigration 8. Los Angeles, California 9. United States 10. Historical fiction
ISBN 0966735242

LC 2004014821

In 1934, twelve-year-old Kai leaves China to join his father in America, but first he must take a long sea voyage, then endure weeks of crowded conditions and harsh examinations on Angel Island, fearing that he or his new friend will be sent home.

"The character Kai is based on a real person, whose photos, then and now, are part of the historical notes at the back of the book. Opposite each page of the intensely moving, detailed text are beautiful full-page watercolor-and-pencil illustrations that capture the crowded holding place, and, in unforgettable closeups, the characters' heartbreak and strength." Booklist.

Curtis, Christopher Paul

★ **Bud,** not Buddy. Christopher Paul Curtis. Delacorte Press, c1999. 245 p.

Grades: 4 5 6 7   **Fic**

1. Depression era (1929-1941) 2. 1930s 3. African American boys 4. Quests 5. Ten-year-old boys 6. African American mother and son 7. Mother-separated boys 8. Michigan 9. Flint, Michigan 10. Historical fiction 11. Classics 12. African American fiction
ISBN 0385323069

LC 9910614

Coretta Scott King Award, Author Category, 2000.
Newbery Medal, 2000.

Ten-year-old Bud, a motherless boy living in Flint, Michigan, during the Great Depression, escapes a bad foster home and sets out in search of the man he believes to be his father—the renowned bandleader, H.E. Calloway of Grand Rapids.

"Curtis says in a afterword that some of the characters are based on real people, including his own grandfathers, so it's not surprising that the rich blend of tall tale, slapstick, sorrow, and sweetness has the wry, teasing warmth of family folklore." Booklist.

★ **Elijah** of Buxton. Christopher Paul Curtis. Scholastic, 2007. 288 p.

Grades: 5 6 7 8   **Fic**

1. 1860s 2. African American boys 3. Freed people 4. Rescues 5. Slavery 6. Black Canadian children 7. Canada 8. Ontario 9. Historical fiction 10. African American fiction
ISBN 0439023440

LC 2007005181

Coretta Scott King Award, Author Category, 2008.
Scott O'Dell Historical Fiction Award, 2008.

In 1859, eleven-year-old Elijah Freeman, the first free-born child in Buxton, Canada, which is a haven for slaves fleeing the American South, uses his wits and skills to try to bring to justice the lying preacher who has stolen money that was to be used to buy a family's freedom.

"Many readers drawn to the book by humor will find themselves at times on the edges of their seats in suspense and, at other moments, moved to tears." Booklist.

The **madman** of Piney Woods. Christopher Paul Curtis. Scholastic Press, 2015. 384 p.

Grades: 4 5 6 7　　　　　**Fic**

　1. 1900s (Decade) 2. Black Canadians 3. Immigrants, Irish 4. Post-traumatic stress disorder 5. Freed people 6. Veterans 7. Canada 8. North Buxton, Ontario 9. Historical fiction 10. African American fiction
ISBN 9780545156646

　　　　　　　　　　LC 2014003493

Even though it is now 1901, the people of Buxton, Canada (originally a settlement of runaway slaves) and Chatham, Canada are still haunted by two events of half a century before—the American Civil War, and the Irish potato famine, and the lasting damage those events caused to the survivors.

　"Humor and tragedy are often intertwined, and readers will find themselves sobbing and chuckling, sometimes in the same scene." Kirkus.

★ The **Watsons** go to Birmingham, 1963: a novel. by Christopher Paul Curtis. Delacorte Press, 1995. 210 p.

Grades: 4 5 6 7　　　　　**Fic**

　1. 1960s 2. African Americans 3. Civil Rights Movement 4. Racism 5. Family visits 6. African American families 7. Alabama 8. Flint, Michigan 9. Historical fiction 10. Classics 11. African American fiction
ISBN 0385321759

　　　　　　　　　　LC 95007091

Golden Kite Award for Fiction, 1995.

The ordinary interactions and everyday routines of the Watsons, an African American family living in Flint, Michigan, are drastically changed after they go to visit Grandma in Alabama in the summer of 1963.

　"Curtis's ability to switch from fun and funky to pinpoint-accurate psychological imagery works unusually well. . . . Ribald humor, sly sibling digs, and a totally believable child's view of the world will make this book an instant hit." School Library Journal.

Cushman, Karen

Catherine, called Birdy. Karen Cushman. Clarion Books, c1994. 169 p.

Grades: 6 7 8 9　　　　　**Fic**

　1. Medieval period (476-1492) 2. 13th century 3. Independence in teenage girls 4. Civilization, Medieval 5. Diary writing 6. Thirteen-year-old girls 7. Teenage girls 8. England 9. Historical fiction 10. Diary novels 11. Classics
ISBN 0395681863

　　　　　　　　　　LC 9323333

Golden Kite Award for Fiction, 1994.

The thirteen-year-old daughter of an English country knight keeps a journal in which she records the events of her life, particularly her longing for adventures beyond the usual role of women and her efforts to avoid being married off.

　"In the process of telling the routines of her young life, Birdy lays before readers a feast of details about medieval England. . . . Superb historical fiction." School Library Journal.

The **loud** silence of Francine Green. by Karen Cushman. Clarion Books, 2006. 225 p.

Grades: 6 7 8 9　　　　　**Fic**

　1. 1940s 2. 1950s 3. Teenage nonconformists 4. Independence in girls 5. Conformity 6. Thirteen-year-old girls 7. Teenage girls 8. Los Angeles, California 9. United States 10. Coming-of-age

stories 11. Historical fiction
ISBN 0618504559

　　　　　　　　　　LC 2005029774

In 1949, thirteen-year-old Francine goes to Catholic school in Los Angeles where she becomes best friends with a girl who questions authority and is frequently punished by the nuns, causing Francine to question her own values.

　"Readers will savor the story of friends and family tensions, the sly humor, and the questions about patriotism, activism, and freedom." Booklist.

The **midwife's** apprentice. Karen Cushman. Clarion Books, c1995. 122 p.

Grades: 6 7 8 9　　　　　**Fic**

　1. Medieval period (476-1492) 2. 14th century 3. Homeless girls 4. Midwives 5. Civilization, Medieval 6. Villages 7. Self-awareness in girls 8. England 9. Historical fiction 10. Classics
ISBN 0395692296

　　　　　　　　　　LC 94013792 /AC

Newbery Medal, 1996.

In medieval England, a nameless, homeless girl is taken in by a sharp-tempered midwife, and in spite of obstacles and hardship, eventually gains the three things she most wants: a full belly, a contented heart, and a place in this world.

　"Earthy humor, the foibles of humans both high and low, and a fascinating mix of superstition and genuinely helpful herbal remedies attached to childbirth make this a truly delightful introduction to a world seldom seen in children's literature." School Library Journal.

Rodzina. by Karen Cushman. Clarion Books, c2003. 215 p.

Grades: 5 6 7 8　　　　　**Fic**

　1. 1880s 2. 19th century 3. Polish American girls 4. Orphan trains 5. Girl orphans 6. Survival 7. Twelve-year-old girls 8. The West (United States) 9. Historical fiction
ISBN 0618133518

　　　　　　　　　　LC 2002015976

A twelve-year-old Polish American girl is boarded onto an orphan train in Chicago with fears about traveling to the West and a life of unpaid slavery.

　"The story features engaging characters, a vivid setting, and a prickly but endearing heroine. . . . Rodzina's musings and observations provide poignancy, humor, and a keen sense of the human and topographical landscape." School Library Journal.

Cypess, Leah

Death sworn. by Leah Cypess. Greenwillow Books, an imprint of HarperCollinsPublishers, [2014] 352 p.: Death sworn

Grades: 7 8 9 10 11 12　　　　　**Fic**

　1. Assassins 2. Secrets 3. Murder 4. Magic 5. Teenage romance 6. High fantasy 7. Fantasy mysteries 8. Fantasy fiction
ISBN 9780062221216

　　　　　　　　　　LC 2013037379

When a young sorceress is exiled to teach magic to a clan of assassins, she will find that secrets can be even deadlier than swords. Provided by publisher.

　"As seventeen-year-old Ileni's magic begins to fade, she's sent to the Black Mountain to tutor assassins in sorcery. With the help of Sorin, her student and assigned protector, she must discover who killed her predecessors before someone kills her. Ileni proves a compelling protagonist, and the blend of romance, assassins, magic, and murder-mystery consistently raises the stakes." Horn Book.

Thornwood. Leah Cypess. Delacorte Books for Young Readers, 2021 272 p.: Sisters ever after

Grades: 4 5 6 7   **Fic**
    1. Sisters 2. Curses 3. Friendship 4. Princes 5. Princesses 6. Fairy tale and folklore-inspired fiction
    ISBN 9780593178836

Placed in a deep sleep along with the rest of the kingdom by her beautiful sister's sleeping curse, a younger sibling awakens to a harrowing truth that nobody else believes, forcing her to embark on a quest to save her loved ones.

"Incorporating surprising twists and subverting tropes to emphasize sibling bonds over romance, Cypess creates a fun tale with a strong heroine whose happily ever after isn't set in stone." Publishers Weekly

Cyprus, Naomi

Sisters of glass. Naomi Cyprus. Harpercollins Children's Books, 2017. 304 p.: Sisters of glass

Grades: 4 5 6 7   **Fic**
    1. Princesses 2. Magic mirrors 3. Kidnapping 4. Rescues 5. Magic 6. Middle Eastern-influenced fantasy 7. Fantasy fiction
    ISBN 9780062458476

Halan is a powerless princess. She is heir to the Magi Kingdom, a blazing desert land ruled by ancient magic. But unlike every royal before her, Halan has no magical powers of her own.

"First in the Shard series, this romp will hook readers with its appealing tween characters, exotic settings that blend old and modern, and empowering fight between right and wrong." Booklist.

D'Lacey, Chris

Dark fire. Chris d'Lacey. Orchard Books, 2010, c2009. 567 p.: Last dragon chronicles

Grades: 6 7 8 9   **Fic**
    1. Authors 2. Dragons 3. Supernatural 4. Good and evil 5. Fire 6. England 7. Arctic regions 8. Fantasy fiction
    ISBN 9780545102728

LC 2009026670

Bestselling author David Rain returns to help Lucy and the Pennykettle dragons try to find and destroy a drop of dark fire before it is discovered and used to birth a darkling, while in the Arctic, enshrouded in mist, hide dragons that have at last returned to Earth.

The **fire** ascending. Chris D'Lacey. Orchard Books, 2012. 576 p.: Last dragon chronicles

Grades: 6 7 8 9   **Fic**
    1. Dragons 2. Apprentices 3. Space and time 4. Good and evil 5. Rain, David (Fictitious character) 6. Fantasy fiction
    ISBN 9780545402163

Young Agawin, apprentice to the healer Yolen, finds that his life is linked to that of the last of the dragons of the Wearle of Hautuuslanden, Galen, and he must journey far in time and space to protect the future of dragon-kind.

The **fire** eternal. Chris d'Lacey. Orchard Books, 2008. 506 p.: Last dragon chronicles

Grades: 6 7 8 9   **Fic**
    1. Authors 2. Dragons 3. Climate change 4. Aliens 5. Supernatural 6. Arctic regions 7. Fantasy fiction
    ISBN 9780545051637

LC 2007046493

As the weather grows wilder and the ice caps melt, Arctic bears starve, dragons awake, the earth goddess Gaia becomes restless, and

Alexa, the daughter of best-selling author David Rain, uses her special abilities in an attempt to save the world from the forces of evil.

Fire star. Chris D'Lacey. Orchard Books 2007. 560 p.: Last dragon chronicles

Grades: 6 7 8 9   **Fic**
    1. Authors 2. College students 3. Dragons 4. College teachers 5. Boarders 6. Arctic Regions 7. Fantasy fiction
    ISBN 0439845823

LC 2006018004

David Rain is faced with the most perilous task yet when Gwilanna returns, this time determined to resurrect the dragon Gawain on the ice cap of the Tooth of Ragnar, unless David and her friends can stop her.

"The story, with its involving and thought-provoking plot full of clever little dragons, mystical polar bears, and spiritual and ecological aspects, will appeal to many fantasy lovers." School Library Journal.

The **fire** within. Chris D'Lacey. Orchard Books 2005. 340 p.: Last dragon chronicles

Grades: 6 7 8 9   **Fic**
    1. Boarders 2. Dragons 3. Writing 4. Creativity 5. Supernatural 6. Massachusetts 7. Fantasy fiction
    ISBN 0439672449

LC 2004058327

When college student David Rain rents a room in an unusual boardinghouse full of clay dragons, he has no idea that they, along with some lively squirrels, will help jumpstart his writing career.

"This has a satisfying domestic reality, spiced with some very unusual dragons." School Library Journal.

Fire world. Chris d'Lacey. Orchard Books, 2011. 562 p.: Last dragon chronicles

Grades: 6 7 8 9   **Fic**
    1. Dragons 2. Mythical birds 3. Parallel universes 4. Supernatural 5. Good and evil 6. Fantasy fiction
    ISBN 9780545283687

LC 2010053114

On the planet Co:per:nica, which is a parallel world to that of Crescent Lane, David is twelve years old and is trying to save a firebird that has been turned to evil by the malevolent Ix.

Icefire. Chris D'Lacey. Orchard Books, 2006. 421 p.: Last dragon chronicles

Grades: 6 7 8 9   **Fic**
    1. College students 2. Essay contests 3. Dragons 4. Supernatural 5. Boarders 6. Arctic regions 7. Fantasy fiction
    ISBN 0439672457

While researching the existence of dragons for an essay that could win him a trip to the Arctic, Chris opens himself to the possibility that a great, ancient treasure exists there, guarded by bears, and that he has some role in its protection.

"Readers will find action and mysteries aplenty in this fantastic tale, as well as a group of appealing dragons who are tricky, heroic, and often charming." School Library Journal.

Dahl, Roald

Skin and other stories. Roald Dahl. Viking, 2000, c1991. 212 p.

Grades: 7 8 9 10   **Fic**
    1. Short stories
    ISBN 9780670891849

A clever collection of thirteen suspenseful and chilling tales for young adults.

"A collection of 13 of the author's short stories written for adults. Full of irony and unexpected twists, they smack of the master's touch—every word carefully chosen, characters fully fleshed out in only a few pages, the sense of place immediate." Booklist.

Dakin, Glenn

The **Society** of Unrelenting Vigilance. Glenn Dakin; [illustrations by Greg Swearingen]. Egmont, 2009. 300 p.: Candle Man

Grades: 4 5 6 7   **Fic**
1. Teenage superheroes 2. Secret societies 3. Vigilantes 4. Guardian and ward 5. Good and evil 6. Steampunk 7. Fantasy fiction
ISBN 9781606840153

                     LC 2009014035

Theo Wickland has been confined to three rooms of his guardian Dr. Saint's mansion for his entire life. But on Theo's 12th birthday, burglars invade Empire Hall—and Theo discovers that he has the ability to melt criminals with merely a touch of his hand. This is only the beginning of Theo's adventures, for he escapes from Empire Hall and joins the Society of Unrelenting Vigilance, whose members reveal the truth about Dr. Saint.

"This is a lighthearted, action-driven adventure. . . . With the help of a cast of appealing characters, the nonstop action rolls to a satisfying conclusion." School Library Journal.

Dallas, Sandra

The **quilt** walk. by Sandra Dallas. Sleeping Bear Press, 2012. 213 p.

Grades: 3 4 5 6 7   **Fic**
1. American Westward Expansion (1803-1899) 2. 1860s 3. 19th century 4. Wagon trains 5. Quilting 6. Frontier and pioneer life 7. Friendship 8. Ten-year-old girls 9. Historical fiction
ISBN 9781585368006

                     LC 2012005863

Ten-year-old Emmy Blue learns the true meaning of friendship—and how to quilt—while making a harrowing wagon journey from Illinois to Colorado with her family in the 1860s.

Damico, Gina

Croak. Gina Damico. Houghton Mifflin Harcourt, 2012. 320 p.: Croak trilogy

Grades: 7 8 9 10   **Fic**
1. Sixteen-year-old girls 2. Supernatural 3. Death 4. Dead 5. Life after death 6. Urban fantasy
ISBN 9780547608327

A delinquent sixteen-year-old girl is sent to live with her uncle for the summer, only to learn that he is a Grim Reaper who wants to teach her the family business.

Danziger, Paula, 1944-2004

The **cat** ate my gymsuit: a novel. Paula Danziger. Delacorte Press, 1974. 147 p.

Grades: 4 5 6 7   **Fic**
1. Junior high school teachers 2. Overweight teenagers 3. Fathers and daughters 4. Self-acceptance in teenagers 5. Junior high schools 6. Realistic fiction 7. Classics
ISBN 0440016967

              LC   74008898

When the unconventional English teacher who helped her conquer many of her feelings of insecurity is fired, a junior high student uses her new found courage to campaign for the teacher's reinstatement.

"Paula Danziger's compassionate and accurate portrayal of a young girl struggling to find her own voice rings as true today as it did 30 years ago. A full cast brings this modern American classic of teenage angst to life with humor and pathos." School Library Journal.

Darrows, Eva

Dead little mean girl. Eva Darrows. Harlequin Teen, 2017. 250 p.

Grades: 7 8 9 10   **Fic**
1. Stepsisters 2. Teenage girls and death 3. Bullying and bullies 4. Teenage girl misfits 5. Death 6. Realistic fiction
ISBN 9780373212415

When proud geek-girl Emma's new stepsister, mean-girl Quinn, moves into the bedroom next door, Emma's world is turned upside down, but when Quinn dies suddenly, Emma realizes there was more to her stepsister than anyone ever realized.

"Darrows' (The Awesome, 2015) new YA novel is a seriously smart, funny, and empathetic look at how someone's manufactured exterior might be hiding inner turmoil, and ultimately advocates for looking past labels and categories." Booklist.

DasGupta, Sayantani

The **force** of fire. Sayantani Dasgupta; illustrations by Vivienne To. Scholastic Press, 2021 368 p.: Kiranmala and the kingdom beyond

Grades: 4 5 6 7   **Fic**
1. East Indian American girls 2. Demon slayers 3. Interdimensional travel 4. Control (Psychology) 5. Insurgency 6. New Jersey 7. Fantasy fiction 8. Fairy tale and folklore-inspired fiction 9. Asian-influenced fantasy
ISBN 9781338636642

A descendent from a long line of demons who build interspecies relationships to fight tyranny works competitively to control her dangerous fire-breathing skills, before a Serpentine Governor's charming son enlists her help to defeat a growing rebellion.

"With masterful storytelling . . . and memorable characters, the story revolves around the question of legacy and how to make decisions for yourself regardless of what others expect." Booklist

Dashner, James, 1972-

The **maze** runner. James Dashner. Delacorte Press, 2009. 384 p.: Maze runner trilogy

Grades: 7 8 9 10 11 12   **Fic**
1. Labyrinths 2. Amnesia 3. Dystopias 4. Cooperation 5. Teenagers with amnesia 6. Dystopian fiction 7. Science fiction
ISBN 9780385737944

                     LC   2009001345

Sixteen-year-old Thomas wakes up with no memory in the middle of a maze and realizes he must work with the community in which he finds himself if he is to escape.

"With a fast-paced narrative steadily answering the myriad questions that arise and an ever-increasing air of tension, Dashner's suspenseful adventure will keep readers guessing until the very end." Publishers Weekly.

Dassu, A. M.

Boy, everywhere. by A. M. Dassu. Tu Books, [2021] 400 p.
Grades: 6 7 8 9   **Fic**
1. Political refugees 2. Immigrants 3. Refugees, Syrian 4. War 5.

Voyages and travels 6. Damascus, Syria
ISBN 9781643791968

LC 2021003482

Sami loves his life in Damascus, Syria, but when war breaks out his parents decide they must flee their home for the safety of the UK.

"A Syrian refugee story that disrupts stereotypes while tugging at readers' heartstrings." Kirkus

Daud, Somaiya

Mirage. Somaiya Daud. Flatiron Books, 2018. 320 p.: Mirage (Daud)

Grades: 8 9 10 11 12 **Fic**
1. Royal pretenders 2. Imaginary kingdoms 3. Teenage kidnapping victims 4. Impostors 5. Mistaken identity 6. Science fiction 7. Afrofuturism and Afrofantasy 8. African American fiction
ISBN 9781250126429

LC 2018013549

After being kidnapped by the Vathek, Amani is forced to work as a body double for the princess who is hated by her conquered people.

Davis, Mandy

Superstar. Mandy Davis. HarperCollins Childrens Books, 2017. 336 p.

Grades: 4 5 6 7 **Fic**
1. Boys with autism 2. Science fairs 3. Adjustment (Child psychology) 4. New students 5. Home schooled boys 6. Realistic fiction
ISBN 9780062377777

Enrolling in public school after years of homeschooling, Lester, a mildly autistic fifth-grader, struggles to adapt and manage symptoms before becoming eager to win a science fair, discovering an unexpected truth along the way.

"This unsentimental portrait of an endearing and memorable protagonist offers powerful insight into living with autism." Publishers Weekly.

Davis, Tanita S.

Mare's war. Tanita S. Davis. Alfred A. Knopf, 2009. 352 p.

Grades: 7 8 9 10 **Fic**
1. United States. Army. Women's Army Corps. 2. 1940s 3. African-American women soldiers 4. Grandmother and granddaughter 5. Automobile travel 6. African Americans 7. Discrimination 8. Europe 9. Historical fiction 10. Epistolary novels
ISBN 9780375957147

LC 2008033744

Teens Octavia and Tali learn about strength, independence, and courage when they are forced to take a car trip with their grandmother, who tells about growing up Black in 1940s Alabama and serving in Europe during World War II as a member of the Women's Army Corps.

"The parallel travel narratives are masterfully managed, with postcards from Octavia and Tali to the folks back home in San Francisco signaling the shift between then and now. Absolutely essential reading." Kirkus.

Day, Christine, 1993-

★ **I** can make this promise. Christine Day. HarperCollins, 2019. 272 p.

Grades: 4 5 6 7 **Fic**
1. Native American girls 2. Adopted girls 3. Family secrets 4. Identity (Psychology) 5. Birthparents -- Identification 6. Seattle, Washington 7. Realistic fiction
ISBN 9780062871992

LC 2019009519

When twelve-year-old Edie finds letters and photographs in her attic that change everything she thought she knew about her Native American mother's adoption, she realizes she has a lot to learn about her family's history and her own identity.

"This debut also offers compelling historical knowledge about the Pacific Northwest Native American tribes, the Indian Child Welfare Act of 1978, and what it means to find one's heritage." Booklist.

The **sea** in winter. Christine Day. Heartdrum, a Harpercollins Imprint, 2021 304 p.

Grades: 4 5 6 7 **Fic**
1. Girl ballet dancers 2. Multiracial girls 3. Sports injuries 4. Anxiety 5. Makah Indians 6. Realistic fiction
ISBN 9780062872043

It's been a hard year for Maisie Cannon, ever since she hurt her leg and could not keep up with her ballet training and auditions. Her blended family is loving and supportive, but Maisie knows that they just can't understand how hopeless she feels. With everything she's dealing with, Maisie is not excited for their family midwinter road trip along the coast, near the Makah community where her mother grew up. But soon, Maisie's anxieties and dark moods start to hurt as much as the pain in her knee. How can she keep pretending to be strong when on the inside she feels as roiling and cold as the ocean?

"Day lifts the narrative beyond the tribulations of another angsty tween heroine by offering an eminently reasonable path forward, paved with physical healing, emotional therapy, and reconnection with friends." Bulletin of the Center for Children's Books

De la Cruz, Melissa, 1971-

Never after: the thirteenth fairy. Melissa De La Cruz. Roaring Brook Press, 2020. 320 p.: Chronicles of never after

Grades: 5 6 7 8 **Fic**
1. Characters and characteristics in fairy tales 2. Adopted girls 3. Middle school students 4. Fairies 5. Imaginary kingdoms 6. Fantasy fiction 7. Fairy tale and folklore-inspired fiction
ISBN 9781250311214

Nothing ever happens in Filomena Jefferson-Cho?s sleepy little suburban town of North Pasadena. But one day, when Filomena is walking home on her own, something strange happens. Filomena is being followed by Jack Stalker, one of the heroes in the Thirteenth Fairy, a series of books she loves about a brave girl and her ragtag group of friends who save their world from an evil enchantress. Soon, Filomena is thrust into the world of evil fairies and beautiful princesses, sorcerers and slayers, where an evil queen drives her ruthless armies to destroy what is left of the Fairy tribes. To save herself and the kingdom of Westphalia, Filomena must find the truth behind the fairytales and set the world back to rights before the cycle of sleep and destruction begins once more.

"Equal parts whimsical and adventure-packed, Filomena's journey will entrance readers and have them rooting for the young, witty heroine." Kirkus

DeStefano, Lauren

A **curious** tale of the in-between. by Lauren DeStefano. Bloomsbury, 2015. 224 p.: Pram Bellamy

Grades: 4 5 6 7 **Fic**
1. Girls and ghosts 2. Psychic ability 3. Loss (Psychology) 4. Girl psychics 5. Aunts 6. Fantasy mysteries
ISBN 9781619636002

"Pram's pregnant mother committed suicide, but the doctors managed to save the baby. Eleven years later, eccentric Pram talks to the dead, and her best friend is ghostly Felix. When she enters the memories of the dead, Pram learns more about her own past, and Felix's, than she bargained for. Fans of Holly Black's Doll Bones may well enjoy this creepy, character-based tale." Horn Book.

DeWoskin, Rachel

Someday we will fly. by Rachel DeWoskin. Viking, 2019. 368 p.

Grades: 7 8 9 10   **Fic**
1. 1940s 2. Jewish teenage girls 3. Immigration and emigration 4. Mother-separated children 5. Sino-Japanese Conflict, 1937-1945 6. Circus performers 7. Shanghai (China) 8. China 9. Historical fiction
ISBN 9780670014965

LC 2018018516

Sydney Taylor Book Award for Teen Readers, 2020.

Lillia, fifteen, flees Warsaw with her father and baby sister in 1940 to try to make a new start in Shanghai, China, but the conflict grows more intense as America and Japan become involved.

"DeWoskin captures the crushing destruction of war and occupation, the unfathomable resilience communities can muster through cross-cultural friendships and acts of kindness, and—the power of the performing arts to foster hope in times of struggle and desperation." Publishers Weekly.

Includes bibliographical references.

Dee, Barbara

★ **Star-crossed**. Barbara Dee. Simon & Schuster 2017 256 p.

Grades: 4 5 6   **Fic**
1. Theater 2. Questioning (Sexual or gender identity) 3. Crushes in girls 4. School plays 5. Middle schools 6. Realistic fiction 7. LGBTQIA fiction
ISBN 9781481478489

LC 2016029743

When Mattie is cast as Romeo in an eighth-grade play, she is confused to find herself increasingly attracted to Gemma, a new classmate who is playing Juliet.

"A fine choice for middle school libraries in need of accessible LG-BTQ stories, and a great option for students reading or performing Romeo and Juliet." School Library Journal

Del Negro, Janice

Passion and poison tales of shape-shifters, ghosts, and spirited women. by Janice M. Del Negro. Marshall Cavendish, 2007. 64 p.

Grades: 5 6 7 8   **Fic**
1. Women 2. Shapeshifters 3. Resourcefulness in women 4. Courage in women 5. Ghosts 6. Ghost stories 7. Gothic fiction 8. Horror
ISBN 9780761453611

LC 2007007237

"Including both original tales and retellings, this collection of seven stories . . . features diverse female protagonists facing challenges and perils—from human bullies to ghosts. More eerie than scary, the tales of bravery, revenge, grief, and redemption share a gothic sensibility. . . . The black-and-white illustrations . . . evoke bygone times." Booklist.

Delacre, Lulu

Us, in progress: short stories about young Latinos. Lulu Delacre. Harper, an imprint of HarperCollinsPublishers, 2017. 42 p.

Grades: 4 5 6 7 8   **Fic**
1. Latin Americans 2. Hispanic Americans 3. Realistic fiction 4.

Short stories
ISBN 9780062392145

A latest collection by the award-winning author of Salsa Stories includes the tales of a girl who has a surprising day of work on her father's burrito truck, two sisters who work to change one's immigration status and a Texas boy who struggles to overcome the prejudices of his Border Patrol family.

"Delacre's collection challenges existing misconceptions by giving readers an intimate and varied look into what it is like to be young and Latino in the United States today." Horn Book.

Delaney, Joseph, 1945-

The **ghost** prison. Joseph Delaney. Sourcebooks Fire, 2013. 112 p.

Grades: 4 5 6 7 8   **Fic**
1. Prisons 2. Teenage boy orphans 3. Haunted places 4. Ghosts 5. Prison guards 6. Horror
ISBN 9781402293184

LC 2013017898

Fifteen-year-old Billy guards a castle prison. But it isn't just criminals he'll be guarding—the ghosts of executed prisoners haunt the place. Provided by publisher.

A **new** darkness. Joseph Delaney. Greenwillow Books, 2014. 416 p.: New Darkness

Grades: 7 8 9 10   **Fic**
1. Apprentices 2. Monsters 3. Witches 4. Supernatural 5. Teenage boys 6. Fantasy fiction 7. Horror
ISBN 9780062334534

LC 2014011963

Although his apprenticeship was not done when John Gregory died, Tom Ward spent years learning to fight boggarts, witches, demons, and more and feels prepared to be the new county Spook, but while his youth causes many people to distrust him, Jenny is determined to be his apprentice.

"A plethora of action involving ghastly creatures, sword fights, and magic coupled with just enough backstory and description make this novel engaging enough to keep even the most reluctant reader turning pages until the end. Tom's story has a doozy of a cliff-hanger that is sure to bring teens back for more." School Library Journal.

★ **Revenge** of the witch. Joseph Delaney; illustrations by Patrick Arrasmith. Greenwillow Books, 2005. 344 p.: Last apprentice

Grades: 5 6 7 8   **Fic**
1. Boy apprentices 2. Witches 3. Revenge 4. Loneliness in boys 5. Loneliness 6. Fantasy fiction 7. Horror
ISBN 0060766182

LC 2004054003

Young Tom, the seventh son of a seventh son, starts work as an apprentice for the village spook, whose job is to protect ordinary folk from "ghouls, boggarts, and all manner of wicked beasties."

"Delaney grabs readers by the throat and gives them a good shake in a smartly crafted story. . . . This is a gristly thriller. . . . Yet the twisted horror is amply buffered by an exquisitely normal young hero, matter-of-fact prose, and a workaday normalcy." Booklist.

Dennard, Susan

Truthwitch. Susan Dennard. Tor Teen, 2016. 415 p.: The Witchlands

Grades: 8 9 10 11 12   **Fic**
1. Witches 2. Political intrigue 3. Friendship 4. Magic 5.

Imaginary empires 6. High fantasy 7. Fantasy fiction
ISBN 9780765379283

On a continent ruled by three empires, some are born with a magical skill that sets them apart from others. Safiya is a Truthwitch, able to discern truth from lie; Iseult, a Threadwitch, can see the invisible ties that bind the lives around her. Safi and Iseult want to be free to live their own lives, but war is coming to the Witchlands. With the help of a Windwitch and the hindrance of a Bloodwitch bent on revenge, the friends must fight emperors, princes, and mercenaries alike, all of whom want to capture Safi.

"A great choice for fans of fantasy adventure and strong female characters." School Library Journal.

Dessen, Sarah

Lock and key: a novel. by Sarah Dessen. Viking, 2008. 422 p.
Grades: 7 8 9 10   Fic
1. Children of alcoholics 2. Abandoned teenagers 3. Sisters 4. Emotional problems 5. Seventeen-year-old girls 6. Realistic fiction
ISBN 9780670010882

LC 2007025370

When she is abandoned by her alcoholic mother, high school senior Ruby winds up living with Cora, the sister she has not seen for ten years, and learns about Cora's new life, what makes a family, how to allow people to help her when she needs it, and that she too has something to offer others.

"The dialogue, especially between Ruby and Cora, is crisp, layered, and natural. The slow unfolding adds to an anticipatory mood. . . . Recommend this one to patient, sophisticated readers." School Library Journal.

The **moon** and more. by Sarah Dessen. Viking, 2013. 384 p.
Grades: 7 8 9 10   Fic
1. Self-discovery in teenage girls 2. Love triangles 3. Fathers and daughters 4. Documentary films -- Production and direction 5. Self-discovery 6. North Carolina 7. Teen chick lit 8. Coming-of-age stories 9. Realistic fiction
ISBN 9780670785605

LC 2012035720

During her last summer at home before leaving for college, Emaline begins a whirlwind romance with Theo, an assistant documentary filmmaker who is in town to make a movie.

"Dessen's characters behave as deliciously unpredictably as people do in real life, and just as in real life, they sometimes have to make difficult choices with not-so-predictable outcomes... Completely engaging." Kirkus.

Saint Anything. Sarah Dessen. Viking Juvenile, 2015. 417 p.
Grades: 7 8 9 10 11 12   Fic
1. Self-discovery in teenage girls 2. Family problems 3. Brothers and sisters 4. Friendship 5. Self-discovery 6. Realistic fiction
ISBN 9780451474704

LC 2014039813

Sydney's charismatic older brother, Peyton, has always been the center of attention in the family but when he is sent to jail, Sydney struggles to find her place at home and the world until she meets the Chathams, including gentle, protective Mac, who makes her feel seen for the first time.

"Once again, Dessen demonstrates her tremendous skill in evoking powerful emotions through careful, quiet prose, while delivering a satisfying romance." Publishers Weekly.

That summer. Sarah Dessen. Orchard Books, 1996. 198 p.

Grades: 7 8 9 10   Fic
1. Children of divorced parents 2. Weddings 3. Family relationships 4. Summer 5. Fifteen-year-old girls 6. Realistic fiction
ISBN 053109538X

During the summer of her divorced father's remarriage and her sister's wedding, fifteen-year-old Haven comes into her own by letting go of the myths of the past.

"Dessen adds a fresh twist to a traditional sister-of-the-bride story with her keenly observant narrative full of witty ironies. Her combination of unforgettable characters and unexpected events generates hilarity as well as warmth." Publishers Weekly.

The **truth** about forever. by Sarah Dessen. Viking, 2004. 382 p.
Grades: 7 8 9 10   Fic
1. Grief 2. Coping in teenage girls 3. Teenage romance 4. Teenage girls 5. Sixteen-year-old girls 6. Realistic fiction
ISBN 0670036390

LC 2003028298

The summer following her father's death, Macy plans to work at the library and wait for her brainy boyfriend to return from camp, but instead she goes to work at a catering business where she makes new friends and finally faces her grief.

"All of Dessen's characters . . . are fully and beautifully drawn. Their dialogue is natural and believable, and their care for one another is palpable. . . . Dessen charts Macy's navigation of grief in such an honest way it will touch every reader who meets her." School Library Journal.

What happened to goodbye. by Sarah Dessen. Viking Childrens Books, c2011. 416 p.
Grades: 8 9 10 11 12   Fic
1. Children of divorced parents 2. Identity (Psychology) 3. Self-discovery in teenage girls 4. Self-discovery 5. Moving, Household 6. Realistic fiction
ISBN 9780670012947

LC 2010041041

Following her parents' bitter divorce as she and her father move from town to town, seventeen-year-old Mclean reinvents herself at each school she attends until she is no longer sure she knows who she is or where she belongs.

"The novel nimbly weaves together familiar story lines of divorce, high-school happiness and angst, and teen-identity struggles with likable, authentic adult and teen characters and intriguing yet credible situations." Booklist.

Deuker, Carl

Golden arm. Carl Deuker. Houghton Mifflin Harcourt, 2020 368 p.
Grades: 6 7 8 9 10   Fic
1. Baseball players 2. Poverty 3. Social classes 4. Baseball 5. Brothers 6. Baseball stories 7. Sports fiction 8. Coming-of-age stories
ISBN 9780358012429

When his pitching talents land him a spot on a wealthier team where he has a chance to be drafted into the majors, a teen navigating poverty and a speech challenge struggles with leaving behind a brother who is increasingly influenced by drug gangs.

"Deuker's realistic novel pits poverty, friendship, teamwork, self-reliance, and supportive adults against wealth, privilege, overambition, and overbearing helicopter parents. Even readers who don't like baseball will be riveted to this human-interest, underdog story." Booklist

Gym candy. by Carl Deuker. Houghton Mifflin Company, c2007. 313 p.

Grades: 7 8 9 10 11 12   **Fic**

    1. High school football players 2. Steroids 3. Integrity 4. Rehabilitation centers 5. Teenage athletes 6. Washington (State) 7. Sports fiction 8. Football stories

ISBN 9780618777136

                                LC   2007012749

Groomed by his father to be a star player, football is the only thing that has ever really mattered to Mick Johnson, who works hard for a spot on the varsity team his freshman year, then tries to hold onto his edge by using steroids, despite the consequences to his health and social life.

"Deuker skillfully complements a sobering message with plenty of exciting on-field action and locker-room drama, while depicting Mick's emotional struggles with loneliness and insecurity as sensitively and realistically as his physical ones." Booklist.

Swagger. Carl Deuker. Houghton Mifflin Harcourt, 2013. 304 p.

Grades: 7 8 9 10 11 12   **Fic**

    1. Teenage basketball players 2. Sex crimes 3. Basketball coaches 4. Basketball 5. Moving to a new state 6. Sports fiction 7. Basketball stories

ISBN 9780547974590

                                LC 2012045062

High school senior point guard Jonas Dolan is on the fast track to a basketball career until an unthinkable choice puts his future on the line.

"When his family moves to Seattle, high school basketball star Jonas befriends new neighbor Levi, who plays power forward. Assistant coach Ryan Hartwell appreciates Jonas's fast-breaking style, but something about Hartwell feels wrong. Eventually his misdeeds lead to tragedy, and Jonas must find the courage to do what's right. Basketball fans will love the realistic hardwood action and the story's quick pacing." Horn Book.

Devlin, Ivy, 1972-

Low red moon. by Ivy Devlin. Bloomsbury Children's Books, 2010. 208 p.

Grades: 7 8 9 10   **Fic**

    1. Grief in teenage girls 2. Teenage werewolves 3. Shapeshifters 4. Shapeshifting 5. Werewolves 6. Paranormal romances 7. Mysteries

ISBN 9781599905105

                                LC 2010003480

Seventeen-year-old Avery can remember nothing to explain her parents' violent death in the woods where they live, but after meeting Ben, a mysterious new neighbor, she begins to believe some of the stories she has heard about creatures of the forest.

"This is an eerie and engrossing paranormal murder mystery. . . . The emotion pouring off the pages should sweep readers into this haunting story." Publishers Weekly.

DiCamillo, Kate

   ★ **Because** of Winn-Dixie. Kate DiCamillo. Candlewick Press, 2000. 182 p.

Grades: 4 5 6 7   **Fic**

    1. Dogs 2. Small town life 3. Girls and dogs 4. Ten-year-old girls 5. Children of clergy 6. Florida 7. Realistic fiction

ISBN 9781536214345

                                LC   99034260

Ten-year-old India Opal Buloni describes her first summer in the town of Naomi, Florida, and all the good things that happen to her because of her big ugly dog Winn-Dixie.

"This well-crafted, realistic, and heartwarming story will be read and reread as a new favorite deserving a long-term place on library shelves." School Library Journal.

   ★ **Beverly,** right here. Kate DiCamillo. Candlewick Press, 2019. 241 p.

Grades: 4 5 6 7 8   **Fic**

    1. 1970s 2. Runaway teenage girls 3. Resilience in girls 4. Home (Concept) 5. Fourteen-year-old girls 6. Friendship 7. Florida 8. Historical fiction 9. Coming-of-age stories

ISBN 9780763694647

Resolved to leave her home for good, a young runaway finds a job and a place to live before forming connections that alter her perspectives about life and herself.

"DiCamillo's Raymie Nightingale (2016) and Louisiana's Way Home (2018) told the stories of two of three good friends. Now it's Beverly Tapinski's turn. Beverly, 14, runs away from home: her beloved dog is dead, and her mother doesn't mind much that she's gone." Booklist.

   ★ **Flora** & Ulysses: the illuminated adventures. Kate DiCamillo; illustrated by K.G. Campbell. Candlewick Press, 2013. 336 p.

Grades: 3 4 5 6   **Fic**

    1. Girls and animals 2. Superheroes 3. Children of divorced parents 4. Comic book fans 5. Squirrels 6. Low fantasy 7. Fantasy fiction 8. Illustrated books

ISBN 9780763660406

                              LC bl2013034499

Newbery Medal, 2014.

Rescuing a squirrel after an accident involving a vacuum cleaner, comic-reading cynic Flora Belle Buckman is astonished when the squirrel, Ulysses, demonstrates astonishing powers of strength and flight after being revived.

   ★ The **magician's** elephant. Kate DiCamillo; illustrated by Yoko Tanaka. Candlewick Press, 2009. 208 p.

Grades: 4 5 6 7   **Fic**

    1. Orphans 2. Missing children 3. Elephants 4. Ten-year-old boys 5. Hope 6. Fantasy fiction

ISBN 9780763644109

                              LC 2009007359

When ten-year-old orphan Peter Augustus Duchene encounters a fortune teller in the marketplace one day and she tells him that his sister, who is presumed dead, is in fact alive, he embarks on a remarkable series of adventures as he desperately tries to find her.

"The profound and deeply affecting emotions at work in the story are buoyed up by the tale's succinct, lyrical text; gentle touches of humor; and uplifting message." Booklist.

   ★ **Raymie** Nightingale. Kate DiCamillo. Candlewick Press, 2016. 272 p.

Grades: 4 5 6 7 8   **Fic**

    1. 1970s 2. Competition in girls 3. Child-separated fathers 4. Loss (Psychology) in children 5. Competition 6. Friendship 7. Florida 8. Historical fiction

ISBN 9780763681173

"The limited third-person narration gives Raymie her distinctive voice and spot-on pre-adolescent perspective of a young girl trying to make sense of the world around her. Here DiCamillo returns—triumphantly—to her Winn-Dixie roots." Horn Book.

DiTerlizzi, Tony

The **battle** for WondLa. Tony DiTerlizzi; with illustrations by the author. Simon & Schuster Books for Young Readers, 2014. 464 p.: WondLa trilogy

Grades: 2 3 4 5   **Fic**

1. Girl adventurers 2. Human/alien encounters 3. Imaginary wars and battles 4. Preteen girls 5. Nine, Eva (Fictitious character) 6. Science fiction

ISBN 9781416983149

LC 2013035219

When all hope for a peaceful coexistence between humankind and aliens seems lost, Eva Nine, with help from an unlikely ally, tries to thwart the evil Loroc's ultimate plan for life on Orbona.

"Of particular interest is Eva's development into a young woman of unwavering compassion and courage, even in the face of betrayal, loss, and injury. DiTerlizzi's beautiful illustrations are worth the price of admission, as usual, and they do much to help the reader distinguish among the plethora of strange creatures." Booklist.

A **hero** for WondLa. Tony DiTerlizzi; with illustrations by the author. Simon & Schuster Books for Young Readers, 2012. 496 p.: WondLa trilogy

Grades: 5 6 7 8   **Fic**

1. Girl adventurers 2. Human/alien encounters 3. Disillusionment 4. Identity (Psychology) 5. Twelve-year-old girls 6. Science fiction

ISBN 9781416983125

LC 2011037031

Raised underground by a robot, twelve-year-old Eva Nine finally finds all she ever wanted in the human colony of New Attica, but something very bad is going on there and unless Eva and her friends stop it, it could mean the end of life on Orbona.

Dickens, Charles, 1812-1870

A **Christmas** carol [Lynch, ill.]. Charles Dickens; illustrated by P.J. Lynch. Candlewick Press, 2006. 160 p.

Grades: 5 6 7 8   **Fic**

1. Ghosts 2. Christmas 3. Miserliness 4. Scrooge, Ebenezer (Fictitious character) 5. Tiny Tim (Fictitious character) 6. Great Britain 7. London, England 8. Christmas stories 9. Classics

ISBN 0763631205

LC 2005058122

A miser learns the true meaning of Christmas when three ghostly visitors review his past and foretell his future.

"Lynch's watercolor-and-gouache illustrations lavishly enhance this handsome edition." School Library Journal.

Dickinson, Peter, 1927-

The **ropemaker**. Peter Dickinson. Delacorte Press, 2001. 375 p.

Grades: 7 8 9 10   **Fic**

1. Wizards 2. Magicians 3. Girls 4. Grandparents 5. Spells (Magic) 6. Coming-of-age stories 7. Fantasy fiction

ISBN 0385729219

LC 2001017422

When the magic that protects their Valley starts to fail, Tilja and her companions journey into the evil Empire to find the ancient magician Faheel, who originally cast those spells.

"The suspense does not let up until the very last pages. While on one level this tale is a fantasy, it is also a wonderful coming-of-age story." School Library Journal.

Divakaruni, Chitra Banerjee, 1956-

The **conch** bearer. by Chitra Banerjee Divakaruni. Roaring Brook Press, c2003. 265 p.: Brotherhood of the conch

Grades: 5 6 7 8   **Fic**

1. Healers 2. Shells 3. Quests 4. Twelve-year-old boys 5. Magic 6. India 7. Fantasy fiction

ISBN 0761319352

LC 2003008578

In India, a healer invites twelve-year-old Anand to join him on a quest to return a magical conch to its safe and rightful home, high in the Himalayan mountains.

"Divakaruni keeps her tale fresh and riveting." Publishers Weekly.

Doctorow, Cory

Pirate cinema. Cory Doctorow. Tor Teen, 2012. 384 p.

Grades: 7 8 9 10   **Fic**

1. Runaway teenage boys 2. Filmmakers 3. Dystopias 4. Copyright 5. Creativity 6. London, England 7. England 8. Science fiction 9. Cyber-thrillers 10. Science fiction thrillers

ISBN 9780765329080

In a dystopian, near-future Britain, sixteen-year-old Trent, obsessed with making movies on his computer, joins a group of artists and activists who are trying to fight a new bill that will criminalize even more harmless internet creativity.

Doherty, Berlie

The **girl** who saw lions. Berlie Doherty. Roaring Brook Press, 2008. 249 p.

Grades: 6 7 8 9   **Fic**

1. Adoption 2. Grief 3. AIDS (Disease) 4. Thirteen-year-old girls 5. Teenage girls 6. Tanzania 7. England

ISBN 9781596433779

LC 2007044054

In alternating voices, thirteen-year-old Rosa and her mother are trying to adopt a Tanzanian child in England, while in Tanzania, nine-year-old Abela watches her family die and her uncle illegally sends her to England, in the hopes of selling her.

"Packs in a great deal of information about the AIDS crisis in Africa, female genital mutilation, international adoptions, the foster care system, and the many challenges facing parentless children and the social workers who try to place them. Girls will love this emotionally powerful novel." Voice of Youth Advocates.

Donnelly, Jennifer

Stepsister. Jennifer Donnelly. Scholastic Press, 2019. 342 p.

Grades: 8 9 10 11 12   **Fic**

1. 18th century 2. Stepsisters 3. Options, alternatives, choices 4. Beauty 5. Ugliness 6. Determination (Personal quality) 7. France 8. Fairy tale and folklore-inspired fiction 9. Historical fantasy 10. Fantasy fiction

ISBN 9781338268461

LC 2019003322

Isabelle is one of Cinderella's ugly stepsisters, who cut off their toes in an attempt to fit into the glass slipper; but there is more to her story than a maimed foot, for the Marquis de la Chance is about to offer her a choice and the opportunity to change her fate—there will be blood and danger, but also the possibility of redemption and triumph, and most of all the chance to find her true self.

"Printz Honor Book author Donnelly offers up a stunningly focused story that rips into the heart of a familiar fairy tale. The gorgeous prose and the fairy tale themes have obvious appeal, but the real strengths here are the depth of character across the board; the examination of the cost of beauty in a world that reveres it; and Isabelle herself, a shattered but not unredeemable girl with a warrior's heart." Booklist.

Donovan, John, 1928-

I'll get there, it better be worth the trip: a novel.. Harper & Row, 1969. 189 p.

Grades: 7 8 9 10 11   **Fic**
1. Thirteen-year-old boys 2. Teenage boys 3. Teenage children of alcoholics 4. Moving, Household 5. Change (Psychology) 6. New York City 7. LGBTQIA fiction 8. Realistic fiction

LC 69015539

Thirteen-year-old Davy has a difficult time adjusting to his grandmother's death and life in New York with his erratic mother.

"Donovan's novel is startlingly outspoken and honest in its presentation of a young teen questioning his sexuality. . . . Such is the author's skill that the reader knows this young man's journey of self-discovery will get him to his there, wherever it may be. This welcome fortieth-anniversary edition of a YA classic is an essential purchase for all libraries." Voice of Youth Advocates.

Donwerth-Chikamatsu, Annie

Beyond me. Annie Donwerth-Chikamatsu. Athenium Books for Young Readers, 2020 304 p.

Grades: 4 5 6 7   **Fic**
1. Multiracial girls 2. Natural disasters 3. Kindness 4. Anxiety 5. Life change events 6. Japan 7. Novels in verse 8. Realistic fiction
ISBN 9781481437899

This novel-in-verse examines the aftershocks of the earthquake and tsunami that devastated Japan in 2011 through the eyes of a young girl who learns that even the smallest kindness can make a difference. Excerpted from publisher description.

Dooley, Sarah

Free verse. Sarah Dooley. Penguin Group USA, 2016. 352 p.
Grades: 5 6 7 8   **Fic**
1. Brothers -- Death 2. Anger in teenage girls 3. Families 4. Teenage poets 5. Foster care 6. West Virginia 7. Realistic fiction
ISBN 9780399165030

When her brother dies in a fire, Sasha Harless has no one left, and nowhere to turn. After her father died in the mines and her mother ran off, he was her last caretaker. They'd always dreamed of leaving Caboose, West Virginia together someday, but instead she's in foster care, feeling more stuck and broken than ever. But then Sasha discovers family she didn't know she had, and learns that life, like poetry, doesn't always take the form you intend.

"Dooley winningly combines engaging plot twists and rich character development with the introspective and thematic power of poetry: not to be missed." Kirkus.

Dorisi-Winget, Dianna

A **million** ways home. Dianna Dorisi Winget. Scholastic Press, 2014. 272 p.
Grades: 4 5 6 7   **Fic**
1. Child murder witnesses 2. Girls and dogs 3. Girl orphans 4. German shepherd dog 5. Dogs 6. Washington (State) 7. Spokane County (Wash)
ISBN 9780545667067

LC 2014005037

When her grandmother and guardian suffers a stroke, twelve-year-old Poppy Parker's life turns upside down—but when she witnesses a murder and has to go into witness protection with Detective Brannigan's mother it becomes hard to believe she will ever find a way home, let alone save Gunner, a beautiful German shepherd with an uncertain future.

"Readers will cheer on this sassy, relatable, pre-teen as they get to know her. Most of her trials are beyond Poppy's years and certainly out of her control. Even reluctant readers will enjoy the journey Poppy takes to find a new, perhaps unexpected, version of family, friendship, and home." Library Media Connection.

Dorris, Michael

Morning Girl. Michael Dorris. Hyperion Books for Children, c1992. 74 p.
Grades: 4 5 6 7   **Fic**
1. Brothers and sisters 2. Taino Indians 3. Indians of the West Indies 4. Taino girls 5. Twelve-year-old girls 6. Western Hemisphere 7. Historical fiction
ISBN 9781562822842

LC 92052989

Scott O'Dell Historical Fiction Award, 1993.

Morning Girl, a Taino child who loves the day, and her younger brother Star Boy, who loves the night, take turns describing their life on an island in pre-Columbian America; in Morning Girl's last narrative, she witnesses the arrival of the first Europeans to her world.

"The author uses a lyrical, yet easy-to-follow, style to place these compelling characters in historical context. . . . Dorris does a superb job of showing that family dynamics are complicated, regardless of time and place. . . . A touching glimpse into the humanity that connects us all." Horn Book.

Sees Behind Trees. Michael Dorris. Hyperion Books for Children, c1996. 104 p.
Grades: 4 5 6 7   **Fic**
1. Native American boys 2. Blindness 3. Quests 4. Native American boys with visual disabilities 5. Native American manhood (Psychology)
ISBN 0786802243

LC 96015859

A Native American boy with a special gift to "see" beyond his poor eyesight journeys with an old warrior to a land of mystery and beauty.

"Set in sixteenth-century America, this richly imagined and gorgeously written rite-of-passage story has the gravity of legend. Moreover, it has buoyant humor and the immediacy of a compelling story that is peopled with multidimensional characters." Booklist.

Dowd, Siobhan

Bog child. Siobhan Dowd. David Fickling Books, c2008. 321 p.
Grades: 8 9 10 11 12   **Fic**
1. Provisional Irish Republican Army. 2. 1980s 3. Bog bodies 4. Smuggling 5. Eighteen-year-old men 6. Decision-making (Ethics) 7. Extortion 8. Northern Ireland 9. Historical fiction
ISBN 9780385751698

LC 2008002998

Carnegie Medal, 2009.

In 1981, the height of Ireland's "Troubles," eighteen-year-old Fergus is distracted from his upcoming A-level exams by his imprisoned brother's hunger strike, the stress of being a courier for Sinn Fein, and dreams of a murdered girl whose body he discovered in a bog.

"Dowd raises questions about moral choices within a compelling plot that is full of surprises, powerfully bringing home the impact of political conflict on innocent bystanders." Publishers Weekly.

★ The **London** Eye mystery. by Siobhan Dowd. David Fickling Books, 2008. 336 p.

Grades: 5 6 7 8 **Fic**

1. London Eye (London, England) 2. Missing boys 3. Children with Asperger's syndrome 4. Cooperation in children 5. Cooperation 6. Asperger's syndrome 7. London, England 8. England 9. Mysteries
ISBN 9780375849763

LC 2007015119

When Ted and Kat's cousin Salim disappears from the London Eye ferris wheel, the two siblings must work together—Ted with his brain that is "wired differently" and impatient Kat—to try to solve the mystery of what happened to Salim.

"Everything rings true here, the family relationships, the quirky connections of Ted's mental circuitry, and . . . the mystery. . . . A page turner with heft." Booklist.

Dowell, Frances O'Roark

The **class**. Frances O'Roark Dowell. Atheneum Books for Young Readers, 2019. 320 p.

Grades: 4 5 6 7 8 **Fic**

1. Middle school students 2. Interpersonal relations 3. Middle schools 4. Middle school teachers 5. Sixth-graders 6. Realistic fiction
ISBN 9781481481793

A sixth-grade class comes together to support a classmate in need, each of them giving their own perspective on the goings on. Provided by publisher.

"Read-aloud possibilities are endless for this fun mystery, which is a must for every sixth-grade classroom library." Booklist.

Dovey Coe. Atheneum Books for Young Readers, 2000. 181 p.

Grades: 5 6 7 8 **Fic**

1. Brothers and sisters 2. Mountain life 3. Murder 4. Girl murder suspects 5. Boys who are deaf 6. North Carolina 7. Historical mysteries
ISBN 0689831749

LC 99046870

When accused of murder in her North Carolina mountain town in 1928, Dovey Coe, a strong-willed twelve-year-old girl, comes to a new understanding of others, including her deaf brother.

"Dowell has created a memorable character in Dovey, quick-witted and honest to a fault. . . . This is a delightful book, thoughtful and full of substance." Booklist.

Falling in. Frances O'Roark Dowell. Atheneum Books for Young Readers, 2010. 272 p.

Grades: 4 5 6 7 **Fic**

1. Grandmothers 2. Misfits (Persons) 3. Misunderstanding 4. Middle school students 5. Parallel universes 6. Gateway fantasy 7. Fantasy fiction
ISBN 9781416950325

LC 2009010412

Middle-schooler Isabelle Bean follows a mouse's squeak into a closet and falls into a parallel universe where the children believe she is the witch they have feared for years, finally come to devour them.

"This perfectly paced story has enough realistic elements to appeal even to nonfantasy readers." Booklist.

The **kind** of friends we used to be. Frances O'Roark Dowell. Atheneum Books for Young Readers, 2009. 240 p.: Secret language of girls trilogy

Grades: 5 6 7 8 **Fic**

1. Preteen girls 2. Friendship 3. Change (Psychology) 4. Identity (Psychology) 5. Best friends 6. Realistic fiction
ISBN 9781416950318

LC 2008022245

Twelve-year-olds Kate and Marylin, friends since preschool, draw further apart as Marylin becomes involved in student government and cheerleading, while Kate wants to play guitar and write songs, and both develop unlikely friendships with other girls and boys.

"Dowell gets middle-school dynamics exactly right, and while her empathetic portraits of Kate and Marylin are genuine and heartfelt, even secondary characters are memorable. A realistic and humorous look at the trials and tribulations of growing up and growing independent." School Library Journal.

The **second** life of Abigail Walker. Frances O'Roark Dowell. Atheneum Books for Young Readers, 2012. 240 p.

Grades: 4 5 6 7 **Fic**

1. Overweight girls 2. Self-confidence in girls 3. Bullying and bullies 4. Self-confidence 5. Friendship
ISBN 9781442405936

LC 2012010646

Bullied by two mean girls in her sixth-grade class, a lonely, plump girl gains self-confidence and makes new friends after a mysterious fox gently bites her.

Shooting the moon. Frances O'Roark Dowell. Atheneum Books for Young Readers, 2008. 176 p.

Grades: 4 5 6 7 **Fic**

1. United States. Army 2. Children of military personnel 3. Brothers and sisters 4. War 5. Photographs 6. Twelve-year-old girls 7. United States 8. Coming-of-age stories 9. Historical fiction
ISBN 9781416926900

LC 2006100347

When her brother is sent to fight in Vietnam, twelve-year-old Jamie begins to reconsider the Army world that she has grown up in.

"The clear, well-paced first-person prose is perfectly matched to this novel's spare setting and restrained plot. . . . This [is a] thoughtful and satisfying story. . . . Readers will find beauty in its resolution, and will leave this eloquent heroine reluctantly." School Library Journal.

Downer, Ann, 1960-

Hatching magic. Ann Downer. Atheneum Books for Young Readers, c2003. 242 p.

Grades: 4 5 6 7 **Fic**

1. 21st century 2. Eleven-year-old girls 3. Wizards 4. Dragons 5. Girls and dragons 6. Dragon babies 7. Boston, Massachusetts 8. Fantasy fiction
ISBN 0689834004

LC 00056570

When a thirteenth-century wizard confronts twenty-first century Boston while seeking his pet dragon, he is followed by a rival wizard and a very unhappy demon, but eleven-year-old Theodora Oglethorpe may hold the secret to setting everything right.

"With likable characters, and laced with plenty of humor and adventure, Downer's fantasy will have solid appeal for young genre fans." Booklist.

Downham, Jenny

Before I die. Jenny Downham. David Fickling Books, c2007. 326 p.

Grades: 8 9 10 11 12 **Fic**
1. Teenagers with terminal illnesses 2. Teenage girls with leukemia 3. Lists 4. Leukemia 5. Families 6. England 7. Realistic fiction
ISBN 9780385751551

LC 2007020284

A terminally ill teenaged girl makes and carries out a list of things to do before she dies.

"Downham holds nothing back in her wrenchingly and exceptionally vibrant story." Publishers Weekly.

Dowswell, Paul

Auslander. Paul Dowswell. Bloomsbury, 2009. 295 p.

Grades: 7 8 9 10 **Fic**
1. Second World War era (1939-1945) 2. 1940s 3. Boy orphans 4. Escapes 5. Courage 6. Identity (Psychology) 7. World War II -- Children 8. Germany 9. Historical fiction 10. Thrillers and suspense
ISBN 9780747589099

"The characters are rich and nuanced; . . . the action is swift and suspenseful; and the juxtaposition of wartime nobility and wartime cruelty is timeless." Horn Book.

Doyle, Marissa

Bewitching season. Marissa Doyle. Henry Holt, 2008. 352 p.: Leland sisters

Grades: 7 8 9 10 **Fic**
1. Georgian era (1714-1837) 2. 1830s 3. 19th century 4. Seventeen-year-old girls 5. Missing persons 6. Governesses 7. Seventeen-year-olds 8. Teenagers 9. London, England 10. Great Britain 11. Historical fantasy
ISBN 9780805082517

LC 2007027317

In 1837, as seventeen-year-old twins, Persephone and Penelope, are starting their first London Season they find that their beloved governess, who has taught them everything they know about magic, has disappeared.

"Doyle takes as much care with characters . . . as with story details. This [is a] delightful mlange of genres." Booklist.

Doyle, Roddy, 1958-

A **greyhound** of a girl. Roddy Doyle. Amulet Books, 2012. 192 p.

Grades: 7 8 9 10 11 12 **Fic**
1. Girls and ghosts 2. Grandmothers 3. Death 4. Last days 5. Mothers and daughters 6. Dublin, Ireland 7. Ireland 8. Fantasy fiction
ISBN 9781419701689

LC 2011042200

Mary O'Hara is a sharp and cheeky twelve-year-old Dublin schoolgirl who is bravely facing the fact that her beloved Gran is dying. But Gran can't let go of life, and when a mysterious young woman turns up in Mary's street with a message for her Gran, Mary gets pulled into an unlikely adventure. Provided by publisher.

Draper, Sharon M. (Sharon Mills)

The **battle** of Jericho. Sharon M. Draper. Atheneum Books for Young Readers, c2003. 304 p.: Jericho trilogy

Grades: 7 8 9 10 **Fic**
1. Initiations (into trades, societies, etc) 2. Friends' death 3. High school juniors 4. Sixteen-year-old boys 5. Cousins 6. Ohio 7. African American fiction
ISBN 0689842325

LC 2002008612

A high school junior and his cousin suffer the ramifications of joining what seems to be a "reputable" school club.

"This title is a compelling read that drives home important lessons about making choices." School Library Journal.

Blended. Sharon M. Draper. Atheneum Books for Young Readers, 2018. 320 p.

Grades: 4 5 6 7 **Fic**
1. Blended families 2. Multiracial girls 3. Race relations 4. Divorce 5. Families 6. Ohio 7. Realistic fiction 8. Coming-of-age stories 9. African American fiction
ISBN 9781442495005

LC 2018025777

Piano-prodigy Isabella, eleven, whose Black father and white mother struggle to share custody, never feels whole, especially as racial tensions affect her school, her parents' both become engaged, and she and her stepbrother are stopped by police.

Double dutch. Sharon M. Draper. Atheneum Books for Young Readers, c2002. 183 p.

Grades: 6 7 8 9 **Fic**
1. Jumping rope -- Tournaments 2. Girls with dyslexia 3. African American girls 4. Middle schools 5. Eighth-grade girls 6. Cincinnati, Ohio 7. African American fiction
ISBN 0689842309

LC 00050247

Three eighth-grade friends, preparing for the International Double Dutch Championship jump rope competition in their home town of Cincinnati, Ohio, cope with Randy's missing father, Delia's inability to read, and Yo Yo's encounter with the class bullies.

"Teens will like the high-spirited, authentic dialogue . . . the honest look at tough issues, and the team workout scenes that show how sports can transform young lives." Booklist.

Fire from the rock. Sharon M. Draper. Dutton Children's Books, 2007. 176 p.

Grades: 6 7 8 9 **Fic**
1. 1950s 2. African American teenage girls 3. School integration 4. Race relations 5. African Americans 6. African American teenagers 7. Little Rock, Arkansas 8. Arkansas
ISBN 9780525477204

LC 2006102952

In 1957, Sylvia Patterson's life—that of a normal African American teenager—is disrupted by the impending integration of Little Rock's Central High when she is selected to be one of the first black students to attend the previously all white school. Includes author's note and related websites.

"This historical fiction novel is a must have. It keeps the reader engaged with vivid depictions of a time that most young people can only imagine." Voice of Youth Advocates.

Just another hero. Sharon M. Draper. Atheneum Books for Young Readers, 2009. 288 p.: Jericho trilogy

Grades: 7 8 9 10   **Fic**

1. School shootings 2. African American teenagers 3. High school seniors 4. Violence in schools 5. Schools 6. Ohio 7. Coming-of-age stories 8. Realistic fiction
ISBN 9781416907008

LC 2008030961

As Kofi, Arielle, Dana, November, and Jericho face personal challenges during their last year of high school, a misunderstood student brings a gun to class and demands to be taken seriously.

"The author presents a timeless theme in a well-crafted, highly readable story." Voice of Youth Advocates.

November blues. Sharon Draper. Atheneum Books for Young Readers, 2007. 320 p.: Jericho trilogy

Grades: 8 9 10 11 12   **Fic**

1. African American teenagers 2. Pregnant teenagers 3. Mothers and daughters 4. Pregnancy 5. High schools 6. Ohio 7. Realistic fiction 8. African American fiction
ISBN 9781416906988

LC 2006101343

A teenaged boy's death in a hazing accident has lasting effects on his pregnant girlfriend and his guilt-ridden cousin, who gives up a promising music career to play football during his senior year in high school.

"Urban teens often ask, 'Where are the books about us, Miss?' and with this novel Draper has . . . given them something meaty and meaningful to read." School Library Journal.

★ **Out** of my mind. Sharon M. Draper. Atheneum Books for Young Readers, 2010. 224 p.

Grades: 5 6 7 8   **Fic**

1. Girls with disabilities 2. Cerebral palsy 3. Photographic memory 4. People with disabilities 5. Communication 6. Realistic fiction 7. African American fiction
ISBN 9781416971702

LC 2009018404

A brilliant, impatient fifth-grader with cerebral palsy discovers a technological device that will allow her to speak for the first time.

"Fifth-grader Melody has cerebral palsy, a condition that affects her body but not her mind. Although she is unable to walk, talk, or feed or care for herself, she can read, think, and feel. A brilliant person is trapped inside her body, determined to make her mark in the world despite her physical limitations. . . . Told in Melody's voice, this highly readable, compelling novel quickly establishes her determination and intelligence and the almost insurmountable challenges she faces. . . . Uplifting and upsetting." Booklist.

★ **Stella** by starlight. Sharon Draper. Atheneum Books for Young Readers, [2015] 288 p.

Grades: 4 5 6 7 8   **Fic**

1. Ku Klux Klan. 2. Depression era (1929-1941) 3. 1930s 4. African American girls 5. Segregation 6. Prejudice 7. Civil rights 8. African Americans 9. North Carolina 10. Historical fiction 11. African American fiction
ISBN 9781442494978

LC 2014038728

When a burning cross set by the Klan causes panic and fear in 1932 Bumblebee, North Carolina, fifth-grader Stella must face prejudice and find the strength to demand change in her segregated town.

"Coretta Scott King Award winner Draper draws inspiration from her grandmother's journal to tell the absorbing story of a young girl growing up in Depression-era, segregated North Carolina...This is an engrossing historical fiction novel with an amiable and humble heroine who does not recognize her own bravery or the power of her words. She provides inspiration not only to her fellow characters but also to readers who will relate to her and her situation. Storytelling at its finest." School Library Journal.

DuPrau, Jeanne

The **city** of Ember. Jeanne DuPrau. Random House, c2003. 270 p.: Books of Ember

Grades: 5 6 7 8   **Fic**

1. Post-apocalypse 2. Resourcefulness in children 3. Underground areas 4. Dystopias 5. Survival 6. Dystopian fiction 7. Science fiction 8. STEM fiction
ISBN 0375822739

LC 2002010239

In the year 241, twelve-year-old Lina trades jobs on Assignment Day to be a Messenger to run to new places in her decaying but beloved city, perhaps even to glimpse Unknown Regions.

"The writing and storytelling are agreeably spare and remarkably suspenseful." Horn Book.

The **diamond** of Darkhold. Jeanne DuPrau. Random House Children's Books, c2008. 285 p.: Books of Ember

Grades: 5 6 7 8   **Fic**

1. Post-apocalypse 2. Dystopias 3. Underground areas 4. Diamonds 5. Survival 6. Science fiction
ISBN 9780375955716

LC 2007047929

When a roamer trades them an ancient book with only a few pages remaining, Lina and Doon return to Ember to seek the machine the book seems to describe in hopes that it will get their new community, Sparks, through the winter.

"A solid and satisfying conclusion to the Ember Saga, set in a post-disaster future." School Library Journal.

The **people** of Sparks. by Jeanne DuPrau. Random House, c2004. 338 p.: Books of Ember

Grades: 5 6 7 8   **Fic**

1. Post-apocalypse 2. Refugees 3. Social conflict 4. Dystopias 5. Sabotage 6. Science fiction
ISBN 0375828249

LC 2003020760

Having escaped to the Unknown Regions, Lina and the others seek help from the village people of Sparks.

"DuPrau clearly explores themes of nonviolence and when to stand up for oneself. The text smoothly involves new readers and fans of the first story, creating a range of three-dimensional characters." Booklist.

The **prophet** of Yonwood. Jeanne DuPrau. Random House, 2006. 289 p.: Books of Ember

Grades: 5 6 7 8   **Fic**

1. Prophets 2. Brainwashing 3. End of the world 4. Prophecies 5. Good and evil 6. North Carolina 7. Science fiction
ISBN 0375875263

LC 2005022423

While visiting the small town of Yonwood, North Carolina, eleven-year-old Nickie makes some decisions about how to identify both good and evil when she witnesses the townspeople's reactions to the apocalyptic visions of one of their neighbors.

"This novel has a great deal of immediacy in light of current world events. It sharply brings home the idea of people blindly following a belief without questioning it." School Library Journal.

Duane, Diane

So you want to be a wizard. Diane Duane. Harcourt Brace, 1996, copyright 1983. 369 p.: Young wizards

Grades: 6 7 8 9 10   **Fic**
1. Teenage wizards 2. Good and evil 3. Bullying and bullies 4. Transformations (Magic) 5. Teenage girls 6. Fantasy fiction
ISBN 0152012397

LC 95-33451

Thirteen-year-old Nita, tormented by a gang of bullies because she won't fight back, finds the help she needs in a library book on wizardry which guides her into another dimension.

Duble, Kathleen Benner

The **sacrifice**. Kathleen Benner Duble. Margaret K. McElderry Books, c2005. 211 p.

Grades: 6 7 8 9   **Fic**
1. Colonial America (1600-1775) 2. 17th century 3. Girls 4. Mothers 5. Mothers and daughters 6. Sisters 7. Child prisoners 8. Andover, Massachusetts 9. Salem, Massachusetts 10. Historical fiction
ISBN 0689876505

LC 2004018355

Two sisters, aged ten and twelve, are accused of witchcraft in Andover, Massachusetts, in 1692 and await trial in a miserable prison while their mother desperately searches for some way to obtain their freedom.

"Well written with accessible language, this book will appeal to a wide range of readers." School Library Journal.

Includes bibliographical references (p. 211).

Duey, Kathleen

Sacred scars. Kathleen Duey; illustrated by Sheila Rayyan. Atheneum Books for Young Readers, 2009. 560 p.: Resurrection of magic

Grades: 7 8 9 10   **Fic**
1. Wizards 2. Loyalty 3. Schools 4. Magic 5. Magicians 6. Fantasy fiction
ISBN 9780689840951

LC 2008056044

In alternate chapters, Sadima works to free captive boys forced to copy documents in the caverns of Limori, and Hahp makes a pact with the remaining students of a wizards' academy in hopes that all will survive their training, as both learn valuable lessons about loyalty.

"The text so successfully portrays Hahp's experience in this grueling, cold-blooded wizard academy—isolation,, starvation, abuse and constant, unsolvable puzzles—that readers may absorb his strain, confusion and desolation themselves. . . . Absorbing and unwaveringly suspenseful." Kirkus.

Skin hunger. by Kathleen Duey. Atheneum Books for Young Readers, 2007. 368 p.: Resurrection of magic

Grades: 7 8 9 10   **Fic**
1. Hunger 2. Punishment 3. Magic -- Study and teaching 4. Fathers -- Death 5. Magicians 6. Fantasy fiction
ISBN 9780689840937

LC 2006034819

In alternate chapters, Sadima travels from her farm home to the city and becomes assistant to a heartless man who is trying to restore knowledge of magic to the world, and a group of boys fights to survive in the academy that has resulted from his efforts.

"This is a compelling new fantasy. . . . Duey sweeps readers up in the page-turning excitement." Horn Book.

Dumas, Firoozeh

It ain't so awful, falafel. Firoozeh Dumas. Clarion Books/ Houghton Mifflin Harcourt, 2016 224 p.

Grades: 4 5 6 7   **Fic**
1. 1970s 2. Iranian Americans 3. Racism 4. Iran Hostage Crisis, 1979-1981 5. Immigrant families 6. Eleven-year-old girls 7. Southern California 8. Historical fiction
ISBN 9780544612310

"On her own journey to maturity, Cindy deftly guides young readers through Iran's complicated realities in this fresh take on the immigrant experience—authentic, funny, and moving from beginning to end." Kirkus.

Dumon Tak, Bibi

Soldier bear. by Bibi Dumon Tak; illustrated by Philip Hopman; translated by Laura Watkinson. Eerdmans Books for Young Readers, 2011. 145 p.

Grades: 4 5 6 7   **Fic**
1. Second World War era (1939-1945) 2. Bears 3. Soldiers 4. Mascots 5. Brown bear 6. World War II 7. Poland 8. Iran 9. Historical fiction
ISBN 9780802853752

LC 2011013963

Mildred L. Batchelder Award, 2012.

An orphaned Syrian brown bear cub is adopted by Polish soldiers during World War II and serves for five years as their mischievous mascot in Iran and Italy. Based on a true story.

"This is smoothly translated and engagingly illustrated with sketches and helpful maps. Funny, fresh and heartwarming." Kirkus.

Duncan, Lois, 1934-2016

I know what you did last summer. Lois Duncan. Little, 1973. 199 p.

Grades: 7 8 9 10 11 12   **Fic**
1. Revenge 2. Accidents 3. Hit-and-run drivers 4. Traffic accidents 5. Teenagers 6. Horror 7. Classics
ISBN 0316195464

LC 73008829

Four teenagers who have desperately tried to conceal their responsibility for a hit-and-run accident are pursued by a mystery person seeking revenge.

"This book has vivid characterization, good balance, and the boding sense of impending danger that adds excitement to the best mystery stories." Bulletin of the Center for Children's Books.

Killing Mr. Griffin. Lois Duncan. Little, Brown, 1978. 243 p.

Grades: 7 8 9 10   **Fic**
1. High school students 2. Teachers 3. Death 4. Teenagers 5. High school teachers 6. Thrillers and suspense
ISBN 0316195499

LC 77027658

A teenager casually suggests playing a cruel trick on the English teacher, but did he intend it to end with murder?

"The author's skillful plotting builds layers of tension that draws readers into the eye of the conflict. The ending is nicely handled in a manner which provides relief without removing any of the chilling implications." School Library Journal.

Locked in time. Lois Duncan. Dell, 1986, c1985. 210 p.

Grades: 7 8 9 10   **Fic**
1. Plantations 2. Blended families 3. Haunted houses 4. Seventeen-year-old girls 5. Teenage girls 6. Louisiana 7. Thrillers

and suspense
ISBN 9780440949428

LC 85000023

Nore arrives at her stepmother's Louisiana plantation to find her new family odd and an aura of evil and mystery about the place.

"The writing style is smooth, the characters strongly developed, and the plot, which has excellent pace and momentum, is an adroit blending of fantasy and realism." Bulletin of the Center for Children's Books.

Stranger with my face. Lois Duncan. Dell, 1982, c1981. 235 p.

Grades: 7 8 9 10   **Fic**
1. Seventeen-year-old girls 2. Paranormal phenomena 3. Astral projection 4. Teenage girls 5. Twins 6. Supernatural mysteries
ISBN 9780440983569

A seventeen-year-old senses she is being spied on and probably impersonated, but when she discovers what actually is occurring, it is more unbelievable than she ever imagined.

"The ghostly Lia is deliciously evil; the idea of astral projection—Lia's method of travel—is novel; the island setting is vivid; and the relationships among the young people are realistic in the smoothly written supernatural tale." Horn Book.

The **third** eye. Lois Duncan Little, Brown, 1984. 220 p.
Grades: 7 8 9   **Fic**
1. Missing children 2. Teenage psychics 3. Extrasensory perception 4. Psychics 5. Teenage detectives 6. Thrillers and suspense
ISBN 0316195537

LC 83026777

High school senior Karen, who worries that her psychic powers will make her seem different from other people, is frightened at first when a young policeman asks her to use her gift to help the police locate missing children.

Dunkle, Clare B.

The **sky** inside. Clare B. Dunkle. Atheneum Books for Young Readers, c2008. 229 p.
Grades: 6 7 8 9   **Fic**
1. Dystopias 2. Suburban life 3. Gifted children 4. Brothers and sisters 5. Missing children 6. Science fiction
ISBN 1416924221

LC bl2008006142

After the disappearance of his sister, Cassie, and other children who ask questions about their carefully choreographed life in a domed suburb cut off from the outside world, Martin and his intelligent dog investigate.

"Dunkle surrounds her protagonists with an enthralling range of settings, a memorable cast of characters. . . . Fans of the author will . . . recognize her evocative storytelling and intricate plotting." Bulletin of the Center for Children's Books.

Dunlap, Susanne Emily

The **musician's** daughter. by Susanne Dunlap. Bloomsbury Children's Books, 2009. 304 p.
Grades: 8 9 10 11 12   **Fic**
1. Haydn, Franz Joseph, 1732-1809 2. 18th century 3. Musicians 4. Murder 5. Fifteen-year-old girls 6. Teenage girls 7. Father-separated teenage girls 8. Vienna, Austria 9. Austria 10. Historical mysteries
ISBN 9781599903323

LC 2008030307

In eighteenth-century Vienna, Austria, fifteen-year-old Theresa seeks a way to help her mother and brother financially while investigat-

ing the murder of her father, a renowned violinist in Haydn's orchestra at the court of Prince Esterhazy, after his body is found near a gypsy camp.

"Dunlap skillfully builds suspense until the final page. . . . Readers will root for courageous Theresa through the exciting intrigue even as they absorb deeper messages about music and art's power to lift souls and inspire change." Booklist.

Dunmore, Helen, 1952-2017

The **deep**. Helen Dunmore; [edited by] Rosemary Brosnan. HarperCollins, 2009. 336 p.: Ingo chronicles
Grades: 6 7 8 9   **Fic**
1. Mermaids 2. Mermen 3. Brothers and sisters 4. Parent and child 5. Magic 6. Cornwall, England 7. Fantasy fiction
ISBN 9780060818586

LC 2008928250

When the ferocious shape-shifting Kraken awakes after thousands of years and threatens the Mer, Sapphire agrees to help them by going with her brother Conor and their friend Faro into the Deep to lull the monster back to sleep.

"The author evokes setting well, and her descriptions of the sea world are lovely. She writes knowledgably about the sperm whale." Voice of Youth Advocates.

Ingo. Helen Dunmore. Harper Collins, 2006. 336 p.: Ingo chronicles
Grades: 6 7 8 9   **Fic**
1. Brothers and sisters 2. Parent and child 3. Mermaids 4. Mermen 5. Divers 6. Cornwall, England 7. England 8. Fantasy fiction
ISBN 0060818522

LC 2005019079

As they search for their missing father near their Cornwall home, Sapphy and her brother Conor learn about their family's connection to the domains of air and of water.

"Strong character development combines with an engaging plot and magical elements to make this a fine choice for fantasy readers, who will look forward to the next installments in this planned trilogy." School Library Journal.

The **tide** knot. Helen Dunmore. Harper Collins Children's, 2006. 336 p.: Ingo chronicles
Grades: 6 7 8 9   **Fic**
1. Brothers and sisters 2. Parent and child 3. Missing persons 4. Mermaids 5. Mermen 6. Cornwall, England 7. England 8. Fantasy fiction
ISBN 9780007204892

"Supporting the brightly adventurous plot are believably flawed and conflicted characters." Horn Book.

Durbin, William, 1951-

The **broken** blade. William Durbin. Delacorte Press, 1997. 163 p.
Grades: 5 6 7 8   **Fic**
1. Voyageurs 2. Fathers and sons 3. Fur industry and trade 4. French-Canadian teenage boys 5. Thirteen-year-old boys 6. Canada 7. Historical fiction 8. Coming-of-age stories
ISBN 0385322240

LC 9622114

In 1800, a teenage boy from Montreal must replace his injured father as a voyageur.

"This look at the early nineteenth-century Canadian fur trade should appeal to reluctant readers as well as adventure buffs, and it may be a welcome suggestion for middle-school historical fiction reports." Bulletin of the Center for Children's Books.

Durham, Paul (Paul Joseph), 1972-

Fork-tongue charmers. Paul Durham; illustrations by Pétur Antonsson. Harper, an imprint of HarperCollinsPublishers, [2015] 304 p.: Luck Uglies trilogy

Grades: 4 5 6 7 8　　　　　　　　　　　　　　**Fic**
1. Monsters 2. Secret societies 3. Islands 4. Family secrets 5. Adventure 6. Fantasy fiction
ISBN 9780062271532

LC 2014038648

When Rye O'Chanter is declared an outlaw from her own village, she finds herself stuck on a strange remote island. But the island comes to feel much less remote when the battle over the future of the Luck Uglies moves to its shores. Provided by publisher.

"There is not a single dull moment in this story, which packs in as many clever twists and fully fleshed characters as the first book. And the writing remains a total delight: witty, richly layered, and capable of creating a world as real as this one. A bittersweet ending assures the reader that Rye's adventures are not over yet." Booklist.

The **Luck** Uglies. Paul Durham; illustrations by Petur Antonsson. Harper, an imprint of HarperCollinsPublishers, 2014. 304 p.: Luck Uglies trilogy

Grades: 4 5 6 7 8　　　　　　　　　　　　　　**Fic**
1. Monsters 2. Secret societies 3. Adventure 4. Friendship 5. Villages 6. Fantasy fiction
ISBN 9780062271501

LC 2013047720

Eleven-year-old Rye O'Chanter and her two friends delve into the secret lore of their village when mysterious creatures of legend reappear on the night of the Black Moon, leading them to the notorious secret society, the Luck Uglies.

"Rye O'Chanter and her friends Quinn and Folly live in Drowning, which is ruled by the tyrannical Earl Longchance, who bans women from reading. When the earl does nothing to protect the villagers from marauding monsters, Drowning's only hope is the Luck Uglies, a notorious outlaw gang—that may or may not exist. Durham's fast-paced narrative and clever characters enhance this humorous and engaging tale." Horn Book.

Durst, Sarah Beth

The **girl** who could not dream. by Sarah Beth Durst. 304 p.

Grades: 4 5 6 7　　　　　　　　　　　　　　**Fic**
1. Dreams 2. Monsters 3. Parent-separated girls 4. Rescues 5. Missing persons 6. Fantasy fiction
ISBN 9780544464971

LC 2015001324

When the secret shop below her parents' bookstore, where dreams are bought and sold, is robbed and her parents go missing, Sophie must unravel the truth with the help of her best friend, a wisecracking and fanatically loyal monster, to save them.

"Sophie's parents run a secret shop beneath their bookstore selling dreams. One night Sophie, who can't dream, steals one and discovers that she has the dangerous power to bring dream-creatures into the waking world. Sophie's dream-friends Monster and the delightfully arrogant unicorn Glitterhoof keep the story merry with their precocious quips, but the adventure does take some turns through dark and perilous territory." Horn Book.

Ice. Sarah Beth Durst. Margaret K. McElderry Books, c2009. 308 p.

Grades: 7 8 9 10　　　　　　　　　　　　　　**Fic**
1. Mother-separated teenage girls 2. Shapeshifters 3. Polar bear 4. Rescues 5. Imprisonment 6. Arctic regions 7. Fantasy fiction 8. Fairy tale and folklore-inspired fiction
ISBN 9781416986430

LC 2009008618

A modern-day retelling of "East o' the Sun, West o' the Moon" in which eighteen-year-old Cassie learns that her grandmother's fairy tale is true when a Polar Bear King comes to claim her for his bride and she must decide whether to go with him and save her long-lost mother, or continue helping her father with his research.

"Told in a descriptive style that perfectly captures the changing settings, Durst's novel is a page-turner that readers who enjoy adventure mixed with fairy-tale romance will find hard to put down." Booklist.

Into the Wild: a novel. by Sarah Beth Durst. Razorbill, 2007. 260 p.

Grades: 6 7 8 9　　　　　　　　　　　　　　**Fic**
1. Characters and characteristics in fairy tales 2. Forests 3. Father-separated girls 4. Mothers and daughters 5. Princes 6. Massachusetts 7. Fantasy fiction 8. Fairy tale and folklore-inspired fiction
ISBN 9781595141569

LC 2007001942

Having escaped from the Wild and the preordained fairy tale plots it imposes, Rapunzel, along with her daughter Julie Marchen, tries to live a fairly normal life, but when the Wild breaks free and takes over their town, it is Julie who has to prevent everyone from being trapped in the events of a story.

Vessel. Sarah Beth Durst. Margaret K. McElderry Books, 2012. 320 p.

Grades: 7 8 9 10　　　　　　　　　　　　　　**Fic**
1. Gods and goddesses 2. Fate and fatalism 3. Kidnapping 4. Survival 5. Deserts 6. High fantasy 7. Fantasy fiction
ISBN 9781442423763

LC 2011044691

When the goddess Bayla fails to take over Liyana's body, Liyana's people abandon her in the desert to find a more worthy vessel, but she soon meets Korbyn, who says the souls of seven deities have been stolen and he needs Liyana's help to find them.

Eagar, Lindsay

Hour of the bees. Lindsay Eagar. Candlewick Press, 2016. 368 p.

Grades: 5 6 7 8　　　　　　　　　　　　　　**Fic**
1. Mexican American girls 2. Grandfather and granddaughter 3. Intergenerational relations 4. People with dementia 5. Storytelling 6. New Mexico 7. Magical realism
ISBN 9780763679224

"Both Carol's journey and Serge's stories seem inherently true, and the juxtaposition of the two results in a moving, atmospheric novel of family, heritage, and fairy tales that are more real than not." Booklist.

Race to the bottom of the sea. Lindsay Eagar. Candlewick Press, 2017. 432 p.

Grades: 4 5 6 7 8　　　　　　　　　　　　　　**Fic**
1. Girl inventors 2. Treasure hunting 3. Pirates 4. Kidnapping 5. Parents -- Death 6. Adventure stories 7. Sea stories
ISBN 9780763679231

When her famous marine scientist parents are killed in a tragic accident, 11-year-old submarine innovator Fidelia is abducted by a treasonous pirate who demands that she help him retrieve a treasure from the ocean floor.

"Earnest and exciting, this swashbuckling voyage of self-discovery sparkles even when threatened by the stormiest seas." Booklist.

Edwardson, Debby Dahl

My name is not easy. Debby Dahl Edwardson. Marshall Cavendish, 2011. 248 p.

Grades: 7 8 9 10   **Fic**
1. 1960s 2. Inupiat 3. Native American residential schools 4. Catholic schools 5. Prejudice 6. Homesickness 7. Alaska 8. Historical fiction
ISBN 9780761459804

Alaskans Luke, Chickie, Sonny, Donna, and Amiq relate their experiences in the early 1960s when they are forced to attend a Catholic boarding school where, despite different tribal affiliations, they come to find a sort of family and home.

"Edwardson's skillful use of dialogue and her descriptions of rural Alaska as well as boarding-school life invoke a strong sense of empathy and compassion in readers. . . Edwardson is to be applauded for her depth of research and her ability to portray all sides of the equation in a fair and balanced manner while still creating a very enjoyable read." School Library Journal.

Efaw, Amy

Battle dress. Amy Efaw. HarperCollins, 2000. 291 p.

Grades: 7 8 9 10   **Fic**
1. United States Military Academy 2. Military cadets 3. Military education 4. Self-confidence in teenage girls 5. Self-confidence 6. Self-esteem 7. New York (State) 8. Realistic fiction 9. Coming-of-age stories
ISBN 0060279435

LC 99034516

As a newly arrived freshman at West Point, seventeen-year-old Andi finds herself gaining both confidence and self esteem as she struggles to get through the grueling six weeks of new cadet training known as the Beast.

"This book by a West Point graduate is a gripping, hard-to-put-down look at a young woman's struggle to succeed in a traditionally all-male environment." Voice of Youth Advocates.

Ehrlich, Esther

Nest. Esther Ehrlich. Wendy Lamb Books, an imprint of Random House Children's Books, 2014. 336 p.

Grades: 4 5 6 7   **Fic**
1. 1970s 2. Children of people with depression 3. Survivors of suicide victims 4. Loss (Psychology) 5. Mothers -- Death 6. Depression 7. Cape Cod, Massachusetts 8. Historical fiction
ISBN 9780385386074

When her peaceful home life in 1972 Cape Cod is devastated by her mother's serious health problem, 11-year-old Chirp finds comfort in a bird watching hobby and a mysterious friend with whom she creates a private world filled with adventure and discovery.

"The focus on nature and the outdoors helps set the pace as the seasonal changes quietly indicate the passage of time. Sensitive readers should be aware of the tough issues that it addresses—suicide, depression, and personal loss. However, the story also offers a hopeful message." School Library Journal.

Elkeles, Simone

How to ruin a summer vacation. Simone Elkeles. Flux, 2006. 234 p.: How to ruin-- series

Grades: 7 8 9 10 11 12   **Fic**
1. Sixteen-year-old girls 2. Teenage girls 3. Teenagers 4. Americans in Israel 5. Grandmother and granddaughter 6. Israel 7. Middle East 8. Realistic fiction 9. Teen chick lit
ISBN 0738709611

LC 2006040592

When sixteen-year-old Amy, a spoiled American, goes to Israel for a three-month summer vacation with a father she barely knows, she is not prepared for his Jewish family and the changes they bring about in her life.

"Amy's feisty attitude and penchant for drama keep the reader engaged. With just a touch of spice to the romance, this [is a] fast read." Voice of Youth Advocates.

How to ruin my teenage life. Simone Elkeles. Flux, 2007. 281 p.: How to ruin-- series

Grades: 7 8 9 10 11 12   **Fic**
1. Seventeen-year-old girls 2. Teenage girls 3. Identity (Psychology) 4. Jewish Americans 5. Israelis in the United States 6. Israel 7. Chicago, Illinois 8. Realistic fiction 9. Teen chick lit
ISBN 9780738710198

LC 2007005535

Living with her Israeli father in Chicago, seventeen-year-old Amy Nelson-Barak feels like a walking disaster, worried about her "non-boyfriend" in the Israeli army, her mother, new stepfather, and the baby they are expecting, a new boy named Nathan who has moved into her apartment building and goes to her school, and whether or not she really is the selfish snob that Nathan says she is.

"This book has laugh-out-loud moments. . . . Amy's thoughtfulness and depth raise this book above most of the chick-lit genre." Voice of Youth Advocates.

How to ruin your boyfriend's reputation. Simone Elkeles. Flux, c2009. 257 p.: How to ruin-- series

Grades: 7 8 9 10 11 12   **Fic**
1. Military bases 2. Basic training (Military education) 3. Teenage boy/girl relations 4. Soldiers 5. Culture conflict 6. Israel 7. Realistic fiction 8. Teen chick lit
ISBN 9780738718798

LC 2009023853

Spoiled Amy Nelson-Barak is excited about going to see her boyfriend, who is in the Israeli Army, until Amy learns that she has to take basic training and her boyfriend is going to be her commanding officer.

"Readers can't help but get drawn in by Amy's fun way of telling her story, and they learn a lot about Israeli teens' mandatory military service." School Library Journal.

Elliott, David, 1947-

Voices: the final hours of Joan of Arc. by David Elliott. Houghton Mifflin Harcourt, 2019. 208 p.

Grades: 7 8 9 10   **Fic**
1. Joan of Arc, Saint, 1412-1431 2. Charles VII, King of France, 1403-1461 3. 15th century 4. Women saints 5. Christian teenage girl martyrs 6. Faith in women 7. Courage in women 8. Leadership in women 9. France 10. Novels in verse 11. Historical fiction 12. Biographical fiction
ISBN 9781328987594

LC 2018025855

A novel in verse explores how Joan of Arc changed the course of history and examines such timely issues as gender, misogyny, and the peril of speaking truth to power.

"An elegant, spirited introduction to classical poetry and to a woman fighting not just for a cause but for a place in a world that undervalued her voice." Booklist.

Elliott, Laura, 1957-

Under a war-torn sky. L.M. Elliott. Hyperion Books For Children, 2001. 284 p.

Grades: 7 8 9 10   **Fic**
1. Second World War era (1939-1945) 2. Nineteen-year-old men 3. Pilots 4. World War II -- Aerial operations 5. Guerrilla warfare 6. Resistance to military occupation 7. France 8. Historical fiction
ISBN 0786824859

LC 2001016633
After his plane is shot down by Hitler's Luftwaffe, nineteen-year-old Henry Forester of Richmond, Virginia, strives to walk across occupied France, with the help of the French Resistance, in hopes of rejoining his unit.

"It's packed with action, intrigue, and suspense, but this novel celebrates acts of kindness and heroism without glorifying war." Booklist.

Ellis, Ann Dee

This is what I did. by Ann Dee Ellis. Little, Brown, 2007. 176 p.

Grades: 6 7 8 9   **Fic**
1. Eighth-graders 2. Teenage boys 3. Teenagers 4. New students 5. Misfits (Persons) 6. Realistic fiction
ISBN 9780316013635

LC 2006001388
Bullied because of an incident in his past, eighth-grader Logan is unhappy at his new school and has difficulty relating to others until he meets a quirky girl and a counselor who believe in him.

"Part staccato prose, part transcript, this haunting first novel will grip readers right from the start. . . . A particularly attractive book design incorporates small drawings between each segment of text." Publishers Weekly.

Ellis, Deborah, 1960-

My name is Parvana. Deborah Ellis. Groundwood Books, 2012. 201 p.: Breadwinner series

Grades: 5 6 7 8   **Fic**
1. Imprisonment 2. Military bases 3. Separated friends, relatives, etc 4. Teenage girls 5. Schools 6. Afghanistan
ISBN 1554982979
Parvana is imprisoned and interrogated by American soldiers when she is found wandering around alone in a bombed-out school in Afghanistan.

Elphinstone, Abi

Casper Tock and the Everdark wings. by Abi Elphinstone. Simon & Schuster, 2020, c2019. 320 p.: Unmapped chronicles

Grades: 4 5 6 7   **Fic**
1. Risk-taking (Psychology) 2. Mythical creatures 3. Self-discovery 4. Boys 5. Good and evil 6. England 7. Gateway fantasy 8. Fantasy fiction
ISBN 9781534443075
A boy who prefers peace and quiet over adventure is unwittingly transported to the sky kingdom of Rumblestar, where his efforts to return home are hampered by an evil harpy, whose thieving plot threatens the magical and human worlds.

"This first series installment is perfect for fans of Narnia in search of more portals into new worlds." Booklist.

Elston, Ashley

The **rules** for disappearing. Ashley Elston. Hyperion, 2013. 320 p.

Grades: 7 8 9 10 11 12   **Fic**
1. Witnesses -- Protection 2. Moving, Household 3. Teenage romance 4. New identities 5. Federal Witness Protection Program 6. Louisiana 7. Natchitoches, Louisiana 8. Realistic fiction 9. Mysteries
ISBN 9781423168973

LC 2012035122
High school student "Meg" has changed identities so often that she hardly knows who she is anymore, and her family is falling apart, but she knows that two of the rules of witness protection are be forgettable and do not make friends—but in her new home in Louisiana a boy named Ethan is making that difficult.

"The fresh first-person narration serves the story well, providing grounding in reality as events spin out of control. Though the plot may seem a bit far-fetched at times, the realistic setting, believable romance and spunky protagonist will make this one worth the trip for mystery and romance fans." Kirkus.

Emerson, Kevin

Last day on Mars. Kevin Emerson. Walden Pond Press, 2017 325 p.: Chronicle of the dark star

Grades: 4 5 6 7 8   **Fic**
1. Life on other planets 2. Space colonies 3. Survival 4. Aliens 5. Time travel 6. Mars (Planet) 7. Science fiction
ISBN 9780062306715
While waiting to leave Mars before it burns up just like the Earth before it, Liam and his friend Phoebe discover some facts about time and space and realize that the human race is just one of the races trying to survive in space.

Emond, Stephen

Bright lights, dark nights. Stephen Emond. Roaring Brook Press, 2015. 320 p.

Grades: 7 8 9 10   **Fic**
1. Children of police 2. Race relations 3. Interracial dating 4. Scandals 5. Racial profiling 6. Realistic fiction 7. Illustrated books
ISBN 9781626722064

LC 2014047413
Walter Wilcox's first love, Naomi, happens to be African American, so when Walter's policeman father is caught in a racial profiling scandal, the teens' bond and mutual love of the Foo Fighters may not be enough to keep them together through the pressures they face at school, at home, and online.

"Readers coming to this story for romance may feel shortchanged, as the relationship here is more true-to-life and awkward than swooningly romantic, but that's what sets Emond's book apart. A real slice of contemporary teenage life that's painfully honest about the below-the-surface racism in today's America." Booklist.

Winter town. by Stephen Emond. Little, Brown, 2011. 336 p.

Grades: 7 8 9   **Fic**
1. Cartoonists 2. Teenage boy/girl relations 3. Self-fulfillment in

teenagers 4. Self-fulfillment 5. Best friends 6. Realistic fiction
ISBN 9780316133326

LC 2011012966

Evan and Lucy, childhood best friends who grew apart after years of seeing one another only during Christmas break, begin a romance at age seventeen but his choice to mindlessly follow his father's plans for an Ivy League education rather than becoming the cartoonist he longs to be, and her more destructive choices in the wake of family problems, pull them apart.

"This is a remarkable illustrated work of contemporary fiction. . . . Interspersed throughout are both realistic illustrations and drawings of a comic strip being created by Evan and Lucy; these black-and-white, almost chibi-style panels form an effective parallel with the plot and appeal mightily on their own. Compelling, honest and true, this musing about art and self-discovery, replete with pitch-perfect dialogue, will have wide appeal." Kirkus.

Engdahl, Sylvia

Enchantress from the stars. Sylvia Engdahl; drawings by Rodney Shackell Collier Books, 1989, c1970 275 p.

Grades: 7 8 9 10 11 12   **Fic**
   1. Space and time 2. Responsibility 3. Options, alternatives, choices 4. Ethics 5. Alien invasions 6. Science fiction 7. Classics
   ISBN 0020430310

LC 8831743

Three civilizations from different planets in widely varying stages of development clash in what could be either a mutually disastrous or beneficial encounter.

"Emphasis is on the intricate pattern of events rather than on characterization, and readers will find fascinating symbolism—and philosophical parallels to what they may have observed or thought. The book is completely absorbing and should have a wider appeal than much science fiction." Horn Book.

Engle, Margarita

Silver people: voices from the Panama Canal. Margarita Engle. Houghton Mifflin Harcourt, [2014] 260 p.

Grades: 5 6 7 8   **Fic**
   1. 1900s (Decade) 2. Teenage abuse victims 3. Racism 4. Discrimination 5. Segregation 6. Fourteen-year-old boys 7. Panama Canal 8. Novels in verse
   ISBN 9780544109414

LC 2013037485

Fourteen-year-old Mateo and other Caribbean islanders face discrimination, segregation, and harsh working conditions when American recruiters lure them to the Panamanian rain forest in 1906 to build the great canal.

"In melodic verses, Engle offers the voices of the dark-skinned workers (known as the 'silver people'), whose backbreaking labor helped build the Panama Canal, along with the perspective of a local girl. Interspersed are occasional echoes from flora and fauna as well as cameo appearances by historical figures. Together, they provide an illuminating picture of the project's ecological sacrifices and human costs." Horn Book.

Includes bibliographical references.

The **wild** book. Margarita Engle. Harcourt Children's Books, 2012. 144 p.

Grades: 5 6 7 8   **Fic**
   1. 20th century 2. Girls with learning disabilities 3. Dyslexia 4. Girls with dyslexia 5. Learning disabilities 6. Kidnapping 7. Cuba

8. Novels in verse 9. Historical fiction
ISBN 9780547581316

LC 2011027320

In early twentieth-century Cuba, bandits terrorize the countryside as a young farm girl struggles with dyslexia. Based on the life of the author's grandmother.

With a star in my hand: Ruben Dario, poetry hero. Margarita Engle. Atheneum Books for Young Readers, 2020 160 p.

Grades: 7 8 9 10   **Fic**
   1. Dario, Ruben, 1867-1916. 2. Poets 3. Creativity 4. Storytelling 5. Storytellers 6. Latin Americans 7. Biographical fiction 8. Novels in verse
   ISBN 9781534424937

A novel in verse about the life and work of Ruben Dario, a Nicaraguan poet who started life as an abandoned child and grew to become the father of a new literary movement. Includes historical notes.

English, Karen

Francie. Karen English. Farrar Straus Giroux, 1999. 199 p.

Grades: 5 6 7 8   **Fic**
   1. 1940s 2. African American girls 3. Poverty 4. Father-separated girls 5. Race relations 6. African Americans 7. Alabama 8. Historical fiction 9. African American fiction
   ISBN 0374324565

LC 98053047

When the sixteen-year-old boy whom she tutors in reading is accused of attempting to murder a white man, Francie gets herself in serious trouble for her efforts at friendship.

"Francie's smooth-flowing, well-paced narration is gently assisted by just the right touch of the vernacular. Characterization is evenhanded and believable, while place and time envelop readers." School Library Journal.

Epstein, Adam Jay

Circle of heroes. Adam Jay Epstein & Andrew Jacobson. Harper, 2012. 400 p.: Familiars

Grades: 4 5 6   **Fic**
   1. Zombies 2. Wizards 3. Cats 4. Good and evil 5. Magic 6. Animal fantasy 7. Fantasy fiction
   ISBN 9780061961144

LC 2012005740

With Vastia under attack from Paksahara's zombie army, the familiars Aldwyn the cat, Skylar the blue jay, and Gilbert the tree frog must gather seven descendants from the most ancient and powerful animals in the queendom to bring Paksahara down.

"In this third installment, cat Aldwyn, frog Gilbert, and blue jay Skylar, the prophesied familiars, embark on a quest to unite seven magical animal descendants before the evil hare Paksahara and her Dead Army of zombie animals forever rid the world of human magic. Rollicking adventure and playful humor add whimsy to this series' theme of fulfilling destiny." Horn Book.

Erdrich, Louise

★ The **birchbark** house. Louise Erdrich with illustrations by the author. Hyperion Books for Children, c1999. 244 p.: Birchbark house

Grades: 5 6 7 8   **Fic**
   1. 1840s 2. 19th century 3. Ojibwa girls 4. Seasons 5. Ojibwa Indians 6. Seven-year-old girls 7. Visitors 8. Lake Superior region

9. Historical fiction 10. Classics
ISBN 0786822414

LC 98046366

Omakayas, a seven-year-old Ojibwe girl lives through the joys of summer and the perils of winter on an island in Lake Superior in 1847 and learns about her past.

"Erdrich crafts images of tender beauty while weaving Ojibwa words seamlessly into the text. Her gentle spot art throughout complements this first of several projected stories that will attempt to retrace [her] own family's history." Horn Book Guide.

The **game** of silence. Louise Erdrich. Harper Collins, 2005. xii, 256 p.: Birchbark house

Grades: 5 6 7 8   **Fic**

1. 19th century 2. 1840s 3. Indians of North America -- Relations with European-Americans 4. Ojibwa girls 5. Frontier and pioneer life 6. Ojibwa Indians 7. Nine-year-old girls 8. Lake Superior Region 9. Historical fiction
ISBN 0060297891

LC 2004006018

Scott O'Dell Historical Fiction Award, 2006.

Nine-year-old Omakayas, of the Ojibwa tribe, moves west with her family in 1849.

"Erdrich's captivating tale of four seasons portrays a deep appreciation of our environment, our history, and our Native American sisters and brothers." School Library Journal.

Makoons. Louise Erdrich. Harper, an imprint of HarperCollins Publishers, [2016] 256 p.: Birchbark house

Grades: 5 6 7 8   **Fic**

1. 1860s 2. 19th century 3. Ojibwa Indians 4. Twin brothers 5. Indians of North America 6. Families 7. Hunting 8. Great Plains (United States) 9. Historical fiction 10. Illustrated books
ISBN 9780060577933

LC 2015038741

Living with their Ojibwe family on the Great Plains of Dakota Territory in 1866, twin brothers Makoons and Chickadee must learn to become buffalo hunters, but Makoons has a vision that foretells great challenges that his family may not be able to overcome.

"Erdrich's simple text and delicate pencil illustrations provide a detailed, honest portrait of Plains life through the antics and experiences of two Ojibwe boys. A warm and welcome addition to the unfolding saga of a 19th-century Ojibwe family." Kirkus.

The **porcupine** year. Louise Erdrich. HarperCollinsPublishers, 2008. 256 p.: Birchbark house

Grades: 5 6 7 8   **Fic**

1. 1850s 2. Ojibwa Indians 3. Forced relocations 4. Indians of North America 5. Indian Removal, 1813-1903 6. Families 7. Lake Superior region 8. Historical fiction
ISBN 9780060297879

In 1852, forced by the United States government to leave their beloved island home, 12-year-old Omakayas and her Ojibwe family travel in search of a place to live. Heading north in hopes of joining Omakayas' aunt in a new settlement, the family faces violent raids, freezing weather, and near-starvation—but they never lose hope.

"Based on Erdrich's own family history, this celebration of life will move readers with its mischief, its anger, and its sadness. What is left unspoken is as powerful as the story told." Booklist.

Erskine, Kathryn

The **absolute** value of Mike. Kathryn Erskine. Philomel Books, 2011. 256 p.

Grades: 5 6 7 8   **Fic**

1. Eccentrics and eccentricities 2. Fund raising 3. Self-acceptance in teenage boys 4. Self-acceptance 5. International adoption 6. Pennsylvania 7. Realistic fiction
ISBN 9780399255052

LC 2010013333

Fourteen-year-old Mike, whose father is a brilliant mathematician but who has no math aptitude himself, spends the summer in rural Pennsylvania with his elderly and eccentric relatives Moo and Poppy, helping the townspeople raise money to adopt a Romanian orphan.

"Erskine weaves together a large but entertaining cast of characters. . . . Despite many laugh-out-loud moments, the heart of the book is essentially serious." Horn Book.

★ **Mockingbird**. Kathryn Erskine. Philomel Books, c2010. 235 p.

Grades: 4 5 6   **Fic**

1. Children with Asperger's syndrome 2. Asperger's syndrome 3. Grief in families 4. Empathy in girls 5. Empathy 6. Virginia 7. Realistic fiction
ISBN 9780399252648

LC 2009006741

National Book Award for Young People's Literature, 2010.

Ten-year-old Caitlin, who has Asperger's Syndrome, struggles to understand emotions, show empathy, and make friends at school, while at home she seeks closure by working on a project with her father.

"The sharp insights into Caitlyn's behavior enhance this fine addition to the recent group of books with narrators with autism and Asbergers." Booklist.

Seeing red. Kathryn Erskine. Scholastic Press, 2013. 352 p.

Grades: 5 6 7 8   **Fic**

1. 1970s 2. Race relations 3. Grief 4. Prejudice 5. Automobile repair shops 6. Families 7. Virginia 8. Historical fiction
ISBN 9780545464406

LC 2013004261

When twelve-year-old Frederick "Red" Porter's father dies in 1972, his mother wants to sell their automobile repair shop and move her two sons back to Ohio, but Red is desperate to stop the sale even if it means unearthing some dark family secrets in a Virginia rife with racial tensions.

Esplin, J. L.

96 miles. J. L. Esplin. Starscape, 2020. 304 p.

Grades: 4 5 6 7 8   **Fic**

1. Survival 2. Brothers 3. Voyages and travels 4. Power failures 5. Deserts 6. Nevada 7. Survival stories 8. Realistic fiction
ISBN 9781250192301

LC 2019044525

During a massive blackout in rural Nevada, two brothers struggle to survive without their self-reliance-obsessed dad and without enough water to cross the desert for help.

"More than just a harrowing survival story, Esplin offers a richly layered look at the frustrations of sibling rivalry, the depths of family loyalty, and the challenges of forgiveness." Publishers Weekly

Eulberg, Elizabeth

Revenge of the girl with the great personality. Elizabeth Eulberg. Point, 2013. 265 p.

Grades: 7 8 9 10   **Fic**
1. Popularity 2. Beauty contests 3. Crushes in teenage girls 4. Teenage boy/girl relations 5. Best friends 6. Realistic fiction 7. Teen chick lit
ISBN 9780545476997
Living in the shadow of her spoiled pageant-queen little sister, Lexi struggles with her school's fixation on appearances and despairs of winning the affections of a crush who regards her as a good buddy before resolving to give herself a makeover.

"Eulberg has an ear for teen dialogue and creates multidimensional characters that both embrace and defy stereotypes." Booklist.

Evans, Lissa

Horten's miraculous mechanisms: magic, mystery, and a very strange adventure. Lissa Evans. Sterling Pub., 2012, c2011. 272 p.
Grades: 3 4 5 6 7   **Fic**
1. Short boys 2. Magicians 3. Missing persons 4. Workshops 5. Triplets 6. Fantasy mysteries
ISBN 9781402798061
Moving away from everything familiar to live in a new house, 10-year-old S. Horten reluctantly befriends the annoying triplets next door and is swept up in a magical quest to find his great-uncle Tony, a famous magician who disappeared along with his fantastical workshop.

Evans, Maz

Who let the gods out? Maz Evans. Chicken House/Scholastic Inc., 2017. 320 p.: Who let the gods out?
Grades: 5 6 7 8   **Fic**
1. Gods and goddesses, Greek 2. Escaped convicts 3. Constellations 4. Thanatos (Greek deity) 5. Good and evil 6. England 7. Stonehenge, England 8. Mythological fiction 9. Fantasy fiction
ISBN 9781338065565
Twelve-year-old Elliot Hooper has many problems: his mother has been behaving strangely, they are in danger of losing their farm to a mean-spirited developer, and he is failing at school, so when he finds a girl in the cowshed, and she announces that she is Virgo, an immortal constellation, it just seems part of the normal chaos—but soon he is swept up in the Gods' hunt for prisoner 42, Thanatos, Daemon of Death, whom Elliot has set free from his prison below Stonehenge.

Evans, Richard Paul

Battle of the Ampere. Richard Paul Evans. Mercury Ink/Simon Pulse, 2013. 307 p.: Michael Vey
Grades: 6 7 8 9   **Fic**
1. Tourette syndrome 2. Electricity 3. Undercover operations 4. Vey, Michael (Fictitious character) 5. Teenage boys 6. Science fiction
ISBN 9781442475113

                               LC 2013026653
To stop Hatch from using the Elgen fleet to gain world power, Michael and the rest of the Electroclan must destroy the lead ship, but divisions within the Electroclan threaten the success of their operation.

"Though the Electroclan's destruction of the Starxource plant was a major victory over the Elgen, the Peruvian government has branded it a terroristic act. Hunted by both the army and the Elgen fleet, Michael and friends must evade capture as they plan their next move against Dr. Hatch. Evans develops character relationships better in this third installment, which continues to be exciting." Horn Book.

The **prisoner** of cell 25. Richard Paul Evans. Threshold Editions, 2011. 320 p.: Michael Vey

Grades: 6 7 8 9   **Fic**
1. Prisoners 2. Electricity 3. Tourette syndrome 4. Superhuman abilities 5. Cheerleaders 6. Science fiction
ISBN 9781451656503
"Short chapters with intriguing titles, excellent writing, and engaging characters make this action-packed story a compulsively entertaining read. The tale progresses with altering points of view. Michael tells his story in first-person and Taylor's tale is narrated in third-person. . . . Though contemporary and edgy, this book contains no bad language, sex, or gratuitous violence. This is a book Rick Riordan's fans will want to read." Voice of Youth Advocates.

Rise of the Elgen. by Richard Paul Evans. Mercury Ink/Simon Pulse, 2012. 336 p.: Michael Vey
Grades: 6 7 8 9   **Fic**
1. Electricity 2. Tourette syndrome 3. Genius 4. Good and evil 5. Friendship 6. Peru 7. Science fiction
ISBN 9781442454149

                               LC 2012022717
Fifteen-year-old Michael Vey, born with Tourette's syndrome and special electromagnetic powers, joins his techno-genius best friend and an alliance of other "electric" teenagers to battle powerful foes in the jungles of Peru, where Michael learns the Order of Elgen's plan to "restructure" the world.

Everman, Cookie Hiponia

We belong. Cookie Hiponia Everman; illustrations by Abigail Dela Cruz. Dial Books for Young Readers, 2021. 208 p.
Grades: 5 6 7 8 9   **Fic**
1. Mothers and daughters 2. Sisters 3. Immigrants 4. Filipino Americans 5. Storytelling 6. Philippines 7. Novels in verse 8. Mythological fiction
ISBN 9780593112205

                               LC 2020047593
Through a bedtime story to her daughters, a woman weaves together her immigration story and Pilipino mythology. Includes glossary, songs, and author's note.

"Deeply poignant, at times involving trauma, the tales are relayed in blue and black type, picking up where the last leaves off in alternating chapters." Publishers Weekly

Eves, Rosalyn

Blood rose rebellion. Rosalyn Eves. Alfred A. Knopf, 2017. 408 p.: Blood rose rebellion
Grades: 7 8 9 10   **Fic**
1. Victorian era (1837-1901) 2. 1840s 3. Nobility 4. Social classes 5. Revolutions 6. Intrigue 7. Magic 8. Hungary 9. Historical fantasy
ISBN 9781101935996
Accidentally breaking her sister's debutante spell, a 16-year-old non-magical girl from a powerful magic-wielding family is exiled to her father's native home in Hungary, where she confronts a difficult choice upon discovering her own latent power.

"Intrigue, romance, and revolution, with enough unanswered questions that fans will cross fingers for a sequel." Kirkus.

Fagan, Deva

Nightingale. Deva Fagan Simon & Schuster, 2021 256 p.
Grades: 4 5 6 7   **Fic**
1. Girl orphans 2. Magic swords 3. Friendship 4. Labor unions 5. Magic 6. Fantasy fiction
ISBN 9781534465787

"Fagan's novel is well paced and will hold readers' attention from the get-go. Lark has gumption and . . . proves the perfect vessel for sympathetic character growth. Significant inclusion of science fiction and political activism elements complement the action in the book and will serve to appeal to a wide audience." Kirkus

Fairlie, Emily

The **magician's** bird: a Tuckernuck mystery. Emily Fairlie; Illustrated by Antonio Javier Caparo. Katherine Tegen Books, an imprint of HarperCollinsPublishers, 2013. 304 p.: Tuckernuck mysteries

Grades: 4 5 6   **Fic**
1. Treasure hunts (Games) 2. Historic buildings 3. Innocence (Law) 4. Murder 5. Schools 6. Mysteries
ISBN 9780062118936

A sequel to The Lost Treasure of Tuckernuck finds seventh graders Laurie, Bud and Misti investigating the murder of a magician while trying to prove the innocence of the beloved school founder, Maria Tutweiler, who has been wrongly accused.

Falls, Kat

Dark life. Kat Falls. Scholastic Press, 2010. 297 p.: Dark life novels (Kat Falls)

Grades: 4 5 6 7   **Fic**
1. Outlaws 2. Ocean bottom 3. Homesteading 4. Undersea colonies 5. Extrasensory perception 6. Science fiction
ISBN 9780545178143

In a near apocalyptic future, rising oceans have resulted in overcrowding around the world. As a result, a few brave pioneers have taken to the sea and started an underwater colony. Ty, who has spent his entire life tending to his family's underwater farm, hopes to have a homestead of his own someday. But when his home is attacked by outlaws, Ty finds himself teaming up with a topsider and facing down a deadly rogue government.

"Ty has lived subsea his entire life. His family members moved below the water to make a better life for themselves. In this future, the climate changes on Earth have been so drastic that hardly any solid ground exits anymore. . . . This book will appeal to middle grade readers, who will enjoy the novel's mystery and suspense. It is a definite must-read for SF fans." Voice of Youth Advocates.

Inhuman. Kat Falls. Scholastic Press, 2013. 384 p.: Fetch
Grades: 7 8 9 10   **Fic**
1. Near future 2. Dystopias 3. Virus diseases 4. Quarantine 5. Survival 6. Science fiction
ISBN 9780545370998

In the aftermath of a cataclysmic war that has caused people and plants throughout the eastern half of the United States to mutate into creatures that exhibit violent animal-like characteristics, 16-year-old Lane forges a dubious agreement with handsome guide Rafe in order to save her missing father.

"Years ago, the U.S. was bisected by a pandemic (spread by biting) that causes humans to mutate into feral human-animal hybrids. When pampered teenager Lane is blackmailed into the Feral Zone, she joins the search for a cure and discovers the gray area between human and feral. While Lane and her love triangle are bland, the zombie-apocalypse-meets-wereanimals-gone-wild setup captures the imagination." Horn Book.

Rip tide. Kat Falls. Scholastic Press, 2011. 320 p.: Dark life novels (Kat Falls)

Grades: 4 5 6 7   **Fic**
1. Undersea colonies 2. Parent-separated teenagers 3. Outlaws 4. Submarines 5. Kidnapping 6. Science fiction
ISBN 9780545178433

Ty and Gemma return to the subsea frontier when Ty's parents are kidnapped by the mysterious Surfs, an abduction that forces the teens into an alliance with the outlaws of the Seablite Gang.

"While preparing to sell the season's seaweed crop, Ty stumbles across an abandoned township, its doors chained shut and its residents murdered. Soon after, the colonists' deal with another township goes bad, and Ty's parents are kidnapped. As Ty and Gemma try to track down those responsible and save their loved ones, they're forced to join up with the notorious Seablite Gang, infiltrate the rough-and-tumble town of Rip Tide, fight for their lives against sea monsters and human predators, and discover who's killing entire townships—and why. . . . There's no shortage of action, intrigue, or daring exploits in this aquatic thriller. Atmospheric and tense, built around an expertly used postapocalyptic meets Wild West setting, this story's a whole lot of fun." Publishers Weekly.

Fantaskey, Beth

Buzz kill. by Beth Fantaskey. Houghton Mifflin Harcourt, 2014. 368 p.
Grades: 8 9 10 11 12   **Fic**
1. Teenage detectives 2. Murder 3. Teenage boy/girl relations 4. Teenage journalists 5. Quarterbacks (Football) 6. Mysteries
ISBN 9780547393100

     LC 2013011423

Seventeen-year-old Millie joins forces with her classmate, gorgeous but mysterious Chase Colton, to try to uncover who murdered head football coach "Hollerin' Hank" Killdare—and why.

"When the head football coach is killed, seventeen-year-old Millie, a school reporter obsessed with Nancy Drew, sets out to learn the truth and clear her assistant-coach father of any suspicion. She gets some unexpected help from dreamy quarterback Chase, who's hiding some secrets. This entertaining sleuth story is a good choice for teens now graduated from books featuring Millie's literary hero." Horn Book.

Jessica's guide to dating on the dark side. Beth Fantaskey. Harcourt, 2009. 354 p.
Grades: 8 9 10 11 12   **Fic**
1. Adopted teenage girls 2. Teenage vampires 3. Arranged marriage 4. Dating (Social customs) 5. Princes 6. Pennsylvania 7. Romania 8. Paranormal romances
ISBN 9780152063849

     LC 2007049002

Seventeen-year-old Jessica, adopted and raised in Pennsylvania, learns that she is descended from a royal line of Romanian vampires and that she is betrothed to a vampire prince, who poses as a foreign exchange student while courting her.

"Fantaskey makes this premise work by playing up its absurdities without laughing at them. . . . The romance sizzles, the plot develops ingeniously and suspensefully, and the satire sings." Publishers Weekly.

Farizan, Sara

Here to stay. Sara Farizan. Algonquin Young Readers, 2018. 272 p.
Grades: 9 10 11 12   **Fic**
1. Arab Americans 2. High school students 3. Cyberbullying 4. Bullying and bullies 5. Basketball 6. Boston, Massachusetts 7. Realistic fiction 8. Basketball stories
ISBN 9781616207007

     LC 2018008382

When a cyberbully sends the entire high school a picture of basketball hero Bijan Majidi, photo-shopped to look like a terrorist, the school administration promises to find and punish the culprit, but Bijan just wants to pretend the incident never happened and move on.

Farmer, Nancy, 1941-

A **girl** named Disaster. by Nancy Farmer. Orchard Books, 1996. 309 p.

Grades: 6 7 8 9   **Fic**

1. 1980s 2. Runaway girls 3. Wilderness survival 4. Eleven-year-old girls 5. Girls 6. Villages 7. Zimbabwe 8. Mozambique 9. Adventure stories 10. Survival stories
ISBN 0531095398

LC 9615141

While journeying to Zimbabwe from Mozambique, eleven-year-old Nhamo struggles to escape drowning and starvation and in so doing comes close to the luminous world of the African spirits.

"This story is humorous and heartwrenching, complex and multilayered." School Library Journal.

The **house** of the scorpion. Nancy Farmer. Atheneum Books for Young Readers, c2002. 380 p.

Grades: 7 8 9 10   **Fic**

1. Clones and cloning 2. Drug dealers 3. Courage in boys 4. Near future 5. Courage 6. Dystopian fiction 7. Science fiction 8. Coming-of-age stories
ISBN 0689852223

LC 2001056594

National Book Award for Young People's Literature, 2002.

In a future where humans despise clones, Matt enjoys special status as the young clone of El Patron, the 142-year-old leader of a corrupt drug empire nestled between Mexico and the United States.

"This is a powerful, ultimately hopeful, story that builds on today's sociopolitical, ethical, and scientific issues and prognosticates a compelling picture of what the future could bring." Booklist.

The **Islands** of the Blessed. Nancy Farmer. Atheneum Books for Young Readers, 2009. 479 p.: Sea of Trolls trilogy

Grades: 5 6 7 8 9   **Fic**

1. Teenage apprentices 2. Spirits 3. Mermaids 4. Changelings 5. Bards and bardism 6. Historical fantasy
ISBN 9781416907374

LC 2008045415

Two years after their adventures in The Land of the Silver Apples, the apprentice bard Jack and his Viking companion Thorgil confront the malevolent spirit of a vengeful mermaid and begin a quest that casts them among the fin folk of Notland.

"This is an exciting story, which contains a cast of lively, multifaceted characters." Booklist.

The **Land** of the Silver Apples. Nancy Farmer. Atheneum Books for Young Readers, c2007. 496 p.: Sea of Trolls trilogy

Grades: 5 6 7 8 9   **Fic**

1. Teenage apprentices 2. Bards and bardism 3. Changelings 4. Child kidnapping victims 5. Kidnapping 6. Historical fantasy
ISBN 9781416907350

LC 2006031433

After escaping from the Sea of Trolls, the apprentice bard Jack plunges into a new series of adventures, traveling underground to Elfland and uncovering the truth about his little sister Lucy.

"Farmer beautifully balances pell-mell action and quieter thematic points. . . . This hearty adventure, as personal as it is epic, will cradle readers in the hollow it its hand." Booklist.

★ The **Sea** of Trolls. Nancy Farmer. Atheneum Books for Young Readers, c2004. 459 p.: Sea of Trolls trilogy

Grades: 5 6 7 8 9   **Fic**

1. Child kidnapping victims 2. Saxons 3. Vikings 4. Boy apprentices 5. Bards and bardism 6. Historical fantasy
ISBN 0689867441

LC 2003019091

After Jack becomes apprenticed to a Druid bard, he and his little sister Lucy are captured by Viking Berserkers and taken to the home of King Ivar the Boneless and his half-troll queen, leading Jack to undertake a vital quest to Jotunheim, home of the trolls.

"This exciting and original fantasy will capture the hearts and imaginations of readers." School Library Journal.

Farrant, Natasha

After Iris. by Natasha Farrant. Dial Books for Young Readers, 2013. 256 p.

Grades: 5 6 7 8   **Fic**

1. Twin sisters -- Death 2. Grief 3. Au pairs 4. Families 5. Videos -- Production and direction 6. Realistic fiction
ISBN 9780803739826

LC 2012039136

Twelve-year-old Bluebell Gadsby's written and video diary chronicles life in a rowdy London family, and how Zoran, the new au pair, and Joss, the troublemaking boy next door, help to pull her out of her shell and cope with the loss of her twin three years before.

Farrey, Brian

The **Grimjinx** rebellion. Brian Farrey; illustrated by Brett Helquist. HarperCollins, 2014. 432 p.: Vengekeep prophecies

Grades: 4 5 6 7   **Fic**

1. Prophecies 2. Thieves 3. Monsters 4. Magic 5. Kidnapping 6. Fantasy fiction
ISBN 9780062049346

"When mage sentinels carry off Jaxter Grimjinx's little sister Aubrin to be their new augur, the family's quest to get her back leads to the opening elements of a prophecy in which Jaxter will save the Five Provinces from a deadly scourge but die doing so. The twisted but coherent puzzle plot unfolds swiftly, speeded along by irreverent Grimjinx humor." Horn Book.

The **secret** of Dreadwillow Carse. Brian Farrey. Algonquin Young Readers, 2016. 240 p.

Grades: 4 5 6 7 8   **Fic**

1. Princesses 2. Twelve-year-old girls 3. Quests 4. Secrets 5. Prophecies 6. Fantasy fiction
ISBN 9781616205058

LC 2015031467

A princess and a peasant girl, who hides a sorrow in a town where everyone lives with unending joy, embark on a dangerous quest to outwit a centuries-old warning foretelling the fall of the Monarchy.

"Part fairy tale, part seemingly utopian society with a dark underbelly, this is a gripping, compelling story that will leave readers mulling over the ethical questions raised." Booklist.

The **Shadowhand** Covenant. Brian Farrey; illustrated by Brett Helquist. Harper, an imprint of HarperCollins, 2013. 304 p.: Vengekeep prophecies

Grades: 4 5 6 7 8   **Fic**
1. Conspiracies 2. Thieves 3. Monsters 4. Kidnapping 5. Magic
6. Fantasy fiction
ISBN 9780062049315

LC 2013021825

Twelve-year-old Jaxter Grimjinx finds himself caught in a conspiracy when he is tapped for a mission by the notorious clan of thieves known as the Shadowhands.

The **Vengekeep** prophecies. Brian Farrey; illustrated by Brett Helquist. HarperCollins, 2012. 304 p.: Vengekeep prophecies
Grades: 4 5 6 7   **Fic**
1. Swindlers and swindling 2. Prophecies 3. Monsters 4. Magic
5. Thieves 6. Fantasy fiction
ISBN 9780062049285

LC 2012025282

A magical tapestry prophesies doom for the town of Vengekeep, and to everyone's surprise twelve-year-old Jaxter Grimjinx and his family of con artists appear to be the town's saviors. Provided by publisher.

Fawcett, Heather (Heather M.)

Even the darkest stars. Heather Fawcett. Balzer & Bray, 2017. 304 p.: Even the darkest stars
Grades: 8 9 10 11 12   **Fic**
1. Mountaineering 2. Talismans 3. Magic 4. Voyages and travels
5. Teenage girls 6. Fantasy fiction
ISBN 9780062463388

Kamzin has always dreamed of becoming one of the Emperor's royal explorers, the elite climbers tasked with mapping the wintry, mountainous Empire and spying on its enemies. She knows she could be the best in the world, if only someone would give her a chance.

"Add in a detailed, well-realized setting, an unsettling villain that lingers just off the page, and buckets of danger to result in an utterly inventive and wholly original debut." Booklist.

Fayers, Claire

The **voyage** to Magical North. Claire Fayers. Henry Holt and Company, 2016. 288 p.: Accidental pirates
Grades: 6 7 8   **Fic**
1. Pirates 2. Wizards 3. Wizards' apprentices 4. Parent-separated girls 5. Pirate ships 6. Fantasy fiction
ISBN 9781627794206

LC 2015022325

Twelve-year-old Brine Seaborne and her friend Peter find themselves in an adventure with pirates, invisible bears, and a seriously evil magician.

"A robust debut, well stocked with heroic exploits, monsters, pirates, explosions, magical transformations, and life-changing adventures, and a promising series starter." Kirkus.

Federle, Tim

Five, six, seven, Nate! Tim Federle. Simon & Schuster Books for Young Readers, 2014. 304 p.: Nate
Grades: 5 6 7 8   **Fic**
1. Musicals 2. Theater 3. Best friends 4. Friendship 5. Thirteen-year-old boys 6. New York City 7. Broadway, New York City 8. Realistic fiction
ISBN 9781442446939

A sequel to Better Nate Than Ever finds small-town theater geek Nate Foster launching rehearsals for the Broadway show of his dreams only to encounter intimidating child stars, cutthroat understudies and a director who cannot remember Nate's name.

"Nate successfully auditioned for Broadway's E.T.: The Musical in Better Nate Than Ever. Of course, he's actually only an understudy's understudy, his chorus part keeps diminishing, and rehearsals are going poorly, but good-humored Nate takes it all in stride. Federle addresses his likable character's burgeoning interest in boys in a laudably straightforward way, making this entertaining backstage pass especially rewarding." Horn Book.

Feinstein, John

Change-up: mystery at the World Series. John Feinstein. Random House Children's Books, 2009. 308 p.: Steve and Susan Carol sports mysteries
Grades: 6 7 8 9   **Fic**
1. Teenage journalists 2. Sportswriters 3. Pitchers (Baseball) 4. Sports -- Corrupt practices 5. Baseball 6. Sports fiction 7. Mysteries 8. Baseball stories
ISBN 9780375956362

While interviewing the new pitcher while covering the World Series, teen reporters Stevie and Susan's interest is piqued by the contradictory answers given and so decide to delve deeper into the story to get to the truth in this exciting sports mystery for middle readers.

"Stevie Thomas and Susan Carol Anderson are back on the newspaper sports beat, this time at the World Series. . . . It seems that Stevie has hit it big when he interviews Norbert Doyle, a pitcher for the Washington Nationals. . . . As Stevie digs for more material for his story, he finds out there is more to Doyle than he first thought. . . . Readers will appreciate the sports details and real-life characters Feinstein includes throughout the novel. . . . This book is an enjoyable trifecta of sports, mystery and journalism for young readers." Voice of Youth Advocates.

Cover-up: mystery at the Super Bowl. John Feinstein. Alfred A. Knopf, c2007. 298 p.: Steve and Susan Carol sports mysteries
Grades: 6 7 8 9   **Fic**
1. Anabolic steroids in sports 2. Sports cover-ups 3. Teenage journalists 4. Football 5. Sports -- Corrupt practices 6. Indianapolis, Indiana 7. Sports fiction 8. Mysteries 9. Football stories
ISBN 0375842470

"This delivers an entertaining mix of mystery, insider detail, . . . and ripped-from-the-headlines subject matter." Booklist.

Last shot: a Final Four mystery. John Feinstein. Knopf, 2005. 256 p.: Steve and Susan Carol sports mysteries
Grades: 6 7 8 9   **Fic**
1. Teenage detectives 2. Basketball tournaments 3. Sportswriters 4. Basketball 5. Thomas, Steve (Fictitious character) 6. New Orleans, Louisiana 7. Sports fiction 8. Mysteries 9. Basketball stories
ISBN 0375831681

LC 2004026535

After winning a basketball reporting contest, eighth graders Stevie and Susan Carol are sent to cover the Final Four tournament, where they discover that a talented player is being blackmailed into throwing the final game.

"The action on the court is vividly described. . . . Mystery fans will find enough suspense in this fast-paced narrative to keep them hooked." School Library Journal.

The **rivalry**: mystery at the Army-Navy game. John Feinstein. Alfred A. Knopf, 2010. 336 p.: Steve and Susan Carol sports mysteries
Grades: 7 8 9 10   **Fic**
1. Teenage detectives 2. Teenage journalists 3. Sports journalism

4. Sportswriters 5. Football 6. Mysteries 7. Sports fiction 8. Football stories
ISBN 9780375865701

LC 2010019614

Eighth-grade sportswriters Stevie and Susan Carol team up to solve a mystery at the famous Army-Navy football game.

"Readers looking for a solid sports story tinged with excitement will enjoy this book. The game details are exciting, the suspense builds in the last fifty pages, and there is both a satisfying conclusion." Voice of Youth Advocates.

Vanishing act: mystery at the U.S. Open. John Feinstein. Knopf, 2006. 288 p.: Steve and Susan Carol sports mysteries
Grades: 6 7 8 9   **Fic**
1. Tennis tournaments 2. Teenage journalists 3. Kidnapping 4. Conspiracies 5. Sportswriters 6. New York City 7. Mysteries 8. Sports fiction
ISBN 037583592X

LC 2005035823

Eighth-grade sports reporters Susan Carol and Stevie reunite at the U.S. Open tennis championships where they investigate the mysterious disappearance of a top Russian player.

"Sports fans will be fascinated by the insider's view of the tournament, and even teens ambivalent about sports will connect with the memorable, high-achieving kids and the messages about maintaining integrity versus selling out—in sports and in life." Booklist.

The **walk-on**. John Feinstein. Alfred A. Knopf, 2014. 359 p.: Triple threat (John Feinstein)
Grades: 6 7 8 9   **Fic**
1. High school football players 2. Children of divorced parents 3. Football 4. Football coaches 5. High schools 6. Pennsylvania 7. Sports fiction 8. Football stories
ISBN 9780385753463

LC 2013044495

After moving to a new town his freshman year in high school, Alex Myers is happy to win a spot on the varsity team as a quarterback but must deal with the idea of not playing for two years since the first-string quarterback is not only a local hero, he is also the son of the corrupt head coach.

"A cliffhanger of a football novel bristling with social, personal, familial and ethical issues to complement the gridiron action, from best-selling sports writer Feinstein." Kirkus.

Ferris, Jean, 1939-
Once upon a Marigold. Jean Ferris. Harcourt, Inc., c2002. 266 p.: Upon a Marigold
Grades: 5 6 7 8   **Fic**
1. Princesses 2. Rulers 3. Conspiracies 4. Trolls 5. Families 6. Fantasy fiction 7. Humorous stories
ISBN 0152167919

LC 2002000311

A young man with a mysterious past and a penchant for inventing things leaves the troll who raised him, meets an unhappy princess he has loved from afar, and discovers a plot against her and her father.

"This complex, fast-paced plot, a mixture of fantasy, romance, comedy, and coming-of-age novel, succeeds because these characters are compelling, well developed, and sympathetic." School Library Journal.

Twice upon a Marigold. Jean Ferris. Harcourt, c2008. 297 p.: Upon a Marigold

Grades: 5 6 7 8   **Fic**
1. Women rulers 2. Amnesia 3. Newlyweds 4. Enemies 5. Wizards 6. Fantasy fiction 7. Humorous stories
ISBN 9780152063825

"Appealing new characters and fresh plot twists give this sequel a life of its own, though fans of the earlier book will enjoy the continuation of its story line, wry humor, and offbeat sense of fun." Booklist.

Fforde, Jasper
The **Eye** of Zoltar. Jasper Fforde. Houghton Mifflin Harcourt, 2014. 405 p.: Chronicles of Kazam
Grades: 7 8 9 10   **Fic**
1. Wizards 2. Magic gems 3. Dragons 4. Greed 5. Rulers 6. Fantasy fiction
ISBN 1443407542

The Mighty Shandar returns to the Ununited Kingdoms and vows to eliminate the dragons once and for all—unless sixteen-year-old Jennifer Strange and her sidekicks from the Kazam house of enchantment can bring him a legendary jewel: The Eye of Zoltar.

"This installment is darker than the first two outings and contains a Grand Canyon-sized cliff-hanger of an ending. Fans of strong, brave, intelligent females will root for Jennifer and her gang, and wait impatiently for the next book." School Library Journal.

The **last** dragonslayer. Jasper Fforde. Harcourt, 2012. 256 p.: Chronicles of Kazam
Grades: 7 8 9 10   **Fic**
1. Dragons 2. Abandoned children 3. Employment agencies 4. Wizards 5. Visions 6. Fantasy fiction
ISBN 9780547738475

Fifteen-year-old Jennifer Strange runs Kazam, an employment agency for soothsayers and sorcerers. Trouble starts when Jennifer has a vision that predicts the death of the last dragon at the hands of a dragonslayer.

The **song** of the quarkbeast. Jasper Fforde. Harcourt, Houghton Mifflin Harcourt, 2013. 290 p.: Chronicles of Kazam
Grades: 7 8 9 10   **Fic**
1. Rulers 2. Wizards 3. Contests 4. Teenage girls 5. Magic 6. Fantasy fiction
ISBN 9780547738482

In an alternate United Kingdom, King Snodd aims to control the world by controlling magic, and only sixteen-year-old Jennifer Strange, acting manager of an employment agency for sorcerers, stands between Snodd and his plans.

Fields, Terri, 1948-
After the death of Anna Gonzales. Terri Fields. Henry Holt, c2002. 100 p.
Grades: 7 8 9 10   **Fic**
1. High school students 2. Suicide victims 3. Teenagers 4. Suicide 5. High schools 6. Novels in verse 7. Realistic fiction
ISBN 080507127X

LC 2002024074

Poems written in the voices of forty-seven people, including students, teachers, and other school staff, record the aftermath of a high school student's suicide and the preoccupations of teen life.

Finneyfrock, Karen
The **sweet** revenge of Celia Door. by Karen Finneyfrock. Viking, 2013. 272 p.

Grades: 7 8 9 10   **Fic**
1. Teenage girl misfits 2. Teenage poets 3. Revenge 4. Gay teenagers 5. Poetry 6. Pennsylvania 7. Hershey, Pennsylvania 8. Realistic fiction
ISBN 9780670012756
                                          LC 2011047221
Fourteen-year-old Celia, hurt by her parents' separation, the loss of her only friend, and a classmate's cruelty, has only her poetry for solace until newcomer Drake Berlin befriends her, comes out to her, and seeks her help in connecting with the boy he left behind.

Fipps, Lisa
Starfish. Lisa Fipps. Nancy Paulson Books, 2021 256 p.
Grades: 5 6 7 8   **Fic**
1. Fat acceptance 2. Overweight girls 3. Self-acceptance 4. Bullying and bullies 5. Swimming 6. Realistic fiction 7. Novels in verse
ISBN 9781984814500
Bullied and shamed her whole life for being fat, twelve-year-old Ellie finally gains the confidence to stand up for herself, with the help of some wonderful new allies.
"As she draws readers in with her smart and succinct voice, Ellie navigates the difficult map of knowing she deserves better treatment while struggling with the conflict that's necessary to achieve it." Booklist

Firestone, Carrie
Dress coded. Carrie Firestone. G. P. Putnam's Sons, 2020. 320 p.
Grades: 5 6 7 8 9   **Fic**
1. Eighth grade girls 2. Sexism 3. Rules 4. Dress codes 5. Protests, demonstrations, vigils, etc 6. Realistic fiction
ISBN 9781984816436
Fed up with sexist dress codes and unfair conduct standards at a school where girls' bodies are considered a distraction, Molly starts a podcast to protest the school's disciplinary inequality before her small rebellion swells into a full-blown empowerment revolution. Atlas Publishing
"Molly's first-person narration, delivered in brief sections—occasionally formatted as bullet points, letters, or transcripts—lends a powerful intimacy to the text. That's good, because this story feels personal, for both Molly and author Firestone. They—and countless others—are fed up, and that energy fuels the beautifully paced pages of this book, full of humor, rage, and heart." Booklist

Fisher, Catherine, 1957-
The **dark** city. by Catherine Fisher. Dial Books for Young Readers, 2011. 384 p.: Relic master
Grades: 6 7 8 9   **Fic**
1. Relics 2. Teenage apprentices 3. Technology 4. Quests 5. Cities and towns 6. Fantasy fiction
ISBN 9780803736733
Sixteen-year-old Raffi, Master Galen, and a mysterious traveler, Carys, enter the ruined city of Tasceron seeking a relic that may save the world, while evading the Watch, a brutal organization opposed to the Order to which Raffi and Galen belong.
"Well-crafted storytelling provides more than the sum of its parts." Kirkus.

The **hidden** Coronet. by Catherine Fisher. Dial Books, 2011. 384 p.: Relic master

Grades: 6 7 8 9   **Fic**
1. Teenage apprentices 2. Relics 3. Quests 4. Antiquities 5. Apprentices 6. Fantasy fiction
ISBN 9780803736757
Sixteen-year-old Raffi and Master Galen continue to evade the Watch as they seek the Coronet, a potent ancient relic that could be their only hope for defeating the power that is destroying Anara.
"The climactic integration of visionary mysticism and gee-whiz gadgetry, rendered bittersweet by all-too human failures, leads directly to a cliffhanger ending." Kirkus.

The **lost** heiress. by Catherine Fisher. Dial Books for Young Readers, 2011. 384 p.: Relic master
Grades: 6 7 8 9   **Fic**
1. Teenage apprentices 2. Heirs and heiresses 3. Protectiveness 4. Relics 5. Apprentices 6. Fantasy fiction
ISBN 9780803736740
Even though the city of Tasceron and its emperor have fallen, when Master Galen and his sixteen-year-old apprentice Raffi hear a rumor that the heiress to the throne still lives, they must try to find her and keep her safe.
"Separate plot threads intertwine in a satisfying climax, posing puzzles to keep readers ensnared while providing pleasing narrative momentum to the overall series." Kirkus.

The **obsidian** mirror. by Catherine Fisher. Dial Books, 2013. 384 p.: Chronoptika
Grades: 7 8 9 10 11 12   **Fic**
1. Magic mirrors 2. Time travel 3. Father-separated teenage boys 4. Changelings 5. Fairies 6. Fantasy fiction
ISBN 9780803739697
                                          LC 2012019459
When his father disappears while experimenting with a black mirror that is a portal to both the past and the future, Jake encounters obstacles when he tries to use the mirror to find his father.

Sapphique. by Catherine Fisher. Dial Books, 2010. 464 p.
Grades: 7 8 9 10   **Fic**
1. Princes 2. Dystopias 3. Artificial intelligence 4. Identity (Psychology) 5. Prisons 6. Dystopian fiction 7. Steampunk 8. Fantasy fiction
ISBN 9780803733978
                                          LC 2009031479
After his escape from the sentient prison, Incarceron, Finn finds that the Realm is not at all what he expected, and he does not know whether he is to be its king, how to free his imprisoned friends, or how to stop Incarceron's quest to be free of its own nature.
"Fisher's superb world-building marks this title, effectively drawing the reader in to a place so rife with secrets even its inhabitants don't entirely understand the depth of its illusions." Bulletin of the Center for Children's Books.

Fitzgerald, Laura Marx
The **gallery**. Laura Marx Fitzgerald. Dial Books for Young Readers, [2016] 336 p.
Grades: 4 5 6 7   **Fic**
1. 1920s 2. Household employees 3. Irish Americans 4. Art 5. Twelve-year-old girls 6. Preteen girls 7. New York City 8. Historical mysteries
ISBN 9780525428657
                                          LC 2015029009

In 1929 New York City, twelve-year-old housemaid Martha O'Doyle suspects that a wealthy recluse may be trying to communicate with the outside world through the paintings on her gallery walls.

"Fitzgerald balances mystery and history in a feminist narrative that invites readers to find out more." Kirkus.

Under the egg. by Laura Marx Fitzgerald. Dial Books for Young Readers, an imprint of Penguin Group (USA) Inc., 2014. 256 p.

Grades: 4 5 6 7   **Fic**
    1. Art 2. Children of celebrities 3. Holocaust survivors 4. Librarians 5. Friendship 6. Greenwich Village, New York City 7. New York City 8. Mysteries
ISBN 9780803740013

                        LC 2013017790
Her grandfather's dying words lead thirteen-year-old Theodora Tenpenny to a valuable, hidden painting she fears may be stolen, but it is her search for answers in her Greenwich Village neighborhood that brings a real treasure.

"Theo's household is vividly portrayed, from her grandfather's creative ingenuity to her mothers tenuous hold on reality. Smart and determined, down-to-earth and insightful, Theo makes an engaging narrator as she follows a winding trail of discovery." Booklist.

Fitzgerald, Sarah Moore, 1965-

The **apple** tart of hope. Sarah Moore Fitzgerald. Holiday House, [2016] 154 p.

Grades: 5 6 7 8   **Fic**
    1. Fourteen-year-olds 2. Missing children 3. First loves 4. Friendship 5. Manipulation (Social sciences) 6. Realistic fiction
ISBN 9780823435616

                        LC 2015022313
Oscar Dunleavy, a teenager who used to make incredible apple tarts, has gone missing and everyone thinks he is dead, but Oscar's best friend Meg and his little brother Stevie, form a band as they try to figure out what happened to him.

"Fully developed secondary characters—such as Oscar's disabled younger brother and Paloma, who tries to take Megs place—add richness and depth to this lyrically written tale, which explores themes of manipulation, self-discovery, hope, and love... This touching novel is one to savor." Booklist.

Fitzmaurice, Kathryn

A **diamond** in the desert. by Kathryn Fitzmaurice. Viking Children's Books, 2012. 256 p.

Grades: 5 6 7 8   **Fic**
    1. Gila River Relocation Center. 2. Second World War era (1939-1945) 3. Japanese Americans -- Forced removal and incarceration, 1942-1945 4. Concentration camps 5. Teenage boys 6. Sick girls 7. Baseball 8. Historical fiction
ISBN 9780670012923

                        LC 2011012041
After the bombing of Pearl Harbor, thirteen-year-old Tetsu and his family are sent to the Gila River Relocation Center in Arizona where a fellow prisoner starts a baseball team, but when Tetsu's sister becomes ill and he feels responsible, he stops playing.

Flake, Sharon

Bang! . by Sharon G. Flake. Jump at the Sun/Hyperion Books for Children, 2005. 298 p.

Grades: 8 9 10 11 12   **Fic**
    1. African American teenage boys 2. Inner city teenage boys 3.

Identity (Psychology) 4. Survival 5. Brothers -- Death 6. Coming-of-age stories 7. African American fiction 8. Realistic fiction
ISBN 0786818441

                        LC 2005047434
A teenage boy must face the harsh realities of inner city life, a disintegrating family, and destructive temptations as he struggles to find his identity as a young man.

"This disturbing, thought-provoking novel will leave readers with plenty of food for thought and should fuel lively discussions." School Library Journal.

Who am I without him?: short stories about girls and the boys in their lives. Sharon G. Flake. Jump at the Sun/Hyperion Books for Children, c2004. 168 p.

Grades: 7 8 9 10   **Fic**
    1. African American teenage girls 2. Identity (Psychology) 3. Dating (Social customs) 4. Boyfriends 5. Teenage boy/girl relations 6. African American fiction 7. Short stories 8. Realistic fiction
ISBN 0786806931

                        LC bl2004004259
A collection of short stories about teenage girls and the issues they must deal with in their relationships with boys.

"Addressing issues and situations that many girls face in today's often complex society, this book is provocative and thought-provoking." School Library Journal.

You don't even know me: stories and poems about boys. Sharon Flake. Jump at the Sun, 2010. 208 p.

Grades: 7 8 9 10   **Fic**
    1. African American teenage boys 2. Urban teenagers 3. City life 4. Teenage boys 5. Street life 6. Short stories
ISBN 9781423100140
The Coretta Scott King Honor author of Who Am I Without Him? shares the thoughts of urban males through their own voices, which are sometimes funny and sometimes intense, but always real.

"This memorable collection of short stories and poems offers a glimpse into the urban lives of several African American boys. . . . Flake offers a vivid, unforgettable collection. . . . The voices ring true. . . . The stories and poetry are quite thought provoking." Voice of Youth Advocates.

Flanagan, John (John Anthony)

The **battle** for Skandia. John Flanagan. Philomel Books, 2008, c2006. 294 p.: Ranger's apprentice.

Grades: 5 6 7 8   **Fic**
    1. Teenage apprentices 2. Teenage heroes and heroines 3. Courage in teenage boys 4. Teenage boys 5. Teenagers 6. High fantasy 7. Fantasy fiction
ISBN 9780399244575

                        LC 2007023646
After Ranger's apprentice Will battles Temujai warriors to rescue Evanlyn, Will's kingdom of Skandia joins forces with rival kingdom Araluen to defeat a common enemy.

"Even readers drawn to the series for its deftly drawn characters and setting may find themselves caught up in the action." Booklist.

The **burning** bridge. John Flanagan. Philomel Books, 2006. 262 p.: Ranger's apprentice.

Grades: 5 6 7 8   **Fic**
    1. Teenage apprentices 2. Boy impersonators 3. Teenage heroes and heroines 4. Bridges 5. Teenage boys 6. High fantasy 7.

Fantasy fiction
ISBN 0399244557

LC 2005033064

"The pace is swift, and action is often at the forefront, but elements of humor and nuances of emotion are apparent as well." Booklist.

The **emperor** of Nihon-ja. John Flanagan. Philomel Books, 2011. 352 p.: Ranger's apprentice.

Grades: 5 6 7 8 **Fic**
1. Teenage heroes and heroines 2. Coups d'etat 3. Warriors 4. Rulers 5. Courage in teenage boys 6. High fantasy 7. Fantasy fiction 8. Asian-influenced fantasy
ISBN 9780399255007

In a faraway land, a young warrior must protect an emperor from an uprising and train an inexperienced army, with assistance from his Ranger friends.

Erak's ransom. John Flanagan. Philomel Books, 2010. 373 p.: Ranger's apprentice.

Grades: 5 6 7 8 **Fic**
1. Teenage heroes and heroines 2. Courage in teenage boys 3. Ransom 4. Deserts 5. Kidnapping victims 6. High fantasy 7. Fantasy fiction
ISBN 9780399252051

On a mission to pay the ransom of a new ally, apprentice Will and his friends find themselves in a desert wasteland awash with enemies.

"Bringing together many favorite characters for a grand adventure, this book delivers both excitement and quiet good times." Booklist.

Halt's peril. John Flanagan. Philomel Books, 2010, c2009. 386 p.: Ranger's apprentice.

Grades: 5 6 7 8 **Fic**
1. Teenage heroes and heroines 2. Cult leaders 3. Assassins 4. Cults 5. Determination in teenage boys 6. High fantasy 7. Fantasy fiction
ISBN 9780399252075

Tennyson, the false prophet of the Outsider cult, has escaped and Halt is determined to stop him before he crosses the border into Araluen, but Genovesan assassins put Will and Halt's extraordinary archery skills to the test.

"Series fans will enjoy the dialogue and camaraderie as much as the action." Booklist.

The **hunters**. John Flanagan. Philomel, 2012. 432 p.: Broth-erband chronicles

Grades: 5 6 7 8 **Fic**
1. Pirates 2. Courage 3. Seafaring life 4. Friendship 5. Imaginary kingdoms 6. High fantasy 7. Fantasy fiction
ISBN 9780399256219

LC 2012020986

Determined to recover the Adomal and to prevent the pirate Zavac from doing more damage, Hal and his brotherband crew persue Zavac to the lawless fortress of Ragusa where, if Hal is to succeed, he will have to go beyond his brotherband training and face the pirate one-on-one in a fight to the finish.

The **icebound** land. John Flanagan. Philomel Books, 2007. 266 p.: Ranger's apprentice.

Grades: 5 6 7 8 **Fic**
1. Teenage apprentices 2. Slave traders 3. Knights and knighthood 4. Enslaved teenagers 5. Teenage heroes and heroines 6. High

fantasy 7. Fantasy fiction
ISBN 0399244565

LC 2006034561

"Flanagan's deft character portrayals and well-paced story will engage readers." Booklist.

The **invaders**. John Flanagan. Philomel, 2012. 432 p.: Broth-erband chronicles

Grades: 5 6 7 8 **Fic**
1. Pirates 2. Seafaring life 3. Courage 4. Adventure 5. Stealing 6. High fantasy 7. Fantasy fiction
ISBN 9780399256202

Hal and the other Herons face many perils as they track down the pirates who stole Skandia's most prized artifact, the Andomal. Provided by publisher.

The **kings** of Clonmel. John Flanagan. Philomel Books, 2010, c2008. 358 p.: Ranger's apprentice.

Grades: 5 6 7 8 **Fic**
1. Teenage heroes and heroines 2. Gold thefts 3. Cult leaders 4. Cults 5. Courage in teenage boys 6. High fantasy 7. Fantasy fiction
ISBN 9780399252068

LC 2009041644

Halt, Will, and Horace set out for Hibernia, where a quasi-religious group, the Outsiders, is sowing confusion and sedition, and they find that secrets from Halt's past may hold the key to restoring order before the last kingdom is undermined.

"There's wit as well as action here, and the revelation of Halt's back-story adds a new dimension to the saga." Booklist.

The **lost** stories. John Flanagan. Philomel Books, 2011. 422 p.: Ranger's apprentice.

Grades: 5 6 7 8 **Fic**
1. Teenage heroes and heroines 2. Teenage apprentices 3. Teenage boy orphans 4. Warriors 5. Imaginary wars and battles 6. High fantasy 7. Fantasy fiction
ISBN 9780399256189

In 1896, an archaeological dig unearths an ancient trunk containing manuscripts that confirm the existence of Araluen Rangers Will and Halt and tell of their first meeting and some of their previously unknown exploits.

"This is a collection of nine stories showing events not recorded in the books [of the Ranger's Apprentice series] and following the familiar characters during certain unrecorded times. In the framework story, set in 1896, an archaeologist discovers the fabled lost stories of the medieval Kingdom of Araluen. . . . Inspired by questions from readers, these short stories retain the adventure and the camaraderis of the novels." Booklist.

★ The **ruins** of Gorlan. John Flanagan. Philomel Books, 2005. 249 p.: Ranger's apprentice.

Grades: 5 6 7 8 **Fic**
1. Teenage apprentices 2. Teenage boy orphans 3. Courage in teenage boys 4. Teenage heroes and heroines 5. Courage 6. High fantasy 7. Fantasy fiction
ISBN 0399244549

LC 2004027735

When fifteen-year-old Will is rejected by battleschool, he becomes the reluctant apprentice to the mysterious Ranger Halt, and winds up protecting the kingdom from danger.

"Flanagan concentrates on character, offering readers a young protagonist they will care about and relationships that develop believably over time." Booklist.

The **siege** of Macindaw. John Flanagan. Philomel Books, 2009. 293 p.: Ranger's apprentice.

Grades: 5 6 7 8 **Fic**
    1. Teenage heroes and heroines 2. Courage in teenage boys 3. Sieges 4. Teenage boys 5. Teenagers 6. High fantasy 7. Fantasy fiction
ISBN 9780399250330

LC 2008032630

Now a full-fledged Ranger, Will must rescue his friend Alyss from a rogue knight and uncover vital information needed to ward off a Scotti invasion.

"Series fans will relish the familiar details of warfare and comradeship as well as the surprising fireworks in both war and love." Booklist.

The **sorcerer** of the north. John Flanagan. Philomel Books, 2008. 295 p.: Ranger's apprentice.

Grades: 5 6 7 8 **Fic**
    1. Teenage heroes and heroines 2. Black magic 3. Hostage taking 4. Poisoning 5. Rescues 6. High fantasy 7. Fantasy fiction
ISBN 0399250328

LC 2008016528

Now a full-fledged Ranger responsible for a sleepy fief, Will finds a new adventure seeking the traitors who poisoned the king, investigating rumors of sorcery, and trying to rescue his friend Alyss, who is taken hostage.

"Flanagan is to be complimented for creating a fantasy world that relies on character and action rather than magic." Voice of Youth Advocates.

The **tournament** at Gorlan. John Flanagan. Philomel Books, an imprint of Penguin Group (USA), [2015] 384 p.: Ranger's apprentice.

Grades: 5 6 7 8 **Fic**
    1. Apprentices 2. Coups d'etat 3. Conspiracies 4. Princes 5. Rulers 6. High fantasy 7. Fantasy fiction
ISBN 9780399163616

LC bl2015029341

Halt and Crowley, discovering that Morgarath has designs on the throne, must tread a dangerous path, one that leads them to the annual tournament at Gorlan, where a series of duels must be fought and won.

Fleischman, Paul

Bull Run. Paul Fleischman; woodcuts by David Frampton. Harper Collins, 1993. 104 p.

Grades: 6 7 8 9 **Fic**
    1. American Civil War era (1861-1865) 2. Children and war 3. Bull Run, 1st Battle, 1861 4. Civil war 5. United States Civil War, 1861-1865 6. United States 7. Historical fiction 8. War stories
ISBN 0060214465

LC 92014745

Scott O'Dell Historical Fiction Award, 1994.

Northerners, Southerners, generals, couriers, dreaming boys and worried sisters describe the glory, the horror, the thrill, and the disillusionment of the first battle of the Civil War.

"Abandoning the conventions of narrative fiction, Fleischman tells a vivid, many-sided story in this original and moving book. An excellent choice for readers' theater in the classroom or on stage." Booklist.

Graven images: three stories. by Paul Fleischman; illustrations by Andrew Glass. Harper & Row, 1982. 85 p.

Grades: 5 6 7 8 **Fic**
    1. Statues 2. Fantasy fiction
ISBN 0060219068

LC 81048649

Three stories about people whose lives are affected by sculptured objects.

"Readers will be delighted with the return to print of [this title] with haunting new acrylic gouache illustrations . . . evoking the spinetingling aspects of this trio of tales. . . . Via a new afterword, the author explains the stories' inspiration and describes this book's significance early in his career." Publishers Weekly.

Seedfolks. Paul Fleischman; illustrations by Judy Pederson. Harper Collins, c1997 69 p.

Grades: 4 5 6 7 **Fic**
    1. Multiethnic neighborhoods 2. Community gardening 3. City life 4. Gardens 5. Empty lots 6. Cleveland, Ohio
ISBN 0060274727

LC 9626696

One by one, a number of people of varying ages and backgrounds transform a trash-filled inner-city into a productive and beautiful garden, and in doing so, the gardeners are themselves transformed.

"This novel tells about an urban garden started by a child and nurtured by people of all ages and ethnic and economic backgrounds. Each of the thirteen chapters is narrated by a different character, allowing the reader to watch as a community develops out of disconnected lives and prior suspicions." Horn Book Guide.

Fleischman, Sid, 1920-2010

★ The **whipping** boy. Illustrations by Peter Sis. Greenwillow Books, 1986. 90 p.

Grades: 5 6 7 8 **Fic**
    1. Role reversal 2. Princes 3. Spoiled children 4. Thieves 5. Adventure stories 6. Classics
ISBN 0688062164

LC 85017555

Newbery Medal, 1987.

A bratty prince and his "whipping boy" have many adventures when they inadvertently trade places after becoming involved with dangerous outlaws.

"A round tale of adventure and humor, this follows the fortunes of Prince Roland (better known as Prince Brat) and his whipping boy, Jemmy, who has received all the hard knocks for the prince's mischief. . . . There's not a moment's lag in pace, and the stock characters, from Hold-Your-Nose Billy to Betsy's dancing bear Petunia, have enough inventive twists to project a lively air to it all." Bulletin of the Center for Children's Books.

Fleming, Candace

On the day I died: stories from the grave. Candace Fleming. Schwartz & Wade Books, 2012. 208 p.

Grades: 6 7 8 9 **Fic**
    1. Teenagers 2. Ghosts 3. Cemeteries 4. Illinois 5. Horror 6. Short stories
ISBN 9780375867811

LC 2011018661

In a lonely Illinois cemetery one cold October night, teen ghosts recount the stories of their deaths in different time periods, from 1870 to the present, to sixteen-year-old Mike, who unknowingly picked up a phantom hitchhiker.

Fletcher, Charlie, 1960-

Ironhand. Charlie Fletcher. Hyperion Books for Children, 2008. 389 p.: Stoneheart trilogy

Grades: 5 6 7 8   **Fic**
1. Statues 2. Parallel universes 3. Kidnapping 4. Rescues 5. Gargoyles 6. London, England 7. Gateway fantasy 8. Fantasy fiction
ISBN 9781423101772

LC 2007042073

Having upset the balance between the warring statues of London, twelve-year-old George is confronted with new challenges as he tries to free his captured friends Edie and The Gunner from the formidable Walker and deal with the three strange veins of marble, bronze, and stone that have begun to grow out of his hand.

"Cliff-hanger chapters . . . will leave readers breathless. George's story is particularly vivid." Booklist.

Silvertongue. Charlie Fletcher. Disney/Hyperion, 2009, c2008. 464 p.: Stoneheart trilogy

Grades: 5 6 7 8   **Fic**
1. Statues 2. Parallel universes 3. Knights and knighthood 4. Space and time 5. Gargoyles 6. London, England 7. Gateway fantasy 8. Fantasy fiction
ISBN 9781423101796

LC bl2009008483

As the battle between the statues and gargoyles of London rages, twelve-year-old George Chapman is stalked by The Dark Knight, while George's friend Edie seeks revenge on the Walker.

"George and Edie's action-packed experiences are told in alternate chapters. . . . The book does not stand on its own, but those familiar with the earlier titles will be satisfied." School Library Journal.

Stoneheart. by Charlie Fletcher. Hyperion Books for Children, 2007. 484 p.: Stoneheart trilogy

Grades: 5 6 7 8   **Fic**
1. Statues 2. Riddles 3. Parallel universes 4. Sphinxes 5. London, England 6. Gateway fantasy 7. Fantasy fiction
ISBN 9781423101758

LC 2007001138

When twelve-year-old George accidentally decapitates a stone statue in London, England, he falls into a parallel dimension where he must battle ancient "live" statues and solve a dangerous riddle.

"This is an action-packed fantasy filled with battles, chases, and an intriguing variety of characters." School Library Journal.

Fletcher, Susan, 1951-

Alphabet of dreams. Susan Fletcher. Atheneum Books for Young Readers, c2006. 304 p.

Grades: 6 7 8 9 10   **Fic**
1. Jesus Christ 2. 1st century BCE 3. Orphans 4. Princesses 5. Teenage girls 6. Brothers and sisters 7. Magi 8. Iran -- History. 9. Historical fiction
ISBN 0689850425

LC 2005036264

Fourteen-year-old Mitra, of royal Persian lineage, and her five-year-old brother Babak, whose dreams foretell the future, flee for their lives in the company of the magus Melchoir and two other Zoroastrian priests, traveling through Persia as they follow star signs leading to a newly-born king in Bethlehem. Includes historical notes.

"The characters are vivid and whole, the plot compelling, and the setting vast." Voice of Youth Advocates.

Dragon's milk. Susan Fletcher. Atheneum, 1989. 242p.: Dragon chronicles

Grades: 7 8 9 10   **Fic**
1. Girl adventurers 2. Dragons 3. Sisters 4. Fantasy fiction
ISBN 0689315791

LC 88035059

Kaeldra, an outsider adopted by an Elythian family as a baby, possesses the power to understand dragons and uses this power to try to save her younger sister who needs dragon's milk to recover from an illness.

"High-fantasy fans will delight in the clash of swords, the flash of magic, the many escape-and-rescue scenes." Booklist.

Flight of the Dragon Kyn. Atheneum, 1993. 213 p.: Dragon chronicles

Grades: 7 8 9 10   **Fic**
1. Dragons 2. Rulers 3. Fifteen-year-old girls 4. Fantasy fiction
ISBN 0689318804

LC 92044787 /AC

Fifteen-year-old Kara is summoned by King Orrik, who believes she has the power to call down the dragons that have been plundering his realm, and she is caught up in the fierce rivalry between Orrik and his jealous brother Rog.

"This is a solid fantasy in a medieval Scandinavian-like setting, and there's plenty of drama, romance, and knavery to keep genre fans happy." Bulletin of the Center for Children's Books.

Sign of the dove. Susan Fletcher. Atheneum Books for Young readers, 1996. 214 p.: Dragon chronicles

Grades: 7 8 9 10   **Fic**
1. Dragon babies 2. Extinction (Biology) 3. Girls and dragons 4. Fantasy fiction
ISBN 0689804601

LC 95584

As the last of the dragon eggs, laid long ago, begin to hatch, Lyf becomes a reluctant friend who tries to save both the dragon mothers and their newly hatched children from their enemies.

"The author offers a stalwart heroine in a rousing story filled with well-realized dragon lore." Booklist.

Flinn, Alex

Beastly. Alex Flinn. HarperTeen, 2007. 320 p.: Kendra chronicles

Grades: 6 7 8 9 10   **Fic**
1. Self-fulfillment in teenage boys 2. Pride and vanity 3. Transformations, Personal 4. Love 5. Transformations (Magic) 6. Manhattan, New York City 7. Fantasy fiction 8. Fairy tale and folklore-inspired fiction
ISBN 9780060874162

LC 2006036241

A modern retelling of "Beauty and the Beast" from the point of view of the Beast, a vain Manhattan private school student who is turned into a monster and must find true love before he can return to his human form.

"This is creative enough to make it an engaging read. . . . [This is an] engrossing tale that will have appeal for fans of fantasy and realistic fiction." Voice of Youth Advocates.

Cloaked. Alex Flinn. HarperTeen, 2011. 256 p.

Grades: 6 7 8 9   **Fic**
1. Witches 2. Transformations (Magic) 3. Magic cloaks 4. Missing persons 5. Shoes -- Repairing 6. Miami, Florida 7. Florida 8. Fantasy fiction 9. Fairy tale and folklore-inspired fiction
ISBN 9780060874223

"A diverting, whimsical romp through fairy-tale tropes." Bulletin of the Center for Children's Books.

A kiss in time. Alex Flinn. HarperTeen, c2009. 371 p.

Grades: 7 8 9 10 11 12 **Fic**
> 1. Princesses 2. Curses 3. Self-awareness in teenagers 4. Self-awareness 5. Kissing 6. Miami, Florida 7. Europe 8. Fantasy fiction 9. Fairy tale and folklore-inspired fiction
ISBN 9780060874193

LC 2008022582

Sixteen-year-old Princess Talia persuades seventeen-year-old Jack, the modern-day American who kissed her awake after a 300-year sleep, to take her to his Miami home, where she hopes to win his love before the witch who cursed her can spirit her away.

"This is a clever and humorous retelling of Sleeping Beauty. . . . Alternating between the teenagers' distinctive points of view, Flinn skillfully delineates how their upbringings set them apart while drawing parallels between their family conflicts. Fans of happily-ever-after endings will delight in the upbeat resolution." Publishers Weekly.

Flores-Scott, Patrick

American road trip. Patrick Flores-Scott. Christy Ottaviano Books, Henry Holt and Company, 2018. 272 p.

Grades: 7 8 9 10 11 12 **Fic**
> 1. Families of military personnel 2. Brothers 3. Mental illness 4. Automobile travel 5. Post-traumatic stress disorder 6. Realistic fiction 7. Coming-of-age stories
ISBN 9781627797412

LC 2018004255

Brothers Teodoro and Manny Avila take a road trip to address Manny's PTSD following his tour in Iraq, and to help T. change his life and win the heart of Wendy Martinez. Includes information and resources about PTSD.

"Featuring a diverse cast of delightful characters, this novel bursts with much-needed optimism." Kirkus.

Foley, Jessie Ann

Sorry for your loss. Jessie Ann Foley. HarperTeen, 2019 336 p.

Grades: 8 9 10 11 12 **Fic**
> 1. Teenage photographers 2. Bereavement 3. Large families 4. Loss (Psychology) 5. Photography 6. Chicago, Illinois 7. Coming-of-age stories 8. Realistic fiction
ISBN 9780062571915

An awkward teen, the youngest of eight children, navigates the loss of a sibling throughout a photography assignment that leads him to secrets, opportunities and an unexpected connection.— Atlas Publishing

"Written with Foley's keen ear for family dynamics, this is definitely a strong choice for fans of her work and those new to the author." School Library Journal.

Foley, Lizzie K.

Remarkable: a novel. by Lizzie K. Foley. Dial Books for Young Readers, 2012. 304 p.

Grades: 3 4 5 6 7 **Fic**
> 1. Twins 2. Pirates 3. Lake monsters 4. Psychic ability 5. Dentists 6. Humorous stories
ISBN 9780803737068

LC 2011021641

Ten-year-old Jane Doe, the only student average enough to be excluded from the town of Remarkable's School for the Remarkably Gifted, is joined at her public school by the trouble-making Grimlet twins, who lead her on a series of adventures involving an out-of-control science fair project, a pirate captain on the run from a mutinous crew, a lonely dentist, and a newly constructed bell tower that endangers Remarkable's most beloved inhabitant—a skittish lake monster named Lucky.

Fombelle, Timothée de, 1973-

Between sky and earth. Timothee de Fombelle. Candlewick Press, 2014, c1997. 432 p.: Vango

Grades: 9 10 11 12 **Fic**
> 1. 1930s 2. Between the Wars (1918-1939) 3. Treasure troves 4. Monks 5. Nazis 6. Murder 7. Murder suspects 8. Historical mysteries
ISBN 9780763671969

LC 2013955696

A gripping mystery-adventure set in the 1930s interwar period about a character desperately searching for his identity.—Publisher's description.

"de Fombelle has written a brilliant, wonderfully exciting story of flight and pursuit, filled with colorful characters and head-scratching mystery. As the novel proceeds, the suspense is ratcheted up to breathtaking levels as the boy remains only one step ahead of his relentless pursuers." Booklist.

Toby alone. Timothée de Fombelle; translated by Sarah Ardizzone; illustrated by Francois Place. Candlewick Press, 2009. 384 p.

Grades: 5 6 7 8 **Fic**
> 1. Miniature persons (Imaginary characters) 2. Trees 3. Environmentalism 4. Children of scientists 5. Oak 6. Fantasy fiction 7. Translations
ISBN 9780763641818

A Lilliputian world. A tree under threat. A boy hunted by his own people must protect his father's secrets in a gripping and witty eco-adventure.

"The impressive debut novel from French playwright de Fombelle deftly weaves mature political commentary, broad humor and some subtle satire into a thoroughly enjoyable adventure." Publishers Weekly.

Toby and the secrets of the tree. Timothée de Fombelle; illustrated by Francois Place. Candlewick Press, 2010. 414 p.

Grades: 5 6 7 8 **Fic**
> 1. Miniature persons (Imaginary characters) 2. Trees 3. Imprisonment 4. Environmentalism 5. Enemies 6. Fantasy fiction 7. Translations
ISBN 9780763646554

LC 2009014833

Thirteen-year-old Toby's tiny world is under greater threat than ever as Leo Blue holds Elisha prisoner while hunting the Grass People and anyone who stands in the way of his devastating plans for the oak Tree in which they all live, but this time Toby is not alone.

"Place's pen-and-ink illustrations are scattered generously throughout and enhance the overall quirkiness. . . . This interesting piece of eco-fantasy provides a satisfying conclusion for those who enjoyed the first book." School Library Journal.

Forbes, Esther

Johnny Tremain: a novel for old and young. Esther Forbes; illustrated by Lynd Ward. Houghton Mifflin, 1943. 256 p.

Grades: 5 6 7 8 **Fic**
> 1. Sons of Liberty. 2. Revolutionary America (1775-1783) 3. 18th century 4. Teenage boys with disabilities 5. Teenage apprentices 6. Children and war 7. Silversmiths 8. Hand -- Wounds and

injuries 9. Boston, Massachusetts 10. United States 11. Historical fiction 12. War stories 13. Classics
ISBN 0395067669

When a fourteen-year-old silversmith apprentice is severely burned by molten silver, he becomes a dispatch rider for the Committee for Public Safety where he meets many Boston patriots involved in the new struggle for independence from England. There he learns that he may be able to overcome his handicap enough to join the fight.

Ford, Christopher, 1981-

Stickman Odyssey.. Christopher Ford. Philomel Books, 2011. 208 p.: Stickman Odyssey

Grades: 5 6 7 8   **Fic**
1. Mythology, Greek 2. Witches 3. Exile (Punishment) 4. Monsters 5. Quests 6. Humorous comics 7. Mythological fiction 8. Comics and Graphic novels
ISBN 9780399254260

LC 2010036900

In this humorous take on the Odyssey, Zozimos, banished from his country by his evil stepmother, has many adventures as he prepares to return home to reclaim the throne that is rightfully his.

"The black-and-white illustrations are occasionally simple to the point of hilarity. . . . There is subtlety and depth here, however, and the contrast between the intentionally plain characters and their seemingly larger-than-life (but ultimately universal) quests . . . makes the final product both the promised Greek epic tale and an examination of the ways in which modern humans are isolated and lost. . . . Ford balances allegory and madcap quest so perfectly that the book inspires reflection even while it is clearly a quick-reading, ridiculous, often gross adventure." Bulletin of the Center for Children's Books.

Forman, Gayle

Where she went. by Gayle Forman. Dutton, 2011. 208 p.: If I stay

Grades: 7 8 9 10   **Fic**
1. Teenage rock musicians 2. Former girlfriends 3. Reunions 4. Cellists 5. Interpersonal relations 6. New York City 7. Realistic fiction
ISBN 9780525422945

Adam, now a rising rock star, and Mia, a successful cellist, reunite in New York and reconnect after the horrific events that tore them apart when Mia almost died in a car accident three years earlier.

"Both characters spring to life, and their pain-filled back story and current realities provide depth and will hold readers fast." Kirkus.

Fox, Janet S.

The **charmed** children of Rookskill Castle. by Janet Fox. Viking, an imprint of Penguin Random House LLC, 2016. 400 p.

Grades: 5 6 7 8 9   **Fic**
1. M I 6 2. Second World War era (1939-1945) 3. 1940s 4. Twelve-year-old girls 5. Spies 6. Witches 7. Missing persons 8. Secrecy 9. Scotland 10. London, England 11. Historical fantasy 12. Gothic fiction 13. Thrillers and suspense
ISBN 9780451476333

LC 2015020813

In 1940, during the Blitz, Katherine, Robbie and Amelie Bateson are sent north to a private school in Rookskill Castle in Scotland, a brooding place, haunted by dark magic from the past—but when some of their classmates disappear Katherine has to find out if the cause is hidden in the past or very much in the present.

"Fox presents readers with a wonderfully paced, exciting story with enough twists to keep the pages turning." School Library Journal.

Foxlee, Karen, 1971-

The **anatomy** of wings. Karen Foxlee. Alfred A. Knopf, 2009, c2007. 361 p.

Grades: 8 9 10 11 12   **Fic**
1. 1980s 2. Death 3. Suicide 4. Grief 5. Ten-year-old girls 6. Sisters -- Death 7. Queensland 8. Australia 9. Realistic fiction
ISBN 9780375856433

With her family falling apart from the sudden death of one of their own, ten-year-old Jennifer is left alone to look for answers to questions about what happened and why in the final month's of her beloved sister's short life in the hopes of finding the closure she so desperately seeks.

"Jenny's observations are . . . poetic and washed with magic realism. . . . With heart-stopping accuracy and sly symbolism, Foxlee captures the small ways that humans reveal themselves, the mysterious intensity of female adolescence, and the surreal quiet of a grieving house, which slowly and with astonishing resilience fills again with sound and music." Booklist.

Fraillon, Zana

The **bone** sparrow. by Zana Fraillon. Disney-Hyperion, 2016. 234 p.

Grades: 4 5 6 7 8   **Fic**
1. Refugees 2. Friendship 3. Grief in girls 4. Immigration prisons 5. Storytelling 6. Australia 7. Realistic fiction
ISBN 9781484781517

LC 2016002391

Subhi's contained world as a refugee in an Australian permanent detention center rapidly expands when Jimmie arrives on the other side of the fence and asks him to read her late mother's stories to her. Provided by publisher.

"Appended with a glimpse at the 'all-too-true reality' of refugee maltreatment, this tale is breathtaking and indispensable." Booklist.

Frank, Steven, 1963-

Armstrong and Charlie. written by Steven B. Frank. Houghton Mifflin Harcourt, 2017. 304 p.

Grades: 5 6 7 8   **Fic**
1. 1970s 2. Interracial friendship 3. Prejudice 4. African Americans 5. Friendship 6. Race relations 7. Los Angeles, California 8. United States 9. Historical fiction
ISBN 9780544826083

LC 2016014199

During the pilot year of a Los Angeles school system integration program, two sixth grade boys, one black, one white, become best friends as they learn to cope with everything from first crushes and playground politics to the loss of loved ones and racial prejudice in the 1970s. Provided by publisher.

"Unforgettable, well-drawn titular characters are the heart of this deeply moving and laugh-out-loud funny story about family, friendship, integrity, and navigating differences." Kirkus.

Frederick, Heather Vogel

Absolutely Truly: a Pumpkin Falls mystery. Heather Vogel Frederick. Simon & Schuster Books for Young Readers, 2014. 384 p.: Pumpkin Falls mysteries

Grades: 4 5 6 7   **Fic**
1. Small towns 2. Bookstores 3. Fathers and daughters 4. Post-traumatic stress disorder 5. Children of military personnel 6. New Hampshire 7. Mysteries
ISBN 9781442429727

Twelve-year-old Truly Lovejoy's family moves to a small town to take over a bookstore. Soon, she has to solve two mysteries involving a missing book and an undelivered letter. Provided by publisher.

Dear pen pal. Heather Vogel Frederick. Simon & Schuster Books for Young Readers, c2009. 406 p.: Mother-Daughter Book Club

Grades: 5 6 7 8   **Fic**
     1. Webster, Jean, 1876-1916. Daddy-Long-Legs 2. Book clubs 3. Mothers and daughters 4. Interpersonal relations 5. Books and reading 6. Friendship 7. Concord, Massachusetts 8. Wyoming 9. Realistic fiction
ISBN 9781416974307

                         LC 2009014982
Four very different friends in Concord, Massachusetts, and their mothers continue their book club, reading Jean Webster's "Daddy Long-Legs," while getting to know their own pen pals from Wyoming.

Home for the holidays. Heather Vogel Frederick. Simon & Schuster Books for Young Readers, c2011. 339 p.: Mother-Daughter Book Club

Grades: 6 7 8 9   **Fic**
     1. Dickens, Charles, 1812-1870. Christmas carol. 2. Mothers and daughters 3. Book clubs 4. Books and reading 5. Christmas 6. Interpersonal relations 7. Realistic fiction
ISBN 9781442406858

Four girls continue their mother-daughter book club, reading Charles Dickens's "A Christmas Carol," but from unexpected blizzards to a sledding disaster, nothing goes as planned.

The **Mother-Daughter** Book Club. Heather Vogel Frederick. Simon & Schuster Books for Young Readers, 2007. 256 p.: Mother-Daughter Book Club

Grades: 4 5 6 7   **Fic**
     1. Alcott, Louisa May, 1832-1888. Little women 2. Book clubs 3. Mothers and daughters 4. Interpersonal relations 5. Books and reading 6. Friendship 7. Concord, Massachusetts 8. Massachusetts 9. Realistic fiction
ISBN 9780689864124

                         LC 2006024818
When the mothers of four sixth-grade girls with very different personalities pressure them into forming a book club, they find, as they read and discuss "Little Women," that they have much more in common than they could have imagined.

Much ado about Anne. Heather Vogel Frederick. Simon & Schuster Books for Young Readers, 2008. 324 p.: Mother-Daughter Book Club

Grades: 4 5 6 7   **Fic**
     1. Montgomery, L. M. (Lucy Maud), 1874-1942. Anne of Green Gables. 2. Book clubs 3. Mothers and daughters 4. Fund-raising 5. Farms 6. Interpersonal relations 7. Concord, Massachusetts 8. Massachusetts 9. Realistic fiction
ISBN 9780689855665

                         LC 2008007324
Entering seventh grade at Walden Middle School, four girls continue their mother-daughter book club, reading Lucy Maud Montgomery's "Anne of Green Gables," while dealing with a mean, troublemaking classmate.

Pies & prejudice. Heather Vogel Frederick. Simon & Schuster Books for Young Readers, 2010. 378 p.: Mother-Daughter Book Club

Grades: 6 7 8 9   **Fic**
     1. Austen, Jane, 1775-1817. Pride and prejudice. 2. Mothers and daughters 3. Book clubs 4. Books and reading 5. Interpersonal relations 6. Moving to a new country 7. Concord, Massachusetts 8. England 9. Realistic fiction
ISBN 9781416974314

                         LC 2010015921
Four girls, and their mothers, continue their mother-daughter book club via videoconference between Massachusetts and England, reading Jane Austen's "Pride and Prejudice," and try to put friendship before romance.

Yours Truly. Heather Vogel Frederick. Simon & Schuster Books for Young Readers, [2017] 272 p.: Pumpkin Falls mysteries

Grades: 4 5 6 7   **Fic**
     1. Sabotage 2. Farms 3. Diaries 4. Maple 5. Small towns 6. New Hampshire 7. New Hampshire 8. Mysteries
ISBN 9781442471863

                         LC 2016031402
When someone tries to sabotage the maple trees on her friend Franklin's family farm, Truly Lovejoy rallies the Pumpkin Falls Private Eyes to investigate.

Freitas, Donna

Unplugged. Donna Freitas. Harperteen, 2016. 448 p.: The wired (Donna Freitas)

Grades: 8 9 10 11   **Fic**
     1. Mother-separated teenage girls 2. Paraphysics 3. Virtual reality 4. Teenage girls 5. Dystopias 6. Dystopian fiction 7. Science fiction
ISBN 9780062118608

Years after being sent by her family to the extravagant virtual App World to live a life of wealth and privilege, Skylar relinquishes the glamour and prestige of her expensive downloads in favor of spending time with her family in the Real World, an effort that is dashed when the borders between worlds suddenly close.

"Despite imperfections, one of the more ambitious and thought-provoking entries in a crowded genre." Kirkus.

French, Jackie

Hitler's daughter. Jackie French. Harper Collins, 2003, c1999. 121 p.

Grades: 4 5 6   **Fic**
     1. Hitler, Adolf, 1889-1945 2. Children 3. Good and evil -- Psychological aspects 4. Genocide -- Moral and ethical aspects 5. Nazism 6. Australia
ISBN 9780060086527

After hearing a fictional tale about Hitler's daughter, Mark, an Australian boy, wonders what it would be like if someone he loved and trusted turned out to be evil.

"French's style is precise and effective. Her descriptions vividly profile even secondary characters." Bulletin of the Center for Children's Books.

French, Susannah T.

Operation Redwood. by S. Terrell French. Amulet Books, 2009. 368 p.

Grades: 4 5 6 7   **Fic**
1. Child heroes 2. Determination (Personal quality) 3. Environmental protection 4. Uncles 5. Determination in children 6. Northern California
ISBN 9780810983540

LC 2008030724

In northern California, Julian Carter-Li and his friends old and new fight to save a grove of redwoods from an investment company that plans to cut them down.

French, Vivian

The **robe** of skulls. Vivian French; illustrated by Ross Collins. Candlewick Press, 2008. 200 p.: Tales from the five kingdoms
Grades: 4 5 6   **Fic**
1. Witches 2. Dresses 3. Transformations (Magic) 4. Princes 5. Identical twins 6. Fantasy fiction 7. Humorous stories
ISBN 9780763635312

LC 2007038290

When she realizes that she has no treasure left with which to purchase a stunning new gown, evil sorceress Lady Lamorna lets loose with a blood-curdling scream heard by everyone in the village of Fracture—everyone, that is, but Gracie Gillypot. Gracie barely hears a peep—but it won't be long before she's called on to help rescue the kingdom's princes, whom Lady Lamorna has turned into frogs.

"Collins' black-and-white line drawings, dropped haphazardly into the text, perfectly complement the story, offering visual metaphors for the heady narrative mix of melodrama and humor." Bulletin of the Center for Children's Books.

Freymann-Weyr, Garret, 1965-

My heartbeat. Garret Freymann-Weyr. Houghton Mifflin Co., 2002. 154 p.
Grades: 7 8 9 10   **Fic**
1. Brothers and sisters 2. Gay teenagers 3. Fourteen-year-old girls 4. Teenagers -- Interpersonal relations 5. Teenage girls -- Family relationships 6. Realistic fiction
ISBN 0618141812

LC 2001047059

As she tries to understand the closeness between her older brother and his best friend, fourteen-year-old Ellen finds her relationship with each of them changing.

"This beautiful novel tells a frank, upbeat story of teen bisexual love in all its uncertainty, pain, and joy. . . . The fast, clipped dialogue will sweep teens into the story, as will Ellen's immediate first-person, present-tense narrative." Booklist.

Friedman, Aimee

Two Summers. Aimee Friedman. Point, 2016. 352 p.
Grades: 7 8 9 10   **Fic**
1. Americans in France 2. Family secrets 3. Self-discovery in teenage girls 4. Self-discovery 5. Fathers and daughters 6. France 7. New York (State) 8. Realistic fiction
ISBN 9780545518079

LC 2015036385

Two possible futures face Summer: either she will spend the summer in Provence with her father, uncovering family secrets, and exploring the old world, or she will stay in upstate New York, coping with her mother, and dreaming of her long time crush—and which future unfolds will depend on whether or not she answers a phone call.

Friedman, Laurie B., 1964-

Can you say catastrophe? by Laurie Friedman. Darby Creek, [2013] 151 p.: Mostly miserable life of April Sinclair
Grades: 5 6 7 8   **Fic**
1. Crushes in teenage girls 2. Humiliation 3. Family vacations 4. Families 5. Teenage girls 6. Realistic fiction
ISBN 9781467709255

LC 2012048867

April Sinclair can't wait to get away from her crazy family for a few weeks and go to summer camp with her two best friends.

"By tale's end, it is evident that this humorous, spirited teen is poised to triumph over the challenges of adolescence." Kirkus.

Friend, Natasha, 1972-

Bounce. Natasha Friend. Scholastic Press, 2007. 188 p.
Grades: 6 7 8 9   **Fic**
1. Blended families 2. Remarriage 3. Popularity 4. Moving to a new state 5. Schools 6. Boston, Massachusetts 7. Massachusetts 8. Realistic fiction
ISBN 9780439853507

LC 2006038126

Thirteen-year-old Evyn's world is turned upside-down when her father, widowed since she was a toddler, suddenly decides to remarry a woman with six children, move with Ev and her brother from Maine to Boston, and enroll her in private school.

"The author presents, through hip conversations and humor, believable characters and a feel-good story with a satisfying amount of pathos." School Library Journal.

How we roll. by Natasha Friend. Farrar Straus Giroux, 2018. 272 p.
Grades: 7 8 9 10 11   **Fic**
1. Self-acceptance 2. People with disabilities 3. Love 4. Alopecia areata 5. People who have had amputations 6. Massachusetts 7. Contemporary romances
ISBN 9780374305666

LC 2017042313

After developing alopecia Quinn lost her friends along with her hair and former football player Jake lost his legs and confidence after an accident, but the two help each other believe in themselves and the possibility of love.

Lush. Natasha Friend. Scholastic Press, 2006. 192 p.
Grades: 7 8 9 10   **Fic**
1. Children of alcoholic fathers 2. Letter writing 3. Family violence 4. Alcoholism 5. Fathers 6. Realistic fiction
ISBN 043985346X

LC 2005031333

Unable to cope with her father's alcoholism, thirteen-year-old Sam corresponds with an older student, sharing her family problems and asking for advice.

"Friend adeptly takes a teen problem and turns it into a believable, sensitive, character-driven story, with realistic dialogue." Booklist.

Perfect. Natasha Friend. Milkweed Editions, 2004. 172 p.
Grades: 6 7 8 9   **Fic**
1. Bulimia 2. Teenage girls with eating disorders 3. Grief in teenage girls 4. Grief 5. Eating disorders 6. Realistic fiction
ISBN 1571316515

LC 2004006371

Following the death of her father, a thirteen-year-old uses bulimia as a way to avoid her mother's and ten-year-old sister's grief, as well as her own.

"Isabelle's grief and anger are movingly and honestly portrayed, and her eventual empathy for her mother is believable and touching." Booklist.

Friesner, Esther M.

Nobody's princess. Esther Friesner. Random House, 2007. 320 p.: Princesses of myth

Grades: 6 7 8 9 10 **Fic**
1. Helen of Troy (Greek mythology) 2. Princesses 3. Young women 4. Gods and goddesses 5. Gender role 6. Mediterranean Region 7. Historical fiction 8. Mythological fiction
ISBN 9780375875281

LC 2006006515

Determined to fend for herself in a world where only men have real freedom, headstrong Helen, who will be called queen of Sparta and Helen of Troy one day, learns to fight, hunt, and ride horses while disguised as a boy, and goes on an adventure throughout the Mediterranean world.

"This is a fascinating portrait. . . . Along the way, Friesner skillfully exposes larger issues of women's rights, human bondage, and individual destiny. It's a rollicking good story." Booklist.

Nobody's prize. Esther Friesner. Random House, c2008. 306 p.: Princesses of myth

Grades: 6 7 8 9 **Fic**
1. Ancient Greece (800 BCE-640 CE) 2. Helen of Troy (Greek mythology) 3. Quests 4. Voyages and travels 5. Princesses 6. Young women 7. Ancient Greece 8. Mediterranean Region 9. Mythological fiction 10. Adventure stories
ISBN 037587531X

LC 2007008395

Still longing for adventure, Princess Helen of Sparta maintains her disguise as a boy to join her unsuspecting brothers as part of the crew of the Argo, the ship commanded by Prince Jason in his quest for the Golden Fleece.

"Friesner is an accomplished writer who is able to interweave a contemporary feel for these ancient characters with pieces of history and mythology. She can also be funny. . . . It is possible for readers to begin with this book. . . . But it is surely best enjoyed as part of a series, and libraries with the first book will want to make sure fans get their second helping." Voice of Youth Advocates.

Sphinx's princess. Esther Friesner. Random House, 2009. 370 p.: Princesses of myth

Grades: 8 9 10 11 12 **Fic**
1. Nefertiti, Queen of Egypt, 14th cent. B.C.E. 2. Ancient Egypt (3100 BCE-640 CE) 3. Women rulers 4. Power (Social sciences) 5. Duty 6. Beauty 7. Aunts 8. Egypt 9. Ancient Egypt. 10. Historical fiction
ISBN 9780375956546

LC 2009013719

Although she is a dutiful daughter, Nefertiti's dancing abilities, remarkable beauty, and intelligence garner attention near and far, so much so that her family is summoned to the Egyptian royal court, where Nefertiti becomes a pawn in the power play of her scheming aunt, Queen Tiye.

"Dramatic plot twists, a powerful female subject, and engrossing details of life in ancient Egypt make for lively historical fiction." Booklist.

Sphinx's queen. Esther Friesner. Random House, 2010. 288 p.: Princesses of myth

Grades: 8 9 10 11 12 **Fic**
1. Nefertiti, Queen of Egypt, 14th cent. B.C.E. 2. Ancient Egypt (3100 BCE-640 CE) 3. Women rulers 4. Malicious accusation 5. Resourcefulness in teenage girls 6. Resourcefulness 7. Justice 8. Egypt 9. Ancient Egypt. 10. Historical fiction
ISBN 9780375856570

LC 2010013769

Chased after by the prince and his soldiers for a crime she did not commit, Nefertiti finds temporary refuge in the wild hills along the Nile's west bank before returning to the royal court to plead her case to the Pharaoh.

"This is written in fine prose that expresses the questioning of religion that most young people experience as they approach maturity. . . . This deeply moral book tells a good story; or, rather, this good story reveals deeply moral truths." School Library Journal.

Threads and flames. by Esther Friesner. Viking, 2010. 304 p.

Grades: 6 7 8 9 10 **Fic**
1. Triangle Shirtwaist Company, Inc., New York City -- Fire, 1911. 2. 1910s 3. Teenage immigrants 4. Fires 5. Immigrants, Polish 6. Jewish teenage girls 7. Thirteen-year-old girls 8. New York City 9. Historical fiction
ISBN 9780670012459

LC 2009050306

After recovering from typhus, thirteen-year-old Raisa leaves her Polish shtetl for America to join her older sister, and goes to work at the Triangle Shirtwaist factory.

"Friesner's sparkling prose makes the immigrant experience in New York's Lower East Side come alive. . . . Readers will turn the pages with rapt attention to follow the characters' intrepid, risk-all adventures in building new lives." Booklist.

Fritz, Jean

Homesick: my own story. by Jean Fritz; illustrated with drawings by Margot Tomes and photographs. G. P. Putnam's Sons, 1982. 163 p.

Grades: 5 6 7 8 **Fic**
1. Fritz, Jean. 2. 1920s 3. Americans in China 4. Children's literature authors, American 20th century 5. Immigrants 6. Politics and culture 7. China 8. Autobiographical fiction
ISBN 0399209336

LC 82007646

National Book Award for Children's Books, 1983.

The author's fictionalized version of her childhood in China in the 1920's.

"The descriptions of places and the times are vivid in a book that brings to the reader, with sharp clarity and candor, the yearnings and fears and ambivalent loyalties of a young girl." Bulletin of the Center for Children's Books.

Frost, Helen, 1949-

All he knew. Helen Frost. Farrar Straus Giroux Books for Young Readers, 2020. 272 p.

Grades: 5 6 7 8 **Fic**
1. Second World War era (1939-1945) 2. Children -- Institutional care 3. People who are deaf 4. Conscientious objectors 5. Institutionalized persons 6. World War II 7. Novels in verse 8. Historical fiction
ISBN 9780374312992

LC 2019033347

Scott O'Dell Historical Fiction Award, 2021.

In 1939 six-year-old Henry, who is deaf, is taken from his family and placed in a home for the feeble-minded where, years later, his friends include a conscientious objector serving there during World War II. Includes historical notes.

"Frost balances descriptions of institutional abuse with strong characters and enduring hope." Publishers Weekly

Diamond Willow. Helen Frost. Farrar, Straus and Giroux, c2008. viii, 111 p.

Grades: 5 6 7 8 **Fic**

1. Spirits 2. Sled dogs 3. Girls and dogs 4. Dogs 5. Families 6. Alaska 7. Novels in verse 8. Adventure stories

ISBN 9780374317768

LC 2006037438

In a remote area of Alaska, twelve-year-old Willow helps her father with their sled dogs when she is not at school, wishing she were more popular, all the while unaware that the animals surrounding her carry the spirits of dead ancestors and friends who care for her.

"Willow relates her story in one-page poems, each of which contains a hidden message printed in darker type. . . . Her poems offer pensive imagery and glimpses of character, and strong emotion. This complex and elegant novel will resonate with readers who savor powerful drama and multifaceted characters." School Library Journal.

Keesha's house. Helen Frost. Frances Foster Books/Farrar, Straus and Giroux, 2003. 116 p.

Grades: 7 8 9 10 **Fic**

1. Teenagers 2. Home (Concept) 3. Family problems 4. Interpersonal relations 5. Homosexuality 6. Novels in verse 7. Urban fiction 8. Realistic fiction

ISBN 0374340641

LC 2002022698

Seven teens facing such problems as pregnancy, closeted homosexuality, and abuse each describe in poetic forms what caused them to leave home and where they found home again.

"Spare, eloquent, and elegantly concise. . . . Public, private, or correctional educators and librarians should put this must-read on their shelves." Voice of Youth Advocates.

Fukuda, Andrew Xia

The **prey**. Andrew Fukuda. St. Martin's Griffin, c2013 326 p.: The hunt trilogy

Grades: 7 8 9 10 11 12 **Fic**

1. Cults 2. Cult leaders 3. Vampires 4. Dystopias 5. Villages 6. Science fiction 7. Horror

ISBN 9781250005113

Struggling to avoid murderous predators in The Vast and haunted by feelings for both Sissy and the girl he left behind, Gene and his group of human survivors join a refuge of exiles in the mountains only to become subject to secretive elders who impose strict and punishing codes of behavior.

Funaro, Gregory

The **alchemist's** shadow. Gregory Funaro. Harper, an imprint of HarperCollinsPublishers, 2020. 240 p.: Watch Hollow

Grades: 4 5 6 7 **Fic**

1. Brothers and sisters 2. Manors 3. Magic clocks and watches 4. Governesses 5. Twins 6. Supernatural mysteries 7. Horror

ISBN 9780062643483

Having defeated the Garr, a vicious tree monster who lived within the enchanted woods of Watch Hollow, Lucy and Oliver Tinker now have the home they've always dreamed of: Blackford House. Powered by a magical clock and full of curious rooms and improbable knick-knacks, Blackford House brims with the promise of new adventures.

Funke, Cornelia, 1958-

Fearless. Cornelia Funke. Little, Brown Books for Young Readers, 2013. 400 p.: Mirrorworld

Grades: 6 7 8 9 **Fic**

1. Curses 2. Shapeshifters 3. Parallel universes 4. Magic mirrors 5. Crossbows 6. Gateway fantasy 7. Fantasy fiction 8. Translations

ISBN 9780316056106

LC 2012028742

Jacob Reckless journeys to the Mirrorworld to tell his shapeshifting friend Fox that a fairy curse—a deadly moth in his chest—means he has only one year to live. The journey in Mirrorworld turns into a search against time and against a Goyl treasure hunter for an enchanted crossbow, which is known to strike down any army it faces, and less well known for its healing power when shot by a loved one. Provided by publisher.

"Adroitly building on layers of European fairy tale, Funke's original, rapid-fire narrative fearlessly transports Jacob and a bevy of ominous, multifaceted fantastical characters through a dark, decaying landscape in which death waits and honor is rare. Provocative, harrowing, engrossing." Kirkus.

Inkdeath. Cornelia Funke; translated from the German by Anthea Bell. Chicken House/Scholastic Inc., 2008. 656 p.: Inkheart trilogy

Grades: 5 6 7 8 **Fic**

1. Kidnapping 2. Books and reading 3. Bookbinding 4. Characters and characteristics in literature 5. Magic 6. Italy 7. Fantasy fiction 8. Metafiction

ISBN 9780439866286

LC 2008019922

As Bluejay—Mo's fictitious double—tries to keep the Book of Immortality from unraveling, Adderhead kidnaps all the children in the kingdom, asking for Bluejay's surrender or the children will be doomed to slavery in the silver mines.

"The assortment of villains is vivid and frightening. . . . The finale includes a thoroughly engrossing climax." School Library Journal.

Inkheart. Cornelia Funke. Scholastic, 2003. 534 p.: Inkheart trilogy

Grades: 5 6 7 8 **Fic**

1. Twelve-year-old girls 2. Books and reading 3. Characters and characteristics in literature 4. Magic 5. Bookbinding 6. Italy 7. Fantasy fiction 8. Metafiction

ISBN 0439531640

LC 2003045844

Twelve-year-old Meggie learns that her father, who repairs and binds books for a living, can "read" fictional characters to life when one of those characters abducts them and tries to force him into service.

"The author proves the power of her imagination; readers will be captivated by the chilling and thrilling world she has created here." Publishers Weekly.

Inkspell. Cornelia Funke; translated from the German by Anthea Bell. Scholastic, 2005 635 p.: Inkheart trilogy

Grades: 5 6 7 8 **Fic**

1. Teenage girls 2. Characters and characteristics in literature 3. Apprentices 4. Villains 5. Parents 6. Italy 7. Fantasy fiction 8. Metafiction

ISBN 0439554004

"This is an involving story that will draw readers smoothly to its conclusion and leave them waiting for the final volume in this projected trilogy." School Library Journal.

The **Thief** Lord. Cornelia Funke; [English translation, Oliver Latsch]. Scholastic, 2002. 345 p.
Grades: 6 7 8 9   **Fic**
    1. Runaway children 2. Thieves 3. Brothers 4. Detectives 5. Venice, Italy 6. Translations
ISBN 0439404371
          LC 2002021037
Mildred L. Batchelder Award, 2003.
    Two brothers, having run away from the aunt who plans to adopt the younger one, are sought by a detective hired by their aunt, but they have found shelter with—and the protection of—Venice's "Thief Lord."
    "This is a compelling tale, rich in ingenious twists, with a setting and cast that will linger in readers' memories." School Library Journal.

Fusco, Kimberly Newton

Beholding Bee. Kimberly Newton Fusco. Alfred A. Knopf, 2013. 336 p.
Grades: 5 6 7 8   **Fic**
    1. 1940s 2. Girl orphans 3. Runaway girls 4. Birthmarks 5. Carnivals 6. Identity (Psychology) 7. Historical fiction
ISBN 9780375868368
          LC 2012005091
In 1942, when life turns sour at the carnival that has always been her home, eleven-year-old Bee takes her dog, Peabody, and piglet, Cordelia, and sets out to find a real home, aided by two women only Bee and her pets can see.

Chasing Augustus. Kimberly Newton Fusco. Random House Childrens Books, 2017. 336 p.
Grades: 4 5 6 7 8   **Fic**
    1. Determination in teenage girls 2. Teenagers and dogs 3. Searching 4. Mother-deserted children 5. Grandfather and granddaughter
ISBN 9780385754019
Rosie's led a charmed life with her loving dad, who runs the town donut shop. It's true her mother abandoned them when Rosie was just a baby, but her dad's all she's ever needed. But now that her father's had a stroke, Rosie lives with her tough-as-nails grandfather. And her beloved dog, Gloaty Gus, has just gone missing. Rosie's determined to find him. With the help of a new friend and her own determination, she'll follow the trail anywhere . . . no matter where it leads. If she doesn't drive the whole world crazy in the meantime.

The **wonder** of Charlie Anne. Kimberly Fusco. Alfred A. Knopf, c2010. 266 p.
Grades: 5 6 7 8   **Fic**
    1. Depression era (1929-1941) 2. 1930s 3. Separated friends, relatives, etc 4. Interracial friendship 5. Depressions 1929-1941 6. Race relations 7. Prejudice 8. Massachusetts , 9. Historical fiction
ISBN 9780375861048
    When her father travels north to find work during the Great Depression, a bereft Charlie Anne consoles herself with memories of her late mother and befriends Phoebe, an African-American girl who has also lost her mother; together the friends learn from and support one another, even in the face of a hatred that is tearing apart the town.
    "Good humor, kindness and courage triumph in this warm, richly nuanced novel that cheers the heart like a song sweetly sung." Kirkus.

Gagnon, Michelle, 1971-

Don't let go. Michelle Gagnon. Harper, an imprint of HarperCollins, 2014. 352 p.: Persefone trilogy (Michelle Gagnon)
Grades: 7 8 9 10 11 12   **Fic**
    1. Hackers 2. Human experimentation in medicine 3. Foster children 4. Experiments 5. Corporations, 6. Thrillers and suspense 7. Cyber-thrillers
ISBN 9780062102966
          LC 2014001880
In his final installment of the Don't Turn Around trilogy, Noa, Peter, and what is left of their army race across the country in their search to destroy Project Persephone before time runs out. Provided by publisher.

Don't look now. Michelle Gagnon. Harper, an imprint of HarperCollins, 2013. 320 p.: Persefone trilogy (Michelle Gagnon)
Grades: 7 8 9 10 11 12   **Fic**
    1. Hackers 2. Human experimentation in medicine 3. Foster children 4. Experiments 5. Rich teenage boys 6. Thrillers and suspense 7. Cyber-thrillers
ISBN 9780062102935
A sequel to Don't Turn Around finds Noa continuing her efforts to protect runaways from the illicit experiments being conducted by sinister corporation Pike & Nolan, while hacker Peter struggles to support her and work against the company on behalf of his victimized girlfriend.
    "Still suffering strange side effects from her stint as a human lab rat at Pike & Dolan, Noa (Don't Turn Around) leads a group of homeless teens bent on sabotaging the corporation. In Boston, her hacktivist friend Peter and his ex-girlfriend, Amanda, uncover new evidence that places them all in danger. This tense, suspenseful tech-thriller will engage readers from beginning to end." Horn Book.

Don't turn around. by Michelle Gagnon. Harper, 2012. 400 p.: Persefone trilogy (Michelle Gagnon)
Grades: 7 8 9 10 11 12   **Fic**
    1. Hackers 2. Conspiracies 3. Human experimentation in medicine 4. Rich teenage boys 5. Teenage girl orphans 6. Thrillers and suspense 7. Cyber-thrillers
ISBN 9780062102904
          LC 2012009691
Noa Torson is a smart and tough computer hacker. As a runaway teenager, Noa thrives living "off the grid"—until the day she wakes up on an operating table with no memory of how she got there. Noa teams up with fellow hacker Peter to discover what happened to her, but the pair soon becomes the target of a dangerous corporation determined to keep them from exposing its deadly secrets.

Strangelets. by Michelle Gagnon. Soho Teen, 2013. 272 p.
Grades: 8 9 10 11 12   **Fic**
    1. Teenagers 2. Near-death experience 3. Dystopias 4. Survival 5. Escapes 6. Science fiction
ISBN 9781616951375
          LC 2012038333
Forcibly sucked into an abyss at the moment of their deaths, six smarter-than-most teenagers wake up in a deadly, desolate future world, where only one of them holds the key to getting everyone back home.

Gaiman, Neil

★ The **graveyard** book. Neil Gaiman; with illustrations by Dave McKean. HarperCollins, c2008. 312 p.
Grades: 5 6 7 8 9 10   **Fic**
    1. Boy orphans 2. Cemeteries 3. Ghosts 4. Supernatural 5.

Werewolves 6. Fantasy fiction 7. Illustrated books
ISBN 9780060530921
Carnegie Medal, 2010.
Newbery Medal, 2009.

Nobody Owens is a normal boy, except that he has been raised by ghosts and other denizens of the graveyard.

"Gaiman writes with charm and humor, and again he has a real winner." Voice of Youth Advocates.

M is for magic. Neil Gaiman; illustrations by Teddy Kristiansen. HarperCollins, c2007. 272 p.

Grades: 7 8 9 10   **Fic**
   1. Magic 2. Cats 3. Ghosts 4. Trolls 5. Detectives 6. Fantasy fiction 7. Science fiction 8. Short stories
ISBN 0061186422

Eleven stories that involve strange and fantastical events.

"Gaiman has selected nine of his short stories and a poem and added a segment from an upcoming children's title for this volume. . . . This well-chosen collection is sure to create a new generation of Gaiman fans who will not need to understand all the allusions to enjoy the stories." Booklist.

MirrorMask. by Neil Gaiman; illustrated by Dave McKean. HarperCollins Publishers, 2005. 80 p.

Grades: 6 7 8 9   **Fic**
   1. Sick women 2. Masks 3. Quests 4. Women rulers 5. Stealing 6. Illustrated books 7. Fantasy fiction 8. Franchise books
ISBN 0060821094

When haunting music draws Helena into a magical realm and her real life is stolen by a runaway from the other side, Helena must rescue the realm from chaos in order to win back the life she once knew.

Stardust. Neil Gaiman; illustrated by Charles Vess. Spike/Avon Books, 1999. 238 p.

Grades: 8 9 10 11 12 Adult   **Fic**
   1. Victorian era (1837-1901) 2. Quests 3. Fairies 4. Magic 5. Walls 6. Gems 7. Historical fantasy 8. Gateway fantasy
ISBN 0380977281

                        LC 988773

Living in a Victorian countryside town overshadowed by an imposing stone barrier, Tristran is compelled to retrieve a fallen star for the woman he loves and crosses to the wondrous other side of the barrier, where he encounters dangerous rivals for the star.

Galante, Cecilia

The **world** from up here. Cecilia Galante. Scholastic Press, 2016. 309 p.

Grades: 4 5 6 7 8   **Fic**
   1. Anxiety in children 2. Self-discovery in girls 3. Children of people with mental illnesses 4. Brothers and sisters of children with autism 5. Women with depression 6. Pennsylvania 7. Realistic fiction
ISBN 9780545848459

                  LC 2015023427

After her mother is hospitalized, Wren Baker and her younger brother go to live with their aunt and her cousin, Silver, but her stress level soars when Silver conceives a plan to climb Creeper Mountain and interview "Witch Weatherly" for the class history project.

Gale, Eric Kahn, 1986-

The **bully** book. Eric Kahn Gale. Harper, c2013. 230 p.

Grades: 4 5 6 7 8   **Fic**
   1. Bullying and bullies 2. Diaries 3. Sixth-grade boys 4. Books 5. Schools 6. Realistic fiction
ISBN 9780062125118

The story of a bullied sixth-grader is conveyed through a series of journal entries that document his efforts to protect himself and are juxtaposed with insights into bully behavior.

"The juxtaposition of Eric's journal against the Bully Book allows readers to see both the bullies' methodology and Eric's unwitting complicity. . . . A compelling and unusual look at a complex and intractable problem that succeeds admirably as story as well." Kirkus.

The **Zoo** at the Edge of the World. by Eric Kahn Gale; illustrations by Matthew Howley. Balzer + Bray, an imprint of HarperCollinsPublishers, 2014. 240 p.

Grades: 4 5 6 7   **Fic**
   1. Human-animal communication 2. Stutterers 3. Captive wild animals 4. Jaguar 5. Zoos 6. Guyana 7. Fantasy fiction
ISBN 9780062125163

                  LC 2014002144

Marlin, a stutterer, can talk smoothly and freely with his father and the jungle animals that populate his father's Zoo at the Edge of the World, a resort where the well-to-do come to experience a last bit of the wild left in the world at the end of the 19th century, until a mysterious black jaguar that his father catches and brings back home confers upon Marlin a powerful gift.

"A secondary plot concerning Marlin's relationships with his father and brother is equally nuanced and powerful, making the book a formidable read on two fronts. The romantic setting and striking prose are icing on the cake, creating an intoxicatingly charming book. Beautiful and fully absorbing." Kirkus.

Gallego Garcia, Laura, 1977-

The **valley** of the Wolves. by Laura Gallego Garcia; translated by Margaret Sayers Peden. Arthur A. Levine Books, 2006. 247 p.

Grades: 6 7 8 9   **Fic**
   1. Ten-year-old girls 2. Rural families 3. Magic 4. Magic -- Study and teaching 5. Wizards 6. Coming-of-age stories 7. Fantasy fiction 8. Translations
ISBN 0439585538

                  LC 2005029987

Chosen to study at an academy of high sorcery known as the Tower, ten-year-old Dana finds herself, as her apprenticeship in magic progresses, growing increasingly curious about the history of the Tower and the true nature of her invisible best friend Kai.

Gallico, Paul, 1897-1976

The **snow** goose. by Paul Gallico; illustrated by Angela Barrett. Alfred A. Knopf, 2008. 48 p.

Grades: 6 7 8 9   **Fic**
   1. Friendship 2. Injured birds 3. Men with disabilities 4. Lighthouse keepers 5. Artists 6. Essex, England 7. Dunkirk, France 8. War stories 9. Historical fiction
ISBN 9780375849787

                  LC 2007008653

Against the backdrop of World War II, friendship develops between a lonely crippled painter and a village girl, when together they minister to an injured snow goose.

"The beautifully written but somewhat complex text uses unfamiliar vocabulary, and the occasional dialogue is rendered in a strong Essex dialect. However, the overall story is clear, poignant, and still relevant years after its original publication (1940). Barrett's inset and full-page pencil drawings, done in soft pastel tones, perfectly complement the tale's serious nature, capturing the spareness of the landscape and the intensity of the characters' feelings." School Library Journal.

Gansworth, Eric L.

Give me some truth: a novel with paintings. Eric Gansworth. Arthur A. Levine Books, 2018. 400 p.

Grades: 8 9 10 11 12   **Fic**

1. 1980s 2. Native American teenagers 3. Indian reservations 4. Teenage musicians 5. Bands (Music) 6. Tuscarora Indians 7. New York (State) 8. Tuscarora Nation Reservation (NY) 9. Historical fiction 10. Coming-of-age stories
ISBN 9781338143546

LC 2017042555

In 1980 life is hard on the Tuscarora Reservation in upstate New York, and most of the teenagers feel like they are going nowhere: Carson Mastick dreams of forming a rock band, and Maggi Bokoni longs to create her own conceptual artwork instead of the traditional beadwork that her family sells to tourists—but tensions are rising between the reservation and the surrounding communities, and somehow in the confusion of politics and growing up Carson and Maggi have to make a place for themselves.

"A rich, honest story of family and friends, of a Nation within a nation." Horn Book.

If I ever get out of here. Eric Gansworth. Arthur A. Levine Books, 2013. 368 p.

Grades: 6 7 8 9   **Fic**

1. 1970s 2. Native American boys 3. Bullying and bullies 4. Poverty 5. Tuscarora Indians 6. Indians of North America 7. New York (State) 8. Tuscarora Nation Reservation (NY) 9. Historical fiction
ISBN 9780545417303

LC 2012030553

Seventh-grader Lewis "Shoe" Blake from the Tuscarora Reservation has a new friend, George Haddonfield from the local Air Force base, but in 1975 upstate New York there is a lot of tension and hatred between Native Americans and whites—and Lewis is not sure that he can rely on friendship.

Gantos, Jack

I am not Joey Pigza. Jack Gantos. Farrar, Straus and Giroux, 2007. 215 p.: Joey Pigza books

Grades: 5 6 7 8   **Fic**

1. Boys with ADHD 2. Forgiveness in children 3. Diners (Restaurants) 4. Pigza, Joey (Fictitious character) 5. Attention-deficit hyperactivity disorder 6. Realistic fiction
ISBN 9780374399412

LC 2006038681

Joey's father returns, calling himself Charles Heinz and apologizing for his past bad behavior, and he swears that once Joey and his mother change their names and help him fix up the old diner he has bought, their lives will change for the better.

"The plot doesn't move so much as careen from one over-the-top event to the next, the achievement being that every one of them feels entirely plausible." Publishers Weekly.

Jack's black book. Jack Gantos. Farrar Straus Giroux, c1997. 165 p.: Jack Henry books

Grades: 5 6 7 8   **Fic**

1. 1960s 2. Humiliation 3. Fiction writing 4. Misadventures 5.

Henry, Jack (Fictitious character) 6. Seventh-grade boys 7. Fort Lauderdale, Florida 8. Florida 9. Humorous stories 10. Diary novels
ISBN 0374336628

LC 96-53107

In these interlinked stories, comic misadventures ensue when seventh-grader Jack tries to write the great American novel.

"The narrative sparkles with wit and, although exaggerated, rings with the authenticity of adolescent humor, embarrassment, and fascination with the absolutely gross." School Library Journal.

Joey Pigza loses control. Jack Gantos. Farrar, Straus and Giroux, 2000. 195 p.: Joey Pigza books

Grades: 5 6 7 8   **Fic**

1. Children of alcoholic fathers 2. Boys with ADHD 3. Baseball 4. Attention-deficit hyperactivity disorder 5. Pigza, Joey (Fictitious character) 6. Realistic fiction
ISBN 0374399891

LC 0020098

Joey, who is still taking medication to keep him from getting too wired, goes to spend the summer with the hard-drinking father he has never known and tries to help the baseball team he coaches win the championship.

"This high-voltage, honest novel mixes humor, pain, fear and courage with deceptive ease." Publishers Weekly.

★ **Joey** Pigza swallowed the key. Jack Gantos. Farrar, Straus and Giroux, c1998. 153 p.: Joey Pigza books

Grades: 5 6 7 8   **Fic**

1. Father-separated boys 2. Boys with ADHD 3. Child abuse victims 4. Children's medication 5. Attention-deficit hyperactivity disorder 6. Realistic fiction 7. Classics
ISBN 0374336644

To the constant disappointment of his mother and teacher, Joey has trouble paying attention or controlling his mood swings when his prescription medicine wears off and he starts acting wired.

"This frenetic narrative pulls at heartstrings and tickles funny bones." School Library Journal.

The **trouble** in me. Jack Gantos. Farrar Straus Giroux, 2015. 256 p.

Grades: 6 7 8 9 10   **Fic**

1. Juvenile delinquency 2. Neighbors 3. Moving, Household 4. Fourteen-year-old boys 5. Teenage boys 6. Florida 7. Fort Lauderdale, Florida 8. Humorous stories 9. Autobiographical fiction
ISBN 9780374379957

"Gantos has won a Newbery Medal, Printz Honor, Sibert Honor, and countless hearts. Readers will want to know how he became one of a kind." Booklist.

What would Joey do? Jack Gantos. Farrar, Straus and Giroux, 2002. 229 p.: Joey Pigza books

Grades: 5 6 7 8   **Fic**

1. Children of divorced parents 2. Boys with ADHD 3. Girls who are blind 4. Pigza, Joey (Fictitious character) 5. Attention-deficit hyperactivity disorder 6. Realistic fiction
ISBN 0374399867

LC 2002022823

Joey tries to keep his life from degenerating into total chaos when his mother sends him to be home-schooled with a hostile blind girl, his divorced parents cannot stop fighting, and his grandmother is dying of emphysema.

"The boy's first-person narration is as frenetically fun as it was in the first two books." School Library Journal.

Garcia, Kami

Beautiful chaos. by Kami Garcia & Margaret Stohl. Little, Brown, 2011. 528 p.: Caster chronicles

Grades: 8 9 10 11   **Fic**

1. Teenage witches 2. Psychic ability 3. Locusts 4. Storms 5. Dreams 6. South Carolina 7. Paranormal romances

ISBN 9780316123525

LC 2011012957

Swarms of locusts, record-breaking heat, and devastating storms ravage Gatlin as Ethan and Lena struggle to understand and control the impact of Lena's claiming, which is even causing her family members' abilities to dangerously misfire.

Beautiful creatures. by Kami Garcia and Margie Stohl. Little, Brown Books for Young Readers, 2009. 576 p.: Caster chronicles

Grades: 7 8 9 10   **Fic**

1. Teenage witches 2. Psychic ability 3. Family secrets 4. Teenage boy/girl relations 5. Supernatural 6. South Carolina 7. Paranormal romances

ISBN 9780316042673

In a small South Carolina town, where it seems little has changed since the Civil War, sixteen-year-old Ethan is powerfully drawn to Lena, a new classmate with whom he shares a psychic connection and whose family hides a dark secret that may be revealed on her sixteenth birthday.

"The intensity of Ethan and Lena's need to be together is palpable, the detailed descriptions create a vivid, authentic world, and the allure of this story is the power of love. The satisfying conclusion is sure to lead directly into a sequel." School Library Journal.

Beautiful darkness. by Kami Garcia & Margaret Stohl. Little, Brown, 2010. 503 p.: Caster chronicles

Grades: 8 9 10 11 12   **Fic**

1. Teenage witches 2. Psychic ability 3. Decision-making 4. Supernatural 5. Teenage romance 6. South Carolina 7. Paranormal romances

ISBN 9780316077057

LC 2010007015

In a small southern town with a secret world hidden in plain sight, sixteen-year-old Lena, who possesses supernatural powers and faces a life-altering decision, draws away from her true love, Ethan, a mortal with frightening visions.

"The southern gothic atmosphere, several new characters, and the surprising fate of one old favorite will keep readers going until the next book, which promises new surprises as 18 moons approaches." Booklist.

Raven. written by Kami Garcia; illustrated by Gabriel Picolo. DC Ink, [2019] 176 p.: Teen Titans (Garcia)

Grades: 7 8 9 10 11 12   **Fic**

1. Orphans 2. Psychic ability 3. Sixteen-year-old girls 4. Secrets 5. Teenage girls -- Identity 6. Superhero comics 7. Comics and Graphic novels

ISBN 9781779507273

LC 2018043961

When a tragic accident takes the life of the only family she's ever known, 16-year-old Raven is sent to New Orleans to start over. She soon

discovers that she can hear the thoughts of others around her...and another, more disturbing, voice in her head.

"Garcia makes great use of teenage emotion and drama in this origin story, and it's nicely carried out in Picolo's expressive artwork, largely in black, white, and gray. Calderon uses cool color washes, featuring lots of purple, for Raven, which emphasizes her powers and keeps the focus of the story on her." Booklist.

Gardner, Kati

Brave enough. Kati Gardner. North Star Editions Inc., 2018. 320 p.

Grades: 7 8 9 10   **Fic**

1. Teenagers with cancer 2. Perfectionism 3. Change 4. Drug addicts 5. Courage in teenagers 6. Realistic fiction

ISBN 9781635830200

"While their peers stretch their wings and aim for the future, these teens learn earlier than most that today is all we have—and that there can be a bracing power to this discovery. The debut author, a cancer survivor and amputee, covers challenging physical and emotional terrain in compelling detail with compassionate insight and strong storytelling skills." Kirkus.

Gardner, Lyn

Into the woods. Lyn Gardner; illustrated by Mini Grey. David Fickling Books, c2006 427 p.

Grades: 4 5 6 7 8   **Fic**

1. Father-separated girls 2. Characters and characteristics in fairy tales 3. Magic flutes 4. Villains 5. Wolves 6. Fantasy fiction

ISBN 9780385751155

LC 2006024350

Pursued by the sinister Dr. DeWilde and his ravenous wolves, three sisters, Storm, the inheritor of a special musical pipe, the elder Aurora, and the baby Any, flee into the woods and begin a treacherous journey filled with many dangers as they try to find a way to defeat their pursuer and keep him from taking the pipe and control of the entire land.

"Gardner's fast-paced fantasy-adventure cleverly borrows from well-known fairy tales, and astute readers will enjoy identifying the many folkloric references. . . . Grey's appealing black-and-white illustrations add humor and detail to the story." Booklist.

Gardner, Sally

The **silver** blade. Sally Gardner. Dial Books, 2009. 368 p.

Grades: 8 9 10 11 12   **Fic**

1. Revolutionary France (1789-1799) 2. 1790s 3. 18th century 4. Romanies 5. Rescues 6. Magic 7. Teenage boys 8. Teenagers 9. France 10. Historical fiction 11. Adventure stories

ISBN 9780803733770

LC 2009009282

As the Revolution descends into the ferocious Reign of Terror, Yann, now an extraordinary practioner of magic, uses his skills to confound his enemies and help spirit refugees out of France, but the question of his true identity and the kidnapping of his true love, Sido, expose him to dangers that threaten to destroy him.

"A luscious melodrama, rich in sensuous detail from horrific to sublime, with an iridescent overlay of magic." Kirkus.

Gardner, Whitney

You're welcome, universe. Whitney Gardner. Alfred A Knopf, 2017 297 p.

Grades: 8 9 10 11 12   **Fic**

1. Teenagers who are deaf 2. Graffiti 3. East Indian American

teenagers 4. Graffiti artists 5. Street art 6. Realistic fiction
ISBN 9780399551413
Schneider Family Book Award for Teens, 2018.

"Gardner brings together Deaf culture, discrimination, sexuality, friendship, body image, trust, betrayal, and even a potential Banksy spotting for this fresh novel, brightened by black-and-white illustrations from Julia's notebooks." Booklist.

Gaughen, A. C.

Scarlet. by A.C. Gaughen. Walker Books for Young Readers, 2012. 292 p.: Scarlet novels (A.C. Gaughen)
Grades: 8 9 10 11 12   **Fic**
 1. Medieval period (476-1492) 2. Outlaws 3. Disguises 4. Civilization, Medieval 5. Thieves 6. Former fiances 7. England 8. Sherwood Forest, England 9. Historical fiction 10. Fairy tale and folklore-inspired fiction
ISBN 9780802723468

LC 2011006395

Will Scarlet shadows Robin Hood, with an unerring eye for finding treasures to steal and throwing daggers with deadly accuracy, but when Gisbourne, a ruthless bounty hunter, is hired by the sheriff to capture Robin and his band of thieves, Robin must become Will's protector risking his own life in the process.

"Thief Will Scarlet keeps Rob and his men informed about doings in Nottinghamshire, and in turn they keep their young messenger's secret—he is really a she (with an enigmatic past). Scar's voice is distinctive, and her unique perspective adds new components to the Robin Hood tale, especially as Rob and other familiar characters all vie for her romantic attention." Horn Book.

Gemeinhart, Dan

The **honest** truth. Dan Gemeinhart. Scholastic Press, [2015] 240 p.
Grades: 5 6 7 8   **Fic**
 1. Children with cancer 2. Runaway boys 3. Boys and dogs 4. Anger in boys 5. Anger 6. Mount Rainier 7. Realistic fiction
ISBN 9780545665735

LC 2014028474

A boy named Mark, tired of being sick with cancer, conceives a plan to climb Mount Rainier, and runs away from home with his dog, Beau—but with over two hundred miles between him and his goal, and only anger at his situation to drive him on nothing will be easy, and only his best friend, Jessie, suspects where he is heading.

Scar Island. Dan Gemeinhart. Scholastic Press, 2017 256 p.
Grades: 6 7 8 9   **Fic**
 1. Juvenile correctional institutions 2. Juvenile delinquents 3. Guilt 4. Guilt in boys 5. Survival 6. Adventure stories
ISBN 9781338053845

Twelve-year-old Jonathan Grisby has been sent to the Slabhenge Reformatory School for Troubled Boys, a former lunatic asylum which is currently run by a sadist who enjoys punishing the boys and setting them against each other; but when a lightning strike kills all the adults the boys find themselves suddenly free—and trapped on Scar Island which seems to be sinking into the ocean.

★ **Some** kind of courage. Dan Gemeinhart. Scholastic Press, 2016. 240 p.
Grades: 4 5 6 7   **Fic**
 1. 1890s 2. Boy orphans 3. Horses 4. Twelve-year-old boys 5. Preteen boys 6. Washington (State) 7. Historical fiction 8.

Westerns
ISBN 9780545665773

In 1890 Washington, the only family Joseph Johnson has left is his half-wild Indian pony, Sarah, so when she is sold by a man who has no right to do so, he sets out to get her back—and he plans to let nothing stop him in his quest.

"Gemeinhart's riveting tale of grit and grief is equally tragic and triumphant." School Library Journal.

George, Jean Craighead, 1919-2012

Julie. Jean Craighead George; illustrated by Wendell Minor. Harper Collins, 1994. 226 p.: Julie of the wolves trilogy
Grades: 6 7 8 9   **Fic**
 1. Inuit teenage girls 2. Girls and wolves 3. Teenage romance 4. Inuit 5. Fathers and daughters 6. Adventure stories
ISBN 9780060235284

LC   93027738 /AC

When Julie returns to her father's village, she struggles to find a way to save her beloved wolves in a changing Arctic world and she falls in love with a young Siberian man.

George, Jessica Day, 1976-

Dragon flight. Jessica Day George. Bloomsbury Children's Books, 2008. 262 p.: Dragon slippers
Grades: 5 6 7 8   **Fic**
 1. Dragons 2. Seamstresses 3. Adventure 4. Imaginary wars and battles 5. Princes 6. Fantasy fiction
ISBN 9781599901107

LC 2007050762

Young seamstress Creel finds herself strategizing with the dragon king Shardas once again when a renegade dragon in a distant country launches a war against their country, bringing an entire army of dragons into the mix.

"Fans of the first book will find the same strengths here: the imaginatively detailed scenes; the thrilling, spell-fueled action; the possibility of romance with a prince; and the appealing, brave heroine." Booklist.

★ **Dragon** slippers. by Jessica Day George. Bloomsbury Childrens Books, 2007. 324 p.: Dragon slippers
Grades: 5 6 7 8   **Fic**
 1. Teenage girl orphans 2. Dragons 3. Slippers 4. Princes 5. Seamstresses 6. Fantasy fiction
ISBN 9781599900575

LC 2006021142

Orphaned after a fever epidemic, Creel befriends a dragon and unknowingly inherits an object that can either save or destroy her kingdom.

"The plot is fast paced with all the right touches of romance and adventure. . . . The characters are wonderfully drawn." Voice of Youth Advocates.

Dragon spear. by Jessica Day George. Bloomsbury, 2009. 248 p.: Dragon slippers
Grades: 5 6 7 8   **Fic**
 1. Teenage girl orphans 2. Dragons 3. Kidnapping 4. Rulers 5. Princes 6. Fantasy fiction
ISBN 9781599903699

LC 2008044414

Creel's adventures continue when she, her brother, and her betrothed travel across the seas to visit their dragon friends and become involved in a battle against an alien group of dragons that has kidnapped Queen Velika, endangering her and her expected litter of hatchlings.

"As in the previous series titles, George creates richly satisfying fantasy realms, from opulent palaces to forest lairs, while the tender romances, genuine friendships, rapid dialogue, and thrilling adventures will continue to delight readers." Booklist.

Princess of the Midnight Ball. Jessica Day George. Blooms-bury, 2009. 280 p.: Princess books (Jessica Day George)

Grades: 6 7 8 9 10 　　　　　　　　　　　　　**Fic**
　　1. 19th century 2. Princesses 3. Curses 4. Dancing 5. Spells (Magic) 6. Magic 7. Fantasy fiction 8. Fairy tale and folklore-inspired fiction
　　ISBN 9781599903224

　　　　　　　　　　　　　　　　　　LC 2008030310
A retelling of the tale of twelve princesses who wear out their shoes dancing every night, and of Galen, a former soldier now working in the king's gardens, who follows them in hopes of breaking the curse.

"Fans of fairy-tale retellings . . . will enjoy this story for its magic, humor, and touch of romance." School Library Journal.

★ **Tuesdays** at the castle. Jessica Day George. Bloomsbury USA, 2011. 288 p.: Castle Glower

Grades: 3 4 5 6 　　　　　　　　　　　　　　**Fic**
　　1. Parent-separated girls 2. Princesses 3. Castles 4. Inheritance and succession 5. Rulers 6. Fantasy fiction
　　ISBN 9781599906447
Eleven-year-old Princess Celie lives with her parents, the king and queen, and her brothers and sister at Castle Glower, which adds rooms or stairways or secret passageways most every Tuesday, and when the king and queen are ambushed while travelling, it is up to Celie to protect their home and save their kingdom.

"Castle Glower is the true star of this charming story of court in-trigue and magic. A satisfying mix of Hogwarts and Howl's Moving Castle, . . . Castle Glower helps its true citizens, but never at the expense of plot or character development." School Library Journal.

Gephart, Donna
　　★ **How** to survive middle school. Donna Gephart. Delacorte Press, 2010. 256 p.

Grades: 5 6 7 8 　　　　　　　　　　　　　　**Fic**
　　1. Videos 2. Popularity 3. Middle school students 4. Internet 5. Television programs 6. Realistic fiction
　　ISBN 9780385907019
His dream of becoming a celebrity interrupted by the realities of middle school, David has a falling out with his best friend that leads to a new relationship with a girl who shares David's love for television and acting, which catapults them to stardom when they post their skit online.

"Gephart crafts for her likable protagonist an engaging, feel-good transition into adolescence that's well stocked with tears and laughter." Booklist.

Gerber, Alyson
　　Braced. Alyson Gerber. Arthur A. Levine Books, 2017. 304 p.

Grades: 5 6 7 8 　　　　　　　　　　　　　　**Fic**
　　1. Scoliosis 2. Girl soccer players 3. Mothers and daughters 4. Medical genetics 5. Orthopedic braces 6. Massachusetts 7. Andover, Massachusetts 8. Realistic fiction
　　ISBN 9780545902144

　　　　　　　　　　　　　　　　　　LC 2016016818
When twelve-year-old Rachel learns that her scoliosis has worsened and she will need to wear a back brace to keep her spine straight, she is devastated; afraid that she will not be able to play soccer, and terri-fied that she will not be able to hide her condition from her friends and classmates—but her mother is determined to spare her the spinal fusion surgery that she herself had as a teenager.

Gibbs, Stuart, 1969-
　　★ **Belly** up: murder at FunJungle. Stuart Gibbs. Simon & Schuster Books for Young Readers, 2010. 294 p.: FunJungle

Grades: 4 5 6 7 　　　　　　　　　　　　　　**Fic**
　　1. Boy detectives 2. Hippopotamus 3. Zoos 4. Amusement parks 5. Zoo animals 6. Texas 7. Mysteries 8. Realistic fiction
　　ISBN 9781416987314

　　　　　　　　　　　　　　　　　　LC 2009034860
Twelve-year-old Teddy investigates when a popular Texas zoo's star attraction—Henry the hippopotamus—is murdered.

"The characters are well-developed and believable, making this book appealing to reluctant readers and those who enjoy animal stories and mysteries." Library Media Connection.

Big game. Stuart Gibbs. Simon & Schuster Books for Young Readers, 2015. 336 p.: FunJungle

Grades: 4 5 6 7 　　　　　　　　　　　　　　**Fic**
　　1. Poaching 2. Zoo animals 3. Boy detectives 4. Zoos 5. Rhinoceros 6. Texas 7. Mysteries
　　ISBN 9781481423335

　　　　　　　　　　　　　　　　　　LC 2014042145
Someone is trying to hunt FunJungle's Asian greater one-horned rhinoceros, and twelve-year-old Teddy Fitzroy is on the case. Provided by publisher.

"Monkey business included, this adventure strikes a neat balance between shenanigans and gravitas to inspire young conservationists." Kirkus.

★ **Charlie** Thorne and the last equation. Stuart Gibbs. Si-mon & Schuster Books for Young Readers, 2019. 400 p.: Char-lie Thorne

Grades: 5 6 7 8 　　　　　　　　　　　　　　**Fic**
　　1. Einstein, Albert, 1879-1955 2. CIA 3. Genius 4. Gifted girls 5. Cryptography 6. Spies 7. Girl adventurers 8. Spy fiction 9. Thrillers and suspense
　　ISBN 9781534424760

　　　　　　　　　　　　　　　　　　LC 2018050572
The CIA forces twelve-year-old Charlotte "Charlie" Thorne, a rebel-lious genius, to use her code-breaking skills on an epic global chase to locate Einstein's last equation before dangerous agents discover it and unlock the solution to harnessing energy.

"Issues of racial and gender diversity are nicely folded into the plot, which moves at breakneck speed from start to literal cliff-hanger finish." Booklist.

Charlie Thorne and the lost city. Stuart Gibbs. Simon & Schuster 2021 384 p.: Charlie Thorne

Grades: 5 6 7 8 　　　　　　　　　　　　　　**Fic**
　　1. Darwin, Charles, 1809-1882 2. CIA 3. Genius 4. Gifted girls 5. Cryptography 6. Spies 7. Girl adventurers 8. Galapagos Islands 9. Spy fiction 10. Thrillers and suspense
　　ISBN 9781534443815
In a daring adventure that takes her across South America, Charlie must crack Darwin's 200-year-old clues to track down his mysterious discovery and stay ahead of the formidable lineup of enemies who are hot on her tail.

"Will appeal to readers who appreciate action-oriented tales." Kirkus

Evil spy school. Stuart Gibbs. Simon & Schuster Books for Young Readers, 2015. 336 p.: Spy school

Grades: 4 5 6 7   **Fic**

1. Boy spies 2. Espionage 3. Undercover operations 4. Good and evil 5. Thirteen-year-old boys 6. Spy fiction
ISBN 9781442494893

After getting expelled from spy school for accidentally shooting a live mortar into the principal's office, thirteen-year-old Ben finds himself recruited by the evil crime organization SPYDER.

Panda-monium: a FunJungle novel. Stuart Gibbs. Simon & Schuster Books for Young Readers, 2017 352 p.: FunJungle

Grades: 4 5 6 7   **Fic**

1. Animal stealing 2. Zoo animals 3. Boy detectives 4. Pandas 5. Rare and endangered animals 6. Texas 7. Mysteries
ISBN 9781481445672

Teddy Fitzroy returns as FunJungle's resident sleuth when the zoo's newest addition goes missing—before she even arrives!

Poached. Stuart Gibbs. Simon & Schuster Books for Young Readers, 2014. 336 p.: FunJungle

Grades: 4 5 6 7   **Fic**

1. Koalas 2. Animal stealing 3. Bullying and bullies 4. Boy detectives 5. Zoo animals 6. Texas 7. Mysteries
ISBN 9781442467774

"I would never have been accused of stealing the koala if Vance Jessup hadn't made me drop a human arm in the shark tank." That's Teddy Fitzroy's explanation for the mess he's in. He was just in the wrong place at the wrong time, and now he's the prime suspect in the theft of a koala from FunJungle, the zoo amusement park where his parents work.

"Gibbs weaves interesting trivia (newborn koalas are jellybean-size) and plenty of humor (a poop-throwing chimp helps ID an industrial spy/saboteur) into his action-packed mystery." Horn Book.

★ **Space** case: a Moon Base Alpha novel. Stuart Gibbs. Simon & Schuster Books for Young Readers, 2014. 352 p.: Moon Base Alpha

Grades: 4 5 6 7   **Fic**

1. Space colonies 2. Human-alien encounters 3. Near future 4. Murder investigation 5. Twelve-year-old boys 6. Moon 7. Mysteries 8. Science fiction
ISBN 9781442494862

Life among the colonists on Moon Base Alpha is surprisingly dull and predictable...until the base's doctor is found dead. Though it looks like an accident, Dash Gibson has reason to believe that Dr. Holtz may have been murdered. There's no shortage of suspects, so Dash recruits two tech-savvy new friends to help with his investigation, never forgetting that they might be trapped in space with a killer.

"Closed quarters and technomumbo-jumbo add delightful color to the proceedings. Thankfully, the author doesn't let the high-concept setting overshadow the novel's mystery. The whodunit is smartly paced and intricately plotted." Kirkus.

Spaced out. Stuart Gibbs. Simon & Schuster Books for Young Readers, [2016] 336 p.: Moon Base Alpha

Grades: 4 5 6 7   **Fic**

1. Space colonies 2. Human-alien encounters 3. Near future 4. Telepathy 5. Missing persons 6. Moon 7. Mysteries 8. Science fiction
ISBN 9781481423366

In 2041 twelve-year-old Dashiell Gibson is a resident of Moon Base Alpha, and at the moment he is faced with a number of problems: coping with the nasty Sjoberg twins, finding out how the commander of the base has managed to disappear from a facility no bigger than a soccer field, and dealing with the alien Zan who communicates with him telepathically from afar—and who is hiding a secret which may threaten the whole Earth.

Spy camp. Stuart Gibbs. Simon & Schuster Books for Young Readers, c2013. 321 p.: Spy school

Grades: 4 5 6 7   **Fic**

1. Boy spies 2. Camps 3. Death threats 4. Survival 5. Summer 6. Spy fiction
ISBN 9781442457539

LC 2012019416

As almost thirteen-year-old Ben, a student at the CIA's academy for future intelligence agents, prepares to go to spy summer camp, he receives a death threat from the evil organization SPYDER.

"After escaping assassination by the top-secret organization SPYDER, Ben Ripley (Spy School) is looking forward to chilling out this summer. But SPYDER is turning up the heat, insisting that Ben come to work for them. Gorgeous fellow-spy-in-training Erica is ready to help, and her legendary grandfather also appears on the scene. Clever descriptions and plot twists make this a top-notch summer read." Horn Book.

★ **Spy** school. Stuart Gibbs. Simon & Schuster Books for Young Readers, 2012. 304 p.: Spy school

Grades: 4 5 6 7   **Fic**

1. Gifted boys 2. Boy spies 3. Moles (Spies) 4. Spies -- Recruiting 5. Boy/girl relations 6. Virginia 7. Spy fiction
ISBN 9781442421820

LC 2011015023

Twelve-year-old Ben Ripley leaves his public middle school to attend the CIA's highly secretive Espionage Academy, which everyone is told is an elite science school.

"Ben is well-defined; he is a math nerd, a geek who has never gotten the girl, but he comes into his own when he is under attack. Similar in many ways to the Alex Rider books for an older audience, this romp is a great choice for reluctant readers of either gender." Booklist.

Spy ski school: a Spy school novel. Stuart Gibbs. Simon & Schuster Books for Young Readers, [2016] 368 p.: Spy school

Grades: 4 5 6 7   **Fic**

1. Boy spies 2. Espionage 3. Undercover operations 4. Skiing 5. Friendship 6. Colorado 7. Vail, Colorado 8. Spy fiction
ISBN 9781481445627

LC 2015037993

Twelve-year-old Ben's unexpected success outside the classroom causes the CIA to activate him for a mission to become friends with Jessica Shang, daughter of a suspected Chinese crime boss.

"Readers will be glad they strapped on their boots and went along for the ride." Kirkus.

Gibney, Shannon

See no color. by Shannon Gibney. Carolrhoda Lab, a division of Lerner Pub. Group, 2015. 196 p.

Grades: 7 8 9 10   **Fic**

1. Multiracial teenage girls 2. Identity (Psychology) 3. Adopted girls 4. Interracial families 5. Sixteen-year-old girls 6. Realistic fiction
ISBN 9781467776820

LC 2015001619

Alex has always identified herself as a baseball player, the daughter of a winning coach, but when she realizes that is not enough she begins to come to terms with her adoption and her race.

Gidwitz, Adam

The **Grimm** conclusion. Adam Gidwitz. Dutton Children's Books, an imprint of Penguin Group (USA) Inc., [2013] 343 p.: Grimm series (Adam Gidwitz)

Grades: 4 5 6 **Fic**
> 1. Characters and characteristics in fairy tales 2. Brothers and sisters 3. Ghouls and ogres 4. Adventure 5. Metafiction 6. Fairy tale and folklore-inspired fiction
> ISBN 9780525426158

LC 2013021686

Sister and brother Jorinda and Joringel fight to keep their promise to stay together throughout a new series of gruesome, twisted, Grimm-inspired stories. Provided by publisher.

★ **In** a glass Grimmly. Adam Gidwitz. Dutton Juvenile, 2012. 192 p.: Grimm series (Adam Gidwitz)

Grades: 4 5 6 7 8 **Fic**
> 1. Magic mirrors 2. Talking animals 3. Characters and characteristics in fairy tales 4. Frogs 5. Quests 6. Fairy tale and folklore-inspired fiction 7. Metafiction
> ISBN 9780525425816

LC 2012015515

Frog joins cousins Jack and Jill in leaving their own stories to seek a magic mirror, encountering such creatures as giants, mermaids, and goblins along the way. Based in part on fairy tales from the Brothers Grimm and Hans Christian Andersen.

Gier, Kerstin

Emerald green. Kerstin Gier; translated from the German by Anthea Bell. Henry Holt and Company, 2013. 448 p.: Ruby red trilogy

Grades: 7 8 9 10 **Fic**
> 1. Time travel (Past) 2. Prophecies 3. Secret societies 4. Time machines 5. Teenage romance 6. London, England 7. England 8. Urban fantasy 9. Translations
> ISBN 9780805092677

LC 2013017885

Since learning she is the Ruby, the final member of the time-traveling Circle of Twelve, nothing has gone right for Gwen and she holds suspicions about both Count Saint-German and Gideon, but as she uncovers the Circle's secrets she finally learns her own destiny.

Sapphire blue. Kerstin Gier; translated from the German by Anthea Bell. Henry Holt, 2012. 368 p.: Ruby red trilogy

Grades: 7 8 9 10 **Fic**
> 1. Time travel (Past) 2. Prophecies 3. Secret societies 4. Time machines 5. Teenage romance 6. London, England 7. England 8. Urban fantasy 9. Translations
> ISBN 9780805092660

LC 2011034011

Sixteen-year-old Gwen, the newest and final member of the secret time-traveling Circle of Twelve, searches through history for the other time-travelers, aided by friend Lesley, James the ghost, Xemerius the gargoyle demon, and Gideon, the Diamond, whose fate seems bound with hers.

Giff, Patricia Reilly., 1935-2021

Genevieve's war. by Patricia Reilly Giff. Holiday House, [2017] 240 p.

Grades: 4 5 6 7 **Fic**
> 1. Second World War era (1939-1945) 2. French Resistance (World War II) 3. Grandmother and granddaughter 4. Self-reliance 5. World War II 6. Americans in France 7. France 8. Historical fiction
> ISBN 9780823438006

LC 2016027038

In August 1939 Genevieve makes an impulsive decision not to get on train to take her to boat back New York and must spend the duration of World War II with her grandmother in a small village in Alsace, France, where she becomes involved with the French resistance. Provided by publisher.

"A well-crafted look at how World War II impacted civilians, with great potential for classroom use." School Library Journal.

Lily's crossing. Patricia Reilly Giff. Delacorte Press, c1997. 180 p.

Grades: 4 5 6 7 **Fic**
> 1. 1940s 2. Child refugees 3. World War II -- Children 4. Children -- Friendship 5. Refugees, Hungarian 6. Beaches 7. United States 8. Historical fiction
> ISBN 0385321422

LC 9623021

During a summer spent at Rockaway Beach in 1944, Lily's friendship with a young Hungarian refugee causes her to see the war and her own world differently.

"Gentle elements of danger and suspense . . . keep the plot moving forward, while the delicate balance of characters and setting gently coalesces into an emotional whole that is fully satisfying." Bulletin of the Center for Children's Books.

Nory Ryan's song. Patricia Reilly Giff. Delacorte Press, c2000. 148 p.

Grades: 5 6 7 8 **Fic**
> 1. Irish Potato Famine (1845-1852) 2. 19th century 3. Twelve-year-old girls 4. Resourcefulness in girls 5. Brothers and sisters 6. Survival 7. Ireland 8. Historical fiction
> ISBN 0385321414

LC 00027690

When a terrible blight attacks Ireland's potato crop in 1845, twelve-year-old Nory Ryan's courage and ingenuity help her family and neighbors survive. Includes glossary.

"Giff brings the landscape and the cultural particulars of the era vividly to life and creates in Nory a heroine to cheer for. A beautiful, heart-wrenching novel that makes a devastating event understandable." Booklist.

Pictures of Hollis Woods. Patricia Reilly Giff. Wendy Lamb Books, c2002. 166 p.

Grades: 5 6 7 8 **Fic**
> 1. Twelve-year-old girls 2. Foster home care 3. Girls and senior women 4. Artists 5. Belonging 6. New York (State) 7. Realistic fiction
> ISBN 0385326556

LC 2002000426

A troublesome twelve-year-old orphan, staying with an elderly artist who needs her, remembers the only other time she was happy in a foster home, with a family that truly seemed to care about her.

"She was named for the place where she was found as an abandoned baby. Twelve-year-old Hollis Woods has been through many foster homes—and she runs away, every time. In her latest placement, with an artist named Josie, the tightly wound Hollis begins to relax ever so slightly. . . . But Josie is slowly slipping into dementia, and Hollis knows that she'll be taken away from her if Josie is found out. . . . Giff has a sure hand with language, and the narrative is taut and absorbing." Booklist.

A **slip** of a girl. by Patricia Reilly Giff. Holiday House, 2019. 240 p.

Grades: 5 6 7 8 **Fic**
1. 19th century 2. Sisters 3. Fugitives 4. Fathers and daughters 5. Children with developmental disabilities 6. Mothers -- Death 7. Ireland 8. Historical fiction 9. Novels in verse
ISBN 9780823439553

Anna's mother has died, and her older siblings have emigrated, leaving Anna and her father to care for a young sister with special needs. And though their family has worked this land for years, they're in danger of losing it as poor crop yields leave them without money to pay their rent. When a violent encounter with the Lord's rent collector results in Anna and her father's arrest, all seems lost. But Anna sees her chance and bolts from the jailhouse. On the run, Anna must rely on her own inner strength to protect her sister—and try to find a way to save her family.

"Giff loosely based the tenacious heroine of this profoundly moving novel on her great-grandmother, who was raised in the town in Ireland where the Drumlish Land War of 1881 took place." Booklist.

Winter sky. by Patricia Reilly Giff. Wendy Lamb Books, 2014. 160 p.

Grades: 4 5 6 7 **Fic**
1. Fire fighters 2. Abandoned dogs 3. Fires 4. Dogs 5. Communities 6. Realistic fiction
ISBN 9780375838927

LC 2013022399

Almost twelve-year-old Siria, who chases firetrucks in the middle of the night to ensure her fire fighter dad's safety, learns about bravery one winter as she tries to mend a broken friendship.

"Worried about her firefighter father's safety, every time a siren wails eleven-year-old Siria sneaks out and chases the truck, watching to make sure he escapes harm. Over Christmas break, Siria notices small fires being set all over town and decides to investigate on her own. Unadorned but engaging prose and Giff's well-drawn characters add depth to a simple story about courage and friendship." Horn Book.

Giles, Chrystal D.

Take back the block. Chrystal D. Giles. Random House Children's Books, 2021 240 p.

Grades: 4 5 6 7 **Fic**
1. Friendship 2. Gentrification of cities 3. Middle school students 4. Belonging 5. Community activism 6. Realistic fiction 7. African American fiction
ISBN 9780593175170

When a real estate developer makes an offer to buy Kensington Oaks, the neighborhood Wes has lived his whole life, everything changes. Wes isn't about to give up the only home he's ever known. Wes has always been good at puzzles, and he knows there has to be a missing piece that will solve this puzzle and save the Oaks. But can he find it . . . before it's too late?

"The story echoes contemporary realities that, as its culmination indicates, take an entire community to confront, and it will undoubtedly push readers into action. An ambitious invitation for young readers that delivers promise for all." Kirkus

Giles, L. R. (Lamar R.)

The **Last** Mirror on the Left. by Lamar Giles; illustrations by Dapo Adeola. Versify, Houghton Mifflin Harcourt, 2020. 272 p.: Legendary Alston Boys adventure

Grades: 4 5 6 7 **Fic**
1. Boy detectives 2. Fugitives 3. Time 4. African American boys 5. Adventurers 6. Virginia 7. Fantasy fiction 8. African American fiction
ISBN 9780358129417

In this new Legendary Alston Boys adventure from Edgar-nominated author Lamar Giles, Otto and Sheed must embark on their most dangerous journey yet, bringing a fugitive to justice in a world that mirrors their own but has its own rules to play by.

"Giles's The Last Last-Day-of-Summer sequel is a complex and exciting fantasy adventure that encourages readers to question what they know about incarceration, justice, laws, and the people who enforce them." School Library Journal

Not so pure and simple. Lamar Giles. HarperTeen, 2020. 304 p.

Grades: 8 9 10 11 12 **Fic**
1. Virginity 2. Masculinity 3. Teenage boys 4. High schools 5. Dating (Social customs) 6. Virginia 7. Coming-of-age stories 8. Realistic fiction
ISBN 9780062349194

LC 2019025683

High school junior Del Rainey unwittingly joins a Purity Pledge class at church, hoping to get closer to his long-term crush, Kiera.

"With true-to-life characters and a straightforward handling of sex, including often ignored aspects of male sexuality, Giles's thoughtful, hilarious read offers a timely viewpoint on religion, toxic masculinity, and teen sexuality." Kirkus.

Overturned. Lamar Giles. Scholastic Press, 2017. 352 p.

Grades: 7 8 9 10 11 12 **Fic**
1. African American teenage girls 2. Casinos 3. Gambling 4. Murder investigation 5. Frameups 6. Las Vegas, Nevada 7. Mysteries 8. African American fiction
ISBN 9780545812504

LC 2016035488

When her father is cleared of murder charges and released from death row, Nikki, who has been saving money to get out of Vegas by playing illegal poker games, joins her father's obsessive search to find the person who framed him.

"A fast-paced, compelling mystery and memorable characters and relationships make this selection a first choice for most YA collections." School Library Journal.

Spin. Lamar Giles. Scholastic Press, 2019. 352 p.

Grades: 7 8 9 10 **Fic**
1. African American teenage girls 2. Murder investigation 3. Media fandom 4. Interpersonal relations 5. Secrets 6. Thrillers and suspense 7. African American fiction
ISBN 9781338219210

LC 2018044097

When DJ ParSec (Paris Secord), rising star of the local music scene, is found dead over her turntables, the two girls who found her, Kya (her pre-fame best friend) and Fuse (her current chief groupie) are torn between grief for Paris and hatred for each other—but when the lack of obvious suspects stalls the investigation, and the police seem to lose interest, despite pressure from social media and ParSec's loyal fans, the two girls unite, determined to find out who murdered their friend.

"This is genre fiction at its best: a taut mystery with rich characterization and a strong sense of place." Kirkus.

Gilman, David

Blood sun. by David Gilman. Delacorte Press, 2011. 336 p.: Danger zone

Grades: 7 8 9 10 11 12   **Fic**

1. Teenage boy adventurers 2. Rain forests 3. Assassins 4. Drug smugglers 5. Environmental protection 6. England 7. Central America 8. Adventure stories

ISBN 9780385735629

Desperate to uncover the secret of his mother's death, fifteen-year-old Max Gordon, pursued by enemies, travels from the bleakness of Dartmoor to the rainforest of Central America, where the environmental devastation hides a sinister secret.

"Max Gordon is a likable character who faces tough challenges with determination, physical strength and a positive attitude.... This is ... a solid read from start to breathless finish." Kirkus.

The **devil's** breath. David Gilman. Random House Childrens Books, 2008, 2007. 336 p.: Danger zone

Grades: 7 8 9 10 11 12   **Fic**

1. Missing persons 2. Father-separated teenage boys 3. Environmentalism 4. Missing persons investigation 5. Kidnapping 6. Namibia 7. Adventure stories

ISBN 9780385905466

When fifteen-year-old Max Gordon's environmentalist-adventurer father goes missing while working in Namibia and Max becomes the target of a would-be assassin at his school in England, he decides he must follow his father to Africa and find him before they both are killed.

"The action is relentless.... Gilman has a flair for making the preposterous seem possible." Booklist.

Ice claw. David Gilman. Random House Children's Books, 2010 336 p.: Danger zone

Grades: 7 8 9 10 11 12   **Fic**

1. Teenage boy adventurers 2. Teenage murder witnesses 3. Extreme sports 4. Teenage boys 5. Ecological disturbances -- Prevention 6. Pyrenees 7. France 8. Adventure stories

ISBN 9780385905473

"The omniscient point of view ... does a lot for clarity, which is his strong suit—few authors are able to depict action scenes so lucidly.... But it's Max's humanity ... that makes Gilman's research and storytelling come alive." Booklist.

Gilmore, Kate

The **exchange** student. Houghton Mifflin 1999. 217 p.

Grades: 7 8 9 10   **Fic**

1. Wildlife conservation 2. Rare and endangered animals 3. Aliens (Humanoid) 4. Exchange students 5. Science fiction

ISBN 0395575117

LC 97047162

When her mother arranges to host one of the young people coming to Earth from Chela, Daria is both pleased and intrigued by the keen interest shown by the Chelan in her work breeding endangered species.

"Gilmore makes a farfetched premise seem more reasonable with everyday details of life in the twenty-first century, sympathetic characters, and logical consequences.... A story that will appeal to readers on many levels." Booklist.

Gino, Alex

Rick. Alex Gino. Scholastic Press, 2020. 240 p.

Grades: 4 5 6 7   **Fic**

1. Preteen boys 2. Questioning (Sexual or gender identity) 3. Self-discovery in boys 4. Bullying and bullies 5. Best friends 6. LGBTQIA fiction 7. Realistic fiction

ISBN 9781338048100

LC 2019047098

Privately struggling with his best friend's bullying personality and his father's jokes about hot girls, a middle school student joins his new school's Rainbow Spectrum club, where other kids of diverse gender identities help him find understanding and a sense of himself.

"An enlightening and important novel about a young person's experience with asexuality. A required purchase for middle grade collections." School Library Journal.

Gipson, Fred, 1908-1973

Old Yeller. Fred Gipson. Harper Perennial, 1956. 184 p.

Grades: 6 7 8 9   **Fic**

1. Frontier and pioneer life 2. Fourteen-year-old boys 3. Children and dogs 4. Families 5. Dogs 6. Texas 7. Classics

ISBN 006080971X

LC 88-45960

About a Texas pioneer family in the 1860s and the big yellow stray dog that affects their lives.

"Travis at fourteen was the man of the family during the hard summer of 1860 when his father drove his herd of cattle from Texas to the Kansas market. It was the summer when an old yellow dog attached himself to the family and won Travis' reluctant friendship. Before the summer was over, Old Yeller proved more than a match for thieving raccoons, fighting bulls, grizzly bears, and mad wolves. This is a skillful tale of a boy's love for a dog as well as a description of a pioneer boyhood and it can't miss with any dog lover." Horn Book.

Glaser, Mechthild

The **book** jumper. Mechthild Gläser; [translated by Romy Fursland] Henry Holt and Company, 2017. 384 p.

Grades: 8 9 10   **Fic**

1. Books 2. Characters and characteristics in literature 3. Thieves 4. Islands 5. Fifteen-year-old girls 6. Scotland 7. Gateway fantasy 8. Fantasy fiction 9. Translations

ISBN 9781250086662

LC 2016007363

A teen girl discovers she is a book jumper—she can leap directly into books, meet the characters, and experience the world of the book. Provided by publisher.

"This offering is the first U.S. title from an award-winning German author and would be a good additional purchase for fans of Cornelia Funke's Inkheart or Kristin Kladstrup's The Book of Story Beginnings." School Library Journal.

Gleason, Colleen

The **clockwork** scarab. Colleen Gleason. Chronicle Books, 2013. 356 p.: Stoker & Holmes novels

Grades: 7 8 9 10   **Fic**

1. Victorian era (1837-1901) 2. 19th century 3. 1880s 4. Secret societies 5. Time travel 6. Scarabs 7. Vampire slayers 8. Detectives 9. London, England 10. Great Britain 11. Historical mysteries 12. Steampunk

ISBN 9781452110707

Roped into respective family businesses when two society girls go missing, Evaline, the sister of Bram Stoker, and Mina, the niece of Sherlock Holmes, overcome a fierce rivalry to investigate three mysterious gentlemen and a strange Egyptian relic.

"Few answers are offered in this outing, but the author's writing exudes energy, romance, and humor, and she gives her heroines strong, vibrant personalities as they puzzle out the expansive mystery unfolding before them." Publishers Weekly.

Gleitzman, Morris

Now. Morris Gleitzman. Henry Holt, 2012, c2010. 176 p.: Once series

Grades: 7 8 9 10   **Fic**

1. Parent-separated girls 2. Wildfires 3. Resilience in girls 4. Resilience (Personal quality) 5. Grandfather and granddaughter 6. Australia 7. Victoria 8. Realistic fiction
ISBN 9780805093780

While her parents are working in Africa, Zelda is living with her grandfather, Holocaust survivor Felix Salinger, in Australia, when a disaster leads them both to deal with unresolved feelings about the first Zelda, Felix's childhood friend.

Goldblatt, Mark, 1957-

Twerp. Mark Goldblatt. Random House, 2013. 304 p.: Julian Twerski books

Grades: 6 7 8   **Fic**

1. 1960s 2. Bullying and bullies 3. Diaries 4. Student suspension 5. Personal conduct 6. Sixth-grade boys 7. Queens, New York City 8. Historical fiction 9. Coming-of-age stories
ISBN 9780375971426

In Queens, New York, in 1969, twelve-year-old Julian Twerski writes a journal for his English teacher in which he explores his friendships and how they are effected by girls, a new student who may be as fast as Julian, and especially an incident of bullying.

Golding, William, 1911-1993

Lord of the flies: a novel. William Golding. Coward-McCann, [1955, c1954] 243 p.

Grades: 8 9 10 11 12 Adult   **Fic**

1. Survival (after airplane accidents, shipwrecks, etc) 2. Human nature 3. Child castaways 4. Teenage boys 5. Boys 6. Psychological fiction 7. Literary fiction 8. Modern classics
ISBN 0884116956

LC 55010081

The classic study of human nature which depicts the degeneration of a group of schoolboys marooned on a desert island.

Gonzales, S., 1992-

Only mostly devastated. Sophie Gonzales. St Martins Pr 2020 288 p.

Grades: 8 9 10 11 12   **Fic**

1. Gay teenagers 2. Summer romance 3. Coming out (Sexual or gender identity) 4. Teenage same-sex romance 5. Teenage boy/boy relations 6. North Carolina 7. LGBTQIA romances 8. Romantic comedies
ISBN 9781250315892

LC 2019044429

When his aunt's illness keeps Ollie in North Carolina, he hopes his summer fling with Will can grow into something more, but at school Will proves to be a completely different—and firmly closeted—man.

Gonzalez, Christina Diaz, 1969-

Moving target. Christina Diaz Gonzalez. Scholastic Press, [2015] 352 p.: Moving target

Grades: 4 5 6 7 8   **Fic**

1. Relics 2. Secret societies 3. Riddles 4. Americans in Italy 5.

Holy Lance 6. Rome, Italy 7. Italy 8. Fantasy fiction
ISBN 9780545773188

LC 2014038851

Twelve-year-old Cassie Arroyo is a student in Rome, but her life changes when a secret organization, the Hastati, shoots her father—and she learns that she is a member of an ancient bloodline that enables her to use the Spear of Destiny, a legendary object that can alter the future.

"An adventure that will keep readers engaged until the cliffhanger ending and leave them waiting for the next book." Kirkus.

Goodman, Alison

The **Dark** Days Club. Alison Goodman. Viking, 2016. 496 p.: Lady Helen novels

Grades: 8 9 10 11 12   **Fic**

1. Charlotte, consort of George III, King of Great Britain, 1744-1818. 2. Regency period (1811-1820) 3. Demons 4. Nobility 5. Balls (Parties) 6. Courts and courtiers 7. Missing persons 8. London, England 9. Great Britain 10. Historical fantasy
ISBN 9780670785476

LC 2015006792

In April 1812, as she is preparing for her debut presentation to Queen Charlotte, Lady Helen Wrexhall finds herself in the middle of a conspiracy reaching to the very top of society, and learns the truth about her mother, who died ten years ago. Provided by publisher.

"Readers willing to embrace the deep, deliberately paced journey will find the pace and tension increasing until the end leaves them eager for the next volume." Kirkus.

Eona: return of the dragoneye. Alison Goodman. Viking, 2011. 531 p.

Grades: 7 8 9 10   **Fic**

1. Teenage girls with disabilities 2. Dragons 3. Gender role 4. Betrayal 5. Sexuality 6. High fantasy 7. Fantasy fiction 8. Asian-influenced fantasy
ISBN 9780670063116

Facing the ultimate battle for control of the land she calls home, Eona finds herself waging an internal battle every bit as devastating as the war threatening to break out across the kingdom.

"One of those rare and welcome fantasies that complicate black-and-white morality." Kirkus.

Gordon, Roderick

Tunnels. by Roderick Gordon and Brian Williams. Chicken House/Scholastic, 2008. 472 p.: Tunnels

Grades: 6 7 8 9   **Fic**

1. Teenage boys 2. Rescues 3. Civilization, Subterranean 4. Archaeological expeditions 5. Tunnels 6. London, England 7. England 8. Science fiction
ISBN 9780439871778

LC 2007009169

When Will Burrows and his friend Chester embark on a quest to find Will's archaeologist father, who has inexplicably disappeared, they are led to a labyrinthine world underneath London, full of sinister inhabitants with evil intentions toward "Topsoilers" like Will and his father.

"This is compelling. . . . The authors add distinctive, vivid touches to the . . . premise . . . and the murderous, refreshingly competant Styx makes an uncommonly challenging adversary." Booklist.

Goto, Hiromi, 1966-

Half World. Hiromi Goto; [illustrations by] Jillian Tamaki. Viking, 2010. 240 p.

Grades: 7 8 9 10   **Fic**
1. Purgatory 2. Soul 3. Balance 4. Spiritual journeys 5. Quests 6. Coming-of-age stories 7. Fantasy fiction 8. Asian-influenced fantasy
ISBN 9780670012206

When her mother is kidnapped, Melanie, the human daughter of parents from the Half World, a limbo between Earth and the afterlife, is forced to follow her missing mother to Half World, from which neither may return alive.

"Raised in impoverished circumstances by her single mother, overweight 14-year-old Melanie is the target of ridicule at school and leads a lonely, introverted life. Then an evil being named Mr. Glueskin kidnaps her mother, forcing Melanie to travel to Half World, a colorless land that has been sundered from the realms of flesh and spirit, its deceased inhabitants cursed to relive the most traumatic moments of their lives. . . . Goto writes the hellish Half World as miserably surreal yet horrifyingly believable. . . . It's a fast-moving and provocative journey with cosmically high stakes, and one that should readily appeal to fans of dark, nightmarish fantasy." Publishers Weekly.

Grabenstein, Chris

The **crossroads**. Chris Grabenstein. Random House, c2008. 325 p.: Haunted mysteries
Grades: 5 6 7 8   **Fic**
1. Ghosts 2. Traffic accidents 3. Revenge 4. Oak 5. Murder 6. Connecticut 7. Supernatural mysteries
ISBN 9780375846977

LC 2007024803

When eleven-year-old Zack Jennings moves to Connecticut with his father and new stepmother, they must deal with the ghosts left behind by a terrible accident, as well as another kind of ghost from Zack's past.

"An absorbing psychological thriller . . . as well as a rip-roaring ghost story, this switches points of view among humans, trees, and ghosts with astonishing élan." Booklist.

★ **Escape** from Mr. Lemoncello's library. Chris Grabenstein. Random House, 2013. 304 p.: Mr. Lemoncello's library
Grades: 5 6 7   **Fic**
1. Libraries 2. Puzzles 3. Games 4. Twelve-year-old boys 5. Preteen boys 6. Mysteries
ISBN 9780375870897

LC 2012048122

Twelve-year-old Kyle wins a coveted spot to be one of 12 children chosen to stay in the new town library—designed by his hero, the famous gamemaker Luigi Lemoncello—for an overnight of fun, food and games, but in the morning, the kids find all the doors still locked and must work together to solve secret puzzles in order to discover the hidden escape route.

★ The **island** of Dr. Libris. Chris Grabenstein. Random House, 2015. 329 p.
Grades: 4 5 6 7   **Fic**
1. Characters and characteristics in literature 2. Books and reading 3. Family problems 4. Islands 5. Inventions 6. Fantasy fiction
ISBN 9780385388443

A twelve-year-old boy, worried that his parents may divorce, discovers that an island in the middle of the lake where he is spending the summer is the testing grounds of the mysterious Dr. Libris, who may have invented a way to make the characters in books come alive.

Mr. Lemoncello's great library race. Chris Grabenstein. Random House, [2017] 304 p.: Mr. Lemoncello's library

Grades: 5 6 7   **Fic**
1. Contests 2. Libraries 3. Books and reading 4. Eccentrics and eccentricities 5. Competition 6. Mysteries
ISBN 9780553536072

LC 2015040525

Mr. Lemoncello holds a contest for his young friends where they must race to bring interesting facts back to his library. Provided by publisher.

"Fans will embrace this new entry, which, like the previous books, features lightning-fast pacing and zany plotlines. Educators will be pleased by the emphasis on careful research and fact-checking." School Library Journal.

Mr. Lemoncello's Library Olympics. Chris Grabenstein. Random House, 2016. 304 p.: Mr. Lemoncello's library
Grades: 5 6 7   **Fic**
1. Libraries 2. Contests 3. Books and reading 4. Competition 5. Censorship 6. Mysteries
ISBN 9780553510409

LC 2015024473

Mr. Lemoncello has invited teams from all across America to compete in the first ever LIBRARY OLYMPICS...but someone is trying to censor what the kids are reading. Provided by publisher.

"This is a successful blend of mystery, adventure, and suspense, with a sizable cast of characters, in a wholly satisfying sequel that easily stands alone." School Library Journal.

The **smartest** kid in the universe. Chris Grabenstein. Random House Children's Books, 2020 304 p.: Smartest kid in the universe
Grades: 4 5 6 7   **Fic**
1. Middle school students 2. Genius 3. Conspiracies 4. Treasure troves 5. School principals 6. Adventure stories 7. Humorous stories
ISBN 9780525647782

LC 2019051235

12-year-old Jake is rendered a child genius by the accidental ingestion of experimental information pills, before using his newfound smarts to save his middle school from being shut down.

"The author crafts a conscientiously diverse cast for his multistranded crowd-pleaser and slips in snatches of dialogue in Spanish along with buckets of random facts and trivia." Booklist

Grabenstein, J. J.

★ **Shine!** . J.J. and Chris Grabenstein. Random House, 2019 224 p.
Grades: 4 5 6 7   **Fic**
1. Prep schools 2. Ability 3. Self-esteem 4. Private schools 5. New students 6. Realistic fiction
ISBN 9781524717667

LC 2017022751

When seventh-grader Piper's father is hired by Chumley Prep, a school where every student seems to be the best at everything, she gets the chance to compete for the prestigious Excelsior Award.

Graff, Lisa (Lisa Colleen), 1981-

★ A **tangle** of knots. Lisa Graff. Philomel Books, 2013. 288 p.
Grades: 3 4 5 6   **Fic**
1. Girl orphans 2. Baking 3. Ability 4. Identity (Psychology) 5. Adopted girls 6. New York (State) 7. Poughkeepsie, New York 8.

Fantasy fiction
ISBN 9780399255175

LC 2012009573

Destiny leads 11-year-old Cady to a peanut butter factory, a family of children searching for their own Talents, and a Talent Thief who will alter her life forever. Provided by publisher. Includes cake recipes.

Grant, Holly

The **league** of beastly dreadfuls. Holly Grant; pictures by Josie Portillo. Random House, 2015. 320 p.: League of beastly dreadfuls

Grades: 4 5 6 7   **Fic**

1. Captives 2. Child kidnapping victims 3. Shapeshifters 4. Kidnapping 5. Shadows 6. Fantasy fiction
ISBN 9780385370073

Moving to a Victorian asylum run by her two eccentric great aunts after her parents die in a tragic vacuum-cleaner accident, 11-year-old Anastasia befriends two mysterious brothers and begins to suspect her aunts are not who they claim to be.

"With just the right mix of humor, magic, maliciousness, and suspense, Grant leaves readers waiting for Anastasias next adventure." Booklist.

Grant, Michael, 1954-

Eve & Adam. Michael Grant and Katherine Applegate. Feiwel and Friends, 2012. 291 p.

Grades: 7 8 9 10   **Fic**

1. Biomedical engineering 2. Traffic accident victims 3. Healing 4. Corporations 5. Mothers and daughters 6. San Francisco, California 7. Science fiction
ISBN 9780312583514

A story told from alternating viewpoints by the husband-and-wife team creators of the Animorphs series follows the efforts of a car accident patient who, while recovering in her mother's research facility, is given the task of creating a perfect boy using detailed simulation technologies.

"Observant, smart, and unencumbered by emotion, this is a tasty read that readers will devour in a flash. Lucky for them, there's a sequel planned." Publishers Weekly.

Fear: a Gone novel. Michael Grant. Katherine Tegen Books, 2012. 576 p.: Gone novels

Grades: 7 8 9 10   **Fic**

1. Survival 2. Parent-separated children 3. Fear 4. Supernatural 5. Good and evil 6. California 7. Science fiction
ISBN 9780061449154

LC 2011019374

As the young residents of Perdido Beach begin to better comprehend the truths of who they are and their relationships to one another, the Darkness finds a new way to be born, bringing their understanding of fear to a new level.

"Fans can count on more excellent storytelling, multidimensional characters who continue to develop in unexpected ways, and some mighty fine eye-popping moments." Voice of Youth Advocates.

Hunger: a Gone novel. Michael Grant. Katherine Tegen Books/HarperTeen, 2009. 590 p.: Gone novels

Grades: 7 8 9 10   **Fic**

1. Parent-separated children 2. Twin brothers 3. Hunger 4. Social conflict 5. Supernatural 6. California 7. Science fiction
ISBN 9780061449079

LC 2008036465

Conditions worsen for the remaining young residents of a small California coastal town isolated by supernatural events when their food supplies dwindle and the Darkness underground awakens.

"Readers will be unable to avoid involuntarily gasping, shuddering, or flinching while reading this suspense-filled story. The tension starts in the first chapter and does not let up until the end." Voice of Youth Advocates.

Lies: a Gone novel. Michael Grant. HarperTeen, 2010 464 p.: Gone novels

Grades: 7 8 9 10   **Fic**

1. Mutants 2. Prophets 3. Life after death 4. Supernatural 5. Good and evil 6. California 7. Science fiction
ISBN 9780061449093

Believing they have defeated Drake after the events in Hunger, Sam and Caine are dismayed by the arrival of an Orsay prophetess who insists they must commit suicide to escape the FAYZ, a situation that is further complicated when Zil and Human Crew set the town on fire.

"This book retains all the action, unexpected twists, and engaging characters of the previous stories; readers will learn answers to old questions but new questions will proliferate. . . . Fascinating, frightening and absolutely worth an obsessive wait for the next installment, mature teen readers will embrace this thrill ride tempered with a touch of smart social commentary." Voice of Youth Advocates.

Light: a Gone novel. Michael Grant. Katherine Tegen Books, 2013. 576 p.: Gone novels

Grades: 7 8 9 10   **Fic**

1. Survival 2. Parent-separated children 3. Fear 4. Supernatural 5. Good and evil 6. California 7. Science fiction
ISBN 9780061449192

A conclusion to the series is set a year after every person over the age of 14 has disappeared from the town of Perdido, where a precarious new existence for young FAYZ survivors is shattered by the rebirth of the Darkness.

Plague: a Gone novel. Michael Grant. Katherine Tegen Books, 2011. 576 p.: Gone novels

Grades: 7 8 9 10   **Fic**

1. Epidemics 2. Plague 3. Survival 4. Supernatural 5. Good and evil 6. California 7. Science fiction
ISBN 9780061449123

LC 2010021834

A deadly, flu-like epidemic and a plague of flesh-eating creatures threaten the lives of the children at Perdido Beach while Sam, Astrid, Caine, and Diana each struggle with doubts and uncertainties.

"Grant's sf-fantasy thrillers continue to be the very definition of page-turner." Booklist.

The **trap**. Michael Grant. Katherine Tegen Books, 2011. 256 p.: Magnificent 12

Grades: 4 5 6   **Fic**

1. Boy heroes 2. Women rulers 3. Exile (Punishment) 4. Clues 5. Good and evil 6. China 7. Fantasy fiction
ISBN 9780061833687

LC 2010040580

Mack MacAvoy, an average-seeming twelve-year-old boy who happens to have special powers, travels to China in an effort to assemble an elite team of his peers to help him thwart the evil Pale Queen.

Gratton, Tessa

Strange grace. Tessa Gratton. Margaret K. McElderry Books, 2018 400 p.

Grades: 8 9 10 11　　　　　　　**Fic**

1. Faustian bargains 2. Human sacrifice 3. Witches 4. Forests 5. Curses 6. Fantasy fiction 7. Horror

ISBN 9781534402089

Every seven years, the people of Three Graces send a sacrifice to the woods. The death of their 'best boy' ensures seven years free from disease, blight, and pain. But this year, the Slaughter Moon has risen early, and three, not one, will run into the forest as a sacrifice. Provided by publisher.

Gratz, Alan, 1972-

Ground Zero. Alan Gratz. Scholastic 2021 336 p.

Grades: 4 5 6 7　　　　　　　**Fic**

1. World Trade Center, New York City 2. 2000s (Decade) 3. 2010s 4. September 11 Terrorist Attacks, 2001 5. Afghan War, 2001- 6. Teenage boys 7. Teenage girls 8. Survival (after disaster) 9. New York City 10. Afghanistan 11. Historical fiction

ISBN 9781338245752

LC 2020041442

Brandon is visiting his dad on the 107th floor of the World Trade Center on September 11, 2001 when the attack comes; Reshmina is a girl in Afghanistan who has grown up in the aftermath of that attack but dreams of peace, becoming a teacher and escaping her village and the narrow role that the Taliban believes is appropriate for women—both are struggling to survive, both changed forever by the events of 9/11.

"The pace is quick (don't blink or you'll miss something!), its emotions deeply authentic, and the highly visual settings resonate with accuracy." Booklist

Prisoner B-3087. by Alan Gratz. Scholastic Press, 2013. 272 p.

Grades: 7 8 9 10　　　　　　　**Fic**

1. Gruener, Jack. 2. Holocaust(1933-1945) 3. Jewish boys 4. Holocaust survivors 5. Ghettoes, Jewish 6. Concentration camps 7. Krakow, Poland 8. Poland 9. Historical fiction 10. Biographical fiction

ISBN 9780545459013

LC 2012012460

Based on the life of Jack Gruener, this book relates his story of survival from the Nazi occupation of Krakow, when he was eleven, through a succession of concentration camps, to the final liberation of Dachau.

★ **Projekt** 1065. Alan Gratz. Scholastic Press, 2016. 320 p.

Grades: 5 6 7 8　　　　　　　**Fic**

1. Hitler Youth. 2. Second World War era (1939-1945) 3. Undercover operations 4. Teenage spies 5. Diplomatic and consular service 6. Espionage 7. Irish in Germany 8. Berlin, Germany 9. Germany 10. Spy fiction 11. Historical fiction

ISBN 9780545880169

LC 2016016960

It is 1943, and thirteen-year-old Michael O'Shaunessey, son of the Irish ambassador to Nazi Germany in Berlin, is also a spy for the British Secret Service, so he has joined the Hitler Youth, and pretending that he agrees with their violence and book-burning is hard enough—but when he is asked to find out more about "Projekt 1065" both his and his parents' lives get a lot more dangerous.

"A rare insider's glimpse into the Hitler Youth: animated, well-researched, and thought-provoking." Kirkus.

Includes bibliographical references.

Refugee. Alan Gratz. Scholastic Press, 2017. 352 p.

Grades: 5 6 7 8　　　　　　　**Fic**

1. 1930s 2. 1990s 3. 2010s 4. Refugees 5. Immigration and emigration 6. Resilience (Personal quality) 7. Jewish boys 8. Survival 9. Germany 10. Cuba 11. Historical fiction

ISBN 9780545880831

LC 2017017544

Sydney Taylor Book Award for Older Readers, 2018.

Separated by decades, Josef, a Jew living in 1930s Nazi Germany; Isabel, a girl trying to escape unrest in 1994 Cuba; and Mahmoud, a Syrian boy in 2015 whose homeland is torn apart by violence, embark on journeys in search of refuge.

"Poignant, respectful, and historically accurate while pulsating with emotional turmoil, adventure, and suspense." Kirkus.

Gray, Claudia

Defy the stars. Claudia Gray. 512 p.: Constellation trilogy

Grades: 7 8 9 10 11 12　　　　　　　**Fic**

1. Teenage soldiers 2. Robots 3. Purpose in life 4. Love 5. Loyalty 6. Space opera 7. Science fiction

ISBN 9780316394031

LC 2016028390

Teenaged soldier Noemi and an enemy robot, Abel, who is programmed to obey her commands, set out on an interstellar quest to save her home planet, Earth colony Genesis.

"Nuanced philosophical discussions of religion, terrorism, and morality advise and direct the high-stakes action, informing the beautiful, realistic ending. Intelligent and thoughtful, a highly relevant far-off speculative adventure." Kirkus.

A **thousand** pieces of you. Claudia Gray. HarperTeen, an imprint of HarperCollinsPublishers, 2014. 368 p.: Firebird trilogy (Claudia Gray)

Grades: 8 9 10 11　　　　　　　**Fic**

1. Interdimensional travel 2. Revenge 3. Children of scientists 4. Space and time 5. Families 6. Science fiction

ISBN 9780062278968

LC 2014001894

When eighteen-year-old Marguerite Caine's father is killed, she must leap into different dimensions and versions of herself to catch her father's killer and avenge his murder.—Provided by publisher.

"Readers will appreciate Marguerite's determination to help her parents, even though she is a misfit, the lone artist in a family of scientific geniuses. The secondary players are equally well rounded, and their various incarnations in each dimension make for intriguing character explorations. In resourceful Marguerite's first-person narration, the story moves quickly, and the science is explained enough to make the plot clear, but not so much as to bog things down." Booklist.

Green, Tim, 1963-

Baseball genius. by Tim Green and Derek Jeter. Jeter Children's/Aladdin, 2017. 344 p.: Baseball genius

Grades: 5 6 7 8　　　　　　　**Fic**

1. Multiracial boys 2. Boy baseball players 3. Professional baseball players 4. Stealing 5. Baseball 6. Baseball stories 7. Sports fiction

ISBN 9781481468640

An everyday kid with a talent for predicting baseball pitches is caught stealing baseballs from his favorite New York Yankees player, who agrees not to press charges if the boy will help him recover from a difficult batting slump

Football champ. Tim Green. HarperCollins Children's Books, c2009. 280 p.: Football genius novels

Grades: 5 6 7 8 **Fic**

1. Atlanta Falcons (Football team) 2. Boy football players 3. Father-deserted children 4. Journalists 5. Secrets 6. Forecasting 7. Atlanta, Georgia 8. Sports fiction 9. Football stories
ISBN 9780061626906

LC 2008051775

Twelve-year-old Troy's uncanny gift for predicting football plays proves a powerful secret weapon for the Atlanta Falcons, but a seedy reporter with a vendetta suspects something is going on and sets out to shred the reputations of Troy and star linebacker Seth Halloway.

"The characters are engaging and the game action is exciting. Short cliffhanger chapters make this a good bet for reluctant readers." School Library Journal.

Football genius. Tim Green. Harper Collins Publishers, 2007. 244 p.: Football genius novels

Grades: 5 6 7 8 **Fic**

1. Atlanta Falcons (Football team) 2. Boy football players 3. Father-deserted children 4. Assertiveness (Psychology) 5. Self-discovery in boys 6. Boys and sports 7. Atlanta, Georgia 8. Sports fiction 9. Football stories
ISBN 9780061122705

LC 2006029470

Troy, a sixth-grader with an unusual gift for predicting football plays before they occur, attempts to use his ability to help his favorite team, the Atlanta Falcons, but he must first prove himself to the coach and players.

"The author imparts many insider details that football fans will love. Green makes Troy a winning hero, and he ties everything together with a fast-moving plot." Booklist.

Football hero. Tim Green. HarperCollinsPublishers, c2008. 297 p.: Football genius novels

Grades: 5 6 7 8 **Fic**

1. New York Jets (Football team) 2. Boy football players 3. Father-deserted children 4. Gambling 5. Mafia 6. Brothers 7. Sports fiction 8. Football stories
ISBN 9780061122750

LC 2007024184

When twelve-year-old Ty's brother Thane is recruited out of college to play for the New York Jets, their Uncle Gus uses Ty to get insider information for his gambling ring, landing Ty and Thane in trouble with the Mafia.

"The novel is briskly paced and undemanding, and might be a good bet for sports-minded reluctant readers." School Library Journal.

Force out. Tim Green. Harper, 2013. 272 p.

Grades: 4 5 6 **Fic**

1. Boy baseball players 2. Competition 3. Best friends 4. Friendship 5. Little League baseball 6. Sports fiction 7. Realistic fiction 8. Baseball stories
ISBN 9780062089595

LC 2012026752

When Joey has to compete with his best friend, Zach, for a single spot on an elite baseball team, he is forced to decide how far he is willing to go to win. Provided by publisher.

"Though Green is no stylist, he does a better job of avoiding the sports fantasy and sticking to real life than usual. There's plenty of play-by-play for those who want the sports to be the focus, but the interactions off the field are never shortchanged. . . . A slice of life for middle school readers who know that their sport is a microcosm of the larger world." Kirkus.

New kid. Tim Green. HarperCollins, 2014. 352 p.: New kids novels

Grades: 4 5 6 7 8 **Fic**

1. Boy baseball players 2. Fathers and sons 3. New students 4. Moving, Household 5. Interpersonal relations 6. New York (State) 7. Sports fiction 8. Baseball stories
ISBN 9780062208729

LC 2013032816

A troubled kid finds his bearings in a new school after a baseball coach offers him a spot on the team. Provided by publisher.

"Best-selling author and former NFL defensive end Green delivers a riveting book about the complexities of being a teenager caught in unusual circumstances beyond his control. His writing is both compelling and intelligent, and even the implausible scenes—like a visit from a baseball great—still maintain a feel of authenticity. Even readers who aren't sports fans will find plenty of familiar drama and entertainment in this book. Exciting, romantic and thought-provoking, this book scores a home run." Kirkus.

Greenwald, Lisa

My life in pink & green. by Lisa Greenwald. Amulet Books, 2009. 272 p.: Pink & green

Grades: 4 5 6 7 **Fic**

1. Family problems 2. Mothers and daughters 3. Cosmetics 4. Green movement 5. Twelve-year-old girls 6. Realistic fiction
ISBN 9780810983526

LC 2008025577

When the family's drugstore is failing, seventh-grader Lucy uses her problem solving talents to come up with solution that might resuscitate the business, along with helping the environment.

"Greenwald deftly blends eco-facts and makeup tips, friendship dynamics, and spot-on middle-school politics into a warm, uplifting story." Booklist.

Greenwald, Tom, 1962-

Charlie Joe Jackson's guide to summer vacation. Tommy Greenwald; illustrated by J. P. Coovert. Roaring Brook Press, 2013. 240 p.: Charlie Joe Jackson's guide to--

Grades: 4 5 6 7 **Fic**

1. Summer camps 2. Boy campers 3. Slackers 4. Student newspapers and periodicals 5. Interpersonal relations 6. Realistic fiction 7. Humorous stories
ISBN 9781596437579

LC 2012034249

Charlie Joe Jackson is back and he's at academic summer camp trying to convert all the other kids to non-academics. Provided by publisher.

Game changer. Tommy Greenwald. Harry N Abrams Inc., 2018. 304 p.

Grades: 6 7 8 9 **Fic**

1. Football players 2. People in comas 3. Hazing 4. Football injuries 5. Sports injuries 6. Mysteries 7. Sports fiction 8. Football stories
ISBN 9781419731433

While thirteen-year-old Teddy fights for his life after a football injury at training camp, his friends and family gather to support him and discuss events leading to his coma. Told through dialogue, text messages, newspaper articles, transcripts, an online forum, and Teddy's inner thoughts.

Gregorio, I. W., 1976-

This is my brain in love. I. W. Gregorio. Little, Brown and Company, 2020. 384 p.

Grades: 8 9 10 11 12   **Fic**

1. Restaurants 2. Family businesses 3. Cooking, Chinese 4. Anxiety in teenagers 5. Teenagers with depression 6. New York State 7. Romantic comedies 8. Contemporary romances
ISBN 9780316423823

LC 2019033954

Schneider Family Book Award for Teens, 2021.

Rising high school juniors Jocelyn Wu and Will Domenici fall in love while trying to save the Wu family restaurant, A-Plus Chinese Garden.

"Deftly navigating issues of race and mental health, as well as giving voice to the reality of American teens born to immigrant families, many of whom grapple with different cultural and familial expectations, Gregorio, a founding member of We Need Diverse Books, has written a heartwarming foodie rom-com." School Library Journal.

Griffin, N.

Just wreck it all. N. Griffin. A Caitlyn Dlouhy Book/Atheneum, 2018. 336 p.

Grades: 7 8 9 10 11   **Fic**

1. Self-destructive behavior in teenage girls 2. Guilt 3. Compulsive eating 4. Teenage girls 5. Teenage runners 6. Realistic fiction
ISBN 9781481465182

LC 2018008167

Crippled with guilt after causing a horrific accident two years earlier, sixteen-year-old Bett's life is a series of pluses and minuses. But when the pluses become too much to outweigh the minuses, Bett is forced to confront her self-harming behavior. Provided by publisher.

Griffin, Paul, 1966-

Saving Marty. by Paul Griffin. Dial Books, 2017. 208 p.

Grades: 5 6 7 8   **Fic**

1. Piglets 2. Best friends 3. Human/animal relationships 4. Father-separated boys 5. Friendship 6. Pennsylvania 7. Realistic fiction
ISBN 9780399539077

LC 2017008131

When Lorenzo adopts Marty, a runt piglet, nothing prepares him for the life-changing bond they form or for the chaos a full grown pig can create.

"Griffin captures a slice of Americana—the flyover farms of middle America—rarely depicted so sensitively in contemporary middle-grade fiction." Booklist.

Skyjacked. Paul Griffin. Scholastic Press, 2019. 240 p.

Grades: 5 6 7 8 9 10 11 12   **Fic**

1. Hijacking of aircraft 2. Hostages 3. Suspicion 4. Kidnapping victims 5. Survival 6. Thrillers and suspense 7. Survival stories
ISBN 9781338047417

LC 2018053889

Five teenagers from the elite Hartwell Academy are on their way back to New York from an end-of-summer camping trip in Idaho when they realize that something has gone wrong; one of them has become violently ill, and their private plane has apparently been hijacked and is headed in the wrong direction—and even if they can somehow break

into the cockpit and manage to overpower the hijacker, they have no idea how to fly the plane, much less land it.

Grimes, Nikki

Bronx masquerade. Nikki Grimes. Dial Books, 2002. 167 p.

Grades: 7 8 9 10   **Fic**

1. African American students 2. Identity (Psychology) 3. Bonding (Interpersonal relations) 4. Ethnicity 5. African Americans 6. Bronx, New York City 7. Novels in verse 8. Realistic fiction
ISBN 0803725698

LC 00031701

Coretta Scott King Award, Author Category, 2003.

While studying the Harlem Renaissance, students at a Bronx high school read aloud poems they've written, revealing their innermost thoughts and fears to their formerly clueless classmates.

"Funny and painful, awkward and abstract, the poems talk about race, abuse, parental love, neglect, death, and body image. . . . Readers will enjoy the lively, smart voices that talk bravely about real issues and secret fears. A fantastic choice for readers' theater." Booklist.

Jazmin's notebook. Nikki Grimes. Dial Books, 1998. 102 p.

Grades: 6 7 8 9   **Fic**

1. 1960s 2. African American girls 3. Fourteen-year-old girls 4. Sisters 5. African American families 6. Harlem, New York City 7. Realistic fiction 8. African American fiction
ISBN 0803722249

LC 97005850

Jazmin, a fourteen-year-old Afro-American girl who lives with her sister in a Harlem apartment, finds strength in writing poetry and keeping a diary.

"An articulate, admirable heroine, Jazmin leaps over life's hurdles with agility and integrity." Publishers Weekly.

Grisham, John

The **abduction**. John Grisham. Dutton Children's Books, 2011. 217 p.: Theodore Boone

Grades: 4 5 6 7   **Fic**

1. Kidnapping investigation 2. Lawyers 3. Courts 4. Kidnapping 5. Family problems 6. Mysteries
ISBN 9780525425571

LC 2011006060

When his best friend disappears from her bedroom in the middle of the night, thirteen-year-old Theo uses his legal knowledge and investigative skills to chase down the truth and save April.

"The book is smoothly written, and there's a mild tutorial on the criminal justice system." Publishers Weekly.

The **accused**. John Grisham. Puffin Books, 2012. 271 p.: Theodore Boone

Grades: 4 5 6 7   **Fic**

1. Malicious accusation 2. Lawyers 3. Robbery 4. Innocence (Law) 5. Courts 6. Mysteries
ISBN 9780525425762

Thirteen-year-old aspiring lawyer Theodore Boone is falsely accused in a robbery and must fight to clear his name.

★ **Theodore** Boone, kid lawyer. John Grisham. Dutton Children's Books, c2010. 263 p.: Theodore Boone

Grades: 4 5 6 7   **Fic**

1. Trials (Murder) 2. Murder witnesses 3. Lawyers 4. Wife killing

5. Truth 6. Mysteries
ISBN 9780525423843

LC bl2010012879

Thirteen-year-old Theodore Boone has always dreamed of being a great trial lawyer someday, but a sensational murder trial forces him into the arena sooner than expected, and he is determined to see that justice prevails.

"Grisham serves up a dandy legal adventure that moves along quickly. Without intruding on the story's trajectory, he gives plenty of background about the legal process and explores various ethical questions." Horn Book Guide.

Grove, S. E.

The **crimson** skew. S.E. Grove. Viking, an imprint of Penguin Random House LLC, 2016. 432 p.: Mapmakers trilogy
Grades: 6 7 8 9 10   **Fic**
1. 1890s 2. Parent-separated teenage girls 3. Maps 4. Pirates 5. Imaginary wars and battles 6. Teenage girls 7. Fantasy fiction
ISBN 9780670785049

LC 2015036703

In a world transformed by 1799's Great Disruption—when all of the continents were flung into different time periods, Sophia Tims journeys home to Boston, anticipating her runion with Theo, but he has been conscripted to fight in the Western War, Prime Minister Broadgirldle's twisted vision of Manifest Destiny.

"Pirates, sea captains, fortunetellers, a dragon, poisonous red fog, former slave traders, and healers populate a story that may introduce young readers to the old-fashioned pleasure of settling into a long, rich, and complicated tale. A triumphant conclusion to a prodigious feat of storytelling." Kirkus.

The **golden** specific. S.E. Grove; maps by Dave A. Stevenson. Viking, an imprint of Penguin Group (USA), 2015. 528 p.: Mapmakers trilogy
Grades: 6 7 8 9 10   **Fic**
1. 1890s 2. Parent-separated teenage girls 3. Maps 4. Missing persons 5. Plague 6. Adventure 7. Fantasy fiction
ISBN 9780670785032

Thirteen-year-old Sophia Tims and her friend Theo continue to search for her parents, explorers who have vanished, as the borders shift within a world transformed by the Great Disruption of 1799.

"Brilliantly imagined and full of wonder." Kirkus.

Gulledge, Laura Lee

Will & Whit. Laura Lee Gulledge. Paw Prints, 2013. 192 p.
Grades: 7 8 9 10   **Fic**
1. Fear of darkness 2. Hurricanes 3. Creativity in teenage girls 4. Coping in teenage girls 5. Communities 6. Comics and Graphic novels
ISBN 9781419705465

Wilhelmina "Will" Huxstep, a creative soul struggling to come to terms with a family tragedy, crafts whimsical lamps, in part to deal with her fear of the dark, which she is forced to confront when a hurricane blows through her town at the end of a summer.

Gurevich, Margaret

Making the cut. by Margaret Gurevich; illustrated by Brooke Hagel. Capstone Young Readers, a Capstone imprint, 2014. 384 p.: Chloe by design
Grades: 5 6 7 8 9   **Fic**
1. Fashion design 2. Reality television programs 3. Competition

4. Fashion designers 5. Frenemies 6. Realistic fiction
ISBN 9781623701123

"Project Runway meets Mean Girls in this fashion-inspired first volume of the Chloe by Design series. Chloe Montgomery has always dreamed of becoming a fashion designer, so when her favorite reality show, Design Diva, offers up a teen version of the show, Chloe knows she has to audition—the show's wild challenges will push her creatively. She gets in, but can she overcome her shy instincts and handle criticism from both the judges and her fashion nemesis?...While the outcome is predictable, Chloe's journey (and the fashions that accompany it) make for an enjoyable, fluffy read. Perfect for readers obsessed with fashion, clothing design, and reality TV." Booklist.

Gutman, Dan

Abner & me: a baseball card adventure. Dan Gutman. Harper Collins, c2005. 166 p.: Baseball card adventures
Grades: 4 5 6 7   **Fic**
1. Doubleday, Abner, 1819-1893 2. Thirteen-year-old boys 3. Time travel (Past) 4. Teenage boys 5. Nurses 6. Mothers and sons 7. United States 8. Fantasy fiction
ISBN 0060534435

LC 2004006315

With his ability to travel through time using baseball cards and photographs, thirteen-year-old Joe and his mother go back to 1863 to ask Abner Doubleday whether he invented baseball, but instead find themselves in the middle of the Battle of Gettysburg.

Babe and me: a baseball card adventure. Dan Gutman. Avon Camelot, c2000. 161 p.: Baseball card adventures
Grades: 4 5 6 7   **Fic**
1. Ruth, Babe, 1895-1948 2. Baseball 3. Time travel (Past) 4. Twelve-year-old boys 5. Baseball cards 6. Fantasy baseball (Game) 7. Fantasy fiction
ISBN 0380977397

LC 99-36778

With their ability to travel through time using vintage baseball cards, Joe and his father have the opportunity to find out whether Babe Ruth really did call his shot when he hit that home run in the third game of the 1932 World Series against the Chicago Cubs.

"Readers will enjoy the action, the rich baseball lore, and the sense of adventure." Booklist.

From Texas with love. Dan Gutman. Harper, an imprint of HarperCollinsPublishers, [2014] 256 p.: Genius Files
Grades: 4 5 6 7   **Fic**
1. Twin brothers and sisters 2. Genius 3. Codes (Communication) 4. Assassins 5. Recreational vehicles 6. Southwest (United States) 7. Thrillers and suspense
ISBN 9780061827730

LC 2013032147

The wackiest road trip in history continues as the McDonald twins travel the Southwest dodging nefarious villains and visiting weird but true American landmarks. Provided by publisher.

Honus and me: a baseball card adventure. Dan Gutman. Avon Books, 1997. 140 p.: Baseball card adventures
Grades: 4 5 6 7   **Fic**
1. Wagner, Honus 1874-1955 2. Twelve-year-old boys 3. Baseball 4. Time travel (Past) 5. Boys and baseball 6. Baseball players 7. Fantasy fiction
ISBN 0380973502

LC 96031439

Twelve-year-old Joe Stoshack, who loves baseball but is not very good at it, finds a valuable 1909 Honus Wagner card and travels back in time to meet the Hall of Famer. Illustrated with black-and-white photos, drawings, and facsimiles.

"This clever adventure will capture the hearts of anyone who has ever held a baseball bat in his or her hands. Gutman's voice rings true from start to finish." School Library Journal.

★ **Jackie** and me: a baseball card adventure. Dan Gutman. Avon Camelot, c1999. 145 p.: Baseball card adventures

Grades: 4 5 6 7   **Fic**
1. Baseball 2. Time travel (Past) 3. Prejudice 4. Baseball cards 5. Fantasy baseball (Game) 6. Fantasy fiction
ISBN 0380976854

LC   98053347

With his ability to travel through time by using baseball cards, Joe goes back to 1947 to meet Jackie Robinson; but he can't predict that his journey will not only change the color of his skin for a time, but it will alter his view of history—and his definition of courage.

"Full of action, this title will spark history discussions and be a good choice for book reports and leisure reading." School Library Journal.

Jim & me: a baseball card adventure. Dan Gutman. HarperCollins Publishers, c2008. 195 p.: Baseball card adventures

Grades: 4 5 6 7   **Fic**
1. Thorpe, Jim, 1887-1953. 2. New York Giants (Baseball team) 3. Baseball 4. Time travel (Past) 5. Thirteen-year-old boys 6. Boys and baseball 7. Baseball players 8. Fantasy fiction
ISBN 0060594942

Joe and his longtime enemy, Bobby Fuller, use a vintage baseball card to travel in time, hoping to stop Jim Thorpe from participating in the 1912 Olympics and losing his medals, but instead they watch Thorpe struggle during his first season with the New York Giants.

License to thrill. Dan Gutman. Harper, an imprint of HaperCollinsPublishers, 2015. 250 p.: Genius Files

Grades: 5 6 7 8   **Fic**
1. Twin brothers and sisters 2. Genius 3. Assassins 4. Recreational vehicles 5. Families 6. Thrillers and suspense
ISBN 9780062236326

Finds Coke and Pepsi McDonald fleeing nefarious villains while visiting such famous landmarks as the Hoover Dam and the Grand Canyon.

Mickey & me: a baseball card adventure. Dan Gutman. Harper Collins, 2003. 160 p.: Baseball card adventures

Grades: 4 5 6 7   **Fic**
1. 1940s 2. Baseball 3. Thirteen-year-old boys 4. Time travel (Past) 5. Baseball cards 6. Gender role 7. Fantasy fiction
ISBN 0060292474

LC   2002005641

When Joe travels back in time to 1944, he meets the Milwaukee Chicks, one of the only all-female professional baseball teams in the history of the game.

"Like the other books in the series, this one delivers a fast-moving plot, lots of action, and colorful depictions of famous sports heroes of the past." Booklist.

The **million** dollar shot. Dan Gutman. Hyperion Books for Children, c1997. 114 p.: Million dollar series (Dan Gutman)

Grades: 4 5 6 7   **Fic**
1. Eleven-year-old boys 2. Basketball 3. Contests 4. Basketball for children 5. Wealth 6. Sports fiction 7. Realistic fiction 8.

Basketball stories
ISBN 0786822759

LC   97006461

Eleven-year-old Eddie gets a chance to win a million dollars by sinking a foul shot at the National Basketball Association finals.

"This will appeal to both sports readers and general audiences. Gutman's subtle humor, exciting sports action, and excruciating suspense make this title an outstanding choice for reluctant readers." School Library Journal.

★ **Miss** Daisy is crazy! Dan Gutman; pictures by Jim Paillot. HarperTrophy, 2004. 83 p.: My weird school

Grades: 1 2 3   **Fic**
1. Second-grade boys 2. Elementary school teachers 3. Elementary schools 4. Reading 5. Schools 6. Humorous stories 7. Realistic fiction
ISBN 0060507004

LC   2003021441

Miss Daisy's unusual teaching methods surprise her second grade students, especially reluctant learner A.J.

★ **Mission** unstoppable. by Dan Gutman. Harper, 2011. 304 p.: Genius Files

Grades: 5 6 7 8   **Fic**
1. Twin brothers and sisters 2. Assassins 3. Genius 4. Recreational vehicles 5. Transcontinental journeys 6. Thrillers and suspense
ISBN 9780061827655

LC   2010009390

On a cross-country vacation with their parents, twins Coke and Pepsi, soon to be thirteen, fend off strange assassins as they try to come to terms with their being part of a top-secret government organization known as The Genius Files.

"Gutman's novel offers a quirky look at Americana that will engage curious minds. . . . Those looking for a fun and suspenseful read . . . will not be disappointed." Booklist.

★ **Never** say genius. Dan Gutman. Harper, 2012. 256 p.: Genius Files

Grades: 4 5 6 7   **Fic**
1. Twin brothers and sisters 2. Assassins 3. Genius 4. Recreational vehicles 5. Transcontinental journeys 6. Thrillers and suspense
ISBN 9780061827679

LC   2011019363

As their cross-country journey with their parents continues through the midwest, twins Coke and Pepsi, now thirteen, again face strange assassins at such places as the first McDonald's restaurant and Cedar Point amusement park.

Ray & me: a baseball card adventure. Dan Gutman. HarperCollins Publishers, c2009. 173 p.: Baseball card adventures

Grades: 4 5 6 7   **Fic**
1. Chapman, Ray, 1891-1920 2. Mays, Carl, 1892-1971 3. 1920s 4. Baseball 5. Time travel (Past) 6. Boys and baseball 7. Boys 8. Sports injuries 9. Fantasy fiction
ISBN 9780061234811

LC   2008019645

After recovering from being hit in the head during a baseball game, Stosh travels back in time to try to save Ray Chapman, a batter who was killed by a pitch in New York in 1920.

Roberto & me: a baseball card adventure. Dan Gutman. Harper, 2010. 192 p.: Baseball card adventures

Grades: 4 5 6 7 **Fic**
   1. Clemente, Roberto, 1934-1972. 2. 1960s 3. Time travel 4. Baseball 5. Thirteen-year-old boys 6. Professional baseball players 7. Boys and baseball 8. Fantasy fiction
   ISBN 9780061234859

                                 LC 2009014267
Stosh travels back to 1969 to try to prevent the untimely death of Roberto Clemente, a legendary baseball player and humanitarian, but upon his return to the present, he meets his own great-grandson who takes him into the future, and what he finds there is more shocking than anything he has encountered in his travels to the past.
   "This series entry is both amusing and informative." Booklist.

Satch & me: a baseball card adventure. Dan Gutman. Harper Collins, c2006. ix, 175 p.: Baseball card adventures
Grades: 4 5 6 7 **Fic**
   1. Paige, Satchel, 1906-1982 2. Thirteen-year-old boys 3. Baseball 4. Time travel (Past) 5. Boys and baseball 6. Baseball players 7. Fantasy fiction
   ISBN 0060594918

                                 LC 2005005717
With his ability to travel through time using vintage baseball cards, Joe takes Flip with him to find out whether Satchel Paige really was the fastest pitcher ever.
   "Enhancing the action-driven story are plenty of well-written baseball scenes, black-and-white photos, and the appearance of Negro League players Josh Gibson, Cool Papa Bell, and Buck ONeil." School Library Journal.

Shoeless Joe & me: a baseball card adventure. Dan Gutman. Harper Collins, c2002. 163 p.: Baseball card adventures
Grades: 4 5 6 7 **Fic**
   1. Jackson, Joe 1888-1951 2. Chicago White Sox (Baseball team) -- History 3. Thirteen-year-old boys 4. Time travel (Past) 5. Baseball 6. Professional baseball players 7. Black Sox Scandal, 1919 8. Fantasy fiction
   ISBN 0060292539

                                 LC 2001024638
Joe Stoshack travels back to 1919, where he meets Shoeless Joe Jackson and tries to prevent the fixing of the World Series in which Jackson was wrongly implicated.
   "Shoeless Joe is compelling, and Joe's adventures are exciting." Voice of Youth Advocates.

Haddix, Margaret Peterson

Among the Barons. Margaret Peterson Haddix. Simon & Schuster Books for Young Readers, 2003. 192 p.: Shadow children
Grades: 5 6 7 8 **Fic**
   1. Impostors 2. Survival 3. Boarding school students 4. Boys 5. Brothers 6. Science fiction
   ISBN 0689839065

                                 LC 2002004534
In a future world of false identities, government lies, and death threats, Luke feels drawn to the younger brother of the boy whose name Luke has taken.
   "This fourth installment in the series that began with Among the Hidden (1998) focuses on shadow child Luke Garner, a third child in a futuristic society that allows families only two children. Luke, who has gone underground to escape the Population Police, reemerges after 12 years in hiding to assume the identity of Lee Grant. . . . The impersonation goes smoothly until Smits, Grant's younger brother, enters the

picture. . . . There is enough background information in the opening chapter to fill in readers new to the series, and series' fans of the books won't be disappointed; there's plenty of suspense, and there are lots of thrilling twists and turns." Booklist.

Among the betrayed. Margaret Peterson Haddix. Simon & Schuster Books for Young Readers, 2002. 156 p.: Shadow children
Grades: 5 6 7 8 **Fic**
   1. Teenage prisoners 2. Escapes 3. Courage in girls 4. Police 5. Betrayal 6. Science fiction
   ISBN 0689839057

                                 LC 2001032214
Thirteen-year-old Nina is imprisoned by the Population Police, who give her the option of helping them identify illegal "third-born" children, or facing death.
   "As a character, Nina is well drawn and believable but it is the agonizing moral decisions that she must make that elevate the book beyond the average tale." School Library Journal.

Among the brave. Margaret Peterson Haddix. Simon & Schuster Books for Young Readers, c2004. 240 p.: Shadow children
Grades: 5 6 7 8 **Fic**
   1. Prisoners 2. Escapes 3. Rescues 4. Police 5. Boys 6. Science fiction
   ISBN 0689857942

                                 LC 2003009602
In a society that allows families to have only two children, a group of third-borns tries to save themselves and others like them.
   "Once again, Haddix makes real how hard ordinary and not-so-ordinary actions would be for kids who've spent most of their lives hidden away. Although this installment could be read on its own, this series works best when read in sequence." School Library Journal

Among the enemy. Margaret Peterson Haddix. Simon & Schuster Books for Young Readers, c2005. 214 p.: Shadow children
Grades: 5 6 7 8 **Fic**
   1. Police 2. Rescues 3. Guilt in teenage boys 4. Guilt 5. Personal conduct 6. Science fiction
   ISBN 0689857969

                                 LC 2004009645
In a society that allows families to have only two children, third child Matthias joins the Population Police to infiltrate their system.
   "The brisk, efficient pacing facilitated by occasionally abrupt plot turns is precisely what has cemented Haddix's strong following among both avid and reluctant readers. Series fans and newcomers alike will devour this whole." Booklist.

Among the free. Margaret Peterson Haddix. Simon & Schuster Books for Young Readers, 2006. 208 p.: Shadow children
Grades: 5 6 7 8 **Fic**
   1. Insurgency 2. Political corruption 3. Freedom 4. Thirteen-year-old boys 5. Teenage boys 6. Science fiction
   ISBN 0689857985

                                 LC 2005013025
When thirteen-year-old Luke Garner unwittingly sets off a rebellion which sweeps the country and ousts the Population Police from power, he quickly realizes that the new regime is corrupt and he may hold the only key to true freedom.

"This is a light, easy read that delivers what it promises. Fans of the series won't be disappointed." School Library Journal.

Among the hidden. Margaret Peterson Haddix. Simon & Schuster Books for Young Readers, c1998. 153 p.: Shadow children

Grades: 5 6 7 8   **Fic**
1. Twelve-year-old boys 2. Population control 3. Hiding 4. Social isolation in children 5. Social isolation 6. Science fiction 7. Classics
ISBN 0689817002

LC 97033052

A government decree allows each family only two children. For Luke, a third child, this has meant a lifetime of hiding. But could a stray glimpse of a child hiding in the house across the way lead to freedom?

Among the impostors. Margaret Peterson Haddix. Simon & Schuster Books for Young Readers, 2001. 172 p.: Shadow children

Grades: 5 6 7 8   **Fic**
1. Impostors 2. Coping in boys 3. Boarding schools 4. Fear in boys 5. Boys -- Interpersonal relations 6. Science fiction
ISBN 0689839049

LC 00058325

In a future where the law limits a family to only two children, third-born Luke has been in hiding for the entire twelve years of his life, until he enters boarding school under an assumed name and is forced to face his fears.

"Luke's quest for selfhood is convincingly portrayed in an unusually tense plot." Horn Book Guide.

Caught. Margaret Peterson Haddix. Simon & Schuster Books for Young Readers, 2012 London Toronto Sydney. 352 p.: The missing

Grades: 5 6 7 8   **Fic**
1. Einstein-Maric, Mileva, 1875-1948. 2. Einstein, Albert, 1879-1955 3. 1900s (Decade) 4. Time travel (Past) 5. Mother and child 6. Space and time 7. Brothers and sisters 8. Switzerland 9. Serbia 10. Science fiction
ISBN 9781416989820

LC 2011018654

When Jonah and Katherine travel to early 1900s Switzerland and Serbia to return Albert Einstein's daughter, Lieserl, to history, her mother Mileva grasps entirely too much about time travel and has no intention of letting her daughter go.

★ **Children** of exile. Margaret Peterson Haddix. Simon & Schuster Books for Young Readers, [2016] 304 p.: Children of exile

Grades: 5 6 7 8 9   **Fic**
1. Parent and child 2. Reunions 3. Families 4. Twelve-year-old girls 5. Preteen girls 6. Science fiction
ISBN 9781442450035

LC 2015031239

A twelve-year-old girl raised in a foster village is returned to her biological parents, and discovers home is not what she expected it to be.

"Haddix gives readers lots to mull over regarding conflict, justice, and prejudice." Publishers Weekly.

Children of refuge. Margaret Peterson Haddix. Simon & Schuster Books for Young Readers, [2017] 272 p.: Children of exile

Grades: 5 6 7 8 9   **Fic**
1. Aliens 2. Brothers and sisters 3. Boarding schools 4. Schools 5. Escapes 6. Science fiction
ISBN 9781442450066

LC 2016028252

Many surprises await twelve-year-old Edwy Watanaboneset when the Freds return him to Cursed Town, including that he has siblings in Refuge City who he will join in boarding school.

"An excellent dystopian adventure for tweens that avoids graphic violence while bringing up issues of social justice and prejudice." Booklist.

The **deceivers**. Margaret Peterson Haddix. Katherine Tegen Books, 2020. 448 p.: Greystone secrets

Grades: 4 5 6 7 8   **Fic**
1. Missing persons 2. Mother-separated children 3. Brothers and sisters 4. Rescues 5. Honesty 6. Ohio 7. Mysteries 8. Science fiction
ISBN 9780062838407

LC 2019026615

Told from separate viewpoints, as Finn, Emma, and Chess Greystone and Natalie Mayhew, ages eight to thirteen, continue their quest to rescue their mothers they must return to the alternate dimension where truth is illegal.

"A perilous, high-action plot—with a cliffhanger." Kirkus.

★ **Found**. Margaret Peterson Haddix. Simon & Schuster Books for Young Readers, c2008. 314 p.: The missing

Grades: 5 6 7 8 9   **Fic**
1. Adopted teenage boys 2. Time travel 3. Identity (Psychology) 4. Quests 5. Thirteen-year-old boys 6. Ohio 7. Science fiction
ISBN 1416954171

When thirteen-year-olds Jonah and Chip, who are both adopted, learn they were discovered on a plane that appeared out of nowhere, full of babies with no adults on board, they realize that they have uncovered a mystery involving time travel and two opposing forces, each trying to repair the fabric of time.

"This is a tantalizing opener to a new series. . . . Readers will be hard-pressed to wait for the next installment." Publishers Weekly.

In over their heads. Margaret Peterson Haddix. Simon & Schuster Books for Young Readers, [2017] 320 p.: Under their skin

Grades: 4 5 6 7   **Fic**
1. Twin brothers and sisters 2. Robots 3. Blended families 4. Humans 5. Extinction (Biology) 6. Science fiction
ISBN 9781481417617

LC 2015039563

Twelve-year-old twins Nick and Eryn and their robot stepsiblings, Jackson and Ava, try to save humanity from killer robots.

"As in the previous book, there are cliff-hangers in every chapter, and the tension builds to a fever-pitch conclusion." Booklist.

Just Ella. Margaret Peterson Haddix. Simon & Schuster Books for Young Readers, c1999 185 p.: Palace chronicles

Grades: 7 8 9 10   **Fic**
1. Princesses 2. Independence in teenage girls 3. Engagement 4. Princes 5. Gender role 6. Fantasy fiction 7. Fairy tale and folklore-inspired fiction
ISBN 0689821867

LC 98008384

In this continuation of the Cinderella story, fifteen-year-old Ella finds that accepting Prince Charming's proposal ensnares her in a suffocating tangle of palace rules and royal etiquette, so she plots to escape.

"In lively prose, with well-developed characters, creative plot twists, wit, and drama, Haddix transforms the Cinderella tale into an insightful coming-of-age story." Booklist.

Remarkables. Margaret Peterson Haddix. Katherine Tegen Books, an imprint of HarperCollins Publishers, [2019] 304 p.
Grades: 4 5 6 7   **Fic**
1. Neighbors 2. Time travel 3. Family relationships 4. Family secrets 5. Guilt 6. Pennsylvania 7. Supernatural mysteries
ISBN 9780062838469
                                                                                    LC 2019000073
Eleven-year-old Marin and her neighbor Charley hope that by preventing a disaster that occurred twenty years ago, they can save Charley's dad from a future of guilt and self-destructive behavior.

"Blending issues that matter to young adolescents with intrigue and a surprise ending, Haddix proves why she's a master of middle-grade fiction." Booklist.

Risked. Margaret Peterson Haddix. Simon & Schuster Books for Young Readers, 2013. 320 p.: The missing
Grades: 5 6 7 8 9   **Fic**
1. Aleksei Nikolaevich Czarevitch, son of Nicholas II, Emperor of Russia 1904-1918. 2. Anastasia Nikolaevna, Grand Duchess, daughter of Nicholas II, Emperor of Russia, 1901-1918 3. Nicholas II, Emperor of Russia, 1868-1918 4. 1910s 5. Time travel (Past) 6. Assassination 7. Brothers and sisters 8. Soviet Union 9. Science fiction
ISBN 9781416989844
                                                                                    LC 2012006770
Jonah, thirteen, and Katherine, eleven, travel through time to 1918 Russia just as Alexei, Anastasia, and the rest of Tsar Nicholas II's family is about to be executed. Author's note includes facts about the Romanov's and the mystery surrounding their deaths.

Sabotaged. Margaret Peterson Haddix. Simon & Schuster Books for Young Readers, 2010. 384 p.: The missing
Grades: 5 6 7 8 9   **Fic**
1. Dare, Virginia, 1587- 2. 16th century 3. Space and time 4. Time travel (Past) 5. Brothers and sisters 6. Sabotage 7. Roanoke Colony 8. Science fiction
ISBN 9781416954248
                                                                                    LC 2009020056
Time-travelers Jonah and Katherine are summoned to help another missing child from history, this time Virginia Dare from the Roanoke Colony, but their journey is sabotaged and goes dangerously awry, leaving them in the wrong time period. Includes author's note about the history of Roanoke Colony and Virginia Dare.

Sent. Margaret Peterson Haddix. Simon & Schuster Books for Young Readers, 2009. 313 p.: The missing
Grades: 5 6 7 8 9   **Fic**
1. Edward V, King of England, 1470-1483 2. Richard, Duke of York, 1472-1483 3. Richard, III, King of England, 1452-1485 4. Tower of London (London, England) 5. Medieval period (476-1492) 6. Plantagenet period (1154-1485) 7. 15th century 8. Princes 9. Time travel (Past) 10. Brothers and sisters 11. Royal pretenders 12. Space and time 13. England 14. Great Britain 15.

Science fiction
ISBN 9781416954224
                                                                                    LC 2008011552
Jonah, Katherine, Chip, and Alex suddenly find themselves in 1483 at the Tower of London, where they discover that Chip and Alex are Prince Edward V and Richard of Shrewsbury, imprisoned by their uncle, King Richard III, but trying to repair history without knowing what is supposed to happen proves challenging. Author's note includes historical facts about the princes and king.

"Haddix conveys quite a bit of real history painlessly to her target audience and even mixes in some physics. . . . Valuable fun for tweens." Kirkus.

Under their skin. Margaret Peterson Haddix. Simon & Schuster Books for Young Readers, [2016] 224 p.: Under their skin
Grades: 4 5 6 7   **Fic**
1. Twin brothers and sisters 2. Robots 3. Blended families 4. Secrets 5. Twelve-year-olds 6. Science fiction
ISBN 9781481417587
From the New York Times best-selling author comes the first book in a brand-new thrilling series about twins who are on a quest to discover the secrets being kept by their new family—specifically, WHY their new stepsiblings are being kept hidden away.

"Haddix offers a gripping blend of science fiction, suspense, and mystery, taking middle graders and teens on a fast-paced ride that will interest even the most reluctant reader." School Library Journal.

Uprising. Margaret Peterson Haddix. Simon & Schuster Books for Young Readers, c2007. 346 p.
Grades: 6 7 8 9 10   **Fic**
1. Triangle Shirtwaist Company, Inc., New York City -- Fire, 1911 2. 1910s 3. Women employees 4. Sweatshops 5. Factories 6. Immigrants 7. Labor disputes 8. New York City 9. Historical fiction
ISBN 1416911715
In 1927, at the urging of twenty-one-year-old Harriet, Mrs. Livingston reluctantly recalls her experiences at the Triangle Shirtwaist factory, including miserable working conditions that led to a strike, then the fire that took the lives of her two best friends, when Harriet, the boss's daughter, was only five years old.

"This deftly crafted historical novel unfolds dramatically with an absorbing story and well-drawn characters who readily evoke empathy and compassion." School Library Journal.

Includes bibliographical references.

Hahn, Mary Downing

All the lovely bad ones: a ghost story. Mary Downing Hahn. Clarion Books, c2008. 182 p.
Grades: 4 5 6 7   **Fic**
1. Brothers and sisters 2. Ghosts 3. Haunted hotels 4. Haunted houses 5. Practical jokes 6. Vermont 7. Ghost stories 8. Historical fiction
ISBN 9780618854677
                                                                                    LC 2007037932
While spending the summer at their grandmother's Vermont inn, two prankster siblings awaken young ghosts from the inn's distant past who refuse to "rest in peace."

"In addition to crafting some genuinely spine-chilling moments, the author takes a unique approach to a well-traversed genre." Publishers Weekly.

Closed for the season: a mystery. by Mary Downing Hahn. Clarion Books, 2009. 192 p.

Grades: 5 6 7 8   **Fic**
  1. Murder 2. Neighbors 3. Friendship 4. Moving, Household 5. Embezzlement 6. Virginia 7. Mysteries
  ISBN 9780547084510

                                          LC 2008046846

When thirteen-year-old Logan and his family move into a run-down old house in rural Virginia, he discovers that a woman was murdered there and becomes involved with his neighbor Arthur in a dangerous investigation to try to uncover the killer.

"This is an enjoyable mystery with just the right amount of frightening and dangerous elements to entice readers. Logan is a sympathetic character." School Library Journal.

Mister Death's blue-eyed girls. by Mary Downing Hahn. Clarion Books, 2012. 384 p.

Grades: 8 9 10 11 12   **Fic**
  1. 1950s 2. Crimes against teenage girls 3. Grief in teenage girls 4. Murder 5. Former boyfriends 6. Teenage murder victims 7. Baltimore, Maryland 8. Historical fiction 9. Coming-of-age stories
  ISBN 9780547760629

                                          LC 2011025950

Narrated from several different perspectives, tells the story of the 1956 murder of two teenaged girls in suburban Baltimore, Maryland.

One for sorrow: a ghost story. Mary Downing Hahn. 224 p.

Grades: 5 6 7 8   **Fic**
  1. Girl ghosts 2. Influenza Epidemic, 1918-1919 3. Bullying and bullies 4. Revenge 5. Friendship 6. Ghost stories 7. Horror 8. Historical fiction
  ISBN 9780544818095

                                          LC 2016010761

When unlikeable Elsie dies in the influenza pandemic of 1918, she comes back to haunt Annie to make sure she'll be Annie's best—and only—friend soon. Provided by publisher.

"Hahn's story is characteristically steeped in eerie atmosphere, and the novel's blend of historical drama, the supernatural, and the intricacies of adolescent friendship is a gripping combination." Publishers Weekly.

Took: a ghost story. Mary Downing Hahn. 272 p.

Grades: 5 6 7 8   **Fic**
  1. Witches 2. Brothers and sisters 3. Moving to a new state 4. Ghosts 5. Teenage boys 6. West Virginia 7. Ghost stories 8. Horror
  ISBN 9780544551534

                                          LC 2014043064

A witch called Old Auntie is lurking near Dan's family's new home. He doesn't believe in her at first, but is forced to accept that she is real and take action when his little sister, Erica, is 'took' to become Auntie's slave for the next fifty years.

Wait till Helen comes: a ghost story. Mary Downing Hahn. Clarion Books, 1986. 184 p.

Grades: 4 5 6   **Fic**
  1. Twelve-year-old girls 2. Stepbrothers and stepsisters 3. Ghosts 4. Ghost stories
  ISBN 0899194532

                                          LC 86002648

Molly and Michael dislike their spooky new stepsister, Heather, but realize that they must try to save her when she seems ready to follow a ghost child to her doom.

"Intertwined with the ghost story is the question of Molly's moral imperative to save a child she truly dislikes. Though the emotional turnaround may be a bit quick for some, this still scores as a first-rate thriller." Booklist.

Hahn, Rebecca

A **creature** of moonlight. Rebecca Hahn. Houghton Mifflin Harcourt, 2014. 320 p.

Grades: 7 8 9 10 11 12   **Fic**
  1. Identity (Psychology) 2. Dragons 3. Princesses 4. Forests 5. Revenge 6. Fantasy fiction
  ISBN 9780544109353

                                          LC 2013020188

Marni, a young flower seller who has been living in exile, must choose between claiming her birthright as princess of a realm whose king wants her dead, and a life with the father she has never known—a wild dragon.

"Marni lives in a shack at the edge of the woods with her Gramps, where she tends flowers, as she's done for most of her life. Yet change is afoot... This book's greatest strength lies in the vivid woodland scenes and the rich detail that describes the mystical pieces of Marni's tale." School Library Journal.

Hale, Shannon

Book of a thousand days. by Shannon Hale; [illustrations by James Noel Smith]. Bloomsbury Children's Books, 2007. 305 p.

Grades: 7 8 9 10   **Fic**
  1. Teenage girl orphans 2. Imprisonment 3. Household employees 4. Nobility 5. Punishment 6. Central Asia 7. Fairy tale and folklore-inspired fiction 8. Fantasy fiction 9. Diary novels
  ISBN 9781599900513

                                          LC 2006036999

Fifteen-year-old Dashti, sworn to obey her sixteen-year-old mistress, the Lady Saren, shares Saren's years of punishment locked in a tower, then brings her safely to the lands of her true love, where both must hide who they are as they work as kitchen maids.

"This is a captivating fantasy filled with romance, magic, and strong female characters." Booklist.

Enna burning. Shannon Hale. Bloomsbury Children's Books, 2004. 317 p.: Books of Bayern

Grades: 6 7 8 9 10   **Fic**
  1. Fire 2. Control (Psychology) 3. Emotions in teenage girls 4. Brothers -- Death 5. Soldiers 6. Fantasy fiction
  ISBN 1582348898

                                          LC 2003065817

Enna hopes that her new knowledge of how to wield fire will help protect her good friend Isi—the Princess Anidori—and all of Bayern against their enemies, but the need to burn is uncontrollable and puts Enna and her loved ones in grave danger.

"With a richly detailed setting, eloquent descriptions, a complex plot, a large cast of characters, and romance, this high fantasy will be welcomed both by fans of The Goose Girl and those who have yet to discover it." School Library Journal.

The **forgotten** sisters. by Shannon Hale. Bloomsbury, 2015. 336 p.: Princess Academy trilogy

Grades: 5 6 7 8   **Fic**
  1. Princesses 2. Tutoring 3. Telepathy 4. Self-confidence 5. Secrets 6. Fantasy mysteries 7. Fantasy fiction
  ISBN 9781619634855

                                          LC 2014013744

Miri is eager to return to her beloved Mount Eskel after a year at the capital, but the king and queen ask her to first journey to a distant swamp and start her own miniature princess academy for three royal cousins, but once there she must solve a mystery before she can return home.

The **goose** girl. by Shannon Hale. Bloomsbury Children's Books, 2003. 383 p.: Books of Bayern
Grades: 6 7 8 9 **Fic**
1. Princesses 2. Inheritance and succession 3. Courage in teenage girls 4. Courage 5. Human/animal communication 6. Fairy tale and folklore-inspired fiction 7. Fantasy fiction
ISBN 158234843X
LC 2002028336
On her way to marry a prince she's never met, Princess Anidori is betrayed by her guards and her lady-in-waiting and must become a goose girl to survive until she can reveal her true identity and reclaim the crown that is rightfully hers.
"A fine adventure tale full of danger, suspense, surprising twists, and a satisfying conclusion." Booklist.

Palace of stone. Shannon Hale. Bloomsbury Childrens, 2012. 336 p.: Princess Academy trilogy
Grades: 5 6 7 8 **Fic**
1. Princesses 2. Telepathy 3. Self-confidence 4. Loyalty 5. Royal weddings 6. Fantasy fiction
ISBN 9781599908731
LC 2012003875
Miri returns to Asland and calls upon all of her knowledge of rhetoric and other useful lessons learned at the Princess Academy when she and the other girls face strong opposition while working for a new, fair charter.
"A literary and engaging coming-of-age story, the elements of class tension, home, family, friendship, and self discovery ring true." Voice of Youth Advocates.

The **storybook** of legends. by Shannon Hale. Little, Brown and Company, 2013. 304 p.: Ever After High (Shannon Hale)
Grades: 4 5 6 7 **Fic**
1. Characters and characteristics in fairy tales 2. Boarding schools 3. Fate and fatalism 4. Friendship 5. Schools 6. Fantasy fiction 7. Metafiction 8. Fairy tale and folklore-inspired fiction
ISBN 9780316401227
LC 2013024496
At Ever After High, a boarding school for the sons and daughters of famous fairy-tale characters, students Apple White and Raven Queen face the moment when they must choose whether to follow their destinies, or change them.
"Raven Queen and Apple White, the daughters of famous fairy-tale characters, begin their much-anticipated Legacy Year at Ever After High. They investigate the mystery of a lost story, and Raven realizes that being evil might not be her only path. Fans of the Inkheart and Sisters Grimm series will enjoy the 'hexellent' fairy-tale-infused lingo and lively characters." Horn Book.

Halpern, Julie, 1975-
Get well soon. Julie Halpern. Feiwel and Friends, 2007. 193 p.
Grades: 7 8 9 10 **Fic**
1. Sixteen-year-old girls 2. Overweight teenage girls 3. Teenage girls 4. Teenagers 5. Mental illness 6. Illinois 7. Epistolary novels 8. Realistic fiction
ISBN 9780312367954

When her parents confine her to a mental hospital, an overweight teenage girl, who suffers from panic attacks, describes her experiences in a series of letters to a friend.
"Halpern creates a narrative that reflects the changes in Anna with each passing day that includes self-reflection and a good dose of humor." Voice of Youth Advocates.

Hamilton, Virginia, 1936-2002
The **house** of Dies Drear. Illustrations by Eros Keith. Macmillan, 1968. 246 p.
Grades: 5 6 7 8 **Fic**
1. African American families 2. Underground Railroad 3. Houses 4. Slavery 5. Mysteries 6. African American fiction 7. Classics
ISBN 0027425002
LC 68023059
An African-American family tries to unravel the secrets of their new home which was once a stop on the Underground Railroad.
"The answer to the mystery comes in a startling dramatic dnouement that is pure theater. This is gifted writing; the characterization is unforgettable, the plot imbued with mounting tension." Saturday Review

The **planet** of Junior Brown. Virginia Hamilton. Macmillan, 1971. 210 p.
Grades: 6 7 8 9 **Fic**
1. Homeless teenagers 2. Overweight teenagers 3. Eighth-graders 4. Teenagers -- Friendship 5. Teenage musicians 6. New York City 7. Realistic fiction 8. African American fiction
ISBN 9780027425109
LC 71155264
Already a leader in New York's underground world of homeless children, Buddy Clark takes on the responsibility of protecting the overweight, emotionally disturbed friend with whom he has been playing hooky from eighth grade all semester.

Hamza, Nina
Ahmed Aziz's epic year. Nina Hamza. Quill Tree Books, 2021 244 p.
Grades: 4 5 6 7 8 **Fic**
1. Middle schools 2. Books and reading 3. Muslims 4. Families -- History 5. Moving to a new state 6. Realistic fiction
ISBN 9780063024892
LC 2020055221
Moving from Hawaii to Minnesota, Ahmed Aziz is having the worst year until he deals with bullies, makes new friends and uncovers his family's past—all while finding himself in three books assigned for his English class.
"Hamza has a lot of nuanced plotlines in play—and she does an admirable job of keeping them all relevant to the main narrative and following them to completion—some of the themes of which are family, finding yourself, faith, dealing with hate crimes, and friendship." Booklist

Han, Jenny
It's not summer without you: a summer novel. Jenny Han. Simon & Schuster Books for Young Readers, 2010. 288 p.: Summer novels (Jenny Han)
Grades: 7 8 9 10 **Fic**
1. Grief in teenagers 2. Crushes in teenage girls 3. Summer romance 4. Vacation homes 5. Grief 6. Realistic fiction 7. Coming-of-age stories
ISBN 9781416995555
LC 2009042180

Teenaged Isobel "Belly" Conklin, whose life revolves around spending the summer at her mother's best friend's beach house, reflects on the tragic events of the past year that changed her life forever.

"Han artfully weaves together Belly's and Jeremiah's back stories, recent and long past, to create a solid fabric of relationship and longing. Flashes of humor, realistic (and often salty) dialogue and growing-up moments both painful and authentic create a convincing and poignant read." Publishers Weekly.

Shug. Jenny Han. Simon & Schuster Books for Young Readers, c2006. 248 p.

Grades: 5 6 7 8   **Fic**

1. Children of alcoholic mothers 2. Crushes in girls 3. Self-esteem in girls 4. Self-esteem 5. Friendship 6. Georgia 7. Realistic fiction 8. Coming-of-age stories
ISBN 1416909427

LC 2005009367

A twelve-year-old girl learns about friendship, first loves, and self-worth in a small town in the South.

"Tall, freckled, gawky seventh-grader Annemarie Wilcox (whose family calls her Shug) has a beautiful, popular older sister; a gorgeous, alcoholic mother who doesn't fit in their small Georgia town; and a father who's always away on business. She also has a huge crush on Mark, the neighborhood boy who has always been her best friend. . . . Shug's direct, honest narration reveals a wholly believable, endearing, hot-tempered young woman who faces painful truths and survives." Booklist.

We'll always have summer: a summer novel. Jenny Han. Simon & Schuster BFYR, c2011. 291 p.: Summer novels (Jenny Han)

Grades: 7 8 9 10   **Fic**

1. Women college students 2. Love triangles 3. Engagement 4. Brothers 5. Beaches 6. Realistic fiction
ISBN 9781416995586

LC 2010046670

The summer after her first year of college, Isobel "Belly" Conklin is faced with a choice between Jeremiah and Conrad Fisher, brothers she has always loved, when Jeremiah proposes marriage and Conrad confesses that he still loves her.

"In Han's conclusion to the trilogy that began with The Summer I Turned Pretty, she both underscores the folly of getting engaged too young and vividly depicts the emotions of a girl on the brink of womanhood." Publishers Weekly.

Hand, Cynthia, 1978-

The **how** & the why. Cynthia Hand. Harperteen, 2019. 464 p.

Grades: 7 8 9 10 11 12   **Fic**

1. Teenage girls 2. Searching 3. Adoption 4. Identity (Psychology) 5. Teenage pregnancy 6. Idaho 7. Coming-of-age stories 8. Realistic fiction
ISBN 9780062693167

A novel told from the viewpoints of an adoptee and the teen mother who gave her up 18 years earlier follows Cassandra's search for clues about her true identity in the letters left behind by her birth mother.

"Hand explores adoption's multiple dimensions with great insight and sensitivity. Inclusive and illustrative an engaging lesson in timeless family values." Kirkus.

The **last** time we say goodbye. Cynthia Hand. HarperTeen, an imprint of HarperCollinsPublishers, [2015] 228 p.

Grades: 8 9 10 11   **Fic**

1. Survivors of suicide victims 2. Grief in teenage girls 3. Guilt 4.

Grief 5. Family problems 6. Nebraska 7. Realistic fiction
ISBN 9780062318473

LC 2014038645

After her younger brother, Tyler, commits suicide, Lex struggles to work through her grief in the face of a family that has fallen apart, the sudden distance between her and her friends, and memories of Tyler that still feel all too real.

My Calamity Jane. Cynthia Hand, Brodi Ashton, Jodi Meadows. HarperTeen, 2020 544 p.: Lady Janies

Grades: 7 8 9 10 11   **Fic**

1. Calamity Jane, 1852-1903 2. Hickok, Wild Bill's, 1837-1876. 3. Oakley, Annie, 1860-1926. 4. American Westward Expansion (1803-1899) 5. 1870s 6. Gunfighters 7. Werewolves 8. Frontier and pioneer life 9. Wild West shows 10. Monster hunters 11. The West (United States) 12. Westerns 13. Historical fantasy
ISBN 9780062652812

A side-splitting follow-up to My Plain Jane finds Wild Bill?s Traveling Show performer Calamity Jane incurring a suspicious bite in the wake of a garou hunt gone wrong before seeking a cure in Deadwood, where she encounters a life-threatening surprise. Atlas Publishing.

Unearthly. Cynthia Hand. HarperTeen, 2011. 320 p.: Unearthly trilogy

Grades: 7 8 9 10   **Fic**

1. Angels 2. Visions 3. High school football players 4. Supernatural 5. Moving to a new state 6. Wyoming 7. Jackson Hole, Wyoming 8. Paranormal romances
ISBN 9780061996160

LC 2010017849

Sixteen-year-old Clara Gardner's purpose as an angel-blood begins to manifest itself, forcing her family to pull up stakes and move to Jackson, Wyoming, where she learns that danger and heartbreak come with her powers.

"Hand avoids overt discussion of religion while telling an engaging and romantic tale with a solid backstory. Her characters deal realistically with the uncertainty of being on the cusp of maturity without wrapping themselves in angst." Publishers Weekly.

Hannigan, Kate

Cape. by Kate Hannigan; illustrated by Patrick Spaziante. Aladdin, 2019. 336 p.: League of Secret Heroes

Grades: 4 5 6 7   **Fic**

1. Second World War era (1939-1945) 2. Girl superheroes 3. World War II 4. Rescues 5. Secrets 6. Nazis 7. Philadelphia, Pennsylvania 8. United States 9. Historical fantasy 10. Superhero stories
ISBN 9781534439115

LC 2018037398

Soon after being recruited by the mysterious Mrs. Boudica to join a secret military intelligence operation, Josie, Mae, and Akiko discover their superhero abilities and use them to thwart a Nazi plot to steal the ENIAC computer.

"Fans of fast-paced action adventures, computer science, and confident main characters will enjoy this series debut that is sure to fly off the shelves." School Library Journal.

Includes bibliographical references.

Mask. by Kate Hannigan; illustrated by Patrick Spaziante. Aladdin, 2020. 304 p.: League of Secret Heroes

Grades: 4 5 6 7   **Fic**

1. Manzanar War Relocation Center, California. 2. Second World

War era (1939-1945) 3. Girl superheroes 4. World War II 5. Codes (Communication) 6. Secrets 7. Spies 8. United States 9. San Francisco, California 10. Historical fantasy 11. Superhero stories
ISBN 9781534439146

LC 2020018906

Akiko, Mae, and Josie, also called the Infinity Trinity, spring into action after learning that a spy is betraying secrets to the Japanese military—and that Akiko's mother may be involved.

"A winning blend of comedy, superheroics, inspirational women from history, and puzzle-solving." Kirkus

Hannigan, Katherine

True (--sort of). by Katherine Hannigan. Greenwillow Books, 2011. 304 p.

Grades: 4 5 6   **Fic**
1. Self-control in children 2. Girls who are mute 3. Emotions in girls 4. Elective mutism 5. Friendship 6. Realistic fiction
ISBN 9780061968747

LC 2010017315

For most of her eleven years, Delly has been in trouble without knowing why, until her little brother, R.B., and a strange, silent new friend, Ferris, help her find a way to be good—and happy—again.

"Told in carefully crafted language that begs to be read aloud, the story runs the gamut from laugh-out-loud funny to emotionally wrenching." School Library Journal.

Hardinge, Frances

Cuckoo song. Frances Hardinge. Amulet Books, 2015. 416 p.

Grades: 7 8 9 10 11 12   **Fic**
1. Between the Wars (1918-1939) 2. 1920s 3. Supernatural 4. Sisters 5. Grief 6. Postwar life 7. Identity (Psychology) 8. England 9. Great Britain 10. Historical fantasy
ISBN 9781419714801

LC 2014045264

In post-World War I England, eleven-year-old Triss nearly drowns in a millpond known as "The Grimmer" and emerges with memory gaps, aware that something is terribly wrong, and to try to set things right, she must meet a twisted architect who has designs on her family.

"Nuanced and intense, this painstakingly created tale mimics the Escher-like constructions of its villainous Architect, fooling the eyes and entangling the emotions of readers willing and able to enter into a world like no other." Kirkus.

Deeplight. Frances Hardinge. Amulet, 2020, c2019. 416 p.
Grades: 7 8 9 10 11 12   **Fic**
1. Gods and goddesses 2. Best friends 3. Sea monsters 4. Islands 5. Scavenging 6. Fantasy fiction
ISBN 9781419743207

The gods are dead. Decades ago, they turned on one another and tore each other apart. Nobody knows why. But are they really gone forever? When 15-year-old Hark finds the still-beating heart of a terrifying deity, he risks everything to keep it out of the hands of smugglers, military scientists, and a secret fanatical cult so that he can use it to save the life of his best friend, Jelt. But with the heart, Jelt gradually and eerily transforms. How long should Hark stay loyal to his friend when he's becoming a monster—and what is Hark willing to sacrifice to save him?

"Equal parts dazzling fantasy, swashbuckling adventure, and tender coming-of-age tale, this ambitious standalone from Hardinge (A Skinful of Shadows) cautions against xenophobia, zealotry, and greed while using boldly drawn characters to illustrate storytelling's power and fear's role in faith." Publishers Weekly.

The **lost** conspiracy. Frances Hardinge. Bowen Press, 2009. 576 p.

Grades: 6 7 8 9 10   **Fic**
1. Intrigue 2. Revenge 3. Sisters 4. Escapes 5. Secrets 6. High fantasy 7. Fantasy fiction
ISBN 9780060880415

LC 2008045380

When a lie is exposed and their tribe turns against them, Hathin must find a way to save her sister Arilou—once considered the tribe's oracle—and herself.

"A deeply imaginative story, with nuanced characters, intricate plotting, and an amazingly original setting. . . . A perfectly pitched, hopeful ending caps off this standout adventure." Booklist.

Harkrader, Lisa

The **adventures** of Beanboy. by Lisa Harkrader. Houghton Mifflin, 2012. 208 p.: Adventures of Beanboy

Grades: 4 5 6 7 8   **Fic**
1. Seventh-grade boys 2. Family problems 3. Money-making projects for children 4. Children of single parents 5. Poverty 6. Realistic fiction
ISBN 9780547550787

LC 2011012161

When aspiring comic-book artist Tucker MacBean enters a contest to create a new sidekick for his favorite superhero, Beanboy , he's got a lot riding on whether or not he wins. Tucker hopes that stardom might make him more popular, and he wants to give the prize, a college scholarship, to his hardworking but exhausted single mom.

Harlow, Joan Hiatt

Thunder from the sea. Joan Hiatt Harlow. Margaret K. McElderry Books, c2004. 256 p.

Grades: 4 5 6 7   **Fic**
1. 1920s 2. Orphans 3. Thirteen-year-old boys 4. Dogs 5. Newfoundland dogs 6. Fishers 7. Newfoundland and Labrador 8. Historical fiction 9. Adventure stories
ISBN 0689864035

LC 2003010687

Just when his dreams of being part of a family and having a dog seem to be coming true, Tom wonders if trouble with neighbors on his new island home and the impending birth of a new baby will change everything. Set in Newfoundland in 1929.

Harper, Charise Mericle

Alien encounter. Charise Mericle Harper. Christy Ottaviano Books, Henry Holt and Company, 2014. 160 p.: Sasquatch and aliens

Grades: 3 4 5 6   **Fic**
1. Nine-year-old boys 2. Aliens (Humanoid) 3. Yeti 4. Friendship 5. Families 6. Pacific Northwest 7. Science fiction 8. Humorous stories
ISBN 9780805096217

LC 2013039906

Nine-year-old Morgan of the Pacific Northwest is fascinated with aliens and the sasquatch, but his real adventures begin when he meets Lewis, whose parents just bought a motel named the Sasquatch Inn.

"With an authentic, zany splash of fourth-grade humor, perspective, and imagination, this inaugural series title targets boys and will captivate elementary readers. . . . Morgan is a spunky, verbal, resourceful protagonist whose nonstop adventures resonate with self-discovery, family relationships, friendships, and creative problem-solving." School Library Journal.

Harrell, Rob

★ **Wink**. Rob Harrell. Dial Books for Young Readers, 2020.
320 p.

Grades: 4 5 6 7   **Fic**
1. Children with cancer 2. Guitarists 3. Middle schools 4. Misfits
(Persons) 5. Individuality 6. Realistic fiction 7. Autobiographical
fiction
ISBN 9781984815149

          LC 2019024068

After being diagnosed with a rare eye cancer, twelve-year-old Ross
discovers how music, art, and true friends can help him survive both
treatment and middle school.

"With its breezy quippiness and exuberant comics, this is a brisk
alternative to Palacio's Wonder in destabilizing the notion of normal."
Bulletin of the Center for Children's Books.

Harrington, Janice N.

Catching a storyfish. Janice N. Harrington. Wordsong, 2016.
240 p.

Grades: 4 5 6 7   **Fic**
1. Moving to a new state 2. African American girls 3. Friendship
4. Grandfather and granddaughter 5. Storytelling 6. Illinois 7.
Realistic fiction 8. Novels in verse 9. African American fiction
ISBN 9781629794297

Keet knows the only good thing about moving away from her Alabama home is that she'll live near her beloved grandfather. When Keet
starts school, it's even worse than she expected, as the kids tease her
about her southern accent. Now Keet, who can "talk the whiskers off
a catfish," doesn't want to open her mouth. Slowly, though, while fishing with her grandfather, she learns the art of listening. Gradually, she
makes her first new friend. But just as she's beginning to settle in, her
grandfather has a stroke, and even though he's still nearby, he suddenly
feels ever-so-far-away.

"A gentle-spirited book about a Black girl who almost gives up her
gift but for love and friendship." Kirkus.

Harrington, Karen, 1967-

Courage for beginners. Karen Harrington. Little, Brown and
Company, 2014. 289 p.

Grades: 4 5 6 7 8   **Fic**
1. Children of people with mental illnesses 2. Family problems 3.
Coping in girls 4. Coping 5. Agoraphobia 6. Texas 7. Realistic
fiction
ISBN 9780316210485

Wishing she were more like a fictional hero who always knows how
to handle such challenges as a best friend's abandonment, her father's
hospitalization and a painful family secret, seventh-grader Mysti taps
her inner courage with the help of a new friend and a hot-air balloon.

"Mysti's curatorial narration—as if she were describing paintings or
book characters—works on multiple levels, showing off her snark and
emphasizing her mothers sheltered influence. Her mother is flawed but
sympathetic; she knows her fears are disproportionate, but their debilitating effect is real.With gallows humor and believable small victories,
this unusual novel is a window into making friends and facing fears."
Kirkus.

Mayday. by Karen Harrington. 352 p.

Grades: 5 6 7 8   **Fic**
1. Coping in boys 2. Grief 3. Children of divorced parents 4.
Airplane accidents 5. Voice 6. Realistic fiction
ISBN 9780316298018

          LC 2015020622

Twelve-year-old Wayne Kovok loses his uncle to war and his voice
to a plane crash in the same year and must learn to speak up as he navigates relationships with his father, grandfather, and new friend, Denny
Rosenblatt. Provided by publisher.

"Wayne is an appealing protagonist with a strong voice who develops believably over the difficult months, as do the other characters. A
well-done book on all levels." Publishers Weekly.

Sure signs of crazy. by Karen Harrington. Little, Brown and
Company, 2013. 288 p.

Grades: 4 5 6 7 8   **Fic**
1. Children of people with mental illnesses 2. Crushes in girls 3.
Summer 4. Children of alcoholic fathers 5. Family problems 6.
Texas 7. Realistic fiction 8. Coming-of-age stories
ISBN 9780316210584

Feeling different from other 12-year-old kids because of her unusual
tastes and separation from a mother who has been in a mental institution
for years, Sarah hopes to settle down in a permanent home with her father and develops a first crush during an extraordinary summer in Texas.

Harrington, Kim, 1974-

Revenge of the Red Club. Kim Harrington. Aladdin, 2019
256 p.

Grades: 5 6 7 8   **Fic**
1. Girl journalists 2. Clubs 3. Protests, demonstrations, vigils, etc
4. Menstruation 5. Feminism 6. Realistic fiction
ISBN 9781534435728

When middle school journalist Riley Dunne learns that an important
and beloved club is being shut down, she uses the power of the pen to
instigate much-needed social change.

"Despite some heavy-handed themes, it's inspiring to see girls
marching through hallways gripping tampons without embarrassment."
Booklist.

Harris, Teresa E.

The **perfect** place. Teresa E. Harris. Clarion Books, Houghton Mifflin Harcourt, 2014. 272 p.

Grades: 5 6 7 8   **Fic**
1. Parent-separated girls 2. African Americans 3. Great-aunts 4.
Jewelry theft 5. Sisters 6. Virginia 7. Realistic fiction 8. Coming-
of-age stories 9. African American fiction
ISBN 9780547255194

"Two months after 12-year-old Treasure's dad left without further
word, her mom decides to search for him, and she takes Treasure and
her younger sister to stay with their cantankerous Great-Aunt Grace in
Black Lake, Virginia... Readers will find sly humor here as well as the
pleasure of seeing justice done on several levels. A satisfying first novel
with a realistic but heartening ending." Booklist.

Harrison, Michelle, 1979-

13 curses. Michelle Harrison. Little, Brown, 2011. 496 p.: 13
treasures trilogy

Grades: 5 6 7 8   **Fic**
1. Fairies 2. Charms 3. Orphans 4. Parallel universes 5. Curses
6. England 7. Fantasy fiction
ISBN 9780316041508

          LC 2010022850

When fairies steal her brother, thirteen-year-old Rowan Fox promises that in exchange for his return she will find the thirteen charms that
the fairies have enchanted and hidden in the human world.

"The sure-handed storytelling creates a completely credible setting-
by turns violent and tender, sinister and poignant. . . . Contrasts between

human emotion and commitment and the cold, often cruel magic and mischief of the fairy realm create terrific tension and afford opportunities for heroism for the young protagonists." Kirkus.

13 secrets. Michelle Harrison; [interior illustrations by Kelly Louise Judd]. Little, Brown, 2012. 421 p.: 13 treasures trilogy

Grades: 5 6 7 8 **Fic**
1. Fairies 2. Changelings 3. Revenge 4. Parallel universes 5. Teenage girls 6. England 7. Fantasy fiction
ISBN 9780316185639

LC 2011033368

Now living at Elvesden Manor under her real name of Rowan, Red attempts to put her past behind her, while fairy messengers try to convince her to participate once more in the changeling trade and she is haunted by dreams of an old enemy who is determined to exact his revenge.

Hartman, Rachel, 1972-

Seraphina: a novel. by Rachel Hartman. Random House, 2012. 480 p.: Seraphina

Grades: 7 8 9 10 11 12 **Fic**
1. Dragons 2. Musicians 3. Conspiracies 4. Identity (Psychology) 5. Secrets 6. High fantasy 7. Fantasy fiction
ISBN 9780375866562

LC 2011003015

In a world where dragons and humans coexist in an uneasy truce and dragons can assume human form, Seraphina, whose mother died giving birth to her, grapples with her own identity amid magical secrets and royal scandals, while she struggles to accept and develop her extraordinary musical talents.

Shadow scale: a companion to Seraphina. Rachel Hartman. Random House, 2015. 480 p.: Seraphina

Grades: 7 8 9 10 11 12 **Fic**
1. Half-human hybrids 2. War 3. Dragons 4. Courts and courtiers 5. Civilization, Medieval 6. High fantasy 7. Fantasy fiction
ISBN 9780375866579

LC 2014017953

Seraphina, half-dragon and half-human, searches for others like her who can make the difference in the war between dragons and humans in the kingdom of Goredd.

"From graceful language to high stakes to daring intrigue, this sequel shines with the same originality, invention, and engagement of feeling that captivated readers in Hartman's debut." Horn Book.

Hashimi, Nadia

★ **One** half from the east. Nadia Hashimi. Harpercollins, 2016 256 p.

Grades: 4 5 6 7 8 **Fic**
1. Gender role 2. Independence (Personal quality) 3. Villages 4. Families 5. Boy impersonators 6. Afghanistan
ISBN 9780062421906

"Well-told through appealing characters, this tale sheds light from a unique cultural perspective on the link between vastly different, rigidly enforced roles for boys and girls and gender-identity issues." Kirkus.

Haskell, Merrie

Handbook for dragon slayers. Merrie Haskell. HarperCollins, 2013. 240 p.

Grades: 6 7 8 **Fic**
1. Princesses 2. Girls with disabilities 3. Dragons 4. Courage 5.

Teenage girls 6. Historical fantasy
ISBN 9780062008169

LC 2012022159

Schneider Family Book Award for Middle School, 2014.

Yearning for life in a cloistered scriptorium, thirteen-year-old Princess Matilda, whose lame foot brings fear of the evil eye, escapes her scheming cousin Ivo and joins her servant Judith and an old friend, Parz, in hunting dragons and writing about them.

Hatfield, Ruth

The **Book** of Storms. Ruth Hatfield. Henry Holt & Co., 2015. 356 p.: Book of Storms

Grades: 5 6 7 8 **Fic**
1. Storms 2. Parent-separated boys 3. Human-animal communication 4. Missing persons 5. Supernatural 6. Fantasy fiction
ISBN 9780805099980

LC 2014029352

When his parents disappear after a fierce storm, eleven-year-old Danny, unaccustomed to acts of bravery, comes to their rescue after finding a valuable shard of wood that enables him to talk to plants and animals and battle terrifyingly powerful enemies, including the demonic Sammael.

"This debut novel is an entertaining fantasy adventure set across a modern European landscape. The book follows 11-year-old Danny O'Neill as he struggles to piece together the seemingly incomprehensible details left behind by a devastating storm. The quest takes him deep within himself where he must find courage that he never knew he possessed...Not only does Hatfield take readers inside the thoughts and minds of all sorts of flora and fauna, but she uses their observable traits to guide their humanistic presence in very believable ways." School Library Journal.

Hautman, Pete, 1952-

All-in. Pete Hautman. Simon & Schuster Books for Young Readers, c2007. 181 p.

Grades: 7 8 9 10 **Fic**
1. Teenage gamblers 2. Poker 3. Winning and losing 4. Gambling 5. Crushes in teenage boys 6. Las Vegas, Nevada 7. Realistic fiction
ISBN 9781416913252

LC 2006023871

Having won thousands of dollars playing high-stakes poker in Las Vegas, seventeen-year-old Denn Doyle hits a losing streak after falling in love with a young casino card dealer named Cattie Hart.

"Skillfully using the multiple-voice approach, Hautman brings to life the intricacies of poker, crafting a thrilling story of loss, good versus evil, and redemption." Voice of Youth Advocates.

Blank confession. Pete Hautman. Simon & Schuster Books for Young Readers, 2010. 176 p.

Grades: 7 8 9 10 **Fic**
1. Teenage drug dealers 2. Bullying and bullies 3. Teenage murderers 4. Confession (Law) 5. High schools 6. Realistic fiction
ISBN 9781416913276

LC 2009050169

A new and enigmatic student named Shayne appears at high school one day, befriends the smallest boy in the school, and takes on a notorious drug dealer before turning himself in to the police for killing someone.

"Masterfully written with simple prose, solid dialogue and memorable characters, the tale will grip readers from the start and keep the reading in one big gulp, in the hope of seeing behind Shayne's mask. A sure hit with teen readers." Kirkus.

Godless. Pete Hautman. Simon & Schuster Books for Young Readers, 2004. 198 p.

Grades: 7 8 9 10   **Fic**
  1. Belief and doubt 2. Idols and images 3. Religion 4. Water towers 5. Spirituality 6. Realistic fiction
  ISBN 0689862784
                     LC 2003010468
National Book Award for Young People's Literature, 2004.

When sixteen-year-old Jason Bock and his friends create their own religion to worship the town's water tower, what started out as a joke begins to take on a power of its own.

"The witty text and provocative subject will make this a supremely enjoyable discussion-starter as well as pleasurable read." Bulletin of the Center for Children's Books.

The **Klaatu** terminus: a Klaatu Diskos novel. Pete Hautman. Candlewick Press, 2014. 358 p.: Klaatu diskos

Grades: 7 8 9 10 11 12   **Fic**
  1. Time travel 2. Pyramids 3. Space and time 4. Love triangles 5. Teenage boys 6. Minnesota 7. Science fiction
  ISBN 9780763654054

"Pulling together elaborate strands of the first two books, this conclusion rewards readers with a surprising yet cogent and satisfying chronicle across time." Horn Book.

The **obsidian** blade. Pete Hautman. Candlewick Press, 2012. 320 p.: Klaatu diskos

Grades: 7 8 9 10   **Fic**
  1. Parent-separated teenagers 2. Time travel 3. Faith 4. Space and time 5. Missing persons 6. Minnesota 7. Science fiction
  ISBN 9780763654030

After thirteen-year-old Tucker Feye's parents disappear, he suspects that the strange disks of shimmering air that he keeps seeing are somehow involved, and when he steps inside of one he is whisked on a time-twisting journey trailed by a shadowy sect of priests and haunted by ghostlike figures.

Road tripped. Pete Hautman. Simon & Schuster Books for Young Readers, 2019 336 p.

Grades: 8 9 10 11 12   **Fic**
  1. Runaway teenagers 2. Cross-country automobile trips 3. Coping in teenage boys 4. Grief 5. Fathers -- Death 6. Psychological fiction 7. Realistic fiction
  ISBN 9781534405905

Seventeen-year-old Steven "Stiggy" Gabel tries to cope with his father's suicide, his mother's depression, and his girlfriend's departure by taking off down the Great River Road from Minnesota to Louisiana.

★ **Slider**. Pete Hautman. Candlewick Press, 2017 288 p.

Grades: 4 5 6 7 8   **Fic**
  1. Competitive eating 2. Contests 3. Brothers and sisters of children with autism 4. Pizza 5. Best friends 6. Realistic fiction
  ISBN 9780763690700

Entering the world's greatest pizza-eating contest after secretly putting thousands of dollars onto his mother's credit card, a young competitive eater finds his efforts complicated by family denial about his younger brother's autism.

"This novel is laugh-out-loud funny and genuinely sweet. . . . ultimately a meaningful book with insight into having a sibling with special

needs and the general ups and downs that come with being a teenager." School Library Journal.

Haydu, Corey Ann
  ★ **One** jar of magic. Corey Ann Haydu. Katherine Tegen Books, 2021. 304 p.

Grades: 4 5 6 7   **Fic**
  1. Magic 2. Families 3. Good luck 4. Belief and doubt 5. Friendship 6. Fantasy fiction
  ISBN 9780062689856

Joining her family in her community's annual New Year's Day magic-capturing ceremony, a 12-year-old girl who has always been lucky captures just one tiny jar of magic, revealing the true nature and beliefs of her loved ones.

"The worldbuilding and magic system are enchanting and expertly crafted, but the core of this gorgeously written story isn't magic at all: it's abuse and it's absolutely heartbreaking and completely realistic." Kirkus

Rules for stealing stars. Corey Ann Haydu. Katherine Tegen Books, an imprint of HarperCollinsPublishers, 2015. 300 p.

Grades: 4 5 6 7 8   **Fic**
  1. Children of alcoholic mothers 2. Mothers and daughters 3. Sisters 4. Magic 5. Family problems 6. New Hampshire 7. Low fantasy
  ISBN 9780062352712
                     LC 2014047921
Four sisters rely on each other—and a bit of mysterious magic—to cope with their mother's illness. Provided by publisher.

The **someday** suitcase. Corey Ann Haydu. Katherine Tegen Books, 2017. 304 p.

Grades: 5 6 7 8   **Fic**
  1. Best friends 2. Children with chronic illnesses 3. Science -- Methodology 4. Sick boys 5. Friendship 6. Realistic fiction
  ISBN 9780062352750

Sharing a best friendship forged over respective interests, Clover and Danny find their bond tested when Danny suddenly falls ill from a mysterious malady that requires numerous visits to the doctor, while Clover uses the scientific method to catalog Danny's symptoms and prove her usefulness toward his recovery.

Hayles, Marsha
  Breathing room. Marsha Hayles. Henry Holt and Co., 2012. 256 p.

Grades: 5 6 7 8   **Fic**
  1. 1940s 2. Tuberculosis 3. Sick girls 4. Hospitals 5. People with tuberculosis 6. Sanatoriums 7. Minnesota 8. Historical fiction
  ISBN 9780805089615
                     LC 2011034055
In 1940, thirteen-year-old Evvy Hoffmeister and her newfound friends struggle to get well at Loon Lake Sanatorium, where they are being treated for tuberculosis.

Headley, Justina Chen, 1968-
  Return to me. by Justina Chen. Little, Brown, 2013. 352 p.

Grades: 7 8 9 10   **Fic**
  1. Teenage girl psychics 2. Children of divorced parents 3. Self-fulfillment in teenage girls 4. Self-fulfillment 5. Architecture 6. Realistic fiction
  ISBN 9780316102551
                     LC 2012001549

Always following her parents' wishes and ignoring her psychic inner voice takes eighteen-year-old Rebecca Muir from her beloved cottage and boyfriend on Puget Sound to New York City, where revelations about herself and her family help her find a path to becoming the architect she wants to be.

Healey, Karen

When we wake. Karen Healey. Little, Brown Books for Young Readers, 2013. 304 p.

Grades: 7 8 9 10 11 12   **Fic**
    1. Sixteen-year-old girls 2. Undead 3. Low temperature engineering 4. Gunshot victims 5. Greed 6. Australia 7. Science fiction
    ISBN 9780316200769

                        LC 2012028739
In 2027, sixteen-year-old Tegan is just like every other girl—playing the guitar, falling in love, and protesting the wrongs of the world with her friends. But then Tegan dies, waking up 100 years in the future as the unknowing first government guinea pig to be cryogenically frozen and successfully revived. Appalling secrets about her new world come to light, and Tegan must choose to either keep her head down or fight for a better future.

Healy, Christopher, 1972-

The **hero's** guide to saving your kingdom. by Christopher Healy; with drawings by Todd Harris. Walden Pond Press, 2012. 320 p.: League of Princes

Grades: 4 5 6 7   **Fic**
    1. Princes 2. Witches 3. Characters and characteristics in fairy tales 4. Quests 5. Good and evil 6. Fantasy fiction 7. Fairy tale and folklore-inspired fiction 8. Humorous stories
    ISBN 9780062117434

                        LC 2011053347
The four princes erroneously dubbed Prince Charming and rudely marginalized in their respective fairy tales form an unlikely team when a witch threatens the whole kingdom.

Heaney, Katie

Girl crushed. Katie Heaney. Knopf Books for Young Readers, 2020 352 p.

Grades: 8 9 10 11 12   **Fic**
    1. Lesbian teenagers 2. Former girlfriends 3. Crushes in teenage girls 4. Former friends 5. First loves 6. San Diego, California 7. LGBTQIA romances 8. Coming-of-age stories
    ISBN 9781984897350

Dumped by her best friend and girlfriend a month before their senior year, a heartbroken Quinn struggles to move on with a new crush when she is unable to completely forget her ex.

"Everything is there: the dramatic 'is she, isn't she?' straight-girl dance; the lesbian hangout on the edge of bankruptcy, run by two aging dykes; the gay-straight alliance that never quite got going—and then Heaney adds in more mainstream concerns about athletic scholarships and plans after high school." Booklist.

Heath, Jack, 1986-

The **lab**. Jack Heath. Scholastic, 2008. 311 p.: Six of Hearts

Grades: 7 8 9 10   **Fic**
    1. Teenage spies 2. Dystopias 3. Genetic engineering 4. Clones and cloning 5. Vigilantes 6. Dystopian fiction 7. Science fiction
    ISBN 9780545068604

Far into the future, the world is devastated by pollution, and the single walled city that remains is controlled entirely by the corrupt Chao-Sonic corporation. The only hope for the downtrodden populace is the Deck, a secret organization that's sworn to take down ChaoSonic—and whose best operative is a product of ChaoSonic's lab, genetically enhanced Agent Six of Hearts. But Agent Six has just been captured.

"A gritty dystopic world exists under the iron rule of the mega-corporation Chao-Sonic, with only a few vigilante groups around to act as resistance. Six of Hearts is easily the best agent on one such group, the Deck, and he is fiercely dedicated to justice, using his extensive genetic modifications to his advantage. . . . The compelling and memorable protagonist stands out even against the intricately described and disturbing city whose vividness makes the place's questionable fate a suspenseful issue in its own right." Bulletin of the Center for Children's Books.

Remote control. Jack Heath. Scholastic Press, c2010. 326 p.: Six of Hearts

Grades: 7 8 9 10   **Fic**
    1. Teenage spies 2. Trust in teenage boys 3. Twin brothers 4. Kidnapping 5. Rescues 6. Dystopian fiction 7. Science fiction
    ISBN 9780545075916

                        LC bl2009035265
Teenage agent Six of Hearts is suspected of being a double agent, which has him on the run from his fellow agents at the Deck while also trying to track down his brother's kidnappers.

"The technothriller begun in The Lab (2008) takes several intriguing twists . . . on its way to a satisfying, if temporary, resolution." Booklist.

Heider, Mary Winn

The **losers** at the center of the galaxy. Mary Winn Heider. Little, Brown and Company, 2021. 304 p.

Grades: 4 5 6 7   **Fic**
    1. Brothers and sisters 2. Middle schools 3. Missing persons 4. Eccentrics and eccentricities 5. Teachers 6. Realistic fiction 7. Coming-of-age stories
    ISBN 9780759555426

                        LC 2020040280
Two years after their father disappeared, Winston and Louise wrestle with their grief while investigating mysterious teachers, innovative science, and a captive bear.

"Madcap antics ensue, but this is still, at its heart, a story of grief over the loss of a father and husband from CTE (chronic traumatic encephalopathy) ." Horn Book

Helgerson, Joseph

Horns and wrinkles. by Joseph Helgerson; illustrations by Nicoletta Ceccoli. Houghton Mifflin, 2006. 368 p.

Grades: 4 5 6 7   **Fic**
    1. Twelve-year-old girls 2. Cousins 3. Girl adventurers 4. Bullying and bullies 5. Magic 6. Mississippi River 7. Fantasy fiction
    ISBN 0618616799

                        LC 2005025448
Along a magic-saturated stretch of the Mississippi River near Blue Wing, Minnesota, twelve-year-old Claire and her bullying cousin Duke are drawn into an adventure involving Bodacious Deepthink the Great Rock Troll, a helpful fairy, and a group of trolls searching for their fathers.

"Tongue-in-cheek humor brings a delightful zing to the playfully inventive storytelling and fast-paced plot. Enchanting sketches foreshadow each chapter, adding to the wonder." School Library Journal.

Hemphill, Stephanie

Wicked girls: a novel of the Salem witch trials. Stephanie Hemphill. Balzer + Bray, 2010. 336 p.

Grades: 7 8 9 10 11 12   **Fic**
1. 1690s 2. 17th century 3. Witches 4. Malicious accusation 5. Trials (Witchcraft) 6. Teenage girls 7. Girls 8. Salem, Massachusetts 9. Historical fiction 10. Novels in verse
ISBN 9780061853289
"Hemphill's raw, intimate poetry probes behind the abstract facts and creates characters that pulse with complex emotion." Booklist.

Your own, Sylvia: a verse portrait of Sylvia Plath. by Stephanie Hemphill. Alfred A. Knopf, c2007. 272 p.
Grades: 8 9 10 11 12   **Fic**
1. Plath, Sylvia 2. Authors, American 20th century 3. Poets, American 4. Rejection (Psychology) 5. Family relationships 6. Poets
ISBN 037583799X
                                              LC 2006007253
"Hemphill's verse, like Plath's, is completely compelling: every word, every line, worth reading." Horn Book.

Henderson, Leah

The **magic** in changing your stars. Leah Henderson. Sterling Pub Co Inc 2020 304 p.
Grades: 4 5 6 7   **Fic**
1. 1930s 2. Grandfather and grandson 3. Time travel (Past) 4. Theater 5. Dancers 6. Actors and actresses 7. Harlem, New York City 8. Low fantasy 9. Historical fiction 10. Classics-inspired fiction
ISBN 9781454934066
                                              LC 2019055928
After bungling his audition to play the Scarecrow in The Wiz, fifth-grader Ailey is magically transported to 1930s Harlem where he meets his own grandfather and legendary tap dancer Bill "Bojangles" Robinson.
"Black excellence, Black fantastic, and Black family combine for a transformational story of passion and persistence." Kirkus

Henkes, Kevin

★ **Bird** Lake moon. by Kevin Henkes. Greenwillow Books, 2008. 179 p.
Grades: 4 5 6 7   **Fic**
1. Children of divorced parents 2. Coping in boys 3. Loss (Psychology) 4. Lakes 5. Friendship 6. Wisconsin 7. Realistic fiction
ISBN 9780061470769
                                              LC 2007036564
Twelve-year-old Mitch and his mother are spending the summer with his grandparents at Bird Lake after his parents separate, and ten-year-old Spencer and his family have returned to the lake where Spencer's little brother drowned long ago, and as the boys become friends and spend time together, each of them begins to heal.
"Characters are gently and believably developed as the story weaves in and around the beautiful Wisconsin setting. The superbly crafted plot moves smoothly and unhurriedly, mirroring a slow summer pace." School Library Journal.

★ **Olive's** ocean. by Kevin Henkes. Greenwillow Books, c2003. 217 p.
Grades: 5 6 7 8   **Fic**
1. Self-perception in girls 2. Summer 3. Grandmother and granddaughter 4. Twelve-year-old-girls 5. Life change events 6. Cape Cod, Massachusetts 7. Massachusetts 8. Realistic fiction
ISBN 0060535431
                                              LC 2002029782

On a summer visit to her grandmother's cottage by the ocean, twelve-year-old Martha gains perspective on the death of a classmate, on her relationship with her grandmother, on her feelings for an older boy, and on her plans to be a writer.
"Rich characterizations move this compelling novel to its satisfying and emotionally authentic conclusion." School Library Journal.

Protecting Marie. Kevin Henkes. Greenwillow Books, c1995. 195 p.
Grades: 5 6 7 8   **Fic**
1. Children of artists 2. Girls and dogs 3. Fathers and daughters 4. Dogs 5. Families 6. Christmas stories 7. Realistic fiction
ISBN 0688139582
                                              LC   94016387 /AC
Relates twelve-year-old Fanny's love-hate relationship with her father, a temperamental artist, who has given Fanny a new dog.
"The characters ring heartbreakingly true in this quiet, wise story; they are complex and difficult—like all of us—and worthy of our attention." Horn Book.

Henry, April

The **lonely** dead. April Henry. Henry Holt & Co., 2019. 240 p.
Grades: 7 8 9 10 11 12   **Fic**
1. Former friends 2. Mediums 3. Murder investigation 4. Murder victims 5. Ghosts 6. Supernatural mysteries 7. Thrillers and suspense
ISBN 9781250157577
                                              LC 2018021064
When schizophrenic Adele, who possesses a paranormal gift, is implicated in an investigation that involves the murder of her ex-best friend Tori, Adele must work with Tori's ghost to find the killer.
"A thriller that manages to be both creepy and fun." Kirkus.

Henry, Katie

Heretics anonymous. Katie Henry. Harpercollins Childrens Books 2018 336 p.
Grades: 8 9 10 11 12   **Fic**
1. Atheists 2. Misfits (Persons) 3. Catholic schools 4. Belief and doubt 5. Secret societies 6. Realistic fiction
ISBN 9780062698872
"The story adeptly asks readers to question what they believe and why, without being preachy, judgmental, or dismissive. Humor interlaced with more serious ideas make for an interesting and enjoyable read." School Library Journal.

Henry, O., 1862-1910

The **gift** of the Magi. O. Henry; illustrated by P.J. Lynch. Candlewick Press, 2008. 40 p.
Grades: 5 6 7 8   **Fic**
1. Self-sacrifice 2. Love 3. Poor people 4. Couples 5. Christmas 6. Christmas stories
ISBN 9780763635305
                                              LC 2007052028
A husband and wife sacrifice treasured possessions in order to buy each other Christmas presents.
"The story enjoys a gentle new interpretation through watercolor illustrations in worn grays and warm brown tones. . . . Lynch's illustrations of wintry landscapes and the protagonists' animated faces add an accessible level of storytelling to the sophisticated prose." Horn Book Guide.

Henson, Heather

Dream of Night. Heather Henson. Atheneum Books for Young Readers, 2010. 224 p.

Grades: 6 7 8 9   **Fic**
> 1. Foster children 2. Race horses 3. Emotional problems of girls 4. Emotional problems 5. Horses 6. Kentucky 7. Realistic fiction
> ISBN 9781416948995

LC 2009026213

Told from their different points of view, twelve-year-old Shiloh, a troubled foster child, Dream of Night, an abused former racehorse, and Jess, a woman who cares for both, find healing by helping one another through their pain.

"[Henson's] novel, like her characters, shimmers with anger and hope. She doesn't pull her punches—the scenes and flashbacks of abuse are realistically graphic—but she also never lets the details overwhelm the narrative, always offering the possibility of redemption." Kirkus.

Hepler, Heather

The **cupcake** queen. Heather Hepler. Dutton, 2009. 242 p.: Cupcake queen

Grades: 6 7 8 9   **Fic**
> 1. Moving, Household 2. Family problems 3. Thirteen-year-old girls 4. Schools 5. Cupcakes 6. New York (State) 7. Realistic fiction 8. Teen chick lit
> ISBN 9780525421573

LC 2008048971

While longing to return to life in New York City, thirteen-year-old Penny helps her mother and grandmother run a cupcake bakery in Hog's Hollow, tries to avoid the beastly popular girls, to be a good friend to quirky Tally, and to catch the eye of enigmatic Marcus.

"An endearing and poignant story about standing up to adversity and finding peace in what it is, rather than holding out for what it could be." Publishers Weekly.

Herbach, Geoff

I'm with stupid. Geoff Herbach. Sourcebooks Fire, [2013], ©2013. 309 p.: Felton Reinstein trilogy

Grades: 7 8 9 10   **Fic**
> 1. High school football players 2. Survivors of suicide victims 3. Bullying and bullies 4. High school football 5. Anxiety 6. Wisconsin 7. Realistic fiction
> ISBN 9781402277917

LC 2012042814

It's nerd-turned-jock Felton Reinstein's last year before college, and the choices he makes now will affect the rest of his life. That's a lot of pressure. Before leaving home forever, Felton will have to figure out just who he is, even if, sometimes, it sucks to be him. Provided by publisher.

Herlong, Madaline

The **great** wide sea. by Madaline Herlong. Viking Childrens Books, 2008. 240 p.

Grades: 7 8 9 10   **Fic**
> 1. Sailing 2. Grief 3. Seafaring life 4. Family relationships 5. Brothers 6. Caribbean Sea 7. Survival stories 8. Adventure stories
> ISBN 9780670063307

LC 2008008384

Still mourning the death of their mother, three brothers go with their father on an extended sailing trip off the Florida Keys and have a harrowing adventure at sea.

"Herlong makes the most of the three boys' characters, each exceptionally well developed here, to make this as much a novel of brotherhood as a sea story." Bulletin of the Center for Children's Books.

Herrera, Robin

Hope is a ferris wheel. Robin Herrera. Amulet Books, 2014. 261 p.

Grades: 4 5 6 7   **Fic**
> 1. Dickinson, Emily, 1830-1886 2. Clubs 3. Poetry 4. Optimism 5. Optimism in girls 6. Mobile home parks 7. California 8. Northern California 9. Realistic fiction
> ISBN 9781419710391

LC 2013026392

After moving from Oregon to a trailer park in California, ten-year-old Star participates in a poetry club, where she learns some important lessons about herself and her own hopes and dreams for the future.

"Herrera has created a delightful narrator with a memorable voice and surrounded her with a unique supporting cast." Booklist.

Herrick, Amy

The **Time** Fetch: a novel. Amy Herrick. Algonquin Young Readers, 2013. 320 p.

Grades: 5 6 7 8   **Fic**
> 1. Loners 2. Space and time 3. Rocks 4. Witches 5. Eighth-grade boys 6. Fantasy fiction
> ISBN 9781616202200

LC 2013008612

When the Time Fetch's foragers gobble up too much time, causing the fabric of the universe to unravel and blur the boundaries between worlds and dimensions, eighth-grade loner Edward and his classmates must band together to save the day.

Hesse, Karen

★ **Brooklyn** Bridge. Karen Hesse. Feiwel and Friends, 2008. 240 p.

Grades: 5 6 7 8 9 10   **Fic**
> 1. 1900s (Decade) 2. Children of immigrants 3. Teddy bears 4. Abandoned children 5. Social classes 6. Families 7. Brooklyn, New York City 8. Historical fiction
> ISBN 9780312378868

LC 2008005624

Sydney Taylor Book Award for Older Readers, 2009.

In 1903 Brooklyn, fourteen-year-old Joseph Michtom's life changes for the worse when his parents, Russian immigrants, invent the teddy bear and turn their apartment into a factory, while nearby the glitter of Coney Island contrasts with the dismal lives of children dwelling under the Brooklyn Bridge.

"Hesse applies her gift for narrative voice to this memorable story. . . . The novel explodes with dark drama before its eerie but moving resolution." Publishers Weekly.

★ **Letters** from Rifka. Karen Hesse. Henry Holt, 1992. 148 p.

Grades: 5 6 7 8   **Fic**
> 1. Ellis Island Immigration Station, New York. 2. 1910s 3. Jewish girls 4. Courage in girls 5. Jewish families 6. Cousins 7. Letter writing 8. Antwerp, Belgium 9. United States 10. Historical fiction 11. Epistolary novels 12. Classics
> ISBN 0805019642

LC 91048007

Sydney Taylor Book Award for Older Readers, 1992.

In letters to her cousin, a young Jewish girl chronicles her family's flight from Russia in 1919 and her own experiences when she must be left in Belgium for a while when the others emigrate to America.

"Based on the true story of the author's great-aunt, the moving account of a brave young girl's story brings to life the day-to-day trials and horrors experienced by many immigrants as well as the resourcefulness and strength they found within themselves." Horn Book.

★ **Out** of the dust. Karen Hesse. Scholastic Press, 1997. 227 p.

Grades: 5 6 7 8   **Fic**
   1. Depression era (1929-1941) 2. 1930s 3. Droughts 4. Depressions 1929-1941. 5. Teenage pianists 6. Discontent in teenage girls 7. Loss (Psychology) 8. Oklahoma 9. Dust Bowl (South Central United States) 10. Historical fiction 11. Coming-of-age stories 12. Novels in verse
ISBN 0590360809
                      LC 96040344
Newbery Medal, 1998.
Scott O'Dell Historical Fiction Award, 1998.
   In a series of poems, fourteen-year-old Billie Jo relates the hardships of living on her family's wheat farm in Oklahoma during the dust bowl years of the Depression.
   "Hesse's writing transcends the gloom and transforms it into a powerfully compelling tale of a girl with enormous strength, courage, and love. The entire novel is written in very readable blank verse." Booklist.

Safekeeping. Karen Hesse. Feiwel and Friends, 2012. 304 p.

Grades: 7 8 9 10 11 12   **Fic**
   1. Survival 2. Parent-separated teenage girls 3. Dystopias 4. Friendship 5. Seventeen-year-old girls 6. New England
ISBN 9781250011343
                    LC bl2012021621
   When Radley returns to the United States after volunteering abroad, she comes back to a country under military rule with strict travel restrictions, and she must find her way back to her Vermont home through the New England woods.

★ **Witness.** Karen Hesse. Scholastic Press, 2001 161 p.

Grades: 6 7 8 9   **Fic**
   1. Ku-Klux Klan. 2. 1920s 3. Racism 4. African American girls 5. Jewish American girls 6. Prejudice 7. Small town life 8. Vermont 9. Historical fiction 10. Novels in verse
ISBN 0439271991
                    LC 00054139
   A series of poems express the views of various people in a small Vermont town, including a young black girl and a young Jewish girl, during the early 1920s when the Ku Klux Klan is trying to infiltrate the town.
   "The story is divided into five acts, and would lend itself beautifully to performance. The plot unfolds smoothly, and the author creates multidimensional characters." School Library Journal.

Hesse, Monica

The **war** outside. Monica Hesse. 336 p.

Grades: 8 9 10 11 12   **Fic**
   1. Second World War era (1939-1945) 2. Teenage girls 3. Concentration camps 4. Japanese Americans -- Forced removal and incarceration, 1942-1945 5. German Americans 6. Friendship 7. Texas 8. Historical fiction
ISBN 9780316316699
                    LC 2018005733
   Teens Haruko, a Japanese American, and Margot, a German American, form a life-changing friendship as everything around them starts falling apart in the Crystal City family internment camp during World War II.
   "Interned in a Texas camp during World War II, Japanese-American Haruko and German-American Margot watch their families fall apart and are driven to depend on each other, even if they should not." Kirkus.

Hesser, Terry Spencer

Kissing doorknobs. Terry Spencer Hesser. Delacorte Press, 1998. 149 p.

Grades: 7 8 9 10   **Fic**
   1. Teenagers with mental illnesses 2. Obsessive-compulsive disorder 3. Fourteen-year-old girls 4. Mental illness 5. Compulsive behavior 6. Realistic fiction
ISBN 0385323298
                    LC 97026937
   Fourteen-year-old Tara describes how her increasingly strange compulsions begin to take over her life and affect her relationships with her family and friends.
   "An honest, fresh, and multilayered story to which readers will instantly relate. . . . The prose is forthright, economical, and peppered with wry humor." School Library Journal.

Hest, Amy

The **summer** we found the baby. Amy Hest. Candlewick Press, 2020 192 p.

Grades: 4 5 6 7   **Fic**
   1. Second World War era (1939-1945) 2. Abandoned children 3. Former friends 4. Sisters 5. Everyday life 6. War and society 7. Long Island, New York 8. Historical fiction
ISBN 9780763660079
   Told from three viewpoints, a brisk historical tale follows the experiences of two sisters who discover an abandoned baby on the library steps, while their estranged friend, racing to complete an important errand for his World War II soldier brother, jumps to the wrong conclusion. Atlas Publishing
   "Each credible voice is distinct yet complementary, shaping a richly layered, cohesive novel that is by turns heartwarming and heartbreaking." Publishers Weekly

Hiaasen, Carl

★ **Flush.** Carl Hiaasen. Alfred A. Knopf, 2005. 263 p.

Grades: 5 6 7 8   **Fic**
   1. Children of environmentalists 2. Environmental crimes 3. Environmental protection 4. Children of prisoners 5. Water -- Pollution 6. Florida 7. Florida Keys 8. Thrillers and suspense
ISBN 0375821821
                    LC 2005005259
   With their father jailed for sinking a river boat, Noah Underwood and his younger sister, Abbey, must gather evidence that the owner of this floating casino is emptying his bilge tanks into the protected waters around their Florida Keys home.
   "This quick-reading, fun, family adventure harkens back to the Hardy Boys in its simplicity and quirky characters." School Library Journal.

★ **Hoot.** by Carl Hiaasen. Alfred A. Knopf, 2002. 227 p.

Grades: 5 6 7 8   **Fic**
   1. Owls 2. Resistance to land development 3. Eco-terrorism 4. Environmental protection 5. Wildlife conservation 6. Florida
ISBN 0375821813
                    LC 2002025478
   Roy, who is new to his small Florida community, becomes involved in another boy's attempt to save a colony of burrowing owls from a proposed construction site.
   "The story is full of offbeat humor, buffoonish yet charming supporting characters, and genuinely touching scenes of children enjoying the wildness of nature." Booklist.

★ **Scat.** Carl Hiaasen. Alfred A. Knopf, c2009. 384 p.

Grades: 5 6 7 8   **Fic**
1. Oil industry and trade 2. Rare and endangered animals 3. Children of parents with disabilities 4. Environmental protection 5. Wildlife conservation 6. Florida 7. Mysteries
ISBN 9780375834868

LC 2008028266

Nick and his friend Marta decide to investigate when a mysterious fire starts near a Florida wildlife preserve and an unpopular teacher goes missing.

"Once again, Hiaasen has written an edge-of-the-seat eco-thriller. . . . From the first sentence, readers will be hooked. . . . This well-written and smoothly plotted story, with fully realized characters, will certainly appeal to mystery lovers." School Library Journal.

Skink--no surrender. Carl Hiaasen. Alfred A. Knopf, 2014. 288 p.
Grades: 8 9 10 11 12   **Fic**
1. Missing teenage girls 2. Internet predators 3. Wilderness areas 4. Cousins 5. Former governors 6. Florida 7. Mysteries
ISBN 9780375870514

LC 2014006036

With the help of an eccentric ex-governor, a teenaged boy searches for his missing cousin in the Florida wilds.

Higgins, F. E.
The **black** book of secrets. F.E. Higgins. Feiwel & Friends, 2007. 273 p.: Tales from the sinister city
Grades: 4 5 6 7   **Fic**
1. Runaway boys 2. Boy apprentices 3. Confession 4. Pawnbrokers 5. Secrets 6. Historical fantasy 7. Mysteries
ISBN 0312368445

"This is an intriguing blend of adventure and historical fiction spiced with a light touch of the fantastic." Voice of Youth Advocates.

The **eyeball** collector. F. E. Higgins. Feiwel & Friends, 2009. 272 p.: Tales from the sinister city
Grades: 7 8 9 10   **Fic**
1. Boy orphans 2. Swindlers and swindling 3. Revenge in boys 4. Revenge 5. Extortion 6. Historical fantasy 7. Mysteries
ISBN 9780312566814

"In what the author dubs a polyquel that partially bridges her Black Book of Secrets (2007) and its prequel Bone Magician (2008), Higgins sends a suddenly penniless young orphan from the filthy streets of Urbs Umida's South Side to an extravagantly rococo estate house in search of vengeance for his family's ruin. . . . Readers with a taste for lurid prose, macabre twists, riddles, exotic poisons, high-society caricatures, murderous schemes and scenes of stomach-churning degeneracy will find some or all of these in every chapter, and though the author trots in multiple characters and references from previous episodes, this one stands sturdily on its own." Kirkus.

The **lunatic's** curse. F. E. Higgins. Feiwel and Friends, 2011. 336 p.: Tales from the sinister city
Grades: 6 7 8 9   **Fic**
1. Psychiatric hospitals 2. Stepmothers 3. Diamonds 4. Swindlers and swindling 5. Fathers 6. Historical fantasy 7. Mysteries
ISBN 9780312566821

"The prosperous town of Oppum Oppidulum, the deep and cold adjacent Lake Beluarum and the Asylum for the Peculiar and Bizarre that sits on an island in said lake all hold horrifying secrets. Young Rex discovers this when his father is confined to the Asylum after suddenly going mad and eating his own hand to the open glee of Rex's sinister new

stepmother Acantha Grammaticus. . . . Strewing her narrative with dark hints, obscure clues, assorted lunatics and, in particular, both macabre cuisine and a panoply of noxious or tantalizingly evocative odors, the author contrives a highly atmospheric experience. Readers with strong stomachs and a taste for melodramatic narratives . . . will devour this yarn with relish." Kirkus.

Higgins, Jack, 1929-
Death run. by Jack Higgins with Justin Richards. Harper Collins, 2007. 336 p.: Rich and Jade
Grades: 6 7 8 9   **Fic**
1. Mafia 2. Twin brothers and sisters 3. Spies 4. Fifteen-year-olds 5. Fathers 6. London, England 7. Spy fiction 8. Thrillers and suspense
ISBN 9780399250811

"This is an enjoyable romp." Booklist.

First strike. Jack Higgins with Justin Richards. G.P. Putnam's Sons, c2010. xxi, 240 p.: Rich and Jade
Grades: 6 7 8 9   **Fic**
1. Twin brothers and sisters 2. Presidents 3. Hostage taking 4. Spies 5. Adventure 6. Spy fiction 7. Thrillers and suspense
ISBN 9780399252402

British twins Rich and Jade are once again thrown into danger as they try to help their spy father, John Chance, save the President of the United States from a radical group holding the White House hostage and attempting to steal the nation's nuclear launch codes.

"Fans of the twins' exploits will enjoy this thrill ride." Booklist.

Sharp shot. Jack Higgins with Justin Richards. G.P. Putnam's Sons, c2009. xxi, 214 p.: Rich and Jade
Grades: 6 7 8 9   **Fic**
1. Twin brothers and sisters 2. Hostage taking 3. Atomic bomb 4. Spies 5. Adventure 6. Middle East 7. Spy fiction 8. Thrillers and suspense
ISBN 9780399252396

LC 2008052886

British twins Rich and Jade Chance are back for a third adventure with their spy father as they try to save the Middle East and the President of the United States from a terrorist government coup.

"Higgins and Richards have crafted another page-turner punctuated with gunfire and highlighted by heroism and explosions." Booklist.

Sure fire. by Jack Higgins with Justin Richards. HarperCollins, 2006. 256 p.: Rich and Jade
Grades: 6 7 8 9   **Fic**
1. Twin brothers and sisters 2. Spies 3. Kidnapping 4. Fifteen-year-olds 5. Mothers -- Death 6. London, England 7. Spy fiction 8. Thrillers and suspense
ISBN 9780007244096

LC 2007008144

Resentful of having to go and live with their estranged father after the death of their mother, fifteen-year-old twins, Rich and Jade, soon find they have more complicated problems when their father is kidnapped and their attempts to rescue him involve them in a dangerous international plot to control the world's oil.

"This is a standout YA spy novel. . . . Each chapter ends with a cliffhanger, maintaining the high level of suspense." Publishers Weekly.

Higgins, Joanna, 1945-
Waiting for the queen. Joanna Higgins. Milkweed Editions, 2013 256 p.

Grades: 6 7 8 9 10   **Fic**
    1. 18th century 2. Quakers 3. Nobility 4. Slavery 5. Social
classes 6. Friendship 7. Pennsylvania 8. France 9. Historical
fiction
ISBN 9781571317001

In 1793, fifteen-year-old Eugenie de la Roque, her family, and other
nobles barely escape the French Revolution and arrive in Pennsylvania, where homesick young Hannah Kimbrell, a Shaker, is among those
charged with preparing New France for the aristocrats' arrival.

Higuera, Donna Barba

Lupe Wong won't dance. Donna Barba Higuera. Levine
Querido, 2020. 256 p.
Grades: 5 6 7 8   **Fic**
    1. Multiracial girls 2. Baseball 3. Middle school students 4.
Pitchers (Baseball) 5. Physical education for children 6. Realistic
fiction 7. Baseball stories
ISBN 9781646140039

Lupe Wong is going to be the first female pitcher in the Major
Leagues. She's also championed causes her whole young life. Lupe
needs an A in all her classes in order to meet her favorite pitcher, Fu Li
Hernandez, who's Chinacan/Mexinese just like her. So when the horror
that is square dancing rears its head in gym? Obviously she's not gonna
let that slide.

"Lupe has a wonderfully diverse group of friends with a wide range
of interests, from Star Trek to soccer, deftly avoiding 'diversity quota'
pitfalls. . . . This one is simply delightful." Kirkus

Hilton, Marilyn

Full cicada moon. by Marilyn Hilton. Dial Books for Young
Readers, 2015. 400 p.
Grades: 4 5 6 7   **Fic**
    1. 1960s 2. Multiracial girls 3. Gender role 4. Moving to a new
state 5. Twelve-year-old girls 6. Preteen girls 7. Vermont 8.
Historical fiction 9. Novels in verse
ISBN 9780525428756

                                             LC 2014044894

In 1969 twelve-year-old Mimi and her family move to an all-white
town in Vermont, where Mimi's mixed-race background and interest in
"boyish" topics like astronomy make her feel like an outsider.

"Mimi Yoshiko Oliver and her family just moved from Berkeley,
California, to Hillsborough, Vermont, where she immediately encounters barrier after barrier to overcome. Mimi's goal is to become an astronaut; however, it's 1969, a time when young girls are encouraged to
become mothers, secretaries, teachers, or nurses. . . . Mimi's voice as
narrator is clear and focused: she must figure out who she is, instead of
answering the question, What are you? Out of respect for her parents, the
decisions she makes pull from both halves to make a whole. Perfect for
readers who straddle societies, feel they don't fit in, or need that confir-
mation of self-celebration." Booklist.

Hinton, S. E.

The **outsiders**. by S. E. Hinton. Puffin Books, 1997, c1967.
180 p.
Grades: 7 8 9 10   **Fic**
    1. Gangs 2. Brothers 3. Teenagers 4. Teenage boys 5. Bullying
and bullies 6. Realistic fiction 7. Classics
ISBN 9780140385724

                                             LC 67013606

Three brothers struggle to stay together after their parents' death, as
they search for an identity among the conflicting values of their adolescent society in which they find themselves "outsiders."

"This remarkable novel by a seventeen-year-old girl gives a moving, credible view of the outsiders from the inside—their loyalty to each
other, their sensitivity under tough crusts, their understanding of self and
society." Horn Book.

Hirahara, Naomi, 1962-

1001 cranes. Naomi Hirahara. Delacorte Press, 2008. 230 p.
Grades: 5 6 7 8   **Fic**
    1. Japanese American girls 2. Origami 3. Japanese American
families 4. Interpersonal relations 5. Change (Psychology) 6. Los
Angeles, California 7. Realistic fiction
ISBN 9780385905411

Moving to L.A. with her family to spend the summer working at
her grandparents' flower shop, twelve-year-old Angela is bored by the
tediousness of her task, but as her skills for folding origami and crane
displays improves, she gains newfound respect for her Japanese culture
and herself in the process.

"Angela's colorful, bold voice captures the excitement of her first
love as well as the anxiety of not understanding the many secrets of
the adults around her. By experiencing her family's support, by learning
about her Japanese heritage, and by acknowledging the various ways
that love is expressed, Angela emerges into a strong, caring person."
School Library Journal.

Hiranandani, Veera

The **whole** story of half a girl. Veera Hiranandani. Delacorte
Press, 2012. 224 p.
Grades: 4 5 6 7   **Fic**
    1. Multiracial children 2. Children of people with depression 3.
Culture shock 4. Identity (Psychology) 5. Belonging 6. Coming-
of-age stories
ISBN 9780375989957

                                             LC 2011026178

When Sonia's father loses his job and she must move from her small,
supportive private school to a public middle school, the half-Jewish half-
Indian sixth-grader experiences culture shock as she tries to navigate
the school's unfamiliar social scene, and after her father is diagnosed
with clinical depression, she finds herself becoming even more confused
about herself and her family.

"Sonia's struggles are painfully realistic. . . True to life, her problems
do not wrap up neatly, but Sonia's growth is deeply rewarding in this
thoughtful and beautifully wrought novel." Publishers Weekly.

Hirsch, Jeff

Breakaway. Jeff Hirsch. Scholastic Inc., [2014] 192 p.: The
39 clues.
Grades: 4 5 6 7   **Fic**
    1. Orphans 2. Brothers and sisters 3. Clues 4. Enemies 5.
Teenagers 6. Adventure stories
ISBN 9780545597104

                                             LC bl2013048233

Dan Cahill and his sister Amy travel from the hottest to the cold-
est regions of the world in order to stop someone from using their own
power against them.

The **eleventh** plague. Jeff Hirsch. Scholastic Press, 2011.
304 p.
Grades: 7 8 9 10   **Fic**
    1. Post-apocalypse 2. Survival 3. Dystopias 4. Practical jokes 5.
Communities 6. Dystopian fiction 7. Science fiction
ISBN 9780545290142

                                             LC 2010048966

Twenty years after the start of the war that caused the Collapse, fifteen-year-old Stephen, his father, and grandfather travel post-Collapse America scavenging, but when his grandfather dies and his father decides to risk everything to save the lives of two strangers, Stephen's life is turned upside down.

"This novel is an impressive story with strong characters. . . . Hirsch delivers a tight, well-crafted story." Publishers Weekly.

Hitchcock, Bonnie-Sue

The **smell** of other people's houses. Bonnie-Sue Hitchcock. Wendy Lamb Books, 2016. 208 p.

Grades: 7 8 9 10 **Fic**
> 1. 1970s 2. Inupiat 3. Teenage girl dancers 4. Children of separated parents 5. Children of prisoners 6. Runaway teenagers 7. Alaska 8. Fairbanks, Alaska 9. Historical fiction
> ISBN 9780553497786

Intertwined stories of love, tragedy, wild luck and salvation on Alaska's wild frontier in the 1970s follows the experiences of four very different teens whose lives become entangled and who try to save each other, sometimes succeeding when they least expect it.

"Less a narrative and more a series of portraits, this is an exquisitely drawn, deeply heartfelt look at a time and place not often addressed. Hitchcock's measured prose casts a gorgeous, almost otherworldly feel over the text, resulting in a quietly lovely look at the various sides of human nature and growing up in a difficult world." Booklist.

Hoang, Van

Girl giant and the Monkey King. Van Hoang. Roaring Brook Press, 2020. 256 p.

Grades: 4 5 6 7 **Fic**
> 1. Preteen girls 2. Tricksters 3. Strength and weakness 4. Vietnamese Americans 5. Magic 6. Georgia 7. Asian-influenced fantasy 8. Mythological fiction 9. Fantasy fiction
> ISBN 9781250240415

Eleven-year-old Thom Ngho is keeping a secret: she's strong. Like suuuuper strong. Freakishly strong. And it's making it impossible for her to fit in at her new middle school. In a desperate bid to get rid of her super strength, Thom makes a deal with the Monkey King, a powerful deity and legendary trickster she accidentally released from his 500-year prison sentence. Thom agrees to help the Monkey King get back his magical staff if he'll take away her strength. Soon Thom is swept up in an ancient and fantastical world in where demons, dragons, and Jade princesses actually exist. But she quickly discovers that magic can't cure everything, and dealing with the trickster god might be more trouble than it's worth.

"A tale that deals with important issues of fitting in and cultural understanding, while soaring into the realms of myth and magical adventure." School Library Journal

Hobbs, Valerie

The **last** best days of summer. Valerie Hobbs. Farrar, Straus and Giroux, 2010. 192 p.

Grades: 5 6 7 8 **Fic**
> 1. Grandmother and granddaughter 2. Children with Down syndrome 3. Memory in senior women 4. Popularity 5. Women potters 6. Coming-of-age stories 7. Realistic fiction
> ISBN 9780374346706

LC 2008047145
During a summer visit, twelve-year-old Lucy must come to terms with both her grandmother's failing memory and how her mentally-challenged neighbor will impact her popularity when both enter the same middle school in the fall.

"The story's finely tuned realism is refreshing, particularly in Lucy's yearning for social acceptance and in the fully drawn and wholly memorable characters." Booklist.

Hobbs, Will

Crossing the wire. by Will Hobbs. HarperCollins, c2006. 216 p.

Grades: 5 6 7 8 **Fic**
> 1. Mexicans 2. Undocumented workers 3. Drug smugglers 4. Fifteen-year-old boys 5. Teenage boys 6. Mexico 7. Arizona 8. Survival stories 9. Adventure stories 10. Realistic fiction
> ISBN 0060741384

LC 2005019697
Fifteen-year-old Victor Flores journeys north in a desperate attempt to cross the Arizona border and find work in the United States to support his family in central Mexico.

"This is an exciting story in a vital contemporary setting." Voice of Youth Advocates.

Go big or go home. Will Hobbs. HarperCollins Publishers, c2008. 185 p.

Grades: 6 7 8 9 **Fic**
> 1. Meteorites 2. Sick persons 3. Extreme sports 4. Bacteria 5. Fourteen-year-old boys 6. South Dakota 7. Black Hills 8. Science fiction
> ISBN 9780060741419

Fourteen-year-old Brady and his cousin Quinn love extreme sports, but nothing could prepare them for the aftermath of Brady's close encounter with a meteorite after it crashes into his Black Hills, South Dakota, bedroom.

"The sense of place is powerful, with bits of lore about the region making the reader feel immersed in the story and its setting, and the characterizations are especially strong." Voice of Youth Advocates.

★ **Jason's** gold. Will Hobbs. Morrow Junior Books, c1999. 221 p.

Grades: 5 6 7 8 **Fic**
> 1. 1890s 2. Gold rush 3. Wilderness survival 4. Voyages and travels 5. Siberian huskies 6. Boys and dogs 7. Yukon Territory 8. Coming-of-age stories 9. Adventure stories 10. Historical fiction
> ISBN 0688150934

LC 99017973
When news of the discovery of gold in Canada's Yukon Territory in 1897 reaches fifteen-year-old Jason, he embarks on a 10,000-mile journey to strike it rich.

"The successful presentation of a fascinating era, coupled with plenty of action, makes this a good historical fiction choice." School Library Journal.

Leaving Protection. by Will Hobbs. HarperCollins, c2004. 178 p.

Grades: 7 8 9 10 **Fic**
> 1. Treasure hunting 2. Salmon fishing 3. Selling -- Antiques 4. Summer employment 5. Secrets 6. Alaska 7. Adventure stories 8. Realistic fiction
> ISBN 0688174752

LC 2003015545
Sixteen-year-old Robbie Daniels, happy to get a job aboard a troller fishing for king salmon off southeastern Alaska, finds himself in danger when he discovers that his mysterious captain is searching for long-buried Russian plaques that lay claim to Alaska and the Northwest.

"This nautical thriller brims with detail about the fishing life and weaves in historical facts as well. . . . Robbie's doubts build to a climactic finale involving a dramatic and fateful storm at sea, grippingly rendered. Fans of maritime tales will relish the atmosphere and the bursts of action." Publishers Weekly.

Never say die. by Will Hobbs. HarperCollins Children's Books, 2012. 192 p.

Grades: 4 5 6 7   **Fic**
1. Inuit 2. Bears 3. Survival 4. Photojournalism 5. Multiracial teenage boys 6. Canada 7. Aklavik, Northwest Territories 8. Survival stories 9. Adventure stories
ISBN 9780061708787

LC 2011053289

Fifteen-year-old half-Inuit Nick meets and shares an adventure on the Firth River in the Canadian Arctic with his white brother, Ryan. They have to face white water, wild animals, and fierce weather as Ryan documents the effects of climate change on caribou for National Geographic magazine.

Take me to the river. by Will Hobbs. HarperCollins, 2011. 192 p.

Grades: 5 6 7 8   **Fic**
1. White-water rafting 2. Fugitives 3. Boy cousins 4. Hurricanes 5. Kidnappers 6. Rio Grande 7. Texas 8. Adventure stories
ISBN 9780060741440

"The story unfolds in a disarming manner. The pace is quick, and the challenges are relentless, but the writing is so grounded in physical details and emotional realism that every turn of events seems convincing within the context of the story." Booklist.

Hodkin, Michelle

The **unbecoming** of Mara Dyer. Michelle Hodkin. Simon & Schuster, 2011. 272 p.: Mara Dyer trilogy

Grades: 7 8 9 10 11 12   **Fic**
1. Post-traumatic stress disorder 2. Supernatural 3. Murder 4. Teenage boy/girl relations 5. High schools 6. Florida 7. Paranormal fiction
ISBN 9781442421769

LC 2010050862

Seventeen-year-old Mara cannot remember the accident that took the lives of three of her friends but, after moving from Rhode Island to Florida, finding love with Noah, and more deaths, she realizes that uncovering something buried in her memory might save her family and her future.

"The characters are real and wonderful, and the supernatural story is riveting." School Library Journal.

Hof, Marjolijn, 1956-

Mother number zero. Marjolijn Hof. Groundwood Books, 2011. 179 p.

Grades: 4 5 6 7   **Fic**
1. Adoption 2. New neighbors 3. Birthmothers 4. Belonging 5. Identity (Psychology)
ISBN 9781554980789

"Fay and his older sister An Bing Wa were both adopted; she was an abandoned baby in China, and he was born to a mother traumatized in the Bosnian conflict. A new girl in the neighborhood, Maud, takes a keen interest in Fay's story and urges him to find his birth mother. . . . Hof . . . writes Fay's narration with a calm, matter-of-fact voice that possesses a literalness and simplicity in keeping with his youth. . . . The story nonetheless treats the characters with quiet percipience. . . . Younger

fans of domestic novels who like a tale with more gravitas if not reading difficulty will appreciate this thoughtful family story." Bulletin of the Center for Children's Books.

Holczer, Tracy

The **secret** hum of a daisy. Tracy Holczer. G. P. Putnam's Sons, an imprint of Penguin Group (USA), 2014. 320 p.

Grades: 5 6 7 8   **Fic**
1. Girl orphans 2. Grandmother and granddaughter 3. Loss (Psychology) 4. Moving, Household 5. Clues 6. Realistic fiction
ISBN 9780399163937

LC 2013039962

After 12-year-old Grace's mother's sudden death, Grace is forced to live with a grandmother she's never met. Then she discovers clues in a mysterious treasure hunt—one that will help her find her true home. Provided by publisher.

"Grace is a multifaceted, relatable protagonist: she's pensive, stubborn, lonely, and caring—much like Grandma, which is why they are able to help heal each other's grief. Their relationship evolves in an honest and tender way in this heartfelt debut about loss and love." Horn Book.

Holland, Elise

The **thorn** queen. Elise Holland. SparkPress, a BookSparks imprint, 2018. 256

Grades: 5 6 7 8   **Fic**
1. Resourcefulness 2. Imaginary places 3. Preteen girls 4. Princes 5. Conspiracies 6. High fantasy 7. Fantasy fiction
ISBN 9781943006793

Twelve-year-old Meylyne longs to impress her brilliant, sorceress mother—but when she accidentally breaks one of Glendoch's First Rules, she accomplishes the opposite of that. Forced to flee, the only way she may return home is with a cure for Glendoch's diseased prince.

Holm, Jennifer L.

Boston Jane: an adventure. Jennifer L. Holm. Harper Collins, 2001. 273 p.: Boston Jane adventures

Grades: 6 7 8 9   **Fic**
1. 19th century 2. Young women 3. Frontier and pioneer life 4. Peck, Jane (Fictitious character) 5. Self-perception 6. Etiquette 7. Washington (State) 8. Historical fiction
ISBN 0060287381

LC 2001016753

Schooled in the lessons of etiquette for young ladies of 1854, Miss Jane Peck of Philadelphia finds little use for manners during her long sea voyage to the Pacific Northwest and while living among the American traders and Chinook Indians of Washington Territory.

"Strong characterizations, meticulous attention to historical details . . . and a perceptive understanding of human nature make this a first-rate story not to be missed." Booklist.

Boston Jane: the claim. Jennifer L. Holm. Harper Collins Publishers, c2004. 230 p.: Boston Jane adventures

Grades: 4 5 6   **Fic**
1. 19th century 2. Young women 3. Frontier and pioneer life 4. Peck, Jane (Fictitious character) 5. Women -- Interpersonal relations 6. Men/women relations 7. Washington (State) 8. Historical fiction
ISBN 0060290455

LC 2003009556

The arrival from Philadelphia of her spiteful nemesis Sally Biddle and the return of her corrupt ex-fiance Richard Baldt spell trouble for seventeen-year-old Miss Jane Peck, who has survived on her own in Shoalwater Bay, a community of white settlers and Chinook Indians in 1850s Washington Territory.

"The story is fast paced and lively, and Holm successfully campaigns for diversity and feminism without making her plot seem like a thinly disguised message." Voice of Youth Advocates.

Boston Jane: wilderness days. Jennifer L. Holm. Harper Collins, c2002. vi, 242 p.: Boston Jane adventures

Grades: 6 7 8 9   **Fic**
   1. 19th century 2. 1850s 3. Young women 4. Frontier and pioneer life 5. Peck, Jane (Fictitious character) 6. Women -- Interpersonal relations 7. Men/women relations 8. Washington (State) 9. Historical fiction
ISBN 0060290439

LC 2002001473
Far from her native Philadelphia, Miss Jane Peck continues to prove that she is more than an etiquette-schooled graduate of Miss Hepplewhite's Young Ladies Academy as she braves the untamed wilderness of Washington Territory in the mid 1850s.

"Holm once again delivers an action-packed story with a strong female protagonist." School Library Journal.

★ The **fourteenth** goldfish. Jennifer L. Holm. Random House, 2014. 224 p.: Fourteenth goldfish

Grades: 4 5 6 7   **Fic**
   1. Aging 2. Scientists 3. Grandfathers 4. Families 5. Middle schools 6. Science fiction 7. STEM fiction
ISBN 9780375870644
Hating change and missing both her best friend and her dead goldfish, 11-year-old Ellie encounters a boy who strongly resembles her immortality-obsessed grandfather, in a story that introduces the work of famous historical scientists.

"With humor and heart, Holm has crafted a story about life, family, and finding one's passion that will appeal to readers willing to imagine the possible." School Library Journal.

★ **Middle** school is worse than meatloaf: a year told through stuff. by Jennifer L. Holm; pictures by Elicia Castaldi. Atheneum Books for Young Readers, c2007. 128 p.: Year told through stuff series

Grades: 5 6 7 8   **Fic**
   1. Children and remarriage 2. Former friends 3. School dances 4. Boy/girl relations 5. Friendship 6. Realistic fiction 7. Diary novels 8. Illustrated books
ISBN 0689852819
"Ginny Davis begins seventh grade with a list of items to accomplish. This list, along with lots of other stuff—including diary entries, refrigerator notes, cards from Grandpa, and IM screen messages—convey a year full of ups and downs. Digitally rendered collage illustrations realistically depict the various means of communication, and the story flows easily from one colorful page to the next. . . . The story combines honesty and humor to create a believable and appealing voice." School Library Journal.

★ **Our** only May Amelia. Jennifer L. Holm. Harper, 2019. 253 p.

Grades: 5 6 7 8   **Fic**
   1. Immigrant families 2. Frontier and pioneer life 3. Gender role 4. Brothers and sisters 5. Finnish American families 6. Washington

(State) 7. Historical fiction
ISBN 9780062881779

LC 98047504
As the only girl in a Finnish American family of seven brothers, May Amelia Jackson resents being expected to act like a lady while growing up in Washington state in 1899.

"The voice of the colloquial first-person narrative rings true and provides a vivid picture of frontier and pioneer life. . . . An afterword discusses Holm's research into her own family's history and that of other Finnish immigrants." Horn Book Guide.

Penny from heaven. by Jennifer L. Holm. Random House Children's Books, 2006. 288 p.

Grades: 5 6 7 8   **Fic**
   1. 1950s 2. Families 3. Italian Americans 4. Secrets 5. Eleven-year-old girls 6. Fathers -- Death 7. New Jersey 8. Coming-of-age stories 9. Historical fiction
ISBN 037583687X

LC 2005013896
As she turns twelve during the summer of 1953, Penny gains new insights into herself and her family while also learning a secret about her father's death.

"Holm impressively wraps pathos with comedy in this coming-of-age story, populated by a cast of vivid characters." Booklist.

The **trouble** with May Amelia. Jennifer L. Holm. Atheneum Books for Young Readers, 2011. 176 p.

Grades: 5 6 7 8   **Fic**
   1. 1900s (Decade) 2. Gender role 3. Frontier and pioneer life 4. Swindlers and swindling 5. Immigrant families 6. Finnish American families 7. Washington (State) 8. Historical fiction
ISBN 9781416913733

LC 2010042092
Living with seven brothers and her father, who thinks girls are useless, a thirteen-year-old Finnish American farm girl is determined to prove her worth when an enterprising gentleman tries to purchase their cash-strapped family settlement in Washington State in 1900.

"Holm gets her heroine just right. Narrating events in dryly witty, plainspoken first-person, this indomitable teen draws readers in with her account, through which her world comes alive." Kirkus.

Holmes, Sara

Operation Yes. Sara Lewis Holmes. Arthur A. Levine Books, 2009. 234 p.

Grades: 5 6 7 8   **Fic**
   1. Teachers 2. Improvisation (Acting) 3. Military dependents 4. Families of military personnel 5. Helpfulness in children 6. Realistic fiction
ISBN 9780545107952

LC 2008053732
In her first ever teaching job, Miss Loupe uses improvisational acting exercises with her sixth-grade students at an Air Force base school, and when she experiences a family tragedy, her previously skeptical class members use what they have learned to help her, her brother, and other wounded soldiers.

"Quick, funny, sad, full of heart, and irresistibly absorbing." Booklist.

Holt, K. A.

Knockout. K.A. Holt. Chronicle Books, [2018] 339 p.

Grades: 5 6 7 8 9   **Fic**
   1. Boxing 2. Children of divorced parents 3. Preteen boys 4.

Boxers (Sports) 5. Brothers 6. Realistic fiction 7. Novels in verse
ISBN 9781452163581

LC 2017042925

Told in assonant free verse, Levi was once a premature baby who
suffered from respiratory problems; he recovered, and now in seventh
grade, he struggles to demonstrate to his divorced mother and overprotective brother that he is okay—so when his father suggests he take up
boxing he falls in love with the sport, but he still must find a way to
convince his family to set him free to follow his dream.

Redwood and Ponytail. K.A. Holt. Chronicle Books, 2019.
424 p.

Grades: 5 6 7 8   **Fic**
1. Middle school students 2. Coming out (Sexual or gender identity)
3. Lesbians 4. Female friendship 5. Interpersonal relations 6.
Novels in verse 7. Realistic fiction
ISBN 9781452172880

Told in verse in two voices, with a chorus of fellow students, this is a
story of two girls, opposites in many ways, who are drawn to each other;
Kate appears to be a stereotypical cheerleader with a sleek ponytail and a
perfectly polished persona, Tam is tall, athletic and frequently mistaken
for a boy, but their deepening friendship inevitably changes and reveals
them in ways they did not anticipate.

"Two middle school girls grapple with their blossoming feelings for
each other in this verse novel." Kirkus.

Holt, Kimberly Willis

The **water** seeker. Kimberly Willis Holt. Henry Holt, 2010.
309 p.

Grades: 4 5 6 7   **Fic**
1. American Westward Expansion (1803-1899) 2. 19th century 3.
Frontier and pioneer life 4. Dowsing 5. Trappers 6. Dowsers 7.
Fathers and sons 8. Historical fiction 9. Coming-of-age stories
ISBN 9780805080209

LC 2009024149

Traces the hard life, filled with losses, adversity, and adventure, of
Amos, son of a trapper and dowser, from 1833 when his mother dies
giving birth to him until 1859, when he himself has grown up and has
a son of his own.

"Drawing on such diverse themes as Manifest Destiny, personal
identity and cross-cultural relationships, the author has crafted a satisfying all-ages story that hosts a dazzling array of richly realized secondary
characters . . . and flows as effortlessly as the Platte River." Kirkus.

★ **When** Zachary Beaver came to town. Kimberly Willis
Holt. Henry Holt, 1999. 192 p.

Grades: 5 6 7 8   **Fic**
1. 1970s 2. Teenage misfits 3. Overweight boys 4. Best friends 5.
Fathers 6. Boys -- Friendship 7. Texas 8. Coming-of-age stories
9. Realistic fiction
ISBN 0805061169

LC 99027998

National Book Award for Young People's Literature, 1999.

During the summer of 1971 in a small Texas town, thirteen-year-old
Toby and his best friend Cal meet the star of a sideshow act, 600-pound
Zachary, the fattest boy in the world.

"Holt writes with a subtle sense of humor and sensitivity, and reading her work is a delightful experience." Voice of Youth Advocates.

Holyoke, Polly

The **Neptune** Project. Polly Holyoke. Disney-Hyperion
Books, [2013], ©2013. 341 p.: Neptune Project

Grades: 4 5 6 7   **Fic**
1. Genetic engineering 2. Children of scientists 3. Dystopias 4.
Genetically engineered children 5. Undersea colonies 6. Science
fiction
ISBN 9781423157564

LC 2013000353

A group of kids who have been genetically altered to survive in the
ocean must embark on a dangerous underwater journey to find refuge—
and maybe even a way to save the world. Provided by publisher.

Hoobler, Dorothy

The **demon** in the teahouse. Dorothy and Thomas Hoobler.
Philomel Books, c2001. 181 p.: Samurai detective series

Grades: 6 7 8 9   **Fic**
1. Ooka, Tadasuke, 1677?-1751? 2. Tokugawa period (1600-1868)
3. 18th century 4. Detectives 5. Geishas 6. Samurai 7. Japan 8.
Historical mysteries 9. Mysteries
ISBN 0399234993

LC 00050184

In eighteenth-century Japan, fourteen-year-old Seikei, a merchant's
son in training to be a samurai, helps his patron investigate a series of
murders and arson in the capital city of Edo, each of which is associated
in some way with a popular geisha.

"Details of Shogun-era Japan are seamlessly woven into a gripping
story." Horn Book Guide.

The **ghost** in the Tokaido Inn. Dorothy and Thomas Hoobler.
Philomel Books, 1999. 214 p.: Samurai detective series

Grades: 6 7 8 9   **Fic**
1. Tokugawa period (1600-1868) 2. 18th century 3. Detectives 4.
Boy detectives 5. Jewelry theft 6. Kabuki 7. Courage in boys 8.
Japan 9. Historical mysteries 10. Mysteries
ISBN 9780399233302

LC 98014089

While attempting to solve the mystery of a stolen jewel, Seikei, a
merchant's son who longs to be a samurai, joins a group of kabuki actors
in eighteenth-century Japan.

"Precise characterization, suspenseful plot twists, and a pace defined
by swift and sometimes violent action make this a lively period thriller."
Bulletin of the Center for Children's Books.

Seven paths to death: a samurai mystery. Dorothy and Thomas Hoobler. Philomel Books, 2008. 192 p.: Samurai detective
series

Grades: 6 7 8 9   **Fic**
1. Ooka, Tadasuke, 1677?-1751? 2. Tokugawa period (1600-1868)
3. Detectives 4. Maps 5. Weapons 6. Tattooing 7. Murder 8.
Japan 9. Historical mysteries 10. Mysteries
ISBN 9780399246104

LC 2007042092

Samurai Seikei and Judge Ooka, his foster-father, seek seven men
who have seven maps on their backs in order to locate a cache of dangerous weapons before they fall into the wrong hands.

"This is a successful historical mystery, chockablock with adventure
. . . and cultural details." Booklist.

The **sword** that cut the burning grass: a samurai mystery.
Dorothy and Thomas Hoobler. Philomel Books, 2005. 211 p.:
Samurai detective series

Grades: 6 7 8 9   **Fic**
1. Ooka, Tadasuke, 1677?-1751? 2. Tokugawa period (1600-1868)
3. Detectives 4. Samurai 5. Japan 6. Historical mysteries 7.

Mysteries
ISBN 0399242724

LC 2004020320

In his latest adventure in eighteenth-century Japan, fourteen-year-old samurai apprentice Seikei, with the help of a servant girl and an imperious old man, sets out to rescue the young Emperor Yasuhito from his kidnappers.

"There's plenty of rousing action to propel the story forward, and, as always, Seikei makes a thoughtful hero." Booklist.

Hooper, Mary, 1948-
Fallen Grace. Mary Hooper. Bloomsbury Childrens Books, 2011. 320 p.
Grades: 7 8 9 10   Fic
1. Victorian era (1837-1901) 2. 1860s 3. Teenage girl orphans 4. Fraud 5. Sisters 6. Poverty 7. Undertakers 8. London, England 9. Great Britain 10. Historical fiction
ISBN 9781599905648

LC 2010025498

In Victorian London, impoverished fifteen-year-old orphan Grace takes care of her older but mentally unfit sister Lily, and after enduring many harsh and painful experiences, the two become the victims of a fraud perpetrated by the wealthy owners of several funeral businesses.

"Hooper packs her brisk Dickensian fable with colorful characters and suspenseful, satisfying plot twists. The sobering realities of child poverty and exploitation are vividly conveyed, along with fascinating details of the Victorian funeral trade." Kirkus.

Hopkins, Ellen
Rumble. Ellen Hopkins. Margaret K. McElderry Books, 2014. 608 p.
Grades: 8 9 10 11 12   Fic
1. Survivors of suicide victims 2. Anger in teenage boys 3. Atheists 4. Anger 5. Censorship 6. Oregon 7. Realistic fiction 8. Novels in verse
ISBN 9781442482845

Matthew Turner doesn't have faith in anything—not in his family, which is in shambles after his younger brother was bullied into suicide; or his so-called friends or some all-powerful creator; but when a horrific event plunges Matt into a dark, silent place, he begins to question everything he's ever disbelieved.

"Matt is a wonderfully faceted character that readers will alternately sympathize with and dislike. His actions are directly related to his emotional turmoil, and teens will understand his pain and admire his intellect, even while shaking their heads over his actions.." School Library Journal.

Hopkinson, Deborah
A **bandit's** tale: the muddled misadventures of a pickpocket. Deborah Hopkinson. Alfred A. Knopf, 2016. 304 p.
Grades: 4 5 6 7 8   Fic
1. 1880s 2. Boy immigrants 3. Child labor 4. Immigrants, Italian 5. Animal welfare 6. Pickpockets 7. New York city 8. Historical fiction
ISBN 9780385754996

"Rocco's conversational voice resounds with humor, compassion, and an inspiring energy for change. A dynamic historical novel ideal for both classroom studies and pleasure reading." Kirkus.

The **great** trouble: a mystery of London, the blue death, and a boy called Eel. Deborah Hopkinson. Alfred A. Knopf 2013 256 p.

Grades: 4 5 6 7 8   Fic
1. Victorian era (1837-1901) 2. 1850s 3. 19th century 4. Cholera 5. Epidemics 6. Boy orphans 7. Epidemiologists 8. London, England 9. Great Britain 10. Historical fiction 11. Diary novels 12. STEM fiction
ISBN 9780375848186

Eel, an orphan, and his best friend Florrie must help Dr. John Snow prove that cholera is spread through water, and not poisonous air, when an epidemic sweeps across their London neighborhood in 1854.

Into the firestorm: a novel of San Francisco, 1906. Deborah Hopkinson. Alfred A. Knopf, 2006. 208 p.
Grades: 5 6 7 8   Fic
1. 1900s (Decade) 2. Earthquakes 3. Fires 4. Survival (after earthquakes) 5. Orphans 6. Boy orphans 7. San Francisco, California 8. Historical fiction
ISBN 0375836527

LC 2005037189

Days after arriving in San Francisco from Texas, eleven-year-old orphan Nicholas Dray tries to help his new neighbors survive the 1906 San Francisco earthquake and the subsequent fires.

"The terror of the 1906 disaster is brought powerfully alive in this fast-paced tale. . . . Nick is a thoroughly developed protagonist, as are the supporting characters." School Library Journal.

Includes afterword and bibliography.

Hopkinson, Nalo
The **Chaos**. Nalo Hopkinson. Margaret K. McElderry Books, 2012. 320 p.
Grades: 7 8 9 10 11 12   Fic
1. Multiracial teenage girls 2. Identity (Psychology) 3. Missing persons 4. Supernatural 5. Brothers and sisters 6. Toronto, Ontario 7. Canada 8. Urban fantasy 9. Afrofuturism and Afrofantasy
ISBN 9781416954880

LC 2011018154

Struggling to fit in because of her mixed-race heritage, 16-year-old Scotch is baffled when her skin becomes covered by a sticky black substance that cannot be removed at the same time her brother is swallowed up by a mysterious bubble of light and their town is overcome by a malevolent supernatural force.

Horowitz, Anthony, 1955-
Evil star. Anthony Horowitz. Scholastic Press, 2006. 318 p.: Gatekeepers (Anthony Horowitz)
Grades: 6 7 8 9   Fic
1. Foster teenagers 2. Incas 3. Gates 4. Fourteen-year-old boys 5. Teenage boys 6. Peru 7. Nazca Lines Site (Peru) 8. Fantasy fiction
ISBN 0439679966

LC 2005022135

Having locked the Raven's gate, fourteen-year-old Matt travels to Peru where he meets the second of the five gatekeepers and works with him to try to stop the opening of a second gate somehow related to the Nazca Lines.

"Though this is the second installment in this series, new readers will catch on quickly. . . . The plot turns and emotional relationships will more than satisfy thrill seekers." School Library Journal.

The **Falcon's** Malteser: a Diamond brothers mystery. Anthony Horowitz. Philomel Books, 2004. 191 p.: Diamond brothers mysteries
Grades: 5 6 7 8   Fic
1. Teenage boy detectives 2. Packages 3. False imprisonment 4.

Murder investigation 5. Murder 6. London, England 7. England
8. Mysteries 9. Humorous stories
ISBN 0399241531

LC 2004048322

After his older brother, a fledgling private detective, agrees to safe-guard a package for a dwarf who does not live long, thirteen-year-old
Nick scampers to solve the mystery while also trying to stay one step
ahead of an assortment of thugs.

"The Diamond Brothers stories are invariably funny and full of ex-citement. Mystery readers with a sense of humor will enjoy [this tale]."
Voice of Youth Advocates.

The **Greek** who stole Christmas: a Diamond Brothers mys-tery. Anthony Horowitz. Puffin Books, 2008, c2007. 105 p.:
Diamond brothers mysteries

Grades: 5 6 7 8   **Fic**

1. Teenage boy detectives 2. Death threats 3. Celebrities 4.
Christmas 5. Brothers 6. London, England 7. England 8.
Mysteries 9. Humorous stories
ISBN 9780142403754

LC 2008025944

Fourteen-year-old Nick and his brother, an ineffectual private detec-tive, try to prevent the threatened murder of an international pop star in
London at Christmas time.

"The witty banter between the characters keeps this short novel
moving at breakneck speed." School Library Journal.

Necropolis. Anthony Horowitz. Scholastic Press, 2009. x,
389 p.: Gatekeepers (Anthony Horowitz)

Grades: 6 7 8 9   **Fic**

1. Corporate greed 2. Fate and fatalism 3. Dreams 4. Supernatural
5. Good and evil 6. Hong Kong 7. Fantasy fiction
ISBN 9780439680035

LC 2008044892

To stop the evil corporation Nightrise from unleashing its devastat-ing power around the globe, fifteen-year-old Matt and three other Gate-keepers travel to Hong Kong to find Scarlet, the final Gatekeeper, whose
fate is inextricably joined to their own.

"There are many action-filled sequences and Scarlett is an interest-ing new addition to the cast of characters. . . . Fans of the series will nat-urally want to read it and prepare themselves for the final great battle."
Voice of Youth Advocates.

Never say die. Anthony Horowitz. Philomel Books, [2017]
368 p.: Alex Rider adventures

Grades: 5 6 7 8   **Fic**

1. Teenage spies 2. Terrorists 3. Missing persons 4. Grief 5.
Quests 6. San Francisco, California 7. Egypt 8. Spy fiction 9.
Thrillers and suspense
ISBN 9781524739300

LC 2017010203

Fifteen-year-old MI6 agent Alex Rider travels from Egypt to Wales,
from luxury yachts to abandoned coal mines, with the goal of destroying
the world's deadliest terrorist organization, Scorpia, once and for all.

"Having given his hyperpopular series something of a breather,
Horowitz now sets it back on track with a fresh caper that roars along to
a (naturally) explosive climax and tidy resolution." Booklist.

Nightrise. Anthony Horowitz. Scholastic Press, 2007. 365
p.: Gatekeepers (Anthony Horowitz)

Grades: 6 7 8 9   **Fic**

1. Foster teenagers 2. Twin brothers 3. Telepathy 4. Dreams 5.

Fourteen-year-old boys 6. Reno, Nevada 7. Nevada 8. Fantasy
fiction
ISBN 9780439680011

LC 2006035882

As fourteen-year-old telepathic twins struggle to escape the clutches
of the Nightrise Corporation, one of them travels through dreams to a
time when the evil Old Ones ruled and learns the role that he, his brother,
and three other Gatekeepers must play to keep the world safe from the
Old Ones' return.

★ **Public** enemy number two: a Diamond brothers mystery.
Anthony Horowitz. Philomel Books, 2004. 190 p.: Diamond
brothers mysteries

Grades: 5 6 7 8   **Fic**

1. Teenage boy detectives 2. Frameups 3. Jewelry theft 4.
Criminals 5. Private investigators 6. London, England 7. England
8. Mysteries 9. Humorous stories
ISBN 039924154X

LC 2004010418

When thirteen-year-old Nick is framed for a jewel robbery, he and
his brother, the bumbling detective Tim Diamond, attempt to clear his
name by capturing the master criminal known as the Fence.

"Horowitz has a knack for puns and humor, and he successfully
combines it with a nonstop action mystery that has everything from hy-draulically controlled buses to secret caverns. A readable and exciting
adventure." School Library Journal.

Raven's gate. Anthony Horowitz. Scholastic Press, 2005.
254 p.: Gatekeepers (Anthony Horowitz)

Grades: 6 7 8 9   **Fic**

1. Foster teenagers 2. Juvenile delinquents (Boys) 3. Witches
4. Gates 5. Fourteen-year-old boys 6. Yorkshire, England 7.
England 8. Fantasy fiction
ISBN 0439679958

LC 2004021512

Sent to live in a foster home in a remote Yorkshire village, Matt, a
troubled fourteen-year-old English boy, uncovers an evil plot involving
witchcraft and the site of an ancient stone circle.

"The creepy activities and the overall atmosphere of fear are well
defined, and once the action starts, it doesn't let up. . . . This power-ful struggle between good and evil is a real page-turner." School
Library Journal.

South by southeast: a Diamond brothers mystery. Anthony
Horowitz. Puffin Books, 2005. 148 p.: Diamond brothers mys-teries

Grades: 5 6 7 8   **Fic**

1. Teenage boy detectives 2. Assassins 3. Art -- Collectors and
collecting 4. Fourteen-year-old boys 5. Teenage boys 6. London,
England 7. England 8. Mysteries 9. Humorous stories
ISBN 0142403741

LC 2005043169

"Horowitz has created another well-written, well-paced spy melo-drama." School Library Journal.

★ **Stormbreaker.** Anthony Horowitz. Philomel Books,
2001. 192 p.: Alex Rider adventures

Grades: 5 6 7 8   **Fic**

1. M I 6 2. Teenage spies 3. Teenage boy orphans 4. Computers
5. Terrorism 6. Intelligence service 7. England 8. Spy fiction 9.

Thrillers and suspense
ISBN 0399236201

LC 00063683

After the death of the uncle who had been his guardian, fourteen-year-old Alex Rider is coerced to continue his uncle's dangerous work for Britain's intelligence agency, MI6.

"Horowitz thoughtfully balances Alex's super-spy finesse with typical teen insecurities to create a likable hero living a fantasy come true. An entertaining, nicely layered novel." Booklist.

Three of diamonds: three Diamond Brothers mysteries. Anthony Horowitz. Puffin Books, 2005. 214 p.: Diamond brothers mysteries

Grades: 5 6 7 8   **Fic**
1. Teenage boy detectives 2. Drug smuggling 3. Missing persons investigation 4. Philanthropists 5. Murderers 6. London, England 7. England 8. Humorous stories 9. Mysteries 10. Short stories
ISBN 0142402982

LC 2004065493

A collection of three Diamond Brothers mysteries in which Tim and Nick bungle their way through a search for a missing philanthropist, find themselves in a Parisian prison, and are stranded on a Scottish island with a murderer.

"Nick is a realistic character with a voice that is sarcastic and fresh, while Tim's lack of intelligence makes even the most dangerous situations laughable. Plenty of plays on words add to the humor." School Library Journal.

Horvath, Polly

The **canning** season. Polly Horvath. Farrar Straus Giroux, 2003. 195 p.

Grades: 6 7 8 9   **Fic**
1. Eccentric aunts 2. Thirteen-year-old girls 3. Abandoned girls 4. Abandoned teenagers 5. Parent-separated girls 6. Maine
ISBN 0374399565

LC 2002066296

National Book Award for Young People's Literature, 2003.

Thirteen-year-old Ratchet spends a summer in Maine with her eccentric great-aunts Tilly and Penpen, hearing strange stories from the past and encountering a variety of unusual and colorful characters.

"Offbeat, slapstick humor is mitigated by poignancy in Horvath's distinctive rollicking style. There is occasional use of strong language, and the family stories are woven with death, often gruesomely described. . . . Readers are in for a wise and wacky ride when they open this novel." School Library Journal.

Everything on a waffle. Polly Horvath. Farrar Straus Giroux, 2000. 149 p.

Grades: 4 5 6 7   **Fic**
1. Parent-separated girls 2. Uncles 3. Foster home care 4. Self-reliance in girls 5. Eleven-year-old girls 6. British Columbia 7. Canada
ISBN 0374322368

LC 00035399

Eleven-year-old Primrose living in a small fishing village in British Columbia recounts her experiences and all that she learns about human nature and the unpredictability of life in the months after her parents are lost at sea.

"The story is full of subtle humor and wisdom, presented through the eyes of a uniquely appealing young protagonist." School Library Journal.

★ **My** one hundred adventures. Polly Horvath. Schwartz & Wade Books, 2008. 160 p.

Grades: 4 5 6 7   **Fic**
1. Brothers and sisters 2. Single-parent families 3. Summer 4. Beaches 5. Adventure 6. Massachusetts 7. Coming-of-age stories
ISBN 9780375845826

Twelve-year-old Jane, who lives at the beach in a run-down old house with her mother, two brothers, and sister, has an eventful summer accompanying her pastor on bible deliveries, meeting former boyfriends of her mother's, and being coerced into babysitting for a family of ill-mannered children.

"With writing as foamy as waves, as gritty as sand, or as deep as the sea, this book may startle readers with the freedom given the heroine. . . . Unconventionality is Horvath's stock and trade, but here the high quirkiness quotient rests easily against Jane's inner story with its honest, childlike core." Booklist.

Northward to the moon. Polly Horvath. Schwartz & Wade Books, 2010. 256 p.

Grades: 4 5 6 7   **Fic**
1. Stepfathers 2. Automobile travel 3. Blended families 4. Family relationships 5. Preteen girls 6. Realistic fiction
ISBN 9780375861109

When Jane's stepfather, Ned, get fired from his job, the family goes on an adventure that takes them across the continent.

"Many characters here are distinct, wonderfully idiosyncratic individuals, and Horvath's fine-tuned observations are conveyed with subtlety and precision." Booklist.

One year in Coal Harbor. Polly Horvath. Schwartz & Wade Books, 2012. 192 p.

Grades: 5 6 7   **Fic**
1. Foster children 2. Matchmaking 3. Fishing villages 4. Cookbook writing 5. Interpersonal relations 6. British Columbia 7. Canada
ISBN 9780375969706

LC 2011023591

In the sequel to Everything on a waffle, Primrose Squarp, who once thought her parents were lost at sea, has another year filled with turmoil. From meddling in her Uncle's romantic life, to trying to help her new friend, Ked, a foster child, to trying to stop the logging on Mendolay Mountain that threatens the world Primrose loves in Coal Harbour.

The **vacation**. Polly Horvath. Farrar, Straus and Giroux, 2005. 208 p.

Grades: 5 6 7 8   **Fic**
1. Aunts 2. Cross-country automobile trips 3. Vacations 4. Twelve-year-old boys 5. Aunt and nephew
ISBN 0374380708

LC 2004057667

When his parents go to Africa to work as missionaries, twelve-year-old Henry's eccentric aunts, Pigg and Mag, take him on a cross-country car trip, allowing him to gain insight into his family and himself.

"Horvath spins another delightfully offbeat yarn, complete with her signature cast of eccentric characters, wacky situations, poignant moments, and snappy dialogue." School Library Journal.

Howard, Abby

The **crossroads** at midnight. Abby Howard. Iron Circus Comics, 2020. 320 p.

Grades: 7 8 9 10 11 12   **Fic**
1. Supernatural 2. Monsters 3. Loneliness 4. Horror comics 5.

Comics and Graphic novels 6. Anthologies
ISBN 9781945820687

LC bl2020034044

In this collection of evocative, unnerving slice-of-life horror, five stories explore what happens when one is desperate enough to seek solace in the unnatural, and what might be waiting for us at the Crossroads at Midnight.

"This anthology is immersive but horror lite, making it an excellent introduction to the genre." School Library Journal

Howard, J. J. (Jennifer Jane), 1972-

That time I joined the circus. J.J. Howard. Point, 2013. 272 p.

Grades: 7 8 9 10   **Fic**
1. Mother-deserted children 2. Fathers -- Death 3. Circus 4. Best friends 5. Friendship 6. Florida 7. New York City 8. Coming-of-age stories
ISBN 9780545433815

LC 2012016715

After her father's sudden death and a break-up with her best friends, seventeen-year-old Lexi has no choice but to leave New York City seeking her long-absent mother, rumored to be in Florida with a traveling circus, where she just may discover her destiny.

Howe, James, 1946-

★ **Addie** on the inside. James Howe. Atheneum Books for Young Readers, 2011. 224 p.: Misfits (James Howe)

Grades: 5 6 7 8   **Fic**
1. Identity (Psychology) 2. Former friends 3. Self-acceptance in teenage girls 4. Self-acceptance 5. Misfits (Persons) 6. New York (State) 7. Realistic fiction 8. Novels in verse
ISBN 9781416913849

LC 2010024497

Outspoken thirteen-year-old Addie Carle learns about love, loss, and staying true to herself as she navigates seventh grade, enjoys a visit from her grandmother, fights with her boyfriend, and endures gossip and meanness from her former best friend.

"Howe's artfully crafted lines show Addie's intelligence and wit, and his imagery evokes the aura of sadness surrounding this purgatory of/ the middle school years/ when so many things/ that never mattered before/ and will never matter again/ matter. Readers will empathize with Addie's anguish and admire her courage to keep fighting." Publishers Weekly.

Also known as Elvis. James Howe. Atheneum Books for Young Readers, 2014. 288 p.: Misfits (James Howe)

Grades: 5 6 7 8 9   **Fic**
1. Bullying and bullies 2. Single-parent families 3. Crushes in teenage boys 4. Crushes (Interpersonal relations) 5. Summer 6. New York (State) 7. Realistic fiction
ISBN 9781442445109

Finds Skeezie Tookis navigating a pivotal summer of tough choices involving a job helping his mom, clashes with a bully and a possible crush on a mercurial girl.

"As an adult, Skeezie reflects on the summer when his absent father returned home seeking reconciliation. As Skeezie tries to hold his fragile family life together, he explores his own emotions toward his parents and sisters, and is surprised by the bonds he feels. A satisfying conclusion to the Misfit books, with glimpses into adulthood for each member of the Gang of Five." Horn Book.

The **misfits**. James Howe. Atheneum Books for Young Readers, 2001. 274 p.: Misfits (James Howe)

Grades: 5 6 7 8   **Fic**
1. Child misfits 2. Overweight boys 3. Student elections 4. Misfits (Persons) 5. Friendship 6. New York (State) 7. Realistic fiction
ISBN 0689839553

LC 00066390

Four students who do not fit in at their small-town middle school decide to create a third party for the student council elections to represent all students who have ever been called names.

"This is a timely, sensitive, laugh-out-loud must-read for all middle school students and teachers." Voice of Youth Advocates.

Totally Joe. by James Howe. Atheneum Books for Young Readers, 2005. 208 p.: Misfits (James Howe)

Grades: 5 6 7 8 9   **Fic**
1. Gay boys 2. Misfits (Persons) 3. Crushes in boys 4. Homosexuality 5. Friendship 6. New York (State) 7. Realistic fiction 8. LGBTQIA fiction 9. Coming-of-age stories
ISBN 068983957X

LC 2004022242

As a school assignment, a thirteen-year-old boy writes an alphabiography—life from A to Z—and explores issues of friendship, family, school, and the challenges of being a gay teenager.

"Joe, one of the characters in The Misfits (2001), has his say, in a voice uniquely his own. Twelve-year-old Joe knows he is gay. He played with Barbies as a young child, prefers cooking to sports, and has a crush on a male classmate...Joe himself often comes off as a cross between Niles Crane and Harvey Fierstein. But he also reacts like a kid, and readers in his situation will wish for the love and support he receives from friends and family, as well as the happy life he so clearly envisions." Booklist.

Howe, Katherine
Conversion. Katherine Howe. G. P. Putnam's Sons, [2014] 448 p.

Grades: 7 8 9 10 11 12   **Fic**
1. Epidemics 2. Private schools 3. Trials (Witchcraft) 4. Schools 5. Friendship 6. Massachusetts 7. Mysteries
ISBN 9780399167775

LC 2014000397

When girls start experiencing strange tics and other mysterious symptoms at Colleen's high school, her small town of Danvers, Massachusetts, falls victim to rumors that lead to full-blown panic, and only Colleen connects their fate to the ill-fated Salem Village, where another group of girls suffered from a similarly bizarre epidemic three centuries ago.

"St. Joan's Academy in Danvers, Massachusetts, a well-to-do private girls school for the best and brightest, is usually only home to hysteria of the college-admissions kind. But when Clara starts convulsing in class, a media frenzy fixates on the St. Joan's mystery disease... A simmering blend of relatable high-school drama with a persistent pinprick of unearthliness in the background." Booklist.

Howe, Peter, 1942-
Waggit's tale. by Peter Howe; drawings by Omar Rayyan. HarperCollinsPublishers, c2008. 276 p.: Waggit

Grades: 5 6 7   **Fic**
1. Dogs 2. Abandoned dogs 3. Pet adoption 4. Survival 5. Animal rescue 6. New York City 7. Central Park, New York City 8. Stories told by animals
ISBN 9780061242618

When Waggit is abandoned by his owner as a puppy, he meets a pack of wild dogs who become his friends and teach him to survive in the city park, but when he has a chance to go home with a kind woman who wants to adopt him, he takes it.

"The novel celebrates the wild freedom of the feral dog pack, while also emphasizing the many hazards of urban life for homeless companion animals." Voice of Youth Advocates.

Howland, Leila

The **forget-me-not** summer. Leila Howland; illustrations by Ji-Hyuk Kim. Harper, an imprint of HarperCollinsPublishers, 2015. 208 p.: Silver sisters

Grades: 4 5 6 7   **Fic**

1. Child actors and actresses 2. Talent shows 3. Summer 4. Coastal towns 5. Aunts 6. Cape Cod, Massachusetts 7. Realistic fiction

ISBN 9780062318695

When their plans for summer vacation are thwarted by a visit to Cape Cod, three sisters adjust to sharing a room and living without a television before being won over by their sunny aunt and local community activities.

"An old-fashioned story well-told, with engaging characters—a beach read for preteens that is as comfortable as the old tennis shoes worn on the Massachusetts shore." Kirkus.

Hughes, Dean, 1943-

Four-Four-Two. Dean Hughes. Atheneum Books for Young Readers, [2016] 256 p.

Grades: 7 8 9 10   **Fic**

1. United States. Army. Regimental Combat Team, 442nd. 2. World War II 3. Japanese Americans -- Forced removal and incarceration, 1942-1945 4. Prejudice 5. Soldiers 6. Loyalty 7. United States 8. War stories 9. Historical fiction

ISBN 9781481462525

LC 2015043700

Forced into an internment camp at the start of World War II, eighteen-year-old Yuki enlists in the Army to fight for the Allies as a member of the "Four-Four-Two," a segregated Japanese American regiment.

"Nuanced and riveting in equal parts." Kirkus.

Includes bibliographical references.

Missing in action. Dean Hughes. Atheneum Books for Young Readers, 2010. 228 p.

Grades: 6 7 8 9   **Fic**

1. Children of military personnel 2. Multiracial boys 3. Prejudice 4. Japanese American boys 5. Interracial friendship 6. Utah 7. Historical fiction

ISBN 9781416915027

LC 2009011276

While his father is missing in action in the Pacific during World War II, twelve-year-old Jay moves with his mother to small-town Utah, where he sees prejudice from both sides, as a part-Navajo himself and through an unlikely friendship with Japanese American Ken from the nearby internment camp.

"Jay's pain and eventual resolution will touch readers in this sure-to-be-popular work of historical fiction." Booklist.

Search and destroy. Dean Hughes. Atheneum Books for Young Readers, c2005. 216 p.

Grades: 7 8 9 10   **Fic**

1. Green Berets 2. Young men 3. High school graduates 4. Soldiers 5. Vietnam War, 1961-1975 6. Family problems 7. Vietnam 8. Long Beach, California 9. War stories 10. Historical

fiction 11. Coming-of-age stories

ISBN 068987023X

LC 2005011255

Recent high school graduate Rick Ward, undecided about his future and eager to escape his unhappy home life, joins the army and experiences the horrors of the war in Vietnam.

"This is a compelling, insightful story about the emotional, physical, and psychological scars that wars leave upon soldiers." Booklist.

Soldier boys. Dean Hughes. Atheneum Books for Young Readers, c2001. 162 p.

Grades: 7 8 9 10   **Fic**

1. World War II 2. Ardennes, Battle of the, 1944-1945 3. Personal conduct 4. Soldiers 5. War stories

ISBN 0689817487

LC 00046920

Two boys, one German and one American, are eager to join their respective armies during World War II, and their paths cross at the Battle of the Bulge.

"This World War II novel tells the parallel stories of two young soldiers fighting on opposite sides of the conflict: a paratrooper from Utah and a Hitler Youth who joins the German army. Spence and Dieter's paths cross briefly on a snow-covered Belgian hill in a scene both compassionate and tragic. Hughes tells their tales in assured prose that's harrowing without being exploitive." Horn Book Guide.

Hughes, Mark Peter

A **crack** in the sky. by Mark Peter Hughes. Delacorte Press, 2010. 405 p.: Greenhouse chronicles

Grades: 5 6 7 8   **Fic**

1. Post-apocalypse 2. End of the world 3. Utopias 4. Survival 5. Thirteen-year-old boys 6. Dystopian fiction 7. Science fiction

ISBN 9780385737081

LC 2009043532

In a post-apocalyptic world, thirteen-year-old Eli, part of the most powerful family in the world, keeps noticing problems with the operations of his domed city but his family denies them, while in the surrounding desert, the Outsiders struggle to survive while awaiting a prophesied savior.

"Hughes keeps his protagonist an individual, and in fact an amiable, scrappy one with whom readers will identify." Bulletin of the Center for Children's Books.

Hughes, Naomi

Refraction. Naomi Hughes. Page Street Kids, 2019. 352 p.

Grades: 8 9 10 11 12   **Fic**

1. Monsters 2. Teenage boys 3. Mirrors 4. Doorways 5. Aliens (Non-humanoid) 6. Dystopian fiction 7. Science fiction

ISBN 9781624148903

After an attack on earth, all reflective surfaces become weapons to release monsters, causing a planet-wide ban on mirrors. Despite the danger, the demand rises, and 17-year-old Marty Callahan becomes a distributor in an illegal mirror trade—until he's caught by the mayor's son, whose slate is far from clean. Both of them are exiled for their crimes to one of the many abandoned cities overrun by fog. But they soon realize their thoughts influence their surroundings and their deepest fears begin to manifest.

"This second novel from Hughes is a fast-paced, mind-bending sf mystery with poignant #OwnVoices OCD representation." Booklist.

Hughes, Pat (Patrice Raccio)

Five 4ths of July. by Pat Raccio Hughes. Viking Childrens Books, 2011. 278 p.

Grades: 7 8 9 10   **Fic**

   1. Revolutionary America (1775-1783) 2. 18th century 3. Teenage prisoners 4. Freedom 5. Imprisonment 6. Soldiers 7. Fourteen-year-old boys 8. Connecticut 9. United States 10. Historical fiction

ISBN 9780670012077

                      LC 2010049521

On July 4th, 1777, fourteen-year-old Jake Mallory and his friends are celebrating their new nation's independence, but over the next four years Jake finds himself in increasingly adventurous circumstances as he battles British forces, barely survives captivity on a prison ship, and finally returns home to Connecticut, war-torn and weary, but hopeful for America's future.

"This is a straightforward and well-conceived novel. . . . A fine addition to collections on the war and an eye-opening look at the horrors of British prison ships." Kirkus.

Hughes, Shirley, 1927-

  ★ **Hero** on a bicycle. Shirley Hughes. Candlewick Press, 2013. 213 p.

Grades: 5 6 7   **Fic**

   1. 1940s 2. World War II 3. Resistance to military occupation 4. Children of military personnel 5. Escaped prisoners of war 6. Families 7. Italy 8. Florence, Italy 9. Historical fiction

ISBN 9780763660376

                      LC 2012943650

When their mother reluctantly joins the Italian Resistance against Nazi occupying forces in World War II Florence, young Paolo and his sister, Costanza, devise a clever way to use their bicycle to assist the movement.

Hulme, John, 1970-

The **glitch** in sleep. by John Hulme and Michael Wexler. Bloomsbury Children's Books: 2007. 288 p.: The Seems

Grades: 4 5 6 7   **Fic**

   1. Twelve-year-old boys 2. Secret societies 3. Sleep 4. Technology 5. Parallel universes 6. New Jersey 7. Fantasy fiction 8. Gateway fantasy

ISBN 9781599901299

                      LC 2007002598

Months after he filled out a very unusual job application on a whim, nine-year-old Becker Drane was taken to The Seems, the secret place where everything about the world as we know it—including Nature, Weather, Time, and Sleep—is manufactured. Now Becker is 12 and has become a full-fledged Fixer, and he's got a whopper of a problem for his first assignment: a glitch in Sleep has created an insomnia epidemic that, left unchecked, could mean the end of reality altogether.

"The story is upbeat and full of humor. . . . Dynamic full-page illustrations appear throughout." School Library Journal.

Hunt, Lynda Mullaly

One for the Murphys. Lynda Mullaly Hunt. Nancy Paulsen Books, 2012. 224 p.

Grades: 5 6 7 8   **Fic**

   1. Foster children 2. Family violence 3. Trust 4. Foster home care 5. Families 6. Connecticut 7. Realistic fiction

ISBN 9780399256158

                      LC 2011046708

Follows the experiences of foster kid Carley, who uses humor and street smarts to cope with her unpredictable life until the loving, bustling Murphy family offers her more stability and a greater sense of belonging than she ever thought possible.

Hunter, Erin

  ★ **Broken** pride. written by Erin Hunter; illustrated by Owen Richardson. Harper, an imprint of HarperCollins Publishers, 2017 319 p.: Bravelands.

Grades: 5 6 7 8   **Fic**

   1. Betrayal 2. Lion 3. Predatory animals 4. Elephants 5. Baboons 6. Africa 7. Animal fantasy

ISBN 9780062642028

When the lone rule of the African plains is violated, the task of keeping the fragile peace between predators and prey is left to a cast-out lion, an intuitive elephant, and an honor-seeking baboon.

"Deep characters, a complex plot, rich mythology, and a stunning setting all come together to prove once again that the Hunter collective are master storytellers." Kirkus.

Code of the clans. Erin Hunter; illustrated by Wayne McLoughlin. HarperCollins, 2009. 176 p.: Warriors (Erin Hunter).

Grades: 6 7 8 9   **Fic**

   1. Cats 2. Warriors 3. Feral cats 4. Rules 5. Codes (Communication) 6. Animal fantasy 7. Fantasy fiction

ISBN 9780061660092

Explores the fifteen rules that govern the daily life of a warrior cat.

A **dangerous** path. Erin Hunter. Harper Collins, c2004. 336 p.: Warriors (Erin Hunter).

Grades: 6 7 8 9   **Fic**

   1. Cats 2. Feral cats 3. Warriors 4. Animals 5. Wild cats 6. Animal fantasy 7. Fantasy fiction

ISBN 0060000066

                      LC 2003013962

Tigerclaw is back and more dangerous than ever as the new leader of ShadowClan, but he is not the most terrifying enemy Fireheart must face as a new force sweeps through the woods.

"With compelling intrigue and fast-paced actions, this is one of the most exciting books in the series." Booklist.

The **darkest** hour. Erin Hunter. Harper Collins, c2004. 315 p.: Warriors (Erin Hunter).

Grades: 6 7 8 9   **Fic**

   1. Cats 2. Feral cats 3. Warriors 4. Animals 5. Heroes and heroines 6. Animal fantasy 7. Fantasy fiction

ISBN 0060000074

                      LC 2003022493

ThunderClan's darkest hour is upon them and Fireheart, the warrior cat, must protect his clan from a threat unlike any the forest has ever seen, as the time comes for prophecies to unfold and heroes to rise.

Dawn. Erin Hunter. Harper Collins, 2005. 352 p.: Warriors (Erin Hunter).

Grades: 6 7 8 9   **Fic**

   1. Cats 2. Feral cats 3. Warriors 4. Animals 5. Heroes and heroines 6. Animal fantasy 7. Fantasy fiction

ISBN 0060744553

                      LC 2005009175

The questing cats return to a forest devastated by the Twolegs, where they must find a way to convince their Clans to leave in search of a new home, even though they have no idea where they are going.

"Fans will relish this eminently satisfying episode." Booklist.

Fire and ice. Erin Hunter. Harper Collins, c2003. 317 p.: Warriors (Erin Hunter).
Grades: 6 7 8 9   **Fic**
1. Cats 2. Feral cats 3. Warriors 4. Animals 5. Wild cats 6. Animal fantasy 7. Fantasy fiction
ISBN 0060000031
          LC 2002014415
Fireheart, a full-fledged warrior cat, must confront questions of loyalty and identity as he faces the possibility of betrayal from within his own forest clan.

"Characters remain true to their feline natures, adding to the plausibility of events in this tension-filled story." Booklist.

Forest of secrets. Erin Hunter. Harper Collins, c2003. 312 p.: Warriors (Erin Hunter).
Grades: 6 7 8 9   **Fic**
1. Cats -- Behavior 2. Feral cats 3. Warriors 4. Animals 5. Wild cats 6. Animal fantasy 7. Fantasy fiction
ISBN 006000004X
          LC 2003000445
The warrior cat Fireheart's determination to uncover the truth about another warrior's death leads him deep into danger, and reveals secrets that test the strength of clan loyalties.

"This exciting book is not for the faint of heart as it is often violent. . . . Fans of the series will lap it up." School Library Journal.

Into the wild. Erin Hunter. Harper Collins, c2003. 272 p.: Warriors (Erin Hunter).
Grades: 6 7 8 9   **Fic**
1. Cats 2. Feral cats 3. Warriors 4. Wild cats 5. Courage 6. Animal fantasy 7. Fantasy fiction
ISBN 0060000023
          LC 2002091791
For generations, four clans of wild cats have shared the forest. When their warrior code is threatened by mysterious deaths, a house cat named Rusty may turn out to be the bravest warrior of all.

"The author has created an intriguing world with an intricate structure and mythology, and an engaging young hero." School Library Journal.

Rising storm. Erin Hunter. Harper Collins, c2004. 315 p.: Warriors (Erin Hunter).
Grades: 6 7 8 9   **Fic**
1. Cats 2. Feral cats 3. Warriors 4. Animals 5. Wild cats 6. Animal fantasy 7. Fantasy fiction
ISBN 0060000058
          LC 2003006982
Fireheart, the warrior cat, faces many challenges in his new role of ThunderClan deputy as his apprentice, Cloudpaw, resists following the warrior code, Bluestar weakens, and Tigerclaw continues to haunt the forest seeking revenge.

"Hunter once again tells a good, suspenseful adventure story that urges readers onward." Booklist.

The **sight**. Erin Hunter. Harper Collins, c2007. 384 p.: Warriors (Erin Hunter).
Grades: 6 7 8 9   **Fic**
1. Cats 2. Warriors 3. Feral cats 4. Clans 5. Brothers and sisters

6. Animal fantasy 7. Fantasy fiction
ISBN 0060892013
"Plenty of action and solid characterizations make this an enticing choice for fans of the long-running enterprise." Booklist.

Hurley, Tonya
    Ghostgirl. by Tonya Hurley. Little Brown, 2008. 328 p.: Ghostgirl
Grades: 7 8 9 10   **Fic**
1. Teenage girl ghosts 2. Life after death 3. Crushes in teenage girls 4. Popularity 5. Death 6. Paranormal fiction
ISBN 9780316113571
          LC 2007031541
After dying, high school senior Charlotte Usher is as invisible to nearly everyone as she always felt, but despite what she learns in a sort of alternative high school for dead teens, she clings to life while seeking a way to go to the Fall Ball with the boy of her dreams.

"Hurley combines afterlife antics, gothic gore, and high school hell to produce an original, hilarious satire. . . . Tim Burton and Edgar Allan Poe devotees will die for this fantastic, phantasmal read." School Library Journal.

Hurston, Zora Neale
    The **skull** talks back and other haunting tales. collected by Zora Neale Hurston; adapted by Joyce Carol Thomas; illustrated by Leonard Jenkins. Harper Collins, c2004. 56 p.
Grades: 4 5 6 7   **Fic**
1. Supernatural 2. Paranormal phenomena 3. Short stories 4. Horror 5. African American fiction
ISBN 0060006315
          LC 2003022215
Inspired by stories from the rural south, a collection of terrifying tales includes a skinless witch, a talking skull, and a man more evil than the devil, as collected by the famous African-American writer Zora Neale Hurston.

"Using a direct style that loses none of the colloquial immediacy of the original voices, Thomas has done a great job of retelling six of Hurston's supernatural tales, and Jenkins' monochromatic collages and silhouettes capture the delicious, shivery glow of skeletons and graveyards." Booklist.

Hurwitz, Michele Weber
    The **summer** I saved the world-- in 65 days. Michele Weber Hurwitz. Wendy Lamb Books, an imprint of Random House Children's Books, a division of Random House, Inc., 2014 208 p.
Grades: 5 6 7 8   **Fic**
1. Helpfulness 2. Kindness 3. Neighbors 4. Summer 5. Personal conduct 6. Illinois 7. Realistic fiction
ISBN 9780385371063
"Insightful writing, realistic dialogue infused with humor, and a sweet romantic element add depth to the story." Booklist.

Hyman, Fracaswell
    Mango Delight. by Fracaswell Hyman. Sterling Children's Books, 2017. 219 p.: Mango Delight
Grades: 4 5 6 7 8   **Fic**
1. African American girls 2. Former friends 3. Friendship 4. Middle school students 5. Twelve-year-old girls 6. Realistic fiction 7. African American fiction
ISBN 9781454923329

A first novel by an award-winning Disney and Nickelodeon writer and producer follows the experiences of a seventh-grader whose clumsy accident costs her social status, her spot on the track team and her father's job before becoming an unexpected YouTube sensation and confronting difficult choices about friendship.

"A short and sweet story that will encourage deeper conversations around shame, honesty, and courage." Kirkus.

Ibbotson, Eva

The **dragonfly** pool. Eva Ibbotson; illustrated by Kevin Hawkes. Dutton Children's Books, 2008. 377 p.

Grades: 5 6 7 8   **Fic**

1. Friendship 2. Courage in teenagers 3. Children and war 4. Teenagers and war 5. Teenage girls 6. Historical fiction

ISBN 9780525420644

"Ibbotson's trademark eccentric characters and strongly contrasted principles of right and wrong brighten and broaden this uplifting tale." Booklist.

★ The **Ogre** of Oglefort. by Eva Ibbotson; [illustrations by Lisa K. Weber]. Dutton Children's Books, 2011. 224 p.

Grades: 4 5 6   **Fic**

1. Boy orphans 2. Ghouls and ogres 3. Princesses 4. Trolls 5. Wizards 6. Fantasy fiction 7. Humorous stories

ISBN 9780525423829

LC 2010038137

When the Hag of Dribble, an orphan boy, and a troll called Ulf are sent to rescue a princess from an ogre, it turns out to be far from the routine magical mission they expect.

"Magical creatures abound in this effervescent fairy tale that effectively merges classic tropes with modern sensibilities." Bulletin of the Center for Children's Books.

★ The **star** of Kazan. Eva Ibbotson; illustrated by Kevin Hawkes. Dutton Children's Books, 2004. 405 p.

Grades: 5 6 7 8   **Fic**

1. 19th century 2. Abandoned children 3. Mothers and daughters 4. Jewelry 5. Twelve-year-old girls 6. Identity (Psychology) 7. Vienna, Austria 8. Austria 9. Historical mysteries

ISBN 0525473475

LC 2004045455

After twelve-year-old Annika, a foundling living in late nineteenth-century Vienna, inherits a trunk of costume jewelry, a woman claiming to be her aristocratic mother arrives and takes her to live in a strangely decrepit mansion in Germany.

"This is a rich saga . . . full of stalwart friends, sly villains, a brave heroine, and good triumphing over evil. . . . An intensely satisfying read." School Library Journal.

Ifueko, Jordan

Raybearer. Jordan Ifueko. Amulet Books, 2020. 368 p.

Grades: 8 9 10 11 12   **Fic**

1. Mothers and daughters 2. Courts and courtiers 3. Competition 4. Fate and fatalism 5. Social isolation 6. Afrofuturism and Afrofantasy 7. High fantasy 8. Fantasy fiction

ISBN 9781419739828

LC 2019053872

Raised in isolation, Tarisai yearns for the closeness she could have as one of the Crown Prince's Council of 11, but her mother, The Lady, has magically compelled Tarisai to kill the Crown Prince.

"The nuanced experiences of the fantasy communities will resonate with global, contemporary marginalized peoples and their struggles against discrimination. A fresh, phenomenal fantasy that begs readers to revel in its brilliant world." Kirkus

Ireland, Justina

★ **Ophie's** ghosts. Justina Ireland Balzer + Bray, 2021 336 p.

Grades: 5 6 7 8   **Fic**

1. 1920s 2. Fathers -- Death 3. Ghosts 4. Household employees 5. Manors 6. Children and ghosts 7. Pittsburgh, Pennsylvania 8. Pennsylvania 9. Historical fiction 10. Supernatural mysteries

ISBN 9780062915894

Discovering her ability to see ghosts when a cruel act ends her father's life and forces her to move in with relatives in 1920s Pittsburgh, young Ophelia forges a helpful bond with a spirit whose own life ended suddenly and unjustly.

"Ireland's first middle-grade novel deftly examines the haunting aftermath of racial trauma and how people can learn to thrive despite it. Equal parts supernatural suspense and historical fiction, this is a compelling spin on the classic whodunit narrative." Booklist

Irving, Washington, 1783-1859

The **legend** of Sleepy Hollow. Washington Irving; illustrated by Gris Grimly. Atheneum Books for Young Readers, c2007. 40 p.

Grades: 4 5 6   **Fic**

1. 19th century 2. Ghosts 3. Teachers 4. Eccentrics and eccentricities 5. Love triangles 6. Mate selection 7. New York (State) 8. United States 9. Ghost stories 10. Classics

ISBN 1416906258

LC 2005027502

A superstitious schoolmaster, in love with a wealthy farmer's daughter, has a terrifying encounter with a headless horseman.

"The tale, . . . slightly condensed but with language and ambiguities intact, is reimagined here with humor, vigor, [and] clarity. . . . Irving's language is challenging . . . but Grimly's numerous Halloween-hued panel and spot illustrations . . . parse it into comprehensible tidbits. The comically amplified emotions and warm yellow and orange tones balance the horror aspects of the text." Horn Book.

Iserles, Inbali

The **taken**. Inbali Iserles. Scholastic Press, 2015 252 p.: Foxcraft

Grades: 4 5 6 7   **Fic**

1. Foxes 2. Separated friends, relatives, etc 3. Brothers and sisters 4. Cities and towns 5. Animal fantasy

ISBN 9780545690812

Using her cunning to navigate the dangers of the wild, young fox Isla and her brother discover that their den has been taken over by hostile foxes, forcing the pair to escape into a human world that compels Isla to master magical arts in order to survive.

"Vivid details, intriguing characters, and a riveting plot are smoothly executed in this exciting new series from one of the authors who write under the pseudonym of Erin Hunter. Beautifully rendered and magical." Kirkus.

Iturbe, Antonio, 1967-

The **librarian** of Auschwitz. Antonio Iturbe; translated by Lilit Thwaites. Henry Holt and Company, 2017, c2012. 432 p.

Grades: 7 8 9 10 11 12   **Fic**

1. Kraus, Dita, 1929- 2. Auschwitz (Concentration camp). 3. Second World War era (1939-1945) 4. Teenage girls 5. Concentration camps 6. Books and reading 7. Jews, Czech 8. Jews 9. Prague, Czech Republic 10. Poland 11. Historical fiction

12. Translations
ISBN 9781627796187
Sydney Taylor Book Award for Teen Readers, 2018.

Follows the true story of Dita Kraus, a fourteen-year-old girl from Prague who after being sent to Auschwitz is chosen to protect the eight volumes prisoners have smuggled past the guards.

"Despite being a fictional retelling of a true story, this novel is one that could easily be recommended or taught alongside Elie Wiesel's Night and The Diary of Anne Frank and a text that, once read, will never be forgotten." School Library Journal.

Jackson, Tiffany D.

Let me hear a rhyme. Tiffany D. Jackson; with lyrics by Malik "Malik-16" Sharif. Katherine Tegen Books, 2019 380 p.

Grades: 8 9 10 11 12   **Fic**

1. 1990s 2. Rap musicians 3. Murder victims 4. Hip-hop culture 5. African American teenagers 6. Music industry and trade 7. Brooklyn, New York City 8. Historical fiction 9. Urban fiction 10. Mysteries
ISBN 9780062840325

LC 2018968472

After their friend Steph is murdered, Quadir, Jarrell, and Steph's sister Jasmine promote his music under a new rap name, the Architect, but when his demo catches a music label rep's attention, the trio must prove his talent from beyond the grave.

"From obscure rap and hip-hop references to invocations of scalding hot combs, Jackson scores a bull's-eye with her passionate homage to Black city life in the late '90s, yet it's her earnest takes on creativity, love, and loss that are timeless." Publishers Weekly.

Monday's not coming. Tiffany D. Jackson. Katherine Tegen Books, 2018. 320 p.

Grades: 8 9 10 11 12   **Fic**

1. Missing persons 2. Child abuse 3. Loss (Psychology) 4. Bullying and bullies 5. Dyslexia 6. African American fiction 7. Mysteries 8. Realistic fiction
ISBN 9780062422675

Monday Charles is missing, and only Claudia seems to notice. Claudia and Monday have always been inseparable—more sisters than friends. So when Monday doesn't turn up for the first day of school, Claudia's worried.

"This is a powerful and emotional novel that is gripping and heart-breaking and hits upon serious topics." Booklist.

Jacobson, Jennifer, 1958-

Paper things. Jennifer Richard Jacobson. Candlewick Press, 2015 376 p.

Grades: 5 6 7 8   **Fic**

1. Homelessness 2. Gifted girls 3. Orphans 4. Brothers and sisters 5. Schools 6. Maine 7. Realistic fiction
ISBN 9780763663230

Leaving with her brother when he decides he can no longer stay with their guardian, Ari endures a life of homelessness that challenges her schoolwork, friendships, and the promise made to her mother that she and her brother would stay together.

"Before her death four years earlier, Ari and Gage's mother had urged them to stay together always. Now it has been two months since nineteen-year-old Gage and eleven-year-old Ari left their overbearing guardian's home to strike out on their own, and the challenges of finding a permanent job and stable living situation have frayed Gage's confidence... In this poignant view of one child's experience with home-lessness, Jacobson deftly shows how easily it can happen, an insidious downward spiral with heart-wrenching consequences." Horn Book.

Small as an elephant. Jennifer Richard Jacobson. Candlewick Press, 2011. 288 p.

Grades: 5 6 7 8   **Fic**

1. Children of people with mental illnesses 2. Abandoned boys 3. Elephants 4. Mothers and sons 5. Self-reliance in boys 6. New England 7. Realistic fiction
ISBN 9780763641559

LC 2010039175

Abandoned by his mother in an Acadia National Park campground, Jack tries to make his way back to Boston before anyone figures out what is going on, with only a small toy elephant for company.

"Jacobson masterfully puts readers into Jack's mind—he loves and understands his mother, but sometimes his judgments are not always good, and readers understand. . . . Jack's journey to a new kind of family is inspiring and never sappy." Kirkus.

Jacques, Brian

The **angel's** command: a tale from the castaways of the Flying Dutchman. Brian Jaques; illustrated by David Elliot. Philomel Books, 2003. 448 p.: Castaways of the Flying Dutchman

Grades: 6 7 8 9   **Fic**

1. Boy heroes 2. Dogs 3. Angels 4. Boys and dogs 5. Pirates 6. Sea stories 7. Fantasy fiction
ISBN 0399239995

LC 2002075279

Ben and Ned, a boy and dog gifted with eternal youth and the ability to communicate with one another nonverbally, encounter pirates on the high seas and rescue a kidnapped prince from a band of gypsy thieves.

"Jacques spins a rousing yarn that fairly bursts at the seams with exciting escapades, exotic locations, poems, shanties, treachery and derring-do." Publishers Weekly.

Castaways of the Flying Dutchman. Brian Jacques; illustrated by Ian Schoenherr. Philomel Books, 2001. 327 p.: Castaways of the Flying Dutchman

Grades: 6 7 8 9   **Fic**

1. Boy heroes 2. Boys and dogs 3. Angels 4. Flying Dutchman 5. Sea stories 6. Fantasy fiction
ISBN 0399236015

LC 00059822

In 1620, a boy and his dog are rescued from the doomed ship, Flying Dutchman, by an angel who guides them in travelling the world, eternally helping those in great need.

"The swashbuckling language brims with color and melodrama; the villains are dastardly and stupid; and buried treasure, mysterious clues, and luscious culinary descriptions . . . keep the pages turning." Booklist.

Mariel of Redwall. Brian Jacques; illustrated by Gary Chalk. Philomel Books, 1992, copyright 1991. 387p.: Redwall

Grades: 5 6 7 8 9   **Fic**

1. Animals 2. Heroes and heroines 3. Good and evil 4. Rats 5. Mice 6. Animal fantasy 7. Fantasy fiction
ISBN 0399221441

LC 91017157

The mousemaid Mariel achieves victory at sea for the animals of Redwall Abbey, fighting the savage pirate rat Gabool the Wild, warlord of rodent corsairs.

"A young mousemaid, Mariel, and her father, Joseph, are captured by the dreaded searat pirates of Terramount Island while trying to deliver a bell Joseph has made for the king of the badgers. Mariel escapes and makes her way to Redwall Abbey, where others, including the spirit of Martin the Warrior, join her to get revenge on the searats." ALAN.

"Jacques' characters are fully developed and true to their natures; his dialectal dialog resounds with wit; the plot is filled with action, drama, and larger-than-life violence; and good conquers all. A satisfying tale with wide appeal that extends beyond its intended audience." Booklist.

Martin the Warrior. Brian Jacques; illustrated by Gary Chalk. Philomel Books, 1994, copyright 1993. 376 p.: Redwall

Grades: 5 6 7 8 9   Fic
    1. Animals 2. Heroes and heroines 3. Good and evil 4. Redwall Abbey (Imaginary place) 5. Rats 6. Animal fantasy 7. Fantasy fiction
    ISBN 0399226702

                                                         LC   93026434 /AC

Captured and enslaved by the corsair stoat Badrang, young mouse warrior Martin vows to end the evil beast's plundering and killing.

"Studded with vibrant and distinct animal characters, Jacques's classically inspired . . . plot-weaving achieves virtuosity as moments of sensitivity shake his fierce heroes off their warrior paths." Publishers Weekly.

Mattimeo. Brian Jacques; illustrated by Gary Chalk. Philomel Books, 1990. 446 p.: Redwall

Grades: 5 6 7 8 9   Fic
    1. Heroes and heroines 2. Animals 3. Good and evil 4. Foxes 5. Mice 6. Animal fantasy 7. Fantasy fiction
    ISBN 039921741x

                                                         LC   89037005

Mattimeo, the son of the warrior mouse Matthias, learns to wake up the sword and joins the other animal inhabitants of Redwall Abbey in resisting Slagar the fox and his band of marauders.

"This is truly thrilling. . . . Jacques's realistically drawn characters are full of personality. . . . The fierceness with which the Redwallers fight back to save their young lends the story credibility within the realm of the animal kingdom, while at the same time taking wonderful liberties with the imagination." Publishers Weekly.

Mossflower. Brian Jacques; illustrated by Gary Chalk. Philomel Books, 1988. 431 p.: Redwall

Grades: 5 6 7 8 9   Fic
    1. Animals 2. Heroes and heroines 3. Good and evil 4. Mice 5. Redwall Abbey (Imaginary place) 6. Animal fantasy 7. Fantasy fiction
    ISBN 0399215492

                                                         LC   88017921

Martin the warrior mouse and Gonff the mousethief set out to find the missing ruler of Mossflower, while the other animal inhabitants of the woodland prepare to rebel against the evil wildcat who has seized power.

"The writing is smooth and swift-paced." School Library Journal.

Pearls of Lutra. Brian Jacques; illustrated by Allan Curless. Philomel Books, 1996. 408 p.: Redwall

Grades: 5 6 7 8 9   Fic
    1. Heroes and heroines 2. Animals 3. Pearls 4. Redwall Abbey (Imaginary place) 5. Good and evil 6. Animal fantasy 7. Fantasy fiction
    ISBN 0399229469

                                                         LC 9618444

A set of pearls is sought by a hedgehog and an evil emperor.

★ **Redwall**. Brian Jacques; illustrated by Gary Chalk. Philomel Books, 2007, c1986. 351p.: Redwall

Grades: 5 6 7 8 9   Fic
    1. Heroes and heroines 2. Animals 3. Good and evil 4. Rats 5. Swords 6. Animal fantasy 7. Fantasy fiction 8. Classics
    ISBN 9780399247941

                                                         LC   86025467

When the peaceful life of ancient Redwall Abbey is shattered by the arrival of the evil rat Cluny and his villainous hordes, Matthias, a young mouse, determines to find the legendary sword of Martin the Warrior which, he is convinced, will help Redwall's inhabitants destroy the enemy.

"Thoroughly engrossing, this novel captivates despite its length. . . . The theme will linger long after the story is finished." Booklist.

Salamandastron. Brian Jacques; illustrated by Gary Chalk. Philomel Books, 1993, c1992. 391 p.: Redwall

Grades: 5 6 7 8 9   Fic
    1. Heroes and heroines 2. Animals 3. Good and evil 4. Badgers 5. Weasels 6. Animal fantasy 7. Fantasy fiction
    ISBN 9780399219924

                                                         LC   91046423

Urthstripe the Strong, a wise old badger, leads the animals of the great fortress of Salamandastron and Redwall Abbey against the weasel Ferahgo the Assassin and his corps of vermin.

"The reader feels included in the Abbey's history as it is being written, and Jacques encourages that empathy by creating animal characters that respond to extraordinary circumstances with compellingly human-like humility and strength. Chalk's black-and-white illustrations above each chapter number are small marvels of nuance and personality." Publishers Weekly.

Jaffe, Nina

The **cow** of no color: riddle stories and justice tales from around the world.. By Nina Jaffe and Steve Zeitlin. Pictures by Whitney Sherman. H. Holt, 1998. 160 p.

Grades: 4 5 6 7   Fic
    1. Justice 2. Guilt 3. Innocence (Law) 4. Forgiveness 5. Mercy 6. Short stories
    ISBN 0805037365

                                                         LC 98-14167

A collection of stories from all over the world, each of which turns on a question of justice. Includes tales from China, Ghana, Balkans, Ireland, Vietnam, ancient Israel, Laos, Nigeria, Cuba, Korea, Mexico, Syria, and Nigeria.

"Sherman's black-and-white line drawings have a stark gracefulness that complements the tales' form and structure; the tales themselves are simply told with little embellishment." Bulletin of the Center for Children's Books.

James, Anna (Anna Lois)

The **bookwanderers**. Anna James. Philomel Books, 2019, c2018. 288 p.: Pages & Co.

Grades: 4 5 6 7   Fic
    1. Books and reading 2. Mother-separated children 3. Characters and characteristics in literature 4. Bookstores 5. Magic 6. England 7. London, England 8. Fantasy fiction
    ISBN 9781984837127

                                                         LC 2019016911

Eleven-year-old Tilly Pages, who has found comfort in her grandparents' bookshop since her mother's disappearance, now learns that she can bookwander into any stories, and decides to seek her mother.

"Steeped in magical world building, James' debut pays loving testament to the power of books, and it functions well as a stand-alone adventure while setting the stage for future installments of enormous potential." Booklist.

The **lost** fairy tales. Anna James; illustrated by Paola Escobar. Philomel Books, 2020, c2019. 400 p.: Pages & Co.

Grades: 5 6 7   **Fic**
1. Books and reading 2. Characters and characteristics in fairy tales 3. Best friends 4. Quests 5. Bookstores 6. France 7. Paris, France 8. Fantasy fiction
ISBN 9781984837295
Tilly Pages is a bookwanderer; she can travel inside books, and even talk to the characters she meets there. But Tilly's powers are put to the test when fairytales start leaking book magic and causing havoc... On a wintery visit to Paris, Tilly and her best friend Oskar bravely bookwander into the land of fairytales to find that characters are getting lost, stories are all mixed-up, and mysterious plot holes are opening without warning. Can Tilly work out who, or what, is behind the chaos so everyone gets their happily-ever-after? The second enthralling tale in the bestselling PAGES & CO series.

"This series is made for book-lovers and attests to the power and importance of stories." School Library Journal

James, Helen Foster, 1951-
Paper son: Lee's journey to America. written by Helen Foster James and Virginia Shin-Mui Loh; illustrated by Wilson Ong. Sleeping Bear Press, 2013. 32 p.: Tales of Young Americans series

Grades: 5 6 7 8   **Fic**
1. Angel Island Immigration Station, California 2. 1920s 3. Immigration and emigration 4. Boy orphans 5. Immigrants, Chinese 6. Immigrants 7. Twelve-year-old boys 8. Angel Island (Calif) 9. Historical fiction
ISBN 9781585368334
                                LC 2012033691
Twelve-year-old Lee, an orphan, reluctantly leaves his grandparents in China for the long sea voyage to San Francisco, where he and other immigrants undergo examinations at Angel Island Immigration Station.

Jennings, Patrick
Odd, weird & little. Patrick Jennings. Egmont USA, 2014. 160 p.

Grades: 4 5 6 7   **Fic**
1. Bullying and bullies 2. Friendship 3. Right and wrong 4. Eccentrics and eccentricities 5. Misfits (Persons) 6. Humorous stories
ISBN 9781606843741
                                LC 2013018248
Befriending a very strange new student, Toulouse, helps outsider Woodrow stand up to the class bullies who have been picking on them both.

Jennings, Richard W. (Richard Walker), 1945-
Ghost town. written and illustrated by Richard W. Jennings. Houghton Mifflin Harcourt, 2009. 167 p.

Grades: 7 8 9 10   **Fic**
1. Teenage boys 2. Ghost towns 3. Paranormal phenomena 4. Cameras 5. Thirteen-year-old boys 6. Kansas 7. Ghost stories 8.

Humorous stories
ISBN 9780547194714
                                LC 2008036781
Thirteen-year-old Spencer Honesty and his imaginary friend, an Indian called Chief Leopard Frog, improbably achieve fame and riches in the abandoned town of Paisley, Kansas, when Spencer begins taking photographs with his deceased father's ancient camera and Chief Leopard Frog has his poems published by a shady businessman in the Cayman Islands.

"Jennings has a dry wit, and the protagonist's matter-of-fact observations make the most outlandish scenes seem possible. This is a coming-of-age story/tall tale that's full of charm." School Library Journal.

Jeter, Derek, 1974-
The contract. Derek Jeter; with Paul Mantell. Jeter Publishing, Simon & Schuster Books for Young Readers, 2014. 160 p.: The contract (Derek Jeter)

Grades: 5 6 7   **Fic**
1. Jeter, Derek, 1974- 2. Boy baseball players 3. Little League baseball 4. Determination (Personal quality) 5. Third-grade boys 6. Eight-year-old boys 7. Baseball stories 8. Sports fiction 9. Autobiographical fiction
ISBN 9781481423120
                                LC 2014004045
In Kalamazoo, Michigan, eight-year-old Derek Jeter, who dreams of playing for the New York Yankees, learns what it takes to be a champion on and off the field.

"A boy named Derek Jeter chases his dreams of playing in the Major Leagues. The author's note states the story is based on some of my experiences growing up and playing baseball, and the book's theme is: Set Your Goals High. Third-grade Derek (the character) is remarkably—and unrealistically—self-possessed and self-aware, but fans will get a kick out of this kid-version of their hero." Horn Book.

Jiménez, Francisco, 1943-
Breaking through. Francisco Jiménez. Houghton Mifflin, 2001. 195 p.

Grades: 7 8 9 10 11 12   **Fic**
1. Mexican American teenage boys 2. Immigrants, Mexican 3. Deportation 4. Migrant agricultural laborers 5. Mexican American families 6. California 7. Autobiographical fiction 8. Short stories
ISBN 0618011730
                                LC 2001016941
Having come from Mexico to California ten years ago, fourteen-year-old Francisco is still working in the fields but fighting to improve his life and complete his education.

"For all its recounting of deprivation, this is a hopeful book, told with rectitude and dignity." Horn Book.

The circuit: stories from the life of a migrant child. Francisco Jiménez. Houghlin Mifflin Co., 1999, c1997. 116 p.

Grades: 7 8 9 10 11 12   **Fic**
1. Jiménez, Francisco, 1943- 2. Mexican American boys 3. Immigrants, Mexican 4. Migrant agricultural laborers 5. Undocumented workers 6. Mexican American families 7. California 8. Autobiographical fiction 9. Short stories 10. Realistic fiction
ISBN 9780395979020
A realistic portrayal of the lives of migrant workers, based on the author's own experiences, movingly chronicles a family's perseverance in the face of extreme hardship.

"The story begins in Mexico when the author is very young and his parents inform him that they are going on a very long trip to El Norte. What follows is a series of stories of the family's unending migration from one farm to another as they search for the next harvesting job. Each story is told from the point of view of the author as a young child. The simple and direct narrative stays true to this perspective. . . . Lifting the story up from the mundane, Jiménez deftly portrays the strong bonds of love that hold this family together." Publishers Weekly.

Reaching out. Francisco Jiménez. Houghlin Mifflin Co., c2008. vi, 196 p.

Grades: 7 8 9 10 11 12   **Fic**
    1. Jiménez, Francisco, 1943- 2. 1960s 3. Mexican American teenage boys 4. College students 5. Mexican American families 6. Immigrants, Mexican 7. Migrant agricultural laborers 8. California 9. Autobiographical fiction

ISBN 9780618038510

Carter G. Woodson Book Awards: Secondary Level, 2009.

In an inspiring sequel to the award-winning Breaking Through, the author describes the many challenges he faced during his quest to continue his education, including poverty, family turmoil, guilt, and self-doubt, and become an academic success.

"Papa's raging depression intensifies young Jiménez personal guilt and conflict in the 1960s. . . . He is the first in his Mexican American migrant family to attend college in California. . . . Like his other fictionalized autobiographies, The Circuit (1997) and Breaking Through (2001), this sequel tells Jiménez personal story in self-contained chapters that join together in a stirring narrative. . . . The spare episodes will draw readers with the quiet daily detail of work, anger, sorrow, and hope." Booklist.

Jinks, Catherine

Evil genius. Catherine Jinks. Harcourt, 2007, c2005. 486 p.: Evil genius books

Grades: 7 8 9 10   **Fic**
    1. Genius 2. Hackers 3. Gifted teenagers 4. Teenage boy prodigies 5. Identity (Psychology) 6. Australia 7. Science fiction

ISBN 0152059881

                        LC 2006014476

Child prodigy Cadel Piggott, an antisocial computer hacker, discovers his true identity when he enrolls as a first-year student at an advanced crime academy.

"Cadel's turnabout is convincingly hampered by his difficulty recognizing appropriate outlets for rage, and Jinks' whiplash-inducing suspense writing will gratify fans of Anthony Horowitz's high-tech spy scenarios." Booklist.

Genius squad. Catherine Jinks. Harcourt, c2008. 436 p.: Evil genius books

Grades: 7 8 9 10   **Fic**
    1. Genius 2. Foster care 3. Secret societies 4. Gifted teenagers 5. Teenage boy prodigies 6. Australia 7. Science fiction

ISBN 9780152059859

                        LC 2007030373

After the Axis Institute is blown up, fifteen-year-old Cadel Piggott is unhappily stuck in foster care with constant police surveillance to protect him from the evil Prosper English until he gets an offer to join a mysterious group called Genius Squad.

"Readers who loved Evil Genius will find this sequel as gripping, devilish and wonderfully dark as its predecessor." Publishers Weekly.

The **genius** wars. Catherine Jinks. Harcourt, 2010, c2009. 384 p.: Evil genius books

Grades: 7 8 9 10   **Fic**
    1. Genius 2. Fugitives 3. Courage in teenage boys 4. Courage 5.

Gifted teenagers 6. Science fiction

ISBN 9780152066192

Fifteen-year-old genius Cadel Piggott Greenaus sets aside his new, crime-free life when his best friend Sonja is attacked, and he crosses oceans and continents trying to track down his nemesis Prosper English, breaking whatever rules he must.

"The climax is taut, absorbing and tantalizingly ambiguous." Kirkus.

★ **How** to catch a bogle. Catherine Jinks. Harcourt Children's Books, Houghton Mifflin Harcourt, 2013. 304 p.: City of orphans

Grades: 5 6 7 8   **Fic**
    1. Victorian era (1837-1901) 2. 19th century 3. 1870s 4. Monsters 5. Girl orphans 6. Girl apprentices 7. Supernatural 8. Ten-year-old girls 9. London, England 10. Great Britain 11. Historical fantasy

ISBN 9780544087088

                        LC 2012045936

In 1870s London, a young orphan girl becomes the apprentice to a man who traps monsters for a living.

The **last** bogler. Catherine Jinks; illustrated by Sarah Watts. 336 p.: City of orphans

Grades: 5 6 7 8   **Fic**
    1. Victorian era (1837-1901) 2. 19th century 3. 1870s 4. Missing children 5. Monsters 6. Orphans 7. Prisons 8. Boy apprentices 9. London, England 10. England 11. Historical fantasy

ISBN 9780544086968

Ned Roach becomes a bogler's apprentice as Victorian London seeks to banish its bogle infestation once and for all in this conclusion to the trilogy featuring young assistants to Victorian London's best monster catcher, Alfred Bunce.

"A highly satisfying conclusion to this wonderfully crafted fantasy series." School Library Journal.

Jobling, Curtis

Rise of the wolf. by Curtis Jobling. Viking Childrens Books, 2011. 412 p.: Wereworld

Grades: 4 5 6 7   **Fic**
    1. Werewolves 2. Shapeshifters 3. Imaginary wars and battles 4. Inheritance and succession 5. Imaginary kingdoms 6. Fantasy fiction

ISBN 9780670013302

                        LC 2010049517

When a vicious beast invades his father's farm and sixteen-year-old Drew suddenly transforms into a werewolf, he runs away from his family, seeking refuge in the most out of the way parts of Lyssia, only to be captured by Lord Bergan's men and forced to battle numerous werecreatures while trying to prove that he is not the enemy.

"Jobling's characterizations are solid, his world-building is complex and fascinating, and the combat scenes are suitably exciting. The book's themes are familiar—lost prince in exile, voyage of self-discovery, young heroes rebelling against injustice and evil—but Jobling uses them to tell a thoroughly enjoyable adventure that makes particularly inventive use of its shapeshifter elements and mythology." Publishers Weekly.

Jocelyn, Marthe

A **big** dose of lucky. Marthe Jocelyn. Orca Book Pub., 2015. 264 p.: Secrets (Orca Book Publishers)

Grades: 7 8 9 10 11 12   **Fic**
    1. 1960s 2. Teenage orphans 3. Black Canadians 4. Ethnic identity 5. Sixteen-year-old girls 6. Prejudice 7. Ontario 8.

Coming-of-age stories 9. Historical fiction
ISBN 9781459806689

After her move to Parry Sound, Malou sees more mixed-race children and wants to learn more about her past.

"Sharp writing keeps this dramatic coming-of-age story from taking a turn toward the saccharine or melodramatic, despite the casual and not-so-casual racism Malou endures outside the sheltered confines of the orphanage. Lovely and easily digestible historical fiction." Booklist.

Viminy Crowe's comic book. Marthe Jocelyn & Richard Scrimger; with comics by Claudia Davila. Tundra Books, c2014. 317 p.

Grades: 4 5 6 7 **Fic**
    1. Comic book fans 2. Steampunk culture 3. Comic books, strips, etc 4. Books and reading 5. Doorways 6. Gateway fantasy 7. Fantasy fiction
ISBN 1770494790

LC 2013943886

A chance encounter between geeky Wylder Wallace and aloof Addy Crowe at Toronto's Comicon results in the pair winding up inside a steam-punk comic book. As they search for a portal back to the real world, the comic book story goes on around them, with every page turn sending them to a thrilling and often dangerous new setting.

"A bathroom portal at ComicFest launches two kids, Wylder Wallace and Addy Crowe, into the pages of a comic book. Suspense builds as the kids' presence affects the story, their adventures shown (in interspersed comic panels) in Davila's clear, humorous illustrations. It's a clever concept that's well executed by Jocelyn and Scrimger." Horn Book.

John, Antony, 1972-
  Five flavors of Dumb. by Antony John. Dial Books, 2010. 337 p.

Grades: 7 8 9 10 **Fic**
    1. Rock groups 2. Teenagers who are deaf 3. Resentfulness 4. Teenage girls with disabilities 5. Supervisors 6. Seattle, Washington 7. Washington (State) 8. Realistic fiction
ISBN 9780803734333

LC 2009044449

Schneider Family Book Award for Teens, 2011.

Eighteen-year-old Piper becomes the manager for her classmates' popular rock band, called Dumb, giving her the chance to prove her capabilities to her parents and others, if only she can get the band members to get along.

"Readers interested in any of the narrative strands . . . will find a solid, satisfyingly complex story here." Bulletin of the Center for Children's Books.

Johnson, Angela, 1961-
  A **certain** October. Angela Johnson. Simon & Schuster Books For Young Readers, 2012. 144 p.

Grades: 7 8 9 10 11 12 **Fic**
    1. Guilt in teenage girls 2. Accidents 3. Children with autism 4. Guilt 5. Death 6. Ohio 7. Realistic fiction 8. African American fiction
ISBN 9780689865053

LC 2012001595

Scotty compares herself to tofu: no flavor unless you add something. And it's true that Scotty's friends, Misha and Falcone, and her brother, Keone, make life delicious. But when a terrible accident occurs, Scotty feels responsible for the loss of someone she hardly knew, and the world goes wrong. She cannot tell what is a dream and what is real. Her friends are having a hard time getting through to her and her family is preoccupied with their own trauma. But the prospect of a boy, a dance, and the possibility that everything can fall back into place soon help Scotty realize that she is capable of adding her own flavor to life. Provided by publisher.

★ A **cool** moonlight. Angela Johnson. Dial Books, 2003. 133 p.

Grades: 4 5 6 **Fic**
    1. Sick girls 2. Light and darkness 3. Skin -- Diseases 4. Sick children 5. Children -- Diseases 6. Sun
ISBN 0803728468

LC 2002031521

Nine-year-old Lila, born with xeroderma pigmentosum, a skin disease that makes her sensitive to sunlight, makes secret plans to feel the sun's rays on her tenth birthday.

"The book's real magic resides in the spell cast by Johnson's spare, lucid, lyrical prose. Using simple words and vivid sensory images, she creates Lila's inner world as a place of quiet intensity." Booklist.

The **first** part last. Angela Johnson. Simon & Schuster Books for Young Readers, 2003. 144 p.: Heaven trilogy

Grades: 7 8 9 10 **Fic**
    1. Teenage fathers 2. African American teenage boys 3. Father and child 4. Sixteen-year-old boys 5. Teenage parents 6. New York City 7. Coming-of-age stories 8. Realistic fiction 9. African American fiction
ISBN 0689849222

LC 2002036512

Coretta Scott King Award, Author Category, 2004.
Michael L. Printz Award, 2004.

When his girlfriend Nia announces that she is pregnant, sixteen-year-old Bobby, a typical urban New York City teenager, must cast aside his life of partying to visit obstetricians and social workers, who try to convince them to give their baby up for adoption, until tragedy strikes.

"Brief, poetic, and absolutely riveting." School Library Journal.

Heaven. Angela Johnson. Simon & Schuster Books for Young Readers, 1998. 138 p.: Heaven trilogy

Grades: 6 7 8 9 **Fic**
    1. Adopted children 2. African American teenage girls 3. Small town life 4. Fourteen-year-old girls 5. Adoption 6. Ohio 7. Realistic fiction 8. African American fiction
ISBN 0689822294

LC 98003291

Coretta Scott King Award, Author Category, 1999.

Fourteen-year-old Marley's seemingly perfect life in the small town of Heaven is disrupted when she discovers that her father and mother are not her real parents.

"In spare, often poetic prose . . . Johnson relates Marley's insightful quest into what makes a family." School Library Journal.

Sweet, hereafter. Angela Johnson. Simon and Schuster Books for Young Readers, 2010. 128 p.: Heaven trilogy

Grades: 7 8 9 10 **Fic**
    1. African American teenage girls 2. Identity (Psychology) 3. Unhappiness 4. Soldiers 5. Interpersonal relations 6. Realistic fiction
ISBN 9780689873850

LC 2009027618

Sweet leaves her family and goes to live in a cabin in the woods with the quiet but understanding Curtis, to whom she feels intensely connected, just as he is called back to serve again in Iraq.

"With heartfelt empathy, we share in Shoogy's personal loss and her need for a new direction. Characters from the two other titles reappear, and we get a glimpse of how their lives are moving forward. This book belongs in all junior and senior high school collections, especially those who already own the first two titles. . . . Johnson now has one more well-woven character development novel to her name." Library Media Connection.

Johnson, Jaleigh

★ The **mark** of the dragonfly. Jaleigh Johnson. Delacorte Press, 2014. 288 p.

Grades: 5 6 7 8   **Fic**
1. Teenage girl orphans 2. Trains 3. Amnesia 4. Voyages and travels 5. Solace (Imaginary place) 6. Steampunk 7. Fantasy fiction
ISBN 9780385376150
                LC 2013019716
Since her father's death in a factory in the Dragonfly territories, thirteen-year-old Piper has eked out a living as a scrapper in Merrow Kingdom, but the arrival of a mysterious girl sends her on a dangerous journey to distant lands.

"Heart, brains and courage find a home in a steampunk fantasy worthy of a nod from Baum. . . . A well-imagined world of veritable adventure." Kirkus.

Johnson, Maureen, 1973-

13 little blue envelopes. Maureen Johnson. Harper Collins, c2005. 317 p.: Little blue envelopes

Grades: 8 9 10 11 12   **Fic**
1. Teenage travelers 2. Growth (Psychology) 3. Letters 4. Seventeen-year-old girls 5. Teenage girls 6. Europe 7. Realistic fiction 8. Teen chick lit
ISBN 0060541415
                LC 2005002658
When seventeen-year-old Ginny receives a packet of mysterious envelopes from her favorite aunt, she leaves New Jersey to criss-cross Europe on a sort of scavenger hunt that transforms her life.

"Equal parts poignant, funny and inspiring, this tale is sure to spark wanderlust." Publishers Weekly.

The **hand** on the wall. Maureen Johnson. Katherine Tegen Books, 2020. 384 p.: Truly Devious

Grades: 8 9 10 11 12   **Fic**
1. Teenage girl detectives 2. Boarding schools 3. Murder investigation 4. Murder 5. Riddles 6. Vermont 7. Mysteries
ISBN 9780062338112
A conclusion to the series that includes The Vanishing Stair finds another death compelling Stevie to navigate mysterious riddles and track down a missing David at the same time a massive storm forces her to confront a killer.

"In this hotly anticipated trilogy finale (beginning with Truly Devious, 2018), Johnson pulls out all the stops, filling the thrillingly nimble narrative with classic mystery conventions." Booklist

The **madness** underneath. Maureen Johnson. G. P. Putnam's Sons, 2013. 304 p.: Shades of London

Grades: 6 7 8 9 10   **Fic**
1. Ghosts 2. Americans in London, England 3. Murder 4. Supernatural 5. Dating (Social customs) 6. London, England 7. England 8. Paranormal fiction
ISBN 9780399256615
            LC 2012026755

After her near-fatal run-in with the Jack the Ripper copycat, Rory Devereaux is back in London to help solve a new string of inexplicable deaths plaguing the city. Provided by publisher.

The **name** of the star. Maureen Johnson. G. P. Putnam's Sons, 2011. 384 p.: Shades of London

Grades: 6 7 8 9 10   **Fic**
1. Teenage murder witnesses 2. Copycat murders 3. Ghosts 4. Serial murders 5. Supernatural 6. London, England 7. England 8. Paranormal fiction
ISBN 9780399256608
            LC 2011009003
Rory, of Boueuxlieu, Louisiana, is spending a year at a London boarding school when she witnesses a murder by a Jack the Ripper copycat and becomes involved with the very unusual investigation.

"Johnson's trademark sense of humor serves to counterbalance some grisly murders in this page-turner, which opens her Shades of London series. . . . As one mutilated body after another turns up, Johnson . . . amplifies the story's mysteries with smart use of and subtle commentary on modern media shenanigans and London's infamously extensive surveillance network. . . . Readers looking for nonstop fun, action, and a little gore have come to the right place." Publishers Weekly.

Scarlett fever. by Maureen Johnson. Point, 2010. 352 p.: Scarlett Martin series

Grades: 7 8 9 10   **Fic**
1. Actors and actresses 2. Dating (Social customs) 3. Hotels 4. Fifteen-year-old girls 5. Teenage boy/girl relations 6. Manhattan, New York City 7. New York City 8. Realistic fiction 9. Teen chick lit
ISBN 9780439899284
            LC 2009019322
Fifteen-year-old Scarlett, who is beginning to get over her break-up with Eric, stays busy as assistant to her theatrical-agent friend who is not only promoting Scarlett's brother Spencer, but also a new client whose bad-boy brother has transferred to Scarlett's school.

"While the novel may be enjoyed for the light if slightly madcap romance that it is, it is notable for its attention to social class and to the Martins' struggles with money." School Library Journal.

The **shadow** cabinet. Maureen Johnson. G. P. Putnam's Sons, an imprint of Penguin Group (USA), 2015. 304 p.: Shades of London

Grades: 6 7 8 9 10   **Fic**
1. Ghosts 2. Kidnapping 3. Cults 4. Americans in London, England 5. Murder 6. London, England 7. England 8. Paranormal fiction
ISBN 9780399256622
            LC 2014031153
Rory, Callum and Boo are still reeling from a series of tragic events, while new dangers lurk around the city from Jane and her nefarious organization. Provided by publisher.

"The plot . . . is among Johnson's finest and incorporates creepy bits of backstory, fascinating historical asides, and truly ghoulish side characters—take, for example, a lumpen cemetery ghost that is 'just a glob of people pieces mixed together.' "Booklist.

Suite Scarlett. Maureen Johnson. Point, 2008. viii, 353 p.: Scarlett Martin series

Grades: 6 7 8 9 10   **Fic**
1. Hotels 2. Women authors 3. Theater 4. Rich women 5. Actors and actresses 6. Manhattan, New York City 7. New York City 8.

Realistic fiction 9. Teen chick lit
ISBN 9780439899277

LC 2007041903

Fifteen-year-old Scarlett Martin is stuck in New York City for the summer working at her quirky family's historic hotel, but her brother's attractive new friend and a seasonal guest who offers her an intriguing and challenging writing project improve her outlook.

"Utterly winning, madcap Manhattan farce, crafted with a winking, urbane narrative and tight, wry dialogue." Booklist.

Truly, Devious. Maureen Johnson. HarperCollins Children's Books, 2018. 320 p.: Truly Devious

Grades: 8 9 10 11 12   **Fic**

1. Boarding schools 2. Murder 3. Teenage girl detectives 4. Crime 5. Teenage girls 6. Vermont 7. Mysteries
ISBN 9780062338051

Ellingham Academy is a famous private school in Vermont for the brightest thinkers, inventors, and artists. It was founded by Albert Ellingham, an early twentieth century tycoon, who wanted to make a wonderful place full of riddles, twisting pathways, and gardens. "A place," he said, "where learning is a game."

"Johnson deftly twists two mysteries together—Stevie's investigation is interspersed with case files and recollections from the Ellington kidnapping—and the result is a suspenseful, attention-grabbing mystery with no clear solution. Invested readers, never fear—this is just the first in a series." Booklist.

The **vanishing** stair. Maureen Johnson. HarperCollins Children's Books, 2019. 384 p.: Truly Devious

Grades: 8 9 10 11 12   **Fic**

1. Boarding schools 2. Murder 3. Teenage girl detectives 4. Investigations 5. Teenage girls 6. Vermont 7. Mysteries
ISBN 9780062338082

Pulled out of Ellingham Academy by her overprotective parents, aspiring detective Stevie Bell makes a deal with the despicable Edward King in hopes of reuniting with her friends and solving the Truly Devious case.

"In this second trilogy installment, Johnson gives and she takes away: a few major mysteries are satisfyingly solved, but other long-standing riddles remain tantalizingly indecipherable, and several new ones come into play by the enigmatic end." Booklist.

Johnson, Terry Lynn

Dog driven. Terry Lynn Johnson. Houghton Mifflin Harcourt, 2019. 240 p.

Grades: 5 6 7 8   **Fic**

1. Girls with disabilities 2. Sled dog racing 3. Wilderness survival 4. Teenage girls 5. People with visual disabilities 6. Survival stories 7. Adventure stories
ISBN 9781328551597

From the author of Ice Dogs, comes a riveting adventure about a musher who sets out to prove her impaired vision won't hold her back from competing in a rigorous sled race through the Canadian wilderness.

"A densely plotted, fast-moving, thematically rich tale set at the intersection of ability and disability." Kirkus.

Ice dogs. by Terry Lynn Johnson. Houghton Mifflin, Houghton Mifflin Harcourt, 2013. 279 p.

Grades: 5 6 7 8 9   **Fic**

1. Dogsledding 2. Survival 3. Wilderness areas 4. Sled dogs 5.

Dogs 6. Alaska 7. Survival stories 8. Adventure stories
ISBN 9780547899268

LC 2012045061

In this survival story set in Alaska, fourteen-year-old Vicky and her dog sled team find an injured sledder in the wilderness.

Johnson, Varian

★ The **great** Greene heist. by Varian Johnson. Arthur A. Levine Books, 2014. 240 p.: Jackson Greene novels

Grades: 5 6 7 8   **Fic**

1. Student elections 2. Practical jokers 3. Middle school students 4. Middle schools 5. Schools 6. Realistic fiction 7. African American fiction
ISBN 9780545525527

When his ex-girlfriend and an ill-intentioned rival with ties to the principal run for school president, reformed con artist Jackson Greene secretly assembles a crack team to ensure the election is run fairly, an effort that is complicated by Jackson's enduring feelings for his ex.

"This fast-paced caper reads like Ocean's 11 for the middle-school set, and thats no coincidence: Johnson (Saving Maddie, 2010) openly credits the film as inspiration, and he has pretty much pulled it off, right down to the dizzying plot twists, incredulous access to the latest tech, and unflappable swagger." Booklist.

The **Parker** inheritance. Varian Johnson. Arthur A. Levine Books, 2018. 336 p.

Grades: 4 5 6 7   **Fic**

1. African American girls 2. Puzzles 3. Treasure hunting 4. Racism 5. Mothers and daughters 6. South Carolina 7. Mysteries 8. African American fiction
ISBN 9780545946179

LC 2017042551

Twelve-year-old Candice Miller is spending the summer in Lambert, South Carolina, in the old house that belonged to her grandmother, who died after being dismissed as city manager for having the city tennis courts dug up looking for buried treasure—but when she finds the letter that sent her grandmother on the treasure hunt, she finds herself caught up in the mystery and, with the help of her new friend and fellow book-worm, Brandon, she sets out to find the inheritance, exonerate her grandmother, and expose an injustice once committed against an African American family in Lambert.

"A dazzling and emotional read that deals with serious topics such as bullying, racism, and divorce." Booklist.

To catch a cheat. Varian Johnson. Arthur A. Levine Books, an imprint of Scholastic Inc., 2016. 256 p.: Jackson Greene novels

Grades: 5 6 7 8   **Fic**

1. Cheating (Education) 2. Extortion 3. Practical jokers 4. Middle school students 5. Middle schools 6. Realistic fiction 7. African American fiction
ISBN 9780545722391

LC 2015025232

Because of his reputation for practical jokes Jackson Greene is the automatic suspect for anything that goes wrong at school—but when he and his friends are framed for a crime they did not commit, Gang Greene sets out to expose the students responsible, who are trying to blackmail Jackson into helping them cheat on an important test.

"Fast-paced antics, clever writing, and a diverse cast of characters give this ample broad appeal." Booklist.

Johnson-Shelton, Nils

The **invisible** tower. Nils Johnson-Shelton. HarperCollins, 2012. 352 p.: Otherworld chronicles

Grades: 4 5 6 7   **Fic**

1. Arthur, King. 2. 21st century 3. Towers 4. Video games 5. Dragons 6. Wolves 7. Quests 8. Pennsylvania 9. Arthurian fantasy

ISBN 9780062070869

LC 2011022928

A twelve-year-old boy learns that he is actually King Arthur brought back to life in the twenty-first century—and that the fate of the universe rests in his hands.

"This new take on the Arthurian legends, told in third-person, pits wisecracking contemporary teens with their contemporary banter. . . . against all manner of obstacles. . . . It's always high-spirited and fun. Gives new life to Arthurian legends and may just send readers back to more traditional tellings." Kirkus.

The **seven** swords. Nils Johnson-Shelton. HarperCollins, c2013. 368 p.: Otherworld chronicles

Grades: 4 5 6 7   **Fic**

1. Arthur, King. 2. 21st century 3. Swords 4. Knights and knighthood 5. Inheritance and succession 6. Kingfisher, Artie (Fictitious character) 7. Arthurian fantasy

ISBN 9780062070944

LC 2012019088

Twelve-year-old Artie Kingfisher has only ten days to gather a team of knights to wield the mythical seven swords, or his mission to save the Otherworld and claim his throne as King Arthur will be lost. Provided by publisher.

Johnston, E. K.

Prairie fire. by E.K. Johnston. Carolrhoda Lab, 2015. 304 p.: Dragon slayer of Trondheim

Grades: 7 8 9 10 11 12   **Fic**

1. Adventurers 2. Dragons 3. Military service 4. Bards and bardism 5. Heroes and heroines 6. Canada 7. Fantasy fiction

ISBN 9781467739092

LC 2014008995

After graduating high school, dragon slayer Owen Thorskard and his friend and bard Siobhan McQuaid sign up for service in the Oil Watch.

"A fantasy YA novel that steers clear of love triangles, teen angst, and a tidy ending is hard to come by; Prairie Fire and its prequel are must-haves." School Library Journal.

The **story** of Owen: dragon slayer of Trondheim. E. K. Johnston. Carolrhoda Lab, 2014. 305 p.: Dragon slayer of Trondheim

Grades: 7 8 9 10 11 12   **Fic**

1. Dragons 2. Bards and bardism 3. Small towns 4. Fame 5. Families 6. Canada 7. Fantasy fiction

ISBN 9781467710664

LC 2013020492

In an alternate world where industrialization has caused many species of carbon-eating dragons to thrive, Owen, a slayer being trained by his famous father and aunt, and Siobahn, his bard, face a dragon infestation near their small town in Canada.

"Humor, pathos and wry social commentary unite in a cleverly drawn, marvelously diverse world. Refreshingly, the focus is on the pair as friends and partners, not on potential romance." Kirkus.

Johnston, Tony, 1942-

Any small goodness: a novel of the barrio. Tony Johnston; illustrations by Raul Colon. Blue Sky Press, c2001. 128 p.

Grades: 4 5 6 7   **Fic**

1. Immigrant families 2. Cultural differences 3. Mexican Americans 4. Mexican American families 5. Hispanic Americans 6. Los Angeles, California 7. East Los Angeles, California

ISBN 0439189365

LC 99059877

Arturo and his family and friends share all kinds of experiences living in the barrio of East Los Angeles—reclaiming their names, playing basketball, championing the school librarian, and even starting their own gang.

"The characters are likable and warm. . . . The message is positive and the episodes, while occasionally serious, are more often humorous and gratifying." School Library Journal.

Beast rider: a boy's journey beyond the border. Tony Johnston and Maria Elena Fontanot de Rhoads. Amulet Books, 2019. 176 p.

Grades: 6 7 8 9   **Fic**

1. Brothers 2. Undocumented immigrants 3. Voyages and travels 4. Immigration and emigration 5. Trains 6. Mexico 7. California 8. Survival stories 9. Realistic fiction

ISBN 9781419733635

LC 2018038535

After his brother leaves their village in Mexico to live in the United States, twelve-year-old Manuel wants to join him, but will have to evade police and drug gangs and survive a dangerous journey aboard the train known as La Bestia.

"Told directly and effectively, this story gives readers an opportunity to be present for one young man's harrowing journey as an immigrant to the U.S." School Library Journal.

Jones, Diana Wynne

Enchanted glass. by Diana Wynne Jones. Greenwillow Books, 2010. 304 p.

Grades: 6 7 8 9   **Fic**

1. Boy orphans 2. Glass 3. Protectiveness 4. Magic 5. Imaginary creatures 6. England 7. Fantasy fiction

ISBN 9780061866845

LC 2009006195

After his grandfather dies, Andrew Hope inherits a house and surrounding land in an English village, but things become very complicated when young orphan Aidan shows up and suddenly a host of variously magical townsfolk and interlopers start intruding on their lives.

"Jones hits all the bases, combining fluid storytelling, sly humor, and exquisitely drawn characters." Booklist.

★ **Howl's** moving castle. Diana Wynne Jones. Greenwillow Books, 1986. 212 p.: Howl's moving castle (Diana Wynne Jones)

Grades: 5 6 7 8   **Fic**

1. Wizards 2. Castles 3. Hatmakers 4. Magic 5. Enchantment 6. Fantasy fiction 7. Humorous stories 8. Classics

ISBN 0688062334

LC 85021981

Eldest of three sisters in a land where it is considered to be a misfortune, Sophie is resigned to her fate as a hat shop apprentice until a witch turns her into an old woman and she finds herself in the castle of the greatly feared wizard Howl.

"Satisfyingly, Sophie meets a fate far exceeding her dreary expectations. This novel is an exciting, multi-faceted puzzle, peopled with vibrant, captivating characters. A generous sprinkling of humor adds potency to this skillful author's spell." Voice of Youth Advocates.

The **islands** of Chaldea. by Diana Wynne Jones; completed by Ursula Jones. Greenwillow Books, 2013. 352 p.

Grades: 4 5 6 7 8   **Fic**
    1. Girl apprentices 2. Wizards 3. Self-confidence 4. Magic 5. Aunts 6. Fantasy fiction
ISBN 9780062295071

LC 2013036422

Aileen's family of magic makers includes Aunt Beck, the most powerful magician on Skarr, but her own magic does not show itself until a mission for the King and a magical cat help her find strength and confidence.

"Diana Wynne Jones's humor, insight, and brisk, inventive style shine in this posthumously published novel. Aileen is embarrassed when she fails her Wise Woman initiation. She discovers her own very vigorous powers on a quest with her Wise Aunt Beck, a prince, and his attendant through the islands of Chaldea. Jones's imaginative vigor is unabated in this last, picaresque novel." Horn Book.

The **tough** guide to Fantasyland. Diana Wynne Jones. Firebird, c2006. 234 p.

Grades: 8 9 10 11 12   **Fic**
    1. Jones, Diana Wynne 2. Fantasy fiction 3. Humorous stories
ISBN 0886778328

A unique guide to fantasy literature helps readers understand such subjects as virginity, why High Priests are always evil, how Dark Lords always have minions, and useful tips on what to do when captured by a Goblin.

"This book contains alphabetic entries for people, places, and events in a fantasy world and information on how travelers can best find their way to the epic final battle. Icons conveniently identify lodging, food, and other necessary elements that travelers will need in their journey. . . . This brilliantly written satire perfectly celebrates and skewers the cliches of the fantasy genre." Voice of Youth Advocates.

Jones, Frewin

Destiny's path. Frewin Jones. HarperTeen, c2009. 329 p.: Warrior princess

Grades: 8 9 10 11 12   **Fic**
    1. 7th century 2. Women warriors 3. Princesses 4. Fate and fatalism 5. Imaginary wars and battles 6. Magic 7. Wales 8. Historical fantasy
ISBN 9780060871468

LC 2009014587

When fifteen-year-old Princess Branwen tries to turn away from her destiny as the one who will save Wales from the Saxons, the Shining Ones send an owl in the form of a young girl called Blodwedd to guide her and Rhodri on the right path.

"Branwen's compelling story leaves readers waiting for the sequel." Booklist.

Jones, Kelly (Kelly Anne), 1976-

Murder, magic, and what we wore. Kelly Jones. Alfred A. Knopf, 2017. 304 p.

Grades: 7 8 9 10 11 12   **Fic**
    1. Regency period (1811-1820) 2. Dressmaking 3. Magic 4. Spies 5. Murder 6. Sixteen-year-old girls 7. London, England 8.

Historical fantasy
ISBN 9780553535204

The year is 1818, the city is London, and 16-year-old Annis Whitworth has just learned that her father is dead and all his money is missing. And so, of course, she decides to become a spy.

"A cross between Jane Austen dramas and Harriet the Spy, this delightful strong female-led title mixes historical fiction and spy mystery with a touch of magic to produce a story filled with adventure." School Library Journal.

Jones, Kimberly, 1957-

Sand dollar summer. Kimberly K. Jones. Margaret K. McElderry Books, 2006. 206 p.

Grades: 5 6 7 8   **Fic**
    1. Twelve-year-old girls 2. Twelve-year-olds 3. Mothers 4. Single mothers 5. Children of single parents 6. Maine 7. Atlantic Ocean 8. Coming-of-age stories 9. Realistic fiction
ISBN 1416903623

LC 2005012740

When twelve-year-old Lise spends the summer on an island in Maine with her self-reliant mother and bright—but oddly mute—younger brother, her formerly safe world is complicated by an aged Indian neighbor, her mother's childhood friend, and a hurricane.

"The drama in [the] smart, tough, first-person narrative is understated; the spaces between the words are as eloquent as what is said. . . . The family story . . . is exquisitely told." Booklist.

Jones, Marcia Thornton

Woodford Brave. Marcia Thornton Jones; illustrations by Kevin Whipple. Calkins Creek, imprint of Highlights, 2015. 192 p.

Grades: 2 3 4 5 6   **Fic**
    1. Second World War era (1939-1945) 2. Family and war 3. Right and wrong 4. Comic book fans 5. Courage 6. Summer 7. Historical fiction 8. Graphic novel hybrids
ISBN 9781629793054

"Jones, best known for her contributions to the Bailey School Kids series, has written a moving period piece that explores heroism and the ghosts we all live with." Booklist.

Jones, Patrick, 1961-

Bridge. Patrick Jones. Lerner Pub Group, 2014. 92 p.: The alternative

Grades: 6 7 8 9 10 11 12   **Fic**
    1. Hispanic American teenage boys 2. Immigrant families 3. Responsibility in teenage boys 4. High school students 5. Truancy 6. Realistic fiction 7. High interest-low vocabulary books
ISBN 9781467744829

"The author's effective use of flashbacks and crisp portraits of positive adult characters add further emotional depth to this emotional glimpse at the high-pressure difficulties facing children in immigrant families. References to O'Brien's book will likely spark the interest of readers in that title as well." Publishers Weekly.

Jones, Traci L.

Silhouetted by the blue. Traci L. Jones. Farrar Straus Giroux, 2011. 208 p.

Grades: 5 6 7 8   **Fic**
    1. African American teenage girls 2. Children of people with depression 3. Theater 4. Responsibility 5. Grief 6. Realistic

fiction 7. African American fiction
ISBN 9780374369149

LC 2010008419

After the death of her mother in an automobile accident, seventh-grader Serena, who has gotten the lead in her middle school play, is left to handle the day-to-day challenges of caring for herself and her younger brother when their father cannot pull himself out of his depression.

"Jones has written another winner with this beautiful, haunting tale rich in story and characterization." Booklist.

Joseph, Lynn

The **color** of my words. Lynn Joseph. Joanna Cotler Books, 2000. 138 p.

Grades: 5 6 7 8   **Fic**
1. Brothers -- Death 2. Families 3. Brothers and sisters 4. Twelve-year-old girls 5. Dominican Republic 6. Coming-of-age stories 7. Realistic fiction
ISBN 0060282320

LC 00022440

When life gets difficult for Ana Rosa, a twelve-year-old would-be writer living in a small village in the Dominican Republic, she can depend on her older brother to make her feel better—until the life-changing events on her thirteenth birthday.

"A finely crafted novel, lovely and lyrical." School Library Journal.

Flowers in the sky. by Lynn Joseph. HarperTeen, 2013. 112 p.

Grades: 8 9 10 11 12   **Fic**
1. Teenage immigrants 2. Dominican Americans 3. Teenage romance 4. Brothers and sisters 5. Fifteen-year-old girls 6. New York City 7. Dominican Republic 8. Realistic fiction 9. Coming-of-age stories
ISBN 9780060297947

LC 2012038122

Fifteen-year-old Nina immigrates from the Dominican Republic to New York to live with her older brother and must reconcile the realities of Washington Heights with the dreams of the U.S. her mami envisioned for her. Provided by publisher.

Juby, Susan, 1969-

The **fashion** committee. by Susan Juby. Viking Books for Young Readers, 2017. 304 p.

Grades: 7 8 9 10   **Fic**
1. Competition 2. Fashion 3. Small towns 4. Children of drug abusers 5. Scholarships and fellowships 6. Canada 7. Realistic fiction
ISBN 9780451468789

Charlie and John are both gunning for the same scholarship to a private arts high school. For this coveted spot, they must compete in a fashion competition—and only one can win.

"Juby's thoughtful bildungsroman excels in showcasing and normalizing those on society's fringe—whether it be in her bold portrayal of differing socio-economic class issues or subtle examination of gender identity." Kirkus.

Jung, Mike

The **boys** in the back row. Mike Jung. Levine Querido, 2020 272 p.

Grades: 4 5 6 7   **Fic**
1. Best friends 2. Moving to a new state 3. Fan conventions 4. Adventure 5. Sneakiness 6. Realistic fiction
ISBN 9781646140114

Best friends Matt and Eric are hatching a plan for one big final adventure together before Eric moves away: during the marching band competition at a Giant Amusement Park, they will sneak away to a nearby comics convention and meet their idol: a famous comic creator. Without cell phones. Or transportation. Or permission.

"It is both refreshing and reassuring to read a tale that explores a loving friendship between two boys who defy societal gender norms and are simply authentic to themselves and one another." Kirkus

Geeks, girls, and secret identities. by Mike Jung; with illustrations by Mike Maihack. Arthur A. Levine Books, 2012. 256 p.

Grades: 3 4 5 6 7   **Fic**
1. Superheroes 2. Fan clubs 3. Robots 4. Middle schools 5. Schools 6. Superhero stories
ISBN 9780545335485

LC 2011042548

Twelve-year-old Vincent and his fellow members of the Captain Stupendous Fan Club help out when someone new becomes Earth's most famous superhero, without knowing anything about him, just as evil Professor Mayhem and his robot arrive in Copperplate City.

Juster, Norton, 1929-2021

The **annotated** Phantom tollbooth. by Norton Juster; illustrations by Jules Feiffer; introduction and notes by Leonard Marcus. Alfred A. Knopf, 2011. 320 p.

Grades: Adult Professional   **Fic**
1. Juster, Norton, 1929- Phantom tollbooth. 2. Boredom in boys 3. Boys and dogs 4. Numbers 5. Words 6. Rescues 7. Fantasy fiction 8. Allegories
ISBN 9780375857157

LC 2011013174

"Still ferrying dazzled readers to Dictionopolis and beyond 50 years after his first appearance, young Milo is accompanied this time through by encyclopedic commentary from our generation's leading (and most readable) expert on the history of children's literature and publishing. . . . Leonard opens with typically lucid and well-organized pictures of both Juster's and Feiffer's formative years and later careers, interwoven with accounts of the book's conception, publication and critical response. In notes running alongside the ensuing facsimile, he puts on an intellectual show. . . . he delivers notes on topics as diverse as the etymological origins of BALDERDASH! and mimetic architecture to textual parallels with the Wizard of Oz and echoes of Winsor McKay and George Grosz in the art. Family photos, scrawled notes and images of handwritten and typescript manuscript pages further gloss a work that never ages nor fails to astonish." Kirkus.

Kade, J. V.

Bot Wars. by J.V. Kade. Dial Books for Young Readers, 2013. 368 p.: Bot Wars

Grades: 5 6 7 8   **Fic**
1. Robots 2. Father-separated boys 3. Dystopias 4. Imaginary wars and battles 5. Missing persons 6. Science fiction
ISBN 9780803738607

LC 2012017682

In a futuristic world where humans and robots are at war, a boy goes on a search to find his missing military father.

Kade, Stacey

The **rules.** Stacey Kade. Hyperion, 2013. 416 p.: Project paper doll

Grades: 7 8 9 10 11 12   **Fic**
1. Genetic engineering 2. Sixteen-year-old girls 3. Secret identity

4. Interpersonal relations 5. High schools 6. Science fiction
ISBN 9781423153283

LC 2012033732

At sixteen, Ariane Tucker has been careful to elude those seeking her since her escape from a genetics lab ten years earlier, but the attention of classmate Zane, both frightening and intoxicating, tempts her to risk violating at least one of her adoptive father's five simple rules.

Kadohata, Cynthia

★ **Cracker!**: the best dog in Vietnam. Cynthia Kadohata. Atheneum Books for Young Readers, 2007. 312 p.

Grades: 5 6 7 8   Fic
1. Teenage soldiers 2. German shepherd dog 3. Vietnam War, 1961-1975 4. Dogs -- War use 5. Animal trainers 6. Vietnam 7. Historical fiction 8. Stories told by animals
ISBN 1416906371

LC 2006022022

A young soldier in Vietnam bonds with his bomb-sniffing dog.

"The author tells a stirring, realistic story of America's war in Vietnam, using the alternating viewpoints of an army dog named Cracker and her 17-year-old handler, Rick Hanski. . . . The heartfelt tale explores the close bond of the scout-dog team." Booklist.

Half a world away. Cynthia Kadohata. Atheneum Books for Young Readers, [2014] 240 p.

Grades: 5 6 7 8   Fic
1. Adopted boys 2. International adoption 3. Emotional problems of boys 4. Emotional problems 5. Abandoned children 6. Kazakhstan 7. Realistic fiction
ISBN 9781442412750

LC 2013031627

Twelve-year-old Jaden, an emotionally damaged adopted boy fascinated by electricity, feels a connection to a small, weak toddler with special needs in Kazakhstan, where Jaden's family is trying to adopt a "normal" baby.

"Twelve-year-old Jaden, adopted from Romania and suffering from attachment disorder, travels to Kazakhstan with his parents, who have decided to adopt a second child. As his parents struggle to bond with an emotionally unresponsive infant, Jaden bonds with disabled toddler Dimash—a breakthrough for Jaden. This story about a troubled adoptee and the equally troubling issues of international adoption is compelling and involving." Horn Book.

★ **Kira-kira**. Cynthia Kadohata. Atheneum Books for Young Readers, c2004. 256 p.

Grades: 5 6 7 8   Fic
1. 1950s 2. Japanese American girls 3. Brothers and sisters of sick children 4. Grief 5. Japanese American families 6. Sisters -- Death 7. Georgia 8. Historical fiction
ISBN 0689856393

LC 2003000737

Newbery Medal, 2005.

Chronicles the close friendship between two Japanese-American sisters growing up in rural Georgia during the late 1950s and early 1960s, and the despair when one sister becomes terminally ill.

"This beautifully written story tells of a girl struggling to find her own way in a family torn by illness and horrendous work conditions. . . . All of the characters are believable and well developed." School Library Journal.

★ A **million** shades of gray. Cynthia Kadohata. Atheneum Books for Young Readers, 2010. 224 p.

Grades: 5 6 7 8   Fic
1. Viet Cong. 2. 1970s 3. Parent-separated teenagers 4. Boys and elephants 5. Escapes 6. Elephants 7. Survival 8. Vietnam 9. Historical fiction
ISBN 9781416918837

LC 2009033307

In 1975 after American troops pull out of Vietnam, a thirteen-year-old boy and his beloved elephant escape into the jungle when the Viet Cong attack his village.

"Kadohata delves deep into the soul of her protagonist while making a faraway place and stark consequences of war seem very near." Publishers Weekly.

Outside beauty. Cynthia Kadohata. Atheneum Books for Young Readers, c2008. 265 p.

Grades: 5 6 7 8   Fic
1. 1980s 2. Japanese American teenage girls 3. Half-sisters 4. Fathers and daughters 5. Mothers and daughters 6. Beauty 7. Chicago, Illinois 8. Realistic fiction
ISBN 9780689865756

LC 2007039711

Thirteen-year-old Shelby and her three sisters must go to live with their respective fathers while their mother, who has trained them to rely on their looks, recovers from a car accident that scarred her face.

"Kadohata's gifts for creating and containing drama and for careful definition of character prove as powerful as ever in this wise, tender and compelling novel." Publishers Weekly.

★ A **place** to belong. Cynthia Kadohata; illustrated by Julia Kuo. Atheneum, 2019. 416 p.

Grades: 4 5 6 7 8   Fic
1. 20th century 2. Japanese American girls 3. Identity (Psychology) 4. Postwar life 5. Immigration and emigration 6. Immigrants 7. Hiroshima, Japan 8. Japan 9. Historical fiction
ISBN 9781481446648

LC 2018043629

Twelve-year-old Hanako and her family, reeling from their confinement in an internment camp, renounce their American citizenship to move to Hiroshima, a city devastated by the atomic bomb dropped by Americans.

★ The **thing** about luck. Cynthia Kadohata; illustrated by Julia Kuo. Atheneum Books for Young Readers, 2013. 288 p.

Grades: 5 6 7 8   Fic
1. Japanese American girls 2. Migrant agricultural laborers 3. Grandparents 4. Brothers and sisters 5. Bad luck 6. Kansas 7. Realistic fiction
ISBN 9781416918820

LC 2012021287

National Book Award for Young People's Literature, 2013.

Just when twelve-year-old Summer thinks nothing else can possibly go wrong in a year of bad luck, an emergency takes her parents to Japan, leaving Summer to care for her little brother while helping her grandmother cook and do laundry for harvest workers.

"Kadohata expertly captures the uncertainties of the tween years as Summer navigates the balance of childlike concerns with the onset of increasingly grown-up responsibilities." School Library Journal.

★ **Weedflower**. Cynthia Kadohata. Atheneum Books for Young Readers, 2006. 272 p.

Grades: 5 6 7 8   Fic
1. 1940s 2. Japanese American girls 3. Determination in girls

4. Japanese American families 5. Japanese Americans -- Forced removal and incarceration, 1942-1945 6. World War II 7. California 8. Arizona 9. Historical fiction
ISBN 0689865740

LC 2004024912

After twelve-year-old Sumiko and her Japanese-American family are relocated from their flower farm in southern California to an internment camp on a Mojave Indian reservation in Arizona, she helps her family and neighbors, becomes friends with a local Indian boy, and tries to hold on to her dream of owning a flower shop.

"Sumiko is a sympathetic heroine, surrounded by well-crafted, fascinating people. The concise yet lyrical prose conveys her story in a compelling narrative." School Library Journal.

Kagawa, Julie

The **eternity** cure. Julie Kagawa. Harlequin Teen, 2013. 304 p.: Blood of Eden
Grades: 7 8 9 10 11 12　　　　　**Fic**
1. Vampires 2. Immortality 3. Viruses 4. Zombies 5. Urban fantasy 6. Apocalyptic fiction
ISBN 9780373210695

Elevated to Queen of the Underworld after attaining immortality, Kate Winters resolves to win the love of Henry despite his increasing secretiveness, a situation that escalates when Henry is abducted by the King of the Titans, triggering a dangerous war and a pact with Henry's first wife, Persephone.

The **forever** song. Julie Kagawa. Harlequin Teen, 2014. 304 p.: Blood of Eden
Grades: 7 8 9 10 11 12　　　　　**Fic**
1. Vampires 2. Immortality 3. Viruses 4. Zombies 5. Urban fantasy 6. Apocalyptic fiction
ISBN 9780373211128

Embracing her vampire side after the death of her beloved Zeke, Allie teams up with her companions to hunt the psychopathic vampire responsible for his murder only to be confronted with brutal surprises.

The **immortal** rules. Julie Kagawa. Harlequin Teen, 2012. 512 p.: Blood of Eden
Grades: 7 8 9 10 11 12　　　　　**Fic**
1. Vampires 2. Immortality 3. Zombies 4. Near future 5. Viruses 6. Urban fantasy 7. Apocalyptic fiction
ISBN 9780373210510

After Allison is forced to flee the city, she joins a band of humans who are seeking a legend—a possible cure to the disease that killed off most of humankind and created the creatures threatening humans and vampires alike.

"Kagawa wraps excellent writing and skillful plotting around a well-developed concept and engaging characters, resulting in a fresh and imaginative thrill-ride that deserves a wide audience." Publishers Weekly.

Talon. Julie Kagawa. Harlequin Books Teen, 2014 400 p.: Talon saga
Grades: 8 9 10 11　　　　　**Fic**
1. Dragons 2. Shapeshifters 3. Twin brothers and sisters 4. Love triangles 5. Teenagers 6. California 7. Urban fantasy
ISBN 9780373211395

Siblings Ember and Dante Hill prepare for destined positions in the world of Talon only to be hunted by a dragon-slaying soldier who questions everything he has been taught.

"Young love, sibling rivalry, rogue dragons, and plots for world domination create an intriguing mix in this new series." Horn Book.

Kapit, Sarah

Get a grip, Vivy Cohen! Sarah Kapit. Dial Books for Young Readers, 2020. 200 p.
Grades: 4 5 6 7 8　　　　　**Fic**
1. Baseball 2. Girls with autism 3. Letter writing 4. Bullying and bullies 5. Pen pals 6. Baseball stories 7. Realistic fiction 8. Epistolary novels
ISBN 9780525554189

In this perfectly pitched novel-in-letters, autistic eleven-year-old Vivy Cohen won't let anything stop her from playing baseball—not when she has a major-league star as her pen pal.

Katcher, Brian

The **improbable** theory of Ana and Zak. Brian Katcher. Katherine Tegen Books, an imprint of HarperCollinsPublishers, [2015] 336 p.
Grades: 7 8 9 10 11 12　　　　　**Fic**
1. Fan conventions 2. Contests 3. Missing teenage boys 4. Science fiction fandom 5. Genius 6. Seattle, Washington 7. Washington (State) 8. Contemporary romances 9. Romantic comedies
ISBN 9780062272775

LC 2014030718

Ana is an honor student obsessed with being successful at everything academic, Clayton is her thirteen-year-old genius brother, the youngest student in their high school and Zak is a gamer who is forced to join the quiz team by his teacher—but when Clayton sneaks off to a science fiction convention in Seattle while they are all there for a quiz bowl tournament, Ana is forced to rely on the unreliable Zak to find him.

"Type-A Ana and relaxed geek Zak take turns narrating as they spend a night searching for Ana's younger brother at a comic-book convention. The he said/she said romance has been done before, of course, but the unconventional setting, quirky convention-goers, and many over-the-top hijinks (e.g., multiple fights, a sci-fi-themed gay wedding, inadvertent drug-running) give this one a unique twist." Horn Book.

Katsoulis, Gregory Scott

Access restricted. Gregory Scott Katsoulis. Harlequin Books 2018 304 p.: Word$
Grades: 7 8 9 10 11 12　　　　　**Fic**
1. Silence and silent things 2. Resistance to government 3. Escapes 4. Sisters 5. Parent-separated teenage girls 6. Dystopian fiction 7. Science fiction
ISBN 9781335016256

After taking down Silas Rog and freeing the city from his grasp, Speth journeys outside the dome in search of her parents, who were sold into indentured servitude years earlier.

Kaufman, Amie

Aurora rising. Amie Kaufman and Jay Kristoff. Alfred A. Knopf, 2019. 480 p.: Aurora cycle
Grades: 8 9 10 11 12　　　　　**Fic**
1. Military cadets 2. Stowaways 3. Space vehicles 4. Fugitives 5. Misfits (Persons) 6. Space 7. Space opera 8. Science fiction thrillers 9. Science fiction
ISBN 9781524720971

LC 2018026944

Relegated by a misguided act of heroism to a squad comprised of his school's hopeless misfits, a graduating cadet in a 24th-century space academy rescues a centuries-hibernating girl from interdimensional space only to be swept up in an interstellar war millions of years in the making.

"Rotating perspectives and never-flagging energy propel this narrative forward, which, if it weren't compelling enough on its own, is given illustrious life by its ragtag, always-at-odds cast." Booklist.

Gemina. Amie Kaufman & Jay Kristoff; journal illustrations by Marie Lu. Alfred A. Knopf, 2016. 672 p.: Illuminae files
Grades: 8 9 10 11 12   **Fic**
    1. Space vehicles 2. Artificial intelligence 3. Space flight 4. Space stations 5. Corporations 6. Space opera 7. Science fiction
ISBN 9780553499155
A sequel to Illuminae follows the experiences of privileged station captain's daughter Hanna and Nik, a reluctant crime family member, who confront the next wave of the BeiTech assault on board the isolated Jump Station Heimdall.
"An action-packed thrill ride and stellar head trip." Kirkus.

Illuminae. Amie Kaufman; Jay Kristoff. Alfred A. Knopf, 2015. 608 p.: Illuminae files
Grades: 8 9 10 11 12   **Fic**
    1. Space flight 2. Artificial intelligence 3. Plague 4. Electronic records 5. Refugees 6. Space opera 7. Science fiction 8. Science fiction thrillers
ISBN 9780553499117
                      LC 2014017908
The planet Kerenza is attacked, and Kady and Ezra find themselves on a space fleet fleeing the enemy, while their ship's artificial intelligence system and a deadly plague may be the end of them all.
"This sci-fi romance novel's minimalist, dynamic format—the story is told entirely through instant messages, transcripts, letters, reports, etc.—increases the sense of tension and adds the reading experience." Horn Book Guide.

Obsidio. Amie Kaufman & Jay Kristoff; with journal illustrations by Marie Lu. Alfred A. Knopf, [2018] 608 p.: Illuminae files
Grades: 8 9 10 11 12   **Fic**
    1. Space vehicles 2. Artificial intelligence 3. Space flight 4. Space stations 5. Corporations 6. Space opera 7. Science fiction
ISBN 9780553499209
                      LC bl2018020416
Kady, Ezra, Hanna, Nik reluctantly return to Kerenza with other refugees, while Asha has joined Kerenza's ragtag underground resistance, and when she reconnects with her old flame Rhys, the two find themselves on opposite sides of the conflict.

The **world** between blinks. Amie Kaufman and Ryan Graudin. Quill Tree Books, 2021. 304 p.: World between blinks
Grades: 4 5 6 7   **Fic**
    1. Cousins 2. Child adventurers 3. Parallel universes 4. Lost articles 5. Treasure hunting maps 6. South Carolina 7. Gateway fantasy 8. Fantasy fiction
ISBN 9780062882240
Whenever Jake and Marisol get together, adventure follows. They have their late Nana to thank for that. Her epic trips and treasure hunts were legendary. With the whole family reuniting for one last summer vacation at Nana's home, the cousins are prepared for an extraordinary trip of their own. Following a map Nana left behind, Jake and Marisol sneak out to a nearby lighthouse, then accidentally slip into another world! The World Between Blinks is a magical place, where all sorts of lost things and people wind up. Everywhere they turn, the cousins find real mysteries from history and a few they thought were just myths, from pilot Amelia Earhart to the fabled city of Atlantis. But the man

who holds the key to Jake and Marisol's journey home doesn't want to be found . . . and if the cousins don't catch him fast, they could end up lost in this world forever.
"Readers will have enormous fun following the cousins as they navigate their strange situation and piece together their place in it, all while learning lessons on the power of love, the value of memories, and the wonders that the world holds." Booklist

Keith, Harold, 1903-1998
Rifles for Watie. Harold Keith. Crowell, 1957. 332 p.
Grades: 6 7 8 9   **Fic**
    1. Watie, Stand, 1806-1871 2. United States Army -- History -- Civil War, 1861-1865 3. Sixteen-year-old boys 4. Teenage soldiers 5. Teenage spies 6. Civil war 7. Union soldiers 8. United States 9. War stories 10. Historical fiction 11. Classics
ISBN 006447030X
                      LC 57010280
Newbery Medal, 1958.
With fighting erupting around his Kansas farm, 16-year-old Jefferson Davis Bussey can hardly wait to join the Union forces. When he infiltrates Colonel Watie's Confederate camp as a spy, he discovers the enemy is much like himself—only fighting for a different cause.
"An exceptionally well-written story of the Civil War as it was fought in the western states." Bulletin of the Center for Children's Books.

Keller, Julia
Back home. Julia Keller. Egmont USA, 2009. 194 p.
Grades: 6 7 8 9   **Fic**
    1. Children of veterans 2. Brain injury 3. Family and war 4. Family problems 5. Thirteen-year-old girls 6. Realistic fiction
ISBN 9781606840481
                      LC 2009015877
Thirteen-year-old Rachel Browning understands that her father will be different after being injured in the Iraq War, but no one is prepared for the impact that his traumatic brain injury and other wounds have on the entire family.
"No one who reads this heartbreaking book will ever forget it. With integrity, authenticity, and immediacy, Keller has captured the extraordinary complexity and challenge of unexpected change and, to her everlasting credit, unsparingly shares the whole truth of it with her readers." Booklist.

Kelly, Erin Entrada
Blackbird fly. by Erin Entrada Kelly; with illustrations by Betsy Peterschmidt. Greenwillow Books, an imprint of HarperCollinsPublishers, 2015. 304 p.
Grades: 4 5 6 7 8   **Fic**
    1. Filipino Americans 2. Bullying and bullies 3. Guitar 4. Asian American girls 5. Music 6. Louisiana 7. Realistic fiction
ISBN 9780062238610
                      LC 2014029444
Bullied at school, eighth-grader Apple, a Filipino American who loves the music of the Beatles, decides to change her life by learning how to play the guitar.
"Debut author Kelly skillfully weaves together the story of misfit Apple, her love of music, and a budding romance with a new boy at school, while never losing focus on the central issue of what it is like to be the 'other. . .' ." Booklist.

★ **Hello,** universe. Erin Entrada Kelly. Greenwillow Books, an imprint of HarperCollins Publishers, [2017] 320 p.

Grades: 4 5 6 7　　　　　　　　　　　　　**Fic**
1. Filipino Americans 2. Bullying and bullies 3. Friendship 4. Missing boys 5. Rescues 6. Realistic fiction
ISBN 9780062414151
　　　　　　　　　　　　　　LC 2016022723
Newbery Medal, 2018.
Lives of four misfits are intertwined when a bully's prank lands shy Virgil at the bottom of a well and Valencia, Kaori, and Gen band together in an epic quest to find and rescue him.
"An original and resonant exploration of interconnectedness and friendship." Kirkus.

The **land** of forgotten girls. by Erin Entrada Kelly. Greenwillow Books, an imprint of HarperCollinsPublishers, 2016. 304 p.
Grades: 3 4 5 6　　　　　　　　　　　　　**Fic**
1. Father-deserted children 2. Sisters 3. Imagination in girls 4. Filipino American girls 5. Filipinos 6. Louisiana 7. Realistic fiction
ISBN 9780062238641
　　　　　　　　　　　　　　LC 2015019330
Abandoned by their father and living in poverty with their heartless stepmother in Louisiana, two sisters from the Philippines, twelve-year-old Sol and six-year-old Ming, learn the true meaning of family.
"Readers will become engrossed in the enchanting plot propelled by delightful narration. This book will appeal to a broad array of readers, as it has a little bit of eveverything: fantasy, realism, sisterhood, friendship, suspense, and humor." School Library Journal.

★ **We** dream of space. Erin Entrada Kelly. Greenwillow Books, 2020 304 p.
Grades: 4 5 6 7 8　　　　　　　　　　　　**Fic**
1. 1980s 2. Brothers and sisters 3. Family problems 4. Interpersonal relations 5. Science projects 6. Middle school students 7. Delaware 8. Historical fiction
ISBN 9780062747303
Cash, Fitch, and Bird Thomas are three siblings in seventh grade together in Park, Delaware. In 1986, as the country waits expectantly for the launch of the Space Shuttle Challenger, they each struggle with their own personal anxieties.
"The author never shies from difficult realities—whether national tragedy or domestic troubles—and offers no tidy solutions, instead allowing her characters a newfound sense of agency and the sweet reward of finding solace in each other. Another wondrous title from a remarkably talented author." Booklist.

Kelly, Jacqueline
★ The **curious** world of Calpurnia Tate. Jacqueline Kelly. Henry Holt and Company, 2015. 352 p.: Calpurnia Tate
Grades: 4 5 6　　　　　　　　　　　　　**Fic**
1. 1900s (Decade) 2. Veterinarians 3. Gender role 4. Hurricanes 5. Families 6. Thirteen-year-old girls 7. Texas 8. Historical fiction
ISBN 9780805097443
　　　　　　　　　　　　　　LC 2015000920
In rural Texas in 1900, when a storm blows change into town in the form of a visiting veterinarian, thirteen-year-old Callie discovers a life and a vocation she desperately wants. But with societal expectations as they are, she will need all her wits and courage to realize her dreams. Provided by publisher.
"Recommended for fans of the original novel and strong readers who enjoy character-driven narratives." School Library Journal.

★ The **evolution** of Calpurnia Tate. Jacqueline Kelly. Henry Holt and Co., 2009. 352 p.: Calpurnia Tate
Grades: 4 5 6 7　　　　　　　　　　　　　**Fic**
1. 1890s 2. Nature study 3. Self-discovery in girls 4. Self-discovery 5. Families 6. Naturalists 7. Texas 8. Historical fiction 9. Coming-of-age stories
ISBN 9780805088410
　　　　　　　　　　　　　　LC 2008040595
In central Texas in 1899, eleven-year-old Callie Vee Tate is instructed to be a lady by her mother, learns about love from the older three of her six brothers, and studies the natural world with her grandfather, the latter of which leads to an important discovery.
"Callie is a charming, inquisitive protagonist; a joyous, bright, and thoughtful creation. . . . Several scenes . . . mix gentle humor and pathos to great effect." School Library Journal.

Kelly, Lynne, 1969-
Chained. Lynne Kelly. Farrar Straus Giroux, 2012. 176 p.
Grades: 4 5 6　　　　　　　　　　　　　**Fic**
1. Boys and elephants 2. Animal welfare 3. Circus 4. Elephants 5. Child labor 6. India
ISBN 9780374312374
　　　　　　　　　　　　　　LC 2011031767
To work off a family debt, ten-year-old Hastin leaves his desert village in India to work as a circus elephant keeper but many challenges await him, including trying to keep Nandita, a sweet elephant, safe from the cruel circus owner.

Kemmerer, Brigid
A **heart** so fierce and broken. by Brigid Kemmerer. Bloomsbury, 2020 450 p.: Cursebreaker series
Grades: 8 9 10 11 12　　　　　　　　　　　**Fic**
1. Heirs and heiresses 2. Inheritance and succession 3. Princes 4. People with post-traumatic stress disorder 5. Post-traumatic stress disorder 6. Fairy tale and folklore-inspired fiction 7. Fantasy fiction 8. First-person narratives
ISBN 9781681195117
The curse is finally broken, but Prince Rhen of Emberfall faces darker troubles still. Rumors circulate that he is not the true heir and that forbidden magic has been unleashed in Emberfall. Loyalties are tested and new love blooms in a kingdom on the brink of war.
"This sweeping, romantic epic repeatedly turns the tables on the fantasy tropes that readers might be expecting." Kirkus.

Kenneally, Miranda
Racing Savannah. Miranda Kenneally. Sourcebooks Fire, 2013 304 p.: Hundred Oaks
Grades: 8 9 10 11 12　　　　　　　　　　　**Fic**
1. Teenage equestrians 2. Teenage girls and horses 3. Horse farms 4. Moving to a new state 5. Teenage romance 6. Tennessee 7. Franklin, Tennessee 8. Contemporary romances 9. Teen chick lit
ISBN 9781402284762
"Kenneally (Stealing Parker, 2012) again looks at sports through a female lens, this time tackling male-dominated horse racing, in this fourth Hundred Oaks novel. Savannah, her widowed horse-trainer father, and her father's pregnant girlfriend move to Tennessee's Cedar Hill, a farm that trains horses for races including the Kentucky Derby... The author's knack for weaving forbidden romance, breezy dialogue, and details of this lesser-known sports venue places it in the winner's circle for reluctant readers and chick-lit fans." Booklist.

Kent, Rose

Kimchi & calamari. Rose Kent. Harper Collins Publishers, 2007. 240 p.

Grades: 4 5 6 7 **Fic**
1. Adoption 2. Interracial adoption 3. Korean Americans 4. Korean American teenage boys 5. Fourteen-year-old boys 6. Realistic fiction
ISBN 0060837691

LC 2006020041

Adopted from Korea by Italian parents, fourteen-year-old Joseph Calderaro begins to make important self-discoveries about race and family after his social studies teacher assigns an essay on cultural heritage and tracing the past.

"Fourteen-year-old Korean adoptee Joseph Calderaro is stumped when his social studies teacher assigns an ancestry essay. . . . Kent's debut novel humorously captures the feelings of a young teen who thoroughly enjoys his Italian-American family but still wonders about his birth parents." Booklist.

Kenyon, Sherrilyn, 1965-

Infinity: chronicles of Nick. Sherrilyn Kenyon. St. Martin's Press, 2010 464 p.: Chronicles of Nick

Grades: 7 8 9 10 11 12 **Fic**
1. Vampires 2. Survival 3. Vampire slayers 4. Good and evil 5. Supernatural 6. Urban fantasy
ISBN 9780312599072

Fourteen-year-old sarcastic, street-savvy Nick is drawn into the world of the Dark-Hunters, but must hide his participation in the battle against werewolves, vampires, and zombies from his mother and high school principal.

Kephart, Beth

Going over. Beth Kephart. Chronicle Books, c2014. 262 p.

Grades: 8 9 10 11 12 **Fic**
1. 1980s 2. Berlin Wall 3. Separated friends, relatives, etc 4. Graffiti 5. Immigrants 6. Families 7. Berlin, Germany 8. Germany 9. Historical fiction
ISBN 9781452124575

LC 2012046894

In the early 1980s Ada and Stefan are young, would-be lovers living on opposite sides of the Berlin Wall—Ada lives with her mother and grandmother and paints graffiti on the Wall, and Stefan lives with his grandmother in the East and dreams of escaping to the West.

"In a present-tense narration alternating between Ada's first-person and Stefan's second-person, the young lovers on opposite sides of the Berlin Wall in 1983 plan for Stefan's escape to the West. Kephart works romantic chemistry into a danger-packed plot with moving results in this captivating glimpse into an underrepresented era that will appeal to older readers with a taste for literary historical fiction." Horn Book.

Includes bibliographical references (p. [259]-262).

The **heart** is not a size. Beth Kephart. HarperTeen/Balzer & Bray, 2010. 256 p.

Grades: 7 8 9 10 **Fic**
1. Self-perception in teenage girls 2. Teenage volunteers 3. Poverty 4. Volunteers 5. Fifteen-year-old girls 6. Mexico 7. Pennsylvania 8. Realistic fiction
ISBN 9780061470486

LC 2008055721

Fifteen-year-old Georgia learns a great deal about herself and her troubled best friend Riley when they become part of a group of suburban Pennsylvania teenagers that go to Anapra, a squatters village in the border town of Juarez, Mexico, to undertake a community construction project.

"Kephart's prose is typically poetic. She pens a faster-paced novel that explores teens' inner selves. . . . The writing is vivid, enabling readers to visualize Anapra's desolation and hope." Voice of Youth Advocates.

This is the story of you. Beth Kephart. Chronicle Books, 2016. 264 p.

Grades: 7 8 9 10 11 12 **Fic**
1. Hurricanes 2. Survival (after hurricanes) 3. Mother-separated teenage girls 4. Island life 5. Seventeen-year-old girls 6. New Jersey 7. Realistic fiction 8. Survival stories
ISBN 9781452142845

LC 2015003765

Seventeen-year-old Mira lives in a small island beach town off the coast of New Jersey year-round, and when a devastating superstorm strikes she will face the storm's wrath and the destruction it leaves behind alone.

"At once an exploration of the unrelenting power of nature and a reminder of the one thing in the world that is irreplaceable: family." Booklist.

Undercover. Beth Kephart. HarperTeen, c2007. 278 p.

Grades: 8 9 10 11 12 **Fic**
1. High school students 2. Teenagers 3. Teenage girls 4. Teenage girl authors 5. Ghostwriters 6. Contemporary romances 7. Classics-inspired fiction
ISBN 9780061238932

LC 2007002981

High school sophomore Elisa is used to observing while going unnoticed except when classmates ask her to write love notes for them, but a teacher's recognition of her talent, a "client's" desire for her friendship, a love of ice skating, and her parent's marital problems draw her out of herself.

"Kephart tells a moving story. . . . Readers will fall easily into the compelling premise and Elisa's memorable, graceful voice." Booklist.

Wild blues. Beth Kephart; illustrated by William Sulit. Simon & Schuster 2018 256 p.

Grades: 5 6 7 8 9 **Fic**
1. Uncle and niece 2. Little people 3. Kidnapping 4. Women with cancer 5. Thirteen-year-old girls 6. Adventure stories
ISBN 9781481491532

Thirteen-year-old Lizzie relates, through a victim statement, her harrowing journey through the Adirondacks seeking her disabled friend, Matias, who was kidnapped by escaped convicts.

Keplinger, Kody

Run. Kody Keplinger. Scholastic Press, 2016. 304 p.

Grades: 7 8 9 10 11 12 **Fic**
1. Runaway teenage girls 2. Teenagers who are blind 3. Female friendship 4. Bisexual teenagers 5. Children of drug abusers 6. Kentucky 7. Realistic fiction
ISBN 9780545831130

A wild girl from a dysfunctional family and a straight-laced, legally blind girl with overbearing parents forge an unlikely best friendship that is tested by a brush with the law that compels the pair to run away, a decision that pits them against the authorities, ugly secrets and their own beliefs.

"A good unlikely friendship story with compelling characters and a nuanced portrait of disability and small-town life." School Library Journal.

That's not what happened. Kody Keplinger. Scholastic Press, 2018. 336 p.

Grades: 7 8 9 10 11 12   **Fic**
1. School shootings 2. Truthfulness and falsehood 3. Teenage girl murder victims 4. Memories 5. Loss (Psychology) 6. Realistic fiction
ISBN 9781338186529

LC 2017060501

In the three years since the Virgil County High School Massacre, a story has grown up around one of the victims, Sarah McHale, that says she died proclaiming her Christian faith—but Leanne Bauer was there, and knows what happened, and she has a choice: stay silent and let people believe in Sarah's martyrdom, or tell the truth.

Kessler, Liz

Emily Windsnap and the castle in the mist. Liz Kessler; illustrated by Natacha Ledwidge. Candlewick Press, 2007. 208 p.: Emily Windsnap

Grades: 3 4 5 6   **Fic**
1. Mermaids 2. Twelve-year-old girls 3. Curses 4. Preteen girls 5. Neptune (Roman deity) 6. Fantasy fiction
ISBN 9780763633301

LC 2006051835

When she incurs Neptune's wrath by finding a diamond ring buried under rocks in the ocean, Emily is put under a curse that will force her to choose to be either a mermaid or a human and split up her parents forever.

Emily Windsnap and the land of the midnight sun. Liz Kessler. Candlewick Press, 2013. 288 p.: Emily Windsnap

Grades: 4 5 6   **Fic**
1. Mermaids 2. Oceans 3. Memory 4. Quests 5. Neptune (Roman deity) 6. Fantasy fiction
ISBN 9780763658243

Continues the undersea adventures of the intrepid young half-mermaid, who plunges into a scheme to reunite with her father.

The **tail** of Emily Windsnap. by Liz Kessler; illustrated by Sarah Gibb. Candlewick Press, 2004. 224 p.: Emily Windsnap

Grades: 4 5 6   **Fic**
1. Twelve-year-old girls 2. Mermaids 3. Family secrets 4. Father-separated children 5. Reunions 6. Fantasy fiction
ISBN 0763624837

LC 2003065284

After finally convincing her mother that she should take swimming lessons, twelve-year-old Emily discovers a terrible and wonderful secret about herself that opens up a whole new world.

When the world was ours. Liz Kessler Aladdin, 2021 352 p.

Grades: 6 7 8 9   **Fic**
1. Second World War era (1939-1945) 2. World War II 3. Best friends 4. Separated friends, relatives, etc 5. Friendship 6. Vienna, Austria 7. Austria 8. Historical fiction
ISBN 9781534499652

Torn apart by the historical events leading up to World War II, three friends from 1936 Vienna are scattered to different countries as darkness spreads throughout Europe, impacting their families and their bonds with each other.

"The Jewish characters' first-person perspectives are based . . . on aspects of Kessler's own family history, while the third-person focalization through Max is chilling as he realistically justifies the new state of the world to himself and is indoctrinated into Nazi ideology." Bulletin of theCenter for Children's Books

Keyser, Amber

Pointe, claw. Amber J. Keyser. Carolrhoda Lab, [2017] 278 p.

Grades: 8 9 10 11 12   **Fic**
1. Teenage girl ballet dancers 2. Former friends 3. Diseases 4. Friendship 5. Zoonoses 6. Realistic fiction
ISBN 9781467775915

LC 2016006114

After eight years of separation childhood best friends are reunited. One is studying to be a professional ballerina, the other has a rare disease that is rapidly taking its toll. Provided by publisher.

"Keyser's writing shimmers with raw emotion and empathy, and her finale, much like in dance, is poetic, bittersweet, and life affirming." Publishers Weekly.

Khan, Hena

Amina's song. Hena Khan. Salaam Reads, [2021] 288 p.: Amina's voice

Grades: 4 5 6 7 8   **Fic**
1. Pakistani American girls 2. Identity (Psychology) 3. Friendship 4. Pakistani Americans 5. Families 6. Pakistan 7. Realistic fiction
ISBN 9781534459885

Feeling pulled between two cultures after a month with family in Pakistan, Amina shares her experiences with Wisconsin classmates through a class assignment and a songwriting project with new student Nico.

"Khan excellently weaves together complex issues of feeling torn between two parts of one's identity, illness in the family, helping others, and finding out that growing up does not have to mean growing apart. Highly recommended." Booklist

★ **Amina's** voice. Hena Khan. Salaam Reads / Simon & Schuster Books for Young Readers, [2017] 384 p.: Amina's voice

Grades: 4 5 6 7 8   **Fic**
1. Muslim girls 2. Pakistani Americans 3. Belonging 4. Prejudice 5. Friendship 6. Wisconsin 7. Realistic fiction 8. Coming-of-age stories
ISBN 9781481492065

LC 2016024621

Amina, a Pakistani-American Muslim girl, struggles to stay true to her family's culture while dealing with the vandalism of the local Islamic Center and mosque and her best friend Soojin's new friendship with their former nemesis.

"A universal story of self-acceptance and the acceptance of others." School Library Journal.

More to the story. Hena Khan. Salaam Reads, 2019. 384 p.

Grades: 4 5 6 7   **Fic**
1. Families 2. Teenage journalists 3. New students 4. Friendship 5. Thirteen-year-old girls 6. Atlanta, Georgia 7. Realistic fiction 8. Classics-inspired fiction
ISBN 9781481492096

LC 2019001352

As features editor of her school newspaper, thirteen-year-old Jameela Mirza wants to impress her father by writing a spectacular story about the new student, but a misunderstanding and family illness complicate matters.

"This contemporary update of Louisa May Alcott's Little Women follows the Muslim, Pakistani-American Mizra family of Atlanta." Publishers Weekly.

Khorram, Adib

Darius the Great is not okay. Adib Khorram. Dial Books, 2018 320 p.

Grades: 7 8 9 10 11 12   **Fic**
  1. Iranian American teenagers 2. Depression 3. Identity (Psychology) 4. Family visits 5. Iranian Americans 6. Iran 7. Realistic fiction 8. Coming-of-age stories
ISBN 9780525552963

LC 2018009825

Clinically-depressed Darius Kellner, a high school sophomore, travels to Iran to meet his grandparents, but it is their next-door neighbor, Sohrab, who changes his life.

"Darius is a well-crafted, awkward but endearing character, and his cross-cultural story will inspire reflection about identity and belonging." School Library Journal.

Khoury, Jessica, 1990-

The **Mystwick** School of Musicraft. Jessica Khoury. Houghton Mifflin Harcourt 2020 352 p.

Grades: 4 5 6 7   **Fic**
  1. Music 2. Magic 3. Preteen girls 4. Orphans 5. Mistaken identity 6. Fantasy fiction
ISBN 9781328625632

Humor and heart shine in this middle-grade fantasy about a girl who attends a boarding school to learn how to use music to create magic.

"The storytelling flows, pulling readers along, and some particularly grand, magical sequences (including a legitimately epic ending) make this stand-alone fantasy a memorable adventure." Booklist.

Kidd, Ronald

Night on fire. Ronald Kidd. Albert Whitman & Company, 2015. 264 p.

Grades: 4 5 6 7 8   **Fic**
  1. 1960s 2. Civil Rights Movement 3. Social change 4. African Americans -- Civil rights -- History 20th century 5. Freedom Riders (Civil rights movement) 6. Violence 7. Alabama 8. Historical fiction
ISBN 9780807570241

"Beautifully written and earnestly delivered, the novel rolls to an inexorable, stunning conclusion readers won't soon forget." Kirkus.

Kim, Graci

The **last** fallen star. Graci Kim. Disney-Hyperion, 2021 336 p.

Grades: 4 5 6 7 8   **Fic**
  1. Adopted children 2. Self-acceptance 3. Witches 4. Preteen girls 5. Belonging 6. Asian-influenced fantasy 7. Mythological fiction
ISBN 9781368059633

"From a compelling and endearing supporting cast to the rich and tantalizing Korean cuisine explored in its pages, this pays homage to traditional Korean magic and mythos while infusing it with a contemporary story line and characters readers will fall in love with in an instant." Booklist

Kim, Jessica, 1980-

Stand up, Yumi Chung! Jessica Kim. Kokila, 2020 320 p.

Grades: 4 5 6 7   **Fic**
  1. Korean American girls 2. Mistaken identity 3. Stand-up comedy 4. Expectation (Psychology) 5. Immigrant families 6. Los Angeles, California 7. Coming-of-age stories 8. Humorous stories 9. Realistic fiction
ISBN 9780525554974

LC 2019040260

When eleven-year-old Yumi Chung stumbles into a kids' comedy camp she is mistaken for another student, so she decides to play the part.

Kincaid, S. J.

Insignia. S.J. Kincaid. Katherine Tegen Books, 2012. 400 p.: Insignia trilogy

Grades: 7 8 9 10 11 12   **Fic**
  1. Gifted teenagers 2. Virtual reality 3. War 4. Fourteen-year-old boys 5. Teenage boys 6. Science fiction 7. Cyber-thrillers 8. Science fiction thrillers
ISBN 9780062092991

LC 2011044634

Tom, a fourteen-year-old genius at virtual reality games, is recruited by the United States Military to begin training at the Pentagon Spire as a Combatant in World War III, controlling the mechanized drones that do the actual fighting off-planet.

Kindl, Patrice

Keeping the castle. by Patrice Kindl. Viking Childrens Books, 2012. 224 p.

Grades: 7 8 9 10 11   **Fic**
  1. Georgian era (1714-1837) 2. Seventeen-year-old girls 3. Castles 4. Teenage girls 5. Rich men 6. Nobility 7. England 8. Great Britain 9. Historical romances
ISBN 9780670014385

LC 2011033185

In order to support her family and maintain their ancient castle in Lesser Hoo, seventeen-year-old Althea bears the burden of finding a wealthy suitor who can remedy their financial problems.

A **school** for brides: a story of maidens, mystery, and matrimony. Patrice Kindl. Viking, an imprint of Penguin Group (USA) LLC, 2015. 272 p.

Grades: 7 8 9 10   **Fic**
  1. Georgian era (1714-1837) 2. 1800s (Decade) 3. Boarding schools 4. Schools 5. Marriage 6. Courtship 7. Teenage girls 8. England 9. Yorkshire, England 10. Historical fiction
ISBN 9780670786084

"This affectionate homage to the genre delivers what's missing: a witty, intelligent plot whose characters—complex, conniving, hypocritical, and hilarious—seek happiness within an ordered world. This airy soufflé of a tale, garnished with quirky charm, is an unmitigated delight from start to finish." Kirkus.

King, A. S. (Amy Sarig), 1970-

The **year** we fell from space. Amy Sarig King. Arthur A. Levine Books, 2019. 262 p.

Grades: 5 6 7 8   **Fic**
  1. Children of separated parents 2. Family problems 3. Parent and child 4. Children of people with depression 5. Magical thinking 6. Realistic fiction
ISBN 9781338236361

LC 2019004550

Seeing remarkable patterns and pictures in a night sky that were introduced to her by her now-absent father, Liberty struggles with inconsistencies in her family's views while trying to map out a better future.

"This is required reading for both children and parents of divorce, all of whom will find themselves reflected in this heartachingly cathartic tale of family, mental health, and coping." Booklist.

King, Wesley

OCDaniel. Wesley King. Simon & Schuster Books for Young Readers, [2016] 304 p.

Grades: 4 5 6 7 8   **Fic**

1. Obsessive-compulsive disorder 2. Mental illness 3. Missing persons 4. Football 5. Crushes in boys 6. Realistic fiction 7. Coming-of-age stories
ISBN 9781481455312

LC 2015029259

A thirteen-year-old boy's life revolves around hiding his obsessive compulsive disorder until a girl at school, who is unkindly nicknamed Psycho Sara, notices him for the first time and he gets a mysterious note that changes everything.

Kinney, Jeff

★ **Cabin** fever. Jeff Kinney. Amulet Books, 2011. 224 p.: Diary of a wimpy kid

Grades: 5 6 7 8   **Fic**

1. Blizzards 2. Vandalism 3. Innocence (Law) 4. Diary writing 5. Diary writing for children 6. Realistic fiction 7. Diary novels 8. Illustrated books
ISBN 9781419702235

The authorities are closing in, but when a surprise blizzard hits, the Heffley family is trapped indoors. Greg knows that when the snow melts he's going to have to face the music, but could any punishment be worse than being stuck inside with your family for the holidays?

The **deep** end. Jeff Kinney. Harry N. Abrams, 2020. 224 p.: Diary of a wimpy kid

Grades: 5 6 7 8   **Fic**

1. Diary writing 2. Family vacations 3. Camp sites, facilities, etc 4. Recreational vehicles 5. Middle school students 6. Realistic fiction 7. Diary novels 8. Humorous stories
ISBN 9781419753787

Greg Heffley and his family hit the road for a cross-country camping trip, ready for the adventure of a lifetime. But things take an unexpected turn, and they find themselves stranded at an RV park that's not exactly a summertime paradise. When the skies open up and the water starts to rise, the Heffleys wonder if they can save their vacation, or if they're already in too deep.

"A witty addition to the long-running series." Kirkus

★ **Diary** of a wimpy kid: Greg Heffley's journal. Jeff Kinney. Amulet Books, c2007. 217 p.: Diary of a wimpy kid

Grades: 5 6 7 8   **Fic**

1. Diary writing 2. Social acceptance in children 3. Popularity 4. Middle school students 5. Best friends 6. Realistic fiction 7. Diary novels 8. Illustrated books
ISBN 9780810993136

LC 2006031847

Greg records his sixth grade experiences in a middle school where he and his best friend, Rowley, undersized weaklings amid boys who need to shave twice daily, hope just to survive, but when Rowley grows more popular, Greg must take drastic measures to save their friendship.

"Kinney's background as a cartoonist is apparent in this hybrid book that falls somewhere between traditional prose and graphic novel. . . . The pace moves quickly. The first of three installments, it is an excellent choice for reluctant readers, but more experienced readers will also find much to enjoy and relate to." School Library Journal.

★ **Dog** days. by Jeff Kinney. Amulet Books, 2009. 224 p.: Diary of a wimpy kid

Grades: 5 6 7 8   **Fic**

1. Diary writing 2. Video games and boys 3. Interpersonal conflict 4. Middle school students 5. Resistance (Psychology) 6. Realistic fiction 7. Diary novels 8. Illustrated books
ISBN 9780810983915

LC 2009024953

In the latest diary of middle-schooler Greg Heffley, he records his attempts to spend his summer vacation sensibly indoors playing video games and watching television, despite his mother's other ideas.

"Kinney's gift for telling, pitch-perfect details in both his writing and art remains." Publishers Weekly.

★ **Hard** luck. Jeff Kinney. Amulet Books, 2013. 224 p.: Diary of a wimpy kid

Grades: 5 6 7 8   **Fic**

1. Bad luck 2. Fate and fatalism 3. Friendship 4. Middle schools 5. Schools 6. Realistic fiction 7. Diary novels 8. Illustrated books
ISBN 9781419711329

LC bl2013040291

After being dumped by his best friend and having a hard time finding new friends in middle school, Greg decides to change his luck and turn all his decisions over to chance.

"Greg Heffley's eighth adventure (but who's counting?) centers on his relationship with his best friend, Rowley—more specifically, the demise of that relationship when Rowley gets a girlfriend... As ever, Kinney strikes his comic target in the bull's-eye, exaggerating the trials of adolescence just enough to make them real while deftly exposing the insecurities behind Greg's bravado with his super, simple drawings. Will Greg and Rowley make up? Either way, devotees need not worry; there is plenty more angst in store." Booklist.

★ The **last** straw. Jeff Kinney. Amulet Books, 2009. 217 p.: Diary of a wimpy kid

Grades: 5 6 7 8   **Fic**

1. Diary writing 2. Courage in boys 3. Threat (Psychology) 4. Fathers and sons 5. Fear in boys 6. Realistic fiction 7. Diary novels 8. Illustrated books
ISBN 9780810970687

LC 2008060022

Middle-schooler Greg Heffley nimbly sidesteps his father's attempts to change Greg's wimpy ways until his father threatens to send him to military school.

"Kinney's spot-on humor and winning formula of deadpan text set against cartoons are back in full force." Publishers Weekly.

★ The **long** haul. by Jeff Kinney. Amulet Books, [2014] 224 p.: Diary of a wimpy kid

Grades: 5 6 7 8   **Fic**

1. Automobile travel 2. Family vacations 3. Families 4. Brothers 5. Middle school students 6. Realistic fiction 7. Diary novels 8. Illustrated books
ISBN 9781419711893

LC bl2014025344

Greg Heffley and his family hit the streets for a wimpy kid-style road trip.

"By taking the Heffleys on the road, Kinney both gives himself an almost universally familiar experience to lampoon and places Greg in the rather unusual position of being almost entirely justified in his misanthropy, which is downright refreshing." Kirkus.

★ **Old** school. by Jeff Kinney. Amulet Books, [2015] 224 p.: Diary of a wimpy kid

Grades: 5 6 7 8 **Fic**

1. Electronics 2. Families 3. Middle school students 4. Middle schools 5. Schools 6. Realistic fiction 7. Diary novels 8. Illustrated books
ISBN 9781419717017

"Mishaps galore and a chilling rumor make for a highly entertaining, and fairly smelly, foray into the great outdoors and, thankfully, back home to modern comforts." Booklist.

★ **Rodrick** rules. by Jeff Kinney. Amulet Books, 2008. 216 p.: Diary of a wimpy kid
Grades: 5 6 7 8 **Fic**

1. Embarrassment in boys 2. Diary writing 3. Sibling rivalry 4. Humiliation 5. Brothers 6. Realistic fiction 7. Diary novels 8. Illustrated books
ISBN 9780810994737

LC 2007032296

Greg Heffley tells about his summer vacation and his attempts to steer clear of trouble when he returns to middle school and tries to keep his older brother Rodrick from telling everyone about Greg's most humiliating experience of the summer.

"Once again diarist Greg chronicles a hilarious litany of problems. . . . As before, he peppers his journal entries with his own cartoons. . . . He comes across as a real kid, and his story is one that will appeal to all those real kids who feel just like him." Booklist.

The **third** wheel. by Jeff Kinney. Amulet Books, 2012. 224 p.: Diary of a wimpy kid
Grades: 5 6 7 8 **Fic**

1. School dances 2. Valentine's Day 3. Best friends 4. Middle schools 5. Schools 6. Realistic fiction 7. Diary novels 8. Illustrated books
ISBN 9781419705847

A Valentine's Day dance at Greg's middle school has turned his world upside down until an unexpected twist gives Greg a partner for the dance and leaves his best friend Rowley the odd man out.

The **ugly** truth. by Jeff Kinney. Amulet Books, 2010. 224 p.: Diary of a wimpy kid
Grades: 5 6 7 8 **Fic**

1. Diary writing 2. Families 3. Friendship 4. Middle school students 5. Responsibility in boys 6. Realistic fiction 7. Diary novels 8. Illustrated books
ISBN 9780810984912

While trying to find a new best friend after feuding with Rowley, middle-school slacker Greg Heffley is warned by older family members that adolescence is a time to act more responsibly and to think seriously about his future.

Kipling, Rudyard, 1865-1936

The **jungle** book. Rudyard Kipling; illustrated by Robert Ingpen. Sterling, 2012. 192 p.
Grades: 4 5 6 7 **Fic**

1. Boys and wild animals 2. Wild children 3. Jungle animals 4. Mowgli (Fictitious character) 5. Cobras 6. India 7. Adventure stories 8. Classics
ISBN 9781402782848

Presents the adventures of Mowgli, the Indian boy brought up by wolves in the jungle, his companions, Baloo and Bagheera, and his enemy, Shere Khan.

Kirby, Matthew J., 1976-

★ The **clockwork** three. Matthew Kirby. Scholastic Press, c2010. 386 p.
Grades: 5 6 7 8 **Fic**

1. 19th century 2. Poor children 3. Clocks and watches 4. Street musicians 5. Magic violin 6. Boy apprentices 7. New England 8. Steampunk 9. Historical fantasy
ISBN 9780545203371

LC 2009037879

As mysterious circumstances bring Giuseppe, Frederick, and Hannah together, their lives soon interlock like the turning gears in a clock and they realize that each one holds a key to solving the others' mysteries.

"This is a riveting historical fantasy. . . . Kirby has assembled all the ingredients for a rousing adventure, which he delivers with rich, transporting prose." Publishers Weekly.

Icefall. by Matthew J. Kirby. Scholastic Press, 2011. 336 p.
Grades: 5 6 7 8 **Fic**

1. Princesses 2. Traitors 3. Sabotage 4. Winter 5. Self-confidence 6. Historical fantasy
ISBN 9780545274241

LC 2011000890

Princess Solveig and her siblings are trapped in a hidden fortress tucked between towering mountains and a frozen fjord, along with her best friend and an army of restless soldiers, all awaiting news of the king's victory in battle, but as they wait for winter's end and the all-encompassing ice to break, acts of treachery make it clear that a traitor lurks in their midst.

"Kirby turns in a claustrophobic, thought-provoking coming-of-age adventure that shows a young woman growing into her own, while demonstrating the power of myth and legend. Kirby's attention to detail and stark descriptions make this an effective mood piece." Publishers Weekly.

A **taste** for monsters. Matthew J. Kirby. Scholastic Press, 2016. 352 p.
Grades: 7 8 9 10 **Fic**

1. Merrick, Joseph Carey, 1862-1890. 2. Jack, the Ripper. 3. Victorian era (1837-1901) 4. 1880s 5. People with disfigurements 6. Household employees 7. Serial murders 8. Ghosts 9. Phosphorus -- Physiological effect 10. London, England 11. Great Britain 12. Historical fiction 13. Paranormal fiction
ISBN 9780545817844

LC 2015048826

In 1888 seventeen-year-old Evelyn Fallow, herself disfigured by the phosphorus in the match factory where she worked, has been hired as a maid to Joseph Merrick, the Elephant Man—but when the Jack the Ripper murders begin she and Merrick find themselves haunted by the ghosts of the slain women, and Evelyn is caught up in the mystery of Jack's identity.

"A lovely, suspenseful, lyrical, imperfect paranormal mystery." Kirkus.

Kisner, Adrienne

Dear Rachel Maddow. Adrienne Kisner. Feiwel & Friends, 2018 272 p.
Grades: 7 8 9 10 11 **Fic**

1. Maddow, Rachel 2. Lesbian teenagers 3. Equality 4. Grief in teenage girls 5. High schools 6. School politics 7. Realistic fiction 8. LGBTQIA fiction 9. Epistolary novels
ISBN 9781250146021

A teen slogging through remedial courses at school in the wake of her sibling's death, a breakup with her first girlfriend and her parents' dysfunctions writes unsent e-mails to her favorite news anchor before becoming involved in a moral and political dilemma involving an honor student's controversial opinions.

Klages, Ellen, 1954-

The **green** glass sea: a novel. Ellen Klages. Viking, c2006. 321 p.

Grades: 5 6 7 8   **Fic**
   1. Manhattan Project (U.S.) 2. 1940s 3. Children of scientists 4. Child misfits 5. Eleven-year-old girls 6. Girls -- Friendship 7. Military secrets 8. Los Alamos, New Mexico 9. New Mexico 10. Historical fiction 11. Coming-of-age stories
ISBN 0670061344

Scott O'Dell Historical Fiction Award, 2007.

"Many readers will know as little about the true nature of the project as the girls do, so the gradual revelation of facts is especially effective, while those who already know about Los Alamos's historical significance will experience the story in a different, but equally powerful, way." School Library Journal.

Out of left field. Ellen Klages. Viking Children's Books, 2018. 224 p.

Grades: 4 5 6 7   **Fic**
   1. 1950s 2. Girl baseball players 3. Baseball teams 4. Girl athletes 5. Baseball 6. San Francisco, California 7. Historical fiction 8. Sports fiction 9. Baseball stories
ISBN 9780425288597

Every boy in the neighborhood knows Katy Gordon is their best pitcher, even though she's a girl. But when she tries out for Little League, it's a whole different story. Girls are not eligible, period.

"The narrative, though rich in details, never gets bogged down. This title also includes substantial back matter, such as a list of female ballplayers, an author's note, a glossary of baseball terms, and further recommended reading. Klages gives Katy a strong voice and helps spotlight the history of marginalized women in sports history. Featuring powerful female characters, this is historical fiction that doesn't drag for a second. A fine purchase." School Library Journal.

Klass, Sheila Solomon

Soldier's secret: the story of Deborah Sampson. Sheila Solomon Klass. Henry Holt, 2009. 215 p.

Grades: 6 7 8 9 10   **Fic**
   1. Gannett, Deborah Sampson, 1760-1827 2. Revolutionary America (1775-1783) 3. 18th century 4. Deception 5. Gender role 6. Women soldiers 7. Soldiers 8. Women and war 9. United States 10. Biographical fiction 11. Historical fiction
ISBN 9780805082005

LC 2008036783

During the Revolutionary War, a young woman named Deborah Sampson disguises herself as a man in order to serve in the Continental Army.

"In this novel, Sampson is strong, brave, and witty. . . . Klass doesn't shy away from the horrors of battle; she also is blunt regarding details young readers will wonder about, like how Sampson dealt with bathing, urination, and menstruation. . . . Sampson's romantic yearnings for a fellow soldier . . . is given just the right notes or restraint and realism." Booklist.

Klise, James, 1967-

The **art** of secrets: a novel. by James Klise Algonquin, 2014. 240 p.

Grades: 6 7 8 9   **Fic**
   1. Secrets 2. Arson 3. Art thefts 4. Outsider art 5. Charity auctions 6. Chicago, Illinois 7. Mysteries
ISBN 9781616201951

LC 2013043222

When some quirky art donated to a school fundraising effort to help a Pakistani American family, victims of a possible hate crime, is revealed to be an unknown work by a famous outsider artist, worth hundreds of thousands of dollars, adults and teenagers alike debate who should get the money and begin to question each other's motivations.

Klise, Kate

Regarding the bathrooms: a privy to the past. by Kate Klise; illustrated by M. Sarah Klise. Harcourt, 2006. 160 p.: Regarding the--

Grades: 4 5 6 7   **Fic**
   1. School principals 2. Middle school students 3. Escaped convicts 4. Criminals 5. Child detectives 6. Missouri 7. Mysteries 8. Humorous stories
ISBN 0152051643

LC 2005016813

In this novel told through letters, newspaper articles, and police reports, a middle school principal's bathroom renovation project leads to the discovery of stolen Roman antiquities.

"Puns abound, and there are a few bathroom jokes, though nothing really crass enough to compromise an entertaining novel that celebrates community and history." Booklist.

★ **Regarding** the fountain: a tale, in letters, of liars, and leaks. Kate Klise; illustrated by M. Sarah Klise. Avon Books, 1998. 138 p.: Regarding the--

Grades: 4 5 6 7   **Fic**
   1. Drinking fountains 2. Creativity in children 3. Fifth-graders 4. Schools 5. Letters 6. Humorous stories 7. Mysteries 8. Epistolary novels
ISBN 0380975386

LC 97018205

When the principal asks a fifth-grader to write a letter regarding the purchase of a new drinking fountain for their school, he finds that all sorts of chaos results.

"Fresh, funny, and a delight to read." School Library Journal.

Regarding the sink: where, oh where, did Waters go? Kate Klise; illustrated by M. Sarah Klise. Gulliver Books/Harcourt, c2004. 127, [8] p.: Regarding the--

Grades: 4 5 6 7   **Fic**
   1. Sixth-graders 2. Missing persons 3. Women designers 4. Elementary school teachers 5. Sixth-grade teachers 6. Epistolary novels 7. Mysteries 8. Humorous stories
ISBN 0152050191

LC 2003026560

A series of letters reveals the selection of the famous fountain designer, Florence Waters, to design a new sink for the Geyser Creek Middle School cafeteria, her subsequent disappearance, and the efforts of a class of sixth-graders to find her.

"Piecing the story and clues together is satisfying. Introduce this book to savvy readers who are ready for the jump to a clever, unconventional reading experience." School Library Journal.

Regarding the trees: a splintered saga rooted in secrets. Kate Klise; illustrated by M. Sarah Klise. Harcourt Inc., c2005. 143 p.: Regarding the--
Grades: 4 5 6 7 **Fic**
    1. Trees 2. Schools 3. School principals 4. Weddings 5. Restaurants 6. Humorous stories 7. Epistolary novels
ISBN 0152051635

LC 2004027211

In this story told primarily through letters, Principal Russ wants the middle school trees to be trimmed before his administrative evaluation, but the project is interrupted by a town gender war, dueling chefs, student tree protests, and a surprise wedding.

Knowles, Johanna, 1970-
    See you at Harry's. Jo Knowles. Candlewick Press, 2012. 310 p.
Grades: 6 7 8 9 10 11 **Fic**
    1. Grief 2. Family problems 3. Brothers and sisters 4. Homosexuality 5. Grief in children
ISBN 9780763654078

LC 2011018619

Twelve-year-old Fern feels invisible in her family, where grumpy eighteen-year-old Sarah is working at the family restaurant, fourteen-year-old Holden is struggling with school bullies and his emerging homosexuality, and adorable, three-year-old Charlie is always the center of attention, and when tragedy strikes, the fragile bond holding the family together is stretched almost to the breaking point.

    Where the heart is. Jo Knowles. Candlewick Press, 2019. 304 p.
Grades: 4 5 6 7 **Fic**
    1. Family problems 2. Identity (Psychology) 3. Girls 4. Questioning (Sexual or gender identity) 5. Summer employment 6. Realistic fiction 7. Coming-of-age stories 8. LGBTQIA fiction
ISBN 9781536200034

An unexpectedly challenging summer job and her parents' financial difficulties are further complicated by 13-year-old Rachel's best friend's changing feelings and her own uncertainty about whether she even likes boys.

"Thirteen-year-old Rachel faces uncertainties about her sexuality, her family's financial situation, and growing up in Knowles' latest." Booklist.

Knox, Elizabeth
    Mortal fire. Elizabeth Knox. Frances Foster Books, 2013. 336 p.
Grades: 7 8 9 10 11 **Fic**
    1. 1950s 2. Gifted teenagers 3. Magic 4. Imprisonment 5. Genius 6. Stepbrothers and stepsisters 7. New Zealand 8. Islands of the Pacific 9. Fantasy fiction
ISBN 9780374388294

LC 2012040872

When sixteen-year-old Canny of the Pacific island, Southland, sets out on a trip with her stepbrother and his girlfriend, she finds herself drawn into enchanting Zarene Valley where the mysterious but dark seventeen-year-old Ghislain helps her to figure out her origins.

Knudsen, Michelle
    The **dragon** of Trelian. Michelle Knudsen. Candlewick Press, 2009. 407 p.: Trelian
Grades: 4 5 6 7 **Fic**
    1. Wizards' apprentices 2. Dragons 3. Princesses 4. Magic 5.

Imaginary kingdoms 6. High fantasy 7. Fantasy fiction
ISBN 9780763634551

LC 2008025378

Excited that her sister's wedding to a prince will end a war between the kingdoms, Princess Meg becomes fearful of a dangerous plot by an evil traitor wishing to destroy the happy day and so works with Calen, a mage-to-be, to stop him in his tracks in order to avert the disaster that is sure to happen if the wedding doesn't take place.

"Knudsen does a fantastic job of creating sympathetic and realistic characters that really drive the story. The tale is adventurous and exciting with many twists and turns along the way." School Library Journal.

Koertge, Ronald
    Shakespeare makes the playoffs. Ron Koertge. Candlewick Press, 2010. 176 p.: Shakespeare bats cleanup
Grades: 6 7 8 9 **Fic**
    1. Teenage poets 2. Teenage baseball players 3. Teenage boy/girl relations 4. Teenage boys 5. Adolescence 6. Realistic fiction 7. Novels in verse
ISBN 9780763644352

LC 2009014519

Fourteen-year-old Kevin Boland, poet and first baseman, is torn between his cute girlfriend Mira and Amy, who is funny, plays Chopin on the piano, and is also a poet.

"The well-crafted poetry is firmly rooted in the experiences of regular teens and addresses subjects that range from breakups to baseball. . . . Appealing and accessible." Booklist.

    Stoner & Spaz. Ron Koertge. Candlewick Press, 2002. 169 p.
Grades: 8 9 10 11 12 **Fic**
    1. Teenage boys with disabilities 2. Self-acceptance in teenage boys 3. Teenage girl drug abusers 4. Cerebral palsy 5. Self-acceptance 6. Humorous stories 7. Realistic fiction
ISBN 0763616087

LC 2001043050

A troubled youth with cerebral palsy struggles toward self-acceptance with the help of a drug-addicted young woman.

"Funny, touching, and surprising, it is a hopeful yet realistic view of things as they are and as they could be." Booklist.

    Strays. Ronald Koertge. Candlewick, 2007. 167 p.
Grades: 7 8 9 10 11 12 **Fic**
    1. Teenage boy orphans 2. Human/animal communication 3. Loneliness 4. Loneliness in teenage boys 5. Sixteen-year-old boys 6. Coming-of-age stories
ISBN 9780763627058

When his parents die in a sudden accident and he is moved into the home of a set of crazy foster parents, sixteen-year-old Ted is forced to cope with his loss while attending a hard inner-city school overrun by delinquents.

"Though Koertge never soft pedals the horrors faced by some foster children, this thoughtful novel about the lost and abandoned is a hopeful one." Booklist.

Konigsberg, Bill
    Openly straight. Bill Konigsberg. Arthur A. Levine Books, c2013. 336 p.: Openly straight
Grades: 8 9 10 11 **Fic**
    1. Gay teenagers 2. Identity (Psychology) 3. Boarding school students 4. Soccer 5. Homosexuality 6. Massachusetts 7.

Realistic fiction 8. LGBTQIA romances
ISBN 9780545509893

LC 2012030552

Tired of being known as "the gay kid", Rafe Goldberg decides to assume a new persona when he comes east and enters an elite Massachusetts prep school—but trying to deny his identity has both complications and unexpected consequences.

"Rafe is sick of being the poster child for all things gay at his uberliberal Colorado high school, so when he gets into a Massachusetts boarding school for his junior year, he decides to reboot himself as openly straight. Konigsberg slyly demonstrates how thoroughly assumptions of straightness are embedded in everyday interactions. For a thought-provoking take on the coming-out story, look no further." Horn Book.

Konigsburg, E. L.

The **mysterious** edge of the heroic world. E. L. Konigsburg. Simon & Schuster, 2007. 240 p.

Grades: 5 6 7 8   **Fic**

1. Sixth-grade boys 2. Neighbors 3. Art thefts -- History 20th century. 4. Nazi plunder 5. Recluses 6. Amsterdam, Netherlands 7. Florida 8. Mysteries
ISBN 1416949720

"this humorous, poignant, tragic, and mysterious story has intertwining plots that peel away like the layers of an onion." School Library Journal.

★ The **view** from Saturday. E. L. Konigsburg. Atheneum for Young Readers, c1996. 163 p.

Grades: 4 5 6 7   **Fic**

1. Women with paraplegia 2. Sixth-graders 3. Competition 4. Children -- Friendship 5. Contests 6. Realistic fiction 7. Classics
ISBN 068980993X

LC 95-52624

Newbery Medal, 1997.

Four students, with their own individual stories, develop a special bond and attract the attention of their teacher, a paraplegic, who chooses them to represent their sixth-grade class in the Academic Bowl competition.

"Glowing with humor and dusted with magic. . . . Wrought with deep compassion and a keen sense of balance." Publishers Weekly.

Korman, Gordon

Collision course. Gordon Korman. Scholastic, c2011. 176 p.: Titanic

Grades: 4 5 6 7   **Fic**

1. Titanic (Steamship) 2. 1910s 3. Stowaways 4. Murder 5. Friendship 6. Shipping lines 7. Children of suffragists 8. Historical fiction 9. Adventure stories
ISBN 9780545123327

Four children aboard the Titanic—Sophie, Paddy, Juliana, and Alfie—believe the famed killer Jack the Ripper is on the ship with them, and the urgency of their mystery deepens as the "unsinkable" ship hits an iceberg.

The **juvie** three. by Gordon Korman. Hyperion, 2008. 256 p.

Grades: 7 8 9 10   **Fic**

1. Group homes 2. Juvenile delinquents 3. Cooperation 4. Second chances 5. Juvenile detention 6. New York City 7. Realistic fiction
ISBN 9781423101581

LC 2008019087

Gecko, Arjay, and Terence, all in trouble with the law, must find a way to keep their halfway house open in order to stay out of juvenile detention.

"Korman keeps lots of balls in the air as he handles each boy's distinct voice and characteras well as the increasingly absurd situationwith humor and flashes of sadness." Booklist.

Linked. Gordon Korman Scholastic, 2021. 256 p.

Grades: 4 5 6 7 8   **Fic**

1. Middle school students 2. Vandalism 3. Racism 4. Middle schools 5. Investigations 6. Colorado 7. Realistic fiction
ISBN 9781338629118

When swastikas begin appearing all over town, Link, Michael and Dana, the only Jewish girl in town, must face crimes both past and present to find the truth.

"Bringing the past into the present and moving beyond pure emotional manipulation, this wrenching story offers much to ponder and few, if any, easy answers." Booklist

★ The **Medusa** plot. Gordon Korman. Scholastic, 2011. 224 p.: The 39 clues.

Grades: 5 6 7   **Fic**

1. Ransom 2. Orphans 3. Clues 4. Codes (Communication) 5. Kidnapping 6. Adventure stories
ISBN 9780545298391

Cahills are being kidnapped by a shadowy group known only as the Vespers. Now Amy and Dan have only days to fulfill a bizarre ransom request or their captured friends will start dying. Amy and Dan don't know what the Vespers want or how to stop them. Only one thing is clear. The Vespers are playing to win, and if they get their hands on the Clues ... the world will be their next hostage.

Notorious. Gordon Korman. Balzer + Bray, 2020. 307 p.

Grades: 4 5 6 7   **Fic**

1. Treasure troves 2. Islands 3. Preteens 4. Pets -- Death 5. Middle school students 6. Canada 7. United States 8. Mysteries
ISBN 9780062798862

LC 2019010133

Moving to an unfamiliar island split between the United States and Canada, Keenan learns about the island?s Prohibition-era smuggling history from an unconventional neighbor who believes her dog has been murdered.

"Korman sketches characters with swift, sure strokes and places them in a distinctive setting: situated on an island in the St. Clair River, their town sits on a zigzagging international border dividing Michigan from Ontario." Booklist.

Pop. by Gordon Korman. Balzer & Bray, 2009. 272 p.

Grades: 7 8 9 10   **Fic**

1. People with Alzheimer's disease 2. Former professional football players 3. New students 4. Sixteen-year-old boys 5. Moving, Household 6. Sports fiction 7. Realistic fiction 8. Football stories
ISBN 9780061742286

LC 2008052106

Lonely after a midsummer move to a new town, sixteen-year-old high-school quarterback Marcus Jordan becomes friends with a retired professional linebacker who is great at training him, but whose childish behavior keeps Marcus in hot water.

"Readers will be sucked into compelling story lines on complicated family situations, peer acceptance, the game of football, and the effects of progressive Alzheimer's disease on the persons involved, their families, and friends—themes that flow seamlessly together." Voice of Youth Advocates.

★ **Restart**. Gordon Korman. Scholastic Press, 2017. 243 p.
Grades: 4 5 6 7 **Fic**
> 1. Bullying and bullies 2. Amnesia 3. Memory 4. Boys with amnesia 5. Self-perception 6. Realistic fiction
> ISBN 9781338053777

When Chase returns to middle school after falling off the roof and losing his memory, he learns that the person he was before the amnesia is not someone he likes.

"Korman shows bullying, regret, and forgiveness from various perspectives and leaves readers with ideas to ponder." Booklist.

Schooled. Gordon Korman. Hyperion, 2007. 224 p.
Grades: 6 7 8 9 **Fic**
> 1. Home schooled teenage boys 2. Middle schools 3. First day of school 4. Home schooling 5. Middle school students 6. Realistic fiction
> ISBN 0786856920

"This rewarding novel features an engaging main character and some memorable moments of comedy, tenderness, and reflection." Booklist.

Slacker. Gordon Korman. Scholastic Press, 2016. 240 p.:
Slacker
Grades: 4 5 6 7 **Fic**
> 1. Clubs 2. Social action 3. Video gamers 4. Responsibility 5. Brothers and sisters 6. Realistic fiction
> ISBN 9780545823159

When eighth-grader Cameron Boxer creates the Positive Action Group at school he intends it as a diversion to fool his parents, teachers, and sister into letting him continue to concentrate on his video-gaming—but before he knows it other kids are taking it seriously, and soon he finds himself president of the P.A.G., and involved in community service, so the boy who never cared about anything is now the center of everything, whether he likes it or not.

Son of the mob. Gordon Korman. Hyperion, 2002. 262 p.
Grades: 7 8 9 10 **Fic**
> 1. Organized crime 2. Seventeen-year-old girls 3. Teenage boys 4. Teenage boy/girl relations 5. Crime bosses 6. New York City 7. Realistic fiction
> ISBN 0786807695

LC 2002068672

Seventeen-year-old Vince's life is constantly complicated by the fact that he is the son of a powerful Mafia boss, a relationship that threatens to destroy his romance with the daughter of an FBI agent.

"The fast-paced, tightly focused story addresses the problems of being an honest kid in a family of outlaws—and loving them anyway. Korman doesn't ignore the seamier side of mob life, but even when the subject matter gets violent . . . he keeps things light by relating his tale in the first-person voice of a humorously sarcastic yet law-abiding wise guy." Horn Book.

★ **Swindle**. Gordon Korman. Scholastic Press, 2008. 252 p.:
Swindle mysteries
Grades: 4 5 6 **Fic**
> 1. Baseball cards 2. Swindlers and swindling 3. Revenge 4. Collectors and collecting 5. Friendship 6. Realistic fiction
> ISBN 0439903440

LC 2007017225

After unscrupulous collector S. Wendell Palamino cons him out of a valuable baseball card, sixth-grader Griffin Bing puts together a band of misfits to break into Palomino's heavily guarded store and steal the card back, planning to use the money to finance his father's failing invention, the SmartPick fruit picker.

"The plot is the main attraction, and it's clever intricacies—silly, deceptively predictable, and seasoned with the occasional unexpected twist—do not disappoint." Booklist.

Ungifted. Gordon Korman. Balzer + Bray, 2012. 244 p.
Grades: 4 5 6 **Fic**
> 1. Practical jokers 2. Gifted children 3. Robotics 4. Robots 5. Personal conduct 6. Realistic fiction
> ISBN 9780061742668

LC 2012008408

When one of Donovan's thoughtless pranks accidentally destroys the school gym during the Big Game he knows he's in for it. But through a strange chain of events, his name gets put on the list for the local school for gifted students. Donovan knows he's not a genius, but he can't miss this chance to escape. Now, he has to figure out a way to stay at ASD and fit in with the kids there.

War stories. Gordon Korman. Scholastic, 2020. 231 p.
Grades: 4 5 6 7 8 **Fic**
> 1. 1940s 2. Grandfather and grandson 3. War 4. Secrecy 5. Truth 6. Military campaigns 7. France 8. War stories 9. Historical fiction
> ISBN 9781338290202

LC 2019047102

Visiting the small French village that his veteran grandfather helped liberate during World War II, an avid young player of war video games begins questioning his family's perspectives about his grandfather's heroism when he uncovers the rest of the story.

"Told in alternating contemporary and historical chapters, this is a fast-paced tale that will engage kids who, like Trevor, would really prefer war to play out on a video screen—furious, glorious, and without irrevocable consequences." Bulletin of the Center for Children's Books

Zoobreak. Gordon Korman. Scholastic Press, 2009. 265 p.:
Swindle mysteries
Grades: 3 4 5 6 **Fic**
> 1. Zoos 2. Animal rescue 3. Students 4. Sixth-graders 5. Stealing 6. Long Island, New York 7. Realistic fiction
> ISBN 9780545124997

LC 2009015456

After a class trip to a floating zoo where animals are mistreated and Savannah's missing pet monkey is found in a cage, Long Island sixth-grader Griffin Bing and his band of misfits plan a rescue.

"Both children and adults will find the story fast moving and enjoyable. The often-unpredictable plot is interesting, full of humor, and good fun." Voice of Youth Advocates.

Kostick, Conor, 1964-
Edda. Conor Kostick. Viking, 2011. 440 p.: Avatar chronicles
Grades: 7 8 9 10 **Fic**
> 1. Weapons 2. Computer games 3. Independence (Personal quality) 4. Fantasy games -- Computer methods 5. Role playing 6. Science fiction
> ISBN 9780670012183

LC 2011003000

In the virtual world of Edda, ruler Scanthax decides he wants to invade another virtual world, embroiling the universes of Edda, Saga, and Epic in war, with only three teenagers to try to restore peace.

"Humans, electronic beings and servers are separated by light years and metaphysics, but Kostick's action-filled series conclusion is immediate and relevant." Kirkus.

Epic. Conor Kostick. Viking, 2007. 320 p.: Avatar chronicles
Grades: 7 8 9 10   **Fic**
    1. Computer games 2. Fantasy games -- Computer methods 3. Exile (Punishment) 4. Role playing 5. Role playing games 6. Dystopian fiction 7. Science fiction
    ISBN 9780670061792

                                    LC 2006019958
On New Earth, a world based on a video role-playing game, fourteen-year-old Erik pursuades his friends to aid him in some unusual gambits in order to save Erik's father from exile and safeguard the futures of each of their families.

"There is intrigue and mystery throughout this captivating pageturner. Veins of moral and ethical social situations and decisions provide some great opportunities for discussion. Well written and engaging." School Library Journal.

Saga. Conor Kostick. Penguin, 2008. 368 p.: Avatar chronicles
Grades: 7 8 9 10   **Fic**
    1. Computer games 2. Fantasy games -- Computer methods 3. Immortality 4. Women rulers 5. Role playing 6. Dystopian fiction 7. Science fiction
    ISBN 9780670062805
As the Dark Queen and controller of Saga sets out to enslave the people of New Earth, Ghost and his street hacker airboard gang of friends must find a way to stop her before the world they have always known is gone forever.

"The plot and pacing are near perfect in this tale of a world cramped by fear and tradition. . . . Compulsively readable and palpable (the descriptions of airboarding are a near-physical experience), it will appeal to SF fans across the board." Voice of Youth Advocates.

Kowitt, Holly
    The **loser** list. H. N. Kowitt. Scholastic Press, 2011. 213 p.: Loser list
Grades: 4 5 6 7   **Fic**
    1. Boy misfits 2. Stealing 3. Drawing 4. Comic books, strips, etc 5. Boy comic strip illustrators 6. Realistic fiction
    ISBN 9780545240048
Danny must set things right again after his attempt to remove his name from the dreaded Loser List lands him in detention, attracts the attention of the school bully, and causes his best friend Jasper to end their friendship.

Kramer, J. Kasper
    The **story** that cannot be told. J. Kasper Kramer. Atheneum, 2019. 384 p.
Grades: 4 5 6 7   **Fic**
    1. 1980s 2. Girl authors 3. Communism 4. Storytelling 5. Revolutions 6. Social change 7. Romania 8. Historical fiction
    ISBN 9781534430686
A powerful middle grade debut draws on folklore and history to tell the story of a girl who finds her voice and courage during the final months of the Communist regime of 1989 Romania.

"Kramer's debut stitches a patchwork of storytelling, folklore, and history together into a narrative about a Romanian girl suffering under her country's Communist rule and the resistance movement it produced." Booklist.

Kraus, Daniel, 1975-
    At the edge of empire. Daniel Kraus. Simon & Schuster, 2015. 688 p.: Death and life of Zebulon Finch
Grades: 9 10 11 12   **Fic**
    1. Undead 2. Redemption 3. Seventeen-year-old boys 4. Soldiers 5. Gangsters 6. Horror 7. Historical fiction
    ISBN 9781481411394
"A hefty volume for fans of historical fiction with an undead twist." School Library Journal.

Krishnaswami, Uma, 1956-
    Step up to the plate, Maria Singh. Uma Krishnaswami. Tu Books, an imprint of Lee & Low Books, 2017 288 p.
Grades: 4 5 6 7 8   **Fic**
    1. Second World War era (1939-1945) 2. Multiracial girls 3. Girl softball players 4. Prejudice 5. Interracial families 6. Nine-year-old girls 7. California 8. Historical fiction
    ISBN 9781600602610
Nine-year-old Maria Singh learns to play softball just like her heroes in the All-American Girls' League, while her parents and neighbors are struggling through World War II, working for India's independence, and trying to stay on their farmland.

"Filled with heart, this tale brings to life outspoken and determined Maria, her love for baseball, and her multicultural community and their challenges and triumphs." Kirkus.

Kristoff, Jay
    Lifel1k3. Jay Kristoff. Knopf Books for Young Readers, 2018. 416 p.: Lifel1k3
Grades: 7 8 9 10 11 12   **Fic**
    1. Memory 2. Robots 3. Secrets 4. Paranormal phenomena 5. Islands 6. Science Fiction 7. Science fiction thrillers 8. Apocalyptic fiction
    ISBN 9781524713928
When Eve learns she can destroy machines with her mind, she becomes a target for a group of puritanical fanatics, and with her new android best friend Ezekiel, faces cyborg assassins.

Kritzer, Naomi
    Catfishing on Catnet. Naomi Kritzer. Tor Teen, 2019. 288 p.: Catnet
Grades: 8 9 10 11 12   **Fic**
    1. Artificial intelligence 2. Virtual community 3. Teenage girls 4. Technology 5. Consciousness 6. Cyber-thrillers 7. Thrillers and suspense
    ISBN 9781250165084
Because her mom is always on the move, Steph hasn't lived anyplace longer than six months. Her only constant is an online community called CatNet, a social media site where users upload cat pictures, a place she knows she is welcome. What Steph doesn't know is that the admin of the site, CheshireCat, is a sentient A.I.

"Alongside the uplifting message about inclusivity, diversity, and found family—characters of various ethnicities identify as gay, bisexual, nonbinary, asexual, and still exploring—Kritzer's take on a benevolent AI is both whimsical and poignant." Publishers Weekly.

Krosoczka, Jarrett

The **frog** who croaked. Jarrett J. Krosoczk. Walden Pond Press, 2013. 226 p.: Platypus Police Squad

Grades: 3 4 5 6 7   **Fic**

  1. Animal detectives 2. Missing persons investigation 3. Fishes 4. Police 5. Platypus 6. Mysteries 7. Animal fantasy 8. Illustrated books

  ISBN 9780062071644

Paired together after a veteran detective retires, platypus police squad members Rick Zengo, a hotshot rookie, and Corey O'Malley, a hard-nosed old-timer, struggle with their differences while tackling their first case involving a missing schoolteacher and a duffle bag filled with illegal fish.

Kuehn, Stephanie

Complicit. Stephanie Kuehn. St. Martin's Griffin, 2014. 224 p.

Grades: 8 9 10 11 12   **Fic**

  1. Amnesia 2. Adopted teenagers 3. Mental illness 4. Brothers and sisters 5. Private schools 6. California 7. Psychological suspense

  ISBN 9781250044594

                  LC 2014008117

Jamie's mother was murdered when he was six, about seven years later his sister Cate was incarcerated for burning down a neighbor's barn, and now Jamie, fifteen, learns that Cate has been released and is coming back for him, blaming him for all the bad things that led to her arrest.

"...every page shows a firm, surprising choice, whether you like it or not. Cate, naturally, is the main event, the alternatingly irrational, gentle, explosive, and enigmatic center of this fast, black whirlpool of a novel." Booklist.

Kuhn, Sarah

I love you so mochi. Sarah Kuhn. Scholastic Press, 2019. 320 p.

Grades: 8 9 10 11 12   **Fic**

  1. Asian American teenage girls 2. Self-discovery in teenage girls 3. Grandparents 4. Family problems 5. Dating (Social customs) 6. Japan 7. Teen chick lit 8. Romantic comedies

  ISBN 9781338302882

Eagerly visiting her estranged grandparents in Japan to distance herself from the mother who disapproves of her fashion ambitions, a talented young designer immerses herself in Kyoto's markets and cherry blossom festival and bonds with a cute med student while uncovering illuminating family secrets.

"Kuhn ... has brought together travel, fashion, food, romance, and family to create an incredibly sweet and heartwarming coming of age romantic comedy. weaving in Japanese vocabulary and slang, she also subtly addresses racism and differences between Japanese and Japanese -American cultures." Kirkus.

Kurtz, Chris, 1960-

The **adventures** of a South Pole pig: a novel of snow and courage. Chris Kurtz; illustrations by Jennifer Black Reinhardt. Harcourt Children's Books, Houghton Mifflin Harcourt, 2012. 144 p.

Grades: 4 5 6 7   **Fic**

  1. Pigs 2. Ships 3. Courage 4. Ocean travel 5. Sled dogs 6. Antarctica 7. Animal fantasy

  ISBN 9780547634555

                  LC 2012027226

Flora the pig ditches the sedentary life on the farm for an adventure in Antarctica, where she escapes the knife and lives her dream of pulling a sled with a team of dogs. Provided by publisher.

Kwaymullina, Ambelin, 1975-

The **things** she's seen. by Ambelin Kwaymullina and Ezekiel Kwaymullina. Alfred A. Knopf, 2019. 208 p.

Grades: 7 8 9 10 11 12   **Fic**

  1. Dead 2. Murder 3. Racism 4. Aboriginal Australians 5. Grief in men 6. Australia 7. Psychological suspense 8. Paranormal fiction

  ISBN 9781984849373

Nothing's been the same for Beth Teller since she died. Her dad, a detective, is the only one who can see and hear her—and he's drowning in grief. But now they have a mystery to solve together regarding a fire at a children's home. As Beth unravels the mystery, she finds a shocking story lurking beneath the surface of a small town, and a friendship that lasts beyond one life and into another. Told in two unforgettable voices, this gripping novel interweaves themes of grief, colonial history, violence, love and family.

Kyi, Tanya Lloyd, 1973-

Shadow warrior. Tanya Lloyd Kyi; illustrated by Celia Krampien. Annick Press, 2017. 64 p.

Grades: 4 5 6 7 8   **Fic**

  1. 16th century 2. Ninja 3. Women warriors 4. Widows 5. Warlords 6. Spies 7. Japan 8. Illustrated books 9. Historical fiction

  ISBN 9781554519668

It's 1558, and warlords across Japan are battling for territory and control. Mochizuki Chiyome is determined to become a ninja, but is married off to the nephew of a fierce warlord. When a tragic event occurs, she sees a chance to fulfill her dream.

"This interesting peek into a lesser-known historical moment tells a compelling story of women intentionally—and expertly—hiding in a male-dominated field." Booklist.

L'Engle, Madeleine

A **swiftly** tilting planet. Madeleine L'Engle. Farrar, Straus and Giroux, 1978. 278 p.: Time quintet

Grades: 5 6 7 8 9 10   **Fic**

  1. Nuclear warfare 2. Genealogy 3. Time travel 4. Fifteen-year-old boys 5. Unicorns 6. Science fiction 7. Classics

  ISBN 0374373620

                  LC 78009648

National Book Award for Children's Books, 1980.

The youngest of the Murry children must travel through time and space in a battle against an evil dictator who would destroy the entire universe.

A **wind** in the door. Madeleine L'Engle. Farrar, Straus and Giroux, 1973. 211 p.: Time quintet

Grades: 5 6 7 8 9 10   **Fic**

  1. Brothers and sisters 2. Good and evil 3. Space and time 4. Love 5. Mitochondria 6. Science fiction 7. Classics

  ISBN 9780374384432

                  LC 73075176

With Meg's help, the dragons her little brother saw in the garden play an important part in his getting well and take her on a journey into space.

"L'Engle mixes classical theology, contemporary family life, and futuristic science fiction to make a completely convincing tale that should put under its spell both readers familiar with the Murrys and those meeting them for the first time." New York Times Book Review.

★ A **wrinkle** in time. Madeleine L'Engle. Farrar, Straus, and Giroux, c1962. 211 p.: Time quintet

Grades: 5 6 7 8 9 10   **Fic**
1. Time travel 2. Father-separated children 3. Brothers and sisters 4. Space and time 5. Rescues 6. Science fiction 7. Classics
ISBN 0374386137

LC   62007203

Newbery Medal, 1963.

Meg and Charles Wallace set out with their friend Calvin in a search for their father. His top secret job as a physicist for the government has taken him away and the children search through time and space to find him.

"This book makes unusual demands on the imagination and consequently gives great rewards." Horn Book.

LaBan, Elizabeth

The **Tragedy** Paper. Elizabeth LaBan. Alfred A. Knopf, 2013. 272 p.

Grades: 7 8 9 10 11 12   **Fic**
1. Boarding school students 2. Albinos and albinism 3. Research papers 4. Teenage boy/girl relations 5. Boarding schools 6. Realistic fiction 7. Coming-of-age stories
ISBN 9780375970405

LC 2012011294

While preparing for the most dreaded assignment at the prestigious Irving School, the Tragedy Paper, Duncan gets wrapped up in the tragic tale of Tim Macbeth, a former student who had a clandestine relationship with the wrong girl, and his own ill-fated romance with Daisy.

LaFleur, Suzanne M.

Beautiful blue world. Suzanne LaFleur. Wendy Lamb Books, [2016] 224 p.: Beautiful blue world

Grades: 5 6 7 8   **Fic**
1. Children and war 2. Imaginary wars and battles 3. Prisoners of war 4. Fear in children 5. Survival 6. Fantasy fiction
ISBN 9780375990892

LC 2015046201

Sofarende is at war and the army is paying families well to recruit children, so if twelve-year-old Mathilde or her best friend Megs is chosen, they hope to help their families but fear they will be separated forever.

"Deeply emotional, compelling, and brilliant." Kirkus.

★ **Love,** Aubrey. Suzanne Lafleur. Wendy Lamb Books, c2009. 262 p.

Grades: 5 6 7 8   **Fic**
1. Abandoned girls 2. Children and death 3. Bereavement in girls 4. Bereavement 5. Loss (Psychology) 6. Vermont 7. Virginia 8. Realistic fiction
ISBN 9780385906869

While living with her Gram in Vermont, eleven-year-old Aubrey writes letters as a way of dealing with losing her father and sister in a car accident, and then being abandoned by her grief-stricken mother.

"Aubrey's detailed progression from denial to acceptance makes her both brave and credible in this honest and realistic portrayal of grief." Kirkus.

Threads of blue. Suzanne LaFleur. Wendy Lamb Books, [2017] 224 p.: Beautiful blue world

Grades: 5 6 7 8   **Fic**
1. Children and war 2. Soldiers 3. Imaginary wars and battles 4. Espionage 5. Friendship 6. Fantasy fiction
ISBN 9781101939994

LC 2016048219

Mathilde escapes war-torn Sofarende and reunites with Megs and the other children who are working for the army to retake Sofarende from the enemy, but Mathilde must come to terms with her past treasonous actions and determine what she must do in order to prove her friendship to Megs.

"Beautifully written in first-person narrative, LaFleur has crafted a tale about the ravages of war and survival, starring an unforgettable heroine." School Library Journal.

LaRocca, Rajani

Midsummer's mayhem. by Rajani LaRocca. Yellow Jacket, [2019] 352 p.

Grades: 4 5 6 7   **Fic**
1. East Indian American girls 2. Baking 3. Enchantment 4. Cooking contests 5. Girl bakers 6. Massachusetts 7. Low fantasy 8. Humorous stories 9. Shakespeare-inspired fiction
ISBN 9781499808889

LC 2019002900

Loosely based on Shakespeare's A Midsummer Night's Dream, eleven-year-old Mimi Mackson entangles herself and her family with mischievous fairies when she seeks to win a baking contest.

"As the curtain raises on this reimagining of A Midsummer Night's Dream, Indian-American Mimi, 11, is reading her favorite cookbook when she hears a song drifting from the woods 'like an irresistible aroma.' Enchantment reigns, yet the author's exploration of family, friendship, and self-esteem are firmly grounded in reality." Kirkus.

Lacey, Josh

Island of Thieves. by Josh Lacey. Houghton Mifflin, 2012. 288 p.

Grades: 4 5 6 7 8   **Fic**
1. Drake, John fl. 1577-1580. 2. Drake, Francis, Sir, 1540?-1596. 3. Treasure hunting 4. Uncle and nephew 5. Gangsters 6. Treasure troves 7. Islands 8. Peru 9. Adventure stories
ISBN 9780547763279

LC 2011033893

After Tom Trelawney accidentally burns down his family's garden shed, Tom's parents, who are away on vacation, send him to stay with his eccentric Uncle Harvey in New York City. But Uncle Harvey is headed for Peru, supposedly to hunt for treasure, and means to leave Tom behind. Maybe Tom wouldn't have worked so hard convincing his uncle to take him along if he'd known what he was getting into.

Lackey, Lindsay

All the impossible things. Lindsay Lackey. Roaring Brook, 2019. 384 p.

Grades: 4 5 6 7   **Fic**
1. Foster children 2. Mother-separated children 3. Senior couples 4. Winds 5. Magic 6. Low fantasy
ISBN 9781250202864

Struggling to control the wind powers that render her skies stormy whenever she feels stressed, a foster-care girl arrives at the petting-zoo home of a quirky couple before her new sense of belonging is challenged by the return of her troubled mother.

"An emotional tale filled with unique characters, heartbreaking realities, and a touch of magical realism." Booklist.

Lai, Remy

★ **Fly** on the wall. Remy Lai. Henry Holt and Company, 2020. 368 p.

Grades: 4 5 6 7   **Fic**

1. Growing up 2. Voyages and travels 3. Families 4. Protectiveness 5. Comic strip drawing 6. Realistic fiction 7. Coming-of-age stories 8. Graphic novel hybrids
ISBN 9781250314116

LC 2019036946

A boy with an overprotective mother who interrogates his friends and forbids him from doing anything independently secretly creates an anonymous gossip cartoon and scrambles to keep his parents from finding out.

"Lai presents Henry's flaws with sympathy and grace, never condemning him and resisting preachiness while allowing readers to come to their own conclusions about what responsibility and independence look like. The cartoony art is crucial to the storytelling, as are the more formal, digital looking illustrations from the vlog." Bulletin of the Center for Children's Books

Lai, Thanhha

Butterfly yellow. Thanhha Lai. Harper, 2019 284 p.

Grades: 8 9 10 11 12   **Fic**

1. 1980s 2. Separated friends, relatives, etc 3. Refugees 4. Reunions 5. Vietnamese in the United States 6. Brothers and sisters 7. Texas 8. Historical fiction
ISBN 9780062229212

Scott O'Dell Historical Fiction Award, 2020.

A Vietnam War refugee in Texas partners with a rodeo aspirant to track down the younger brother she was forced to leave behind before discovering that he no longer remembers her.

"Remarkable. Told with ample grace, Lai's finely drawn narrative and resilient characters offer a memorable, deeply felt view of the Vietnam War's impact." Publishers Weekly.

★ **Inside** out & back again. Thanhha Lai. HarperCollins, 2011. 262 p.

Grades: 4 5 6 7   **Fic**

1. 1970s 2. Immigrants, Vietnamese 3. Father-separated girls 4. Vietnamese Americans 5. Immigration and emigration 6. Cultural differences 7. Vietnam 8. Alabama 9. Novels in verse 10. Historical fiction
ISBN 9780061962783

LC 2010007855

National Book Award for Young People's Literature, 2011.

Through a series of poems, a young girl chronicles the life-changing year of 1975, when she, her mother, and her brothers leave Vietnam and resettle in Alabama.

"Based on Lai's personal experience, this first novel captures a child-refugee's struggle with rare honesty. Written in accessible, short free-verse poems." Booklist.

★ **Listen,** slowly. Thanhha Lai. Harper, 2015. 272 p.

Grades: 4 5 6 7 8   **Fic**

1. Twelve-year-old girls 2. Vietnamese American girls 3. Families 4. Translating and interpreting 5. Friendship 6. Vietnam 7. Coming-of-age stories
ISBN 9780062229182

"Gracefully written and enriched by apposite figures of speech, Listen, Slowly is a superb, sometimes humorous, always thought-provoking coming-of-age story." Booklist.

Lancaster, Mike A.

Human.4. Mike A. Lancaster. Egmont USA, 2011. 240 p.

Grades: 7 8 9 10   **Fic**

1. Fourteen-year-old boys 2. Computer programs 3. Human/computer interaction 4. Technological innovations 5. Families 6. England 7. Science fiction
ISBN 9781606840993

LC 2010030313

Twenty-first century fourteen-year-old Kyle was hypnotized when humanity was upgraded to 1.0 and he, incompatible with the new technology, exposes its terrifying impact in a tape-recording found by the superhumans of the future.

"Lancaster fashions a fast-paced, upsetting little thriller punctuated by ominous editorial notes that translate Kyle's details for the futuristic audience." Booklist.

Landman, Tanya

Hell and high water. Tanya Landman. Candlewick Press, 2017. 320 p.

Grades: 7 8 9 10   **Fic**

1. 18th century 2. Georgian era (1714-1837) 3. Multiracial persons 4. Fathers -- Death 5. Family secrets 6. Poor people 7. Prejudice 8. Devon, England 9. Historical mysteries 10. Coming-of-age stories
ISBN 9780763688752

Set in eighteenth-century Devon, this is the story of Caleb, the son of a poor puppeteer. When his father is wrongfully accused of theft and sentenced to transportation, Caleb is left all alone in the world. As a mixed race boy living in an age of slavery, he has always been treated with fear and mistrust. Without his father he is more vulnerable than ever, and is forced to seek out his estranged aunt. After a body washes up on a nearby beach, a shattered Caleb finds himself involved in a dastardly plot: a plot that places him and his newfound family in mortal danger.

"Murder and mystery abound in this engrossing and atmospheric tale set in 18th-century England." Kirkus.

Landy, Derek

The **faceless** ones. by Derek Landy. Bowen Press, 2009. 432 p.: Skulduggery Pleasant

Grades: 4 5 6 7   **Fic**

1. Detectives 2. Skeleton 3. Parallel universes 4. Wizards 5. Magic 6. Ireland 7. Fantasy fiction
ISBN 9780061240911

LC 2008051714

Fourteen-year-old Valkyrie and the skeleton mage, Skulduggery Pleasant, try to foil a plot set in motion fifty years before to find and open the gate that will allow the Faceless Ones to return to this reality.

"A gifted storyteller, the author will hook readers on the first page and leave them on the last as wrung out as he leaves his teenage protagonist—who pays a high price indeed for killing a god or two. Rattling good fun." Kirkus.

Playing with fire. by Derek Landy. HarperCollins, c2008. 389 p.: Skulduggery Pleasant

Grades: 4 5 6 7   **Fic**

1. Detectives 2. Skeleton 3. Apprentices 4. Quests 5. Magic 6. Ireland 7. Fantasy fiction
ISBN 9780061240881

LC 2007032444

When the evil Baron Vengeous escapes from prison, Detective Skulduggery Pleasant and his apprentice, Valkyrie Cain, have just two days to recapture him or the Baron's creature, the Grotesquery, may summon the Faceless Ones back to their world.

"The style is cinematic, and the action nonstop. Skullduggery's subtle humorous asides . . . lighten the mood, and magical details, such as Valkyrie's ability to throw fireballs, add to the fun." Booklist.

★ **Skulduggery** Pleasant. by Derek Landy. HarperCollins Publishers, 2007. 400 p.: Skulduggery Pleasant

Grades: 4 5 6 7   **Fic**
1. Detectives 2. Skeleton 3. Revenge 4. Heirs and heiresses 5. Murder 6. Ireland 7. Fantasy fiction
ISBN 0061231150

LC 2006029403

When twelve-year-old Stephanie inherits her weird uncle's estate, she must join forces with Skulduggery Pleasant, a skeleton mage, to save the world from the Faceless Ones.

"This is a rich fantasy that is as engaging in its creative protagonists and villains as it is in the lightning-paced plot and sharp humor." Bulletin of the Center for Children's Books.

Lane, Kathleen, 1967-

Pity party: stories. by Kathleen Lane. Little, Brown and Company, 2021. 208 p.

Grades: 5 6 7 8   **Fic**
1. Middle school students 2. Growing up 3. Middle schools 4. Short stories
ISBN 9780316417365

A grab bag of deliciously dark short fiction set in middle school that explores anxieties and twists them into funny, resonant, and reassuring psychological thrills. Provided by publisher.

"Some pieces are funny, others a bit twisted, but all of them work to recognize the myriad experiences of young people trying to conform to, or push back against, societal pressures to be attractive, popular, and perfect." Booklist

Lange, Erin Jade

Butter. Erin Jade Lange. Bloomsbury, 2012. 296 p.

Grades: 8 9 10 11 12   **Fic**
1. Overweight teenage boys 2. Obesity 3. Loneliness in teenage boys 4. Loneliness 5. Internet 6. Arizona 7. Scottsdale, Arizona 8. Realistic fiction
ISBN 9781599907802

LC 2011045509

Unable to control his binge eating, a morbidly obese teenager nicknamed Butter decides to make a live webcast of his last meal as he attempts to eat himself to death.

Langrish, Katherine

The **shadow** hunt. Katherine Langrish. Harper, 2010 322 p.

Grades: 6 7 8 9   **Fic**
1. Runaway boys 2. Girls who are mute 3. Demons 4. Supernatural 5. Revenge 6. Wales 7. Historical fantasy
ISBN 9780061116766

"Thirteen-year-old Wolf is running away from the abbey where he was raised when he unexpectedly meets renowned knight Sir Hugo. Together, they capture a mysterious elf-child and return to Hugo's castle, where Wolf will be allowed to stay—if he gets the elf-child to speak. . . . In this medieval fantasy, Langrish . . . provides a vividly rendered, engrossing tale. Epic themes—good and evil, faith and doubt, sin and redemption—are made personal and poignant through the losses and longings of the notably well-drawn, dimensional main characters." Booklist.

Lapinski, L.D.

The **Strangeworlds** Travel Agency. by L.D. Lapinski. Aladdin, 2021, 384 p.: Strangeworlds Travel Agency trilogy

Grades: 4 5 6 7   **Fic**
1. Child heroes 2. Voyages and travels 3. End of the world 4. Quests 5. Luggage 6. Magical realism
ISBN 9781534483514

Pack your suitcase for a magical adventure! At Strangeworlds Travel Agency, each suitcase transports you to a different world. All you have to do is step inside. When 12-year-old Flick Hudson accidentally ends up in the Strangeworlds Travel Agency, she uncovers a fantastic secret: there are hundreds of other worlds just steps away from ours. All you have to do to visit them is jump into the right suitcase. Flick gets the invitation of a lifetime: join Strangeworlds' magical travel society and explore other worlds. But, unknown to Flick, the world at the very centre of it all, a city called Five Lights, is in danger. Buildings and even streets are mysteriously disappearing. Once Flick realizes what's happening she must race against time, travelling through unchartered worlds, seeking a way to fix Five Lights before it collapses into nothingness and takes our world with it.

"Lapinski's debut is captivating, particularly in its descriptions of new worlds, and while evoking shades of Doctor Who and His Dark Materials . . . this still feels like a wonderful world of its own." Booklist

Larocca, Rajani

Red, white, and whole. Rajani Larocca. Harpercollins Childrens Books 2021 256 p.

Grades: 5 6 7 8 9   **Fic**
1. 1980s 2. East Indian American girls 3. Cultural differences 4. Loss (Psychology) 5. Middle school students 6. Leukemia 7. India 8. Historical fiction 9. Coming-of-age stories 10. Realistic fiction
ISBN 9780063047426

"Composed of short, metaphor-rich poems, this verse novel weaves together complex narrative strands with sophistication. It does the double duty of giving voice to the hyphenated American experience and navigation of dual identities." Horn Book

Larson, Kirby

★ **Dash**. Kirby Larson. Scholastic Press, 2014. 256 p.: Dogs of World War II

Grades: 4 5 6 7   **Fic**
1. Puyallup Assembly Center (Puyallup, Wash.) 2. Second World War era (1939-1945) 3. Japanese Americans -- Forced removal and incarceration, 1942-1945 4. Girls and dogs 5. World War II 6. Japanese American girls 7. Eleven-year-old girls 8. Washington (State) 9. Historical fiction
ISBN 9780545416351

Scott O'Dell Historical Fiction Award, 2015.

Forced to move with her family to an internment camp after the attack on Pearl Harbor, Japanese-American Mitsi mourns her separation from her beloved dog and tries to keep up with the outside world with the help of a friendly neighbor back home.

"Spot-on dialogue, careful cultural details and the inclusion of specific historical characters such as artist Eddie Sato make this an educational read as well as a heartwarming one. An author's note adds further authenticity.This emotionally satisfying and thought-provoking book will have readers pulling for Mitsi and Dash." Kirkus.

Hattie Big Sky. Kirby Larson. Delacorte Press, 2006. 289 p.

Grades: 6 7 8 9 10   **Fic**
1. First World War era (1914-1918) 2. 1910s 3. Teenage girl

orphans 4. Homesteading 5. Neighbors 6. Prejudice 7. Frontier and pioneer life 8. Montana 9. Historical fiction
ISBN 0385733135

LC 2005035039

After inheriting her uncle's homesteading claim in Montana, sixteen-year-old orphan Hattie Brooks travels from Iowa in 1917 to make a home for herself and encounters some unexpected problems related to the war being fought in Europe.

"This is a richly textured novel full of memorable characters." Booklist.

Includes bibliographical references.

Lasky, Kathryn

A **journey** to the New World: the diary of Remember Patience Whipple. Kathryn Lasky. Scholastic, 1996. 173 p.: Dear America

Grades: 5 6 7 8   **Fic**

1. Mayflower (Ship) 2. Colonial America (1600-1775) 3. Twelve-year-old girls 4. Pilgrims (New England settlers) 5. Immigrants 6. Massachusetts 7. United States 8. Historical fiction 9. Diary novels
ISBN 059050214X

LC 95-25715

Twelve-year-old Mem presents a diary account of the trip she and her family made on the Mayflower in 1620 and their first year in the New World.

Lone wolf. by Kathryn Lasky. Scholastic Press, 2010. 240 p.: Wolves of the Beyond

Grades: 5 6 7 8   **Fic**

1. Wolf pups 2. Abandoned infants 3. Survival 4. Wolves 5. Courage 6. Animal fantasy 7. Fantasy fiction
ISBN 9780545093101

LC 2009017007

Abandoned by his pack, a baby wolf with a mysterious mark on his deformed paw survives and embarks on a journey that will change the world of the wolves of the Beyond.

"Lasky merges anthropomorphic fantasy with realistic details about wolves and bears to produce an almost plausible emotional narrative, complete with dialogue and personalities. . . . The author builds a captivating world of forest, snow and volcanoes populated by intelligent animals and weaves a compelling story sure to bring readers back for the second installment." Kirkus.

Lauren, Ruth

Prisoner of ice and snow. by Ruth Lauren. Bloomsbury, April 2017. 256 p.

Grades: 4 5 6 7   **Fic**

1. Twin sisters 2. Prisons 3. Prisoners 4. Escapes 5. Thirteen-year-old girls 6. Russia 7. Fantasy fiction
ISBN 9781681191317

LC 2016025579

When thirteen-year-old Valor is arrested, she could not be happier. Demidova's prison for criminal children is exactly where she wants to be. Valor's sister Sasha is already serving a life sentence for stealing from the royal family, and Valor is going to help her escape . . . from the inside. Provided by publisher.

"Anyone who likes adventure, survival stories, folktales, or novels with strong female protagonists will not be able to put this down." School Library Journal.

Lavender, William, 1921 December 23-

Aftershocks. William Lavender. Harcourt, 2006. 343 p.

Grades: 8 9 10 11 12   **Fic**

1. 1900s (Decade) 2. Gender role 3. Fathers and daughters 4. Fourteen-year-old girls 5. Teenage girls 6. Teenagers 7. San Francisco, California 8. California 9. Diary novels 10. Historical fiction
ISBN 0152058826

LC 2005019695

In San Francisco from 1903 to 1908, teenager Jessie Wainwright determines to reach her goal of becoming a doctor while also trying to care for the illegitimate child of a liaison between her father and their Chinese maid.

"This is readable historical fiction about an engrossing event in U.S. history." Voice of Youth Advocates.

Law, Ingrid, 1970-

★ **Savvy**. by Ingrid Law. Dial Books for Young Readers, c2008. 342 p.: Savvy (Ingrid Law)

Grades: 4 5 6 7   **Fic**

1. Hospital patients 2. Bus travel 3. Self-discovery in teenage girls 4. Self-discovery 5. Magic 6. Fantasy fiction
ISBN 9780803733060

LC 2007039814

Recounts the adventures of Mibs Beaumont, whose thirteenth birthday has revealed her "savvy"—a magical power unique to each member of her family—just as her father is injured in a terrible accident.

"Short chapters and cliffhangers keep the pace quick, while the mix of traditional language and vernacular helps the story feel both fresh and timeless. . . . [This is] a vibrant and cinematic novel that readers are going to love." Publishers Weekly.

★ **Scumble**. by Ingrid Law. Dial Books for Young Readers, 2010. 400 p.: Savvy (Ingrid Law)

Grades: 4 5 6 7   **Fic**

1. Disappointment 2. Girl journalists 3. Family secrets 4. Magic 5. Families 6. Wyoming 7. Fantasy fiction
ISBN 9780803733077

LC 2010002444

Mibs's cousin Ledge is disappointed to discover that his "savvy"—the magical power unique to each member of their family—is to make things fall apart, which endangers his uncle Autry's ranch and reveals the family secret to future reporter Sarah.

"This provides a satisfying plot, delightful characters, alliterative language, and rich imagery." Booklist.

Switch. by Ingrid Law. Dial Books for Young Readers, [2015] 224 p.: Savvy (Ingrid Law)

Grades: 4 5 6 7   **Fic**

1. Visions 2. Superhuman abilities 3. Grandmothers 4. Alzheimer's disease 5. Magic 6. Fantasy fiction
ISBN 9780803738621

LC 2015006965

Gypsy Beaumont's magical savvy switches to its opposite when she learns that her mean and decidedly non-magical grandma has Alzheimer's and is going to move in with her family. Provided by publisher.

"Law tenderly handles the challenges of having a grandparent with Alzheimers, highlighting the power of familial love. Though no explanation for the switch is given, readers will be caught up in this snowy, magical adventure and the characters efforts to balance their true, sparkly selves with growing up." Booklist.

Lawrence, Iain, 1955-

The **smugglers**. Iain Lawrence. Delacorte Press, c1999. 183 p.: High seas trilogy

Grades: 5 6 7 8   **Fic**

1. 19th century 2. Courage in teenage boys 3. Smuggling 4. Pirates 5. Sixteen-year-old boys 6. Teenage boys 7. England 8. Historical fiction 9. Adventure stories 10. Sea stories

ISBN 0385326637

LC 98041582

In nineteenth-century England, after his father buys a schooner called the Dragon, sixteen-year-old John sets out to sail it from Kent to London and becomes involved in a dangerous smuggling scheme.

"The book's nonstop action, fast-paced plot, and picturesque characters make for a real page-turner." School Library Journal.

★ The **wreckers**. Iain Lawrence. Delacorte Press, c1998. 196 p.: High seas trilogy

Grades: 5 6 7 8   **Fic**

1. Georgian era (1714-1837) 2. 1790s 3. 18th century 4. Shipwrecks 5. Survival (after airplane accidents, shipwrecks, etc) 6. Escapes 7. Fourteen-year-old boys 8. Teenage boys 9. England 10. Cornwall, England 11. Historical fiction 12. Sea stories 13. Adventure stories

ISBN 0385325355

LC 97031625

Shipwrecked after a vicious storm, fourteen-year-old John Spencer attempts to save his father and himself while also dealing with an evil secret about the English coastal town where they are stranded.

"In 1799 fourteen-year-old John Spencer survives a shipwreck on the coast of Cornwall. To his horror, he soon learns that the villagers are not rescuers, but pirates who lure ships ashore in order to plunder their cargoes. . . . Lawrence creates an edge-of-the-chair survival/mystery story. Fast-moving, mesmerizing." Horn Book Guide.

Lawson, Jessica, 1980-

Nooks & crannies. Jessica Lawson; illustrated by Natalie Andrewson Simon & Schuster Books for Young Readers, 2015. 316 p.

Grades: 3 4 5 6 7   **Fic**

1. Edwardian era (1901-1914) 2. Inheritance and succession 3. Counts and countesses 4. Murder 5. Eleven-year-old girls 6. Ghosts 7. Great Britain 8. Historical mysteries

ISBN 9781481419215

LC 2014023223

Eleven-year-old Tabitha Crum, whose parents were just about to abandon her, is invited to the country estate of a wealthy countess along with five other children and told that one of them will become her heir.

"Lawson offers a compelling puzzle, vividly drawn characters, and a clever and capable young detective, who bravely sniffs out clues before the final secrets are revealed—with everyone together in the parlor, naturally." Booklist.

Le Guin, Ursula K., 1929-2018

Powers. Ursula K. Le Guin. Harcourt, c2007. 502 p.: Annals of the Western Shore

Grades: 7 8 9 10   **Fic**

1. Grief 2. Psychic ability 3. Slavery 4. Teenage boy psychics 5. Fourteen-year-old boys 6. Fantasy fiction

ISBN 9780152057701

LC 2006013549

When young Gavir's sister is brutally killed, he escapes from slavery and sets out to explore the world and his own psychic abilities.

"Le Guin uses her own prodigious power as a writer to craft lyrical, precise sentences, evoking a palpable sense of place and believable characters." School Library Journal.

Tales from Earthsea. Ursula K. Le Guin. Harcourt, c2001. 320 p.: Earthsea series

Grades: 11 12 Adult   **Fic**

1. Magic 2. Wizards 3. Dragons 4. Spells (Magic) 5. Earthsea 6. High fantasy 7. Fantasy fiction

ISBN 0151005613

LC 2001016554

Explores further the magical world of Earthsea through five tales of events which occur before or after the time of the original novels, as well as an essay on the people, languages, history and magic of the place.

"Inhabited by people no better or worse than ourselves, Earthsea is dominated by the practice of magic as precise as any science and as unpredictable in its social consequences. Since it is based entirely on language, Earthsea's magic serves as a metaphor for the writer's own sorcery. Yet despite Le Guin's strong bias toward the didactic there is no hint of by-the-numbers allegory here." New York Times Book Review.

Voices. Ursula K. Le Guin. Harcourt, 2006. 352 p.: Annals of the Western Shore

Grades: 7 8 9 10   **Fic**

1. Magic 2. Power (Social sciences) 3. Revenge 4. Censorship 5. Resistance to government 6. Fantasy fiction

ISBN 0152056785

LC 2005020753

Young Memer takes on a pivotal role in freeing her war-torn homeland from its oppressive captors.

"While her prose is simple and unadorned, Le Guin's superior narrative voice and storytelling power make even small moments ring with truth, and often with beauty." School Library Journal.

A **wizard** of Earthsea. by Ursula K. Le Guin. Atheneum, 1991, c1968. 197 p.: Earthsea series

Grades: 6 7 8 9   **Fic**

1. Child wizards 2. Magic -- Study and teaching 3. Dragons 4. Students 5. Islands 6. High fantasy 7. Fantasy fiction 8. Classics

ISBN 9780689317200

LC 9023884

During a spell recalling the dead, the boy Sparrowhawk, a sorcerer's apprentice, unwittingly unleashes evil on the land. He grows to manhood while attempting to subdue the evil he unleashed on the world.

LeZotte, Ann Clare

★ **Show** me a sign. Ann Clare LeZotte. Scholastic Press, 2020. 288 p.

Grades: 4 5 6 7 8   **Fic**

1. 1800s (Decade) 2. People who are deaf 3. Human experimentation in medicine 4. Prejudice 5. Preteen girls 6. Sign language 7. Martha's Vineyard, Massachusetts 8. Massachusetts 9. Historical fiction

ISBN 9781338255812

LC 2019027510

Schneider Family Book Award for Middle School, 2021.

It is 1805 and Mary Lambert has always felt safe among the deaf community of Chilmark on Martha's Vineyard where practically everyone communicates in a shared sign language, but recent events have shattered her life; her brother George has died, land disputes between English settlers and the Wampanoag people are becoming increasingly bitter, and a "scientist" determined to discover the origins of the islands' widespread deafness has decided she makes the perfect "live specimen" and kidnaps her.

Lean, Sarah

★ A **dog** called Homeless. Sarah Lean. Katherine Tegen Books, 2012. 208 p.

Grades: 3 4 5 6 7 **Fic**
   1. Grief in girls 2. Coping in girls 3. Girls who are mute 4. Grief 5. Dogs 6. Realistic fiction
ISBN 9780062122209

LC 2011044628

Schneider Family Book Award for Middle School, 2013.

Fifth-grader Cally Louise Fisher stops talking, partly because her father and brother never speak of her mother who died a year earlier, but visions of her mother, friendships with a homeless man and a disabled boy, and a huge dog ensure that she still communicates.

Leavitt, Martine, 1953-

Calvin. Martine Leavitt. Margaret Ferguson Books, Farrar Straus Giroux, 2015. 224 p.

Grades: 7 8 9 10 11 12 **Fic**
   1. Watterson, Bill 2. Teenagers with schizophrenia 3. Mental illness 4. Schizophrenia 5. Teenage boys with mental illnesses 6. High schools 7. Lake Erie 8. Realistic fiction
ISBN 9780374380731

LC 2015002574

Governor General's Literary Award for English-Language Children's Literature, 2016

Seventeen-year-old Calvin, who was born on the day that the last Calvin and Hobbes comic strip was published, is stricken by a schizophrenic episode and begins having conversations with the tiger, Hobbes. Struggling to regain control of his mind and destiny, Calvin becomes convinced that he'll get better if the strip's creator, Bill Watterson, will draw just one more comic.

"Funny, intellectual, and entertaining, its a sensitive yet irreverent adventure about a serious subject." Publishers Weekly.

My book of life by Angel. Martine Leavitt. Margaret Ferguson Books/Farrar Straus Giroux, 2012. 352 p.

Grades: 8 9 10 11 **Fic**
   1. Teenage prostitutes 2. Drug abuse 3. Prostitution 4. Missing persons 5. Sixteen-year-old girls 6. Vancouver, British Columbia 7. Canada 8. Novels in verse 9. Realistic fiction
ISBN 9780374351236

LC 2011044563

Angel, a sixteen-year-old girl working the streets of Vancouver's Downtown Eastside, befriends Melli, an 11-year-old girl in the same situation and realizes she must do all that she can to save Melli and perhaps save herself at the same time.

Lecesne, James

Absolute brightness. James Lecesne. HarperTeen, c2008. 472 p.

Grades: 7 8 9 10 **Fic**
   1. Gay teenagers 2. Difference (Psychology) 3. Homophobia 4. Adolescence 5. Teenagers 6. New Jersey 7. Coming-of-age stories 8. Realistic fiction
ISBN 0061256285

LC 2007002988

In the beach town of Neptune, New Jersey, Phoebe's life is changed irrevocably when her gay cousin moves into her house and soon goes missing.

Lee, Harper

To kill a mockingbird. Harper Lee. Lippincott, 1960. 296 p.: To kill a mockingbird

Grades: 8 9 10 11 12 Adult **Fic**
   1. Racism 2. Single-parent families 3. Fathers and daughters 4. Race relations 5. Trials (Rape) 6. Southern States 7. Alabama 8. Coming-of-age stories 9. Modern classics 10. Literary fiction
ISBN 0397001517

LC 60007847

Scout Finch, daughter of the town lawyer, likes to spend her summers building treehouses, swimming, and catching lightning bugs with her big brother Jem. But one summer, when a black man is accused of raping a white woman, Scout's carefree days come to an end. In the county courtroom, she will join her father in a desperate battle against ignorance and prejudice.

Lee, Julie

Brother's keeper. Julie Lee. Holiday House, 2020. 320 p.

Grades: 4 5 6 7 8 **Fic**
   1. 1950s 2. Separated friends, relatives, etc 3. Refugees 4. Escapes 5. Voyages and travels 6. Survival 7. North Korea 8. War stories 9. Historical fiction
ISBN 9780823444946

LC 2019052526

Twelve-year-old Sora and her eight-year-old brother, Youngsoo, must try to escape North Korea's oppressive Communist regime on their own in 1950. Includes historical notes, photographs of the author's mother, glossary of Korean words, and timeline.

"Lee captures Sora's internal journey alongside the physical one. . . . Even after Sora arrives at her destination, her battles do not end, as she still must combat the social norms that deny her agency simply for being female. An amazing debut and an important book that explores a part of history few younger readers are taught in school." Booklist

Lee, Mackenzi

The **gentleman's** guide to vice and virtue. Mackenzi Lee. Katherine Tegen Books, 2017. 528 p.: Montague siblings

Grades: 7 8 9 10 11 12 **Fic**
   1. 18th century 2. Rich teenage boys 3. Teenage boy/boy relations 4. Pirates 5. Multiracial teenage boys 6. Brothers and sisters 7. Europe 8. Historical fantasy 9. LGBTQIA fiction
ISBN 9780062382801

LC 2016949692

Two friends on a Grand Tour of 18th-century Europe stumble across a magical artifact that leads them from Paris to Venice in a dangerous manhunt shaped by pirates, highwaymen and their growing attraction to one another.

"Austen, Wilde, and Indiana Jones converge in this deliciously anachronistic bonbon." Kirkus.

Loki: where mischief lies. by Mackenzi Lee; illustrated by Stephanie Hans. Disney Press, 2019. 336 p.

Grades: 6 7 8 9 10 **Fic**
   1. 19th century 2. Sibling rivalry 3. Murder 4. Assassins 5. Loki (Norse deity) 6. Secret societies 7. London, England 8. Historical fantasy 9. Superhero stories 10. Franchise books
ISBN 9781368022262

After the banishment of his only friend, the sorceress Amora, to Earth, a young Loki travels to nineteenth-century London to investigate a string of murders but finds much more than he expects.

"This deft, nuanced examination of identity, destiny, and agency is a surprisingly tender addition to the Marvel canon." Kirkus.

Lee, Stacey (Stacey Heather)

The **downstairs** girl. Stacey Lee. G.P. Putnam's Sons, 2019. 384 p.

Grades: 7 8 9 10 11 12   **Fic**
1. 1890s 2. 19th century 3. Chinese American teenage girls 4. Household employees 5. Advice columns 6. Teenage girl journalists 7. Social reformers 8. Atlanta, Georgia 9. Southern States 10. Historical fiction
ISBN 9781524740955

LC 2018018881

1890, Atlanta. By day, seventeen-year-old Jo Kuan works as a lady's maid for the cruel Caroline Payne, the daughter of one of the wealthiest men in Atlanta. But by night, Jo moonlights as the pseudonymous author of a newspaper advice column for 'the genteel Southern lady'.

"Unflinching in its portrayals of racism yet ultimately hopeful and heartfelt, this narrative places voices frequently left out of historical fiction center stage." School Library Journal

Outrun the moon. Stacey Lee. G. P. Putnam's Sons, [2016]. 400 p.

Grades: 7 8 9 10   **Fic**
1. 1900s (Decade) 2. Chinese American teenage girls 3. Earthquakes 4. Boarding schools 5. Survival 6. San Francisco Earthquake and Fire, Calif, 1906 7. San Francisco, California 8. Chinatown, San Francisco, California 9. Historical fiction
ISBN 9780399175411

LC 2015032478

On the eve of the San Francisco Earthquake of 1906, Mercy Wong—daughter of Chinese immigrants—is struggling to hold her own among the spoiled heiresses at prestigious St. Clare's School. When tragedy strikes, everyone must band together to survive. Provided by publisher.

Lee, Stan, 1922-2018

Convergence. Stan Lee, Stuart Moore, Andie Tong [illustrator]. Disney Press, 2015. 304 p.: Zodiac legacy

Grades: 4 5 6 7   **Fic**
1. Chinese zodiac 2. Chinese Americans 3. Good and evil 4. Chinese American teenage boys 5. Teenage boys 6. Superhero stories 7. Illustrated books 8. Asian-influenced fantasy
ISBN 9781423180852

Follows the experiences of a Chinese-American teen who is thrown into the middle of an epic global chase involving the release of twelve magical superpowers.

Lee, Y. S. (Ying S.), 1974-

The **body** at the tower. Y.S. Lee Candlewick Press, 2010. 352 p.: The Agency

Grades: 8 9 10 11 12   **Fic**
1. Westminster Hall, London, England. 2. Victorian era (1837-1901) 3. 1850s 4. Teenage girl detectives 5. Role reversal 6. Poor boys 7. Teenage girl orphans 8. Teenage girls 9. Great Britain 10. London, England 11. Historical mysteries 12. Mysteries
ISBN 9780763649685

As a nearly full-fledged member of the Agency, the all-female detective unit based in Miss Scrimshaw's Academy for Girls, Mary Quinn, disguised as a poor apprentice builder, must brave the sinister underworld of Victorian London in order to unmask a murderer.

"Mary Quinn returns in another case for the Agency, a covert all-female detective agency in Victorian London. A man has recently fallen out of the soon-to-be-completed clock tower of the Houses of Parliament. Mary disguises herself as an errand boy and attempts to infiltrate the work site to discover potential suspects. . . . This second book is much stronger than the first, both in terms of character development and the central mystery." School Library Journal.

A **spy** in the house. Y.S. Lee. Candlewick Press, 2010. 352 p.: The Agency

Grades: 8 9 10 11 12   **Fic**
1. Victorian era (1837-1901) 2. 1850s 3. Teenage girl orphans 4. Swindlers and swindling 5. Girl thieves 6. Smuggling 7. Seventeen-year-old girls 8. Great Britain 9. London, England 10. Historical mysteries 11. Mysteries
ISBN 9780763640675

LC 2009032736

Mary graduates from Miss Scrimshaw's Academy for Girls with admirable skills, including being an undercover investigator. Working in the guise of a lady's companion, she infiltrates a merchant's home to try to trace his missing cargo ships. She then finds that that household is full of dangerous secrets.

"Lee fills the story with classic elements of Victorian mystery and melodrama. Class differences, love gone awry, racial discrimination, London's growing pains in the 1850s, and the status of women in society are all addressed. Historical details are woven seamlessly into the plot, and descriptive writing allows readers to be part of each scene." School Library Journal.

Legrand, Claire, 1986-

Some kind of happiness. Claire Legrand. Simon & Schuster Books for Young Readers, 2016. 304 p.

Grades: 4 5 6 7   **Fic**
1. Depression 2. Writing 3. Family secrets 4. Anxiety 5. Family problems 6. Realistic fiction
ISBN 9781442466012

"A quiet magic is at work in Legrand's novel, in which she adeptly interweaves Fin's imaginative writing with the real-life narrative, underpinning all with an appeal to honesty and self-acceptance. This beautiful and reflective tale carries echoes of Katherine Patterson's The Bridge to Terabithia (1977) and will resonate with thoughtful readers who enjoy pondering life's bigger questions." Booklist.

Lennon, Tom

When love comes to town. Tom Lennon. Albert Whitman, 2013. 288 p.

Grades: 8 9 10 11 12   **Fic**
1. 1990s 2. Gay teenagers 3. Coming out (Sexual or gender identity) 4. Rejection (Psychology) 5. Closeted gay teenagers 6. Teenage boys 7. Ireland 8. Realistic fiction 9. LGBTQIA fiction
ISBN 9780807589168

LC 2012020160

Neil Byrne, a teenager in Dublin, Ireland, in the 1990s, comes to terms with the fact that he is gay and seeks acceptance from his friends and family.

Leno, Katrina

The **lost** & found. Katrina Leno. HarperTeen, an imprint of HarperCollinsPublishers, 2016 352 p.

Grades: 7 8 9 10 11   **Fic**
1. Loss (Psychology) 2. Automobile travel 3. Lost articles 4. Teenagers 5. Realistic fiction
ISBN 9780062231208

Forging a friendship through an online support group, Frannie and Louis, teens whose losses are tied to mysterious disappearances, search for answers during a road trip to Austin, where they find magical things that the other has lost.

"This is a beautiful exploration of loss in many forms and the emotional toll it can take on those who are affected. . . . An emotional journey that's well worth the ride." School Library Journal.

Lerangis, Peter

The **colossus** rises. Peter Lerangis. Harper, 2013. 304 p.: Seven wonders

Grades: 4 5 6 7 8 9   **Fic**
1. Atlantis (Legendary place) 2. Teenage adventurers 3. Seven Wonders of the World 4. Relics 5. Covert operations 6. Fantasy fiction 7. Mythological fiction
ISBN 9780062070401

LC 2012025334

Teens Jack, Marco, Aly, and Cass begin a quest to find seven pieces of Atlantis' power that were hidden long ago and that will, if returned to Atlantis, save them from certain death due to the genetic abnormality that also gives them superior abilities.

Lost in babylon. Peter Lerangis; [illustrated by Torstein Nordstrand]. HarperCollins, 2013. 373 p.: Seven wonders

Grades: 4 5 6 7 8 9   **Fic**
1. Seven Wonders of the World 2. Teenage adventurers 3. Atlantis (Legendary place) 4. Adventure 5. Babylon (Extinct city) 6. Babylonia 7. Fantasy fiction 8. Mythological fiction
ISBN 9780062070432

LC 2013942765

Journeying to the ancient city of Babylon when Bhegad tracks down Marco, the companions face a daunting choice involving a dire trap and a long-lost figure from Jack's past.

The **tomb** of shadows. Peter Lerangis; illustrations by Torstein Norstrand. Harper, an imprint of HarperCollins Publishers, 2014 338 p.: Seven wonders

Grades: 4 5 6 7 8 9   **Fic**
1. Teenage adventurers 2. Seven Wonders of the World 3. Betrayal 4. Mausoleum (Halicarnassus) 5. Adventure 6. Fantasy fiction 7. Mythological fiction
ISBN 9780062070463

Struggling with the ruin of Babylon and a devastating betrayal, Jack McKinley and his friends hone their growing G7W powers while continuing their journey to the most formidable of the Wonders.

"Jack, Ally, and Cass continue their quest to save the world—even as their friend Marco joins the enemy's side. Epic battles and fast-moving chapters will keep fans of this Percy Jackson-like series engaged." School Library Journal.

Lesperance, Nicole

The **nightmare** thief. Nicole Lesperance. Sourcebooks Inc 2021 304 p.: Nightmare thief

Grades: 4 5 6 7   **Fic**
1. Sisters 2. Family businesses 3. Dreams 4. Magic 5. Extortion 6. New England 7. Fantasy fiction
ISBN 9781728215341

LC 2020034485

When Maren breaks the strict rules of her family's dream shop to help her comatose sister, she is caught and blackmailed by a woman with evil plans for the town of Rockpool Bay.

"In this debut, Lesperance has crafted a wonderfully original world, similar to ours in many ways but completely extraordinary in others, with small amounts of magic neatly tucked alongside normal bits of life. . . . There is magic and mayhem, horror and hope, and the thread of family and friendship weaving it all together." Booklist

Lester, Julius

Day of tears: a novel in dialogue. Hyperion Books for Children, 2005. 176 p.

Grades: 7 8 9 10   **Fic**
1. Antebellum America (1820-1861) 2. 19th century 3. Slave trade 4. Cruelty 5. Enslaved people 6. African Americans 7. Slaveholders 8. Savannah, Georgia 9. Southern States 10. Historical fiction
ISBN 0786804904

Coretta Scott King Award, Author Category, 2006.

"The horror of the auction and its aftermath is unforgettable. . . . The racism is virulent (there's widespread use of the n-word). The personal voices make this a stirring text for group discussion." Booklist.

Guardian. by Julius Lester. Amistad/HarperTeen, 2008. 160 p.

Grades: 7 8 9 10   **Fic**
1. 1940s 2. Lynching 3. Racism 4. Race relations 5. Judicial error 6. African Americans 7. Southern States 8. Historical fiction
ISBN 9780061558900

In a rural southern town in 1946, a white man and his son witness the lynching of an innocent black man. Includes historical note on lynching.

"The author's understated, haunting prose is as compelling as it is dark; . . . [the story] leaves a deep impression." Publishers Weekly.

Includes bibliographical references.

Time's memory. Julius Lester. Farrar Straus Giroux, 2006. 240 p.

Grades: 8 9 10 11 12   **Fic**
1. 1860s 2. Slavery 3. African Americans -- History 19th century 4. Loss (Psychology) 5. African American families 6. Dogon (African people) -- Religion 7. Virginia 8. Historical fiction 9. African American fiction 10. Mythological fiction
ISBN 0374371784

LC 2005047716

Ekundayo, a Dogon spirit brought to America from Africa, inhabits the body of a young African American slave on a Virginia plantation, where he experiences loss, sorrow, and reconciliation in the months preceding the Civil War.

"More than a picture of slavery through the eyes of those enslaved or their captors, Lester's narrative evokes spiritual images of Mali's Dogon people." School Library Journal.

Levenseller, Tricia

Daughter of the pirate king. Tricia Levenseller. Feiwel & Friends, 2017. 272 p.: Daughter of the pirate king

Grades: 8 9 10 11   **Fic**
1. Girl pirates 2. Maps 3. Undercover operations 4. Captivity 5. Pirates 6. Fantasy fiction
ISBN 9781250095961

"Resourceful and confident, Alosa swaggers through the pages with style and panache, and her supporting cast is just as delightful." Publishers Weekly.

Levine, Gail Carson

A **ceiling** made of eggshells. Gail Carson Levine. HarperCollins, 2020. 397 p.

Grades: 5 6 7 8   **Fic**
1. 15th century 2. Jews -- Persecutions 3. Grandfather and child 4. Jewish girls 5. Voyages and travels 6. Inquisition 7. Spain 8.

Historical fiction
ISBN 9780062878205

LC 2019040581

From age seven, Loma relishes traveling with her beloved grandfather across fifteenth-century Spain, working to keep the Jews safe, but soon realizes she must also make sacrifices to help her people. Includes historical notes, recipe, glossary, and a link to a bibliography.

"Levine skillfully juxtaposes the larger religious battles taking place in Spain with Loma's dreams for her future." School Library Journal

Ella enchanted. Gail Carson Levine. Harper Collins Publishers, c1997. 232 p.: Ella enchanted

Grades: 5 6 7 8   **Fic**
    1. Obedience 2. Curses 3. Resourcefulness in girls 4. Resourcefulness 5. Fairies 6. Fantasy fiction 7. Fairy tale and folklore-inspired fiction 8. Classics
    ISBN 0060275103

LC 96-30734

In this novel based on the story of Cinderella, Ella struggles against the childhood curse that forces her to obey any order given to her.

"As finely designed as a tapestry, Ella's story both neatly incorporates elements of the original tale and mightily expands them." Booklist.

Ever. Gail Carson Levine. Harper Collins Publishers, 2008. 256 p.

Grades: 5 6 7 8   **Fic**
    1. Human sacrifice 2. Immortality 3. Quests 4. Teenage boy/girl relations 5. Fourteen-year-olds 6. Fantasy fiction
    ISBN 9780061229626

LC 2007032289

Fourteen-year-old Kezi and Olus, Akkan god of the winds, fall in love and together try to change her fate—to be sacrificed to a Hyte god because of a rash promise her father made—through a series of quests that might make her immortal.

"Levine conducts a riveting journey, offering passion and profound pondering along the way." Publishers Weekly.

Fairest. Gail Carson Levine. Harper Collins, 2006. 336 p.

Grades: 6 7 8 9   **Fic**
    1. Self-acceptance in teenage girls 2. Teenage girl singers 3. Ugliness 4. Fifteen-year-old girls 5. Teenage girls 6. Fantasy fiction 7. Fairy tale and folklore-inspired fiction
    ISBN 0060734086

LC 2006000337

In a land where beauty and singing are valued above all else, Aza eventually comes to reconcile her unconventional appearance and her magical voice, and learns to accept herself for who she truly is.

"The plot is fast-paced, and Aza's growth and maturity are well crafted and believable." School Library Journal.

The **lost** kingdom of Bamarre. Gail Carson Levine. Harper, 2017. 385 p.

Grades: 5 6 7 8   **Fic**
    1. Identity (Psychology) 2. Prejudice 3. Adopted teenage girls 4. Disguises 5. Fairies 6. Fantasy fiction
    ISBN 9780062074669

In a romantic prequel to the best-selling The Two Princesses of Bamarre, a noble girl learns that her parents were of the despised underclass and that she must raise a rebellion on behalf of her people.

"Levine riffs gently on Rapunzel and delivers an arch appraisal of discrimination and bigotry, cloaked in a magical, medieval, vaguely European fairy-tale setting." Kirkus.

A **tale** of Two Castles. Gail Carson Levine. HarperCollins, 2011. 336 p.: Tale of Two Castles

Grades: 4 5 6   **Fic**
    1. Girl apprentices 2. Dragons 3. Poisoning 4. Reasoning 5. False imprisonment 6. Fantasy mysteries 7. Fantasy fiction
    ISBN 9780061229657

Twelve-year-old Elodie journeys to Two Castles in hopes of studying acting but instead becomes apprentice to a dragon, who teaches her to be observant and use reasoning, thus helping her to uncover who is poisoning the king.

"Readers are certain to be pulled, like Elodie herself, right into the midst of the rich and swirling life of Two Castles." School Library Journal.

Levine, Kristin (Kristin Sims), 1974-

★ The **lions** of Little Rock. Kristin Levine. G. P. Putnam's Sons, 2012. 304 p.

Grades: 5 6 7 8   **Fic**
    1. 1950s 2. Twelve-year-old girls 3. School integration 4. Race relations 5. Racism 6. Shyness in children 7. Little Rock, Arkansas 8. Historical fiction
    ISBN 9780399256448

LC 2011031835

In 1958 Little Rock, Arkansas, painfully shy twelve-year-old Marlee sees her city and family divided over school integration, but her friendship with Liz, a new student, helps her find her voice and fight against racism.

The **paper** cowboy. Kristin Levine. G.P. Putnam's Sons, an imprint of Penguin Group (USA), [2014] 341 p.

Grades: 5 6 7 8   **Fic**
    1. 1950s 2. Newspaper carriers 3. Bullying and bullies 4. Neighbors 5. Family problems 6. Communists 7. Illinois 8. Historical fiction
    ISBN 9780399163289

LC 2014004421

In a small town near Chicago in 1953, twelve-year-old Tommy faces escalating problems at home, among his Catholic school friends, and with the threat of a communist living nearby, but taking over his hospitalized sister's paper route introduces him to neighbors who he comes to rely on for help.

"Twelve-year-old Tommy wants to be a cowboy. That's not so easy, though, in 1950s Downers Grove, Illinois. After he plays a prank that ends up costing the local grocery store owner his business, a remorseful Tommy goes about becoming a different kind of cowboy—one who stands up for others. Themes of bullying, community, and growing up in a dysfunctional family are explored sensitively." Horn Book.

Levithan, David

The **mysterious** disappearance of Aidan S.: (as told to his brother). David Levithan. Knopf Books for Young Readers, 2021. 224 p.

Grades: 5 6 7 8   **Fic**
    1. Missing children 2. Truthfulness and falsehood 3. Imaginary places 4. Reality 5. Letting go (Psychology) 6. Realistic fiction 7. Mysteries 8. LGBTQIA fiction
    ISBN 9781984848604

Aidan disappeared for six days. Six agonizing days of searches and police and questions and constant vigils. Then, just as suddenly as he vanished, Aidan reappears. Where has he been? The story he tells is simply. . . impossible. But it's the story Aidan is sticking to. His brother, Lucas, wants to believe him. But Lucas is aware of what other people, including their parents, are saying: that Aidan is making it all up to disguise the fact that he ran away. When the kids in school hear Aidan's story, they taunt him. But still Aidan clings to his story. And as he becomes more of an outcast, Lucas becomes more and more concerned. Being on Aidan's side would mean believing in the impossible. But how can you believe in the impossible when everything and everybody is telling you not to?

"A stellar novel that deftly examines the uncomfortable reality that not everything has a satisfying answer." Bulletin of the Center for Children's Books

Two boys kissing. David Levithan. Alfred A. Knopf, 2013. 208 p.

Grades: 8 9 10 11 12   **Fic**

    1. Gay teenagers 2. Kissing 3. AIDS (Disease) 4. Dating (Social customs) 5. Former boyfriends 6. LGBTQIA romances 7. Realistic fiction 8. Contemporary romances

    ISBN 9780307931900

                            LC 2012047089

A chorus of men who died of AIDS observes and yearns to help a cross-section of today's gay teens who navigate new love, long-term relationships, coming out, self-acceptance, and more in a society that has changed in many ways.

"Craig and Harry attempt to break the world record for longest kiss, which, in turn, affects the lives of the people around them. Narrated by a ghostly chorus of past generations of gay men who died of AIDS, Levithan's latest novel weaves together an informed (sometimes melodramatic) perspective on the past with the present-day stories of seven boys constructing their own sexual identities." Horn Book.

Levy, Dana Alison

    Above all else. Dana Alison Levy. Charlesbridge, 2020. 320 p.

Grades: 8 9 10 11 12   **Fic**

    1. Best friends 2. Mountaineering 3. Wilderness survival 4. Teenage boy/girl relations 5. Teenagers 6. Mount Everest 7. Survival stories

    ISBN 9781623541408

                            LC 2019034453

Eighteen-year-olds Rose and Tate are best friends and climbing buddies, and now they are embarking on the greatest climb of all—Mount Everest; but as the climbers encounter physical and emotional challenges the higher they go, the expedition starts to slide toward disaster, testing the teens' courage, determination, and their feelings for each other. Provided by publisher.

"Levy's fast-paced novel mirrors the frantic, heartrending, and blood-pumping journey undertaken by her characters. Thanks to a detailed map of the mountain routes, readers can track Rose and Tate's adventures as they wind around each other like climbing ropes, their stories dovetailing into a passionate, climactic romance." Booklist

    The **family** Fletcher takes Rock Island. Dana Alison Levy. Delacorte Press, [2016] 256 p.: Family Fletcher novels

Grades: 4 5 6 7   **Fic**

    1. Families 2. Summer 3. Lighthouses 4. Cats 5. Kayaking 6. Humorous stories 7. Realistic fiction

    ISBN 9780553521306

                            LC 2015014134

Summertime brings the Fletcher Family back to Rock Island where the good times never end, but this summer the boys' favorite lighthouse is all boarded up and with the help from their new neighbors, the Garcia girls, the boys are determined to find out what is really happening with their lighthouse and saving it, no matter what the cost.

"There is constant action and delightful humor, but there are also realistic present-day problems and happy solutions. An old-fashioned summer adventure set in a very modern world, this lively family tale will leave readers impatient for more." Kirkus.

The **misadventures** of the family Fletcher. Dana Alison Levy. Delacorte Press, 2014. 192 p.: Family Fletcher novels

Grades: 4 5 6 7   **Fic**

    1. Family relationships 2. Adopted boys 3. Nontraditional families 4. Brothers 5. Interethnic families 6. Realistic fiction

    ISBN 9780385376525

                            LC 2013026320

Relates the adventures of a family with two fathers, four adopted boys, and a variety of pets as they make their way through a school year, Kindergarten through sixth grade, and deal with a grumpy new neighbor.

"Four adopted (and racially diverse) brothers and two dads star in this Penderwicks-esque chronicle of a year in their lives. Focusing each chapter on one boy while still keeping the whole family in the picture, Levy provides a compelling, compassionate, and frequently hilarious look at their daily concerns. Readers will want to be part of (or at least friends with) this delightful family." Horn Book.

This would make a good story someday. Dana Alison Levy. Delacorte Press, 2017. 320 p.

Grades: 4 5 6 7 8   **Fic**

    1. Twelve-year-old girls 2. Railroad travel 3. Nontraditional families 4. Lesbian mothers 5. Transcontinental journeys 6. Realistic fiction 7. Humorous stories

    ISBN 9781101938171

                            LC 2016032310

Although not thrilled when her summer plans are upended for a surprise cross-country train trip with her family and embarrassed because one of her moms is writing a tell-all book about the trip, twelve-year-old Sara Johnston-Fischer finds herself changing along with the landscape outside the train windows.

Lewis, C. S. (Clive Staples), 1898-1963

    The **horse** and his boy. C.S. Lewis; illustrated by Pauline Baynes. HarperCollins, 1994, c1954. 224 p.: Chronicles of Narnia

Grades: 4 5 6 7   **Fic**

    1. Magic 2. Good and evil 3. Boy adventurers 4. Boys and horses 5. Princes 6. High fantasy 7. Fantasy fiction 8. Classics

    ISBN 9780060234881

                            LC 54012817

A boy and a talking horse share an adventurous and dangerous journey to Narnia to warn of invading barbarians.

    The **last** battle. C.S. Lewis; illustrated by Pauline Baynes. HarperTrophy, 1994, c1956. 228 p.: Chronicles of Narnia

Grades: 4 5 6 7   **Fic**

    1. Good and evil 2. Magic 3. Child adventurers 4. Imaginary wars and battles 5. Narnia (Imaginary place) 6. Fantasy fiction 7. Classics 8. Gateway fantasy

    ISBN 9780064471084

    Carnegie Medal, 1956.

When evil comes to Narnia, Jill and Eustace help fight the great last battle, and Aslan leads his people to a glorious new paradise.

★ The **lion,** the witch and the wardrobe: a story for children. C.S. Lewis; illustrated by Pauline Baynes. HarperCollins, 1997, c1950. 174 p.: Chronicles of Narnia

Grades: 4 5 6 7   **Fic**
1. Magic 2. Good and evil 3. Child adventurers 4. Spells (Magic) 5. Witches 6. Fantasy fiction 7. Classics 8. Gateway fantasy
ISBN 9780060234829

Four English school children find their way through the back of a wardrobe into the magic land of Narnia and assist Aslan, the golden lion, to triumph over the White Witch, who has cursed the land with eternal winter.

"This begins the Narnia stories, outstanding modern fairy tales with an underlying theme of good overcoming evil. Child Books Too Good to Miss

The **magician's** nephew. C.S. Lewis; illustrated by Pauline Baynes. HarperCollins, 1994, c1955. 202 p.: Chronicles of Narnia
Grades: 4 5 6 7   **Fic**
1. Magic 2. Good and evil 3. Spells (Magic) 4. Witches 5. Lion 6. Fantasy fiction 7. Classics 8. Gateway fantasy
ISBN 9780060234973

When Digory and Polly try to return the wicked witch Jadis to her own world, the magic gets mixed up and they all land in Narnia where they witness Aslan blessing the animals with human speech.

Prince Caspian: the return to Narnia. C.S. Lewis; illustrated by Pauline Baynes. HarperCollins, 1994, c1951. 223 p.: Chronicles of Narnia
Grades: 4 5 6 7   **Fic**
1. Magic 2. Good and evil 3. Quests 4. Princes 5. Lion 6. Fantasy fiction 7. Classics 8. Gateway fantasy
ISBN 9780060234836

Four children help Prince Caspian and his army of Talking Beasts to free Narnia from evil. Includes map.

The **silver** chair. C.S. Lewis; illustrated by Pauline Baynes. HarperCollins, 1994, c1953. 243 p.: Chronicles of Narnia
Grades: 4 5 6 7   **Fic**
1. Magic 2. Good and evil 3. Rescue work 4. Princes 5. Witches 6. Fantasy fiction 7. Classics 8. Gateway fantasy
ISBN 9780060234959

Two English school children share hair-raising adventures as they go on a search and rescue mission for the missing Prince Rilian, who is held captive in the underground kingdom of the Emerald Witch.

The **voyage** of the Dawn Treader. C.S. Lewis; illustrated by Pauline Baynes. HarperCollins, 1994, c1952. 248 p.: Chronicles of Narnia
Grades: 4 5 6 7   **Fic**
1. Cousins 2. Dragons 3. Transformations (Magic) 4. Magic 5. Good and evil 6. Fantasy fiction 7. Classics 8. Gateway fantasy
ISBN 9780060234867

Lucy, Edmund, and their peevish cousin Eustace sail to the land of Narnia, where Eustace is temporarily transformed into a green dragon because of his selfish behavior and skepticism.

Lewis, Gill
Gorilla dawn. by Gill Lewis; illustrated by Susan Meyer. Atheneum Books for Young Readers, 2017. 408 p.
Grades: 5 6 7 8 9   **Fic**
1. Hostages 2. Child soldiers 3. Gorillas 4. Rain forests 5. Congo (Democratic Republic) 6. Thrillers and suspense
ISBN 9781481486576

"A riveting survival adventure with an important message." Kirkus.

One white dolphin. Gill Lewis; illustrated by Raquel Aparicio. Atheneum Books for Young Readers, 2012. 192 p.
Grades: 5 6 7   **Fic**
1. Dolphins 2. Wildlife rescue 3. Environmental protection 4. Girls with dyslexia 5. Boys with cerebral palsy 6. England 7. Realistic fiction
ISBN 9781442414471

LC 2012009182

When a baby albino dolphin caught in old fishing netting washes ashore, Paralympics sailing hopeful Felix and English school girl Kara work with veterinarians and specialists to save and reunite the dolphin with her mother, setting off a chain of events that might just save the reef from the environmental effects of proposed dredging.

Lewis, J. Patrick
★ **And** the soldiers sang. by J. Patrick Lewis; illustrations by Gary Kelley. Creative Editions, 2011. 32 p.
Grades: 2 3 4 5 6   **Fic**
1. First World War era (1914-1918) 2. Soldiers 3. Western Front (World War I) 4. War 5. Christmas Truce, 1914 6. Trench warfare 7. War stories 8. Historical fiction
ISBN 9781568462202

"This offers a terse yet lyrical text and stark, dramatic illustrations. . . . Kelley's compelling artwork features mostly dark shades and strong, angular compositions. . . . Grim, upsetting and utterly beautiful, this is both a strong antiwar statement and a fascinating glimpse of a little-known historical event." Kirkus.

Lim, Elizabeth
Spin the dawn. Elizabeth Lim. Random House Children's Books, 2019 416 p.: Blood of stars
Grades: 9 10 11 12   **Fic**
1. Seamstresses 2. Contests 3. Enchantment 4. Imaginary empires 5. Disguises 6. Asian-influenced fantasy 7. High fantasy 8. Fantasy fiction
ISBN 9780525646990

Risking her life by disguising herself as a boy to secure the position of imperial tailor, Maia is given the impossible task of sewing three magic gowns representing the sun, moon and stars for the emperor's reluctant bride-to-be.

"Beautifully written with a can't-wait-for-the-sequel ending, this breathtaking and fast-paced Silk-road inspired fantasy from the author of Mulan-retelling Reflection is sure to enchant readers beginning to end." Booklist

Lin, Grace
★ **Starry** River of the Sky. by Grace Lin. Little, Brown, 2012. 304 p.: Starry River of the Sky
Grades: 3 4 5 6   **Fic**
1. Runaway boys 2. Inns 3. Storytelling 4. Villages 5. China 6. Moon 7. Fantasy fiction
ISBN 9780316125956

LC 2012012651

An innkeeper's chore boy discovers that a visitor's stories hold the key to returning the moon to the Starry River of the Sky.

★ **When** the sea turned to silver. Grace Lin. 384 p.: Starry River of the Sky
Grades: 4 5 6 7   **Fic**
1. Kidnapping 2. Storytellers 3. Adventure 4. Quests 5.

Grandmothers 6. China 7. Fantasy fiction 8. Fairy tale and folklore-inspired fiction 9. Illustrated books
ISBN 9780316125925

LC 2015041876

When her grandmother is kidnapped, Pinmei, accompanied by her friend Yishan, embarks on a search for the Luminous Stone That Lights the Night, which she intends to give the cruel Tiger Emperor in exchange for her grandmother.

"A stunning addition to a deservedly beloved set of novels." School Library Journal.

Includes bibliographical references.

★ **Where** the mountain meets the moon. by Grace Lin. Little, Brown and Co., 2009. 278 p.: Starry River of the Sky
Grades: 4 5 6 7   **Fic**
1. Poor girls 2. Adventure 3. Greed 4. Dragons 5. Quests 6. Moon 7. Fantasy fiction 8. Asian-influenced fantasy
ISBN 9780316114271

LC 2008032818

Minli, an adventurous girl from a poor village, buys a magical goldfish, and then joins a dragon who cannot fly on a quest to find the Old Man of the Moon in hopes of bringing life to Fruitless Mountain and freshness to Jade River.

"With beautiful language, Lin creates a strong, memorable heroine and a mystical land. . . . Children will embrace this accessible, timeless story about the evil of greed and the joy of gratitude." Booklist.

Lindelauf, Benny, 1964-

Fing's war. Benny Lindelauf; translated from the Dutch by John Nieuwenhuizen. Consortium Book Sales & Dist., 2019. 411 p.
Grades: 4 5 6   **Fic**
1. Second World War era (1939-1945) 2. Families 3. War 4. Anger in teenagers 5. Eccentrics and eccentricities 6. Teenage girls -- Career aspirations 7. Netherlands 8. Historical fiction 9. Translations
ISBN 9781592702695

LC 2019011185

Follows teenaged Fing Boon and her large, impoverished, eccentric family as they navigate the changes World War II visits upon their little town on the border of the Netherlands and Germany.

Nine Open Arms. Benny Lindelauf; translated from the Dutch by John Nieuwenhuizen; jacket and interior art by Dasha Tolstikova. Enchanted Lion Books, 2014. 180 p.
Grades: 5 6 7 8 9   **Fic**
1. 1930s 2. Single-parent families 3. Romanies 4. Grandmothers 5. Families 6. Twelve-year-old girls 7. Netherlands 8. Historical fiction 9. Translations
ISBN 9781592701469

"Every element of the tale has a purpose, and in the end, the multiple layers of past and present separate and come together in surprising, often discomfiting twists and turns. A challenging and entirely unique Dutch import." Kirkus.

Lipsyte, Robert

The **contender**. Robert Lipsyte. Harper & Row, 1967. 182 p.
Grades: 7 8 9 10   **Fic**
1. African American teenage boys 2. Persistence in teenage boys 3. Boxing 4. Courage in teenage boys 5. Gangs 6. Sports fiction
ISBN 9780060239206

LC   67019623

Against great odds, a black high school drop-out trains to become a championship boxer.

Lisle, Janet Taylor

Quicksand Pond. Janet Taylor Lisle. Atheneum Books for Young Readers, [2017] 256 p.
Grades: 5 6 7 8   **Fic**
1. Friendship 2. Murder 3. Recluses 4. Ponds 5. Summer 6. New England 7. Realistic fiction
ISBN 9781481472227

LC 2016009707

Twelve-year-old Jessie spends the summer with her family on Quicksand Pond, a New England vacation spot, where she develops a star-crossed friendship with independent Terri, and meets a reclusive old lady whose connection to a murder that took place decades ago still informs her present—and affects Terri in ways that Jessie gradually comes to understand the more time they spend together.

"A strong purchase for fans of layered, realistic mysteries and drama." School Library Journal.

Little, Kimberley Griffiths

Circle of secrets. Kimberley Griffiths Little. Scholastic Press, 2011. 336 p.
Grades: 5 6 7 8   **Fic**
1. Mothers and daughters 2. Ghosts 3. Bayous 4. Guilt 5. Reconciliation 6. Louisiana
ISBN 9780545165617

LC 2011000889

A year after her mother has deserted the family, eleven-year-old Shelby goes to stay with her, deep in the Louisiana bayou, where they both confront old hurts and regrets.

"The gently spooky ghost angle is handled nicely with some religious overtones. A very dramatic climax leads to a sweet, satisfying ending with some surprising twists and with reconciliation occurring for several characters." Kirkus.

Littlewood, Kathryn

Bliss. Kathryn Littlewood. Katherine Tegen Books, 2012. 256 p.: Bliss novels
Grades: 3 4 5 6   **Fic**
1. Twelve year-old girls 2. Bakeries 3. Magic 4. Books and reading 5. Bakers 6. Fantasy fiction
ISBN 9780062084231

LC 2011019390

Twelve-year-old Rose Bliss wants to work magic in her family's bakery as her parents do, but when they are called away and Rose and her siblings are left in charge, the magic goes awry and a beautiful stranger tries to talk Rose into giving her the Bliss Cookery Booke.

Littman, Sarah

Backlash. Sarah Darer Littman. Scholastic Press, 2015. 336 p.
Grades: 7 8 9   **Fic**
1. Cyberbullying 2. Suicide 3. Teenage girls 4. Teenage boy/girl relations 5. Social status 6. Realistic fiction
ISBN 9780545651264

LC 2014020226

When Christian, a boy she knows only through Facebook, posts a lot of nasty comments on her page, fifteen-year-old Lara tries to kill herself—but that is only the beginning of the backlash for her sister, Sydney; her former friend Bree; and her classmates.

"The depression and bullying are handled realistically without su-garcoating, and fortunately, consequences are applied. An excellent choice for any antibullying campaign." Booklist.

Lloyd, Natalie

★ A **snicker** of magic. by Natalie Lloyd. Scholastic Press, 2014. 320 p.

Grades: 4 5 6 7   **Fic**
1. Curses 2. Single-parent families 3. Talent shows 4. Boy wheelchair users 5. Moving, Household 6. Tennessee 7. Fantasy fiction
ISBN 9780545552707

LC 2013027779

Arriving in a town where magic has been driven away by a curse, 12-year-old Felicity, a girl who possesses a supernatural ability to see words around the people and places she visits, befriends mysterious do-gooder Jonah, who introduces shimmering new words while helping her break the curse.

"The unusual language, showing a tinge of Tennessee mountain dia-lect, spins a web around the story that touches on helping others, bud-ding friendships, and strength of family." Booklist.

Lloyd, Saci

The **carbon** diaries 2015. by Saci Lloyd. Holiday House, 2009. 330 p.

Grades: 8 9 10 11 12   **Fic**
1. Rationing 2. Energy conservation 3. Climate change 4. Global warming 5. Families 6. London, England 7. Diary novels 8. Science fiction
ISBN 9780823421909

LC 2008019712

In 2015, when England becomes the first nation to introduce carbon dioxide rationing in a drastic bid to combat climate change, sixteen-year-old Laura documents the first year of rationing as her family spirals out of control.

"Deeply compulsive and urgently compulsory reading." Booklist.

Lloyd-Jones, Emily

The **bone** houses. Emily Lloyd-Jones. Little, Brown and Company, 2019 352 p.

Grades: 7 8 9 10 11   **Fic**
1. Teenage girl orphans 2. Apprentices 3. Undead 4. Curses 5. Villages 6. Fantasy fiction 7. Horror
ISBN 9780316418416

When risen corpses called 'bone houses' threaten Ryn's village be-cause of a decades-old curse, she teams up with a mapmaker named Ellis to solve the mystery of the curse and destroy the bone houses forever. Provided by publisher.

"The story serves as a meditation on the complicated relationship be-tween the living and the dead, combining fear, humor and enchantment in equal measure, and alloying them with humor." Publishers Weekly.

Lockhart, E.

The **disreputable** history of Frankie Landau-Banks. E. Lockhart. Hyperion, 2008. 345 p.

Grades: 7 8 9 10 11 12   **Fic**
1. Self-perception in teenage girls 2. Secret societies 3. Social acceptance 4. Dating (Social customs) 5. Teenage girls 6. Coming-of-age stories 7. Realistic fiction 8. Teen chick lit
ISBN 9780786838189

Tells of the life and transformation of Frankie Landau-Banks who began her teenage years as a quiet member of the Debate Club and grew to become a sixteen-year-old criminal mastermind with an attitude to match.

"On her return to Alabaster Prep . . . [Frankie] attracts the attention of gorgeous Matthew . . . [who] is a member of the Loyal Order of the Basset Hounds, an all-male Alabaster secret society. . . . Frankie engi-neers her own guerilla membership by assuming a false online identity. . . . Lockhart creates a unique, indelible character. . . . Teens will be galvanized." Booklist.

Dramarama. by E. Lockhart. Hyperion Books for Children, 2007. 320 p.

Grades: 7 8 9 10 11 12   **Fic**
1. Arts camps 2. Teenage actors and actresses 3. Gay teenagers 4. Best friends 5. Teenagers -- Interpersonal relations 6. Ohio 7. Realistic fiction 8. Teen chick lit
ISBN 0786838159

LC 2006049599

Spending their summer at Wildewood Academy, an elite boarding school for the performing arts, tests the bond between teens Sadye and her best friend Demi.

"Teens will identify strongly with both the heartbreak and the hu-mor in this authentic portrayal of friendships maturing and decaying." School Library Journal.

Genuine fraud. E. Lockhart Delacorte, 2017. 288 p.

Grades: 7 8 9 10 11 12   **Fic**
1. Impostors 2. Social classes 3. Disguises 4. Impersonation 5. Murderers 6. Thrillers and suspense
ISBN 9780385744775

Imogen is a runaway heiress, an orphan, a cook, and a cheat. Jule is a fighter, a social chameleon, and an athlete. An intense friendship. A disappearance. A murder, or maybe two. A bad romance, or maybe three. Blunt objects, disguises, blood, and chocolate. The American dream, su-perheroes, spies, and villains. A girl who refuses to give people what they want from her. A girl who refuses to be the person she once was.

"This quietly unsettling, cinematic novel is deliciously suspenseful, and while it's slim, it packs a real punch." Booklist.

We were liars. E. Lockhart. Delacorte Press, 2014. 240 p.

Grades: 7 8 9 10 11 12   **Fic**
1. Rich families 2. Amnesia 3. Islands 4. Friendship 5. Teenage romance 6. Massachusetts 7. Thrillers and suspense
ISBN 9780385741262

LC 2013042127

Spending the summers on her family's private island off the coast of Massachusetts with her cousins and a special boy named Gat, teenaged Cadence struggles to remember what happened during her fifteenth summer.

"Cadence Sinclair Easton comes from an old-money family, headed by a patriarch who owns a private island off of Cape Cod. Each sum-mer, the extended family gathers at the various houses on the island, and Cadence, her cousins Johnny and Mirren, and friend Gat (the four Liars), have been inseparable since age eight....The story, while lightly touching on issues of class and race, more fully focuses on dysfunctional fam-ily drama, a heart-wrenching romance between Cadence and Gat, and, ultimately, the suspense of what happened during that fateful summer. The ending is a stunner that will haunt readers for a long time to come." School Library Journal.

Lockington, Mariama

★ **For** black girls like me. Mariama J. Lockington. Farrar Straus Giroux, 2019. 336 p.

Grades: 4 5 6 7   **Fic**
1. African American girls 2. Adopted girls 3. Children of people with mental illnesses 4. Interracial adoption 5. Identity (Psychology) 6. Albuquerque, New Mexico 7. Realistic fiction 8. African American fiction
ISBN 9780374308049

LC 2018035461
Eleven-year-old Makeda dreams of meeting her African American mother, while coping with serious problems in her white adopted family, a cross-country move, and being homeschooled.

"A transracial adoptee navigates a new school, a mentally ill parent, and questions about her identity…The myriad themes explored are compelling, but the execution gets in the way." Kirkus.

Loftin, Nikki

Nightingale's nest. Nikki Loftin. Razorbill , a division of Penguin Young Readers Group, 2014. 256 p.
Grades: 4 5 6 7   **Fic**
1. Singing 2. Foster children 3. Grief 4. Family problems 5. Birds 6. Texas 7. Magical realism 8. Fairy tale and folklore-inspired fiction
ISBN 9781595145468

LC 2013047556
In this twist on "The Nightingale," Little John, despite his own poverty and grief, reaches out to Gayle, an unhappy foster child living next-door who sings beautifully and hides a great secret.

"John narrates his story in fluid, lyrical prose, Loftin blending the raw realism of a boy who makes the wrong choice with the fairy-tale magic of a girl with a nightingale voice. Unusual, finely crafted story of loss, betrayal and healing." Kirkus.

Wish girl. by Nikki Loftin. Razorbill, a division of Penguin Young Readers Group, 2015. 256 p.
Grades: 4 5 6 7   **Fic**
1. Bullying and bullies 2. Children with cancer 3. Friendship 4. Individuality 5. Best friends 6. Texas 7. Magical realism
ISBN 9781595146861

LC 2014031004
Twelve-year-old Peter has never felt at home with his noisy family, but begins to find the strength to live and to be himself when he discovers a special valley in the Texas Hill Country and meets Annie, a girl dying of cancer who knows and accepts him from the start.

"This thoughtful entry into realistic fiction for young teens explores family dysfunction and discord, the depression and emotional issues that plague young people trying to find their way, the importance of mentors, the unfortunate effects of bullying, and last but not least, cancer's impact on children and their families." Voice of Youth Advocates.

London, Alex

Black wings beating. Alex London. Farrar Straus Giroux, 2018. 432 p.: Skybound saga
Grades: 8 9 10 11 12   **Fic**
1. Twin brothers and sisters 2. Quests 3. Falconry 4. Twins 5. Birds 6. Fantasy fiction 7. Asian-influenced fantasy
ISBN 9780374306823

LC 2018001439
Twins Kylee and Brysen must fight for survival in a remote valley called Six Villages as war approaches, she by rejecting her ancient gifts for falconry and Brysen by striving to find greatness.

Proxy. Alex London. Philomel Books, an imprint of Penguin Group (USA) Inc., [2013] 368 p.: Proxy

Grades: 7 8 9 10   **Fic**
1. Dystopias 2. Spoiled teenage boys 3. Children -- Punishment 4. Sixteen-year-old boys 5. Teenage boy orphans 6. Dystopian fiction 7. Science fiction
ISBN 9780399257766

LC 2012039704
Privileged Syd and and his proxy, Knox, are thrown together to overthrow the system. Provided by publisher.

Red skies falling. Alex London. Farrar Straus Giroux, 2019. 480 p.: Skybound saga
Grades: 8 9 10 11 12   **Fic**
1. Twin brothers and sisters 2. Birds 3. Political intrigue 4. Imaginary wars and battles 5. Falconry 6. Fantasy fiction 7. Asian-influenced fantasy
ISBN 9780374306847

LC 2018046457
Orphaned twins Kylee and Brysen continue to fight for survival and power in the remote valley of the Six Villages.

"Readers clamoring for a YA Game of Thrones will easily fall prey to this trilogy and await the final installment. Arresting." Kirkus.

London, Jack, 1876-1916

The **call** of the wild. Jack London; illustrations by Philippe Munch. Viking, 1996. 126 p.
Grades: 5 6 7 8 9 10 11 12 Adult   **Fic**
1. Sled dogs 2. Wolves 3. Prospectors 4. Men and dogs 5. Dogs 6. Klondike gold fields 7. Alaska 8. Adventure stories 9. Classics
ISBN 9780670869183

LC 95-61728
The adventures of an unusual dog, part St. Bernard, part Scotch Shepherd, that was kidnapped and shipped off to Alaska to work on the Klondike Gold Rush. Buck the dog quickly learns how to survive in the wild and also learns the call of the wolf.

Longo, Jennifer

What I carry. Jennifer Longo. Random House, [2020] 336 p.
Grades: 8 9 10 11 12   **Fic**
1. Foster teenagers 2. Control (Psychology) 3. Belonging 4. Familial love 5. Foster family 6. Washington (State) 7. Bainbridge Island, Washington 8. Coming-of-age stories 9. Realistic fiction
ISBN 9780553537727

LC 2019001923
In her final year in foster care, seventeen-year-old Muir tries to survive her senior year before aging out of the system.

"The power of relationship both those experienced and those denied is expertly explored throughout this novel with nuance and humanity." Kirkus.

Lopez, Diana

Ask my mood ring how I feel. by Diana Lopez. Little, Brown, 2013. 336 p.
Grades: 4 5 6 7   **Fic**
1. Hispanic American teenage girls 2. Children of people with cancer 3. Fund-raising 4. Children of people with breast cancer 5. Promises 6. Texas 7. San Antonio, Texas 8. Realistic fiction
ISBN 9780316209960

LC 2012029856
When thirteen-year-old Erica "Chia" Montenegro finds out her mother has breast cancer, she makes a promise to God to raise money

for breast cancer awareness and discovers that when family and friends work together, miracles can happen.

Confetti girl. by Diana Lopez. Little, Brown, 2009. 198 p.
Grades: 4 5 6 7   **Fic**
1. Single-parent families 2. Fathers and daughters 3. Hispanic American girls 4. Mexican American girls 5. Sixth-grade girls 6. Texas 7. Coming-of-age stories 8. Realistic fiction
ISBN 9780316029551

LC 2008032819

After the death of her mother, Texas sixth-grader Lina's grades and mood drop as she watches her father lose himself more and more in books, while her best friend uses Lina as an excuse to secretly meet her boyfriend.

"Lopez effectively portrays the Texas setting and the characters' Latino heritage. . . . This . . . novel puts at its center a likable girl facing realistic problems on her own terms." Booklist.

Lord, Cynthia
Half a chance. Cynthia Lord. Scholastic Press, 2014. 224 p.
Grades: 4 5 6 7   **Fic**
1. Girl photographers 2. Father-separated girls 3. Photography 4. Dementia 5. Friendship 6. New Hampshire 7. Realistic fiction
ISBN 9780545035330

Moving to an old house on a lake that she struggles to view artistically in accordance with her photographer father's teachings, Lucy, fearing the pictures she takes will never meet his high standards, anonymously enters a photo contest that he is judging.

"The story is moving, and readers will find themselves caught up in sensitive Lucy's honest and thoughtful narration." Horn Book.

★ **Rules**. Cynthia Lord. Scholastic Press, 2006. 200 p.
Grades: 4 5 6 7   **Fic**
1. Twelve-year-old girls 2. Younger brothers and sisters 3. Brothers and sisters 4. People with disabilities 5. Children with autism 6. Realistic fiction
ISBN 0439443822

LC 2005017519

Schneider Family Book Award for Middle School, 2007.

Frustrated at life with an autistic brother, twelve-year-old Catherine longs for a normal existence but her world is further complicated by a friendship with a young paraplegic.

"The details of autistic behavior are handled well, as are depictions of relationships. . . . A heartwarming first novel." Booklist.

Touch blue. by Cynthia Lord. Scholastic Press, 2010. 192 p.
Grades: 4 5 6 7   **Fic**
1. Foster home care 2. Schools 3. Island life 4. Loneliness in girls 5. Families 6. Maine 7. Realistic fiction
ISBN 9780545035316

LC 2009042306

When the state of Maine threatens to shut down their island's one-room schoolhouse because of dwindling enrollment, eleven-year-old Tess, a strong believer in luck, and her family take in a trumpet-playing foster child, to increase the school's population.

"Aaron's relationship with his foster family . . . develops believably. The tight-knit community and lobster-catching details make for a warm, colorful environment. This is a feel-good story." Booklist.

Lord, Emery
When we collided. by Emery Lord. Bloomsbury, 2016. 380 p.

Grades: 8 9 10 11 12   **Fic**
1. Teenage girls with mental illnesses 2. Grief 3. Children of people with depression 4. Family problems 5. Teenagers with bipolar disorder 6. California 7. Realistic fiction 8. Love stories
ISBN 9781619638457

LC 2015011933

Schneider Family Book Award for Teens, 2017.

Can seventeen-year-old Jonah save his family restaurant from ruin, his mother from her sadness, and his danger-seeking girlfriend Vivi from herself?

"As much about the fragility of the human experience as it is about mental illness, this offers a refreshing perspective on a spectrum of mental health disorders. This love story veers away from tragedy, instead firmly entrenching itself in hope and possibility." Booklist.

Lord, Emma
Tweet cute. Emma Lord. Wednesday Books, 2020. 362 p.
Grades: 7 8 9 10 11 12   **Fic**
1. Business competition 2. Social media 3. Teenagers -- Interpersonal relations 4. Teenage boy/girl relations 5. Fast food restaurants, chains, etc 6. New York City 7. Romantic comedies 8. Teen chick lit
ISBN 9781250237323

LC 2019036362

A reimagining of You've Got Mail follows the unlikely romance between an overachiever from a successful family and the class clown, who exchange snarky tweets that escalate into a viral Twitter war.

"This plugged-in romance will likely be seen as a precursor to the way teen love stories will be told for years to come." Booklist.

Love, D. Anne
Semiprecious. D. Anne Love. Margaret K. McElderry Books, 2006. 304 p.
Grades: 5 6 7 8   **Fic**
1. 1960s 2. Families 3. Mothers and daughters 4. Twelve-year-old girls 5. Preteen girls 6. Parent-separated children 7. Oklahoma 8. Texas 9. Coming-of-age stories 10. Historical fiction
ISBN 0689856385

LC 2005014906

Uprooted and living with an aunt in 1960s Oklahoma, thirteen-year-old Garnet and her older sister Opal brave their mother's desertion and their father's recovery from an accident, learning that "the best home of all is the one you make inside yourself."

"An involving novel of hurt, healing, and adjustment." Booklist.

Love, Damien
Monstrous devices. Damien Love. Viking, [2018] 352 p.: Monstrous devices
Grades: 5 6 7 8 9   **Fic**
1. Grandfather and grandson 2. Assassins 3. Robots 4. Chases 5. Golem 6. Europe 7. Fantasy fiction
ISBN 9780451478580

LC 2017053893

Alex, nearly thirteen, flees with his grandfather across snowy Europe to escape the human and mechanical assassins that pursue them, trying to retrieve a powerful object.

"A well-knit debut generously stocked with chills, thrills, and chancy exploits." Kirkus

The **shadow** arts. Damien Love. Viking, 2020. 352 p.: Monstrous devices

Grades: 5 6 7 8 9 **Fic**
1. Voyages and travels 2. Grandfather and grandson 3. Robots 4. Rescues 5. Grandfathers 6. Europe 7. Fantasy fiction
ISBN 9780451478610

A few months ago, Alex's world changed...forever. Now, just when it seems life is almost getting back to normal, Alex's grandfather crashes back into the picture with grave news: their friend Harry has fallen into the clutches of a familiar foe, and the old man needs Alex's help to rescue him.

"Breathlessly paced adventure with rousingly eerie and icky notes." Kirkus

Lowry, Lois

Anastasia at your service. Lois Lowry; decorations by Diane DeGroat. Houghton Mifflin, 1982. 149 p.: Anastasia Krupnik
Grades: 4 5 6 **Fic**
1. Children and seniors 2. Household employees 3. Twelve-year-old girls 4. Krupnik, Anastasia (Fictitious character) 5. Misadventures 6. Realistic fiction

LC 82009231

Twelve-year-old Anastasia has a series of disastrous experiences when, expecting to get a job as a lady's companion, she is hired instead to be a maid.

★ **Anastasia** Krupnik. by Lois Lowry; decorations by Diane deGroat. Houghton Mifflin, 1979. 113 p.: Anastasia Krupnik
Grades: 4 5 6 **Fic**
1. New baby in family 2. Children and seniors 3. Ten-year-old girls 4. Krupnik, Anastasia (Fictitious character) 5. Jealousy 6. Realistic fiction
ISBN 0395286298

LC 79018625

Anastasia's 10th year has some good things like falling in love and really getting to know her grandmother and some bad things like finding out about an impending baby brother.

"Anastasia's father and mother—an English professor and an artist—are among the most humorous, sensible, and understanding parents to be found in . . . children's fiction, and Anastasia herself is an amusing and engaging heroine." Horn Book.

Gathering blue. Lois Lowry. Houghton Mifflin, c2000. 215 p.: Giver quartet
Grades: 5 6 7 8 **Fic**
1. Dystopias 2. Girl orphans 3. Embroidery 4. Girls with disabilities 5. Far future 6. Dystopian fiction 7. Science fiction
ISBN 0618055819

LC 00024359

Lame and suddenly orphaned, Kira is mysteriously removed from her squalid village to live in the palatial Council Edifice, where she is expected to use her gifts as a weaver to do the bidding of the all-powerful Guardians.

"Lowry has once again created a fully realized world full of drama, suspense, and even humor." School Library Journal.

★ The **giver**. Lois Lowry. Houghton Mifflin, 1993. 180 p.: Giver quartet
Grades: 5 6 7 8 9 10 **Fic**
1. Dystopias 2. Twelve-year-old boys 3. Memories 4. Far future 5. Dystopian fiction 6. Coming-of-age stories 7. Classics
ISBN 9780395645666

LC 92015034

Newbery Medal, 1994.

Living in a "perfect" world without social ills, a boy approaches the time when he will receive a life assignment from the Elders, but his selection leads him to a mysterious man who reveals the dark secrets behind the utopian facade.

"A riveting, chilling story that inspires a new appreciation for diversity, love, and even pain. Truly memorable." School Library Journal.

★ **Number** the stars. Lois Lowry. Houghton Mifflin, 1989. 137 p.
Grades: 4 5 6 7 **Fic**
1. Second World War era (1939-1945) 2. Holocaust (1933-1945) 3. Ten-year-old girls 4. World War II 5. Jews 6. Children 7. Denmark 8. Copenhagen, Denmark 9. Historical fiction 10. Classics
ISBN 0395510600

LC 88037134

Newbery Medal, 1990.
Sydney Taylor Book Award for Older Readers, 1989.

In 1943, during the German occupation of Denmark, ten-year-old Annemarie learns how to be brave and courageous when she helps shelter her Jewish friend from the Nazis.

"The appendix details the historical incidents upon which Lowry bases her plot. . . . The whole work is seamless, compelling, and memorable." Horn Book.

Son. by Lois Lowry. Houghton Mifflin, 2012. 288 p.: Giver quartet
Grades: 6 7 8 9 10 11 12 **Fic**
1. Utopias 2. Birthmothers 3. Mother and child 4. Separation (Psychology) 5. Coastal towns 6. Dystopian fiction 7. Science fiction
ISBN 9780547887203

LC 2012014034

Unlike the other Birthmothers in her utopian community, teenaged Claire forms an attachment to her baby, feeling a great loss when he is taken to the Nurturing Center to be adopted by a family unit.

Lu, Marie, 1984-

Champion: a Legend novel. Marie Lu. G.P. Putnam's Sons, 2013 384 p.: Legend (Marie Lu)
Grades: 8 9 10 11 12 **Fic**
1. 22nd century 2. Post-apocalypse 3. Dystopias 4. Plague 5. Far future 6. Fugitives 7. Los Angeles, California 8. Dystopian fiction 9. Science fiction
ISBN 9780399256776

June and Day's hopes for peace are shattered by a plague outbreak that renews warfare throughout the panicked Colonies, a situation that forces the Republic to consider a means of defense that threatens everything Day has worked for.

"Having been diagnosed with a terminal illness, Day (Legend; Prodigy) takes care of his brother, Eden, victim of the Republic's experiments in biological warfare. International diplomacy raises the stakes in this final volume of the trilogy, but readers will likely care more about whether Day and June (the Republic's prodigy) can repair their passionate romance. Lu's storytelling is compulsively readable." Horn Book.

The **Kingdom** of Back. Marie Lu. G.P. Putnam's Sons, 2020 336 p.
Grades: 7 8 9 10 11 12 **Fic**
1. Berchtold zu Sonnenburg, Maria Anna Mozart, Reichsfreiin von, 1751-1829 2. Mozart, Wolfgang Amadeus, 1756-1791 3. 18th century 4. Musicians 5. Faustian bargains 6. Women's role

7. Brothers and sisters 8. Fairies 9. Austria 10. Europe 11. Historical fantasy
ISBN 9781524739010

Nannerl Mozart has just one wish—to be remembered forever. But she has little hope she'll ever become the acclaimed composer she longs to be. As Nannerl's hope grows dimmer with each passing year, the talents of her beloved younger brother, Wolfgang, only seem to shine brighter. His brilliance begins to eclipse her own, until one day a mysterious stranger from a magical land appears with an irresistible offer—but his help may cost her everything. Adapted from publisher description.

Legend. Marie Lu. G. P. Putnam's Sons, 2011. 336 p.: Legend (Marie Lu)

Grades: 8 9 10 11 12   **Fic**
1. 22nd century 2. Post-apocalypse 3. Plague 4. Dystopias 5. Revenge 6. Resistance to government 7. Los Angeles, California 8. Dystopian fiction 9. Science fiction
ISBN 9780399256752

LC 2011002003

In a dark future, when North America has split into two warring nations, fifteen-year-olds Day, a famous criminal, and prodigy June, the brilliant soldier hired to capture him, discover that they have a common enemy.

"The characters are likable, the plot moves at a good pace, and the adventure is solid." School Library Journal.

Prodigy: a Legend novel. Marie Lu. G. P. Putnam's Sons, 2012. 288 p.: Legend (Marie Lu)

Grades: 8 9 10 11 12   **Fic**
1. 22nd century 2. Post-apocalypse 3. Dystopias 4. Fugitives 5. Resistance to government 6. Assassination 7. Los Angeles, California 8. Dystopian fiction 9. Science fiction
ISBN 9780399256769

LC 2012003773

June and Day make their way to Las Vegas where they join the rebel Patriot group and become involved in an assassination plot against the Elector in hopes of saving the Republic.

"This is a well-molded mixture of intrigue, romance, and action, where things can change with almost any turn of the page, and frequently do." Booklist.

Rebel. Marie Lu. Roaring Brook Press, 2019. 378 p.: Legend (Marie Lu)

Grades: 8 9 10 11 12   **Fic**
1. Post-apocalypse 2. Dystopias 3. Brothers 4. Far future 5. Hiding 6. Antarctica 7. Dystopian fiction 8. Science fiction
ISBN 9781250221704

LC bl2019024462

As Day and Eden struggle with who they've become since their time in the Republic, a new danger creeps into the distance between them, and Eden finds himself drawn into Ross City's dark side, where his legendary brother may not be able to save him.

"This tale of intrigue, alliances, and love will draw Legend fans and new readers into a fascinating world whose combined layers of privilege and surveillance draw comparisons to many present-day social ills." Kirkus.

Warcross. Marie Lu. G.P. Putnam's Sons Books for Young Readers, 2017. 416 p.: Warcross

Grades: 8 9 10 11 12   **Fic**
1. Computer games 2. Teenage hackers 3. Undercover operations 4. Computer crimes 5. Virtual reality games 6. Tokyo, Japan 7.

Japan 8. Science fiction 9. STEM fiction
ISBN 9780399547966

After hacking into the Warcross Championships' opening game to track illegal betting, bounty hunter Emika Chen is asked by the game's creator to go undercover to investigate a security problem, and she uncovers a sinister plot.

"Readers will move effortlessly through Lu's fantastic writing, and they will enjoy getting to know this international cast of characters. The author adeptly weaves together exciting video games scenes, virtual reality, and romance." School Library Journal.

Wildcard. Marie Lu. G.P. Putnam's Sons Books for Young Readers, 2018. 352 p.: Warcross

Grades: 8 9 10 11 12   **Fic**
1. Computer games 2. Teenage hackers 3. Undercover operations 4. Computer crimes 5. Virtual reality games 6. Tokyo, Japan 7. Japan 8. Science fiction 9. STEM fiction
ISBN 9780399547997

LC 2018011748

For the millions who log in every day, Warcross isn't just a game—it's a way of life. And teenage hacker Emika Chen has found herself caught up in a conflict that could change the world. Warcross creator, Hideo Tanaka, wants to use the game to control peoples' thoughts and feelings, effectively ending free will. Zero, a mysterious (and dangerous) hacker, wants to stop him. Now Emika must decide who she will fight for. The game is on!

"The plotting is exquisite, with tiny details connecting back to the first book, big twists that never feel forced, and emotional power drawn from character growth." Kirkus.

The **young** elites. Marie Lu. G. P. Putnam's Sons, 2014. 336 p.: Young elites

Grades: 8 9 10 11 12   **Fic**
1. Teenage girl heroes 2. Imaginary kingdoms 3. Survival (after epidemics) 4. Plague 5. Pariahs 6. High fantasy 7. Fantasy fiction
ISBN 9780399167836

Scarred and cast out after surviving the blood plague, Adelina finds a place for herself among the Young Elites who use their magic to advocate on behalf of young innocents and who are targeted by the soldiers of the Inquisition Axis.

"In a gorgeously constructed world that somewhat resembles Renaissance Italy but with its own pantheon, geography and fauna, the multiethnic and multisexual Young Elites offer a cinematically perfect ensemble of gorgeous-but-unusual illusionists, animal speakers, fire summoners and wind callers. A must for fans of Kristin Cashore's Fire (2009) and other totally immersive fantasies." Kirkus.

Lubar, David

Character, driven. David Lubar. Tor Teen, a Tom Doherty Associates book, 2016. 300 p.

Grades: 8 9 10 11 12   **Fic**
1. Children of unemployed parents 2. Fathers and sons 3. Teenage boy/girl relations 4. High school seniors 5. Virginity 6. New Jersey 7. Realistic fiction 8. Coming-of-age stories
ISBN 9780765316332

In his last year of high school, seventeen-year-old virgin Cliff Sparks has to figure out what to do with his life, including how to meet new girl Jillian and how to deal with old issues with his unemployed father.

"This exquisitely crafted coming-of-age novel gets down and dirty—and even rebellious—without sacrificing honesty, thoughtfulness, or respect." Booklist.

Hidden talents. David Lubar. TOR, 1999. 213 p.

Grades: 6 7 8 9   **Fic**
1. Teenage boy psychics 2. Psychic ability 3. Teenage misfits 4. Teenage boys -- Friendship 5. Supernatural 6. Science fiction
ISBN 0312866461

LC 99024560

A 13-year-old boy who has been sent to an alternative school for mouthing off, discovers that he and his classmates have psychic powers.

"The author serves up great fun, along with an insight or two for those whose powers are only too human." Publishers Weekly.

True talents. David Lubar. Tom Doherty Associates, 2007. 320 p.

Grades: 6 7 8 9   **Fic**
1. Teenage boy psychics 2. Psychic ability 3. Teenage misfits 4. Extrasensory perception 5. Kidnapping 6. Science fiction
ISBN 0765309777

LC 2006039763

Over a year after fourteen-year-old Eddie "Trash" Thalmeyer and his friends from Edgeview Alternative School find out about their psychic abilities, Trash is kidnapped and Torchie, Cheater, Lucky, Flinch, and Martin must join forces to rescue their friend, discovering their true talents in the process.

"This is a gripping page-turner, with a flawlessly structured plot and compelling, struggling characters who never let each other down." Voice of Youth Advocates.

Lucier, Makiia

A **death-struck** year. Makiia Lucier. Houghton Mifflin Harcourt, [2014] 282 p.

Grades: 9 10 11 12   **Fic**
1. Red Cross. 2. American National Red Cross 3. Epidemics 4. Diseases 5. Self-reliance in teenage girls 6. Death 7. Red Cross workers 8. Portland, Oregon 9. Historical fiction
ISBN 9780544164505

LC 2013037482

When the Spanish influenza epidemic reaches Portland, Oregon, in 1918, seventeen-year-old Cleo leaves behind the comfort of her boarding school to work for the Red Cross.

"A teen girl struggles to survive the Spanish influenza pandemic of 1918...Readers will be swept up in the story as Cleo builds friendships and manages to find hope amid disease and death. A notable debut." Kirkus.

Includes bibliographical references (page 280).

Song of the abyss. Makiia Lucier. Houghton Mifflin Harcourt 2019 368 p.: Tower of winds

Grades: 7 8 9   **Fic**
1. Explorers 2. Missing persons 3. Seafaring life 4. Cartographers 5. Inheritance and succession 6. High fantasy 7. Sea stories 8. Fantasy fiction
ISBN 9780544968585

LC 2018052136

When men start vanishing at sea without a trace, seventeen-year-old Reyna, a Master Explorer, must travel to a country shrouded in secrets to solve the mystery before it is too late.

Luddy, Karon

Spelldown. Karon Luddy. Simon & Schuster Books for Young Readers, 2007. 224 p.

Grades: 5 6 7 8   **Fic**
1. 1960s 2. Thirteen-year-old girls 3. Teenage girls 4. Middle school students 5. Spelling bees 6. Family problems 7. South Carolina
ISBN 1416916105

LC 2006021956

In 1969, the town of Red Clover, South Carolina, led by an enthusiastic new Latin teacher, supports thirteen-year-old Karlene as she wins her school spelling bee and strives to qualify for the National Bee, despite family problems and a growing desire for romance.

"This heartrending and funny debut novel deftly evokes place, time and character." Publishers Weekly.

Lukoff, Kyle

★ **Too** bright to see. Kyle Lukoff Penguin Group USA, 2021 192 p.

Grades: 4 5 6 7 8   **Fic**
1. Transgender children 2. Identity (Psychology) 3. Self-discovery in children 4. Ghosts 5. Grief in children 6. LGBTQIA fiction 7. Ghost stories
ISBN 9780593111154

It's the summer before middle school and eleven-year-old Bug's best friend Moira has decided the two of them need to use the next few months to prepare. For Moira, this means figuring out the right clothes to wear, learning how to put on makeup, and deciding which boys are cuter in their yearbook photos than in real life. But none of this is all that appealing to Bug, who doesn't particularly want to spend more time trying to understand how to be a girl. Besides, there's something more important to worry about: A ghost is haunting Bug's eerie old house in rural Vermont...and maybe haunting Bug in particular. As Bug begins to untangle the mystery of who this ghost is and what they're trying to say, an altogether different truth comes to light—Bug is transgender.

"[The] message of hope and compassion is frequently lacking from other trans narratives and desperately needed for other trans kids of Bug's age and beyond. The spooks and mysteries are an added bonus that sets this narrative apart from similar titles." Bulletin of the Center for Children's Books

Lundin, Britta

Ship it. by Britta Lundin. 384 p.

Grades: 7 8 9 10 11 12   **Fic**
1. Actors and actresses 2. Media fandom 3. Prejudice 4. Blogs 5. Popularity 6. Coming-of-age stories 7. LGBTQIA fiction 8. Realistic fiction
ISBN 9781368003131

LC 2017034202

Told from two viewpoints, Forest, a television actor who needs more fans, and Claire, a teen fan fiction blogger, are teamed to raise his profile despite their disagreement over whether his character is gay.

Lupica, Mike

The **batboy**. Mike Lupica. Philomel Books, 2010. 276 p.

Grades: 5 6 7 8   **Fic**
1. Detroit Tigers (Baseball team) 2. Children of separated parents 3. Bat boys and bat girls 4. Professional baseball players 5. Baseball 6. Fathers and sons 7. Detroit, Michigan 8. Baseball stories 9. Sports fiction
ISBN 9780399250002

LC 2009015067

Even though his mother feels baseball ruined her marriage to his father, she allows fourteen-year-old Brian to become a bat boy for the Detroit Tigers, who have just drafted his favorite player back onto the team.

"Lupica gives his readers a behind-the-scenes look at major league sports. In this novel, he adds genuine insights into family dynamics and the emotional state of his hero." Booklist.

The **big** field. Mike Lupica. Philomel Books, 2008. 288 p.
Grades: 5 6 7 8   **Fic**
　　1. Fathers and sons 2. Baseball 3. Baseball players 4. Friendship 5. Family relationships 6. Florida 7. Sports fiction 8. Baseball stories
　　ISBN 9780399246258

LC 2007023647

When fourteen-year-old baseball player Hutch feels threatened by the arrival of a new teammate named Darryl, he tries to work through his insecurities about both Darryl and his remote and silent father, who was once a great ballplayer too.

"Writing in typically fluid prose and laying in a strong supporting lineup, Lupica strikes the right balance between personal issues and game action." Booklist.

Fantasy league. Mike Lupica. Philomel, an imprint of Penguin Group (USA), [2014] 304 p.
Grades: 5 6 7 8   **Fic**
　　1. Football 2. Fame 3. Friendship 4. Football teams 5. Fantasy football (Game) 6. Los Angeles, California 7. Football stories 8. Sports fiction
　　ISBN 9780399256073

LC 2014007442

In Los Angeles, twelve-year-old Charlie's skill at fantasy football gains the attention of both the local media and the owner of a professional football team.

"Usually a football book is about whether or not the kid makes the team and the problems that follow. So it's refreshing that those issues are only a part of 12-year-old Charlie Gains' story. See, Charlie is known as the Brain, because he is a football stats genius. He understands which players should be playing where and why. . . . There's a lot of football here: pro and fantasy teams and Charlie's own Pop Warner career. Veteran sportswriter Lupica handles it all very well. However, it's the heart and depth he adds to the story depicting Charlie's relationships with a sterling cast of characters that make this unique. This Moneyball story with kids is on the money." Booklist.

Heat. Mike Lupica. Philomel Books, 2006. 324 p.
Grades: 5 6 7 8   **Fic**
　　1. Yankee Stadium (New York, N.Y.: 1923-2009) 2. Little League baseball 3. Baseball 4. Boy baseball players 5. Cuban Americans 6. Twelve-year-old boys 7. New York City 8. South Bronx, New York City 9. Coming-of-age stories 10. Sports fiction 11. Baseball stories
　　ISBN 0399243011

LC 2005013521

Pitching prodigy Michael Arroyo is on the run from social services after being banned from playing Little League baseball because rival coaches doubt he is only twelve years old and he has no parents to offer them proof.

"The dialogue crackles, and the rich cast of supporting characters' . . . nearly steals the show. Topnotch entertainment." Booklist.

Hero. Mike Lupica. Philomel Books, 2010. 304 p.
Grades: 6 7 8 9   **Fic**
　　1. Teenage superheroes 2. Attempted assassination 3. Grief in teenage boys 4. Grief 5. Good and evil 6. New York City 7.

Superhero stories
ISBN 9780399252839

LC 2010001772

Fourteen-year-old Zach learns he has the same special abilities as his father, who was the President's globe-trotting troubleshooter until "the Bads" killed him, and now Zach must decide whether to use his powers in the same way at the risk of his own life.

"Lupica effectively unfolds this high-adventure story." Booklist.

Miracle on 49th Street. Mike Lupica. Philomel Books, 2006. 256 p.
Grades: 5 6 7 8   **Fic**
　　1. Boston Celtics (Basketball team) 2. Children of athletes 3. Fathers and daughters 4. Professional basketball players 5. Birthparents -- Identification 6. Mothers -- Death 7. Boston, Massachusetts 8. Realistic fiction 9. Sports fiction 10. Basketball stories
　　ISBN 0399244883

LC 2005032648

After her mother's death, twelve-year-old Molly learns that her father is a basketball star for the Boston Celtics.

"Lupica creates intriguing, complex characters . . . and he paces his story well, with enough twists and cliff-hangers to keep the pages turning." School Library Journal.

The **only** game. Mike Lupica. Simon & Schuster Books for Young Readers, 2015. 320 p.: Home team novels
Grades: 4 5 6 7   **Fic**
　　1. Boy baseball players 2. Grief in boys 3. Friendship 4. Baseball 5. Softball 6. Baseball stories 7. Sports fiction
　　ISBN 9781481409957

LC 2014015989

Sixth grade is supposed to be the year that Jack Callahan would lead his team to a record-shattering season and the Little League World Series, but after the death of his brother he loses interest in baseball and only Cassie, star of the girls' softball team, seems to understand.

"Although the story is sports related, this is more than a baseball book and will appeal to a wide variety of readers. A must-buy." School Library Journal.

Play makers. Mike Lupica. Scholastic, 2013. 201 p.: Game changers
Grades: 3 4 5 6 7   **Fic**
　　1. Boy athletes 2. Basketball 3. Teamwork (Sports) 4. Friendship 5. Boy basketball players 6. Sports fiction 7. Basketball stories
　　ISBN 9780545381833

Starting the basketball season after an incredible football championship win, Ben McBain and his crew, including the talented Shawn O'Brien, are challenged by newcomer Chase Braggs, whose point guard abilities outstrip Ben's and who attracts Lily's attention while Ben is busy practicing.

Strike zone. Mike Lupica. Philomel Books, 2019. 272 p.
Grades: 5 6 7 8   **Fic**
　　1. U.S. Immigration and Customs Enforcement 2. Dominican Americans 3. Immigrant families 4. Boy baseball players 5. Little League baseball 6. Baseball 7. Bronx, New York City 8. New York City 9. Realistic fiction 10. Baseball stories 11. Sports fiction
　　ISBN 9780525514886

LC 2019014207

Twelve-year-old Nick Garcia dreams of winning MVP of his summer baseball league, of finding a cure for his sister, of meeting his hero,

Yankee pitcher Michael Arroyo, and of no longer living in fear of the government and ICE agents.

Summer ball. Mike Lupica. Philomel Books, 2007. 256 p.: Danny Walker

Grades: 6 7 8 9   **Fic**

1. Sports camps 2. Boy basketball players 3. Basketball 4. Children of athletes 5. Basketball camps 6. Sports fiction 7. Basketball stories
ISBN 9780399244872

LC 2006021781

Thirteen-year-old Danny must prove himself all over again for a disapproving coach and against new rivals at a summer basketball camp.

"Lupica breathes life into both characters and story. Danny is . . . sympathetic and engaging. He is surrounded by a cast of supporting characters who add humor and whose interactions ring true." School Library Journal.

Lyga, Barry

The **astonishing** adventures of Fanboy & Goth Girl. by Barry Lyga. Houghton Mifflin, 2006. 311 p.

Grades: 8 9 10 11 12   **Fic**

1. Teenage misfits 2. Comic book writers 3. Self-perception in teenagers 4. Fifteen-year-old boys 5. Teenagers 6. Realistic fiction
ISBN 9780618723928

LC 2005033259

A fifteen-year-old "geek" who keeps a list of the high school jocks and others who torment him, and pours his energy into creating a great graphic novel, encounters Kyra, Goth Girl, who helps change his outlook on almost everything, including himself.

"This engaging first novel has good characterization with genuine voices. . . . The book is compulsively readable." Voice of Youth Advocates.

Lynch, Chris, 1962-

Casualties of war. Chris Lynch. Scholastic Press, 2013. 192 p.: Vietnam

Grades: 8 9 10 11 12   **Fic**

1. United States. Air Force. 2. Teenage soldiers 3. Vietnam War, 1961-1975 4. Airmen 5. Agent Orange 6. Soldiers 7. Vietnam 8. War stories 9. Historical fiction
ISBN 9780545270236

LC 2012014434

One of four friends who have volunteered to fight in the Vietnam War, the intellectual Beck is in the Air Force, where he is part of a crew spraying Agent Orange, but the destruction of the jungle and his isolation from the fighting going on below is starting to effect him.

Inexcusable. Chris Lynch. Atheneum Books for Young Readers, c2005. 165 p.: Inexcusable

Grades: 8 9 10 11 12   **Fic**

1. High school football players 2. Date rape 3. Self-deception 4. Teenage boy/girl relations 5. Violence in teenage boys 6. Realistic fiction
ISBN 0689847890

LC 2004030874

High school senior and football player Keir sets out to enjoy himself on graduation night, but when he attempts to comfort a friend whose date has left her stranded, things go terribly wrong.

"This finely crafted and thought-provoking page-turner carefully conveys that it is simply inexcusable to whitewash wrongs, and that those responsible should (and hopefully will) pay the price." School Library Journal.

Lyons, Mary E.

Letters from a slave boy: the story of Joseph Jacobs. Mary Lyons. Atheneum Books for Young Readers, 2007. 208 p.

Grades: 6 7 8 9   **Fic**

1. Jacobs, Joseph, b. 1829 2. 19th century 3. Letter writing 4. Enslaved boys 5. Enslaved people 6. Slavery 7. African Americans 8. North Carolina 9. United States 10. Epistolary novels 11. Historical fiction
ISBN 0689878672

LC 2006001277

A fictionalized look at the life of Joseph Jacobs, son of a slave, told in the form of letters that he might have written during his life in pre-Civil War North Carolina, on a whaling expedition, in New York, New England, and finally in California during the Gold Rush.

"The letters are short and the pace is quick. The dialect and spelling give authenticity without making the text difficult to read and understand. . . . This title stands on its own, but children who appreciated the forthright perspective of the first book will want to read this one as well." School Library Journal.

Letters from a slave girl: the story of Harriet Jacobs. Mary E. Lyons. Scribner, 1992. 146 p.

Grades: 6 7 8 9   **Fic**

1. Jacobs, Harriet, 1818-1896 2. 19th century 3. Letter writing 4. Enslaved girls 5. Slavery 6. African American women 7. North Carolina 8. Epistolary novels 9. Historical fiction
ISBN 0684194465

LC 91045778

Golden Kite Award for Fiction, 1992.

A fictionalized version of the life of Harriet Jacobs, told in the form of letters that she might have written during her slavery in North Carolina and as she prepared for escape to the North in 1842.

"This is historical fiction at its best. . . . Mary Lyons has remained faithful to Jacobs's actual autobiography throughout her readable, compelling novel. . . . Her observations of the horrors of slavery are concise and lucid. The letters are written in dialect, based on Jacobs's own writing and on other slave narrations of the period." Horn Book.

Includes bibliographical references (p. 143-146).

Maas, Sarah J.

Catwoman: Soulstealer. Sarah J. Maas. Random House Childrens Books 2018. 320 p.: DC icons

Grades: 7 8 9 10   **Fic**

1. Superheroes 2. Women criminals 3. Catwoman (Fictitious character) 4. Women villains 5. Supervillains 6. Superhero stories 7. Franchise books
ISBN 9780399549694

Two years after escaping Gotham City's slums, Selina Kyle returns as the mysterious and wealthy Holly Vanderhees. She quickly discovers that with Batman off on a vital mission, Gotham City looks ripe for the taking.

Maberry, Jonathan

The **orphan** army. Jonathan Maberry. Simon & Schuster Books for Young Readers, 2015. 400 p.: The Nightsiders

Grades: 5 6 7 8   **Fic**

1. Aliens (Non-humanoid) 2. Boy heroes 3. Monsters 4.

Supernatural 5. Magic 6. Fantasy fiction 7. Science fiction
ISBN 9781481415750

LC 2014014576

In the future, bug-like aliens are taking over Earth and young Milo
Silk learns through dreams and strange encounters that there are other,
ancient monsters on the planet that are also threatened by the aliens, and
that he may be the hero destined to lead his friends in saving the universe.

"Maberry's prowess in fiction as well as comic books is evident in
his well-crafted story, which balances over-the-top battle scenes with
the quiet moments between characters that give substance to what could
be a heartless thriller. This first book in an explosive new series is the
perfect mix of science fiction and magic." Kirkus.

Rot & Ruin. Jonathan Maberry. Simon & Schuster Books for
Young Readers, c2010. 458 p.: Benny Imura books

Grades: 9 10 11 12   **Fic**
    1. Zombies 2. Bounty hunters 3. Stepbrothers 4. Rationing 5.
    Survival 6. California 7. Apocalyptic fiction 8. Science fiction
    9. Horror
    ISBN 9781442402324

LC 2009046041

After the zombie apocalypse, teens must find work by the age of 15
if they want to keep their food ration. And that's why lazy, resentful,
15-year-old Benny reluctantly leaves the safety of home and joins his
bounty-hunting half-brother Tom in the zombie-riddled wilds of the Rot
and Ruin. As the brothers encounter villains far more inhuman than the
undead, Benny begins to question his understanding not only of Tom,
but also of life, death, and what bravery really means.

"In turns mythic and down-to-earth, this intense novel combines
adventure and philosophy to tell a truly memorable zombie story."
Publishers Weekly.

Mac, Carrie, 1975-

10 things I can see from here. Carrie Mac. Alfred A. Knopf,
[2017] 320 p.

Grades: 7 8 9 10 11 12   **Fic**
    1. Lesbian teenagers 2. Anxiety disorders 3. Anxiety in teenagers
    4. Fathers and daughters 5. Love 6. Vancouver, British Columbia
    7. Realistic fiction 8. LGBTQIA fiction
    ISBN 9780399556258

LC 2015046690

Maeve, a sufferer of severe anxiety, moves in with her recovering
alcoholic father and her very pregnant stepmother and falls for a girl
who is not afraid of anything.

"With Maeve, Mac delivers a character who's heartwarmingly real
and sympathetic, and her story provides a much needed mirror for anxious queer girls everywhere." Kirkus.

MacColl, Michaela

Prisoners in the palace: how Victoria became queen with the
help of her maid, a reporter, and a scoundrel. by Michaela Mac-
Coll. Chronicle Books, 2010. 304 p.

Grades: 7 8 9 10   **Fic**
    1. Victoria, Queen of Great Britain, 1819-1901 2. 1830s 3. Teenage
    girl orphans 4. Household employees 5. Libel and slander 6. Self-
    reliance in teenage girls 7. Self-reliance 8. London, England 9.
    Great Britain 10. Historical fiction
    ISBN 9780811873000

LC 2010008257

Recently orphaned and destitute, seventeen-year-old Liza Hastings
earns a position as a lady's maid to sixteen-year-old Princess Victoria
at Kensington Palace in 1836, the year before Victoria becomes Queen
of England.

"This novel is full of historical detail, vivid settings, and richly
drawn characters, and themes of friendship and romance give the story
teen appeal." Booklist.

Promise the night. by Michaela MacColl. Chronicle Books,
2011. 256 p.

Grades: 6 7 8 9   **Fic**
    1. Markham, Beryl, 1902-1986 2. 1910s 3. Pilots 4. British in
    Africa 5. Interracial friendship 6. Women air pilots 7. Kenya 8.
    Biographical fiction 9. Historical fiction
    ISBN 9780811876254

LC 2011010938

Explores the early life of Beryl Markham, who grew up on a farm in
Kenya, and became the first person to fly solo across the Atlantic from
east to west.

"MacColl vividly portrays her headstrong protagonist . . . with
fierce, exuberant spirit." Booklist.

Rory's promise. Michaela MacColl, Rosemary Nichols.
Calkins Creek, an imprint of Highlights, 2014. 288 p.: Hidden
histories

Grades: 5 6 7 8   **Fic**
    1. New York Foundling Hospital 2. 1900s (Decade) 3. Girl
    orphans 4. Orphan trains 5. Stowaways 6. Sisters 7. Orphanages
    8. New York (State) 9. Historical fiction
    ISBN 9781620916230

"Outspoken twelve-year-old Rory, who lives in NYC's Catholic
Foundling Hospital in 1904, vows to protect her sister, Violet. When
Violet is placed with a family in racially divided Arizona Territory, Rory
sneaks aboard the train headed west. Despite some lackluster dialogue
and underdeveloped characters, Rory is a feisty and compelling protagonist in an action-packed story based on historical events." Horn Book.

MacCullough, Carolyn

Once a witch. by Carolyn MacCullough. Clarion Books,
2009. 292 p.

Grades: 8 9 10 11 12   **Fic**
    1. Teenage witches 2. Sibling rivalry 3. Time travel 4. Witches
    5. Ability 6. New York City 7. Urban fantasy
    ISBN 9780547223995

LC 2008049234

Born into a family of witches, seventeen-year-old Tamsin is raised
believing that she alone lacks a magical "Talent," but when her beautiful
and powerful sister is taken by an age-old rival of the family in an attempt to change the balance of power, Tamsin discovers her true destiny.

"The book will appeal to teen readers who enjoy stories with romance, magic, or time travel, along with hardcore fantasy aficionados, and it is appropriate for all young adult collections." Voice of
Youth Advocates.

MacHale, D. J.

The **lost** city of Faar. D.J. MacHale. Aladdin Paperbacks,
2003. 385 p.: Pendragon series

Grades: 7 8 9 10   **Fic**
    1. Teenage heroes and heroines 2. Shapeshifters 3. Demons 4.
    Imaginary wars and battles 5. Underwater cities 6. Fantasy fiction
    7. Gateway fantasy
    ISBN 0743437322

LC 2002108580

"The ideas are clever and the descriptions inviting and easy to picture. . . . The teenaged protagonists enlist readers' sympathy and involve-

ment and the nonstop plot developments keep the many pages turning and readers wanting more." School Library Journal.

The **merchant** of death. by D.J. MacHale. Aladdin, c2002. 375 p.: Pendragon series

Grades: 7 8 9 10 **Fic**
1. Teenage heroes and heroines 2. Parallel universes 3. Shapeshifters 4. Demons 5. Imaginary wars and battles 6. Fantasy fiction 7. Gateway fantasy
ISBN 0743437314

LC 2002210164
Bobby Pendragon is a seemingly normal fourteen-year-old boy. He has a family, a home, and even Marley, his beloved dog. But there is something very special about Bobby. He is going to save the world. ...Before he can object, he is swept off to an alternate dimension known as Denduron, a territory inhabited by strange beings, ruled by a magical tyrant, and plagued by dangerous revolution.

The **never** war. D.J. MacHale. Aladdin Paperbacks, 2003. 336 p.: Pendragon series

Grades: 7 8 9 10 **Fic**
1. 1930s 2. Teenage heroes and heroines 3. Shapeshifters 4. Time travel 5. Demons 6. Space and time 7. New York City 8. Fantasy fiction 9. Gateway fantasy
ISBN 0743437330

LC 2002116463
Bobby and the Traveler from Cloral—Spader—have flumed to New York City, 1937. Against a backdrop of gangsters, swing music, and the distant sound of a brewing war, the two must uncover the evil Saint Dane's newest plot.
"This book has a fast pace, suspenseful plotting, and cliffhanger chapter endings that will make it popular." School Library Journal.

The **reality** bug. D.J. MacHale. Aladdin Paperbacks, c2003. 375 p.: Pendragon series

Grades: 7 8 9 10 **Fic**
1. Teenage heroes and heroines 2. Shapeshifters 3. Virtual reality 4. Demons 5. Space and time 6. Fantasy fiction 7. Gateway fantasy
ISBN 0743437349

LC 2003105075
In his ongoing battle to save Earth and its parallel worlds from the demon Saint Dane, fifteen-year-old Bobby Pendragon travels to Veelox, a world whose inhabitants have abandoned their real lives in favor of virtual reality.

MacLachlan, Patricia
Kindred souls. Patricia MacLachlan. HarperCollins, 2012. 128 p.

Grades: 4 5 6 **Fic**
1. Grandfather and grandson 2. Intergenerational relations 3. Sick grandfathers 4. Sod houses 5. Families
ISBN 9780060522988

LC 2011016617
Ten year-old Jake shares a special bond with his grandfather, Billy, but when Billy asks Jake to build him a sod house, Jake is not sure he wants to do it.

Macdonald, Maryann
Odette's secrets. by Maryann Macdonald. Bloomsbury, 2013. 240 p.

Grades: 6 7 8 9 **Fic**
1. Meyers, Odette 2. Second World War era (1939-1945) 3. 1940s 4. Jewish girls 5. World War II 6. Identity (Psychology) 7. Parent-separated girls 8. Holocaust (1933-1945) 9. France 10. Historical fiction 11. Novels in verse
ISBN 9781599907505

LC 2012015549
When Odette Meyer's father is sent to a Nazi work camp, her mother sends Odette from Paris to the French countryside where she must pretend to be a Catholic peasant to remain safe, while secrets burn within her.

Machale, D. J.
SYLO. D.J. MacHale. Razorbill, 2013 407 p.: SYLO chronicles

Grades: 5 6 7 8 9 **Fic**
1. Quarantine 2. Conspiracies 3. Drugs 4. Escapes 5. Islands 6. Maine 7. Science fiction
ISBN 9781595146656

When everyone is quarantined on a once-peaceful island off the coast of Maine, Tucker questions a secret branch of the military claiming that residents have been infected by a deadly virus.

Mack, W. C., 1972-
Athlete vs. mathlete. by W.C. Mack. Bloomsbury: 2013. 208 p.: Athlete vs. mathlete series

Grades: 5 6 7 **Fic**
1. Twin brothers 2. Jealousy in boys 3. Jealousy 4. Basketball 5. Competition 6. Realistic fiction 7. Sports fiction 8. Basketball stories
ISBN 9781599909158

LC 2012014146
When their two worlds collide in seventh grade, fraternal twins and opposites Owen and Russell find themselves in direct competition at school, on the court, and at home.

Mackel, Kathryn, 1950-
Boost. by Kathy Mackel. Dial Books, 2008. 256 p.

Grades: 6 7 8 9 **Fic**
1. Anabolic steroid abuse 2. Basketball 3. Teenagers and moving 4. Teenage girls 5. New students 6. Realistic fiction
ISBN 9780803732407

LC 2007049441
Thirteen-year-old Savvy Christopher is 6'2" and a talented basketball player; her big sis, Callie, is a cheerleader. When an injury ruins their dad's golf career, the family moves from their swanky New Mexico home to an aunt's sheep farm in Rhode Island. Savvy is thrilled when she makes the exclusive 18-and-under basketball team The Fire; getting to play on a great travel team makes up for having to share a room with Callie, being teased about her height, and having to work on the sheep farm. But when steroids are found in Savvy's gym bag, she'll have to fight for her spot on the team. A bit of mystery, complex family relationships, and plenty of exciting on-court action make Boost a riveting read.
"Mackel has turned a tough subject in the world of teen competitive sports into a highly readable blend of intense action, interfamily relationships, and intrigue." School Library Journal.

Mackler, Carolyn
The **Earth,** my butt, and other big, round things. Carolyn Mackler. Candlewick Press, 2003. 246 p.: Earth, my butt, and other big, round things

Grades: 7 8 9 10   **Fic**
1. Fifteen-year-old girls 2. Self-perception in teenage girls 3. Assertiveness in teenage girls 4. Family problems 5. Weight control 6. New York City 7. Realistic fiction 8. Teen chick lit
ISBN 0763619582

LC 2002073921

Virginia Shreves is insecure—and comparing herself to the tall, dark, and slender over-achievers who make up the rest of her family doesn't help. Add in even more criticism than usual from her exercise-obsessed mom and the fact that Virginia's best friend has moved away, and it's sure be a bad year of epic proportions. Or is it? This funny, sexy, no-holds-barred story of a girl who's about to learn that her "perfect" family isn't so perfect. .

"The e-mails [Virginia] exchanges . . . and the lists she makes (e.g., The Fat Girl Code of Conduct) add both realism and insight to her character. The heroine's transformation into someone who finds her own style and speaks her own mind is believable—and worthy of applause." Publishers Weekly.

Mae, Natalie
The **kinder** poison. Natalie Mae. Razorbill, 2020. 416 p.: Kinder poison novels
Grades: 8 9 10 11 12   **Fic**
1. Magic 2. Rulers 3. Teenage girls 4. Imaginary kingdoms 5. Running races 6. Fantasy fiction 7. Middle Eastern-influenced fantasy
ISBN 9781984835215

LC 2019051803

When her magical kingdom's ailing ruler invokes an ancient tradition to identify his successor, a lowly stable girl who possesses the ability to commune with animals is chosen as a human sacrifice during a high-risk desert crossing involving three ruthless heirs.

Maetani, Valynne E.
Ink & ashes. Valynne E. Maetani. Tu Books, an imprint of Lee & Low Books, Inc., 2015. 386 p.
Grades: 7 8 9 10   **Fic**
1. Japanese American teenage girls 2. Organized crime 3. Grief in teenage girls 4. Fathers -- Death 5. Blended families 6. Utah 7. Thrillers and suspense
ISBN 9781620142110

LC 2015006632

When Japanese American Claire Takata finds out that her deceased father was once a member of the yakuza, a Japanese crime syndicate, danger enters her life that could end up killing someone. Provided by publisher.

"Maetani's fast-paced debut will appeal to readers who like their intrigue with a generous helping of romance." Booklist.

Mafi, Tahereh
Furthermore: a novel. by Tahereh Mafi. Dutton Children's Books, an imprint of Penguin Random House, [2016] 432 p.
Grades: 4 5 6 7 8   **Fic**
1. Twelve-year-old girls 2. Missing persons 3. Adventure 4. Fathers 5. Fantasy 6. Fantasy fiction
ISBN 9781101994764

LC 2015044898

Yearning to find her missing father, 12-year-old Alice Alexis Queensmeadow embarks on an adventure to find him by traveling through the mythical, upside-down, dangerous land of Furthermore along with a boy named Oliver, whose own magical ability is based in lies and deceit.

"While Oliver and Alice start off at odds, their friendship, forged in adversity, is the best part of a fast-paced, funny, and richly imaginative story that embraces and celebrates individuality." Publishers Weekly.

A **very** large expanse of sea. Tahereh Mafi. HarperTeen, 2018. 304 p.
Grades: 8 9 10 11 12   **Fic**
1. First loves 2. Prejudice 3. Muslim girls 4. Sixteen-year-old girls 5. Stereotypes (Social psychology) 6. Realistic fiction 7. Love stories
ISBN 9780062866561

LC 2018945999

"Shirin and Ocean's interactions are palpable, and the discussions and exploration of what it means to be a Muslim in politically charged America will resonate with many teens and will be enlightening for some." School Library Journal.

Whichwood. by Tahereh Mafi. Dutton Children's Books Young Readers/Penguin Random House LLC, [2017] 368 p.
Grades: 4 5 6 7 8   **Fic**
1. Thirteen-year-old girls 2. Sick girls 3. Ghosts 4. Adventure 5. Fantasy 6. Fantasy fiction
ISBN 9781101994795

LC 2017020411

Laylee, thirteen, is nearly worn out from washing and packaging corpses for the Otherwhere and being shunned by villagers when two strangers, Alice and Oliver, arrive determined to help.

"Memorable new characters experience the restorative power of friendship in this darkly fascinating, somewhat ghoulish sequel to Furthermore." Kirkus.

Magoon, Kekla
Camo girl. Kekla Magoon. Aladdin Paperbacks, 2011. 218 p.
Grades: 5 6 7 8   **Fic**
1. Multiracial girls 2. Misfits (Persons) 3. Loyalty in girls 4. Loyalty 5. Girl misfits 6. Las Vegas, Nevada 7. Realistic fiction 8. African American fiction
ISBN 9781416978046

A biracial girl living in the suburbs of Las Vegas examines the friendships that grow out of, and despite, her race.

"Magoon . . . offers a sensitive and articulate portrayal of a pair of middle-school outsiders. . . . This poetic and nuanced story addresses the courage it takes to truly know and support someone, as well as the difficult choices that come with growing up." Publishers Weekly.

Fire in the streets. Kekla Magoon. Aladdin, 2012. 288 p.
Grades: 7 8 9 10   **Fic**
1. Black Panther Party 2. 1960s 3. African American teenage girls 4. Civil Rights Movement 5. Racism 6. Former boyfriends 7. Brothers and sisters 8. Chicago, Illinois 9. United States 10. Historical fiction 11. African American fiction
ISBN 9781442422308

In the aftermath of Dr. King's assassination in 1968, Chicago fourteen-year-old Maxie longs to join the Black Panthers, whether or not her brother Raheem, ex-boyfriend Sam, or her friends like it, and is soon caught up in the violence of anti-war and civil rights demonstrations.

The **rock** and the river. Kekla Magoon. Aladdin, 2009. 290 p.
Grades: 7 8 9 10   **Fic**
1. Black Panther Party 2. 1960s 3. Civil Rights Movement 4. Racism 5. Brothers 6. African Americans 7. Fourteen-year-old

boys 8. Chicago, Illinois 9. United States 10. Historical fiction
11. African American fiction
ISBN 9781416975823

LC 2008029170

It's 1968, and Chicago teen Sam is torn. He's always looked up to his father, a civil rights leader dedicated to nonviolence. His older brother Stick, however, has left home to join the revolutionary Black Panther Party. At first Sam is skeptical of the Panthers' militant approach to ending racial injustice, but after one of his friends is brutally beaten by the police, Sam starts to question his father's nonviolent beliefs.

"This novel will make readers feel what it was like to be young, black, and militant 40 years ago, including the seething fury and desperation over the daily discrimination that drove the oppressed to fight back." Booklist.

Maguire, Gregory

Egg & spoon. Gregory Maguire. Candlewick Press, 2014. 496 p.

Grades: 7 8 9 10 11 12   **Fic**
     1. 1900s (Decade) 2. Mistaken identity 3. Witches 4. Baba Yaga (Legendary character) 5. Princes 6. Social classes 7. Russia 8. Historical fantasy 9. Metafiction
ISBN 9780763672201

Enduring a brutal life of poverty in the Russian countryside, young Elena Rudina is swept up by a passing noble family into an escapade involving mistaken identity, an imprisoned monk, an anonymous prince and the mythological Baba Yaga.

"With one brother conscripted into the Tsar's army and another bound to serve a local landowner, Elena is left alone to care for her widowed and ailing mother in early 20th-century Russia. When an elegant train bearing a noble her age rolls through their barren village, Elena and her counterpart, Cat, accidentally swap places. . . . The author weaves a lyrical tale full of magic and promise, yet checkered with the desperation of poverty and the treacherous prospect of a world gone completely awry. Egg and Spoon is a beautiful reminder that fairy tales are at their best when they illuminate the precarious balance between lighthearted childhood and the darkness and danger of adulthood." School Library Journal.

Mah, Adeline Yen, 1937-

Chinese Cinderella and the Secret Dragon Society. Adeline Yen Mah. Harper Collins, c2005. xiii, 242 p.: Chinese Cinderella

Grades: 5 6 7 8   **Fic**
     1. Second World War era (1939-1945) 2. 1940s 3. 20th century 4. Twelve-year-old girls 5. Runaway girls 6. Runaways 7. Stepmothers 8. Courage in girls 9. China 10. Historical fiction
ISBN 0060567341

LC 2004008852

During the Japanese occupation of parts of China, twelve-year-old Ye Xian is thrown out of her father's and stepmother's home, joins a martial arts group, and tries to help her aunt and the Americans in their struggle against the Japanese invaders. Includes historical notes.

"Full of adventure and contrivance, this somewhat old-fashioned, plot-driven novel is clear about the values that are important to the author. . . . These young people are courageous, creative, and open-minded." School Library Journal.

Includes bibliographical references (p. 241-242).

Makechnie, Amy

Ten thousand tries. Amy Makechnie Simon & Schuster, 2021 256 p.

Grades: 4 5 6 7 8   **Fic**
     1. Grief in children 2. Children of sick persons 3. Children of people with terminal illnesses 4. Amyotrophic lateral sclerosis 5. Eighth graders 6. Realistic fiction 7. Coming-of-age stories
ISBN 9781534482296

With his home life spiraling out of control, 12-year-old Golden Maroni pushes himself to become the captain of his soccer team and master of his eighth-grade universe, which alienates those around him.

"The strength of this novel lies in Makechnie's ability to create a compelling protagonist who strives to persevere despite great odds. Whether or not they are a fan of soccer, this title is sure to make readers laugh and cry." Booklist

Maldonado, Torrey

Secret Saturdays. Torrey Maldonado. G.P. Putnam's Sons, c2010. 195 p.

Grades: 6 7 8 9   **Fic**
     1. Father-separated boys 2. African American boys 3. Shame 4. Children of prisoners 5. Inner city boys 6. Brooklyn, New York City 7. Realistic fiction
ISBN 9780399251580

LC 2009010361

Twelve-year-old boys living in a rough part of New York confront questions about what it means to be a friend, a father, and a man.

"Maldonado convincingly portrays roughneck playgrounds where boys are expected to be hard and . . . Justin's narration resonates with the authenticity of a preteen doing his best in an urban landscape that has taught him all he knows. . . . The book remains a moving portrayal of the hope to be found through honest relationships." Publishers Weekly.

★ **Tight**. Torrey Maldonado. Nancy Paulsen Books, 2018. 160 p.

Grades: 4 5 6 7   **Fic**
     1. Personal conduct 2. Inner city 3. Friendship 4. Families 5. African Americans 6. Brooklyn, New York City 7. Realistic fiction
ISBN 9781524740559

LC 2018007927

After his quick-tempered father gets in a fight and is sent back to jail, sixth-grader Bryan, known for being quiet and thoughtful, snaps and follows new friend Mike into trouble.

"Through Bryan's believable, emotionally honest first-person narration, Maldonado skillfully shows a boy trying to navigate parental desires and the societal expectations of his Brooklyn neighborhood while trying to figure himself out. Readers will be rooting for Bryan to make the right choices even as they understand the wrong ones." Kirkus.

Mandanna, Sangu

Color outside the lines: stories about love. edited by Sangu Mandanna. Soho Teen, [2019] 312 p.

Grades: 8 9 10 11 12   **Fic**
     1. Hope 2. Teenage romance 3. Love 4. Interpersonal relations 5. Interracial romance 6. Anthologies 7. Love stories 8. LGBTQIA romances
ISBN 9781641290463

LC 2019017621

This modern, groundbreaking YA anthology explores the complexity and beauty of interracial and LGBTQ+ relationships where differences are front and center.

"From dealing with a racist bully to facing the impact of colonialism and handling Asian fever, the authors delve into a number of cultures, races, religions, and ethnicities Moroccan, Indian, black, Hmong, Chinese, Jewish, Latinx, Palestinian, and Irish, among others." Kirkus.

Mann, Jennifer Ann

What every girl should know: Margaret Sanger's journey: a novel. by J. Albert Mann. Atheneum, 2019. 240 p.

Grades: 7 8 9 10 11 12   **Fic**

1. Sanger, Margaret 1879-1966 2. Planned Parenthood Federation of America. 3. 19th century 4. Children of sick persons 5. Poor families 6. Gender role 7. Feminists 8. Women social reformers 9. New York (State) 10. Biographical fiction 11. Historical fiction
ISBN 9781534419322

In this fictionalized biography, a teenage Maggie Higgins struggles to balance her responsibilities to her family, society's expectations for women, and her desire to pursue her education and plan for the future.

"An important, readable novel about Sanger, who changed the fate of millions of women through access to contraception." Kirkus.

Manzano, Sonia

The **revolution** of Evelyn Serrano. Sonia Manzano. Scholastic, 2012. 224 p.

Grades: 6 7 8 9 10   **Fic**

1. 1960s 2. Puerto Ricans 3. Protest movements 4. Grandmothers 5. Identity (Psychology) 6. Families 7. New York City 8. East Harlem, New York City 9. Historical fiction
ISBN 9780545325059

LC 2012009240

It is 1969 in Spanish Harlem, and fourteen-year-old Evelyn Serrano is trying hard to break free from her conservative Puerto Rican surroundings, but when her activist grandmother comes to stay and the neighborhood protests start, things get a lot more complicated—and dangerous.

Marchetta, Melina, 1965-

Finnikin of the rock. Melina Marchetta. Candlewick Press, 2010, c2008. 399 p.: Lumatere chronicles

Grades: 8 9 10 11 12   **Fic**

1. Royal houses 2. Curses 3. Heirs and heiresses 4. Imaginary kingdoms 5. Impostors 6. High fantasy 7. Fantasy fiction
ISBN 9780763643614

Now on the cusp of manhood, Finnikin, who was a child when the royal family of Lumatere was brutally murdered and replaced by an imposter, reluctantly joins forces with an enigmatic young novice and fellow-exile, who claims that her dark dreams will lead them to a surviving royal child and a way to regain the throne of Lumatere.

"The skillful world building includes just enough detail to create a vivid sense of place, and Marchetta maintains suspense with unexpected story arcs. It is the achingly real characters, though, and the relationships that emerge through the captivating dialogue that drive the story. Filled with questions about the impact of exile and the human need to belong, this standout fantasy quickly reveals that its real magic lies in its accomplished writing." Booklist.

Marcus, Kimberly

Exposed. by Kimberly Marcus. Random House, 2011. 288 p.

Grades: 8 9 10   **Fic**

1. Teenage girl photographers 2. Rape 3. Rapists 4. Best friends 5. Brothers and sisters 6. Cape Cod, Massachusetts 7. Massachusetts 8. Realistic fiction 9. Novels in verse
ISBN 9780375866937

"The narrative largely zooms in on Liz's pain and her struggle to ground herself in her photography and gain admission to art school as events swirl around her. As a result of tethering the narrative to Liz's perspective, the ongoing discussion of Kate's rape and ensuing trial are not heavyhanded or gratuitous. In Liz, Marcus has created a sympathetic lead. A worthy addition to any collection." School Library Journal.

Margolis, Leslie

Girl's best friend. by Leslie Margolis. Bloomsbury USA Childrens Books, 2010. 272 p.: Maggie Brooklyn mysteries

Grades: 4 5 6 7   **Fic**

1. Girl detectives 2. Twin brothers and sisters 3. Dognapping 4. Pet thefts 5. Dog walking 6. Brooklyn, New York City 7. Mysteries
ISBN 9781599905259

LC 2010000562

In Brooklyn, New York, twelve-year-old dog-walker Maggie, aided by her twin brother Finn and best friend Lucy, investigates someone she believes is stealing pets.

"Characters are well-developed, typical preteens. Readers will easily identify with these seventh graders, and they will love the eccentric landlady who adds a bit of humor. Mystery fans will enjoy this lighthearted whodunit." School Library Journal.

Marillier, Juliet

Cybele's secret. Juliet Marillier. Alfred A. Knopf, 2008. 448 p.

Grades: 7 8 9 10   **Fic**

1. Antiquities 2. Supernatural 3. Fathers and daughters 4. Voyages and travels 5. Merchants 6. Istanbul, Turkey 7. Turkey 8. Historical fantasy 9. Fantasy fiction 10. Middle Eastern-influenced fantasy
ISBN 9780375833656

LC 2008004758

Scholarly eighteen-year-old Paula and her merchant father journey from Transylvania to Istanbul to buy an ancient pagan artifact rumored to be charmed, but others, including a handsome Portuguese pirate and an envoy from the magical Wildwood, want to acquire the item, as well.

"This is a honeyed draught of a [novel]. . . . Marillier embroiders Ottoman Empire cultural details into every fold and drape of her story." Booklist.

Wildwood dancing. Juliet Marillier. Knopf, 2007. 407 p.

Grades: 7 8 9 10   **Fic**

1. Supernatural 2. Magic 3. Sisters 4. Fathers and daughters 5. Secrets 6. Transylvania, Romania 7. Gateway fantasy 8. Fantasy fiction 9. Fairy tale and folklore-inspired fiction
ISBN 0375833641

LC 2006016075

Five sisters who live with their merchant father in Transylvania use a hidden portal in their home to cross over into a magical world, the Wildwood.

"This is told with a striking sense of place, magical elements, beautifully portrayed characters, strong heroines, and an emotional core that touches the heart." Voice of Youth Advocates.

Marks, Janae

★ **From** the desk of Zoe Washington. Janae Marks. Katherine Tegen Books, 2020. 256 p.

Grades: 4 5 6 7   **Fic**

1. Fathers and daughters 2. Prisoners families 3. African American girls 4. Baking 5. Girl bakers 6. Realistic fiction 7. African American fiction
ISBN 9780062875853

LC 2019026849

Avid baker Zoe Washington receives a letter on her twelfth birthday from her biological father, who is in prison for a terrible crime.

"Debut author Marks seamlessly weaves timely discussions about institutionalized racism into this uplifting and engaging story that packs an emotional punch." Publishers Weekly.

Marr, Melissa

Ink exchange. Melissa Marr. HarperTeen, c2008. 325 p.: Wicked lovely

Grades: 8 9 10 11 12   **Fic**
1. Fairies 2. Tattooing 3. Teenage rape victims 4. Options, alternatives, choices 5. Slavery 6. Urban fantasy
ISBN 9780061214684

LC 2007040106

Seventeen-year-old Leslie wants a tattoo as a way of reclaiming control of herself and her body, but the eerie image she selects pulls her into the dangerous Dark Court of the faeries, where she draws on inner strength to make a horrible choice.

"Readers will be drawn in by Marr's darkly poetic imagery and language, her vivid portrayal of the art of tattooing, and her shadowy love triangle. This is indeed a delicious, smoky delight." Bulletin of the Center for Children's Books.

Wicked lovely. Melissa Marr. HarperTeen, c2007. 328 p.: Wicked lovely

Grades: 8 9 10 11 12   **Fic**
1. Fairies 2. Rulers 3. Options, alternatives, choices 4. Secrets 5. Magic 6. Urban fantasy
ISBN 9780061214653

LC 2007009143

Seventeen-year-old Aislinn, who has the rare ability to see faeries, is drawn against her will into a centuries-old battle between the Summer King and Winter Queen, and the survival of her life, her love, and summer all hang in the balance.

"This story explores the themes of love, commitment, and what it really means to give of oneself for the greater good to save everyone else. It is the unusual combination of past legends and modern-day life that gives a unique twist to this fairy tale." School Library Journal.

Marsden, John, 1950-

Tomorrow, when the war began. John Marsden. Houghton Mifflin, 1995. 286 p.: Tomorrow series

Grades: 7 8 9 10   **Fic**
1. Resourcefulness in teenagers 2. Hiding 3. Imprisonment 4. Resourcefulness 5. Determination in teenagers 6. Australia 7. Apocalyptic fiction 8. Classics
ISBN 0395706734

LC 94029299 /AC

Seven Australian teenagers return from a camping trip in the bush to discover that their country has been invaded and they must hide to stay alive.

"The novel is a riveting adventure through which Marsden explores the capacity for evil and the necessity of working together to oppose it." Horn Book.

Marsh, Katherine

Jepp, who defied the stars. Katherine Marsh. Hyperion, 2012. 384 p.

Grades: 6 7 8 9 10   **Fic**
1. Renaissance (1300-1600) 2. 16th century 3. Little people 4. Courts and courtiers 5. Quests 6. Teenage boys 7. Fate and fatalism 8. Europe 9. Historical fiction 10. Coming-of-age stories
ISBN 9781423135005

LC 2011053065

Jepp, a teenage dwarf living in sixteenth-century Europe, leaves home to seek his destiny.

Nowhere boy. Katherine Marsh. Roaring Brook Press, 2018 368 p.

Grades: 5 6 7 8 9   **Fic**
1. Refugees, Syrian 2. Prejudice 3. Resilience (Personal quality) 4. Immigrants 5. Friendship 6. Brussels, Belgium 7. Realistic fiction
ISBN 9781250307576

Fourteen-year-old Ahmed, a Syrian refugee, and thirteen-year-old Max, an American boy, are bound by a secret that sets them on the adventure of a lifetime.

Marshall, Kate Alice

I am still alive. Kate Alice Marshall. Viking Books for Young Readers, 2018. 352 p.

Grades: 8 9 10 11   **Fic**
1. Wilderness survival 2. Revenge 3. Fathers -- Death 4. Endurance in women 5. Grief in women 6. Canada 7. Survival stories 8. Adventure stories
ISBN 9780425290989

Stranded in the woods with few supplies and survival skills, a disabled girl and her dog fervently prepare for the coming winter while evaluating how her mother's death, a dysfunctional foster-care system and her survivalist father led to her predicament.

Martin, Ann M., 1955-

Better to wish. Ann M. Martin. Scholastic Press, 2013. 240 p.: Family tree (Ann M. Martin)

Grades: 3 4 5 6 7   **Fic**
1. Depression era (1929-1941) 2. 1930s 3. Prejudice 4. Independence in girls 5. Independence (Personal quality) 6. Families 7. Maine 8. Historical fiction
ISBN 9780545359429

LC 2012047940

In 1930 Abby Nichols is an eight-year-old girl growing up in Maine, but as the Depression deepens, and her mother dies, the responsibility of taking care of her family falls to her, and she has to put her dreams of going to college and becoming a writer on hold.

A **corner** of the universe. Ann M. Martin. Scholastic Press, 2002. 208 p.

Grades: 5 6 7 8   **Fic**
1. 1960s 2. Uncles 3. Carnivals 4. Families 5. Small town life 6. Girls 7. Historical fiction
ISBN 0439388805

LC 2001057611

The summer that Hattie turns twelve, she meets the childlike uncle she never knew and becomes friends with a girl who works at the carnival that comes to Hattie's small town.

"Martin delivers wonderfully real characters and an engrossing plot through the viewpoint of a girl who tries so earnestly to connect with those around her." School Library Journal.

Everything for a dog. Ann M. Martin. Feiwel and Friends, 2009. 211 p.

Grades: 5 6 7 8   **Fic**
1. Boys and dogs 2. Human/animal relationships 3. Dogs 4.

Loneliness in boys 5. Grief in boys 6. Stories told by animals
ISBN 9780312386511

LC 2008034747

In parallel stories, Bone, an orphaned dog, finds and loses a series of homes, Molly, a family pet, helps Charlie through the grief and other after-effects of his brother's death, and lonely Henry pleads for a dog of his own.

"This is a sensitive, gentle read that surrounds its occasional heartbreak with plenty of hope and warm feelings." Booklist.

★ **Rain** Reign. Ann M. Martin. Feiwel & Friends, 2014. 272 p.

Grades: 4 5 6 7   **Fic**
1. Girls with autism 2. Girls and dogs 3. Lost dogs 4. Uncle and niece 5. Children with Asperger's syndrome
ISBN 9780312643003

Schneider Family Book Award for Middle School, 2015.

Struggling with the challenges of OCD and Asperger's syndrome, Rose, a homonym enthusiast, shares an inseparable bond with a beloved dog, but when the dog goes missing during a storm, Rose is forced to confront the limits of her comfort levels, even if it means leaving her routines and safe places in order to search for her pet.

"Rose, a fifth-grader who has been diagnosed with Asperger syndrome, is often teased at school about her obsession with homonyms and her steadfast conviction that everyone should follow the rules at all times. Rose lives with her harsh, troubled father, but it's Uncle Weldon who cares for her in the ways that matter most. Still, her father did give her Rain, a stray dog that comforts and protects Rose. After Rain is lost in a storm and recovered, Rose learns that her dog has an identification microchip...Rose is driven by the unwavering belief that she must follow the rules, find Rain's former owners, and give the dog back to them... Readers will be moved by the raw portrayal of Rose's difficult home life, her separation from other kids at school, and her loss of the dog that has loved her and provided a buffer from painful experiences. A strong story told in a nuanced, highly accessible way." Booklist.

Martin, Laura

The **ark** plan. Laura Martin. Harper, an imprint of HarperCollinsPublishers, 2016. 304 p.: Edge of extinction

Grades: 4 5 6 7 8   **Fic**
1. Dinosaurs 2. Father-separated girls 3. Post-apocalypse 4. Twelve-year-old girls 5. Preteen girls 6. Science fiction
ISBN 9780062416223

A century and a half after cloned dinosaurs forced humans to move into underground compounds, Sky discovers a clue to the whereabouts of her long-missing father and ventures above ground on a quest that has the potential to save the world.

Martin, Maggie Ann

To be honest. Maggie Ann Martin. Swoon Reads, 2018. 304 p.

Grades: 8 9 10 11 12   **Fic**
1. Body image 2. High school seniors 3. Mothers and daughters 4. Overweight teenage girls 5. Sisters 6. Realistic fiction
ISBN 9781250183156

LC bl2018180829

After her older sister goes to college, Savannah is left home alone with her weight-obsessed mother, and must find consolation in a new relationship with George, who has insecurities of his own.

Martinez, Claudia Guadalupe, 1978-

Pig park. Claudia Guadalupe Martinez. Cinco Puntos Press, 2014. 248 p.

Grades: 8 9 10 11   **Fic**
1. Neighborhoods 2. Bakeries 3. Hispanic Americans 4. Families 5. Building 6. Chicago, Illinois 7. Coming-of-age stories 8. Realistic fiction
ISBN 9781935955764

LC 2013040645

Seventeen-year-old Masi Burciaga's barrio becomes more like a ghost town every day, but when she and other youths are recruited to erect a giant pyramid in hopes of attracting tourists, she wonders about the entrepreneur behind the scheme—and his attractive son.

"Martinez uses nicely specific physical details to relate Masi's experiences, and the moments in the bakery seem particularly authentic and are suffused with love. The warm, diverse community setting and the realistic family interactions help overcome the somewhat jumbled plotlines." Kirkus.

The **smell** of old lady perfume. by Claudia Guadalupe Martinez. Cinco Puntos Press, c2008. 249 p.

Grades: 5 6 7 8   **Fic**
1. Mexican American families 2. Determination in girls 3. Strokes 4. Sixth-grade girls 5. Families 6. El Paso, Texas 7. Coming-of-age stories 8. Realistic fiction
ISBN 1933693185

LC 2007038296

When sixth-grader Chela Gonzalez's father has a stroke and her grandmother moves in to help take care of the family, her world is turned upside down.

"Short, well-crafted chapters offer perceptive glimpses into life on the border, the dynamics of middle-grade girls, and a family in turmoil." Horn Book Guide.

Martinez, Jessica

Virtuosity. Jessica Martinez. Simon Pulse, 2011. 294 p.

Grades: 8 9 10 11 12   **Fic**
1. Teenage musicians 2. Competition 3. Mothers and daughters 4. Teenage boy/girl relations 5. Home schooled teenage girls 6. Chicago, Illinois 7. Realistic fiction
ISBN 9781442420526

LC 2010042513

Just before the most important violin competition of her career, seventeen-year-old prodigy Carmen faces critical decisions about her antianxiety drug addiction, her controlling mother, and a potential romance with her most talented rival.

"This is a riveting novel. . . . The portrayal of Carmen's world . . . is unique and convincing. . . . Even readers without much interest in music will enjoy this exceptional novel." School Library Journal.

Mass, Wendy, 1967-

★ **Every** soul a star. by Wendy Mass. Little, Brown and Co., 2008. 322 p.

Grades: 5 6 7 8   **Fic**
1. Solar eclipses 2. Camp sites, facilities, etc 3. Teenage boy misfits 4. Friendship 5. Interpersonal relations 6. Moon 7. Realistic fiction 8. Coming-of-age stories
ISBN 9780316002561

LC 2008009259

Ally, Bree, and Jack meet at the one place the Great Eclipse can be seen in totality, each carrying the burden of different personal problems, which become dim when compared to the task they embark upon and the friendship they find.

"Mass combines astronomy and storytelling for a well-balanced look at friendships and the role they play in shaping identity. . . . Information about solar eclipses and astronomy is carefully woven into the plot to build drama and will almost certainly intrigue readers." Publishers Weekly.

Jeremy Fink and the meaning of life. Wendy Mass. Little, Brown, c2006. 289 p.

Grades: 5 6 7 8   **Fic**
1. Father-separated boys 2. Purpose in life 3. Self-fulfillment in boys 4. Self-fulfillment 5. Boxes 6. New York City 7. Realistic fiction
ISBN 0316058297

"Mass fashions an adventure in which both journey and destination are worth the trip." Horn Book.

A **mango-shaped** space: a novel. by Wendy Mass. Little, Brown, c2003. 220 p.

Grades: 5 6 7 8   **Fic**
1. Synesthesia 2. Pets -- Death 3. Coping in teenage girls 4. Coping 5. Cats 6. Realistic fiction 7. Coming-of-age stories
ISBN 0316523887

LC 2002072989

Schneider Family Book Award for Middle School, 2004.

Afraid that she is crazy, thirteen-year-old Mia, who sees a special color with every letter, number, and sound, keeps this a secret until she becomes overwhelmed by school, changing relationships, and the loss of something important to her.

"Mass skillfully conveys Mia's emotions, and readers will be intrigued with this fictional depiction of an actual, and fascinating, condition." Horn Book Guide.

Pi in the sky. Wendy Mass. Little, Brown and Company, 2013. 256 p.

Grades: 3 4 5 6 7   **Fic**
1. Pies 2. Space and time 3. Cosmogony 4. Adventure 5. Teenage boys 6. Earth 7. Space 8. Science fiction
ISBN 9780316089166

LC 2012030638

Relegated to the humble duty of delivering pies due to his lack of motivation, young Joss, a seventh son of a prestigious family of overachievers, is tasked with recovering a suddenly missing Earth with the assistance of an outspoken Earth girl.

Matas, Carol, 1949-
After the war. Carol Matas. Simon & Schuster Books for Young Readers, c1996. 116 p.

Grades: 7 8 9 10   **Fic**
1. Berihah (Organization) 2. Jewish teenage girls 3. Antisemitism 4. Refugees, Jewish 5. Courage in teenage girls 6. Courage 7. Poland 8. Historical fiction
ISBN 0689803508

LC 9543613

After being released from Buchenwald at the end of World War II, fifteen-year-old Ruth joins the underground organization Berihah, and risks her life to lead a group of children across Europe to Palestine.

"Rich in texture and simple in its honesty, this story resonates with feeling." Voice of Youth Advocates.

Matson, Morgan
Since you've been gone. Morgan Matson. Simon & Schuster Books for Young Readers, 2014. 400 p.

Grades: 7 8 9 10   **Fic**
1. Self-discovery in teenage girls 2. Separated friends, relatives, etc 3. Teenage boy/girl relations 4. Self-discovery 5. Self-reliance 6. Connecticut 7. Realistic fiction
ISBN 9781442435001

LC 2013041617

Quiet Emily's sociable and daring best friend, Sloane, has disappeared leaving nothing but a random list of bizarre tasks for her to complete, but with unexpected help from popular classmate Frank Porter, Emily gives them a try.

"Emily feels lost when her best friend, Sloane, disappears without explanation. But Sloane left Emily a daunting to-do list (with items like 'kiss a stranger'), and Emily bravely takes on each task, finding new friends, confidence, and a crush along the way. A perfectly awkward protagonist; well-rounded, quirky supporting characters; and spot-on dialogue make this novel of self-discovery stand out." Horn Book.

Matti, Truus, 1961-
Departure time. Truus Matti; translated by Nancy Forest-Flier. Namelos, c2010. 214 p.

Grades: 5 6 7 8   **Fic**
1. Ten-year-old girls 2. Father-separated girls 3. Grief in girls 4. Lost girls 5. Death
ISBN 9781608980871

"A 10-year-old girl is lost in a surrealistic landscape, a red-earth desert threatened by an approaching storm. Nothing looks familiar. She can't remember how she got to this place. Alternating with this classic bad-dream setting, which is narrated in the third person, is a first-person, furious tirade by a girl who feels abandoned by her father and neglected by her mother. Readers will be intrigued by the way Matti interweaves these stories and tantalizes with the possible connections between them. . . . Remarkable and arresting and wholly original, this novel lingers in the mind long after the last page has been read." School Library Journal.

Mister orange. Truus Matti; translated from the Dutch by Laura Watkinson; [jacket and interior art by Jenni Desmond]. Enchanted Lion Books, 2013. 159 p.

Grades: 5 6 7 8   **Fic**
1. Second World War era (1939-1945) 2. 1940s 3. Artists 4. Children and war 5. World War II 6. Delivery services 7. World War II home front 8. New York City 9. Manhattan, New York City 10. Historical fiction 11. Translations
ISBN 9781592701230

Mildred L. Batchelder Award, 2014.

Assuming his older brother's job as a grocery store delivery boy when his brother leaves to fight in World War II, young Linus Muller befriends an enigmatic European artist who orders a crate of oranges every week and who discusses with Linus respective views on the war, the future and creative freedom.

Mazer, Harry, 1925-2016
A **boy** at war: a novel of Pearl Harbor. Harry Mazer. Simon & Schuster Books for Young Readers, 2001. 104 p.

Grades: 7 8 9 10   **Fic**
1. Arizona (Battleship) 2. Pearl Harbor, Attack on, 1941 3. Fathers and sons 4. Missing in action 5. Teenage children of military personnel 6. World War II 7. Hawaii
ISBN 0689841612

LC 00049687

While fishing with his friends off Honolulu on December 7, 1941, teenaged Adam is caught in the midst of the Japanese attack and through the chaos of the subsequent days tries to find his father, a naval officer who was serving on the U.S.S. Arizona when the bombs fell.

"Mazer's graphic, sensory descriptions give the narrative immediacy, putting readers alongside Adam, watching with him as pieces of the ship and pieces of men rained down around him. . . . This is a thought-provoking, sobering account of the human costs of war." Horn Book Guide.

Heroes don't run: a novel of the Pacific War. Harry Mazer. Simon & Schuster Books for Young Readers, 2005. 128 p.
Grades: 7 8 9 10   **Fic**
1. United States. Marine Corps 2. Second World War era (1939-1945) 3. Seventeen-year-old boys 4. Teenage boys 5. Teenage soldiers 6. Children of military personnel 7. Loss (Psychology) 8. Hawaii 9. Okinawa Island, Japan 10. War stories 11. Historical fiction
ISBN 0689855346
                                            LC 2004010935
To honor his father who died during the Japanese invasion of Pearl Harbor, seventeen-year-old Adam eagerly enlists in the Marines in 1944, survives boot camp, and faces combat on the tiny island of Okinawa.

"The clear first-person narrative is terse and gripping, graphic about the slaughter and heartfelt about the loss." Booklist.

The **last** mission. Harry Mazer. Delacorte Press, 1979. 182 p.
Grades: 7 8 9 10   **Fic**
1. 1940s 2. Jewish American teenage boys 3. Teenage soldiers 4. Fifteen-year-olds 5. World War II -- Aerial operations 6. World War II -- Prisoners and prisons, German 7. Historical fiction 8. War stories
ISBN 0385286627
                                            LC   79050674
Jack is a freshman in high school when he decides that he wants to be a hero. One small lie gets him a job as a gunner in a B-17 flying combat mission across Europe in 1944. But he wasn't prepared for the terror of night missions or getting shot down.

"Told in a rapid journalistic style, occasionally peppered with barrack-room vulgarities, the story is a vivid and moving account of a boy's experience during World War II as well as a skillful, convincing portrayal of his misgivings as a Jew on enemy soil and of his ability to size up—in mature human fashion—the misery around him." Horn Book.

Somebody please tell me who I am. Harry Mazer and Peter Lerangis. Simon & Schuster Books for Young Readers, 2012. 160 p.
Grades: 6 7 8 9 10 11 12   **Fic**
1. Men with brain injuries 2. Memory 3. Rehabilitation 4. Soldiers 5. Coma 6. Realistic fiction
ISBN 9781416938958
                                            LC 2011006010
Schneider Family Book Award for Teens, 2013.
Wounded in Iraq while his Army unit is on convoy and treated for many months for traumatic brain injury, the first person Ben remembers from his earlier life is his autistic brother.

Mazer, Norma Fox, 1931-2009

The **missing** girl. Norma Fox Mazer. HarperTeen, 2008. 284 p.
Grades: 7 8 9 10   **Fic**
1. Stalkers 2. Sisters 3. Kidnapping victims 4. Teenagers 5.

Teenage girls 6. New York (State) 7. Psychological suspense
ISBN 9780066237763

"Fans of . . . classic tales of high-tension peril will appreciate the way this successfully plays on their deepest fears." Bulletin of the Center for Children's Books.

Mbalia, Kwame

★ **Tristan** Strong destroys the world. by Kwame Mbalia. Disney-Hyperion 2020 320 p.: Tristan Strong
Grades: 4 5 6 7 8   **Fic**
1. Preteen boys 2. Characters and characteristics in mythology 3. Kidnapping 4. Supernatural 5. Grandparents 6. Alabama 7. Fairy tale and folklore-inspired fiction 8. African American fiction
ISBN 9781368042383
                                            LC 2020005493
Seventh-grader Tristan must return to Alke and enlist the help of African gods and black folktale heroes when Nana is abducted from the Strong family farm in Alabama.

"Mbalia's universe continues to excite through sheer conceptual brilliance, nonstop action and adventure, and—let's be honest—the comical aggression of sidekick god Gum Baby." Booklist

★ **Tristan** Strong punches a hole in the sky. by Kwame Mbalia. Disney HYPERION, 2019. 496 p.: Tristan Strong
Grades: 4 5 6 7 8   **Fic**
1. Preteen boys 2. Characters and characteristics in mythology 3. Loss (Psychology) 4. Best friends -- Death 5. Survivor guilt 6. Alabama 7. Fairy tale and folklore-inspired fiction 8. African American fiction
ISBN 9781368039932
                                            LC 2018057192
Haunted by the bus accident that ended his best friend's life, seventh grader Tristan Strong dreads a visit to his grandparents' Alabama farm before a bizarre living doll snatches away his friend's notebook and draws him into a world of burning seas, iron monsters and exhausted black folk heroes.

"Perfectly paced, this cinematic adventure never lags." Booklist.

McCaffrey, Anne

Dragon's fire. Anne McCaffrey, Todd McCaffrey. Del Rey Books, 2006. 384 p.: Dragonriders of Pern
Grades: 7 8 9 10 11 12   **Fic**
1. Apprentices 2. Orphans 3. Dragons 4. Pern (Imaginary place) 5. Mines and mineral resources 6. Science fiction 7. Coming-of-age stories 8. Science fantasy
ISBN 9780345480286
                                            LC 2006040236
When a mine containing firestone, the mineral that gives the dragons of Pern their ability to breathe fire, explodes, killing the miners trapped there, young Cristov volunteers to take over the dangerous task of retrieving the explosive rock for the dragons.

"The deadly Thread has not fallen on Pern for nearly 200 turns, but it is due to in another 18, and the firestone needed by the dragons to breathe fire and fight Thread is in short supply. . . . A number of well-limned major characters move the plot forward with the long series' expected momentum, and as usual, the interactions between humans, dragons, fire lizards, and whers put the richly detailed story on a par with the rest of the Pern canon." Booklist

Dragonflight. Anne McCaffrey. Ballantine Books, 1968. 303 p.: Dragonriders of Pern

Grades: 8 9 10 11 12 Adult **Fic**
1. Women rulers 2. Household employees 3. Dragons 4. Biological invasions 5. Survival 6. Science fiction 7. Science fantasy
ISBN 9780345276940

At a time when the number of Dragonriders has fallen too low for safety and only one Weyr trains the creatures and their riders, the Red Star approaches Pern, threatening it with disaster.

McCall, Guadalupe Garcia

All the stars denied. by Guadalupe Garcia McCall. Tu Books, an imprint of Lee & Low Books Inc., 2018 336 p.
Grades: 6 7 8 9 10 **Fic**
1. 1930s 2. Mexican American families 3. Deportation 4. Racism 5. Mexican American girls 6. Race relations 7. Texas 8. Mexico (City) 9. Historical fiction 10. Diary novels
ISBN 9781620142813

LC 2017058034

When resentment surges during the Great Depression in a Texas border town, Estrella, fifteen, organizes a protest against the treatment of tejanos and soon finds herself with her mother and baby brother in Mexico.

Under the mesquite. by Guadalupe Garcia McCall. Lee & Low Books, 2011. 224 p.
Grades: 7 8 9 10 11 12 **Fic**
1. Mexican American teenage girls 2. Children of people with cancer 3. Responsibility in teenage girls 4. Responsibility 5. Acting 6. Texas 7. Realistic fiction 8. Novels in verse
ISBN 9781600604294

LC 2010052567

Pura Belpré Award for Narrative, 2012.

Throughout her high school years, as her mother battles cancer, Lupita takes on more responsibility for her house and seven younger siblings, while finding refuge in acting and writing poetry. Includes glossary of Spanish terms.

"With poignant imagery and well-placed Spanish, the author effectively captures the complex lives of teenagers in many Latino and/or immigrant families." Kirkus.

McCaughrean, Geraldine

The **kite** rider: a novel. by Geraldine McCaughrean. HarperCollins, 2002. xi, 272 p.
Grades: 6 7 8 9 **Fic**
1. Kublai Khan, 1216-1294. 2. 13th century 3. Mediums 4. Circus 5. Kites 6. Mongols 7. Fathers -- Death 8. China 9. Adventure stories 10. Historical fiction
ISBN 0066238749

LC 2001039522

In thirteenth-century China, after trying to save his widowed mother from a horrendous second marriage, twelve-year-old Haoyou has life-changing adventures when he takes to the sky as a circus kite rider and ends up meeting the great Mongol ruler Kublai Khan.

"The story is a genuine page-turner. . . . McCaughrean fully immerses her memorable characters in the culture and lore of the ancient Chinese and Mongols, which make this not only a solid adventure story but also a window to a fascinating time and place." Booklist.

Where the world ends. Geraldine McCaughrean. Flatiron Books, 2019, c2017 324 p.
Grades: 8 9 10 11 12 **Fic**
1. Georgian era (1714-1837) 2. 1720s 3. Castaways 4. Wilderness survival 5. Islands 6. End of the world 7. Hunting 8. Outer Hebrides 9. Scotland 10. Historical fiction
ISBN 9781250225498

LC 2019019749

Carnegie Medal, 2018.

In the summer of 1727, Quill and his friends are put ashore on a remote sea stac to harvest birds for food, and only the end of the world can explain why no boat returns to collect them.

"McCaughrean takes the bones of a real event, wraps it in immersive, imaginative detail and thoroughly real emotion, and creates an unforgettable tale of human survival. A masterpiece." Kirkus

McClintock, Norah

Out of tune. Norah McClintock. Orca Book Publishers, [2017] 222 p.: Riley Donovan mysteries
Grades: 7 8 9 10 **Fic**
1. Teenage detectives 2. Murder 3. Murder suspects 4. Violinists 5. Donovan, Riley (Fictitious character) 6. Mysteries
ISBN 1459814657

When Alicia, a talented violinist at Riley Donovan's high school, is found dead, Riley goes searching for the truth.

"The plot is complex and tightly woven, the reveal is both surprising and satisfying, the violence is prominent but tastefully presented, and Riley continues to be a strong and relatable protagonist with good moral fiber." Booklist.

She said/she saw. Norah McClintock. Orca Book Publishers, 2011. 211 p.
Grades: 7 8 9 10 **Fic**
1. Teenage murder witnesses 2. Crimes against teenage girls 3. Friends' death 4. Trust 5. Best friends -- Death 6. Mysteries 7. Realistic fiction
ISBN 9781554693351

"The brisk pace, solid character development and inventive structuring make for fast, page-turning reading, and it all wraps up with an unpredictable plot twist and ending. Mysterious and haunting, packed with hard truths about adolescence." Kirkus.

Taken. Norah McClintock. Orca Book Publishers, 2009. 176 p.
Grades: 7 8 9 10 **Fic**
1. Wilderness survival 2. Serial murderers 3. Fourteen-year-old girls 4. Survival 5. Teenage girls 6. Thrillers and suspense
ISBN 9781554691524

LC 2009925695

"After two girls from a nearby town go missing everyone goes on high alert, suspecting a serial killer, and while walking home, Stephanie is grabbed from behind and injected with a drug that knocks her out. She awakens hours later to find herself tied up in an abandoned cabin deep in a densely wooded area. . . . Her harrowing journey back to safety propels this plot-driven, fast-paced tale forward. . . . Told in the first person, this suspenseful survival story is sure to have strong appeal." Kirkus.

McCormick, Patricia, 1956-

Cut. Patricia McCormick. Front Street, 2000. 136 p.
Grades: 7 8 9 10 **Fic**
1. Teenagers with mental illnesses 2. Psychiatric clinics 3. Self-harm in teenage girls 4. Cutting (Self-harm) 5. Self-destructive behavior in teenage girls 6. Realistic fiction
ISBN 1886910618

LC 0003484

While confined to a mental hospital, thirteen-year-old Callie slowly comes to understand some of the reasons behind her self-mutilation, and gradually starts to get better.

"Realistic, sensitive, and heartfelt." Voice of Youth Advocates.

Purple heart. by Patricia McCormick. Balzer & Bray, 2009. 176 p.

Grades: 7 8 9 10   **Fic**

1. Soldiers 2. People with brain injuries 3. Iraq War, 2003-2011 4. Memory 5. Suspicion 6. Iraq 7. War stories

ISBN 9780061730900

LC 2009001757

While recuperating in a Baghdad hospital from a traumatic brain injury sustained during the Iraq War, eighteen-year-old soldier Matt Duffy struggles to recall what happened to him and how it relates to his ten-year-old friend, Ali.

"Strong characters heighten the drama. . . . McCormick raises moral questions without judgment and will have readers examining not only this conflict but the nature of heroism and war." Publishers Weekly.

McCoy, Mary, 1976-

I, Claudia. Mary McCoy. Carolrhoda Lab, 2018. 424 p.

Grades: 8 9 10 11 12   **Fic**

1. High school students 2. Betrayal 3. Student government 4. Historians 5. Power (Social sciences) 6. Los Angeles, California 7. Psychological fiction

ISBN 9781512448467

LC 2017038714

Over the course of her high school years, awkward Claudia McCarthy finds herself unwittingly drawn into the dark side of her school's student government, with dire consequences. Provided by publisher.

"Smart, witty, and featuring an unforgettable (and possibly unreliable) narrator, as well as a seamless stream of political history, the audience that finds this novel will be unable to put it down." Booklist.

McCrite, K. D. (Kathaleen Deiser)

In front of God and everybody. by K. D. McCrite. Thomas Nelson, 2011. 304 p.: Confessions of April Grace

Grades: 4 5 6 7   **Fic**

1. 1980s 2. Eleven-year-old girls 3. Rural families 4. Christian life 5. Swindlers and swindling 6. Friendship -- Religious aspects -- Christianity 7. Arkansas 8. Christian fiction

ISBN 9781400317226

In the summer of 1986, eleven-year-old April Grace, who lives on a rural Arkansas farm with her family, across a field from her grandmother, has her sense of Christian charity tested when a snooty couple from San Francisco moves into a dilapidated house down the road and her grandmother takes up with a loud, obnoxious, and suspicious-acting Texan.

"With keen eyes and good humor, April Grace notes the quirks, presumptions, and motivations of family and neighbors; she has plenty of fodder—the characters' personalities are dialed up to 11." Publishers Weekly.

McCulloch, Amy, 1986-

Jinxed. Amy McCulloch. Sourcebooks Young Readers, 2020, c2018. 336 p.: Jinxed (McCulloch)

Grades: 4 5 6 7   **Fic**

1. Robots 2. Engineering 3. Gifted girls 4. Girls and cats 5. Father-separated children 6. Toronto, Ontario 7. Canada 8. STEM fiction 9. Science fiction

ISBN 9781492683742

LC 2019024230

After fourteen-year-old Lacey Chu repairs a highly advanced smartphone/robotic pet companion, or baku, called Jinx, the baku gets her into her dream school, Profectus, where she is exposed to dangerous secrets.

"With a sharp eye toward the rising awareness of device addiction and a keen sense of wonder, McCulloch's tale is a feast for the imagination that celebrates women in STEM fields." Publishers Weekly.

McDaniel, Lurlene

Breathless. Lurlene McDaniel. Delacorte Press, c2009. 165 p.

Grades: 8 9 10 11 12   **Fic**

1. Teenage athletes 2. Teenagers with cancer 3. Assisted suicide 4. Teenage boy divers 5. Teenage boy/girl relations 6. Alabama 7. Realistic fiction

"This is a heartstrings-tugging read that retains the central character's dignity and peace in the face of insurmountable odds. A sensitive book on a delicate topic." School Library Journal.

Hit and run. Lurlene McDaniel. Delacorte Press, 2007. 180 p.

Grades: 8 9 10 11 12   **Fic**

1. Teenage athletes 2. Hit-and-run accidents 3. Guilt in teenage boys 4. Guilt 5. Popularity 6. North Carolina 7. Asheville, North Carolina 8. Realistic fiction

ISBN 9780385731614

Events surrounding the hit and run accident of a popular high school student are told from the viewpoints of those involved, including the victim.

"This demonstrates the power of love and making choices. McDaniel, known for her inspiring novels, has a simplistic style, but a weighty message—it's the way you respond to a given situation that defines who you are and who you will be." School Library Journal.

McGarry, Katie

Only a breath apart. Katie McGarry. Tor Teen, 2019. 368 p.

Grades: 8 9 10 11 12   **Fic**

1. Former friends 2. Inheritance and succession 3. Farms 4. Secrets 5. Love 6. Kentucky 7. Contemporary romances 8. Realistic fiction

ISBN 9781250193858

LC 2018044554

Told in two voices, childhood best friends Jessie and Scarlett reconnect at his grandmother's funeral and start to share their secrets and feelings for each other.

"The novel manages to tackle domestic violence in a way that never feels clichéd, and the romance is sure to win over even the most cynical reader." Booklist.

McGinnis, Mindy

Be not far from me. Mindy McGinnis. Katherine Tegen Books, 2020 240 p.

Grades: 8 9 10 11   **Fic**

1. Wilderness survival 2. Wilderness areas 3. Infection 4. Wounds and injuries 5. Survival 6. Great Smoky Mountains (NC and Tenn) 7. Tennessee 8. Survival stories

ISBN 9780062561626

Lost in the Great Smoky Mountains, rising high school senior Ashley Hawkins must fight for survival without any tools, growing in awareness that the world is not tame, and neither are people.

McGuigan, Mary Ann

Morning in a different place. Mary Ann McGuigan. Front Street, c2009. 195 p.

Grades: 7 8 9 10 **Fic**
    1. 1960s 2. Interracial friendship 3. Race relations 4. Racism 5. Eighth-grade girls 6. Teenage girls 7. Bronx, New York City 8. New York City 9. Historical fiction
    ISBN 9781590785515

    LC 2007017547
    In 1963 in the Bronx, New York, eighth-graders Fiona and Yolanda help one another face hard decisions at home despite family and social opposition to their interracial friendship, but Fiona is on her own when popular classmates start paying attention to her and give her a glimpse of both a different way of life and a new kind of hatefulness.

    "This book is never didactic. McGuigan's writing is spare and low-key, and her metaphors are acute." Booklist.

McKay, Hilary

Binny for short. Hilary McKay. Margaret K. McElderry Books, 2013. 291 p.: Binny Cornwallis

Grades: 4 5 6 7 **Fic**
    1. Coping in girls 2. Loss (Psychology) 3. Girls and dogs 4. Dogs 5. Moving, Household 6. Realistic fiction
    ISBN 9781442482753

    LC 2013000053
    Eleven-year-old Binny struggles to cope with her father's death and the loss of her beloved dog while she adjusts to a new home that might be haunted by her horrible Aunt Violet.

Caddy ever after. Hilary McKay. Margaret K. McElderry Books, 2006. 218 p.: Casson family

Grades: 5 6 7 8 **Fic**
    1. Eccentric families 2. Disasters, Minor 3. Weddings 4. Children -- Interpersonal relations 5. Engagement 6. England 7. Realistic fiction
    ISBN 1416909303

    LC 2005031449
    The four eccentric Casson siblings each contribute written accounts of the events—which include a Valentine's Day dance, the appearance of a sinister balloon, and the breakdown of a car—that lead to Caddy's wedding day.

    "The depth of the story is conveyed in the dynamic of this family that is at times both touching and hilarious." School Library Journal.

Forever Rose. Hilary McKay. Margaret K. McElderry Books, 2008. 291 p.: Casson family

Grades: 5 6 7 8 **Fic**
    1. Children of artists 2. Eccentric families 3. School field trips 4. Mischief 5. Eleven-year-old girls 6. England 7. Realistic fiction
    ISBN 9781416954866

    As Christmas approaches, eleven-year-old Rose, the youngest member of the eccentric Casson family, discovers that life is filled with both catastrophic problems and wonderful surprises.

    "Those who know the characters will rejoice in this final sly, celebratory view of a messy, imperfect, and fiercely loving family." Booklist.

Indigo's star. Hilary McKay. Margaret K. McElderry Books, 2004. 265 p.: Casson family

Grades: 5 6 7 8 **Fic**
    1. Children of divorced parents 2. Bullying and bullies 3. Eccentric families 4. Twelve-year-old boys 5. Friendship 6. England 7.

Realistic fiction
ISBN 0689865635

    LC 2003009941
    Spurred on by his youngest sister, Rose, twelve-year-old Indigo sticks up for himself and an American boy who has replaced him as the primary target of the school bullies.

    "This offers sly humor, deft characterization, and brisk pacing. . . . Readers will love revisiting the chaotic but loving Casson household." School Library Journal.

Saffy's angel. by Hilary McKay. Margaret K. McElderry Books, 2002, c2001. 152 p.: Casson family

Grades: 5 6 7 8 **Fic**
    1. Adopted teenage girls 2. Eccentric families 3. Searching 4. Belonging 5. Brothers and sisters 6. England 7. Italy 8. Realistic fiction
    ISBN 0689849338

    LC 2001044110
    After learning that she was adopted, thirteen-year-old Saffron's relationship with her eccentric, artistic family changes, until they help her go back to Italy where she was born to find a special memento of her past.

    "Like the Casson household itself, the plot is a chaotic whirl that careens off in several directions simultaneously. But McKay always skillfully draws each clearly defined character back into the story with witty, well-edited details; rapid dialogue; and fine pacing." Booklist.

★ The **time** of green magic. Hilary McKay. Margaret K. McElderry Books, 2020, 224 p.

Grades: 4 5 6 7 **Fic**
    1. Blended families 2. Moving, Household 3. Imaginary creatures 4. Stepbrothers and stepsisters 5. Adjustment (Psychology) 6. Low fantasy
    ISBN 9781534462762

    When eleven-year-old Abi moves with her father and new stepfamily into an eerie old house, something magical makes her books more real and brings a not-so-imaginary friend to stepbrother Louis.

    "McKay's own magic is the ability to portray individuals, their quirky differences, and their shifting relationships in ways that seem realistic and uncommonly absorbing. Within the story, tension builds steadily on several fronts, then resolves as the characters begin to form bonds of trust and even kinship, along with the unspoken realization that they can rely on each other." Booklist

McKay, Sharon E.

Thunder over Kandahar. Sharon E. McKay; photographs by Rafal Gerszak. Annick Press, c2010. 260 p.

Grades: 7 8 9 10 11 12 **Fic**
    1. Taliban. 2. Runaway teenage girls 3. Arranged marriage 4. Religious persecution 5. Best friends 6. Friendship 7. Afghanistan 8. Realistic fiction
    ISBN 9781554512676

    LC bl2010021366
    Teenage best friends Tamanna and Yasmine face arranged marriages and persecution by the Taliban in their Afghan village, so they flee through dangerous mountain passes with only one another to rely upon.

    "When her British and American-educated parents' return to Afghanistan is cut short by a terrible attack, 14-year-old Yasmine is sent to Kandahar for safety. Instead, the driver abandons her and her friend Tamanna along the way, and they must travel on their own through Taliban-controlled mountains. . . . In spite of unrelenting violence, along with grinding poverty, restrictive customs, and the horrors of war, what shines through this sad narrative is the love Afghans have for their country. . . . [The author] traveled to Afghanistan and provides numerous credits for this gripping tale." School Library Journal.

McKernan, Victoria

The **devil's** paintbox. Victoria McKernan. Alfred A. Knopf, 2009. 368 p.

Grades: 6 7 8 9 10 **Fic**
1. American Westward Expansion (1803-1899) 2. 1860s 3. 19th century 4. Frontier and pioneer life 5. Overland journeys to the Pacific 6. Brothers and sisters 7. Orphans 8. Fifteen-year-old boys 9. The West (United States) 10. Seattle, Washington 11. Historical fiction
ISBN 9780375837500

LC 2008004749

In 1866, fifteen-year-old Aidan and his thirteen-year-old sister Maddy, penniless orphans, leave drought-stricken Kansas on a wagon train hoping for a better life in Seattle, but find there are still many hardships to be faced.

"This is a gripping novel. . . . Attention to detail and steady pacing keep readers fully engaged." Publishers Weekly.

Shackleton's stowaway. Victoria McKernan. Knopf, 2005. 317 p.

Grades: 7 8 9 10 **Fic**
1. Blackborow, W. Perce, 1894-1949 2. Shackleton, Ernest Henry, Sir, 1874-1922. 3. Endurance (Ship) 4. Explorers 5. Survival (after airplane accidents, shipwrecks, etc) 6. Expeditions 7. Voyages and travels 8. Cold 9. Antarctica 10. Survival stories 11. Adventure stories 12. Historical fiction
ISBN 0375826912

LC 2004010313

A fictionalized account of the adventures of eighteen-year-old Perce Blackborow, who stowed away for the 1914 Shackleton Antarctic expedition and, after their ship Endurance was crushed by ice, endured many hardships, including the loss of the toes of his left foot to frostbite, during the nearly two-year return journey across sea and ice.

"This book provides historical information for history and geography classes who are interested in exploration, the Antarctic, and early history of great sea voyages." Library Media Connection.

Includes bibliographical references.

McKinley, Robin

Beauty: a retelling of the story of Beauty & the beast. Robin McKinley. Harper & Row, c1978. 247 p.

Grades: 7 8 9 10 **Fic**
1. Enchantment 2. Self-sacrifice 3. Spells (Magic) 4. Love 5. Kindness 6. Fantasy romances 7. Fairy tale and folklore-inspired fiction
ISBN 0060241497

LC 77025636

Kind Beauty grows to love the Beast at whose castle she is compelled to stay and through her love releases him from the spell which had turned him from a handsome prince into an ugly beast.

The **blue** sword. Robin McKinley. Greenwillow Books, c1982. 272 p.

Grades: 7 8 9 10 **Fic**
1. Girl heroes 2. Girl kidnapping victims 3. Courage in girls 4. Girl adventurers 5. Swordfighters 6. High fantasy 7. Fantasy fiction
ISBN 0688009387

LC 82002895

Harry, bored with her sheltered life in the remote orange-growing colony of Daria, discovers magic in herself when she is kidnapped by a Hillfolk king with mysterious powers.

"This is a zesty, romantic, heroic fantasy with an appealing stalwart heroine, a finely realized mythical kingdom, and a grounding in reality." Booklist.

Chalice. Robin McKinley. G.P. Putnam's Sons, 2008. 272 p.
Grades: 7 8 9 10 11 12 **Fic**
1. Beekeepers 2. Nature 3. Duty 4. Women political consultants 5. Priests 6. Fantasy fiction
ISBN 9780399246760

LC 2008000704

A beekeeper by trade, Mirasol's life changes completely when she is named the new Chalice, the most important advisor to the new Master, a former priest of fire.

"The fantasy realm is evoked in thorough and telling detail. . . . A lavish and lasting treat." Publishers Weekly.

Fire: tales of elemental spirits. Robin McKinley and Peter Dickinson. G. P. Putnam's Sons, 2009. 304 p.: Tales of elemental spirits
Grades: 7 8 9 10 **Fic**
1. Imaginary creatures 2. Fire 3. Four elements 4. Supernatural 5. Self-discovery 6. Fantasy fiction 7. Short stories
ISBN 9780399252891

LC 2009004730

Spanning a time period of thousands of years, this collection for young adults offers five suspenseful stories incorporating the powerful and enchanting element of fire.

"The settings of these five tales range from ancient to modern, but they are all united by encounters with magical creatures with an affinity for fire. . . . This collection of beautifully crafted tales will find a warm welcome from fans of either author, as well as from fantasy readers in general." School Library Journal.

The **hero** and the crown. Robin McKinley. Greenwillow Books, c1985. 246 p.
Grades: 6 7 8 9 **Fic**
1. Princesses 2. Wizards 3. Inheritance and succession 4. Dragons 5. Heroes and heroines 6. High fantasy 7. Fantasy fiction
ISBN 0688025935

LC 84004074

Newbery Medal, 1985.

Aerin, with the guidance of the wizard Luthe and the help of the blue sword, wins the birthright due her as the daughter of the Damarian king and a witchwoman of the mysterious, demon-haunted North.

"The author has in this suspenseful prequel . . . created an utterly engrossing fantasy, replete with a fairly mature romantic subplot as well as adventure." New York Times Book Review.

The **outlaws** of Sherwood. Robin McKinley. Greenwillow Books, c1988. 282 p.
Grades: 8 9 10 11 12 **Fic**
1. Richard I, King of England, 1157-1199 2. 12th century 3. Robin Hood (Legendary character) 4. Outlaws 5. Nobility -- History 12th century. 6. Heroes and heroines 7. Adventurers 8. England 9. Sherwood Forest, England 10. Historical fiction 11. Fairy tale and folklore-inspired fiction
ISBN 0688071783

LC 88045227

The author retells the adventures of Robin Hood and his band of outlaws who live in Sherwood Forest in twelfth-century England.

"McKinley takes a fresh look at a classic, changing some of the events or deviating from standard characterization to gain new dimensions. Her afterword explains her artistic compromise with myth and history, her wish to write a version that is historically unembarrassing. With a few exceptions, she has done that admirably, creating a story that has pace and substance and style, and that is given nuance and depth by the characterization." Bulletin of the Center for Children's Books.

Pegasus. Robin McKinley. G.P. Putnam's Sons, 2010. 400 p.
Grades: 8 9 10 11 12 **Fic**
    1. Princesses 2. Winged horses 3. Telepathy 4. Wizards 5. Alliances 6. High fantasy 7. Fantasy fiction
ISBN 9780399246777

                LC 2010002279
Because of a thousand-year-old alliance between humans and pegasi, Princess Sylvi is ceremonially bound to Ebon, her own pegasus, on her twelfth birthday, but the closeness of their bond becomes a threat to the status quo and possibly to the safety of their two nations.

"McKinley's storytelling is to be savored. She lavishes page after page upon rituals and ceremonies, basks in the awe of her intricately constructed world, and displays a masterful sense of pegasi physicality and mannerisms." Booklist.

Rose daughter. Robin McKinley. Greenwillow Books, c1997. 306 p.
Grades: 7 8 9 10 **Fic**
    1. Enchantment 2. Roses 3. Love 4. Beauty 5. Rose growing 6. Fantasy romances 7. Fairy tale and folklore-inspired fiction
ISBN 0688154395

                LC 96048783
Beauty grows to love the Beast at whose castle she is compelled to stay, and through her love he is released from the curse that had turned him from man to beast.

"Compared to Beauty, this is fuller bodied, with richer characterizations and a more mystical, darker edge. . . . There is more background on the Beast in this version . . . and Beauty's choice at the end, a departure from that in Beauty, is just so right. Readers will be enchanted, in the best sense of the word." Booklist.

Water: tales of elemental spirits. Robin McKinley, Peter Dickinson. G. P. Putnam's, c2002. 266 p.: Tales of elemental spirits
Grades: 7 8 9 10 **Fic**
    1. Sea monsters 2. Oceans 3. Magic 4. Mermen 5. Mermaids 6. Fantasy fiction 7. Short stories 8. Sea stories
ISBN 0399237968

                LC 2001041642
"The masterfully written stories all feature distinct, richly detailed casts and settings . . . and focus as strongly on action as on character. There's plenty here to excite, enthrall, and move even the pickiest readers." School Library Journal.

McKissack, Pat, 1944-2017

★ The **dark-thirty:** Southern tales of the supernatural. Patricia C. McKissack; illustrated by Brian Pinkney. Knopf, 1992. iv, 122 p.
Grades: 4 5 6 7 **Fic**
    1. Ghosts 2. Ghost stories 3. Horror 4. Short stories
ISBN 9780679818632

                LC 92003021

Coretta Scott King Award, Author Category, 1993.

A collection of ghost stories with African American themes, designed to be told during the Dark Thirty—the half hour before nightfall—when ghosts seem all too believable.

"Strong characterizations are superbly drawn in a few words. The atmosphere of each selection is skillfully developed and sustained to the very end. Pinkney's stark scratchboard illustrations evoke an eerie mood, which heightens the suspense of each tale." School Library Journal.

A **friendship** for today. by Patricia C. McKissack. Scholastic Press, 2007. 240 p.
Grades: 4 5 6 7 **Fic**
    1. 1950s 2. Twelve-year-old girls 3. African American girls 4. School integration 5. Interracial friendship 6. Racism 7. Missouri 8. Historical fiction
ISBN 043966098X

                LC 2006029293
In 1954, when desegregation comes to Kirkland, Missouri, ten-year-old Rosemary faces many changes and challenges at school and at home as her parents separate.

"A real, at times raw tale about a winning and insightful young heroine during a bittersweet era." Publishers Weekly.

NzinghaWarrior Queen of Matamba. Scholastic, 2000. 136 p.: Royal diaries
Grades: 5 6 7 8 **Fic**
    1. Nzingha, Queen of Matamba, 1582?-1663 2. 16th century 3. 17th century 4. Girls 5. Princesses 6. Mbundu (African people) 7. Slave-trade 8. Gender role 9. Angola 10. Historical fiction 11. Diary novels
ISBN 0439112109

                LC 00024216
Presents the diary of thirteen-year-old Nzingha, a sixteenth-century West African princess who loves to hunt and hopes to lead her kingdom one day against the invasion of the Portuguese slave traders. Includes Kiluanji family tree, pronunciation guide, and glossary of characters, places, and things.

"The diary format will appeal to readers and the author's use of time lines, seasons, and actual place names makes the story believable and interesting." School Library Journal.

★ **Porch** lies: tales of slicksters, tricksters, and other wily characters. Patricia C. McKissack; illustrated by Andre Carillho. Schwartz & Wade Books, c2006. 160 p.
Grades: 4 5 6 7 **Fic**
    1. African Americans 2. Tricksters 3. Storytelling 4. African American fiction 5. Horror 6. Humorous stories
ISBN 0375836195

                LC 2005022048
"The original tales in this uproarious collection draw on African American oral tradition and blend history and legend with sly humor, creepy horror, villainous characters, and wild farce. McKissack based the stories on those she heard as a child while sitting on her grandparents' porch. . . . Carrilho's full-page illustrations—part cartoon, part portrait in silhouette—combine realistic characters with scary monsters." Booklist.

McLemore, Anna-Marie

Blanca & Roja. Anna-Marie McLemore. Feiwel & Friends, 2018. 320 p.
Grades: 8 9 10 11 **Fic**
    1. Curses 2. Sisters 3. Love 4. Swans 5. Duty 6. Magical

realism

ISBN 9781250162717

The del Cisne girls have never just been sisters; they're also rivals, Blanca as obedient and graceful as Roja is vicious and manipulative. They know that, because of a generations-old spell, their family is bound to a bevy of swans deep in the woods. They know that, one day, the swans will pull them into a dangerous game that will leave one of them a girl, and trap the other in the body of a swan. But when two local boys become drawn into the game, the swans' spell intertwines with the strange and unpredictable magic lacing the woods, and all four of their fates depend on facing truths that could either save or destroy them ... The story of the ugly duckling was never about the cygnet discovering he is lovely. It is about the sudden understanding that you are something other than what you thought you were. Publisher's description.

McManis, Charlene Willing, 1953-2018

★ **Indian** no more. Charlene Willing Mcmanis; with Traci Sorell. Tu Books, 2019. 211 p.

Grades: 4 5 6 7   **Fic**

1. 1950s 2. Native American girls 3. Identity (Psychology) 4. Life change events 5. Native American families 6. Home (Concept) 7. Los Angeles, California 8. Historical fiction 9. Coming-of-age stories 10. Autobiographical fiction

ISBN 9781620148396

When Regina's Umpqua tribe is legally terminated and her family must relocate from Oregon to Los Angeles, she goes on a quest to understand her identity as an Indian despite being so far from home.

"Readers will be moved as they become invested in Regina's predicament. Is she still Indian, American, or both? And what does that mean for her and her family?" School Library Journal.

McMann, Lisa

Cryer's cross. by Lisa McMann. Simon Pulse, 2011. 240 p.

Grades: 7 8 9 10   **Fic**

1. Obsessive-compulsive disorder 2. Missing teenagers 3. Ambition in teenage girls 4. Supernatural 5. Farm life 6. Montana 7. Horror

ISBN 9781416994817

Seventeen-year-old Kendall, who suffers from obsessive-compulsive disorder, lives with her parents on a potato farm in a tiny community in Montana, where two teenagers go missing within months of each other, with no explanation.

"Kendall is a unique character, and the details of her OCD compulsions are well drawn. Haunting passages from another world, which provide just enough detail to intrigue and disturb readers, are intertwined with Kendall's story. Part mystery, part ghost story, and part romance, this book has enough to satisfy a variety of readers." Booklist.

Wake. Lisa McMann. Simon Pulse, 2008. 210 p.: Wake trilogy (Lisa McMann)

Grades: 7 8 9 10   **Fic**

1. Children of alcoholic mothers 2. Dreams 3. Teenagers and seniors 4. Lucid dreams 5. High schools 6. Supernatural mysteries

ISBN 9781416953579

Ever since she was eight years old, high school student Janie Hannagan has been uncontrollably drawn into other people's dreams, but it is not until she befriends an elderly nursing home patient and becomes involved with an enigmatic fellow-student that she discovers her true power.

"A fast pace, a great mix of teen angst and supernatural experiences, and an eerie, attention-grabbing cover will make this a hit." Booklist.

McMullan, Margaret

How I found the Strong. by Margaret McMullan. Houghton Mifflin, 2004. 136 p.

Grades: 5 6 7 8   **Fic**

1. American Civil War era (1861-1865) 2. Eleven-year-old boys 3. Children and war 4. Enslaved people 5. Battles 6. Racism 7. Mississippi 8. United States 9. Historical fiction 10. Coming-of-age stories

ISBN 061835008X

LC 2003012294

Frank Russell, known as Shanks, wishes he could have gone with his father and brother to fight for Mississippi and the Confederacy, but his experiences with the war and his changing relationship with the family slave, Buck, change his thinking.

"The crisply written narrative is full of regional speech and detail, creating a vivid portrait." Voice of Youth Advocates.

Sources of light. by Margaret McMullan. Houghton Mifflin Harcourt, 2010. 233 p.

Grades: 6 7 8 9   **Fic**

1. 1960s 2. Racism 3. Segregation 4. Teenage girls 5. Fourteen-year-old girls 6. Race relations 7. Mississippi 8. Coming-of-age stories 9. Historical fiction

ISBN 9780547076591

LC 2009049708

Fourteen-year-old Samantha and her mother move to Jackson, Mississippi, in 1962 after her father is killed in Vietnam, and during the year they spend there Sam encounters both love and hate as she learns about photography from a new friend of her mother's and witnesses the prejudice and violence of the segregationists of the South.

"When 14-year-old Samantha Thomas moves to Jackson, Miss., in 1962, following her father's death in Vietnam, she learns about love and hate all in the same year. Her mother meets Perry Walker, a photographer who teaches Sam about taking photographs and seeing the world in new ways, but what she begins seeing and pondering is the racial situation in Jackson: lunch-counter sit-ins, voter-registration protests and the violent reprisals of many in the white community, including the father of the boy she begins to like. . . . This offers a superb portrait of a place and time and a memorable character trying to make sense of a world both ugly and beautiful." Kirkus.

When I crossed No-Bob. Margaret McMullan. Houghton Mifflin Company, 2007. 224 p.

Grades: 5 6 7 8   **Fic**

1. Ku-Klux Klan -- History 2. Twelve-year-old girls 3. Farm life 4. Abandoned children 5. Integrity 6. Children and war 7. Mississippi 8. Historical fiction

ISBN 9780618717156

LC 2007012753

Ten years after the Civil War's end, twelve-year-old Addy, abandoned by her parents, is taken from the horrid town of No-Bob by schoolteacher Frank Russell and his bride, but when her father returns to claim her she must find another way to leave her O'Donnell past behind.

"The simple prose can be pure poetry. . . . Readers will be drawn by the history close-up and by the elemental moral choice." Booklist.

McMullen, Beth, 1969-

Mrs. Smith's Spy School for Girls. by Beth McMullen. Aladdin, 2017. 256 p.: Mrs. Smith's Spy School for Girls

Grades: 4 5 6 7 8   **Fic**

1. Girl spies 2. Boarding schools 3. Mother-separated girls 4.

Missing persons 5. Spies 6. New York City 7. Spy fiction
ISBN 9781481490207

LC 2016042030

Twelve-year-old Abigail is shocked to discover her elite boarding school is really a cover for a huge spy ring, and must undergo Spy Training 101 in order to save her mother, who happens to be the spy ring's top agent.

"Abigails entertaining narration tempers suspense with levity, and readers will have a blast accompanying her through sticky situations." Booklist.

McNab, Andy, 1959-

Avenger. by Andy McNab and Robert Rigby. G. P. Putnam's Sons, 2007. 263 p.: Watts family adventures

Grades: 7 8 9 10   **Fic**
1. Great Britain. Army. Special Air Service 2. 2000s (Decade) 3. Seventeen-year-old boys 4. Seventeen-year-olds 5. Teenage girls 6. Teenagers 7. Spies 8. England 9. London, England 10. Spy fiction 11. Thrillers and suspense 12. Adventure stories
ISBN 9780399246852

LC 2007008153

Seventeen-year-old Danny, his grandfather, Fergus, who is an ex-SAS explosives expert, and friend Elena set out to stop the evil computer hacker who is sending teenaged suicide bombers to their deaths around the world.

McNeal, Tom

Far far away. by Tom McNeal. Alfred A. Knopf Books for Young Readers, 2013. 371 p.

Grades: 7 8 9 10   **Fic**
1. Grimm, Jacob, 1785-1863. 2. Revenge 3. Ghosts 4. Bakers 5. Supernatural 6. Friendship 7. Fantasy fiction 8. Fairy tale and folklore-inspired fiction
ISBN 9780375849725

LC 2012020603

After his mother left and his father became a recluse, Jeremy Johnson Johnson (whose mother and father both had the same last name) was left to support the family, but he's been aided by the ghost of Jacob Grimm, one half of the infamous Brothers Grimm writing duo, and when provocative local girl Ginger Boultinghouse takes an interest in Jeremy (and his unique abilities), a grim chain of events is put into motion.

McQuerry, Maureen, 1955-

The **Peculiars**: a novel. Maureen Doyle McQuerry. Amulet Books, 2012. 288 p.

Grades: 7 8 9 10 11 12   **Fic**
1. Father-separated teenage girls 2. Librarians 3. Identity (Psychology) 4. Eighteen-year-old women 5. Teenage girls 6. Steampunk
ISBN 9781419701788

LC 2012000844

Eighteen-year-old Lena Mattacascar sets out for Scree, a weird place inhabited by Peculiars, seeking the father who left when she was young, but on the way she meets young librarian Jimson Quiggley and handsome marshall Thomas Saltre, who complicate her plans.

Medina, Meg

★ **Merci** Suarez can't dance. Meg Medina. Candlewick Press, 2021. 416 p.: Merci Suarez

Grades: 4 5 6 7 8   **Fic**
1. Preteen girls 2. School dances 3. Cuban American girls 4. Crushes in girls 5. Grandfather and granddaughter 6. Florida 7.

Realistic fiction 8. Coming-of-age stories
ISBN 9780763690502

A follow-up to the Newbery Medal-winning Merci Suarez Changes Gears finds Merci embarking on a seventh grade year shaped by high teacher expectations, a crush on a school-store co-worker and a bossy classmate's plan for the annual Heart Ball.

"The plot moves along at a consistent and page-turning pace, and as usual Medina's characters are excellently written and developed. Medina also touches on racism and how shared cultural heritage can bring people together unexpectedly." School Library Journal

Mejia, Tehlor Kay

Paola Santiago and the river of tears. Tehlor Kay Mejia. Disney-Hyperion, 2020 368 p.: Paola Santiago

Grades: 3 4 5 6 7   **Fic**
1. Mexican American girls 2. Imaginary places 3. Mythical creatures 4. Rescues 5. Monsters 6. Fairy tale and folklore-inspired fiction 7. Fantasy fiction
ISBN 9781368049177

"With this adventure, Mejia draws upon her Latinx heritage to conjure creatures from folklore, such as chupacabras, La Llorona, and disembodied hands, arming Paola and her allies with fantastical weapons and layering in realistic plot points: socioeconomic and immigration concerns, the tension between science and superstition." Publishers Weekly

Melleby, Nicole

How to become a planet. Nicole Melleby. Algonquin Young Readers, 2021. 288 p.

Grades: 4 5 6 7   **Fic**
1. Depression 2. Anxiety disorders 3. Preteen girls 4. Friendship 5. Children with mental illnesses 6. New Jersey 7. Realistic fiction
ISBN 9781643750361

LC 2020039373

After an entire summer trying to figure out how to go back to being the person she was before her depression and anxiety diagnosis, twelve-year-old Pluto finds out—with the help of the Hayden Planetarium hotline, a new tutor, and a new friend—that there is no old or new Pluto, there's just Pluto, growing up. Provided by publisher.

"Sprinkled with astronomy-related metaphors related to a planet's properties, this acutely observed, authentically told tale by Melleby thoughtfully portrays Pluto's relationship with her worried single mother, the girl's urgent desire to 'be fixed,' and her intense . . .. depressive episodes." Publishers Weekly

In the role of Brie Hutchens . . .. Nicole Melleby. Algonquin Young Readers, 2020. 272 p.

Grades: 5 6 7 8   **Fic**
1. Mothers and daughters 2. Coming out (Sexual or gender identity) 3. Catholic schools 4. Lesbians 5. Secrets 6. Coming-of-age stories 7. LGBTQIA fiction 8. Realistic fiction
ISBN 9781616209070

LC 2019045980

When strong-willed, drama-loving eighth grader Brie Hutchens tells a lie because she isn't quite ready to come out to her mother, she must navigate the consequences in her relationships with her family, friends, and faith. Provided by publisher.

"This funny, tender, and heart-wrenching story will have readers calling for an encore." Kirkus

Meloy, Colin

Under Wildwood. by Colin Meloy; illustrated by Carson Ellis. Balzer + Bray, 2012. 560 p.: Wildwood chronicles

Grades: 5 6 7 8   **Fic**
1. Underground areas 2. Child labor exploitation 3. Talking animals 4. Orphans 5. Animals 6. Portland, Oregon 7. Oregon 8. Fantasy fiction
ISBN 9780062024718

LC 2012019040

Prue and Curtis are thrown together again to save themselves and the lives of their friends, and to bring unity to the divided country of Wildwood.

★ **Wildwood.** Colin Meloy; illustrations by Carson Ellis. Balzer + Bray, 2011. 560 p.: Wildwood chronicles
Grades: 5 6 7 8   **Fic**
1. Missing boys 2. Forests 3. Talking animals 4. Kidnapping 5. Adventure 6. Portland, Oregon 7. Oregon 8. Fantasy fiction
ISBN 9780062024688

When her baby brother is kidnapped by crows, seventh-grader Prue McKeel ventures into the forbidden Impassable Wilderness—a dangerous and magical forest in the middle of Portland, Oregon—and soon finds herself involved in a war among the various inhabitants.

"Illustrations by Ellis . . . bring forest and inhabitants to gently whimsical life. A satisfying blend of fantasy, adventure story, eco-fable and political satire with broad appeal." Kirkus.

Wildwood imperium. Colin Meloy; illustrations by Carson Ellis. Balzer + Bray, an imprint of HarperCollinsPublishers, 2014 580 p.: Wildwood chronicles
Grades: 5 6 7 8   **Fic**
1. Talking animals 2. Orphans 3. Hostages 4. Animals 5. Rescues 6. Portland, Oregon 7. Oregon 8. Animal fantasy 9. Fantasy fiction
ISBN 9780062024749

In the aftermath of a young's girl's midnight seance that awakens a long-slumbering, malevolent spirit, a band of runaway orphans teams up with an underground collective of saboteurs to rescue friends imprisoned in an industrial wasteland.

"Dramatic shifts in tone and mood—by turns politically astute and subversively witty, elegiac, droll and philosophical—are par for the course, while narrative style ranges from intimate to intergalactically distant." Kirkus.

Meloy, Maile

The **apothecary.** Maile Meloy; illustrated by Ian Schoenherr. G. P. Putnam's Sons, 2011. 353 p.: Apothecary series
Grades: 6 7 8 9   **Fic**
1. 1950s 2. Pharmacists 3. Rare books 4. Moving, Household 5. Nuclear warfare 6. Spies 7. London, England 8. Great Britain 9. Historical fantasy
ISBN 9780399256271

LC 2010045003

Follows a fourteen-year-old American girl whose life unexpectedly transforms when she moves to London in 1952 and gets swept up in a race to save the world from nuclear war.

"With evocative, confident prose and equally atmospheric spot art from Schoenherr, adult author Meloy's first book for young readers is an auspicious one." Publishers Weekly.

Menon, Sandhya

10 things I hate about Pinky. Sandhya Menon. Simon Pulse, 2020 368 p.
Grades: 7 8 9 10 11   **Fic**
1. East Indian Americans 2. Summer 3. Coastal towns 4. Dating (Social customs) 5. Teenage boy/girl relations 6. Cape Cod, Massachusetts 7. Romantic comedies 8. Multicultural romances
ISBN 9781534416819

A latest entry in the series that includes There's Something About Sweetie finds Ashish's friends, Pinky and Samir, pretending to date each other to achieve respective goals during a Cape Cod summer, with disastrously uproarious results. Atlas Publishing.

From Twinkle, with love. Sandhya Menon. Simon Pulse, 2018. 336 p.
Grades: 7 8 9 10 11 12   **Fic**
1. Teenage filmmakers 2. Twin brothers 3. Filmmaking 4. East Indian Americans 5. Teenage girls 6. Romantic comedies 7. Epistolary novels
ISBN 9781481495400

LC 2017048138

Told through letters, aspiring filmmaker and wallflower Twinkle Mehra learns a lesson about love while directing a movie for the Midsummer Night arts festival, in which her longtime crush and his twin brother are also participating.

"This is an often laugh-out-loud funny journey through the tribulations of high school that's tempered by Twinkle's very real feelings of isolation . . . A charming addition to the rom-com canon." Booklist.

There's something about Sweetie. by Sandhya Menon. Simon Pulse, 2019. 384 p.
Grades: 7 8 9 10   **Fic**
1. Dating (Social customs) 2. East Indian Americans 3. Teenage boy/girl relations 4. Self-discovery in teenagers 5. Families 6. Romantic comedies 7. Contemporary romances 8. Multicultural romances
ISBN 9781534416789

LC 2019004082

Told in two voices, disappointed-in-love Ashish Patel and self-proclaimed fat athlete Sweetie Nair begin to find their true selves while dating under contract.

"This companion book to her successful debut, When Dimple Met Rishi (2017), hits all the right notes and delivers a joyful relationship that discards society's dictates about appearance in favor of loving the whole person. Give this to readers who love a good rom-com with a message." Booklist.

When Dimple met Rishi. Sandhya Menon. Simon Pulse, 2017. 384 p.
Grades: 7 8 9 10   **Fic**
1. Arranged marriage 2. East Indian Americans 3. First loves 4. East Indian American teenagers 5. Teenage romance 6. California 7. Contemporary romances 8. Romantic comedies 9. Multicultural romances
ISBN 9781481478687

LC 2016023129

When Dimple Shah and Rishi Patel meet at a Stanford University summer program, Dimple is avoiding her parents' obsession with "marriage prospects" but Rishi hopes to woo her into accepting arranged marriage with him.

"The strength of the story comes from its blending of Indian culture and values into a modern-day romance that scores of readers can enjoy. This novel touches on issues of identity while remaining light and fun." School Library Journal.

Merrill, Jean Fairbanks

★ The **pushcart** war. by Jean Merrill. With illustrations by Ronni Solbert. W. R. Scott, 1964. 222 p.

Grades: 5 6 7 8   **Fic**

1. Peddlers 2. City life 3. Guerrilla warfare 4. Urban problems 5. Truck drivers 6. New York City

ISBN 9780812453218

LC 84043131

The outbreak of a war between truck drivers and pushcart peddlers brings the mounting problems of traffic to the attention of both the city of New York and the world.

"A book that is both humorous and downright funny. . . . Such a lively book will need little introducing." Horn Book.

Messner, Kate

The **brilliant** fall of Gianna Z. by Kate Messner. Walker, 2009. 198 p.

Grades: 5 6 7 8   **Fic**

1. Girl runners 2. School projects 3. Procrastination 4. Grandmothers 5. Friendship 6. Vermont 7. Realistic fiction

ISBN 9780802798428

LC 2008046979

Gianna has less than one week to complete her leaf project if she wants to compete in the upcoming cross-country sectionals, but issues like procrastination, disorganization—and her grandmother's declining health—seem destined to keep her from finishing.

"Youngsters will find much to relate to in this likable protagonist's struggle to balance family and academic commitments. . . . Plot twists keep readers engaged, and Messner's warm and humorous tone will capture even reluctant readers." School Library Journal.

Chirp. Kate Messner. Bloomsbury, 2020. 240 p.

Grades: 5 6 7 8   **Fic**

1. Gymnastics 2. Preteen girls 3. Family businesses 4. Crickets (Insects) 5. Friendship 6. Vermont 7. Coming-of-age stories 8. Realistic fiction 9. Mysteries

ISBN 9781547602810

LC 2019019160

Moving to Vermont the summer after seventh grade, a young gymnast hides a secret as she makes new friends and investigates her grandmother's claim that someone is trying to destroy her cricket farm.

"As Mia's trauma is slowly revealed, Messner incorporates others' #MeToo experiences, providing her with a strong support system of women. This book directly addresses a relevant topic rarely discussed with middle-schoolers—and it's not the lively debate over whether people should eat crickets." Booklist

The **seventh** wish. by Kate Messner. Bloomsbury, [2016] 240 p.

Grades: 4 5 6 7   **Fic**

1. Wishing and wishes 2. Crushes in girls 3. Drug abuse 4. Magic 5. Sisters 6. New York (State) 7. Low fantasy 8. Fairy tale and folklore-inspired fiction

ISBN 9781619633766

LC 2015036430

Unsure of how to get her family's attention, Charlie comes across the surprise of her life one day while ice-fishing...in the form of a floppy, scaly fish offering to grant her a wish in exchange for its freedom. Provided by publisher.

"Hopeful, empathetic, and unusually enlightening." Kirkus.

Meyer, L. A. (Louis A.), 1942-2014

Bloody Jack: being an account of the curious adventures of Mary "Jacky" Faber, Ship's Boy. L.A. Meyer. Harcourt, 2002. 278 p.: Bloody Jack adventures

Grades: 7 8 9 10   **Fic**

1. Great Britain Royal Navy -- History -- 18th century 2. 1790s 3. 18th century 4. Teenage girl orphans 5. Impostors 6. Teenage girl impostors 7. Thirteen-year-old girls 8. Teenage girls 9. Historical fiction 10. Adventure stories 11. Sea stories

ISBN 0152167315

LC 2002000759

Reduced to begging and thievery in the streets of London, a thirteen-year-old orphan disguises herself as a boy and connives her way onto a British warship set for high sea adventure in search of pirates.

"From shooting a pirate in battle to foiling a shipmate's sexual attack to surviving when stranded alone on a Caribbean island, the action in Jacky's tale will entertain readers with a taste for adventure." Booklist.

Meyer, Marissa

Cinder. Marissa Meyer. Feiwel & Friends, 2012. 400 p.: Lunar chronicles

Grades: 7 8 9 10 11 12   **Fic**

1. Cyborgs 2. Plague 3. Mind control 4. Aliens 5. Princes 6. Science fiction 7. Fairy tale and folklore-inspired fiction

ISBN 9780312641894

As plague ravages the overcrowded Earth, observed by a ruthless lunar people, Cinder, a gifted mechanic and cyborg, becomes involved with handsome Prince Kai and must uncover secrets about her past in order to protect the world in this futuristic take on the Cinderella story.

Cress. Marissa Meyer. Feiwel & Friends, 2014. 552 p.: Lunar chronicles

Grades: 7 8 9 10 11 12   **Fic**

1. Cyborgs 2. Hackers 3. Imprisonment 4. Aliens 5. Mechanics 6. Science fiction 7. Fairy tale and folklore-inspired fiction

ISBN 9780312642976

"Cress is locked away in a floating satellite. She dreams of visiting Earth, the planet she has been forced to spy on, and meeting Carswell Thorne, the handsome ship captain who teamed up with Cinder in Scarlet (Feiwel & Friends, 2013)....Cress fills in more historical details about Earth and Luna's relationship—most of which will be of no surprise to the reader—and Cinder's rebirth as a cyborg. Fans of Scarlet and Wolf may be disappointed that their relationship takes a backseat to the newly introduced pairing. As always, Meyer excels at interweaving new characters that extend beyond the archetypes of their fairy tale into the main story. Readers will eagerly await the final installment of this highly appealing and well-constructed series." School Library Journal.

Heartless. Marissa Meyer. Feiwel & Friends, 2016. 464 p.

Grades: 7 8 9 10   **Fic**

1. Rulers 2. Fools and jesters 3. Characters and characteristics in literature 4. Teenage romance 5. Women rulers 6. Fantasy fiction 7. Classics-inspired fiction

ISBN 9781250044655

LC 2015021393

In this prequel to Alice in Wonderland, Cath would rather open a bakery and marry for love than accept a proposal from the King of Hearts, especially after meeting the handsome and mysterious court jester.

"If you only read one fractured fairy tale this year, make it Heartless. A must-have title." School Library Journal.

Scarlet. Marissa Meyer. Feiwel and Friends, 2013. 464 p.:
Lunar chronicles
Grades: 7 8 9 10 11 12   **Fic**
1. Cyborgs 2. Missing persons 3. Imprisonment 4. Aliens 5.
Mechanics 6. Science fiction 7. Fairy tale and folklore-inspired
fiction
ISBN 9780312642969

LC 2012034060
Scarlet Benoit and Wolf, a street fighter who may have information
about her missing grandmother, join forces with Cinder as they try to
stay one step ahead of the vicious Lunar Queen Levana in this story
inspired by Little Red Riding Hood.

Meyer, Stephenie, 1973-
Breaking dawn. Stephenie Meyer. Little, Brown and Co.,
2008. 768 p.: Twilight saga
Grades: 8 9 10 11 12   **Fic**
1. Eighteen-year-old women 2. Teenage vampires 3. Pregnant
teenagers 4. Marriage 5. Teenage girls 6. Washington (State) 7.
Seattle, Washington 8. Paranormal romances
ISBN 9780316067928

LC 2008928027
"For those who find it hard to say farewell to Bella and company,
take heart: it may not be goodbye." Booklist.

Eclipse. Stephenie Meyer. Little, Brown, 2007. 640 p.: Twi-
light saga
Grades: 8 9 10 11 12   **Fic**
1. Teenage vampires 2. Teenage werewolves 3. Love triangles 4.
Decision-making 5. Revenge 6. Washington (State) 7. Seattle,
Washington 8. Paranormal romances
ISBN 9780316160209

LC 2007012325
Bella must choose between her friendship with Jacob and her relationship with Edward, both vampires, but when Seattle is ravaged
by a mysterious string of killings, the three of them need to decide
whether their personal lives are more important than the well-being of
an entire city.
"Meyer knows what her fans want: thrills, chills, and a lot of romance, and she delivers on all counts." School Library Journal.

New moon. by Stephenie Meyer. Little, Brown and Co.,
2006. 576 p.: Twilight saga
Grades: 8 9 10 11 12   **Fic**
1. Teenage werewolves 2. Breaking up (Interpersonal relations)
3. Teenage girls with depression 4. Eighteen-year-old women 5.
Friendship 6. Washington (State) 7. Paranormal romances
ISBN 0316160199

LC 2006012309
When the Cullens, including her beloved Edward, leave Forks rather
than risk revealing that they are vampires, it is almost too much for eighteen-year-old Bella to bear, but she finds solace in her friend Jacob until
he is drawn into a "cult" and changes in terrible ways.
"Vampire aficionados will voraciously consume this mighty tome in
one sitting, then flip back and read it once more. It maintains a brisk pace
and near-genius balance of breathtaking romance and action." Voice of
Youth Advocates.

Twilight. Stephenie Meyer. Little, Brown and Co., 2005. 498
p.: Twilight saga
Grades: 8 9 10 11 12   **Fic**
1. Teenage vampires 2. First loves 3. Crushes in teenagers 4.

Vampires 5. Teenage boy/girl relations 6. Washington (State) 7.
Paranormal romances
ISBN 0316160172

LC 2004024730
When seventeen-year-old Bella leaves Phoenix to live with her
father in Forks, Washington, she meets an exquisitely handsome boy
at school for whom she feels an overwhelming attraction and who she
comes to realize is not wholly human.
"Realistic, subtle, succinct, and easy to follow, . . . [this book] will
have readers dying to sink their teeth into it." School Library Journal.

Michael, Jan, 1947-
City boy. Jan Michael. Clarion Books, 2009. 192 p.
Grades: 5 6 7 8   **Fic**
1. Orphans 2. Rural life 3. Blacks 4. Children of people with
AIDS 5. Families 6. Malawi 7. Coming-of-age stories
ISBN 9780547223100

LC 2008037418
In the southern African country of Malawi, after the AIDS-related
deaths of both of his parents, a boy leaves his affluent life in the city
to live in a rural village, sharing a one-roomed hut with his aunt, his
cousins, and other orphans.
"This is a powerful portrait of poverty and hardship, evenly balanced with shades of hope. Michael's simple prose subtly layers detail,
building full-bodied descriptions of landscapes and characters, leaving
no room for shortcuts. . . . A stoic tale of surviving life's uncertainties."
Kirkus.

Mieville, China
Railsea. China Mieville. Del Rey/Ballantine Books, 2012.
424 p.
Grades: 7 8 9 10   **Fic**
1. Trains 2. Monsters 3. Orphans 4. Prairies 5. Treasure hunting
6. Fantasy fiction
ISBN 9780345524522

LC 2012009516
On board the moletrain Medes, Sham Yes ap Soorap watches in awe
as he witnesses his first moldywarpe hunt: the giant mole bursting from
the earth, the harpoonists targeting their prey, the battle resulting in one's
death & the other's glory. But no matter how spectacular it is, Sham
can't shake the sense that there is more to life than traveling the endless
rails of the railsea—even if his captain can think only of the hunt for the
ivory-colored mole she's been chasing since it took her arm all those
years ago. When they come across a wrecked train, at first it's a welcome
distraction. But what Sham finds in the derelict—a kind of treasure map
indicating a mythical place untouched by iron rails—leads to considerably more than he'd bargained for. Soon he's hunted on all sides, by
pirates, trainsfolk, monsters, and salvage-scrabblers. And it might not
be just Sham's life that's about to change. It could be the whole of the
railsea. Here is a novel for readers of all ages, a gripping and brilliantly
imagined take on Herman Melville's Moby-Dick that confirms China
Mieville's status as "the most original & talented voice to appear in several years" (Science Fiction Chronicle). Provided by publisher.

Mikaelsen, Ben, 1952-
Ghost of Spirit Bear. Ben Mikaelsen. HarperCollins, c2008.
154 p.
Grades: 6 7 8 9   **Fic**
1. Self-fulfillment in teenage boys 2. Bullying and bullies 3.
Change (Psychology) 4. Self-fulfillment 5. High schools 6.
Minneapolis, Minnesota 7. Realistic fiction
ISBN 9780060090074

LC 2007036732

After a year in exile on an Alaskan island as punishment for severely beating a fellow student, Cole Matthews returns to school in Minneapolis having made peace with himself and his victim—but he finds that surviving the violence and hatred of high school is even harder than surviving in the wilderness.

Touching Spirit Bear. by Ben Mikaelsen. HarperCollins, 2001. 241 p.

Grades: 6 7 8 9 **Fic**
> 1. Juvenile delinquents (Boys) 2. Anger in teenage boys 3. Wilderness survival 4. Self-fulfillment in teenage boys 5. Self-fulfillment 6. Alaska 7. Survival stories 8. Adventure stories 9. Coming-of-age stories
> ISBN 9780380977444

LC 00040702
After his anger erupts into violence, Cole, in order to avoid going to prison, agrees to participate in a sentencing alternative based on the native American Circle Justice, and he is sent to a remote Alaskan Island where an encounter with a huge Spirit Bear changes his life.

"Mikaelsen's portrayal of this angry, manipulative, damaged teen is dead on. . . . Gross details about Cole eating raw worms, a mouse, and worse will appeal to fans of the outdoor adventure/survival genre." School Library Journal.

Milford, Kate
Bluecrowne. Kate Milford; with illustrations by Nicole Wong. Clarion Books, 2018. 272 p.: Greenglass House

Grades: 5 6 7 8 **Fic**
> 1. 1810s 2. Brothers and sisters 3. Time travel 4. Seafaring life 5. Secrets 6. Fireworks 7. Fantasy mysteries 8. Historical fantasy
> ISBN 9781328466884

LC 2018006963
In 1810, Lucy Bluecrowne, twelve, is bored living ashore with her stepmother and half brother until two nefarious strangers identify her little brother as the pyrotechnical prodigy they need for their evil plan.

The **Boneshaker**. Kate Milford; with illustrations by Andrea Offermann. Clarion Books, 2010. 372 p.

Grades: 5 6 7 8 9 **Fic**
> 1. 1910s 2. Courage in teenage girls 3. Machinery 4. Courage 5. Medicine shows 6. Supernatural 7. Missouri 8. Historical fantasy 9. Steampunk
> ISBN 9780547241876

LC 2009045350
When Jake Limberleg brings his traveling medicine show to a small Missouri town in 1913, thirteen-year-old Natalie senses that something is wrong and, after investigating, learns that her love of automata and other machines makes her the only one who can set things right.

"Natalie is a well-drawn protagonist with sturdy supporting characters around her. The tension built into the solidly constructed plot is complemented by themes that explore the literal and metaphorical role of crossroads and that thin line between good and evil." Kirkus.

Ghosts of Greenglass House. Kate Milford. Clarion Books, Houghton Mifflin Harcourt, 2017. 384 p.: Greenglass House

Grades: 5 6 7 8 **Fic**
> 1. Adopted boys 2. Inns 3. Maps 4. Ghosts 5. Smugglers 6. Fantasy mysteries
> ISBN 9780544991460

"A brainy, satisfying assemblage of puzzles with an immensely likable protagonist." Kirkus.

Greenglass House. by Kate Milford; with illustrations by Jaime Zollars. Clarion Books, Houghton Mifflin Harcourt, 2014. 176 p.: Greenglass House

Grades: 5 6 7 8 **Fic**
> 1. Adopted boys 2. Inns 3. Smugglers 4. Role playing games 5. Magic 6. Fantasy mysteries
> ISBN 9780544052703

LC 2013036212
At Greenglass House, a smuggler's inn, twelve-year-old Milo, the innkeepers' adopted son, plans to spend his winter holidays relaxing but soon guests are arriving with strange stories about the house sending Milo and Meddy, the cook's daughter, on an adventure.

The **Left-Handed** Fate. Kate Milford; illustrated by Eliza Wheeler. Henry Holt and Company, 2016. 352 p.

Grades: 5 6 7 8 **Fic**
> 1. 1810s 2. Ships 3. Quests 4. Ocean travel 5. Magic 6. United States 7. Historical fantasy
> ISBN 9780805098006

LC 2015033437
A quest story to find the three pieces of a magical engine which can either win the War of 1812...or stop it altogether. Provided by publisher.

"Rich and strange of place and premise; suspenseful and thought-provoking." Kirkus.

The **raconteur's** commonplace book. Kate Milford, Barry Goldblatt Literary Agency (COR). Clarion Books, 2021 320 p.: Greenglass House

Grades: 5 6 7 8 **Fic**
> 1. Hospitality 2. Inns 3. Magic 4. Secrets 5. Storytelling 6. Historical fantasy 7. Fairy tale and folklore-inspired fiction 8. Fantasy mysteries
> ISBN 9781328466907

A standalone mystery set in the world of the best-selling Greenglass House series follows the experiences of 12 guests at a flooded-in tavern who tell stories reflecting diverse examples of folklore and each narrator's respective secrets.

"At times wryly humorous and at others marvelously unnerving and superbly menacing, this novel delights." Kirkus

The **thief** knot. Kate Milford. Clarion Books, 2020 464 p.: Greenglass House

Grades: 5 6 7 8 **Fic**
> 1. Preteen girls 2. Kidnapping investigation 3. Family secrets 4. Kidnapping 5. Families 6. Fantasy mysteries
> ISBN 9781328466891

When Marzana's parents are recruited to solve an odd crime, she assembles her own team, including a ghost, to investigate the kidnapping.

"Milford's Nagspeake stories are always a treat, but this one, with its tight, clever plotting; heartening emotional growth; and dynamic setting, shines extra brightly." Booklist.

Miller, Jessica
Elizabeth and Zenobia. Jessica Miller; illustrated by Yelena Bryksenkova. Amulet Books, 2017, c2016. 208 p.

Grades: 4 5 6 7 8 **Fic**
> 1. Shyness in girls 2. Friendship 3. Haunted houses 4. Manors 5. Missing persons 6. Mysteries
> ISBN 9781419727245

"Miller's painstaking crafting of language and attention to atmospheric detail create a clever story where nothing is as it seems. Drawings reminiscent of Gorey and references to gloomy classic poetry add beguiling texture. Eerie and dazzling—a perfect book for a dark and stormy afternoon or a favorite graveyard reading spot." Kirkus.

Miller, Kirsten, 1973-

The **eternal** ones. Kirsten Miller. Razorbill, 2010. 411 p.: Eternal ones novels (Kirsten Miller)

Grades: 6 7 8 9 10   **Fic**

1. Reincarnation 2. Murder suspects 3. Teenage romance 4. Dressmakers 5. Identity (Psychology) 6. New York City 7. Tennessee 8. Paranormal romances

ISBN 9781595143082

LC 2010022775

"Miller's writing elevates the supernatural romance well beyond typical fare, and Haven's mix of naïveté and determination makes her a solid, credible heroine." Publishers Weekly.

Inside the shadow city. by Kirsten Miller. Bloomsbury Children's Books: 2006. 250 p.: Kiki Strike novels

Grades: 5 6 7 8   **Fic**

1. Underground cities 2. Secret societies 3. Girl spies 4. Twelve-year-old girls 5. Secret places 6. Manhattan, New York City 7. New York City 8. Mysteries 9. Adventure stories

ISBN 9781582349602

LC 2005030945

Life becomes more interesting for Ananka Fishbein when, at the age of twelve, she discovers an underground room in the park across from her New York City apartment and meets a mysterious girl called Kiki Strike who claims that she, too, wants to explore the subterranean world.

"If a 12-year-old can be a hardboiled detective, Ananka Fishbein is one. Her narration is fresh and funny, and the author's unadorned, economical, yet descriptive style carries her character through with verve." School Library Journal.

Miller, Sarah Elizabeth, 1979-

The **lost** crown. Sarah Miller. Atheneum Books for Young Readers, 2011. 448 p.

Grades: 8 9 10 11 12   **Fic**

1. Nicholas II, Emperor of Russia, 1868-1918 2. Anastasia Nikolaevna, Grand Duchess, daughter of Nicholas II, Emperor of Russia, 1901-1918 3. Romanov Dynasty (1613-1917) 4. 1910s 5. First World War era (1914-1918) 6. Sisters 7. Revolutions 8. World War I 9. Rulers 10. Teenage girls 11. Russia 12. Historical fiction

ISBN 9781416983408

LC 2010037001

In alternating chapters, Grand Duchesses Olga, Tatiana, Maria, and Anastasia tell how their privileged lives as the daughters of the tsar in early twentieth-century Russia are transformed by world war and revolution.

"Each Grand Duchess comes across as a unique personality. . . . Like the best historical novels, this allows modern-day teens to see themselves in very different people." Booklist.

Miss Spitfire: reaching Helen Keller. Sarah Miller. Atheneum, 2007. 240 p.

Grades: 7 8 9 10 11   **Fic**

1. Sullivan, Annie, 1866-1936. 2. Keller, Helen, 1880-1968. 3. Teacher-student relationships 4. People who are blind and deaf 5. People who are blind 6. People who are deaf 7. People with disabilities 8. Alabama 9. Historical fiction

ISBN 1416925422

Told from Anne Sullivan's point of view, the process of teaching Helen Keller, a young girl who was deaf, blind, and out of control, to communicate with the world was a challenge like no other—one she was willing to face with fierce conviction and determination when all others had given up hope.

"This excellent novel is compelling reading even for those familiar with the Keller/Sullivan experience." School Library Journal.

Mills, Emma, 1989-

Famous in a small town. Emma Mills. Henry Holt & Co, 2019 320 p.

Grades: 7 8 9 10 11   **Fic**

1. New neighbors 2. Small town life 3. Celebrities 4. Marching bands 5. Crushes in teenage girls 6. Illinois 7. Realistic fiction 8. Teen chick lit

ISBN 9781250179630

Loving her small community, school and best friends, Sophie develops an unexpected crush on a quiet, alluring new next-door neighbor, August, who seems to prefer keeping others at arm's length. Atlas Publishing.

"A comfortable, readable tale of deep friendship, small towns, and big love in all its guises." Booklist.

Mills, Geraldine

Gold. Geraldine Mills. Trafalgar Square Books 2017 241 p.

Grades: 4 5 6 7 8   **Fic**

1. Twin brothers 2. Survival (after environmental catastrophe) 3. Gold 4. Post-apocalypse 5. Risk-taking (Psychology) 6. Apocalyptic fiction 7. Adventure stories 8. Dystopian fiction

ISBN 9781910411551

Dystopian fiction meets classic adventure in this tale of twin brothers travelling to forbidden islands in search of gold.

"Strong world-building and thought-provoking themes make this ideal for tweens looking for dystopian tales." School Library Journal.

Mills, Wendy, 1973-

All we have left. Wendy Mills. Bloomsbury USA, 2016. 272 p.

Grades: 8 9 10 11 12   **Fic**

1. September 11 Terrorist Attacks, 2001 2. Muslim teenagers 3. Prejudice 4. Terrorism 5. Sixteen-year-old girls 6. New York City 7. Realistic fiction

ISBN 9781619633438

"This outstanding, touching look at a national tragedy promotes healing and understanding and belongs in every Library." School Library Journal.

Mlynowski, Sarah

Don't even think about it. Sarah Mlynowski. Delacorte Press, [2014] 336 p.

Grades: 7 8 9 10   **Fic**

1. Extrasensory perception 2. Teenage psychics 3. Teenage boy/girl relations 4. High school sophomores 5. High schools 6. New York City 7. Tribeca (New York City) 8. Paranormal fiction

ISBN 9780385737388

LC 2012050777

A group of Tribeca high school kids go in for flu shots . . . and they discover that they now have telepathic abilities.

"When a group of Manhattan 10th graders inadvertently receives telepathic abilities from tainted flu shots, things rapidly get chaotic (and noisy). Finding out too much information dramatically upends family relationships, friendships, and romances. . . . Filled with heartbreak, hilarity, and some brutal truths, Mlynowski's novel will leave readers thinking about the gaps between our private and public selves and the lies we tell others and ourselves." Publishers Weekly.

Ten things we did (and probably shouldn't have). Sarah Mlynowski. HarperTeen, 2011. 368 p.

Grades: 7 8 9 10   **Fic**

   1. Parent-separated teenage girls 2. Independence (Personal quality) 3. Self-reliance in teenage girls 4. Self-reliance 5. Sexuality 6. Connecticut 7. Teen chick lit 8. Realistic fiction

   ISBN 9780061701245

                 LC 2010045556

Sixteen-year-old April, a high school junior, and her friend Vi, a senior, get a crash course in reality as the list of things they should not do becomes a list of things they did while living parent-free in Westport, Connecticut, for the semester.

"With wit, energy, and an uncanny understanding of teenage logic, Mlynowski . . . weighs the pros and cons of independence in this modern cautionary tale. . . . Mlynowski avoids sermonizing, offering 10 madcap and remarkably tense escapades that will have readers laughing, cringing, and guessing how April will get out of the next pickle." Publishers Weekly.

Mobley, Jeannie

Katerina's wish. Jeannie Mobley. Margaret K. McElderry Books, 2012. 240 p.

Grades: 4 5 6 7   **Fic**

   1. 1900s (Decade) 2. Immigrants 3. Wishing and wishes 4. Coal mining towns 5. Families 6. Fishes 7. Colorado 8. Historical fiction

   ISBN 9781442433434

                 LC 2011044392

Thirteen-year-old Trina's family left Bohemia for a Colorado coal town to earn money to buy a farm, but by 1901 she doubts that either hard work or hoping will be enough, even after a strange fish seems to grant her sisters' wishes.

Moderow, Hannah

Lily's mountain. written by Hannah Moderow. 192 p.

Grades: 4 5 6 7   **Fic**

   1. Mountaineering 2. Father-separated girls 3. Rescues 4. Fathers and daughters 5. Sisters 6. Alaska 7. Mount Denali (Alaska) 8. Adventure stories

   ISBN 9780544978003

                 LC 2016037231

Unable to believe their father died while climbing Mount Denali, twelve-year-old Lily and her older sister, Sophie, climb the mountain in order to rescue him.

"There is strong character development, and readers will be inspired by Lily's and Sophie's ambition, perseverance, and self-determination." School Library Journal.

Molope, Kagiso Lesego, 1976-

This book betrays my brother. Kagiso Lesego Molope. Mawenzi House Pub 2018 187 p.

Grades: 8 9 10 11 12   **Fic**

   1. Brothers and sisters 2. Teenage girls 3. Rape 4. Family relationships 5. Personal conduct 6. South Africa 7. Coming-of-age stories 8. Realistic fiction

   ISBN 9781988449296

All her life, Naledi has been in awe of Basi, her charming and outgoing older brother. They've shared their childhood, with its jokes and secrets, the alliances and stories about the community. Having reached thirteen, she is preparing to go to the school dance. Then she sees Basi commit an act that violates everything she believes about him. How will she live her life now?—Excerpted from publisher description

Monir, Alexandra

The **girl** in the picture. Alexandra Monir. Delacorte Press, 2016. 272 p.

Grades: 7 8 9 10   **Fic**

   1. Prep schools 2. Teenage girl musicians 3. Rich teenagers 4. Murder 5. Secrets 6. Supernatural mysteries

   ISBN 9780385743907

                 LC 2015042550

When a popular high school boy is found murdered, everyone is surprised he carried pictures of himself with Nicole Morgan, a shy "music geek" no one knew was close to him.

"Teens will enjoy the cleverly crafted ride of this whodunit." School Library Journal.

Monninger, Joseph

Whippoorwill. by Joseph Monninger. 288 p.

Grades: 7 8 9 10   **Fic**

   1. Teenagers and dogs 2. Neighbors 3. Dogs -- Training 4. Labrador retrievers 5. Animal welfare 6. New Hampshire 7. Realistic fiction

   ISBN 9780544531239

                 LC 2014046833

In rural New Hampshire, sixteen-year-old Clair Taylor and her neighbor, eighteen-year-old Danny Stewart, fall into an unlikely relationship as they work together to save Wally, a loveable but mistreated dog kept chained in a junk-filled yard by Danny's cruel father.

"Monninger revitalizes the boy-and-his-dog trope in this sweet novel." School Library Journal.

Moore, David Barclay

The **stars** beneath our feet. David Barclay Moore. Alfred A. Knopf, 2017 304 p.

Grades: 5 6 7 8   **Fic**

   1. West Indian Americans 2. Children of LGBTQIA parents 3. LEGO toys 4. Gangs 5. People with autism 6. Harlem, New York City 7. New York City 8. Realistic fiction

   ISBN 9781524701246

Unable to celebrate the holidays in the wake of his older brother's death in a gang-related shooting, 12-year-old Lolly Rachpaul struggles to avoid being forced into a gang himself while constructing a fantastically creative LEGO city at the Harlem community center.

"Moore imbues his first novel with a strong voice and includes a diverse cast." Booklist.

Moore, Peter, 1963-

V is for villain. Peter Moore. Hyperion, 2014. 336 p.

Grades: 7 8 9 10   **Fic**

   1. Telepathy 2. Superheroes 3. Secrets 4. Good and evil 5. Villains 6. Superhero stories

   ISBN 9781423157496

                 LC 2013026304

In a smart, action-packed superhero/villain showdown that offers a surprising take on good versus evil, Brad Baron and his friend Layla discover dangerous secrets about the superheroes who are running their society, a finding that pulls them into a web of nefarious criminals, high-stakes battles and startling family secrets.

"Well-crafted characters, moral nuance, and a tale with nice, believable twists make this a great addition to the teen-superhero genre." Kirkus.

Moore, Stuart

Batman: Nightwalker. novel written by Marie Lu; adapted by Stuart Moore; art by Chris Wildgoose; color by Laura Trinder; letters by Troy Peteri. DC Comics, [2019] 208 p.

Grades: 7 8 9 10 11 12   Fic

1. Orphans 2. Billionaires 3. High school students 4. Eighteen-year-old men 5. Psychiatric hospitals 6. Superhero comics 7. Comics and Graphic novels

ISBN 9781401280048

LC 2019021229

A ruthless new gang of criminals known only as Nightwalkers is terrorizing Gotham, and the city's elite are being taken out one by one. On the way home from his 18th birthday party, newly minted billionaire Bruce Wayne makes an impulsive choice that puts him in their crosshairs and lands him in Arkham Asylum, the once-infamous mental hospital. There, he meets Madeleine Wallace, a brilliant killer...and Bruce's only hope. Madeleine is the mystery Bruce must unravel, but is he convincing her to divulge her secrets, or is he feeding her the information she needs to bring Gotham City to its knees? Provided by publisher.

"Wildgoose's illustrations adeptly depict awkward adolescent exchanges as well as tense interrogations and violent standoffs." School Library Journal

Moranville, Sharelle Byars

27 magic words. Sharelle Byars Moranville. Holiday House, [2016] 199 p.

Grades: 5 6 7 8   Fic

1. Ten-year-old girls 2. Grief in girls 3. Moving to a new country 4. Parents -- Death 5. Loss (Psychology) 6. Realistic fiction

ISBN 9780823436576

LC 2015049142

Although Kobi's parents sailed into a storm five years ago, she believes they are alive, and when she is sent from her grandmother's luxurious Paris apartment to live with an uncle in Iowa, Kobi tells lies that soon catch up with her.

"Distinctive, well-drawn characters drive the plot and provide their own magical contributions to Kobi's widening world. Both tragic and uplifting, this winsome tale perfectly depicts some of the many aspects of magic." Kirkus.

Moreci, Michael

The **lost** carnival: a Dick Grayson graphic novel. written by Michael Moreci; illustrated by Sas Milledge with Phil Hester; colored by David Calderon; lettered by Steve Wands. DC Comics, 2020 208 p.

Grades: 7 8 9 10   Fic

1. Trapeze and high-wire performers 2. Circus 3. Identity (Psychology) 4. Teenage boys 5. Circus performers 6. Superhero comics 7. Fantasy comics 8. Comics and Graphic novels

ISBN 9781401291020

LC 2020000770

Before Batman trained him to be Robin, Dick Grayson was star of his family of trapeze artists, but when an enchanting new attraction opens nearby and threatens to lure away their remaining customers, Dick is among those drawn to its magical glow and may be too mesmerized to recognize the dangers ahead.

"A solid introduction to the creepy side of the DC universe." School Library Journal.

Moreno, Nina

Don't date Rosa Santos. Nina Moreno. Hyperion, 2019 336 p.

Grades: 8 9 10 11   Fic

1. Cuban Americans 2. Studying abroad 3. Family curses 4. Dating (Social customs) 5. Family relationships 6. Florida 7. Romantic comedies 8. Multicultural romances 9. Teen chick lit

ISBN 9781368039703

Rosa Santos, a Cuban American, works to save her Florida town, seeks admittance to study abroad in her homeland, and wonders if love can break her family's curse.

"Full of complex family relationships, a diverse community, and plenty of swoonworthy moments, fans of rom-coms won't be able to put this one down." Kirkus.

Moriarty, Jaclyn

A **corner** of white. Jaclyn Moriarty. Arthur A. Levine Books, 2013, r2012. 384 p.: Colors of Madeleine trilogy

Grades: 7 8 9 10 11 12   Fic

1. Parallel universes 2. Princesses 3. Pen pals 4. Color 5. Magic 6. Cambridge, England 7. England 8. Fantasy fiction 9. Gateway fantasy

ISBN 9780545397360

LC 2012016582

Fourteen-year-old Madeleine of Cambridge, England, struggling to cope with poverty and her mother's illness, and fifteen-year-old Elliot of the Kingdom of Cello in a parallel world where colors are villainous and his father is missing, begin exchanging notes through a crack between their worlds and find they can be of great help to each other.

"Australian writer Moriarty's marvelously original fantasy is quirky and clever... [she] captures the proud iconoclasm of many homeschoolers and does not shy away from tenderness and poignancy." Booklist.

The **cracks** in the Kingdom. Jaclyn Moriarty. Arthur A. Levine Books, an imprint of Scholastic Inc., 2014. 480 p.: Colors of Madeleine trilogy

Grades: 7 8 9 10 11 12   Fic

1. Parallel universes 2. Teenagers 3. Searching 4. Teenage boys 5. Rural boys 6. Fantasy fiction 7. Gateway fantasy

ISBN 9780545397384

A follow-up to A Corner of White finds Elliot continuing to search for his father while using his connections to Madeleine to secretly help Princess Ko track down her own missing family, who may be trapped in the World with no memory of their true lives.

"In this lively follow-up to A Corner of White (Scholastic, 2013), Moriarty chronicles the ever-intertwining lives of Cambridge resident Madeline Tully and her secret correspondent Elliot Baranski, a quick-witted farm boy from the Kingdom of Cello...The RYA's work around Cello expands an already complex and intricately drawn world. Readers will be clamoring for the next title after the thrilling yet satisfying conclusion." School Library Journal.

Feeling sorry for Celia: a novel. Jaclyn Moriarty. St. Martin's Press, 2001, c2000. 276 p.: Ashbury/Brookfield books

Grades: 7 8 9 10 11 12   Fic

1. Teenage girls 2. Letter writing 3. Friendship 4. Fathers and daughters 5. High school students 6. Australia 7. Coming-of-age stories 8. Teen chick lit 9. Epistolary novels

ISBN 0312269234

LC 00045969

Life is pretty complicated for Elizabeth Clarry. Her best friend Celia keeps disappearing, her absent father suddenly reappears, and her communication with her mother consists entirely of wacky notes left on the fridge. On top of everything else, because her English teacher wants to rekindle the "Joy of the Envelope," a Complete and Utter Stranger knows more about Elizabeth than anyone else.

"Moriarty poignantly captures the trials of adolescent friendships and the bittersweet evolution of the teenage subconscious." Booklist.

Morpurgo, Michael

The **day** the world stopped turning. Michael Morpurgo. Feiwel & Friends, 2019. 288 p.

Grades: 5 6 7 8   **Fic**
1. Second World War era (1939-1945) 2. Children and war 3. World War II 4. Boys with autism 5. Romani girls 6. Romanies 7. Camargue, France 8. France 9. Historical fiction 10. War stories
ISBN 9781250107077

"Most notable are the portrayal of Lorenzo, whose clear limitations pale next to his strengths, and the inclusion of a compassionate German soldier who helps the families when he can." Booklist.

Half a man. Michael Morpurgo; illustrated by Gemma O'Callaghan. Candlewick Press, 2015, c2014. 47 p.

Grades: 7 8 9 10   **Fic**
1. Grandfather and grandson 2. People with disfigurements 3. World War II veterans 4. World War II -- Naval operations, British 5. Grandparent and child 6. Realistic fiction 7. Illustrated books
ISBN 9780763677473

A coming-of-age tale about the physical and mental scars of war follows the experiences of a young man who after years of being told not to ask his World War II veteran grandfather about his injuries learns how his grandfather survived a torpedo attack on his ship.

"With our returning wounded warriors of today, this is a timely and superb addition to all collections and not to be missed." School Library Journal.

Listen to the moon. Michael Morpurgo. Feiwel & Friends, 2015. 352 p.

Grades: 5 6 7 8 9   **Fic**
1. Lusitania (Steamship) 2. First World War era (1914-1918) 3. 1910s 4. Convalescence 5. Families 6. War 7. Forgiveness 8. Hope
ISBN 9781250042040

A tale inspired by the sinking of the Lusitania during World War I follows the experiences of a young British boy and his father, who take in a lost girl who is suspected of being a German.

"A framing device, built around the research of Lucy's future grandson, allows Morpurgo to shift among multiple narrators as he unspools the mystery of where she came from. Along the way, Morpurgo offers powerful descriptions of shipwreck, mass drowning, and devastation, as well as healing and growth." Publishers Weekly.

Private Peaceful. by Michael Morpurgo. Scholastic Press, 2004. 202 p.

Grades: 7 8 9 10   **Fic**
1. First World War era (1914-1918) 2. Teenage soldiers 3. Duty 4. World War I 5. Trench warfare 6. Brothers 7. England 8. France 9. War stories 10. Historical fiction
ISBN 0439636485

LC 2003065347

When Thomas Peaceful's older brother is forced to join the British Army, Thomas decides to sign up as well, although he is only fourteen years old, to prove himself to his country, his family, his childhood love, Molly, and himself.

"In this World War I story, the terse and beautiful narrative of a young English soldier is as compelling about the world left behind as about the horrific daily details of trench warfare. . . . Suspense builds right to the end, which is shocking, honest, and unforgettable." Booklist.

War horse. by Michael Morpurgo. Scholastic, 2007. 176 p.

Grades: 5 6 7 8   **Fic**
1. First World War era (1914-1918) 2. 1910s 3. War horses 4. Boys and horses 5. World War I 6. Soldiers 7. Young men 8. Historical fiction 9. War stories 10. Stories told by animals
ISBN 9780439796637

LC 2006044368

Joey the horse recalls his experiences growing up on an English farm, his struggle for survival as a cavalry horse during World War I, and his reunion with his beloved master.

"At times deeply affecting, the story balances the horror with moments of respite and care." Horn Book Guide.

Morris, Gerald, 1963-

The **squire's** tale. Gerald Morris. Houghton Mifflin, 1998. 212 p.: Squire's Tale series

Grades: 6 7 8 9   **Fic**
1. Arthur, King 2. Boys -- Identity 3. Friendship 4. Wizards 5. Orphans 6. Identity (Psychology) 7. Great Britain 8. Historical fantasy 9. Arthurian fantasy
ISBN 0395869595

LC 97012447

In medieval England, fourteen-year-old Terence finds his tranquil existence suddenly changed when he becomes the squire of the young Gawain of Orkney and accompanies him on a long quest, proving Gawain's worth as a knight and revealing an important secret about his own true identity.

"Well-drawn characters, excellent, snappy dialogue, detailed descriptions of medieval life, and a dry wit put a new spin on this engaging tale of the characters and events of King Arthur's time." Booklist.

Morris, Paula

Ruined: a novel. Paula Morris. Point, c2009. 309 p.: Haunted city series

Grades: 6 7 8 9 10   **Fic**
1. Teenage girls and ghosts 2. Teenage girl murder victims 3. Curses 4. Voodoo 5. Teenage girl ghosts 6. New Orleans, Louisiana 7. Louisiana 8. Supernatural mysteries
ISBN 9780545042154

"Set in New Orleans, this is the story of 15-year-old Rebecca Brown, a proud New Yorker sent to live with a family friend while her father travels overseas. Ostracized as an outsider, Rebecca struggles to fit in and cope with her new surroundings. When she befriends Lisette, a ghost who has haunted the cemetery ever since her mysterious death 155 years earlier, Rebecca is drawn into an eerie story of betrayal, loss, old curses and family secrets. . . . This moody tale thoroughly embraces the rich history, occult lore and complex issues of race, ethnicity, class and culture that have defined New Orleans for centuries." Publishers Weekly.

Morrison, Megan, 1976-

Grounded: the adventures of Rapunzel. Megan Morrison. Arthur A. Levine Books, an imprint of Scholastic Inc., 2015. 384 p.: Tyme

Grades: 5 6 7 8   **Fic**
1. Characters and characteristics in fairy tales 2. Fairies 3. Witches 4. Magic 5. Innocence (Personal quality) 6. Fantasy fiction 7.

Fairy tale and folklore-inspired fiction
ISBN 9780545638265

Rapunzel believes she is the luckiest person in Tyme, because Witch tells her so, but when Jack climbs into her tower to steal an enchanted rose, he hints that Witch is not telling the whole truth and Rapunzel, driven by her anger and fear, descends to the ground for the first time.

Mosier, Paul

Train I ride. Paul Mosier. Harper, an imprint of HarperCollinsPublishers,s, 2017 192 p.

Grades: 6 7 8 9 10   **Fic**
1. Self-acceptance 2. Railroad travel 3. Loss (Psychology) 4. Self-acceptance in teenage girls 5. Thirteen-year-old girls 6. Realistic fiction
ISBN 9780062455734

Taking a train journey from her elderly grandmother's home in California to live in Chicago with an unknown relative, young Rydr holds a suitcase filled with memories and bonds with fellow passengers while seeking the hope and forgiveness she needs to start over.

"A harrowing, moving, immersive, and ultimately uplifting debut novel." Kirkus.

Moskowitz, Hannah

Sick kids in love. Hannah Moskowitz. Entangled Teen, 2019. 317 p.

Grades: 8 9 10 11 12   **Fic**
1. People with chronic illnesses 2. Teenage romance 3. Dating (Social customs) 4. Teenage boy/girl relations 5. Chronic pain 6. New York City 7. Contemporary romances
ISBN 9781640637320

Isabel has one rule: no dating. She's got issues. She's got secrets. She's got rheumatoid arthritis. But then she meets another sick kid. He's got a chronic illness Isabel's never heard of, something she can't even pronounce. He understands what it means to be sick. He understands her more than her healthy friends. He understands her more than her own father who's a doctor. He's gorgeous, fun, and foul-mouthed. And totally into her."—adapted from publisher's description.

"Thoughtful without being heavy-handed or improbable in its teen characterization, Sick Kids In Love has a cinematic feel reminiscent of mid-00s romantic comedies, without feeling dated." Booklist.

Mosley, Walter

47. by Walter Mosley. Little, Brown, 2005. 232 p.

Grades: 7 8 9 10   **Fic**
1. 19th century 2. Enslaved people 3. Aliens (Humanoid) 4. Enslaved boys 5. African American teenage boys 6. Fourteen-year-old boys 7. Georgia 8. Afrofuturism and Afrofantasy 9. Science fiction 10. African American fiction
ISBN 0316110353

                                        LC 2004012500

Number 47, a fourteen-year-old slave boy growing up under the watchful eye of a brutal master in 1832, meets the mysterious Tall John, who introduces him to a magical science and also teaches him the meaning of freedom.

"Time travel, shape-shifting, and intergalactic conflict add unusual, provocative elements to this story. And yet, well-drawn characters; lively dialogue filled with gritty, regional dialect; vivid descriptions; and poignant reflections ground it in harsh reality." School Library Journal.

Mukherjee, Sonya

Gemini. Sonya Mukherjee. Simon & Schuster Books for Young Readers, [2016] 384 p.

Grades: 8 9 10 11 12   **Fic**
1. Conjoined twins 2. Identity (Psychology) 3. High school seniors 4. Small towns 5. High schools 6. California 7. Realistic fiction
ISBN 9781481456777

                                        LC 2015019774

In a small town, as high school graduation approaches, two conjoined sisters must weigh the importance of their dreams as individuals against the risk inherent in the surgery that has the potential to separate them forever.

"Even for sisters, Clara and Hailey are close. They have to be—theyre conjoined twins attached at the spine. . . . [T]his debut is a well-researched and particularly heartfelt account of a rare medical condition and the people it affects. Though they share a body, Clara and Hailey are two very different people with different dreams, and their fight for a normal life will resonate with many." Booklist.

Mull, Brandon, 1974-

Sky raiders. by Brandon Mull. Aladdin, 2014. 432 p.: Five kingdoms

Grades: 4 5 6 7   **Fic**
1. Sixth-graders 2. Parallel universes 3. Rescues 4. Doorways 5. Magic 6. Gateway fantasy 7. Fantasy fiction
ISBN 9781442497009

                                        LC 2013032734

Whisked through a portal to The Outskirts, an in-between world, sixth-grader Cole must rescue his friends and find his way back home—before his existence is forgotten.

"Although Mull packs quite a bit into this initial installment, he skillfully mixes the capricious logic of dreams with high stakes and constant danger. The intriguing premise, strong world-building, and numerous twists make this a real page-turner." Publishers Weekly.

Wild born. Brandon Mull. Scholastic Inc., 2013. 224 p.: Spirit animals.

Grades: 4 5 6 7   **Fic**
1. Human/animal relationships 2. Talismans 3. Shapeshifting 4. Good and evil 5. Eleven-year-olds 6. Fantasy fiction
ISBN 9780545522434

Discovering when they come of age that they share a bond with special spirit animals who wield great powers, four children become lone protectors of their world against a dark force that threatens to destroy everyone they love, in a debut installment in a role-playing action adventure series by the best-selling author of the Fablehaven books.

A world without heroes. Brandon Mull. Aladdin, 2011. 464 p.: Beyonders

Grades: 4 5 6 7   **Fic**
1. Wizards 2. Words 3. Teenage heroes and heroines 4. Quests 5. Magic 6. Gateway fantasy 7. Fantasy fiction
ISBN 9781416997924

                                        LC 2010023437

Fourteen-year-old Jason Walker is transported to a strange world called Lyrian, where he joins Rachel, who was also drawn there from our world, and a few rebels, to piece together the Word that can destroy the malicious wizard emperor, Surroth.

"Mull moves his story at a brisk pace, preventing the tragedies from overwhelming the adventure, while offering ample action and feisty dialogue to keep fantasy lovers entertained." Publishers Weekly.

Mulligan, Andy

Trash. Andy Mulligan. David Fickling Books, 2010. 240 p.

Grades: 6 7 8 9   **Fic**

1. Homeless children 2. Poverty 3. Garbage collection 4. Political corruption 5. Garbage collectors 6. Developing countries 7. Mysteries
ISBN 9780385752145

Fourteen-year-olds Raphael and Gardo team up with a younger boy, Rat, to figure out the mysteries surrounding a bag Raphael finds during their daily life of sorting through trash in a third-world country's dump.

"While on the surface the book reads like a fast-paced adventure title, it also makes a larger statement about the horrors of poverty and injustice in the world. . . . Trash is a compelling read." School Library Journal.

Munda, Rosaria

Fireborne. Rosaria Munda. G. P. Putnam's Sons, 2019 448 p.: Aurelian cycle

Grades: 7 8 9 10 11 12   **Fic**

1. Teenage orphans 2. Dragons 3. Power (Social sciences) 4. Competition 5. Social classes 6. High fantasy 7. Fantasy fiction
ISBN 9780525518211

When a brutal revolution opens dragonrider classes to everyone, two orphans from very different backgrounds become rising stars in a new regime that is challenged by violent survivors of the former government.

"Munda seamlessly moves between breathless action and an unflinching examination of horrors inflicted in pursuit of noble ideals, and the difficulty of escaping cycles of power and violence." Publishers Weekly.

Murdock, Catherine Gilbert

Da Vinci's cat: a novel. Catherine Gilbert Murdock. Greenwillow Books, an imprint of HarperCollins Publishers, 2021. 288 p.

Grades: 4 5 6 7   **Fic**

1. Michelangelo Buonarroti, 1475-1564 2. Raphael, 1483-1520 3. Time travel 4. Drawing 5. European Renaissance 6. Art 7. Cats 8. Rome, Italy 9. New Jersey 10. Science fiction
ISBN 9780063015258

LC 2020053868

Using a mysterious wardrobe that allows them to travel through time, two eleven-year-olds, Federico a boy from the Italian Renaissance and Bee a girl from present-day New Jersey, work together to prevent the bickering between two great artists from changing the future.

"Murdock keeps her story fresh with tight, fast-paced writing that incorporates history by bringing it engagingly to life and tying it meaningfully to the present." Booklist.

Dairy queen: a novel. by Catherine Gilbert Murdock. Houghton Mifflin, 2006. 275 p.: Dairy queen trilogy

Grades: 7 8 9 10   **Fic**

1. Rural teenagers 2. Girl football players 3. Self-discovery in teenage girls 4. Self-discovery 5. Teenage girl athletes 6. Wisconsin 7. Sports fiction 8. Realistic fiction 9. Football stories
ISBN 9780618683079

LC 2005019077

After spending her summer running the family farm and training the quarterback for her school's rival football team, sixteen-year-old D.J. decides to go out for the sport herself, not anticipating the reactions of those around her.

"D. J.'s voice is funny, frank, and intelligent, and her story is not easily pigeonholed." Voice of Youth Advocates.

The **off** season. by Catherine Gilbert Murdock. Houghton Mifflin, 2007. 277 p.: Dairy queen trilogy

Grades: 7 8 9 10   **Fic**

1. Rural teenagers 2. Teenage girl athletes 3. Sports injuries 4. High school football 5. Lesbian teenagers 6. Wisconsin 7. Sports fiction 8. Realistic fiction 9. Football stories
ISBN 9780618686957

LC 2006029278

High school junior D.J. staggers under the weight of caring for her badly injured brother, her responsibilities on the dairy farm, a changing relationship with her friend Brian, and her own athletic aspirations.

"This depicts a believably maturing D.J., a young woman whose character shines through even as she struggles to find her voice. Readers will root for her at every tragicomic turn." School Library Journal.

Princess Ben: being a wholly truthful account of her various discoveries and misadventures, recounted to the best of her recollection, in four parts. written by Catherine Gilbert Murdock. Houghton Mifflin, 2008. 344 p.

Grades: 7 8 9 10   **Fic**

1. Princesses 2. Arranged marriage 3. Self-fulfillment in teenage girls 4. Self-fulfillment 5. Magic 6. Fantasy fiction 7. Coming-of-age stories
ISBN 9780618959716

LC 2007034300

A girl is transformed, through instruction in life at court, determination, and magic, from sullen, pudgy, graceless Ben into Crown Princess Benevolence, a fit ruler of the kindgom of Montagne as it faces war with neighboring Drachensbett.

"Murdock's prose sweeps the reader up and never falters, blending a formal syntax and vocabulary with an intimate tone that bonds the reader with Ben." Horn Book.

Murphy, Julie, 1985-

★ **Dear** Sweet Pea. Julie Murphy. Balzer + Bray, 2019. 288 p.

Grades: 4 5 6 7 8   **Fic**

1. Children of divorced parents 2. Preteen girls 3. Advice columns 4. Divorced parents 5. Advice columnists 6. Texas 7. Realistic fiction
ISBN 9780062473073

Struggling to adjust to her parents' sudden divorce at the same time she is forced to sit next to her former best friend in class, a teen finds herself in the unlikely role of a community advice columnist.

"Sweet Pea is a treasure of a protagonist. She's fat without it being a cause for shame (though it comes with realistic challenges, like shopping in the junior's section), and she's not shy, popular, or an outcast: she's gloriously normal." Booklist.

Ramona Blue. Julie Murphy. Balzer + Bray, an imprint of HarperCollinsPublishers, 2017. 432 p.

Grades: 8 9 10 11   **Fic**

1. Lesbian teenagers 2. Questioning (Sexual or gender identity) 3. Swimming 4. African American teenage boys 5. Teenage boy/girl relations 6. Mississippi 7. Realistic fiction 8. Coming-of-age stories 9. LGBTQIA fiction
ISBN 9780062418357

LC 2016950250

Struggling with the loss of her home and her dysfunctional family after Hurricane Katrina, gay teen Ramona finds solace in a new swimming hobby while developing confusing feelings for a boy who challenges her perceptions.

"An exquisite, thoughtful exploration of the ties that bind and the fluidity of relationships, sexuality, and life." Kirkus.

Mussi, Sarah

The **door** of no return. Sarah Mussi. Margaret K. McElderry Books, 2008. 394 p.

Grades: 8 9 10 11 12   **Fic**
    1. Treasure hunting 2. Political corruption 3. Murder 4. Sixteen-year-old boys 5. Teenage boys 6. Ghana 7. Adventure stories
ISBN 9781416915508

Sixteen-year-old Zac Baxter never believed his grandfather's tales about their enslaved ancestors being descended from an African king, but when his grandfather is murdered and the villains come after Zac, he sets out for Ghana to find King Baktu's long-lost treasure before the murderers do.

"This exciting narrative takes place in England and Africa; in jungles, dark caves, and on the sea. . . . Overall, this is a complex, masterful story for confident readers." School Library Journal.

Myers, Walter Dean, 1937-2014

145th Street: short stories. Walter Dean Myers. Delacorte Press, 2000. 151 p.

Grades: 7 8 9 10   **Fic**
    1. Inner city teenagers 2. Short stories 3. Realistic fiction 4. African American fiction
ISBN 0385321376

Ten stories portray life on a block in Harlem.

"These ten powerful stories create a vivid mosaic of life in the Harlem neighborhood of 145th Street. Memorable characters range from outgoing Big Joe, who decides to stage his own funeral party in Big Joe's funeral, to book-loving Monkeyman, who outsmarts the Tigros gang. . . . Beautifully told, Myers's stories offer an enticing collection for teens." Voice of Youth Advocates.

Darius & Twig. Walter Dean Myers. Harper, an imprint of HarperCollinsPublishers, [2013] 208 p.

Grades: 8 9 10 11 12   **Fic**
    1. Best friends 2. Teenage authors 3. Bullying and bullies 4. Friendship 5. Teenage runners 6. Harlem, New York City 7. New York City
ISBN 9780061728235

                     LC 2012050678

Two best friends, a writer and a runner, deal with bullies, family issues, social pressures, and their quest for success coming out of Harlem. Provided by publisher.

"This encouraging text may inspire teens who feel trapped by their surroundings...Told in Darius's voice, the prose is poetic but concise. This would be a worthwhile addition to any middle or high school media center or public Library shelf and would make a valuable book for discussion in a middle school classroom." Voice of Youth Advocates.

Dope sick. Walter Dean Myers. HarperTeen/Amistad, 2009. 192 p.

Grades: 8 9 10 11 12   **Fic**
    1. Teenage boys 2. Options, alternatives, choices 3. Second chances 4. Seventeen-year-old boys 5. Personal conduct 6. Harlem, New York City 7. Magical realism 8. Literary fiction 9. African American fiction
ISBN 9780061214783

                     LC 2008010568

Seeing no way out of his difficult life in Harlem, seventeen-year-old Jeremy "Lil J" Dance flees into a house after a drug deal goes awry and meets a weird man who shows different turning points in Lil J's life when he could have made better choices.

"Myers uses street-style lingo to cover Lil J's sorry history of drug use, jail time, irresponsible fatherhood and his own childhood grief. A didn't-see-that-coming ending wraps up the story on a note of well-earned hope and will leave readers with plenty to think about." Publishers Weekly.

Fallen angels. Walter Dean Myers. Scholastic, 1988. 309 p.

Grades: 8 9 10 11 12   **Fic**
    1. Vietnam War, 1961-1975 -- African-American troops 2. Vietnam War, 1961-1975 3. Seventeen-year-old boys 4. African-American teenage soldiers 5. Battles 6. War stories 7. Coming-of-age stories 8. African American fiction
ISBN 0590409425

                 LC 87023236

Coretta Scott King Award, Author Category, 1989.

Seventeen-year-old Richie Perry, just out of his Harlem high school, enlists in the Army in the summer of 1967 and spends a devastating year on active duty in Vietnam.

"Except for occasional outbursts, the narration is remarkably direct and understated; and the dialogue, with morbid humor sometimes adding comic relief, is steeped in natural vulgarity, without which verisimilitude would be unthinkable. In fact, the foul talk, which serves as the story's linguistic setting, is not nearly as obscene as the events." Horn Book.

Hoops: a novel. Walter Dean Myers. Delacorte Press, 1981. 183 p.

Grades: 7 8 9 10   **Fic**
    1. African American basketball players 2. Sports betting 3. Teenage athletes 4. Sports -- Corrupt practices 5. Seventeen-year-old boys 6. Realistic fiction 7. African American fiction
ISBN 0440938848

                 LC 81065497

A teenage basketball player from Harlem is befriended by a former professional player who, after being forced to quit because of a point shaving scandal, hopes to prevent other young athletes from repeating his mistake.

"This story offers the reader some fast, descriptive basketball action, a love story between Lonnie and girlfriend Mary-Ann, peer friendship problems, and gangster intrigues. Most importantly, however, it portrays the growth of a trusting and deeply caring father-son relationship between [the coach] Cal and [fatherless] Lonnie." Voice of Youth Advocates.

Lockdown. Walter Dean Myers. HarperTeen/Amistad, 2010. 256 p.

Grades: 8 9 10 11 12   **Fic**
    1. Juvenile delinquents (Boys) 2. African American teenage boys 3. Juvenile jails 4. Self-perception in teenage boys 5. Personal conduct 6. Realistic fiction 7. African American fiction
ISBN 9780061214813

                 LC 2009007287

Teenage Reese, serving time at a juvenile detention facility, gets a lesson in making it through hard times from an unlikely friend with a harrowing past.

"Reese's first-person narration rings with authenticity. . . . Myers' storytelling skills ensure that the messages he offers are never heavy-handed." Booklist.

Monster. by Walter Dean Myers; illustrations by Christopher Myers. Harper Collins, 1999. 281 p.

Grades: 7 8 9 10   **Fic**
    1. Teenage prisoners 2. Trials (Murder) 3. Prisons 4. Teenage

murder suspects 5. African-American teenage prisoners 6. Realistic fiction 7. African American fiction
ISBN 0060280778

LC 98040958 /AC

Michael L. Printz Award, 2000.

While on trial as an accomplice to a murder, sixteen-year-old Steve Harmon records his experiences in prison and in the courtroom in the form of a film script as he tries to come to terms with the course his life has taken.

"Balancing courtroom drama and a sordid jailhouse setting with flashbacks to the crime, Myers adeptly allows each character to speak for him or herself, leaving readers to judge for themselves the truthfulness of the defendants, witnesses, lawyers, and, most compellingly, Steve himself." Horn Book Guide.

Scorpions. by Walter Dean Myers. Harper & Row, 1988. 216 p.

Grades: 6 7 8 9 **Fic**
1. African American gangs 2. Ghettoes, African American 3. African American teenage boys 4. Gangs 5. Harlem, New York City 6. Realistic fiction 7. African American fiction 8. Classics
ISBN 0060243643

LC 85045815

After reluctantly taking on the leadership of the Harlem gang, the Scorpions, Jamal finds that his enemies treat him with respect when he acquires a gun until a tragedy occurs.

Slam! Walter Dean Myers. Scholastic Press, 1996. 266 p.

Grades: 7 8 9 10 **Fic**
1. Seventeen-year-old boys 2. High school basketball players 3. African American teenage boys 4. Inner city teenage boys 5. African American basketball players 6. Coming-of-age stories 7. Realistic fiction 8. African American fiction
ISBN 0590486675

LC 95-46647

Coretta Scott King Award, Author Category, 1997.

Seventeen-year-old "Slam" Harris is counting on his basketball talents to get him out of the inner city and give him a chance to succeed in life, but his coach sees things differently.

"Myers descriptions of Slam on the court . . . use crisp details, not flowery language, to achieve their muscular poetry, and Myers is equally vivid in relating the torment Slam feels as he stares at a page of indecipherable algebra formulas. . . . [This is an] admirably realistic coming-of-age novel." Booklist.

Street love. Walter Dean Myers. Amistad, 2006. 144 p.

Grades: 8 9 10 11 12 **Fic**
1. Inner city teenagers 2. Street life 3. Gangs 4. Poverty 5. Love 6. Harlem, New York City 7. Realistic fiction 8. Novels in verse 9. African American fiction
ISBN 0060280794

LC 2006002457

This story told in free verse is set against a background of street gangs and poverty in Harlem in which seventeen-year-old African American Damien takes a bold step to ensure that he and his new love will not be separated.

"The realistic drama on the street and at home tells a gripping story." Booklist.

Sunrise over Fallujah. Walter Dean Myers. Scholastic Press, 2008. 304 p.

Grades: 8 9 10 11 12 **Fic**
1. African American soldiers 2. Psychic trauma in men 3. Life change events 4. Human nature 5. Culture conflict 6. Baghdad, Iraq 7. Iraq 8. Coming-of-age stories 9. War stories
ISBN 9780439916240

LC 2007025444

Robin Perry, from Harlem, is sent to Iraq in 2003 as a member of the Civilian Affairs Battalion, and his time there profoundly changes him.

"Instead of heading to college as his father wishes, Robin leaves Harlem and joins the army to stand up for his country after 9/11. While stationed in Iraq with a war looming that he hopes will be averted, he begins writing letters home to his parents and to his Uncle Richie. . . . Myers brilliantly freeze-frames the opening months of the current Iraq War by realistically capturing its pivotal moments in 2003 and creating a vivid setting. Memorable characters share instances of wry levity that balance the story without deflecting its serious tone." School Library Journal.

What they found: love on 145th street. Walter Dean Myers. Wendy Lamb Books, 2007. 256 p.

Grades: 8 9 10 11 12 **Fic**
1. Love 2. Fathers 3. Familial love 4. Teenagers -- Interpersonal relations 5. Teenagers -- Sexuality 6. Harlem, New York City 7. Iraq 8. Short stories
ISBN 9780385321389

LC 2007007057

Fifteen interrelated stories explore different aspects of love, such as a dying father's determination to help start a family business—a beauty salon—and the relationship of two teens who plan to remain celibate until they marry.

"Rich in both character and setting, these urban tales combine heartbreak and hope into a vivid tableau of a community. A priority purchase for all libraries, especially those in urban settings." School Library Journal.

Myklusch, Matt

Jack Blank and the Imagine Nation. Matt Myklusch. Aladdin, 2011. 470 p.: Jack Blank adventures

Grades: 4 5 6 7 **Fic**
1. Superheroes 2. Boy orphans 3. Identity (Psychology) 4. Robots 5. Giants 6. Superhero stories
ISBN 9781416995616

LC 2009023533

Jack Blank—so called because he has no memories of either his parents or his real name—lives in a bleak orphanage in New Jersey and finds his only solace in reading comic books. But when a robot zombie straight from the pages of one of Jack's comics shows up at St. Barnaby's Home for the Hopeless, Abandoned, Forgotten, and Lost, Jack somewhat accidentally destroys the mechanical beast and is then whisked away to the Imagine Nation, an island populated entirely by beings with superpowers.

"This creates a richly imagined world with strong appeal to fans of comics. The island is populated by a fun cast of heroes and villains. . . . Brisk narration captures the superhero world with a mixture of fast-paced action, wry humor, and occasional heartfelt speeches about courage and friendship." School Library Journal.

Myracle, Lauren, 1969-

Luv ya bunches. by Lauren Myracle. Amulet Books, 2009. 352 p.: Flower power books

Grades: 4 5 6 **Fic**
1. Online identities 2. Revenge 3. Interracial friendship 4. African American girls 5. Muslim girls 6. Realistic fiction
ISBN 9780810942110

LC 2009012585

Four friends—each named after a flower—navigate the ups and downs of fifth grade. Told through text messages, blog posts, screenplay, and straight narrative.

"Myracle displays a shining awareness of and sensitivity to the highly textured society of tween girls. . . . This is a fun, challenging, and gently edifying story." Booklist.

Na, An, 1972-

A **step** from heaven. An Na. Front Street, 2000. 156 p.
Grades: 7 8 9 10　　　　　　　　　　　　　　　　　Fic
　　1. Koreans in the United States 2. Child immigrants 3. Alcoholic fathers 4. Immigrant families 5. Immigration and emigration 6. Realistic fiction 7. Coming-of-age stories
ISBN 1886910588
　　　　　　　　　　　　　　　　　　LC　00041083
Michael L. Printz Award, 2002.
A young Korean girl and her family find it difficult to learn English and adjust to life in America.

"This isn't a quick read, especially at the beginning when the child is trying to decipher American words and customs, but the coming-of-age drama will grab teens and make them think of their own conflicts between home and outside. As in the best writing, the particulars make the story universal." Booklist.

Wait for me. An Na. G. P. Putnam's Sons, 2006. 240 p.
Grades: 8 9 10 11 12　　　　　　　　　　　　　　Fic
　　1. High school seniors 2. Korean American teenage girls 3. Expectation (Psychology) 4. Seventeen-year-old girls 5. Korean Americans 6. California 7. Realistic fiction 8. Coming-of-age stories
ISBN 0399242759
　　　　　　　　　　　　　　　　　　LC　2005030931
As her senior year in high school approaches, Mina yearns to find her own path in life but working at the family business, taking care of her little sister, and dealing with her mother's impossible expectations are as stifling as the southern California heat, until she falls in love with a man who offers a way out.

"This is a well-crafted tale, sensitively told. . . . The mother-daughter conflict will resonate with teens of any culture who have wrestled parents for the right to choose their own paths." Bulletin of the Center for Children's Books.

Naidoo, Beverley

The **other** side of truth. by Beverley Naidoo. Harper Collins, 2001. 227 p.
Grades: 5 6 7 8　　　　　　　　　　　　　　　　Fic
　　1. Abandoned children 2. Refugees 3. Nigerians in England 4. Homeless children 5. Brothers and sisters 6. London, England 7. Nigeria 8. Realistic fiction
ISBN 0060296283
　　　　　　　　　　　　　　　　　　LC　00054112
Carnegie Medal, 2000.
Smuggled out of Nigeria after their mother's murder, Sade and her younger brother are abandoned in London when their uncle fails to meet them at the airport and they are fearful of their new surroundings and of what may have happened to their journalist father back in Nigeria.

"Part survival adventure, part docudrama, the narrative stays true to Sade's viewpoint. . . . This powerful novel brings the news images very close." Booklist.

Out of bounds: seven stories of conflict and hope. Beverley Naidoo. Harper Collins, 2003. xv, 175 p.

Grades: 5 6 7 8　　　　　　　　　　　　　　　　　Fic
　　1. 20th century 2. Apartheid 3. Racism 4. State-sponsored terrorism 5. Coping in children 6. Children 7. South Africa 8. Short stories
ISBN 0060507993
　　　　　　　　　　　　　　　　　　LC　2002068901
Seven stories, spanning the time period from 1948 to 2000, chronicle the experiences of young people from different races and ethnic groups as they try to cope with the restrictions placed on their lives by South Africa's apartheid laws.

"Naidoo's book reveals our humanity and inhumanity with starkness and precision. . . . She honors her country's past, present, and future with these brave tales." Horn Book.

Napoli, Donna Jo, 1948-

Beast. Donna Jo Napoli. Atheneum Books for Young Readers, 2000. 260 p.
Grades: 7 8 9 10　　　　　　　　　　　　　　　Fic
　　1. Princes 2. Curses 3. Fathers and sons 4. Survival 5. Voyages and travels 6. Iran 7. Fantasy fiction 8. Fairy tale and folklore-inspired fiction 9. Middle Eastern-influenced fantasy
ISBN 0689835892
　　　　　　　　　　　　　　　　　　LC　99089923
Elaborates on the tale of Beauty and the Beast told from the point of view of the beast and set in Persia.

"In this take on Beauty and the Beast, Napoli focuses on Beast before French beauty Belle enters his life. The first-person story begins in Persia, where proud prince Orasmyn, who loves roses, makes an unfortunate decision that sets in motion a curse: he becomes a lion who can only be restored by the love of a woman." Booklist.

Bound. Donna Jo Napoli. Atheneum Books for Young Readers, 2004. 192 p.
Grades: 8 9 10 11 12　　　　　　　　　　　　　　Fic
　　1. Stepmothers 2. Footbinding 3. Princes 4. Slippers 5. Fourteen-year-old girls 6. China 7. Historical fiction 8. Fairy tale and folklore-inspired fiction
ISBN 0689861753
　　　　　　　　　　　　　　　　　　LC　2004000365
In a novel based on Chinese Cinderella tales, fourteen-year-old stepchild Xing-Xing endures a life of neglect and servitude, as her stepmother cruelly mutilates her own child's feet so that she alone might marry well.

"The author fleshes out and enriches the story with well-rounded characters and with accurate information about a specific time and place in Chinese history; the result is a dramatic and masterful retelling." School Library Journal.

Hush: an Irish princess' tale. Donna Jo Napoli. Atheneum Books for Young Readers, 2007. 320 p.
Grades: 8 9 10 11 12　　　　　　　　　　　　　　Fic
　　1. Medieval period (476-1492) 2. 10th century 3. Fifteen-year-old girls 4. Slavery 5. Mutism 6. Kidnapping 7. Kidnapping victims 8. Ireland 9. Historical fiction
ISBN 9780689861765
　　　　　　　　　　　　　　　　　　LC　2007002676
Fifteen-year-old Melkorka, an Irish princess, is kidnapped by Russian slave traders and not only learns how to survive but to challenge some of the brutality of her captors, who are fascinated by her apparent muteness and the possibility that she is enchanted.

"This is a powerful survival story. . . . Napoli does not shy from detailing practices that will make readers wince . . . and the Russian crew repeatedly gang-rapes an older captive. . . . The tension over Mel's hopes for escape paces this story like a thriller." Publishers Weekly.

Stones in water. Donna Jo Napoli. Dutton Children's Books, c1997. 209 p.

Grades: 5 6 7 8   **Fic**
> 1. Second World War era (1939-1945) 2. World War II 3. Forced labor 4. Nazis 5. Escapes 6. Thirteen-year-old boys 7. Germany 8. Historical fiction 9. War stories
> ISBN 0525458425

LC   97014253

Golden Kite Award for Fiction, 1997.
Sydney Taylor Book Award for Older Readers, 1998.
After being taken by German soldiers from a local movie theater along with other Italian boys including his Jewish friend, Roberto is forced to work in Germany, escapes into the Ukrainian winter, before desperately trying to make his way back home to Venice.
"This is a gripping, meticulously researched story (loosely based on the life of an actual survivor)." Publishers Weekly.

Zel. Dutton Children's Books, 1996. 227 p.

Grades: 7 8 9 10   **Fic**
> 1. 15th century 2. Teenage romance 3. Mothers and daughters 4. Nobility 5. Switzerland 6. Fantasy romances 7. Fairy tale and folklore-inspired fiction
> ISBN 0525456120

LC 96-15135

Based on the fairy tale Rapunzel, the story is told in alternating chapters from the point of view of Zel, her mother, and the prince, and delves into the psychological motivations of the characters.
"This version, with its Faustian overtones, will challenge readers to think about this old story on a deeper level. It begs for discussion in literature classes." School Library Journal.

Nayeri, Daniel

Everything sad is untrue: a true story. Daniel Nayeri. Levine Querido, 2020 368 p.

Grades: 7 8 9 10 11 12   **Fic**
> 1. Refugees 2. Everyday life 3. Storytelling 4. Storytellers 5. Memory 6. Oklahoma 7. Biographical fiction 8. Realistic fiction
> ISBN 9781646140008
> Michael L. Printz Award, 2021.

At the front of a middle school classroom in Oklahoma, a boy named Khosrou (whom everyone calls "Daniel") stands, trying to tell a story. His story. But no one believes a word he says. To them he is a dark-skinned, hairy-armed boy with a big butt whose lunch smells funny; who makes things up and talks about poop too much. Like Scheherazade in a hostile classroom, Daniel weaves a tale to save his own life: to stake his claim to the truth. Adapted from publisher description
"It's the book's focus on the themes of storytelling and memory and the stubborn authenticity of young Khousrou/Daniel's child view that result in a story that soars sometimes despite, sometimes because of, its sorrows." Bulletin of the Center for Children's Books

Naylor, Phyllis Reynolds

★ **Shiloh**. Phyllis Reynolds Naylor. Atheneum, 1991. 144 p.: Shiloh quartet

Grades: 4 5 6   **Fic**
> 1. Boys and dogs 2. Animal welfare 3. Beagle (Dog breed) 4. Courage in boys 5. Nastiness in men 6. West Virginia 7. Realistic

fiction 8. Classics
> ISBN 0440407524

LC   90000603

Newbery Medal, 1992.
When he finds a lost beagle in the hills behind his West Virginia home, Marty tries to hide it from his family and the dog's real owner, a mean-spirited man known to shoot deer out of season and to mistreat his dogs.
"A credible plot and characters, a well-drawn setting, and nicely paced narration combine in a story that leaves the reader feeling good." Horn Book.

Nazemian, Abdi

Like a love story. Abdi Nazemian. Balzer + Bray, 2019. 432 p.

Grades: 8 9 10 11 12   **Fic**
> 1. ACT UP. 2. 1980s 3. Gay teenagers 4. Iranians in the United States 5. Teenage boy/boy relations 6. Teenage same-sex romance 7. First loves 8. New York City 9. LGBTQIA fiction 10. Historical fiction
> ISBN 9780062839367

An Iranian youth who hides his sexual orientation from his family, an openly gay photographer and an aspiring fashion designer with an HIV-positive uncle fall in love and find their voices as activists during the height of the AIDS crisis in New York City.
"This is a beautifully written exploration of first love's fragility in the face of a world full of hate and fear. But just as compelling is its look into a friendship that isn't shattered by a betrayal; instead, its cracks are revealed as two friends grow into the people they're meant to be." Booklist.

Nelson, Theresa, 1948-

Ruby electric. Theresa Nelson. Atheneum Books for Young Readers, 2003. 272 p.

Grades: 5 6 7 8   **Fic**
> 1. Twelve-year-old girls 2. Father-separated girls 3. Fathers and daughters 4. Brothers and sisters 5. Younger brothers and sisters 6. Los Angeles, California 7. California 8. Realistic fiction
> ISBN 0689838522

LC 2002008034

Twelve-year-old Ruby Miller, movie buff and aspiring screen writer, tries to resolve the mysteries surrounding her little brother's stuffed woolly mammoth and their father's five year absence.
"Ruby's voice is electric, and she is an unforgettable character with courage, a cause, and imagination." Booklist.

Nelson, Vaunda Micheaux

No crystal stair. by Vaunda Micheaux Nelson; illustrated by R. Gregory Christie. Carolrhoda Lab, c2012. 208 p.

Grades: 6 7 8 9 10 11 12   **Fic**
> 1. Michaux, Lewis H., 1885-1976. 2. African Americans 3. Bookstores 4. Books and reading 5. Booksellers 6. African American men 7. Harlem, New York City 8. New York City 9. Biographical fiction 10. Historical fiction
> ISBN 9780761361695

LC 2011021251

Told by a banker that he should sell fried chicken rather than books, since "Negroes don't read," Lewis Michaux defies the odds to build Harlem's National Memorial African Bookstore, an intellectual center and gathering place from 1939 to 1975.

Nesbet, Anne

Cloud and Wallfish. Anne Nesbet. Candlewick Press, 2016 385 p.

Grades: 5 6 7 8   **Fic**

1. 1980s 2. Children of spies 3. Stutterers 4. Friendship 5. Families 6. Eleven-year-old boys 7. East Germany 8. Berlin, Germany 9. Historical fiction

ISBN 9780763688035

Picked up by his parents and taken to the airport with stern instructions to avoid answering questions, Noah is rushed to East Berlin, where he confronts astonishing secrets about his and his family's true identity.

"Noah's friendship with his neighbor Claudia is genuinely touching, and some truly tense scenes unfold as secrets are revealed and readers witness events leading to the fall of the Berlin Wall." Booklist.

Daring Darleen, queen of the screen. Anne Nesbet. Candlewick Press, 2020 357 p.

Grades: 4 5 6 7   **Fic**

1. 1910s 2. Child actors and actresses 3. Heirs and heiresses 4. Kidnapping 5. Publicity stunts 6. Conspiracies 7. New Jersey 8. Historical fiction 9. Adventure stories

ISBN 9781536206197

LC 2020902571

When a publicity stunt goes terribly wrong, a 12-year-old silent-film star finds herself navigating murderous plots and a runaway air balloon to rescue a kidnapped heiress from a band of dastardly criminals.

"Film studies professor Nesbet writes her intrepid heroine with swashbuckling verve and sweet familial affection, incorporating extensive knowledge of early-20th-century filmmaking into a well-paced, gripping tale of staying true to oneself while stretching limitations." Publishers Weekly.

Ness, Patrick, 1971-

And the ocean was our sky. Patrick Ness; illustrated by Rovina Cai. HarperTeen, 2018. 176 p.

Grades: 7 8 9 10 11 12   **Fic**

1. Whales 2. Ships 3. Hostages 4. Prisoners 5. Oceans 6. Fantasy fiction 7. Classics-inspired fiction

ISBN 9780062860729

With harpoons strapped to their backs, the proud whales of Bathsheba's pod live for the hunt, fighting in the ongoing war against the world of men. When they attack a ship bobbing on the surface of the Abyss, they expect to find easy prey. Instead, they find the trail of a myth, a monster, perhaps the devil himself...

"Ness mines Moby-Dick for incidents and motifs, pitting men against whales in a futuristic alternate world. . . . The story, though far shorter than its progenitor, conjures similar allegorical weight by pairing the narrative's rolling cadences with powerful, shadowy illustrations featuring looming whales, an upside-down ship in full sail, and swarms of red-eyed sharks, all amid dense swirls of water and blood." Kirkus.

The **Ask** and the Answer: a novel. by Patrick Ness. Candlewick Press, 2009. 528 p.: Chaos walking

Grades: 8 9 10 11 12   **Fic**

1. Space colonies 2. Telepathy 3. Dystopias 4. Teenagers 5. Teenage boy/girl relations 6. Dystopian fiction 7. Science fiction

ISBN 9780763644901

LC 2009007329

Alternate chapters follow teenagers Todd and Viola, who become separated as the Mayor's oppressive new regime takes power in New Prentisstown, a space colony where residents can hear each other's thoughts.

"Provocative questions about gender bias, racism, the meaning of war and the price of peace are thoughtfully threaded throughout a breathless, often violent plot peopled with heartbreakingly real characters." Kirkus.

The **knife** of never letting go. Patrick Ness. Candlewick Press, 2008. 492 p.: Chaos walking

Grades: 8 9 10 11 12   **Fic**

1. Dystopias 2. Telepathy 3. Space colonies 4. Social problems 5. Human/animal communication 6. Dystopian fiction 7. Science fiction

ISBN 9780763639310

LC 2007052334

Pursued by power-hungry Prentiss and mad minister Aaron, young Todd and Viola set out across New World searching for answers about his colony's true past and seeking a way to warn the ship bringing hopeful settlers from Old World.

"This troubling, unforgettable opener to the Chaos Walking trilogy is a penetrating look at the ways in which we reveal ourselves to one another, and what it takes to be a man in a society gone horribly wrong." Booklist.

A **monster** calls: a novel. by Patrick Ness; inspired by an idea from Siobhan Dowd; illustrations by Jim Kay. Candlewick Press, 2011. 224 p.

Grades: 6 7 8 9 10   **Fic**

1. Monsters 2. Children of people with cancer 3. Self-fulfillment in teenage boys 4. Self-fulfillment 5. Schools 6. England 7. Magical realism 8. Illustrated books

ISBN 9780763655594

LC 2010040741

Carnegie Medal, 2012.

Thirteen-year-old Conor awakens one night to find a monster outside his bedroom window, but not the one from the recurring nightmare that began when his mother became ill—an ancient, wild creature that wants him to face truth and loss.

"This is a profoundly moving, expertly crafted tale of unaccountable loss. . . . A singular masterpiece, exceptionally well-served by Kay's atmospheric and ominous illustrations." Publishers Weekly.

Neumeier, Rachel

The **keeper** of the mist. Rachel Neumeier. Alfred A. Knopf, 2016. 400 p.

Grades: 7 8 9 10 11 12   **Fic**

1. Rulers 2. Inheritance and succession 3. Illegitimate children of royalty 4. Magic 5. Imaginary places 6. High fantasy 7. Fantasy fiction

ISBN 9780553509281

Required by ancient magic to assume the dangerous position previously held by the father she barely knew, Keri relies on her three clever guides and struggles to outmaneuver her treacherous half-brothers while working to repair a failing boundary between her people and land-hungry neighbors.

"This is a beautifully written story that emphasizes intelligence and diplomacy. Recommend to fans of Patricia Wrede and Tamora Pierce, as well as lovers of traditional fantasy." School Library Journal.

Nicholls, Sally, 1983-

Season of secrets. Sally Nicholls. Arthur A. Levine Books, 2011. 225 p.

Grades: 4 5 6   **Fic**

1. Grief in girls 2. Invisibility 3. Seasons 4. Nature 5. Grief 6.

Fantasy fiction
ISBN 9780545218252

Staying with their grandparents while their father mourns the loss of their mother, Molly and Hannah find their lives transformed by a relationship with an injured man who seems to possess wondrous magical abilities.

"Written in gently flowing prose, the plot appropriately transitions from autumn into summer as Molly emerges from grief to acceptance and hope. A poignant story of healing tinged with mystery." Kirkus.

Ways to live forever. Sally Nicholls. Arthur A. Levine Books, 2008. 212 p.

Grades: 4 5 6 7   **Fic**
    1. Children with leukemia 2. Children and death 3. Writing 4. Leukemia 5. Children with terminal illnesses 6. Realistic fiction
    ISBN 9780545069489

LC 2007047341

Eleven-year-old Sam McQueen, who has leukemia, writes a book during the last three months of his life, in which he tells about what he would like to accomplish, how he feels, and things that have happened to him.

"This skirts easy sentiment to confront the hard questions head-on, intelligently and realistically and with an enormous range of feeling." Publishers Weekly.

Nicholson, William

Seeker. William Nicholson. Harcourt, 2006. 432 p.: Noble warriors

Grades: 7 8 9 10   **Fic**
    1. Self-fulfillment 2. Personal conduct 3. Faith 4. Sixteen-year-old boys 5. Teenage boys 6. Fantasy fiction
    ISBN 0152057684

LC 2005017171

Having been rejected by the Nomana—the revered warrior-monk order they long to join—sixteen-year-olds Seeker and Morning Star, along with a curious pirate named Wildman, attempt to prove that they are worthy of joining the community, after all.

"The classic coming-of-age tale is combined with a rich setting of cold villains, strange powers, and disturbing warriors." Voice of Youth Advocates.

Nielsen, Jennifer A.

The **false** prince. by Jennifer A. Nielsen. Scholastic Press, 2012. 368 p.: Ascendance trilogy

Grades: 4 5 6 7 8   **Fic**
    1. Impersonation 2. Orphans 3. Princes 4. Courts and courtiers 5. Secrets 6. High fantasy 7. Fantasy fiction
    ISBN 9780545284134

LC 2011006692

In the country of Carthya, a devious nobleman engages four orphans in a brutal competition to be selected to impersonate the king's long-missing son in an effort to avoid a civil war.

Resistance. Jennifer A. Nielsen. Scholastic Press, 2018 400 p.

Grades: 6 7 8 9 10   **Fic**
    1. Second World War era (1939-1945) 2. Jewish teenage girls 3. Resistance to military occupation 4. Ghettoes, Jewish 5. Jewish resistance and revolts 6. Jews -- Persecutions 7. Poland 8. Warsaw, Poland 9. Historical fiction 10. War stories
    ISBN 9781338148473

After a smuggling mission to an isolated Jewish ghetto goes wrong and her colleagues are arrested, Chaya Lindner, a Jewish girl living in Nazi-occupied Poland, decides to go to Warsaw, where an uprising is in the works.

"Historical fiction at its finest, this informs, enlightens, and engages young readers. A first purchase." School Library Journal

The **runaway** king. Jennifer A. Nielsen. Scholastic Press, 2013. 352 p.: Ascendance trilogy

Grades: 4 5 6 7 8   **Fic**
    1. Rulers 2. Identity (Psychology) 3. Attempted assassination 4. Conspiracies 5. Princesses 6. High fantasy 7. Fantasy fiction
    ISBN 9780545284158

LC 2012035290

Young King Jaron has taken the throne of Carthya, but after enemies attempt to assassinate him, and a neighboring kingdom threatens invasion, he finds that he has no friends in the palace, not even his bride-to-be, princess Amarinda—and his regents think it would be better for Carthya if he just disappeared again.

The **shadow** throne. Jennifer A. Nielsen. Scholastic Press, 2014. 384 p.: Ascendance trilogy

Grades: 4 5 6 7 8   **Fic**
    1. Rulers 2. Identity (Psychology) 3. Attempted assassination 4. Conspiracies 5. Princesses 6. High fantasy 7. Fantasy fiction
    ISBN 9780545284172

Finds Jaron embarking on his final adventure.

"There's enough adventure, mystery, and romance in this concluding volume to please a variety of genre readers." Horn Book.

Nielsen, Susin, 1964-

No fixed address. Susin Nielsen. Wendy Lamb Books, 2018 288 p.

Grades: 6 7 8 9   **Fic**
    1. Homelessness 2. Mothers and sons 3. Self-reliance in boys 4. Television game shows 5. Community life 6. Vancouver, British Columbia 7. Realistic fiction
    ISBN 9781524768348

Twelve-year-old Felix's appearance on a television game show reveals that he and his mother have been homeless for a while, but also restores some of his faith in other people.

Word nerd. Susin Nielsen. Tundra Books of Northern New York, 2008. 256 p.

Grades: 5 6 7 8   **Fic**
    1. Boy misfits 2. Scrabble (Game) 3. Overprotectiveness in mothers 4. Former convicts 5. Allergy 6. Vancouver, British Columbia 7. Realistic fiction
    ISBN 9780887768750

LC 2007938541

When some bullies at his new school almost kill him by slipping a peanut into his sandwich, friendless nerd Ambrose, forced to be home-schooled by his overprotective mother, coerces his neighbor Cosmo into taking him to the West Side Scrabble Club, where people accept him for who he is.

"This is a tender, often funny story with some really interesting characters. It will appeal to word nerds, but even more to anyone who has ever longed for acceptance or had to fight unreasonable parental restrictions." School Library Journal.

Nimmo, Jenny

Midnight for Charlie Bone. Jenny Nimmo. Orchard Books, 2003. 401 p.: Children of the Red King

Grades: 5 6 7 8   **Fic**

   1. Child wizards 2. Missing girls 3. Photographs 4. Magic 5. Villains 6. England 7. Fantasy fiction

   ISBN 0439474299

                          LC 2002030738

Charlie Bone's life with his widowed mother and two grandmothers undergoes a dramatic change when he discovers that he can hear people in photographs talking.

"This marvelous fantasy is able to stand on its own despite inevitable comparisons to the students of Hogwarts." Voice of Youth Advocates.

Nix, Garth

Abhorsen. Garth Nix. HarperCollins Publishers, c2003. 358 p.: Old Kingdom

Grades: 7 8 9 10   **Fic**

   1. Teenage girl orphans 2. Wizards 3. Courage in teenagers 4. Courage 5. Good and evil 6. High fantasy 7. Fantasy fiction

   ISBN 0060278250

                          LC 2002003151

Abhorsen-In-Waiting Lirael and Prince Sameth, a Wallmaker, must confront and bind the evil spirit Oranis before it can destroy all life.

"The tension throughout the story is palatable, and despite a solid, satisfying conclusion, Nix leaves himself a bit of room to revisit his intricately designed universe." Booklist.

Clariel: the lost Abhorsen. Garth Nix. 2014. 400 p.: Old Kingdom

Grades: 7 8 9 10   **Fic**

   1. Revenge 2. Good and evil 3. Murder 4. Parents -- Death 5. Spirits 6. High fantasy 7. Fantasy fiction

   ISBN 9780061561559

Ignoring rumors about her family's claim to the throne after moving to the city of Belisaere, Clariel dreams of escaping to a hunter's life while trying to outmaneuver a Free Magic creature, an unwanted betrothal and a plot against King Orrikan.

"Nix's intricate world building reveals more Old Kingdom history and its ever-shifting alliance between the political and magical. Themes of freedom and destiny underpin Clariel's harrowing, bittersweet story, and readers will delight in the telling." Booklist.

Goldenhand: an Old Kingdom novel. Garth Nix; maps by Mike Schley. Harper,, 2016 344 p.: Old Kingdom

Grades: 7 8 9 10   **Fic**

   1. Imaginary kingdoms 2. Magic 3. Rescues 4. Good and evil 5. Teenage girls 6. High fantasy 7. Fantasy fiction

   ISBN 9780061561580

"A masterfully spun tale well worth the years-long wait." Kirkus.

Lirael, daughter of the Clayr. Garth Nix. HarperCollins, c2001. 487 p.: Old Kingdom

Grades: 7 8 9 10   **Fic**

   1. Teenage girl orphans 2. Courage in teenagers 3. Imaginary wars and battles 4. Courage 5. Princes 6. High fantasy 7. Fantasy fiction

   ISBN 0060278234

                          LC 00059707

When a dangerous necromancer threatens to unleash a long-buried evil, Lirael and Prince Sameth are drawn into a battle to save the Old Kingdom and reveal their true destinies.

"The Clayr Lirael is 14, but is unable to be initiated as a Clayr because she has not had a vision. To ease her disappointment, Lirael is made Third Assistant Librarian. This allows Lirael an opportunity to study volumes of forgotten magic, and she uses one spell to turn a stone carving of a dog into a living creature. Lirael gradually increases her knowledge, and, with Disreputable Dog, explores forgotten passages in the Library. . . . With her special powers, Lirael leaves the enclave to help save the Old Kingdom." Book Rep.

"Sound world-building, swift plotting, and superb characterization, including some of the strongest animal characters in recent fantasy, make this sequel must reading for those who have read the first volume and a brisk, involving experience for those who have not." Voice of Youth Advocates.

Mister Monday. Garth Nix. Scholastic, c2003. 361 p.: Keys to the kingdom

Grades: 6 7 8 9   **Fic**

   1. Magic keys 2. Plague 3. Boy heroes 4. Seventh-grade boys 5. Boys with asthma 6. Fantasy fiction

   ISBN 0439551234

                       LC BL2003009595

Although Arthur Penhaligon is supposed to die, he is saved by a key shaped like the minute hand of a clock, and now some bizarre creatures—including Mister Monday, his avenging messengers, and an army of dog-faced Fetchers—will stop at nothing to get the key.

"The first in a seven part series for middle graders is every bit as exciting and suspenseful as the author's previous young adult novels." School Library Journal.

Sabriel. Garth Nix. HarperCollins, c1995. xi, 292 p.: Old Kingdom

Grades: 7 8 9 10   **Fic**

   1. Wizards 2. Courage in teenage girls 3. Spirits 4. Good and evil 5. Teenage girls 6. High fantasy 7. Fantasy fiction

   ISBN 0060273224

                       LC 96001295

Sabriel, daughter of the necromancer Abhorsen, must journey into the mysterious and magical Old Kingdom to rescue her father from the Land of the Dead.

"The final battle is gripping, and the bloody cost of combat is forcefully presented. The story is remarkable for the level of originality of the fantastic elements . . . and for the subtle presentation, which leaves readers to explore for themselves the complex structure and significance of the magic elements." Horn Book.

To hold the bridge. Garth Nix. HarperCollins Children's Books, 2015. 416 p.

Grades: 6 7 8 9 10 11 12   **Fic**

   1. Fantasy fiction 2. Science fiction 3. Horror

   ISBN 9780062292520

"This anthology's titular novella is a suspenseful prequel to The Old Kingdom Chronicles. Eighteen other tales are organized by theme, with a satisfying variety of genres and tones. Some pay homage to famous speculative fiction (Hellboy; John Carter of Mars), others are companion pieces to Nix's own work; the majority stand alone. Nix's superb world-building and tight plotting are evident here." Horn Book.

Nolan, Han

Crazy. Han Nolan. Harcourt, 2010. 352 p.

Grades: 7 8 9 10   **Fic**

   1. High school students 2. Fathers with mental illnesses 3. Family problems 4. Group psychotherapy 5. Missing persons 6. Realistic

fiction
ISBN 9780152051099

LC 2009049969

Fifteen-year-old loner Jason struggles to hide father's declining mental condition after his mother's death, but when his father disappears he must confide in the other members of a therapy group he has been forced to join at school.

"Nolan leavens this haunting but hopeful story with spot-on humor and a well-developed cast of characters." Booklist.

A **summer** of Kings. Han Nolan. Harcourt, c2006. 334 p.
Grades: 6 7 8 9   **Fic**
1. 1960s 2. Fourteen-year-old girls 3. Fourteen-year-olds 4. Eighteen-year-old men 5. Eighteen-year-olds 6. African Americans 7. Westchester County, New York 8. Washington, DC 9. Historical fiction
ISBN 0152051082

LC 2005019487

After being accused of killing a white man in Alabama and sent north by his mother to escape a lynch mob, King-Roy finds his way to a home where he meets Esther, a young white girl looking for excitement and attention, where an unexpected friendship develops that transforms both of their lives while coming to terms with what they deem just and right.

"Infused with rhetoric that is as meaningful today as it was two generations ago, this young teen's account of a life-changing summer not only opens a window to history, but also displays Nolan's brilliant gift for crafting profoundly appealing protagonists." School Library Journal.

North, Phoebe

Starglass. Phoebe North. Simon & Schuster Books for Young Readers, 2013. 448 p.: Starglass
Grades: 7 8 9 10   **Fic**
1. Jews 2. Dystopias 3. Space flight 4. Space vehicles 5. Insurgency 6. Dystopian fiction 7. Science fiction
ISBN 9781442459533

LC 2012021171

For all of her sixteen years, Terra has lived on a city within a spaceship that left Earth five hundred years ago seeking refuge, but as they finally approach the chosen planet, she is drawn into a secret rebellion that could change the fate of her people.

Northrop, Michael

Polaris. Michael Northrop. Scholastic Press, 2017. 288 p.
Grades: 4 5 6 7 8   **Fic**
1. 1830s 2. Cabin boys 3. Mutiny 4. Ships 5. Fungi 6. Seafaring life 7. Horror 8. Sea stories 9. Historical fiction
ISBN 9780545297165

LC 2016059059

When the adult crew of the Polaris mutinies and abandons ship off the coast of Brazil in the 1830s, cabin boy Owen Ward and the ship's young deckhands attempt to steer the ship to safety.

"This fast-moving adventure-survival novel with a science-fiction focus . . . will appeal to reluctant readers who like thrills and chills." Booklist.

Noyes, Deborah

The **ghosts** of Kerfol. Deborah Noyes. Candlewick Press, 2008. 163 p.
Grades: 8 9 10 11 12   **Fic**
1. Haunted houses 2. Ghosts 3. Supernatural 4. Manors 5.

France 6. Ghost stories 7. Short stories
ISBN 0763630004

LC 2007051884

Over the centuries, the inhabitants of author Edith Wharton's fictional mansion, Kerfol, are haunted by the ghosts of dead dogs, fractured relationships, and the bitter taste of revenge.

"This collection includes five wonderfully chilling short stories." Publishers Weekly.

Nunn, Malla

When the ground is hard. Malla Nunn. G.P. Putnam's Sons Books for Young Readers, 2019. 272 p.
Grades: 8 9 10 11   **Fic**
1. Bronte, Charlotte, 1816-1855. Jane Eyre 2. 1960s 3. Boarding school students 4. Social classes 5. Multiracial persons 6. Human skin color -- Social aspects 7. Christian schools 8. Swaziland 9. Coming-of-age stories 10. Historical fiction
ISBN 9780525515579

LC 2018040602

At Swaziland's Keziah Christian Academy, where the wealth and color of one's father determines one's station, once-popular Adele bonds with poor Lottie over a book and a series of disasters.

"In Swaziland, wealth and privilege are tightly bound to race. As a mixed-race girl, Adele considers herself above the native Zulus, but her relatively privileged status is compromised by the fact that her white father lives with his 'real' family in Johannesburg." Booklist.

Nye, Naomi Shihab

Habibi. Naomi Shihab Nye. Simon & Schuster Books for Young Readers, 1997. 259 p.
Grades: 7 8 9 10   **Fic**
1. Fourteen-year-old girls 2. Arab American families 3. Palestinian Americans 4. Arab American teenage girls 5. Teenagers 6. Jerusalem, Israel 7. Realistic fiction
ISBN 0689801491

LC 97010943

When fourteen-year-old Liyanna, her younger brother, and her parents move from St. Louis to a new home between Jerusalem and the Palestinian village where her father was born, they face many changes and must deal with the tensions between Jews and Palestinians.

"Poetically imaged and leavened with humor, the story renders layered and complex history understandable through character and incident." School Library Journal.

There is no long distance now: very short stories. Naomi Shihab Nye. Harpercollins Childrens Books, 2011. 256 p.
Grades: 7 8 9 10 11 12   **Fic**
1. Young adults 2. Emotions 3. Short stories
ISBN 9780062019653

"Very short stories offer glimpses into the everyday lives of young people. . . . As she does in her poetry, Nye achieves a perfect marriage of theme and structure in stories that reflect the moments, glimpses and epiphones of growing up." Kirkus.

O'Brien, Caragh M.

Birthmarked. Caragh M. O'Brien. Roaring Brook Press, 2010. 368 p.: Birthmarked trilogy
Grades: 6 7 8 9 10   **Fic**
1. Teenage apprentices 2. Midwives 3. Dystopias 4. Infants 5. Genetic engineering 6. Dystopian fiction 7. Science fiction
ISBN 9781596435698

In a futureworld decimated by climate change, apprentice midwife Gaia lives along the shore of what used to be Lake Michigan, helping her mother deliver babies and making sure to "advance" the required three newborns per month to the exclusive, walled-in Enclave. Gaia is forced to infiltrate the Enclave herself after her parents are arrested as traitors, and though she finds help (maybe even love?) from someone unexpected, she also uncovers devastating secrets that shatter her understanding of her society.

"Readers who enjoy adventures with a strong heroine standing up to authority against the odds will enjoy this compelling tale." School Library Journal.

O'Brien, Robert C.

★ **Mrs.** Frisby and the rats of NIMH. Robert C. O'Brien; illustrated by Zena Bernstein. Atheneum, 1971. 233 p.

Grades: 4 5 6 7   **Fic**
    1. United States. National Institute of Mental Health. 2. Sick children 3. Laboratory animals 4. Escapes 5. Rats 6. Rats as laboratory animals 7. Animal fantasy 8. Fantasy fiction 9. Classics
ISBN 0689704135

                  LC   74134818

Newbery Medal, 1972.

When a little field mouse falls ill, his mother, Mrs. Frisby, seeks help from the other animals and discovers a secret laboratory.

"The story is fresh and ingenious, the style witty, and the plot both hilarious and convincing. Saturday Rev

Z for Zachariah. Robert C. O'Brien. Atheneum, 1975. 249 p.

Grades: 7 8 9 10   **Fic**
    1. Survival (after nuclear warfare) 2. Nuclear holocaust survivors 3. Escapes 4. Radiation victims 5. Dystopias 6. Apocalyptic fiction 7. Science fiction
ISBN 0689304420

                  LC   74076736

Seemingly the only person left alive after a nuclear war, a sixteen-year-old girl is relieved to see a man arrive into her valley until she realizes that he is a tyrant and she must somehow escape.

"The journal form is used by O'Brien very effectively, with no lack of drama and contrast, and the pace and suspense of the story are adroitly maintained until the dramatic and surprising ending." Bulletin of the Center for Children's Books.

O'Connor, Barbara

★ **How** to steal a dog: a novel. by Barbara O'Connor. Farrar, Straus & Giroux, 2007. 170 p.

Grades: 4 5 6   **Fic**
    1. Father-deserted families 2. Dognapping 3. Homelessness 4. Right and wrong 5. Girls 6. North Carolina 7. Realistic fiction
ISBN 0374334978

                  LC 2005040166

Living in the family car in their small North Carolina town after their father leaves them virtually penniless, Georgina, desperate to improve their situation and unwilling to accept her overworked mother's calls for patience, persuades her younger brother to help her in an elaborate scheme to get money by stealing a dog and then claiming the reward that the owners are bound to offer.

"This is told in stripped-down, unsentimental prose. . . . The myriad effects of homelessness and the realistic picture of a moral quandary will surely generate discussion." Booklist.

O'Connor, Sheila

★ **Sparrow** Road. Sheila O'Connor. G. P. Putnam's Sons, 2011. 247 p.

Grades: 5 6 7 8   **Fic**
    1. Artists colonies 2. Mansions 3. Self-discovery in girls 4. Self-discovery 5. Secrets 6. Realistic fiction
ISBN 9780399254581

                  LC 2010028290

Twelve-year-old Raine spends the summer at a mysterious artists' colony and discovers a secret about her past.

"This is a beautifully written novel. . . . Readers finding themselves in this quiet world will find plenty of space to imagine and dream for themselves." Kirkus.

O'Dell, Scott, 1898-1989

★ **Island** of the Blue Dolphins. Scott O'Dell; illustrated by Ted Lewin. Houghton Mifflin, 1990. 181 p.

Grades: 5 6 7 8   **Fic**
    1. Survival 2. Native American girls 3. Islands 4. Loneliness 5. Resourcefulness in girls 6. Survival stories 7. Adventure stories 8. Classics
ISBN 0395536804

                  LC   90035331

Newbery Medal, 1961.

Left alone on a beautiful but isolated island off the coast of California, a young Indian girl spends eighteen years, not only merely surviving through her enormous courage and self-reliance, but also finding a measure of happiness in her solitary life.

"The edition illustrated by Ted Lewin features twelve full-page, full-color watercolors in purple and blue hues that are appropriate to the island setting. This handsome gift-edition version includes a new introduction by Lois Lowry to commemorate the book's fiftieth anniversary." Horn Book Guide.

Sing down the moon. Scott O'Dell. Houghton Mifflin, 1970. 137 p.

Grades: 5 6 7 8   **Fic**
    1. 19th century 2. Navajo girls 3. Indian Removal, 1813-1903 4. Fourteen-year-old girls 5. Navajo Indians -- Relocation 6. Indians of North America -- Wars 7. Westerns 8. Classics
ISBN 0395109191

                  LC   71098513

A young Navajo girl recounts the events of 1864 when her tribe was forced to march to Fort Sumner as prisoners of the white soldiers.

"This story is told through the eyes of a young Navaho girl as she sees the rich harvest in the Canyon de Chelly in 1864 destroyed by Spanish slavers and the subsequent destruction by white soldiers which forces the Navahos on a march to Fort Sumner." Publishers Weekly.

"There is a poetic sonority of style, a sense of identification, and a note of indomitable courage and stoicism that is touching and impressive." Saturday Rev

Streams to the river, river to the sea: a novel of Sacagawea. Scott O'Dell. Houghton Mifflin, 1986. ix, 191 p.

Grades: 5 6 7 8   **Fic**
    1. Sacagawea 2. Native American women 3. Guides (Persons) 4. Expeditions 5. Exploration 6. Shoshoni women 7. Historical fiction 8. Biographical fiction 9. Classics
ISBN 9780395404300

                  LC   86000936

Scott O'Dell Historical Fiction Award, 1987.

A young Shoshoni woman, accompanied by her infant and cruel husband, experiences joy and heartbreak when she joins the Lewis and Clark Expedition seeking a way to the Pacific.

"An informative and involving choice for American history students and pioneer-adventure readers." Bulletin of the Center for Children's Books.

Zia. Scott O'Dell. Houghton, 1976. 179 p.

Grades: 5 6 7 8   **Fic**
1. San Gabriel Mission (California) 2. Indians of North America 3. Native American girls 4. Family traditions 5. Aunts 6. California 7. Realistic fiction
ISBN 9788434586116

LC   75044156

A young Indian girl, Zia, caught between the traditional world of her mother and the present world of the Mission, is helped by her Aunt Karana whose story was told in The Island of the Blue Dolphins.

"Zia is an excellent story in its own right, written in a clear, quiet, and reflective style which is in harmony with the plot and characterization." School Library Journal.

O'Hart, Sinead

The **starspun** web. Sinead O'Hart. Alfred A. Knopf, 2019. 368 p.

Grades: 4 5 6 7   **Fic**
1. Parallel universes 2. Girl orphans 3. Space and time 4. Girl scientists 5. Tarantulas as pets 6. Ireland 7. Fantasy fiction
ISBN 9781101935071

LC 2019019770

Tess de Sousa leaves Miss Ackerbee's orphanage to live with her new guardian in Roedeer Lodge, taking with her a fondness for scientific experimentation, a pet tarantula named Violet, and a device that allows her to travel to parallel universes.

"Fantasy readers will appreciate the foray into interdimensionality and multiple and alternate realities as well as the flecks of other fantasy and science-fiction influences that will feel familiar." Kirkus.

O'Neal, Eilis

The **false** princess. Eilis O'Neal. Egemont USA, 2010. 336 p.

Grades: 6 7 8 9   **Fic**
1. Princesses 2. Wizards' apprentices 3. Conspiracies 4. Wizards 5. Identity (Psychology) 6. Fantasy fiction
ISBN 9781606840795

LC 2009040903

For sixteen years, Nalia has been raised as the princess of Thorvaldor, but one day she learns that her real name is Sinda and that she is part of a complicated plot that would change the future of her country forever.

"This is a compelling fantasy, which is filled with magic, political drama, and romance." Publishers Weekly.

O'Reilly, Jane H.

The **notations** of Cooper Cameron. Jane O'Reilly. Carolrhoda Books, [2017] 320 p.

Grades: 5 6 7 8   **Fic**
1. Compulsive behavior 2. Loss (Psychology) 3. Obsessive-compulsive disorder 4. Family problems 5. Vacation homes 6. Realistic fiction
ISBN 9781512404159

LC 2016042763

At the family cabin by the lake where his grandfather died two years ago, eleven-year-old Cooper Cameron spends the summer trying to rid himself of the rituals that allow him to cope with his grief and fear.

"The novel provides a heartfelt portrayal of one boy's experience with obsessive-compulsive disorder. Cooper is helped by a cast of supporting characters, who shine almost as brightly as he does." School Library Journal.

O'Shaughnessy, Kate

The **lonely** heart of Maybelle Lane. Kate O'Shaughnessy. Alfred A. Knopf, 2020 288 p.

Grades: 4 5 6 7   **Fic**
1. Father-separated girls 2. Girl musicians 3. Cross-country automobile trips 4. Searching 5. Resilience (Personal quality) 6. Realistic fiction
ISBN 9781984893840

Experiencing her world through the evocative sounds she collects, 11-year-old Maybelle becomes convinced that a new radio DJ is her absent father before entering a singing contest that the DJ will be judging in Nashville. Atlas Publishing.

O'Sullivan, Joanne

Between two skies. Joanne O'Sullivan. Candlewick Press, 2017. 272 p.

Grades: 7 8 9 10 11 12   **Fic**
1. Hurricane Katrina, 2005 2. Teenage boy/girl relations 3. Teenagers 4. Sixteen-year-old girls 5. Social classes 6. Louisiana 7. Love stories 8. Historical fiction
ISBN 9780763690342

Enjoying a quiet life in a tiny Louisiana fishing town, sixteen-year-old Evangeline is set adrift by Hurricane Katrina and must work through difficult political and cultural challenges to regain her sense of belonging.

"Told in a strong, purposeful voice filled with controlled emotion and hope, the impact of Katrina on families is as compelling as Evangeline's drive to regain her sense of self and belonging." Booklist.

Oaks, J. Adams (Jeffrey Adams)

Why I fight: a novel. J. Adams Oaks. Atheneum Books for Young Readers, c2009. 228 p.

Grades: 8 9 10 11 12   **Fic**
1. Teenage boys 2. Uncles 3. Bare knuckle boxing 4. Emotional problems of teenage boys 5. Boxing 6. Coming-of-age stories 7. Realistic fiction
ISBN 9781416911777

LC 2007046433

When he was 12 years old, Wyatt left his neglectful parents and went on the road with his traveling-salesman uncle, Spade. Their life is unpredictable, poor, and more than a little sketchy. Always looking for a way to make a buck, Uncle Spade hits on the idea of promoting Wyatt—who is big, strong, and has a violent temper—as a bare-knuckle fighter, and for a while it seems as though Wyatt will never lose. No ordinary sports novel, Why I Fight is a gritty, disturbing read that digs deep into Wyatt's tortured psyche and yet offers hope that he can create a better life on his own terms.

"Oaks' first novel is a breathtaking debut with an unforgettable protagonist. . . . The voice Oaks has created for Wyatt to tell his painful and poignant story is a wonderful combination of the unlettered and the eloquent." Booklist.

Oates, Joyce Carol, 1938-

Big Mouth & Ugly Girl. Joyce Carol Oates. Harper Tempest, 2002. 266 p.

Grades: 7 8 9 10   **Fic**

1. Teenage misfits 2. Malicious accusation 3. Courage in teenagers 4. Courage 5. Bomb threats 6. Realistic fiction
ISBN 0066237564

LC 2001024601

When sixteen-year-old Matt is falsely accused of threatening to blow up his high school and his friends turn against him, an unlikely classmate comes to his aid.

"Readers will be propelled through these pages by an intense curiosity to learn how events will play out. Oates has written a fast-moving, timely, compelling story." School Library Journal.

Odhiambo, Eucabeth A.

Auma's long run. Eucabeth Odhiambo. Carolrhoda Books, [2017] 304 p.

Grades: 5 6 7 8 9   **Fic**

1. 1980s 2. AIDS (Disease) 3. Orphans 4. Running 5. Africans 6. Ambition 7. Kenya 8. Historical fiction
ISBN 9781512427844

LC 2016041225

When AIDS devastates thirteen-year-old Auma's village in Kenya during the 1980s, Auma must choose between staying to help her family and working toward a track scholarship that will take her away from home.

"The novel spans two years, and Odhiambo smoothly weaves in medical details throughout, along with the evolving understanding of AIDS. A hard-hitting story of a resilient and intelligent girl who bravely confronts a devastating health crisis." Publishers Weekly.

Oh, Ellen

Spirit hunters. Ellen Oh. Harper, an imprint of HarperCollins Publishers, 2017 276 p.: Spirit hunters

Grades: 4 5 6 7   **Fic**

1. Haunted houses 2. Spirit possession 3. Moving, Household 4. Multiracial girls 5. Korean American girls 6. Washington, DC 7. Horror 8. Ghost stories
ISBN 9780062430083

Feeling uncomfortable from the moment she arrives in her new home, Harper is dismayed by local rumors that her house is haunted and that every family that has ever lived there has suffered terrible tragedies, a situation that turns sinister when her cheerful little brother begins acting in alarming ways.

"Even more impressive than the shiver factor is the way the author skillfully uses the compelling premise to present a strong, consistent message of not rejecting what you don't understand—a most welcome message." Booklist.

Okorafor, Nnedi

Akata witch. Nnedi Okorafor. Viking, 2011. 352 p.: Akata series

Grades: 6 7 8 9 10   **Fic**

1. Girl misfits 2. Albinos and albinism 3. Witches 4. Witchcraft 5. Nigerian Americans 6. Nigeria 7. Africa 8. Fantasy fiction 9. African American fiction 10. Afrofuturism and Afrofantasy
ISBN 9780670011964

Twelve-year-old Sunny Nwazue, an American-born albino child of Nigerian parents, moves with her family back to Nigeria, where she learns that she has latent magical powers which she and three similarly gifted friends use to catch a serial killer.

"This vividly imagined, original fantasy shows what life is like in today's Nigeria, while it beautifully explores an alternate magical reality. Sunny must deal with cultural stereotypes, a strict father who resents her being female, and older brothers who pick on her because she's better at soccer than they are. This is a consistently surprising, inventive read that will appeal to more thoughtful, patient fantasy readers because it relies less on action and more on exploring the characters' gradual mastery of their talents." School Library Journal.

Ikenga. Nnedi Okorafor. Penguin Group USA 2020 240 p.

Grades: 5 6 7 8   **Fic**

1. Children of murder victims 2. Superhuman abilities 3. Murder investigation 4. Magic 5. Revenge 6. Nigeria 7. Afrofuturism and Afrofantasy
ISBN 9780593113523

LC 2019057715

In southeastern Nigeria, twelve-year-old Mnamdi is determined to avenge his police chief father, who was murdered while triyng to rid the town of criminals, but Nnamdi feels powerless until he receives a magical object which gives him superpowers.

"Details, including Igbo phrases, villain names, and food descriptions, evoke a vivid sense of place. . . . Fans of classic superheroes—including Nnamdi's favorite, the Incredible Hulk—and readers looking for a young superhero will find a champion in Nnamdi." Publishers Weekly

Older, Daniel Jose

Thunder run. Daniel Jose Older. Scholastic Press, 2020. 305 p.: Dactyl Hill Squad

Grades: 4 5 6 7   **Fic**

1. 1860s 2. United States Civil War, 1861-1865 3. Orphans 4. Dinosaurs 5. Cuban Americans 6. African Cubans 7. Mexico 8. United States 9. Historical fantasy
ISBN 9781338268874

LC 2019047468

Entrusted by General Grant with a top-secret mission to disrupt a plot against Union forces, Magdalys and her friends find their dino-wrangling skills pushed to the limit when they find themselves battling enemies on two fronts.

Oliver, Lauren, 1982-

Liesl & Po. by Lauren Oliver; illustrated by Kei Acedera. HarperCollins Childrne's Books, 2011. 320 p.

Grades: 4 5 6 7   **Fic**

1. Girl orphans 2. Boy apprentices 3. Alchemists 4. Ghosts 5. Stepmothers 6. Fantasy fiction
ISBN 9780062014511

A mix-up involving the greatest magic in the world has tremendous consequences for Liesl, an orphan who has been locked in an attic; Will, an alchemist's runaway apprentice; and Po, a ghost, as they are pursued by friend and foe while making an important journey.

"This is a charming, insightful fantasy. . . . This original fairy tale, told by a wise and humorous omniscient narrator and peopled with broadly drawn but instantly recognizable characters, avoids sentimentality to show the magic of accepting loss without letting go and finding joy in the lives left behind." Booklist.

★ The **magnificent** monsters of Cedar Street. Lauren Oliver; illustrated by Ethan Aldridge. Harpercollins Childrens Books, 2020 384 p.

Grades: 4 5 6 7   **Fic**

1. 19th century 2. Imaginary creatures 3. Missing persons 4. Fathers and daughters 5. Monsters 6. Secrecy 7. Boston,

Massachusetts 8. Massachusetts 9. Historical fantasy 10. Fantasy fiction
ISBN 9780062345073

Helping to protect the remarkable creatures that her neighbors in late 19th-century Boston call "monsters," Cordelia teams up with human and fantastical friends when her beloved father and several of the creatures in his care go missing.

"Cordelia and Gregory face instances of peril that are exciting without feeling too dangerous, and the book's secondary characters, both human and monster, add much to the story." Horn Book

★ The **spindlers**. by Lauren Oliver; illustrated by Iacopo Bruno. Harper, 2012. 256 p.

Grades: 4 5 6   **Fic**
    1. Soul 2. Courage in girls 3. Underground areas 4. Courage 5. Quests 6. Fantasy fiction
ISBN 9780061978081

                            LC 2012009698

Accompanied by an eccentric, human-sized rat, Liza embarks on a perilous quest through an underground realm to save her brother Patrick, whose soul has been stolen by the evilest of creatures—the spiderlike spindlers.

Olson, Arielle North

Ask the bones: scary stories from around the world. selected and retold by Arielle North Olson and Howard Schwartz; illustrated by David Linn. Viking, 1999. ix, 145 p.

Grades: 4 5 6 7   **Fic**
    1. Fear 2. Supernatural 3. Horror 4. Short stories 5. Folklore Collection (mixed).
ISBN 0670875813

                            LC 98019108

A collection of scary folktales from countries around the world including China, Russia, Spain, and the United States.

"David Linn's bone-chilling black-and-white illustrations . . . will stay with the reader long after the book is closed. Excellent for reading aloud, this collection will satisfy even jaded genre fans." Booklist.

Includes bibliographical references (p.141-145).

More bones: scary stories from around the world. selected and retold by Arielle North Olson and Howard Schwartz; illustrated by E.M. Gist. Viking, 2008. ix, 145 p.

Grades: 4 5 6 7   **Fic**
    1. Horror 2. Short stories 3. Folklore
ISBN 9780670063390

Red-haired maidens, serpents, magic, and more are featured in an exciting compilation of scary tales from Egypt, Iceland, and other countries around the world.

"This tour of the world's shadowy corners is full of dark wizards, unkind witches, and other untrustworthy creatures. . . . The 22 tales, as retold by Olson and Schwartz, give a vivid glimpse into unfamiliar, unnerving territory. . . . The atmospheric illustrations, while not intricately detailed, are somewhat startling in their imagery." Booklist.

Onome, Louisa

Like home. Louisa Onome. Delacorte Press, 2021. 320 p.

Grades: 9 10 11 12   **Fic**
    1. City life 2. Vandalism 3. Friendship 4. Police 5. Urban planning 6. Realistic fiction 7. Coming-of-age stories
ISBN 9780593172599

                            LC 2020043213

Remaining steadfast to her community after an act of violence compels several of her neighbors to move, Nelo lands in the center of a high-profile fight involving disputes with the police, urban redevelopment plans and an estrangement from her best friend.

"Chinelo's youthful, down-to-earth voice is humorous and utterly believable. The serious topics of gentrification, stereotyping, and inequality are ruthlessly examined without getting in the way of an engaging story of a young woman trying to find her place in a changing world." Kirkus

Oppel, Kenneth, 1967-

Airborn. Kenneth Oppel. Eos, c2004. 368 p.: Airborn adventures

Grades: 7 8 9 10   **Fic**
    1. Airships 2. Cabin boys 3. Rich girls 4. Teenage boy/girl relations 5. Teenagers 6. Fantasy fiction 7. Steampunk
ISBN 0060531800

                            LC 2003015642

Governor General's Literary Award for English-Language Children's Literature, 2004.

Matt, a young cabin boy aboard an airship, and Kate, a wealthy young girl traveling with her chaperone, team up to search for the existence of mysterious winged creatures reportedly living hundreds of feet above the Earth's surface.

"This rousing adventure has something for everyone: appealing and enterprising characters, nasty villains, and a little romance." School Library Journal.

Bloom. Kenneth Oppel. Knopf Books for Young Readers, 2020 320 p.: Overthrow

Grades: 5 6 7 8 9   **Fic**
    1. Plant invasions 2. Carnivorous plants 3. Teenagers 4. Plants 5. Alien plants 6. Vancouver, British Columbia 7. British Columbia 8. Science fiction 9. Apocalyptic fiction
ISBN 9781524773014

The invasion begins—but not as you'd expect. It begins with rain. Rain that carries seeds. Seeds that sprout—overnight, everywhere. These new plants take over crop fields, twine up houses, and burrow below streets. They bloom—and release toxic pollens. They bloom—and form Venus flytrap-like pods that swallow animals and people. They bloom—everywhere, unstoppable. Or are they? Three kids on a remote island seem immune to the toxic plants. Anaya, Petra, Seth. They each have strange allergies—and yet not to these plants. What's their secret? Can they somehow be the key to beating back this invasion? They'd better figure it out fast, because it's starting to rain again....

"In this fast-paced thriller, Oppel spins a richly drawn, incredibly fascinating world. Beginning with the brilliantly unique premise of a botanical alien invasion, the plot unravels satisfyingly, building readers' curiosity by creating 10 new questions for every answer given." Kirkus

★ The **Boundless**. Kenneth Oppel. Simon & Schuster Books for Young Readers, 2014. 336 p.

Grades: 4 5 6 7 8   **Fic**
    1. 1880s 2. Trains 3. Robbery 4. Voyages and travels 5. Railroad travel 6. Circus performers 7. Canada 8. Historical fantasy 9. Steampunk
ISBN 9781442472884

                            LC 2013009879

Aboard "The Boundless," the greatest train ever built, on its maiden voyage across Canada, teenaged Will enlists the aid of a traveling circus to save the train from villains.

"Will's father is driving the Boundless, the longest train ever, on her maiden voyage. After a series of adventures (involving a sasquatch and a murder), Will finds himself stranded in the caboose, where, with the help of a cute tightrope walker, he dodges a nefarious villain. The third-person present-tense narrative creates suspense as the well-drawn characters travel through an alternate-universe Canadian wilderness." Horn Book.

Half brother. Kenneth Oppel. Scholastic Press, 2010. 375 p.
Grades: 7 8 9 10   **Fic**
1. 1970s 2. Children of scientists 3. Chimpanzees 4. Teenagers and moving 5. Human/animal communication 6. Science -- Experiments 7. Victoria, British Columbia 8. Canada 9. Historical fiction
ISBN 9780545229258
                                                LC 2010002696
In 1973, when a renowned Canadian behavioral psychologist pursues his latest research project—an experiment to determine whether chimpanzees can acquire advanced language skills—he brings home a baby chimp named Zan and asks his thirteen-year-old son to treat Zan like a little brother.

"Oppel has taken a fascinating subject and molded it into a topnotch read. Deftly integrating family dynamics, animal-rights issues, and the painful lessons of growing up, Half Brother draws readers in from the beginning and doesn't let go." School Library Journal.

★ The **nest**. Kenneth Oppel; illustrated by Jon Klassen. Simon & Schuster Books for Young Readers, 2015. 256 p.
Grades: 4 5 6 7   **Fic**
1. Wasps 2. Anxiety 3. Infants 4. Anxiety in boys 5. Supernatural 6. Horror 7. Illustrated books
ISBN 9781481432320
Agonizing over his sick baby brother's struggles to survive, Steve is visited in his dreams by a mysterious wasp queen who offers to save his brother at a formidable cost.

"Klassen's eerie, atmospheric illustrations, all shadowy corners and half-concealed shapes, contribute to the spooky mood. With subtle, spine-chilling horror at its heart, this tale of triumph over monsters— both outside and in—is outstanding." Booklist.

Silverwing. Kenneth Oppel. Simon & Schuster Books for Young Readers, 1997. 217 p.: Silverwing saga
Grades: 5 6 7 8   **Fic**
1. Bats 2. Voyages and travels 3. Animal migration 4. Self-reliance 5. Growth (Psychology) 6. Animal fantasy 7. Fantasy fiction
ISBN 9780689815294
                                                LC 97010977
A young bat becomes separated from his flock while they are migrating.

"Oppel's bats are fully developed characters who, if not quite cuddly, will certainly earn readers' sympathy and respect. In Silverwing the author has created an intriguing microcosm of rival species, factions, and religions." Horn Book.

This dark endeavor. Kenneth Oppel. Simon & Schuster Books for Young Readers, c2011. 304 p.: Apprenticeship of Victor Frankenstein
Grades: 7 8 9 10   **Fic**
1. 18th century 2. Twin brothers 3. Alchemy 4. Alchemists 5. Love triangles 6. Sick teenage boys 7. Geneva (Republic) 8. Horror 9. Gothic fiction 10. Classics-inspired fiction
ISBN 9781442403154
                                                LC 2011016974

When his twin brother falls ill in the family's chateau in the independent republic of Geneva in the eighteenth century, sixteen-year-old Victor Frankenstein embarks on a dangerous and uncertain quest to create the forbidden Elixir of Life described in an ancient text in the family's secret Biblioteka Obscura.

"Written in a readable approximation of early 19th-century style, Oppel's . . . tale is melodramatic, exciting, disquieting, and intentionally over the top." Publishers Weekly.

Thrive. Kenneth Oppel. Alfred A. Knopf , 2021. 416 p.: Overthrow
Grades: 5 6 7 8 9   **Fic**
1. Human-alien hybrids 2. Biological invasions 3. Teenagers 4. Rebels 5. Aliens (Insectoid) 6. Earth 7. Science fiction 8. Apocalyptic fiction
ISBN 9781984894816
First the alien plant life bloomed, next their terrifying creatures hatched, and now the aliens themselves have arrived on Earth for a final showdown. Alien-hybrids Anaya, Petra and Seth will have to push themselves further than they ever thought possible if they want to forge an alliance with the alien rebels that will allow their planet to thrive once and for all.

"Despite its post-apocalyptic setting, the story is fundamentally character driven, and it is incredibly satisfying to watch each protagonist overcome their inner battles within the context of the larger human-alien war." Kirkus.

Orenstein, Denise Gosliner, 1950-
The **secret** twin. Denise Gosliner Orenstein. Katherine Tegen Books, 2007. 400 p.
Grades: 7 8 9 10   **Fic**
1. Thirteen-year-old boys 2. Nurses 3. Snipers 4. Teenage boys 5. Teenagers
ISBN 0060785640
                                                LC 2006003876
Born a conjoined twin, thirteen-year-old Noah bears the secret guilt of being the only survivor, and now finds himself in the care of a stranger with a secret of her own.

"This spellbinding story will entangle readers at the first sentence. . . . Orenstein's writing is magic—every word and phrase precisely chosen." Booklist.

Orlev, Uri, 1931-
Run, boy, run: a novel. by Uri Orlev; translated from the Hebrew by Hillel Halkin. Houghton Mifflin, 2003. 192 p.
Grades: 7 8 9 10   **Fic**
1. Fridman, Yoram 2. Orphans 3. Boy orphans 4. Jews, Polish 5. Parent-separated children 6. Boys -- Identity 7. Poland 8. Historical fiction 9. Translations
ISBN 0618164650
                                                LC 2003001550
Mildred L. Batchelder Award, 2004.
Based on the true story of a nine-year-old boy who escapes the Warsaw Ghetto and must survive throughout the war in the Nazi-occupied Polish countryside.

"The story is totally engrossing as it vividly describes the hardships faced by so many youngsters during the war. Orlev has . . . successfully used historical fiction to illustrate the Holocaust experience." School Library Journal.

Ormsbee, Kathryn

The **house** in Poplar Wood. K.E. Ormsbee. Chronicle Books, [2018] 344 p.

Grades: 5 6 7 8 **Fic**

1. Twin brothers 2. Alliances 3. Murder investigation 4. Death 5. Child detectives 6. Tennessee 7. Fantasy mysteries 8. Mysteries
ISBN 9781452149868

LC 2017058843

The Vickery twins, Lee and Felix, live in a house in Poplar Wood, where, because of the "Agreement," their mother serves Memory, and their father assists Death, and only Lee is allowed to leave the house, except for Halloween; but when a local girl is murdered, Gretchen Whipple, daughter of the mayor, offers the boys a deal—help her solve the crime and she will help them break the Agreement, and regain their freedom.

Orr, Wendy, 1953-

Dragonfly song. Wendy Orr. Pajama Press, 2017, c2016 408 p.

Grades: 5 6 7 8 **Fic**

1. Pariahs 2. Bulls 3. Human sacrifice 4. Children who are mute 5. Islands 6. Fantasy fiction
ISBN 9781772780376

There are whispers that the Lady, an island priestess, gave birth to a deformed child, and because of this she was rejected and doomed to a life of servitude as a lowly mute no-name. Aissa wonders about the scars along her wrists and her connection with animals. When the soldiers of Crete arrive demanding children as a tribute for their god-king's bull dances, Aissa decides to take matters into her own scarred hands.

"[Wendy] Orr tells her tale in both narrative poetry and prose for an effect that is both fanciful and urgent, drawing a rich fantasy landscape filled with people and creatures worthy of knowing. . . . As mesmerizing as a mermaid's kiss, the story dances with emotion, fire, and promise." Kirkus.

Orwell, George, 1903-1950

Animal farm. George Orwell. Signet Classics, 1996, c1945. 140 p.

Grades: 7 8 9 10 11 12 Adult **Fic**

1. Totalitarianism 2. Dystopias 3. Farm animals 4. Talking animals 5. Domestic animals 6. Political fiction 7. Allegories 8. Satirical fiction
ISBN 9780451526342

A satire on totalitarianism in which farm animals overthrow their human owner and set up their own government.

Oseman, Alice

Heartstopper. Alice Oseman. Scholastic, 2020, 288 p.: Heartstopper

Grades: 7 8 9 10 11 12 **Fic**

1. High schools 2. Coming out (Sexual or gender identity) 3. Crushes in teenage boys 4. Friendship 5. Mental illness 6. Comics and graphic novels 7. LGBTQIA comics 8. LGBTQIA romances
ISBN 9781338617443

Charlie and Nick are at the same school, but they've never met until one day when they're made to sit together. They quickly become friends, and soon Charlie is falling hard for Nick, even though he doesn't think he has a chance. But love works in surprising ways, and Nick is more interested in Charlie than either of them realised.

"An adorable diary of love's gut punches." Kirkus

Heartstopper.. Alice Oseman. Graphix, 2020, c2019. 320 p.: Heartstopper

Grades: 7 8 9 10 11 12 **Fic**

1. High schools 2. Coming out (Sexual or gender identity) 3. Crushes in teenage boys 4. Best friends 5. Friendship 6. Comics and graphic novels 7. LGBTQIA comics 8. LGBTQIA romances
ISBN 9781338617498

Nick and Charlie are best friends. Nick knows Charlie's gay, and Charlie is sure that Nick isn't. But love works in surprising ways, and Nick is discovering all kinds of things about his friends, his family ... and himself. Heartstopper is about friendship, loyalty and mental illness. It encompasses all the small stories of Nick and Charlie's lives that together make up something larger, which speaks to all of us. This is the second volume of Heartstopper, with more to come.

"Nick and Charlie's lighthearted and tender romance is delightful, and the genuine heart present in the characters makes for a wholesome and uplifting ride." Kirkus

Oshiro, Mark

Anger is a gift: a novel. Mark Oshiro. Tor Teen, 2018 464 p.

Grades: 8 9 10 11 12 **Fic**

1. African American teenage boys 2. Gay teenagers 3. Protests, demonstrations, vigils, etc 4. High schools 5. Racism 6. Oakland, California 7. California 8. Realistic fiction
ISBN 9781250167026

Schneider Family Book Award for Teens, 2019.

A young adult debut by the popular social media personality and critic reflects the racial and economic struggles of today's teens in the story of high school junior Moss, who in the face of a racist school administration decides to organize a protest that escalates into violence.

"Oshiro deftly captures the simmering rage that ultimately transforms Moss from a quiet teenager to a committed activist against a brutal, menacing system." Publishers Weekly.

Ostertag, Molly

The **girl** from the sea. Molly Knox Ostertag; color by Maarta Laiho. Graphix, an imprint of Scholastic, 2021. 208 p.

Grades: 7 8 9 10 **Fic**

1. Teenage girls 2. Teenage romance 3. Lesbian teenagers 4. Selkies 5. Secrets 6. Canada 7. Romance comics 8. LGBTQIA comics 9. Fantasy comics
ISBN 9781338540581

Fifteen-year-old Morgan has a secret: she can't wait to escape the perfect little island where she lives. She's desperate to finish high school and escape her sad divorced mom, her volatile little brother, and worst of all, her great group of friends...who don't understand Morgan at all. Because really, Morgan's biggest secret is that she has a lot of secrets, including the one about wanting to kiss another girl. Then one night, Morgan is saved from drowning by a mysterious girl named Keltie. The two become friends and suddenly life on the island doesn't seem so stifling anymore. But Keltie has some secrets of her own. And as the girls start to fall in love, everything they're each trying to hide will find its way to the surface...whether Morgan is ready or not. Back cover.

"With a timely environmentalism subplot about how tourism and pollution affect seal habitats, the romance and coming-of-age narrative wind together in a story about identity, family, and friendship." School Library Journal

Ostlere, Cathy

Karma. Cathy Ostlere. Puffin Canada, 2011. 528 p.

Grades: 7 8 9 10 11 12 **Fic**

1. Children of suicide victims 2. Sikhs 3. Culture conflict 4.

Fifteen-year-old girls 5. Travelers 6. India
ISBN 9780670064526

In 1984, following her mother's suicide, 15-year-old Maya and her Sikh father travel to New Delhi from Canada to place her mother's ashes in their final resting place. On the night of their arrival, Prime Minister Indira Gandhi is assassinated, Maya and her father are separated when the city erupts in chaos, and Maya must rely on Sandeep, a boy she has just met, for survival.

"The novel's pace and tension will compel readers to read at a gallop, but then stop again and again to turn a finely crafted phrase, whether to appreciate the richness of the language and imagery or to reconsider the layers beneath a thought. This is a book in which readers will consider the roots and realities of destiny and chance. Karma is a spectacular, sophisticated tale that will stick with readers long after they're done considering its last lines." School Library Journal.

Owen, Margaret, 1986-

The **merciful** Crow. Margaret Owen. Henry Holt and Company, 2019 384 p.: Merciful Crow

Grades: 7 8 9 10   **Fic**
1. Witches 2. Fugitives 3. Staged deaths 4. Teenage girls 5. Euthanasia 6. Fantasy fiction
ISBN 9781250191922

LC 2018038716

Fie, a sixteen-year-old chieftain from a lowly caste of mercy-killers, must rely on her wits and bone magic to smuggle the crown prince of Sabor to safety.

"Memorable and filled with diverse characters with fluid sexualities and identities, this tale is both a satisfying standalone and the first half of a planned duology." Publishers Weekly

Padian, Maria

How to build a heart. Maria Padian. Algonquin, 2020. 352 p.
Grades: 8 9 10 11 12   **Fic**
1. Habitat for Humanity 2. Home (Concept) 3. Multiracial teenage girls 4. Social classes 5. Hispanic American families 6. Neighbors 7. Realistic fiction
ISBN 9781616208493

LC 2019007625

Izzy Crawford's family has been selected for a new home by Habitat for Humanity, near where the very attractive Sam lives, but just when her neighbor and best friend needs her most.

"While navigating the remnants of her Methodist father's legacy and her mother's deeply rooted Catholicism, Izzy must also explore her relationship with both sides of her family." Kirkus.

Paige, Danielle

Mera: tidebreaker. written by Danielle Paige; illustrated by Stephen Byrne. DC Ink, 2019. 192 p.
Grades: 7 8 9 10 11 12   **Fic**
1. Coups d'etat 2. Women superheroes 3. Rulers -- Succession 4. Teenage girls 5. Penal colonies 6. Superhero comics 7. Comics and Graphic novels
ISBN 9781401283391

LC 2018043960

When the Xebellian military plots to overthrow Atlantis and break free of its oppressive regime, Mera seizes the opportunity to take control over her own destiny by assassinating Arthur Curry—the long-lost prince and heir to the kingdom of Atlantis. But her mission gets sidetracked when Mera and Arthur unexpectedly fall in love. Will Arthur Curry be the king at Mera's side, or will he die under her blade as she attempts to free her people from persecution?

"An exciting and romantic look at a lesser-known superhero, for DC comics followers and newcomers alike." School Library Journal.

Palacio, R. J.

★ **Wonder**. by R.J. Palacio. Alfred A. Knopf, 2012. 315 p.
Grades: 3 4 5 6   **Fic**
1. Boys with disfigurements 2. Birth defects 3. Middle school students 4. Self-acceptance in boys 5. Kindness in children 6. Realistic fiction
ISBN 9780375869020

LC 2011027133

Ten-year-old Auggie Pullman, who was born with extreme facial abnormalities and was not expected to survive, goes from being homeschooled to entering fifth grade at a private middle school in Manhattan, which entails enduring the taunting and fear of his classmates as he struggles to be seen as just another student.

Pancholy, Maulik, 1974-

The **best** at it. Maulik Pancholy. Balzer + Bray, [2019] 336 p.
Grades: 5 6 7 8   **Fic**
1. East Indian American boys 2. Identity (Psychology) 3. Self-acceptance 4. Questioning (Sexual or gender identity) 5. Gay boys 6. Indiana 7. Coming-of-age stories 8. Realistic fiction
ISBN 9780062866417

LC 2019009804

Twelve-year-old Rahul Kapoor, an Indian-American boy growing up in small-town Indiana, struggles to come to terms with his identity, including that he may be gay.

"An Indian American boy struggles with his sexuality and mental health while finding a place for himself in seventh grade. Rings true." Kirkus.

Paolini, Christopher

Eragon. Christopher Paolini. Alfred A. Knopf, 2003. 528 p.: Inheritance cycle (Christopher Paolini)
Grades: 7 8 9 10   **Fic**
1. Dragons 2. Fifteen-year-old boys 3. Revenge 4. Boys and dragons 5. Magic 6. High fantasy 7. Fantasy fiction
ISBN 0375826688

LC 2003047481

When fifteen-year-old Eragon comes to learn that he is a gifted Dragon Rider, he realizes that his destiny is to fight the evil powers that will bring complete destruction to the Empire and so leaves his quiet life as a farm boy to succeed in his one true mission in life.

"This unusual, powerful tale . . . is the first book in the planned Inheritance trilogy. . . . The telling remains constantly fresh and fluid, and [the author] has done a fine job of creating an appealing and convincing relationship between the youth and the dragon." Booklist.

Park, Linda Sue

Forest of wonders. Linda Sue Park; illustrated by Jim Madsen. HarperCollins, 2016. 352 p.: Wing & claw
Grades: 4 5 6 7   **Fic**
1. Talking animals 2. Transformations (Magic) 3. Botany 4. Bats 5. Magic 6. High fantasy 7. Fantasy fiction
ISBN 9780062327383

When an injured bat crashes into Raffa's life, he invents a cure from a rare crimson vine that he finds deep in the forest. The powers of the vine are stronger than Raffa could have imagined. His remedy saves the animal but also transforms it into something much more than an ordinary bat, with far-reaching consequences. Raffa's experiments lead him away from home to the forbidding city of Gilden, where troubling discoveries make him question who he can trust.

"With its engaging hero, talking animals, arcane magic, moral issues, and unresolved plot, this first of a proposed trilogy promises more exciting forest wonders." Kirkus.

Keeping score. Linda Sue Park. Clarion Books, c2008. 202 p.

Grades: 4 5 6 7   **Fic**
    1. 1950s 2. Baseball fans 3. Korean War veterans 4. Intergenerational friendship 5. Soldiers 6. Traumatic shock 7. Brooklyn, New York City
ISBN 0618927999

LC 2007046522

In Brooklyn in 1951, a die-hard Giants fan teaches nine-year-old Maggie, who is a "Bums" (Dodgers) fan, how to use a technique to keep score of a baseball game which creates a special friendship between them.

"Maggie's perspective is authentically childlike and engaging, and her relations with her family and friends ring true. . . . This finely crafted novel should resonate with a wide audience of readers." School Library Journal.

A **long** walk to water: based on a true story. by Linda Sue Park. Clarion Books, 2009. 128 p.

Grades: 6 7 8 9 10   **Fic**
    1. Dut, Salva, 1974- 2. Refugees 3. Civil war 4. Survival 5. Eleven-year-old boys 6. Water 7. Sudan 8. Realistic fiction
ISBN 9780547251271

LC 2009048857

When the Sudanese civil war reaches his village in 1985, eleven-year-old Salva becomes separated from his family and must walk with other Dinka tribe members through southern Sudan, Ethiopia, and Kenya in search of safe haven. Based on the life of Salva Dut, who, after emigrating to America in 1996, began a project to dig water wells in Sudan.

"This is a spare, immediate account. . . . Young readers will be stunned by the triumphant climax of the former refugee who makes a difference." Booklist.

★ The **one** thing you'd save. by Linda Sue Park; illustrated by Robert Sae-Heng. Clarion Books, 2021. 72 p.

Grades: 4 5 6 7 8   **Fic**
    1. Middle school students 2. Disasters 3. Emotions 4. Personal belongings 5. Homework 6. Novels in verse 7. Illustrated books
ISBN 9781328515131

If your house were on fire, what one thing would you save? Newbery Medalist Linda Sue Park explores different answers to this provocative question in linked poems that capture the diverse voices of a middle school class. Illustrated with black-and-white art.

"This is a combination of piquant premise and accessible, engaging text, resulting in an unexpected hi-lo title that will invite both reluctant and enthusiastic literati to reconsider their possessions. It also cries out to be a classroom read or—even readaloud or readers' theater." Bulletin of the Center for Children's Books

★ **Prairie** lotus. Linda Sue Park. Clarion Books, 2020 272 p.

Grades: 4 5 6 7   **Fic**
    1. 1880s 2. Multiracial teenage girls 3. Fathers and daughters 4. Prejudice 5. Frontier and pioneer life 6. Dressmaking 7. Dakota Territory 8. Historical fiction
ISBN 9781328781505

LC 2019007372

In Dakota Territory in the 1880s, half-Chinese Hanna and her white father face racism and resistance to change as they try to make a home for themselves.

"Fans of the Little House books will find many of the small satisfactions of Laura's stories—the mouthwatering descriptions of victuals, the attention to smart building construction, the glorious details of pleats and poplins—here in abundance. Park brings new depth to these well-trodden tales, though, as she renders visible both the xenophobia of the town's white residents, which ranges in expression from microaggressions to full-out assault, and Hanna's fight to overcome it with empathy and dignity." Kirkus

Project Mulberry: a novel. by Linda Sue Park. Clarion Books, c2005. 225 p.

Grades: 5 6 7 8   **Fic**
    1. Toleration in children 2. Silkworms 3. Interracial friendship 4. Korean American girls 5. African American boys 6. Illinois 7. Realistic fiction
ISBN 0618477861

LC 2004018159

While working on a project for an after-school club, Julia, a Korean American girl, and her friend Patrick learn not just about silkworms, but also about tolerance, prejudice, friendship, patience, and more. Between the chapters are short dialogues between the author and main character about the writing of the book.

"The unforgettable family and friendship story, the quiet, almost unspoken racism, and the excitement of the science make this a great cross-curriculum title." Booklist.

★ A **single** shard. Linda Sue Park. Clarion Books, c2001. 152 p.

Grades: 5 6 7 8   **Fic**
    1. 12th century 2. Boy orphans 3. Potters 4. Twelve-year-old boys 5. Preteen boys 6. Pottery 7. Korea 8. Historical fiction
ISBN 0395978270

LC 00043102

Newbery Medal, 2002.

Tree-ear, a twelve-year-old orphan in medieval Korea, lives under a bridge in a potters' village, and longs to learn how to throw the delicate celadon ceramics himself.

"This quiet, but involving, story draws readers into a very different time and place. . . . A well-crafted novel with an unusual setting." Booklist.

Storm warning. Linda Sue Park. Scholastic, 2010. 190 p.: The 39 clues.

Grades: 4 5 6 7   **Fic**
    1. Child adventurers 2. Brothers and sisters 3. Treasure troves 4. Voyages and travels 5. Orphans 6. Adventure stories
ISBN 9780545090674

Finds Amy and Dan learning the truth about the Madrigals and Grace Cahill's alternate will, discoveries that lead to the revelation of a secret about their family and a showdown with the Man in Black.

Trust no one. Linda Sue Park. Scholastic, 2012. 192 p.: The 39 clues.

Grades: 4 5 6 7   **Fic**
    1. Orphans 2. Kidnapping 3. Moles (Spies) 4. Ransom 5. Clues 6. Adventure stories
ISBN 9780545298438

Returned by a surprising twist to their first mission on U.S. soil since the beginning of the Clue hunt, Amy and Dan discover evidence of a mole in their organization who proves to be one of their closest confidantes and who reveals, even more disturbingly, the true agenda of the Vespers.

★ **When** my name was Keoko. by Linda Sue Park. Clarion Books, 2002. 199 p.

Grades: 5 6 7 8   **Fic**

     1. Second World War era (1939-1945) 2. 1940s 3. Courage in children 4. Military occupation 5. Resistance to government 6. Determination (Personal quality) 7. Culture conflict 8. Korea 9. Historical fiction
     ISBN 0618133356

           LC 2001032487

With national pride and occasional fear, a brother and sister face the increasingly oppressive occupation of Korea by Japan during World War II, which threatens to suppress Korean culture entirely.

"Park is a masterful prose stylist, and her characters are developed beautifully. She excels at making traditional Korean culture accessible to Western readers." Voice of Youth Advocates.

Includes bibliographical references (p. 197-199).

Parker, Morgan

Who put this song on? Morgan Parker. Delacorte Press, 2019 325 p.

Grades: 7 8 9 10 11   **Fic**

     1. African American teenage girls 2. Teenage girls with depression 3. Misfits (Persons) 4. Depression 5. Christian schools 6. California 7. Coming-of-age stories 8. Realistic fiction 9. African American fiction
     ISBN 9780525707516

           LC 2018051979

17-year-old Morgan is a black teen triumphantly figuring out her identity when her conservative town deems depression as a lack of faith, and blackness as something to be politely ignored. Provided by publisher.

"This fresh read provides a positive and inclusive take on mental health and wellness and offers readers some tools to survive on their own." Booklist.

Parker, Natalie C.

Seafire. Natalie C. Parker. Razorbill, 2018 384 p.: Seafire trilogy

Grades: 7 8 9 10 11 12   **Fic**

     1. Women ship captains 2. Revenge 3. Seafaring life 4. Ship captains 5. Insurgency 6. Sea stories 7. Dystopian fiction
     ISBN 9780451478801

           LC 2018012935

Follows Caledonia Styx, captain of her own ship, the Mors Navis, and its all-female crew as they strive to defeat the powerful fleet of Aric Athair, the vicious warlord who has taken their homes and families.

"Along with openly feminist themes, the crew is racially diverse and in this future world, skin color appears to carry no connotations." Kirkus.

Steel tide. by Natalie C. Parker. Razorbill, 2019. 384 p.: Seafire trilogy

Grades: 7 8 9 10 11 12   **Fic**

     1. Women ship captains 2. Seafaring life 3. Insurgency 4. Warlords 5. Adventure 6. Sea stories 7. Dystopian fiction
     ISBN 9780451478832

           LC 2019016804

Rescued by the Blades, a nomadic crew hiding from Aric Athair, Caledonia seeks their help to find the Mors Navis and her sisters, defeat Aric's fleet, and take back the Bullet seas.

"A strong purchase for YA fantasy shelves." School Library Journal.

Parkinson, Siobhan

Blue like Friday. by Siobhan Parkinson. Roaring Brook Press, 2008. 160 p.

Grades: 4 5 6 7   **Fic**

     1. Practical jokes 2. Synesthesia 3. Family problems 4. Stepfathers 5. Fathers -- Death 6. Ireland 7. Realistic fiction
     ISBN 9781596433403

           LC 2007031106

When Olivia helps her quirky friend Hal, whose synesthesia causes him to experience everything in colors, with a prank intended to get rid of Hal's potential stepfather, there are unexpected consequences, including the disappearance of Hal's mother.

"Parkinson creates a warm, moving story of real families facing real problems. . . . The economy of her prose is admirable; all the characters are well drawn." Booklist.

Partridge, Elizabeth

Dogtag summer. Elizabeth Partridge. Bloomsbury Books for Young Readers, 2011. 240 p.

Grades: 4 5 6 7   **Fic**

     1. 1980s 2. Vietnamese American girls 3. Adopted girls 4. Vietnam veterans 5. Adoption 6. Families 7. California 8. Historical fiction
     ISBN 9781599901831

           LC 2010025515

In the summer of 1980 before she starts junior high school in Santa Rosa, California, Tracy, who was adopted from Vietnam when she was six years old, finds an old ammo box with a dog tag and picture that bring up painful memories for both her Vietnam-veteran father and her.

"This gripping yet tender coming-of-age story reveals multiple nuanced perspectives of the Vietnam War and its aftermath. . . . Powerful historical fiction." Publishers Weekly.

Pasternack, Sofiya

Anya and the nightingale. by Sofiya Pasternack. New York: 2020. 416 p.: Anya

Grades: 5 6 7   **Fic**

     1. 10th century 2. Medieval period (476-1492) 3. Jewish girls 4. Dragons 5. Best friends 6. Rescues 7. Folktales, Russian 8. Kievan Rus 9. Russia 10. Historical fantasy 11. Mythological fiction
     ISBN 9780358006022

           LC 2019041632

Thirteen-year-old Anya sets out to find her missing father but instead travels to Kiev, where she meets the tsar, dines with a rabbi, and rescues two brothers from a dangerous monster lurking beneath the city.

"Once again, Pasternak pens a lively tale woven with magic and the Jewish faith, wherein friendships are tested both by circumstance and new romantic feelings, and threats are effectively neutralized through communication and compassion." Booklist

Paterson, Katherine

Bread and roses, too. by Katherine Paterson. Clarion Books, 2006. 288 p.

Grades: 5 6 7 8   **Fic**

     1. 1910s 2. Labor unions 3. Strikes -- Textile industry 4. Child labor 5. Labor-management relations 6. Working class 7.

Lawrence, Massachusetts 8. Massachusetts 9. Historical fiction 10. Coming-of-age stories
ISBN 0618654798

LC 2005031702

Jake and Rosa, two children, form an unlikely friendship as they try to survive and understand the 1912 Bread and Roses strike of mill workers in Lawrence, Massachusetts.

"Paterson has skillfully woven true events and real historical figures into the fictional story and created vivid settings, clearly drawn characters, and a strong sense of the hardship and injustice faced by the mostly immigrant mill workers." School Library Journal.

★ **Bridge** to Terabithia. Katherine Paterson; illustrated by Donna Diamond. Crowell, 1977. 128 p.

Grades: 4 5 6 7 **Fic**

1. Children and death 2. Rural life 3. Boy/girl relations 4. Ten-year-olds 5. Imagination in children 6. Realistic fiction 7. Classics
ISBN 0690013590

LC 77002221

Newbery Medal, 1978.

Ten-year-old Jesse Aarons, who has lived all his life on a farm in Virginia, becomes friends with Leslie Burke, a "city girl" who has moved into a farmhouse down the road and opens doors to culture and imaginative play. But then tragedy strikes.

"Jess and his family are magnificently characterized; the book abounds in descriptive vignettes, humorous sidelights on the clash of cultures, and realistic depictions of rural school life." Horn Book.

★ The **great** Gilly Hopkins. Crowell, 1978. 148 p.

Grades: 5 6 7 8 **Fic**

1. Foster children 2. Mother-separated girls 3. Eleven-year-old girls 4. Fear in children 5. Foster home care 6. Realistic fiction 7. Classics
ISBN 0690038380

LC 77027075

National Book Award for Children's Books, 1979.

"A well-structured story, [this] has vitality of writing style, natural dialogue, deep insight in characterization, and a keen sense of the fluid dynamics in human relationships." Bulletin of the Center for Children's Books.

Jacob have I loved. Katherine Paterson. Crowell, 1980. 216 p.

Grades: 5 6 7 8 **Fic**

1. Sisters 2. Twins 3. Sibling rivalry 4. Girls -- Identity 5. Self-fulfillment 6. Chesapeake Bay Region 7. Classics
ISBN 0690040784

LC 80000668

Newbery Medal, 1981.

Feeling deprived all her life of schooling, friends, mother, and even her name by her twin sister, Louise finally begins to find her identity.

"Each incident and feeling in the life of her young protagonist rings true because the younger voice is so alive and direct. This is a book full of humor and compassion and sharpness." Bulletin of the Center for Children's Books.

Lyddie. Katherine Paterson. Lodestar Books, 1991. 182 p.

Grades: 5 6 7 8 9 **Fic**

1. 19th century 2. Poor girls 3. Textile mills 4. Child labor exploitation 5. Women textile workers 6. Self-reliance in girls 7. Lowell, Massachusetts 8. Historical fiction 9. Classics
ISBN 9780525673385

LC 90042944

Impoverished Vermont farm girl Lyddie Worthen is determined to gain her independence by becoming a factory worker in Lowell, Massachusetts, in the 1840s.

"Not only does the book contain a riveting plot, engaging characters, and a splendid setting, but the language—graceful, evocative, and rhythmic—incorporates the rural speech patterns of Lyddie's folk, the simple Quaker expressions of the farm neighbors, and the lilt of fellow mill girl Bridget's Irish brogue. . . . A superb story of grit, determination, and personal growth." Horn Book.

The **same** stuff as stars. Katherine Paterson. Clarion Books c2002. 242 p.

Grades: 5 6 7 8 **Fic**

1. Family problems 2. Brothers and sisters 3. Great-grandmothers 4. Self-reliance 5. Abandoned children
ISBN 0618247440

LC 2002003967

When Angel's self-absorbed mother leaves her and her younger brother with their poor great-grandmother, the eleven-year-old girl worries not only about her mother and brother, her imprisoned father, the frail old woman, but also about a mysterious man who begins sharing with her the wonder of the stars.

"Paterson's deft hand at characterization, her insight into the human soul, and her glorious prose make this book one to rejoice over." Voice of Youth Advocates.

Patrick, Cat

Revived. by Cat Patrick. Little, Brown, 2012. 352 p.

Grades: 7 8 9 10 11 12 **Fic**

1. Death 2. Emotions in teenage girls 3. Teenagers and death 4. Fifteen-year-old girls 5. Drugs 6. Science fiction
ISBN 9780316094627

LC 2011026950

Having been brought back from the dead repeatedly by a top-secret government super drug called Revive, and forced to move so the public does not learn the truth, fifteen-year-old Daisy meets people worth living for and begins to question the heavy-handed government controls she has dealt with for eleven years.

Patrick, Denise Lewis

A **matter** of souls. Denise Lewis Patrick. Carolrhoda Lab, [2014] 186 p.

Grades: 7 8 9 10 11 12 **Fic**

1. African Americans 2. Race relations 3. Slavery 4. Southern States 5. Short stories 6. African American fiction
ISBN 9780761392804

LC 2013017597

A series of vignettes reveal life in the Deep South for African Americans as they experience discrimination in a doctor's office, lynching, and other forms of oppression, especially during the 1960s.

"Eight short stories with long memory cut to the quickall the more as they could be true. Patrick's tales from the distant and not-so-distant past shed fresh light on interracial and intraracial conflicts that shape and often distort the realities of African-Americans. . . . The plots and characters change from one story to the next, but each one artfully tells a poignant truth without flinching. Shocking, informative and powerful, this volume offers spectacular literary snapshots of black history and culture." Kirkus.

Patterson, James, 1947-

Ali Cross. James Patterson. Jimmy Patterson, 2019. 320 p.: Ali Cross

Grades: 4 5 6 7   **Fic**
1. Boy detectives 2. Fathers and sons 3. Missing children 4. Best friends 5. Clues 6. Mysteries
ISBN 9780316530415

Published to coincide with the release of the 25th entry in Patterson's best-selling Alex Cross thrillers, a series debut starring Alex's son, Ali, follows his desperate search for a missing friend and clues proving his father's innocence against a backdrop of neighborhood burglaries.

The **angel** experiment. by James Patterson. Little, Brown, 2005. 432 p.: Maximum Ride
Grades: 7 8 9 10   **Fic**
1. Genetically engineered teenagers 2. Genetic engineering 3. Human experimentation in medicine 4. Kidnapping 5. Rescues 6. Science fiction
ISBN 031615556X

LC 2004018623

After the mutant Erasers abduct the youngest member of their group, the "birdkids," who are the result of genetic experimentation, take off in pursuit and find themselves struggling to understand their own origins and purpose.

"Smart-mouthed sympathetic characters and copious butt-kicking make this fast read pure escapist pleasure." Horn Book Guide.

★ **Becoming** Muhammad Ali. James Patterson, Kwame Alexander; Dawud Anyabwile. JIMMY Patterson Books/Little Brown and Company, 2020. 224 p.
Grades: 4 5 6 7 8   **Fic**
1. Ali, Muhammad, 1942-2016 2. Boy boxers 3. African American boys 4. Racism 5. Segregation 6. African American boxers 7. Kentucky 8. Biographical fiction 9. Novels in verse
ISBN 9780316498166

Before he was a household name, Cassius Clay was a kid with struggles like any other. Kwame Alexander and James Patterson join forces to vividly depict his life up to age seventeen in both prose and verse, including his childhood friends, struggles in school, the racism he faced, and his discovery of boxing. Readers will learn about Cassius' family and neighbors in Louisville, Kentucky, and how, after a thief stole his bike, Cassius began training as an amateur boxer at age twelve. Before long, he won his first Golden Gloves bout and began his transformation into the unrivaled Muhammad Ali.

"Told in 'Ten Rounds,' this utterly delightful story about Ali's childhood is a smash hit. Patterson handles narrator Lucky's prose while Alexander crafts Cassius's poetry." School Library Journal

Best nerds forever. James Patterson and Chris Grabenstein. Little Brown & Co 2021 288 p.
Grades: 4 5 6 7   **Fic**
1. Misfits (Persons) 2. Hit-and-run victims 3. Death 4. Ghosts 5. Middle school students 6. Fantasy fiction
ISBN 9780316500241

Being "nerdy" in middle school isn't a bad thing—I should know! Me and my friends are nerds. Some of us are geeky but funny, smart but never boring. One is a jock but not a jerk. We don't quite fit. But we're funny. We're fun. We're total chaos. And we own it—until one of us is targeted by a maniac. It will take all of our nerdiest skills to Sherlock Holmes our way out of one dangerous mess.

"However somber the premise, the creators inject a lively underlying current and a sense of optimism as the new friends make the most of their spectral status and face the unknown future." Publishers Weekly

Homeroom diaries. by James Patterson and Lisa Papademetriou; illustrated by Keino. 272 p.
Grades: 7 8 9 10   **Fic**
1. Foster teenagers 2. Teenage girl misfits 3. Cliques 4. High schools 5. Schools 6. Realistic fiction 7. Diary novels 8. Illustrated books
ISBN 9780316207621

LC 2013016061

Seventeen-year-old Margaret "Cuckoo" Clark keeps a journal detailing the trials and tribulations of high school life as she and her close-knit group of outcast friends try to break down the barriers between their school's "warring nations."

"Despite the fact that serious issues (a negligent mother, an attempted sexual assault, and an incident of cyberbullying) are at play, the lighthearted tone adds levity to the work. The novel is fully illustrated with humorous artwork that contributes to the story in a meaningful way. Fans of the popular diary fiction genre (as well as those simply looking for an approachable and quick read) will find much to enjoy here." School Library Journal.

House of robots. James Patterson and Chris Grabenstein; illustrated by Juliana Neufeld. 336 p.: House of robots
Grades: 4 5 6 7 8   **Fic**
1. Robots 2. Inventions 3. Middle schools 4. Schools 5. Families 6. Metafiction 7. Science fiction 8. Humorous stories
ISBN 9780316405911

LC 2013041672

Fifth-grader Sammy Hayes-Rodriguez struggles to fit in when his inventor mother requires him to take her latest creation, a robotic 'brother,' to school with him to learn to become a student. Provided by publisher.

"A fast-moving plot, lots of jokes, and a host of weird robots will draw readers in." School Library Journal.

Like father, like son. James Patterson Jimmy Patterson, 2021. 320 p.: Ali Cross
Grades: 4 5 6 7   **Fic**
1. Boy detectives 2. Fathers and sons 3. Gunshot victims 4. Best friends 5. Clues 6. Mysteries
ISBN 9780316500135

Ali Cross is back in the gripping sequel to Ali Cross, the best-selling mystery that introduced readers to detective Alex Cross's son. In Ali's toughest case ever, his friend Zoe is in trouble after Ali and his friends witnessed a crime in Anacostia Park, and it's up to Ali to figure out why Zoe is lying to the police—and who she's protecting.

"Overall, this is a solid follow-up that shows Ali developing as a sleuth even as he's a young boy trying to make sense of his world. Important messages regarding social justice are imparted." Kirkus

★ **Middle** school: the worst years of my life. James Patterson and Chris Tebbetts; illustrated by Laura Park. Little, Brown, 2011. 288 p.: Middle school (James Patterson)
Grades: 4 5 6 7   **Fic**
1. Rules 2. Misbehavior in boys 3. Children and single parent dating 4. Misbehavior 5. Personal conduct 6. Realistic fiction
ISBN 9780316101875

LC 2010022852

When Rafe Kane enters middle school, he teams up with his best friend, "Leo the Silent," to create a game to make school more fun by trying to break every rule in the school's code of conduct.

"The book's ultrashort chapters, dynamic artwork, and message that normal is boring should go a long way toward assuring kids who don't fit the mold that there's a place for them, too." Publishers Weekly.

Pattou, Edith

East. Edith Pattou. Harcourt, 2003. 498 p.

Grades: 7 8 9 10   **Fic**

1. Bears 2. Spells (Magic) 3. Enchantment 4. Trolls 5. Fourteen-year-old girls 6. Fantasy fiction 7. Fairy tale and folklore-inspired fiction
ISBN 0152045635

LC 2003002338

A young woman journeys to a distant castle on the back of a great white bear who is the victim of a cruel enchantment.

"Readers with a taste for fantasy and folklore will embrace Pattou's . . . lushly rendered retelling of 'East of the Sun and West of the Moon'." Publishers Weekly.

Paulsen, Gary

Brian's return. Delacorte Press, 1999. 117 p.: Brian's saga

Grades: 6 7 8 9   **Fic**

1. Self-reliance in teenagers 2. Wilderness survival 3. Self-reliance 4. Teenage boys 5. Children of divorced parents 6. Adventure stories
ISBN 0385325002

LC 9824278

After having survived alone in the wilderness, Brian finds that he can no longer live in the city but must return to the place where he really belongs.

"This work is bold, confident and persuasive, its transcendental themes powerfully seductive." Publishers Weekly.

Brian's winter. Delacorte Press, 1996. 133 p.: Brian's saga

Grades: 6 7 8 9   **Fic**

1. Wilderness survival 2. Survival (after airplane accidents, shipwrecks, etc) 3. Winter 4. Children of divorced parents 5. Thirteen-year-old boys 6. Canada 7. Adventure stories 8. Survival stories
ISBN 0385321988

LC 95041337 /AC

Instead of being rescued from a plane crash, as in the author's book Hatchet, this story portrays what would have happened to Brian had he been forced to survive a winter in the wilderness with only his survival pack and hatchet.

"The same formula that worked before is successful here: the driving pace of the narration, the breathtaking descriptions of nature, and the boy who triumphs on the merits of efficient problem solving. The author's ability to cast a spell, mesmerize his audience, and provide a clinic in winter survival is reason enough to buy this novel." School Library Journal.

Hatchet. Gary Paulsen. Bradbury Press, 1987. 195 p.: Brian's saga

Grades: 6 7 8 9   **Fic**

1. Airplane accidents 2. Wilderness survival 3. Survival (after airplane accidents, shipwrecks, etc) 4. Children of divorced parents 5. Thirteen-year-old boys 6. Canada 7. Survival stories 8. Adventure stories 9. Classics
ISBN 0027701301

LC 87006416

After a plane crash, thirteen-year-old Brian spends fifty-four days in the wilderness, learning to survive initially with only the aid of a hatchet given him by his mother, and learning also to survive his parents' divorce.

"Paulsen's knowledge of our national wilderness is obvious and beautifully shared." Voice of Youth Advocates.

Notes from the dog. Gary Paulsen. Wendy Lamb Books, c2009. 133 p.

Grades: 5 6 7 8   **Fic**

1. People with breast cancer 2. House sitters 3. Neighbors 4. Teenage boys 5. Self-confidence 6. Realistic fiction
ISBN 9780385738453

LC 2009013300

When Johanna shows up at the beginning of summer to house-sit next door to Finn, he has no idea of the profound effect she will have on his life by the time summer vacation is over.

"The plot is straightforward, but Paulsen's thoughtful characters are compelling and their interactions realistic. This emotional, coming-of-age journey about taking responsibilty for one's own happiness and making personal connections will not disappoint." Publishers Weekly.

Soldier's heart: being the story of the enlistment and due service of the boy Charley Goddard in the First Minnesota Volunteers: a novel of the Civil War.. Delacorte Press, 1998. 106 p.

Grades: 7 8 9 10   **Fic**

1. United States. Army. Minnesota Infantry Regiment, 1st (1861-1864) 2. American Civil War era (1861-1865) 3. Children and war 4. Post-traumatic stress disorder 5. Fifteen-year-old boys 6. Teenage boys 7. Teenage soldiers 8. United States 9. Historical fiction 10. War stories 11. Classics
ISBN 0385324987

LC 98010038

Eager to enlist, fifteen-year-old Charley has a change of heart after experiencing both the physical horrors and mental anguish of Civil War combat.

The **Transall** saga. Delacorte Press, 1998. 248 p.

Grades: 5 6 7 8   **Fic**

1. Time travel 2. Thirteen-year-old boys 3. Wilderness survival 4. Teenagers 5. Survival 6. Science fiction
ISBN 0385321961

LC 97040773

While backpacking in the desert, thirteen-year-old Mark falls into a tube of blue light and is transported into a more primitive world, where he must use his knowledge and skills to survive.

"A riveting tale of adventure and action." Voice of Youth Advocates.

Woods runner. Gary Paulsen. Wendy Lamb Books, c2010. 164 p.

Grades: 6 7 8 9   **Fic**

1. Revolutionary America (1775-1783) 2. 1770s 3. Prisoners 4. Trackers 5. Tracking and trailing 6. Colonists 7. Frontier and pioneer life 8. Pennsylvania 9. United States 10. Historical fiction
ISBN 9780385907514

LC 2009027397

From his 1776 Pennsylvania homestead, thirteen-year-old Samuel, who is a highly-skilled woodsman, sets out toward New York City to rescue his parents from the band of British soldiers and Indians who kidnapped them after slaughtering most of their community. Includes historical notes.

"Paulsen fortifies this illuminating and gripping story with interspersed historical sections that offer details about frontier life and the war (such as technology, alliances, and other period information), helping place Sam's struggles in context." Publishers Weekly.

Pausewang, Gudrun

Dark hours. Annick Press, 2006. 212 p.

Grades: 6 7 8 9   **Fic**
1. Second World War era (1939-1945) 2. Bombing 3. World War II -- Children 4. World War II -- Refugees, German 5. World War II -- Moral and ethical aspects 6. Fifteen-year-old girls 7. Germany 8. Historical fiction 9. Translations
ISBN 1554510422
"Well written with suspense and powerful sentiments, this story will spark discussion." School Library Journal.

Traitor. Gudrun Pausewang; translated from the German by Rachel Ward. Carolrhoda Books, 2006. 220 p.
Grades: 7 8 9 10   **Fic**
1. Hitler Youth. 2. Second World War era (1939-1945) 3. 1940s 4. Prisoners of war 5. Escaped prisoners of war 6. Fifteen-year-old girls 7. Teenage girls 8. Teenagers 9. Germany 10. Historical fiction 11. War stories 12. Thrillers and suspense
ISBN 0822561956
                                               LC 2005033379
During the closing months of World War II, a fifteen-year-old German girl must decide whether or not to help an escaped Russian prisoner of war, despite the serious consequences if she does so.
"Pausewang presents an exciting and thought-provoking novel." School Library Journal.

Pearsall, Shelley
All of the above. by Shelley Pearsall. Little, Brown, 2006. 256 p.
Grades: 5 6 7 8   **Fic**
1. School projects 2. Middle school students 3. Inner city 4. Interpersonal relations 5. Seventh-graders 6. Realistic fiction
ISBN 031611524X
                                               LC 2005033109
Five urban middle school students, their teacher, and other community members relate how a school project to build the world's largest tetrahedron affects the lives of everyone involved.
"Pearsall's novel, based on a real event in 2002, is a delightful story about the power of a vision and the importance of a goal. The authentic voices of the students and the well-intentioned, supportive adults surrounding them illustrate all that is good about schools, family, friendship, and community." Booklist.

The **seventh** most important thing. Shelley Pearsall. Knopf Books for Young Readers, 2015. 192 p.
Grades: 5 6 7 8   **Fic**
1. Hampton, James, 1909-1964. 2. 1960s 3. Artists 4. Loss (Psychology) 5. Community service (Punishment) 6. Folk art 7. African Americans 8. Historical fiction 9. Coming-of-age stories
ISBN 9780553497281
                                               LC 2014047761
In 1963, 13-year-old Arthur is sentenced to community service helping the neighborhood Junk Man after he throws a brick at the old man's head in a moment of rage, but the junk he collects might be more important than he suspects. Inspired by the work of American folk artist James Hampton.
"A middle school student learns the meaning of redemption in this excellent coming-of-age story. For the rest of the country, it was the year President Kennedy was assassinated. For Arthur Owens, it would always be the year his Dad died." School Library Journal.

Pearson, Mary (Mary E.)
The **adoration** of Jenna Fox. Mary E. Pearson. Henry Holt, 2008. 272 p.: Jenna Fox chronicles

Grades: 7 8 9 10 11 12   **Fic**
1. Biotechnology 2. People in comas 3. Self-perception in teenage girls 4. Self-perception 5. Traffic accident victims 6. Science fiction
ISBN 9780805076684
                                               LC 2007027314
In the not-too-distant future, when biotechnological advances have made synthetic bodies and brains possible but illegal, a seventeen-year-old girl, recovering from a serious accident and suffering from memory lapses, learns a startling secret about her existence.
"The science . . . and the science fiction are fascinating, but what will hold readers most are the moral issues of betrayal, loyalty, sacrifice, and survival." Booklist.

Dance of thieves. Mary E. Pearson. Henry Holt and Company, 2018 512 p.: Dance of thieves
Grades: 8 9 10 11 12   **Fic**
1. Outlaws 2. Guards 3. Loyalty 4. Imaginary kingdoms 5. Thieves 6. High fantasy 7. Fantasy fiction
ISBN 9781250159014
When outlaw leader meets reformed thief, a cat-and-mouse game of false moves ensues, bringing them intimately together in a battle that may cost them their lives—and their hearts.

Vow of thieves. Mary E. Pearson. Henry Holt and Company, 2019 496 p.: Dance of thieves
Grades: 9 10 11 12   **Fic**
1. Thieves 2. Warriors 3. Loyalty 4. Imaginary wars and battles 5. Enemies 6. High fantasy 7. Fantasy fiction
ISBN 9781250162656
A sequel to Dance of Thieves finds an ominous warning overshadowing Kazi and Jase's return to Tor's Watch before a violent attack separates the pair, forcing them to pursue unexpected alliances.— Atlas Publishing.
"The two volumes work most effectively as a pair—the seeds for this book were planted skillfully throughout the first, but it is here that they take glorious root." Booklist

Peck, Richard, 1934-2018
Are you in the house alone? Richard Peck. Viking, 1976. 156 p.
Grades: 8 9 10 11 12   **Fic**
1. Stalking 2. Teenage rape victims 3. Threat (Psychology) 4. Rape case prosecution 5. High school girls 6. New York (State) 7. Realistic fiction 8. Thrillers and suspense
ISBN 0440902274
                                               LC 76028810
Gail, a rape victim, learns she must prove her assailant's guilt in order to see him convicted.

★ The **best** man. Richard Peck. Dial Books for Young Readers, [2016] 240 p.
Grades: 4 5 6 7   **Fic**
1. Role models 2. Bullying and bullies 3. Weddings 4. Families 5. Schools 6. Realistic fiction 7. Coming-of-age stories
ISBN 9780803738393
                                               LC 2015049803
Archer has four important role models in his life—his dad, his grandfather, his uncle Paul, and his favorite teacher, Mr. McLeod. When Uncle Paul and Mr. McLeod get married, Archer's sixth-grade year becomes one he'll never forget.

"It's an indelible portrait of what it looks like to grow up in an age of viral videos and media frenzies, undergirded by the same powerful sense of family that characterizes so much of Peck's work." Publishers Weekly.

Fair weather. by Richard Peck. Dial Books, c2001. 130 p.
Grades: 5 6 7 8 **Fic**
    1. Buffalo Bill, 1846-1917 2. Russell, Lillian, 1861-1922 3. 1890s 4. Family vacations 5. Exhibitions 6. Aunts 7. Thirteen-year-old girls 8. Families 9. Chicago, Illinois 10. Humorous stories 11. Historical fiction
ISBN 0803725167
                    LC   00055561
In 1893, thirteen-year-old Rosie and members of her family travel from their Illinois farm to Chicago to visit Aunt Euterpe and attend the World's Columbian Exposition which, along with an encounter with Buffalo Bill and Lillian Russell, turns out to be a life-changing experience for everyone.
"Peck's unforgettable characters, cunning dialogue and fast-paced action will keep readers in stitches." Publishers Weekly.

★ A **long** way from Chicago: a novel in stories. Richard Peck. Dial Books for Young Readers, 1998. 148 p.
Grades: 5 6 7 8 **Fic**
    1. Depression era (1929-1941) 2. Depressions 1929-1941 3. Social problems 4. Grandmother and child 5. Small town life 6. Rural life 7. Illinois 8. Historical fiction
ISBN 0803722907
                    LC   98010953
A boy recounts his annual summer trips to rural Illinois with his sister during the Great Depression to visit their larger-than-life grandmother.
"The novel reveals a strong sense of place, a depth of characterization, and a rich sense of humor." Horn Book.

★ A **season** of gifts. Richard Peck. Dial Books for Young Readers, 2009. 176 p.
Grades: 5 6 7 8 **Fic**
    1. 1950s 2. Moving, Household 3. Neighbors 4. Twelve-year-old boys 5. Senior women 6. Churches 7. Illinois 8. Historical fiction 9. Humorous stories
ISBN 9780803730823
                    LC   2008048050
Relates the surprising gifts bestowed on twelve-year-old Bob Barnhart and his family, who have recently moved to a small Illinois town in 1958, by their larger-than-life neighbor, Mrs. Dowdel.
"The type of down-home humor and vibrant characterizations Peck fans have come to adore re-emerge in full as Peck resurrects Mrs. Dowdel, the irrepressible, self-sufficient grandmother featured in A Year Down Yonder and A Long Way from Chicago." Publishers Weekly.

The **teacher's** funeral: a comedy in three parts. Richard Peck. Dial Books, c2004. 190 p.
Grades: 5 6 7 8 **Fic**
    1. 1900s (Decade) 2. Women teachers 3. Rural life 4. Brothers and sisters 5. Fifteen-year-old boys 6. Education 7. Middle West 8. Indiana 9. Historical fiction 10. Humorous stories
ISBN 0803727364
                    LC   2004004361
In rural Indiana in 1904, fifteen-year-old Russell's dream of quitting school and joining a wheat threshing crew is disrupted when his older sister takes over the teaching at his one-room schoolhouse after mean, old Myrt Arbuckle "hauls off and dies."

"The dry wit and unpretentious tone make the story's events comical, its characters memorable, and its conclusion unexpectedly moving." Booklist.

★ A **year** down yonder. Richard Peck. Dial Books for Young Readers, 2000. 130 p.
Grades: 5 6 7 8 **Fic**
    1. 1930s 2. Recession (Economics) 3. Grandmother and granddaughter 4. Social problems 5. Grandmothers 6. Rural life 7. Illinois 8. Historical fiction
ISBN 0803725183
                    LC   99043159
Newbery Medal, 2001.
During the recession of 1937, fifteen-year-old Mary Alice is sent to live with her feisty, larger-than-life grandmother in rural Illinois and comes to a better understanding of this fearsome woman.
"Peck has created a delightful, insightful tale that resounds with a storyteller's wit, humor, and vivid description." School Library Journal.

Peet, Mal
Tamar: a novel of espionage, passion and betrayal. Mal Peet. Candlewick Press, 2007. 424 p.
Grades: 8 9 10 11 12 **Fic**
    1. Second World War era (1939-1945) 2. 1990s 3. 1940s 4. Soldiers 5. Granddaughters 6. Undercover operations 7. World War II 8. Resistance to military occupation 9. Netherlands 10. Love stories 11. Historical fiction
ISBN 9780763634889
Carnegie Medal, 2005.
"Peet's plot is tightly constructed, and striking, descriptive language, full of metaphor, grounds the story." Booklist.

Pellegrino, Marge
Journey of dreams. Marge Pellegrino. Frances Lincoln Children's Books, 2009. 256 p.
Grades: 6 7 8 9 **Fic**
    1. 1980s 2. Mayan girls 3. Civil war 4. Storytelling 5. State-sponsored terrorism 6. Hiding 7. Guatemala 8. Historical fiction
ISBN 9781847800619
Set during the period of the "scorched earth" campaign by the Guatemalan army in the 1980's, Tomasa endures great hardship and heartbreak as death and destruction encircles her small village, her brother is forced into hiding to avoid being forced into recruitment, and the only home she has ever known is smashed to the ground.
"This novel will captivate both Latin American survivors of civil war and their peers. Outstanding." Kirkus.

Pena, Matt de la
We were here. Matt de la Pena. Delacorte Press, c2009. 357 p.
Grades: 7 8 9 10 11 12 **Fic**
    1. Multiracial teenage boys 2. Juvenile delinquents (Boys) 3. Runaway teenage boys 4. Identity (Psychology) 5. Self-discovery 6. California 7. Diary novels 8. Realistic fiction 9. Coming-of-age stories
ISBN 9780385736671
                    LC   2008044568
Haunted by the event that sentences him to time in a group home, Miguel breaks out with two unlikely companions and together they begin their journey down the California coast hoping to get to Mexico and a new life.

"The contemporary survival adventure will keep readers hooked, as will the tension that builds from the story's secrets." Booklist.

Pennypacker, Sara, 1951-

★ **Pax**. Sara Pennypacker; [illustrated by Jon Klassen]. Balzer + Bray, [2016] 224 p.: Pax

Grades: 4 5 6 7   **Fic**

1. Children of military personnel 2. Boys and animals 3. Human-animal relationships 4. Foxes 5. Boys and foxes 6. Adventure stories 7. Stories told by animals
ISBN 9780062377012

LC 2015015400

When his father enlists in the military and makes him return his beloved pet fox to the wild, Peter, who has been sent to live with his grandfather hundreds of miles away, embarks on a journey filled with astonishing discoveries in order to be reunited with his fox.

"Every moment in the graceful, fluid narrative is believable. Klassen's cover art has a sense of contained, powerful stillness. (Interior illustrations not seen.) Moving and poetic." Kirkus.

★ The **summer** of the gypsy moths. Sara Pennypacker. Balzer + Bray, 2012. 288 p.

Grades: 4 5 6   **Fic**

1. Foster children 2. Self-sufficiency 3. Resilience in girls 4. Resilience (Personal quality) 5. Loss (Psychology) 6. Cape Cod, Massachusetts 7. Realistic fiction
ISBN 9780061964206

LC 2011026095

A foster child named Angel and eleven-year-old Stella, who are living with Stella's great-aunt Louise at the Linger Longer Cottage Colony on Cape Cod, secretly assume responsibility for the vacation rentals when Louise unexpectedly dies and the girls are afraid of being returned to the foster care system.

Perera, Anna

Guantanamo boy. by Anna Perera. Albert Whitman, 2011. 352 p.

Grades: 7 8 9 10 11 12   **Fic**

1. Guantanamo Bay Detention Camp. 2. False imprisonment 3. Teenage prisoners 4. Muslim teenagers 5. Torture 6. False arrest 7. Guantanamo Bay Naval Base, Cuba 8. Pakistan 9. Realistic fiction
ISBN 9780807530771

LC 2010048016

Six months after the events of September 11, 2001, Khalid, a Muslim fifteen-year-old boy from England, is kidnapped during a family trip to Pakistan and imprisoned in Guantanamo Bay, Cuba, where he is held for two years suffering interrogations, water-boarding, isolation, and more for reasons unknown to him.

"Readers will feel every ounce of Khalid's terror, frustration, and helplessness in this disturbing look at a sad, ongoing chapter in contemporary history." Publishers Weekly.

Perez, Ashley Hope

What can(t) wait. by Ashley Hope Perez. Carolrhoda, 2011. 234 p.

Grades: 7 8 9 10   **Fic**

1. Mexican American teenage girls 2. Options, alternatives, choices 3. Self-fulfillment in teenage girls 4. Self-fulfillment 5. Expectation (Psychology) 6. Texas 7. Houston, Texas 8. Realistic

fiction
ISBN 9780761361558

LC 2010028175

Marooned in a broken-down Houston neighborhood—and in a Mexican immigrant family where making ends meet matters much more than making it to college—smart, talented Marissa seeks comfort elsewhere when her home life becomes unbearable.

"Prez fills a hole in YA lit by giving Marisa an authentic voice that smoothly blends Spanish phrases into dialogue and captures the pressures of both Latina life and being caught between two cultures." Kirkus.

Peréz, Celia C., 1972-

★ The **first** rule of punk. by Celia C. Peréz. Viking, 2017 304 p.

Grades: 3 4 5 6   **Fic**

1. Mexican American girls 2. Bands (Music) 3. Identity (Psychology) 4. Punk rock music 5. Moving to a new state 6. Chicago, Illinois 7. Illinois 8. Realistic fiction
ISBN 9780425290408

Twelve-year-old Maraia Luisa O'Neill-Morales (who really prefers to be called Malú reluctantly moves with her Mexican-American mother to Chicago and starts seventh grade with a bang—violating the dress code with her punk rock aesthetic and spurning the middle school's most popular girl in favor of starting a band with a group of like-minded weirdos.

"With tenderness and humor, Peréz explores the joys and challenges of being biracial. Readers will connect with Malú, a strong protagonist who leaps off the page and whose zine-inspired artistry boldly illustrates how she deals with life." School Library Journal.

Perez, Marlene

Dead is the new black. Marlene Perez. Harcourt, c2008. 190 p.: Dead is--

Grades: 7 8 9 10   **Fic**

1. Cheerleading 2. Psychic ability 3. Teenage girl detectives 4. Teenage detectives 5. Teenage boy/girl relations 6. California 7. Fantasy mysteries 8. Urban fantasy
ISBN 9780152064082

LC 2007027677

While dealing with her first boyfriend and suddenly being pressed into service as a substitute cheerleader, seventeen-year-old Daisy Giordano, daughter and sister of psychics but herself a "normal," attempts to help her mother discover who is behind a series of bizarre attacks on teenage girls in their little town of Nightshade, California.

"This is the witty and humorous first installment in a series; it provides romance, mystery, friendship, adventure, and the supernatural all rolled up in a fast-paced, plot-twisting story." School Library Journal.

Perkins, Lynne Rae

As easy as falling off the face of the earth. Lynne Rae Perkins. Greenwillow Books, 2010. 368 p.

Grades: 8 9 10 11 12   **Fic**

1. Teenage boys 2. Disasters, Minor 3. Voyages and travels 4. Accidents 5. Bad luck 6. Montana 7. Realistic fiction
ISBN 9780061870903

LC 2009042524

A teenaged boy encounters one comedic calamity after another when his train strands him in the middle of nowhere, and everything comes down to luck.

"The real pleasure is Perkins' relentlessly entertaining writing. . . . Wallowing in the wry humor, small but potent truths, and cheerful implausibility is an absolute delight." Booklist.

★ **Criss** cross. by Lynne Rae Perkins. Greenwillow Books, 2005. 368 p.

Grades: 6 7 8 9   **Fic**

1. 1960s 2. Small towns 3. Fourteen-year-olds 4. Teenagers -- Identity 5. Friendship 6. Interpersonal relations 7. Historical fiction 8. Coming-of-age stories
ISBN 0060092726

LC 2004054023

Newbery Medal, 2006.

Teenagers in a small town in the 1960s experience new thoughts and feelings, question their identities, connect, and disconnect as they search for the meaning of life and love.

"Debbie . . . and Hector . . . narrate most of the novel. Both are 14 years old. Hector is a fabulous character with a wry humor and an appealing sense of self-awareness. . . . The descriptive, measured writing includes poems, prose, haiku, and question-and-answer formats. There is a great deal of humor in this gentle story." School Library Journal.

Perkins, Mitali
Bamboo people. Mitali Perkins. Charlesbridge, 2010. 272 p.
Grades: 5 6 7 8   **Fic**

1. Boy soldiers 2. Boy refugees 3. Trust 4. Jungles 5. Revenge 6. Burma 7. War stories
ISBN 9781580893282

LC 2009005495

Two Burmese boys, one a Karenni refugee and the other the son of an imprisoned Burmese doctor, meet in the jungle and in order to survive they must learn to trust each other.

"Perkins seamlessly blends cultural, political, religious, and philosophical context into her story, which is distinguished by humor, astute insights into human nature, and memorable characters." Publishers Weekly.

Secret keeper. Mitali Perkins. Delacorte Press, 2009. 272 p.
Grades: 7 8 9 10   **Fic**

1. 1970s 2. Sisters 3. Arranged marriage 4. Gender role 5. Individuality in teenage girls 6. Family relationships 7. India
ISBN 9780385733403

LC 2008021475

In 1974 when her father leaves New Delhi, India, to seek a job in New York, Ashi, a tomboy at the advanced age of sixteen, feels thwarted in the home of her extended family in Calcutta where she, her mother, and sister must stay, and when her father dies before he can send for them, they must remain with their relatives and observe the old-fashioned traditions that Ashi hates.

"The plot is full of surprising secrets rooted in the characters' conflicts and deep connections with each other. The two sisters and their mutual sacrifices are both heartbreaking and hopeful." Booklist.

Tiger boy. Mitali Perkins; illustrated by Jamie Hogan. Charlesbridge, [2015] 140 p.
Grades: 3 4 5 6   **Fic**

1. Animal rescue 2. Scholarships and fellowships 3. Dilemmas 4. Poachers 5. Tigers 6. India 7. Sundarbans (Bangladesh and India)
ISBN 9781580896603

LC 2013049028

A tiger cub has escaped from a reserve in the Sunderbans in West Bengal, India, and Neel, a poor boy from the islands, is determined to find her in order to save her from being captured and sold on the black market by Mr. Gupta and his men.

Perkins, Stephanie
Anna and the French kiss. Stephanie Perkins. Dutton, 2010. 384 p.
Grades: 7 8 9 10   **Fic**

1. Children of authors 2. Studying abroad 3. Crushes in teenage girls 4. Teenage boy/girl relations 5. Boarding schools 6. Paris, France 7. France 8. Contemporary romances 9. Teen chick lit
ISBN 9780525423270

LC 2009053290

Who wouldn't jump at the chance to spend her senior year at a boarding school in Paris? Anna Oliphant, that's who. Besides barely speaking French, Anna is perfectly happy at home in Atlanta, Georgia. But Anna's father insists, so Paris it is. And Anna does warm up to the city...especially after she meets gorgeous Etienne St. Clair, who seems to return her interest but already has a girlfriend.

"Perkin's debut surpasses the usual chick-lit fare with smart dialogue, fresh characters and plenty of tingly interactions, all set amid pastries, parks and walks along the Seine in arguably the most romantic city in the world." Kirkus.

Perl, Erica S
The **capybara** conspiracy: a novel in three acts. Erica S. Perl. Alfred A. Knopf Books for Young Readers, 2016. 208 p.
Grades: 5 6 7 8   **Fic**

1. Dramatists 2. Animal stealing 3. Middle schools 4. Theater 5. Schools 6. Humorous stories
ISBN 9780399551710

LC 2015047497

Fed up with their sports-obsessed school, seventh-grade playwright Olive and her best friend Reynaldo decide to kidnap the school's capybara mascot in an attempt to get more benefits and respect for non-athletes.

"Staged over three acts, Perl's novel zips along thanks to all the back-and-forth dialogue, and is well suited to be performed. An unexpected ending and comprehensive notes on how to stage the play round out an amusing tale." Publishers Weekly.

Peterfreund, Diana
Omega City. Diana Peterfreund. Balzer + Bray, an imprint of HarperCollinsPublishers, 2015. 324 p.: Omega City
Grades: 4 5 6 7   **Fic**

1. Bunkers (Fortification) 2. Fathers and daughters 3. Inventions 4. Children of divorced parents 5. Twelve-year-old girls 6. Science fiction
ISBN 9780062310859

Determined to prove her conspiracy theorist father's beliefs about lost Cold War technology, Gillian, her skeptical brother, and their friends journey to the ruins of a vast doomsday bunker before they are confronted by dangerous adversaries.

Peters, Julie Anne
Define "normal": a novel. Julie Anne Peters. Little, Brown, c2000. 196 p.
Grades: 7 8 9 10   **Fic**

1. Children of divorced parents 2. Children of people with depression 3. Peer counseling 4. Punk culture 5. Family problems 6. Realistic fiction
ISBN 0316706310

LC 99042774

When she agrees to meet with Jasmine as a peer counselor at their middle school, Antonia never dreams that this girl with the black lipstick and pierced eyebrow will end up helping her deal with the serious problems she faces at home and become a good friend.

Petrucha, Stefan

Teen, Inc. Stefan Petrucha. Walker: 2007. 244 p.

Grades: 8 9 10 11 12   **Fic**
> 1. Orphans 2. Teenage orphans 3. Teenage environmentalists 4. Fourteen-year-old boys 5. Teenage boys 6. Humorous stories
ISBN 0802796508

Fourteen-year-old Jaiden has been raised by NECorp since his parents were killed when he was a baby, so when he discovers that the corporation has been lying about producing illegal levels of mercury emissions, he and his two friends decide to try to do something about it.

"Witty and provocative without being preachy, this novel has both daring characters and a heady plot." Booklist.

Pfeffer, Susan Beth, 1948-

Life as we knew it. Susan Beth Pfeffer. Harcourt, c2006. 352 p.: Life as we knew it

Grades: 7 8 9 10   **Fic**
> 1. Survival (after environmental catastrophe) 2. Meteors 3. Sixteen-year-old girls 4. Survival 5. Life change events 6. Pennsylvania 7. Science fiction 8. Diary novels 9. Apocalyptic fiction
ISBN 0152058265

LC 2005036321

Through journal entries sixteen-year-old Miranda describes her family's struggle to survive after a meteor hits the moon, causing worldwide tsunamis, earthquakes, and volcanic eruptions.

"Each page is filled with events both wearying and terrifying and infused with honest emotions. Pfeffer brings cataclysmic tragedy very close." Booklist.

Philbrick, W. R. (W. Rodman)

★ The **mostly** true adventures of Homer P. Figg. Rodman Philbrick. Blue Sky Press, c2009. 224 p.

Grades: 5 6 7 8   **Fic**
> 1. American Civil War era (1861-1865) 2. 1860s 3. Runaway boys 4. Separated brothers 5. Boy orphans 6. Brothers 7. Civil war 8. United States 9. Historical fiction
ISBN 9780439668187

LC 2008016925

Twelve-year-old Homer, a poor but clever orphan, has extraordinary adventures after running away from his evil uncle to rescue his brother, who has been sold into service in the Civil War.

"The book wouldn't be nearly as much fun without Homer's tall tales, but there are serious moments, too, and the horror of war and injustice of slavery ring clearly above the din of playful exaggerations." Publishers Weekly.

Wild river: a novel. Rodman Philbrick. Scholastic 2021 208 p.

Grades: 4 5 6 7   **Fic**
> 1. Middle school students 2. Survival 3. Disasters 4. Dam failures 5. Friendship 6. Montana 7. Survival stories 8. Adventure stories 9. First-person narratives
ISBN 9781338647273

LC 2020011013

When a dam fails and rushing waters sweep away their adult supervisors, five middle schoolers on a white-water rafting adventure are left alone with few supplies and the opportunity to forge powerful bonds as well as develop dangerous disagreements.

"As he did with Wildfire (2019), Newbery Honoree Philbrick has crafted another action tale for young readers that's impossible to put down. Readers will need to strap on their helmets and prepare for a wild ride." Kirkus

Wildfire: a novel. Rodman Philbrick. Blue Sky Press, an imprint of Scholastic Inc., 2019. 208 p.

Grades: 4 5 6 7   **Fic**
> 1. Wildfires 2. Preteen boys 3. Survival 4. Natural disasters 5. Forest fires 6. Maine 7. Survival stories 8. Adventure stories 9. First-person narratives
ISBN 9781338266900

LC 2018051703

Twelve-year-old Sam Castine is at summer camp while his mother is in rehab, but when the camp is evacuated ahead of a fast moving wildfire, he makes the mistake of going back for his phone, and finds himself left behind, disoriented, and running for his life, together with a girl, Delphy, from a different camp—finding an old jeep keeps them going, but in the wilds of Maine, there are only logging roads and the deadly crown fire is everywhere.

"Short chapters, outstanding cover art, and a breathless pace make this a fine choice for reluctant readers. Interesting backmatter regarding wildfires and survival tips rounds out a thrilling tale. Outstanding suspense." Kirkus.

Zane and the hurricane: a story of Katrina. Rodman Philbrick. The Blue Sky Press, an imprint of Scholastic Inc., 2014. 192 p.

Grades: 5 6 7 8   **Fic**
> 1. Hurricanes 2. Survival (after hurricanes) 3. Multiracial boys 4. Boys and dogs 5. Hurricane Katrina, 2005 6. New Orleans, Louisiana
ISBN 9780545342384

A twelve-year-old boy and his dog become trapped in New Orleans during the horrors of Hurricane Katrina.

"Careful attention to detail in representations of the storm, the city and local dialect give this tale a realistic feel. Zane's perspective as an outsider allows Philbrick to weave in social commentary on race, class, greed and morality, offering rich fodder for reflection and discussion." Kirkus.

Philippe, Ben

The **field** guide to the North American teenager. Ben Philippe. Balzer + Bray, 2018. 384 p.

Grades: 8 9 10   **Fic**
> 1. Stereotypes (Social psychology) 2. New students 3. Moving, Household 4. Cynicism 5. Making friends 6. Austin, Texas 7. Texas 8. Coming-of-age stories 9. Realistic fiction
ISBN 9780062824110

LC 2018014221

When Norris, a Black French Canadian, starts his junior year at an Austin, Texas, high school, he views his fellow students as cliches from "a bad 90s teen movie."

Pierce, Tamora

Alanna: the first adventure. by Tamora Pierce. Atheneum, 1983. 241 p.: Song of the lioness

Grades: 7 8 9 10   **Fic**
> 1. Girl adventurers 2. Knights and knighthood 3. Disguises 4. Girl healers 5. Tortall (Imaginary place) 6. High fantasy 7.

Fantasy fiction 8. Classics
ISBN 0689309945

LC 83002595

Eleven-year-old Alanna, who aspires to be a knight even though she is a girl, disguises herself as a boy to become a royal page, and learns many hard lessons along her path to high adventure.

Bloodhound. Tamora Pierce. Random House, 2009. 240 p.: Beka Cooper

Grades: 7 8 9 10 **Fic**
1. Counterfeits and counterfeiting 2. Rookie police 3. Girl psychics 4. Criminal investigation 5. Police 6. High fantasy 7. Fantasy fiction 8. Diary novels
ISBN 9780375814693

Having been promoted from "Puppy" to "Dog," Beka, now a full-fledged member of the Provost's Guard, and her former partner head to a neighboring port city to investigate a case of counterfeit coins.
"Quirky, endearing characters save the story." Booklist.

Briar's book. Scholastic Press, 1999. 258 p.: Circle of magic (Tamora Pierce)

Grades: 6 7 8 9 **Fic**
1. Teenage wizards 2. Teenage misfits 3. Plague 4. Wizards 5. Diseases 6. Fantasy fiction
ISBN 0590553593

LC 98026148

Briar, a young mage-in-training, and his teacher Rosethorn must use their magic to fight a deadly plague that is ravaging Summersea.
"This fast-paced, imaginative fantasy could be read and enjoyed on its own, but it works better as part of the quartet, which covers the span of a year and begins with Sandry's Book." School Library Journal.

Daja's book. Scholastic Press, 1998. 234 p.: Circle of magic (Tamora Pierce)

Grades: 6 7 8 9 **Fic**
1. Teenage wizards 2. Teenage misfits 3. Forest fires 4. Wizards 5. Teenagers -- Friendship 6. Fantasy fiction
ISBN 0590553585

While at Gold Ridge Castle, Daja and 3 other mages-in-training develop their unique magical talents as they try to stop a devastating forest fire.
"The fantasy elements of the series as a whole are satisfyingly well imagined, as are the main characters, and readers who have not read the first two novels will understand what is going on." School Library Journal.

First test. Random House, 1999. 216 p.: Protector of the small

Grades: 6 7 8 9 **Fic**
1. Knights and knighthood 2. Gender role 3. Royal pages 4. Determination in girls 5. Ten-year-old girls 6. High fantasy 7. Fantasy fiction
ISBN 0679889140

LC 98030903

Ten-year-old Keladry of Mindalen, daughter of nobles, serves as a page but must prove herself to the males around her if she is ever to fulfill her dream of becoming a knight.
"Pierce spins a whopping good yarn, her plot balanced on a solid base of action and characterization." Bulletin of the Center for Children's Books.

Lady knight. Tamora Pierce. Random House, c2002. 429 p.: Protector of the small

Grades: 6 7 8 9 **Fic**
1. Knights and knighthood 2. Gender role 3. Refugee camps 4. Women knights 5. Tortall (Imaginary place) 6. High fantasy 7. Fantasy fiction
ISBN 0375814655

LC 2002069862

When she became a knight, eighteen-year-old Kel hoped to be given a combat post, but instead she finds herself named commander of an outpost of refugees, where she must face the unnatural forces of the evil Balyce.
"Kel's world is completely realized in quick, precise detail." Booklist.

Mastiff. Tamora Pierce. Random House, 2011. 560 p.: Beka Cooper

Grades: 7 8 9 10 **Fic**
1. Girl psychics 2. Missing persons 3. Political corruption 4. Engaged persons 5. Extrasensory perception 6. High fantasy 7. Fantasy fiction 8. Diary novels
ISBN 9780375914706

"This novel provides both crackerjack storytelling and an endearingly complex protagonist." Kirkus.

Melting stones. Tamora Pierce. Scholastic, 2008. 312 p.: Circle reforged

Grades: 8 9 10 11 12 **Fic**
1. Teenage magicians 2. Volcanoes 3. Islands 4. Magic 5. Teenage girls 6. Fantasy fiction
ISBN 9780545052641

Researching strange happenings on the island of Starns, young stone mage Evvy learns about the dangers facing the islanders hidden in a dormant volcano and so must work to save those who live there using the skills she developed from her mentor Rosethorn.
"This is a riveting story that has many inventive and exciting plot twists and turns. . . . The story features excellent character development." School Library Journal.

Page. Random House, 2000. 257 p.: Protector of the small

Grades: 6 7 8 9 **Fic**
1. Knights and knighthood 2. Gender role 3. Royal pages 4. Eleven-year-old girls 5. Tortall (Imaginary place) 6. High fantasy 7. Fantasy fiction
ISBN 0679889159

LC 99089894

Keladry of Mindelan continues her training to become a squire with the aid of a new maid, the support of her friends, interference from some other pages, and some serious, even dangerous opposition. Includes "Cast of characters" and glossary.
"The plot is engaging and Kel's character growth continues." School Library Journal.

Sandry's book. Tamora Pierce. Scholastic, 1997. 252 p.: Circle of magic (Tamora Pierce)

Grades: 6 7 8 9 **Fic**
1. Teenage wizards 2. Teenage misfits 3. Orphans 4. Misfits (Persons) 5. Wizards 6. Fantasy fiction
ISBN 0590553569

LC 95039540

"Pierce has created an excellent new world where magic is a science and utterly believable and populated it with a cast of well-developed characters." Booklist.

Squire. by Tamora Pierce. Random House, 2001. 399 p.: Protector of the small

Grades: 6 7 8 9   **Fic**
   1. Knights and knighthood 2. Gender role 3. Squires 4. Tortall (Imaginary place) 5. Keladry of Mindelan (Fictitious character) 6. High fantasy 7. Fantasy fiction
ISBN 0679889167

                          LC 2001019280
After becoming a squire to Lord Raoul, commander of the King's Own, Kel of Mindelan, must face a terrifying test in the Chamber of the Ordeal before she can be a knight.

"The novel expertly juxtaposes outward action and introspection, as Kel matures in both her knightly skills and personal outlook." Horn Book Guide.

Terrier. Tamora Pierce. Random House, 2006. 592 p.: Beka Cooper

Grades: 7 8 9 10   **Fic**
   1. Girl psychics 2. Extrasensory perception 3. Rookie police 4. Cooper, Rebakah (Fictitious character) 5. Teenage girls 6. High fantasy 7. Fantasy fiction 8. Diary novels
ISBN 9780375814686

                          LC 2006014834
When sixteen-year-old Beka becomes "Puppy" to a pair of "Dogs," as the Provost's Guards are called, she uses her police training, natural abilities, and a touch of magic to help them solve the case of a murdered baby in Tortall's Lower City.

"Pierce deftly handles the novel's journal structure, and her clear homage to the police-procedural genre applies a welcome twist to the girl-legend-in-the-making story line." Booklist.

Trickster's choice. Tamora Pierce. Random House, c2003. 422 p.: Trickster series (Tamora Pierce)

Grades: 7 8 9 10   **Fic**
   1. Sixteen-year-old girls 2. Girl spies 3. Enslaved girls 4. Tortall (Imaginary place) 5. Alianne 6. Fantasy fiction 7. Asian-influenced fantasy
ISBN 0375814663

                          LC 2003005202
Alianne must call forth her mother's courage and her father's wit in order to survive on the Copper Isles in a royal court rife with political intrigue and murderous conspiracy.

"This series opener is packed with Pierce's alluring mix of fantasy, adventure, romance, and humor, making the book an essential purchase for school and public libraries." Voice of Youth Advocates.

Tris's book. by Tamora Pierce. Scholastic Press, 1998 251 p.: Circle of magic (Tamora Pierce)

Grades: 6 7 8 9   **Fic**
   1. Teenage wizards 2. Teenage misfits 3. Pirates 4. Wizards 5. Magic 6. Fantasy fiction
ISBN 0590553577

                          LC 97008521
With the defenses of Winding Circle Temple seriously weakened by an earthquake, Tris and her fellow mages-in-training try to join their different magic powers to protect the Winding Circle community from a pirate attack.

"Pierce has created another gripping adventure that's sure to please her many fans." School Library Journal.

Wild magic. Tamora Pierce. Atheneum, 1992. 259 p.: Immortals (Tamora Pierce)

Grades: 6 7 8 9 10   **Fic**
   1. Thirteen-year-old girls 2. Human/animal communication 3. Women knights 4. Magic 5. Wizards 6. High fantasy 7. Fantasy fiction
ISBN 0689317611

                          LC   91043909
The mage Numair, the knight Alanna, and Queen Thayet enlist thirteen-year-old Daine's help to battle the dreadful immortal creatures that have recently begun to attack the kingdom of Tortall.

The **will** of the empress. by Tamora Pierce. Scholastic Press, 2005. 560 p.: Circle reforged

Grades: 8 9 10 11 12   **Fic**
   1. Wizards' apprentices 2. Former friends 3. Courts and courtiers 4. Telepathy 5. Young women 6. Fantasy fiction
ISBN 0439441714

                          LC 2005002874
On a visit to Namorn to visit her vast landholdings and her devious cousin, Empress Berenene, eighteen-year-old Sandry must rely on her childhood friends and fellow mages, Daja, Tris, and Briar, despite the distance that has grown between them.

"This novel begins two years after the Circle of Magic and The Circle Opens series. . . . Readers will enjoy being reacquainted with these older but still very well-developed characters." School Library Journal.

Pierpoint, Eric, 1950-

The **last** ride of Caleb O'Toole. Eric Pierpoint. Sourcebooks Jabberwocky, 2013. 288 p.

Grades: 4 5 6 7   **Fic**
   1. American Westward Expansion (1803-1899) 2. 1870s 3. 19th century 4. Orphans 5. Wagon trains 6. Brothers and sisters 7. Adventure 8. Twelve-year-old boys 9. Oregon Trail 10. The West (United States) 11. Historical fiction
ISBN 9781402281716

                          LC 2013011800
During a thirteen hundred mile journey from Kansas to the Bitterroot Mountains, Caleb O'Toole faces deserts, tornadoes, wolves, and the infamous Blackstone Gang as he tries to honor his promise to his dying mother and keep his sisters safe.

The **secret** mission of William Tuck. Eric Pierpoint. Sourcebooks Jabberwocky, [2015] 304 p.

Grades: 4 5 6 7 8   **Fic**
   1. Revolutionary America (1775-1783) 2. 1780s 3. Spies 4. Revolutions 5. Voyages and travels 6. Twelve-year-old boys 7. Preteen boys 8. United States. 9. Historical fiction 10. War stories
ISBN 9781402281747

                          LC 2015009887
After seeing his brother murdered by the British, William leaves home to join the Patriot effort. While on a mission to deliver a secret message, William meets Rebecca, posing as a boy. Together they embark on a cross-colony journey through a secret network of Patriot spies that leads them on a quest to find General Washington himself. Provided by publisher.

"Richly detailed and exhilarating." Kirkus.

Pierson, D. C.

The **boy** who couldn't sleep and never had to: a novel. by DC Pierson. Vintage Books, 2010. 240 p.

Grades: 11 12 Adult   **Fic**
    1. Sleep 2. Misfits (Persons) 3. Dreams 4. Friendship 5. High schools 6. Science fiction 7. Humorous stories
    ISBN 9780307474612

           LC 2009021984

Fifteen-year-old Darren, a social misfit who spends his time at school trying not to be noticed while drawing characters for a planned film series and book tie-ins, befriends Eric, another outcast who reveals that he never sleeps.

Pike, Aprilynne

Earthbound. Aprilynne Pike. Razorbill, 2013. 336 p.: Earthbound

Grades: 7 8 9 10   **Fic**
    1. Airplane accidents 2. Conspiracies 3. Love triangles 4. Teenage romance 5. Teenage girls 6. Fantasy fiction
    ISBN 9781595146502

Finds Tavia, the sole survivor of a plane crash that killed her parents, experiencing visions of a boy she has never met before discovering the truth about her identity and her ability to stop an evil society from manipulating the world.

"The characters are well developed and the narrative is easy to follow... Pike does take a while to get to the heart of the matter, but overall the story is compelling. Readers of supernatural romances will be clamoring." School Library Journal.

Glitter. Aprilynne Pike. Random House, [2016] 320 p.: Glitter (Aprilynne Pike)

Grades: 8 9 10 11   **Fic**
    1. Near future 2. Courts and courtiers 3. Drugs 4. Drug dealers 5. Rulers 6. Versailles, France 7. Science fiction
    ISBN 9781101933701

           LC 2015039116

A teenager living in an alternate-history futuristic Versailles must escape its walls by selling a happy-enducing makeup called Glitter. Provided by publisher.

"Poufy gowns and corsets in a futuristic setting make for an interesting spin on a perennially popular genre." Kirkus.

Pileggi, Leah

Prisoner 88. Leah Pileggi. Charlesbridge, c2013. 142 p.

Grades: 4 5 6 7 8   **Fic**
    1. 1880s 2. 19th century 3. Prisoners 4. Prisons 5. Farms 6. Boy prisoners 7. Ten-year-old boys 8. Idaho 9. Historical fiction
    ISBN 9781580895606

           LC 2012024443

In 1885, ten-year-old Jake is sent to prison for killing a man who threatened his father, and struggles to survive the harsh realities of prison life in the Idaho Territory.

Pinkney, Andrea Davis

★ **Bird** in a box. by Andrea Davis Pinkney. Little, Brown, 2011. 256 p.

Grades: 4 5 6 7   **Fic**
    1. Louis, Joe, 1914-1981 2. 1930s 3. African American children 4. Orphanages 5. Orphans 6. Grief 7. Grief in children 8. New York (State) 9. Historical fiction
    ISBN 9780316074032

           LC 2010022851

In 1936, three children meet at the Mercy Home for Negro Orphans in New York State, and while not all three are orphans, they are all dealing with grief and loss which together, along with the help of a sympathetic staff member and the boxing matches of Joe Louis, they manage to overcome. Includes author's notes.

"Pinkney weaves quite a bit of 1930s history into her story and succeeds admirably in showing how Louis came to represent so much more than his sport. Her detailed notes make this an accessible and inspiring piece of historical fiction that belongs in most collections." School Library Journal.

Loretta Little looks back: three voices go tell it!: a monologue novel. by Andrea Davis Pinkney; paintings by Brian Pinkney. Little Brown & Co 2020 224 p.

Grades: 4 5 6 7 8 9   **Fic**
    1. 20th century 2. African Americans 3. Sharecroppers 4. Civil Rights Movement 5. Racism 6. African American families 7. Mississippi 8. Historical fiction 9. African American fiction
    ISBN 9780316536776

           LC 2020005755

Loretta, Roly, and Aggie B. Little relate their Mississippi family's struggles and triumphs from 1927 to 1968 while struggling as sharecroppers, living under Jim Crow, and fighting for Civil Rights.

"The choice of oral storytelling is inspired, both for its cultural significance and because it allows readers to empathize with these events. Stage notes, free verse poems, and black-and-white spot art introduce most monologues, effectively representing the characters and emphasizing their resilience." Booklist

★ The **red** pencil. by Andrea Davis Pinkney; illustrated by Shane W. Evans. Little, Brown and Company, 2014. 336 p.

Grades: 4 5 6 7   **Fic**
    1. Girl refugees 2. Education 3. Refugees 4. Pencils 5. Refugees, Sudanese 6. Sudan 7. Novels in verse
    ISBN 9780316247801

           LC 2013044753

After her tribal village is attacked by militants, Amira, a young Sudanese girl, must flee to safety at a refugee camp, where she finds hope and the chance to pursue an education in the form of a single red pencil and the friendship and encouragement of a wise elder. Provided by publisher.

"Amira's thoughts and drawings are vividly brought to life through Pinkney's lyrical verse and Evans's lucid line illustrations, which infuse the narrative with emotional intensity." School Library Journal.

With the might of angels: the diary of Dawnie Rae Johnson. Andrea Davis Pinkney. Scholastic, 2011. 336 p.: Dear America

Grades: 5 6 7 8   **Fic**
    1. 1950s 2. African American girls 3. School integration 4. Tomboys 5. Schools 6. Race relations 7. Virginia 8. Historical fiction 9. Diary novels
    ISBN 9780545297059

           LC 2011001363

In 1955 Hadley, Virginia, twelve-year-old Dawnie Rae Johnson, a tomboy who excels at baseball and at her studies, becomes the first African American student to attend the all-white Prettyman Coburn school, turning her world upside down. Includes historical notes about the period.

"Dawnie's journal is realistic, encompassing thoughts and emotions one would expect of someone so stressed. . . . The author seamlessly incorporates historical events into the child's journal. The end matter contains age-appropriate photographs, a time line, and brief biographical sketches of the people mentioned. A first purchase." School Library Journal.

Pinkwater, Daniel Manus, 1941-

Bushman lives! written by Daniel Pinkwater; illustrated by Calef Brown. Houghton Mifflin Harcourt, 2012. 320 p.: Neddiad

Grades: 5 6 7 8   **Fic**
1. 1960s 2. Artists 3. Self-discovery 4. Gorillas 5. Drawing 6. Teenage boys 7. Chicago, Illinois 8. Humorous stories 9. Coming-of-age stories
ISBN 9780547385396

LC 2011048211

In the 1960s, Harold Knishke, a Chicago teenager with a special place in his heart for Bushman, the famed departed gorilla of the Lincoln Park Zoo, embarks on a hometown adventure, in a quest to become a great artist and figure out how he became the object of a famous folk song.

The **Neddiad**: how Neddie took the train, went to Hollywood, and saved civilization. written by Daniel Pinkwater. Houghton Mifflin, 2007. 200 p.: Neddiad

Grades: 5 6 7 8   **Fic**
1. 1940s 2. Boys 3. Turtles 4. Material culture 5. Trains 6. Train rides 7. Los Angeles, California 8. California 9. Adventure stories 10. Humorous stories
ISBN 0618594442

LC 2006033944

When shoelace heir Neddie Wentworthstein and his family take the train from Chicago to Los Angeles in the 1940s, he winds up in possession of a valuable Indian turtle artifact whose owner is supposed to be able to prevent the impending destruction of the world, but he is not sure exactly how.

"A bright and breezy adventure with a smart and funny narrator. . . . [This is a] goofy and lovingly nostalgic historical fantasy." School Library Journal.

Pitcher, Annabel

Silence is goldfish: a novel. by Annabel Pitcher. 352 p.

Grades: 7 8 9 10   **Fic**
1. Teenage girls who are mute 2. Family secrets 3. Identity (Psychology) 4. Fathers 5. Bullying and bullies 6. England 7. Manchester, England 8. Realistic fiction 9. Coming-of-age stories
ISBN 9780316370752

LC 2015024312

Fifteen-year-old Tess Turner of Manchester, England, decides to stop speaking in the wake of discovering a heartbreaking family secret. Provided by publisher.

"Tess, fifteen, is an offbeat English introvert with a highly involved dad. After she discovers his startling blog post recounting her own birth ('It wasn't my daughter. It was...some sperm donor's'), her anger emboldens her to stand up against Dad's expectations. Her rebellion of choice is silence, but her narrative voice speaks loudly—Tess is a witty and appealing protagonist." Horn Book.

Pixley, Marcella Fleischman

Freak. Farrar, 2007. 144 p.

Grades: 6 7 8 9 10   **Fic**
1. Seventh-grade girls 2. Bullying and bullies 3. Misfits (Persons) 4. Middle school students 5. Sisters 6. Realistic fiction
ISBN 9780374324537

When her sister blossoms into a beautiful being and makes new friends, seventh grader Miriam is left alone to deal with her freak status and now must face the harsh criticism and teasing of the popular club whose merciless abuse pushes her to the breaking point.

"The story's conflicts are exceptionally riveting and believable." Booklist.

Without Tess. Marcella Pixley. Farrar Straus Giroux, 2011. 288 p.

Grades: 7 8 9 10   **Fic**
1. Fifteen-year-old girls 2. Family and mental illness 3. Sisters -- Death 4. Family relationships 5. Death 6. Psychological fiction 7. Realistic fiction 8. First person narratives
ISBN 9780374361747

LC 2011001469

Fifteen-year-old Lizzie Cohen recalls what it was like growing up with her imaginative but disturbed older sister Tess, and how she is striving to reclaim her own life since Tess died.

"The author plumbs the emotional depths of a tough subject with sensitivity and insight into the complexities of human nature and sibling bonds." Kirkus.

Plozza, Shivaun

Tin heart. Shivaun Plozza. Penguin Random House Australia, 2018. 320 p.

Grades: 8 9 10 11 12   **Fic**
1. Transplant recipients 2. Identity (Psychology) 3. Chronic diseases 4. Second chances 5. Family feuds 6. Coming-of-age stories 7. Romantic comedies
ISBN 9780143786276

"Funny and direct, this book by Plozza . . . is capable of balancing heartbreak, first love, mortality, and the absurd." Publishers Weekly.

Poblocki, Dan

The **haunting** of Gabriel Ashe. Dan Poblocki. Scholastic Press, 2013. 288 p.

Grades: 6 7 8   **Fic**
1. Monsters 2. Neighbors 3. Imagination 4. Friendship 5. Games 6. Massachusetts 7. Horror
ISBN 9780545402705

LC 2013004009

Since eighth-grader Gabriel Ashe moved into his grandmother's house he has been spending a lot of time playing in the woods with his new friend Seth, but the games Seth invents involve a child-eating monster called the Hunter, and Gabriel is not sure how much is imagination and how much is real.

Poe, Edgar Allan, 1809-1849

Edgar Allan Poe's tales of death and dementia. Edgar Allan Poe; illustrated by Gris Grimly. Atheneum Books for Young Readers, 2009. 144 p.

Grades: 7 8 9 10   **Fic**
1. Horror 2. Gothic fiction 3. Classics
ISBN 9781416950257

LC 2009003056

Four short stories, abridged and illustrated, by the nineteenth-century American writer best known for his tales of horror.

"Four of Poe's morbid short stories are adapted for teens in this heavily illustrated presentation: The Tell-Tale Heart, The System of Dr. Tarr and Professor Fether, The Oblong Box, and The Facts in the Case of M. Valdemar. Grimly intersperses his horror-infused ink-and-watercolor cartoon art throughout Poe's putrid prose. The effect is an offering that bridges graphic and traditional print formats. Great for readers who adore the gothic and the gruesome." School Library Journal.

Edgar Allan Poe's tales of mystery and madness. Edgar Allan Poe; illustrated by Gris Grimly. Atheneum Books for Young Readers, c2004. 135 p.

Grades: 8 9 10 11 12   **Fic**
  1. Costume parties 2. Black cats 3. Manors 4. Dwarves (Fantasy characters) 5. Frights 6. Horror 7. Short stories 8. Gothic fiction
ISBN 9780689848377

    LC 2003010565

Presents four classic tales of the macabre enhanced by appropriately ghoulish illustrations.

"With high-production values and gothic sensibilities thoroughly reflected in both text and art, this is an essential purchase for libraries. Adults can use it to lead young people to some great literature; readers will pluck it off the shelves themselves for creepy, entertaining fun." Booklist.

Polak, Monique

What world is left. Monique Polak. Orca Book Publishers, 2008. 232 p.

Grades: 7 8 9 10 11 12   **Fic**
  1. Theresienstadt (Concentration camp) 2. 1940s 3. Jewish girls 4. Concentration camps 5. Holocaust (1933-1945) 6. Fathers 7. Families 8. Netherlands 9. Czechoslovakia
ISBN 9781551438474

    LC 2008927295

When the Nazis invade Holland in 1942, Anneke's pampered life changes as she and her family are deported to Theresienstadt, a concentration camp in Czechoslovakia which the Nazis are touting as an idyllic place where European Jews are thriving under the Nazi regime.

"Growing up in a secular Jewish home in Holland, Anneke cares little about Judaism, so she has no faith to lose when, in 1943, her family is deported to Theresienstadt, the Nazi concentration camp. . . . Based on the experiences of the author's mother . . . this novel is narrated in Anneke's first-person, present-tense voice. The details are unforgettable. . . . An important addition to the Holocaust curriculum." Booklist.

Polisner, Gae

The **pull** of gravity. Gae Polisner. Frances Foster Books, 2011. 208 p.

Grades: 6 7 8 9   **Fic**
  1. Steinbeck, John, 1902-1968. Of mice and men. 2. Family problems 3. Death 4. Grief 5. Grief in teenagers 6. Teenagers 7. Rochester, New York 8. Realistic fiction 9. Coming-of-age stories
ISBN 9780374371937

    LC 2010021749

When their friend Scooter dies of a rare disease, teenagers Nick Gardner and Jaycee Amato set out on a secret journey to find the father who abandoned "The Scoot" when he was an infant, and give him a signed first edition of "Of Mice and Men."

"Polisner's first novel begins with a bang and ends with another . . . . There is a great deal to enjoy throughout, and literary kids will surely enjoy a subplot involving John Steinbeck." Booklist.

Pollen, Samuel

The **year** I didn't eat. Samuel Pollen. Yellow Jacket, 2019, c2019. 400 p.

Grades: 6 7 8 9   **Fic**
  1. People with anorexia 2. Teenage boys 3. Eating disorders 4. Anorexia nervosa 5. Fourteen-year-old boys 6. England 7.

Realistic fiction
ISBN 9781499808087

A 14-year-old boy with anorexia records his efforts to control his eating disorder in a therapist-prescribed journal that documents the progression of his illness and its impact on his perspectives and family.

"Max is a thoughtful, appealing narrator to whom readers will relate, and his story brings attention to an illness most commonly associated with girls and older teens or adults." Booklist.

Polonsky, Ami

Gracefully Grayson. Ami Polonsky. Disney/Hyperion, 2014. 256 p.

Grades: 6 7 8 9   **Fic**
  1. Transgender children 2. Girl orphans 3. School plays 4. Theater 5. Self-acceptance 6. Chicago, Illinois 7. Realistic fiction 8. LGBTQIA fiction
ISBN 9781423185277

    LC 2014010155

Grayson, a transgender twelve-year-old, learns to accept her true identity and share it with the world. Provided by publisher.

"Sixth grader Grayson daydreams about being a girl, despite being seen by everyone as male. Grayson keeps people at a distance until Amelia moves to town. After landing the (female) lead in a play, Grayson fights for the right to present her truest self to others—both on and off stage. Polonsky captures her protagonist's loneliness, then courage, in an immediate and intimate narrative." Horn Book.

Threads. Ami Polonsky. Disney-Hyperion, [2016] 256 p.

Grades: 4 5 6 7   **Fic**
  1. Human trafficking 2. Child labor 3. Loss (Psychology) 4. Grief 5. Escapes 6. Illinois 7. China 8. Realistic fiction
ISBN 9781484746905

    LC 2015043621

An American girl finds a note written by a Chinese girl forced to work in a factory in Beijing.

"Based on a true incident, this is an engaging offering for readers who seek to broaden their global perspective. Especially good for teachers to use as a spark for classroom conversation." School Library Journal.

Ponti, James

Framed! James Ponti. Aladdin, 2016. 304 p.: T.O.A.S.T. mysteries

Grades: 5 6 7 8   **Fic**
  1. FBI 2. Art thefts 3. Child detectives 4. Undercover operations 5. Friendship 6. Kidnapping 7. Washington, DC 8. Mysteries
ISBN 9781481436304

    LC 2015045506

In Washington, D.C., twelve-year-old Florian Bates, a consulting detective for the FBI, and his best friend Margaret help thwart the biggest art heist in United States history.

Trapped! by James Ponti. Aladdin, 2018. 384 p.: T.O.A.S.T. mysteries

Grades: 5 6 7 8   **Fic**
  1. FBI. 2. Child detectives 3. Private schools 4. Middle schools 5. Undercover operations 6. Libraries 7. Washington, DC 8. Mysteries
ISBN 9781534408913

    LC 2018005076

Middle schoolers Florian and Margaret are determined to catch a spy who is implicating their FBI supervisor, Marcus Rivers, in a variety of crimes—even if they have to break into, and out of, the Library of Congress to do it.

Vanished! James Ponti. Aladdin, 2017. 304 p.: T.O.A.S.T. mysteries

Grades: 5 6 7 8   **Fic**
1. FBI 2. Child detectives 3. Practical jokes 4. Private schools 5. Middle schools 6. Undercover operations 7. Washington, DC 8. Mysteries
ISBN 9781481436335

LC 2016041962

In Washington, D.C., twelve-year-old Florian Bates, a consulting detective for the FBI, and his best friend Margaret must uncover the truth behind a series of private middle school pranks that may or may not involve the daughter of the President of the United States.

Pool, Katy Rose

There will come a darkness. Katy Rose Pool. Henry Holt and Company, 2019. 496 p.: Age of Darkness (Katy Rose Pool)

Grades: 8 9 10 11 12   **Fic**
1. Prophets 2. Prophecies 3. End of the world 4. Fate and fatalism 5. Free will and determinism 6. High fantasy 7. Fantasy fiction
ISBN 9781250211750

LC 2019017243

For generations the Seven Prophets guided humanity with their visions, ending wars and uniting nations—until the day they vanished, leaving behind the promise of a looming Age of Darkness and the birth of a Prophet who could be the world's salvation . . . or the cause of its destruction. Provided by publisher.

"A well-crafted, surprising, and gripping start to a new trilogy." Kirkus.

Powell, Laura, 1979-

Burn mark. by Laura Powell. Bloomsbury Children's Books: 2012. 304 p.: Burn mark

Grades: 7 8 9 10 11 12   **Fic**
1. Witches 2. Conspiracies 3. Undercover operations 4. Crime 5. Fifteen-year-olds 6. London, England 7. England 8. Urban fantasy
ISBN 9781599908434

LC 2011034464

In an alternate London, England, the lives of a fifteen-year-old girl eagerly awaiting the development of her "fae," or witch abilities, and the son of a man who sentences witches to death by burning, intersect when the son makes a startling discovery.

The **game** of triumphs. Laura Powell. Alfred A. Knopf, 2011. 288 p.

Grades: 7 8 9 10   **Fic**
1. Tarot 2. Teenage girl orphans 3. Interdimensional travel 4. Supernatural 5. Murder 6. London, England 7. Urban fantasy
ISBN 9780375865879

Fifteen-year-old Cat and three other London teens are drawn into a dangerous game in which Tarot cards open doorways into a different dimension and while there is everything to win, losing can be fatal.

"Original and engrossing." Kirkus.

Powell, Patricia Hruby, 1951-

Loving vs. Virginia: a documentary novel of the landmark civil rights case. by Patricia Hruby Powell; artwork by Shadra Strickland. Chronicle Books, [2017] 260 p.

Grades: 7 8 9 10   **Fic**
1. Loving, Richard Perry 2. Loving, Mildred Jeter 3. 1950s 4. 1960s 5. Interracial marriage 6. Race relations 7. Civil Rights Movement 8. African American women 9. Imprisonment 10. Virginia 11. Historical fiction 12. Novels in verse 13. Illustrated books
ISBN 9781452125909

A tale inspired by the landmark 1955 civil rights case follows the relationship between two young people who challenged period segregation, prejudice and injustice to pursue a relationship at the center of a Supreme Court case that legalized interracial marriage.

"A powerful and riveting account of an American couple in love when that love was ruled illegal in many American states." Kirkus.

Power, Rory

Wilder girls. Rory Power. Random House Childrens Books, 2019. 368 p.

Grades: 8 9 10 11 12   **Fic**
1. Quarantine 2. Survival 3. Climate change 4. Diseases 5. Missing persons 6. Maine 7. Thrillers and suspense 8. Horror
ISBN 9780525645580

Friends Hetty, Byatt, and Reece go to extremes trying to uncover the dark truth about the mysterious disease that has had them quarantined at their boarding school on a Maine island.

"Power's evocative, haunting, and occasionally gruesome debut will challenge readers to ignore its bewitching presence." Booklist

Pratchett, Terry

The **amazing** Maurice and his educated rodents. Terry Pratchett. Harper Collins Publishers, 2002. 241 p.: Discworld (Young adult)

Grades: 7 8 9 10   **Fic**
1. Rats 2. Cats 3. Musicians 4. Swindlers and swindling 5. Human/animal relationships 6. Fantasy fiction 7. Humorous stories 8. Fairy tale and folklore-inspired fiction
ISBN 006001234X

LC 2001042411

Carnegie Medal, 2001.

A talking cat, intelligent rats, and a strange boy cooperate in a Pied Piper scam until they try to con the wrong town and are confronted by a deadly evil rat king.

"In this laugh-out-loud fantasy, his first Discworld novel for younger readers, Pratchett rethinks a classic story and comes up with a winner." School Library Journal.

Dodger. by Terry Pratchett. HarperCollins, 2012. 336 p.

Grades: 7 8 9 10   **Fic**
1. Dickens, Charles, 1812-1870. 2. Victorian era (1837-1901) 3. 19th century 4. Homeless teenagers 5. Criminals 6. Todd, Sweeney (Legendary character) 7. Fourteen-year-old boys 8. Teenage boys 9. London, England 10. Great Britain 11. Humorous stories 12. Historical fiction
ISBN 9780062009494

LC 2012022155

Surviving by his wits in an alternative-universe London ruled by a young Queen Victoria, the intrepid young Dodger inadvertently foils a murderous Sweeney Todd's operation and encounters numerous fictional and historical characters, including Darwin, Disraeli and Dickens.

I shall wear midnight. Terry Pratchett. Harper, 2010. 272 p.: Discworld (Young adult)

Grades: 7 8 9 10 **Fic**
1. Teenage witches 2. Hate 3. Memory 4. Villains 5. Witches 6. Fantasy fiction 7. Humorous stories
ISBN 9780061433047

LC bl2010019256

Combines comedy and action in the final adventure of Tiffany Aching and the Wee Free Men as the young witch faces an insidious new foe, one who whispers threats of violence and quietly unleashes mayhem.

"The final adventure in Pratchett's Tiffany Aching series brings this subset of Discworld novels to a moving and highly satisfactory conclusion." Publishers Weekly.

Nation. Terry Pratchett. HarperCollins, 2008. 272 p.
Grades: 7 8 9 10 11 12 **Fic**
1. Tsunamis 2. Survival 3. Interpersonal relations 4. Island life 5. Survival (after environmental catastrophe) 6. Survival stories 7. Adventure stories
ISBN 9780061433016

After a devastating tsunami destroys all that they have ever known, Mau, an island boy, and Daphne, an aristocratic English girl, together with a small band of refugees, set about rebuilding their community and all the things that are important in their lives.

"Quirky wit and broad vision make this a fascinating survival story on many levels." Booklist.

★ **Only** you can save mankind: if not you, who else? by Terry Pratchett. Harper Collins, 2005. xi, 207 p.: Johnny Maxwell trilogy
Grades: 5 6 7 8 **Fic**
1. 1990s 2. Twelve-year-old boys 3. Computer games 4. Life on other planets 5. Misfits (Persons) 6. Space and time 7. Fantasy fiction 8. Humorous stories
ISBN 0060541857

LC 2004004341

Twelve-year-old Johnny endures tensions between his parents, watches television coverage of the Gulf War, and plays a computer game called Only You Can Save Mankind, in which he is increasingly drawn into the reality of the alien ScreeWee.

"This is a wild ride, full of Pratchett's trademark humor; digs at primitive, low-resolution games . . .; and some not-so-subtle philosophy about war and peace." Booklist.

The **Wee** Free Men. Terry Pratchett. Harper Collins Publishers, c2003. 263 p.: Discworld (Young adult)
Grades: 7 8 9 10 **Fic**
1. Preteen girls 2. Miniature persons (Imaginary characters) 3. Fairies 4. Witches 5. Warriors 6. Fantasy fiction 7. Humorous stories
ISBN 0060012366

LC 2002015396

A young witch-to-be named Tiffany teams up with the Wee Free Men, a clan of six-inch-high blue men, to rescue her baby brother and ward off a sinister invasion from Fairyland.

"Pratchett invites readers into his well-established realm of Discworld where action, magic, and characters are firmly rooted in literary reality. Humor ripples throughout, making tense, dangerous moments stand out in stark contrast." Bulletin of the Center for Children's Books.

Preller, James
Bystander. by James Preller. Feiwel and Friends, c2009. 226 p.

Grades: 5 6 7 8 **Fic**
1. Bullying and bullies 2. Personal conduct 3. Middle schools 4. Thirteen-year-old boys 5. Teenage boys 6. Long Island, New York 7. Realistic fiction
ISBN 9780312379063

LC 2008028554

Thirteen-year-old Eric discovers there are consequences to not standing by and watching as the bully at his new school hurts people, but although school officials are aware of the problem, Eric may be the one with a solution.

"Although there are no pat answers, the message (that a bystander is hardly better than an instigator) is clear, and Preller's well-shaped characters, strong writing, and realistic treatment of middle-school life deliver it cleanly." Booklist.

The **courage** test. James Preller. Feiwel & Friends, 2016. 212 p.
Grades: 4 5 6 7 **Fic**
1. Fathers and sons 2. Voyages and travels 3. Children of divorced parents 4. Adventure travel 5. Runaways 6. Lewis and Clark National Historic Trail 7. Realistic fiction 8. Coming-of-age stories
ISBN 9781250093912

"Additionally, not only does the author slip cogent historical facts and insights into his simply told narrative without disturbing its flow, he offers more detail, plus sources of information, in an afterword." Booklist.

Six innings: a game in the life. James Preller. Feiwel and Friends, 2008. 147 p.
Grades: 4 5 6 7 **Fic**
1. Sick children 2. Baseball 3. Friendship 4. Group games 5. Children with cancer 6. Sports fiction 7. Baseball stories
ISBN 0312367635

LC 2007032846

Earl Grubb's Pool Supplies plays Northeast Gas & Electric in the Little League championship game, while Sam, who has cancer and is in a wheelchair, has to call the play-by-play instead of participating in the game.

"The outcome is predictable but the journey is nailbitingly tense. Kids will be nodding in agreement at the truths laid bare." Publishers Weekly.

Preus, Margi
Enchantment Lake: a Northwoods mystery. Margi Preus. University of Minnesota Press, 2015. 200 p.: Enchantment Lake mysteries
Grades: 6 7 8 9 10 **Fic**
1. Murder investigation 2. Parent-separated teenage girls 3. Small towns 4. Lakes 5. Treasure troves 6. Minnesota 7. Mysteries
ISBN 9780816683024

"Preus offers intriguing characters, suspenseful moments, and a love interest—plenty to keep readers involved." Booklist.

Heart of a samurai: based on the true story of Nakahama Manjiro. by Margi Preus. Amulet Books, 2010. 320 p.
Grades: 7 8 9 10 11 12 **Fic**
1. Nakahama, Manjiro, 1827-1898 2. 19th century 3. Samurai 4. Japanese in the United States 5. Fourteen-year-old boys 6. Rescues 7. Teenage boys 8. Japan -- Foreign relations -- United States 9. United States -- Foreign relations -- Japan 10. Historical fiction
ISBN 9780810989818

LC 2009051634

In 1841, rescued by an American whaler after a terrible shipwreck leaves him and his four companions castaways on a remote island, fourteen-year-old Manjiro, who dreams of becoming a samurai, learns new laws and customs as he becomes the first Japanese person to set foot in the United States.

"The author mixes fact with fiction in a tale that is at once adventurous, heartwarming, sprawling, and nerve-racking in its depictions of early anti-Asian sentiment. She succeeds in making readers feel every bit as other as Manjiro, while showing America at its best and worst through his eyes." Publishers Weekly.

Shadow on the mountain a novel inspired by the true adventures of a wartime spy. by Margi Preus. Amulet Books, 2012. 286 p.

Grades: 6 7 8 9   **Fic**
1. Second World War era (1939-1945) 2. 1940s 3. Spies 4. World War II 5. Resistance to military occupation 6. Underground newspapers 7. Fourteen-year-old boys 8. Norway 9. Historical fiction
ISBN 9781419704246

LC 2012015623

In Nazi-occupied Norway, fourteen-year-old Espen joins the resistance movement, graduating from deliverer of illegal newspapers to courier and spy.

Village of scoundrels: based on a true story of courage during WWII. Margi Preus; illustrations by S.M. Vidaurri. Amulet Books, 2020 320 p.

Grades: 5 6 7 8 9   **Fic**
1. 1940s 2. World War II 3. Refugees 4. Holocaust (1933-1945) 5. Jews 6. Nazis 7. France 8. Historical fiction
ISBN 9781419708978

In the 1940s, remote Les Lauzes, France, houses Jews, unregistered foreigners, forgers, and others who take great risks to shelter refugees and smuggle them to safety in Switzerland.

"Named as Righteous Among the Nations by Yad Vashem, these characters are based on real people from the village of Le Chambon sur Lignon, and Preus tells their afterstories in a well-researched, comprehensive epilogue. Deeply emotional, intense, and thought-provoking." Kirkus

Includes bibliographical references (pages 300-302).

★ **West** of the moon. Margi Preus. Amulet Books, 2014. 224 p.

Grades: 5 6 7 8   **Fic**
1. 19th century 2. Child trafficking 3. Father-separated girls 4. Child trafficking victims 5. Immigration and emigration 6. Teenage girls 7. Norway 8. Historical fantasy
ISBN 9781419708961

LC 2013023250

In nineteenth-century Norway, fourteen-year-old Astri, whose aunt has sold her to a mean goat herder, dreams of joining her father in America.

"In the Scandinavian fairy tale 'East of the Sun and West of the Moon,' a young girl is taken from her home to a magnificent castle by a great bear, whom she discovers is really a prince. . . . Preus (Heart of a Samurai, 2010) interweaves the mesmerizing tale of Astri's treacherous and harrowing mid-nineteenth-century immigration to America with bewitching tales of magic. A fascinating author's note only adds to the wonder." Booklist.

Includes bibliographical references.

Price, Charlie
Desert Angel. Charlie Price. Farrar Straus Giroux, 2011. 176 p.

Grades: 8 9 10 11 12   **Fic**
1. Children of drug abusers 2. Loners 3. Survival 4. Violence 5. Mexican Americans 6. California 7. Thrillers and suspense
ISBN 9780374317751

LC 2010044122

In the California desert, fourteen-year-old Angel is on the run from the man who abused her, killed her mother, and intends to kill her too.

"Price's pacing is tight, aided by direct, clipped prose that underscores Scotty's brutality and Angel's fragile emotional state. Both the best and worst of humanity shine through in this gripping novel." Publishers Weekly.

Price, Lissa
Starters. Lissa Price. Delacorte Press, 2012. 336 p.

Grades: 7 8 9 10   **Fic**
1. Body swapping 2. Teenage girl orphans 3. Dystopias 4. Murder 5. Seniors 6. Dystopian fiction 7. Science fiction
ISBN 9780375990601

LC 2011040820

To support herself and her younger brother in a future Beverly Hills, sixteen-year-old Callie hires her body out to seniors who want to experience being young again, and she lives a fairy-tale life until she learns that her body will commit murder, unless her mind can stop it.

Priest, Cherie
I am Princess X. by Cherie Priest; illustrated by Kali Ciesemier. Arthur A. Levine, 2015. 256 p.

Grades: 7 8 9 10 11 12   **Fic**
1. Best friends -- Death 2. Subcultures 3. Suspicion 4. Teenage girls 5. Traffic accidents 6. Seattle, Washington 7. Mysteries 8. Graphic novel hybrids
ISBN 9780545620857

Best friends Libby Deaton and May Harper invented Princess X when they were in fifth grade, but when the car Libby is in goes off a bridge, she is presumed dead, and the story came to an end—except now, three years later, Princess X is suddenly everywhere, with a whole underground culture focused on a webcomic, and May believes her friend must be alive

"May and Libby created Princess X on the day they met in fifth grade. That was before Libby and her mother died in a car crash. Now May is 16 and looking at another long, lonely summer in Seattle when she spots a Princess X sticker on the corner of a store window. Suddenly she starts seeing Princess X everywhere, including in a webcomic at IAmPrincessX.com, where the princess story is eerily similar to Libby's. . . . An excellent book with loads of cross-genre and cross-format appeal." School Library Journal.

Prineas, Sarah
The **magic** thief. Sarah Prineas. HarperCollins Childrens Books, 2008. 417 p.: Magic thief

Grades: 4 5 6 7   **Fic**
1. Wizards 2. Magic 3. Thieves 4. Boy thieves 5. Wizards' apprentices 6. Fantasy fiction
ISBN 9780061375873

When a local pickpocket puts his hand in the pocket belonging to the wizard Nevery, Conn gets more than he expected when he is drawn into the world of wizardry as a result of his mischievous deed.

"Conn is a thief but, through desire and inevitability, becomes a wizard . . . This evolution begins when Conn picks the pocket of the wizard

Nevery. . . . What works wonderfully well here is the boy's irresistable voice." Booklist.

Proimos, James
12 things to do before you crash and burn. James Proimos. Roaring Brook Press, 2011. 128 p.
Grades: 7 8 9 10   **Fic**
1. Sixteen-year-old boys 2. Fathers -- Death 3. Grief in teenage boys 4. Teenage boys 5. Teenage boy/girl relations 6. Baltimore, Maryland 7. Maryland 8. Realistic fiction
ISBN 9781596435957

LC 2010043935
Sixteen-year-old James "Hercules" Martino completes twelve tasks while spending two weeks in Baltimore with his Uncle Anthony, and gains insights into himself, his uncle, and his recently deceased father, a self-help author and daytime talk show host who was beloved by the public but a terrible father.

"Proimos fully inhabits the mind and voice of his hero, whose almost mythic journey offers moments hilarious, heartbreaking, and triumphant." Publishers Weekly.

Pullman, Philip, 1946-
The **amber** spyglass. Philip Pullman. A. A. Knopf, 2000. 518 p.: His dark materials
Grades: 7 8 9 10 11 12   **Fic**
1. Girl heroes 2. Familiars (Spirits) 3. Quests 4. Fathers and daughters 5. Dark matter (Astronomy) 6. Fantasy fiction 7. Steampunk 8. Classics
ISBN 0679879269

LC 00044776
Lyra and Will find themselves at the center of a battle between the forces of the Authority and those gathered by Lyra's father, Lord Asriel.

The **book** of dust: la belle sauvage. Philip Pullman. Alfred A. Knopf Books for Young Readers, 2017. 464 p.: Book of dust
Grades: 8 9 10 11 12   **Fic**
1. University of Oxford 2. Familiars (Spirits) 3. Eleven year old boys 4. Totalitarianism 5. Dust 6. Freedom of speech 7. Oxford, England 8. England 9. Fantasy fiction
ISBN 9780375815300
Set in the parallel world of His Dark Materials, this tale begins 10 years before the events of The Golden Compass and centers on the early childhood of Lyra, her daemon Pantalaimon, and the struggle between totalitarians and supporters of free speech.

"Magisterial storytelling will sweep readers along; the cast is as vividly drawn as ever; and big themes running beneath the surface invite profound responses and reflection." Kirkus.

The **book** of dust: the secret commonwealth Philip Pullman. Alfred A. Knopf, 2019. 656 p.: Book of dust
Grades: 8 9 10 11 12   **Fic**
1. University of Oxford 2. Familiars (Spirits) 3. Young women 4. College teachers 5. College students 6. Dark matter (Astronomy) 7. Oxford, England 8. England 9. Fantasy fiction
ISBN 9780553510669
Unaware of her professor's role in bringing her and the alethiometer to Jordan College, 20-year-old undergraduate Lyra and her daemon, Pantalaimon, receive secrets from a dying man about a daemon-haunted city and the origins of Dust.

"Magisterial storytelling will sweep readers along; the cast is as vividly drawn as ever; and big themes running beneath the surface invite profound responses and reflection." Kirkus.

The **golden** compass. Philip Pullman. A.A. Knopf, 1995. 399 p.: His dark materials
Grades: 7 8 9 10 11 12   **Fic**
1. Familiars (Spirits) 2. Girl heroes 3. Quests 4. Child kidnapping victims 5. Transformations (Magic) 6. Arctic regions 7. Fantasy fiction 8. Steampunk 9. Classics
ISBN 0679879242

LC 9533397
Carnegie Medal, 1995.
Accompanied by her shape-shifting daemon, Lyra Belacqua sets out to prevent her best friend and other kidnapped children from becoming the subject of gruesome experiments in the Far North.

"This first title in a fantasy trilogy introduces the characters and sets up the basic conflict, namely, a race to unlock the mystery of a newly discovered type of charged particles simply called Dust that may be a bridge to an alternate universe. The action follows 11-year-old protagonist Lyra Belacqua from her home at Oxford University to the frozen wastes of the North on a quest to save dozens of kidnapped children from the evil Gobblers, who are using them as part of a sinister experiment involving Dust." Library Journal.

Once upon a time in the North. by Philip Pullman; engravings by John Lawrence. Alfred A. Knopf, 2008. 112 p.: His dark materials
Grades: 7 8 9 10 11 12   **Fic**
1. Political corruption 2. Familiars (Spirits) 3. Polar bear 4. Balloonists 5. Ship captains 6. Fantasy fiction 7. Steampunk
ISBN 9780375845109

LC 2007043993
In a time before Lyra Silvertongue was born, the tough American balloonist Lee Scoresby and the great armoured bear Iorek Byrnison meet when Lee and his hare daemon Hester crash-land their trading balloon onto a port in the far Arctic North and find themselves right in the middle of a political powder keg.

"The precise narrative prose is spiced up with Lee's flights of oratorical flamboyancy, and the sardonic banter between Lee and his daemon Hester is as amusing as ever. [Illustrated with] engraved spot illustrations and reproduced documents." Horn Book.

The **subtle** knife. Philip Pullman. A.A. Knopf, 1997. 326 p.: His dark materials
Grades: 7 8 9 10 11 12   **Fic**
1. Girl heroes 2. Familiars (Spirits) 3. Quests 4. Magic 5. Transformations (Magic) 6. Fantasy fiction 7. Steampunk 8. Classics
ISBN 0679879250

LC 97673
As the boundaries betweens worlds begin to dissolve, Lyra and her daemon help Will Parry in his search for his father and for a powerful, magical knife.

"More than fulfilling the promise of The Golden Compass, this second volume in the His Dark Materials trilogy starts off at a heart-thumping pace and never slows down." Publishers Weekly.

Two crafty criminals!: and how they were captured by the daring detectives of the New Cut Gang. Philip Pullman. Knopf Books for Young Readers, 2012. 277 p.

Grades: 5 6 7 8   **Fic**
1. Victorian era (1837-1901) 2. 19th century 3. 1890s 4. Child
detectives 5. Counterfeits and counterfeiting 6. Crime 7. Burglary
8. Gangs 9. London, England 10. Great Britain 11. Historical
mysteries 12. Humorous stories 13. Mysteries
ISBN 9780375970290

LC 2011042391

Eleven-year-old Benny Kaminsky leads a rag-tag gang of neighborhood children as they use improbable disguises and crazy ruses
while investigating such crimes as counterfeiting and stolen silver in
1894 London.

Pyron, Bobbie

The **dogs** of winter. by Bobbie Pyron. Arthur A. Levine
Books, 2012. 320 p.

Grades: 5 6 7 8   **Fic**
1. 1990s 2. Wild children 3. Boys and dogs 4. Boy orphans 5.
Homeless children 6. Human/animal relationships 7. Russia 8.
Moscow, Russia
ISBN 9780545399302

LC 2011051519

Brought to Moscow in 1990s Russia by his mother's abusive boyfriend, five-year-old Mishka is forced by a gang of homeless children to
lie and steal until he finds comfort and love with a pack of dogs. Includes
historical note.

Lucky strike. Bobbie Pyron. Arthur A. Levine Books, an imprint of Scholastic Inc., [2015] 272 p.

Grades: 4 5 6 7   **Fic**
1. Lightning 2. Boy orphans 3. Good luck 4. Life change events
5. Best friends 6. Florida 7. Franklin County (Fla) 8. Realistic
fiction
ISBN 9780545592178

LC 2014013764

Nathaniel Harlow lives with his grandfather in a trailer park in
Franklin County, Florida, and he has always been unlucky—but when
he is struck by lightning on his eleventh birthday and survives, it seems
like his luck starts to change.

"The quirkiness of the characters and the town never goes too far,
and there is an overall cozy feeling to the book. Genesis's dad is the
preacher at The Church of the One True Redeemer and Everlasting
Light, but she is a scientist through and through, which adds complexity
to the text, including musings on destiny, fate, probability, and weather."
School Library Journal.

Qamar, Amjed

Beneath my mother's feet. Amjed Qamar. Atheneum Books
for Young Readers, 2008. 198 p.

Grades: 7 8 9 10   **Fic**
1. Women 2. Women's role 3. Determination in teenage girls 4.
Fourteen-year-old girls 5. Teenage girls 6. Pakistan
ISBN 9781416947288

LC 2007019001

When her father is injured, fourteen-year-old Nazia is pulled away
from school, her friends, and her preparations for an arranged marriage,
to help her mother clean houses in a wealthy part of Karachi, Pakistan,
where she finally rebels against the destiny that is planned for her.

"This novel provides a fascinating glimpse into a world remarkably
distant from that of most American teens, and would be an excellent
suggestion for readers who want to know about how other young people
live." School Library Journal.

Quigley, Dawn, 1970-

Apple in the middle. Dawn Quigley. North Dakota State
University Press, 2018 264 p.

Grades: 6 7 8 9 10   **Fic**
1. Multiracial teenage girls -- Identity 2. Indian reservations 3.
Adjustment (Psychology) 4. Native American teenage girls 5.
Native American families 6. North Dakota 7. Coming-of-age
stories 8. Realistic fiction
ISBN 9781946163073

Apple in the Middle is a coming-of-age novel with an unexpected
look at what happens when two cultures collide and our only tour guide
is a quirky, offbeat outcast.— North Dakota State University Press

Ramee, Lisa Moore

★ A **good** kind of trouble. Lisa Ramee. Balzer + Bray, 2019
368 p.

Grades: 4 5 6 7 8   **Fic**
1. African American girls 2. Race relations 3. Protest movements
4. Black Lives Matter movement 5. Girls -- Interpersonal relations
6. Coming-of-age stories 7. African American fiction 8. Realistic
fiction
ISBN 9780062836687

Strictly following the rules to pursue her junior-high ambitions,
12-year-old Shayla is forced to choose between her education and her
identity when her sister joins the Black Lives Matter movement in the
wake of a powerful protest.

"This is a solid story for middle-schoolers dealing with issues such
as friendship across racial lines, being strong girls, #BLM, #MeToo,
civil rights, diversity, and justice." Booklist.

Something to say. Lisa Moore Ramee. Balzer + Bray, 2020
304 p.

Grades: 3 4 5 6 7   **Fic**
1. Loners 2. African American girls 3. Making friends 4. Family
relationships 5. Debates and debating 6. Realistic fiction 7.
African American fiction
ISBN 9780062836717

A friendless girl who has developed a knack for keeping her head
down at school resists a red-headed newcomer who wants to make
friends, before the two are paired for a class assignment that she hopes
will secure her position on the debate team. Atlas Publishing.

Raskin, Ellen

The **Westing** game. Ellen Raskin. Dutton, 1978. 185 p.

Grades: 5 6 7 8   **Fic**
1. Eccentrics and eccentricities 2. Inheritance and succession
3. Murder investigation 4. Apartment houses 5. Neighbors 6.
Chicago, Illinois 7. Illinois 8. Mysteries 9. Classics
ISBN 9780593118108

LC   77018866

Newbery Medal, 1979.

The mysterious death of an eccentric millionaire brings together an
unlikely assortment of heirs who must uncover the circumstances of his
death before they can claim their inheritance.

"The rules of the game make eight pairs of the players; each oddly matched couple is given a ten thousand dollar check and a set of
clues. The result is a fascinating medley of word games, disguises,
multiple aliases and subterfuges, in a demanding but rewarding book."
Horn Book.

Reed, M. K.

Americus. MK Reed; illustrations by Jonathan David Hill. First Second, 2011. 208 p.

Grades: 8 9 10 11 12   **Fic**

1. Banned books 2. Teenage social advocates 3. Books and reading 4. Censorship 5. Librarians 6. Comics and Graphic novels
ISBN 9781596436015

LC 2010051586

Oklahoma teen Neal Barton stands up for his favorite fantasy series, The Chronicles of Apathea Ravenchilde, when conservative Christians try to bully the town of Americus into banning it from the public library.

"The clever mix of fantasy and realistic fiction, thoughtful pacing, authentic dialogue, and expressive art perfectly captures the angst of a nerdy teen who is at first ostracized but then finds his niche as he finds his voice." Booklist.

Reeve, Philip

Fever Crumb. by Philip Reeve. Scholastic Press, 2010. 336 p.: Hungry city chronicles.

Grades: 6 7 8 9 10   **Fic**

1. Abandoned children 2. Prejudice 3. Identity (Psychology) 4. Girl apprentices 5. Orphans 6. London, England 7. England 8. Science fiction 9. Steampunk
ISBN 9780545207195

LC 2009015457

Foundling Fever Crumb has been raised as an engineer although females in the future London, England, are not believed capable of rational thought, but at age fourteen she leaves her sheltered world and begins to learn startling truths about her past while facing danger in the present.

"Reeve's captivating flights of imagination play as vital a role in the story as his endearing heroine, hiss-worthy villains, and nifty array of supporting characters." Booklist.

Scrivener's moon. Philip Reeve. Scholastic Press, 2012. 352 p.: Hungry city chronicles.

Grades: 6 7 8 9 10   **Fic**

1. Mutants 2. Technology 3. Identity (Psychology) 4. Mutation (Biology) 5. Teenage girls 6. London, England 7. Science fiction 8. Steampunk
ISBN 9780545222181

When she returns home after two years, Fever finds that her Scriven mother's creation, New London, the city on wheels, is nearly complete and ready to fight the nomad tribes of Britain—and Fever must journey to the north to find the ancient birthplace of the Scriven mutants and solve the mystery of her own past.

A **web** of air. Philip Reeve. Scholastic, 2011. 304 p.: Hungry city chronicles.

Grades: 6 7 8 9 10   **Fic**

1. Engineers 2. Flying-machines 3. Men recluses 4. Circus 5. Orphans 6. Science fiction 7. Steampunk
ISBN 9780545222167

LC 2010043341

In Mayda, a post-apocalyptic city off the coast of Portugal, a brilliant young engineer and a mysterious recluse race to build a flying machine, unaware that powerful enemies will kill to possess—or destroy—their new technology.

"It's clear that Reeve . . . is building toward an epic, and his remarkable storytelling gifts, coupled with a trenchant understanding of human nature, make these projected volumes worth the wait." Horn Book.

Reichs, Brendan

Chrysalis. Brendan Reichs. G.P. Putnam's Sons Books for Young Readers, 2019. 416 p.: Project Nemesis

Grades: 8 9 10 11 12   **Fic**

1. Survival 2. Cooperation 3. Teenagers 4. Alliances 5. Conspiracies 6. Idaho 7. Apocalyptic fiction 8. Science fiction
ISBN 9780525517054

LC 2018051632

After the test subjects of Project Nemesis find themselves in the dangerous Fire Lake valley and discover that they may not be alone, they realize that they have to overcome their old conflicts and work together if they hope to survive.

Genesis. Brendan Reichs. G. P. Putnam's Sons, [2018] 320 p.: Project Nemesis

Grades: 8 9 10 11 12   **Fic**

1. Survival 2. Conspiracies 3. Couples 4. Betrayal 5. Computer programs 6. Idaho 7. Science fiction 8. Science fiction thrillers
ISBN 9780399544965

LC 2017028972

Min, Noah, and the sophomores of Fire Lake must fight to survive in the second phase of Project Nemesis. Provided by publisher.

"Nemesis was a page-turner, and Genesis has plenty of fevered action and startling surprises, especially as the book nears its conclusion. ...Fans of the first book will certainly want to read this and look forward to the trilogys conclusion." Booklist.

Reinhardt, Dana

The **things** a brother knows. Dana Reinhardt. Wendy Lamb Books, c2010. 288 p.

Grades: 7 8 9 10 11 12   **Fic**

1. Soldiers 2. Post-traumatic stress disorder 3. Walking 4. Brothers 5. Former Marines 6. Boston, Massachusetts 7. Washington, DC 8. Realistic fiction
ISBN 9780375844553

LC 2009035867

Sydney Taylor Book Award for Teen Readers, 2011.

Although they have never gotten along well, seventeen-year-old Levi follows his older brother Boaz, an ex-Marine, on a walking trip from Boston to Washington, D.C. in hopes of learning why Boaz is completely withdrawn.

"Reinhardt's poignant story of a soldier coping with survivor's guilt and trauma, and his Israeli American family's struggle to understand and help, is timely and honest." Booklist.

Reiss, Johanna

★ The **upstairs** room. Johanna Reiss. Harper & Row, 1987, c1972. 179 p.

Grades: 3 4 5 6 7 8   **Fic**

1. Reiss, Johanna 2. Hiding 3. World War II 4. Jews, Dutch 5. Netherlands 6. Autobiographical fiction
ISBN 0690851278

LC 77187940

A Dutch Jewish girl describes the two-and-one-half years she spent in hiding in the upstairs bedroom of a farmer's house during World War II.

"In a vital, moving account the author recalls her experiences as a Jewish child hiding from the Germans occupying her native Holland during World War II. . . . Ten-year-old Annie and her twenty-year-old sister Sini, . . . are taken in by a Dutch farmer, his wife, and mother who hide the girls in an upstairs room of the farm house. Written from the perspective of a child the story affords a child's-eye-view of the war." Booklist.

Revis, Beth

Give the dark my love. Beth Revis. Razorbill, an imprint of Penguin Random House LLC, 2018. 320 p.: Give the dark my love

Grades: 9 10 11 12   **Fic**
1. Magic (Occultism) 2. Plague 3. Risk-taking (Psychology) 4. Teenagers 5. Anger in teenage girls 6. Fantasy fiction
ISBN 9781595147172

LC 2018013398

Told in two voices, seventeen-year-old alchemy student Nedra turns to dark magic when a deadly plague sweeps through her homeland leaving her new friend, Grey, to pull her from the darkness.

Rex, Adam

Champions of breakfast. Adam Rex. Balzer + Bray, an imprint of HarperCollins Publishers, 2014. 288 p.: Cold cereal saga

Grades: 4 5 6 7   **Fic**
1. Fairies 2. Breakfast cereals 3. Corporations 4. Trolls 5. Dragons 6. New Jersey 7. Fantasy fiction
ISBN 9780062060082

LC 2013021387

Eighth-grader Scott Doe and his companions must save the world from a terrible faerie invasion and put an end to the diabolical cereal company Goodco once and for all.

"Scott, Polly, Emily, and Erno, together with a large supporting cast, rescue the miniaturized Queen of England and quell a fairy invasion by killing the dragon Saxbriton and healing the rift between the worlds. The superabundance of characters is hard to keep track of, but for readers following the Arthurian-reimagining trilogy, action, magic, and humor combine for a whiz-bang conclusion." Horn Book.

★ **Cold** cereal. Adam Rex. Balzer + Bray, 2012. 288 p.: Cold cereal saga

Grades: 4 5 6 7   **Fic**
1. Boy misfits 2. Experiments 3. Corporations 4. Breakfast cereals 5. Twin brothers and sisters 6. New Jersey 7. Fantasy fiction
ISBN 9780062060020

LC 2011019538

A boy who may be part changeling, twins involved in a bizarre secret experiment, and a clurichaun in a red tracksuit try to save the world from an evil cereal company whose ultimate goal is world domination.

"The author tucks in portrait illustrations and hilariously odd TV-commercial storyboards, along with a hooded Secret Society, figures from Arthurian legend, magical spells and potions, a certain amount of violence, many wonderful throwaway lines. . . . All in all, it's a mad scramble that culminates in the revelation of a dastardly plot that will require sequels to foil." Kirkus.

Smek for president! Adam Rex. 304 p.: Smek (Adam Rex)

Grades: 5 6 7 8   **Fic**
1. Human/alien encounters 2. Aliens 3. Space flight 4. Adventure 5. Time travel 6. Saturn (Planet) 7. Science fiction 8. Illustrated books 9. Humorous stories
ISBN 9781484709511

LC 2014010764

Gratuity Tucci and her alien friend, J.Lo, journey to New Boovworld, one of Saturn's moons, to clear J.Lo's name after a string of misunderstandings. Provided by publisher.

"Rex packs his sequel with loads of action and a steady spotlight on friendship; plus, he adds witty send-ups of political elections, time travel, and even sports rules (again using cartoon panels to good effect). And his humor is, as it was in Smekday, laugh-out-loud funny." Horn Book.

★ The **true** meaning of Smekday. Adam Rex. Hyperion, c2007. 423 p.: Smek (Adam Rex)

Grades: 5 6 7 8   **Fic**
1. UFO abductions 2. Mother-separated girls 3. Aliens 4. Human/alien encounters 5. Cats 6. Earth. 7. United States 8. Science fiction 9. Illustrated books 10. Humorous stories
ISBN 9780786849000

In the chaotic turmoil that follows the Boov invasion of Earth, eleven-year-old Gratuity Tucci finds herself driving her mother's car to Florida, where all of the humans are being relocated, with her cat and a renegade extraterrestrial named J. Lo as her copilots.

"Incorporating dozens of his weird and wonderful illustrations and fruitfully manipulating the narrative structure, Rex skewers any number of subjects." Publishers Weekly.

Unlucky charms. Adam Rex. Balzer + Bray, 2013. 432 p.: Cold cereal saga

Grades: 4 5 6 7   **Fic**
1. Boy misfits 2. Kidnapping 3. Corporations 4. Space and time 5. Breakfast cereals 6. England 7. Fantasy fiction
ISBN 9780062060051

LC 2012026714

Three kids must save the world from the diabolical schemes of an evil breakfast cereal company, which has been luring magical creatures to our world through a rift in the time-space continuum. Provided by publisher.

Reynolds, Jason

The **boy** in the black suit. Jason Reynolds. Atheneum Books for Young Readers, 2015. 272 p.

Grades: 7 8 9 10   **Fic**
1. African American teenage boys 2. Grief in teenage boys 3. Funeral homes 4. Grief 5. Funerals 6. Brooklyn, New York City 7. Realistic fiction 8. African American fiction
ISBN 9781442459502

Working in the local funeral home to support his family after his mother's death and his father's descent into alcoholism, Matt falls in love with a tough girl who never cries and who understands his loneliness.

"High-school senior Matt has a job at Mr. Ray's funeral home, but he's also in mourning, for his mother who died and his long-on-the-wagon father who's returned to drink. While all this sounds like heavy problem-novel territory, it isn't. Reynolds writes about urban African American kids in a warm and empathetic way that the late Walter Dean Myers would have applauded." Horn Book.

★ **Ghost**. Jason Reynolds. Atheneum Books for Young Readers, 2016 192 p.: Track (Jason Reynolds)

Grades: 4 5 6 7   **Fic**
1. Runners 2. African American boys 3. Children of prisoners 4. Fathers and sons 5. Sprinting 6. Realistic fiction 7. African American fiction
ISBN 9781481450157

"Reynolds has created a wonderfully dynamic character in Ghost; his first-person narrative is one with which young readers will readily identify." Horn Book.

Long way down. Jason Reynolds. Atheneum, 2017. 240 p.

Grades: 6 7 8 9 10 11 12 **Fic**
1. Revenge 2. Grief 3. Violence and guns 4. Loss (Psychology)
5. Ghosts 6. Novels in verse 7. African American fiction
ISBN 9781481438254

Driven by the secrets and vengeance that mark his street culture, 15-year-old Will contemplates over the course of 60 psychologically suspenseful seconds whether or not he is going to murder the person who killed his brother.

"Teens are left with an unresolved ending that goes beyond the simple question of whether Will will seek revenge. Told in verse, this title is fabulistic in its simplicity and begs to be discussed." School Library Journal.

★ **Look** both ways: a tale told in ten blocks. Jason Reynolds; illustrations by Alexander Nabaum. Atheneum/Caitlyn Dlouhy Books, 2019. 208 p.
Grades: 5 6 7 8 **Fic**
1. Students 2. Interpersonal relations 3. City life 4. African Americans 5. School buses 6. Short stories 7. African American fiction
ISBN 9781481438285
LC 2019010095

Carnegie Medal, 2021.

A whimsical exploration of the role detours play in life follows a group of students who become so engaged in everyday activities while taking 10 different routes home from school that they fail to notice a school bus that has dropped from the sky.

"This is storytelling at its finest, a true masterpiece from one of kidlit's brightest ambassadors." Booklist.

Miles Morales. Jason Reynolds. Marvel Press, 2017. 416 p.
Grades: 7 8 9 10 11 12 **Fic**
1. Multiracial teenage boys 2. Teenage superheroes 3. Identity (Psychology) 4. Prep schools 5. Schools 6. Brooklyn, New York City 7. Superhero stories 8. African American fiction 9. Franchise books
ISBN 9781484787489

After a misunderstanding leads him to be suspended from school, Miles Morales feels conflicted about his identity as the new Spider-Man, but when his scholarship is threatened, he uncovers a plot that puts his friends and neighborhood at risk.

"Reynolds builds on a comic book plot and neatly ties in Miles' Marvel Universe background, but he focuses more on his 16-year-old protagonist's struggle with self-doubt in a vividly rendered urban setting stocked with engaging supporting characters." Booklist.

Patina. Jason Reynolds. Atheneum Books for Young Readers, 2017 192 p.: Track (Jason Reynolds)
Grades: 4 5 6 7 **Fic**
1. African American girls 2. Runners 3. Track and field 4. Children of people with diabetes 5. Family problems 6. Realistic fiction 7. African American fiction
ISBN 9781481450188

"The second entry in the four-book Track series, this serves as a complete, complex, and sparkling stand-alone novel." Booklist.

Rhodes, Jewell Parker

Black brother, black brother. Jewell Parker Rhodes. Little, Brown and Company, 2020. 240 p.
Grades: 4 5 6 7 **Fic**
1. Multiracial teenagers 2. Racism 3. Bullying and bullies 4. Colorism 5. Fencing 6. Massachusetts 7. Realistic fiction 8.

African American fiction
ISBN 9780316493802
LC 2019034929

Suspended unjustly from elite Middlefield Prep, Donte Ellison studies fencing with a former champion, hoping to put the racist fencing team captain in his place.

"This novel offers a solid story, with relatable, three-dimensional characters considering identity, that will teach readers about colorism's effects." Publishers Weekly

★ **Ghost** boys. by Jewell Parker Rhodes. Little Brown & Co., 2018 256 p.
Grades: 4 5 6 7 8 **Fic**
1. Till, Emmett, 1941-1955 2. Police shootings 3. Racism 4. African American boys -- Death 5. Death 6. Ghosts 7. Chicago, Illinois 8. Magical realism 9. African American fiction
ISBN 9780316262286
LC 2017019240

After seventh-grader Jerome is shot by a white police officer, he observes the aftermath of his death and meets the ghosts of other fallen black boys including historical figure Emmett Till. Provided by publisher.

★ **Ninth** Ward. by Jewell Parker Rhodes. Little, Brown and Co., 2010. 217 p.
Grades: 5 6 7 8 **Fic**
1. African American girls 2. Hurricane Katrina, 2005 3. Spirits 4. Survival (after hurricanes) 5. Resilience (Personal quality) 6. New Orleans, Louisiana 7. Coming-of-age stories 8. African American fiction
ISBN 9780316043076
LC 2009034423

In New Orleans' Ninth Ward, twelve-year-old Lanesha, who can see spirits, and her adopted grandmother have no choice but to stay and weather the storm as Hurricane Katrina bears down upon them.

"The dynamics of the diverse community enrich the survival story, and the contemporary struggle of one brave child humanizes the historic tragedy." Booklist.

Sugar. Jewell Parker Rhodes. Little, Brown, 2013. 160 p.
Grades: 3 4 5 6 7 8 **Fic**
1. 1870s 2. Freed people 3. Race relations 4. Reconstruction (United States history) 5. African American girls 6. Plantation life 7. Louisiana 8. Historical fiction 9. African American fiction
ISBN 9780316043052
LC 2012026218

In 1870, Reconstruction brings big changes to the Louisiana sugar plantation where spunky ten-year-old Sugar has always lived, including her friendship with Billy, the son of her former master, and the arrival of workmen from China.

"Sugar's clipped narration is personable and engaging, strongly evoking the novel's historical setting and myriad racial tensions, making them accessible and meaningful to beginning readers." Publishers Weekly.

Rhuday-Perkovich, Olugbemisola

Two Naomis. Olugbemisola Rhuday-Perkovich & Audrey Vernick. Balzer + Bray, 2016. 208 p.
Grades: 4 5 6 7 **Fic**
1. Children and single parent dating 2. Ten-year-old girls 3. Names 4. Girls -- Names 5. Mother-separated girls 6. Realistic fiction 7.

African American fiction
ISBN 9780062414250

A realistic contemporary story of two girls, both named Naomi, whose divorced parents begin to date.

"A smart, endearing story about two girls who are blending families, growing up, and building a friendship." Kirkus.

Ribay, Randy

Patron saints of nothing. Randy Ribay. Kokila, 2019. 352 p.
Grades: 8 9 10 11 12   **Fic**
1. Murder 2. Cousins 3. Filipino American boys 4. Drug traffic 5. Identity (Psychology) 6. Philippines 7. Realistic fiction 8. Coming-of-age stories
ISBN 9780525554912

LC 2018044009

When seventeen-year-old Jay Reguero learns his Filipino cousin and former best friend, Jun, was murdered as part of President Duterte's war on drugs, he flies to the Philippines to learn more.

"By deftly weaving key details into Jay's quest for the truth, Ribay provides a much-needed window for young people of the West to better understand the Filipino history of colonization, occupation, and revolution." Booklist.

Includes bibliographical references.

Richards, Jame

Three rivers rising: a novel of the Johnstown flood. Jame Richards. Alfred A. Knopf, c2010. 293 p.
Grades: 6 7 8 9 10   **Fic**
1. 1880s 2. Rich teenage girls 3. Floods 4. Classism 5. Social classes 6. Teenage boy/girl relations 7. Pennsylvania 8. Novels in verse 9. Historical fiction
ISBN 9780375958854

LC 2009004251

Sixteen-year-old Celestia is a wealthy member of the South Fork Fishing and Hunting Club, where she meets and falls in love with Peter, a hired hand who lives in the valley below, and by the time of the torrential rains that lead to the disastrous Johnstown flood of 1889, she has been disowned by her family and is staying with him in Johnstown. Includes an author's note and historical timeline.

"This is a striking novel in verse. . . . Richards builds strong characters with few words and artfully interweaves the lives of these independent thinkers." Publishers Weekly.

Riggs, Ransom

Hollow City: the second novel of Miss Peregrine's Home for Peculiar Children. Ransom Riggs. Quirk Books, 2014. 400 p.: Miss Peregrine
Grades: 6 7 8 9 10   **Fic**
1. 1940s 2. Orphans 3. Animals 4. Escapes 5. Supernatural 6. Teenage boys 7. London, England 8. Wales 9. Fantasy fiction 10. Illustrated books
ISBN 9781594746123

In 1940, Jacob and his new friends escape from Miss Peregrine's island and travel to London where they encounter new allies, a menagerie of peculiar animals, and other unexpected surprises.

"Like the first volume, this one is generously illustrated with peculiar period photographs that capture and enhance the eerie mood and mode." Booklist.

Library of souls: the third novel of Miss Peregrine's peculiar children. Ransom Riggs. Quirk Books, 2015. 400 p.: Miss Peregrine

Grades: 6 7 8 9 10   **Fic**
1. 1940s 2. Orphans 3. Rescues 4. Supernatural 5. Teenage boys 6. London, England 7. Wales 8. Fantasy fiction 9. Illustrated books
ISBN 9781594747588

The adventure that began with Miss Peregrine's Home for Peculiar Children and continued in Hollow City comes to a thrilling conclusion with Library of Souls. As the story opens, sixteen-year-old Jacob discovers a powerful new ability, and soon he's diving through history to rescue his peculiar companions from a heavily guarded fortress. Accompanying Jacob on his journey are Emma Bloom, a girl with fire at her fingertips, and Addison MacHenry, a dog with a nose for sniffing out lost children.

"As in the previous books, Riggs builds atmosphere with eerie vintage photos that amplify the curious nature of his imagined world. This novel proves perhaps too neat a conclusion to Jacob's story arc, but satisfying answers are given to long-standing questions about peculiardom, and all major story lines see resolution. Fans will easily lose themselves in this most peculiar tale of all." Booklist.

A map of days. Ransom Riggs. Dutton Children's Books, 2018. 496 p.: Miss Peregrine
Grades: 6 7 8 9 10   **Fic**
1. Orphanages 2. Time travel (Past) 3. Abandoned property 4. Grandfathers -- Death 5. Supernatural 6. Florida 7. Fantasy fiction 8. Illustrated books
ISBN 9780735232143

LC bl2018179834

Jacob Portman is back in Florida and this time Miss Peregrine, Emma, and their peculiar friends are with him, but when he finds a secret underground bunker owned by his grandfather Abe, Jacob is thrust into a new adventure.

Miss Peregrine's home for peculiar children: a novel. by Ransom Riggs. Quirk Books, 2011. 352 p.: Miss Peregrine
Grades: 6 7 8 9 10   **Fic**
1. Orphanages 2. Time travel (Past) 3. Abandoned property 4. Grandfathers -- Death 5. Islands 6. Wales 7. Fantasy fiction 8. Illustrated books
ISBN 9781594744761

After a family tragedy, Jacob feels compelled to explore an abandoned orphanage on an island off the coast of Wales, discovering disturbing facts about the children who were kept there.

"Nearly 50 unsettling vintage photographs appear throughout, forming the framework of this dark but empowering tale, as Riggs creates supernatural backstories and identities for those pictured in them. . . . It's an enjoyable, eccentric read, distinguished by well-developed characters, a believable Welsh setting, and some very creepy monsters." Publishers Weekly.

Tales of the Peculiar. Ransom Riggs; illustrated by Andrew Davidson. Dutton Books for Young Readers, 2016. 208 p.: Miss Peregrine
Grades: 7 8 9 10   **Fic**
1. Time travel 2. Secrets 3. Shapeshifters 4. Cannibals 5. Princesses 6. Fantasy fiction 7. Short stories 8. Illustrated books
ISBN 9780399538537

"Elegantly detailed engravings from Davidson open each story, setting the tone for the tale that follows." Publishers Weekly.

Riley, James, 1977-

Secret origins. by James Riley. Aladdin, 2017. 352 p.: Story thieves

Grades: 5 6 7 8   **Fic**
1. Superheroes 2. Comic book characters 3. Magic 4. Adventure 5. Rescues 6. Fantasy fiction 7. Metafiction
ISBN 9781481461252

LC 2016025387

Aided by old friends and new, Owen and Bethany try to bring the light back to Jupiter City, a comic book world where they discover a link between the Dark and Bethany's father.

"A literary hall of mirrors, with plenty of thrills and laughs to keep 'nonfictionals' in the game." Kirkus.

Riordan, Rick

The **battle** of the Labyrinth. Rick Riordan. Hyperion Books for Children, 2008. 320 p.: Percy Jackson & the Olympians

Grades: 5 6 7 8 9   **Fic**
1. Teenage boy adventurers 2. Demigods 3. Labyrinths 4. Friendship 5. Cheerleaders 6. Fantasy fiction 7. Mythological fiction
ISBN 9781423101468

LC 2007042957

When demonic cheerleaders invade his high school, Percy Jackson hurries to Camp Half Blood, from whence he and his demigod friends set out on a quest through the Labyrinth, while the war between the Olympians and the evil Titan lord Kronos draws near.

"The wit, rousing swordplay and breakneck pace will once again keep kids hooked." Publishers Weekly.

The **blood** of Olympus. Rick Riordan. Disney Press, 2014. 528 p.: Heroes of Olympus

Grades: 5 6 7 8   **Fic**
1. Demigods 2. Giants 3. Gods and goddesses, Greek 4. Prophecies 5. Gaia (Greek deity) 6. Fantasy fiction 7. Mythological fiction
ISBN 9781423146735

LC 2014017392

The Greek and Roman demigods must simultaneously prevent the earth mother, Gaea, from waking and stop war from breaking out at Camp Half-Blood. Provided by publisher.

"Readers looking forward to the battle scenes will find plenty here, but the young heroes also rely on their wits as they dupe, charm, and negotiate their way through a series of encounters with gods, goddesses, and mythological creatures." Booklist.

The **burning** maze. Rick Riordan. Disney-Hyperion, 2018. 448 p.: Trials of Apollo

Grades: 5 6 7 8   **Fic**
1. Gods and goddesses, Greek 2. Oracles 3. Demigods 4. Apollo (Greek deity) 5. Bisexual teenagers 6. Southwest (United States) 7. Mythological fiction 8. Fantasy fiction
ISBN 9781484746431

LC 2017059850

The Greek god Apollo, cast down to earth as the ungifted human teenager Lester Papadopoulos, and his demigod friends must go through the Labyrinth to find the third emperor—and an Oracle who speaks in word puzzles—somewhere in the American Southwest.

"Amid the cinematic pacing and well-choreographed action scenes, Riordan squeezes plenty of character development into the expanding cast of characters, even minor ones who don't get a lot of page space." Booklist

The **dark** prophecy. Rick Riordan. Disney-Hyperion, 2017. 320 p.: Trials of Apollo

Grades: 5 6 7 8   **Fic**
1. Gods and goddesses, Greek 2. Oracles 3. Demigods 4. Apollo (Greek deity) 5. Bisexual teenagers 6. Mythological fiction 7. Fantasy fiction
ISBN 9781484746424

"Riordan's characters continue to be an impressively diverse group. . . . This latest has Riordan's signature wry narration, nonstop action, and mythology brought to life." School Library Journal

The **hammer** of Thor. Rick Riordan. Disney-Hyperion, 2016. 528 p.: Magnus Chase and the gods of Asgard

Grades: 5 6 7 8 9   **Fic**
1. Gods and goddesses, Norse 2. Magic hammers 3. Giants 4. Quests 5. Loki (Norse deity) 6. Mythological fiction 7. Fantasy fiction
ISBN 9781423160922

"An entertaining sequel that will whet fans appetites for the next installment." Kirkus.

The **hidden** oracle. Rick Riordan. Disney-Hyperion, 2016. 384 p.: Trials of Apollo

Grades: 5 6 7 8   **Fic**
1. Gods and goddesses, Greek 2. Demigods 3. Apollo (Greek deity) 4. Enemies 5. Bisexual teenagers 6. New York City 7. Mythological fiction 8. Fantasy fiction
ISBN 9781484732748

"A clash of mythic intrigues and centuries of pop culture to thrill die-hard and new fans alike." Kirkus.

The **house** of Hades. Rick Riordan. Disney-Hyperion, 2013. 608 p.: Heroes of Olympus

Grades: 5 6 7 8   **Fic**
1. Giants 2. Demigods 3. Prophecies 4. Gods and goddesses, Greek 5. Hera (Greek deity) 6. Fantasy fiction 7. Mythological fiction
ISBN 9781423146728

LC 2013015946

Greek and Roman demigods from the Prophecy of Seven must work together to seal the Doors of Death—and help Percy and Annabeth escape the Underworld in the process. Provided by publisher.

"In this fourth in Riordan's series pitting Roman and Greek demigods against an awakening goddess Gaea, Percy and Annabeth trek through Tartarus to escape through the Doors of Death, while their friends fight their way to the Doors' mortal side to rescue them. The wisecracking teens reveal emotional depths while overcoming monsters and personal obstacles in this high velocity continuation of the gripping franchise." Horn Book.

The **last** Olympian. Rick Riordan. Hyperion Books for Children, c2009. 381 p.: Percy Jackson & the Olympians

Grades: 5 6 7 8 9   **Fic**
1. Teenage boy adventurers 2. Demigods 3. Fate and fatalism 4. Gods and goddesses, Greek 5. Titans (Mythology) 6. New York City 7. Mount Olympus, Greece 8. Fantasy fiction 9. Mythological fiction
ISBN 9781423101475

The long-awaited prophecy surrounding Percy Jackson's sixteenth birthday unfolds as he leads an army of young demigods to stop Kronos in his advance on New York City, while the Olympians struggle to contain the rampaging monster, Typhon.

"Riordan masterfully orchestrates the huge cast of characters and manages a coherent, powerful tale at once exciting, philosophical and tear-jerking." Kirkus.

★ The **lightning** thief. Rick Riordan. Miramax, 2006, c2005. 377 p.: Percy Jackson & the Olympians

Grades: 5 6 7 8 9   **Fic**

1. Boy adventurers 2. Demigods 3. Lightning 4. Camps 5. Hostages 6. New York City 7. Los Angeles, California 8. Fantasy fiction 9. Mythological fiction

ISBN 9780786838653

After learning that the father he never knew is Poseidon, God of the Sea, Percy Jackson is transferred from boarding school to Camp Half-Blood, a summer camp for demigods, and becomes involved in a quest to prevent a war between the gods.

"Riordan's fast-paced adventure is fresh, dangerous, and funny." Booklist.

The **lost** hero. Rick Riordan. Disney/Hyperion Books, 2010. 576 p.: Heroes of Olympus

Grades: 5 6 7 8   **Fic**

1. Demigods 2. Gods and goddesses, Greek 3. Imprisonment 4. Rescues 5. Quests 6. Fantasy fiction 7. Mythological fiction

ISBN 9781423113393

LC 2010015469

Jason, Piper, and Leo, three students from a school for "bad kids," find themselves at Camp Half-Blood, where they learn that they are demigods and begin a quest to free Hera, who has been imprisoned by Mother Earth herself.

"Completely in control of pacing and tone, . . . [Riordan] . . . balances a faultless comic banter against deeper notes that reveal the characters' vulnerabilities." Horn Book.

The **mark** of Athena. Rick Riordan. Hyperion, 2012. 608 p.: Heroes of Olympus

Grades: 5 6 7 8   **Fic**

1. Giants 2. Demigods 3. Prophecies 4. Camps 5. Monsters 6. Greece 7. Fantasy fiction 8. Mythological fiction

ISBN 9781423140603

LC 2012017264

The Greek and Roman demigods will have to cooperate in order to defeat the giants released by the Earth Mother, Gaea. Then they will have to sail together to the ancient land—Greece itself—to find the Doors of Death. Provided by publisher.

"With Gaea awakening and pitting the Greek demigods against their Roman counterparts, Percy Jackson, Jason, and their companions travel to Rome so Annabeth can search for her mother Athena's statue, stolen by the Romans in antiquity. Its return might heal the rift between the camps. Riordan's likable, strong, distinct characters drive the narrative in this rousing continuation of the saga." Horn Book.

★ The **maze** of bones. Rick Riordan. Scholastic Press, 2008. 224 p.: The 39 clues.

Grades: 4 5 6 7   **Fic**

1. Child adventurers 2. Inheritance and succession 3. Clues 4. Orphans 5. Codes (Communication) 6. Adventure stories

ISBN 0545060397

LC 2007938689

"Adeptly incorporating a genuine kids' perspective, the narrative unfolds like a boulder rolling downhill and keeps readers glued to the pages. . . . The book dazzles with suspense, plot twists, and snappy humor." School Library Journal.

Percy Jackson's Greek gods. Rick Riordan; illustrated by John Rocco. Disney-Hyperion, [2014] 336 p.

Grades: 5 6 7 8   **Fic**

1. Gods and goddesses, Greek 2. Jackson, Percy (Fictitious character) 3. Mythological fiction 4. Fantasy fiction

ISBN 9781423183648

LC 2013034612

Percy Jackson, a modern-day demigod, tells the origin stories of the gods of Olympus and provides an insider's point of view while offering a personal take on his ancient associates.

"Combining the sarcasm and wit of Percy Jackson with the original Greek myths is a great way to hook tweens and teens on the stories without boring them. The beautiful illustrations by John Rocco enhance each story without taking away from the action and drama." Voice of Youth Advocates.

★ The **red** pyramid. by Rick Riordan. Hyperion Books for Children, c2010. 516 p.: Kane chronicles

Grades: 4 5 6 7   **Fic**

1. Multiracial children 2. Gods and goddesses, Egyptian 3. Egyptologists 4. Quests 5. Voyages and travels 6. Brooklyn, New York City 7. England 8. Fantasy fiction 9. Mythological fiction

ISBN 9781423113386

Brilliant Egyptologist Dr. Julius Kane accidentally unleashes the Egyptian god Set, who banishes the doctor to oblivion and forces his two children to embark on a dangerous journey, bringing them closer to the truth about their family and its links to a secret order that has existed since the time of the pharaohs.

"The first-person narrative shifts between Carter and Sadie, giving the novel an intriguing dual perspective made more complex by their biracial heritage and the tension between the siblings. . . . This fantasy adventure delivers . . . young protagonists with previously unsuspected magical powers, a riveting story marked by headlong adventure, a complex background rooted in ancient mythology, and wry, witty twenty-first-century narration." Booklist.

The **sea** of monsters. Rick Riordan. Miramax, c2006. 279 p.: Percy Jackson & the Olympians

Grades: 5 6 7 8 9   **Fic**

1. Teenage boy adventurers 2. Magic trees 3. Demigods 4. Monsters 5. Gods and goddesses, Greek 6. New York City 7. Bermuda Triangle 8. Fantasy fiction 9. Mythological fiction

ISBN 0786856866

When Camp Half-Blood, the only safe haven for demigods, comes close to being overrun by mythological monsters, Percy must find his best friend Grover, who is prisoner on an island in the Bermuda Triangle, and then set out to save the Camp.

"Adventure follows chaotic adventure at a rapid pace, and readers with even a passing acquaintance with the Odyssey will enjoy this fresh use of familiar stories." School Library Journal.

The **serpent's** shadow. Rick Riordan Disney/Hyperion, 2012. 416 p.: Kane chronicles

Grades: 4 5 6 7   **Fic**

1. Snakes 2. Gods and goddesses, Egyptian 3. Multiracial children 4. Spells (Magic) 5. Shadows 6. Fantasy fiction 7. Mythological fiction

ISBN 9781423140573

Carter and Sade prepare for the ultimate confrontation with the chaos snake Apophis at the same time the House of Life magicians launch a civil war, compelling the Kanes to tap the power of an ancient spell.

The **ship** of the dead. Rick Riordan. Disney Press, 2017. 528 p.: Magnus Chase and the gods of Asgard

Grades: 5 6 7 8   **Fic**

1. Teenage boys 2. Voyages and travels 3. Gods and goddesses, Norse 4. Quests 5. Chase, Magnus (Fictitious character) 6. Mythological fiction 7. Fantasy fiction
ISBN 9781423160939

Magnus and his friends set sail for the farthest borders of Jotunheim and Niflheim in pursuit of Asgard's greatest threat, Loki's demonic ship full of zombies.

The **son** of Neptune. Rick Riordan. Disney/Hyperion Books, 2011. 384 p.: Heroes of Olympus

Grades: 5 6 7 8   **Fic**

1. Demigods 2. Prophecies 3. Death 4. Gods and goddesses, Greek 5. Quests 6. Fantasy fiction 7. Mythological fiction
ISBN 9781423140597

LC 2011017658

Demigod Percy Jackson, still with no memory, and his new friends from Camp Jupiter, Hazel and Frank, go on a quest to free Death, but their bigger task is to unite the Greek and Roman camps so that the Prophecy of Seven can be fulfilled.

The **sword** of summer. Rick Riordan. Disney Hyperion, 2015. 528 p.: Magnus Chase and the gods of Asgard

Grades: 5 6 7 8   **Fic**

1. Gods and goddesses, Norse 2. Demigods 3. Giants 4. Swords 5. Death 6. Boston, Massachusetts 7. Fantasy fiction 8. Mythological fiction
ISBN 9781423160915

"There's appeal for new readers, but Percy Jackson fans will also undoubtedly snap this up, and there's even some overlap: Magnus's cousin is Annabeth Chase." Booklist.

The **throne** of fire. Rick Riordan. Disney/Hyperion Books, c2011. 452 p.: Kane chronicles

Grades: 4 5 6 7   **Fic**

1. Multiracial children 2. Gods and goddesses, Egyptian 3. Magical books 4. Ra (Egyptian deity) 5. Magic 6. Mythological fiction 7. Fantasy fiction
ISBN 9781423140566

LC bl2011009343

Carter and Sadie, offspring of the brilliant Egyptologist Dr. Julius Kane, embark on a worldwide search for the Book of Ra, but the House of Life and the gods of chaos are determined to stop them.

"Lit by flashes of humor, this fantasy adventure is an engaging addition to the Kane Chronicles series." Booklist.

The **Titan's** curse. Rick Riordan. Miramax Books/Hyperion Books for Children, c2007. 320 p.: Percy Jackson & the Olympians

Grades: 5 6 7 8 9   **Fic**

1. Teenage boy adventurers 2. Demigods 3. Missing women 4. Friendship 5. Prophecies 6. Fantasy fiction 7. Mythological fiction
ISBN 9781423101451

LC 2006035731

When the goddess Artemis disappears while hunting a rare, ancient monster, a group of her followers joins Percy and his friends in an attempt to find and rescue her before the winter solstice, when her influence is needed to sway the Olympian Council regarding the war with the Titans.

"Intricate prophecies and relationships are neatly braided into the adventurous plot." School Library Journal.

★ The **tower** of Nero. Rick Riordan. 448 p.: Trials of Apollo

Grades: 5 6 7 8   **Fic**

1. Gods and goddesses, Greek 2. Oracles 3. Demigods 4. Apollo (Greek deity) 5. Bisexual teenagers 6. New York City 7. San Francisco Bay Area 8. Mythological fiction 9. Fantasy fiction
ISBN 9781484746455

A conclusion to the best-selling series finds Lester teaming up with his demigod master, Meg, to follow a prophecy that leads to an ultimate confrontation with Python at the Tower of Nero.

Ritter, John H., 1951-

The **boy** who saved baseball. John H. Ritter. Philomel Books, c2003. 216 p.

Grades: 5 6 7 8   **Fic**

1. Twelve-year-old boys 2. Boy baseball players 3. Former professional baseball players 4. Baseball coaches 5. Baseball players 6. California
ISBN 0399236228

LC 2002015792

The fate of a small California town rests on the outcome of one baseball game, and Tom Gallagher hopes to lead his team to victory with the secrets of the now disgraced player, Dante Del Gato.

"This tale is peppered with both optimism and dilemmas; it has plenty of play-by-play action, lots of humor, and a triumphant ending." School Library Journal.

Ritter, William, 1984-

Changeling. William Ritter. Algonquin Young Readers, 2019. 272 p.: Oddmire

Grades: 4 5 6 7   **Fic**

1. Twin brothers 2. Changelings 3. Goblins 4. Preteen boys 5. Magic 6. Fantasy fiction
ISBN 9781616208394

LC 2018033941

Twelve-year-olds Tinn and Cole, raised as human twins in sleepy Endsborough, risk their lives in the Wild Wood, Oddmire Swamp, and the Deep Dark to learn which is a goblin changeling with an important mission.

"A human boy and a goblin changeling are raised as brothers...a delightful series opener." Kirkus.

Deepest, darkest. written and illustrated by William Ritter. Algonquin Young Readers, 2021. 320 p.: Oddmire

Grades: 4 5 6 7   **Fic**

1. Missing persons 2. Twin brothers 3. Changelings 4. Goblins 5. Preteen boys 6. Fantasy fiction
ISBN 9781643750927

LC 2020041304

Determined to solve the mystery of their long-missing father, brothers Cole and Tinn, with the help of their friends, set out on a dangerous quest to the deepest, most deadly limits of the Wild Wood to find the truth.

"This is very much an action story, with abundant visual description and an accessible writing style that ranges from epic prophecy to contemporary vernacular." Horn Book

The **dire** king. William Ritter. Algonquin Young Readers, 2017. 352 p.: Jackaby

Grades: 7 8 9 10   **Fic**
   1. 1890s 2. Detectives 3. Shapeshifters 4. Eccentrics and eccentricities 5. Rulers 6. Zombies 7. New England 8. Supernatural mysteries 9. Historical mysteries
   ISBN 9781616206703

                   LC 2017002941

In this conclusion to the Jackaby series, the eccentric detective and his assistant Abigail Rook find themselves in the middle of a war between magical worlds.

"A humorous, energetic, action-packed, and magical conclusion." Kirkus.

Jackaby. R. William Ritter. Algonquin Young Readers, 2014. 304 p.: Jackaby

Grades: 7 8 9 10 11 12   **Fic**
   1. 1890s 2. 19th century 3. Serial murder investigation 4. Serial murderers 5. Murder 6. Supernatural 7. Imaginary creatures 8. New England 9. Supernatural mysteries
   ISBN 9781616203535

                   LC 2014014706

Newly arrived in 1892 New England, Abigail Rook becomes assistant to R. F. Jackaby, an investigator of the unexplained with the ability to see supernatural beings, and she helps him delve into a case of serial murder which, Jackaby is convinced, is due to a nonhuman creature.

The **unready** queen. written and illustrated by William Ritter. Algonquin Young Readers, 2020. 272 p.: Oddmire

Grades: 4 5 6 7   **Fic**
   1. Forests 2. Rulers 3. Armistices 4. Magic 5. Preteens 6. Fantasy fiction
   ISBN 9781616208400

                   LC 2019057639

Fable, the half-human daughter of the Queen of the Deep Dark, and her friends, the human and goblin brothers Cole and Tinn, discover that humans are destroying the Wild Wood, breaking the unspoken truce between the people of Endsborough and the inhabitants of the Wild Wood and leading them to war.

Rivera, Kaela

★ **Cece** Rios and the Desert of Souls. Kaela Rivera HarperCollins, 2021. 352 p.

Grades: 4 5 6 7 8   **Fic**
   1. Spirits 2. Kidnapping 3. Quests 4. Preteen girls 5. Twelve-year-old girls 6. Fantasy fiction 7. Coming-of-age stories
   ISBN 9780062947550

                   LC 2020937705

Privately questioning her remote community's superstitions about dangerous powerful spirits in their Devil's Alley home, Cecelia Rios experiments with the forbidden art of brujera to rescue her kidnapped sister.

"With excellent pacing and rich world-building, debut author Rivera flawlessly immerses readers in the landscape of Tierra del Sol and Cece's journey. An enthralling, finely crafted read." Publishers Weekly

Rivers, Karen, 1970-

Finding Ruby Starling. Karen Rivers. Scholastic, 2014. 288 p.

Grades: 5 6 7 8   **Fic**
   1. Twin sisters 2. Separated twins 3. Email 4. Sisters 5. Realistic fiction 6. Epistolary novels
   ISBN 9780545534796

A tale inspired by The Parent Trap is told through emails, letters, Tumblr entries and movie scripts that trace the reunion of two identical twins who learn the truth about their separation while sharing respective social and family challenges.

"In this epistolary, dual-narrator story, Ruth, an American twelve-year-old, e-finds her identical twin, Ruby, in England. As with any novel in letters (in this case emails, handwritten notes, and the occasional Tumblr posting), voice is everything, and Ruth and Ruby have distinctive, convincing, and entertaining writing styles. Subplots abound, including the backstory of two complicated families. Hectic, highly textured, and good-natured without being soppy." Horn Book.

The **girl** in the well is me. Karen Rivers. Algonquin Young Readers, [2016] 224 p.

Grades: 5 6 7 8 9   **Fic**
   1. Bullying and bullies 2. Self-perception 3. Nastiness in girls 4. Friendship 5. Wells 6. Texas 7. Realistic fiction
   ISBN 9781616205690

                   LC 2015023956

Eleven-year-old Kammie reflects on her life as she fights claustrophobia while waiting to be rescued from a well she fell into while trying to impress some mean girls.

"A different sort of bullying book, with the spotlight never leaving the victim, it should strike a chord with its tween audience." Booklist.

Love, Ish. Karen Rivers. Algonquin Young Readers, 2017. 304 p.

Grades: 6 7 8 9   **Fic**
   1. Children with cancer 2. Adopted girls 3. Friendship 4. Brain -- Tumors 5. New students 6. Mars (Planet) 7. Realistic fiction
   ISBN 9781616205706

                   LC 2016038086

Twelve-year-old Mischa "Ish" Love's longtime dream has been to someday live on Mars, but when she collapses on the first day of seventh grade, Ish receives a diagnosis which threatens her future plans.

Roat, Sharon Huss

How to disappear. Sharon Huss Roat. HarperTeen, an imprint of HarperCollins Publishers, 2017 377 p.

Grades: 7 8 9 10 11 12   **Fic**
   1. Introverts 2. Social media 3. Kindness 4. Anxiety 5. Loneliness 6. Realistic fiction
   ISBN 9780062291752

Living life strictly below the radar after her only friend moves away, Vicky, determined to put off her mother's intervention, Photoshops herself into pictures that she posts online before meeting numerous people who feel just as alone and ignored as she does.

"This is a witty, hard-to-put-down novel that's appropriate for younger teens. However, the lack of grittiness won't deter older teens, who will be carried along by familiar lingo and references to social networks and celebrities." School Library Journal.

Robinet, Harriette Gillem

Walking to the bus-rider blues. Atheneum Books for Young Readers, 2000. 146 p.

Grades: 5 6 7 8   **Fic**
   1. African Americans 2. Twelve-year-old boys 3. Montgomery Bus Boycott 4. Montgomery, Alabama
   ISBN 0689831919

                   LC   99029054

Twelve-year-old Alfa Merryfield, his older sister, and their grandmother struggle for rent money, food, and their dignity as they participate in the Montgomery, Alabama bus boycott in the summer of 1956.

"Ingredients of mystery, suspense, and humor enhance and personalize this well-constructed story that offers insight into a troubled era." School Library Journal.

Robinson, Gary, 1950-

Little Brother of War. Gary Robinson. 7th Generation, 2013. 120 p.

Grades: 6 7 8   **Fic**

1. Native American teenage boys 2. Teenage athletes 3. Fathers and sons 4. Individuality 5. Ball games 6. Mississippi 7. Realistic fiction

ISBN 9781939053022

LC 2013013182

Sixteen-year-old Mississippi Choctaw Randy Cheska lives under the shadow of his brother who was a football hero, later killed in Iraq, until proves himself to his parents and others through the ancient game of stickball.

Standing strong. Gary Robinson. Orca Book Pub 2019 120 p.

Grades: 7 8 9   **Fic**

1. Native American teenage girls 2. Protests, demonstrations, vigils, etc 3. Suicidal behavior 4. Environmental protection 5. Oil industry and trade 6. Standing Rock Reservation, North Dakota 7. Montana 8. Realistic fiction

ISBN 9781939053220

LC 2019002633

After a failed suicide attempt, seventeen-year-old Rhonda Runningcrane is inspired to help a crew protesting against an oil company running a pipeline through sacred Native land in North Dakota.

"A book for reluctant readers that highlights the heroism of young activists." Kirkus.

Rodgers, Mary, 1931-

Freaky Friday. Mary Rodgers. Harper, 1972. 145 p.

Grades: 4 5 6 7   **Fic**

1. Role reversal 2. Teenage girls 3. Mothers and daughters 4. Disasters, Minor 5. Lost children 6. Fantasy fiction 7. Classics 8. Humorous stories

ISBN 0060250488

LC 74183158

A teenage girl and her mother get their wish as they magically exchange places one day.

"Readers will giggle in anticipation as Annabel plunges madly from one disaster to another trying to cope with various adult situations." Publishers Weekly.

Rodkey, Geoff, 1970-

The **Tapper** twins go to war (with each other). Geoff Rodkey. Little, Brown and Company, 2015. 224 p.: Tapper twins

Grades: 4 5 6 7   **Fic**

1. Twin brothers and sisters 2. Practical jokes 3. Revenge 4. Internet games 5. Families 6. New York City 7. Realistic fiction

ISBN 9780316297790

"Through oral-history interviews, text messages, e-mails, chat-room comments, photographs, and margin notes, Claudia documents the history of the Tapper twins' war. . . . Thanks to the inclusion of various points of view, Claudia's reasonably balanced narrative offers plenty of humorous insight, and occasional doodles and photos keep it peppy." Booklist.

Roe, Robin

A **list** of cages. Robin Roe. 320 p.

Grades: 8 9 10 11   **Fic**

1. Teenage abuse victims 2. Child abuse 3. Teenage boy orphans 4. Teenage boys with ADHD 5. Teenagers with dyslexia 6. Realistic fiction

ISBN 9781484763803

LC 2015045422

Landing a coveted elective to serve as an aide to the school psychologist, Adam, a student struggling with ADHD, is assigned to track down a troubled freshman he discovers is the foster brother he has not seen in five years.

"A triumphant story about the power of friendship and of truly being seen." Kirkus.

Rogerson, Margaret

An **enchantment** of ravens. Margaret Rogerson. Margaret K. McElderry Books, 2017. 300 p.

Grades: 7 8 9 10   **Fic**

1. Teenage girl artists 2. Portraits 3. Fairies 4. Princes 5. Imaginary kingdoms 6. High fantasy 7. Fantasy fiction

ISBN 9781481497589

A superbly skilled portrait artist who includes among her patrons the sinister, immortal fair folk who covet her talents, Isobel makes the terrible mistake of revealing an autumn faerie prince's sorrow in his portrait, a choice that strands them both in a hostile land where they risk their lives to pursue forbidden feelings for each other.

"Rogerson ably builds this fantasy world through canny details and contemporary dialogue, allowing for an enjoyable read by fantasy and non-fantasy readers alike. She also craftily depicts the power imbalance between Isobel and Rook, offering a refreshing dynamic in which Isobel often comes out on top." School Library Journal.

Rose, Caroline Starr

May B.: a novel. by Caroline Starr Rose. Schwartz & Wade Books, 2012. 224 p.

Grades: 4 5 6 7   **Fic**

1. 19th century 2. Girls with dyslexia 3. Frontier and pioneer life 4. Blizzards 5. Survival 6. Poor families 7. Kansas 8. Historical fiction 9. Novels in verse

ISBN 9781582464121

LC 2010033222

When a failed wheat crop nearly bankrupts the Betterly family, Pa pulls twelve-year-old May from school and hires her out to a couple new to the Kansas frontier.

"If May is a brave, stubborn fighter, the short, free-verse lines are one-two punches in this Laura Ingalls Wilder-inspired ode to the human spirit." Kirkus.

Rosen, Michael J., 1954-

Sailing the unknown: around the world with Captain Cook. written by Michael J. Rosen; illustrated by Maria Cristina Pritelli. Creative Editions, 2012. 40 p.

Grades: 3 4 5 6 7   **Fic**

1. Cook, James, 1728-1779. 2. Endeavour (Ship) 3. 18th century 4. Boy sailors 5. Trips around the world 6. Explorers 7. Diaries 8. Sailors -- History 18th century 9. Oceania 10. Australia 11. Sea

stories 12. Historical fiction
ISBN 9781568462165

LC 2011040840

A sailor boy named Nick travels the uncharted world of the late 1700s in this illustrated account of the historic three-year voyage of the British vessel Endeavour and its captain, James Cook. Provided by publisher.

The **tale** of rescue. Michael J. Rosen; illustrated by Stan Fellows. Candlewick Press, 2015. 103 p.

Grades: 4 5 6 7 8   **Fic**

1. Blizzards 2. Dogs 3. Rescue dogs 4. Rescues 5. Families 6. Adventure stories 7. Illustrated books
ISBN 9780763671679

"Lavishly illustrated in full-page watercolors, the book is visually beautiful and will appeal to adults looking for a feel-good dog story to share with a child." Booklist.

Rosenberg, Madelyn, 1966-

This is just a test. a novel by Madelyn Rosenberg and Wendy Wan-Long Shang. Scholastic Press, 2017. 243 p.

Grades: 4 5 6 7 8   **Fic**

1. 1980s 2. Families 3. Jewish boys 4. Chinese American boys 5. Friendship 6. Grandmothers 7. Virginia 8. Historical fiction
ISBN 9781338037722

LC 2016037804

In 1983 seventh-grader David Da-Wei Horowitz has a lot to worry about—his bar mitzvah is coming soon, his Jewish and Chinese grandmothers argue about everything, his teammates for the upcoming trivia contest, Scott and Hector, do not like each other, he is beginning to notice girls, and Scott has persuaded him to begin digging a fallout shelter just in case the Cold War heats up.

"An appealing historical novel, even for readers resistant to the genre." Booklist.

Ross, Elizabeth (Elizabeth Anne)

Belle epoque. Elizabeth Ross. Delacorte Press, 2013. 272 p.

Grades: 7 8 9 10 11 12   **Fic**

1. Belle Epoque (1871-1914) 2. 19th century 3. Sixteen-year-old girls 4. Class conflict 5. Beauty 6. Social classes 7. Teenage girls 8. Paris, France 9. France 10. Historical fiction
ISBN 9780385741460

LC 2012034694

Sixteen-year-old Maude Pichon, a plain, impoverished girl in Belle Epoque Paris, is hired by Countess Dubern to make her headstrong daughter, Isabelle, look more beautiful by comparison but soon Maude is enmeshed in a tangle of love, friendship, and deception.

"Ross models her plot on an 1866 story by Zola, Les Repoussoirs, expanding its focus to highlight Maude's plight and using that to illuminate the chasm that existed between the wealthy and the poor... A refreshingly relevant and inspiring historical venture." Kirkus.

Ross, Joel N., 1968-

The **Fog** diver. Joel Ross. HarperCollins, 2015. 336 p.: Fog diver novels

Grades: 4 5 6 7   **Fic**

1. Post-apocalypse 2. Fog 3. Airships 4. Orphans 5. Survival 6. Science fiction
ISBN 9780062352934

LC 2014034154

In this futuristic high-stakes adventure, humanity clings to cities on the highest mountain peaks above the deadly Fog, and airships transport the pirates of the skies. Daring 13-year-old tetherboy Chess and his salvage crew must face the dark plans of Lord Kodoc and work to save their beloved Mrs. E. Provided by publisher.

"[A] fresh approach, convincingly delivered, with overtones reminiscent of Dickens; the only thing missing is a sequel, which readers will hope won't be far behind." Kirkus.

Rossetti, Rinsai

The **girl** with borrowed wings. by Rinsai Rossetti. Dial Books, c2012. 290 p.

Grades: 7 8 9 10 11 12   **Fic**

1. Shapeshifters 2. Overprotectiveness in fathers 3. Flight 4. Freedom 5. Shapeshifting 6. Fantasy fiction 7. Middle Eastern-influenced fantasy
ISBN 9780803735668

LC 2011027164

Seventeen-year-old Frenenqer lives a controlled and restricted life in the desert, like everyone else there, but when she meets Sangris, a Free, winged shape-shifter, everything changes.

Rossi, Veronica

Under the never sky. Veronica Rossi. Harpercollins Childrens Books, 2012. 400 p.: Under the never sky trilogy

Grades: 6 7 8 9 10 11 12   **Fic**

1. Post-apocalypse 2. Dystopias 3. Quests 4. Teenage boy/girl relations 5. Seventeen-year-old girls 6. Science fiction 7. Apocalyptic fiction
ISBN 9780062072030

Aria and Perry, two teens from radically different societies—one highly advanced, the other primitive—hate being dependent on one another until they overcome their prejudices and fall in love, knowing they can't stay together.

Rothenberg, Jess

The **Kingdom**. Jess Rothenberg. Henry Holt and Company, 2019. 343 p.

Grades: 7 8 9 10   **Fic**

1. Cyborgs 2. Trials (Murder) 3. Amusement parks 4. Posthumanism 5. Artificial intelligence 6. Science fiction
ISBN 9781250293855

LC 2018038696

Ana, a half-android, half-human employee of a futuristic fantasy theme park, the Kingdom, faces a charge of murder in a tale told through flashbacks and court transcripts.

"A layered and fast-paced mystery with an ethical backbone." Booklist

Rowell, Rainbow

Carry on: a novel. Rainbow Rowell. Griffin, [2015] 528 p.: Simon Snow

Grades: 8 9 10 11 12   **Fic**

1. Wizards 2. Boarding schools 3. Monsters 4. Teenage boy/boy relations 5. Magic 6. Fantasy fiction
ISBN 9781250049551

During his last year at Watford School of Magicks, Simon Snow, the Chosen One, faces a magic-eating monster wearing his face, a break-up, and a missing nemesis.

"The novel playfully twists genre conventions—there are plenty of wink-wink, nudge-nudge moments to satisfy faithful fantasy readers—but it also stands alone as a modern bildungsroman." Kirkus.

Wayward son. Rainbow Rowell. Wednesday Books, 2019. 368 p.: Simon Snow

Grades: 8 9 10 11 12   **Fic**

1. Cross-country automobile trips 2. Misadventures 3. Wizards 4. Vampires 5. Teenage boy/boy relations 6. United States 7. Fantasy fiction

ISBN 9781250146076

LC 2019028910

Finds an overwhelmed Simon joining Penny and Baz on a trip to the American West in a vintage convertible, only to be confronted by dragons, vampires and gun-toting skunks.

"Carefully plotted, the book is a classic page-turner right to the open ending which, o frabjous day, promises a sequel to the sequel! One can hardly wait." Booklist

Rowling, J. K.

Harry Potter and the Chamber of Secrets. J. K. Rowling; illustrations by Mary GrandPre. Arthur A. Levine Books, 1999. 341 p.: Harry Potter (Original series)

Grades: 4 5 6 7 8 9 10   **Fic**

1. Child wizards 2. Boarding schools 3. Magic -- Study and teaching 4. Schools 5. Potter, Harry (Fictitious character) 6. England 7. Fantasy fiction 8. Classics

ISBN 9780439064866

LC 98-46370

When the Chamber of Secrets is opened again at the Hogwarts School for Witchcraft and Wizardry, second-year student Harry Potter finds himself in danger from a dark power that has once more been released on the school.

Harry Potter and the deathly hallows. J. K. Rowling; illustrated by Mary GrandPre. Arthur A. Levine Books, 2007. 784 p.: Harry Potter (Original series)

Grades: 4 5 6 7 8 9 10   **Fic**

1. Teenage wizards 2. Boarding schools 3. Self-fulfillment 4. Magic -- Study and teaching 5. Schools 6. England 7. Fantasy fiction 8. Classics

ISBN 9780545010221

LC 2007925449

The seventh and final book of the blockbuster Harry Potter series follows the wizard's last year at Hogwarts School of Witchcraft and Wizardry.

"Throughout, Rowling returns to and embellishes the hallmark themes of the series: the importance of parental influences, the redemptive power of sacrifice, and the strength found in love. These truths are the underpinnings of a finale that is worthy of fans' hopes and expectations." Booklist

Harry Potter and the goblet of fire. J. K. Rowling; illustrations by Mary GrandPre. A. A. Levine Books, 2000. 734 p.: Harry Potter (Original series)

Grades: 4 5 6 7 8 9 10   **Fic**

1. Teenage wizards 2. Boarding schools 3. Magic -- Study and teaching 4. Schools 5. Potter, Harry (Fictitious character) 6. England 7. Fantasy fiction 8. Classics

ISBN 9780439139595

Fourteen-year-old Harry Potter joins the Weasleys at the Quidditch World Cup, then enters his fourth year at Hogwarts Academy where he is mysteriously entered in an unusual contest that challenges his wizarding skills, friendships and character, amid signs that an old enemy is growing stronger.

Harry Potter and the Order of the Phoenix. J. K. Rowling; illustrated by Mary GrandPre. Arthur A. Levine Books, 2003. 896 p.: Harry Potter (Original series)

Grades: 4 5 6 7 8 9 10   **Fic**

1. Boarding schools 2. Teenage boy orphans 3. Magic -- Study and teaching 4. Schools 5. Potter, Harry (Fictitious character) 6. England 7. Fantasy fiction 8. Classics

ISBN 9780439358064

LC 2003102525

When the government of the magic world and authorities at Hogwarts School of Witchcraft and Wizardry refuse to believe in the growing threat of a freshly revived Lord Voldemort, fifteen-year-old Harry Potter finds support from his loyal friends in facing the evil wizard and other new terrors.

Harry Potter and the prisoner of Azkaban. J. K. Rowling; illustrations by Mary GrandPre. A. A. Levine Books, 1999. 435 p.: Harry Potter (Original series)

Grades: 4 5 6 7 8 9 10   **Fic**

1. Boarding schools 2. Teenage boy orphans 3. Magic -- Study and teaching 4. Schools 5. Potter, Harry (Fictitious character) 6. England 7. Fantasy fiction 8. Classics

ISBN 9780439136358

During his third year at Hogwarts School for Witchcraft and Wizardry, Harry Potter must confront the devious and dangerous wizard responsible for his parents' death.

★ **Harry** Potter and the sorcerer's stone. J. K. Rowling; illustrations by Mary GrandPre. A. A. Levine Books, 1997. vi, 309 p.: Harry Potter (Original series)

Grades: 4 5 6 7 8 9 10   **Fic**

1. Child wizards 2. Boarding schools 3. Magic -- Study and teaching 4. Schools 5. Eleven-year-old boys 6. England 7. Fantasy fiction 8. Classics

ISBN 9780590353403

LC 9739059

Rescued from the outrageous neglect of his aunt and uncle, a young boy with a great destiny proves his worth while attending Hogwarts School of Witchcraft and Wizardry.

"This is a brilliantly imagined and beautifully written fantasy." Booklist.

The **tales** of Beedle the Bard. J. K. Rowling. Arthur A. Levine Books, 2008. 128 p.: Harry Potter (Companion volumes)

Grades: 5 6 7 8 9 10 11 12   **Fic**

1. Wizards 2. Self-awareness 3. Magic wands 4. Enchantment 5. Magic 6. Fantasy fiction

ISBN 9780545128285

LC 2008934360

A collection of fairy tales for young wizards and witches, with each story followed by observations on Wizarding history, personal reminiscences, and information on the story's key elements by Hogwarts headmaster, Albus Dumbledore.

"The introduction is captivating . . . [and] the tales themselves are entertaining. . . . Rowling is at the top of her game as a superb storyteller, providing her legions of fans with an enchanting collection of wizard folklore." Voice of Youth Advocates.

Roy, Jennifer Rozines, 1967-

Mindblind. Jennifer Roy. Marshall Cavendish, c2010. 248 p.

Grades: 7 8 9 10 11   **Fic**
1. Gifted teenagers 2. Rock groups 3. Asperger's syndrome 4. Songwriting 5. Genius 6. Realistic fiction
ISBN 9780761457169

LC 2010006966

Fourteen-year-old Nathaniel Clark, who has Asperger's Syndrome, tries to prove that he is a genius by writing songs for his rock band, so that he can become a member of the prestigious Aldus Institute, the premier organization for the profoundly gifted.

"Mature readers will empathize with Nathaniel as his friends, Jessa and Cooper, do. This book is for teens who appreciate a story about self-discovery, dreams, and friendship." Voice of Youth Advocates.

Yellow star. by Jennifer Roy. Marshall Cavendish, c2006. 227 p.
Grades: 5 6 7 8   **Fic**
1. Second World War era (1939-1945) 2. 1930s 3. 1940s 4. Families 5. Jewish girls 6. Girls 7. Jewish families 8. Holocaust survivors 9. Poland 10. Biographical fiction 11. Historical fiction
ISBN 076145277X

LC 2005050788

From 1939, when Syvia is four and a half years old, to 1945 when she has just turned ten, a Jewish girl and her family struggle to survive in Poland's Lodz ghetto during the Nazi occupation.

"In a thoughtful, vividly descriptive, almost poetic prose, Roy retells the true story of her Aunt Syvia's experiences. . . . This book is a standout in the genre of Holocaust literature." School Library Journal.

Rubens, Michael
Sons of the 613. Mike Rubens. Clarion Books, 2012. 384 p.
Grades: 7 8 9 10   **Fic**
1. Jewish boys 2. Bar mitzvah 3. Masculinity 4. Brothers 5. Jews 6. Minnesota 7. Realistic fiction 8. Coming-of-age stories 9. Humorous stories
ISBN 9780547612164

LC 2011044352

Isaac is struggling to prepare for his Bar Mitzvah when his older brother Josh, a self-proclaimed "Super Jew" and undefeated wrestler, forces him into a quest to become a man by shooting a gun, riding a motorcycle, falling in love, and more.

Rubin, Lance, 1981-
Crying laughing. Lance Rubin. Alfred A. Knopf, 2019 336 p.
Grades: 7 8 9 10 11   **Fic**
1. Improvisation (Acting) 2. Teenage girls 3. Family problems 4. Stand-up comedy 5. High school students 6. Realistic fiction 7. Coming-of-age stories
ISBN 9780525644682

The author of Denton Little's Deathdate gives us a tragicomic story of bad dates, bad news, bad performances, and one girl's determination to find the funny in high school.

"This book is for anyone who's ever attended high school, had a crush, gotten news they weren't prepared to deal with, or learned that someone close to them isn't quite who they thought they were—in short, for everyone." Booklist.

Ruby, Laura
The **clockwork** ghost. Laura Ruby. Walden Pond Press, an imprint of HarperCollinsPublishers, 2019. 464 p.: York (Laura Ruby)

Grades: 5 6 7 8   **Fic**
1. Codes (Communication) 2. Puzzles 3. Twin brothers and sisters 4. Neighbors 5. Jewish children 6. New York City 7. Fantasy mysteries 8. Steampunk
ISBN 9780062306968

Continuing their efforts to solve the Morningstarr cipher in the aftermath of their home's destruction, the Biedermann twins and their friend Jaime encounter dangerous enemies who are attempting to claim the cipher's treasure.

"Ruby takes a classic puzzle mystery and compellingly draws it out, both in the time the puzzles take and by giving the characters room to contemplate their feelings." Booklist.

The **shadow** cipher. Laura Ruby. Walden Pond Press, an imprint of HarperCollinsPublishers, 2017 476 p.: York (Laura Ruby)
Grades: 5 6 7 8 9   **Fic**
1. Codes (Communication) 2. Puzzles 3. Twin brothers and sisters 4. Neighbors 5. Real estate developers 6. New York City 7. Fantasy mysteries 8. Steampunk
ISBN 9780062306937

A debut entry in an alternate-history series depicts three kids who try to solve a modern-world puzzle and complete a treasure hunt laid into the streets and buildings of New York City.

Ruiz Zafon, Carlos, 1964-2020
Marina. Carlos Ruiz Zafon. Little, Brown and Company, 2014. 336 p.
Grades: 8 9 10 11 12   **Fic**
1. Boarding school students 2. Secrets 3. Tombs 4. Loyalty 5. Mansions 6. Barcelona, Spain 7. Spain 8. Gothic fiction 9. Translations
ISBN 9780316044714

An English-language release of a popular story for older teens relates the experiences of a boarding school student who witnesses a shrouded woman's macabre ritual at a cemetery, then follows her on a journey that transports him and his companion, Marina, to a forgotten post-war Barcelona, where they uncover a dark secret.

"Set in Barcelona, Spain from late 1979 to May 1980, this gothic novel centers around 15-year-old boarding school student Oscar Drai. Instead of studying during his free time, the teen explores the city, and one day ends up in an area that seems deserted. Drawn in by music coming from an old dilapidated house, Oscar is given a scare by the owner, an eccentric and haunted German artist...With elements of romance, mystery, and horror, none of them overwhelming the other, this complex volume that hints at Mary Shelley's Frankenstein manages to weave together three separate stories for a cohesive and eerie result." School Library Journal.

The **Midnight** Palace. Carlos Ruiz Zafon; translated by Lucia Graves. Little, Brown, 2011. 304 p.
Grades: 7 8 9 10   **Fic**
1. British Raj (1858-1947) 2. 1930s 3. Twin brothers and sisters 4. Secret societies 5. Supernatural 6. Villains 7. Teenage orphans 8. Calcutta, India 9. India 10. Historical fantasy 11. Translations
ISBN 9780316044738

LC 2010043131

When a mysterious threat reenters the lives of twins Ben and Sheere, separated as babies and reunited as teenagers in 1930s Calcutta, the siblings must confront an unspeakable terror, with the help of their secret society of fellow orphans.

"The sense of dread and mystery that pervades the story, and the themes of lost innocence and sacrifice keep readers turning the pages." School Library Journal.

The **prince** of mist. Carlos Ruiz Zafon. Little, Brown, 2010. 208 p.

Grades: 6 7 8 9 10   **Fic**
   1. Coastal towns 2. Shipwrecks 3. Magicians 4. Good and evil 5. Gardens 6. Horror
ISBN 9780316044776

In 1943, in a seaside town where their family has gone to be safe from war, thirteen-year-old Max Carver and sister, fifteen-year-old Alicia, with new friend Roland, face off against an evil magician who is striving to complete a bargain made before he died.

"Zafon is a master storyteller. From the first page, the reader is drawn into the mystery and suspense that the young people encounter when they move into the Fleischmann house. . . . This book can be read and enjoyed by every level of reader." Voice of Youth Advocates.

Rundell, Katherine

★ **Cartwheeling** in thunderstorms. Katherine Rundell, Melissa Castrillon. Simon & Schuster, 2014. 256 p.

Grades: 4 5 6 7 8   **Fic**
   1. Twelve-year-old girls 2. Independence in girls 3. Resilience (Personal quality) 4. New students 5. Belonging 6. London, England 7. Zimbabwe 8. Realistic fiction
ISBN 9781442490611

Wilhelmina Silver lives half-wild on an African farm with her horse, her monkey and her best friend, but when her home is sold and Will is sent away to boarding school in England, the world becomes impossibly difficult—lions and hyenas are nothing compared to the packs of vicious schoolgirls she encounters.

"Wilhelmina, daughter of William Silver, white foreman of the Two Tree Hill Farm in Zimbabwe, leads a 'wildcat' life. Her idyll ends abruptly and tragically with her father's death from malaria, after which she's shipped off to boarding school in England. Rundell's finely drawn etchings of the people in Will's sphere and rich descriptions of African colonial farm life sprawl across the pages." Horn Book.

★ **Rooftoppers**. Katherine Rundell; with illustrations by Terry Fan. Simon & Schuster Books for Young Readers, 2013. 256 p.

Grades: 4 5 6 7   **Fic**
   1. Guardian and ward 2. Mother-separated girls 3. Orphans 4. Missing persons 5. Roofs 6. Paris, France 7. France 8. Adventure stories
ISBN 9781442490581

LC 2012049469

When authorities threaten to take Sophie, twelve, from Charles who has been her guardian since she was one and both survived a shipwreck, the pair goes to Paris to try to find Sophie's mother, and they are aided by Matteo and his band of "rooftoppers."

The **wolf** wilder. Katherine Rundell. Simon & Schuster Books for Young Readers, [2015] 256 p.

Grades: 4 5 6 7 8   **Fic**
   1. Mothers and daughters 2. Rescues 3. Wolves 4. Prisoners 5. Voyages and travels 6. Russia 7. Historical fiction 8. Survival stories
ISBN 9781481419420

LC 2014048206

In the days before the Russian Revolution, twelve-year-old Feodora sets out to rescue her mother when the Tsar's Imperial Army imprisons her for teaching tamed wolves to fend for themselves.

"Her spirited, half-wild nature shines brightly on the page, even as her vulnerabilities endear her to readers' hearts. It is a wonderful thing to see Feo's quest inspire a nation to stand up and fight, and readers will cheer her on every step of the way." Booklist.

Rupp, Rebecca

After Eli. Rebecca Rupp. Candlewick Press, 2012. 245 p.

Grades: 4 5 6 7 8   **Fic**
   1. Teenagers and death 2. First loves 3. Loss (Psychology) 4. Teenage boy/girl relations 5. Brothers -- Death 6. Realistic fiction
ISBN 9780763658106

LC 2011048344

After the death of his older brother, Daniel Anderson became engrossed in recording details about dead people, how they died, and whether their deaths mattered but he is eventually drawn back into interaction with the living.

Russell, Chris

Songs about a girl. Chris Russell. Flatiron Books, 2017 362 p.

Grades: 7 8 9 10   **Fic**
   1. Boy bands 2. Photographers 3. Best friends 4. Bullying and bullies 5. Teenage girl photographers 6. England 7. Realistic fiction
ISBN 9781250095169

Accepting a job taking band photos for a former classmate, aspiring photographer Charlie Bloom is surprised when the unexpectedly popular band catapults her into the world of fandom and paparazzi before a love triangle, a creative rivalry and a personal secret threaten her prospects.

Russell, Rachel Renee

Tales from a not-so-fabulous life. by Rachel Renee Russell. Aladdin Paperbacks, 2009. 282 p.: Dork diaries

Grades: 4 5 6 7   **Fic**
   1. Popularity 2. Private schools 3. Crushes in teenage girls 4. Friendship 5. Middle schools 6. Diary novels 7. Realistic fiction
ISBN 9781416980063

LC 2008048567

Fourteen-year-old Nikki Maxwell writes in her diary of her struggle to be popular at her exclusive new private school, then of finding her place after she gives up on being part of the elite group.

"Nikki's journey of self-discovery will appeal to preadolescent readers struggling to find their places in the world." Kirkus.

Rutkoski, Marie

The **Cabinet** of Wonders. Marie Rutkoski. Farrar, Straus and Giroux, 2008. viii, 258 p.: Kronos chronicles

Grades: 5 6 7 8   **Fic**
   1. Clocks and watches 2. Eye 3. Princes 4. Romanies 5. Spiders 6. Historical fantasy
ISBN 9780374310264

LC 2007037702

Twelve-year-old Petra, accompanied by her magical tin spider, goes to Prague hoping to retrieve the enchanted eyes the Prince of Bohemia took from her father, and is aided in her quest by a Roma boy and his sister.

"Add this heady mix of history and enchantment to the season's list of astonishingly accomplished first novels. . . . Infusions of folklore (and

Rutkowski's embellishments of them) don't slow the fast plot but more deeply entrance readers." Publishers Weekly.

The **Celestial** Globe. Marie Rutkoski. Farrar, Straus and Giroux, 2009. 304 p.: Kronos chronicles

Grades: 5 6 7 8   **Fic**

1. Spies 2. Murder investigation 3. Globes 4. Pirates 5. Romanies 6. Historical fantasy

ISBN 9780374310271

LC 2008035599

Thirteen-year-old Petra, her tin spider Astrophil, and their Roma friends Neel and Tomik are surprised by revelations about Dee, Kit, and Petra's father as they face Prince Rodolfo of Bohemia, who will do anything to possess a powerful object, the Celestial Globe.

"This stellar sequel to The Cabinet of Wonders surpasses its predecessor by navigating the intelligent fantasy adventure outside 16th-century Bohemia and deepening the scope of its magic. . . . Strong characters and fast-paced plotting let this compelling installment stand independently, but the ending will leave readers eager for the next." Publishers Weekly.

The **winner's** crime. Marie Rutkoski. Farrar Straus Giroux Books for Young Readers, 2015. 352 p.: Winner's trilogy

Grades: 7 8 9 10 11 12   **Fic**

1. Aristocracy 2. Spies 3. Loyalty 4. Secrets 5. Engagement 6. High fantasy 7. Fantasy fiction

ISBN 9780374384708

LC 2014025185

The engagement of Lady Kestrel to Valoria's crown prince is the event of a lifetime, but to Kestrel it means living in a cage of her own making, so as she aches to tell the truth about her engagement, she becomes a skilled practitioner of deceit and as a spy passes information and gets close to uncovering a shocking secret.

"A rich and complex story of political intrigue, missed opportunities, and thwarted trust fill the pages of this sequel to The Winner's Curse (2014). Rutkoski's world is splendid in its cruelty and beauty, with characters that continue to claim our hearts." Booklist.

The **winner's** curse. Marie Rutkoski. Farrar, Straus and Giroux, 2014. 368 p.: Winner's trilogy

Grades: 7 8 9 10 11 12   **Fic**

1. Slavery 2. Aristocracy 3. Loyalty 4. Enslaved people 5. Interpersonal attraction 6. High fantasy 7. Fantasy fiction

ISBN 9780374384678

Limited by her warmongering empire to join the military or get married, 17-year-old general's daughter Kestrel finds herself falling in love with compelling slave Arin, who hides a dangerous secret.

"Full-bodied characters explore issues of loyalty, class, and values (for example, arts versus military strengths), without sacrificing any of the relationship-related tension that is a hallmark of this kind of story." Booklist.

The **winner's** kiss. Marie Rutkoski. Farrar Straus Giroux Books for Young Readers, 2016 352 p.: Winner's trilogy

Grades: 7 8 9 10 11 12   **Fic**

1. Aristocracy 2. Slavery 3. Imaginary wars and battles 4. Secrets 5. Teenage girls 6. High fantasy 7. Fantasy fiction

ISBN 9780374384739

Arin fights in the war between the East and the Empire as he tries to forget Kestrel, the woman he believes betrayed her people, while Kestrel struggles to escape from a labor camp before discovering terrible secrets.

Ryan, Pam Munoz

★ The **dreamer**: a novel. by Pam Munoz Ryan; [illustrations by Peter Sís. Scholastic Press, 2010. 384 p.

Grades: 4 5 6 7   **Fic**

1. Neruda, Pablo, 1904-1973 2. Shyness in boys 3. Creativity in boys 4. Poets, Chilean 5. Shyness 6. Creativity 7. Chile 8. Biographical fiction 9. Illustrated books

ISBN 9780439269704

LC 2009010274

Pura Belpré Award for Narrative, 2011.

A fictionalized biography of the Nobel Prize-winning Chilean poet Pablo Neruda, who grew up a painfully shy child, ridiculed by his overbearing father, but who became one of the most widely-read poets in the world.

"Ryan loads the narrative with vivid sensory details. And although it isn't poetry, it eloquently evokes the sensation of experiencing the world as someone who savors the rhythms of words and gets lost in the intricate surprises of nature. The neat squares of Sís meticulously stippled illustrations, richly symbolic in their own right, complement and deepen the lyrical quality of the book." Booklist.

Includes bibliographical references.

Echo. Pam Munoz Ryan. Scholastic Press, 2015 592 p.

Grades: 4 5 6 7 8   **Fic**

1. Harmonica 2. Music 3. Fate and fatalism 4. Curses 5. Orphans 6. Germany 7. Pennsylvania 8. Historical fiction

ISBN 9780439874021

Decades after a man is entwined in a prophecy-based quest involving three mysterious sisters and a harmonica, three individuals from different areas of the world confront daunting challenges involving the same harmonica.

"The harmonica and the love of music serve as the unifying threads for these tales of young people who save the lives and spirits of their families and neighbors, each in a time marked by bigotry and violence. It's an ambitious device, but Ryan's storytelling prowess and vivid voice lead readers expertly through a hefty tome illuminated by layers of history, adventure, and the seemingly magical but ultimately very human spirit of music." Horn Book.

Esperanza rising. Pam Munoz Ryan. Scholastic Press, 2000. 262 p.

Grades: 5 6 7 8   **Fic**

1. Depression era (1929-1941) 2. 1930s 3. Mexican American teenage girls 4. Mexican American migrant agricultural laborers 5. Social classes 6. Mexican Americans 7. Mothers and daughters 8. California 9. Historical fiction

ISBN 0439120411

LC 00024186

Pura Belpré Award for Narrative, 2002.

Esperanza and her mother are forced to leave their life of wealth and privilege in Mexico to go work in the labor camps of Southern California, where they must adapt to the harsh circumstances facing Mexican farm workers on the eve of the Great Depression.

"Ryan writes movingly in clear, poetic language that children will sink into, and the [book] offers excellent opportunities for discussion and curriculum support." Booklist.

Rylant, Cynthia

A **fine** white dust. Cynthia Rylant. Bradbury Press, 1986. 106 p.

Grades: 5 6 7 8   **Fic**

1. Thirteen-year-old boys 2. Faith 3. Betrayal 4. Christian life 5.

Teenage boys -- Friendship 6. North Carolina 7. Realistic fiction
ISBN 0027772403

LC 86001003

The visit of the traveling Preacher Man to his small North Carolina town gives new impetus to thirteen-year-old Peter's struggle to reconcile his own deeply felt religious belief with the beliefs and non-beliefs of his family and friends.

"Blending humor and intense emotion with a poetic use of language, Cynthia Rylant has created a taut, finely drawn portrait of a boy's growth from seeking for belief, through seduction and betrayal, to a spiritual acceptance and a readiness for something whole." Horn Book.

★ **God** went to beauty school. by Cynthia Rylant. Harper Collins, 2003. 56 p.

Grades: 5 6 7 8 **Fic**

1. God 2. Everyday life 3. Life 4. New experiences 5. Novels in verse
ISBN 0060094338

LC 2002069068

A novel in poems that reveal God's discovery of the wonders and pains in the world He has created.

Missing May. Cynthia Rylant. Orchard Books, 1992. 89 p.

Grades: 5 6 7 8 **Fic**

1. Twelve-year-old girls 2. Children and death 3. Grief 4. Grief in children 5. Aunts 6. West Virginia
ISBN 9780531059968

LC 91023303

Newbery Medal, 1993.

After the death of the beloved aunt who has raised her, twelve-year-old Summer and her uncle Ob leave their West Virginia trailer in search of the strength to go on living.

"There is much to ponder here, from the meaning of life and death to the power of love. That it all succeeds is a tribute to a fine writer who brings to the task a natural grace of language, an earthly sense of humor, and a well-grounded sense of the spiritual." School Library Journal.

Ryon, Loriel

Into the tall, tall grass. Loriel Ryon. Margaret K. McElderry Books, 2020 336 p.

Grades: 5 6 7 8 **Fic**

1. Magic 2. Ability 3. Family secrets 4. Twin sisters 5. Grandmothers 6. Magical realism
ISBN 9781534449671

LC 2019032230

Hiding her lack of magical powers from her family of witches, Yolanda agrees to accompany her estranged twin and friend on a quest to uncover long-buried secrets that have overshadowed her loved ones.

"The tinge of whimsical magic permeating the Rodriguez line creates the perfect ambiance for stirring up, and resolving, conflict among Yolanda, those she cares for, and the town." School Library Journal

Sachar, Louis, 1954-

The **cardturner**. Louis Sachar. Delacorte Press, 2010. 192 p.

Grades: 8 9 10 11 12 **Fic**

1. Rich men 2. Intergenerational relations 3. Bridge (Game) 4. Card games 5. Men who are blind 6. Realistic fiction
ISBN 9780385736626

Alton Richards doesn't have much going for him the summer after his junior year of high school and his parents insist he drive his wealthy, elderly uncle to his bridge club and be his cardturner. Alton soon finds himself intrigued by his uncle, by the game of bridge, and by pretty and shy Toni Castaneda. As the summer goes on, he tries to figure out the meaning of his life.

"Alton gets roped into serving as a card turner for his great-uncle, Lester Trapp, a bridge whizz who recently lost his eyesight. . . . To Alton's surprise, he becomes enamored of the game and begins to bond with his crusty uncle. . . . With dry, understated humor, Alton makes the intricacies of bridge accessible, while his relationships with and observations about family members and friends . . . form a portrait of a reflective teenager whose life is infinitely enriched by connections he never expected to make." Publishers Weekly.

★ **Holes**. Louis Sachar. Farrar, Straus and Giroux, 1998 233 p.

Grades: 5 6 7 8 **Fic**

1. Juvenile delinquents 2. Holes 3. Juvenile correctional institutions 4. Teenage prisoners 5. Yelnats, Stanley (Fictitious character) 6. Texas 7. Classics
ISBN 0374332657

LC 97045011

National Book Award for Young People's Literature, 1998.
Newbery Medal, 1999.

As further evidence of his family's bad fortune which they attribute to a curse on a distant relative, Stanley Yelnats is sent to a hellish correctional camp in the Texas desert where he finds his first real friend, a treasure, and a new sense of himself.

"This delightfully clever story is well-crafted and thought-provoking, with a bit of a folklore thrown in for good measure." Voice of Youth Advocates.

Small steps. Louis Sachar. Delacorte Press, 2006. 272 p.

Grades: 5 6 7 8 **Fic**

1. Ticket scalping 2. Money-making projects for boys 3. People with disabilities 4. Teenage boys 5. African American teenage boys 6. Austin, Texas
ISBN 0385733143

LC 2005009102

Schneider Family Book Award for Teens, 2007.

Three years after being released from Camp Green Lake, Armpit is trying hard to keep his life on track, but when his old pal X-Ray shows up with a tempting plan to make some easy money scalping concert tickets, Armpit reluctantly goes along.

"This is a story of redemption, of the triumph of the human spirit, of self-sacrifice, and of doing the right thing. Sachar is a master storyteller who creates memorable characters." School Library Journal.

Saeed, Jamal, 1959-

Yara's spring. Jamal Saeed & Sharon E. McKay. Annick Press, 2020. 264 p.

Grades: 6 7 8 9 **Fic**

1. Girl refugees 2. Survival 3. Arab Spring, 2010- 4. Parent-separated children 5. Children and war 6. Jordan 7. Syria 8. Realistic fiction 9. Coming-of-age stories
ISBN 9781773214405

Coming of age against all odds in the midst of the Arab Spring.

"The narrative is fast-paced and descriptive, and the dialogue so charged with the characters' emotions that readers will be immediately drawn into Yara's plight. They will not only learn about how the Syrian war is affecting ordinary lives but also how people rely on social media to connect and keep abreast—and how they have to negotiate myriad complications in order to gain refuge." Booklist

Sage, Angie

StarChaser. Angie Sage; illustrations by Mark Zug. Katherine Tegen Books, an imprint of HarperCollinsPublishers, 2016. 471 p.: TodHunter Moon

Grades: 5 6 7   **Fic**
   1. Wizards 2. Wizards' apprentices 3. Witches 4. Quests 5. Magic 6. High fantasy 7. Fantasy fiction
   ISBN 9780062272515

"Pencil drawings sprinkled throughout enhance the narrative and substantiate the book's setting in an alternative, medieval-ish, largely white world. A delightful ending to a Magykal ride." Kirkus.

Twilight hauntings. Angie Sage. Katherine Tegen Books, 2020. 368 p.: Enchanter's child

Grades: 4 5 6 7   **Fic**
   1. Foster children 2. Enchanters 3. Magic 4. Betrayal 5. Brothers and sisters 6. Fantasy fiction
   ISBN 9780062875143

A debut installment in a planned duology finds a secret practitioner of forbidden magic and her little brother forced to flee in the wake of a betrayal before finding themselves targeted by mysterious magical predators.

"Sage deftly crafts an endearing and familiar fantasy story, expertly characterizing distinct, extreme personalities. Other appeals include the avoidance of genre stereotypes, age-appropriate horror, and wry humor through dramatic irony." Bulletin of the Center for Children's Books.

Saint-Exupery, Antoine de, 1900-1944

The **little** prince: deluxe pop-up book. Antoine de Saint-Exupery. HMH Books, 2009. 60 p.

Grades: 4 5 6   **Fic**
   1. Princes 2. Pride and vanity 3. Pilots 4. Purpose in life 5. Boy adventurers 6. Sahara 7. Allegories 8. Translations 9. Pop-up books
   ISBN 9780547260693

An aviator whose plane is forced down in the Sahara Desert encounters a little prince from a small planet who relates his adventures in seeking the secret of what is important in life.

"This volume is a beautiful piece of bookmaking that actually extends the classic story. In 3-D form, the original artwork feels new, and inventive design elements . . . add whimsy while focusing even more attention on the images." Booklist.

Salazar, Aida

The **land** of the cranes. Aida Salazar. Scholastic Press, 2020 240 p.

Grades: 4 5 6 7   **Fic**
   1. United States. Bureau of Immigration and Customs Enforcement. 2. Child refugees 3. Voyages and travels 4. Immigration and emigration 5. Immigration prisons 6. Refugees 7. Novels in verse
   ISBN 9781338343809

A story in verse of nine-year-old Betita, a young Latinx girl who learns to hold on to hope and love even in the darkest of places: a family detention center for migrants and refugees.

"Salazar's lyrical verse fashions empowerment out of indignity and suffering, creating a stirring and accessible, all-too-timely story." Publishers Weekly

Saldana, Rene

Dancing with the devil and other tales from beyond = Bailando con el diablo y otros cuentos del mas alla. by = por Rene Saldana, Jr.; Spanish translation by = traduccion al espanol de Gabriela Baeza Ventura. Pinata Books, c2012. 164 p.

Grades: 5 6 7 8 9   **Fic**
   1. Mexican Americans 2. Supernatural 3. Texas 4. Mexican-American Border Region 5. Short stories 6. Bilingual materials
   ISBN 9781558857445

                  LC 2012008729

A collection of traditional tales based on Mexican American lore with a contemporary twist.

Salisbury, Graham

Banjo. Graham Salisbury. Wendy Lamb Books, an imprint of Random House Children's Books, 2019. 224 p.

Grades: 4 5 6 7 8   **Fic**
   1. Humans and dogs 2. Human-animal relationships 3. Cowboys 4. Ranch life 5. Border collies 6. Realistic fiction
   ISBN 9780375940699

Danny, a rising rodeo star whose border collie, Banjo, has been wounded by neighbors, and Meg, who has a way with animals, come together to keep Banjo safe, aided by Danny's brother.

"A page-turner that doesn't offer all the answers." Kirkus.

Eyes of the emperor. Graham Salisbury. Wendy Lamb Books, 2005. 229 p.: Prisoners of the empire

Grades: 7 8 9 10   **Fic**
   1. Second World War era (1939-1945) 2. Japanese American teenage boys 3. Teenage soldiers 4. Japanese Americans 5. Dogs -- War use -- History World War II. 6. Racism 7. Hawaii 8. United States 9. Historical fiction 10. War stories
   ISBN 0385729715

                  LC 2004015142

Following orders from the United States Army, several young Japanese-American men train K-9 units to hunt Asians during World War II.

"Based on the experiences of 26 Hawaiian-Americans of Japanese ancestry, this novel tells an uncomfortable story. Yet it tells of belief in honor, respect, and love of country." Library Media Connection.

Samphire, Patrick

Secrets of the dragon tomb. by Patrick Samphire; with illustrations by Jeremy Holmes. Henry Holt and Company, 2016. 336 p.: Secrets of the dragon tomb

Grades: 4 5 6 7   **Fic**
   1. 19th century 2. Parent-separated children 3. Kidnapping 4. Rescues 5. Families 6. Twelve-year-old boys 7. Mars (Planet) 8. Steampunk 9. Science fiction
   ISBN 9780805099065

                  LC 2015004517

While dreaming of being a spy like those in his favorite magazine, twelve-year-old Edward has been stuck holding his eccentric family together but when his parents are kidnapped, he leads his sisters and cousin in an effort to rescue them across the danger-filled landscape of nineteenth-century Mars.

"Abundant humor, intricate worldbuilding details, and precisely timed slapstick and mayhem mesh as neatly as the gears and levers of the water abacus, producing a gorgeously articulated clockwork of a novel." Publishers Weekly.

San Souci, Robert D.

Dare to be scared: thirteen stories to chill and thrill. Robert San Souci; illustrations by David Ouimet. Cricket Books, c2003. 159 p.: Dare to be scared

Grades: 4 5 6 7   Fic
1. Ghosts 2. Monsters 3. Cell phones 4. Nightmares 5. Haunted houses 6. Short stories 7. Horror 8. Ghost stories
ISBN 0812626885

LC 2002152827

"With crisp, straightforward delivery and some intriguing endings, these 13 tales are great fun for young readers who like to be spooked." Booklist.

Haunted houses. Robert D. San Souci; illustrated by Kelly Murphy and Antoine J.D. Revoy. Henry Holt, 2010. 288 p.: Are you scared yet?
Grades: 4 5 6 7   Fic
1. Haunted houses 2. Ghosts 3. Supernatural 4. Horror
ISBN 9780805087505

LC 2009050763

"The stories are well paced and satisfyingly startling. . . . This book won't stay on the shelves for long. Murphy and Revoy's black-and-white illustrations heighten the fright factor, making San Souci's collection even more riveting." School Library Journal.

Sanchez, Alex, 1957-
Bait. Alex Sanchez. Simon & Schuster Books for Young Readers, c2009. 239 p.
Grades: 7 8 9 10   Fic
1. Hispanic American teenage boys 2. Sexual violence victims 3. Anger in teenage boys 4. Parole officers 5. Emotional problems of teenage boys 6. LGBTQIA fiction 7. Coming-of-age stories 8. Realistic fiction
ISBN 9781416937722

LC 2008038815

Diego keeps getting into trouble because of his explosive temper until he finally finds a probation officer who helps him get to the root of his anger so that he can stop running from his past.

"This groundbreaking novel brings to life an appealing young man who is neither totally a victim nor a victimizer, one who struggles to handle conflicts that derail many young lives. . . . High interest and accessible, this coming-of-age story belongs in every collection." School Library Journal.

Sanderson, Brandon
Alcatraz versus the evil librarians. Brandon Sanderson. Scholastic, c2007. 308 p.: Alcatraz Smedry adventures
Grades: 4 5 6 7   Fic
1. Foster teenagers 2. Librarians 3. Clumsiness 4. Sand 5. Good and evil 6. Fantasy fiction 7. Humorous stories
ISBN 0439925509
On his thirteenth birthday, foster child Alcatraz Smedry receives a bag of sand which is immediately stolen by the evil Librarians who are trying to take over the world, and Alcatraz is introduced to his grandfather and his own special talent, and told that he must use it to save civilization.

"Readers whose sense of humor runs toward the subversive will be instantly captivated. . . . This nutty novel isn't for everyone, but it's also sure to win passionate fans." Publishers Weekly.

The **dark** talent. Brandon Sanderson; illustrations by Hayley Lazo. Starscape, 2016 300 p.: Alcatraz Smedry adventures
Grades: 4 5 6 7   Fic
1. Librarians 2. Girls in comas 3. Fathers and sons 4. Good and evil 5. Rescues 6. Fantasy fiction 7. Humorous stories
ISBN 9780765381408

Having broken the Smedry Talents while saving the kingdom of Mokia from the Evil Librarian army, Alcatraz Smedry infiltrates the Highbrary as part of a desperate plan to save his comatose friend, Batille.

"As in previous volumes, the narrative is rife with bizarre situations, thrilling seat-of-the-pants action, and metafictional musings; the ending will set readers back on their heels." Horn Book.

Skyward. Brandon Sanderson. Delacorte Press, [2018] 513 p.: Skyward (Brandon Sanderson)
Grades: 7 8 9 10   Fic
1. Survival 2. War 3. Pilots 4. Girls 5. Courage in girls 6. Science fiction
ISBN 9780399555770

LC 2018026175

When a long-term attack against her world by the alien Krell escalates, Spensa's dream of becoming a pilot may come true, despite her deceased father being labeled a deserter.

Sands, Kevin
The **Blackthorn** key. by Kevin Sands. Aladdin, 2015. 371 p.: Blackthorn key
Grades: 4 5 6 7 8   Fic
1. 1660s 2. Restoration England (1660-1688) 3. Stuart period (1603-1714) 4. 17th century 5. Apprentices 6. Codes (Communication) 7. Alchemy 8. Secrets 9. Chemistry 10. London, England 11. Great Britain 12. Fantasy mysteries 13. Historical fantasy
ISBN 9781481446518

LC 2014048032

In 1665 London, fourteen-year-old Christopher Rowe, apprentice to an apothecary, and his best friend, Tom, try to uncover the truth behind a mysterious cult, following a trail of puzzles, codes, pranks, and danger toward an unearthly secret with the power to tear the world apart.

"This stunning and smart mystery is made even better by well-researched historical detail, intriguing characters, and genuinely funny moments." Kirkus.

Sangster, Caitlin
Last star burning. by Caitlin Sangster. Simon Pulse, 2017. 400 p.: Last star burning
Grades: 7 8 9 10 11 12   Fic
1. Epidemics 2. Teenage fugitives 3. Survival 4. Sixteen-year-old girls 5. Fantasy fiction
ISBN 9781481486132

LC 2016046285

To escape execution for a crime she didn't commit, seventeen-year-old Sev is forced to run away from her city into the wilderness. With nowhere to turn, Sev has to figure out who she can trust in a world where trusting the wrong person could mean not only her life but the lives of everyone she loves. Provided by publisher.

"Brimming with rich detail in an Asian-inflected alternative world that's lightly touched with Maoist terminology and concepts and helmed by achingly real characters, Sevvy's story is thrilling to get lost in. . . . Incredibly immersive and tightly plotted." Kirkus.

Saunders, Kate, 1960-
The **Whizz** Pop Chocolate Shop. Kate Saunders. Delacorte Press, c2013. 293 p.
Grades: 5 6 7 8   Fic
1. Twin brothers and sisters 2. Immortality 3. Talking animals 4. Great-uncles 5. Chocolate 6. London, England 7. Fantasy fiction
ISBN 9780385743013

Eleven-year-old twins Oz and Lily are recruited by a talking cat to assist her and M16 in foiling the dastardly plans of their great-great-uncle, a chocolatier who used magic to make a candy that bestows immortality.

Savit, Gavriel

Anna and the Swallow Man. Gavriel Savit. Alfred A. Knopf, [2016] 240 p.

Grades: 8 9 10 11 12   **Fic**

1. Second World War era (1939-1945) 2. Girl orphans 3. Seven-year-old girls 4. World War II 5. Bonding (Interpersonal relations) 6. Innocence (Psychology) 7. Poland 8. Germany 9. Historical fiction

ISBN 9780553513349

Sydney Taylor Book Award for Teen Readers, 2017.

Left alone when her intellectual father is arrested by the Germans during World War II, Anna, a child growing up in occupied Krakow, Poland, finds shelter with a talented illusionist who hides a sinister nature.

"Full of sophisticated questions and advanced vocabulary, Savit's debut occasionally feels like an adult novel, but young readers with the patience for his gauzy pacing and oblique plot turns will be rewarded by a moving, thought-provoking story about coming-of-age in the midst of trauma." Booklist.

Schlitz, Laura Amy

Amber and Clay. Laura Amy Schlitz, with illustrations by Julia Iredale. Candlewick Press, 2021 544 p.

Grades: 6 7 8 9   **Fic**

1. Friendship 2. Enslaved people 3. Ghosts 4. Gods and goddesses, Greek 5. Spirituality 6. Ancient Greece 7. Historical fantasy 8. Mythological fiction

ISBN 9781536201222

Bound by destiny, Melisto and Rhaskos—Amber and Clay—never meet in the flesh. By the time they do, one of them is a ghost. But the thin line between life and death is just one boundary their unlikely friendship crosses. It takes an army of snarky gods and fearsome goddesses, slaves and masters, mothers and philosophers to help shape their story into a gorgeously distilled, symphonic tour de force.

"Curation, historical fiction, performance piece—Schlitz brings a bundle of learning, artifice, and intentionality to this highly stylized tale of ancient Greece." Horn Book

The **hired** girl. Laura Amy Schlitz. Candlewick Press, 2015. 400 p.

Grades: 7 8 9 10   **Fic**

1. 1910s 2. Household employees 3. Catholics 4. Jewish families 5. Crushes in teenage girls 6. Fourteen-year-old girls 7. Baltimore, Maryland 8. Pennsylvania 9. Historical fiction 10. Coming-of-age stories 11. Diary novels

ISBN 9780763678180

Scott O'Dell Historical Fiction Award, 2016.

Sydney Taylor Book Award for Teen Readers, 2016.

"A wonderful look into the life of strong girl who learns that she needs the love of others to truly grow up." School Library Journal.

Splendors and glooms. Laura Amy Schlitz. Candlewick, 2012. 400 p.

Grades: 4 5 6 7   **Fic**

1. Victorian era (1837-1901) 2. 19th century 3. 1860s 4. Witches 5. Orphans 6. Puppeteers 7. Kidnapping 8. Good and evil 9. London, England 10. Great Britain 11. Historical fantasy

ISBN 9780763653804

LC 2011048366

When Clara vanishes after the puppeteer Grisini and two orphaned assistants were at her twelfth birthday party, suspicion of kidnapping chases the trio away from London and soon the two orphans are caught in a trap set by Grisini's ancient rival, a witch with a deadly inheritance to shed before it is too late.

Schmatz, Pat

Bluefish. Pat Schmatz. Candlewick Press, 2011. 240 p.

Grades: 7 8 9 10   **Fic**

1. Loners 2. Illiteracy 3. Resentfulness in teenagers 4. Resentfulness 5. Family problems 6. Realistic fiction

ISBN 9780763653347

LC 2010044815

Everything changes for thirteen-year-old Travis, a new student who is trying to hide his illiteracy, when he meets a sassy classmate with her own secrets and a remarkable teacher.

"A cast of richly developed characters peoples this work of contemporary fiction, told in the third person from Travis' point of view, with first-person vignettes from Velveeta's perspective peppered throughout. . . . A story rife with unusual honesty and hope." Kirkus.

Schmidt, Gary D.

Just like that. Gary D. Schmidt. Houghton Mifflin Harcourt, 2021 400 p.

Grades: 5 6 7 8   **Fic**

1. 1960s 2. Grief in teenage girls 3. Friends' death 4. Boarding schools 5. Belonging 6. Homeless teenagers 7. Maine 8. Historical fiction

ISBN 9780544084773

With insight and a light touch, best-selling, author Gary D. Schmidt tells two poignant, linked stories: that of a grieving girl and a boy trying to escape his violent past.

"[Schmidt] writes like a modern-day Dickens, at one point, Meryl Lee says that 'there are times when words can't do what you want them to do,' but Schmidt can, and this is a masterwork of old-fashioned storytelling." Horn Book

Lizzie Bright and the Buckminster boy. by Gary D. Schmidt. Clarion Books, c2004. 219 p.

Grades: 7 8 9 10   **Fic**

1. 1910s 2. Children of clergy 3. Interracial friendship 4. African American girls 5. Poor girls 6. Assertiveness in teenage boys 7. Maine 8. Historical fiction

ISBN 0618439293

LC 2003020967

In 1911, Turner Buckminster hates his new home of Phippsburg, Maine, but things improve when he meets Lizzie Bright Griffin, a girl from a poor, nearby island community founded by former slaves that the town fathers—and Turner's—want to change into a tourist spot.

"Although the story is hauntingly sad, there is much humor, too. Schmidt's writing is infused with feeling and rich in imagery. With fully developed, memorable characters and a fascinating, little-known piece of history, this novel will leave a powerful impression on readers." School Library Journal.

Orbiting Jupiter. Gary D. Schmidt. Clarion Books, Houghton Mifflin Harcourt, [2015] 192 p. cm

Grades: 6 7 8 9   **Fic**

1. Teenage fathers 2. Father-separated children 3. Foster children 4. Friendship 5. Emotional problems 6. Realistic fiction

ISBN 9780544462229

LC 2015001338

Jack, 12, tells the gripping story of Joseph, 14, who joins his family as a foster child. Damaged in prison, Joseph wants nothing more than to find his baby daughter, Jupiter, whom he has never seen. When Joseph has begun to believe he'll have a future, he is confronted by demons from his past that force a tragic sacrifice. Provided by publisher.

"The matter-of-fact narrative voice ensures that the tragic plot never overwhelms this wrenching tale of growth and loss." School Library Journal.

★ The **Wednesday** wars. by Gary D. Schmidt. Clarion Books, c2007. 256 p.

Grades: 5 6 7 8   **Fic**
   1. Shakespeare, William, 1564-1616. Plays. 2. 1960s 3. Teacher-student relationships 4. Growth (Psychology) 5. Junior high schools 6. Schools 7. Families 8. Long Island, New York 9. Coming-of-age stories 10. Historical fiction
ISBN 0618724834

                       LC 2006023660

During the 1967 school year, on Wednesday afternoons when all his classmates go to either Catechism or Hebrew school, seventh-grader Holling Hoodhood stays in Mrs. Baker's classroom where they read the plays of William Shakespeare and Holling learns much of value about the world he lives in.

"The serious issues are leavened with ample humor, and the supporting cast . . . is fully dimensional. Best of all is the hero." Publishers Weekly.

Schrefer, Eliot, 1978-
  Endangered. Eliot Schrefer. Scholastic Press, 2012. 264 p.: Ape quartet

Grades: 7 8 9 10 11 12   **Fic**
   1. Bonobos 2. Wilderness survival 3. Coups d'etat 4. Rescues 5. Animal rescue 6. Congo (Democratic Republic) 7. Adventure stories
ISBN 9780545165761

                       LC 2012030877

Sophie is not happy to be back in the Congo for the summer, but when she rescues an abused baby bonobo she becomes more involved in her mother's sanctuary—and when fighting breaks out and the sanctuary is attacked, it is up to Sophie to rescue the apes and somehow survive in the jungle.

Gogi's gambit. Eliot Schrefer. Katerine Tegen Books, an imprint of HarperCollins Publishers, 2019 368 p.: Lost rainforest

Grades: 4 5 6 7   **Fic**
   1. Rain forests 2. Good and evil 3. Rain forest animals 4. Jungles 5. Jungle animals 6. Animal fantasy 7. Fantasy fiction
ISBN 9780062491114

Gogi and the other shadowwalkers race to save their magical rainforest home before the Ant Queen makes it her own. Provided by publisher.

Rumi's riddle. Eliot Schrefer; illustrated by Emilia Dziubak. Katherine Tegen Books, 2020. 320 p.: Lost rainforest

Grades: 4 5 6 7   **Fic**
   1. Rain forests 2. Good and evil 3. Rain forest animals 4. Jungles 5. Jungle animals 6. Animal fantasy 7. Fantasy fiction
ISBN 9780062491206

After the Ant Queen is defeated by the shadowwalkers, the magical rainforest begins to rumble, and Rumi, a scholarly frog, must rally the other animals to save their home.

Threatened. Eliot Schrefer. Scholastic Press, 2014. 288 p.: Ape quartet

Grades: 7 8 9 10 11 12   **Fic**
   1. Chimpanzees 2. Teenage boy orphans 3. Jungles 4. Survival 5. Teenage boys 6. Africa 7. Gabon 8. Adventure stories
ISBN 9780545551434

Escaping his jailer by fleeing into the forest with a scientist who is not entirely what he seems, an African street youth helps the scientist with his studies of chimpanzees and must join the chimps to save their habitat from unwelcome intruders.

"The book is filled with sensory detail—the city and jungle settings pulse with vitality—and the characters, human and nonhuman alike, are well drawn." Horn Book.

Schroder, Monika, 1965-
  My brother's shadow. Monika Schroder. Farrar Straus Giroux, 2011. 240 p.

Grades: 6 7 8 9 10   **Fic**
   1. Teenage boys 2. Personal conduct 3. World War I 4. War 5. Sixteen-year-old boys 6. Germany 7. War stories 8. Historical fiction
ISBN 9780374351229

                       LC 2010033107

In 1918 Berlin, Germany, sixteen-year-old Moritz struggles to do what is right on his newspaper job, in his relationship with his mother and sister who are outspoken socialists, and with his brother, who returns from the war physically and emotionally scarred.

"In this nuanced and realistic work of historical fiction, Schrder . . . immerses readers in her setting with meticulous details and dynamic characters that contribute to a palpable sense of tension." Publishers Weekly.

Schwartz, Alvin, 1927-1992
  ★ **More** scary stories to tell in the dark. collected from folklore and retold by Alvin Schwartz, with drawings by Stephen Gammell J. B. Lippincott 1984 100 p.

Grades: 4 5 6 7   **Fic**
   1. Ghosts 2. Horror 3. Ghost stories 4. Folklore United States
ISBN 0808579959

                       LC 83049494

More traditional and modern-day stories of ghosts, witches, vampires, "jump" stories, and scary songs.

"Helquist's new illustrations for Schwartz's classic [collection] of ghost stories inhabit an altogether more benign universe than the nightmarish Stephen Gammell originals. [This edition is] handsome and accessible, ceding the stories themselves pride of place." Horn Book Guide.

★ **Scary** stories 3: more tales to chill your bones. collected from folklore and retold by Alvin Schwartz; drawings by Stephen Gammell. HarperCollins Publishers, 1991 115 p.

Grades: 4 5 6 7   **Fic**
   1. Ghosts 2. Horror 3. Ghost stories 4. Folklore
ISBN 0060217944

                       LC 90047474

More traditional and modern-day stories of ghosts, haunts, superstitions, monsters, and horrible scary things.

"The book is well paced and continually captivates, surprises, and entices audiences into reading just one more page. Gammell's gauzy, cobwebby, black-and-white pen-and-ink drawings help to sustain the overall creepy mood." School Library Journal.

Scott, Michael, 1959-

The **alchemyst**. Michael Scott. Delacorte Press, 2007. 400 p.: Secrets of the immortal Nicholas Flamel

Grades: 7 8 9 10   **Fic**

1. Flamel, Nicolas, d. 1418. 2. Machiavelli, Niccolo, 1469-1527. 3. Dee, John, 1527-1608. 4. Twin brothers and sisters 5. Alchemists 6. Rare books 7. Magic 8. Supernatural 9. San Francisco, California 10. California 11. Fantasy fiction

ISBN 9780385733571

LC 2006024417

Having discovered the secret to eternal youth, 14th-century alchemist Nicholas Flamel and his wife are alive and well in present-day San Francisco, California. But they won't stay well if 15-year-old twins Sophie and Josh Newman don't fulfill their prophesied role of either saving or destroying the world, starting by getting back an ancient text stolen from Flamel's bookstore. (The stolen volume contains the key to the Flamels' immortality, which they must renew every month).

"Scott uses a gigantic canvas for this riveting fantasy. . . . A fabulous read." School Library Journal.

Sedgwick, Marcus

Midwinterblood. Marcus Sedgwick. Roaring Brook Press, 2013. 272 p.

Grades: 7 8 9 10 11 12   **Fic**

1. Reincarnation 2. Islands 3. Love 4. Painters 5. Journalists 6. Scandinavia 7. Magical realism

ISBN 9781596438002

LC 2012013302

Michael L. Printz Award, 2014.

Seven linked vignettes unfold on a Scandinavian island inhabited—throughout various time periods—by Vikings, vampires, ghosts, and a curiously powerful plant. Provided by publisher.

Revolver. Marcus Sedgwick. Roaring Brook Press, 2010. 204 p.

Grades: 7 8 9 10   **Fic**

1. 1910s 2. Decision-making 3. Guns 4. Cabins 5. Gold rush 6. Fathers -- Death 7. Alaska 8. Arctic regions 9. Historical mysteries 10. Adventure stories 11. Mysteries

ISBN 9781596435926

In a tense, psychological drama set in the snowy wilderness of the Arctic Circle during the Alaska Gold Rush, 14-year-old Sig confronts a stranger who has come to take revenge on his dead father.

"Tight plotting and a wealth of moral concerns—good versus evil; faith, love, and hope; the presence of God; survival in a bleak landscape; trusting the lessons parents teach—make this a memorable tale." Horn Book.

She is not invisible. Marcus Sedgwick. Roaring Brook Press, 2014, c2013. 224 p.

Grades: 7 8 9 10 11 12   **Fic**

1. Teenagers who are blind 2. Father-separated children 3. Missing persons 4. Brothers and sisters 5. Blindness 6. New York City 7. London, England 8. Mysteries

ISBN 9781596438019

LC 2013029561

A London teenager who is blind and her younger brother travel to New York to find their missing father, using clues from his notebook.

"Laureth is sixteen, smart, self-doubting, and blind. She is also desperate to find her missing famous writer father—desperate enough to boost her mother's credit card to buy two plane tickets from London to New York City, forge travel documents, and abduct her beloved seven-year-old brother in order to disguise her blindness... Laureth herself is worth the journey. The tricks she uses to negotiate in a sighted world... her determination to fight the tendency of sighted people to treat blind people as stupid or deaf or, most insidiously, invisible—all are presented matter-of-factly and sympathetically. Readers will applaud Laureth's believable evolution into a more confident—and definitely more visible—young woman." Horn Book.

White crow. Marcus Sedgwick. Roaring Brook Press, 2011. 240 p.

Grades: 8 9 10 11 12   **Fic**

1. Life after death 2. Priests 3. Coastal towns 4. Good and evil 5. Friendship 6. England 7. East Anglia, England 8. Horror

ISBN 9781596435940

LC 2010034053

Sixteen-year-old Rebecca moves with her father from London to a small, seaside village, where she befriends another motherless girl and they spend the summer together exploring the village's sinister history.

"Showing his customary skill with a gothic setting and morally troubled characters, Sedgwick keeps readers guessing to the very end." Publishers Weekly.

Selznick, Brian

★ The **invention** of Hugo Cabret: a novel in words and pictures. by Brian Selznick. Scholastic Press, 2007. 544 p.

Grades: 4 5 6 7   **Fic**

1. Melies, Georges, 1861-1938. 2. 1930s 3. Boy orphans 4. Clocks and watches -- Repairing and adjusting 5. Robots 6. Railroad stations 7. Boy thieves 8. Paris, France 9. France 10. Historical fiction 11. Graphic novel hybrids

ISBN 0439813786

LC 2006007119

Caldecott Medal, 2008.

When twelve-year-old Hugo, an orphan living and repairing clocks within the walls of a Paris train station in 1931, meets a mysterious toy-seller and his goddaughter, his undercover life and his biggest secret are jeopardized.

"With characteristic intelligence, exquisite images, and a breathtaking design, Selznick shatters conventions related to the art of bookmaking." School Library Journal.

The **Marvels**. Brian Selznick. Scholastic Press, 2015. 640 p.

Grades: 5 6 7 8   **Fic**

1. 1990s 2. Runaway boys 3. Uncle and nephew 4. Theater 5. Grief 6. Loss (Psychology) 7. London, England 8. England 9. Historical fiction 10. Graphic novel hybrids

ISBN 9780545448680

LC 2015023161

In 1766, a boy, Billy Marvel, is shipwrecked, rescued, and goes on to found a brilliant family of actors that flourishes in London until 1900—and nearly a century later, Joseph Jervis, runs away from home, seeking refuge with his uncle in London, and is captivated by the Marvel house, with its portraits and ghostly presences.

"This brilliant journey through time in words and pictures is also a story of a theatrical family and their fortunes. This heavy tome opens to tell of one family, the Marvels, from 1766 to 1900 as their connection to the Royal Theatre in London begins and perhaps ends. In the first half of the book, all of this complex history is vividly conveyed through illustrations, with minor hints from playbills, cards, and letters that appear as part of the art. . . . Complex, entertaining, and full of gorgeous art and writing, this is a powerhouse of a book." School Library Journal.

★ **Wonderstruck**. Brian Selznick. Scholastic, 2011. 608 p.

Grades: 4 5 6 7   **Fic**
1. American Museum of Natural History 2. 1970s 3. 1920s 4. Boys who are deaf 5. Runaway children 6. Families 7. Dioramas 8. People with disabilities 9. New York City 10. Graphic novel hybrids
ISBN 9780545027892

LC 2011009113
Schneider Family Book Award for Middle School, 2012.

Having lost his mother and his hearing in a short time, twelve-year-old Ben leaves his Minnesota home in 1977 to seek the father he never knew in New York City, and meets there Rose, who is also longing for something missing from her life. Ben's story is told in words; Rose's in pictures.

"Readers know that the two stories will converge, but Selznick keeps them guessing, cutting back and forth with expert precision. . . . Both stories are equally immersive and impeccably paced. . . . Visually stunning, completely compelling." Kirkus.

Includes bibliographical references.

Sendak, Maurice

My brother's book. Maurice Sendak. Michael di Capua Books, 2013. 32 p.
Grades: 4 5 6 7 8   **Fic**
1. Brothers 2. Separated brothers 3. Familial love 4. Separated friends, relatives, etc 5. Desire
ISBN 9780062234896

Presents a poem Sendak wrote to pay homage to his late brother, Jack, whom he credited for his passion for writing and drawing.

"As the ultimate not-for-little-children Sendak, this profoundly personal book about loss and healing should find its audience among thoughtful adults (and perhaps some teenagers)." Horn Book.

Sepetys, Ruta

Between shades of gray. Ruta Sepetys. Philomel Books, 2011. 352 p.
Grades: 8 9 10 11 12   **Fic**
1. 1940s 2. Teenage girl artists 3. Forced labor 4. Survival 5. Fifteen-year-old girls 6. Teenage girls 7. Lithuania 8. Siberia 9. Historical fiction
ISBN 9780399254123

LC 2009050092
Golden Kite Award for Fiction, 2011.

In 1941, fifteen-year-old Lina, her mother, and brother are pulled from their Lithuanian home by Soviet guards and sent to Siberia, where her father is sentenced to death in a prison camp while she fights for her life, vowing to honor her family and the thousands like hers by burying her story in a jar on Lithuanian soil. Based on the author's family, includes a historical note.

"A harrowing page-turner, made all the more so for its basis in historical fact, the novel illuminates the persecution suffered by Stalin's victims (20 million were killed), while presenting memorable characters who retain their will to survive even after more than a decade in exile." Publishers Weekly.

Salt to the sea: a novel. Ruta Sepetys. Philomel Books, 2016. 391 p.
Grades: 8 9 10 11 12   **Fic**
1. Wilhelm Gustloff (Ship) 2. Second World War era (1939-1945) 3. 1940s 4. Refugees 5. World War II 6. Nurses 7. Pregnant teenagers 8. Soldiers 9. Europe 10. Historical fiction
ISBN 9780399160301
Carnegie Medal, 2017.
Golden Kite Award for Fiction, 2017

As World War II draws to a close, refugees try to escape the war's final dangers, only to find themselves aboard a ship with a target on its hull. Provided by publisher.

"Sepetys describes an almost unknown maritime disaster whose nearly 9,000 casualties dwarfed those of both the Titanic and the Lusitania. Told alternately from the perspective of each of the main characters, the novel also highlights the struggle and sacrifices that ordinary people—children—were forced to make. At once beautiful and heart-wrenching, this title will remind readers that there are far more casualties of war than are recorded in history books." Library Journal.

Shang, Wendy Wan-Long

The **way** home looks now. Wendy Wan-Long Shang. Scholastic, 2015. 272 p.
Grades: 4 5 6 7 8   **Fic**
1. 1970s 2. Baseball 3. Grief in families 4. Grief 5. Chinese Americans 6. Twelve-year-old boys 7. Historical fiction
ISBN 9780545609562

"The first-person narration is smooth and believable. This is a fine story of family, loss, growing up and learning to play baseball, raised to a higher level by gracefully incorporated themes of feminism and kindness." Kirkus.

Sharenow, Rob

The **Berlin** Boxing Club. Robert Sharenow. HarperTeen, 2011. 384 p.
Grades: 7 8 9 10   **Fic**
1. Hitler Youth. 2. 1930s 3. Jewish teenage boys 4. Boxing 5. Holocaust (1933-1945) 6. Teenage cartoonists 7. Fourteen-year-old boys 8. Historical fiction 9. Coming-of-age stories
ISBN 9780061579684
Sydney Taylor Book Award for Teen Readers, 2011.

"Readers will be drawn by the sports detail and by the close-up narrative of the daily oppression." Booklist.

Shaw, Susan, 1951-

Safe. by Susan Shaw. Dutton Children's Books, 2007. 208 p.
Grades: 7 8 9 10   **Fic**
1. Thirteen-year-old girls 2. Mother-separated teenage girls 3. Teenage rape victims 4. Rape 5. Mothers 6. Realistic fiction
ISBN 9780525478294

LC 2006036428
When thirteen-year-old Tracy, whose mother died when she was three years old, is raped and beaten on the last day of school, all her feelings of security disappear and she does not know how to cope with the fear and dread that engulf her.

"This is an extraordinarily tender novel. . . . Intimate, first-person narrative honestly expresses Tracy's full range of emotions." Publishers Weekly.

Shelley, T. C.

The **monster** who wasn't. T. C. Shelley. Bloomsbury Children's Books, 2020, 320 p.
Grades: 4 5 6 7 8   **Fic**
1. Monsters 2. Gargoyles 3. Ghouls and ogres 4. Rulers 5. Fate and fatalism 6. Fantasy fiction
ISBN 9781547604562

This is the story of a creature who is both strange and unique. When he hatches down in the vast underground lair where monsters dwell, he looks just like a human boy. Even the grumpy gargoyles who adopt him and nickname him 'Imp' only want him to steal chocolate for them. He's a child with feet in both worlds, and he doesn't know where he fits. But little does Imp realise that the king of the ogres has a great and dangerous destiny in mind for him, and he'll stop at nothing to see it come to pass.

"Shelley creates a lavish tapestry of monsters, bringing together frightening creatures from a range of traditions. Her choice of language is taut and precise, filled with gorgeous metaphors and unexpected plot twists that will keep readers engaged." Kirkus

Shen, E. L.

The **comeback**: a figure skating novel. E. L. Shen. Farrar Straus Giroux Books for Young Readers, 2021. 272 p.
Grades: 4 5 6 7   **Fic**
> 1. Chinese American girls 2. Sports rivalry 3. Figure skating 4. Ice skating 5. Preteen girls 6. Lake Placid, New York 7. New York (State) 8. Sports fiction 9. Realistic fiction
> ISBN 9780374313791

LC 2020009861

Twelve-year-old Maxine Chen dreams of being a figure skating champion, but a remarkably talented new girl at the arena and a racist classmate at school test her resolve.

"With fast-paced prose and an ear for authentic dialogue, Shen brings big emotions and ideas to the hyper-focused world of the obsessive skater." New York Times

Shepherd, Megan

Midnight beauties. by Megan Shepherd. Houghton Mifflin Harcourt 2019 448 p.: Grim lovelies
Grades: 9 10 11 12   **Fic**
> 1. Magic (Occultism) 2. Witches 3. Princes 4. Transformations (Magic) 5. Enemies 6. Paris, France 7. London, England 8. Urban fantasy 9. Fairy tale and folklore-inspired fiction
> ISBN 9781328811905

LC 2018060799

Seventeen-year-old Anouk is forced into a sinister deal with Crown Prince Rennar in order to help her friends, who are trapped in their animal forms, and save Paris from the Coven at Oxford.

Sheth, Kashmira

Keeping corner. Kashmira Sheth. Hyperion, 2007. 288 p.
Grades: 7 8 9 10 11 12   **Fic**
> 1. Gandhi, Mahatma, 1869-1948 2. British Raj (1858-1947) 3. 1940s 4. Families 5. Widows 6. National self-determination 7. Child marriage 8. Mourning customs 9. India
> ISBN 9780786838592

LC 2007015314

In India during World War I, thirteen-year-old Leela's happy, spoiled childhood ends when her husband since age nine, whom she barely knows, dies, leaving her a widow whose only hope of happiness could come from Mahatma Ghandi's social and political reforms.

"Sheth sets up a thrilling premise in which politics become achingly personal." Booklist.

Shevah, Emma

Dara Palmer's major drama. Emma Shevah. Sourcebooks Jabberwocky, [2016] 288 p.
Grades: 4 5 6 7   **Fic**
> 1. Adopted girls 2. Child actors and actresses 3. Prejudice 4. Cambodians 5. Self-confidence 6. Great Britain 7. Realistic fiction
> ISBN 9781492631385

LC 2015031876

Dara Palmer dreams of being an actress, but when she does not get a part in the school play she wonders if it is because of her different looks as an adopted girl from Cambodia, so Dara becomes determined not to let prejudice stop her from being in the spotlight.

"Crawford-White's charming doodle illustrations along the margins reflects Dara's inner monologues throughout the book.This funny, charismatic heroine will capture her readers' hearts." Kirkus.

Shivering, William

Ghosts of Weirdwood. William Shivering; illustrated by Anna Early. Henry Holt & Co 2021 352 p.: Thieves of Weirdwood
Grades: 4 5 6 7   **Fic**
> 1. Thieves 2. Preteen boys 3. Gangs 4. Ghosts 5. Magic 6. Fantasy fiction
> ISBN 9781250302908

LC 2020022085

Twelve-year-old reformed thieves Arthur and Wally's determination to succeed as Novitiates of the Wardens of Weirdwood pits them against the Order of Eldar and the ghosts they released for their own gain.

"This second action-packed Weirdwood adventure is as exciting as the first. Secondary characters get more developed backstories, adding interesting layers to the story, and the villains are fantastic." Kirkus

Thieves of Weirdwood. William Shivering; illustrated by Anna Early. Henry Holt and Company, 2020. 352 p.: Thieves of Weirdwood
Grades: 4 5 6 7   **Fic**
> 1. Thieves 2. Preteen boys 3. Gangs 4. Magic 5. Manors 6. Fantasy fiction
> ISBN 9781250302885

LC 2019019333

Wally Cooper and Arthur Benton, who resorted to thievery to pay off family debts, unwittingly find themselves at the center of a battle between the Fae and the mages tasked with protecting humanity.

Shofner, Corabel

Almost paradise. Corabel Shofner. Farrar, Straus and Giroux, 2017. 288 p.
Grades: 5 6 7   **Fic**
> 1. Aunt and niece 2. Children of prisoners 3. Tomboys 4. Single-parent families 5. Nuns 6. Texas 7. Realistic fiction
> ISBN 9780374303785

LC 2016038518

When twelve-year-old Ruby's mother goes to jail, Ruby finds her Aunt Eleanor, an ornery nun with some dark secrets, who Ruby hopes will help free her mother.

"Shofner has taken all the established, important elements of a good middle-grade novel, given them a brisk shake, and served them up to readers in a way that both entertains and enlightens." Booklist.

Shulman, Mark, 1962-

Scrawl. Mark Shulman. Roaring Brook Press, 2010. 240 p.
Grades: 6 7 8 9 10   **Fic**
> 1. Bullying and bullies 2. Punishment 3. Writing 4. Diaries 5. Student counselors 6. Realistic fiction
> ISBN 9781596434172

LC 2010010521

When eighth-grade school bully Tod and his friends get caught committing a crime on school property, his penalty—staying after school and writing in a journal under the eye of the school guidance counsellor—reveals aspects of himself that he prefers to keep hidden.

"Blackmail, cliques, and a sense of hopelessness from both students and teachers sets up an unexpected ending that will leave readers with a new appreciation for how difficult high school can be. With the potential to occupy the rarified air of titles like S.E. Hinton's The Outsiders and Chris Crutcher's Staying Fat for Sarah Byrnes . . ., Scrawl paints the stereotypical school bully in a different, poignant light." Voice of Youth Advocates.

Shulman, Polly

The **Grimm** legacy. Polly Shulman. G.P. Putnam's Sons, 2010. 336 p.: Repository series

Grades: 5 6 7 8   **Fic**

1. Library employees 2. Suspicion 3. Stealing 4. Transformations (Magic) 5. Magic 6. New York City 7. Fantasy fiction 8. Fairy tale and folklore-inspired fiction
ISBN 9780399250965

LC 2009028919

New York high school student Elizabeth gets an after-school job as a page at the "New-York Circulating Material Repository," and when she gains coveted access to its Grimm Collection of magical objects, she and the other pages are drawn into a series of frightening adventures involving mythical creatures and stolen goods.

"This modern fantasy has intrigue, adventure, and romance, and the magical aspects of the tale are both clever and intricately woven. . . . Shulman's prose is fast paced, filled with humor, and peopled with characters who are either true to life or delightfully bizarre." School Library Journal.

The **Poe** estate. Polly Shulman. Nancy Paulsen Books, an imprint of Penguin Group (USA), [2015] 272 p.: Repository series

Grades: 5 6 7 8   **Fic**

1. Books and reading 2. Haunted houses 3. Ghosts 4. Family secrets 5. Supernatural 6. Fantasy fiction 7. Classics-inspired fiction
ISBN 9780399166143

LC 2014042105

Sukie braves the twists and turns of the spooky Poe Annex at the New-York Circulating Material Repository to untangle ancient family secrets, find hidden treasure, and help the ghosts who are haunting her house.

"Shulman's novel stands alone and is all the richer for readers who know the backstory of the Grimm Collection, and the treasures kept in the Repository." School Library Journal.

Shurtliff, Liesl

Rump: the true story of Rumpelstiltskin. Liesl Shurtliff. Alfred A. Knopf, 2013. 264 p.

Grades: 3 4 5 6 7   **Fic**

1. Curses 2. Names, Personal 3. Gold 4. Rumpelstiltskin (Fictitious character) 5. Magic 6. Fantasy fiction 7. Fairy tale and folklore-inspired fiction 8. Humorous stories
ISBN 9780307977939

LC 2012005093

Relates the tale of Rumpelstiltskin's childhood and youth, explaining why his name is so important, how he is able to spin straw into gold, and why a first-born child is his reward for helping the miller's daughter-turned-queen.

"Debut author Shurtliff upends the traditional characterization of this fairy tale's antihero, recasting Rumpelstiltskin as a sympathetic and tragically doomed protagonist.... [T]he picaresque-style narrative gives the maligned character a refreshingly plainspoken voice, while honoring the original story's hauntingly strange events." Publishers Weekly.

Shusterman, Neal

Antsy does time. by Neal Shusterman. Dutton Children's Books, 2008. 256 p.: Antsy Bonano

Grades: 7 8 9 10   **Fic**

1. Teenagers with terminal illnesses 2. Death 3. Interpersonal attraction 4. Family problems 5. Fourteen-year-old boys 6. Brooklyn, New York City 7. Realistic fiction
ISBN 9780525478256

LC 2008000459

Fourteen-year-old Anthony "Antsy" Bonano learns about life, death, and a lot more when he tries to help a friend with a terminal illness feel hopeful about the future.

"Featuring a terrific supporting cast led by Antsy's wise, acerbic mother, an expert blend of comedy and near tragedy, and the wry observations of a narrator . . . this will keep tween readers hooked from start to finish." Booklist.

Dry. Neal Shusterman and Jarrod Shusterman. Simon & Schuster Books for Young Readers, 2018. 352 p.

Grades: 7 8 9 10 11 12   **Fic**

1. Droughts 2. Survival 3. Nature -- Effect of humans on 4. Ecology 5. Brothers and sisters 6. California 7. Survival stories 8. Realistic fiction
ISBN 9781481481960

The drought—or the Tap-Out, as everyone calls it—has been going on for a while now. Everyone's lives have become an endless list of don'ts: don't water the lawn, don't fill up your pool, don't take long showers. Until the taps run dry. Suddenly, Alyssa's quiet suburban street spirals into a warzone of desperation; neighbours and families turned against each other on the hunt for water. And when her parents don't return and her life—and the life of her brother—is threatened, Alyssa has to make impossible choices if she's going to survive.

Scythe. Neal Shusterman. Simon & Schuster Books for Young Readers, [2016] 352 p.: Arc of a scythe

Grades: 8 9 10 11 12   **Fic**

1. Death 2. Murder 3. Teenage apprentices 4. Competition 5. Corruption 6. Dystopian fiction 7. Science fiction
ISBN 9781442472426

LC 2016006502

In a world where disease has been eliminated, the only way to die is to be randomly killed ('gleaned') by professional reapers ('scythes'). Two teens must compete with each other to become a scythe—a position neither of them wants. The one who becomes a scythe must kill the one who doesn't.

"Elegant and elegiac, brooding but imbued with gallows humor, Shusterman's dark tale thrusts realistic, likable teens into a surreal situation and raises deep philosophic questions." Kirkus.

The **toll**. Neal Shusterman. Simon & Schuster Books for Young Readers, [2019] 640 p.: Arc of a scythe

Grades: 7 8 9 10 11 12   **Fic**

1. Fugitives 2. Artificial intelligence 3. Death 4. Executions and executioners 5. Corruption 6. Dystopian fiction 7. Science fiction
ISBN 9781481497060

LC 2019035943

Citra and Rowan have disappeared. Endura is gone. It seems like nothing stands between Scythe Goddard and absolute dominion over the world scythedom. With the silence of the Thunderhead and the reverberations of the Great Resonance still shaking the earth to its core, the question remains: Is there anyone left who can stop him? The answer lies in the Tone, the Toll, and the Thunder. Provided by publisher.

"Long but strong, a furiously paced finale that reaches for the stars." Kirkus.

Silberberg, Alan

Milo: sticky notes and brain freeze. by Alan Silberberg. Aladdin, 2010. 256 p.

Grades: 5 6 7 8   **Fic**
> 1. Boy misfits 2. Grief in boys 3. New students 4. Grief 5. Mothers -- Death 6. Realistic fiction
> ISBN 9781416994305

LC 2010012708

In love with the girl he sneezed on the first day of school and best pals with Marshall, the "One Eyed Jack" of friends, seventh-grader Milo Cruikshank misses his mother whose death has changed everything at home.

"This is more than just another funny story about a middle school misfit who is the new kid in the neighborhood. While Milo does struggle with all the normal tween anxieties and self-consciousness about his family, there is more. Silberberg details the daily events with Wimpy Kid-like drawings and quick-witted humor that will keep the pages turning. Milo's new friendships with classmates Marshall and Hillary and elderly neighbor Sylvia Poole allow readers to glimpse at the deeper truth—Milo's mother's deat—has it emerges between laugh lines. Silberberg takes on a tough topic and always stays true to the age of the character through dialogue and artwork while maintaining that wisecracking, 12-year-old humor." School Library Journal.

Silvera, Adam, 1990-

Infinity son. Adam Silvera. HarperTeen, 2020 368 p.: Infinity cycle

Grades: 8 9 10 11 12   **Fic**
> 1. Twin brothers 2. Gangs 3. Magic 4. Teenage boys 5. Ability 6. New York City 7. Urban fantasy 8. Fantasy fiction
> ISBN 9780062457820

LC 2019033533

Manifesting supernatural phoenix fire abilities when he turns 18, Emil becomes a reluctant defender against the specters that overshadow his world and reluctantly joins a vigilante team that his powerless brother idolizes.

"Fans of Cassandra Clare, Mackenzie Lee's Loki, Brandon Sanderson's Steelheart, Kiersten White's Slayer and Marissa Meyer's Renegades series will love this magical book that embodies it all: romance, heartbreak, deceit, shifting loyalties, revenge, power struggles, violence, and complicated origin stories." School Library Journal.

Silvey, Craig, 1982-

Jasper Jones: a novel. Craig Silvey. Alfred A. Knopf, 2011, c2009. 312 p.

Grades: 6 7 8 9 10   **Fic**
> 1. 1960s 2. Teenage boys 3. Misfits (Persons) 4. Life change events 5. Small towns 6. Secrets 7. Western Australia 8. Australia 9. Literary fiction 10. Coming-of-age stories
> ISBN 9780375866661

In small-town Australia, teens Jasper and Charlie form an unlikely friendship when one asks the other to help him cover up a murder until they can prove who is responsible.

"Silvey infuses his prose with a musician's sensibility—Charlie's pounding heart is echoed in the terse staccato sentences of the opening scenes, alternating with legato phrases laden with meaning. The author's keen ear for dialogue is evident in the humorous verbal sparring between Charlie and Jeffrey, typical of smart 13-year-old boys. . . . A richly rewarding exploration of truth and lies by a masterful storyteller." Kirkus.

Simon, Francesca

The **monstrous** child. Francesca Simon. Faber & Faber: 2017 320 p.

Grades: 7 8 9 10   **Fic**
> 1. Gods and goddesses, Norse 2. Crushes in teenage girls 3. Demigods 4. Rulers 5. Brothers and sisters 6. Fantasy fiction 7. Mythological fiction
> ISBN 9780571330270

A stunning, operatic, epic drama, like no other. Meet Hel, an ordinary teenager—and goddess of the Underworld. Why is life so unfair? Hel tries to make the best of it, creating gleaming halls in her dark kingdom and welcoming the dead who she is forced to host for eternity. Until eternity itself is threatened.

"Readers may enjoy Hel's flippant insolence . . . while others may find the quirky presentation of Norse mythology a good companion to Rick Riordan's Magnus Chase and the Gods of Asgard series." Booklist.

Sitomer, Alan Lawrence

Homeboyz. by Alan Lawrence Sitomer. Jump at the Sun/ Hyperion Books For Children, c2007. 283 p.: Hoopster trilogy

Grades: 7 8 9 10   **Fic**
> 1. Revenge 2. Violence 3. Loss (Psychology) 4. Grief in teenage boys 5. African Americans 6. Urban fiction
> ISBN 1423100301

When his attempt to exact revenge on his little sister's killer places him under house arrest, Teddy Anderson is forced by his probation officer to tutor a twelve-year-old orphan—a community service assignment that eventually helps him to save his family and himself.

"Still, the tale's violent, rough-hewn plot and street-inflected language supply sufficient intensity to carry the heavy agenda." Booklist.

The **secret** story of Sonia Rodriguez. by Alan Lawrence Sitomer. Jump at the Sun/Hyperion Books For Children, 2008. 320 p.

Grades: 7 8 9 10   **Fic**
> 1. Mexican American teenage girls 2. Determination in teenage girls 3. Family problems 4. Undocumented immigrants 5. Mexican American families 6. Realistic fiction
> ISBN 1423110722

LC 2007045265

Tenth-grader Sonia reveals secrets about her life and her Hispanic family as she studies hard to become the first Rodriguez to finish high school.

"Sonia's immediate voice will hold teens with its mix of anger, sorrow, tenderness, and humor." Booklist.

Skrypuch, Marsha Forchuk

Making bombs for Hitler. Marsha Forchuk Skrypuch. Scholastic Press, 2017. 230 p.: WW2

Grades: 5 6 7 8   **Fic**
> 1. Second World War era (1939-1945) 2. Separated sisters 3. Concentration camps 4. World War II -- Children 5. Concentration camp inmates 6. Child prisoners 7. Historical fiction
> ISBN 9780545931915

When Lida and her sister are caught by the Nazis they are separated. Lida is sent to a slave labour camp and must work from dawn to dusk on bread and soup, without shoes and wearing only a thin dress. Even if she survives the war, will Lida ever see her sister again?

"A well-told story of persistence, lost innocence, survival, and hope." Kirkus.

Sleator, William

Interstellar pig. William Sleator. Dutton, 1984. 197 p.
Grades: 5 6 7 8   **Fic**
  1. Aliens (Non-humanoid) 2. Board games 3. Treasure troves
4. Science fiction games 5. Ship captains 6. New England 7.
Science fiction
ISBN 0525440984

          LC 84004132
Barney's boring seaside vacation suddenly becomes more interesting when the cottage next door is occupied by three exotic neighbors who are addicted to a game they call "Interstellar Pig."
  "The author draws the reader in with intimations of danger and horror, but the climactic battle is more slapstick than horrific, and the victor's prize could scarcely be more ironic. Problematic as straight science fiction but great fun as a spoof on human-alien contact." Booklist.

Oddballs: stories. by William Sleator. Dutton Children's Books, c1993. 134 p.
Grades: 6 7 8 9 10   **Fic**
  1. Brothers and sisters 2. Families 3. Growing up 4. Friendship
5. Short stories 6. Autobiographical fiction
ISBN 9780525450573

          LC 92027666
A collection of stories based on experience from the author's youth and peopled with an unusual assortment of family and friends.
  "Fresh, funny, and slightly gross, the quasi-autobiographical glimpses will grab the reader's attention." Horn Book Guide.

Sloan, Holly Goldberg, 1958-

Counting by 7s. by Holly Goldberg Sloan. Dial Books for Young Readers, 2012. 384 p.
Grades: 4 5 6 7   **Fic**
  1. Girl orphans 2. Genius 3. Girl misfits 4. Fatal traffic accidents
5. Parents -- Death 6. Realistic fiction
ISBN 9780803738553

          LC 2012004994
Twelve-year-old genius and outsider Willow Chance must figure out how to connect with other people and find a surrogate family for herself after her parents are killed in a car accident.

The **elephant** in the room. Holly Goldberg Sloan. Dial Books for Young Readers, 2021. 250 p.
Grades: 4 5 6 7   **Fic**
  1. Separation (Psychology) 2. Intergenerational relations 3.
Friendship 4. Separated friends, relatives, etc 5. Grief 6. Realistic fiction
ISBN 9780735229945

          LC 2020049193
Missing her mother who has returned to Turkey to resolve an immigration problem, sixth-grader Sila welcomes a very large distraction in her life when she helps a surprising new friend rescue a circus elephant.
  "Writing from multiple points of view, old and young, animal and human, Sloan captures the importance of compassion and bravery when facing life's challenges." Kirkus

I'll be there. by Holly Goldberg Sloan. Little, Brown, 2011. 400 p.
Grades: 7 8 9 10   **Fic**
  1. Teenage musicians 2. Survival 3. Violence in men 4. Elective mutism 5. Boys who are mute 6. Realistic fiction
ISBN 9780316122795

          LC 2010042994
Raised by an unstable father who keeps constantly on the move, Sam Border has long been the voice of his silent younger brother, Riddle, but everything changes when Sam meets Emily Bell and, welcomed by her family, the brothers are faced with normalcy for the first time.
  "This riveting story will keep readers interested and guessing until the end." School Library Journal.

Short. Holly Goldberg Sloan. Dial Books for Young Readers, [2017] 288 p.
Grades: 4 5 6 7 8   **Fic**
  1. Theater 2. Short girls 3. Self-acceptance in girls 4. Self-acceptance 5. Summer 6. Realistic fiction
ISBN 9780399186219

          LC 2016013964
Very short for her age, Julia grows into her sense of self while playing a munchkin in a summer regional theater production of The Wizard of Oz.
  "Her self-acceptance is inspiring, and the joy she experiences in her foray into theater is irresistible." Booklist.

Smiley, Jane

The **Georges** and the Jewels. Jane Smiley. Random House Childrens Books, 2009. 256 p.: Horses of Oak Valley Ranch
Grades: 4 5 6 7   **Fic**
  1. 1960s 2. Girls and horses 3. Horses 4. Fathers and daughters
5. Girls 6. Horse farms 7. California 8. Historical fiction 9.
Horse stories
ISBN 9780375862274
Instructed by her father to not become attached to the horses on their ranch because they are to be sold, Abby does her best to abide, but after a series of personal dramas with her friends and the sudden departure of her brother, Abby's heart suddenly develops a soft spot for one particular gelding who behaves as stubbornly as a mule.
  "As might be expected from the skilled hands of Smiley . . . there are synchronous storylines . . . [and] many will find it difficult to say goodbye to Abby, Jack and especially to Ornery George." Publishers Weekly.

Smith, Alexander Gordon, 1979-

Death sentence. Alexander Gordon Smith. Farrar Straus Giroux, 2011. 272 p.: Escape from Furnace
Grades: 7 8 9 10   **Fic**
  1. Monsters 2. Cruelty 3. Teenage prisoners 4. Prisoners 5.
Fourteen-year-old boys 6. Science fiction 7. Horror
ISBN 9780374324940

          LC 2010010938
After his failed attempt to escape from Furnace Penitentiary, Alex struggles to survive the bloodstained laboratories beneath where monsters are manufactured, with a death sentence—or worse—hanging over his head.
  "Smith strikes the ideal balance between action and introspection. Readers will feel genuine sympathy for antihero Alex." Kirkus.

Lockdown. Alexander Gordon Smith. Farrar, Straus and Giroux, 2009. 273 p.: Escape from Furnace
Grades: 7 8 9 10   **Fic**
  1. Prisons 2. Teenage prisoners 3. False imprisonment 4. Escapes
5. Monsters 6. Horror 7. Science fiction
ISBN 9780374324919

          LC 2008043439
When fourteen-year-old Alex is framed for murder, he becomes an inmate in the Furnace Penitentiary, where brutal inmates and sadistic

guards reign, boys who disappear in the middle of the night sometimes return weirdly altered, and escape might just be possible.

"Once a plot is hatched, readers will be turning pages without pause, and the cliffhanger ending will have them anticipating the next installment. Most appealing is Smith's flowing writing style, filled with kid-speak, colorful adjectives, and amusing analogies." School Library Journal.

Solitary. Alexander Gordon Smith. Farrar Straus Giroux, 2010. 240 p.: Escape from Furnace

Grades: 7 8 9 10 **Fic**
1. Teenage prisoners 2. Solitary confinement 3. False imprisonment 4. Judicial error 5. Prisons 6. Horror 7. Science fiction
ISBN 9780374324926

LC 2009030843

Imprisoned for a murder he did not commit, fourteen-year-old Alex Sawyer thinks that he has escaped the hellish Furnace Penitentiary, but instead he winds up in solitary confinement, where new horrors await him.

"The author knows what keeps his readers locked to the page and delivers it soundly." Kirkus.

Smith, Hope Anita

Keeping the night watch. Hope Anita Smith; with illustrations by E.B. Lewis. Henry Holt, 2008. 73 p.

Grades: 4 5 6 7 **Fic**
1. African American teenage boys 2. Father-separated teenage boys 3. Emotions in teenage boys 4. Emotions 5. Anger in teenage boys 6. Novels in verse
ISBN 0805072020

LC 2007012372

A thirteen-year-old African American boy chronicles what happens to his family when his father, who temporarily left, returns home and they all must deal with their feelings of anger, hope, abandonment, and fear.

"The words are simple . . . and the beautiful watercolor pictures of the African American family have the same quiet intensity as pictures in the first book. . . . Although mainly in free verse, there's also a sonnet." Booklist.

Smith, Icy

Half spoon of rice: a survival story of the Cambodian genocide. written by Icy Smith; illustrated by Sopaul Nhem. East West Discovery Press, 2010. 44 p.

Grades: 5 6 7 8 **Fic**
1. 1970s 2. Genocide 3. Courage in boys 4. Courage 5. Parent-separated boys 6. Survival (in concentration camps, prisons, etc) 7. Cambodia 8. Historical fiction
ISBN 9780982167588

LC 2009002973

Nine-year-old Nat and his family are forced from their home on April 17, 1975, marched for many days, separated from each other, and forced to work in the rice fields, where Nat concentrates on survival. Includes historical notes and photographs documenting the Cambodian genocide.

"Bold, impressionistic oil paintings, mainly full page but some full spreads, speak volumes, and archival photographs are appended. This powerful child's eye view of war is harsh and realistic—like its subject—though accessible and thought-provoking." School Library Journal.

Smith, Jennifer E., 1980-

Field notes on love. Jennifer E. Smith. Delacorte Press, [2019] 288 p.

Grades: 7 8 9 10 11 12 **Fic**
1. British in the United States 2. Teenage filmmakers 3. Railroad travel 4. Strangers 5. New experiences 6. Coming-of-age stories 7. Contemporary romances 8. Romantic comedies
ISBN 9780399559419

LC 2018023440

Two teens, Hugo and Mae, are strangers until they share a cross-country train trip that teaches them about love, each other, and the futures they can build for themselves.

"A coming-of-age story as well as a romance, it offers authentic, complementary protagonists while capturing the thrill of exploring new territory." Booklist.

The **geography** of you and me. Jennifer E. Smith. Little, Brown and Company, 2014. 352 p.

Grades: 7 8 9 10 11 12 **Fic**
1. Long-distance romance 2. Loss (Psychology) 3. Power failures 4. Voyages and travels 5. Teenagers 6. New York City 7. Contemporary romances
ISBN 9780316254779

Stuck in an elevator during a blackout in New York City, Lucy from the 24th floor and basement-dwelling Owen manage to escape and spend the rest of the blackout bonding on the darkened streets, a night they remember with longing when their respective lives separate them.

"Owen and Lucy meet during a citywide blackout in New York and spend a memorable (chaste) night together. Soon afterward, Lucy's parents take her to Europe, and Owen and his dad move to San Francisco, but even on opposite sides of the world, they think about each other. Smith's fans will recognize the alternating narration; reflective, deliberate writing style; and serendipitous coincidences." Horn Book.

Smith, Roland, 1951-

Chupacabra. Roland Smith. Scholastic Press, 2013. 285 p.: Cryptid hunters series

Grades: 5 6 7 8 **Fic**
1. Chupacabras 2. Kidnapping 3. Cryptozoology 4. Cousins 5. Uncles 6. Adventure stories
ISBN 9780545178174

Searching faraway world regions for Grace, who has been kidnapped by a ruthless grandfather who has also stolen two dinosaur hatchlings, Marty and his cryptozoologist uncle, Travis Wolfe, are distracted by a sighting of an elusive blood-drinking cryptid.

"Plunging readers in where Tentacles (Scholastic, 2009) left off, this fast-paced novel opens right after Grace discovers that her twin brother, Marty, is in fact her cousin, and that her father's unscrupulous enemy, Noah Blackwood, is actually her grandfather...Though this sequel suffers in comparison to the previous books in the series, Smith adeptly adds enough new characters, dangers, and cool science to reel in reluctant readers and keep them turning pages long after their lights should have been turned off." School Library Journal.

Peak. Roland Smith. Harcourt Children's Books, c2007. 246 p.: Peak

Grades: 7 8 9 10 **Fic**
1. Mountaineers 2. Mountaineering 3. Resentfulness in teenagers 4. Survival 5. Teenage mountaineers 6. Mount Everest 7. Coming-of-age stories 8. Adventure stories 9. Survival stories
ISBN 9780152024178

LC 2006024325

A fourteen-year-old boy attempts to be the youngest person to reach the top of Mount Everest.

"This is a thrilling, multifaceted adventure story. Smith includes plenty of mountaineering facts told in vivid detail. . . . But he also explores other issues, such as the selfishness that nearly always accompanies the intensely single-minded." Booklist.

Smith, Ronald L. (Ronald Lenard), 1959-

Hoodoo. by Ronald L. Smith. 176 p.
Grades: 4 5 6 7 **Fic**
  1. 1930s 2. Twelve-year-old boys 3. Supernatural 4. Magic 5. African Americans 6. Families 7. Alabama 8. Gothic fiction 9. Horror 10. Historical fiction
  ISBN 9780544445253
                    LC 2014046838
  In 1930s Alabama, twelve-year-old Hoodoo Hatcher is the only member of his family who seems unable to practice folk magic, but when a mysterious man called the Stranger puts the entire town at risk from his black magic, Hoodoo must learn to conjure to defeat him.
  "Folks in the insular 1930s African American community of Sardis, Alabama, believe in God and in folk magick, or hoodoo. Twelve-year-old Hoodoo Hatcher's father tried to cheat death by transporting part of his soul into Hoodoo. To free him, Hoodoo must destroy the evil Stranger. This creepy Southern Gothic ghost story is steeped in time and place; Hoodoo's folksy asides relieve tension." Horn Book.

Smith, Sherri L.

Flygirl. Sherri L. Smith. G.P. Putnam's Sons, 2009. 256 p.
Grades: 7 8 9 10 **Fic**
  1. Women Airforce Service Pilots (U.S.) 2. Second World War era (1939-1945) 3. 1940s 4. World War II -- Women's participation 5. Women pilots 6. African American women 7. Racism 8. Prejudice 9. Historical fiction
  ISBN 9780399247095
                    LC 2008025407
  During World War II, a light-skinned African American girl "passes" for white in order to join the Women Airforce Service Pilots.
  "The details about navigation are exciting, but tougher than any flight maneuver are Ida Mae's loneliness, shame, and fear that she will be thrown out of the the military, feelings that culminate in an unforgettable climax." Booklist.

Smy, Pam

Thornhill. Pam Smy. Roaring Brook Press, 2017 544 p.
Grades: 5 6 7 8 9 **Fic**
  1. 1980s 2. 2010s 3. Girl orphans 4. Orphanages 5. Bullying and bullies 6. Revenge 7. Ghosts 8. Ghost stories 9. Diary novels 10. Illustrated books
  ISBN 9781626726543
  Parallel, interwoven stories set in different times—one told through intimate diary entries and the other through bold, striking art—converge as a girl unravels the mystery of the abandoned building next door. Pam Smy's Thornhill is a haunting exploration of human connection, breathtakingly illustrated and masterfully told.
  "Dual stories set decades apart unfold together in this hybrid novel told in diary entries and eerie grayscale illustrations." Booklist.

Snicket, Lemony

"Who could that be at this hour?"**. by Lemony Snicket; art by Seth. Little, Brown, 2012. 258 p.: All the wrong questions
Grades: 4 5 6 7 **Fic**
  1. Boy apprentices 2. Statues 3. Stealing 4. Investigations 5. Eccentrics and eccentricities 6. Mysteries
  ISBN 9780316123082
                    LC 2012012657
  In a fading town, far from anyone he knew or trusted, a young Lemony Snicket began his apprenticeship in an organization nobody knows about. He started by asking questions that shouldn't have been on his mind. Now he has written an account that should not be published, in four volumes that shouldn't be read. This is the first volume.

Sniegoski, Tom

Quest for the spark: book one.. written by Tom Sniegoski; illustrated by Jeff Smith; color by Steve Hamaker. Graphix, 2011. 224 p.: Bone trilogy
Grades: 4 5 6 7 **Fic**
  1. Boy adventurers 2. Dreams 3. Visions 4. Sleep 5. Raccoons 6. Fantasy fiction
  ISBN 9780545141017
                    LC 2010017002
  Twelve-year-old Tom Elm, his raccoon friend Roderick, Percival, Abbey, and Barclay Bone, warrior-priest Randolf, and forest-woman Lorimar join in a quest to find the pieces of the Spark that can save Dreaming—and the Waking World—from a Darkness created by the Nacht.
  "At long last . . . we return to the Valley that was the setting for Smith's comics-landscape-changing Bone, though this adventure takes place in prose rather than panels. . . . As long as fans are not expecting a repeat of the old magic and not too disappointed that there isn't nearly enough of Smith's always excellent full-color, full-page artwork helping out, it looks as if they're in for a cheery jaunt back through a beloved world." Booklist.

Quest for the spark: book two. written by Tom Sniegoski; illustrated by Jeff Smith; color by Steve Hamaker. Graphix, 2012. 234 p.: Bone trilogy
Grades: 4 5 6 7 **Fic**
  1. Boy adventurers 2. Dreams 3. Dragons 4. Magic 5. Quests 6. Fantasy fiction
  ISBN 9780545141031
                    LC 2011020281
  Twelve-year-old Tom and his cohorts continue their seemingly impossible quest to find the pieces of the Spark that will save Dreaming—and the Waking World—from the evil Nacht.

Snyder, Laurel

My Jasper June. Laurel Snyder. Harpercollins Childrens Books, 2019. 304 p.
Grades: 5 6 7 **Fic**
  1. Friendship 2. Loss (Psychology) 3. Grief in teenage girls 4. Beauty 5. Summer 6. Atlanta, Georgia 7. Coming-of-age stories 8. Realistic fiction
  ISBN 9780062836625
  "Snyder tackles heavy topics (death and grief, abuse and homelessness) straightforwardly in this coming-of-age story. Her adept characterization of Jasper, whose hope and sincerity are palpable, offers buoyancy, and the joyful, almost ethereal friendship the two girls form is refreshingly and intensely honest." Publishers Weekly.

Sones, Sonya

Stop pretending: what happened when my big sister went crazy. Sonya Sones. HarperCollins, c1999. 149 p.
Grades: 6 7 8 9 **Fic**
  1. Teenage girls with mental illnesses 2. Sisters 3. Healing 4. Families 5. Friendship 6. Novels in verse 7. Realistic fiction
  ISBN 0060283874
                    LC 99011473
  A younger sister has a difficult time adjusting to life after her older sister has a mental breakdown.

"Based on the journals Sones wrote at the age of 13 when her 19-year-old sister was hospitalized due to manic depression, the simply crafted but deeply felt poems reflect her thoughts, fears, hopes, and dreams during that troubling time." School Library Journal.

What my girlfriend doesn't know. Sonya Sones. Simon & Schuster Books for Young Readers, 2007. 304 p.

Grades: 7 8 9 10   **Fic**
1. Teenage artists 2. Social acceptance in teenagers 3. Self-esteem in teenage boys 4. Dating (Social customs) 5. Teenagers 6. Boston, Massachusetts 7. Novels in verse 8. Realistic fiction
ISBN 9780689876028

LC 2006014682

Fourteen-year-old Robin Murphy is so unpopular at high school that his name is slang for "loser," and so when he begins dating the beautiful and popular Sophie her reputation plummets, but he finds acceptance as a student in a drawing class at Harvard.

"Robin's believable voice is distinctive, and Sones uses her spare words (and a few drawings) to expert effect." Booklist.

What my mother doesn't know. by Sonya Sones. Simon & Schuster Books for Young Readers, c2001. 259 p.

Grades: 7 8 9 10   **Fic**
1. Crushes in teenage girls 2. Love 3. Teenage boy/girl relations 4. Crushes (Interpersonal relations) 5. Dating (Social customs) 6. Novels in verse 7. Realistic fiction
ISBN 0689841140

LC 00052634

A series of poems reflect the thoughts and feelings of Sophie, a fifteen-year-old-girl, as she describes her relationships with a series of boys and as she searches for Mr. Right.

"Fourteen-year-old Sophia is searching for Mr. Right. In a story written in poetry form, Sophia describes her relationships with sexy Dylan, suspicious cyberboy, and, finally, with the mysterious masked stranger who dances with her on Halloween and then disappears." Book Rep.

"This is a fast, funny, touching book. . . . The very short, sometimes rhythmic lines make each page fly. Sophie's voice is colloquial and intimate." Booklist.

Sonnenblick, Jordan

After ever after. by Jordan Sonnenblick. Scholastic Press, 2010. 272 p.

Grades: 5 6 7 8   **Fic**
1. Cancer survivors 2. Eighth-graders 3. Middle schools 4. Cancer 5. Adolescence 6. New Jersey 7. Realistic fiction
ISBN 9780439837064

LC 2009010430

Schneider Family Book Award for Middle School, 2011.

Although Jeff and Tad, encouraged by a new friend, Lindsey, make a deal to help one another overcome after effects of their cancer treatments in preparation for eighth-grade graduation, Jeff still craves advice from his older brother Stephen, who is studying drums in Africa.

"Sonnenblick imbues Jeffrey with a smooth, likable, and unaffected voice. . . . As hilarious as it is tragic, and as honest as it is hopeful . . . [this book is] irresistable reading." Booklist.

Notes from the midnight driver. by Jordan Sonnenblick. Scholastic Press, 2006. 272 p.

Grades: 8 9 10 11 12   **Fic**
1. Sixteen-year-old boys 2. Intergenerational friendship 3. Community service (Punishment) 4. Teenage boys 5. Senior men

6. Realistic fiction
ISBN 0439757797

LC 2005027972

After being assigned to perform community service at a nursing home, sixteen-year-old Alex befriends a cantankerous old man who has some lessons to impart about jazz guitar playing, love, and forgiveness.

"The author deftly infiltrates the teenage mind to produce a first-person narrative riddled with enough hapless confusion, mulish equivocation, and beleaguered deadpan humor to have readers nodding with recognition, sighing with sympathy, and gasping with laughter—often on the same page." Horn Book.

Zen and the art of faking it. by Jordan Sonnenblick. Scholastic Press, 2007. 264 p.

Grades: 5 6 7 8   **Fic**
1. Fourteen-year-old boys 2. Identity (Psychology) 3. Zen Buddhism 4. Teenage boys 5. Chinese American boys 6. Pennsylvania 7. Realistic fiction
ISBN 9780439837071

LC 2006028841

When thirteen-year-old San Lee moves to a new town and school for the umpteenth time, he is looking for a way to stand out when his knowledge of Zen Buddhism, gained in his previous school, provides the answer—and the need to quickly become a convincing Zen master.

"The author gives readers plenty to laugh at. . . . Mixed with more serious scenes, . . . lighter moments take a basic message about the importance of honesty and forgiveness and treat it with panache." Publishers Weekly.

Sonnichsen, A. L.

Red butterfly. A.L. Sonnichsen. Schuster Books for Young Readers, 2015. 400 p.

Grades: 4 5 6 7   **Fic**
1. Girl orphans 2. Orphanages 3. International adoption 4. Hand -- Abnormalities 5. Eleven-year-old girls 6. China 7. Florida 8. Realistic fiction 9. Novels in verse
ISBN 9781481411097

An uplifting story in verse follows the experiences of a young orphan in modern China who spends her days with an adoptive parent and wishes that her Mama and she could leave Tianjin and live with Daddy in Montana.

"Sympathetic readers will appreciate that Kara learns to build trust with those who demonstrate their compassion in constructive attempts to right some of the wrongs of her difficult beginnings." Booklist.

Soontornvat, Christina

★ A **wish** in the dark. Christina Soontornvat. Candlewick Press, 2020. 384 p.

Grades: 4 5 6 7   **Fic**
1. Boy prisoners 2. Fugitives 3. Classism 4. Social justice 5. Prison employees 6. Fantasy fiction 7. Asian-influenced fantasy
ISBN 9781536204940

Escaping from the prison where he was born, Pong discovers harrowing truths about the gap between the world's privileged ruling class and impoverished laborers, while the prison warden's daughter who is hunting him uncovers other daunting secrets.

Sorosiak, Carlie

Wild blue wonder. Carlie Sorosiak. Harpercollins Childrens Books 2018 320 p.

Grades: 7 8 9 10 11   **Fic**
1. Best friends 2. Survivor guilt 3. Boating accidents 4. Grief 5.

Teenage boys -- Death 6. Maine 7. Realistic fiction
ISBN 9780062563996

Following a tragic boating accident during the summer before her senior year of high school, Quinn goes through life in a daze of grief until the new boy in town, Alexander, helps her begin to understand the truth about love and loss.

Soto, Gary

Baseball in April and other stories. Gary Soto. Harcourt Brace Jovanovich, 1990. 111 p.

Grades: 5 6 7 8   **Fic**

  1. Mexican American children 2. Mexican American teenagers 3. Hispanic American children 4. Hispanic American teenagers 5. Fresno, California 6. Short stories
ISBN 015205720X

LC   89036460

Eleven short stories focusing on the everyday adventures of young Chicanos growing up in Fresno, California.

"Each story gets at the heart of some aspect of growing up. The insecurities, the embarrassments, the triumphs, the inequities of it all are chronicled with wit and charm. Soto's characters ring true and his knowledge of, and affection for, their shared Mexican-American heritage is obvious and infectious." Voice of Youth Advocates.

Help wanted: stories. Gary Soto. Harcourt, c2005. 216 p.

Grades: 6 7 8 9   **Fic**

  1. Mexican American teenage girls 2. Mexican American teenagers 3. Teenage girls 4. Teenage boys 5. Families 6. Short stories
ISBN 0152052011

LC   2004007510

Ten stories portray some of the struggles and hopes of young Mexican Americans.

"The stories are sometimes funny, often poignant, and occasionally provocative." Booklist.

Local news. Harcourt Brace Jovanovich, 1993. 148 p.

Grades: 5 6 7 8   **Fic**

  1. Mexican American children 2. Mexican American teenagers 3. Short stories
ISBN 0152481176

LC   92037905

A collection of thirteen short stories about the everyday lives of Chicano young people in California's Central Valley.

"These stories resonate with integrity, verve, and compassion." Horn Book.

Sovern, Megan Jean

The **meaning** of Maggie. Megan Jean Sovern. Chronicle Books, 2014 224 p.

Grades: 4 5 6 7   **Fic**

  1. 1980s 2. Children of sick persons 3. Multiple sclerosis 4. Gifted girls 5. Families 6. Middle schools 7. Realistic fiction
ISBN 9781452110219

"Maggie's self-realizations come quickly, but her distinct voice, with a snarky superiority that often masks her true vulnerability, creates a character who's not easy to love but tough to forget." Horn Book.

Speare, Elizabeth George

★ The **witch** of Blackbird Pond. Elizabeth George Speare. Houghton, 1958. 249 p.

Grades: 6 7 8 9   **Fic**

  1. Colonial America (1600-1775) 2. 18th century 3. Puritans

-- History 18th century 4. Independence (Personal quality) 5. Witchcraft 6. Prejudice 7. Connecticut 8. United States 9. Historical fiction 10. Classics
ISBN 0395071143

LC   58011063

Newbery Medal, 1959.

A young woman brought up in Barbados comes to live with her uncle in Connecticut, and finds their Puritan way of life difficult after her unconventional upbringing.

Spinelli, Jerry

Crash. Jerry Spinelli. Knopf, c1996. 162 p.

Grades: 5 6 7 8   **Fic**

  1. Empathy 2. Aggressiveness (Psychology) 3. Racing 4. Bullying and bullies 5. Empathy in boys 6. Realistic fiction
ISBN 0679979573

LC 95-30942

Seventh-grader John "Crash" Coogan has always been comfortable with his tough, aggressive behavior, until his relationship with an unusual Quaker boy and his grandfather's stroke make him consider the meaning of friendship and the importance of family.

"Crash is a star football player. He torments Penn, a classmate who is everything Crash is not—friendly, small, and a pacifist. When his beloved grandfather comes to live with his family and suffers a debilitating stroke, Crash begins to see value in many of the things he has scorned." Horn Book Guide.

Dead Wednesday. Jerry Spinelli Knopf Books for Young Readers, 2021. 240 p.

Grades: 6 7 8 9   **Fic**

  1. Teenage boys 2. Children and ghosts 3. Mortality 4. Teenagers -- Death 5. Self-discovery in teenagers 6. Pennsylvania 7. Paranormal fiction
ISBN 9780593306673

When the school assigns each eighth-grader the name of a teenager who died in the past year as a lesson in mortality, Worm Tarnauer, who thrives on being invisible, doesn't count on Becca Finch, the 17-year-old car crash victim who changes everything.

"Spinelli writes with wry humor that still makes room for sweetness and a belief in the impossible. A stellar pick for tween collections." Booklist

Hokey Pokey. Jerry Spinelli. Alfred A. Knopf Books for Young Readers, 2013. 272 p.

Grades: 5 6 7 8   **Fic**

  1. Growing up 2. Childhood 3. Play 4. Growth (Psychology) 5. Children 6. Coming-of-age stories
ISBN 9780375831980

An inventive fable of growing up and letting go, of leaving childhood and its imaginative play behind for the more dazzling adventures of adolescence, and of learning to accept not only the sunny part of day, but also the unwelcome arrival of night.

Maniac Magee: a novel. by Jerry Spinelli. Little, Brown, c1990. 184 p.

Grades: 5 6 7 8   **Fic**

  1. Runaway boys 2. Racism 3. Running 4. Segregation 5. Race relations 6. Allegories 7. Realistic fiction 8. Classics
ISBN 0316807222

LC   89027144

Newbery Medal, 1991.

After his parents die, Jeffrey Lionel Magee's life becomes legendary, as he accomplishes athletic and other feats which awe his contemporaries.

"Orphaned at three, Jeffery Lionel Magee, after eight unhappy years with relatives, one day takes off running. A year later, he ends up 200 miles away in Two Mills, a highly segregated community. Part tall tale and part contemporary realistic fiction, this unusual novel magically weaves timely issues of homelessness, racial prejudice, and illiteracy into an energetic story that bursts with creativity, enthusiasm, and hope for the future. In short, it's a celebration of life." Booklist.

Stargirl. Jerry Spinelli. Alfred A. Knopf, 2000. 176 p.
Grades: 7 8 9 10   **Fic**
    1. Nonconformity 2. Popularity 3. First loves 4. Eccentric teenage girls 5. Teenagers 6. Arizona 7. Realistic fiction 8. Classics
ISBN 0679886370

LC 99087944

In this story about the perils of popularity, the courage of nonconformity, and the thrill of first love, an eccentric student named Stargirl changes Mica High School forever.

"As always respectful of his audience, Spinelli poses searching questions about loyalty to one's friends and oneself and leaves readers to form their own answers." Publishers Weekly.

Wringer. Jerry Spinelli. HarperCollins, c1997. 228 p.
Grades: 4 5 6 7   **Fic**
    1. Courage in boys 2. Initiation rites for boys 3. Pigeons 4. Bullying and bullies 5. Ten-year-old boys 6. Pennsylvania 7. Realistic fiction
ISBN 0060249145

LC 9637897

As Palmer comes of age he must either accept the violence of being a wringer at his Pennsylvania town's annual Pigeon day or find the courage to oppose it.

"During the annual pigeon shoot, it is a town tradition for 10-year-old boys to break the necks of wounded birds. In this riveting story told with verve and suspense, Palmer rebels." School Library Journal.

Spratt, R. A.

Friday Barnes, girl detective. R.A. Spratt; illustration by Phil Gosier. Roaring Brook Press, 2016. 256 p.: Friday Barnes mysteries
Grades: 4 5 6 7   **Fic**
    1. Eleven-year-old girls 2. Girl detectives 3. Boarding schools 4. Cleverness in girls 5. Genius 6. Mysteries
ISBN 9781626722972

A genius girl detective discovers her ultra exclusive boarding school is a hotbed of crime, from missing homework and stolen lemon tarts to a mysterious yeti haunting the school swamp. Provided by publisher.

"Delightful, highly logical, and well-informed fun." Kirkus.

Springer, Nancy

The **case** of the bizarre bouquets: an Enola Holmes mystery. Nancy Springer. Philomel Books, 2008. 176 p.: Enola Holmes mysteries
Grades: 5 6 7 8   **Fic**
    1. Victorian era (1837-1901) 2. Teenage girl detectives 3. Missing persons 4. Missing persons investigation 5. Fourteen-year-old girls 6. Holmes, Enola (Fictitious character) 7. London, England 8. Great Britain 9. Historical mysteries 10. Mysteries 11. Classics-inspired fiction
ISBN 9780399245183

LC 2007020435

Fourteen-year-old Enola Holmes, disguised as a beautiful woman, finds clues in floral bouquets as she searches for the missing Doctor Watson, a companion of her famous older brother, Sherlock.

"Springer's descriptions of late-19th-century England are vivid, the mystery is intriguing, and Enola's cleverness and capability will appeal to readers who like their heroines both sprightly and savvy." School Library Journal.

The **case** of the cryptic crinoline. Nancy Springer. Philomel Books, c2009. 160 p.: Enola Holmes mysteries
Grades: 5 6 7 8   **Fic**
    1. Nightingale, Florence, 1820-1910 2. Victorian era (1837-1901) 3. 19th century 4. Teenage girl detectives 5. Missing persons investigation 6. Kidnapping 7. Missing persons 8. Crimean War, 1853-1856 9. London, England 10. Great Britain 11. Historical mysteries 12. Mysteries 13. Classics-inspired fiction
ISBN 9780399247811

LC 2008040475

In late nineteenth-century London, fourteen-year-old Enola Holmes, much younger sister of detective Sherlock Holmes, turns to Florence Nightingale for help when her investigation into the disappearance of a Crimean War widow grows cold.

"From the riveting prologue to the satisfying conclusion, readers are hurled headlong into Enola Holmes's latest case." School Library Journal.

The **case** of the gypsy goodbye. Nancy Springer. Philomel Books, 2010. 166 p.: Enola Holmes mysteries
Grades: 5 6 7 8   **Fic**
    1. Victorian era (1837-1901) 2. 19th century 3. Teenage girl detectives 4. Kidnapping 5. Missing persons investigation 6. Brothers and sisters 7. Characters and characteristics in literature 8. London, England 9. Great Britain 10. Historical mysteries 11. Mysteries 12. Classics-inspired fiction
ISBN 9780399252365

LC 2009027141

After fourteen-year-old Enola Holmes seeks the missing Duquessa Del Campo in the seedy underbelly of nineteenth-century London, she finally reaches an understanding with her brothers Sherlock and Mycroft.

"The series that features Enola Holmes, the (much) younger sister of Sherlock, continues to be flat-out among the best mysteries being written for young people today. Not only are the mysteries sharp attention holders but the conclusions are well thought out, with i's dotted and t's crossed in true Holmesian fashion." Booklist.

The **case** of the left-handed lady: an Enola Holmes mystery. Nancy Springer. Philomel Books, 2007. 192 p.: Enola Holmes mysteries
Grades: 5 6 7 8   **Fic**
    1. Victorian era (1837-1901) 2. Teenage girl detectives 3. Kidnapping 4. Kidnapping investigation 5. Holmes, Enola (Fictitious character) 6. Holmes, Sherlock (Fictitious character) 7. London, England 8. Great Britain 9. Historical mysteries 10. Mysteries 11. Classics-inspired fiction
ISBN 0399245170

LC 2006008261

Pursued by her much older brother, famed detective Sherlock Holmes, fourteen-year-old Enola, disguised and using false names, attempts to solve the kidnapping of a baronet's sixteen-year-old daughter in nineteenth-century London.

"Enola is beautifully drawn, as are the sights and sounds of late-nineteenth-century London." Booklist.

★ The **case** of the missing marquess: an Enola Holmes mystery. Nancy Springer. Philomel Books, 2006. 224 p.: Enola Holmes mysteries

Grades: 5 6 7 8 **Fic**

1. Victorian era (1837-1901) 2. 1880s 3. Teenage girl detectives 4. Missing persons investigation 5. Private investigators 6. Missing persons 7. Heirs and heiresses 8. London, England 9. England 10. Historical mysteries 11. Mysteries 12. Classics-inspired fiction
ISBN 0399243046

LC 2005013260

Enola Holmes, much younger sister of detective Sherlock Holmes, must travel to London in disguise to unravel the disappearance of her missing mother.

"Enola's loneliness, intelligence, sense of humor, and sheer pluck make her an extremely appealing heroine." School Library Journal.

The **case** of the peculiar pink fan: an Enola Holmes mystery. Nancy Springer. Philomel Books, c2008. 183 p.: Enola Holmes mysteries

Grades: 5 6 7 8 **Fic**

1. Victorian era (1837-1901) 2. Teenage girl detectives 3. Arranged marriage 4. Kidnapping 5. Characters and characteristics in literature 6. Fourteen-year-old girls 7. London, England 8. Great Britain 9. Historical mysteries 10. Mysteries 11. Classics-inspired fiction
ISBN 9780399247804

LC 2008006933

While fourteen-year-old Enola Holmes endeavors to save her friend Lady Cecily Alistair from an unwelcome arranged marriage, she meets with some assistance from her older brother, Sherlock, and interference by the eldest, Mycroft.

"This features a strong mystery, intriguing family relationships, and the continuing thread of a daughter and mother lost to each other. . . . A rousing read with plenty of terrific Victorian detail." Booklist.

Springstubb, Tricia

Every single second. Tricia Springstubb, Diana Sudyka. Harpercollins Childrens Books, 2016. 288 p.

Grades: 4 5 6 7 8 **Fic**

1. Twelve-year-old girls 2. Shooting 3. Time 4. Change 5. Brothers 6. Coming-of-age stories
ISBN 9780062366283

"The narrative structure of then and now, with short chapters devoted to the musings of a statue, sometimes intrudes upon the story, but this is rich in complex issues that include caring for the elderly, the problems of friendship, and the role of God in everyday life. Lots of plates here, but Springstubb keeps them spinning to a satisfying end." Booklist.

The **most** perfect thing in the universe. by Tricia Springstubb. Margaret G. Ferguson Books, 2021 176 p.

Grades: 4 5 6 7 **Fic**

1. Mothers and daughters 2. Adventurers 3. Birds 4. Ornithologists 5. Survival 6. Adventure stories 7. Survival stories
ISBN 9780823447572

LC 2021003233

When her mother, a noted ornithologist, is lost at the top of the world, unadventurous 11-year-old Loah Londonderry, with the help of a new friend, must step out of her comfort zone to save her lost mother.

"Through metaphor and imagery, Springstubb's tender, sensitively written story captures the essences of places and characters." Publishers Weekly

Includes bibliographical references.

Stamper, Phil

The **gravity** of us. Phil Stamper. Bloomsbury, 2020. 352 p.

Grades: 8 9 10 11 12 **Fic**

1. United States. National Aeronautics and Space Administration 2. Journalism 3. Family problems 4. Teenage boy/boy relations 5. Astronauts 6. Teenage romance 7. LGBTQIA romances 8. Realistic fiction
ISBN 9781547600144

LC 2019019167

When his volatile father is picked to become an astronaut for NASA's mission to Mars, seventeen-year-old Cal, an aspiring journalist, reluctantly moves from Brooklyn to Houston, Texas, and looks for a story to report, finding an ally (and crush) in Jeremy, the son of another astronaut.

"In his debut novel, Stamper crafts a sweet fish-out-of-water tale that also shrewdly explores the intersection between social class and modern media culture." Kirkus

Stanley, Diane

Bella at midnight: the thimble, the ring, and the slippers of glass. Diane Stanley; illustrated by Bagram Ibatoulline. HarperCollins, 2006. 278 p.

Grades: 5 6 7 8 **Fic**

1. Mother-separated children 2. Magic 3. Princes 4. Girl orphans 5. Fathers and daughters 6. Historical fiction 7. Fairy tale and folklore-inspired fiction
ISBN 0060775734

LC 2005005906

Raised by peasants, Bella discovers that she is actually the daughter of a knight and finds herself caught up in a terrible plot that will change her life and the kingdom forever.

"What raises this above other recreated fairy tales is the quality of the writing, dotted with jeweled description and anchored by the strong values: loyalty, truth, honor." Booklist.

The **princess** of Cortova. Diane Stanley. Harper, an imprint of HarperCollins, 2013. 320 p.: Silver bowl trilogy

Grades: 5 6 7 8 **Fic**

1. Princesses 2. Clairvoyance 3. Rulers 4. Courts and courtiers 5. Magic 6. Fantasy fiction
ISBN 9780062047304

LC 2013021824

With tensions rising between the kingdoms of Westria and Austlind, Molly and Tobias accompany King Alaric to Cortova, where he hopes to form an alliance with the powerful King Gonzalo—an alliance that would be sealed by Alaric's marriage to Gonzalo's daughter, the beautiful princess Elizabetta. Provided by publisher.

The **silver** bowl. Diane Stanley. Harper, 2011. 272 p.: Silver bowl trilogy

Grades: 5 6 7 8 **Fic**

1. Household employees 2. Clairvoyance 3. Family curses 4. Curses 5. Rulers 6. Fantasy fiction
ISBN 9780061575433

"Molly is a young scullery maid in the castle of King Edmund, and like her mother before her, she sees visions and hears voices that offer glimpses of the future. But is this a blessing or a curse?. . . . The girl's choice of silence . . . is challenged when she learns that a rumored curse on the royal family is true and only by sharing her visions might they be saved. Combining carefully chosen details of setting with a richly realized fantasy premise, Stanley succeeds in creating a believable world large enough to accommodate not only menace and evil but also loyalty, enduring friendship, and love." Booklist.

Staples, Suzanne Fisher

Haveli. Suzanne Fisher Staples. Knopf, 1993. 259 p.

Grades: 8 9 10 11 12   **Fic**
   1. Gender role 2. Family feuds 3. Women 4. Pakistan 5. Realistic fiction
   ISBN 9780679841579

LC   92029054

Having relented to the ways of her people in Pakistan and married the rich older man to whom she was pledged against her will, Shabanu is now the victim of his family's blood feud and the malice of his other wives.

"Staples brews a potent mix here: the issue of a woman's role in a traditional society, page-turning intrigue, tough women characters, and a fluidity of writing that blends it all together." Booklist.

Under the persimmon tree. Suzanne Fisher Staples. Farrar, Straus and Giroux, 2005. 288 p.

Grades: 7 8 9 10   **Fic**
   1. Taliban 2. 21st century 3. Girls 4. Afghans 5. Refugees 6. Child refugees 7. Women 8. Afghanistan 9. Peshawar, Pakistan 10. War stories
   ISBN 0374380252

LC   2004053256

Alternating between the stories of Najmah, a 12-year-old Afghan girl, and Nusrat, a young American woman, this powerful, poignant novel depicts the emotional cost of the war in Afghanistan. Nusrat longs for the return of her husband, Faiz, who left to open a medical clinic in Afghanistan. Meanwhile, Najmah, whose mother and baby brother were killed by American bombs, desperately searches for her father and older brother, who were forced to fight for the Taliban. When Najmah and Nusrat meet at a refugee camp in Pakistan, they forge a friendship that reveals the heartbreak and hope of surviving the devastation of war. .

"Staples weaves a lot of history and politics into her story. . . . But . . . it's the personal story . . . that compels as it takes readers beyond the modern stereotypes of Muslims as fundamentalist fanatics. There are no sweet reunions, but there's hope in heartbreaking scenes of kindness and courage." Booklist.

Starmer, Aaron, 1976-

The **storyteller.** Aaron Starmer. Farrar Straus Giroux, 2016. 256 p.: Riverman trilogy

Grades: 5 6 7 8 9   **Fic**
   1. Parallel universes 2. Missing children 3. Soul 4. Storytelling 5. Brothers and sisters 6. New York (State) 7. Gateway fantasy 8. Fantasy fiction
   ISBN 9780374363130

LC 2015004696

Along with stories, Keri Cleary records in her diary the strange and terrifying events surrounding the disappearance of Fiona Loomis and Alistair Cleary's efforts to find her in Aquavania, a world where wishes can nearly come true, as well as the repercussions of the shooting of Kyle Dwyer.

"In a subsection of publishing where trilogies often seem formulaic or forced, this refreshing take challenges traditionally reiterated narrative devices by never dealing in absolutes and not tying things off into neat bows. Fans of fantasy and realistic fiction alike will find something to love about this book, in which narrative ambiguity has never been so well leveraged." School Library Journal.

The **whisper.** Aaron Starmer. Farrar Straus Giroux, 2015. 256 p.: Riverman trilogy

Grades: 5 6 7 8   **Fic**
   1. 1980s 2. Parallel universes 3. Missing children 4. Friendship 5. Preteen boys 6. Cleary, Alistair (Fictitious character) 7. New York (State) 8. Gateway fantasy 9. Fantasy fiction
   ISBN 9780374363116

LC 2014013168

Twelve-year-old Alistair continues his quest to find his missing friend, Fiona, in Aquavania, a world where wishes can nearly come true, but he learns that the Whisper, once a boy named Charlie from his own world, has plans for Alistair and has used Fiona to try to get to him.

"A riveting, imaginative, disconcerting, inscrutable, unresolved sequel, guaranteed to leave readers anxious for the finale." Kirkus.

Stead, Rebecca

First light. Rebecca Stead. Wendy Lamb Books, c2007. 328 p.

Grades: 5 6 7 8   **Fic**
   1. Children of scientists 2. Global warming 3. Underground areas 4. Secrets 5. Adventure 6. Greenland 7. Adventure stories
   ISBN 9780375840173

LC   2006039733

When twelve-year-old Peter and his family arrive in Greenland for his father's research, he stumbles upon a secret his mother has been hiding from him all his life, and begins an adventure he never imagines possible.

"This novel is an exciting, engaging mix of science fiction, mystery, and adventure. . . . Peter and Thea are fully developed main characters." School Library Journal.

★ **Goodbye** stranger. Rebecca Stead. Wendy Lamb Books, an imprint of Random House Children's Books, 2015. 192 p.

Grades: 5 6 7 8 9   **Fic**
   1. Friendship 2. Boy/girl relations 3. Love 4. Best friends 5. Middle schools 6. New York City 7. Manhattan, New York City 8. Realistic fiction
   ISBN 9780385743174

"Ah, seventh grade! A year when your friends transform inexplicably, your own body and emotions perplex you, and the world seems fraught with questions, and the most confusing ones of all concern the nature of love. Stead focuses on Bridge Barsamian, her best girlfriends, and her newest friend Sherma, a boy who is definitely not her boyfriend (probably). . . . An immensely satisfying addition for Stead's many fans." School Library Journal.

Liar & spy. by Rebecca Stead. Wendy Lamb Books, 2012. 208 p.

Grades: 4 5 6 7 8   **Fic**
   1. Boy spies 2. Apartment houses 3. Home schooled boys 4. Neighbors 5. Friendship 6. Brooklyn, New York City 7. New York City 8. Realistic fiction
   ISBN 9780385737432

LC 2011042674

Seventh-grader Georges adjusts to moving from a house to an apartment, his father's efforts to start a new business, his mother's extra shifts as a nurse, being picked on at school, and Safer, a boy who wants his help spying on another resident of their building.

★ The **list** of things that will not change. Rebecca Stead. Wendy Lamb Books, 2020. 224 p.

Grades: 4 5 6 7 **Fic**

1. Children of divorced parents 2. Secrets 3. Gay fathers 4. Weddings 5. Remarriage 6. Realistic fiction

ISBN 9781101938102

Despite her parents' divorce, her father's coming out as gay, and his plans to marry his boyfriend, ten-year-old Bea is reassured by her parents' unconditional love, excited about getting a stepsister, and haunted by something she did last summer at her father's lake house.

"Stead's greatest strength may be her understanding of the middle-grade psyche. Her work shows great respect for the complexity of children's feelings, and this remarkable book is, more than anything, about feelings." Booklist

★ **When** you reach me. Rebecca Stead. Wendy Lamb Books, 2009. 199 p.

Grades: 5 6 7 8 **Fic**

1. 1970s 2. Latchkey children 3. Space and time 4. Children of single parents 5. Television game shows 6. Friendship 7. New York City 8. Science fiction

ISBN 9780385737425

LC 2008024998

Newbery Medal, 2010.

As her mother prepares to be a contestant on the 1980s television game show, "The $20,000 Pyramid," a twelve-year-old New York City girl tries to make sense of a series of mysterious notes received from an anonymous source that seems to defy the laws of time and space.

"The '70s New York setting is an honest reverberation of the era; the mental gymnastics required of readers are invigorating; and the characters . . . are honest bits of humanity." Booklist.

Steele, Hamish

DeadEndia: the watcher's test. Hamish Steele. Nobrow, 2018 212 p.

Grades: 7 8 9 10 11 12 **Fic**

1. Best friends 2. Amusement parks 3. Paranormal phenomena 4. Friendship 5. Haunted places 6. Paranormal comics 7. Webcomics 8. LGBTQIA comics

ISBN 9781910620472

Barney and his best friend Norma are just trying to get by and keep their jobs, but working at the Dead End theme park also means battling demonic forces, time traveling wizards, and scariest of all—their love lives!

Stephens, John, 1972-

The **emerald** atlas. John Stephens. Alfred A. Knopf, 2011. 400 p.: Books of beginning

Grades: 4 5 6 **Fic**

1. Parent-separated children 2. Magical books 3. Time travel (Past) 4. Space and time 5. Witches 6. Fantasy fiction

ISBN 9780375868702

Ten years ago, siblings Kate, Michael, and Emma were taken from their parents' home and have lived in orphanage after orphanage ever since. Newly arrived at their latest abode, they find an enchanted old atlas that transports them back in time...and into the clutches of an evil countess who's seeking the book that they've found.

"This fast-paced, fully imagined fantasy is by turns frightening and funny, and the siblings are well-crafted and empathetic heroes. Highly enjoyable, it should find many readers." Publishers Weekly.

The **fire** chronicle. John Stephens. Alfred A. Knopf, 2012. 400 p.: Books of beginning

Grades: 4 5 6 **Fic**

1. Magical books 2. Time travel (Past) 3. Parent-separated children 4. Space and time 5. Monsters 6. New York City 7. Fantasy fiction

ISBN 9780375868719

LC 2012016139

In the second book in the Books of Beginning Trilogy, Michael and Emma must track down the Chronicle of Life, while Kate must find a way back to present day from the year 1899.

Stevens, Robin, 1988-

First class murder. Robin Stevens. Simon & Schuster Books for Young Readers, [2017] 256 p.: Wells & Wong mysteries

Grades: 4 5 6 7 **Fic**

1. 1930s 2. Between the Wars (1918-1939) 3. Girl detectives 4. Murder investigation 5. Orient Express (Train) 6. Trains 7. Murder 8. Historical mysteries

ISBN 9781481422185

On holiday with Hazel's father, Daisy and Hazel secretly investigate a murder on the Orient Express, rushing to solve it before another murder occurs, or someone else finds the killer.

Murder is bad manners. Robin Stevens. Simon & Schuster Books for Young Readers, 2015. 320 p.: Wells & Wong mysteries

Grades: 4 5 6 7 **Fic**

1. 1930s 2. Between the Wars (1918-1939) 3. Boarding school students 4. Girl detectives 5. Murder 6. Friendship 7. Boarding schools 8. England 9. Historical mysteries

ISBN 9781481422123

"Heres a mystery import, set in the 1930s, that does justice to its British roots. Hazel Wong has come from Hong Kong to attend Deepdean boarding school. An outcast until she is accepted by upper-crust Daisy Wells, Hazel is happy to be half of a two-girl detective agency. . . . Hazel makes a good narrator, and while the mystery plods a bit and has too many teachers—though a cast list helps—not every reader will guess the ending. Nancy Drew, meet Wells and Wong." Booklist.

Poison is not polite. Robin Stevens. Simon & Schuster Books for Young Readers, [2016] 256 p.: Wells & Wong mysteries

Grades: 4 5 6 7 **Fic**

1. 1930s 2. Between the Wars (1918-1939) 3. Murder 4. Girl detectives 5. Poisoning 6. Girl students 7. Birthday parties 8. England 9. Great Britain 10. Historical mysteries

ISBN 9781481422154

Murder mystery set in the 1930s. Schoolgirl detectives Daisy Wells and Hazel Wong are at Daisy's family home for the holidays. Daisy's mother invites her whole extended family around for a tea party to celebrate Daisy's birthday. But what is her real motive for inviting them round? When a guest is poisoned Daisy and Hazel investigate.

"A first-rate whodunit, reminiscent of a game of Clue and terrific preparation for the works of Agatha Christie." Kirkus.

Stevenson, Robert Louis, 1850-1894

Kidnapped: being memoirs of the adventures of David Balfour in the year 1751 how he was kidnapped and cast away .... written by himself and now set forth by Robert Louis Stevenson; illustrated by N.C. Wyeth. Scribner, 1982, c1886. xiv, 289 p.

Grades: 7 8 9 10 11 12 Adult **Fic**

1. 1750s 2. Uncles 3. Jacobites 4. Teenage kidnapping victims 5. Teenage adventurers 6. Kidnapping 7. Highlands, Scotland 8.

Adventure stories 9. Classics
ISBN 0684177943

A seventeen-year-old orphan is kidnapped by his villainous uncle, but later escapes and becomes involved in the struggle of the Scottish Highlanders against English rule.

Treasure Island. Robert Louis Stevenson; illustrated by John Lawrence. Candlewick Press, 2009. 269 p.
Grades: 5 6 7 8 9 10 11 12 Adult   **Fic**
1. Treasure hunting 2. Pirates 3. Adventurers 4. Silver, Long John (Fictitious character) 5. Treasure troves 6. Caribbean Area 7. Adventure stories 8. Sea stories 9. Classics
ISBN 9780763644451

LC 2009007338

While going through the possessions of a deceased guest who owed them money, the mistress of the inn and her son find a treasure map that leads them to a notorious pirate's fortune.

"Lawrence evokes the essence of classic adventure stories with his vinyl-cut illustrations, as thick black shapes are tempered by muted tones of blue, gold and green. . . . Readers will feel they've discovered a true relic with this edition." Publishers Weekly.

Treasure Island. by Robert Louis Stevenson; illustrated by Robert Ingpen. Sterling, 2011. 192 p.
Grades: 5 6 7 8 9 10 11 12 Adult   **Fic**
1. Adventurers 2. Pirates 3. Treasure hunting 4. Silver, Long John (Fictitious character) 5. Mothers and sons 6. Adventure stories 7. Sea stories 8. Classics
ISBN 9781402775451

LC bl2011005443

While going through the possessions of a deceased guest who owed them money, Jim Hawkins and his innkeeper mother find a treasure map that leads to a pirate's fortune.

"This unabridged version of Stevenson's classic, following the adventures of young Jim Hawkins, Long John Silver, and the crew of the Hispaniola on Treasure Island, features new art by Ingpen. The heavy pages of this edition have the look of parchment paper and the illustrations bring to mind old oil-on-canvas paintings, providing a pleasing aesthetic." Horn Book Guide.

Stewart, Trenton Lee

The **mysterious** Benedict Society. written by Trenton Lee Stewart; illustrated by Carson Ellis. Little, Brown, 2007. 485 p.: Mysterious Benedict Society
Grades: 5 6 7 8   **Fic**
1. Orphans 2. Gifted children 3. Brainwashing 4. Schools 5. Undercover operations 6. Adventure stories
ISBN 0316057770

LC 2006009925

After passing a series of mind-bending tests, four children are selected for a secret mission that requires them to go undercover at the Learning Institute for the Very Enlightened, where the only rule is that there are no rules.

"Stewart's unusual characters, threatening villains, and dramatic plot twists will grab and hold readers' attention." School Library Journal.

The **secret** keepers. Trenton Lee Stewart; illustrated by Diana Sudyka. Little, Brown and Company, 2016. 512 p.
Grades: 3 4 5 6   **Fic**
1. Invisibility 2. Magic clocks and watches 3. Immortality 4. Family secrets 5. Magic 6. Fantasy fiction 7. Illustrated books
ISBN 9780316389556

"This epic story filled with adventure and twists and turns is certain to keep readers' interest from beginning to end." School Library Journal.

Stiefvater, Maggie, 1981-

The **anatomy** of curiosity. Maggie Stiefvater, Tessa Gratton, Brenna Yovanoff. Carolrhoda Lab, 2015. 286 p.
Grades: 8 9 10 11   **Fic**
1. Creativity 2. Fiction writing 3. Teenage fiction writing 4. Characters and characteristics in literature 5. Short stories
ISBN 9781467723985

LC 2014046862

An anthology of stories with comments by the authors on their writing process, explores the way in which creativity is cultivated in different ways.

"At its best, this is an accessible guidebook for creating fiction that illustrates the complexity of the process while offering practical tips for managing it." Kirkus.

Call down the hawk. Maggie Stiefvater. Scholastic Press, 2019. 480 p.: Dreamer trilogy
Grades: 7 8 9 10 11 12   **Fic**
1. Dreams 2. End of the world 3. Prophecies 4. Brothers 5. Magic 6. Washington, DC 7. Urban fantasy
ISBN 9781338188325

While dreamers Ronan Lynch and Jordan Hennessy work to control their powers and stop destructive dreaming, government agent Carmen Farooq-Lane is hunting dreamers to prevent the prophesied apocalypse.

"Stiefvater delivers a stunningly imaginative tale that is by turns dark, funny, tragic, romantic, and surreal. Exquisitely drawn characters and witty, graceful prose complement the artfully crafted plot, which thrills while examining issues of individuality and mortality." Publishers Weekly.

The **dream** thieves. Maggie Stiefvater. Scholastic Press, 2013. 416 p.: Raven cycle
Grades: 8 9 10 11 12   **Fic**
1. Dreams 2. Family secrets 3. Gay teenagers 4. Clairvoyance 5. Rich teenage boys 6. Urban fantasy
ISBN 9780545424943

While Ronan struggles with intensifying and pervasive dreams triggered by the resurrected ley lines around Cabeswater, Ganey's search for clues to a local puzzle is threatened by dangerous adversaries.

"In this darker second book (The Raven Boys), Gansey, Blue, and the search for Glendower take a backseat to the exploration of Ronan's and Adam's tortured personalities. Stiefvater's descriptive prose reveals a complicated plot, multiple viewpoints, and detailed backstories. Many mysteries remain, but the cliffhanger ending makes it clear that Glendower will resurface as the main focus of book three." Horn Book.

The **raven** boys. Maggie Stiefvater. Scholastic Press, 2012. 390 p.: Raven cycle
Grades: 8 9 10 11 12   **Fic**
1. Clairvoyance 2. Rich teenage boys 3. Psychics 4. Spirits 5. Love 6. Urban fantasy
ISBN 9780545424929

Blue Sargent's gift seems to be that she makes other people's talents stronger, and when she meets Gansey, one of the Raven Boys from the Aglionby Academy, she discovers that together their talents are a dangerous mix.

The **raven** king. Maggie Stiefvater. Scholastic Press, 2014. 400 p.: Raven cycle

Grades: 8 9 10 11 12   **Fic**
1. Clairvoyance 2. Psychics 3. Rich teenage boys 4. Dreams 5. Supernatural 6. Urban fantasy
ISBN 9780545424981

A conclusion to the best-selling series finds a skeptical Blue confronting the prophecy that she will cause the death of her true love as she is increasingly caught up in the strange and sinister world of the Raven Boys.

"Stiefvater excels at building an intricately layered narrative with twisting, unpredictable turns, and her ability to introduce new, complex characters and storylines while also tying up previous loose ends is remarkable." Voice of Youth Advocates.

The **Scorpio** races. Maggie Stiefvater. Scholastic Press, 2011. 400 p.
Grades: 8 9 10 11 12   **Fic**
1. Horse racing 2. Competition 3. Teenage girl orphans 4. Horses 5. Islands 6. Fantasy fiction
ISBN 9780545224901

LC 2011015775

Nineteen-year-old returning champion Sean Kendrick competes against Puck Connolly, the first girl ever to ride in the annual Scorpio Races, both trying to keep hold of their dangerous water horses long enough to make it to the finish line.

"Stiefvater's narration is as much about atmospherics as it is about event, and the water horses are the environment in which Sean and Puck move, allies and rivals to the end. It's not a feel-good story—dread, loss, and hard choices are the islanders' lot. As a study of courage and loyalty tested, however, it is an utterly compelling read." Publishers Weekly.

Stone, Nic

Clean getaway. Nic Stone. Crown Publishing, 2020. 240 p.
Grades: 4 5 6 7   **Fic**
1. Automobile travel 2. Racism 3. Multiracial children 4. Grandmothers 5. Spring break 6. African American fiction 7. Realistic fiction
ISBN 9781984892980

An 11-year-old boy confronts the realities of race relations, past and present, and the mysterious agenda of his unconventional grandmother during an unplanned spring break road trip through the once-segregated American South.

"Adding Scoob's wry conversational observations about the odyssey to maps and a Green Book, an essential travel guide for African Americans designed to help them find accommodations willing to admit them and avoid towns known for terrorizing Black people, contributes levity and realism to what could have been a topic too emotionally heavy for middle-grade readers ... An absolute firecracker of a book and a must-have for children's collections." Booklist.

Stone, Phoebe, 1947-

The **Romeo** and Juliet code. by Phoebe Stone. Arthur A. Levine Books, 2011. 288 p.
Grades: 4 5 6 7   **Fic**
1. Second World War era (1939-1945) 2. Parent-separated girls 3. Codes (Communication) 4. World War II 5. Evacuation of civilians 6. World War II 7. Maine 8. Historical fiction
ISBN 9780545215114

LC 2010030005

During World War II, eleven-year-old Felicity is sent from London to Bottlebay, Maine, to live with her grandmother, aunt, uncle, and a reclusive boy who helps her decode mysterious letters that contain the truth about her missing parents.

"Felicity is endearingly portrayed, and the back story, so gradually revealed, provides a peek into the depths of the souls of some of the adults. The pacing is deliberately slow, yet Felicity's growing awareness of how she can help heal the troubled adults makes this an eminently satisfying read." Kirkus.

Stork, Francisco X.

Disappeared. Francisco X. Stork. Arthur A. Levine Books, 2017. 336 p.: Disappeared (Stork)
Grades: 7 8 9 10   **Fic**
1. Journalists 2. Missing persons 3. Criminals 4. Crime 5. Poverty 6. Mexico 7. Ciudad Juarez, Mexico 8. Thrillers and suspense
ISBN 9780545944472

LC 2017017320

Four months ago Sara Zapata's best friend, Linda, disappeared from the streets of Juarez, and ever since Sara has been using her job as a reporter to draw attention to the girls who have been kidnapped by the criminals who control the city, but now she and her family are being threatened—meanwhile her younger brother, Emiliano, is being lured into the narcotics business by the promise of big money, and soon the only way for both of them to escape is to risk the dangerous trek across the desert to the United States border.

"Stork (The Memory of Light) crafts a narrative that is both riveting and eye-opening. Part thriller, part sociological study, the novel sheds light on poverty, corruption, and greed while bringing readers intimately close to the plight of those who illegally cross borders with the hope of a brighter future." Publishers Weekly.

The **last** summer of the Death Warriors. Francisco X. Stork. Arthur A. Levine Books, 2010. 352 p.
Grades: 8 9 10 11 12   **Fic**
1. People with cancer 2. Caregivers 3. Revenge 4. Seventeen-year-old boys 5. Teenage boys 6. New Mexico 7. Classics-inspired fiction
ISBN 9780545151337

LC 2009019853

Seventeen-year-old Pancho is bent on avenging the senseless death of his sister, but after he meets D.Q, who is dying of cancer, and Marisol, one of D.Q.'s caregivers, both boys find their lives changed by their interactions.

"This novel, in the way of the best literary fiction, is an invitation to careful reading that rewards serious analysis and discussion. Thoughtful readers will be delighted by both the challenge and Stork's respect for their abilities." Booklist.

Marcelo in the real world. Francisco X. Stork. Arthur A. Levine Books, 2009. 320 p.
Grades: 8 9 10 11 12   **Fic**
1. God (Christianity) -- Will 2. Teenagers with autism 3. Injustice 4. Romantic love 5. Teenage boys 6. Realistic fiction
ISBN 9780545054744

LC 2008014729

Schneider Family Book Award for Teens, 2010.

Marcelo Sandoval, a seventeen-year-old boy on the high-functioning end of the autistic spectrum, faces new challenges, including romance and injustice, when he goes to work for his father in the mailroom of a corporate law firm.

"Stork introduces ethical dilemmas, the possibility of love, and other real world conflicts, all the while preserving the integrity of his characterizations and intensifying the novel's psychological and emotional stakes." Publishers Weekly.

Strange, Lucy

The **secret** of Nightingale Wood. Lucy Strange. Scholastic, 2017. 304 p.

Grades: 4 5 6 7   **Fic**

1. 1910s 2. Mental illness 3. Books and reading 4. Characters and characteristics in fairy tales 5. Twelve-year-old girls 6. Death 7. England 8. Historical fiction 9. First-person narratives
ISBN 9781338157475

Finding herself alone in the wake of her mother's illness, her father's job abroad and her caregiver's busy schedule, Henrietta, a girl growing up in the early 20th century, explores ghostly secrets in her new home.

"An evocative, beautifully written, mesmerizing debut tale with lush fairy-tale themes and a poignant exploration of mental illness—enthralling." Kirkus.

Strasser, Todd

Boot camp. Todd Strasser. Simon & Schuster Books for Young Readers, 2007. 256 p.

Grades: 8 9 10 11 12   **Fic**

1. Fifteen-year-old boys 2. Juvenile delinquency 3. Prison boot camps 4. Teenage boys 5. Teenagers 6. Realistic fiction
ISBN 9781416908487

LC 2006013634

After ignoring several warnings to stop dating his teacher, Garrett is sent to Lake Harmony, a boot camp that uses unorthodox and brutal methods to train students to obey their parents.

"The ending is both realistic and disturbing. . . . Writing in the teen's mature and perceptive voice, Strasser creates characters who will provoke strong reactions from readers. . . . [This is a] fast-paced and revealing story." School Library Journal.

Fallout. Todd Strasser. Candlewick Press, 2013 258 p.

Grades: 5 6 7 8   **Fic**

1. 1960s 2. Cuban Missile Crisis, 1962 3. Fallout shelters 4. Cold War 5. Racism 6. Families 7. Thrillers and suspense
ISBN 9780763655341

When an unthinkable nuclear attack occurs in an alternate-reality 1962, Scott is forced into his father's bomb shelter with his family and neighbors, where they rapidly consume limited supplies and fear the worst about the fate of the world outside.

No place. Todd Strasser. Simon & Schuster, 2014. 272 p.

Grades: 7 8 9 10   **Fic**

1. High school seniors 2. Poverty 3. Homelessness 4. Young men 5. Teenage boys 6. Realistic fiction
ISBN 9781442457218

Rendered homeless by circumstances beyond his middle-class family's control, Dan, a popular school baseball star, is forced to move to Tent City, where he becomes involved in the efforts of people fighting for better conditions only to be targeted by an adversary who wants to destroy the impoverished region.

"With the consummate skill of the best young adult writers, Strasser avoids sermonizing as he seamlessly combines real-time information about the social and economic conditions in contemporary society with a realistic and readable story of high school life. This exceptionally thought-provoking novel should be part of all collections serving teens." VOYA.

Price of duty. Todd Strasser. Simon & Schuster, 2018. 224 p.

Grades: 8 9 10 11   **Fic**

1. United States. Army. Reserve Officers' Training Corps. 2. Veterans 3. Post-traumatic stress disorder 4. War 5. Heroes and heroines 6. Addiction 7. Realistic fiction
ISBN 9781481497091

Hailed as a hero, twenty-year-old Jake returns to his pro-military hometown and family injured physically and emotionally, unsure if he can return to active duty but uncomfortable with the alternative.

Stroud, Jonathan

The **amulet** of Samarkand. Jonathan Stroud. Hyperion Books For Children, 2003. 464 p.: Bartimaeus trilogy

Grades: 7 8 9 10   **Fic**

1. Boy apprentices 2. Genies 3. Revenge 4. Magic 5. Twelve-year-old boys 6. London, England 7. Fantasy fiction 8. Middle Eastern-influenced fantasy
ISBN 078681859X

LC 2003049904

Nathaniel, a magician's apprentice, summons up the djinni Bartimaeus and instructs him to steal the Amulet of Samarkand from the powerful magician Simon Lovelace.

"There is plenty of action, mystery, and humor to keep readers turning the pages. This title, the first in a trilogy, is a must for fantasy fans." School Library Journal.

The **creeping** shadow. Jonathan Stroud. Disney-Hyperion, 2016. 400 p.: Lockwood & Co.

Grades: 4 5 6 7   **Fic**

1. Psychic ability 2. Ghosts 3. Resourcefulness 4. Supernatural 5. Crime 6. London, England 7. England 8. Fantasy fiction
ISBN 9781484709672

"Stroud's scene setting and storytelling are second to none, but its his ability to create credible, idiosyncratic characters and relationships that makes avid fans of the Lockwood & Co. series." Booklist.

The **golem's** eye. by Jonathan Stroud. Hyperion Books for Children, 2004. 574 p.: Bartimaeus trilogy

Grades: 7 8 9 10   **Fic**

1. Teenage apprentices 2. Power (Social sciences) 3. Genies 4. Golem 5. Fourteen-year-old boys 6. London, England 7. Prague, Czech Republic 8. Fantasy fiction 9. Middle Eastern-influenced fantasy
ISBN 0786818603

LC 2004054232

In their continuing adventures, magician's apprentice Nathaniel, now fourteen years old, and the djinni Bartimaeus travel to Prague to locate the source of a golem's power before it destroys London.

"The characters are well developed and the action never lets up. A must-purchase for all fantasy collections." School Library Journal.

Heroes of the valley. Jonathan Stroud. Hyperion, 2009. 480 p.

Grades: 7 8 9 10   **Fic**

1. Teenage adventurers 2. Practical jokes 3. Hero worship 4. Quests 5. Fifteen-year-old boys 6. Fantasy fiction 7. Coming-of-age stories
ISBN 9781423109662

When young Halli Sveinsson takes one of his practical jokes too far, he is forced to leave the House of Svein and go on a hero's quest where he encounters highway robbers, terrifying monsters, and a girl who may be as fearless as he is.

"Smart, funny dialogue and prose, revealing passages about the exploits of the hero Svein, bouts of action and a touch of romance briskly move the story along." Publishers Weekly.

The **hollow** boy. Jonathan Stroud. Disney-Hyperion, 2015. 400 p.: Lockwood & Co.

Grades: 4 5 6 7   **Fic**
> 1. Psychic ability 2. Ghosts 3. Assassins 4. Supernatural 5. London, England 6. England 7. Fantasy fiction
> ISBN 9781484709689

"As always, the descriptions of the hauntings are genuinely frightening, especially that of a spindly, humanoid creature that crawls on all fours and whispers Lucy's name." School Library Journal.

Ptolemy's gate. Jonathan Stroud. Hyperion Books For Children, 2006. 512 p.: Bartimaeus trilogy

Grades: 7 8 9 10   **Fic**
> 1. Teenage magicians 2. Genies 3. Conspiracies 4. Seventeen-year-old boys 5. Magic 6. London, England 7. Egypt 8. Fantasy fiction 9. Middle Eastern-influenced fantasy
> ISBN 0786818611

LC 2005052655

Dangerous adventures continue for the djinni Bartimaeus and his master, seventeen-year-old Nathaniel, a powerful magician who is serving as England's minister of information.

"This is an exciting and eminently satisfying conclusion to the trilogy. . . . literate, entertaining, and exciting." School Library Journal.

The **ring** of Solomon: a Bartimaeus novel. by Jonathan Stroud. Disney/Hyperion Books, 2010. 512 p.: Bartimaeus trilogy

Grades: 7 8 9 10   **Fic**
> 1. Solomon, King of Israel. 2. Genies 3. Magic rings 4. Women assassins 5. Magic 6. Wizards 7. Jerusalem, Israel 8. Fantasy fiction 9. Middle Eastern-influenced fantasy
> ISBN 9781423123729

LC 2010015468

Wise-cracking djinni Bartimaeus finds himself at the court of King Solomon with an unpleasant master, a sinister servant, and King Solomon's magic ring.

"In this exciting prequel set in ancient Israel, Stroud presents an early adventure of his sharp-tongued djinn, Bartimaeus. . . . This is a superior fantasy that should have fans racing back to those books." Publishers Weekly.

★ The **screaming** staircase. by Jonathan Stroud. Disney-Hyperion Books, 2013. 384 p.: Lockwood & Co.

Grades: 4 5 6 7   **Fic**
> 1. Haunted houses 2. Psychic ability 3. Ghosts 4. Supernatural 5. Resourcefulness 6. London, England 7. England 8. Fantasy fiction
> ISBN 9781423164913

When London is overrun by malevolent spirits, a talented group of young psychic detectives compete against other ghostbusting agencies in the debut of a new series that finds three intrepid colleagues investigating one of England's most haunted houses.

The **whispering** skull. Jonathan Stroud. Disney-Hyperion, 2014. 448 p.: Lockwood & Co.

Grades: 4 5 6 7   **Fic**
> 1. Psychic ability 2. Ghosts 3. Supernatural 4. Resourcefulness 5. Exhumation 6. London, England 7. England 8. Fantasy fiction
> ISBN 9781423164920

LC 2014014683

Lockwood & Co. are hired to investigate Edmund Bickerstaff, a Victorian doctor who reportedly tried to communicate with the dead, while Lucy is distracted by urgent whispers coming from the skull in a ghost jar. Provided by publisher.

"Stroud writes with a fine ear for dialogue, a wry sense of humor, and a knack for describing haunted places. Creating tension that ebbs and flows, he slowly builds the dramatic narrative to a resounding crescendo, and he makes the quieter scenes that follow just as compelling." Booklist.

Sugiura, Misa

It's not like it's a secret. Misa Sugiura. HarperTeen, 2017. 400 p.

Grades: 7 8 9 10 11   **Fic**
> 1. Japanese American teenage girls 2. Secrets 3. First loves 4. Teenage romance 5. Extramarital affairs 6. California 7. Realistic fiction 8. Coming-of-age stories
> ISBN 9780062473417

LC 2016961849

A girl whose life revolves around big and small secrets struggles with differences between two diverse groups of friends, a boy's sweet but unrequited affection, her crush on her best friend and her father's increasingly obvious affair.

"Well-paced, brimming with drama, and utterly vital." Kirkus.

Summers, Courtney

This is not a test. Courtney Summers. St. Martin's Griffin, 2012. 326 p.

Grades: 7 8 9 10 11 12   **Fic**
> 1. Zombies 2. Survival (after disaster) 3. End of the world 4. High schools 5. Family problems 6. Apocalyptic fiction 7. Horror
> ISBN 0312656742

Sloane Price is barricaded in Cortege High with five other teens while zombies try to get in. She observes her fellow captives become more unpredictable and violent as time passes although they each have much more reason to live than she has.

Sumner, Jamie

Roll with it. Jamie Sumner. Atheneum, 2019. 256 p.

Grades: 4 5 6 7   **Fic**
> 1. Girls with disabilities 2. Moving, Household 3. New students 4. Children with cerebral palsy 5. Friendship 6. Oklahoma 7. Realistic fiction
> ISBN 9781534442559

Twelve-year-old Ellie, who has cerebral palsy, finds her life transformed when she moves with her mother to small-town Oklahoma to help care for her grandfather, who has Alzheimer's Disease.

★ **Tune** it out. Jamie Sumner. Atheneum Books for Young Readers, 2020. 256 p.

Grades: 5 6 7 8   **Fic**
> 1. Girl singers 2. Sensory disorders 3. Mothers and daughters 4. Child custody 5. Friendship 6. Realistic fiction
> ISBN 9781534457003

Twelve-year-old Lou Montgomery's life has been centered on her mother's terrifying plan to make her a singing star, but a crisis reveals Lou's sensory processing disorder and people determined to help her address it.

"Her voice alternately wry, naive, and wise beyond her years, Lou confronts sensory overload, self-consciousness, and her simultaneous love for and anger toward her mother in poetic, poignant prose. . . . A vivid, sensitive exploration of invisible disability, family bonds, and the complex reality of happily-ever-after." Kirkus

Svingen, Arne, 1967-

The **ballad** of a broken nose. Arne Svingen, Kari Dickson. Simon & Schuster, 2016. 304 p.

Grades: 5 6 7   **Fic**

   1. Optimism 2. Teenage boys 3. Dysfunctional families 4. Children of alcoholics 5. Twelve-year-old boys 6. Norway 7. Humorous stories

ISBN 9781481415422

"An absorbing, well-paced story with a heartening conclusion." Booklist.

Sweeney, Diana

The **minnow**. by Diana Sweeney. The Text Publishing Company, 2014. 263 p.

Grades: 8 9 10 11 12   **Fic**

   1. Pregnant teenagers 2. Grief 3. Teenage girl orphans 4. Floods 5. Grief in teenage girls 6. Realistic fiction

ISBN 9781922182012

"Readers who can accept the ambiguous chronology and Tom's glib ability to communicate beyond worlds will be rewarded: the universe into which Minnow is born and will undoubtedly thrive is engaging and extraordinary. A promising and welcome debut." Booklist.

Swift, Jonathan, 1667-1745

Gulliver's travels. Jonathan Swift. Dover Publications, 1996, c1735. xiii, 226 p.

Grades: 7 8 9 10 11 12 Adult   **Fic**

   1. 19th century 2. Voyages and travels 3. Giants 4. Lilliputians (Fictitious characters) 5. Sailing 6. Miniature persons (Imaginary characters) 7. Fantasy classics 8. Fantasy fiction 9. Satirical fiction

ISBN 9780486292731

Gullible ship's doctor Lemuel Gulliver experiences extraordinary travels, in which he goes through a series of apparently child-like fantasy worlds of tiny people and giants, floating islands and talking horses.

Talley, Robin

Pulp. Robin Talley. Harlequin Teens, 2018 406 p.

Grades: 8 9 10 11 12   **Fic**

   1. 1950s 2. Lesbian teenagers 3. Women authors 4. Books and reading 5. Young women 6. Teenage same-sex romance 7. Washington, DC 8. Love stories 9. Novels-within-novels

ISBN 9781335012906

Duel narratives follow an eighteen-year-old closeted lesbian in 1955 keeping a secret romance and wanting to write her own stories and another young woman sixty-two years later studying 1950s lesbian pulp fiction for her senior project.

Tamaki, Mariko

Harley Quinn: breaking glass: a graphic novel. Mariko Tamaki; illustrated by Steve Pugh. DC Ink, 2019. 128 p.

Grades: 7 8 9 10 11 12   **Fic**

   1. Supervillains 2. Teenage girls 3. Social advocacy 4. Anarchism 5. Social justice 6. Superhero comics 7. Comics and Graphic novels

ISBN 9781401283292

LC 2019012179

With just $5 and a knapsack to her name, fifteen-year-old Harleen Quinzel is sent to live in Gotham City. To combat the destructive gentrification of her new neighborhood, she must choose between supporting Ivy, her friend from high school and an impassioned activist, or the Joker, an anarchist of questionable motives.

"The fast-paced plot enhanced by Harley's trademark style of speech examines the impact of gentrification, and Harley's character development follows a redemptive arc that will have readers rooting for her and her colorful family." Kirkus.

Saving Montgomery Sole. Mariko Tamaki. Roaring Brook Press, 2016. 288 p.

Grades: 7 8 9 10   **Fic**

   1. Children of LGBTQIA parents 2. Clubs 3. Homophobia 4. Self-perception 5. Friendship 6. California 7. Realistic fiction

ISBN 9781626722712

LC 2015004007

An outcast teen girl explores the mysteries of friendship, family, faith, and phenomena, including the greatest mystery of all—herself. Provided by publisher.

"Montgomery's slow confrontation with reality creates a realistic, satisfying arc, and Tamaki's economical storytelling results in dimensional characters whose struggles feel viscerally real." Publishers Weekly.

Unicorn power! Mariko Tamaki; illustrated by Brooke Allen. Amulet Books, 2017. 256 p.: Lumberjanes (Chapter books)

Grades: 3 4 5 6 7 8   **Fic**

   1. Unicorns 2. Girl campers 3. Scouting (Youth activity) 4. Mountains 5. Camps 6. Fantasy fiction 7. Illustrated books

ISBN 9781419727252

LC 2017028472

Welcome to Miss Qiunzella Thiskwin Penniquiqul Thistle Crumpet's Camp for Hardcore Lady Types. The five scouts of Roanoke cabin?Jo, April, Molly, Mal, and Ripley—love their summers at camp. They get to hang out with their best friends, earn Lumberjane scout badges, annoy their no-nonsense counselor Jen . . . and go on supernatural adventures. That last one? A pretty normal occurrence at Miss Qiunzella's, where the woods contain endless mysteries.

"The primary focus, however, is on the rollicking adventure and the power of friendship, and Lumberjanes fans will be satisfied on that front. Occasionally, the cartoonish action and pace of the story, which was so successful in the comics, doesn't quite land in narrative form, but that's a fairly minor quibble unlikely to bother readers eager for anything and everything Lumberjanes." Booklist.

Tamani, Liara

All the things we never knew. Liara Tamani. Greenwillow Books, 2020. 384 p.

Grades: 8 9 10 11 12   **Fic**

   1. African American teenagers 2. First loves 3. Basketball 4. Teenage basketball players 5. Teenage romance 6. Texas 7. Multicultural romances 8. Contemporary romances 9. African American fiction

ISBN 9780062656919

LC 2019060207

Carli and Rex have an immediate connection, an understanding that must mean first love, but family secrets, disappointments—and basketball, which holds center stage in both their lives—all create complications. Provided by publisher.

"The immediacy of Tamani's writing, imbued with wonderful sensory moments as the two protagonists let their guards down, will ensure that this engaging story has wide appeal." School Library Journal.

Tan, Shaun

Cicada. Shaun Tan. Arthur A. Levine Books, 2019, c2018. 32 p.

Grades: 6 7 8 9   **Fic**
  1. Cicadas 2. Office workers 3. Ingratitude 4. Offices 5. Insects
ISBN 9781338298390

Cicada works in an office, dutifully toiling day after day for unappreciative bosses and being bullied by his coworkers. But one day, Cicada goes to the roof of the building, and something truly extraordinary happens.

★ **Lost** & found. three by Shaun Tan. Arthur A. Levine Books, 2011. 128 p.
Grades: 5 6 7 8   **Fic**
  1. Loss (Psychology) 2. Lost articles 3. Rabbits 4. Trees 5. Short stories
ISBN 9780545229241

LC 2010030936

Three stories explore how we lose and find what matters most to us, as a girl finds a bright spot in a dark world, a boy leads a strange, lost being home, and a group of peaceful creatures loses its home to cruel invaders.

"The Red Tree follows a solitary girl through a single, not very good day, exploring her feelings as they shift from disappointment and confusion to alienation and despair. The spare, lyrical text provides an anchor for Tan's large, moody, beautiful paintings. The Lost Thing is a more upbeat tale of a boy who discovers an unusual object and then must decide what to do with it. Freedom and imagination are the themes in this story, and here the art includes fascinating and sometimes humorous bits of technical drawings. The prose of John Marsden's The Rabbits, an allegory about imperialism, is so simple and melodic that it verges on poetry. The artist emphasizes the invasive foreignness of the rabbits by dressing them in baroque uniforms, drawing mystifying, gigantic machines and buildings for them to build and deploy in their inexorable drive to dominate." School Library Journal.

Tales from outer suburbia. Shaun Tan. Arthur A. Levine Books, 2008. 96 p.
Grades: 7 8 9 10   **Fic**
  1. Suburban life 2. Water buffalo 3. Exchange students 4. Australia 5. Short stories 6. Illustrated books
ISBN 9780545055871

LC 2008013784

Fifteen illustrated short stories, some humorous and some haunting, set in the Australian suburbs.

"The term suburbia may conjure visions of vast and generic sameness, but in his hypnotic collection of 15 short stories and meditations, Tan does for the sprawling landscape what he did for the metropolis in The Arrival . . . . Ideas and imagery both beautiful and disturbing will linger." Publishers Weekly.

Tales from the inner city. Shaun Tan. Arthur A. Levine Books, 2018. 219 p.
Grades: 7 8 9 10 11 12   **Fic**
  1. Human/animal relationships 2. Animals 3. City life 4. Cities and towns 5. Allegories 6. Short stories 7. Illustrated books
ISBN 9781338298406

A collection of illustrated short stories, each one about the relationship of humans and the animals, both wild and domestic, that share the urban environment of the inner city.

"In contrast to the neighborhood settings of Tales from Outer Suburbia (2009), this collection of 25 illustrated poems and stories explores the dynamics between animals and humans amid breathtakingly imaginative scenes in skyscrapers and gutters." Kirkus.

Tanner, Lian
  Ice breaker. Lian Tanner. Feiwel & Friends, 2015. 256 p.: Icebreaker trilogy
Grades: 5 6 7 8   **Fic**
  1. Ships 2. Misfits (Persons) 3. Icebergs 4. Secrets 5. Twelve-year-old girls 6. South Pole 7. Science fiction
ISBN 9781250052162

Living on an ancient icebreaker in a war-stricken world ruled by Anti-Machinists, twelve-year-old Petrel hides a stowaway only to discover that her new friend has been sent to destroy a secret object.

Tanquary, Kathryn
  The **night** parade. Kathryn Tanquary. Sourcebooks Jabberwocky, 2016. 336 p.
Grades: 5 6 7 8   **Fic**
  1. Curses 2. Supernatural 3. Rites and ceremonies 4. Villages 5. Summer 6. Mythology, Japanese 7. Fantasy fiction 8. Mythological fiction
ISBN 9781492623243

During summer vacation thirteen-year-old Saki Yamamoto unintentionally invokes a death curse at her old family graveyard and now she must enter the dangerous spirit world of the Night Parade where three different guides will see if she can perform the deeds that will allow her to overcome the curse.

"Vivid details and realistic situations ensure accessibility, and subtle teaching moments are wrapped in wide-eyed enchantment." Publishers Weekly.

Tarshis, Lauren
  The **battle** of Gettysburg, 1863. by Lauren Tarshis; illustrated by Scott Dawson. Scholastic, c2013. 89 p.: I survived
Grades: 3 4 5 6   **Fic**
  1. American Civil War era (1861-1865) 2. 1860s 3. African American boys 4. Slavery 5. Civil war 6. Gettysburg, Battle of, 1863 7. Brothers and sisters 8. United States 9. Survival stories 10. Historical fiction
ISBN 9780545459365

Witnessing the harrowing events of the Civil War from the sidelines, eleven-year-old Henry endures the most grueling challenges of his life throughout a hot July week when he becomes inadvertently involved in the historic battle.

Taylor, Laini
  Blackbringer. Laini Taylor. G. P. Putnam's Sons, c2007. 437 p.: Dreamdark
Grades: 6 7 8 9   **Fic**
  1. Fairies 2. Demons 3. Genies 4. Crows 5. Magic 6. Fantasy fiction
ISBN 9780399246302

LC 2006026540

Magpie Windwitch, faerie, devil hunter, and granddaughter of the West Wind, must defeat an ancient evil creature, the Blackbringer, who has escaped from his bottle and threatens to unmake all of creation.

"Taylor drives the story forward by slowly teasing the reader with twists and turns in the plot. . . . Teen readers will identify with this faerie's humanness." Voice of Youth Advocates.

Daughter of smoke and bone. by Laini Taylor. Little, Brown, 2011. 432 p.: Daughter of smoke and bone trilogy
Grades: 8 9 10 11 12   **Fic**
  1. Teenage girl artists 2. Angels 3. Chimera (Greek mythology) 4. Mythical creatures 5. Supernatural 6. Prague, Czech Republic 7.

Czech Republic 8. Urban fantasy
ISBN 9780316134026

LC 2010045802

Seventeen-year-old Karou, a lovely, enigmatic art student in a Prague boarding school, carries a sketchbook of hideous, frightening monsters—the chimaerae who form the only family she has ever known.

"Taylor again weaves a masterful mix of reality and fantasy with cross-genre appeal. Exquisitely written and beautifully paced." Publishers Weekly.

Days of blood & starlight. Laini Taylor. Little, Brown Books for Young Readers, 2012. 528 p.: Daughter of smoke and bone trilogy

Grades: 9 10 11 12 **Fic**
1. Angels 2. Chimera (Greek mythology) 3. Imaginary wars and battles 4. Demons 5. Revenge 6. Morocco 7. Urban fantasy
ISBN 9780316133975

A sequel to Daughter of Smoke and Bone finds Karou struggling to come to terms with her nature while pursuing revenge for her people.

Dreams of gods & monsters. Laini Taylor. Little, Brown, 2014. 304 p.: Daughter of smoke and bone trilogy

Grades: 8 9 10 11 12 **Fic**
1. Angels 2. Chimera (Greek mythology) 3. Imaginary wars and battles 4. Supernatural 5. Parallel universes 6. Urban fantasy
ISBN 9780316134071

Karou and Akiva join their rival human armies against brutal angel invaders, an alliance that is tested by Karou's inability to forgive Akiva for killing the only family she has ever known.

"New revelations, characters, multiple love stories, and constant plot twists and suspense will not disappoint Taylor's many fans, who will also appreciate the novel's subtle philosophical undercurrents about racial harmony and the profound difficulty of making choices that reconcile duty, the greater good, and personal happiness." Booklist.

Taylor, Mildred D.

All the days past, all the days to come. Mildred D. Taylor. Viking Childrens Books, 2020. 496 p.: Logan family (Mildred D. Taylor)

Grades: 8 9 10 11 12 **Fic**
1. 20th century 2. Racism 3. African American families 4. Civil Rights Movement 5. Interracial marriage 6. Grief in women 7. Southern States 8. Historical fiction 9. Family sagas 10. African American fiction
ISBN 9780399257308

A long-awaited conclusion to the story that began in the Newbery Medal-winning Roll of Thunder, Hear My Cry finds young adult Cassie Logan searching for a sense of belonging before joining the civil rights movement in 1960s Mississippi.

"Taylor is unsparing in her depiction of the years of segregation and of the Black experience of white racism, bigotry, and injustice." Booklist.

★ The **friendship**. Mildred D. Taylor; pictures by Max Ginsburg. Dial Books for Young Readers, 1987. 53 p.: Logan family (Mildred D. Taylor)

Grades: 4 5 6 7 **Fic**
1. 1930s 2. Racism 3. Freed people 4. African American senior men 5. Logan, Cassie (Fictitious character) 6. Logan family (Fictitious characters: Taylor) 7. Mississippi 8. Historical fiction

9. Family sagas 10. African American fiction
ISBN 0803704178

LC 86029309

Coretta Scott King Award, Author Category, 1988.

Four children witness a confrontation between an elderly man and a white storekeeper in rural Mississippi in the 1930s.

"This story about race relations in rural Mississippi during the Depression focuses on an incident between an old Black man, Mr. Tom Bee, and a white storekeeper, Mr. John Wallace. Indebted to Tom for saving his life as a young man, John had promised they would always be friends. But now, years later, John insists that Tom call him Mister and shoots the old man for defiantly—and publicly—calling him by his first name. Narrator Cassie Logan and her brothers . . . are verbally abused by Wallace's villainous sons before witnessing the encounter." Bulletin of the Center for Children's Books.

★ The **gold** Cadillac. Mildred D. Taylor; pictures by Michael Hays. Dial Books for Young Readers, 1987. 43 p.

Grades: 4 5 6 7 **Fic**
1. 1950s 2. African American families 3. Racism 4. Cadillac automobile 5. Pride and vanity 6. Southern States 7. Historical fiction
ISBN 9780803703421

LC 86011526

Two black girls living in the North are proud of their family's beautiful new Cadillac until they take it on a visit to the South and encounter racial prejudice for the first time.

"Full-page sepia paintings effectively portray the characters, setting, and mood of the story events as Hays ably demonstrates his understanding of the social and emotional environments which existed for Blacks during this period." School Library Journal.

The **land**. Mildred D. Taylor. Phyllis Fogelman Books, 2001. 375 p.: Logan family (Mildred D. Taylor)

Grades: 7 8 9 10 **Fic**
1. 19th century 2. Racism 3. African American families 4. Multiracial persons 5. Prejudice 6. Fathers and sons 7. Mississippi 8. Southern States 9. Historical fiction 10. Family sagas 11. Coming-of-age stories
ISBN 0803719507

LC 00039329

Scott O'Dell Historical Fiction Award, 2002.
Coretta Scott King Award, Author Category, 2002.

After the Civil War, Paul, the son of a white father and a black mother, finds himself caught between the two worlds of colored folks and white folks as he pursues his dream of owning land of his own.

"Taylor masterfully uses harsh historical realities to frame a powerful coming-of-age story that stands on its own merits." Horn Book Guide.

★ **Let** the circle be unbroken. Mildred D. Taylor. Dial Press, 1981. 394 p.: Logan family (Mildred D. Taylor)

Grades: 4 5 6 7 **Fic**
1. Depression era (1929-1941) 2. 1930s 3. African American families 4. Racism 5. Depressions 1929-1941 6. Self-esteem in African American children 7. Logan, Cassie (Fictitious character) 8. Mississippi 9. Southern States 10. Historical fiction 11. Family sagas 12. African American fiction
ISBN 0140348921

LC 81065854

Coretta Scott King Award, Author Category, 1982.

Four black children growing up in rural Mississippi during the Depression experience racial antagonisms and hard times, but learn from their parents the pride and self-respect they need to survive.

"The author provides her readers with a literal sense of witnessing important American history. . . . Moreover, [she] never neglects the details of her volatile 9-year-old heroine's interior life. The daydreams, the jealousy, the incredible ardor of that age come alive." New York Times Book Review.

★ The **road** to Memphis. Mildred D. Taylor. Dial Books, 1990. 290 p.: Logan family (Mildred D. Taylor)
Grades: 4 5 6 7   **Fic**
1. Second World War era (1939-1945) 2. 1940s 3. African American families 4. Racism 5. Violence against African-Americans 6. Rural families 7. Interracial friendship 8. Southern States 9. Family sagas 10. Historical fiction 11. Coming-of-age stories
ISBN 0803703406
                                                LC   88033654
Coretta Scott King Award, Author Category, 1991.
Sadistically teased by two White boys in 1940's rural Mississippi, a Black youth severely injures one of the boys with a tire iron and enlists Cassie's help in trying to flee the state.
"Taylor's continued smooth, easy language provides readability for all ages, with a focus on universal human pride, worthy values, and individual responsibility. This action-packed drama is highly recommended." Voice of Youth Advocates.

★ **Roll** of thunder, hear my cry. Mildred D. Taylor. Dial Press, c1976. 276 p.: Logan family (Mildred D. Taylor)
Grades: 4 5 6 7 8 9   **Fic**
1. 1930s 2. African American families 3. Racism 4. Rural families 5. African American girls 6. African American children 7. Southern States 8. Historical fiction 9. Family sagas 10. African American fiction
ISBN 014034893X
                                                LC   76002287
Newbery Medal, 1977.
A Black family living in the South during the 1930s is faced with prejudice and discrimination which their children don't understand.

★ The **well**: David's story. Mildred D. Taylor. Dial Books for Young Readers, 1995. 92 p.: Logan family (Mildred D. Taylor)
Grades: 4 5 6 7   **Fic**
1. 1900s (Decade) 2. Racism 3. African American boys 4. Rural life 5. Droughts 6. Ten-year-old boys 7. Mississippi 8. Historical fiction 9. Family sagas 10. African American fiction
ISBN 0803718020
                                                LC   94025360 /AC
In Mississippi in the early 1900s ten-year-old David Logan's family generously shares their well water with both White and Black neighbors in an atmosphere of potential racial violence.
"This story delivers an emotional wallop in a concentrated span of time and action. . . . This story reverberates in the heart long after the final paragraph is read." Horn Book.

Taylor, Nandi
Given. Nandi Taylor. Wattpad Books, 2020 352 p.
Grades: 7 8 9 10 11 12   **Fic**
1. Women warriors 2. Dragons 3. Fate and fatalism 4. Imaginary empires 5. Warriors 6. Afrofuturism and Afrofantasy 7. Mythological fiction 8. Fantasy fiction
ISBN 9781989365045
Yenni has never been this far from home. With only her wits, her strength, and her sacred runelore, the fierce Yirba warrior princess is alone in the Empire of Cresh. It's a land filled with strange magics and even stranger people—all of whom mistrust anyone who's different. But Yenni will prove herself, and find the cure for her father's wasting illness. She will not fail. But no one warned her about the dragons. Especially not about him.—Adapted from publisher description.
"The captivating worldbuilding of magical lands and well-paced plot and character development combined with intriguing twists will have readers looking forward to more." Kirkus

Taylor, Theodore, 1921-2006
★ The **cay**. Theodore Taylor. Doubleday, 1969. 137 p.
Grades: 5 6 7 8   **Fic**
1. Children who are blind 2. Shipwrecks 3. Interracial friendship 4. African-West Indians 5. Survival (after airplane accidents, shipwrecks, etc) 6. West Indies 7. Caribbean Area 8. Survival stories 9. Adventure stories 10. Classics
ISBN 9780385079068
                                                LC   69015161
When the freighter on which they are traveling is torpedoed by a German submarine during World War II, a teenage white boy, blinded by a blow on the head, and an old Black man are stranded on a tiny Caribbean island where the boy acquires a new kind of vision, courage, and love from his old companion.
"Starkly dramatic, believable and compelling." Saturday Rev.

Timothy of the cay. Harcourt Brace, 1993. 161 p.
Grades: 5 6 7 8   **Fic**
1. African-West Indians 2. Twelve-year-old boys 3. Rescues 4. Prejudice 5. Survival (after airplane accidents, shipwrecks, etc) 6. Caribbean Area 7. Adventure stories
ISBN 0152883584
                                                LC   93007898 /AC
Having survived being blinded and shipwrecked on a tiny Caribbean island with the old Afro-West Indian Timothy, twelve-year-old white Phillip is rescued and hopes to regain his sight with an operation. Alternate chapters follow the life of Timothy from his days as a young cabin boy during the late eighteen-hundreds.
"Somewhat more thoughtful than its well-loved antecedent, this boldly drawn novel is no less commanding." Publishers Weekly.

Taylor, Thomas, 1973-
Malamander. Thomas Taylor; illustrated by Tom Booth. Candlewick Press, 2019. 320 p.: Legends of Eerie-on-Sea
Grades: 4 5 6 7   **Fic**
1. Missing persons 2. Searching 3. Sea monsters 4. Parent-separated girls 5. Seaside resorts 6. Fantasy fiction
ISBN 9781536207224
Assisting a fearless girl in an investigation into the mysterious loss of her parents years earlier, Herbert Lemon learns that some of his fellow townspeople are hunting a sea monster that is believed to convey a surprising gift.
"In this endearingly strange middle grade adventure set against the backdrop of a seaside resort town during the off-season, two orphans are caught up in a local legend. Taylor (Haunters) combines atmospheric descriptions with tongue-in-cheek humor, off-kilter concepts (a mechanical mermonkey that prescribes books), and quirky characters to create an unusual series opener. Meanwhile, exaggerated, stylized illustrations from Booth (This Is Christmas) bring both cast and setting to life, capturing the feel of this fantastical, energetic mystery." Publishers Weekly.

Teague, Mark
★ The **doom** machine. by Mark Teague. Blue Sky Press, 2009. 376 p.

Grades: 4 5 6 7   **Fic**
1. 1950s 2. Human/alien encounters 3. UFO abductions 4. Teenagers 5. Aliens 6. Space vehicles 7. Earth 8. Science fiction 9. Humorous stories
ISBN 9780545151429

LC 2009014262

When a spaceship lands in the small town of Vern Hollow in 1956, juvenile delinquent Jack Creedle and prim, studious Isadora Shumway form an unexpected alliance as they try to keep a group of extraterrestrials from stealing eccentric Uncle Bud's space travel machine.

"This book is filled with humor and dramatic figurative language that makes the setting completely approachable. It is a great fit for science fiction, humor, and adventure genre fans." Voice of Youth Advocates.

Teller, Janne, 1964-

Nothing. Janne Teller; translated by Martin Aitken. Atheneum Books for Young Readers, 2010. 240 p.

Grades: 7 8 9 10 11 12   **Fic**
1. Semantics (Philosophy) 2. Purpose in life 3. Self-sacrifice 4. Interpersonal relations 5. Schools 6. Realistic fiction
ISBN 9781416985792

LC 2009019784

When thirteen-year-old Pierre Anthon leaves school to sit in a plum tree and train for becoming part of nothing, his seventh grade classmates set out on a desperate quest for the meaning of life.

"Indelible, elusive, and timeless, this uncompromising novel has all the marks of a classic." Booklist.

Temblador, Alex

Secrets of the Casa Rosada. by Alex Temblador. Pinata Books, an imprint of Arte Publico Press, [2018] 160 p.

Grades: 8 9 10 11 12   **Fic**
1. 1990s 2. Grandmother and granddaughter 3. Healers 4. Mexican American teenage girls 5. Family secrets 6. Healing 7. Texas 8. Coming-of-age stories 9. Realistic fiction
ISBN 9781558858701

LC 2018029355

Sixteen-year-old Martha's life is transformed when her mother leaves her in Laredo, Texas, in 1990 with a grandmother she never knew, who is a revered curandera.

Thomas, Shelley Moore

The **last** rabbit. Shelley Moore Thomas. Wendy Lamb Books, 2021 288 p.

Grades: 4 5 6 7   **Fic**
1. Second World War era (1939-1945) 2. Magic 3. Transformations (Magic) 4. Sisters 5. Rabbits 6. Magicians 7. Fantasy fiction
ISBN 9780593173534

"Forced to abandoned her sinking island home, an enchanted rabbit visits her human sisters to find a place to call home, before a mistake leads to unexpected consequences that test her family bonds.

Thomas, Sherry (Sherry M.)

The **magnolia** sword: a ballad of Mulan. Sherry Thomas. Tu Books, 2019. 352 p.

Grades: 7 8 9 10   **Fic**
1. 5th century 2. Women warriors 3. Impostors 4. Martial arts 5. Battles 6. Power (Social sciences) 7. China 8. Fairy tale and folklore-inspired fiction 9. Historical fiction
ISBN 9781620148044

LC 2019003668

When her ailing father is conscripted to fight invaders from the north, Mulan dresses as a man to take his place in the army, but an old enemy and an attraction for her troop's commander complicate her mission.

"Skillful martial arts scenes combine with crucial discourse on power, gender, and the impact of language on history in this gripping, thoughtfully layered reinterpretation." Publishers Weekly

Thompson, Holly

The **language** inside. Holly Thompson. Delacorte Press, 2013. 528 p.

Grades: 7 8 9 10 11 12   **Fic**
1. Teenage volunteers 2. Moving to a new country 3. Children of people with cancer 4. Tsunamis 5. Refugees 6. Massachusetts 7. Japan 8. Realistic fiction 9. Novels in verse
ISBN 9780385739795

LC 2012030596

Raised in Japan, American-born tenth-grader Emma is disconcerted by a move to Massachusetts for her mother's breast cancer treatment, because half of Emma's heart remains with her friends recovering from the tsunami.

Thompson, John

The **girl** from Felony Bay. John Thompson. Walden Pond Press, an imprint of HarperCollinsPublishers, [2013] 304 p.

Grades: 4 5 6 7   **Fic**
1. Frameups 2. People in comas 3. Children of lawyers 4. Plantations 5. Families 6. Charleston, South Carolina 7. South Carolina 8. Mysteries
ISBN 9780062104465

LC 2012025338

When Abbey's father falls into a coma and is accused of a crime he didn't commit, Abbey sets out to prove his innocence—and repay a century-old debt. Provided by publisher.

Thor, Annika

Deep sea. Annika Thor; translated from the Swedish by Linda Schenck. Delacorte Press, 2015. 224 p.: Steiner sisters quartet

Grades: 7 8 9 10 11 12   **Fic**
1. Second World War era (1939-1945) 2. World War II -- Refugees 3. Refugees 4. Jews 5. Sisters 6. Schools 7. Sweden 8. Goteborg, Sweden 9. Historical fiction 10. Translations
ISBN 9780385743853

LC 2014005586

Nearly four years after leaving Vienna to escape the Nazis, Stephie Steiner, now sixteen, and her sister Nellie, eleven, are still living in Sweden, worrying about their parents and striving to succeed in school, and at odds with each other despite their mutual love.

"This novel about coming of age during a complicated, tragic time in history is both delicate and poignant, as when Stephie and Nellie sit on the dock, remembering a lullaby their mother sang. Thor's novel capably demonstrates the loneliness, powerlessness, and prejudice Stephie faces, as well as her growing inner strength." Publishers Weekly.

A **faraway** island. Annika Thor; translated by Linda Schenck. Delacorte Press, c2009. 256 p.: Steiner sisters quartet

Grades: 4 5 6 7   **Fic**
1. Second World War era (1939-1945) 2. Jewish children 3. Sisters 4. World War II 5. Children and war 6. Parent-separated children 7. Sweden 8. Historical fiction
ISBN 9780385905909

Mildred L. Batchelder Award, 2010.

In 1939 Sweden, two Jewish sisters wait in seperate foster homes for their parents to join them in fleeing the Nazis in Austria, but while eight-year-old Nellie settles in quickly, twelve-year-old Stephie feels stranded at the end of the world, with a foster mother who is as cold and unforgiving as the island on which they live.

"Children will readily empathize with Stephie's courage. Both sisters are well-drawn, likable characters. This is the first of four books Thor has written about the two girls." School Library Journal.

The **lily** pond. Annika Thor; translated from the Swedish by Linda Schenck. Delacorte Press, c2011. 256 p.: Steiner sisters quartet

Grades: 4 5 6 7 **Fic**
1. Second World War era (1939-1945) 2. Jewish girls 3. World War II 4. Children and war 5. Foster family 6. City life 7. Sweden 8. Historical fiction 9. Translations
ISBN 9780385908382

Having left Nazi-occupied Vienna a year ago, thirteen-year-old Jewish refugee Stephie Steiner adapts to life in the cultured Swedish city of Gothenburg, where she attends school, falls in love, and worries about her parents who were not allowed to emigrate.

Thornburgh, Blair

Ordinary girls. Blair Thornburgh. HarperTeen, 2019. 368 p.
Grades: 7 8 9 10 11 12 **Fic**
1. Sisters 2. Family problems 3. Mothers and daughters 4. Father-separated teenage girls 5. Single mothers 6. Philadelphia, Pennsylvania 7. Realistic fiction 8. Coming-of-age stories 9. Classics-inspired fiction
ISBN 9780062447814

A lighthearted contemporary retelling of Sense and Sensibility finds two sisters, complete opposites in temperament, who discover that the secrets they have been keeping make them more alike than they realized.

"A smart, character-driven contemporary novel with a timeless feel." School Library Journal.

Tingle, Tim

Danny Blackgoat, Navajo prisoner. Tim Tingle. 7th Generation, 2013. 160 p.: Danny Blackgoat

Grades: 6 7 8 **Fic**
1. 1860s 2. 19th century 3. Native American teenage boys 4. Prisoners 5. Navajo Indians 6. Indians of North America 7. Escapes 8. Fort Davis (Tex: Fort) 9. Historical fiction
ISBN 9781939053039

LC 2013013183

Danny Blackgoat, a sixteen-year-old Navajo, is labeled a troublemaker during the Long Walk of 1864 and sent to a prisoner outpost in Texas, where fellow captive Jim Davis saves him from a bully and starts him on the road to literacy—and freedom.

How I became a ghost: a Choctaw Trail of Tears story. Tim Tingle. RoadRunner Press, 2013. 141 p.: How I became a ghost

Grades: 4 5 6 7 **Fic**
1. 19th century 2. 1830s 3. Native American boys 4. Visions 5. Choctaw Indians -- Relocation 6. Ghosts 7. Boy ghosts 8. Historical fiction 9. Ghost stories
ISBN 9781937054533

Isaac, a Choctaw boy, tells of his tribe's removal from its homeland and how the exodus led him to become a ghost—one able to help those left behind.

When a ghost talks, listen: a Choctaw Trail of Tears story. Tim Tingle. RoadRunner Press, 2018 188 p.: How I became a ghost

Grades: 7 8 9 10 **Fic**
1. 1830s 2. 19th century 3. Native American boys 4. Visions 5. Choctaw Indians -- Relocation 6. Ghosts 7. Boy ghosts 8. Oklahoma 9. Washington, DC 10. Historical fiction 11. Ghost stories
ISBN 9781937054519

Ten-year-old Isaac, now a ghost, continues with his people as they walk the Choctaw Trail of Tears headed to Indian Territory in what will one day become Oklahoma. There have been surprises aplenty on their trek, but now Isaac and his three Choctaw comrades learn they can time travel—making for an unexpected adventure. The foursome heads back in time to Washington, D.C., to bear witness for Choctaw Chief Pushmataha who has come to the nation's capital at the invitation of Andrew Jackson. Provided by publisher.

Tolan, Stephanie S.

Surviving the Applewhites. by Stephanie S. Tolan. Harper Collins, 2002. 216 p.: Applewhites

Grades: 5 6 7 8 **Fic**
1. Thirteen-year-old boys 2. Families 3. Eccentrics and eccentricities 4. Home schooling 5. Theater 6. North Carolina 7. Realistic fiction
ISBN 0066236029

LC 2002001474

Jake, a budding juvenile delinquent, is sent for home schooling to the arty and eccentric Applewhite family's Creative Academy, where he discovers talents and interests he never knew he had.

"This is a thoroughly enjoyable book with humor, well-drawn characters, and a super cover." Voice of Youth Advocates.

Tolkien, J. R. R. (John Ronald Reuel), 1892-1973

The **hobbit,** or, there and back again. J. R. R. Tolkien. Ballantine, 1996, c1937. 306 p.: Lord of the rings

Grades: 5 6 7 8 9 10 11 12 Adult **Fic**
1. Adventurers 2. Quests 3. Dragons 4. Hobbits (Fictitious characters) 5. Wizards 6. Epic fantasy 7. Fantasy classics
ISBN 9780345339683

LC 77-8025

Bilbo Baggins, a respectable, well-to-do hobbit, lives comfortably in his hobbit-hole until the day the wandering wizard Gandalf chooses him to take part in an adventure from which he may never return.

The **lord** of the rings. J.R.R. Tolkien. Houghton Mifflin, 2004. xxv, 1157 p., 3 p. of plates

Grades: 7 8 9 10 11 12 Adult **Fic**
1. Dwarves (Fantasy characters) 2. Magic rings 3. Quests 4. Good and evil 5. Elves 6. Epic fantasy 7. Fantasy classics
ISBN 9780618517657

LC 2004275215

Presents the epic depicting the Great War of the Ring, a struggle between good and evil in Middle-earth, following the odyssey of Frodo the hobbit and his companions on a quest to destroy the Ring of Power.

Toro, Guillermo del, 1964-

Pan's labyrinth: the labyrinth of the faun. Guillermo del Toro and Cornelia Funke. Katherine Tegen Books, an imprint of HarperCollinsPublishers, 2019. 272 p.

Grades: 6 7 8 9 **Fic**
1. Second World War era (1939-1945) 2. 1940s 3. Imaginary

places 4. Fauns (Roman mythology) 5. Thirteen-year-old girls 6. Labyrinths 7. Fairies 8. Spain 9. Historical fantasy
ISBN 9780062414465

"Del Toro's Oscar-winning film Pan's Labyrinth is a natural pick for novelization, steeped as it is in books and storytelling. But perhaps novelization is too limiting a word, for Funke beautifully expands the story's mythologies and deftly transposes Del Toro's highly visual world to the page." Booklist.

Towell, Katy

Skary childrin and the carousel of sorrow. by Katy Towell. Alfred A. Knopf, 2011. 272 p.

Grades: 4 5 6 7   **Fic**
1. Merry-go-round 2. Girl misfits 3. Missing persons 4. Supernatural 5. Schools
ISBN 9780375868597

In Widowsbury, an isolated village where people believe "known is good, new is bad," three outcasts from the girls' school join forces with a home-schooled boy to uncover and combat the evil that is making people disappear.

"Towell tucks violent tempests, maggoty slime, hideous transformations, nightmares, sudden terrors and like atmosphere-building elements into a rousingly melodramatic literary debut." Kirkus.

Townley, Rod

The **blue** shoe: a tale of thievery, villainy, sorcery, and shoes. by Roderick Townley; illustrated by Mary GrandPre. Alfred A. Knopf, 2009. 272 p.

Grades: 4 5 6 7   **Fic**
1. Apprentices 2. Shoes 3. Mines and mineral resources 4. Shoemakers 5. Stealing 6. Fantasy fiction 7. Illustrated books
ISBN 9780375956003

                                    LC 2008043851
A mysterious stranger commissions a single, valuable shoe from a humble cobbler, changing the cobbler's life and the life of his young apprentice forever.

"This is a fun, whimsical fairy tale. . . . The good-versus-evil plotline, dynamic cast of characters, . . . light romance between Hap and Sophia, and copious amounts of magic and intrigue will be a hit with a wide range of readers." Booklist.

Trebincevic, Kenan, 1980-

World in between: based on a true refugee story. Kenan Trebincevic, Susan Shapiro Houghton Mifflin Harcourt 2021. 256 p.

Grades: 5 6 7 8   **Fic**
1. Trebincevic, Kenan, 1980- 2. Immigration and emigration 3. Child refugees 4. Children and war 5. Hope 6. Refugees 7. Bosnia and Hercegovina 8. Autobiographical fiction 9. Realistic fiction
ISBN 9780358439875

Based on a true refugee story, this moving novel follows Kenan and his family as they make it out of war-torn Bosnia alive, which is only the beginning of their journey.

"Highly recommended for its emotional and historical perspectives, this is an insightful starting point for understanding one family's refugee experience, as well as the complexities of the Bosnian War." Booklist

Trevayne, Emma

The **accidental** afterlife of Thomas Marsden. Emma Trevayne. Simon & Schuster Books for Young Readers, 2015. 224 p.

Grades: 5 6 7 8   **Fic**
1. Victorian era (1837-1901) 2. Grave robbing 3. Fairies 4. Identity (Psychology) 5. Changelings 6. Magic 7. London, England 8. Great Britain 9. Historical fantasy
ISBN 9781442498822

                                    LC 2014032574
At age twelve, grave robber Thomas Marsden discovers a boy who looks just like him in an unmarked grave and begins a journey of discovery as he learns of faeries trapped in London and their hope that he can return them to their realm.

"Full of hidden messages, midnight graveyard escapades, unlikely friendships, magic, and deceit, it's an engaging tale of one boy's efforts to find himself and his way back home." Publishers Weekly.

Tripp, Ben, 1966-

The **accidental** highwayman: being the tale of Kit Bristol, his horse Midnight, a mysterious princess, and sundry magical persons besides. Ben Tripp. Tor Teen, 2014. 304 p.: Accidental highwayman trilogy

Grades: 7 8 9 10   **Fic**
1. 18th century 2. Teenage boy orphans 3. Princesses 4. Voyages and travels 5. Fairies 6. Teenage boys 7. England 8. Ireland 9. Historical fantasy 10. Illustrated books
ISBN 9780765335494

Donning his wounded master's riding cloak to seek help in 18th-century England, young Kit Bristol is mistaken as an outlaw and catapulted into a world of magic, imperiled princesses and dark omens.

"Readers will root for star-crossed lovers, Kit and Morgana, and delight in their 'opposites attract' romance, drawn onward by a rollicking plot . . . Fantasy readers, especially fans of Cathrynne Valente's work, will enjoy the author's elegant turns of phrase. A first purchase for all fantasy collections." School Library Journal.

Trueman, Terry

Inside out. Terry Trueman. Harper Tempest, c2003. 117 p.

Grades: 7 8 9 10   **Fic**
1. People with schizophrenia 2. Hostages 3. Robbery 4. Children of unemployed parents 5. Children of people with cancer 6. Thrillers and suspense 7. Realistic fiction
ISBN 0066239621

                                    LC 2002151604
A sixteen-year-old with schizophrenia is caught up in the events surrounding an attempted robbery by two other teens who eventually hold him hostage.

"Trueman sometimes captures moments of heartbreaking truth, and his swift, suspenseful plot will have particular appeal to reluctant readers." Booklist.

Stuck in neutral. Terry Trueman. Harper Collins Publishers, c2000. ix, 114 p.

Grades: 7 8 9 10   **Fic**
1. Father-separated teenage boys 2. Teenage boys with disabilities 3. Euthanasia 4. Gifted teenagers 5. Dilemmas 6. Seattle, Washington 7. Realistic fiction
ISBN 0060285192

                                    LC 99037098
Fourteen-year-old Shawn McDaniel, who suffers from severe cerebral palsy and cannot function, relates his perceptions of his life, his family, and his condition, especially as he believes his father is planning to kill him.

"Trueman has created a compelling novel that poses questions about ability and existence while fostering sympathy for people with severe physical limitations." Bulletin of the Center for Children's Books.

Tucholke, April Genevieve

The **Boneless** Mercies. April Genevieve Tucholke. Farrar Straus Giroux, 2018. 352 p.

Grades: 7 8 9 10 11 12 **Fic**
1. Women warriors 2. Monsters 3. Mercenaries 4. Voyages and travels 5. Ambition in women 6. High fantasy 7. Mythological fiction
ISBN 9780374307066

LC 2018003350

Four female mercenaries known as Boneless Mercies, weary of roaming Vorseland, ignored and forgotten until they are needed for mercy killings, decide to seek glory by going after a legendary monster in this reimagining of Beowulf.

"Frey's earnest narrative voice creates a strong sense of the center of this fantasy: female solidarity. Bodily closeness, a shared quest for justice, and sheer joy in physical capacity are only part of it: collaboration and attentive respect are the true underpinning of Tucholke's creation." Horn Book

Seven endless forests. April Genevieve Tucholke. Farrar, Straus & Giroux, 2020 330 p.

Grades: 8 9 10 11 12 **Fic**
1. Sisters 2. Kidnapping 3. Rescues 4. Imaginary creatures 5. Quests 6. Arthurian fantasy 7. High fantasy 8. Fantasy fiction
ISBN 9780374307097

A fierce and lyrical retelling of the King Arthur legend. On the heels of a devastating plague, Torvi's sister Morgunn is stolen from the family farm by Uther, a flame-loving wolf-priest who leads a pack of ragged, starving girls. Torvi leaves the only home she's ever known and joins a shaven-headed druid and a band of roaming Elsh artists known as the Butcher Bards. They set out on a quest to rescue Torvi's sister, and find a mythical sword. On their travels, Torvi and her companions will face wild, dangerous magic that leads to love, joy, tragedy, and death...

"References to the Arthur legend loosely make their way into the narrative—a sword lodged in a stone tree, Mort Darthur River, a wizard who unlocks the path to Avalon—but even readers without an intimate knowledge of the legend will fall beneath Tucholke's spell. A lovely tale of quests and camaraderie." Booklist

Tucker, Laura, 1973-

All the Greys on Greene Street. Laura Tucker. Viking Books for Young Readers, 2019 320 p.

Grades: 5 6 7 8 **Fic**
1. 1980s 2. Girl artists 3. Missing men 4. Family problems 5. Runaway wives, husbands, etc 6. Secrets 7. SoHo, New York City 8. New York City 9. Historical fiction 10. Mysteries 11. Illustrated books
ISBN 9780451479532

A 12-year-old artist in 1981 SoHo searches for answers when her father, a restorer of antique paintings, abruptly disappears in the middle of the night amid questions about a partner's suspicious behavior and a missing work or art.— Atlas Publishing.

"Tucker skillfully balances themes of mental illness, friendship, and creativity under tough circumstances in her memorable debut. The vibrant, eccentric characters are authentic, the early-1980s SoHo setting is clearly wrought (rich with descriptive details such as fad diets and artist-in-residence lofts), and the Konigsburg-tinged art mystery satisfies." Publishers Weekly.

Turnage, Sheila

★ The **ghosts** of Tupelo Landing. by Sheila Turnage. Kathy Dawson Books, an imprint of Penguin Group (USA) Inc., 2014. 256 p.: Tupelo Landing

Grades: 5 6 7 8 **Fic**
1. Hotels 2. Haunted places 3. Small town life 4. Ghosts 5. Communities 6. North Carolina 7. Mysteries
ISBN 9780803736719

LC 2013019376

After her teacher offers extra credit to the student who can interview the oldest citizen of Tupelo Landing, North Carolina, budding detective Mo LoBeau and her best friend Dale decide to one-up the competition and interview the ghost that haunts the Tupelo Inn.

The **odds** of getting even. by Sheila Turnage. Kathy Dawson Books, an imprint of Penguin Group (USA) Inc., [2015] 352 p.: Tupelo Landing

Grades: 5 6 7 8 **Fic**
1. Child detectives 2. Fathers 3. Small town life 4. Crime 5. Best friends 6. North Carolina 7. Mysteries
ISBN 9780803739611

LC 2015008293

Desperado Detectives—aka Mo Lo Beau and her best friend Dale, along with newly-appointed intern, Harm Crenshaw—must take on a new case when Dale's daddy goes on the lam just before his trial is about to start. Provided by publisher.

"The author gracefully weaves a laundry list of characters with a plot that has a lot of moving pieces, and she does it with charm and humor, hitting the sweet spot for young readers searching for more-complex tales but not ready to leave the silly behind." Kirkus.

★ **Three** times lucky. by Sheila Turnage. Dial Books for Young Readers, 2012. 256 p.: Tupelo Landing

Grades: 5 6 7 8 **Fic**
1. Abandoned girls 2. Small town life 3. Restaurants 4. Murder 5. Murder suspects 6. North Carolina 7. Mysteries
ISBN 9780803736702

Washed ashore as a baby in tiny Tupelo Landing, North Carolina, Mo LoBeau, now eleven, and her best friend Dale turn detective when the amnesiac Colonel, owner of a cafe and co-parent of Mo with his cook, Miss Lana, seems implicated in a murder.

Turner, Megan Whalen

A **conspiracy** of kings. by Megan Whalen. Greenwillow Books, c2010. 316 p.: Queen's thief

Grades: 7 8 9 10 **Fic**
1. Princes 2. Kidnapping victims 3. Slavery 4. Power (Social sciences) 5. Rulers 6. High fantasy 7. Fantasy fiction
ISBN 9780061870934

LC 2009023052

Kidnapped and sold into slavery, Sophos, an unwilling prince, tries to save his country from being destroyed by rebellion and exploited by the conniving Mede empire.

"Given the complexity of Turner's plot, readers should reread the first three books before beginning this one, which derives its power from the intricate construction of Turner's imagined world, a realm in which her founding mythology is as impressive as her descriptions of the land itself. . . . Strong evidence emerges that the story doesn't end here, and fans will savor this while they wait for more." Publishers Weekly.

The **king** of Attolia. Megan Whalen Turner. Greenwillow Books, c2006. 387 p.: Queen's thief

Grades: 7 8 9 10   **Fic**
1. Guards 2. Rulers 3. Attempted assassination 4. Soldiers 5.
Eugenides 6. High fantasy 7. Fantasy fiction
ISBN 006083577X

LC 2005040303

Eugenides, still known as a Thief of Eddis, faces palace intrigue and
assassins as he strives to prove himself both to the people of Attolia and
to his new bride, their queen.

"Fans who've been waiting . . . for the sequel to The Queen of Attolia (2000) and The Thief (1996. . .) can finally rejoice. . . . To appreciate
the amazingly charismatic and beguiling character of Eugenides fully,
its best to read the titles in order." School Library Journal.

The **queen** of Attolia. Megan Whalen Turner. Greenwillow
Books, c2000. 279 p.: Queen's thief
Grades: 6 7 8 9   **Fic**
1. Thieves 2. Women rulers 3. Amputation 4. Eugenides
(Fictitious character) 5. Prisoners 6. High fantasy 7. Fantasy
fiction
ISBN 068817423X

LC 99026916

Forsaken by the gods and left to his own devices, Eugenides, Royal
Thief of Eddis, summons all his wit and wiles in an attempt to conquer
the rival Queen of Attolia.

"The intense read is thoroughly involving and wholly satisfying on
all fronts." Horn Book.

Return of the thief. Megan Whalen Turner. Greenwillow
Books, an imprint of HarperCollins Publishers, 2020. 352 p.:
Queen's thief
Grades: 9 10 11 12   **Fic**
1. Rulers 2. Prophecies 3. Imaginary wars and battles 4.
Imaginary kingdoms 5. Attolia (Imaginary place) 6. High fantasy
7. Fantasy fiction
ISBN 9780062874474

A conclusion to the best-selling series finds high king Eugenides preparing to defend the Lesser Peninsula from an invasion by the ruthless
Mede empire, an effort that is complicated by a prophecy that foretells
a king's death.

Thick as thieves: a Queen's thief novel. Megan Whalen
Turner. Greenwillow Books, an imprint of HarperCollins Publishers, [2017] 400 p.: Queen's thief
Grades: 7 8 9 10 11 12   **Fic**
1. Enslaved people 2. Soldiers 3. Kidnapping victims 4. Rulers
5. Imaginary kingdoms 6. High fantasy 7. Fantasy fiction
ISBN 9780062568243

LC 2016047028

Kamet, a secretary and slave to his Mede master, has the ambition
and the means to become one of the most powerful people in the Empire. But with a whispered warning the future he envisioned is wrenched
away, and he is forced onto a very different path. Provided by publisher.

"This series fifth can stand alone without reading the rest of the
books. . . . This invites an older audience, but . . . offer[s] more teen
appeal than the political drama of earlier Queen's Thief novels." Kirkus.

The **thief**. Megan Whalen Turner. Greenwillow Books,
c1996. 219 p.: Queen's thief
Grades: 7 8 9 10   **Fic**
1. Thieves 2. Gems 3. Stealing 4. Prisoners 5. Quests 6. High

fantasy 7. Fantasy fiction
ISBN 0688146279

LC 95-41040

Gen flaunts his ingenuity as a thief and relishes the adventure which
takes him to a remote temple of the gods where he will attempt to steal
a precious stone.

"A tantalizing, suspenseful, exceptionally clever novel. . . . The author's characterization of Gen is simply superb." Horn Book.

Turtschaninoff, Maria, 1977-
Maresi. Maria Turtschaninoff. Amulet Books,, 2017. 256 p.:
Red Abbey chronicles
Grades: 8 9 10 11   **Fic**
1. Abbeys 2. Revenge 3. Sexism 4. Novitiate 5. Kinship-
based society 6. Historical fantasy 7. Coming-of-age stories 8.
Translations
ISBN 9781419722691

"Utterly satisfying and completely different from standard YA fantasy, this Finnish import seems primed to win over American readers."
Booklist.

Twain, Mark, 1835-1910
★ The **adventures** of Tom Sawyer. Mark Twain; illustrated
by Scott McKowen. Sterling Pub., 2004, c1875. vii, 224 p.
Grades: 5 6 7 8   **Fic**
1. 19th century 2. Small town life -- History 19th century 3. Boy
adventurers 4. Mischief in boys 5. Personal conduct 6. Boys 7.
Mississippi River 8. Missouri 9. Adventure stories 10. Humorous
stories 11. Classics
ISBN 1402714602

LC 2004016066

The adventures and pranks of a mischievous boy growing up in a
19th-century Mississippi River town as he plays hooky on an island,
witnesses a crime, hunts for pirate's treasure, and becomes lost in a cave.

The **prince** and the pauper: a tale for young people of all
ages. by Mark Twain; illustrated by W. Hatherall. Harper &
Brothers, c1881. x, 309 p., 26 leaves of plates
Grades: 5 6 7 8 9 10 11 12 Adult   **Fic**
1. Edward VI, King of England, 1537-1553 2. Tudor period (1485-
1603) 3. Role reversal 4. Mistaken identity 5. Impostors 6. Poor
children 7. Princes 8. London, England 9. Great Britain 10.
Historical fiction 11. Adventure stories
ISBN 9780241378496

LC 95227373

Two boys who look alike, one of them poor, the other heir to the
English throne, decide to switch places. When young Edward VI and the
poor boy exchange places, each learns something about the other's very
different station in life.

Uchida, Yoshiko
The **best** bad thing. Yoshiko Uchida. Atheneum, 1983. 120 p.
Grades: 5 6 7 8   **Fic**
1. Tsujimura, Rinko (Fictitious character) 2. Japanese American
girls 3. Japanese Americans 4. Poverty
ISBN 9780689502903

LC 83002833

At first dismayed at having to spend the last month of her summer
vacation helping out in the household of recently widowed Mrs. Hata.
Rinko discovers there are pleasant surprises for her, but then bad things
start to happen.

★ A **jar** of dreams. Yoshiko Uchida. Atheneum, 1981. 131 p.
Grades: 5 6 7 8   **Fic**
  1. 1930s 2. Racism 3. Ethnic identity 4. Eleven-year-old girls
5. Tsujimura, Rinko (Fictitious character) 6. Japanese American
families 7. California
ISBN 9780689502101

LC   81003480

A young girl grows up in a closely-knit Japanese American family in
California during a time of great prejudice.

"Rinko in her guilelessness is genuine and refreshing, and her
worries and concerns seem wholly natural, honest, and convincing."
Horn Book.

Uehashi, Nahoko

Moribito: Guardian of the Spirit. Nahoko Uehashi; trans-
lated by Cathy Hirano; illustrated by Yuko Shimizu. Arthur A.
Levine Books, 2008. 248 p.: Moribito
Grades: 6 7 8 9   **Fic**
  1. Heroes and heroines 2. Bodyguards 3. Spirit possession 4.
Young women 5. Princes 6. Japan 7. Fantasy fiction 8. Asian-
influenced fantasy
ISBN 9780545005425

LC 2007036383

Mildred L. Batchelder Award, 2009.

The wandering warrior Balsa is hired to protect Prince Chagum from
both a mysterious monster and the prince's father, the Mikado.

"This book is first in a series of ten that have garnered literary and
popular success in Japan. . . . Balsa and Chagum's story is brought to
America with a strong translation. . . . Readers who are fans of action
manga, especially with strong female characters, will enjoy the ninja-
like fighting scenes. . . . The exciting premise, combined with an attractive cover, should insure that this title will circulate well." Voice of
Youth Advocates.

Moribito II: guardian of the darkness. Nahoko Uehashi;
translated by Cathy Hirano; illustrated by Yuko Shimizu. Arthur
A. Levine Books, 2009. 245 p.: Moribito
Grades: 6 7 8 9   **Fic**
  1. Girl warriors 2. Conspiracies 3. Teenage girls 4. Heroes and
heroines 5. Young women 6. Japan 7. Fantasy fiction 8. Asian-
influenced fantasy
ISBN 9780545102957

LC 2008037444

The wandering female bodyguard Balsa returns to her native country of Kanbal, where she uncovers a conspiracy to frame her mentor
and herself.

"Once again, Uehashi immerses readers in the culture, traditions, mythology—even diet—of the populace, creating a full, captivating world. . . . This growing series has something for everyone."
Publishers Weekly.

Umminger, Alison

American girls. Alison Umminger. Flatiron Books, 2016.
304 p.
Grades: 8 9 10 11   **Fic**
  1. Runaway teenage girls 2. Film industry and trade 3. Sisters
4. Teenage romance 5. Fifteen-year-old girls 6. Los Angeles,
California 7. Realistic fiction 8. Coming-of-age stories
ISBN 9781250075000

Fifteen-year-old Anna runs away to Los Angeles where her half-
sister takes her in, but after spending days on television and movie sets,
she learns LA is not the glamorous escape she imagined.

"An insightful, original take on the coming-of-age story, this novel
plumbs the depths of American culture to arrive at a poignant emotional
truth." Kirkus.

Unsworth, Tania

The **one** safe place: a novel. by Tania Unsworth. Algonquin
Young Readers, 2014. 224 p.
Grades: 6 7 8 9 10   **Fic**
  1. Near future 2. Abandoned children 3. Dystopias 4. Orphans 5.
Survival 6. Science fiction
ISBN 9781616203290

LC 2013043145

In a near future world of heat, greed, and hunger, Devin earns a
coveted spot in a home for abandoned children that promises unlimited
food and toys and the hope of finding a new family, but Devin discovers
the home's horrific true mission when he investigates its intimidating
Administrator and the zombie-like sickness that afflicts some children.

"Orphaned twelve-year-old Devin is invited to live at the paradisa-
ical Home for Childhood, but something terrifying is happening to the
children there. Devin's synesthesia, which makes him interesting to the
Home's sinister Administrator, may provide the key to their escape. Set
in a world of post climate change desperation, Unsworth's story thoughtfully explores the theme of adults' nostalgia for childhood." Horn Book.

Urban, Linda

The **center** of everything. Linda Urban. Harcourt, c2013.
197 p.
Grades: 4 5 6 7   **Fic**
  1. Grief in girls 2. Loss (Psychology) 3. Parades 4. Grief 5.
Grandmothers -- Death 6. New Hampshire 7. Realistic fiction
ISBN 9780547763484

Twelve-year-old Ruby finds her life spinning out of control in the
wake of questionable choices and dreads an upcoming reading of her
award-wining essay.

Ursu, Anne

★ **Breadcrumbs**. Anne Ursu; drawings by Erin McGuire.
Walden Pond Press, c2011. 304 p.
Grades: 4 5 6 7   **Fic**
  1. Adopted girls 2. Magic mirrors 3. Forests 4. Women rulers 5.
Rescues 6. Minnesota 7. Fantasy fiction 8. Fairy tale and folklore-
inspired fiction 9. Coming-of-age stories
ISBN 9780062015051

LC 2010045666

Hazel and Jack are best friends until an accident with a magical mirror and a run-in with a villainous queen find Hazel on her own, entering
an enchanted wood in the hopes of saving Jack's life.

"Fifth-grader Hazel embarks on a memorable journey into the Minnesota woods to find her best friend Jack, who vanishes after a shard
of glass pierces his eye. . . . Hazel enters the woods to find an entirely
different place, populated by creatures from the pages of Hans Christian
Andersen. . . . [This is a] multi-layered, artfully crafted, transforming
testament to the power of friendship." Kirkus.

Vail, Rachel

Well, that was awkward. Rachel Vail. Viking, 2017 288 p.
Grades: 5 6 7 8   **Fic**
  1. Crushes (Interpersonal relations) 2. Boy/girl relations 3. Best
friends 4. Text messaging 5. Identity (Psychology) 6. New York
City 7. Realistic fiction 8. Classics-inspired fiction
ISBN 9780670013081

Setting aside her crush on a boy who prefers her best friend, Gracie plays Cyrano de Bergerac to help her friend write clever texts to the boy, whose equally witty replies suggest that he may be getting assistance with his own romantic communiques.

"Hilarious and heartfelt." Kirkus.

Valente, Catherynne M., 1979-

The **boy** who lost Fairyland. Catherynne M. Valente; illustrated by Ana Juan. Feiwel & Friends, 2015. 256 p.: Fairyland series (Catherynne M. Valente)

Grades: 5 6 7 8   **Fic**
1. Trolls 2. Changelings 3. Parallel universes 4. Imaginary kingdoms 5. Winds 6. Chicago, Illinois 7. Fantasy fiction 8. Gateway fantasy
ISBN 9781250023490

LC 2014042417

Stolen by the Golden Wind from Fairyland and rendered a changeling in the human world, young troll Hawthorn struggles with his troll nature before stumbling upon a way back home, where he confronts power-hungry fairies that have imposed an Endless Summer.

"In this fourth book in the fantastical series, a young troll named Hawthorn is stolen away by the Golden Wind and brought to live in Chicago as a changeling. When he turns 12, he finds a way back to Fairyland, a place now much changed from the magical realm he left...While readers unfamiliar with the series can certainly jump in with this novel, most will want to start at the beginning. A phenomenal fantasy series worthy of a spot in every library collection." School Library Journal.

★ The **girl** who circumnavigated Fairyland in a ship of her own making. Catherynne Valente. Feiwel and Friends, 2011, c2009. 256 p.: Fairyland series (Catherynne M. Valente)

Grades: 4 5 6 7 8   **Fic**
1. Talismans 2. Marquis and marchionesses 3. Quests 4. Imaginary kingdoms 5. Parallel universes 6. Fantasy fiction 7. Gateway fantasy
ISBN 9780312649616

LC 2010050895

Twelve-year-old September's ordinary life in Omaha turns to adventure when a Green Wind takes her to Fairyland to retrieve a talisman the new and fickle Marquess wants from the enchanted woods.

"The book's appeal is crystal clear from the outset: this is a kind of The Wonderful Wizard of Oz by way of Alice's Adventures in Wonderland, made vivid by Juan's Tenniel-inflected illustrations. . . . Those who thrill to lovingly wrought tales of fantasy and adventure . . . will be enchanted." Publishers Weekly.

The **girl** who fell beneath Fairyland and led the revels there. Catherynne M. Valente, Ana Juan. Feiwel & Friends 2012 256 p.: Fairyland series (Catherynne M. Valente)

Grades: 4 5 6 7 8   **Fic**
1. Quests 2. Voyages and travels 3. Shadows 4. Teenage girls 5. Rulers 6. Fantasy fiction 7. Gateway fantasy
ISBN 9780312649623

After returning to Fairyland, September discovers that her stolen shadow has become the Hollow Queen, the new ruler of Fairyland Below, who is stealing the magic and shadows from Fairyland folk and refusing to give them back.

The **girl** who soared over Fairyland and cut the moon in two. by Catherynne M. Valente; with illustrations by Ana Juan. Feiwel and Friends, 2013. 248 p.: Fairyland series (Catherynne M. Valente)

Grades: 4 5 6 7 8   **Fic**
1. Imaginary kingdoms 2. Adventure 3. Yeti 4. Teenage girls 5. Moon 6. Fantasy fiction 7. Gateway fantasy
ISBN 9781250023506

LC bl2013040330

Longing for a new adventure that will reunite her with Ell, the Wyverary, and Saturday, September is spirited away to the moon and charged with saving Fairyland from a moon-Yeti who wields mysterious powers.

"In this third volume, following The Girl Who Fell Beneath Fairyland and Led the Revels There, September returns to Fairyland and finds herself on a mission to stop a vengeful yeti from destroying his Fairy abusers—and everyone else on the moon. September is now wiser and sadder, and longs for autonomy; likewise, Fairyland and its inhabitants have become darker and more adult." Horn Book.

The **Glass** Town game. Catherynne M. Valente; illustrated by Rebecca Green. Margaret K. McElderry Books, 2017. 535 p.

Grades: 4 5 6 7 8   **Fic**
1. Bronte, Charlotte, 1816-1855 2. Bronte, Emily, 1818-1848 3. Bronte, Patrick Branwell, 1817-1848. 4. Bronte, Anne, 1820-1849 5. Bronte family 6. 1820s 7. Toy soldiers 8. Brothers and sisters 9. Loss (Psychology) 10. Kidnapping 11. Imagination 12. England 13. Haworth, England 14. Gateway fantasy 15. Historical fantasy
ISBN 9781481476966

Whisked away to a magical historical land of their own invention as they are about to depart for boarding school, sisters Charlotte and Emily Bronte find themselves fighting Napoleon to obtain a potion that raises the dead, a situation that is complicated by the abduction of their siblings.

"A lovely, fanciful piece of middle-grade fiction about the worlds we make, and the lives they can take on." Booklist.

Van Draanen, Wendelin

The **running** dream. Wendelin Van Draanen. Alfred A. Knopf, 2011. 256 p.

Grades: 7 8 9 10 11 12   **Fic**
1. Teenage girls who have had amputations 2. Teenage girl athletes 3. Running 4. Prosthesis 5. Traffic accident injuries 6. Realistic fiction
ISBN 9780375966675

LC 2010007072

Schneider Family Book Award for Teens, 2012.

When a school bus accident leaves sixteen-year-old Jessica an amputee, she returns to school with a prosthetic limb and her track team finds a wonderful way to help rekindle her dream of running again.

"It's a classic problem novel in a lot of ways. . . . Overall, though, this is a tremendously upbeat book. . . . Van Draanen's extensive research into both running and amputees pays dividends." Booklist.

★ **Sammy** Keyes and the hotel thief. by Wendelin Van Draanen. A. A. Knopf, c1998. 168 p.: Sammy Keyes mysteries

Grades: 4 5 6 7   **Fic**
1. Teenage girl detectives 2. Robbery 3. Witnesses 4. Teenage girls 5. Keyes, Sammy (Fictitious character) 6. Mysteries
ISBN 067988839X

LC 97-40776

Seventh grader Sammy's penchant for speaking her mind gets her in trouble when she involves herself in the investigation of a robbery at the "seedy" hotel across the street from the seniors' building where she is living with her grandmother.

"This is a breezy novel with vivid characters." Bulletin of the Center for Children's Books.

Van Vleet, Carmella

Eliza Bing is (not) a big, fat quitter. Carmella Van Vleet. Holiday House, [2014] 165 p.

Grades: 3 4 5 6 7 **Fic**
1. Children with ADHD 2. Determination in girls 3. Martial arts for children 4. Tae kwon do 5. Eleven-year-old girls 6. Realistic fiction
ISBN 9780823429448

LC 2013015279

After learning she cannot take a cake decorating class with her best friend, partly because her parents consider her a quitter, eleven-year-old Eliza tries to prove herself by sticking with a taekwondo class all summer.

"Fast moving and humorous with chapter titles such as 'Sticky Note to Self: Wear White Underwear on Wednesdays and Saturdays,' feisty Eliza will have readers, especially those with ADHD, rooting for her." School Library Journal.

Van de Ruit, John

Spud. John van de Ruit. Razorbill, 2007. 352 p.

Grades: 6 7 8 9 10 **Fic**
1. Thirteen-year-old boys 2. Boarding schools 3. Schools 4. Choirboys 5. Families 6. South Africa 7. Diary novels 8. Humorous stories 9. Realistic fiction
ISBN 9781595141705

LC 2007006065

In 1990, thirteen-year-old John "Spud" Milton, a prepubescent choirboy, keeps a diary of his first year at an elite, boys-only boarding school in South Africa, as he deals with bizarre housemates, wild crushes, embarrassingly dysfunctional parents, and much more.

"This raucous autobiographical novel about a scholarship boy in an elite boys' boarding school in 1990 is mainly farce but also part coming-of-age tale." Booklist.

Vance, Alexander P. (Alexander Phillip), 1978-

The **Heartbreak** Messenger. Alexander Vance. Feiwel and Friends, 2013. 283 p.

Grades: 6 7 8 **Fic**
1. Breaking up (Interpersonal relations) 2. Children of single parents 3. Couriers 4. Single-parent families 5. Seventh-grade boys 6. Realistic fiction
ISBN 9781250029690

When doing a favor for a friend leads him to begin a service that allows his classmates to gently break up with each other by proxy, Quentin enjoys unexpected initial success before becoming discouraged by the constant exposure to broken hearts.

Vande Velde, Vivian

All Hallows' Eve: 13 stories. Vivian Vande Velde. Harcourt, 2006. 225 p.

Grades: 7 8 9 10 **Fic**
1. Halloween 2. Vampires 3. Practical jokes 4. Ghosts 5. Supernatural 6. Horror 7. Short stories
ISBN 0152055762

LC 2006005439

Presents thirteen tales of Halloween horrors, including ghosts, vampires, and pranks gone awry.

"This mistress of the macabre draws readers in with her familiar conversational tone and easily recognizable situations . . . before skillfully shifting the narratives in unsettling, sometimes terrifying, directions. . . . Vande Velde's narrative tricks are a treat." Horn Book.

Being dead: stories. Vivian Vande Velde. Harcourt, 2001. 203 p.

Grades: 7 8 9 10 **Fic**
1. Teenagers and death 2. Death 3. Ghosts 4. Dead 5. Supernatural 6. Horror 7. Short stories
ISBN 0152163204

LC 00012996

Seven supernatural stories, all having something to do with death.

"Often humorous and sometimes evoking sympathy, this anthology will be enjoyed by lovers of mild horror as well as by those who like clever short stories." Voice of Youth Advocates.

The **book** of Mordred. by Vivian Vande Velde; [illustrations by Justin Gerard]. Houghton Mifflin, 2005. 342 p.

Grades: 8 9 10 11 12 **Fic**
1. Arthur, King 2. Medieval period (476-1492) 3. Knights and knighthood 4. Wizards 5. Camelot (Legendary place) 6. Kidnapping 7. Mordred (Legendary character) 8. Great Britain 9. Historical fantasy 10. Arthurian fantasy
ISBN 061850754X

LC 2004028223

As the peaceful King Arthur reigns, the five-year-old daughter of Lady Alayna, newly widowed of the village-wizard Toland, is abducted by knights who leave their barn burning and their only servant dead.

"All of the characters are well developed and have a strong presence throughout. . . . [This] provides an intriguing counterpoint to anyone who is interested in Arthurian legend." School Library Journal.

Cloaked in red. by Vivian Vande Velde. Marshall Cavendish Children, 2010. 128 p.

Grades: 7 8 9 10 **Fic**
1. Wolves 2. Grandmothers 3. Lumber workers 4. Little Red Riding Hood (Fictitious character) 5. Deception 6. Humorous stories 7. Short stories 8. Fairy tale and folklore-inspired fiction
ISBN 9780761457930

LC 2009051753

Presents eight twists on the traditional tale of Little Red Riding Hood, exploring such issues as why most characters seem dim-witted and what, exactly, is the theme.

"The stories blend wry contemporary commentary with fractured-fairy-tale elements, horror, and a subtle bit of sensuality. . . . The wacky tales can easily be used to inspire teens to make up versions of their own." Booklist.

Frogged. Vivian Vande Velde. Harcourt Children's Books, Houghton Mifflin Harcourt, 2013 208 p.

Grades: 5 6 7 8 **Fic**
1. Princesses 2. Transformations (Magic) 3. Self-perception 4. Spells (Magic) 5. Frogs 6. Fantasy fiction 7. Fairy tale and folklore-inspired fiction
ISBN 9780547942155

When almost-thirteen-year-old Princess Imogene is turned into a frog, she puts into practice lessons from the book, The Art of Being a Princess, as she tries to become her less-than-perfect self again.

Heir apparent. Vivian Vande Velde. Harcourt, 2002. 315 p.: Rasmussem Corporation

Grades: 6 7 8 9 **Fic**
1. Determination in teenage girls 2. Virtual reality games 3. Protests, demonstrations, vigils, etc 4. Censorship 5. Role playing

games 6. Science fiction
ISBN 0152045600

LC 2002002441

While playing a total immersion virtual reality game of kings and intrigue, fourteen-year-old Giannine learns that demonstrators have damaged the equipment to which she is connected, and she must win the game quickly or be damaged herself.

"This adventure includes a cast of intriguing characters and personalities. The feisty heroine has a funny, sarcastic sense of humor and succeeds because of her ingenuity and determination." School Library Journal.

Tales from the Brothers Grimm and the Sisters Weird. Vivian Vande Velde. Harcourt Brace, c1995. 128 p.

Grades: 7 8 9 10   **Fic**
1. Transformations (Magic) 2. Magic 3. Fractured fairy tales and folklore
ISBN 0152002200

LC 94026341 /AC

Presents thirteen twisted versions of such familiar fairy tales as Red Riding Hood, Jack and the Beanstalk, Hansel and Gretel, and The Three Billy Goats Gruff.

"Vande Velde challenges readers' notions of good, bad, and ugly. . . . Modern references and sensibilities . . . add to the humor (often the gallows variety). Entertaining and provocative, these selections make good read-alouds and can be used to spark discussion or creative writing exercises." School Library Journal.

Vanderpool, Clare

★ **Moon** over Manifest. Clare Vanderpool. Delacorte Press, c2010. 351 p.

Grades: 5 6 7 8   **Fic**
1. Depression era (1929-1941) 2. 1930s 3. Father-separated girls 4. Communities 5. Depressions 1929-1941 6. Fathers 7. Railroad workers 8. Kansas 9. Historical fiction
ISBN 9780385738835
Newbery Medal, 2011.

Jumping off a train in Kansas to learn more about her father's exciting past, Abilene Tucker is initially disappointed by the run-down Depression town she encounters before finding a hidden box of mementos and letters that mention a spy who played an important role in the town's secret history.

"The absolute necessity of story as a way to redemption and healing past wounds is at the heart of this beautiful debut, and readers will cherish every word up to the heartbreaking yet hopeful and deeply gratifying ending." Kirkus.

Vanhee, Jason

Engines of the broken world. Jason Vanhee. Henry Holt and Company, 2013. 262 p.

Grades: 8 9 10 11 12   **Fic**
1. End of the world 2. Undead 3. Shapeshifters 4. Brothers and sisters 5. Supernatural 6. Horror
ISBN 9780805096293

LC 2013026768

In a rural village far distant from the dead and dying cities, twelve-year-old Merciful discovers horrible secrets and must make decisions that may save or doom her world.

"Unlike most action-packed dystopias, the story's slower pace . . . allows readers to feel the fog encroaching on Merciful and Gospel's rustic home, and hear every scratch of their dead mother's awkward movements upon the cellar stairs." Booklist.

Vaughn, Carrie

Steel. Carrie Vaughn. HarperTeen, 2011. 304 p.

Grades: 7 8 9 10   **Fic**
1. 18th century 2. Fencers 3. Pirate ships 4. Time travel (Past) 5. Pirates 6. Fencing 7. Caribbean Area 8. Fantasy fiction
ISBN 9780061547911

When Jill, a competitive high school fencer, goes with her family on vacation to the Bahamas, she is magically transported to an early-eighteenth-century pirate ship in the middle of the ocean.

"This is thoroughly enjoyable. . . . Through her assertive, appealing protagonist and a satisfying plot that sheds light on lesser-known aspects of pirate life, Vaughn introduces readers to an intriguing sport with an ancient pedigree." Kirkus.

Vaught, Susan, 1965-

Things too huge to fix by saying sorry. Susan Vaught. Simon & Schuster Books for Young Readers, 2016. 240 p.

Grades: 5 6 7 8   **Fic**
1. University of Mississippi -- History. 2. Multiracial girls 3. Feuds 4. Civil Rights Movement 5. Women with Alzheimer's disease 6. Middle school students 7. Oxford, Mississippi 8. Mysteries
ISBN 9781481422796

LC 2015025579

A family mystery leads Dani Beans to investigate the secrets of Ole Miss and the dark history of race relations in Oxford, Mississippi. Provided by publisher.

"Combining middle-school mystery and civil rights history with reflections on dying, friendship, and the ethics of writing another's story from a racially different perspective, this novel is ambitious, thought provoking, and very readable." Booklist.

Vawter, Vince

Copyboy. by Vince Vawter; illustrated by Alessia Trunfio. Capstone Editions, [2018] 240 p.: Capstone Editions

Grades: 7 8 9 10   **Fic**
1. Automobile travel 2. Stuttering 3. Newspaper employees 4. Legacies 5. Self-esteem 6. Memphis, Tennessee -- 7. New Orleans, Louisiana 8. Historical fiction 9. Coming-of-age stories
ISBN 9781630791056

LC 2018001840

Newspaper copyboy Victor Vollmer sets out from Memphis to spread the ashes of Mr. Spiro, his friend and mentor, at the mouth of the Mississippi River, and with the help of new friend Philomene he may meet the challenge.

★ **Paperboy.** Vince Vawter. Delacorte Press, 2013. 256 p.

Grades: 5 6 7 8   **Fic**
1. 1950s 2. Stuttering 3. Newspaper carriers 4. Interpersonal relations 5. Self-esteem 6. Race relations 7. Tennessee 8. Memphis, Tennessee 9. Historical fiction 10. Coming-of-age stories
ISBN 9780385742443

LC 2012030546

When an eleven-year-old boy takes over a friend's newspaper route in July, 1959, in Memphis, his debilitating stutter makes for a memorable month.

"Carefully crafted language, authenticity of setting and quirky characters that ring fully true all combine to make this a worthwhile read. Although Little Man's stutter holds up dialogue, that annoyance also powerfully reflects its stultifying impact on his life. An engaging and heartfelt presentation that never whitewashes the difficult time and situation as Little Man comes of age." Kirkus.

Venkatraman, Padma

The **bridge** home. Padma Venkatraman. Nancy Paulsen Books, 2019. 208 p.

Grades: 5 6 7 8   **Fic**

> 1. Homeless children 2. Familial love 3. Runaways 4. Poverty 5. Homeless persons 6. India 7. Epistolary novels 8. Realistic fiction
> ISBN 9781524738112
>
>   LC 2018035686

Golden Kite Award for Middle Grade/Young Reader Fiction, 2020.

Four determined homeless children make a life for themselves in Chennai, India.

"An unforgettable tale of families lost, found, and moving ahead without leaving those they love behind." School Library Journal.

Climbing the stairs. Padma Venkatraman. G.P. Putnam's Sons, 2008. 201p.

Grades: 6 7 8 9 10   **Fic**

> 1. British Raj (1858-1947) 2. 1940s 3. Families 4. Women's role 5. Prejudice 6. Brain injury 7. Fifteen-year-old girls 8. India 9. Historical fiction
> ISBN 9780399247460
>
>   LC 2007021757

In India, in 1941, when her father becomes brain-damaged in a non-violent protest march, fifteen-year-old Vidya and her family are forced to move in with her father's extended family and become accustomed to a totally different way of life.

"Venkatraman paints an intricate and convincing backdrop of a conservative Brahmin home in a time of change. . . . The striking cover art . . . will draw readers to this vividly told story." Booklist.

A **time** to dance. Padma Venkatraman. Nancy Paulsen Books, an imprint of Penguin Group (USA) Inc., [2014] 320 p.

Grades: 8 9 10 11 12   **Fic**

> 1. Dancers 2. People who have had amputations 3. Teenage girls with disabilities 4. Teenage girl dancers 5. Resilience (Personal quality) 6. India 7. Chennai, India 8. Novels in verse 9. Realistic fiction
> ISBN 9780399257100
>
>   LC 2013024244

In India, a girl who excels at Bharatanatyam dance refuses to give up after losing a leg in an accident.

"This free-verse novel set in contemporary India stars Veda, a teenage Bharatanatyam dancer. After a tragic accident, one of Veda's legs must be amputated below the knee. Veda tries a series of customized prosthetic legs, determined to return to dancing as soon as possible. Brief lines, powerful images, and motifs of sound communicate Veda's struggle to accept her changed body." Horn Book.

Ventrella, Kim

The **secret** life of Sam. Kim Ventrella. Harpercollins Childrens Books 2020 208 p.

Grades: 4 5 6 7   **Fic**

> 1. Fathers and sons 2. Grief in boys 3. Parallel universes 4. Supernatural 5. Sadness 6. Oklahoma 7. Fantasy fiction
> ISBN 9780062941183
>
>   LC 2020000846

After his father's death, seventh-grader Sam West is whisked from Louisiana to Oklahoma, where he discovers a mysterious tree trunk that leads to a world where Pa is still alive.

"Ventrella brilliantly renders Sam's gentle nature, defensiveness, and deep sadness; her evocative prose and the small but resonant cast shine, and Sam's voice effectively relays his path toward the other side of grief." Publishers Weekly

Verne, Jules, 1828-1905

★ **20,000** leagues under the sea. Jules Verne; with an introduction by Bruce Coville. F. Watts, 2007. viii, 322 p.

Grades: 5 6 7 8 9 10 11 12 Adult   **Fic**

> 1. Underwater exploration 2. Submarines 3. Survival 4. Oceans 5. Nemo, Captain (Fictitious character) 6. Sea stories 7. Translations 8. Classics
> ISBN 0531169626
>
>   LC 2006007533

Retells the adventures of a French professor and his two companions as they sail above and below the world's oceans as prisoners on the fabulous electric submarine of the deranged Captain Nemo.

Vernick, Shirley Reva

The **blood** lie: a novel. by Shirley Reva Vernick. Cinco Puntos Press, 2011. 224 p.

Grades: 5 6 7 8   **Fic**

> 1. 1920s 2. Jewish teenage boys 3. Antisemitism 4. Prejudice 5. Missing girls 6. Crushes in teenage boys 7. New York (State) 8. Historical fiction
> ISBN 9781933693842
>
>   LC 2011011429

In 1928 in Massena, New York, Jewish sixteen-year-old Jack Pool, in love with his Christian neighbor, is accused of killling her little sister for a blood sacrifice.

"Based on an actual incident in Massena in 1928, the slim novel effectively mines layers of ignorance, fear, intolerance and manipulation, and it connects the incident to Henry Ford's anti-Semitic writing and to the lynching of Jewish businessman Leo Frank in 1915." Kirkus.

Vernon, Ursula

Castle Hangnail. by Ursula Vernon. Dial Books for Young Readers, an imprint of Penguin Group (USA) Inc., 2015. 320 p.

Grades: 5 6 7 8 9   **Fic**

> 1. Witches 2. Secrets 3. Twelve-year-old girls 4. Magic 5. Witchcraft 6. Humorous stories 7. Fantasy fiction 8. Illustrated books
> ISBN 9780803741294
>
>   LC 2014017106

When little, twelve-year-old Molly arrives at Castle Hangnail to fill the vacancy for a wicked witch, the minions who dwell there have no choice but to give her the job and at first it seems she will be able to keep the castle open, but Molly has quite a few secrets that could cause trouble.

"Creatively drawn characters—from a Minotaur cook to a donkey-dragon to clockwork bees—enjoy mutual respect and will sacrifice whatever is needed to safeguard the castle and its master. The illustrations add whimsy to this delightful tale." Booklist.

Villasante, Alexandra

The **grief** keeper. Alexandra Villasante. G. P. Putnam's Sons, 2019 320 p.

Grades: 8 9 10 11 12   **Fic**

> 1. Undocumented immigrants 2. Medical research 3. Teenage girl/girl relations 4. Grief 5. Empathy 6. Science fiction 7. LGBTQIA fiction
> ISBN 9780525514022

Wanting to enjoy an amazing life in America like her favorite television characters, an undocumented 17-year-old bargains for her asylum by becoming a grief keeper to save someone else's life.—Atlas Publishing.

"Villasante builds her novel about undocumented immigrants into a suspenseful story with credible relationships, satisfying character development, and elements of science fiction." Kirkus.

Vivat, Booki

Frazzled.. Booki Vivat. Harper, an imprint of HarperCollinsPublishers, 2016. 225 p.: Frazzled

Grades: 4 5 6 7   **Fic**

1. Chinese American girls 2. Leadership in girls 3. Anxiety in girls 4. Anxiety 5. Friendship 6. Realistic fiction 7. Illustrated books
ISBN 9780062398796

"Abbie's phobias and worries are charmingly depicted in this heavily illustrated hybrid novel. The humorous, doodlelike artwork makes her struggles entertaining and relatable." School Library Journal.

Vivian, Siobhan

The list. Siobhan Vivian. Scholastic, 2012. 336 p.

Grades: 7 8 9 10 11 12   **Fic**

1. Beauty 2. Ugliness 3. Self-perception in teenage girls 4. Self-perception 5. Self-esteem in teenage girls 6. Realistic fiction
ISBN 9780545169172

Enduring a cruel annual ritual through which an anonymous list is posted naming each grade's prettiest and ugliest girl, eight selected high school girls explore how they see themselves and each other.

"Offering a well-differentiated cast of complex characters and a thoughtful focus on femininity, sisterhood, relationships, eating disorders, and what it means to be singled out, Vivian proves that beauty and ugliness aren't always a matter of appearance." Publishers Weekly.

Vlahos, Len

Life in a fishbowl. by Len Vlahos. Bloomsbury, 2017. 336 p.

Grades: 7 8 9 10   **Fic**

1. Reality television programs 2. Children of people with cancer 3. Terminal illness 4. Brain -- Tumors 5. Families 6. Realistic fiction
ISBN 9781681190358

LC 2016022364

Fifteen-year-old Jackie is determined to reclaim her family's privacy and dignity by ending a reality television program about her father's terminal brain tumor.

"From page one, its evident that the ending will not be a happy one, but numerous laugh-out-loud moments and beautifully drawn characters make for a powerful journey that will leave a lasting imprint on readers." Publishers Weekly.

Voelkel, Jon

The end of the world club. J&P Voelkel. Egmont USA, 2011. 384 p.: Jaguar stones

Grades: 4 5 6 7   **Fic**

1. Children of archaeologists 2. Magic rocks 3. Gods and goddesses, Mayan 4. Monkeys 5. Spirits 6. Spain 7. Mythological fiction 8. Fantasy fiction
ISBN 9781606840726

With the end of the Mayan calendar fast approaching, fourteen-year-old Max Murphy and his friend Lola, the Maya girl who saved his life in the perilous jungle, race against time to outwit the twelve villainous Lords of Death, following the trail of the conquistadors into a forgotten land steeped in legend and superstition.

"The authors use Maya mythology and terms and add interesting facts about Spain and Spanish culture. This is a fast-paced book, and the action starts right away." School Library Journal.

Voigt, Cynthia

The book of kings. Cynthia Voigt; illustrated by Iacopo Bruno. Alfred A. Knopf, 2015. 352 p.: Mister Max

Grades: 5 6 7 8   **Fic**

1. 1900s (Decade) 2. Parent-separated boys 3. Self-reliance 4. Captives 5. Adventure 6. Problem solving 7. South America 8. Historical mysteries 9. Adventure stories
ISBN 9780307976871

Solutioneer Max Starling travels to a fictional South American country to rescue his parents who have become embroiled in a political power grab. Provided by publisher.

The book of lost things. by Cynthia Voigt; illustrated by Iacopo Bruno. Alfred A. Knopf, [2013] 400 p.: Mister Max

Grades: 5 6 7 8   **Fic**

1. 1900s (Decade) 2. Parent-separated boys 3. Self-reliance 4. Children of actors and actresses 5. Problem solving 6. Twelve-year-old boys 7. Historical mysteries 8. Adventure stories
ISBN 9780307976819

LC 2012033823

When Max's parents leave the country without him, he must rely on his wits to get by, and before long he is running his own—rather unusual—business.

The book of secrets. Cynthia Voigt; illustrated by Iacopo Bruno. Alfred A. Knopf, 2014. 384 p.: Mister Max

Grades: 5 6 7 8   **Fic**

1. 1900s (Decade) 2. Parent-separated boys 3. Self-reliance 4. Vandalism 5. Arson investigation 6. Children of actors and actresses 7. Historical mysteries 8. Adventure stories
ISBN 9780307976840

LC 2013050301

Self-reliant Max Starling, a twelve-year-old detective and problem solver, struggles to keep his identity a secret as he investigates a case of arson, while cryptic messages from his still missing parents indicate that they need rescuing.

"The mayor asks young solutioneer Max to discover who's behind the city's rash of vandalism. Meanwhile, Max's parents appear to be acting as royalty in a tiny (fictional) South American country. Voigt's talent for balancing various narrative threads ensures that any one subplot can take the lead and then recede without losing tension. Bruno's black-and-white pencil and ink drawings entertainingly highlight Max's disguises." Horn Book.

Dicey's song. Cynthia Voigt. Atheneum, 1982. 196 p.: Tillerman family

Grades: 5 6 7 8   **Fic**

1. Abandoned children 2. Grandmothers 3. Teenage girls 4. Tillerman family (Fictitious characters) 5. Brothers and sisters 6. Classics 7. Realistic fiction
ISBN 0689309449

LC 82003882

Newbery Medal, 1983.

Now that the four abandoned Tillerman children are settled in with their grandmother, Dicey must decide what she wants for her siblings and herself.

"The vividness of Dicey is striking; Voigt has plumbed and probed her character inside out to fashion a memorable protagonist." Booklist.

Homecoming. Atheneum, 1981. 312 p.: Tillerman family
Grades: 6 7 8 9 **Fic**
   1. Abandoned children 2. Thirteen-year-old girls 3. Survival 4. Independence in teenage girls 5. Tillerman family (Fictitious characters) 6. Realistic fiction 7. Classics
ISBN 0689308337
                       LC 80036723
Abandoned by their mother, four children begin to search for a home and an identity.
   "The characterizations of the children are original and intriguing, and there are a number of interesting minor characters encountered in their travels." School Library Journal.

Izzy, willy-nilly. by Cynthia Voigt. Atheneum, 1986. 258 p.
Grades: 7 8 9 10 **Fic**
   1. Teenage girls who have had amputations 2. Traffic accidents 3. Teenagers with disabilities 4. Girls who have had amputations 5. Fifteen-year-old girls 6. Coming-of-age stories
ISBN 9780689312021
                       LC 85022933
A car accident causes fifteen-year-old Izzy to lose one leg and face the need to start building a new life as an amputee.
   "Voigt shows unusual insight into the workings of a 15-year-old girl's mind. . . . Just as Voigt's perceptive empathy brings Izzy to life, other characterizations are memorable, whether of Izzy's shallow former friends or of her egocentric 10-year-old sister." Publishers Weekly. [review of 1986 edition]

A **solitary** blue. by Cynthia Voigt. Atheneum, 1983. 189 p.: Tillerman family
Grades: 7 8 9 10 **Fic**
   1. Children of divorced parents 2. Fathers and sons 3. Abandoned children 4. Mother-deserted families 5. Tillerman family (Fictitious characters) 6. Classics
ISBN 0689310080
                       LC 83006007
Jeff's mother, who deserted the family years before, reenters his life and widens the gap between Jeff and his father, a gap that only truth, love, and friendship can heal.
   "This is the most mature and sophisticated of Voigt's novels. . . . Beautifully knit . . . compelling and intelligent." Bulletin of the Center for Children's Books.

Volponi, Paul
   Black and white. by Paul Volponi. Viking, 2005. 160 p.
Grades: 7 8 9 10 **Fic**
   1. Interracial friendship 2. High school basketball players 3. Criminal justice system 4. Racism 5. Juvenile delinquents 6. Long Island, New York 7. Realistic fiction
ISBN 0670060062
                     LC 2004024543
Two star high school basketball players, one black and one white, experience the justice system differently after committing a crime together and getting caught.
   "These complex characters share a mutual respect and struggle with issues of loyalty, honesty, and courage. Social conflicts, basketball fervor, and tough personal choices make this title a gripping story." School Library Journal.

Hurricane song: a novel of New Orleans. Paul Volponi. Viking Juvenile, 2008. 144 p.
Grades: 7 8 9 10 11 12 **Fic**
   1. Fathers and sons 2. Hurricanes 3. Survival 4. Family relationships 5. Hurricane Katrina, 2005 6. New Orleans, Louisiana 7. Louisiana
ISBN 9780670061600
Having little in common with his father, Miles' move to New Orleans is not what he expected, but when Hurricane Katrina strikes and he is forced to move into the Superdome with his musician father, the bond between the two grows strong as they ride out the deadly storm and its horrific aftermath together.
   "A brilliant blend of reality and fiction, this novel hits every chord just right." Voice of Youth Advocates.

Rikers High. by Paul Volponi. Viking Childrens Books, 2010. 256 p.
Grades: 8 9 10 11 12 **Fic**
   1. African American teenage boys 2. Juvenile delinquency 3. Teacher-student relationships 4. Jails 5. Teenage prisoners 6. Rikers Island (NY) 7. New York City 8. Realistic fiction
ISBN 9780670011070
                     LC 2009022471
Arrested on a minor offense, a New York City teenager attends high school in the jail facility on Rikers Island, as he waits for his case to go to court.
   "The author draws authentic situations and characters from his six years of teaching at Rikers. . . . An absorbing portrait of life in the stir. . . . Rare is the reader who won't find his narrative sobering." Booklist.

Rucker Park setup. by Paul Volponi. Viking, 2007. 149 p.
Grades: 7 8 9 10 11 12 **Fic**
   1. African American boys 2. Basketball 3. Murder 4. Personal conduct 5. Teenage boys 6. Harlem, New York City 7. Realistic fiction 8. Basketball stories
ISBN 9780670061303
                     LC 2006028463
While playing in a crucial basketball game on the very court where his best friend was murdered, Mackey tries to come to terms with his own part in that murder and decide whether to maintain his silence or tell J.R.'s father and the police what really happened.
   "The author's description of playing pickup ball on one of the toughest courts in the world feels wholly authentic. The characters also feel real." Voice of Youth Advocates.

Vrettos, Adrienne Maria
   Sight. Adrienne Maria Vrettos. Margaret K. McElderry Books, c2007. 254 p.
Grades: 7 8 9 10 **Fic**
   1. Sixteen-year-old girls 2. Teenage girls 3. Teenage psychics 4. Psychics 5. Teenagers 6. Mysteries
ISBN 9781416906575
                     LC 2006035999
Sixteen-year-old Dylan uses her psychic abilities to help police solve crimes against children, but keeps her extracurricular activities secret from her friends at school.
   "Vrettos has created a creepy scenario with a taut plot and a gripping climax. . . . She has crafted a believable setting and characters." Bulletin of the Center for Children's Books.

Wagner, Hilary

Nightshade City. Hilary Wagner. Holiday House, c2010. x, 262 p.: Nightshade chronicles

Grades: 5 6 7 8   **Fic**

1. Rats 2. Underground areas 3. Insurgency 4. Resistance to government 5. Cities and towns 6. Animal fantasy 7. Fantasy fiction

ISBN 9780823422852

LC 2010002474

Eleven years after the cruel Killdeer took over the Catacombs far beneath the human's Trillium City, Juniper Belancourt, assisted by Vincent and Victor Nightshade, leads a maverick band of rats to escape and establish their own city.

"The themes of love, loss and loyalty resonate through the novel, and the moments of darkness and violence are ultimately overpowered by hope and redemption. A good story well-told." Kirkus.

Walden, Mark

H.I.V.E.: Higher-Institute-of-Villainous-Education. Mark Walden. Simon & Schuster Books for Young Readers, 2007. 309 p.: H.I.V.E.: the Higher Institute of Villainous Education

Grades: 5 6 7 8   **Fic**

1. Gifted teenagers 2. Teenage boy orphans 3. Teenage kidnapping victims 4. Villains 5. Criminals 6. Science fiction

ISBN 9781416935711

"H.I.V.E. is operated on a volcanic island in a distant ocean by G.L.O.V.E., a shadowy organization of worldwide wickedness. And, as 13-year-old master of mischief Otto Malpense soon discovers, here the slickest of young tricksters, thieves, and hackers have been brought against their will to be trained as the next generation of supervillains. . . . [This] novel is a real page-turner; those who love superhero stories will eat it up." School Library Journal.

Wallace, Rich

One good punch. Rich Wallace. Alfred A. Knopf, 2007. 114 p.

Grades: 7 8 9 10 11 12   **Fic**

1. Track and field athletes 2. Dilemmas 3. Journalism 4. Marijuana 5. Friendship 6. Pennsylvania 7. Realistic fiction

ISBN 0375813527

Eigtheen-year-old Michael Kerrigan, writer of obituaries for the Scranton Observer and captain of the track team, is ready for the most important season of his life—until the police find four joints in his school locker, and he is faced with a choice that could change everything.

"This novel's success is in creating a multidimensional male character in a format that will appeal to all readers. The moral dilemma . . . makes this novel ripe for ethical discussions." Voice of Youth Advocates.

Perpetual check. Rich Wallace. Alfred A. Knopf, 2009. 112 p.

Grades: 8 9 10 11   **Fic**

1. Brothers 2. Frustration 3. Chess -- Tournaments 4. Competition 5. Frustration in teenage boys 6. Pennsylvania 7. Realistic fiction

ISBN 9780375840586

Frustrated with his younger, more geeky brother being the better athlete, better chess player, and the first one of the two to get a girlfriend, Zeke is determined to set the record straight when they come head-to-head in the final round of the regional chess competition.

"Wallace cleverly positions Randy and Zeke for a win-win conclusion in this satisfying, engaging, and deceptively simple story." School Library Journal.

War and watermelon. Rich Wallace. Viking, c2011. 184 p.

Grades: 6 7 8 9   **Fic**

1. 1960s 2. Boy football players 3. Brothers 4. Fathers and sons 5. Vietnam War, 1961-1975 6. Woodstock Festival, 1969 7. New Jersey 8. Historical fiction

ISBN 9780670011520

LC 2010041043

As the summer of 1969 turns to fall in their New Jersey town, twelve-year-old Brody plays football in his first year at junior high while his older brother's protest of the war in Vietnam causes tension with their father.

"Sixties culture and events . . . are well integrated into the story, and humorous vignettes . . . help lighten the mood." Booklist.

Wrestling Sturbridge. Rich Wallace. Alfred A. Knopf, 1996. 133 p.

Grades: 7 8 9 10   **Fic**

1. Teenage athletes 2. Wrestling 3. Frustration 4. Frustration in teenage boys 5. High school seniors 6. Pennsylvania 7. Sports fiction 8. Realistic fiction

ISBN 0679878033

LC 9520468

Stuck in small town Sturbridge, Pennsylvania, where no one ever leaves, and relegated by his wrestling coach to sit on the bench while his best friend Al becomes state champion, Ben decides he can't let his last high school wrestling season slip by without challenging his friend and the future.

"The wresting scenes are thrilling. . . . Like Ben, whose voice is so strong and clear here, Wallace weighs his words carefully, making every one count in this excellent, understated first novel." Booklist.

Waller, Sharon Biggs, 1966-

A **mad,** wicked folly. Sharon Biggs Waller. Viking, published by the Penguin Group, 2014. 384 p.

Grades: 8 9 10 11 12   **Fic**

1. Edwardian era (1901-1914) 2. 1900s (Decade) 3. Seventeen-year-old girls 4. Gender role 5. Teenage girls 6. Teenage artists 7. Nobility 8. London, England 9. Great Britain 10. Historical fiction

ISBN 9780670014682

LC 2013029858

In 1909 London, as the world of debutante balls and high society obligations closes in around her, seventeen-year-old Victoria must figure out just how much she is willing to sacrifice to pursue her dream of becoming an artist.

"Victoria's dream of becoming an artist leads her naively into scandals, tempts her into a convenient marriage, and drives her to join the Women's Social and Political Union. Persistence eventually triumphs, and friendships, love, and art lessons are her rewards. Sound historical research provides the backbone for this warm novel about the development of women's opportunities in Edwardian London." Horn Book.

Includes bibliographical references.

Walrath, Dana

Like water on stone. Dana Walrath. Delacorte Press, 2014. 368 p.

Grades: 8 9 10 11 12   **Fic**

1. 1910s 2. Twin brothers and sisters 3. Armenian genocide, 1915-1923 4. Armenians in Turkey -- History 20th century 5. Genocide 6. Escapes 7. Turkey 8. Historical fiction 9. Novels in verse

ISBN 9780385743976

"This beautiful, yet at times brutally vivid, historical verse novel will bring this horrifying, tragic period to life for astute, mature readers.... A cast of characters, and author note with historical background are thoughtfully included." School Library Journal.

Walsh, Alice, 1958-

A **long** way from home. by Alice Walsh. Second Story Press, 2012. 232 p.

Grades: 7 8 9 10 **Fic**
1. September 11 Terrorist Attacks, 2001 2. Refugees 3. Muslims 4. Muslim teenagers 5. Refugees, Afghan 6. Newfoundland and Labrador
ISBN 9781926920795

It is September 11, 2001. Rabia, her mother, and younger brother are on their way from Afghanistan to New York hoping to start a new life away from the brutal rule of the Taliban. On the same flight is Colin and his mother, returning home after a holiday. Rabia is worried about the future, and Colin is troubled by the prospect of his parents' impending divorce. Their plane is diverted to Gander Newfoundland, where they are each taken under the wing of a Gander family and shown unexpected kindness and hope for the future.

Walsh, Pat, 1954-

★ The **Crowfield** curse. Pat Walsh. Chicken House, 2010. 319 p.: Crowfield series

Grades: 5 6 7 8 **Fic**
1. 14th century 2. Teenage boy orphans 3. Curses 4. Angels 5. Tombs 6. Goblins 7. Great Britain 8. Historical fantasy
ISBN 9780545229227

In 1347, when fourteen-year-old orphan William Paynel, an impoverished servant at Crowfield Abbey, goes into the forest to gather wood and finds a magical creature caught in a trap, he discovers he has the ability to see fays and becomes embroiled in a strange mystery involving Old Magic, a bitter feud, and ancient secrets.

"This suspenseful and spooky story will thrill readers. . . . With fascinating attention to detail and an edgy battle between evil and good, Walsh sweeps readers almost effortlessly into another time and place." School Library Journal.

Walter, Jon, 1964-

My name is not Friday. by Jon Walter. David Fickling Books/ Scholastic Inc., 2016. 368 p.

Grades: 7 8 9 10 **Fic**
1. American Civil War era (1861-1865) 2. Slavery 3. African American teenage boys 4. Separated brothers 5. Brothers 6. Teenage boy orphans 7. United States 8. Historical fiction 9. Coming-of-age stories
ISBN 9780545855228

LC 2015035464

Samuel and his younger brother, Joshua, are free black boys living in an orphanage during the Civil War, but when Samuel takes the blame for his brother's prank, he is sent South, given a new name, and sold into slavery—and somehow he must survive both captivity and the war, to find his way back to his brother.

"While readers on the young end of the age range and those unfamiliar with religious concepts may find the opening chapters somewhat confusing, Samuel's endearing, immersive narration makes the novel a fascinating and unforgettable account of a brutal and shameful chapter in America's history. A heartbreaking story about family, justice, and the resilience of the human spirit." Kirkus.

Walters, Eric, 1957-

Broken strings. Eric Walters and Kathy Kacer. Puffin Books, 2019 288 p.

Grades: 5 6 7 8 9 **Fic**
1. 2000s (Decade) 2. Grandfather and granddaughter 3. Jewish girls 4. Music 5. School plays 6. September 11 Terrorist Attacks, 2001 7. New York City 8. Historical fiction
ISBN 9780735266247

"A tale that teaches both history and compassion; a great choice for middle grade readers." School Library Journal.

The **money** pit mystery. Eric Walters. Harper Collins Publishers, c1999. 249 p.

Grades: 4 5 6 7 **Fic**
1. Kidd, William, d. 1701 2. Grandfathers 3. Treasure hunting 4. Alzheimer's disease 5. Brothers and sisters 6. Mothers 7. Oak Island Treasure Site, Nova Scotia 8. Nova Scotia 9. Mysteries 10. Adventure stories
ISBN 9780006481515

When Sam and Beth go with their mother to visit their grandfather on Oak Island, they find that his mental state and living conditions have deteriorated. Although he is developing Alzheimer's disease, the old man continues his lifelong quest to find the Oak Island treasure. When his grandfather's efforts fail, Sam gets involved and gives his grandfather a chance to realise his dream in a dramatic and dangerous race against time.

"This is a well-thought-out mystery with lots of suspense and a fully realized picture of a struggling family." School Library Journal.

Walton, Julia, 1986-

Words on bathroom walls. Julia Walton. Random House, 2017. 304 p.

Grades: 7 8 9 10 11 12 **Fic**
1. Teenagers with schizophrenia 2. Diary writing 3. Schizophrenia 4. Teenage boys 5. Teenage boys with mental illnesses 6. Realistic fiction 7. Diary novels
ISBN 9780399550881

LC 2016017419

Adam is a recently diagnosed schizophrenic and journals to his therapist about family, friends, and first loves as he undergoes a new drug trial for the mental illness that allows him to keep his secret for only so long. Provided by publisher.

"First-time author Walton creates a psychologically tense story with sympathetic characters while dispelling myths about a much-feared condition." Publishers Weekly.

Ward, David, 1967-

Beneath the mask. David Ward. Amulet Books, 2008, c2003. 243 p.: Grassland trilogy

Grades: 7 8 9 10 **Fic**
1. Freedom 2. Guilt 3. Extortion 4. Self-discovery in teenagers 5. Guards 6. Coming-of-age stories 7. Fantasy fiction
ISBN 9780810970748

"This is an excellent continuation of a trilogy fraught with daring escapes, dangerous situations, and genuine characters." Voice of Youth Advocates.

Escape the mask. David Ward. Amulet Books, 2008, c2001. 171 p.: Grassland trilogy

Grades: 7 8 9 10 **Fic**
1. Teenage kidnapping victims 2. Forced labor 3. Guards 4.

Masks 5. Slavery 6. Coming-of-age stories 7. Fantasy fiction
ISBN 9780810994775

"Ward's novel bursts with action and is laden with tense scenes. His excellent descriptive writing allows the reader to visualize the action. In addition, Ward's fantasy world is so believable that the text almost reads as historical fiction." Voice of Youth Advocates.

Ward, Rachel, 1964-

The **chaos**. Rachel Ward. Chicken House/Scholastic, 2011. 352 p.: Numbers

Grades: 8 9 10 11 12   **Fic**

1. Teenage boy orphans 2. Psychic ability 3. Disasters 4. Death 5. Interpersonal relations 6. London, England 7. England 8. Science fiction
ISBN 9780545242691

LC 2010018294

Like his mother, Jem, when sixteen-year-old Adam looks in people's eyes he can see the dates of their deaths and now he sees the same date, six months in the future, in nearly everyone around him in the London of 2026.

"In this sequel to Numbers a fascinating premise is again worked out through gripping episodes and a lightly handled metaphysical dilemma." Horn Book.

Num8ers. Rachel Ward. Chicken House/Scholastic, 2010. 336 p.: Numbers

Grades: 8 9 10 11 12   **Fic**

1. London Eye (London, England) 2. Foster teenagers 3. Psychic ability 4. Terrorism 5. Bombings 6. Death 7. London, England 8. England 9. Science fiction
ISBN 9780545142991

LC 2008055440

Fifteen-year-old Jem knows when she looks at someone the exact date they will die, so she avoids relationships and tries to keep out of the way, but when she meets a boy named Spider and they plan a day out together, they become more involved than either of them had planned.

"Ward's debut novel is gritty, bold, and utterly unique. Jem's isolation and pain, hidden beneath a veneer of toughness, are palpable, and the ending is a real shocker." School Library Journal.

Warga, Jasmine

The **shape** of thunder. Jasmine Warga Harpercollins Childrens Books 2021 288 p.

Grades: 4 5 6 7 8   **Fic**

1. Best friends 2. School shootings 3. Brothers and sisters 4. Grief in children 5. Guilt in children 6. Realistic fiction
ISBN 9780062956675

Estranged from the best friend whose brother killed her sister in a school shooting, a grieving Cora receives a message on her twelfth birthday from her friend, asking for her help with creating a time portal to prevent the tragedy.

"Warga tells a quiet story despite the dramatic events that led up to it, presenting a sad but not overwhelming narrative." Horn Book

Warman, Janice

The **world** beneath. Janice Warman. Candlewick Press, 2016 176 p.

Grades: 8 9 10 11   **Fic**

1. 1970s 2. Apartheid 3. Racism 4. Anti-apartheid activists 5. Fugitives 6. Eleven-year-old boys 7. South Africa 8. Historical fiction
ISBN 9780763678562

Growing up in the maid's room of a wealthy white employer's home in 1970s South Africa, young Joshua rescues a stranger amid anti-apartheid riots sweeping through the country, which compel him to make heartbreaking choices.

"A good complement to nonfiction about apartheid South Africa, a little-explored place and period in children's literature." Kirkus.

Wasserman, Robin

Awakening. Robin Wasserman. Scholastic, c2007. 207 p.: Chasing yesterday

Grades: 6 7 8 9   **Fic**

1. Thirteen-year-old girls 2. Teenage girls with amnesia 3. People with amnesia 4. Amnesia 5. Nightmares 6. Thrillers and suspense
ISBN 9780439933384

Thirteen-year-old J.D. struggles to understand who she is, where she came from, and why she has nightmares.

"[Wasserman's] characters are well developed and believable, her plot is suspenseful, and her backgrounds . . . are nicely detailed." Voice of Youth Advocates.

The **book** of blood and shadow. by Robin Wasserman. Alfred A. Knopf, 2012. 352 p.

Grades: 7 8 9   **Fic**

1. Secret societies 2. Conspiracies 3. Manuscripts 4. Supernatural 5. Murder 6. Prague, Czech Republic 7. New England 8. Thrillers and suspense
ISBN 9780375968761

LC 2011003920

While working on a project translating letters from sixteenth-century Prague, high school senior Nora Kane discovers her best friend murdered with her boyfriend the apparent killer and is caught up in a dangerous web of secret societies and shadowy conspirators, all searching for a mysterious ancient device purported to allow direct communication with God.

Watkins, Steve, 1954-

Great Falls. Steve Watkins. Candlewick Press, 2016. 245 p.

Grades: 8 9 10 11   **Fic**

1. Post-traumatic stress disorder 2. Brothers 3. Veterans 4. Canoeing 5. Seventeen-year-old boys 6. Virginia 7. Realistic fiction
ISBN 9780763671556

"Watkins (Juvie) delivers a powerful, emotionally raw tale, heartbreaking in its portrayal of damaged veterans, the price some pay to serve, and the toll it takes on their friends and family. It's also a raw coming-of-age journey for Shane as he struggles with his own feelings, especially toward 'the Colonel,' the brothers' emotionally abusive, micromanaging, ex-military stepfather." Publishers Weekly.

Watkins, Yoko Kawashima

★ **So** far from the bamboo grove. by Yoko Kawashima Watkins. Lothrop, Lee & Shepard, 1986. 183 p.

Grades: 6 7 8 9   **Fic**

1. World War II 2. Girls 3. Eight-year-old girls 4. Child refugees 5. Korea 6. Japan 7. Coming-of-age stories 8. Historical fiction 9. Classics
ISBN 0688061109

LC 85015939

A fictionalized autobiography in which eight-year-old Yoko escapes from Korea to Japan with her mother and sister at the end of World War II.

"An admirably told and absorbing novel." Horn Book.

Watson, Cristy, 1964-

Benched. Cristy Watson. Orca Book Publishers, 2011. 106 p.
Grades: 7 8 9 10 11 12 **Fic**
1. Gangs 2. Bereavement in teenagers 3. Stealing 4. Brothers
-- Death 5. Grief 6. High interest-low vocabulary books
ISBN 9781554694099
Cody and his friends are pressured into stealing a park bench, without realizing the serious consequences of their actions.
"This Orca Currents title packs in a lot of issues for one small paperback, but reluctant readers, especially, will be hooked as the tension builds, and the realistic story, which avoids a slick resolution, will spark discussion." Booklist

Watson, Jude

Beyond the grave. Jude Watson. Scholastic Inc., 2009. 192 p.: The 39 clues.
Grades: 4 5 6 7 **Fic**
1. Orphans 2. Clues 3. Family fortunes 4. Brothers and sisters 5. Child adventurers 6. Egypt 7. Adventure stories
ISBN 9780545090612
A clue found in Book 3 sends Amy and Dan jetting off to Egypt to find out what's behind the fierce rivalry between the Tomas and Ekaterina branches of the Cahill family. Was a clue stolen from the Tomas branch? Where is it now? And, most important, can Amy and Dan get their hands on it before their rivals do?
"Like the previous books, historical information is woven into the fast-paced adventure." School Library Journal.

Loot. Jude Watson. Scholastic Press, an imprint of Scholastic Inc., [2014] 272 p.
Grades: 4 5 6 7 **Fic**
1. Jewelry theft 2. Twin brothers and sisters 3. Curses 4. Jewel thieves 5. Orphans 6. Thrillers and suspense
ISBN 9780545468022
LC 2014001218
When Alfie McQuinn, the notorious jewel thief, is killed on a job, his last words to his son, March, are to "find jewels" and this instruction leads the boy to Jules, the twin sister he never knew he had—and the perfect partner to carry on the family business.
"Pitch-perfect characters, from scheming criminals to a twisted former cop to the twins' father, move in and out of the narrative, but it's the four young teens that drive the tale forward with enviable schemes and ingenious plans.Taut, engrossing and unstoppable." Kirkus.

Nowhere to run. Jude Watson. Scholastic, 2013. 266 p.: The 39 clues.
Grades: 4 5 6 7 **Fic**
1. Orphans 2. Brothers and sisters 3. Stealing 4. Clues 5. Teenagers 6. Adventure stories
ISBN 9780545597067
LC bl2013034538
Guardians of the 39 Clues, Dan Cahill and his sister Amy discover that the serum is missing and must race against time to get it back before catastrophe strikes
"Six months after sixteen-year-old Amy and thirteen-year-old Dan defeated the Vespers, the Cahill siblings set out on another quest to stop the serum their family has protected for centuries from wreaking havoc on the world. This first entry in a new spinoff series is formulaic, but the suspense and high stakes that 39 Clues fans love are front and center." Horn Book.

Watson, Renee

Piecing me together. by Renee Watson. Bloomsbury, 2017 320 p.
Grades: 7 8 9 10 11 12 **Fic**
1. African American teenage girls 2. Mentoring 3. Private schools 4. Schools 5. Social classes 6. Portland, Oregon 7. Oregon 8. Realistic fiction 9. African American fiction
ISBN 9781681191058
Coretta Scott King Award, Author Category, 2018.
"A timely, nuanced, and unforgettable story about the power of art, community, and friendship." Kirkus.

Some places more than others. Renee Watson. Bloomsbury Children's Books, 2019. 208 p.
Grades: 4 5 6 7 **Fic**
1. African American girls 2. Family visits 3. Family relationships 4. African American families 5. School projects 6. Harlem, New York City 7. New York City 8. Coming-of-age stories 9. Realistic fiction 10. African American fiction
ISBN 9781681191089
LC 2019003857
Amara visits her father's family in Harlem for her twelfth birthday, hoping to better understand her family and herself, but New York City is not what she expected.
"Amara's search for her roots is tender and empowering. An essential purchase for all middle grade libraries." School Library Journal.

Watch us rise. by Renee Watson and Ellen Hagan. Bloomsbury, 2019. 368 p.
Grades: 7 8 9 10 11 12 **Fic**
1. Women's rights 2. Student organizations 3. Best friends 4. Feminists 5. Bloggers 6. New York City 7. Coming-of-age stories 8. Realistic fiction
ISBN 9781547600083
LC 2018045153
Jasmine and Chelsea are best friends on a mission. Sick of the way that young women are treated at their 'progressive' New York City high school, they decide to start a Women's Right's Club. One problem - no one shows up. That won't stop them though!
"Told from the viewpoints of Chelsea and Jasmine, this thought-provoking novel explores ideas of body-shaming, racial stereotypes, and gender inequality." School Library Journal.

Weaver, Will

Saturday night dirt. Will Weaver. Farrar, Straus and Giroux, 2008. 163 p.: Motor series
Grades: 8 9 10 11 **Fic**
1. Automobile racing 2. Teenagers 3. Small town life 4. Automobile racing drivers 5. Stock car drivers 6. Minnesota 7. Sports fiction 8. Realistic fiction
ISBN 9780374350604
LC 2007006988
In a small town in northern Minnesota, the much-anticipated Saturday night dirt-track race at the old-fashioned, barely viable, Headwaters Speedway becomes, in many ways, an important life-changing event for all the participants on and off the track.
"Weaver presents compelling character studies. . . . Young racing fans . . . will find much that rings true here." Booklist.

Weeks, Sarah

Jumping the scratch. by Sarah Weeks. Laura Geringer Books, 2006. 167 p.

Grades: 5 6 7 8   **Fic**
1. Eleven-year-old boys 2. Child sexual abuse 3. Memory 4. Aunt and nephew 5. Secrets 6. Michigan 7. Realistic fiction
ISBN 0060541091

LC 2005017776

After moving with his mother to a trailer park to care for an injured aunt, eleven-year-old Jamie Reardon struggles to cope with a deeply buried secret.

"Weeks alludes to sexual abuse, but with a broad brush and no graphic details. . . . Weeks perfectly captures not only the guilt, shame, and pain of the abused boy but also the tenor of a fifth-grade classroom from the point of view of a new student who is friendless, targeted, and belittled by an insensitive teacher. Touches of humor ameliorate the pain and poignancy." School Library Journal.

★ **Pie**. Sarah Weeks. Scholastic Press, 2011. 183 p.
Grades: 4 5 6 7   **Fic**
1. 1950s 2. Pies 3. Recipes 4. Cats 5. Aunts -- Death 6. Small towns 7. Pennsylvania 8. Historical mysteries
ISBN 9780545270113

After the death of Polly Portman, whose award-winning pies put the town of Ipswitch, Pennsylvania, on the map in the 1950s, her devoted niece Alice and Alice's friend Charlie investigate who is going to extremes to find Aunt Polly's secret pie crust recipe.

"Weeks deftly leavens moments of hilarity with the process of grieving in this sweet coming-of-age story in which Alice learns from Aunt Polly to follow her heart and to open it as well. Readers will close the book with a satisfied sigh and may seek out an adult to help them bake a pie. Recipes included." School Library Journal.

Wees, Alyssa
The **waking** forest. Alyssa Wees. Delacorte Press, [2019] 304 p.
Grades: 8 9 10 11 12   **Fic**
1. Dreams 2. Witches 3. Forests 4. Visions 5. Wishing and wishes 6. Fantasy fiction 7. Gothic fiction
ISBN 9780525581161

LC 2018022935

When the lives of a girl, who has terrifying visions, and a witch, who grants wishes to children in the woods, collide in the most unexpected of ways, a dark, magical truth threatens to doom them both. Provided by publisher.

"Dreams and stories—their power to escape reality and to restore it—are in the bones of this masterfully woven fantasy debut. And at its heart? The power of revolution in the face of coldly violent injustice." Kirkus.

Wegelius, Jakob
The **murderer's** ape. Jakob Wegelius; translated from the Swedish by Peter Graves. Delacorte Press, [2017] 608 p.
Grades: 7 8 9 10   **Fic**
1. Innocence (Law) 2. Gorillas 3. Adventure 4. Friendship 5. Human-animal relationships 6. Historical mysteries 7. Stories told by animals 8. Illustrated books
ISBN 9781101931752

LC 2016010508

Mildred L. Batchelder Award, 2018.

When her best friend, the sailor Henry Koskela, is falsely accused of murder, a gorilla named Sally Jones visits the run-down docks of Lisbon, embarks on a dizzying journey across the seven seas, and calls on the Maharaja of Bhapur's magnificent court—all in an attempt to clear Henry's name.

"While the sheer length and thoughtful pace of Sally Jones journey might discourage some, those who persevere will have a richly imagined and thoroughly unique adventure in store." Booklist.

Weil, Cynthia
I'm glad I did. Cynthia Weil. Soho Teen, [2015] 272 p.
Grades: 8 9 10 11 12   **Fic**
1. 1960s 2. Songwriters 3. Music industry and trade 4. Popular music 5. Internship programs 6. African Americans 7. New York City 8. Historical mysteries 9. Coming-of-age stories
ISBN 9781616953560

LC 2014025047

In 1963 sixteen-year-old JJ Green, a songwriter interning at New York City's famous Brill Building, finds herself a writing partner in Luke Silver, a boy who seems to connect instantly with her music, and they start cutting their first demo with Dulcie Brown, a legend who has fallen on hard times, with a secret past.

"Grammy-winning songwriter Weil makes an impressive YA debut with this period novel set against the rapidly changing music industry of the early 1960s. . . [s]howing both the bright and the dark sides of the music business, Weil crafts an enticing tale of a sheltered teenagers induction into a world where ambitions and morals are repeatedly tested." Publishers Weekly.

Wein, Elizabeth
Black dove, white raven. Elizabeth Wein. Disney-Hyperion, 2015. 368 p.
Grades: 8 9 10 11 12   **Fic**
1. 1930s 2. Pilots 3. Race relations 4. Italo-Ethiopian War, 1935-1936 5. Americans in Ethiopia 6. Brothers and sisters 7. Ethiopia 8. Historical fiction
ISBN 9781423183105

LC 2014044446

Rhoda who is white and Delia who is black are stunt pilots who perform daring aerobatics. Both women dream of living in a world free of racial discrimination. When Delia is killed in a tragic accident, Rhoda is determined to make that dream come true. She leaves the United States for Ethiopia with her daughter, Em, and Delia's son, Teo and all three fall in love with the beautiful, peaceful country. But peace is soon shattered with the threat of war with Italy, and Em and Teo are drawn into the conflict.

"The intellectual, psychological, and emotional substance of this story is formidable, and Wein makes it all approachable and engaging." Horn Book.

The **pearl** thief. by Elizabeth Wein. Hyperion, 2017. 304 p.: Code name Verity
Grades: 8 9 10 11   **Fic**
1. 1930s 2. Between the Wars (1918-1939) 3. Missing persons 4. Stealing 5. Prejudice 6. Friendship 7. Summer 8. Scotland 9. Historical mysteries
ISBN 9781484717165

LC 2016041527

Fifteen-year-old Julia Beaufort-Stuart wakes up in a hospital not knowing how she was injured, and soon befriends Euan McEwen, the Scottish Traveller boy who found her, and later, when a body is discovered, she experiences the prejudices his family has endured and tries to keep them from being framed for the crime.

"A finely crafted book that brings one girl's coming-of-age story to life, especially poignant for those who already know her fate." Booklist.

Weissman, Elissa Brent

The **length** of a string. Elissa Brent Weissman. Dial Books, 2018 384 p.

Grades: 5 6 7 8   **Fic**
1. African American girls 2. Adoption 3. Identity (Psychology) 4. Jewish girls 5. Twelve-year-old girls 6. Baltimore, Maryland 7. Realistic fiction 8. First-person narratives
ISBN 9780735229471

LC 2017043498

Twelve-year-old Imani, the only black girl in Hebrew school, is preparing for her bat mitzvah and hoping to find her birthparents when she discovers the history of adoption in her own family through her great-grandma Anna's Holocaust-era diary.

Welford, Ross

Time traveling with a hamster. Ross Welford. Schwartz & Wade Books, [2016] 432 p.

Grades: 5 6 7 8   **Fic**
1. Time travel (Past) 2. Time machines 3. Fathers and sons 4. Death 5. Accidents 6. England 7. Science fiction
ISBN 9780399551499

LC 2015036913

Twelve-year-old Al Chaudhury discovers his late dad's time machine and travels back to 1984 with his pet hamster to prevent the go-kart accident that killed his father.

"Welford addresses all the complications of time travel, including the impossibility of being in two places at the same time and the threat of obliterating one's present self. Nods to classic time travel stories will delight some readers; those merely looking for a page-turning adventure will find that and more." Kirkus.

Wells, Robison E.

Variant. Robison Wells. HarperTeen, 2011. 356 p.: Variant (Robison Wells)

Grades: 7 8 9 10   **Fic**
1. Foster teenagers 2. Survival 3. Boarding schools 4. Schools 5. Interpersonal relations 6. New Mexico 7. Science fiction
ISBN 9780062026088

LC 2010042661

When Benson Fisher is accepted into Maxfield Academy, he's relieved to escape from the foster care system and excited to make a fresh start. But soon after the doors of the boarding school lock behind him, Benson realizes that he's made a huge mistake. Students at Maxfield are trapped, under constant surveillance, and at war with each other—and the punishment for rule-breakers is death.

"Hard to put down from the very first page, this fast-paced novel with Stepford overtones answers only some of the questions it poses, holding some of the most tantalizing open for the next installment in a series that is anything but ordinary." Kirkus.

Wells, Rosemary

My Havana: memories of a Cuban boyhood. Rosemary Wells with Secundino Fernandez; illustrated by Peter Ferguson. Candlewick Press, 2010. 65 p.

Grades: 4 5 6 7   **Fic**
1. Fernandez, Secundino 2. 1950s 3. Revolutions 4. Immigrants 5. Architects 6. Architecture 7. Families 8. Havana, Cuba 9. Cuba 10. Historical fiction
ISBN 9780763643058

LC 2009012053

Relates events in the childhood of architect Secundino Fernandez, who left his beloved Havana, Cuba, with his parents, first to spend a year in Spain, and later to move to New York City.

"Wells has chosen anecdotes wisely, and Ferguson's illustrations are atmospheric, capturing Dino's childlike enthusiasm and longing." Kirkus.

Red moon at Sharpsburg. Rosemary Wells. Viking, 2007. 240 p.

Grades: 6 7 8 9 10   **Fic**
1. 1860s 2. Teenage girls 3. War 4. Thirteen-year-old girls 5. Neighbors 6. Scientists 7. United States
ISBN 0670036382

Finding courage she never thought she had, a young Southern girl musters the strength and wit to survive the ravages of the Civil War and keep her family together through it all.

"This powerful novel is unflinching in its depiction of war and the devastation it causes, yet shows the resilience and hope that can follow such a tragedy. India is a memorable, thoroughly believable character." School Library Journal.

Welsh, M. L.

Mistress of the Storm: a Verity Gallant tale. by M.L. Welsh. David Fickling Books, 2011. 320 p.: Verity Gallant tales

Grades: 5 6 7 8   **Fic**
1. Witches 2. Books 3. Storms 4. Friendship 5. Sailing 6. Fantasy fiction
ISBN 9780385752442

After a stranger gives an ancient book to unpopular, twelve-year-old Verity Gallant, she and her new-found friends, Henry and Martha, uncover secrets stirring in the harbor town of Wellow and use them to face a powerful, vengeful witch.

"Welsh's prose is lovely, her characters are well-drawn, and the atmosphere of the town is palpable. In creating a place in the world where a story read aloud can become true, Welsh offers a benediction of sorts to readers, that every child who is alone or out of place will find the friends they need, and the love they deserve." Publishers Weekly.

Werlin, Nancy

Double helix. Nancy Werlin. Dial Books, c2004. 252 p.

Grades: 7 8 9 10   **Fic**
1. Genetic engineering 2. Bioethics 3. People with Huntington's disease 4. Huntington's disease 5. Eighteen-year-old men 6. Thrillers and suspense
ISBN 0803726066

LC 2003012269

Eighteen-year-old Eli discovers a shocking secret about his life and his family while working for a Nobel Prize-winning scientist whose specialty is genetic engineering.

"Werlin clearly and dramatically raises fundamental bioethical issues for teens to ponder. She also creates a riveting story with sharply etched characters and complex relationships that will stick with readers long after the book is closed." School Library Journal.

Extraordinary. by Nancy Werlin. Dial Books for Young Readers, 2010. 256 p.: Impossible series

Grades: 8 9 10 11 12   **Fic**
1. Fairies 2. Promises 3. Self-esteem in teenage girls 4. Self-esteem 5. Secrets 6. Fantasy fiction
ISBN 9780803733725

LC 2010002086

Phoebe, a member of the wealthy Rothschilds family, befriends Mallory, an awkward new girl in school, and the two become as close as sisters, but Phoebe does not know that Mallory is a faerie, sent to the human world to trap the ordinary human girl into fulfilling a promise made by her ancestor Mayer to the queen of the faeries.

"The carefully nuanced, often sensual prose delivers a highly effective narrative. Characterizations are arresting and complex." School Library Journal.

Impossible: a novel. Nancy Werlin. Dial Books, 2008. 384 p.: Impossible series

Grades: 7 8 9 10   **Fic**
    1. Pregnant teenagers 2. Curses 3. Riddles 4. Magic 5. Elves 6. Fantasy fiction
    ISBN 9780803730021

                  LC 2008006633

When seventeen-year-old Lucy discovers her family is under an ancient curse by an evil Elfin Knight, she realizes to break the curse she must perform three impossible tasks before her daughter is born in order to save them both.

"Werlin earns high marks for the tale's graceful interplay between wild magic and contemporary reality." Booklist.

The **killer's** cousin. Nancy Werlin. Delacorte Press, c1998. 229 p.

Grades: 7 8 9 10   **Fic**
    1. Guilt in teenage boys 2. Emotional problems of girls 3. Secrets 4. Dysfunctional families 5. Seventeen-year-old boys 6. Massachusetts 7. Cambridge, Massachusetts 8. Psychological suspense
    ISBN 0385325606

                  LC 98012950

After being acquitted of murder, seventeen-year-old David goes to stay with relatives in Cambridge, Massachusetts, where he finds himself forced to face his past as he learns more about his strange young cousin Lily.

"Teens will find this tautly plotted thriller, rich in complex, finely drawn characters, an absolute page-turner." Booklist.

The **rules** of survival. Nancy Werlin. Dial Books, 2006. 272 p.

Grades: 8 9 10 11 12   **Fic**
    1. Child abuse 2. Mothers with mental illnesses 3. Fear in children 4. Seventeen-year-old boys 5. Teenage boys 6. Thrillers and suspense 7. Realistic fiction
    ISBN 0803730012

                  LC 2006001675

Seventeen-year-old Matthew recounts his attempts, starting at a young age, to free himself and his sisters from the grip of their emotionally and physically abusive mother.

"The author tackles the topic of child abuse with grace and insight. . . . Teens will empathize with these siblings and the secrets they keep in this psychological horror story." School Library Journal.

West, Jacqueline, 1979-

A **storm** of wishes. Jacqueline West. Greenwillow Books, 2019. 304 p.: Collectors (Jacqueline West)

Grades: 4 5 6 7   **Fic**
    1. Wishing and wishes 2. Collectors and collecting 3. Best friends 4. Misfits (persons) 5. Rescues 6. Fantasy fiction
    ISBN 9780062691729

                  LC 2019012390

A follow-up to The Collectors finds 11-year-old Van Markson embarking on a quest of magic and adventure to rescue his best friend from a dangerous wish collector, a quest that is complicated by his mother's injury and dangerous Wish Eater creatures.

"The author skillfully employs the classic setup of a regular kid swept up in magical events. In the end, Van and readers both must question right and wrong in a fairy tale in which the good guys use questionable methods and the monsters might not be so monstrous after all." Kirkus.

West, Kasie

Pivot point. Kasie West. HarperTeen, c2013. 320 p.

Grades: 7 8 9 10   **Fic**
    1. Children of divorced parents 2. Options, alternatives, choices 3. Teenage romance 4. Decision-making 5. Murder 6. Paranormal romances
    ISBN 9780062117373

                  LC 2012019089

A girl with the power to search alternate futures lives out six weeks of two different lives in alternating chapters. Both futures hold the potential for love and loss, and ultimately she is forced to choose which fate she is willing to live through. Provided by publisher.

"Both love interests are developed well, and readers will be able to see Addie with either. The worldbuilding isn't as on point—the Compound raises logistical questions that are glossed over for the sake of the plot's strong pace. Minor missteps are easy to forgive given the underlying suspense of multiple mysteries. West's debut showcases riveting storytelling." Kirkus.

Westerfeld, Scott

Behemoth. written by Scott Westerfeld; illustrated by Keith Thompson. Simon Pulse, 2010. 496 p.: Leviathan trilogy

Grades: 7 8 9 10   **Fic**
    1. 1910s 2. Princes 3. Teenagers and war 4. Genetically engineered animals 5. Warships 6. Genetic engineering 7. Steampunk 8. Alternate histories 9. Science fiction
    ISBN 9781416971757

Continues the story of Austrian Prince Alek who, in an alternate 1914 Europe, eludes the Germans by traveling in the Leviathan to Constantinople, where he faces a whole new kind of genetically-engineered warships.

"This exciting and inventive tale of military conflict and wildly reimagined history should captivate a wide range of readers. Thompson's evocative and detailed spot art (as well as the luridly gorgeous endpapers) only sweetens the deal." Publishers Weekly.

Extras. Scott Westerfeld. Simon & Schuster, 2007. 417 p.: Uglies

Grades: 7 8 9 10   **Fic**
    1. Teenage rebels 2. Fame 3. Dystopias 4. Beauty 5. Image 6. Dystopian fiction 7. Science fiction
    ISBN 9781416951179

                  LC 2007928439

Now that the world is in a complete cultural renaissance, fifteen-year-old Aya Fuse, an Extra, just wants to lay low, so when she discovers the secret lives of the Sly Girls, she wants to report their story, but Aya knows that would propel her into celebrity—a status she's not prepared for.

"Aya is an extra (face rank stuck in the mid-400,000s) in a city run on a reputation economy. If Aya can win fame as a kicker, reporting with her trusty hovercam on a story that captures the city's imagination, her face rank will soar. . . . Westerfeld shows he has a finger on the pulse of our reputation economy, alchemizing the cult of celebrity, advertising's constant competition for consumer attention." Horn Book.

Goliath. written by Scott Westerfeld; illustrated by Keith Thompson. Simon Pulse, 2011. 432 p.: Leviathan trilogy

Grades: 7 8 9 10 **Fic**

1. 1910s 2. Princes 3. Teenagers and war 4. World War I 5. Warships 6. Genetically engineered animals 7. Steampunk 8. Alternate histories 9. Science fiction

ISBN 9781416971771

Alek and Deryn are on the last leg of their round-the-world quest to end World War I, reclaim Alek's throne as prince of Austria, and finally fall in love.

"The alternative-history steampunk extravaganza that began with Leviathan (2009) ends with this third volume, and it does not disappoint. Westerfeld propels the story to a satisfying close. . . . Once again, Thompson's evocative art enlivens the narrative." Booklist.

Leviathan. by Scott Westerfeld; illustrated by Keith Thompson. Simon Pulse, 2009. 440 p.: Leviathan trilogy

Grades: 7 8 9 10 **Fic**

1. 1910s 2. Princes 3. Teenagers and war 4. Genetic engineering 5. Conspiracies 6. Genetically engineered animals 7. Steampunk 8. Alternate histories 9. Science fiction

ISBN 9781416971733

LC 2009000881

In an alternate 1914 Europe, fifteen-year-old Austrian Prince Alek, on the run from the Clanker Powers who are attempting to take over the globe using mechanical machinery, forms an uneasy alliance with Deryn who, disguised as a boy to join the British Air Service, is learning to fly genetically-engineered beasts.

"The protagonists' stories are equally gripping and keep the story moving, and Thompson's detail-rich panels bring Westerfeld's unusual creations to life." Publishers Weekly.

Pretties. Scott Westerfeld. Simon Pulse, 2005. 370 p.: Uglies

Grades: 7 8 9 10 **Fic**

1. Self-perception in teenage girls 2. Dystopias 3. Transformations, Personal 4. Plastic surgery 5. Beauty 6. Dystopian fiction 7. Science fiction

ISBN 0689865392

LC 2004118120

"Riveting and compulsively readable, this action-packed sequel does not disappoint." Booklist.

Shatter city. Scott Westerfeld. Scholastic Press, 2019. 416 p.: Impostors (Scott Westerfeld)

Grades: 6 7 8 9 10 **Fic**

1. Twins 2. Impersonation 3. Missing persons 4. Searching 5. Dystopias 6. Dystopian fiction 7. Science fiction

ISBN 9781338150414

Assuming her twins identity, Frey works to destroy her father, but when a rebel uprising strands her in a city that comes under attack, Frey must step out of the shadows to find her missing sister and take action against her tyrant father.

"Page-turning action made even more engrossing by a rare emotional core." Kirkus.

So yesterday: a novel. by Scott Westerfeld. Razorbill, c2004. 225 p.

Grades: 7 8 9 10 **Fic**

1. Cool (Personal quality) 2. Missing women 3. Consumerism 4.

Conspiracies 5. Advertising 6. New York City 7. Mysteries 8. Realistic fiction

ISBN 159514000X

LC 2004002302

Hunter Braque, a New York City teenager who is paid by corporations to spot what is "cool," combines his analytical skills with girlfriend Jen's creative talents to find a missing person and thwart a conspiracy directed at the heart of consumer culture.

"This hip, fascinating thriller aggressively questions consumer culture. . . . Teens will inhale this wholly entertaining, thought-provoking look at a system fueled by their purchasing power." Booklist.

Specials. Scott Westerfeld. Simon Pulse, c2006. 372 p.: Uglies

Grades: 7 8 9 10 **Fic**

1. Teenage nonconformists 2. Brainwashing 3. Dystopias 4. Image 5. Teenage boy/girl relations 6. Dystopian fiction 7. Science fiction

ISBN 0689865406

LC 2005933890

"Readers who enjoyed Uglies and Pretties . . . will not want to miss Specials. . . . Westerfeld's themes include vanity, environmental conservation, Utopian idealism, fascism, violence, and love." School Library Journal.

Uglies. Scott Westerfeld. Simon Pulse, 2005. 448 p.: Uglies

Grades: 7 8 9 10 **Fic**

1. Moles (Spies) 2. Plastic surgery 3. Dystopias 4. Rebels 5. Image 6. Dystopian fiction 7. Science fiction

ISBN 0689865384

LC 2004106866

Just before their sixteenth birthdays, when they will be transformed into beauties whose only job is to have a great time, Tally's best friend runs away and Tally must find her and turn her in, or never become pretty at all.

"Fifteen-year-old Tally's eerily harmonious, postapocalyptic society gives extreme makeovers to teens on their sixteenth birthdays. . . . When a top-secret agency threatens to leave Tally ugly forever unless she spies on runaway teens, she agrees to infiltrate the Smoke, a shadowy colony of refugees from the tyranny of physical perfection." Booklist.

Weston, Carol

Speed of life. Carol Weston. Sourcebooks Jabberwocky, 2017. 352 p.

Grades: 7 8 9 10 **Fic**

1. Grief 2. Children and single parent dating 3. First loves 4. Multiracial teenage girls 5. Advice columnists 6. New York City 7. Realistic fiction

ISBN 9781492654490

Missing her mother who died last year, fourteen-year-old Sofia finds an anonymous outlet for her personal questions and deep, dark secrets in the Dear Kate advice columnist, until, much to her horror, Sofia's father starts dating Kate.

Weston, Robert Paul

★ **Zorgamazoo**. by Robert Paul Weston. Razorbill, 2008. 192 p.

Grades: 4 5 6 7 **Fic**

1. Girl adventurers 2. Imaginary creatures 3. Parallel universes 4. Quests 5. Girls 6. Novels in verse 7. Fantasy fiction

ISBN 9781595141996

LC 2007051682

Dear Reader, is your day-to-day living a bore? Are coming and going becoming a chore? Need adventure? We have just the right cure for your curse—a whale of a tale penned completely in verse! Come and listen, if you can find someone to read, or recite for yourself these most valiant of deeds—in which thrills and enchantment are stolen from Earth, and a young girl, Katrina Katrell, proves her worth. What's more, there's a zorgle from Zorgamazoo; his name's Morty, and his mettle gets tested, too.

"This book is a natural descendant to the works of Dr. Seuss and Roald Dahl." Booklist.

Whelan, Gloria

All my noble dreams and then what happens. Gloria Whelan. Simon & Schuster Books for Young Readers, 2013. 224 p.

Grades: 6 7 8 9 10   **Fic**
    1. Windsor, Edward, Duke of, 1894-1972. 2. British Raj (1858-1947) 3. 1920s 4. Children of military personnel 5. British in India 6. National liberation movements 7. Families 8. Teenage girls 9. India 10. London, England 11. Historical fiction
    ISBN 9781442449763

                                                    LC 2012018599

As Rosalind continues to straddle the proper English world of her family and the culture of 1920s India where they live, her support of Gandhi and his followers in opposing British rule grows and she considers trying to carry the rebels' message to Edward, Prince of Wales, during his visit.

★ **Homeless** bird. Gloria Whelan. Harper Collins, 2000. 216 p.

Grades: 6 7 8 9 10   **Fic**
    1. Homeless teenagers 2. Abandoned teenagers 3. Self-sufficiency 4. Independence in teenage girls 5. Thirteen-year-old girls 6. India 7. Coming-of-age stories
    ISBN 0060284544

                                                    LC 9933241

National Book Award for Young People's Literature, 2000.

Kali discovers that the husband her parents have chosen for her is sickly.

"This beautifully told, inspiring story takes readers on a fascinating journey through modern India and the universal intricacies of a young woman's heart." Booklist.

Small acts of amazing courage. Gloria Whelan. Simon & Schuster Books for Young Readers, 2011. 160 p.

Grades: 6 7 8 9 10   **Fic**
    1. British Raj (1858-1947) 2. 1910s 3. Independence in teenage girls 4. Children of military personnel 5. Independence (Personal quality) 6. Aunts 7. British in India 8. India 9. London, England 10. Historical fiction
    ISBN 9781442409316

                                                    LC 2010013164

In 1919, independent-minded fifteen-year-old Rosalind lives in India with her English parents, and when they fear she has fallen in with some rebellious types who believe in Indian self-government, she is sent "home" to London, where she has never been before and where her older brother died, to stay with her two aunts.

"Whelan balances the facts with distinctive, sometimes comical characterizations and vibrant, original sensory descriptions. . . . Whelan's vibrant, episodic story explores the tension between doing what's right, rather than what's expected, and the infinite complexities of colonialism." Booklist.

Whipple, Natalie

House of ivy and sorrow. Natalie Whipple. HarperTeen, an imprint of HarperCollinsPublishers, 2014. 352 p.

Grades: 8 9 10 11 12   **Fic**
    1. Witches 2. Curses 3. Black magic 4. Witchcraft 5. Grandmothers 6. Iowa 7. Urban fantasy
    ISBN 9780062120182

When a mysterious Curse that killed her mother and other members of her family strikes, Jo Hemlock realizes that her secret identity as a witch is threatening the human life she has struggled to protect.

"Josephine, 17, lives with her grandmother in a house under the interstate where it's rumored that an old witch can make someone love you if you're willing to give her your pinkie finger. Jo knows that the rumors are true, because her grandmother is that witch...This is a fast-paced fantasy, with just the right amount of romance and realism. Readers will relate to Jo's relationships with her family, crush, and two best friends. Despite the current glut of supernatural and urban fantasy, this tale will stand out." School Library Journal.

White, Ellen Emerson

White House autumn. Ellen Emerson White Feiwel & Friends, 2008, c1985. 343 p.: President's daughter series

Grades: 7 8 9 10   **Fic**
    1. Seventeen-year-old girls 2. Mass media 3. Attempted assassination 4. High school seniors 5. Teenage girls 6. United States 7. Washington, DC
    ISBN 0312374895

The President's teenage daughter is a victim of kidnapping by terrorists.

"Apart from its novelistic merits, the book prompts thought on the burdens of public office, the need for character in the elect and their families." Publishers Weekly.

White, J. A.

A **path** begins. J.A. White. Katherine Tegen Books, an imprint of HarperCollinsPublishers, 2014. 320 p.: The thickety

Grades: 5 6 7 8   **Fic**
    1. Forests 2. Magical books 3. Magic 4. Twelve-year-old girls 5. Preteen girls 6. Fantasy fiction
    ISBN 9780062257246

Shunned by villagers who convicted her mother of witchcraft years earlier, Kara is lured by an unusual bird into a forbidden magical forest where she discovers a strange book of unspeakable power that may have belonged to her mother.

"When Kara was just a child, she was accused of witchcraft and forced to watch her mother executed for the same crime. Ever after, she and her family have lived in their isolated theocratic community as pariahs...White's persistent dark imagery, along with Offermann's eerie silhouette spot illustrations, adds to the overall dark atmosphere." Booklist.

White, Kiersten

The **Guinevere** deception. Kiersten White. Delacorte Press, 2019. 352 p.: Camelot rising (Kiersten White)

Grades: 7 8 9 10 11 12   **Fic**
    1. Arthur, King 2. Knights and knighthood 3. Women wizards 4. Changelings 5. Impostors 6. Magic 7. Arthurian fantasy 8. Fantasy fiction 9. Fairy tale and folklore-inspired fiction
    ISBN 9780525581673

Deadly jousts, duplicitous knights, and forbidden romances are nothing compared to the greatest threat of all: the girl with the long black hair, riding on horseback through the dark woods toward Arthur.

Because when your whole existence is a lie, how can you trust even yourself?

"More diverse than many Camelot representations , this is a retelling designed for a modern audience more interested in people than battles and more intrigued by identity and affection than honor and questing." Kirkus.

Paranormalcy. Kiersten White. HarperTeen, 2010. 335 p.: Paranormalcy trilogy

Grades: 7 8 9 10 11 12   **Fic**
1. Prophecies 2. Fairies 3. Shapeshifters 4. Supernatural 5. Identity (Psychology) 6. Urban fantasy 7. Paranormal romances
ISBN 0061985848

LC 9780061985843 (trade bdg.)
Evie, the only known human with the ability to see through supernatural "glamours," works for the International Paranormal Containment Agency (IPCA) tracking down dangerous creatures. (Really, she finds the work dull and would rather be shopping, watching TV, or at the very least at home painting her weapons pink.) But when a mysterious shape-shifter invades the IPCA and brings news of a string of paranormal murders, things start to heat up.

"White shows the technique and polish of a pro in this absorbing romance, which comes closer than most to hitting the Buffy mark. . . . The action is fast; fun and fear are in abundance; and Lend's father is actually a cool grownup." Publishers Weekly.

Supernaturally. Kiersten White. HarperTeen, 2011. 320 p.: Paranormalcy trilogy

Grades: 7 8 9 10   **Fic**
1. Fairies 2. Vampires 3. Prophecies 4. Shapeshifters 5. Supernatural 6. Urban fantasy 7. Paranormal romances
ISBN 9780061985867

LC 2010040426
Sixteen-year-old Evie thinks she has left the International Paranormal Containment Agency, and her own paranormal activities, behind her when she is recruited to help at the Agency, where she discovers more about the dark faerie prophecy that threatens her future.

"Evie's voice is the best part of the story, as she balances her supernatural abilities against typical teen concerns and obsessions." Kirkus.

White, Ruth, 1942-

★ **Belle** Prater's boy. Ruth White. Farrar Straus Giroux, 1996 196 p.

Grades: 5 6 7 8   **Fic**
1. Coal towns 2. Grief in children 3. Cousins 4. Appalachian Region 5. Realistic fiction
ISBN 0374306680
Cousins living in a Virginia coal town have both experienced the loss of someone dear to them. Through the stories they tell each other and the adventures they share, they learn to look beyond grief and imagine better lives for themselves.

"White's prose evokes the coal mining region of Virginia and the emotional quality of her characters' transformations." Horn Book Guide.

The **treasure** of Way Down Deep. Ruth White. Margaret Ferguson Books, 2013. 176 p.

Grades: 5 6 7 8   **Fic**
1. 1950s 2. Treasure troves 3. Orphans 4. Small towns 5. Boarding houses 6. Abandoned children 7. West Virginia 8. Historical fiction
ISBN 9780374380670

In 1954, when mine closings bring an economic crisis to Way Down Deep, West Virginia, foundling Ruby Jolene Hurley makes a thirteenth-birthday wish to find the treasure rumored to have been buried by one of the town's founders.

★ **Way** Down Deep. Ruth White. Farrar Straus Giroux, 2007. 208 p.

Grades: 5 6 7 8   **Fic**
1. 1950s 2. Abandoned children 3. Community life 4. Identity (Psychology) 5. Orphans 6. Boarding houses 7. West Virginia 8. Historical fiction
ISBN 0374382514

LC 2006046324
In the West Virginia town of Way Down Deep in the 1950s, a foundling called Ruby June is happily living with Miss Arbutus at the local boarding house when suddenly, after the arrival of a family of outsiders, the mystery of Ruby's past begins to unravel.

"This is a story as tender as a breeze and as sharp as a tack. . . . At the heart of the story are profound questions that readers will enjoy puzzling out." Booklist.

White, T. H. (Terence Hanbury), 1906-1964

The **once** and future king. T.H. White. G. P. Putnam's Sons, 1958. 677 p.: Once and future king

Grades: 8 9 10 11 12 Adult   **Fic**
1. Arthur, King 2. Knights and knighthood 3. Grail 4. Merlin (Legendary character) 5. Wizards 6. Magic 7. Great Britain 8. Arthurian fantasy 9. Historical fantasy 10. Modern classics
ISBN 0399105972

LC 58010760
Merlyn instructs Arthur and his brother Sir Kay in the ways of the world. One of them will need it— the king has died leaving no heir, and a rightful one must be found by pulling a sword from an anvil resting on a stone. In the second and third parts of the novel, Arthur has become king and the kingdom is threatened from the north. In the final two books, the aging king faces his greatest challenge, when his own son threatens to overthrow him. In The Book of Merlyn, Arthur's tutor Merlyn reappears, and teaches him that, even in the face of apparent ruin, there is hope.

Whitman, Emily

Wildwing. Emily Whitman. Greenwillow Books, c2010. 359 p.

Grades: 7 8 9 10   **Fic**
1. Medieval period (476-1492) 2. 13th century 3. 1910s 4. Plantagenet period (1154-1485) 5. Teenage girl household employees 6. Time travel (Past) 7. Social classes 8. Mistaken identity 9. Falconers 10. Great Britain 11. Fantasy fiction
ISBN 9780061724527

LC 2009044189
In 1913 London, fifteen-year-old Addy is a lowly servant, but when she gets inside an elevator car in her employer's study, she is suddenly transported to a castle in 1240 and discovers that she is mistaken for the lord's intended bride.

"Whitman populates both of her worlds with vivid, believable characters. . . . This historical novel with a time-travel twist of sci-fi will find an avid readership." School Library Journal.

Whitney, Daisy

When you were here. by Daisy Whitney. Little, Brown and Company, 2013. 272 p.

Grades: 7 8 9 10   **Fic**
1. Grief in teenage boys 2. Children of people with cancer
3. Mothers and sons 4. Loss (Psychology) 5. Breaking up
(Interpersonal relations) 6. Tokyo, Japan 7. Los Angeles, California
8. Realistic fiction 9. Coming-of-age stories
ISBN 9780316209748

LC 2012031409

When his mother dies three weeks before his high school graduation, Danny goes to Tokyo, where his mother had been going for cancer treatments, to learn about the city his mother loved and, with the help of his friends, come to terms with her death.

"Danny's mother has recently died from cancer, his father died years ago, his estranged sister lives in China, and he and Holland, the love of his life, have broken up. A trip to Japan is enlightening and helps him handle a shocking secret he learns about Holland. The extent of Danny's problems stretches credulity, but readers will be caught up in the drama." Horn Book.

Whittemore, Jo, 1977-

Odd girl in. Jo Whittemore. Aladdin, Simon and Schuster Childrens, 2011. 240 p.

Grades: 4 5 6   **Fic**
1. Practical jokers 2. Practical jokes 3. Crushes in girls 4. Personal conduct 5. Interpersonal relations 6. Realistic fiction
ISBN 9781442412842

"Spunky 12-year-old Alex doesn't really want friends or a social life. . . . She hates girly giggling parties and doesn't see any other girls in her middle school that she'd want to have as a friend, so she just concentrates on following in the footsteps of her prankster older twin brothers. . . . Alex's absent mother provides an element of drama in this otherwise witty, laugh-out-loud romp. Whittemore handles not only the comedy but deftly portrays Alex's and her brothers' advancement into a more mature state of mind. It should keep middle-schoolers laughing from start to finish." Kirkus.

Whyman, Matt

Goldstrike: a thriller. Matt Whyman. Atheneum Books for Young Readers, 2010. 272 p.

Grades: 7 8 9 10   **Fic**
1. CIA 2. Qaida (Organization) 3. Fugitives 4. Hackers 5. Resourcefulness in teenage boys 6. Bounty hunters 7. Teenage fugitives 8. London, England 9. Thrillers and suspense
ISBN 9781416995104

LC 2009017830

After escaping Camp Twilight, eighteen-year-old Carl Hobbes and Beth, his girlfriend, begin a new life in London, England, where he attempts to program Sphynx Cargo's highly intelligent supercomputer to help protect them from the CIA and assassins.

"The action sequences are believable and often realistically brutal, and the climactic battle is intense and entertaining." Publishers Weekly.

Icecore: a Carl Hobbes thriller. Matt Whyman. Atheneum Books for Young Readers, 2007 307 p.

Grades: 7 8 9 10   **Fic**
1. Hackers 2. Prisoners 3. Torture 4. Military bases 5. Seventeen-year-old boys 6. Arctic regions 7. Fort Knox, Kentucky 8. Adventure stories 9. Thrillers and suspense
ISBN 9781416949077

LC 2007002674

Seventeen-year-old Englishman Carl Hobbes meant no harm when he hacked into Fort Knox's security system, but at Camp Twilight in the Arctic Circle, known as the Guantanamo Bay of the north, he is tortured to reveal information about a conspiracy of which he was never a part.

"Powered by a fast-paced narrative, this exploration of numerous timely themes . . . gives the eminently readable adventure a degree of depth." Publishers Weekly.

Wiechman, Kathy Cannon

Like a river: a Civil War novel. Kathy Cannon Wiechman. Calkins Creek, an imprint of Highlights, 2015. 336 p.

Grades: 5 6 7 8   **Fic**
1. American Civil War era (1861-1865) 2. 1860s 3. Teenage soldiers 4. Friendship 5. Secrets 6. Union soldiers 7. Prisons 8. United States 9. Historical fiction
ISBN 9781629792095

"Three years have passed since the beginning of the Civil War, when two underage teens, West Virginian Paul Settles and Ohioan Leander Jordan, both with secrets to guard, enlist in the Union Army. Their paths cross in a military hospital, where their mysteries begin to unravel, but the plot takes them in separate directions...A truly excellent first purchase for all fans of historical fiction who enjoy a hint of romance." School Library Journal.

Wiggins, Bethany

Stung. Bethany Wiggins. Walker & Co., 2013. 294 p.

Grades: 7 8 9 10 11 12   **Fic**
1. Post-apocalypse 2. Survival (after epidemics) 3. Dystopias 4. Seventeen-year-old girls 5. Vaccines 6. Apocalyptic fiction 7. Science fiction
ISBN 9780802734181

LC 2012027183

When a vaccine to save endangered bees causes their sting to turn children into ferocious killer beasts, the uninfected build a wall to keep the beasts out, but Fiona wakes up on the wrong side of the wall.

"Wiggins. . . muses on the dangers of science and medicine and deftly maps out the chain of events that has led to catastrophe, creating a violent world vastly different from ours but still recognizable. With a stirring conclusion and space for a sequel, it's an altogether captivating story." Kirkus.

Wiles, Deborah

Anthem. Deborah Wiles. Scholastic, 2019. 480 p.: Sixties trilogy

Grades: 5 6 7 8   **Fic**
1. 1960s 2. Vietnam War, 1961-1975 3. Teenagers 4. Voyages and travels 5. Cousins 6. Draft 7. United States 8. Historical fiction
ISBN 9780545106092

The remarkable story of two cousins who must take a road trip across American in 1969 in order to let a teen know he's been drafted to fight in Vietnam. Full of photos, music, and figures of the time, this is the masterful story of what it's like to be young and American in troubled times.

"It's all complicated, of course, but the novel is wonderfully true to the reality and spirit of the time." Booklist.

Includes bibliographical references.

★ The **Aurora** County All-Stars. Deborah Wiles. Harcourt, c2007. 242 p.: Aurora County trilogy

Grades: 4 5 6   **Fic**
1. Boy baseball players 2. Race relations 3. Pageants 4. Baseball 5. Death 6. Mississippi 7. Realistic fiction 8. Coming-of-age stories
ISBN 0152060685

LC 2006102551

For most boys in a small Mississippi town, the biggest concern one hot summer is whether their annual July 4th baseball game will be cancelled due to their county's anniversary pageant, but after the death of the old man to whom twelve-year-old star pitcher House Jackson has been secretly reading for a year, House uncovers secrets about the man and the history of baseball in Aurora County that could fix everything.

"Quotations from Walt Whitman's poetry, baseball players and Aurora County news dispatches pepper the story and add color. . . . A home run for Wiles." Publishers Weekly.

★ **Countdown**. Deborah Wiles. Scholastic, c2010. 377 p.: Sixties trilogy
Grades: 5 6 7 8   **Fic**
    1. 1960s 2. Children of military personnel 3. Cuban Missile Crisis, 1962 4. Families 5. Growing up 6. Best friends 7. Maryland 8. Historical fiction
    ISBN 9780545106054
The fearful events of the 1962 Cuban Missile Crisis are witnessed by eleven-year-old Franny, who finds her life and perspectives changing throughout the course of a week that is also marked by difficult family issues.

"Wiles skillfully keeps many balls in the air, giving readers a story that appeals across the decades as well as offering enticing paths into the history." Booklist.

Kent State. Deborah Wiles. Scholastic Press, 2020. 144 p.
Grades: 7 8 9 10 11 12   **Fic**
    1. Kent State University. 2. 1970s 3. Kent State shootings, May 4, 1970 4. College students -- Political activity -- History 20th century 5. Vietnam War, 1961-1975 -- Protest movements 6. Student movements -- History 20th century 7. Ohio 8. Historical fiction 9. Novels in verse
    ISBN 9781338356281

                                      LC 2019047100
Told from different points of view—protesters, students, National Guardsmen, and "townies"—recounts the story of what happened at Kent State in May 1970, when four college students were killed by National Guardsmen, and a student protest was turned into a bloody battlefield.

"The tangle of voices is stunningly realized, making this not only a thought-provoking private read but also an stellar candidate for group performance." Bulletin of the Center for Children's Books.

★ **Revolution**. Deborah Wiles. Scholastic Press 2014. 495 p.: Sixties trilogy
Grades: 5 6 7 8   **Fic**
    1. 1960s 2. Blended families 3. African American boys 4. Voter registration 5. Twelve-year-old girls 6. Preteen girls 7. Mississippi 8. Historical fiction
    ISBN 9780545106078
Golden Kite Award for Fiction, 2015.
Struggling to adapt within her newly blended family in 1964 Mississippi, young Sunny witnesses increasingly scary community agitation when activists from the North arrive in town to help register African-Americans to vote.

"Wiles does an excellent job of entwining the two plot strands and seamlessly integrating her exhaustive research, which is detailed at the book's conclusion. . . . As in Countdown, the outstanding period artwork, photographs, snippets of sayings, and songs interspersed throughout bring a troubled time close." Booklist.

Wilkinson, Lili, 1981-
    Pink. Lili Wilkinson. HarperTeen, 2011. 310 p.
Grades: 7 8 9 10 11 12   **Fic**
    1. Lesbian teenagers 2. Popularity 3. Identity (Psychology) 4. Self-discovery in teenage girls 5. Self-discovery 6. Australia 7.

Realistic fiction 8. LGBTQIA fiction
    ISBN 9780061926532
"The novel is in turn laugh-out-loud funny, endearing, and heartbreaking as Ava repeatedly steps into teenage social land mines with unexpected results. Because Wilkinson doesn't rely on stereotypes, the characters are well-developed, and interactions between them feel genuine." Voice of Youth Advocates.

Willey, Margaret
    Beetle boy. by Margaret Willey. Carolrhoda Lab, [2014] 208 p.
Grades: 8 9 10 11   **Fic**
    1. Eighteen-year-old men 2. Psychic trauma in men 3. Memories 4. Teenage boy/girl relations 5. Beetles
    ISBN 9781467726399

                                        LC 2013036853
Terrible memories resurface when Charlie's girlfriend asks questions about his childhood.

"Willey takes readers along on Charlie's painful journey back to physical and emotional health via a meandering timeline of flashbacks, dreams and wrenching conversations, skillfully weaving together the bits and pieces of his life. Innovative use of type brings an immediacy to Charlie's struggles as he slowly looks the truth—and his brother—squarely in the face." Kirkus.

Williams, Alicia, 1970-
    Genesis begins again. Alicia D. Williams. Atheneum, 2019. 336 p.
Grades: 5 6 7 8   **Fic**
    1. African Americans 2. Self-esteem 3. Racism 4. Family problems 5. Human skin color 6. Realistic fiction 7. African American fiction
    ISBN 9781481465809

                                        LC 2018030079
Thirteen-year-old Genesis tries again and again to lighten her black skin, thinking it is the root of her family's troubles, before discovering reasons to love herself as is.

"With its relatable and sympathetic protagonist, complex setting, and exceptional emotional range, this title is easy to recommend." Publishers Weekly.

Williams, Carol Lynch
    The **chosen** one. Carol Lynch Williams. St. Martin's Griffin, 2009. 288 p.
Grades: 7 8 9 10   **Fic**
    1. Cults 2. Polygamy 3. Arranged marriage 4. Families 5. Thirteen-year-old girls 6. Coming-of-age stories 7. Realistic fiction
    ISBN 9780312555115

                                        LC 2009004800
In a polygamous cult in the desert, Kyra, not yet fourteen, sees being chosen to be the seventh wife of her uncle as just punishment for having read books and kissed a boy, in violation of Prophet Childs' teachings, and is torn between facing her fate and running away from all that she knows and loves.

"This book is a highly emotional, terrifying read. It is not measured or objective. Physical abuse, fear, and even murder are constants. It is a girl-in-peril story, and as such, it is impossible to put down and holds tremendous teen appeal." Voice of Youth Advocates.

Williams, Ismee
    Water in May. Ismee Williams. Amulet Books, 2017. 309 p.

Grades: 7 8 9 10 11 12   **Fic**
   1. Pregnant teenagers 2. Hispanic Americans 3. Heart -- Diseases 4. Decision-making 5. Teenage pregnancy 6. Realistic fiction
ISBN 9781419725395
                                    LC 2017008518

Pregnant at fifteen, Mari Pujols believes the baby will supply the family love she yearns for but when she learns the fetus has a heart defect, her friends, sometimes boyfriend, and doctor are there for her.

"Debut author Williams creates an unforgettable young character who will make readers reconsider their assumptions about teen moms, in particular Latina teen moms." Kirkus.

Williams, Michael, 1962-

Diamond boy. Michael Williams. Little, Brown and Company, 2014. 400 p.

Grades: 7 8 9 10   **Fic**
   1. Diamond mines and mining 2. Corruption 3. Blended families 4. Shona (African people) 5. Survival 6. Zimbabwe
ISBN 9780316320696

"Written in diary format, the story brings the reader into the mind and soul of a young refugee suffering in a hell created by the greed and violence of powerful adults. More than simply a good read, Diamond Boy is a multilayered, teachable novel with a variety of approaches and is highly recommended for middle and high school collections." Voice of Youth Advocates.

Now is the time for running. Michael Williams. Little, Brown, 2011, c2009. 240 p.

Grades: 6 7 8 9 10   **Fic**
   1. Refugees 2. Brothers and sisters of children with disabilities 3. Soccer 4. Brothers 5. People with developmental disabilities 6. Zimbabwe 7. Realistic fiction
ISBN 9780316077903
                                    LC 2010043460

When soldiers attack a small village in Zimbabwe, Deo goes on the run with Innocent, his older, mentally disabled brother, carrying little but a leather soccer ball filled with money, and after facing prejudice, poverty, and tragedy, it is in soccer that Deo finds renewed hope.

"There is plenty of material to captivate readers: fast-paced soccer matches every bit as tough as the players; the determination of Deo and his fellow refugees to survive unthinkably harsh conditions; and raw depictions of violence.... But it's the tender relationship between Deo and Innocent, along with some heartbreaking twists of fate, that will endure in readers' minds." Publishers Weekly.

Williams, Suzanne, 1949-

Bull rider. Suzanne Williams. Margaret K. McElderry Books, 2009. 256 p.

Grades: 7 8 9 10   **Fic**
   1. Iraq War veterans 2. Bull riding 3. Brothers 4. Fourteen-year-old boys 5. Skateboards and skateboarding 6. Realistic fiction
ISBN 9781416961307
                                    LC 2007052518

When his older brother, a bull-riding champion, returns from the Iraq War partially paralyzed, fourteen-year-old Cam takes a break from skateboarding to enter a bull-riding contest, in hopes of winning the $15,000 prize and motivating his depressed brother to continue with his rehabilitation.

"The mix of wild macho action with family anguish and tenderness will grab teens.... [This is a] powerful contemporary story of family, community, and work." Booklist.

Williams-Garcia, Rita

★ **Gone** crazy in Alabama. Rita Williams-Garcia. Amistad, an imprint of HarperCollinsPublishers, 2015. 224 p.: Gaither sisters

Grades: 4 5 6 7 8   **Fic**
   1. 1960s 2. Family visits 3. African American families 4. Grandmothers 5. Families 6. African American girls 7. Alabama 8. Historical fiction 9. African American fiction
ISBN 9780062215871

Coretta Scott King Award, Author Category, 2016.

"This well-crafted depiction of a close-knit community in rural Alabama works beautifully, with language that captures its humor, sorrow and resilience. Rich in all areas, Delphine and her sisters' third outing will fully satisfy the many fans of their first two." Kirkus.

Jumped. Rita Williams-Garcia. HarperTeen, 2009. 169 p.

Grades: 8 9 10 11 12   **Fic**
   1. Urban teenagers 2. Anger in teenage girls 3. Violence in schools 4. Dilemmas 5. Bullying and bullies 6. Realistic fiction 7. African American fiction
ISBN 9780060760915
                                    LC 2008022381

The lives of Leticia, Dominique, and Trina are irrevocably intertwined through the course of one day in an urban high school after Leticia overhears Dominique's plans to beat up Trina and must decide whether or not to get involved.

"In alternating chapters narrated by Leticia, Trina, and Dominique, Williams-Garcia has given her characters strong, individual voices that ring true to teenage speech, and she lets them make their choices without judgment or moralizing." School Library Journal.

Like sisters on the homefront. Rita Williams-Garcia. Lodestar Books, c1995. 165 p.

Grades: 7 8 9 10   **Fic**
   1. Teenage mothers 2. African American teenage girls 3. Christian teenage girls 4. Families 5. Cousins 6. Georgia 7. Realistic fiction 8. African American fiction
ISBN 0525674659
                                  LC 95003690 /AC

Troubled fourteen-year-old Gayle is sent down South to live with her uncle and aunt, where her life begins to change as she experiences the healing power of the family.

"Beautifully written, the text captures the cadence and rhythm of New York street talk and the dilemma of being poor, black, and uneducated. This is a gritty, realistic, well-told story." School Library Journal.

★ **One** crazy summer. Rita Williams-Garcia. HarperCollins, 2010. 224 p.: Gaither sisters

Grades: 4 5 6 7 8   **Fic**
   1. Black Panther Party. 2. 1960s 3. African American girls 4. Mother-deserted children 5. Sisters 6. Mothers 7. Poets 8. Oakland, California 9. California 10. Historical fiction 11. African American fiction
ISBN 9780060760885
                                    LC 2009009293

Coretta Scott King Award, Author Category, 2011.
Scott O'Dell Historical Fiction Award, 2011.

In the summer of 1968, after travelling from Brooklyn to Oakland, California, to spend a month with the mother they barely know, eleven-year-old Delphine and her two younger sisters arrive to a cold welcome as they discover that their mother, a dedicated poet and printer, is resentful of the intrusion of their visit and wants them to attend a nearby Black Panther summer camp.

"Delphine's growing awareness of injustice on a personal and universal level is smoothly woven into the story in poetic language that will stimulate and move readers." Publishers Weekly.

★ **P.S.** be eleven. Rita Williams-Garcia. Amistad Press, 2013. 288 p.: Gaither sisters

Grades: 4 5 6 7 8   **Fic**
  1. 1960s 2. African American girls 3. Children and single parent dating 4. Mother-separated girls 5. Independence (Personal quality) 6. Sisters 7. Brooklyn, New York City 8. Historical fiction 9. African American fiction
ISBN 9780061938634
Coretta Scott King Award, Author Category, 2014.

A sequel to One Crazy Summer finds the Gaither sisters returning to Brooklyn, where they adapt to new feelings of independence while managing changes large and small, from Pa's new girlfriend to a very different Uncle Darnell's return from Vietnam.

"Soars as a finely drawn portrait of a family in flux and as a memorable slice of a specific time in our nations history." Booklist.

Williamson, Victoria

The **fox** girl and the white gazelle. Victoria Williamson. Kelpies, 2018. 272 p.

Grades: 5 6 7 8 9   **Fic**
  1. Refugees, Syrian 2. Girl runners 3. Animal rescue 4. Bullying and bullies 5. Foxes 6. Realistic fiction
ISBN 9781782504900

An unlikely friendship between twelve-year-old refugee Reema and her bullying neighbor Caylin forms after they find an injured fox.

Wilson, Diane L.

Black storm comin'. Diane Lee Wilson. Margaret K. McElderry Books, 2005. 304 p.

Grades: 7 8 9 10   **Fic**
  1. Twelve-year-old boys 2. Multiracial children 3. Multiracial boys 4. Pony Express 5. Slavery 6. The West (United States) 7. United States 8. Historical fiction
ISBN 0689871376

         LC 2004009438

Twelve-year-old Colton, son of a black mother and a white father, takes a job with the Pony Express in 1860 after his father abandons the family on their California-bound wagon train, and risks his life to deliver an important letter that may affect the growing conflict between the North and South.

"Wilson masterfully creates a multidimensional character in Colton. . . . Readers will absorb greater lessons as they become engrossed in the excitement, beauty, and terror of Colton's journey to California and manhood." Booklist.

Firehorse. Diane Lee Wilson. Margaret K. McElderry Books, 2006. 336 p.

Grades: 7 8 9 10   **Fic**
  1. 19th century 2. Fifteen-year-old girls 3. Teenage girls 4. Girls and horses 5. Teenage girls and horses 6. Veterinary medicine 7. Boston, Massachusetts 8. Historical fiction
ISBN 1416915516

         LC 2005030785

Spirited fifteen-year-old horse lover Rachel Selby determines to become a veterinarian, despite the opposition of her rigid father, her proper mother, and the norms of Boston in 1872, while that city faces a serial arsonist and an epidemic spreading through its firehorse population.

"Wilson paces the story well, with tension building. . . . The novel's finest achievement, though, is the convincing depiction of family dynamics in an era when men ruled the household and and women, who had few opportunities, folded their dreams and put them away with the linens they embroidered." Booklist.

Wilson, John, 1951 August 2-

Ghost moon. John Wilson. Orca Book Publishers, 2011. 171 p.: Desert legends trilogy

Grades: 6 7 8 9   **Fic**
  1. 1870s 2. Outlaws 3. Gunfights 4. Murder 5. Violence 6. Sixteen-year-old boys 7. New Mexico 8. Westerns
ISBN 9781554698790

The year is 1878, and young Jim is not yet ready to return to Canada. Instead he heads up to New Mexico in hopes of finding work and building a life. On the way he meets Bill Bonney (later to be known as Billy the Kid), who takes him to a ranch south of the town of Lincoln, where they both find work as cowboys. Little does Jim know that he is about to get caught up in a vicious battle for the lucrative army contracts with nearby Fort Stanton.

"A young wanderer lands in the middle of New Mexico's Lincoln County War. . . . 16-year-old James Doolen falls in with Bill Bonney (not yet known as Billy the Kid) a charming but decidedly mercurial teenager who hares off on a vicious killing spree after their new boss, John Tunstall, is murdered by a rival merchant's gang of hired gunmen. . . . Action fans will thrill to the gunplay and other dangers. James' conflicting feelings about his archetypically dangerous friend . . . introduce thought provoking elements. A tale of the Old West with a sturdy historical base and nary a dull moment." Kirkus.

Victorio's war. John Wilson. Orca Book Pub., 2012. 157 p.: Desert legends trilogy

Grades: 6 7 8 9   **Fic**
  1. 1870s 2. Outlaws 3. Gunfights 4. Sixteen-year-old boys 5. Doolen, James (Fictitious character) 6. Teenage boys 7. New Mexico 8. Westerns
ISBN 9781554698820

Now a scout for the army, Jim Doolen finds himself involved in a battle to force Victorio's Apaches onto a reservation far from their traditional lands.

Written in blood. John Wilson. Orca Book Publishers, c2010. 157 p.: Desert legends trilogy

Grades: 6 7 8 9   **Fic**
  1. 1870s 2. Father-deserted children 3. Violence 4. Voyages and travels 5. Fathers 6. Sixteen-year-old boys 7. Westerns
ISBN 9781554692705

"Told in a terse, present-tense narrative, James' adventures will thrill all fans of traditional pulp-style oaters." Booklist.

Wilson, Kip

White Rose. by Kip Wilson. Houghton Mifflin Harcourt, [2019] 368 p.

Grades: 7 8 9 10 11 12   **Fic**
  1. Scholl, Sophie, 1921-1943. 2. Scholl, Hans, 1918-1943. 3. Munich University -- Riot, 1943. 4. Second World War era (1939-1945) 5. Resistance to government 6. Courage in women 7. Nazism 8. White Rose (Anti-Nazi group) 9. Anti-Nazi movement 10. Germany 11. Biographical fiction 12. Novels in verse 13.

Historical fiction
ISBN 9781328594433

LC 2018026607

Tells the story of Sophie Scholl, a young German college student who challenges the Nazi regime during World War II as part of the White Rose, a non-violent resistance group.

"Real events made deeply personal in an intense, bone-chilling reading experience. " Kirkus.

Includes bibliographical references.

Wilson, Nathan D.

The **dragon's** tooth. N.D. Wilson. Random House, 2011. 485 p.: Ashtown burials

Grades: 5 6 7 8   **Fic**

1. Parent-separated children 2. Secret societies 3. Apprentices 4. Parallel universes 5. Magic 6. Fantasy fiction
ISBN 9780375864391

After a mysterious, violent incident that results in the kidnapping of their older brother, Cyrus and Antigone Smith discover that they're now part of the Order of Brendan, a secret society for explorers. The siblings head to the Order's headquarters in Ashtown in search of answers, but instead they encounter immortal enemies, mythological creatures, magical artifacts, and shocking family secrets.

"This fast-paced fantasy quickly draws readers in to its alternate reality. . . . Allusions to mythology and complex character development . . . make Wilson's first in a proposed series a gem." Booklist.

Winerip, Michael, 1951-

Adam Canfield of the Slash. Michael Winerip. Candlewick Press, 2005. 326 p.: Adam Canfield

Grades: 5 6 7 8   **Fic**

1. Middle school students 2. Students 3. Journalists 4. Child journalists 5. Authority (Psychology) 6. Mysteries
ISBN 0763623407

LC 2004061843

Adam Canfield is already sorry that he agreed to be co-editor of his school's newspaper, The Slash. He's made for courting danger while digging up the truth—not for supervising over-eager third-grade cub reporters. But there is something strange going on at Harris Elementary/Middle School, and it's up to Adam, his co-editor Jennifer, and the rest of the newspaper's staff to bring the story to light.

"This is a deceptively fun read that somehow manages to present kids with some of the most subtle social and ethical questions currently shaping their futures." School Library Journal.

Winfrey, Kerry

Things Jolie needs to do before she bites it. Kerry Winfrey. Feiwel & Friends 2018 256 p.

Grades: 8 9 10 11   **Fic**

1. Surgery 2. Teenage girls 3. Fear in teenage girls 4. Fear of death 5. Teenage boy/girl relations 6. Realistic fiction
ISBN 9781250119544

Anticipating surgery for a lifelong dental condition that has caused pain and unpopularity, Jolie is alarmed by a worst-case-scenario reality show and decides she wants to live life to the fullest just in case the surgery does not go as expected.

Winters, Ben H.

The **secret** life of Ms. Finkleman. Ben H. Winters. Harper, c2010. 247 p.

Grades: 4 5 6 7   **Fic**

1. Music teachers 2. Rock concerts 3. Tutoring 4. Punk rock

musicians 5. Music -- Competitions 6. Mysteries
ISBN 9780061965418

LC 2010004601

Spurred by a special project from her social studies teacher, seventh-grader Bethesda Fielding uncovers the secret identity of her music teacher, which leads to a most unusual concert performance and a tutoring assignment.

"Liberally laced with humor and featuring an upbeat heroine, unexpected friendship and rock-music trivia, this witty middle-school drama offers a lighthearted lesson in the importance of getting the facts straight." Kirkus.

Winters, Cat

In the shadow of blackbirds. Cat Winters. Amulet Books, 2013. 304 p.

Grades: 8 9 10 11 12   **Fic**

1. First World War era (1914-1918) 2. 1910s 3. Spiritualism 4. Influenza Epidemic, 1918-1919 5. World War I 6. Ghosts 7. Sixteen-year-old girls 8. San Diego, California 9. Historical fiction 10. Ghost stories
ISBN 9781419705304

LC 2012039262

In San Diego in 1918, as deadly influenza and World War I take their toll, sixteen-year-old Mary Shelley Black watches desperate mourners flock to seances and spirit photographers for comfort and, despite her scientific leanings, must consider if ghosts are real when her first love, killed in battle, returns.

"Winters strikes just the right balance between history and ghost story . . . . Vintage photographs contribute to the authenticity of the atmospheric and nicely paced storytelling." Kirkus.

Odd & true. by Cat Winters. Amulet Books, 2017. 368 p.

Grades: 8 9 10 11 12   **Fic**

1. 1900s(Decade) 2. Sisters -- Family relationships 3. Demon slayers 4. Missing persons investigation 5. Girls with poliomyelitis 6. Poliomyelitis 7. Historical fantasy
ISBN 9781419723100

LC 2017009966

Told from separate viewpoints, Odette returns in 1909 after a two-year absence, promising to rescue her disabled sister, Tru, from the monsters they were taught to believe in.

"Winters has woven an intricate and innovative pattern of structure, genre, and history that cannot fail to capture readers' imaginations." Kirkus.

Winthrop, Elizabeth

Counting on Grace. Elizabeth Winthrop. Wendy Lamb Books, 2006. 144 p.

Grades: 5 6 7 8   **Fic**

1. Hine, Lewis Wickes, 1874-1940 2. 1910s 3. Twelve-year-old girls 4. Mill workers 5. Child labor -- History 6. Child labor exploitation 7. Work environment 8. Pownal, Vermont 9. Vermont 10. Historical fiction
ISBN 038574644X

It's 1910 in Pownal, Vermont. At 12 Grace and her best friend Arthur must go to work in the mill, helping their mothers work the looms. Together Grace and Arthur write a secret letter to the Child Labor Board about underage children working in the mill. A few weeks later, Lewis Hine, a famous reformer arrives undercover to gather evidence. Grace meets him and appears in some of his photographs, changing her life forever.

"Much information on early photography and the workings of the textile mills is conveyed, and history and fiction are woven seamlessly together in this beautifully written novel." School Library Journal.

Wiseman, Eva, 1947-

Puppet. Eva Wiseman. Tundra Books, 2008. 243 p.

Grades: 7 8 9 10 11 12   **Fic**

1. 1880s 2. 19th century 3. Blood libel 4. Jews -- Persecutions 5. Trials (Murder) 6. Murder investigation 7. Household employees 8. Hungary 9. Historical fiction

ISBN 9780887768286

A fictionalized account of the last blood libel trial in Hungary in 1882 is told through the eyes of Julie, a friend of the murdered servant girl Esther and a servant at the jail where Morris Scharf, the accused, is imprisoned.

"Times are hard in Julie Vamosi's Hungarian village in the late nineteenth-century, and the townspeople . . . blame the Jews. After Julie's best friend, Esther, . . . disappears, the rumor spreads that the Jews cut her throat and drained her blood to drink with their Passover matzos. . . . Based on the records of a trial in 1883, this searing novel dramatizes virulent anti-Semitism from the viewpoint of a Christian child. . . . The climax is electrifying." Booklist.

Wiseman, Rosalind, 1969-

Boys, girls, and other hazardous materials. Rosalind Wiseman. G.P. Putnam's Sons, c2010. 282 p.

Grades: 8 9 10 11 12   **Fic**

1. Social acceptance in teenagers 2. Crushes in teenage girls 3. Hazing 4. Bullying and bullies 5. Social acceptance 6. Realistic fiction

ISBN 9780399247965

            LC 2009018446

Transferring to a new high school, freshman Charlotte "Charlie" Healey faces tough choices as she tries to shed her "mean girl" image.

"Wiseman succeeds in delivering realistic, likable characters whose challenges and mistakes are all too relatable." Bulletin of the Center for Children's Books.

Wisler, G. Clifton

Red Cap. Lodestar Books, 1991. 160 p.

Grades: 4 5 6 7   **Fic**

1. Powell, Ransom J., 1849-1899 2. Andersonville, Georgia Military Prison 3. American Civil War era (1861-1865) 4. Prisoners of war, Confederate 5. Thirteen-year-old boys 6. Teenage soldiers 7. Courage in teenage boys 8. Teenage boys -- Friendship 9. United States 10. Historical fiction 11. War stories

ISBN 0140369368

            LC 91021944

Ransom J. Powell, Yankee drummer boy, displays great courage when he's captured and sent to Andersonville Prison.

"The author presents a well-researched view of the war. He effectively interweaves the known facts of Powell's life with first-person accounts of other soldiers and prisoners to create an exciting story." School Library Journal.

Withers, Pam

First descent. Pam Withers. Tundra Books, 2011. 272 p.

Grades: 7 8 9 10   **Fic**

1. Kayaking 2. Grandfather and grandson 3. Seventeen-year-old boys 4. Rivers 5. Indigenous peoples 6. Colombia 7. Coming-of-age stories

ISBN 9781770492578

Rex is excited when he is given the opportunity to go kayaking on the El Furiso River in southwest Colombia. When he is there, he and an indígena named Myriam Calambás become caught up in the clash beteween paramilitaries and guerrillas.

"Withers flings the reader from one perilous adventure to another." Booklist.

Wittlinger, Ellen

Hard love. Ellen Wittlinger. Simon & Schuster Books for Young Readers, c1999. 224 p.

Grades: 7 8 9 10   **Fic**

1. Loneliness in teenage boys 2. Zines 3. Emotions in teenage boys 4. Loneliness 5. Writing 6. Realistic fiction

ISBN 0689821344

            LC 98006668

After starting to publish a zine in which he writes his secret feelings about his lonely life and his parents' divorce, sixteen-year-old John meets an unusual girl and begins to develop a healthier personality.

"John, cynical yet vulnerable, thinks he's immune to emotion until he meets bright, brittle Marisol, the author of his favorite zine. He falls in love, but Marisol, a lesbian, just wants to be friends. A love story of a different sort—funny, poignant, and thoughtful." Booklist.

Parrotfish. Ellen Wittlinger. Simon & Schuster Books for Young Readers, c2007. 304 p.

Grades: 7 8 9 10   **Fic**

1. Identity (Psychology) 2. Social acceptance 3. Transgender teenagers 4. Transgender teenage boys 5. Teenagers 6. LGBTQIA fiction 7. Coming-of-age stories 8. Realistic fiction

ISBN 9781416916222

            LC 2006009689

Grady, a transgendered high school student, yearns for acceptance by his classmates and family as he struggles to adjust to his new identity as a male.

"The author demonstrates well the complexity faced by transgendered people and makes the teen's frustration with having to fit into a category fully apparent." Publishers Weekly.

Wolf, Allan

The **watch** that ends the night: voices from the Titanic. Allan Wolf. Candlewick Press, 2011. 480 p.

Grades: 7 8 9 10   **Fic**

1. Titanic (Steamship) 2. 1910s 3. Shipwrecks 4. Social classes 5. Millionaires 6. Socialites 7. Historical fiction 8. Novels in verse

ISBN 9780763637033

            LC 2010040150

Recreates the 1912 sinking of the Titanic as observed by millionaire John Jacob Astor, a beautiful young Lebanese refugee finding first love, "Unsinkable" Molly Brown, Captain Smith, and others including the iceberg itself.

"A lyrical, monumental work of fact and imagination that reads like an oral history revved up by the drama of the event." Kirkus.

Includes bibliographical references.

Who killed Christopher Goodman?: based on a true crime. Allan Wolf. Candlewick Press, 2017. 269 p.

Grades: 8 9 10 11 12   **Fic**

1. 1970s 2. Guilt 3. Small towns 4. Murder investigation 5. Murder 6. Teenage murder victims 7. Virginia 8. Historical mysteries

ISBN 9780763656133

Everybody likes Chris Goodman, but when he is found dead, no one understands how something like this could happen.

Wolff, Virginia Euwer

Make lemonade. Virginia Euwer Wolff. H. Holt, c1993. 200 p.: Make lemonade trilogy

Grades: 8 9 10 11 12   **Fic**
1. Inner city teenage girls 2. Single teenage mothers 3. Babysitters 4. Poor families 5. Inner city 6. Realistic fiction 7. Novels in verse
ISBN 9780805022285
                                                   LC   92041182
Golden Kite Award for Fiction, 1993.

In order to earn money for college, fourteen-year-old LaVaughn babysits for a teenage mother of two. Written in 66 chapters, with text lines that break at natural speaking phrases.

"Fourteen-year-old LaVaughn accepts the job of babysitting Jolly's two small children but quickly realizes that the young woman, a seventeen-year-old single mother, needs as much help and nurturing as her two neglected children. The four become something akin to a temporary family, and through their relationship each makes progress toward a better life. Sixty-six brief chapters, with words arranged on the page like poetry, perfectly echo the patterns of teenage speech." Horn Book Guide.

The **Mozart** season. Virginia Euwer Wolff. Holt, c1991. 249 p.

Grades: 6 7 8 9   **Fic**
1. Jewish American girls 2. Girl violinists 3. Music -- Competitions 4. Self-discovery in girls 5. Self-discovery 6. Portland, Oregon 7. Oregon 8. Realistic fiction
ISBN 080501571X
                                                   LC   90023635
Allegra Leah Shapiro spends her twelfth summer practicing a Mozart concerto of a violin competition and finding many significant connections in her world.

"With a clear, fresh voice that never falters, Wolff gives readers a delightful heroine, a fully realized setting, and a slowly building tension that reaches a stunning climax." School Library Journal.

Probably still Nick Swansen. Virginia Euwer Wolff. H. Holt, c1988. 144 p.

Grades: 7 8 9 10   **Fic**
1. Teenagers with learning disabilities 2. Coping in teenage boys 3. Self-acceptance in teenage boys 4. Sisters -- Death 5. Teenage boy/girl relations 6. Portland, Oregon 7. Realistic fiction
ISBN 0805007016
                                                   LC   88013175
Sixteen-year-old learning-disabled Nick struggles to endure a life in which the other kids make fun of him, he has to take special classes, his date for the prom makes an excuse not to go with him, and he is haunted by the memory of his older sister who drowned while he was watching.

"It is a poignant, gentle, utterly believable narrative." Booklist.

Wolk, Lauren

★ **Echo** Mountain. Lauren Wolk. Dutton Books for Young Readers, 2020. 368 p.

Grades: 5 6 7 8   **Fic**
1. Depression era (1929-1941) 2. Depressions 1929-1941 3. Children of sick persons 4. Poverty 5. People in comas 6. Moving, Household 7. Maine 8. United States 9. Historical fiction
ISBN 9780525555568

When twelve-year-old Ellie and her family lose livelihood and move to a mountain cabin in 1934, she quickly learns to be an outdoors woman and, when needed, a healer.

"Wolk is, as usual, a writer of quiet beauty in depicting a past era, and Ellie's world of forest wandering, honey retrieval, and barter for the family's needs is distinct and believable. Human dynamics are also compelling, with Ellie taking on responsibility for her father's accident to shield her siblings from their culpability." Bulletin of the Center for Children's Books.

Wolk, Lauren, 1956-

★ **Beyond** the bright sea. Lauren Wolk. Dutton Children's Books, 2017. 283 p.

Grades: 5 6 7 8   **Fic**
1. 1920s 2. Girl orphans 3. Identity (Psychology) 4. Islands 5. Families 6. Twelve-year-old girls 7. Massachusetts 8. Historical fiction
ISBN 9781101994856
Scott O'Dell Historical Fiction Award, 2018.

Set adrift on the ocean in a small skiff as a newborn, twelve-year-old Crow embarks on a quest to find the missing pieces of her history.

"This is a tear-jerking yet ultimately uplifting tale of establishing one's place in the world and realizing that sometimes your family is the one you make, not the one you are born into." School Library Journal.

★ **Wolf** Hollow: a novel. by Lauren Wolk. Dutton Children's Books, an imprint of Penguin Random House LLC, [2016] 250 p.

Grades: 4 5 6 7 8   **Fic**
1. Second World War era (1939-1945) 2. Bullying and bullies 3. Homeless persons 4. World War I veterans 5. World War II home front 6. Families 7. Pennsylvania 8. Historical fiction
ISBN 9781101994825
                                                   LC 2015038506
Twelve-year-old Annabelle must learn to stand up for what's right in the face of a manipulative and violent new bully who targets people Annabelle cares about, including a homeless World War I veteran. Provided by publisher.

"Wolk is relentless in her message: lies and secrets, even for the most noble of reasons, have unintended consequences, as Annabelle's poignant dilemma reminds us long after the last page is turned.' ." Booklist.

Wolkenstein, M. Evan

Turtle boy. M. Evan Wolkenstein. Delacorte Press, 2020 400 p.

Grades: 5 6 7 8   **Fic**
1. Misfits (Persons) 2. Bullying and bullies 3. Boys with disabilities 4. Jewish boys 5. Hospitals 6. Realistic fiction
ISBN 9780593121573
Sydney Taylor Book Award for Older Readers, 2021.

A seventh grader struggles through a new school year marked by bullying, his teacher's insistence that he return captured turtles to the wild and a bar mitzvah community service project that requires him to spend time visiting a terminally ill boy in the hospital. Atlas Publishing.

"Debut author Wolkenstein's well-plotted novel is a model of acute psychology and fully formed characters, even minor ones. The tone, too, is just right, and incidents are seamlessly integrated. Turtle Boy—both boy and book—is a winner." Booklist

Wood, Fiona (Fiona Anna)

Cloudwish. Fiona Wood. Pan Macmillan, 2015. 288 p.

Grades: 7 8 9 10 **Fic**
1. Teenage girls 2. Change 3. Teenage boy/girl relations 4. Adolescence 5. Wishing and wishes 6. Melbourne, Victoria
ISBN 9781743533123
"It's an inspiring story with a sympathetic heroine, who will especially appeal to those who feel pressured to follow paths they don't want to travel." Publishers Weekly.

Wood, Maryrose

Nightshade. by Maryrose Wood; based on a concept by the Duchess of Northumberland. Balzer + Bray, 2011. 288 p.: Poison diaries trilogy
Grades: 8 9 10 **Fic**
1. Georgian era (1714-1837) 2. 18th century 3. Poisons 4. Lost love 5. Pharmacists 6. Humans and plants 7. Medicinal plants 8. England 9. Northumberland, England 10. Historical fantasy
ISBN 9780061802423
"Promising Weed's continued pursuit (and, hopefully, reviving the intriguing issue of Mr. Luxton's poisoning), part three's sure to levy as much page-turning enthrallment as its predecessors." Kirkus.

The **poison** diaries. by Maryrose Wood; based on a concept by the Duchess of Northumberland. Balzer + Bray, c2010. 278 p.: Poison diaries trilogy
Grades: 8 9 10 11 **Fic**
1. Georgian era (1714-1837) 2. 18th century 3. Gardens 4. Poisons 5. Pharmacists 6. Humans and plants 7. Medicinal plants 8. England 9. Northumberland, England 10. Historical fantasy
ISBN 9780061802362
LC 2009054427
In late eighteenth-century Northumberland, England, sixteen-year-old Jessamine Luxton and the mysterious Weed uncover the horrible secrets of poisons growing in Thomas Luxton's apothecary garden.
"This intriguing fantasy has many tendrils to wrap around teen hearts.... The haunting ending will leave readers wanting to talk about the themes of cruelty, honesty, and loyalty." Booklist.

Wooding, Chris, 1977-

Malice. Chris Wooding; illustrated by Dan Chernett. Scholastic Press, 2009. 384 p.: Malice (Chris Wooding)
Grades: 6 7 8 9 10 **Fic**
1. Comic books, strips, etc 2. Good and evil 3. Imagination 4. Teenagers 5. Parallel universes 6. London, England 7. Fantasy fiction 8. Horror 9. Gateway fantasy
ISBN 9780545160438
Having read all about the sinister world in which the villainous Tall Jake resides, fans Luke, Seth, and Kady learn more about it than they ever wanted when they are suddenly pulled into the pages of their comic book and come face-to-face with Tall Jake himself!
"This nail-biter will keep readers glued to the story until the very last page is turned.... Seth and Kady are strong and exciting characters." School Library Journal.

Silver. Chris Wooding. Scholastic Press, 2014 320 p.
Grades: 7 8 9 10 11 12 **Fic**
1. Boarding school students 2. Beetles 3. Survival 4. Boarding schools 5. Schools 6. England 7. Horror
ISBN 9780545603928
"When strange insects assault a remote boarding school in England, the kids try to save the day in this tense page-turner...Skillfully managed subplots keep the pages flying. It looks like the end of the world is nigh.... It's just all kinds of white-knuckle fun." Kirkus.

Woodruff, Elvira

Dear Austin: letters from the Underground Railroad. Elvira Woodruff; with illustrations by Nancy Carpenter. A. Knopf, 1998. 137 p.
Grades: 4 5 6 **Fic**
1. Eleven-year-old boys 2. Underground Railroad 3. Freedom seekers 4. Interracial friendship 5. African American boys 6. United States 7. Epistolary novels 8. Historical fiction
ISBN 0679885943
LC 98005314
In 1853, in letters to his older brother, eleven-year-old Levi describes his adventures in the Pennsylvania countryside with his Black friend Jupiter and his experiences with the Underground Railroad.
"The smoothly written text is fast paced." Horn Book Guide.

George Washington's spy: a time travel adventure. Elvira Woodruff. Scholastic Press, 2010. 229 p.
Grades: 4 5 6 **Fic**
1. Franklin, Benjamin, 1706-1790. 2. 1770s 3. Spies 4. Time travel (Past) 5. Space and time 6. Boats 7. Loyalists (United States history) 8. Boston, Massachusetts 9. Adventure stories
ISBN 9780545104876
LC 2009032700
Ten-year-old Matt and six other children travel to 1776 Boston, living out American history as they meet Benjamin Franklin, learn about colonial medicine, and become part of a rebel spy ring.
"Woodruff does an excellent job of conveying the complexities of war.... This is a great introduction to the Revolutionary period.... The story is fast paced, exciting, and informative." School Library Journal.

The **ravenmaster's** secret: escape from the Tower of London. Elvira Woodruff. Scholastic Press, 2003. 225 p.
Grades: 5 6 7 8 **Fic**
1. Tower of London (London, England) 2. Georgian era (1714-1837) 3. 1730s 4. 18th century 5. Eleven-year-old boys 6. Girls 7. Prisoners 8. Friendship 9. Jacobites 10. Great Britain 11. London, England 12. Historical fiction
ISBN 0439281334
LC 2002015963
The eleven-year-old son of the Ravenmaster at the Tower of London befriends a Jacobite rebel being held prisoner there.
"An absorbing historical adventure with a unique and colorful setting.... The novel can be read for its exciting plot and sympathetic characters, but readers will also sense its underlying theme of courage." Booklist.

Woods, Brenda (Brenda A.)

My name is Sally Little Song. by Brenda Woods. G.P. Putnam's Sons, 2006. 176 p.
Grades: 4 5 6 7 **Fic**
1. 1800s (Decade) 2. 19th century 3. Slavery 4. Freedom seekers 5. African Americans 6. Seminole Indians 7. Indians of North America 8. Florida 9. Georgia 10. Historical fiction 11. African American fiction
ISBN 0399243127
LC 2005032651
When their owner plans to sell one of them in 1802, twelve-year-old Sally and her family run away from their Georgia plantation to look for both freedom from slavery and a home in Florida with the Seminole Indians.
"Based on historical accounts, this novel provides readers with an alternative view of the realities of slavery—an escape to the South rather

than North. . . . This accessible tale will prove a rich resource for study and discussion." School Library Journal.

The **unsung** hero of Birdsong USA. Brenda Woods. Nancy Paulsen Books, 2019. 208 p.

Grades: 5 6 7 8 **Fic**

1. 1940s 2. Intergenerational friendship 3. Racism 4. Twelve-year-old boys 5. African American men 6. World War II veterans 7. South Carolina 8. Southern States 9. Historical fiction 10. African American fiction
ISBN 9781524737092

LC 2018022806

Forging a close friendship with an African American World War II veteran who has recently returned to their unwelcoming Jim Crow community, a 12-year-old white boy worries for his heroic friend's safety when racist locals threaten the man's family.

Woodson, Jacqueline

After Tupac and D Foster. Jacqueline Woodson. G.P. Putnam's Sons, 2008. 160 p.

Grades: 7 8 9 10 **Fic**

1. Shakur, Tupac, 1971-1996 2. 1990s 3. African American teenage girls 4. Street life 5. Independence in teenage girls 6. Best friends 7. Mother-deserted children 8. Queens, New York City 9. Coming-of-age stories 10. Realistic fiction 11. African American fiction
ISBN 0399246541

LC 2007023725

In the New York City borough of Queens in 1996, three girls bond over their shared love of Tupac Shakur's music, as together they try to make sense of the unpredictable world in which they live.

"The subtlety and depth with which the author conveys the girls' relationships lend this novel exceptional vividness and staying power." Publishers Weekly.

★ **Before** the ever after. Jacqueline Woodson. Nancy Paulsen Books, 2020. 176 p.

Grades: 5 6 7 8 **Fic**

1. 2000s (Decade) 2. Fathers and sons 3. Memory 4. African American boys 5. Football 6. Chronic traumatic encephalopathy 7. Realistic fiction 8. Novels in verse 9. African American fiction
ISBN 9780399545436

LC 2020018310

Coretta Scott King Award, Author Category, 2021.

ZJ's friends Ollie, Darry and Daniel help him cope when his father, a beloved professional football player, suffers severe headaches and memory loss that spell the end of his career.

"Woodson again shows herself to be a masterful writer, and her meaningful exploration of concussions and head injuries in football, a subject rarely broached in middle-grade fiction, provides young athletes with necessary insights into into the sport's less glamorous side." Booklist

Feathers. Jacqueline Woodson. G.P. Putnam's Sons, 2007. 208 p.

Grades: 4 5 6 7 **Fic**

1. 1970s 2. African American girls 3. Interracial friendship 4. Sixth-graders 5. Race relations 6. Friendship 7. Historical fiction 8. African American fiction
ISBN 0399239898

LC 2006024713

When a new, white student nicknamed "The Jesus Boy" joins her sixth grade class in the winter of 1971, Frannie's growing friendship with him makes her start to see some things in a new light.

"Woodson creates in Frannie a strong protagonist who thinks for herself and recognizes the value and meaning of family. The story ends with hope and thoughtfulness while speaking to those adolescents who struggle with race, faith, and prejudice." School Library Journal.

From the notebooks of Melanin Sun. Jacqueline Woodson. Scholastic, 1995. 141 p.

Grades: 7 8 9 10 **Fic**

1. Thirteen-year-old boys 2. Children of LGBTQIA parents 3. African American teenage boys 4. African American mother and son 5. Lesbian mothers 6. Brooklyn, New York City 7. Realistic fiction 8. African American fiction
ISBN 0590458809

LC 93034158 /AC

Thirteen-year-old Melanin Sun's comfortable, quiet life is shattered when his mother reveals she has fallen in love with a woman.

"Offering no easy answers, Woodson teaches the reader that love can lead to acceptance of all manner of differences." Publishers Weekly.

Harbor me. Jacqueline Woodson. Nancy Paulsen Books, [2018] 288 p.

Grades: 5 6 7 8 **Fic**

1. Friendship 2. Interpersonal relations 3. Bonding (Interpersonal relations) 4. Listening 5. Safety 6. Realistic fiction 7. African American fiction
ISBN 9780399252525

LC 2018019373

When six students are chosen to participate in a weekly talk with no adults allowed, they discover that when they're together, it's safe to share the hopes and fears they have to hide from the rest of the world. Provided by publisher.

"Woodson tells stories torn from headlines but personalizes them with poetry and memories, blunting their trauma with understanding and love. Haley's history weaves in and out, drawing readers close. These children become each other's safe harbors, and Woodson brilliantly shows readers how to find the connections we all need." Booklist.

If you come softly. G. P. Putnam's Sons, 1998. 181 p.

Grades: 7 8 9 10 **Fic**

1. Prep school students 2. Interracial romance 3. Racism 4. Teenage romance 5. African American teenage boys 6. Manhattan, New York City 7. New York City 8. Love stories 9. Realistic fiction 10. African American fiction
ISBN 0399231129

"The gentle and melancholy tone of this book makes it ideal for thoughtful readers and fans of romance." Voice of Youth Advocates.

Lena. Jacqueline Woodson. Delacorte Press, 1999. 115 p.

Grades: 6 7 8 9 **Fic**

1. Thirteen-year-old girls 2. Runaway girls 3. Sisters 4. Family and child abuse 5. African American fiction
ISBN 0385323085

LC 98024317

Thirteen-year-old Lena and her younger sister Dion mourn the death of their mother as they hitchhike from Ohio to Kentucky while running away from their abusive father.

"Soulful, wise and sometimes wrenching, this taut story never loses its grip on the reader." Publishers Weekly.

Peace, Locomotion. Jacqueline Woodson. G.P. Putnam's Sons, 2009. 144 p.

Grades: 4 5 6 7 **Fic**
    1. Foster home care 2. Brothers and sisters 3. Letters 4. Peace 5. African American boys 6. Realistic fiction 7. African American fiction
ISBN 9780399246555

LC 2008018583

Through letters to his little sister, who is living in a different foster home, sixth-grader Lonnie, also known as "Locomotion," keeps a record of their lives while they are apart, describing his own foster family, including his foster brother who returns home after losing a leg in the Iraq War.

"Woodson creates a full-bodied character in kind, sensitive Lonnie. Readers will understand his quest for peace, and appreciate the hard work he does to find it." Publishers Weekly.

Wrede, Patricia C., 1953-
    Calling on dragons. Patricia C. Wrede. J. Yolen Books; Harcourt Brace Jovanovich, 1993. 244 p.: Enchanted forest chronicles

Grades: 5 6 7 8 **Fic**
    1. Women rulers 2. Wizards 3. Spells (Magic) 4. Swords 5. Dragons 6. Fantasy fiction
ISBN 0152009507

LC 92035469

Queen Cimorene turns to her friends Morwen, Telemain, and Kazul for help when troublesome wizards make their way back to the Enchanted Forest and begin to soak up its magic.

"Wrede's strengths are numerous: sparkling dialogue, amusingly fractured fairy-tale conventions, solid characterization, plenty of action, and truly terrific chapter headings." School Library Journal.

Dealing with dragons. Harcourt Brace Jovanovich, 1990. 212 p.: Enchanted forest chronicles

Grades: 5 6 7 8 **Fic**
    1. Dragons 2. Runaway teenagers 3. Princesses 4. Wizards 5. Spells (Magic) 6. Fantasy fiction
ISBN 0152229000

LC 89024599

Bored with traditional palace life, a princess goes off to live with a group of dragons and soon becomes involved with fighting against some disreputable wizards who want to steal away the dragons' kingdom.

"A decidedly diverting novel with plenty of action and many slightly skewed fairy-tale conventions that add to the laugh-out-loud reading pleasure and give the story a wide appeal." Booklist.

Searching for dragons. Patricia C. Wrede. Harcourt Brace Jovanovich, 1991. 242 p.: Enchanted forest chronicles

Grades: 5 6 7 8 **Fic**
    1. Princesses 2. Dragons 3. Quests 4. Wizards 5. Spells (Magic) 6. Fantasy fiction
ISBN 0152008985

With the aid of King Mandanbar, Princess Cimorene rescues the dragon Kazul and saves the Enchanted Forest from a band of wicked wizards.

"Wrede's tongue-in-cheek humor balances well with sweet adolescent discovery, and the result is another winning chapter in a delightful tale." School Library Journal.

Talking to dragons. Patricia C. Wrede. Harcourt Brace Jovanovich, 1985. x, 255 p.: Enchanted forest chronicles

Grades: 5 6 7 8 **Fic**
    1. Teenage adventurers 2. Spells (Magic) 3. Magic 4. Wizards 5. Sixteen-year-old boys 6. Fantasy fiction
ISBN 0152842470

LC 9240719

Queen Cimorene sends her sixteen-year-old son Daystar into the Enchanted Forest with the only weapon that can combat an evil wizard's magic in an effort to restore the balance of power in the kingdom.

"This grand adventure is both suspenseful and hilarious." Booklist.

The **thirteenth** child. Patricia C. Wrede. Scholastic Press, 2009. 344 p.: Frontier magic

Grades: 7 8 9 10 11 12 **Fic**
    1. Magic 2. Frontier and pioneer life 3. Brothers and sisters 4. Memories 5. Universities and colleges 6. Coming-of-age stories 7. Historical fantasy
ISBN 9780545033428

LC 2008034048

Eighteen-year-old Eff must finally get over believing she is bad luck and accept that her special training in Aphrikan magic, and being the twin of the seventh son of a seventh son, give her extraordinary power to combat magical creatures that threaten settlements on the western frontier.

"Wrede creates a rich world where steam dragons seem as normal as bears, and a sympathetic character in Eff." Publishers Weekly.

Wright, Barbara, 1951-
    Crow. Barbara Wright. Random House, 2012. 320 p.

Grades: 4 5 6 7 **Fic**
    1. 1890s 2. 19th century 3. Riots 4. African American boys 5. Racism 6. Families 7. Race relations 8. Wilmington, North Carolina 9. Historical fiction
ISBN 9780375969287

LC 2011014892

Struggling with early adolescence, family conflicts and distance from his best friend at the end of the 19th century, 11-year-old Moses begins teaching his grandmother how to read while learning about her experiences as a slave and witnessing important political changes unfolding in the country.

"An intensely moving, first-person narrative of a disturbing historical footnote told from the perspective of a very likable, credible young hero." Kirkus.

Wright, Bil
    Putting makeup on the fat boy. Bil Wright. Simon & Schuster Books for Young Readers, 2011. 208 p.

Grades: 7 8 9 10 11 12 **Fic**
    1. Makeup artists 2. Hispanic American teenage boys 3. Gay teenagers 4. Dating violence 5. Crushes in boys 6. New York City, 7. Realistic fiction 8. LGBTQIA fiction 9. African American fiction
ISBN 9781416939962

LC 2010032450

Sixteen-year-old Carlos Duarte is on the verge of realizing his dream of becoming a famous make-up artist, but first he must face his jealous boss at a Macy's cosmetics counter, his sister's abusive boyfriend, and his crush on a punk-rocker classmate.

"Obviously, there's a whole lot going on in Wright's novel, but it's handled deftly and, for the most part, believably. Best of all, Carlos is not completely defined by his homosexuality." Booklist.

When the black girl sings. Bil Wright. Simon & Schuster Books for Young Readers, c2008. 266 p.

Grades: 6 7 8 9 10   **Fic**

　　1. African Americans 2. African American girls 3. Fourteen-year-olds 4. Fourteen-year-old girls 5. Teenagers 6. Connecticut 7. African American fiction

　　ISBN 9781416939955

　　　　　　　　　　　　　　LC 2006030837

Adopted by white parents and sent to an exclusive Connecticut girls' school where she is the only black student, fourteen-year-old Lahni Schuler feels like an outcast, particularly when her parents separate, but after attending a local church where she hears gospel music for the first time, she finds her voice.

"Readers will enjoy the distinctive characters, lively dialogue, and palette of adolescent and racial insecurities in this contemporary, upbeat story." School Library Journal.

Wulffson, Don L.

Soldier X. Don L. Wulffson. Viking, c2001. viii, 226 p.

Grades: 7 8 9 10   **Fic**

　　1. World War II 2. Military campaigns 3. Teenage soldiers 4. Sixteen-year-old boys 5. Soviet Union 6. Germany

　　ISBN 067088863X

　　　　　　　　　　　　　　LC 9904918

In 1943 sixteen-year-old Erik experiences the horrors of war when he is drafted into the German army and sent to fight on the Russian front.

"Erik's first-person narrative records battlefield sequences with an unflinching—and occasionally numbing—brutality, in a story notable for its unusual perspective." Horn Book Guide.

Wunder, Wendy

The **museum** of intangible things. Wendy Wunder. Razorbill, 2014. 304 p.

Grades: 8 9 10 11 12   **Fic**

　　1. Children of alcoholics 2. Bipolar disorder 3. Cross-country automobile trips 4. Best friends 5. Friendship 6. New Jersey 7. Realistic fiction

　　ISBN 9781595145147

　　　　　　　　　　　　　　LC 2013030169

Best friends Hannah and Zoe, seventeen, leave their down-and-out New Jersey town and drive west chasing storms, making new friends, and seeking the intangibles—audacity, insouciance, happiness—that their lives have lacked.

"As Hannah and best friend Zoe (diagnosed bipolar) embark on a cross-country road trip, Zoe gives Hannah intangible lessons (e.g., Hannah learns insouciance when they overnight in an IKEA). When Zoe's irrationality gets scary, Hannah learns betrayal and, later, forgiveness. With each lesson, Hannah becomes more confident, building her own distinct identity. Meanwhile, Zoe is a complex character—intelligent, loyal, and funny." Horn Book.

Yancey, Richard (Rick)

The **extraordinary** adventures of Alfred Kropp. by Rick Yancey. Bloomsbury, 2005. 339 p.: Alfred Kropp adventures

Grades: 7 8 9 10   **Fic**

　　1. Teenage boy orphans 2. Teenage boy misfits 3. Magic swords 4. Uncles 5. Excalibur (Sword) 6. Tennessee 7. Fantasy fiction

　　ISBN 1582346933

　　　　　　　　　　　　　　LC 2005013044

Through a series of dangerous and violent misadventures, teenage loser Alfred Kropp rescues King Arthur's legendary sword Excalibur from the forces of evil.

"True to its action-adventure genre, the story is lighthearted, entertaining, occasionally half-witted, but by and large fun." School Library Journal.

The **seal** of Solomon. by Rick Yancey. Bloomsbury Children's Books, 2007. 336 p.: Alfred Kropp adventures

Grades: 7 8 9 10   **Fic**

　　1. Teenage boy misfits 2. Teenage kidnapping victims 3. Demons 4. Antiquities 5. Quests 6. Tennessee 7. Fantasy fiction

　　ISBN 9781599900452

　　　　　　　　　　　　　　LC 2006024989

The last descendant of Sir Lancelot, teenage misfit Alfred Kropp is drawn back into the OIPEP to battle a group of demons bent on freeing themselves from the confines of an ancient relic.

"This tells a rip-roaring story that teens will love and won't be able to put down." School Library Journal.

Yang, Dori Jones

Daughter of Xanadu. Dori Jones Yang. Delacorte Press, 2011. 352 p.

Grades: 7 8 9 10 11 12   **Fic**

　　1. Kublai Khan, 1216-1294 2. Polo, Marco, 1254-1323? 3. 13th century 4. Mongols 5. Teenage girl soldiers 6. Explorers 7. Gender role 8. Interpersonal attraction 9. China 10. Historical fiction

　　ISBN 9780385739238

　　　　　　　　　　　　　　LC 2009053652

Emmajin, the sixteen-year-old eldest granddaughter of Khublai Khan, becomes a warrior and falls in love with explorer Marco Polo in thirteenth-century China.

"Daughter of Xanadu offers rich descriptions and vivid depictions of fictional characters and historical figures, making them charming and believable. A colorful and compelling read." School Library Journal.

Yee, F. C.

The **epic** crush of Genie Lo: a novel. by F.C. Yee. Amulet Books, 2017. 320 p.: Genie Lo novels

Grades: 7 8 9 10   **Fic**

　　1. Chinese American teenage girls 2. Reincarnation 3. Demons 4. Overachievers 5. Teenage boy/girl relations 6. Urban fantasy 7. Mythological fiction

　　ISBN 9781419725487

　　　　　　　　　　　　　　LC 2017018271

The struggle to get into a top-tier college consumes sixteen-year-old Genie's every waking thought. But when she discovers she's a celestial spirit who's powerful enough to bash through the gates of heaven with her fists, her perfectionist existence is shattered.

"Hard-driving, hyperachieving Chinese-American sophomore Genie Lo may have to put her take-no-prisoners rush to the Ivy Leagues aside so she can save the world, or at least the local region of California currently under attack by Chinese demons. . . . Loads of action, a touch of comedy, a bit of well-controlled lust, and even some serious discussion of Eastern philosophy should leave readers eager for a return performance." Bulletin of the Center for Children's Books.

The **iron** will of Genie Lo. by F. C. Yee. Amulet Books, 2020. 304 p.: Genie Lo novels

Grades: 7 8 9 10   **Fic**

　　1. Chinese American teenage girls 2. Parallel universes 3. Gods and goddesses 4. Demons 5. Demon slayers 6. Urban fantasy 7.

Mythological fiction
ISBN 9781419731457

LC 2019035133

When Genie Lo learns of a cosmos-threatening force while the Jade Emperor is absent, she leads a party of quarrelsome Chinese gods through multiple planes of reality on a quest that will require sacrifice, not strength.

"The politics of the gods, criticism of Silicon Valley VC funding, college parties, and the uncertainty of the future on this plane of existence (plus all the others) are all explored with Genie's hilarious and biting voice especially when she's at her most vulnerable." School Library Journal.

Yee, Lisa

Millicent Min, girl genius. by Lisa Yee. Arthur A. Levine Books, c2003. 248 p.: Millicent Min series

Grades: 5 6 7   **Fic**
   1. Eleven-year-old girls 2. Chinese Americans 3. Child prodigies 4. Friendship 5. Genius 6. Diary novels 7. Realistic fiction
ISBN 0439425190

LC 2003003747

In a series of journal entries, eleven-year-old child prodigy Millicent Min records her struggles to learn to play volleyball, tutor her enemy, deal with her grandmother's departure, and make friends over the course of a tumultuous summer.

"At the tender age of eleven, Millicent Min has completed her junior year of high school. Summer school is Millie's idea of fun, so she is excited that her parents are allowing her to take a college poetry course. . . . The tension between Millie's formal, overly intellectual way of expressing herself and her emotional immaturity makes her a very funny narrator. . . . Readers considerably older than Millicent's eleven years will enjoy this strong debut novel." Voice of Youth Advocates.

Warp speed. by Lisa Yee. Arthur A. Levine Books, 2011. 320 p.

Grades: 5 6 7 8   **Fic**
   1. Boy misfits 2. Bullying and bullies 3. Popularity 4. Running 5. Track and field 6. California 7. Realistic fiction
ISBN 9780545122764

"Yee's combination of humor and sympathy works a charm here, giving Marley a life of his own and a chance at success in this solid addition to her prismatic look at middle school." Kirkus.

Yee, Paul

Learning to fly. Paul Yee. Orca Book Publishers, 2008. 112 p.

Grades: 7 8 9 10   **Fic**
   1. Popularity 2. Friendship 3. Teenage immigrants 4. Immigrant families 5. Belonging 6. High interest-low vocabulary books 7. Realistic fiction
ISBN 9781551439532

"Jason Chen, 17, wants to leave his small town in Canada and return to China. . . . His white high-school teachers do not know how smart he is, and his classmates jeer at him. Driven to join the crowd of potheads, he bonds especially with his Native American classmate, Charles (Chief). Narrated in Jason's wry, first-person, present-tense narrative, Yee's slim novel packs in a lot. . . . The clipped dialogue perfectly echoes the contemporary scene, the harsh prejudice felt by the new immigrant and the Native American, and their gripping friendship story." Booklist.

Yelchin, Eugene

★ **Breaking** Stalin's nose. Eugene Yelchin. Henry Holt, 2011. 144 p.

Grades: 4 5 6 7   **Fic**
   1. Father-separated boys 2. Communism 3. Disillusionment 4. Fathers and sons 5. Schools 6. Soviet Union 7. Historical fiction 8. Illustrated books
ISBN 9780805092165

LC 2011005792

In the Stalinist era of the Soviet Union, ten-year-old Sasha idolizes his father, a devoted Communist, but when police take his father away and leave Sasha homeless, he is forced to examine his own perceptions, values, and beliefs.

"Readers will quickly pick up on the dichotomy between Sasha's ardent beliefs and the reality of life under Stalinism, and be glad for his ultimate disillusion, even as they worry for his future. An author's note concisely presents the chilling historical background and personal connection that underlie the story." Publishers Weekly.

The **haunting** of Falcon House. written and illustrated by Eugene Yelchin. Henry Holt and Company, 2016. 310 p.

Grades: 4 5 6 7 8   **Fic**
   1. 1890s 2. Haunted houses 3. Princes 4. Aunts 5. Extrasensory perception 6. Twelve-year-old boys 7. Russia 8. St Petersburg, Russia 9. Ghost stories
ISBN 9780805098457

Golden Kite Award for Middle Grade/Young Reader Fiction, 2017.

A long-undisturbed bedroom. A startling likeness. A mysterious friend. When twelve-year-old Prince Lev Lvov goes to live with his aunt at Falcon House, he takes his rightful place as heir to the Lvov family estate. Prince Lev dreams of becoming a hero of Russia like his great ancestors. But he'll discover that dark secrets haunt this house. Prince Lev is the only one who can set them free. Will he be the hero his family needs?

"This is a haunting tale at its very best." Booklist.

Spy runner. Eugene Yelchin. Henry Holt & Co., 2019. 352 p.

Grades: 5 6 7 8 9   **Fic**
   1. 1950s 2. Suspicion 3. Anti-Communism 4. Children of military personnel 5. Investigations 6. Twelve-year-old boys 7. Thrillers and suspense 8. Spy fiction 9. Historical fiction
ISBN 9781250120816

A Cold War noir mystery by the Newbery Honor-winning author of Breaking Stalin's Nose finds a 12-year-old boy targeting a Russian boarder in his home with suspicion in his determination to learn the fate of his father, who went missing in action during World War II.

"Well-plotted and -paced, Yelchin's thriller will be a favorite among readers who have an interest in history and intrigue." Publishers Weekly.

Yep, Laurence, 1948-

City of fire. Laurence Yep. Tom Doherty Associates, 2009. 320 p.: City trilogy (Laurence Yep)

Grades: 5 6 7 8   **Fic**
   1. 1940s 2. Dragons 3. Princesses 4. Revenge 5. Shapeshifters 6. Magic 7. Hawaii 8. Fantasy fiction 9. Asian-influenced fantasy
ISBN 9780765319241

LC 2009016737

Twelve-year-old Scirye and her companions travel to Houlani, a new Hawaiian island created by magic, where they enlist the help of volcano goddess Pele in an attempt to stop an evil dragon and a mysterious man from altering the universe.

"Readers will be on tenterhooks awaiting the next episode of this exhilarating chase." Booklist.

A **dragon's** guide to making your human smarter. Laurence Yep & Joanne Ryder; illustrations by Mary GrandPre. Crown Books for Young Readers, 2016. 304 p.: Dragon's guide

Grades: 4 5 6 7   **Fic**

    1. Dragons 2. Schools 3. Grandfathers 4. Magic 5. Girls and dragons 6. San Francisco, California 7. Fantasy fiction
    ISBN 9780385392327

"Winnie's straightforward narration alternates with passages from Miss Drake, whose wry tone adds light humor to the story. An appealing black-and-white drawing opens each chapter." School Library Journal.

A **dragon's** guide to the care and feeding of humans. Laurence Yep & Joanne Ryder; Illustrations by Mary GrandPré. Crown Books for Young Readers, 2015. 160 p.: Dragon's guide

Grades: 4 5 6 7   **Fic**

    1. Dragons 2. Drawing 3. Imaginary creatures 4. Magic 5. Friendship 6. San Francisco, California 7. Fantasy fiction
    ISBN 9780385392280

"With a black-and-white spot illustration opening most chapters, an engaging narrator, and a consistently fluid writing style, this title makes a fine dragon choice for readers not yet ready for more weighty fantasy novels." School Library Journal.

Dragonwings. Laurence Yep. Harper & Row, c1975. 248 p.: Golden mountain chronicles

Grades: 6 7 8 9   **Fic**

    1. 1900s (Decade) 2. Fathers and sons 3. Immigrants, Chinese 4. Prejudice 5. Aviation 6. Airplanes 7. San Francisco, California 8. Chinatown, San Francisco, California 9. Historical fiction
    ISBN 9780060267377

        LC   74002625

In the early twentieth century a young Chinese boy joins his father in San Francisco and helps him realize his dream of making a flying machine.

Hiroshima: a novella. by Laurence Yep. Scholastic, 1995. 56 p.

Grades: 4 5 6 7   **Fic**

    1. Second World War era (1939-1945) 2. 1940s 3. Girls and war 4. Atomic bomb 5. World War II 6. Girls with disfigurements 7. Hiroshima Maidens 8. Hiroshima, Japan 9. Historical fiction
    ISBN 0590208322

        LC   94018195 /AC

Describes the dropping of the atomic bomb on Hiroshima, Japan, particularly as it affects Sachi, who becomes one of the Hiroshima Maidens.

The **star** maker. Laurence Yep. HarperCollins, 2011. 128 p.

Grades: 5 6 7 8   **Fic**

    1. 1950s 2. Chinese American boys 3. Chinese New Year 4. Firecrackers 5. Uncles 6. Money 7. Chinatown, San Francisco, California 8. San Francisco, California 9. Historical fiction
    ISBN 9780060253158

With the help of his Uncle Chester, Artie, a Chinese-American boy who feels like the outsider of the family, tries hard to fulfill a promise to have firecrackers for everyone on the Chinese New Year in 1954.

"Yep skillfully portrays the significance and emotional nature of common childhood dramas, from fears of going back on one's word to worries of losing a favorite uncle to a new girlfriend. . . . Yep has crafted

other memorable characters, including Chinatown itself, which sparkle with energy and camaraderie." Publishers Weekly.

Yohalem, Eve

The **truth** according to Blue. Eve Yohalem. Little, Brown and Company, 2020 352 p.

Grades: 4 5 6 7   **Fic**

    1. Children with diabetes 2. Treasure hunting 3. Making friends 4. Friendship 5. Girls and dogs 6. Realistic fiction
    ISBN 9780316424370

Embarking on a secret hunt for a legendary ship of gold with ties to her ancestors, 13-year-old Blue and her diabetes alert dog clash with a rival treasure hunter and a movie star's bratty daughter, who reveals her own knack for adventure. Atlas Publishing.

Yolen, Jane

Briar Rose. Jane Yolen. Tor Books, 1992. 190 p.: Fairy tales: a series of fantasy novels retelling classic tales

Grades: 8 9 10 11 12 Adult   **Fic**

    1. Jewish American women 2. Storytelling 3. Holocaust survivors 4. Grandmothers 5. Grandmother and granddaughter 6. Poland 7. Contemporary fantasy 8. Fantasy fiction 9. Adaptations, retellings, and spin-offs
    ISBN 9780312851354

        LC   92025456

Takes the fairy tale of Briar Rose, the Sleeping Beauty, and tells it anew—set this time against the terrifying backdrop of the Holocaust.

"Yolen takes the story of Briar Rose (commonly known as Sleeping Beauty) and links it to the Holocaust. . . . Rebecca Berlin, a young woman who has grown up hearing her grandmother Gemma tell an unusual and frightening version of the Sleeping Beauty legend, realizes when Gemma dies that the fairy tale offers one of the very few clues she has to her grandmother's past. . . . By interpolating Gemma's vivid and imaginative story into the larger narrative, Yolen has created an engrossing novel." Publishers Weekly.

Includes bibliographical references (p. [187]-190).

Dragon's blood: a fantasy. by Jane Yolen. Harcourt Brace, 1996, c1982. xi, 292 p.: Pit dragon chronicles

Grades: 6 7 8 9   **Fic**

    1. Animal fighting 2. Enslaved teenagers 3. Dragons 4. Teenage boys 5. Boys and dragons 6. Coming-of-age stories 7. Fantasy fiction
    ISBN 9780152051266

        LC   9522853

Jakkin, a bond boy who works as a Keeper in a dragon nursery on the planet Austar IV, secretly trains a fighting pit dragon of his own in hopes of winning his freedom.

"An original and engrossing fantasy." Horn Book.

Foiled. written by Jane Yolen; artwork by Mike Cavallaro. First Second, 2010. 160 p.

Grades: 7 8 9 10   **Fic**

    1. Fencers 2. Teenage girl heroes 3. Imaginary kingdoms 4. Magic 5. Fairies 6. New York City 7. Fantasy comics 8. Comics and Graphic novels
    ISBN 9781596432796

Outcast Aliera Carstairs may not fit in at school, but she's always a star in her fencing class, so when Avery Castle walks into her first period biology class, she must find a way to be noticed by the possible Prince Charming.

"Besting competitors twice her age in tournaments, and keeping a strict routine of fencing practice, homework, and role-playing games, Aliera is a loner and likes it that way—until she becomes lab partners with the cutest boy in school. . . . Turns out her new ruby-handled foil is the key to his interest in her, and to the yet-unseen magical dimension she must keep in balance. . . . [Yolen] has created a strong, conflicted, and relatable girl hero. . . . Cavallaro's artwork suits Aliera's monochrome existence, but burst into life when she finally sees (in color!) the faerie beasties cheering her on." Booklist.

Mapping the bones. Jane Yolen. Philomel Books, [2018] 432 p.

Grades: 6 7 8 9   **Fic**
1. 1940s 2. Twins 3. Jews 4. Escapes 5. Ghettoes, Jewish 6. Concentration camps 7. Poland 8. Historical fiction
ISBN 9780399257780

LC 2016059474
Golden Kite Award for Fiction, 2019
In Poland in the 1940s, twins Chaim and Gittel rely on each other to endure life in a ghetto, escape through forests, and the horrors of a concentration camp.

"Using the framework of the Hansel and Gretel story, Yolen does a superb job of dramatizing the horrors of WWII and the Holocaust, bringing vivid fear and suspense to her captivating story. It makes for altogether memorable and essential reading." Booklist.

The **queen's** own fool: a novel of Mary Queen of Scots. by Jane Yolen and Robert J. Harris. Philomel Books, 2000. 390 p.: Stuart quartet

Grades: 7 8 9 10   **Fic**
1. Mary, Queen of Scots, 1542-1587 2. Medieval period (476-1492) 3. Scottish Stewart period (1371-1603) 4. 16th century 5. Fools and jesters 6. Women rulers 7. Nobility 8. Scotland 9. Historical fiction
ISBN 9780399233807

LC 99055070
When twelve-year-old Nicola leaves Troupe Brufort and serves as the fool for Mary, Queen of Scots, she experiences the political and religious upheavals in both France and Scotland.

"The authors have woven fiction and historical fact into a seamless tapestry." Horn Book Guide.

Yoon, Nicola
The **sun** is also a star. Nicola Yoon. Delacorte Press, 2016. 384 p.

Grades: 8 9 10 11 12   **Fic**
1. Undocumented immigrants 2. Deportation 3. Asian American teenage boys 4. Korean American teenage boys 5. Teenage romance 6. New York City 7. Brooklyn, New York City 8. Realistic fiction
ISBN 9780553496680
Natasha, whose family is hours away from being deported, and Daniel, a first generation Korean American who strives to live up to his parents' expectations, unexpectedly fall in love and must determine which path they will choose in order to be together.

"With appeal to cynics and romantics alike, this profound exploration of life and love tempers harsh realities with the beauty of hope in a way that is both deeply moving and satisfying." Kirkus.

Young, Brian
Healer of the water monster. Brian Young. Heartdrum, an imprint of HarperCollins Publishers 2021. 384 p.

Grades: 5 6 7 8   **Fic**
1. Preteen boys 2. Grandmother and child 3. Mythical creatures 4. Quests 5. Navajo Indians -- Religion 6. New Mexico 7. Navajo Indian Reservation 8. Mythological fiction 9. Fantasy fiction
ISBN 9780062990402
A debut novel inspired by Native-American culture follows the experiences of a boy whose summer at his grandmother's reservation home is shaped by his uncle's addictions and an encounter with a sacred being from the Navajo Creation Story.

"Young's narrative weaves traditional folklore, language, and mythos with modern emotion to craft a poignant tale of family, friendship, and protecting what you love most." Booklist

Young, Brigit
The **prettiest**. Brigit Young. Roaring Brook Press, 2020 320 p.

Grades: 5 6 7 8   **Fic**
1. Eighth-grade girls 2. Beauty 3. Feminism 4. Objectification (Social psychology) 5. Competition 6. Realistic fiction
ISBN 9781626729230
The Prettiest is an incisive, empowering novel by Brigit Young about young women fighting back against sexism and objectification.

"Written using language that middle schoolers will find relatable, Young conveys a timely message about bullying and sexism, digging beneath the surface to show her protagonists' intelligence, distinct talents, and misguided preconceptions." Publishers Weekly.

Young, Ethan, 1983-
The **dragon** path. Ethan Young. Graphix, an imprint of Scholastic, 2021. 208 p.

Grades: 5 6 7 8   **Fic**
1. Princes 2. Monsters 3. Mythical creatures 4. Voyages and travels 5. Prophecies 6. Asian-influenced fantasy 7. Steampunk 8. Fantasy comics
ISBN 9781338363302
The Wong Clan must leave their ruined homeland for a better life in the mythical Old Land, but to get there they must follow the dragon path, where their sworn enemies, the Dragon Tribe, rule. During a surprise attack, Prince Sing is separated from his clan. With the help of Ming, a powerful mystic from the Old Land, and Midnight, a monstrous warrior beast, Prince Sing must do all he can to save both his family and the Dragon Tribe from mutual destruction. Provided by publisher.

"Themes of betrayal and true identities, with magic woven throughout, create an action-packed adventure." Kirkus

Young, Karen Romano
Doodlebug: a novel in doodles. Karen Romano Young. Feiwel & Friends, 2010. 105 p.

Grades: 4 5 6 7   **Fic**
1. Moving, Household 2. New students 3. Drawing 4. Guilt 5. Guilt in children 6. San Francisco, California 7. Realistic fiction
ISBN 9780312561567
When Doreen "Dodo" Bussey's family moves to a new home, her mother gives her a blank notebook in which Dodo documents her new life, from the move and first days in a new city, to her new school and friends.

"This offers an engaging, originial heroine, a satisfying story and lots of great pictures. . . . Some details, like the fact that the family is interracial, are shown but not stated, rewarding careful examination of the artwork. . . . Charming and thoughtful." Kirkus

Hundred percent. by Karen Romano Young. Chronicle Books, [2016] 256 p.

Grades: 5 6 7 **Fic**

    1. Twelve-year-old girls 2. Identity (Psychology) 3. Friendship 4. Sixth grade (Education) 5. Families

ISBN 9781452138909

        LC 2015047481

Christine Gouda, called Tink, and her best friend Jackie are entering sixth grade, and suddenly everything seems awkward and just plain wrong—boys are behaving differently, clothes do not fit the way they should, long term friendships suddenly seem tenuous, and most of all she needs a new nickname because "Tink" just does not fit anymore.

"Romano's characters jump off the page in a thoughtful and realistic look at what it means to be on the precipice of adolescence." Publishers Weekly.

Young, Moira

Blood red road. Moira Young. Margaret K. McElderry Books, 2011. 464 p.: Dustlands trilogy

Grades: 6 7 8 9 10 **Fic**

    1. Twin brothers and sisters 2. Martial arts 3. Orphans 4. Kidnapping 5. Brothers and sisters 6. Science fiction

ISBN 9781442429987

In a distant future, eighteen-year-old Lugh is kidnapped, and while his twin sister Saba and nine-year-old Emmi are trailing him across bleak Sandsea they are captured, too, and taken to brutal Hopetown, where Saba is forced to be a cage fighter until new friends help plan an escape.

"Readers will . . . be riveted by the book's fast-paced mix of action and romance. It's a natural for Hunger Games fans." Publishers Weekly.

Youngblood, Leslie C.

Forever this summer. Leslie C. Youngblood. Little, Brown and Company, 2021 256 p.: Love like sky

Grades: 4 5 6 **Fic**

    1. Blended families 2. Family businesses 3. Small towns 4. Sisters 5. African Americans 6. Louisiana 7. Realistic fiction 8. African American fiction

ISBN 9780759555204

Georgie has no idea what to expect when she, Mama, and Peaches are plopped down in the middle of small town USA—AKA Bogalusa, Louisiana. G-baby wants to help out at the once-famous family diner that once served celebrities like the Jackson 5 and the Supremes, but with restaurateur Great Aunt Elvie needing help remembering day-to-day things, everyone is too busy to show G-baby the ropes. G-baby makes friends with Markie, a foster kid under Aunt Elvie's care, who has a limb difference and a huge singing voice. When G-baby's best friend, Nikki, comes to visit they realize that the kids in town don't have a place to hang out like their Boys & Girls club in Atlanta and that the diner is in danger of closing. G-baby, Nikki, and Markie embark on a mission to start a club of their own: the Bogalusa Summer Club. And save the diner. Since it takes funds to accomplish these goals, they decide to put on a talent show to raise money. Along the way, G-baby will discover an unexpected talent of her own: fighting for what's fair and right even when everything is stacked against you.

"A dynamic cast, intriguing plot, and essential advice make this a recommended purchase." School Library Journal

Love like sky. Leslie C. Youngblood. Disney-Hyperion, 2018. 288 p.: Love like sky

Grades: 4 5 6 **Fic**

    1. Blended families 2. Children of divorced parents 3. Sisters 4.

Divorce 5. Sick children 6. Georgia 7. Realistic fiction

ISBN 9781368016506

        LC 2018002695

Eleven-year-old Georgie is still adjusting to leaving Atlanta for a small town, having a stepfather, and being unable to get close to her stepsister when her six-year-old sister, Peaches, suddenly becomes very ill.

Yu, Mimi

The **Girl** King. Mimi Yu. Bloomsbury, 2019 496 p.

Grades: 7 8 9 10 **Fic**

    1. Inheritance and succession 2. Heirs and heiresses 3. Sibling rivalry 4. Sisters 5. Women rulers 6. Asian-influenced fantasy 7. Fantasy fiction

ISBN 9781681198897

When their father names a male cousin as next ruler of the Empire of the First Flame, Lu must go on the run to reclaim her birthright, leaving her younger, timid sister, Min, to discover her own hidden power.

Zaczek, Alyssa

Martin McLean, middle school queen. Alyssa Zaczek. Sterling, 2020 272 p.

Grades: 4 5 6 7 8 **Fic**

    1. Multiracial boys 2. Questioning (Sexual or gender identity) 3. Self-esteem in boys 4. Middle schools 5. Middle school students 6. Coming-of-age stories 7. LGBTQIA fiction 8. Realistic fiction

ISBN 9781454935704

Martin McLean has always been surrounded by people who can express themselves, but he's not great at speaking up unless he's at a Mathletes competition. Then his Tio Billy introduces him to the world of drag, inspiring Martin to create a fabulous drag queen alter ego.

"The theme of being true to oneself is wonderfully done. Zaczek also does a terrific job of making sure the drag queen aspect is age-appropriate for the audience, even having the drag event set in a coffee house instead of a bar." School Library Journal.

Zail, Suzy, 1966-

Playing for the commandant. Suzy Zail. Candlewick Press, 2014, c2012. 245 p.

Grades: 7 8 9 10 11 12 **Fic**

    1. Birkenau Extermination Camp 2. 1940s 3. Holocaust (1933-1945) 4. Pianists 5. Concentration camp inmates 6. Interpersonal attraction 7. Jewish families 8. Historical fiction

ISBN 9780763664039

Hanna, a young Jewish pianist at Auschwitz who is desperate to save her family, is chosen to play at the camp commandant's house, but staying alive isn't supposed to include falling in love with the commandant's son.

"Zail's story is as gut-wrenching as any Holocaust tale . . . The haunting, matter-of-fact tone of Hanna's story will likely resonate with teens learning about the Holocaust." Booklist.

Zarr, Sara

How to save a life. Sara Zarr. Little, Brown, 2011. 352 p.

Grades: 6 7 8 9 10 11 12 **Fic**

    1. Adoption 2. Pregnant teenagers 3. Grief in teenage girls 4. Grief 5. Fathers -- Death 6. Colorado 7. Denver, Colorado 8. Realistic fiction

ISBN 9780316036061

        LC 2010045832

Told from their own viewpoints, seventeen-year-old Jill, in grief over the loss of her father, and Mandy, nearly nineteen, are thrown together when Jill's mother agrees to adopt Mandy's unborn child but nothing turns out as they had anticipated.

The **Lucy** variations. Sara Zarr. Little, Brown, 2013. 304 p.
Grades: 7 8 9 10 11 12   **Fic**
   1. Teenage girl pianists 2. Self-fulfillment in teenage girls 3. Piano teachers 4. Child prodigies 5. Pianists 6. San Francisco, California 7. Realistic fiction
ISBN 9780316205016

LC 2012029852

Sixteen-year-old San Franciscan Lucy Beck-Moreau once had a promising future as a concert pianist. Her chance at a career has passed, and she decides to help her ten-year-old piano prodigy brother, Gus, map out his own future, even as she explores why she enjoyed piano in the first place.

"The third-person narration focuses entirely on Lucy but allows readers enough distance to help them understand her behavior in ways Lucy cannot. Occasional flashbacks fill out the back story. The combination of sympathetic main character and unusual social and cultural world makes this satisfying coming-of-age story stand out." Kirkus.

Once was lost: a novel. by Sara Zarr. Little, Brown, 2009. 224 p.
Grades: 7 8 9 10   **Fic**
   1. Teenage children of alcoholics 2. Self-perception in teenage girls 3. Belief and doubt 4. Kidnapping 5. Faith 6. Realistic fiction 7. Christian fiction
ISBN 9780316036047

LC 2009025187

As the tragedy of a missing girl enfolds in her small town, fifteen-year-old Samara, who feels emotionally abandoned by her parents, begins to question her faith.

"This multilayered exploration of the intersection of the spiritual life and imperfect people features suspense and packs an emotional wallop." School Library Journal.

Roomies. Sara Zarr and Tara Altebrando. Little, Brown and Company, 2013. 288 p.
Grades: 9 10 11 12   **Fic**
   1. Email 2. Roommates 3. Friendship 4. Leaving home 5. High school graduates 6. New Jersey 7. California 8. Realistic fiction 9. Epistolary novels
ISBN 9780316217491

LC 2012048431

While living very different lives on opposite coasts, seventeen-year-old Elizabeth and eighteen-year-old Lauren become acquainted by email the summer before they begin rooming together as freshmen at UC-Berkeley.

"Jersey girl Elizabeth (EB) and San Franciscan Lauren, soon to be college roommates, correspond throughout the summer; chapters with alternating perspectives unwrap each girl's backstory, personality, and coming-to-terms with changes looming on the horizon. The premise will have mass appeal with teens who fantasize about their post-high-school futures, and the authors succeed in presenting two distinct and relatable narrative voices." Horn Book.

Zettel, Sarah

Bad luck girl. Sarah Zettel. Random House, 2014. 368 p.: American fairy trilogy
Grades: 7 8 9 10   **Fic**
   1. 1930s 2. Fairies 3. Prophecies 4. Magic 5. Teenage girls 6. LeRoux, Callie (Fictitious character) 7. Chicago, Illinois 8.

Historical fantasy
ISBN 9780375869402

A conclusion to the trilogy that began with Dust Girl and Golden Girl finds Callie caught up in the war between the fairies of the Midnight Throne and the Sunlit Kingdoms before discovering a race of half-fairy misfits who need her help.

"Half-fairy, half-human Callie (Golden Girl; Dust Girl) has reunited with her family, thus starting a war between the two fairy kingdoms. Fleeing Los Angeles for Chicago, Callie realizes that to end the war she must stand and fight. Zettel brings the street life, locales, and culture of jazz-age Chicago into the imagery of her fantasy, packing the story with incident and adventure." Horn Book.

A **most** dangerous deception: being a true, accurate, and complete account of the scandalous and wholly remarkable adventures of Margaret Preston Fitzroy, counterfeit lady, accused thief, and confidential agent at the court of his majesty, King George I. Sarah Zettel. Harcourt, Houghton Mifflin Harcourt, 2013 320 p.: Palace of spies
Grades: 8 9 10   **Fic**
   1. 18th century 2. Georgian era (1714-1837) 3. Spies 4. Teenage girl orphans 5. Artists 6. Courts and courtiers 7. Teenage romance 8. London, England 9. Great Britain 10. Historical mysteries
ISBN 9780544074118

Coerced into impersonating a lady-in-waiting at the palace of King George I, 16-year-old Peggy, a clever and well-bred orphan, begins to suspect that the girl she is impersonating has been murdered and that she is doomed to the same terrible fate unless she can navigate the malicious intrigues of the court.

"In eighteenth-century London, destitute orphan Peggy Fitzroy agrees to impersonate the recently deceased spy Lady Francesca as maid of honor to Princess Caroline. With a war of succession, jilted love, and religious turmoil in the mix, Peggy must navigate intrigue and shady liaisons to uncover the truth behind her predecessor's death. The feisty narrator and lush period details will garner fans for this new series." Horn Book.

Zevin, Gabrielle

Memoirs of a teenage amnesiac. Gabrielle Zevin. Farrar, Straus, and Giroux, 2007. 288 p.
Grades: 7 8 9 10   **Fic**
   1. Amnesia 2. Identity (Psychology) 3. Accidents 4. Teenage girls with amnesia 5. People with amnesia 6. Realistic fiction
ISBN 0374349460

"This is a sensitive, joyful novel. . . . Pulled by the the heart-bruising love story, readers will pause to contemplate irresistible questions." Booklist.

Zindel, Paul

The **pigman**: a novel. Paul Zindel. Dell, 1970, copyright 1968. 159 p.
Grades: 7 8 9 10   **Fic**
   1. High school sophomores 2. Social isolation 3. Teenagers and seniors 4. Intergenerational friendship 5. Friends -- Death 6. Coming-of-age stories 7. Classics
ISBN 0030547032

LC 68010784

A teenage boy and girl, high school sophomores from unhappy homes, tell of their bizarre relationship with an old man.

Zink, Michelle

Prophecy of the sisters. by Michelle Zink. Little, Brown, 2009. 343 p.: Prophecy of the sisters trilogy

Grades: 7 8 9 10   **Fic**
   1. 1890s 2. 19th century 3. Twin sisters 4. Prophecies 5. Supernatural 6. Teenage girl orphans 7. Good and evil 8. New York (State) 9. Historical fantasy 10. Gothic fiction
   ISBN 9780316027427

                       LC 2008045290

Soon after their father dies under mysterious circumstances, orphaned twin sisters Lia and Alice Milthorpe discover that an ancient prophecy has pitted them against one another in a mystical battle between good and evil. One of them will save the world—if she can prevent the other from bringing about its end. But which one is which? Set in a small town in upstate New York in the 19th century and written with a distinct Victorian air, this haunting novel features richly drawn characters, psychological nuances, spells, fallen angels, and murder most foul.

"This arresting story takes readers to other planes of existence." Booklist.

Zinn, Bridget

Poison. Bridget Zinn. Disney*Hyperion, 2013. 288 p.

Grades: 7 8 9 10 11 12   **Fic**
   1. Teenage fugitives 2. Poisons 3. Visions 4. Magic 5. Princesses 6. High fantasy 7. Fantasy fiction
   ISBN 9781423139935

                       LC 2012008693

When sixteen-year-old Kyra, a potions master, tries to save her kingdom by murdering the princess, who is also her best friend, the poisoned dart misses its mark and Kyra becomes a fugitive, pursued by the King's army and her ex-boyfriend Hal.

Zoboi, Ibi Aanu

Pride. Ibi Zoboi. Balzer+Bray, 2018 304 p.

Grades: 8 9 10 11 12   **Fic**
   1. Gentrification of cities 2. Multiracial teenage girls 3. First loves 4. Neighborhoods 5. Dysfunctional families 6. Brooklyn, New York City 7. New York City 8. Classics-inspired fiction 9. Contemporary romances
   ISBN 9780062564047

In a timely update of Jane Austen's Pride and Prejudice, critically acclaimed author Ibi Zoboi skillfully balances cultural identity, class, and gentrification against the heady magic of first love in her vibrant reimagining of this beloved classic.

"This lively, innovative Pride and Prejudice retelling starring a fully rounded Afro-Latinx character hits the familiar notes of Austen's Bennet sisters while inventively modernizing the original's commentary about social class." Horn Book Guide.

Zuckerman, Linda

A **taste** for rabbit. Linda Zuckerman. Arthur A. Levine Books, c2007. 310 p.

Grades: 7 8 9 10   **Fic**
   1. Rabbits 2. Resistance to government 3. Missing persons 4. Brothers 5. Foxes 6. Fantasy fiction
   ISBN 9780439869775

                       LC 2007007787

Quentin, a rabbit who lives in a walled compound run by a militaristic government, must join forces with Harry, a fox, to stop the sinister disappearances of outspoken and rebellious rabbit citizens.

"The blend of adventure, mystery and morality in this heroic tale of honor and friendship will appeal to middle-school fantasy fans." Publishers Weekly.

Zusak, Markus

The **book** thief. by Markus Zusak. Alfred A. Knopf, 2006. 552 p.

Grades: 8 9 10 11 12   **Fic**
   1. Second World War era (1939-1945) 2. Death (Personification) 3. Girl orphans 4. Book thefts 5. World War II -- Jews -- Rescue 6. Righteous Gentiles in the Holocaust 7. Germany 8. Historical fiction
   ISBN 9780375831003

                       LC 2005008942

Sydney Taylor Book Award for Teen Readers, 2007.

Trying to make sense of the horrors of World War II, Death relates the story of Liesel—a young German girl whose book-stealing and story-telling talents help sustain her family and the Jewish man they are hiding, as well as their neighbors.

"This hefty volume is an achievement—a challenging book in both length and subject, and best suited to sophisticated older readers." Publishers Weekly.

AUTHOR, TITLE, AND SUBJECT INDEX

This index to the books in the Classified Collection includes author, title, and subject entries; added entries for publishers' series, illustrators, joint authors, and editors of works entered under title; and name and subject cross-references; all arranged in one alphabet.

The number or symbol in boldface type at the end of each entry refers to the Dewey Decimal Classification or to the Fiction (Fic) section where the main entry for the book will be found. Works classed in Biography (B) will be found under the headings for the biographies' subject.

Anderson, L. H. Fever 1793	**Fic**
Gardner, S. The silver blade	**Fic**
Hale, N. Blades of freedom	**972.94**
Lawrence, I. The wreckers	**Fic**
Meyer, L. A. Bloody Jack	**Fic**

17TH CENTURY

Aliki. William Shakespeare & the Globe	**792**
Duble, K. B. The sacrifice	**Fic**
Hemphill, S. Wicked girls	**Fic**
Huff, T. E. An age of science and revolutions 1600-1800	**909**
Mandell, D. R. King Philip's war	**973.2**
McKissack, P. Nzingha	**Fic**
Messner, K. The Mayflower	**974.4**
Philbrick, N. The Mayflower and the Pilgrims' new world	**973.2**
Saari, P. Colonial America primary sources	**973.2**
Sands, K. The Blackthorn key	**Fic**
Schanzer, R. Witches!	**133.4**
Turnbull, S. R. The most daring raid of the samurai	**952**

180 days. Gallagher, K.	**428.4071**

1800S (DECADE)

Bertozzi, N. Lewis & Clark	**741.5**
Bodden, V. Through the American West	**917.804**
Kindl, P. A school for brides	**Fic**
LeZotte, A. C. Show me a sign	**Fic**
St. George, J. The duel	**973.4**
Woods, B. My name is Sally Little Song	**Fic**

1810S

Milford, K. Bluecrowne	**Fic**
Milford, K. The Left-Handed Fate	**Fic**

1820S

Valente, C. M. The Glass Town game	**Fic**

1830S

Avi. The true confessions of Charlotte Doyle	**Fic**
Barker, M. P. Mending horses	**Fic**
Doyle, M. Bewitching season	**Fic**
MacColl, M. Prisoners in the palace	**Fic**
Northrop, M. Polaris	**Fic**
Tingle, T. How I became a ghost	**Fic**
Tingle, T. When a ghost talks listen	**Fic**

1840S

Avi. Gold rush girl	**Fic**
Brown, S. To stay alive	**Fic**
Bruchac, J. Walking two worlds	**Fic**
DiConsiglio, J. The Mexican-American War	**973.6**
Erdrich, L. The birchbark house	**Fic**
Erdrich, L. The game of silence	**Fic**
Eves, R. Blood rose rebellion	**Fic**
Olson, T. How to get rich in the California Gold Rush	**979.4**

1850S

Carriger, G. Curtsies & conspiracies	**Fic**
Carriger, G. Etiquette & espionage	**Fic**
Carriger, G. Waistcoats & weaponry	**Fic**
Erdrich, L. The porcupine year	**Fic**
Holm, J. L. Boston Jane wilderness days	**Fic**
Hopkinson, D. The great trouble	**Fic**

Lee, Y. S. The body at the tower	**Fic**
Lee, Y. S. A spy in the house	**Fic**

1860S

Curtis, C. P. Elijah of Buxton	**Fic**
Dallas, S. The quilt walk	**Fic**
Erdrich, L. Makoons	**Fic**
Harrell, R. Monster on the hill	**741.5**
Hooper, M. Fallen Grace	**Fic**
Jurmain, S. Murder on the Baltimore Express	**973.7092**
Larson, H. Compass south	**741.5**
Lester, J. Time's memory	**Fic**
McKernan, V. The devil's paintbox	**Fic**
Older, D. J. Thunder run	**Fic**
Otfinoski, S. The Civil War	**973.7**
Philbrick, W. R. The mostly true adventures of Homer P. Figg	**Fic**
Rees, B. The Civil War	**973.7**
Schlitz, L. A. Splendors and glooms	**Fic**
Tarshis, L. The battle of Gettysburg 1863	**Fic**
Tingle, T. Danny Blackgoat Navajo prisoner	**Fic**
Warren, A. Under siege!	**973.7**
Wells, R. Red moon at Sharpsburg	**Fic**
Wiechman, K. C. Like a river	**Fic**

1870S

Avi. The seer of shadows	**Fic**
Carey, E. Heap House	**Fic**
Goldstone, L. Unpunished murder	**976.3**
Hand, C. My Calamity Jane	**Fic**
Jinks, C. How to catch a bogle	**Fic**
Jinks, C. The last bogler	**Fic**
Pierpoint, E. The last ride of Caleb O'Toole	**Fic**
Rhodes, J. P. Sugar	**Fic**
Sheinkin, S. Lincoln's grave robbers	**973.7092**
Wallace, S. N. Bound by ice	**910.4**
Weltig, M. S. The aftermath of the Anglo-Zulu war	**968.4**
Wilson, J. Ghost moon	**Fic**
Wilson, J. Victorio's war	**Fic**
Wilson, J. Written in blood	**Fic**

1880S

Bolden, T. Inventing Victoria	**Fic**
Cushman, K. Rodzina	**Fic**
Gleason, C. The clockwork scarab	**Fic**
Hopkinson, D. A bandit's tale	**Fic**
Kirby, M. J. A taste for monsters	**Fic**
Koestler-Grack, R. A. Johnstown flood of 1889	**974.8**
Oppel, K. The Boundless	**Fic**
Park, L. S. Prairie lotus	**Fic**
Pileggi, L. Prisoner 88	**Fic**
Richards, J. Three rivers rising	**Fic**
Springer, N. The case of the missing marquess	**Fic**
Wiseman, E. Puppet	**Fic**

1890S

Avi. City of orphans	**Fic**
Beatty, R. Serafina and the twisted staff	**Fic**
Gemeinhart, D. Some kind of courage	**Fic**
Grove, S. E. The crimson skew	**Fic**
Grove, S. E. The golden specific	**Fic**

Hobbs, W. Jason's gold | **Fic**
Kelly, J. The evolution of Calpurnia Tate | **Fic**
Lee, S. The downstairs girl | **Fic**
Peck, R. Fair weather | **Fic**
Pullman, P. Two crafty criminals! | **Fic**
Ritter, W. The dire king | **Fic**
Ritter, W. Jackaby | **Fic**
Wright, B. Crow | **Fic**
Yelchin, E. The haunting of Falcon House | **Fic**
Zink, M. Prophecy of the sisters | **Fic**

18TH CENTURY

Anderson, L. H. Ashes | **Fic**
Anderson, L. H. Chains | **Fic**
Anderson, L. H. Fever 1793 | **Fic**
Anderson, L. H. Forge | **Fic**
Avi. The fighting ground | **Fic**
Avi. Sophia's war | **Fic**
Beil, K. M. What Linnaeus saw | **508.092**
Blackwood, G. L. The year of the hangman | **Fic**
Donnelly, J. Stepsister | **Fic**
Dunlap, S. E. The musician's daughter | **Fic**
Forbes, E. Johnny Tremain | **Fic**
Gardner, S. The silver blade | **Fic**
Hale, N. Blades of freedom | **972.94**
Hansen, J. Breaking ground breaking silence | **305.5**
Higgins, J. Waiting for the queen | **Fic**
Hoobler, D. The demon in the teahouse | **Fic**
Hoobler, D. The ghost in the Tokaido Inn | **Fic**
Huff, T. E. An age of science and revolutions 1600-1800 | **909**
Hughes, P. Five 4ths of July | **Fic**
Kiernan, D. Signing their rights away | **973.3**
Klass, S. S. Soldier's secret | **Fic**
Landman, T. Hell and high water | **Fic**
Lawrence, I. The wreckers | **Fic**
Lee, M. The gentleman's guide to vice and virtue | **Fic**
Lu, M. The Kingdom of Back | **Fic**
McClafferty, C. K. Buried lives | **306.3**
McKissack, P. Black hands white sails | **639.2**
Meyer, L. A. Bloody Jack | **Fic**
Oppel, K. This dark endeavor | **Fic**
Roberts, C. Founding mothers | **973.3**
Rosen, M. J. Sailing the unknown | **Fic**
Saari, P. Colonial America primary sources | **973.2**
Speare, E. G. The witch of Blackbird Pond | **Fic**
Tripp, B. The accidental highwayman | **Fic**
Vaughn, C. Steel | **Fic**
Wood, M. Nightshade | **Fic**
Wood, M. The poison diaries | **Fic**
Woodruff, E. The ravenmaster's secret | **Fic**
Zettel, S. A most dangerous deception | **Fic**
19 varieties of gazelle. Nye, N. S. | **811**

1900S (DECADE)

Blundell, J. A city tossed and broken | **Fic**
Bolden, T. Saving Savannah | **Fic**
Chibbaro, J. Deadly | **Fic**
Choldenko, G. Chasing secrets | **Fic**

Curtis, C. P. The madman of Piney Woods | **Fic**
Engle, M. Silver people | **Fic**
Haddix, M. P. Caught | **Fic**
Hesse, K. Brooklyn Bridge | **Fic**
Holm, J. L. The trouble with May Amelia | **Fic**
Hopkinson, D. Into the firestorm | **Fic**
Jarrow, G. Bubonic panic | **614.5**
Jurmain, S. The secret of the yellow death | **614.5**
Kelly, J. The curious world of Calpurnia Tate | **Fic**
Lavender, W. Aftershocks | **Fic**
Lee, S. Outrun the moon | **Fic**
MacColl, M. Rory's promise | **Fic**
Maguire, G. Egg & spoon | **Fic**
Mobley, J. Katerina's wish | **Fic**
Peck, R. The teacher's funeral | **Fic**
Slavicek, L. C. The San Francisco earthquake and fire of 1906 | **979.4**
Taylor, M. D. The well | **Fic**
Voigt, C. The book of kings | **Fic**
Voigt, C. The book of lost things | **Fic**
Voigt, C. The book of secrets | **Fic**
Waller, S. B. A mad wicked folly | **Fic**
Yep, L. Dragonwings | **Fic**

1900S(DECADE)

Winters, C. Odd & true | **Fic**

1910S

Armstrong, J. Shipwreck at the bottom of the world | **919.8**
Avi. The button war | **Fic**
Barber, N. World War I | **940.3**
Bascomb, N. The grand escape | **940.4**
Batten, J. The war to end all wars | **940.3**
Bertozzi, N. Shackleton | **919.89**
Davis, K. C. More deadly than war | **614.5**
Friesner, E. M. Threads and flames | **Fic**
Haddix, M. P. Risked | **Fic**
Haddix, M. P. Uprising | **Fic**
Hesse, K. Letters from Rifka | **Fic**
Jarrow, G. Fatal fever | **614.5**
Korman, G. Collision course | **Fic**
Kupperberg, P. The influenza pandemic of 1918-1919 | **614.5**
Larson, K. Hattie Big Sky | **Fic**
MacColl, M. Promise the night | **Fic**
Marrin, A. Flesh & blood so cheap | **974.7**
Milford, K. The Boneshaker | **Fic**
Miller, S. E. The lost crown | **Fic**
Morpurgo, M. Listen to the moon | **Fic**
Morpurgo, M. War horse | **Fic**
Nesbet, A. Daring Darleen queen of the screen | **Fic**
Paterson, K. Bread and roses too | **Fic**
Sandler, M. W. 1919 | **973.91**
Schlitz, L. A. The hired girl | **Fic**
Schmidt, G. D. Lizzie Bright and the Buckminster boy | **Fic**
Sedgwick, M. Revolver | **Fic**
Strange, L. The secret of Nightingale Wood | **Fic**
Swain, G. World War I | **940.3**
Walker, S. M. Blizzard of glass | **971.6**

Walrath, D. Like water on stone	Fic	Peck, R. A year down yonder	Fic
Westerfeld, S. Behemoth	Fic	Phelan, M. The storm in the barn	741.5
Westerfeld, S. Goliath	Fic	Pinkney, A. D. Bird in a box	Fic
Westerfeld, S. Leviathan	Fic	Roy, J. R. Yellow star	Fic
Whelan, G. Small acts of amazing courage	Fic	Ruiz Zafon, C. The Midnight Palace	Fic
Whitman, E. Wildwing	Fic	Ryan, P. M. Esperanza rising	Fic
Winters, C. In the shadow of blackbirds	Fic	Selznick, B. The invention of Hugo Cabret	Fic
Winthrop, E. Counting on Grace	Fic	Sharenow, R. The Berlin Boxing Club	Fic
Wolf, A. The watch that ends the night	Fic	Smith, R. L. Hoodoo	Fic
1919. Sandler, M. W.	**973.91**	Stanley, J. Children of the Dust Bowl	371.96
1920S		Stevens, R. First class murder	Fic
Blumenthal, K. Six days in October	**332.64**	Stevens, R. Murder is bad manners	Fic
Bryant, J. Ringside 1925	Fic	Stevens, R. Poison is not polite	Fic
Finkelstein, N. H. Three across	**629.130973**	Taylor, M. D. The friendship	Fic
Fitzgerald, L. M. The gallery	Fic	Taylor, M. D. Let the circle be unbroken	Fic
Fritz, J. Homesick	Fic	Taylor, M. D. Roll of thunder hear my cry	Fic
Gutman, D. Ray & me	Fic	Uchida, Y. A jar of dreams	Fic
Hardinge, F. Cuckoo song	Fic	Vanderpool, C. Moon over Manifest	Fic
Harlow, J. H. Thunder from the sea	Fic	Walker, S. M. Fossil fish found alive	597.3
Hesse, K. Witness	Fic	Weatherford, C. B. You can fly	811
Ireland, J. Ophie's ghosts	Fic	Wein, E. Black dove white raven	Fic
James, H. F. Paper son	Fic	Wein, E. The pearl thief	Fic
Macy, S. Breaking through	**796.082**	Yang, G. L. The shadow hero	741.5
Phelan, M. Snow White	**741.5**	Zettel, S. Bad luck girl	Fic
Selznick, B. Wonderstruck	Fic	**1940S**	
Vernick, S. R. The blood lie	Fic	Allen, T. B. Remember Pearl Harbor	940.54
Whelan, G. All my noble dreams and then what happens	Fic	Ambrose, S. E. The good fight	940.53
Wolk, L. Beyond the bright sea	Fic	Atkinson, R. D-Day	940.54
1930S		Bartoletti, S. C. The boy who dared	Fic
Adams, C. Queens of the ice	**796.962082**	Blankman, A. The blackbird girls	Fic
Alban, A. Anya's war	Fic	Blundell, J. What I saw and how I lied	Fic
Baldwin, J. Go tell it on the mountain	Fic	Bolden, T. FDR's Alphabet soup	973.917
Bolden, T. FDR's Alphabet soup	**973.917**	Bowers, R. Superman versus the Ku Klux Klan	741.5
Brimner, L. D. Accused!	**345.761**	Boyne, J. The boy in the striped pajamas	Fic
Brown, D. The boys in the boat	**797.12**	Bradley, K. B. The war that saved my life	Fic
Brown, D. The great American Dust Bowl	**978**	Brimner, L. D. Blacklisted!	323
Burgan, M. Olympic gold 1936	**796.42**	Callery, S. World War II	940.53
Callery, S. World War II	**940.53**	Cline-Ransome, L. Being Clem	Fic
Choldenko, G. Al Capone does my shirts	Fic	Cline-Ransome, L. Leaving Lymon	Fic
Currier, K. S. Kai's journey to Gold Mountain	Fic	Colman, P. Rosie the riveter	331.4
Curtis, C. P. Bud not Buddy	Fic	Cornioley, P. W. Code name Pauline	940.54
Deem, J. M. Kristallnacht	**940.53**	Cushman, K. The loud silence of Francine Green	Fic
Draper, S. M. Stella by starlight	Fic	Davis, T. S. Mare's war	Fic
Fombelle, T. d. Between sky and earth	Fic	DeWoskin, R. Someday we will fly	Fic
Fradin, J. B. Droughts	**363.34**	Dowswell, P. Auslander	Fic
Friedman, I. R. The other victims	**940.53**	Edsel, R. M. The greatest treasure hunt in history	940.53
Fusco, K. N. The wonder of Charlie Anne	Fic	English, K. Francie	Fic
Gillette, R. H. Escape to Virginia	**975.5**	Fox, J. S. The charmed children of Rookskill Castle	Fic
Gratz, A. Refugee	Fic	Freedman, R. We will not be silent	943.086
Henderson, L. The magic in changing your stars	Fic	Friedman, I. R. The other victims	940.53
Hesse, K. Out of the dust	Fic	Fusco, K. N. Beholding Bee	Fic
Levy, D. The year of goodbyes	**811**	Giff, P. R. Lily's crossing	Fic
Lindelauf, B. Nine Open Arms	Fic	Gutman, D. Mickey & me	Fic
MacHale, D. J. The never war	Fic	Haugen, D. M. The attack on Pearl Harbor	940.54
Maraniss, A. Games of deception	**796.48**	Hayles, M. Breathing room	Fic
Martin, A. M. Better to wish	Fic	Hoose, P. M. The boys who challenged Hitler	940.53
McCall, G. G. All the stars denied	Fic	Houston, J. W. Farewell to Manzanar	940.54

O'Reilly, B. Kennedy's last days	973.922092	Wiles, D. Kent State	Fic
Partridge, E. Boots on the ground	959.704	Wolf, A. Who killed Christopher Goodman?	Fic
Pearsall, S. The seventh most important thing	Fic	Woodson, J. Feathers	Fic
Perkins, L. R. Criss cross	Fic	**1980S**	
Pinkwater, D. M. Bushman lives!	Fic	Avery, T. Not as we know it	Fic
Powell, P. H. Loving vs. Virginia	Fic	Blankman, A. The blackbird girls	Fic
Rocco, J. How we got to the moon	629.45	Brashear, A. The incredible true story of the making of the	
Sandler, M. W. Apollo 8	629.45	Eve of Destruction	Fic
Schmidt, G. D. Just like that	Fic	Brown, S. Caminar	Fic
Schmidt, G. D. The Wednesday wars	Fic	Burgan, M. Miracle on ice	796.962
Silvey, C. Jasper Jones	Fic	Charles, T. Becoming Beatriz	Fic
Smiley, J. The Georges and the Jewels	Fic	Charles, T. Like Vanessa	Fic
Stein, R. C. Cuban Missile Crisis	972.9106	Dowd, S. Bog child	Fic
Stone, T. L. Almost astronauts	629.450092	Farmer, N. A girl named Disaster	Fic
Strasser, T. Fallout	Fic	Foxlee, K. The anatomy of wings	Fic
Swanson, J. L. "The president has been shot!"	973.922092	Gansworth, E. L. Give me some truth	Fic
Wallace, R. War and watermelon	Fic	Kadohata, C. Outside beauty	Fic
Watson, B. Freedom Summer for young people	323.1196	Kelly, E. E. We dream of space	Fic
Weil, C. I'm glad I did	Fic	Kephart, B. Going over	Fic
Wiles, D. Anthem	Fic	Kramer, J. K. The story that cannot be told	Fic
Wiles, D. Countdown	Fic	Lai, T. Butterfly yellow	Fic
Wiles, D. Revolution	Fic	Larocca, R. Red white and whole	Fic
Williams-Garcia, R. Gone crazy in Alabama	Fic	McCrite, K. D. In front of God and everybody	Fic
Williams-Garcia, R. One crazy summer	Fic	Nazemian, A. Like a love story	Fic
Williams-Garcia, R. P.S. be eleven	Fic	Nesbet, A. Cloud and Wallfish	Fic
1968. Aronson, M.	909.82	Odhiambo, E. A. Auma's long run	Fic
1968. Kaufman, M. T.	909.82	Partridge, E. Dogtag summer	Fic
1970S		Pellegrino, M. Journey of dreams	Fic
Budhos, M. T. The long ride	Fic	Rosenberg, M. This is just a test	Fic
Burg, A. E. All the broken pieces	Fic	Smy, P. Thornhill	Fic
Cao, W. Bronze and Sunflower	Fic	Sovern, M. J. The meaning of Maggie	Fic
Compestine, Y. C. Revolution is not a dinner party	Fic	Starmer, A. The whisper	Fic
DiCamillo, K. Beverly right here	Fic	Tucker, L. All the Greys on Greene Street	Fic
DiCamillo, K. Raymie Nightingale	Fic	Yoo, P. From a whisper to a rallying cry	305.895
Dumas, F. It ain't so awful falafel	Fic	**1990S**	
Dunstan, S. Entebbe	967.6104	Asher, J. The future of us	Fic
Ehrlich, E. Nest	Fic	Crowder, M. An uninterrupted view of the sky	Fic
Erskine, K. Seeing red	Fic	Curato, M. Flamer	Fic
Frank, S. Armstrong and Charlie	Fic	Gratz, A. Refugee	Fic
Gansworth, E. L. If I ever get out of here	Fic	Jackson, T. D. Let me hear a rhyme	Fic
Hitchcock, B. The smell of other people's houses	Fic	Lennon, T. When love comes to town	Fic
Holm, J. L. Sunny side up	741.5	Peet, M. Tamar	Fic
Holm, J. L. Swing it Sunny	741.5	Pratchett, T. Only you can save mankind	Fic
Holt, K. W. When Zachary Beaver came to town	Fic	Pyron, B. The dogs of winter	Fic
Kadohata, C. A million shades of gray	Fic	Selznick, B. The Marvels	Fic
Lai, T. Inside out & back again	Fic	Temblador, A. Secrets of the Casa Rosada	Fic
Oppel, K. Half brother	Fic	Tolstikova, D. A year without Mom	741.5
Partridge, E. Boots on the ground	959.704	Woodson, J. After Tupac and D Foster	Fic
Pearson, P. O. Conspiracy	973.924	**19TH CENTURY**	
Perkins, M. Secret keeper	Fic	Angleberger, T. Horton Halfpott or The fiendish mystery of	
Selznick, B. Wonderstruck	Fic	Smugwick Manor or The loosening of M'Lady Luggertuck's	
Shang, W. W. The way home looks now	Fic	corset	Fic
Smith, I. Half spoon of rice	Fic	Avi. The true confessions of Charlotte Doyle	Fic
Sonneborn, L. The Khmer Rouge	959.604	Barker, M. P. Mending horses	Fic
Stead, R. When you reach me	Fic	Bartoletti, S. C. Growing up in coal country	331.3
Thimmesh, C. Team moon	629.45	Beatty, R. Willa of Dark Hollow	Fic
Warman, J. The world beneath	Fic	Bolden, T. Inventing Victoria	Fic

Sandler, M. W. 1919	973.91
Taylor, M. D. All the days past all the days to come	**Fic**

21ST CENTURY

Brown, D. In the shadow of the fallen towers	973.931
Corrigan, J. The 2000s decade in photos	973.93
Downer, A. Hatching magic	**Fic**
Johnson-Shelton, N. The invisible tower	**Fic**
Johnson-Shelton, N. The seven swords	**Fic**
Staples, S. F. Under the persimmon tree	**Fic**
21st-century counselors. Flath, C.	362.2

22ND CENTURY

Bertagna, J. Exodus	**Fic**
Lu, M. Champion	**Fic**
Lu, M. Legend	**Fic**
Lu, M. Prodigy	**Fic**
24 girls in 7 days. Bradley, A.	**Fic**
27 magic words. Moranville, S. B.	**Fic**
3 willows. Brashares, A.	**Fic**
3-D printers. Bow, J.	621.988

3-D PRINTING

Bow, J. 3-D printers	621.988
Koch, M. 3D printing	621.9
3D printing. Koch, M.	621.9
47. Mosley, W.	**Fic**
47 things you can do for the environment. Petronis, L.	333.72
5 principles of the modern mathematics classroom. Aungst, G.	510.71

50 Cent

Playground	**Fic**
50 things you should know about the Vietnam War. McNab, C.	959.704

5TH CENTURY

Thomas, S. The magnolia sword	**Fic**
6+1 traits of writing. Culham, R.	372.62

7TH CENTURY

Jones, F. Destiny's path	**Fic**
911. Cart, M.	810.8
The 911 attacks. Murray, L. K.	973.931
96 miles. Esplin, J. L.	**Fic**

A

Aaseng, Nathan

Construction	624
Weird meat-eating plants	583

Abadzis, Nick

Laika	741.5

ABANDONED ANIMALS

Appelt, K. The underneath	**Fic**

ABANDONED BOYS

Blackwood, S. Jinx	**Fic**
Jacobson, J. Small as an elephant	**Fic**

ABANDONED CATS

Myron, V. Dewey the library cat	636.80092

ABANDONED CHILDREN

Almond, D. Raven summer	**Fic**
Fforde, J. The last dragonslayer	**Fic**

Gaiman, N. Hansel & Gretel	398.20943
Hesse, K. Brooklyn Bridge	**Fic**
Hest, A. The summer we found the baby	**Fic**
Ibbotson, E. The star of Kazan	**Fic**
Kadohata, C. Half a world away	**Fic**
McMullan, M. When I crossed No-Bob	**Fic**
Naidoo, B. The other side of truth	**Fic**
Paterson, K. The same stuff as stars	**Fic**
Reeve, P. Fever Crumb	**Fic**
Unsworth, T. The one safe place	**Fic**
Voigt, C. Dicey's song	**Fic**
Voigt, C. Homecoming	**Fic**
Voigt, C. A solitary blue	**Fic**
White, R. The treasure of Way Down Deep	**Fic**
White, R. Way Down Deep	**Fic**

ABANDONED DOGS

Cleary, B. Strider	**Fic**
Giff, P. R. Winter sky	**Fic**
Howe, P. Waggit's tale	**Fic**

ABANDONED GIRLS

Horvath, P. The canning season	**Fic**
LaFleur, S. M. Love Aubrey	**Fic**
Turnage, S. Three times lucky	**Fic**

ABANDONED INFANTS

Alban, A. Anya's war	**Fic**
Lasky, K. Lone wolf	**Fic**

ABANDONED PROPERTY

Riggs, R. A map of days	**Fic**
Riggs, R. Miss Peregrine's home for peculiar children	**Fic**

ABANDONED TEENAGERS

Dessen, S. Lock and key	**Fic**
Horvath, P. The canning season	**Fic**
Whelan, G. Homeless bird	**Fic**

ABANDONMENT (PSYCHOLOGY)

Boteju, T. Kings queens and in-betweens	**Fic**

ABBEYS

Turtschaninoff, M. Maresi	**Fic**

ABBOTT, BERENICE, 1898-1991

Sullivan, G. Berenice Abbott photographer	**B**

Abbott, Tony, 1952-

The forbidden stone	**Fic**
The summer of Owen Todd	**Fic**
Wade and the scorpion's claw	**Fic**

Abdel-Fattah, Randa

Does my head look big in this?	**Fic**
Ten things I hate about me	**Fic**
Where the streets had a name	**Fic**
The abduction. Grisham, J.	**Fic**

Abdul-Jabbar, Kareem, 1947-

Stealing the game	**Fic**

Abell, Tracy

Artificial intelligence ethics and debates	170
Abhorsen. Nix, G.	**Fic**

ABILITY

Aster, A. Curse of the forgotten city	**Fic**
Black, P. J. Urban outlaws	**Fic**
Grabenstein, J. J. Shine!	**Fic**

Graff, L. A tangle of knots — Fic

MacCullough, C. Once a witch — Fic

McKinney, L. L. Nubia — 741.5

Ryon, L. Into the tall tall grass — Fic

Silvera, A. Infinity son — Fic

Abilock, Debbie

Growing schools — 370.71

Abner & me. Gutman, D. — Fic

ABOLITIONISTS

Marrin, A. A volcano beneath the snow — 973.7

ABORIGINAL AUSTRALIANS

Arnold, C. Uluru Australia's Aboriginal heart — 994.01

Kwaymullina, A. The things she's seen — Fic

ABORIGINAL AUSTRALIANS -- HISTORY

Connolly, S. The Americas and the Pacific — 970.004

ABORIGINAL AUSTRALIANS -- RELIGION

Arnold, C. Uluru Australia's Aboriginal heart — 994.01

ABORTION

Merino, N. Abortion — 362.1988

Stevenson, R. My body my choice — 362.1988

Wilcox, C. Thinking critically — 362.1988

ABORTION -- HISTORY

Stevenson, R. My body my choice — 362.1988

ABORTION -- LAW AND LEGISLATION

Blumenthal, K. Jane against the world — 342.7308

Higgins, M. Roe v. Wade — 345.73

Merino, N. Abortion — 362.1988

ABORTION -- MORAL AND ETHICAL ASPECTS

Merino, N. Abortion — 362.1988

Wilcox, C. Thinking critically — 362.1988

Abortion. Merino, N. — 362.1988

Above all else. Levy, D. A. — Fic

Above and beyond. Rhuday-Perkovich, O. — 629.40973

The **abracadabra** kid. Fleischman, S. — B

Abraham Lincoln and Frederick Douglass. Freedman, R. — 973.7092

Abraham Lincoln the writer. Lincoln, A. — B

Abraham Lincoln. Aronson, B. — B

Abrahams, Roger D.

African folktales — 398.2

Abramovitz, Melissa, 1954-

Amazing feats of biological engineering — 660.6

Deadliest sharks — 597.3

Abrams, Dennis, 1960-

Ernesto "Che" Guevara — B

Abramson, Jill, 1954-

Obama — B

Absolute brightness. Lecesne, J. — Fic

Absolute expert. Strother, R. — 599.789

The **absolute** value of Mike. Erskine, K. — Fic

Absolutely normal chaos. Creech, S. — Fic

Absolutely Truly. Frederick, H. V. — Fic

ABU AL-QASIM KHALAF IBN ABBAS AL-ZAHRAWI, D. 1013?

Ramen, F. Albucasis (Abu al-Qasim al-Zahrawi) — B

Abuse and violence information for teens. Omnigraphics, I. — 303.60835

ABUSE OF ADMINISTRATIVE POWER

Pearson, P. O. Conspiracy — 973.924

ABUSED WOMEN

Byars, B. C. Cracker Jackson — Fic

ACADEMIC ACHIEVEMENT

Brulles, D. The cluster grouping handbook — 371.2

ACADEMIC RIVALRY

Johnson, R. L. Battle of the dinosaur bones — 560.97309

Acampora, Paul

Rachel Spinelli punched me in the face — Fic

Access restricted. Katsoulis, G. S. — Fic

The **accidental** afterlife of Thomas Marsden. Trevayne, E. — Fic

The **accidental** highwayman. Tripp, B. — Fic

ACCIDENTS

Bauer, M. D. On my honor — Fic

Duncan, L. I know what you did last summer — Fic

Johnson, A. A certain October — Fic

Perkins, L. R. As easy as falling off the face of the earth — Fic

Welford, R. Time traveling with a hamster — Fic

Zevin, G. Memoirs of a teenage amnesiac — Fic

ACCIDENTS -- PREVENTION

MacRae, S. Deer hunting — 799.2

ACCLIMATIZATION

Collard, S. B. Hopping ahead of climate change — 599.32

The **accursed** vampire. McGrane, M. — 741.5

The **accused**. Grisham, J. — Fic

Accused! Brimner, L. D. — 345.761

Ace your exercise and nutrition science project. Gardner, R. — 612.7

Ace your human biology science project. Gardner, R. — 612

Ace your plant science project. Gardner, R. — 580.78

ACHILLES (GREEK MYTHOLOGY)

Fleischman, P. Dateline Troy — 398.2

Homer. The Iliad — 883

Landmann, B. The fate of Achilles — 883

ACOLYTES

Almond, D. Clay — Fic

ACORNS

Hirsch, A. Trees — 582.16

ACOUSTICAL ENGINEERING

Rooney, A. Audio engineering and the science of sound-waves — 621.389

Across the wide ocean. Young, K. R. — 623.89

ACT UP.

Nazemian, A. Like a love story — Fic

ACTING

Belli, M. L. Acting for young actors — 792.02

Detrick, E. Actor's choice — 808.82

McCall, G. G. Under the mesquite — Fic

Michael, T. Starry-eyed — Fic

Ratliff, G. L. Millennium monologs — 792

Schumacher, T. How does the show go on? — 792.02

Surface, M. H. Short scenes and monologues for middle school actors — 812

ACTING -- AUDITIONS

Ellis, R. New audition scenes and monologs from contemporary playwrights — 808.82

Carter, C. Forever or a long long time **Fic**
Johnson, A. Heaven **Fic**
Kim, G. The last fallen star **Fic**
Skrypuch, M. F. Last airlift **959.704**
Skrypuch, M. F. One step at a time **618.92**
Warren, A. Escape from Saigon **959.704**

ADOPTED GIRLS

Barnhill, K. R. The girl who drank the moon **Fic**
Bowling, D. Insignificant events in the life of a cactus **Fic**
Day, C. I can make this promise **Fic**
De la Cruz, M. Never after **Fic**
Gibney, S. See no color **Fic**
Graff, L. A tangle of knots **Fic**
Lockington, M. For black girls like me **Fic**
Partridge, E. Dogtag summer **Fic**
Rivers, K. Love Ish **Fic**
Shevah, E. Dara Palmer's major drama **Fic**
Ursu, A. Breadcrumbs **Fic**

ADOPTED TEENAGE BOYS

Haddix, M. P. Found **Fic**

ADOPTED TEENAGE GIRLS

Fantaskey, B. Jessica's guide to dating on the dark side **Fic**
Levine, G. C. The lost kingdom of Bamarre **Fic**
McKay, H. Saffy's angel **Fic**

ADOPTED TEENAGERS

Kuehn, S. Complicit **Fic**

ADOPTION

Benway, R. Far from the tree **Fic**
Burg, A. E. All the broken pieces **Fic**
Doherty, B. The girl who saw lions **Fic**
Hand, C. The how & the why **Fic**
Hof, M. Mother number zero **Fic**
Johnson, A. Heaven **Fic**
Kent, R. Kimchi & calamari **Fic**
Langwith, J. Adoption **362.7340973**
Partridge, E. Dogtag summer **Fic**
Weissman, E. B. The length of a string **Fic**
Zarr, S. How to save a life **Fic**
Adoption. Langwith, J. **362.7340973**
The **adoration** of Jenna Fox. Pearson, M. **Fic**

ADVENTURE

Anderson, M. T. He laughed with his other mouths **Fic**
Armstrong, A. W. Looking for Marco Polo **Fic**
Armstrong, J. Shipwreck at the bottom of the world **919.8**
Auxier, J. Peter Nimble and his fantastic eyes **Fic**
Auxier, J. Sophie Quire and the last Storyguard **Fic**
Blackwood, S. Jinx **Fic**
Durham, P. Fork-tongue charmers **Fic**
Durham, P. The Luck Uglies **Fic**
Flanagan, J. The invaders **Fic**
George, J. D. Dragon flight **Fic**
Gidwitz, A. The Grimm conclusion **Fic**
Grove, S. E. The golden specific **Fic**
Higgins, J. First strike **Fic**
Higgins, J. Sharp shot **Fic**
Horvath, P. My one hundred adventures **Fic**
Jung, M. The boys in the back row **Fic**

Lerangis, P. Lost in babylon **Fic**
Lerangis, P. The tomb of shadows **Fic**
Lin, G. When the sea turned to silver **Fic**
Lin, G. Where the mountain meets the moon **Fic**
Mafi, T. Furthermore **Fic**
Mafi, T. Whichwood **Fic**
Mass, W. Pi in the sky **Fic**
McCaughrean, G. Odysseus **398.2**
Meloy, C. Wildwood **Fic**
Parker, N. C. Steel tide **Fic**
Pearson, L. Hildafolk **741.5**
Petersen, D. Mouse guard **741.5**
Pierpoint, E. The last ride of Caleb O'Toole **Fic**
Rex, A. Smek for president! **Fic**
Riley, J. Secret origins **Fic**
Stead, R. First light **Fic**
Valente, C. M. The girl who soared over Fairyland and cut the moon in two **Fic**
Voigt, C. The book of kings **Fic**
Wallace, S. N. Bound by ice **910.4**
Wegelius, J. The murderer's ape **Fic**

ADVENTURE STORIES

Abbott, T. Wade and the scorpion's claw **Fic**
Alonzo, S. Riding invisible **Fic**
Avi. Gold rush girl **Fic**
Avi. The true confessions of Charlotte Doyle **Fic**
Baker, M. If you find this **Fic**
Bodeen, S. A. The raft **Fic**
Bowling, D. The canyon's edge **Fic**
Eagar, L. Race to the bottom of the sea **Fic**
Farmer, N. A girl named Disaster **Fic**
Fleischman, S. The whipping boy **Fic**
Friesner, E. M. Nobody's prize **Fic**
Frost, H. Diamond Willow **Fic**
Gardner, S. The silver blade **Fic**
Gemeinhart, D. Scar Island **Fic**
George, J. C. Julie **Fic**
Gilman, D. Blood sun **Fic**
Gilman, D. The devil's breath **Fic**
Gilman, D. Ice claw **Fic**
Grabenstein, C. The smartest kid in the universe **Fic**
Harlow, J. H. Thunder from the sea **Fic**
Herlong, M. The great wide sea **Fic**
Hirsch, J. Breakaway **Fic**
Hobbs, W. Crossing the wire **Fic**
Hobbs, W. Jason's gold **Fic**
Hobbs, W. Leaving Protection **Fic**
Hobbs, W. Never say die **Fic**
Hobbs, W. Take me to the river **Fic**
Johnson, T. L. Dog driven **Fic**
Johnson, T. L. Ice dogs **Fic**
Kephart, B. Wild blues **Fic**
Kipling, R. The jungle book **Fic**
Korman, G. Collision course **Fic**
Korman, G. The Medusa plot **Fic**
Lacey, J. Island of Thieves **Fic**
Landmann, B. The incredible voyage of Ulysses **398.2**

Lawrence, I. The smugglers — Fic
Lawrence, I. The wreckers — Fic
London, J. The call of the wild — Fic
Marshall, K. A. I am still alive — Fic
McCaughrean, G. The kite rider — Fic
McKernan, V. Shackleton's stowaway — Fic
McNab, A. Avenger — Fic
Meyer, L. A. Bloody Jack — Fic
Mikaelsen, B. Touching Spirit Bear — Fic
Miller, K. Inside the shadow city — Fic
Mills, G. Gold — Fic
Moderow, H. Lily's mountain — Fic
Mussi, S. The door of no return — Fic
Nesbet, A. Daring Darleen queen of the screen — Fic
O'Dell, S. Island of the Blue Dolphins — Fic
Park, L. S. Storm warning — Fic
Park, L. S. Trust no one — Fic
Paulsen, G. Brian's return — Fic
Paulsen, G. Brian's winter — Fic
Paulsen, G. Hatchet — Fic
Pennypacker, S. Pax — Fic
Philbrick, W. R. Wild river — Fic
Philbrick, W. R. Wildfire — Fic
Pinkwater, D. M. The Neddiad — Fic
Pratchett, T. Nation — Fic
Riordan, R. The maze of bones — Fic
Riordan, R. Vespers rising — Fic
Rosen, M. J. The tale of rescue — Fic
Rundell, K. Rooftoppers — Fic
Schrefer, E. Endangered — Fic
Schrefer, E. Threatened — Fic
Sedgwick, M. Revolver — Fic
Smith, R. Chupacabra — Fic
Smith, R. Peak — Fic
Springstubb, T. The most perfect thing in the universe — Fic
Stead, R. First light — Fic
Stevenson, R. L. Kidnapped — Fic
Stevenson, R. L. Treasure Island — Fic
Stewart, T. L. The mysterious Benedict Society — Fic
Taylor, T. The cay — Fic
Taylor, T. Timothy of the cay — Fic
Twain, M. The adventures of Tom Sawyer — Fic
Twain, M. The prince and the pauper — Fic
Voigt, C. The book of kings — Fic
Voigt, C. The book of lost things — Fic
Voigt, C. The book of secrets — Fic
Walters, E. The money pit mystery — Fic
Watson, J. Beyond the grave — Fic
Watson, J. Nowhere to run — Fic
Whyman, M. Icecore — Fic
Woodruff, E. George Washington's spy — Fic

ADVENTURE TRAVEL
Preller, J. The courage test — Fic

ADVENTURERS
Alexander, L. The golden dream of Carlo Chuchio — Fic
Cleare, J. Epic climbs — 796.522092
Colfer, E. Airman — Fic

Giles, L. R. The Last Mirror on the Left — Fic
Hicks, F. E. The divided earth — 741.5
Homer. The Odyssey — 883
Johnston, E. K. Prairie fire — Fic
Kerley, B. The world is waiting for you — 910
Krull, K. Lives of the explorers — 910.92
Landmann, B. The incredible voyage of Ulysses — 398.2
McKinley, R. The outlaws of Sherwood — Fic
Mundy, R. Epic voyages — 910.4
Park, L. S. Click — Fic
Petersen, D. Mouse guard — 741.5
Phelan, M. Around the world — 910.4
Springstubb, T. The most perfect thing in the universe — Fic
Stevenson, R. L. Treasure Island — Fic
Tolkien, J. R. R. The hobbit or there and back again — Fic
Adventures in graphica. Thompson, T. — 372.41
The **adventures** of a South Pole pig. Kurtz, C. — Fic
The **adventures** of Beanboy. Harkrader, L. — Fic
The **adventures** of Medical Man. Evans, M. — 610
The **adventures** of Molly Whuppie and other Appalachian folktales. Shelby, A. — 398.2
The **adventures** of Tom Sawyer. Twain, M. — Fic
Adventures on the ancient Silk Road. Galloway, P. — 950

ADVERTISING
Fyvie, E. Mad for ads — 659.1
Westerfeld, S. So yesterday — Fic

ADVERTISING AGENCIES
Fyvie, E. Mad for ads — 659.1

ADVERTISING AND CHILDREN
Fyvie, E. Mad for ads — 659.1

ADVICE
Carter, A. Dear Ally how do you write a book? — 808.02
Earl, R. Your brain needs a hug — 616.85
Kipling, R. If — 821
Weinstein, B. D. Is it still cheating if I don't get caught? — 170.842

ADVICE COLUMNISTS
Murphy, J. Dear Sweet Pea — Fic
Weston, C. Speed of life — Fic

ADVICE COLUMNS
Lee, S. The downstairs girl — Fic
Murphy, J. Dear Sweet Pea — Fic

AERIAL PHOTOGRAPHY
Belmont, H. Looking at aerial photographs — 910

AERIAL PHOTOGRAPHY IN GEOLOGY
Collier, M. Over the mountains — 557

AERONAUTICS
Anderson, D. Flight and motion — 629.13
Collins, M. Airborne — 629.13
Graham, I. The science of flight — 629.13

AERONAUTICS -- HISTORY
Anderson, D. Flight and motion — 629.13
Aerospace engineer Aprille Ericsson. Waxman, L. H. — B

AEROSPACE ENGINEERING
Rooney, A. Aerospace engineering and the principles of flight — 629.1
Aerospace engineering and the principles of flight. Rooney,

Maldonado, T. Secret Saturdays	Fic	Bond, V. Zora and me	Fic
Mbalia, K. Black boy joy	Fic	Booth, C. Kinda like brothers	Fic
Park, L. S. Project Mulberry	Fic	Callender, K. King and the dragonflies	Fic
Patterson, J. Becoming Muhammad Ali	Fic	Charles, T. Becoming Beatriz	Fic
Reynolds, J. Ghost	Fic	Charles, T. Like Vanessa	Fic
Tarshis, L. The battle of Gettysburg 1863	Fic	Chase, P. J. Dough boys	Fic
Taylor, M. D. The well	Fic	Chase, P. J. So done	Fic
Volponi, P. Rucker Park setup	Fic	Chase, P. J. Turning point	Fic
Wiles, D. Revolution	Fic	Cline-Ransome, L. Being Clem	Fic
Woodruff, E. Dear Austin	Fic	Cline-Ransome, L. Leaving Lymon	Fic
Woodson, J. Before the ever after	Fic	Colbert, B. The revolution of Birdie Randolph	Fic
Woodson, J. Locomotion	811	Craft, J. Class act	741.5
Woodson, J. Peace Locomotion	Fic	Craft, J. New kid	741.5
Wright, B. Crow	Fic	Curtis, C. P. Bud not Buddy	Fic

AFRICAN AMERICAN BOYS -- DEATH

Rhodes, J. P. Ghost boys	Fic	Curtis, C. P. Elijah of Buxton	Fic

AFRICAN AMERICAN CHILDREN

Curtis, C. P. The madman of Piney Woods — Fic

Neri, G. Yummy	741.5	Curtis, C. P. The Watsons go to Birmingham 1963	Fic
Pinkney, A. D. Bird in a box	Fic	Daud, S. Mirage	Fic
Taylor, M. D. Roll of thunder hear my cry	Fic	Draper, S. M. The battle of Jericho	Fic

AFRICAN AMERICAN CHILDREN -- HISTORY 20TH CENTURY

Draper, S. M. Blended — Fic
Draper, S. M. Double dutch — Fic
Draper, S. M. November blues — Fic

Mayer, R. H. When the children marched — 323.1196

Draper, S. M. Out of my mind — Fic

AFRICAN AMERICAN CHILDREN -- POLITICAL AC-TIVITY -- HISTORY 20TH CENTURY

Draper, S. M. Stella by starlight — Fic
English, K. Francie — Fic

Partridge, E. Marching for freedom — 323.1196

Flake, S. Bang! — Fic

AFRICAN AMERICAN CIVIL RIGHTS WORKERS

Flake, S. Who am I without him? — Fic

Bausum, A. The March against Fear	323.1196	Giles, C. D. Take back the block	Fic
Mayer, R. H. When the children marched	323.1196	Giles, L. R. The Last Mirror on the Left	Fic
Pinkney, A. D. Martin rising	811	Giles, L. R. Overturned	Fic
Ribeiro, M. The assassination of Medgar Evers	976.2	Giles, L. R. Spin	Fic
Watson, B. Freedom Summer for young people	323.1196	Grimes, N. Jazmin's notebook	Fic

AFRICAN AMERICAN COLLEGE STUDENTS

Hamilton, V. The house of Dies Drear — Fic

Bausum, A. The March against Fear	323.1196	Hamilton, V. The planet of Junior Brown	Fic
Watson, B. Freedom Summer for young people	323.1196	Harrington, J. N. Catching a storyfish	Fic

AFRICAN AMERICAN FAMILIES

Harris, T. E. The perfect place — Fic

Armstrong, W. H. Sounder	Fic	Hurston, Z. N. The skull talks back and other haunting tales	Fic
Burg, A. E. Unbound	Fic	Hyman, F. Mango Delight	Fic
Colbert, B. The revolution of Birdie Randolph	Fic	Jackson, T. D. Monday's not coming	Fic
Curtis, C. P. The Watsons go to Birmingham 1963	Fic	Johnson, A. A certain October	Fic
Grimes, N. Jazmin's notebook	Fic	Johnson, A. The first part last	Fic
Hamilton, V. The house of Dies Drear	Fic	Johnson, A. Heaven	Fic
Lester, J. Time's memory	Fic	Johnson, V. The great Greene heist	Fic
Pinkney, A. D. Loretta Little looks back	Fic	Johnson, V. The Parker inheritance	Fic
Taylor, M. D. All the days past all the days to come	Fic	Johnson, V. To catch a cheat	Fic
Taylor, M. D. The gold Cadillac	Fic	Jones, T. L. Silhouetted by the blue	Fic
Taylor, M. D. The land	Fic	Lester, J. Time's memory	Fic
Taylor, M. D. Let the circle be unbroken	Fic	Lockington, M. For black girls like me	Fic
Taylor, M. D. The road to Memphis	Fic	Magoon, K. Camo girl	Fic
Taylor, M. D. Roll of thunder hear my cry	Fic	Magoon, K. Fire in the streets	Fic
Watson, R. Some places more than others	Fic	Magoon, K. The rock and the river	Fic
Williams-Garcia, R. Gone crazy in Alabama	Fic	Marks, J. From the desk of Zoe Washington	Fic

AFRICAN AMERICAN FICTION

Mbalia, K. Black boy joy — Fic

50 Cent. Playground	Fic	Mbalia, K. Tristan Strong destroys the world	Fic
Alexander, K. Booked	Fic	Mbalia, K. Tristan Strong punches a hole in the sky	Fic
Bolden, T. Crossing Ebenezer Creek	Fic	McKissack, P. Porch lies	Fic
Bolden, T. Inventing Victoria	Fic		

Mosley, W. 47   Fic

Myers, W. D. 145th Street   Fic

Myers, W. D. Dope sick   Fic

Myers, W. D. Fallen angels   Fic

Myers, W. D. Hoops   Fic

Myers, W. D. Lockdown   Fic

Myers, W. D. Monster   Fic

Myers, W. D. Scorpions   Fic

Myers, W. D. Slam!   Fic

Myers, W. D. Street love   Fic

Okorafor, N. Akata witch   Fic

Parker, M. Who put this song on?   Fic

Patrick, D. L. A matter of souls   Fic

Pinkney, A. D. Loretta Little looks back   Fic

Ramee, L. M. A good kind of trouble   Fic

Ramee, L. M. Something to say   Fic

Reynolds, J. The boy in the black suit   Fic

Reynolds, J. Ghost   Fic

Reynolds, J. Long way down   Fic

Reynolds, J. Look both ways   Fic

Reynolds, J. Miles Morales   Fic

Reynolds, J. Patina   Fic

Rhodes, J. P. Black brother black brother   Fic

Rhodes, J. P. Ghost boys   Fic

Rhodes, J. P. Ninth Ward   Fic

Rhodes, J. P. Sugar   Fic

Rhuday-Perkovich, O. Two Naomis   Fic

Stone, N. Clean getaway   Fic

Tamani, L. All the things we never knew   Fic

Taylor, M. D. All the days past all the days to come   Fic

Taylor, M. D. The friendship   Fic

Taylor, M. D. Let the circle be unbroken   Fic

Taylor, M. D. Roll of thunder hear my cry   Fic

Taylor, M. D. The well   Fic

Watson, R. Piecing me together   Fic

Watson, R. Some places more than others   Fic

Williams, A. Genesis begins again   Fic

Williams-Garcia, R. Gone crazy in Alabama   Fic

Williams-Garcia, R. Jumped   Fic

Williams-Garcia, R. Like sisters on the homefront   Fic

Williams-Garcia, R. One crazy summer   Fic

Williams-Garcia, R. P.S. be eleven   Fic

Woods, B. My name is Sally Little Song   Fic

Woods, B. The unsung hero of Birdsong USA   Fic

Woodson, J. After Tupac and D Foster   Fic

Woodson, J. Before the ever after   Fic

Woodson, J. Feathers   Fic

Woodson, J. From the notebooks of Melanin Sun   Fic

Woodson, J. Harbor me   Fic

Woodson, J. If you come softly   Fic

Woodson, J. Lena   Fic

Woodson, J. Peace Locomotion   Fic

Wright, B. Putting makeup on the fat boy   Fic

Wright, B. When the black girl sings   Fic

Youngblood, L. C. Forever this summer   Fic

African American folklore. Currie, S.   398.08996

AFRICAN AMERICAN GANGS

Myers, W. D. Scorpions   Fic

AFRICAN AMERICAN GIRLS

Alexander, E. Miss Crandall's school for young ladies & little misses of color   811

Antieau, K. Ruby's imagine   Fic

Barron, R. Maya and the rising dark   Fic

Bolden, T. Maritcha   974.7

Bond, V. Zora and me   Fic

Chase, P. J. Turning point   Fic

Dias, M. Marley Dias gets it done   305.23089

Draper, S. M. Double dutch   Fic

Draper, S. M. Stella by starlight   Fic

English, K. Francie   Fic

Grimes, N. Jazmin's notebook   Fic

Harrington, J. N. Catching a storyfish   Fic

Hesse, K. Witness   Fic

Hyman, F. Mango Delight   Fic

Johnson, V. The Parker inheritance   Fic

Lockington, M. For black girls like me   Fic

Marks, J. From the desk of Zoe Washington   Fic

McKissack, P. A friendship for today   Fic

Myracle, L. Luv ya bunches   Fic

Pinkney, A. D. With the might of angels   Fic

Ramee, L. M. A good kind of trouble   Fic

Ramee, L. M. Something to say   Fic

Reynolds, J. Patina   Fic

Rhodes, J. P. Ninth Ward   Fic

Rhodes, J. P. Sugar   Fic

Schmidt, G. D. Lizzie Bright and the Buckminster boy   Fic

Taylor, M. D. Roll of thunder hear my cry   Fic

Watson, R. Some places more than others   Fic

Weissman, E. B. The length of a string   Fic

Williams-Garcia, R. Gone crazy in Alabama   Fic

Williams-Garcia, R. One crazy summer   Fic

Williams-Garcia, R. P.S. be eleven   Fic

Woodson, J. Feathers   Fic

Wright, B. When the black girl sings   Fic

AFRICAN AMERICAN HIGH SCHOOL STUDENTS

Tougas, S. Little Rock girl 1957   379.2

AFRICAN AMERICAN INVENTORS

Young, J. C. Inspiring African-American inventors   608.996

AFRICAN AMERICAN LAWYERS

Wallace, S. N. Race against time   976.7

AFRICAN AMERICAN LEADERSHIP

Haskins, J. African-American religious leaders   920

AFRICAN AMERICAN MEN

Baldwin, J. Go tell it on the mountain   Fic

Joseph, F. The Black friend   305.8

Nelson, V. M. No crystal stair   Fic

Pinkney, A. D. Hand in hand   973

Woods, B. The unsung hero of Birdsong USA   Fic

AFRICAN AMERICAN MEN -- DISEASES -- HISTORY

Uschan, M. V. The Tuskegee experiments   174.2

AFRICAN AMERICAN MOTHER AND SON

Curtis, C. P. Bud not Buddy   Fic

Woodson, J. From the notebooks of Melanin Sun   Fic

AFRICAN AMERICAN MUSIC

Cooper, M. L. Slave spirituals and the Jubilee Singers **782.42162**

Giovanni, N. On my journey now **782.25**

AFRICAN AMERICAN MUSIC -- POLITICAL ASPECTS -- HISTORY 20TH CENTURY

Turck, M. Freedom song **323.0973**

AFRICAN AMERICAN MUSICIANS

Ellis, R. M. With a banjo on my knee **787**

Hillstrom, K. The Harlem Renaissance **810.9**

Pinkney, A. D. Rhythm ride **781.64409774**

Tate, E. E. African American musicians **780**

African American musicians. Tate, E. E. **780**

AFRICAN AMERICAN NEIGHBORHOODS

Nelson, M. My Seneca village **811**

AFRICAN AMERICAN PARENTING

Coates, T. The beautiful struggle **305.896**

AFRICAN AMERICAN PHYSICISTS

Bailey, D. Physics **530.092**

AFRICAN AMERICAN PILOTS -- HISTORY

Weatherford, C. B. You can fly **811**

AFRICAN AMERICAN POETRY

Adoff, A. I am the darker brother **811**

Clinton, C. I too sing America **811**

Giovanni, N. Ego-tripping and other poems for young people **811**

Grimes, N. Legacy **811**

Hudson, W. Poetry from the masters **811.009**

Hughes, L. The dream keeper and other poems **811**

Hughes, L. Langston Hughes **811**

Myers, W. D. Harlem **811**

Rochelle, B. Words with wings **811.008**

Shange, N. Freedom's a-calling me **811**

Shange, N. We troubled the waters **811**

AFRICAN AMERICAN POETS

Grimes, N. Legacy **811**

Hudson, W. Poetry from the masters **811.009**

Hughes, L. Langston Hughes **811**

AFRICAN AMERICAN QUILTS

Rubin, S. G. The quilts of Gee's Bend **746.4609761**

AFRICAN AMERICAN SCIENTISTS

Bailey, D. Physics **530.092**

Saucier, C. A. P. Explore the cosmos like Neil DeGrasse Tyson **520.92**

AFRICAN AMERICAN SENIOR MEN

Taylor, M. D. The friendship **Fic**

AFRICAN AMERICAN SHARECROPPERS

Armstrong, W. H. Sounder **Fic**

AFRICAN AMERICAN SINGERS

Lowinger, K. Give me wings **782.42162**

AFRICAN AMERICAN SOLDIERS

Myers, W. D. Sunrise over Fallujah **Fic**

Shepard, R. Now or never! **973.7**

Stone, T. L. Courage has no color **940.54**

AFRICAN AMERICAN SOLDIERS -- HISTORY CIVIL WAR, 1861-1865

Reis, R. A. African Americans and the Civil War **973.7**

AFRICAN AMERICAN STUDENTS

Alexander, E. Miss Crandall's school for young ladies & little misses of color **811**

Grimes, N. Bronx masquerade **Fic**

AFRICAN AMERICAN STUDENTS -- HISTORY

Magoon, K. Today the world is watching you the Little Rock Nine and the fight for school integration 1957 **379.2**

Stokes, J. A. Students on strike **371.829**

Walker, P. R. Remember Little Rock **379.2**

AFRICAN AMERICAN STUDENTS -- HISTORY 20TH CENTURY

Levinson, C. We've got a job **323.1196**

AFRICAN AMERICAN TEENAGE BOYS

50 Cent. Playground **Fic**

Anderson, L. H. Forge **Fic**

Chase, P. J. Dough boys **Fic**

Crisler, C. L. Tough boy sonatas **811**

Crowe, C. Getting away with murder **364.15**

Flake, S. Bang! **Fic**

Flake, S. You don't even know me **Fic**

Gallo, D. R. Destination unexpected **Fic**

Johnson, A. The first part last **Fic**

Lipsyte, R. The contender **Fic**

Mbalia, K. Black boy joy **Fic**

Mosley, W. 47 **Fic**

Murphy, J. Ramona Blue **Fic**

Myers, W. D. Lockdown **Fic**

Myers, W. D. Scorpions **Fic**

Myers, W. D. Slam! **Fic**

Nelson, M. A wreath for Emmett Till **811**

Oshiro, M. Anger is a gift **Fic**

Reynolds, J. The boy in the black suit **Fic**

Sachar, L. Small steps **Fic**

Smith, H. A. Keeping the night watch **Fic**

Volponi, P. Rikers High **Fic**

Walter, J. My name is not Friday **Fic**

Woodson, J. From the notebooks of Melanin Sun **Fic**

Woodson, J. If you come softly **Fic**

AFRICAN AMERICAN TEENAGE GIRLS

Boyce, J. A. A. This promise of change **379.2**

Caldwell, P. A phoenix first must burn **Fic**

Charles, T. Like Vanessa **Fic**

Colbert, B. The revolution of Birdie Randolph **Fic**

Draper, S. M. Fire from the rock **Fic**

Flake, S. Who am I without him? **Fic**

Giles, L. R. Overturned **Fic**

Giles, L. R. Spin **Fic**

Johnson, A. Heaven **Fic**

Johnson, A. Sweet hereafter **Fic**

Jones, T. L. Silhouetted by the blue **Fic**

Magoon, K. Fire in the streets **Fic**

McKinney, L. L. Nubia **741.5**

Parker, M. Who put this song on? **Fic**

Watson, R. Piecing me together **Fic**

Whitley, J. Princeless **741.5**

Williams-Garcia, R. Like sisters on the homefront **Fic**

Woodson, J. After Tupac and D Foster **Fic**

AFRICAN AMERICAN TEENAGERS

Youngblood, L. C. Forever this summer **Fic**

AFRICAN AMERICANS -- CIVIL RIGHTS
Aretha, D. Martin Luther King Jr. and the 1963 March on Washington **323.092**

Beals, M. March forward girl **379.2**

Bowers, R. The spies of Mississippi **323.1196**

Brimner, L. D. Accused! **345.761**

Brimner, L. D. Twelve days in May **323.11**

Cates, D. Plessy v. Ferguson segregation and the separate but equal policy **342.7308**

Gallagher, J. Policing and race **363.2**

Goldstone, L. Separate no more **323.1196**

King, M. L. The words of Martin Luther King Jr. **323.4**

Levinson, C. We've got a job **323.1196**

Pinkney, A. D. Martin rising **811**

Rubin, S. G. Brown v. Board of Education **344.73**

Rubin, S. G. Freedom summer **323.1196**

Shange, N. We troubled the waters **811**

AFRICAN AMERICANS -- CIVIL RIGHTS -- HISTORY
Archer, J. They had a dream **323**

Aretha, D. The trial of the Scottsboro boys **345.761**

Blohm, C. E. The civil rights movement **323.1196**

Ohnaka, K. Key civil rights laws **342.73**

Pinkney, A. D. Let it shine **920**

AFRICAN AMERICANS -- CIVIL RIGHTS -- HISTORY 20TH CENTURY
Aretha, D. The story of the civil rights March on Washington for Jobs and Freedom in photographs **975.3**

Brimner, L. D. Birmingham Sunday **323.1196**

Brimner, L. D. Black & white **323.1196**

Freedman, R. Freedom walkers **323.1196**

Kidd, R. Night on fire **Fic**

Lowery, L. B. Turning 15 on the road to freedom **323.1196**

Mayer, R. H. When the children marched **323.1196**

Osborne, L. B. Miles to go for freedom **305.896**

Partridge, E. Marching for freedom **323.1196**

Sheinkin, S. The Port Chicago 50 **940.54**

Tougas, S. Birmingham 1963 **323.1196**

Turck, M. Freedom song **323.0973**

Venable, R. The civil rights movement **323.1196**

Watson, B. Freedom Summer for young people **323.1196**

AFRICAN AMERICANS -- DISCRIMINATION
Nelson, M. A wreath for Emmett Till **811**

AFRICAN AMERICANS -- EDUCATION
Finkelstein, N. H. Schools of hope **371.829**

AFRICAN AMERICANS -- EDUCATION -- HISTORY
Walker, P. R. Remember Little Rock **379.2**

AFRICAN AMERICANS -- EMPLOYMENT
Mullenbach, C. Double victory **940.5308**

AFRICAN AMERICANS -- HISTORY
Dolbear, E. Juneteenth **394.263**

Giovanni, N. On my journey now **782.25**

Goss, L. Talk that talk **398.2**

Magoon, K. Today the world is watching you the Little Rock Nine and the fight for school integration 1957 **379.2**

Osborne, L. B. Traveling the freedom road **973.7**

Raatma, L. The Underground Railroad **973.7**

Ribeiro, M. The assassination of Medgar Evers **976.2**

Tarrant-Reid, L. Discovering Black America **973**

Wallace, S. N. Race against time **976.7**

AFRICAN AMERICANS -- HISTORY 1863-1877
Bolden, T. Emancipation Proclamation **973.7**

AFRICAN AMERICANS -- HISTORY 18TH CENTURY
Hansen, J. Breaking ground breaking silence **305.5**

AFRICAN AMERICANS -- HISTORY 19TH CENTURY
Lester, J. Time's memory **Fic**

AFRICAN AMERICANS -- HISTORY 20TH CENTURY
Madigan, T. The burning **976.6**

AFRICAN AMERICANS -- HISTORY CIVIL WAR, 1861-1865
Reis, R. A. African Americans and the Civil War **973.7**

AFRICAN AMERICANS -- INTELLECTUAL LIFE
Hill, L. C. Harlem stomp! **810.9**

AFRICAN AMERICANS -- MIGRATIONS
Lawrence, J. The great migration **759.13**

AFRICAN AMERICANS -- MUSEUMS
Bolden, T. How to build a museum **973**

AFRICAN AMERICANS -- RELATIONS WITH INDIANS
Katz, W. L. Black Indians **970**

AFRICAN AMERICANS -- SOCIAL CONDITIONS
Bolden, T. Wake up our souls **704.03**

Coates, T. The beautiful struggle **305.896**

AFRICAN AMERICANS -- SOCIAL CONDITIONS 19TH CENTURY
Bolden, T. Maritcha **974.7**

AFRICAN AMERICANS -- SOCIAL CONDITIONS 20TH CENTURY
Bausum, A. Marching to the mountaintop **323.092**

AFRICAN AMERICANS -- SOCIAL CONDITIONS 21ST CENTURY
Gallagher, J. Policing and race **363.2**

Marcovitz, H. Black in America **305.896**

AFRICAN AMERICANS -- SOCIAL LIFE AND CUSTOMS
Dolbear, E. Juneteenth **394.263**

AFRICAN AMERICANS -- SOCIAL LIFE AND CUSTOMS 19TH CENTURY
Bolden, T. Maritcha **974.7**

AFRICAN AMERICANS -- SOCIAL LIFE AND CUSTOMS 20TH CENTURY
Hughes, L. Langston Hughes **811**

AFRICAN AMERICANS -- SUFFRAGE
Anderson, C. One person no vote **324.6**

Lowery, L. B. Turning 15 on the road to freedom **323.1196**

Rubin, S. G. Freedom summer **323.1196**

AFRICAN AMERICANS -- SUFFRAGE -- HISTORY
Goldstone, L. Stolen justice **324.6**

AFRICAN AMERICANS -- SUFFRAGE -- HISTORY 20TH CENTURY
Watson, B. Freedom Summer for young people **323.1196**

African Americans and the Civil War. Reis, R. A. **973.7**

AFRICAN AMERICANS IN ART
Lawrence, J. The great migration **759.13**

Alice Paul and the fight for women's rights. Kops, D.   **B**

ALIEN ABDUCTION

Karst, K. Alien abductions   **001.942**

Alien abductions. Karst, K.   **001.942**

Alien encounter. Harper, C. M.   **Fic**

ALIEN INVASIONS

Engdahl, S. Enchantress from the stars   **Fic**

ALIEN PLANTS

Oppel, K. Bloom   **Fic**

ALIENATION (SOCIAL PSYCHOLOGY)

Andrews, J. Me and Earl and the dying girl   **Fic**

Cameron, S. Last bus to Everland   **Fic**

ALIENS

Anderson, M. T. He laughed with his other mouths   **Fic**

Bunker, L. Felix Yz   **Fic**

Clark, H. What we found in the sofa (and how it saved the world)   **Fic**

D'Lacey, C. The fire eternal   **Fic**

Emerson, K. Last day on Mars   **Fic**

Haddix, M. P. Children of refuge   **Fic**

Hale, N. One trick pony   **741.5**

Karst, K. Area 51   **358.4**

Meyer, M. Cinder   **Fic**

Meyer, M. Cress   **Fic**

Meyer, M. Scarlet   **Fic**

Rex, A. Smek for president!   **Fic**

Rex, A. The true meaning of Smekday   **Fic**

Stine, R. L. Fear   **Fic**

Teague, M. The doom machine   **Fic**

ALIENS (HUMANOID)

Adams, D. The hitchhiker's guide to the galaxy   **Fic**

Card, O. S. Ender's game   **Fic**

Gilmore, K. The exchange student   **Fic**

Harper, C. M. Alien encounter   **Fic**

Mosley, W. 47   **Fic**

ALIENS (INSECTOID)

Oppel, K. Thrive   **Fic**

ALIENS (LAW)

Bausum, A. Denied detained deported   **325.73**

ALIENS (NON-HUMANOID)

Alexander, W. Ambassador   **Fic**

Alexander, W. Nomad   **Fic**

Grine, C. Animorphs   **741.5**

Hughes, N. Refraction   **Fic**

Maberry, J. The orphan army   **Fic**

Sleator, W. Interstellar pig   **Fic**

Alifirenka, Caitlin

I will always write back   **305.235**

Aliki

William Shakespeare & the Globe   **792**

Alive in the killing fields. Keat, N.   **B**

All aboard! Zimmermann, K. R.   **385**

All about anxiety. Lewis, C.   **155.4**

All about electric and hybrid cars and who's driving them. Bearce, S.   **629.22**

All about Japan. Moore, W.   **952**

All about sleep from a to zzzzzz. Scott, E.   **612.8**

All fall down. Carter, A.   **Fic**

All Hallows' Eve. Vande Velde, V.   **Fic**

All he knew. Frost, H.   **Fic**

All in the family. Otfinoski, S.   **398.2**

All my noble dreams and then what happens. Whelan, G.   **Fic**

All of the above. Pearsall, S.   **Fic**

All rise for the honorable Perry T. Cook. Connor, L.   **Fic**

All summer long. Larson, H.   **741.5**

All the broken pieces. Burg, A. E.   **Fic**

All the days past all the days to come. Taylor, M. D.   **Fic**

All the dirt. Ashenburg, K.   **613.4**

All the Greys on Greene Street. Tucker, L.   **Fic**

All the impossible things. Lackey, L.   **Fic**

All the lovely bad ones. Hahn, M. D.   **Fic**

All the stars denied. McCall, G. G.   **Fic**

All the things we never knew. Tamani, L.   **Fic**

All the truth that's in me. Berry, J.   **Fic**

All the wrong people have self esteem. Rosenwald, L.   **305.235**

All thirteen. Soontornvat, C.   **796.52**

All together now. Larson, H.   **741.5**

All we have left. Mills, W.   **Fic**

All we know of love. Baskin, N. R.   **Fic**

All's faire in middle school. Jamieson, V.   **741.5**

All-American girl. Cabot, M.   **Fic**

All-American Muslim girl. Courtney, N. J.   **Fic**

All-in. Hautman, P.   **Fic**

Allaby, Michael

National Geographic visual encyclopedia of Earth   **550**

Allan, Tony, 1946-

Exploring the life myth and art of the Vikings   **948**

ALLEGORIES

Juster, N. The annotated Phantom tollbooth   **Fic**

Orwell, G. Animal farm   **Fic**

Saint-Exupery, A. d. The little prince   **Fic**

Sfar, J. The little prince   **741.5**

Spinelli, J. Maniac Magee   **Fic**

Tan, S. Tales from the inner city   **Fic**

Allen, John, 1957-

Careers in environmental and energy technology   **621.042023**

Thinking critically   **363.330973**

Allen, Thomas B.

Harriet Tubman secret agent   **B**

Mr. Lincoln's high-tech war   **973.7**

Remember Pearl Harbor   **940.54**

Allergic. Lloyd, M. W.   **741.5**

ALLERGY

Ballard, C. Explaining food allergies   **616.97**

Bellenir, K. Allergy information for teens   **618.9297**

Lloyd, M. W. Allergic   **741.5**

Nielsen, S. Word nerd   **Fic**

ALLERGY IN CHILDREN

Bellenir, K. Allergy information for teens   **618.9297**

Allergy information for teens. Bellenir, K.   **618.9297**

ALLIANCES

McKinley, R. Pegasus   **Fic**

Ormsbee, K. The house in Poplar Wood   **Fic**

Reichs, B. Chrysalis   **Fic**

Gemeinhart, D. The honest truth	Fic
Hopkins, E. Rumble	Fic

ANGER IN BOYS

Gemeinhart, D. The honest truth	Fic

ANGER IN GIRLS

Arnold, E. K. Far from fair	Fic

ANGER IN TEENAGE BOYS

Bass, K. Graffiti knight	Fic
Hopkins, E. Rumble	Fic
Mikaelsen, B. Touching Spirit Bear	Fic
Sanchez, A. Bait	Fic
Smith, H. A. Keeping the night watch	Fic

ANGER IN TEENAGE GIRLS

Dooley, S. Free verse	Fic
Revis, B. Give the dark my love	Fic
Williams-Garcia, R. Jumped	Fic

ANGER IN TEENAGERS

Blume, J. Tiger eyes	Fic
Lindelauf, B. Fing's war	Fic
Anger is a gift. Oshiro, M.	Fic

Angleberger, Tom

Darth Paper strikes back	Fic
Emperor Pickletine rides the bus	Fic
Fuzzy	Fic
Horton Halfpott or The fiendish mystery of Smugwick Manor or The loosening of M'Lady Luggertuck's corset	Fic
Princess Labelmaker to the rescue!	Fic
The strange case of Origami Yoda	Fic

ANGLICANS

Capaccio, G. Religion in colonial America	200.973

Angliss, Sarah

Gold	669

ANGLO-SAXONS

Rumford, J. Beowulf a hero's tale retold	398.2

ANGOLA

McKissack, P. Nzingha	Fic

ANIMAL ATTACKS

Hamilton, S. L. Ambushed by a cougar	599.75
Hamilton, S. L. Mauled by a bear	599.78

ANIMAL BEHAVIOR

Allman, T. Animal life in groups	591.56
Buchanan, S. C. Animal senses	573.8
Castaldo, N. F. Beastly brains	591.5
Clutton-Brock, J. Horse	636.1
Cotton, K. Counting lions	591.68
Cusick, D. Get the scoop on animal puke	591.5
Downer, A. The animal mating game	591.56
Downer, A. Elephant talk	599.67
Hirsch, A. Cats	599.75
Johnson, J. Animal tracks & signs	591.47
Johnson, R. L. When lunch fights back	591.47
Montgomery, H. L. Who gives a poop?	612.3
O'Connell, C. Bridge to the wild	636.088
O'Sullivan, J. Migration nation	591.56
Safina, C. Beyond words	591.56
Stefoff, R. The rodent order	599.35
Yolen, J. Animal stories	591

ANIMAL BEHAVIOR -- RESEARCH

Woog, A. SCRATCHbot	629.8

ANIMAL COMMUNICATION

Downer, A. Elephant talk	599.67

ANIMAL CONSERVATION

Anderson, T. Giraffe extinction	599.638
Castaldo, N. F. Polar bear rescue	599.786
Montgomery, S. Chasing cheetahs	599.75
Montgomery, S. Saving the ghost of the mountain	599.75

ANIMAL DEFENSES

Johnson, R. L. When lunch fights back	591.47

ANIMAL DETECTIVES

Krosoczka, J. The frog who croaked	Fic

ANIMAL FANTASY

Appelt, K. The true blue scouts of Sugar Man Swamp	Fic
Appelt, K. The underneath	Fic
Avi. Old wolf	Fic
Beckhorn, S. W. The wolf's boy	Fic
Epstein, A. J. Circle of heroes	Fic
Hunter, E. Broken pride	Fic
Hunter, E. Code of the clans	Fic
Hunter, E. A dangerous path	Fic
Hunter, E. The darkest hour	Fic
Hunter, E. Dawn	Fic
Hunter, E. Fire and ice	Fic
Hunter, E. Forest of secrets	Fic
Hunter, E. Into the wild	Fic
Hunter, E. Rising storm	Fic
Hunter, E. The sight	Fic
Iserles, I. The taken	Fic
Jacques, B. Mariel of Redwall	Fic
Jacques, B. Martin the Warrior	Fic
Jacques, B. Mattimeo	Fic
Jacques, B. Mossflower	Fic
Jacques, B. Pearls of Lutra	Fic
Jacques, B. Redwall	Fic
Jacques, B. Redwall the graphic novel	741.5
Jacques, B. Salamandastron	Fic
Krosoczka, J. The frog who croaked	Fic
Kurtz, C. The adventures of a South Pole pig	Fic
Lasky, K. Lone wolf	Fic
Meloy, C. Wildwood imperium	Fic
O'Brien, R. C. Mrs. Frisby and the rats of NIMH	Fic
Oppel, K. Silverwing	Fic
Schrefer, E. Gogi's gambit	Fic
Schrefer, E. Rumi's riddle	Fic
Wagner, H. Nightshade City	Fic
Animal farm. Orwell, G.	Fic

ANIMAL FIGHTING

Yolen, J. Dragon's blood	Fic

ANIMAL GROUPS

Allman, T. Animal life in groups	591.56

ANIMAL HEROES

Campbell, J. Daisy to the rescue	636
Markle, S. Animal heroes	636.088
Animal heroes. Markle, S.	636.088
Animal hospital. Coey, J.	639.9

ANTIRACIST LITERATURE

Behnke, A. Racial profiling	363.2
Emdin, C. For white folks who teach in the hood-- and the rest of y'all too	370.9173
Hudson, W. The talk	305.8
Jewell, T. This book is anti-racist	305.800973
Joseph, F. The Black friend	305.8
Kendi, I. X. Stamped	305.800973
Levinson, C. We've got a job	323.1196
Mendoza, J. An indigenous peoples' history of the United States for young people	970.004
Pinkney, A. D. Hand in hand	973
Pinkney, A. D. Let it shine	920
Stevenson, B. Just mercy	340.092

ANTISEMITISM

Matas, C. After the war	Fic
Vernick, S. R. The blood lie	Fic

ANTISEMITISM IN SPORTS -- HISTORY

Bascomb, N. The racers	796.72092

ANTIVENINS

Hofer, C. Snakebite!	597.96

Antonio Lopez de Santa Anna. Santa Anna, A. L. d.	B
Antsy does time. Shusterman, N.	Fic

ANTWERP, BELGIUM

Hesse, K. Letters from Rifka	Fic

ANXIETY

Day, C. The sea in winter	Fic
Denkmire, H. The truth about anxiety and depression	616.85
Donwerth-Chikamatsu, A. Beyond me	Fic
Herbach, G. I'm with stupid	Fic
Kemper, B. Teens and phobias	618.92
Legrand, C. Some kind of happiness	Fic
Nijkamp, M. Unbroken	Fic
Oppel, K. The nest	Fic
Roat, S. H. How to disappear	Fic
Vivat, B. Frazzled	Fic

ANXIETY DISORDERS

Kemper, B. Teens and phobias	618.92
Mac, C. 10 things I can see from here	Fic
Melleby, N. How to become a planet	Fic
Mooney, C. What is anxiety disorder?	616.85
Scarlet, J. Superhero therapy	616.85

ANXIETY IN BOYS

Oppel, K. The nest	Fic

ANXIETY IN CHILDREN

Galante, C. The world from up here	Fic
Lewis, C. All about anxiety	155.4
Telgemeier, R. Guts	155.4

ANXIETY IN GIRLS

Blume, J. Are you there God? It's me Margaret	Fic
Vivat, B. Frazzled	Fic

ANXIETY IN TEENAGERS

Gregorio, I. W. This is my brain in love	Fic
Mac, C. 10 things I can see from here	Fic

Any small goodness. Johnston, T.	Fic
Anya and the nightingale. Pasternack, S.	Fic
Anya's ghost. Brosgol, V.	741.5
Anya's war. Alban, A.	Fic
Anything but typical. Baskin, N. R.	Fic

APACHE INDIANS -- GOVERNMENT RELATIONS

Jastrzembski, J. C. The Apache wars	970.004

APACHE INDIANS -- SOCIAL CONDITIONS

Jastrzembski, J. C. The Apache wars	970.004

APACHE INDIANS -- WARS

Jastrzembski, J. C. The Apache wars	970.004
The **Apache** wars. Jastrzembski, J. C.	970.004

APARTHEID

Downing, D. Apartheid in South Africa	323.168
Naidoo, B. Out of bounds	Fic
Sonneborn, L. The end of apartheid in South Africa	968.06
Warman, J. The world beneath	Fic
Apartheid in South Africa. Downing, D.	323.168

APARTMENT HOUSES

Raskin, E. The Westing game	Fic
Stead, R. Liar & spy	Fic

Apelfeld, Aharon

Adam and Thomas	Fic

APOCALYPTIC FICTION

Bertagna, J. Exodus	Fic
Bick, I. J. Ashes	Fic
Block, F. L. Love in the time of global warming	Fic
Bruchac, J. Killer of enemies	Fic
Kagawa, J. The eternity cure	Fic
Kagawa, J. The forever song	Fic
Kagawa, J. The immortal rules	Fic
Kristoff, J. Lifel1k3	Fic
Maberry, J. Rot & Ruin	Fic
Marsden, J. Tomorrow when the war began	Fic
Mills, G. Gold	Fic
O'Brien, R. C. Z for Zachariah	Fic
Oppel, K. Bloom	Fic
Oppel, K. Thrive	Fic
Pfeffer, S. B. Life as we knew it	Fic
Reichs, B. Chrysalis	Fic
Rossi, V. Under the never sky	Fic
Summers, C. This is not a test	Fic
Wiggins, B. Stung	Fic

APOLLO (GREEK DEITY)

Riordan, R. The burning maze	Fic
Riordan, R. The dark prophecy	Fic
Riordan, R. The hidden oracle	Fic
Riordan, R. The tower of Nero	Fic

APOLLO 11 (SPACECRAFT)

Brouwer, S. Moon mission	629.45
Maurer, R. Destination moon	629.45

APOLLO 11 (SPACECRAFT) -- HISTORY

Bodden, V. To the moon	629.45
Thimmesh, C. Team moon	629.45

APOLLO 13 (SPACECRAFT)

Edge, L. B. Apollo 13	629.45
Holden, H. M. Danger in space	629.45
Apollo 13. Edge, L. B.	629.45

APOLLO 17 (SPACECRAFT)

Nardo, D. The blue marble — 525

APOLLO 8 (SPACECRAFT)

Sandler, M. W. Apollo 8 — 629.45

Apollo 8. Sandler, M. W. — 629.45

APOLLO THEATRE

Marx, T. Steel drumming at the Apollo — 785

The **apothecary.** Meloy, M. — Fic

Appalachia. Rylant, C. — 974

APPALACHIAN REGION

White, R. Belle Prater's boy — Fic

APPALACHIAN REGION -- DESCRIPTION AND TRAVEL

Rylant, C. Appalachia — 974

APPALACHIAN REGION -- SOCIAL LIFE AND CUSTOMS

Shelby, A. The adventures of Molly Whuppie and other Appalachian folktales — 398.2

APPALACHIAN REGION, SOUTHERN -- SOCIAL LIFE AND CUSTOMS

Rylant, C. Appalachia — 974

Appelt, Kathi, 1954-

Keeper — Fic

Kissing Tennessee and other stories from the Stardust Dance — Fic

Maybe a fox — Fic

The true blue scouts of Sugar Man Swamp — Fic

The underneath — Fic

APPENDECTOMY

Alexander, K. Booked — Fic

Appignanesi, Richard

Romeo and Juliet — 741.5

Apple. Gansworth, E. L. — B

Apple for the teacher. Yolen, J. — 782.42

Apple in the middle. Quigley, D. — Fic

The **apple** tart of hope. Fitzgerald, S. M. — Fic

Applegate, Katherine

Home of the brave — Fic

The one and only Ivan — Fic

Wishtree — Fic

Appleman, Deborah

Critical encounters in Secondary English — 820.71

APPLESEED, JOHNNY, 1774-1845

Worth, R. Johnny Appleseed — B

APPOMATTOX CAMPAIGN, 1865

Benoit, P. The surrender at Appomattox — 973.7

APPRENTICES

Alexander, L. Westmark — Fic

D'Lacey, C. The fire ascending — Fic

Delaney, J. A new darkness — Fic

Fisher, C. The hidden Coronet — Fic

Fisher, C. The lost heiress — Fic

Flanagan, J. The tournament at Gorlan — Fic

Funke, C. Inkspell — Fic

Landy, D. Playing with fire — Fic

Lloyd-Jones, E. The bone houses — Fic

McCaffrey, A. Dragon's fire — Fic

Sands, K. The Blackthorn key — Fic

Townley, R. The blue shoe — Fic

Wilson, N. D. The dragon's tooth — Fic

AQUARIUMS

Igarashi, D. Children of the sea — 741.5

AQUATIC ANIMALS

Cerullo, M. M. Sharks of the deep — 597.3

Hoyt, E. Weird sea creatures — 591.77

Rake, M. Creatures of the deep — 591.77

ARAB AMERICAN FAMILIES

Nye, N. S. Habibi — Fic

ARAB AMERICAN TEENAGE GIRLS

Nye, N. S. Habibi — Fic

ARAB AMERICANS

Farizan, S. Here to stay — Fic

Nye, N. S. 19 varieties of gazelle — 811

ARAB AMERICANS -- HISTORY

Dennis, Y. W. A kid's guide to Arab American history — 973

ARAB COUNTRIES

Brownlie Bojang, A. Sudan in our world — 962.404

King, D. C. United Arab Emirates — 953.57

O'Shea, M. Kuwait — 953.67

ARAB COUNTRIES -- HISTORY -- 20TH CENTURY

Immell, M. Israel — 956.04

Robinson, A. Young Palestinians speak — 956.95

ARAB COUNTRIES -- IMMIGRATION AND EMIGRATION

Dennis, Y. W. A kid's guide to Arab American history — 973

Arab science and invention in the golden age. Blanchard, A. — 509

ARAB SPRING, 2010-

Saeed, J. Yara's spring — Fic

The **Arab** world thought of it. Hussain, S. S. — 909

ARAB-ISRAELI CONFLICT

Ellis, D. Three wishes — 956.9405

Immell, M. Israel — 956.04

Robinson, A. Young Palestinians speak — 956.95

Sokolower, J. Determined to stay — 305.235

Tolan, S. The lemon tree — 956.9405092

Woolf, A. The Arab-Israeli War since 1948 — 956.04

ARAB-ISRAELI CONFLICT 1993-

Abdel-Fattah, R. Where the streets had a name — Fic

Immell, M. Israel — 956.04

ARAB-ISRAELI RELATIONS

Sokolower, J. Determined to stay — 305.235

The **Arab-Israeli** War since 1948. Woolf, A. — 956.04

ARACHNIDA -- IDENTIFICATION

Milne, L. J. The Audubon Society field guide to North American insects and spiders — 595.7097

ARACHNIDS

Hirschmann, K. Deadliest spiders — 595.4

Markle, S. Black widows — 595.4

Markle, S. Crab spiders — 595.4

Markle, S. Jumping spiders — 595.4

Markle, S. Mites — 595.4

Markle, S. Orb weavers — 595.4

The pick-up game	Fic
The real revolution	973.3
Robert F. Kennedy	B
The skull in the rock	569.9096822
Sugar changed the world	664
Trapped	363.11
The world made new	910.9
Around the world in a hundred years. Fritz, J.	920
Around the world. Phelan, M.	910.4

ARRANGED MARRIAGE

Ahdieh, R. Flame in the mist	Fic
Fantaskey, B. Jessica's guide to dating on the dark side	Fic
McKay, S. E. Thunder over Kandahar	Fic
Menon, S. When Dimple met Rishi	Fic
Murdock, C. G. Princess Ben	Fic
Perkins, M. Secret keeper	Fic
Springer, N. The case of the peculiar pink fan	Fic
Williams, C. L. The chosen one	Fic
The **arrival**. Tan, S.	741.5

Arruda, Suzanne Middendorf, 1954-

Freedom's martyr	B

ARSON

Chambliss Bertman, J. The unbreakable code	Fic
Klise, J. The art of secrets	Fic

ARSON INVESTIGATION

Voigt, C. The book of secrets	Fic

ART

Bolden, T. Wake up our souls	704.03
Boldt, C. Think and make like an artist	702.8
Brooks, S. Get into art	704.9
Claybourne, A. Surrealism	709.04
Finger, B. 13 American artists children should know	709.73
Fitzgerald, L. M. The gallery	Fic
Fitzgerald, L. M. Under the egg	Fic
Green, G. Paper artist	736
Gunderson, J. Impressionism	709.03
Gunderson, J. Realism	709.03
Gunderson, J. Romanticism	709.03
Harman, A. Modern art explorer	709.04
Heine, F. Impressionism	759.05
Hume, H. D. The art teacher's book of lists	702
Murdock, C. G. Da Vinci's cat	Fic
Rochelle, B. Words with wings	811.008
Rubin, S. G. Everybody paints!	759.13
Self, C. Chinese brush painting	751.4
Wenzel, A. 13 sculptures children should know	730
Wood, A. Urban 'street' art	709.173
Yancey, D. Art deco	709.04

ART -- COLLECTORS AND COLLECTING

Horowitz, A. South by southeast	Fic

ART -- STUDY AND TEACHING (ELEMENTARY)

Hogan, J. Studio thinking from the start	372.5
Hume, H. D. The art teacher's survival guide for elementary and middle schools	707.1

ART -- STUDY AND TEACHING (MIDDLE SCHOOL)

Hume, H. D. The art teacher's survival guide for elementary and middle schools	707.1

ART -- STUDY AND TEACHING (SECONDARY)

Hume, H. D. The art teacher's survival guide for secondary schools	707.1

ART -- TECHNIQUE

Luxbacher, I. The jumbo book of art	702.8
Peot, M. Inkblot	751.4
Wenzel, A. 13 art techniques children should know	702.8

ART ACTIVITIES FOR CHILDREN AND STUDENTS

Pitamic, M. Fine art adventures	701

ART AND SOCIETY

Wood, A. Urban 'street' art	709.173

ART AND WAR

Edsel, R. M. The greatest treasure hunt in history	940.53

ART APPRECIATION

Brooks, S. Get into art	704.9
D'Harcourt, C. Masterpieces up close	759
An eye for art	708.153
Finger, B. 13 American artists children should know	709.73
Gunderson, J. Impressionism	709.03
Gunderson, J. Realism	709.03
Meyerowitz, J. Seeing things	770
Pitamic, M. Fine art adventures	701
Pitamic, M. Modern art adventures	709.04
Raczka, B. Before they were famous	704
Raczka, B. Name that style	709
Raczka, B. Unlikely pairs	750
Wenzel, A. 13 artists children should know	920
Wenzel, A. 13 sculptures children should know	730

ART APPRECIATION FOR CHILDREN

An eye for art	708.153
Finger, B. 13 American artists children should know	709.73
Raczka, B. Before they were famous	704
Raczka, B. Name that style	709
Raczka, B. Unlikely pairs	750
Wenzel, A. 13 sculptures children should know	730

ART DECO

Yancey, D. Art deco	709.04
Art deco. Yancey, D.	709.04
Art from her heart. Whitehead, K.	B

ART HISTORY

Pitamic, M. Fine art adventures	701
Raczka, B. Name that style	709
Wenzel, A. 13 art techniques children should know	702.8
Wenzel, A. 13 artists children should know	920

ART MOVEMENTS

Barsony, P. The stories of the Mona Lisa	759.06
Gunderson, J. Romanticism	709.03
Raczka, B. Name that style	709
Yancey, D. Art deco	709.04
Art of comprehension. Bryan, T. A.	372.47
The **art** of secrets. Klise, J.	Fic
The **art** of stone skipping and other fun old-time games. Ferrer, J. J.	790.1
The **art** of the catapult. Gurstelle, W.	623.4
The **art** of Walt Disney. Finch, C.	791.43092

ART POTTERY, AMERICAN

Greenberg, J. The mad potter	738.092

Charleyboy, L. Dreaming in Indian — 700.89
Claybourne, A. Surrealism — 709.04
Crispino, E. Van Gogh — 759.9492
Finger, B. 13 American artists children should know — 709.73
Gallico, P. The snow goose — Fic
Giff, P. R. Pictures of Hollis Woods — Fic
Gilberti, F. Yayoi Kusama covered everything in dots and wasn't sorry — 709.2
Greenberg, J. Christo & Jeanne-Claude — 709.2
Gunderson, J. Romanticism — 709.03
Krull, K. Leonardo da Vinci — 509
Lewis, J. P. Self-portrait with seven fingers — 811
Matti, T. Mister orange — Fic
Pearsall, S. The seventh most important thing — Fic
Peters, S. T. Groundbreaking guys — 920.71
Pinkwater, D. M. Bushman lives! — Fic
Raczka, B. Before they were famous — 704
Raczka, B. Name that style — 709
Reef, C. Frida & Diego — 759.972
Rubin, S. G. Everybody paints! — 759.13
Rubin, S. G. Maya Lin — 720.92
Rubin, S. G. Wideness and wonder — 759.13
Schumann, B. 13 women artists children should know — 920
Spence, D. Manet — 759.4
Spence, D. Michelangelo — 709.2
Taylor, D. C. The Renaissance artists — 709.45
Wenzel, A. 13 artists children should know — 920
Whiting, J. Vincent Van Gogh — 759.9492
Zettel, S. A most dangerous deception — Fic

ARTISTS 19TH CENTURY
Sabbeth, C. Monet and the Impressionists for kids — 759.05
ARTISTS COLONIES
O'Connor, S. Sparrow Road — Fic
ARTS
Lusted, M. A. Entertainment — 791
ARTS -- STUDY AND TEACHING
Sousa, D. A. From STEM to STEAM — 372.5
Arts and culture in the early Islamic world. Flatt, L. — 700.9
ARTS CAMPS
Lockhart, E. Dramarama — Fic
ARTS, NATIVE AMERICAN
January, B. Native American art & culture — 704.03
As easy as falling off the face of the earth. Perkins, L. R. — Fic
Ashenburg, Katherine
All the dirt — 613.4
Asher, Jay, 1975-
The future of us — Fic
Thirteen reasons why — Fic
Ashes. Anderson, L. H. — Fic
Ashes. Bick, I. J. — Fic
ASHEVILLE, NORTH CAROLINA
Beatty, R. Serafina and the twisted staff — Fic
McDaniel, L. Hit and run — Fic
Ashkar, Michael
Islam — 297
Ashley Bryan's African tales uh-huh. Bryan, A. — 398.2
Ashley Bryan's puppets. Bryan, A. — 811

ASIA
Lee, J. M. I once was a monkey — 294.3
ASIA -- ENVIRONMENTAL CONDITIONS
Auld, M. Pathways through Asia — 304.2
ASIA -- HISTORY
Morris, N. Asian civilisations — 950
ASIA, CENTRAL -- HISTORY
Hinds, K. Huns — 936
ASIAN AMERICAN GIRLS
Kelly, E. E. Blackbird fly — Fic
ASIAN AMERICAN TEENAGE BOYS
Yoon, N. The sun is also a star — Fic
ASIAN AMERICAN TEENAGE GIRLS
Kuhn, S. I love you so mochi — Fic
ASIAN AMERICANS
Amara, P. Awesome Asian Americans — 920
Chao, G. Our wayward fate — Fic
Yang, G. L. The shadow hero — 741.5
ASIAN AMERICANS -- RELIGION
Mann, G. S. Buddhists Hindus and Sikhs in America — 294
ASIAN CANADIANS
Stephens, R. D. Henry Chow and other stories from the Asian Canadian Writers' Workshop — Fic
Asian civilisations. Morris, N. — 950
ASIAN CIVILIZATION
Morris, N. Asian civilisations — 950
ASIAN LONGHORNED BEETLE
Burns, L. G. Beetle busters — 595.76
ASIAN-INFLUENCED FANTASY
Ahdieh, R. Flame in the mist — Fic
Alexander, L. The iron ring — Fic
Alexander, L. The remarkable journey of Prince Jen — Fic
Arni, S. Sita's Ramayana — 741.5
Chapman, E. Caster — Fic
DasGupta, S. The force of fire — Fic
Flanagan, J. The emperor of Nihon-ja — Fic
Goodman, A. Eona — Fic
Goto, H. Half World — Fic
Hicks, F. E. The divided earth — 741.5
Hicks, F. E. The Nameless City — 741.5
Hicks, F. E. The Stone Heart — 741.5
Hoang, V. Girl giant and the Monkey King — Fic
Kim, G. The last fallen star — Fic
Lee, S. Convergence — Fic
Lim, E. Spin the dawn — Fic
Lin, G. Where the mountain meets the moon — Fic
London, A. Black wings beating — Fic
London, A. Red skies falling — Fic
Pierce, T. Trickster's choice — Fic
Soontornvat, C. A wish in the dark — Fic
Uehashi, N. Moribito — Fic
Uehashi, N. Moribito II — Fic
Yep, L. City of fire — Fic
Young, E. The dragon path — Fic
Yu, M. The Girl King — Fic
ASIANS -- MIGRATIONS
Morris, N. Asian civilisations — 950

ASIATIC BLACK BEAR

Montgomery, S. The golden moon bear | 599.78

Asimov, Isaac, 1920-1992

I robot | Fic

The **Ask** and the Answer. Ness, P. | Fic

Ask me no questions. Budhos, M. T. | Fic

Ask my mood ring how I feel. Lopez, D. | Fic

Ask the astronaut. Jones, T. | 629.4

Ask the bones. Olson, A. N. | Fic

Asking about sex & growing up. Cole, J. | 649

Asperger's rules! Grossberg, B. N. | 618.92

ASPERGER'S SYNDROME

Dowd, S. The London Eye mystery | Fic

Erskine, K. Mockingbird | Fic

Grossberg, B. N. Asperger's rules! | 618.92

Rodriguez, A. M. Autism spectrum disorders | 616.85

Roy, J. R. Mindblind | Fic

ASPERGER'S SYNDROME -- PATIENTS

Price, J. Take control of Asperger's syndrome | 618.92

ASPERGER'S SYNDROME IN ADOLESCENCE -- PATIENTS

Price, J. Take control of Asperger's syndrome | 618.92

ASPERGER'S SYNDROME IN CHILDREN -- PATIENTS

Price, J. Take control of Asperger's syndrome | 618.92

Aspromonte, John, 1977-

ADHD | 616.85

ASSAM, INDIA

Chodosh, J. The elephant doctor of India | 599.67

An **assassin's** guide to love and treason. Boecker, V. | Fic

ASSASSINATION

Coulthurst, A. Of fire and stars | Fic

Giblin, J. C. Good brother bad brother | 920

Haddix, M. P. Risked | Fic

Lu, M. Prodigy | Fic

Nardo, D. Assassination and its aftermath | 973.922092

O'Reilly, B. Kennedy's last days | 973.922092

Ribeiro, M. The assassination of Medgar Evers | 976.2

Swanson, J. L. "The president has been shot!" | 973.922092

Assassination and its aftermath. Nardo, D. | 973.922092

The **assassination** of Martin Luther King Jr.. Bodden, V. | B

The **assassination** of Medgar Evers. Ribeiro, M. | 976.2

ASSASSINATION PLOTS

Boecker, V. An assassin's guide to love and treason | Fic

Jurmain, S. Murder on the Baltimore Express | 973.7092

ASSASSINS

Blackburne, L. Midnight thief | Fic

Boecker, V. An assassin's guide to love and treason | Fic

Colfer, E. The reluctant assassin | Fic

Cypess, L. Death sworn | Fic

Flanagan, J. Halt's peril | Fic

Giblin, J. C. Good brother bad brother | 920

Gilman, D. Blood sun | Fic

Gutman, D. From Texas with love | Fic

Gutman, D. License to thrill | Fic

Gutman, D. Mission unstoppable | Fic

Gutman, D. Never say genius | Fic

Horowitz, A. South by southeast | Fic

Lee, M. Loki | Fic

Love, D. Monstrous devices | Fic

Stohl, M. Forever red | 741.5

Stroud, J. The hollow boy | Fic

ASSATEAGUE ISLAND NATIONAL SEASHORE (MD AND VA)

Frydenborg, K. The wild horse scientists | 599.665

ASSERTIVENESS (PSYCHOLOGY)

Green, T. Football genius | Fic

ASSERTIVENESS IN TEENAGE BOYS

Schmidt, G. D. Lizzie Bright and the Buckminster boy | Fic

ASSERTIVENESS IN TEENAGE GIRLS

Mackler, C. The Earth my butt and other big round things | Fic

ASSIMILATION (SOCIOLOGY)

Applegate, K. Home of the brave | Fic

Tan, S. The arrival | 741.5

ASSISTED SUICIDE

Benwell, F. The last leaves falling | Fic

McDaniel, L. Breathless | Fic

Tate, N. Choosing to live choosing to die | 179.7

Aster, Alex

Curse of the forgotten city | Fic

Curse of the Night Witch | Fic

ASTEROIDS -- COLLISIONS WITH EARTH

Rusch, E. Impact! | 551.3

ASTHMA

Marcovitz, H. Asthma | 616.2

Royston, A. Explaining asthma | 616.2

Asthma. Marcovitz, H. | 616.2

The **astonishing** adventures of Fanboy & Goth Girl. Lyga, B. | Fic

ASTRAL PROJECTION

Duncan, L. Stranger with my face | Fic

Astronaut Academy. Roman, D. | 741.5

ASTRONAUTICS

Bortz, A. B. Seven wonders of space technology | 629.4

Carlisle, R. P. Exploring space | 629.4

Chaikin, A. Mission control this is Apollo | 629.45

Cherrix, A. E. In the shadow of the moon | 629.45

Harris, J. Space exploration | 629.4

Hartman, E. Mission to Mars | 629.45

Jones, T. Ask the astronaut | 629.4

Mara, W. Space exploration | 629.4

Rusch, E. The mighty Mars rovers | 523.43

Saucier, C. A. P. Explore the cosmos like Neil DeGrasse Tyson | 520.92

Stott, C. Space exploration | 629.4

Woolf, A. The science of spacecraft | 629.47

ASTRONAUTICS -- HISTORY

Benoit, P. The space race | 629.4

Crompton, S. W. SputnikExplorer 1 | 629.4

Ottaviani, J. T-minus | 629.4

Ottaviani, J. T-minus | 629.4

Rhuday-Perkovich, O. Above and beyond | 629.40973

ASTRONAUTICS -- TECHNOLOGY TRANSFER

Harris, J. Space exploration | 629.4

ASTRONAUTS

Aldrin, B. Welcome to Mars	523.43
Brouwer, S. Moon mission	629.45
Dell, P. Man on the moon	629.45
Goodman, S. E. Ultimate field trip 5	629.45
Green, C. R. Spacewalk	629.45
Holden, H. M. Danger in space	629.45
Jenkins, M. Exploring space	520.9
Jones, T. Ask the astronaut	629.4
Mara, W. Space exploration	629.4
Ottaviani, J. T-minus	629.4
Sandler, M. W. Apollo 8	629.45
Stamper, P. The gravity of us	Fic
Thimmesh, C. Team moon	629.45

ASTRONAUTS -- HISTORY

Rhuday-Perkovich, O. Above and beyond	629.40973

ASTRONAUTS -- TRAINING

Goodman, S. E. Ultimate field trip 5	629.45

ASTRONOMERS

Atkins, J. Finding wonders	Fic

ASTRONOMY

Aguilar, D. A. Cosmic catastrophes	520
Bodden, V. To the moon	629.45
Dickinson, T. Nightwatch	523.8
Garlick, M. A. Atlas of the universe	523.1
Gater, W. The practical astronomer	520
Gilliland, B. Rocket science for the rest of us	520
Green, D. Astronomy	520
Jackson, E. B. The mysterious universe	523.8
Jennings, K. Outer space	523
Kenney, K. L. Exoplanets	523.2
Latta, S. L. Black holes	523.8
Miller, R. Natural satellites	520
Mitchell, C. How do astronauts wee in space?	520
Simon, S. Earth	525
Simon, S. The moon	559.9
Stott, C. Space exploration	629.4

ASTRONOMY -- HISTORY

Carson, M. K. Beyond the solar system	520.9
Jenkins, M. Exploring space	520.9
Astronomy. Green, D.	520

ASTROPHYSICISTS

Loomis, I. Eclipse chaser	523.7
Saucier, C. A. P. Explore the cosmos like Neil DeGrasse Tyson	520.92

ASTROPHYSICS

Gilliland, B. Rocket science for the rest of us	520
Mara, W. Space exploration	629.4

ASYLUM, RIGHT OF

Amnesty International. Free?	Fic
At home beneath the sea. Mallory, K.	551.46
At home in her tomb. Liu-Perkins, C.	931
At the edge of empire. Kraus, D.	Fic
Athans, Sandra K., 1958-	
Secrets of the sky caves	796.522

ATHEISTS

Henry, K. Heretics anonymous	Fic

Hopkins, E. Rumble	Fic

ATHENS, GREECE

Mann, E. The Parthenon	938

ATHENS, GREECE -- HISTORY

Mann, E. The Parthenon	938
Athlete vs. mathlete. Mack, W. C.	Fic

ATHLETES

Adams, C. Queens of the ice	796.962082
Berman, L. The greatest moments in sports	796
Bryant, H. Legends	796.357
Cronn-Mills, K. LGBTQ+ athletes claim the field	796.086
Ellis, C. Wrestling	796.812
Ignotofsky, R. Women in sports	796.092
Johnson, R. Great athletes	796
Lipsyte, R. Heroes of baseball	920
Macy, S. Swifter higher stronger	796.48

ATHLETES -- DRUG USE

Sommers, M. A. The NFL	362.29

ATHLETES -- PSYCHOLOGY

Afremow, J. A. The young champion's mind	796
Atkin, S. Beth	
Gunstories	363.33
Atkins, Jeannine, 1953-	
Borrowed names	811
Finding wonders	Fic
Atkins, Laura	
Fred Korematsu speaks up	B
Atkinson, E. J. (Elizabeth Jane), 1961-	
I Emma Freke	Fic
Atkinson, Rick	
D-Day	940.54

ATLANTA FALCONS (FOOTBALL TEAM)

Green, T. Football champ	Fic
Green, T. Football genius	Fic

ATLANTA ZOO

O'Connell, C. Bridge to the wild	636.088

ATLANTA, GEORGIA

Carlton, S. K. In the neighborhood of true	Fic
Green, T. Football champ	Fic
Green, T. Football genius	Fic
Khan, H. More to the story	Fic
Lee, S. The downstairs girl	Fic
Snyder, L. My Jasper June	Fic

ATLANTIC OCEAN

Avi. The true confessions of Charlotte Doyle	Fic
Jones, K. Sand dollar summer	Fic

ATLANTIS (LEGENDARY PLACE)

Hawkins, J. Atlantis and other lost worlds	001.94
Lerangis, P. The colossus rises	Fic
Lerangis, P. Lost in babylon	Fic
Atlantis and other lost worlds. Hawkins, J.	001.94
Atlas of the universe. Garlick, M. A.	523.1

ATOMIC BOMB

Higgins, J. Sharp shot	Fic
Yep, L. Hiroshima	Fic

ATOMIC BOMB -- HISTORY

Burgan, M. Hiroshima	940.54

Alvarez, J. How Tia Lola came to (visit) stay	Fic	
Baskin, N. R. Ruby on the outside	Fic	
DeStefano, L. A curious tale of the in-between	Fic	
Friesner, E. M. Sphinx's princess	Fic	
Horvath, P. The vacation	Fic	
Howland, L. The forget-me-not summer	Fic	
Jones, D. W. The islands of Chaldea	Fic	
O'Dell, S. Zia	Fic	
Peck, R. Fair weather	Fic	
Rylant, C. Missing May	Fic	
Whelan, G. Small acts of amazing courage	Fic	
Yelchin, E. The haunting of Falcon House	Fic	

AUNTS -- DEATH
Weeks, S. Pie	Fic
The **Aurora** County All-Stars. Wiles, D.	Fic
Aurora rising. Kaufman, A.	Fic

AUSCHWITZ (CONCENTRATION CAMP)
Bornstein, M. Survivors club	940.53
Boyne, J. The boy in the striped pajamas	Fic
Deem, J. M. Auschwitz	940.53
Iturbe, A. The librarian of Auschwitz	Fic
Jackson, L. E. B. I have lived a thousand years	940.53
Sender, R. M. The cage	940.53
Auschwitz. Deem, J. M.	940.53
Auslander. Dowswell, P.	Fic

Austen, Catherine, 1965-
Walking backward	Fic

AUSTEN, JANE, 1775-1817
Reef, C. Jane Austen	B

AUSTEN, JANE, 1775-1817. PRIDE AND PREJUDICE
Frederick, H. V. Pies & prejudice	Fic

AUSTIN, TEXAS
Philippe, B. The field guide to the North American teenager	Fic
Sachar, L. Small steps	Fic

AUSTRALIA
Abdel-Fattah, R. Does my head look big in this?	Fic
Bateson, C. Being Bee	Fic
Crowley, C. Words in deep blue	Fic
Einfeld, J. Life in the Australian Outback	994
Foxlee, K. The anatomy of wings	Fic
Fraillon, Z. The bone sparrow	Fic
French, J. Hitler's daughter	Fic
Gleitzman, M. Now	Fic
Healey, K. When we wake	Fic
Jinks, C. Evil genius	Fic
Jinks, C. Genius squad	Fic
Kwaymullina, A. The things she's seen	Fic
Leppman, E. J. Australia and the Pacific	994
Marsden, J. Tomorrow when the war began	Fic
Marshall, J. V. Stories from the Billabong	398.2
Moriarty, J. Feeling sorry for Celia	Fic
Patent, D. H. Saving the Tasmanian devil	599.2
Rosen, M. J. Sailing the unknown	Fic
Silvey, C. Jasper Jones	Fic
Tan, S. Tales from outer suburbia	Fic
Turner, K. Australia	994

Turner, P. S. The dolphins of Shark Bay	599.53
Wilkinson, L. Pink	Fic

AUSTRALIA -- ENVIRONMENTAL CONDITIONS
Morganelli, A. Pathways through Australia	304.2

AUSTRALIA -- SOCIAL LIFE AND CUSTOMS
Einfeld, J. Life in the Australian Outback	994
Australia. Turner, K.	994
Australia and the Pacific. Leppman, E. J.	994

AUSTRALOPITHECINES
Thimmesh, C. Lucy long ago	569.9

AUSTRALOPITHECUS AFARENSIS
Thimmesh, C. Lucy long ago	569.9

AUSTRIA
Dunlap, S. E. The musician's daughter	Fic
Ibbotson, E. The star of Kazan	Fic
Kessler, L. When the world was ours	Fic
Lu, M. The Kingdom of Back	Fic

AUTHORITARIANISM
Bailey, D. Dictatorship	321.9

AUTHORITY (PSYCHOLOGY)
Winerip, M. Adam Canfield of the Slash	Fic

AUTHORS
Anderson, J. J. Writing fantastic fiction	808.3
Aronson, M. 1968	909.82
Carter, A. Dear Ally how do you write a book?	808.02
Cooney, C. B. Janie face to face	Fic
D'Lacey, C. Dark fire	Fic
D'Lacey, C. The fire eternal	Fic
D'Lacey, C. Fire star	Fic
Fleischman, P. Alphamaniacs	809
Frost, R. Poetry for kids	811
Marcus, L. S. The wand in the word	813.009

AUTHORS, AMERICAN
Frost, R. Poetry for kids	811

AUTHORS, AMERICAN 19TH CENTURY
Noyes, D. A hopeful heart	813
Rasmussen, R. K. Mark Twain for kids	818

AUTHORS, AMERICAN 20TH CENTURY
Hemphill, S. Your own Sylvia	Fic
Marcus, L. S. The wand in the word	813.009
Paulsen, G. Woodsong	796.5

AUTHORS, ENGLISH
Aliki. William Shakespeare & the Globe	792

AUTHORS, ENGLISH 19TH CENTURY
Reef, C. The Bronte sisters	920

AUTHORS, ENGLISH 20TH CENTURY
Marcus, L. S. The wand in the word	813.009

AUTHORS, ENGLISH EARLY MODERN, 1500-1700
Krueger, S. H. The tempest	822.3
Sobran, J. A midsummer night's dream	822.3

AUTISM
Baskin, N. R. Anything but typical	Fic
Ginsberg, B. Episodes	616.858820092
Grossberg, B. N. Asperger's rules!	618.92
McCreary, M. Funny you don't look autistic	616.85
Rodriguez, A. M. Autism spectrum disorders	616.85
Snedden, R. Explaining autism	616.85

Goldstone, L. Higher steeper faster — 629.13
Langley, W. Women of the wind — 920
White, R. Cleared for takeoff — 629.133
Awakening. Wasserman, R. — Fic
AWARENESS
Chopra, M. Just breathe — 158.1
Awesome Asian Americans. Amara, P. — 920
Awkward. Chmakova, S. — 741.5
Axelrod, Amy
Your friend in fashion Abby Shapiro — Fic
AXES
Petersen, D. Mouse guard — 741.5
AYMARA INDIANS
Crowder, M. An uninterrupted view of the sky — Fic
Azad, Nafiza
The candle and the flame — Fic
AZTEC ARCHITECTURE
Lourie, P. Hidden world of the Aztec — 972
Aztec civilization. Nardo, D. — 972
The **Aztec** empire. Bingham, J. — 972
AZTECS
Bingham, J. The Aztec empire — 972
Croy, A. Ancient Aztec and Maya — 972
Heinrichs, A. The Aztecs — 972
Nardo, D. Aztec civilization — 972
Schomp, V. The Aztecs — 972
AZTECS -- ANTIQUITIES
Cooke, T. National Geographic investigates ancient Aztec — 972
AZTECS -- HISTORY
Lourie, P. Hidden world of the Aztec — 972
Nardo, D. Aztec civilization — 972
AZTECS -- MATERIAL CULTURE
Cooke, T. National Geographic investigates ancient Aztec — 972
AZTECS -- RELIGION
Lourie, P. Hidden world of the Aztec — 972
AZTECS -- SOCIAL LIFE AND CUSTOMS
Nardo, D. Aztec civilization — 972
The **Aztecs**. Heinrichs, A. — 972
The **Aztecs**. Schomp, V. — 972

B

BABA YAGA (LEGENDARY CHARACTER)
Maguire, G. Egg & spoon — Fic
McCoola, M. Baba Yaga's assistant — 741.5
Baba Yaga's assistant. McCoola, M. — 741.5
Babbitt, Natalie
Tuck everlasting — Fic
Babe and me. Gutman, D. — Fic
Babe conquers the world. Wallace, R. — B
Babe Didrikson Zaharias. Freedman, R. — B
Babe Didrikson Zaharias. Lobby, M. — B
BABOONS
Hunter, E. Broken pride — Fic
BABY BOOM GENERATION -- POLITICAL ACTIVITY

Hill, L. C. America dreaming — 303.48
BABY SITTERS
Byars, B. C. Cracker Jackson — Fic
BABYLON (EXTINCT CITY)
Lerangis, P. Lost in babylon — Fic
BABYLONIA
Lerangis, P. Lost in babylon — Fic
The **babysitter's** survival guide. Chasse, J. D. — 649
BABYSITTERS
Telgemeier, R. Claudia and mean Janine — 741.5
Telgemeier, R. Kristy's great idea — 741.5
Wolff, V. E. Make lemonade — Fic
BABYSITTING
Chasse, J. D. The babysitter's survival guide — 649
Bachmann, Stefan
The cabinet of curiosities — Fic
Bacigalupi, Paolo
The Drowned Cities — Fic
Ship breaker — Fic
Tool of war — Fic
Back from the brink. Castaldo, N. F. — 333.95
Back home. Keller, J. — Fic
Backlash. Littman, S. — Fic
Backyard biology. Latham, D. — 570.78
Backyard birds. Latimer, J. P. — 598
BACTERIA
Brown, J. Micro mania — 579.3
Eamer, C. Inside your insides — 579
Gardy, J. It's catching — 579.3
Hobbs, W. Go big or go home — Fic
Koch, F. Plagues — 614.5
BACTERIAL DISEASES
Gardy, J. It's catching — 579.3
Bad boy. Myers, W. D. — B
Bad boys of fashion. Croll, J. — 391.1
BAD BREATH
Donovan, S. Hawk & drool — 612.3
Bad burns. Markle, S. — 617.1
Bad girls. Yolen, J. — 920
Bad Island. TenNapel, D. — 741.5
BAD LUCK
Kadohata, C. The thing about luck — Fic
Kinney, J. Hard luck — Fic
Perkins, L. R. As easy as falling off the face of the earth — Fic
Bad luck girl. Zettel, S. — Fic
Bad machinery. Allison, J. — 741.5
Badcott, Nicholas
Pocket timeline of Islamic civilizations — 909
BADGERS
Jacques, B. Salamandastron — Fic
A **bag** of marbles. Kris. — 741.5
BAGHDAD ZOO
Halls, K. M. Saving the Baghdad Zoo — 590.73
BAGHDAD, IRAQ
Halls, K. M. Saving the Baghdad Zoo — 590.73
Myers, W. D. Sunrise over Fallujah — Fic
Baha'i faith. Hartz, P. — 297.9

Circus Mirandus	Fic
The **Beast**. Condie, A. B.	Fic
Beast. Napoli, D. J.	Fic
Beast rider. Johnston, T.	Fic
Beastly. Flinn, A.	Fic
Beastly brains. Castaldo, N. F.	591.5
The **beastly** bride. Datlow, E.	Fic
BEATLES (MUSICAL GROUP)	
Quinn, J. The Beatles	920
The **Beatles**. Quinn, J.	920
The **Beatles**. Roberts, J.	B
Beatty, Robert, 1963-	
Serafina and the twisted staff	Fic
Willa of Dark Hollow	Fic
Beaty, Andrea	
Cicada summer	Fic
Beaufrand, Mary Jane	
Useless Bay	Fic
Beauties and beasts. Hearne, B. G.	398.21
Beautiful blue world. LaFleur, S. M.	Fic
Beautiful chaos. Garcia, K.	Fic
Beautiful creatures. Garcia, K.	Fic
Beautiful darkness. Garcia, K.	Fic
The **beautiful** stories of life. Rylant, C.	398.2
The **beautiful** struggle. Coates, T.	305.896
BEAUTY	
Cashore, K. Fire	Fic
Donnelly, J. Stepsister	Fic
Friesner, E. M. Sphinx's princess	Fic
Kadohata, C. Outside beauty	Fic
McKinley, R. Rose daughter	Fic
Phelan, M. Snow White	741.5
Platt, R. They wore what?!	391.009
Ross, E. Belle epoque	Fic
Snyder, L. My Jasper June	Fic
Vivian, S. The list	Fic
Westerfeld, S. Extras	Fic
Westerfeld, S. Pretties	Fic
Young, B. The prettiest	Fic
Beauty. McKinley, R.	Fic
BEAUTY AND THE BEAST(TALE)	
Hearne, B. G. Beauties and beasts	398.21
BEAUTY CARE -- HISTORY	
Platt, R. They wore what?!	391.009
BEAUTY CONTESTANTS	
Bray, L. Beauty queens	Fic
BEAUTY CONTESTS	
Bray, L. Beauty queens	Fic
Charles, T. Like Vanessa	Fic
Eulberg, E. Revenge of the girl with the great personality	Fic
Beauty queens. Bray, L.	Fic
BEAVERS	
Gish, M. Beavers	599.37
Beavers. Gish, M.	599.37
Because I am furniture. Chaltas, T.	Fic
Because of Mr. Terupt. Buyea, R.	Fic
Because of Winn-Dixie. DiCamillo, K.	Fic

Beccaloni, George	
Biggest bugs life-size	595.714
Beccia, Carlyn	
Monstrous	001.944
Becker, Helaine	
Funny business	792.7028
Beckhorn, Susan Williams, 1953-	
The wolf's boy	Fic
BECKWITH, BYRON DE LA, 1920-2001	
Ribeiro, M. The assassination of Medgar Evers	976.2
Become a leader like Michelle Obama. Moss, C.	973.932
Becoming. Obama, M.	B
Becoming Beatriz. Charles, T.	Fic
Becoming Maria. Manzano, S.	B
Becoming Muhammad Ali. Patterson, J.	Fic
BEDBUGS	
Gleason, C. Feasting bedbugs mites and ticks	614.4
Bedford, Allan	
The unofficial LEGO builder's guide	790.133
Bedford, Martyn	
Flip	Fic
Bednar, Sylvie	
Flags of the world	929.9
BEDROOMS	
Weaver, J. It's your room!	747.7
The **bee** book. Chadwick, F.	595.79
BEE CULTURE	
Chadwick, F. The bee book	595.79
BEEHIVES	
Markle, S. The case of the vanishing honey bees	595.79
BEEKEEPERS	
McKinley, R. Chalice	Fic
Beers, G. Kylene, 1957-	
Disrupting thinking	418
Notice & note	372.6
BEES	
Blobaum, C. Explore honey bees!	595.79
Chadwick, F. The bee book	595.79
Hirsch, R. E. Where have all the bees gone?	595.79
Hosler, J. The way of the hive	741.5
Markle, S. The case of the vanishing honey bees	595.79
Nye, N. S. Honeybee	811
BEES -- BEHAVIOR	
Hosler, J. The way of the hive	741.5
Beetle & the Hollowbones. Layne, A.	741.5
The **beetle** book. Jenkins, S.	595.76
Beetle boy. Willey, M.	Fic
Beetle busters. Burns, L. G.	595.76
BEETLES	
Burns, L. G. Beetle busters	595.76
Jenkins, S. The beetle book	595.76
Willey, M. Beetle boy	Fic
Wooding, C. Silver	Fic
Before Columbus. Mann, C. C.	970.01
Before Columbus. Wulffson, D. L.	970.01
Before I die. Downham, J.	Fic
Before the ever after. Woodson, J.	Fic

Before they were famous. Raczka, B.	704	Traitor's son	Fic
Before we were free. Alvarez, J.	Fic	**Bell, Juliet**	
Beginning genealogy. Ollhoff, J.	929	Kepler's Dream	Fic
BEHAN, TEJU		**Bell-Rehwoldt, Sheri**	
Behan, T. Drawing from the city	B	The kids' guide to jumping rope	796.2
Behan, Teju		**Bella** at midnight. Stanley, D.	Fic
Drawing from the city	B	**BELLE EPOQUE (1871-1914)**	
Behar, Ruth, 1956-		Ross, E. Belle epoque	Fic
Lucky broken girl	Fic	**Belle** epoque. Ross, E.	Fic
BEHAVIOR		**Belle** Prater's boy. White, R.	Fic
McIntyre, T. The behavior survival guide for kids	649	**Bellenir, Elizabeth**	
Post, P. Emily Post's the guide to good manners for kids	395.1	Fitness information for teens	613.7
		Bellenir, Karen	
BEHAVIOR AND CULTURE		Alcohol information for teens	613.81
Gascoigne, I. Papua New Guinea	995.3	Allergy information for teens	618.9297
The **behavior** survival guide for kids. McIntyre, T.	649	**Beller, Susan Provost, 1949-**	
Behemoth. Westerfeld, S.	Fic	Billy Yank & Johnny Reb	973.7
Behnke, Alison		The history puzzle	901
Death of a dreamer	B	**Belli, Mary Lou**	
Racial profiling	363.2	Acting for young actors	792.02
Beholding Bee. Fusco, K. N.	Fic	**Belly** up. Gibbs, S.	Fic
BEIJING, CHINA		**Belmont, Helen**	
Hay, J. The Tiananmen Square protests of 1989	951.05	Looking at aerial photographs	910
Marx, T. Elephants and golden thrones	951	**BELONGING**	
Beil, Karen Magnuson		Bird, J. The brave	Fic
What Linnaeus saw	508.092	Brosgol, V. Anya's ghost	741.5
Beil, Michael D.		Bunker, L. Zenobia July	Fic
The ring of Rocamadour	Fic	Carlton, S. K. In the neighborhood of true	Fic
The vanishing violin	Fic	Cavanaugh, N. J. This journal belongs to Ratchet	Fic
Being Bee. Bateson, C.	Fic	Chmakova, S. Brave	741.5
Being Clem. Cline-Ransome, L.	Fic	Craft, J. New kid	741.5
Being dead. Vande Velde, V.	Fic	Giff, P. R. Pictures of Hollis Woods	Fic
Being Jazz. Jennings, J.	306.76	Giles, C. D. Take back the block	Fic
Being Toffee. Crossan, S.	Fic	Hiranandani, V. The whole story of half a girl	Fic
Being transgender in America. Harris, D.	306.76	Hof, M. Mother number zero	Fic
Beker, Jeanne		Jamieson, V. All's faire in middle school	741.5
Strutting it	746.9	Khan, H. Amina's voice	Fic
BELGIUM -- HISTORY -- GERMAN OCCUPATION, 1940-1945		Kim, G. The last fallen star	Fic
		Locke, K. It's a whole spiel	Fic
Deem, J. M. The prisoners of Breendonk	940.53	Longo, J. What I carry	Fic
BELIEF AND DOUBT		McKay, H. Saffy's angel	Fic
Hautman, P. Godless	Fic	Rundell, K. Cartwheeling in thunderstorms	Fic
Haydu, C. A. One jar of magic	Fic	Schmidt, G. D. Just like that	Fic
Henry, K. Heretics anonymous	Fic	Yee, P. Learning to fly	Fic
Zarr, S. Once was lost	Fic	The **beloved** world of Sonia Sotomayor. Sotomayor, S.	B
BELIZE		**Belton, Blair**	
Jermyn, L. Belize	972.82	How coal is formed	553.2
Belize. Jermyn, L.	972.82	**Benazir** Bhutto. Naden, C. J.	B
BELL, ALEXANDER GRAHAM, 1847-1922		**Benazir** Bhutto. Price, S.	B
Carson, M. K. Alexander Graham Bell	B	**Benched**. Watson, C.	Fic
Carson, M. K. Alexander Graham Bell for kids	621.385092	**Bender, Lionel**	
Helfand, L. They changed the world	621.3	Explaining blindness	617.7
BELL, CECE		Explaining epilepsy	616.8
Bell, C. El Deafo	B	**Beneath** my mother's feet. Qamar, A.	Fic
Bell, Cece		**Beneath** the mask. Ward, D.	Fic
El Deafo	B	**Beneath** the surface. Hugstad, K.	616.89
Bell, Hilari		**BENEFICIAL INSECTS**	

Brashares, A. 3 willows — Fic
Brashares, A. The sisterhood of the traveling pants — Fic
Budhos, M. T. Tell us we're home — Fic
Callender, K. King and the dragonflies — Fic
Chase, P. J. Dough boys — Fic
Chase, P. J. Turning point — Fic
Cohen, M. The Inn Between — Fic
Crowley, C. Words in deep blue — Fic
Dowell, F. O. The kind of friends we used to be — Fic
Emond, S. Winter town — Fic
Eulberg, E. Revenge of the girl with the great personality — Fic
Federle, T. Five six seven Nate! — Fic
Gino, A. Rick — Fic
Green, T. Force out — Fic
Griffin, P. Saving Marty — Fic
Hale, S. Friends forever — 302
Hardinge, F. Deeplight — Fic
Hautman, P. Slider — Fic
Haydu, C. A. The someday suitcase — Fic
Holt, K. W. When Zachary Beaver came to town — Fic
Howard, J. J. That time I joined the circus — Fic
James, A. The lost fairy tales — Fic
Jung, M. The boys in the back row — Fic
Kessler, L. When the world was ours — Fic
Kinney, J. Diary of a wimpy kid — Fic
Kinney, J. The third wheel — Fic
Levy, D. A. Above all else — Fic
Lockhart, E. Dramarama — Fic
Loftin, N. Wish girl — Fic
Marcus, K. Exposed — Fic
McKay, S. E. Thunder over Kandahar — Fic
Myers, W. D. Darius & Twig — Fic
Oseman, A. Heartstopper — 741.5
Pasternack, S. Anya and the nightingale — Fic
Patterson, J. Ali Cross — Fic
Patterson, J. Like father like son — Fic
Pyron, B. Lucky strike — Fic
Russell, C. Songs about a girl — Fic
Soo, K. Jellaby — 741.5
Sorosiak, C. Wild blue wonder — Fic
Stead, R. Goodbye stranger — Fic
Steele, H. DeadEndia — Fic
Stevenson, N. Lumberjanes — 741.5
Turnage, S. The odds of getting even — Fic
Vail, R. Well that was awkward — Fic
Warga, J. The shape of thunder — Fic
Watson, R. Watch us rise — Fic
West, J. A storm of wishes — Fic
Wiles, D. Countdown — Fic
Woodson, J. After Tupac and D Foster — Fic
Wunder, W. The museum of intangible things — Fic

BEST FRIENDS -- DEATH
Anderson, L. H. Wintergirls — Fic
Benjamin, A. The thing about jellyfish — Fic
Mbalia, K. Tristan Strong punches a hole in the sky — Fic
McClintock, N. She saidshe saw — Fic
Priest, C. I am Princess X — Fic

The **best** man. Peck, R. — Fic
Best nerds forever. Patterson, J. — Fic
Best science fair workshops -- bug science. Young, K. R. — 595.7078
BESTIARIES
Baynes, P. Questionable creatures — 398.24
BETHESDA, MARYLAND
Brashares, A. 3 willows — Fic
BETRAYAL
Barnholdt, L. Sometimes it happens — Fic
Goodman, A. Eona — Fic
Haddix, M. P. Among the betrayed — Fic
Hunter, E. Broken pride — Fic
Lerangis, P. The tomb of shadows — Fic
McCoy, M. I Claudia — Fic
Reichs, B. Genesis — Fic
Rylant, C. A fine white dust — Fic
Sage, A. Twilight hauntings — Fic
Better to wish. Martin, A. M. — Fic
Between shades of gray. Sepetys, R. — Fic
Between sky and earth. Fombelle, T. d. — Fic
BETWEEN THE WARS (1918-1939)
Fombelle, T. d. Between sky and earth — Fic
Hardinge, F. Cuckoo song — Fic
Stevens, R. First class murder — Fic
Stevens, R. Murder is bad manners — Fic
Stevens, R. Poison is not polite — Fic
Wein, E. The pearl thief — Fic
Between two skies. O'Sullivan, J. — Fic
BEVERAGES
Furgang, A. Carbonated beverages — 613.2
Beverly right here. DiCamillo, K. — Fic
Bewitching season. Doyle, M. — Fic
Beyond bullets. Gerszak, R. — 958.1
Beyond courage. Rappaport, D. — 940.53
Beyond invert & multiply. McNamara, J. — 372.7
Beyond Jupiter. Bortz, A. B. — B
Beyond magenta. Kuklin, S. — 306.76
Beyond me. Donwerth-Chikamatsu, A. — Fic
Beyond the bright sea. Wolk, L. — Fic
Beyond the dance. Goh, C. H. — B
Beyond the grave. Watson, J. — Fic
Beyond the great mountains. Young, E. — 811
Beyond the solar system. Carson, M. K. — 520.9
Beyond words. Safina, C. — 591.56
Bezdecheck, Bethany
Directing — 792.602
BHUTTO, BENAZIR, 1953-2007
Naden, C. J. Benazir Bhutto — B
Price, S. Benazir Bhutto — B
Bial, Raymond
Nauvoo — 289.3
The Shoshone — 978
Tenement — 307.76
The **Bible**. Carroll, R. P. — 220.5
BIBLE STORIES
Connolly, S. New Testament miracles — 226.7

Ehrlich, A. With a mighty hand **221.9**

Lottridge, C. B. Stories from Adam and Eve to Ezekiel **221.9**

Lottridge, C. B. Stories from the life of Jesus **225.9**

Napoli, D. J. Treasury of Bible stories **220.95**

Spirin, G. Jesus **232.9**

BIBLIOGRAPHICAL CITATIONS

Gaines, A. Don't steal copyrighted stuff! **808**

Bick, Ilsa J.

Ashes **Fic**

BICYCLE MOTOCROSS

Adamson, T. K. BMX racing **796.6**

BICYCLES

Al-Mansour, H. The green bicycle **Fic**

Lakin, P. Bicycles **629.227**

Mulder, M. Pedal it! **629.227**

Robinson, L. Cyclist bikelist **796.6**

BICYCLES -- DESIGN AND CONSTRUCTION

Lakin, P. Bicycles **629.227**

BICYCLES -- EQUIPMENT AND SUPPLIES

Lakin, P. Bicycles **629.227**

BICYCLES -- HISTORY

Macy, S. Wheels of change **796.6**

Bicycles. Lakin, P. **629.227**

BICYCLING

Adamson, T. K. BMX racing **796.6**

Bradbury, J. Shift **Fic**

Mulder, M. Pedal it! **629.227**

Robinson, L. Cyclist bikelist **796.6**

BICYCLING FOR WOMEN

Macy, S. Wheels of change **796.6**

Biddy Mason speaks up. White, A. **B**

BIDEN, JOSEPH R., 1942-

Gormley, B. Joe Biden **B**

BIEBER, JUSTIN, 1994-

Bieber, J. Justin Bieber **782.42164**

Bieber, Justin, 1994-

Justin Bieber **782.42164**

Biesty, Stephen

Stephen Biesty's cross-sections **940.1**

BIG BAND MUSIC

Nelson, M. Sweethearts of rhythm **781.65**

BIG BANDS

Nelson, M. Sweethearts of rhythm **781.65**

BIG BANG THEORY (ASTRONOMY)

Brown, D. Older than dirt **551.7**

The **big** book of details. Linder, R. **372.62**

The **big** book of monsters. Johnson, H. **001.944**

The **big** book of soccer. Weighill, D. **796.334**

BIG DATA

Martin, B. S. Big data and machine learning **005.7**

Big data and machine learning. Martin, B. S. **005.7**

A **big** dose of lucky. Jocelyn, M. **Fic**

The **big** field. Lupica, M. **Fic**

BIG GAME HUNTING

Peterson, J. M. Big game hunting **799.2**

Big game hunting. Peterson, J. M. **799.2**

Big game. Gibbs, S. **Fic**

Big Mouth & Ugly Girl. Oates, J. C. **Fic**

The **big** questions book of sex and consent. Freitas, D. **176**

Big talk. Fleischman, P. **811**

Bigelow, Lisa Jenn

Hazel's theory of evolution **Fic**

Starting from here **Fic**

Biggest bugs life-size. Beccaloni, G. **595.714**

Bildner, Phil

A high five for Glenn Burke **Fic**

BILES, SIMONE, 1997-

Biles, S. Courage to soar **B**

Biles, Simone, 1997-

Courage to soar **B**

BILINGUAL MATERIALS

Argueta, J. Somos como las nubes **811**

Saldana, R. Dancing with the devil and other tales from beyond **Fic**

BILINGUAL MATERIALS ENGLISH/SPANISH

Camper, C. Lowriders in space **741.5**

Camper, C. Lowriders to the center of the Earth **741.5**

Carlson, L. M. Cool salsa **811**

Carlson, L. M. Red hot salsa **811.008**

Hayes, J. Dance Nana dance **398.2**

Herrera, J. F. Laughing out loud I fly **811**

Janeczko, P. B. A foot in the mouth **821.008**

Mora, P. The desert is my mother **811**

Bill Nye's great big world of science. Nye, B. **500**

The **Bill** of Rights. Baxter, R. **342.7308**

Billie Jean King. Gitlin, M. **B**

Billingsley, Bonnie S.

A survival guide for new special educators **371.90973**

Billingsley, Franny, 1954-

Chime **Fic**

BILLIONAIRES

Moore, S. Batman **Fic**

Billions of years amazing changes. Pringle, L. **576.8**

Billy Yank & Johnny Reb. Beller, S. P. **973.7**

BILOXI, MISSISSIPPI

Greenberg, J. The mad potter **738.092**

BILTMORE ESTATE (ASHEVILLE, N.C.)

Beatty, R. Serafina and the twisted staff **Fic**

BIN LADEN, OSAMA, 1957-2011

Elish, D. Inside the situation room **B**

Lunis, N. The takedown of Osama bin Laden **B**

BINFORD, GRETA

Lasky, K. Silk and venom **595.4**

Bingham, Jane

The Aztec empire **972**

The Gulf Wars with Iraq **956.7044**

Bingham, Kelly L., 1967-

Shark girl **Fic**

Binny for short. McKay, H. **Fic**

Bio diversity. Perdew, L. **333.95**

BIODIVERSITY

Kallen, S. A. What is the impact of declining biodiversity? **333.95**

The **bird** king. Tan, S.   741.64092
Bird Lake moon. Henkes, K.   Fic

BIRD WATCHING
Alderfer, J. K. Bird guide of North America   598.097
Hoose, P. M. Moonbird   598.072
Wolf, S. The robin makes a laughing sound   598

Bird, Betsy
Funny girl   Fic

Bird, James
The brave   Fic

BIRDS
Alderfer, J. K. Bird guide of North America   598.097
Burnie, D. Bird   598
Collard, S. B. Fire birds   634.9
Fleischman, P. I am Phoenix   811
Gish, M. Peacocks   598.6
Hirsch, R. E. Birds vs. blades?   578.77
Hoena, B. A. Everything birds of prey   598.9
Hoose, P. M. Moonbird   598.072
Hutto, J. When I was a turkey   598.6
Larson, J. Hummingbirds   598.7
Latimer, J. P. Backyard birds   598
Loftin, N. Nightingale's nest   Fic
London, A. Black wings beating   Fic
London, A. Red skies falling   Fic
Peterson, R. T. Peterson field guide to birds of eastern and central North America   598.097
Peterson, R. T. Peterson field guide to birds of North America   598.097
Peterson, R. T. Peterson field guide to birds of Western North America   598.097
Springstubb, T. The most perfect thing in the universe   Fic
Thornhill, J. The tragic tale of the great auk   598.3
Turner, P. S. Crow smarts   598.8

BIRDS -- BEHAVIOR
Wolf, S. The robin makes a laughing sound   598

BIRDS -- IDENTIFICATION
Bull, J. L. The National Audubon Society field guide to North American birds   598.097
Latimer, J. P. Backyard birds   598

BIRDS -- MIGRATION
Hoose, P. M. Moonbird   598.072

BIRDS -- ORIGIN
Guiberson, B. Z. Feathered dinosaurs   567.9

BIRDS OF PREY
Hoena, B. A. Everything birds of prey   598.9
Latimer, J. P. Birds of prey   598.9

BIRDS OF PREY -- IDENTIFICATION
Latimer, J. P. Birds of prey   598.9
Birds of prey. Latimer, J. P.   598.9
Birds vs. blades? Hirsch, R. E.   578.77

Birdsall, Jeanne
The Penderwicks   Fic
The Penderwicks at last   Fic
The Penderwicks at Point Mouette   Fic
The Penderwicks in spring   Fic
The Penderwicks on Gardam Street   Fic

Birkemoe, Karen, 1974-
Strike a pose   613.7

BIRKENAU EXTERMINATION CAMP
Zail, S. Playing for the commandant   Fic
Birmingham 1963. Tougas, S.   323.1196
Birmingham Sunday. Brimner, L. D.   323.1196

BIRMINGHAM, ALABAMA -- HISTORY
Brimner, L. D. Birmingham Sunday   323.1196
Levinson, C. We've got a job   323.1196

BIRMINGHAM, ALABAMA -- RACE RELATIONS
Brimner, L. D. Black & white   323.1196
Mayer, R. H. When the children marched   323.1196

BIRMINGHAM, ALABAMA -- RACE RELATIONS -- HISTORY -- 20TH CENTURY
Tougas, S. Birmingham 1963   323.1196

Birmingham, Maria
Weird zone   796.1

BIRTH CONTROL
Lasky, J. Birth control   363.9

BIRTH CONTROL -- HISTORY
Blumenthal, K. Jane against the world   342.7308
Birth control. Lasky, J.   363.9

BIRTH DEFECTS
Giddings, S. Cystic fibrosis   616.3
Levete, S. Explaining cerebral palsy   616.8
Palacio, R. J. Wonder   Fic
The **birth** of Christianity. Nardo, D.   270.1
The **birth** of Islam. Nardo, D.   297.09
The **birth** of modern nations. Malam, J.   940.2

BIRTHDAY PARTIES
Stevens, R. Poison is not polite   Fic

BIRTHDAYS
Birdsall, J. The Penderwicks in spring   Fic

BIRTHFATHERS -- IDENTIFICATION
Creech, S. Absolutely normal chaos   Fic
Birthmarked. O'Brien, C. M.   Fic

BIRTHMARKS
Fusco, K. N. Beholding Bee   Fic

BIRTHMOTHERS
Hof, M. Mother number zero   Fic
Lowry, L. Son   Fic

BIRTHPARENTS -- IDENTIFICATION
Day, C. I can make this promise   Fic
Lupica, M. Miracle on 49th Street   Fic

BISEXUAL STUDENTS
Cianciotto, J. LGBT youth in America's schools   371.826

BISEXUAL TEENAGE GIRLS
Cashore, K. Jane unlimited   Fic

BISEXUAL TEENAGERS
Keplinger, K. Run   Fic
Riordan, R. The burning maze   Fic
Riordan, R. The dark prophecy   Fic
Riordan, R. The hidden oracle   Fic
Riordan, R. The tower of Nero   Fic

Bishop, Kay, 1942-
Connecting libraries with classrooms   375
Bison. Gish, M.   599.64

Blackwood, Sage

Jinx	Fic
Jinx's fire	Fic
Jinx's magic	Fic
Miss Ellicott's school for the magically minded	Fic

Blades of freedom. Hale, N. — 972.94

Blake, Ashley Herring

Hazel Bly and the deep blue sea	Fic

Blake, Kendare

Anna dressed in blood	Fic
Two dark reigns	Fic

Blakemore, Megan Frazer

The friendship riddle	Fic

BLALOCK, ALFRED, 1899-1964

Murphy, J. Breakthrough!	617
Yount, L. Alfred Blalock Helen Taussig and Vivien Thomas	617.4

Blanca & Roja. McLemore, A. — Fic

Blanchard, Anne

Arab science and invention in the golden age	509

Blank confession. Hautman, P. — Fic

Blankman, Anne

The blackbird girls	Fic

Blashfield, Jean F.

Argentina	982
Golda Meir	B
Iowa	977.7
Ireland	941.7
Italy	945
Maryland	975.2
Wisconsin	977.5

Blauer, Ettagale

Mali	966.23
Mauritania	966.1
Portugal	946.9

Blaz, Deborah

Differentiated instruction	418

BLEDSOE, LUCY JANE

Bledsoe, L. J. How to survive in Antarctica	B

Bledsoe, Lucy Jane

How to survive in Antarctica	B

Bleed blister puke and purge. Younker, J. M. — 610.9

Blended. Draper, S. M. — Fic

BLENDED FAMILIES

Abbott, T. Wade and the scorpion's claw	Fic
Barrett, T. The stepsister's tale	Fic
Birdsall, J. The Penderwicks at last	Fic
Birdsall, J. The Penderwicks in spring	Fic
Draper, S. M. Blended	Fic
Duncan, L. Locked in time	Fic
Friend, N. Bounce	Fic
Haddix, M. P. In over their heads	Fic
Haddix, M. P. Under their skin	Fic
Horvath, P. Northward to the moon	Fic
Maetani, V. E. Ink & ashes	Fic
McKay, H. The time of green magic	Fic
Wiles, D. Revolution	Fic

Williams, M. Diamond boy	Fic
Youngblood, L. C. Forever this summer	Fic
Youngblood, L. C. Love like sky	Fic

BLENDED LEARNING

Tucker, C. R. Blended learning in action	371.3
Tucker, C. R. Power up blended learning	371.3

Blended learning in action. Tucker, C. R. — 371.3

Blevins, Wiley

Teaching phonics & word study in the intermediate grades	372.46

BLINDNESS

Bender, L. Explaining blindness	617.7
Dorris, M. Sees Behind Trees	Fic
Markle, S. Lost sight	617.7
Sedgwick, M. She is not invisible	Fic

Bliss. Littlewood, K. — Fic

Bliss, John, 1958-

Art that moves	791.43

BLISTERS

Markle, S. Bad burns	617.1

Blizzard of glass. Walker, S. M. — 971.6

BLIZZARDS

Brown, S. To stay alive	Fic
Kinney, J. Cabin fever	Fic
Rose, C. S. May B.	Fic
Rosen, M. J. The tale of rescue	Fic

Blobaum, Cindy, 1966-

Explore honey bees!	595.79

Block, Francesca Lia

Love in the time of global warming	Fic

BLOGGERS

Watson, R. Watch us rise	Fic

BLOGS

Levine, G. C. Writer to writer	808.02
Lundin, B. Ship it	Fic

Blohm, Craig E., 1948-

The civil rights movement	323.1196

BLOOD

Aveyard, V. Red queen	Fic
Lew, K. Clot & scab	617.1
Newquist, H. P. The book of blood	612.1
Winner, C. Circulating life	615

BLOOD -- CIRCULATION

Rose, S. Circulatory system	612.1

BLOOD -- DISEASES

Markle, S. Leukemia	616.99

BLOOD -- TRANSFUSION

Winner, C. Circulating life	615

Blood Brother. Wallace, R. — B

BLOOD LIBEL

Wiseman, E. Puppet	Fic

The **blood** lie. Vernick, S. R. — Fic

The **blood** of Olympus. Riordan, R. — Fic

Blood red road. Young, M. — Fic

Blood rose rebellion. Eves, R. — Fic

Blood sun. Gilman, D. — Fic

Bloodhound. Pierce, T. — Fic

BOATS

Farndon, J. Stickmen's guide to watercraft	**623.82**
Weitzman, D. Pharaoh's boat	**932**
Woodruff, E. George Washington's spy	**Fic**
Wurdinger, S. D. Kayaking	**797.122**

Bob Marley. Paprocki, S. **B**

Bobrick, Benson, 1947-
The Battle of Nashville **B**

Bock, Caroline
Lie **Fic**

Bodden, Valerie

The assassination of Martin Luther King Jr.	**B**
The Deepwater Horizon oil spill	**363.11**
Samuel Houston	**B**
Through the American West	**917.804**
To the moon	**629.45**
To the South Pole	**B**

Bodeen, S. A. (Stephanie A.), 1965-

The compound	**Fic**
The raft	**Fic**

Bodies from the ash. Deem, J. M. **937**
Bodies from the bog. Deem, J. M. **569.9**
Body 2.0. Latta, S. L. **610.28**
The **body** at the tower. Lee, Y. S. **Fic**

BODY AWARENESS
Rissman, R. Yoga for your mind and body **613.7**

The **body** book for boys. Mar, J. **613**

BODY COVERING (ANATOMY)

Klosterman, L. Skin	**612.7**
Lew, K. Clot & scab	**617.1**

BODY FLUIDS

Donovan, S. Hawk & drool	**612.3**
Larsen, C. S. Crust and spray	**612.8**

BODY IMAGE

Carter, C. How to be a girl in the world	**Fic**
Freitas, D. The big questions book of sex and consent	**176**
Jensen, K. Body talk	**306.4**
Jones, V. Conquering negative body image	**616.85**
Manfredi, A. The (other) F word	**306.4**
Martin, M. A. To be honest	**Fic**
Petro-Roy, J. You are enough	**616.85**
Smith, R. P. Self-image and eating disorders	**616.85**

BODY IMAGE IN TEENAGERS
Smith, R. P. Self-image and eating disorders **616.85**

BODY LANGUAGE
Jackson, D. M. Every body's talking **153.6**

BODY MODIFICATION
Nagle, J. Why people get tattoos and other body art **391.6**

BODY SIZE
Manfredi, A. The (other) F word **306.4**

BODY SWAPPING

Bedford, M. Flip	**Fic**
Price, L. Starters	**Fic**

Body talk. Jensen, K. **306.4**

BODY WEIGHT
Chandler, M. Understanding obesity **618.92**

BODYGUARDS

Uehashi, N. Moribito	**Fic**

Boecker, Virginia
An assassin's guide to love and treason **Fic**

BOG BODIES

Deem, J. M. Bodies from the bog	**569.9**
Dowd, S. Bog child	**Fic**

Bog child. Dowd, S. **Fic**

Bolden, Tonya

Capital days	**B**
Crossing Ebenezer Creek	**Fic**
Emancipation Proclamation	**973.7**
FDR's Alphabet soup	**973.917**
How to build a museum	**973**
Inventing Victoria	**Fic**
M.L.K.	**B**
Maritcha	**974.7**
Pathfinders	**920**
Portraits of African-American heroes	**920**
Saving Savannah	**Fic**
Searching for Sarah Rector	**B**
Strong voices	**815.08**
Take-off!	**784.4**
Wake up our souls	**704.03**

Boldt, Claudia
Think and make like an artist **702.8**

BOLIVAR, SIMON, 1783-1830
Reis, R. A. Simon Bolivar **B**

BOLIVIA

Crowder, M. An uninterrupted view of the sky	**Fic**
Yomtov, N. Bolivia	**984**

Bolivia. Yomtov, N. **984**
Bomb. Sheinkin, S. **623.4**

BOMB RECONNAISSANCE
Perritano, J. Bomb squad technician **363.17**

Bomb squad technician. Perritano, J. **363.17**
Bomb squad. Newton, M. **363.17**

BOMB SQUADS

Newton, M. Bomb squad	**363.17**
Perritano, J. Bomb squad technician	**363.17**

BOMB THREATS

Oates, J. C. Big Mouth & Ugly Girl	**Fic**
Perritano, J. Bomb squad technician	**363.17**

BOMBERS
Jackson, R. 101 great bombers **623.74**

BOMBERS (TERRORISTS)
Denson, B. The Unabomber **364**

BOMBING
Pausewang, G. Dark hours **Fic**

BOMBING INVESTIGATION

Denson, B. The Unabomber	**364**
Perritano, J. Bomb squad technician	**363.17**

The **bombing** of Pearl Harbor. Wukovits, J. F. **940.54**

BOMBINGS

Carlton, S. K. In the neighborhood of true	**Fic**
Haugen, D. M. The attack on Pearl Harbor	**940.54**
Ward, R. Num8ers	**Fic**

BOMBINGS -- HISTORY 20TH CENTURY

Kibuishi, K. Explorer	**741.5**
Mass, W. Jeremy Fink and the meaning of life	**Fic**
TenNapel, D. Cardboard	**741.5**

BOXING

Holt, K. A. Knockout	**Fic**
Lipsyte, R. The contender	**Fic**
Oaks, J. A. Why I fight	**Fic**
Sharenow, R. The Berlin Boxing Club	**Fic**

BOXING MATCHES

Burgan, M. Ali's knockout punch	**796.83092**
Boy. Dahl, R.	**B**

BOY ACTORS

Cooper, S. King of shadows	**Fic**

BOY ADVENTURERS

Lewis, C. S. The horse and his boy	**Fic**
Riordan, R. The lightning thief	**Fic**
Saint-Exupery, A. d. The little prince	**Fic**
Sniegoski, T. Quest for the spark	**Fic**
Twain, M. The adventures of Tom Sawyer	**Fic**
Venditti, R. The lightning thief	**741.5**

BOY APPRENTICES

Delaney, J. Revenge of the witch	**Fic**
Farmer, N. The Sea of Trolls	**Fic**
Higgins, F. E. The black book of secrets	**Fic**
Jinks, C. The last bogler	**Fic**
Kirby, M. J. The clockwork three	**Fic**
Oliver, L. Liesl & Po	**Fic**
Snicket, L. "Who could that be at this hour?"	**Fic**
Stroud, J. The amulet of Samarkand	**Fic**

BOY ARTISTS

Craft, J. New kid	**741.5**
A **boy** at war. Mazer, H.	**Fic**

BOY ATHLETES

Lupica, M. Play makers	**Fic**

BOY BANDS

Russell, C. Songs about a girl	**Fic**

BOY BASEBALL PLAYERS

Bildner, P. A high five for Glenn Burke	**Fic**
Green, T. Baseball genius	**Fic**
Green, T. Force out	**Fic**
Green, T. New kid	**Fic**
Jeter, D. The contract	**Fic**
Lupica, M. Heat	**Fic**
Lupica, M. The only game	**Fic**
Lupica, M. Strike zone	**Fic**
Ritter, J. H. The boy who saved baseball	**Fic**
Wiles, D. The Aurora County All-Stars	**Fic**

BOY BASKETBALL PLAYERS

Alexander, K. The crossover	**Fic**
Lupica, M. Play makers	**Fic**
Lupica, M. Summer ball	**Fic**

BOY BOXERS

Patterson, J. Becoming Muhammad Ali	**Fic**

BOY CAMPERS

Greenwald, T. Charlie Joe Jackson's guide to summer vacation	**Fic**

BOY COAL MINERS -- HISTORY

Bartoletti, S. C. Growing up in coal country	**331.3**

BOY COMIC STRIP ILLUSTRATORS

Kowitt, H. The loser list	**Fic**

BOY COUSINS

Hobbs, W. Take me to the river	**Fic**

BOY DETECTIVES

Cody, M. Powerless	**Fic**
Gibbs, S. Belly up	**Fic**
Gibbs, S. Big game	**Fic**
Gibbs, S. Panda-monium	**Fic**
Gibbs, S. Poached	**Fic**
Giles, L. R. The Last Mirror on the Left	**Fic**
Hoobler, D. The ghost in the Tokaido Inn	**Fic**
Patterson, J. Ali Cross	**Fic**
Patterson, J. Like father like son	**Fic**
Boy everywhere. Dassu, A. M.	**Fic**

BOY FOOTBALL PLAYERS

Green, T. Football champ	**Fic**
Green, T. Football genius	**Fic**
Green, T. Football hero	**Fic**
Wallace, R. War and watermelon	**Fic**

BOY GHOSTS

Tingle, T. How I became a ghost	**Fic**
Tingle, T. When a ghost talks listen	**Fic**

BOY HEROES

Grant, M. The trap	**Fic**
Hatke, B. Mighty Jack	**741.5**
Jacques, B. The angel's command	**Fic**
Jacques, B. Castaways of the Flying Dutchman	**Fic**
Maberry, J. The orphan army	**Fic**
Nix, G. Mister Monday	**Fic**
Renier, A. The unsinkable Walker Bean	**741.5**
Roman, D. Astronaut Academy	**741.5**

BOY IMMIGRANTS

Currier, K. S. Kai's journey to Gold Mountain	**Fic**
Hopkinson, D. A bandit's tale	**Fic**

BOY IMPERSONATORS

Flanagan, J. The burning bridge	**Fic**
Hashimi, N. One half from the east	**Fic**
The **boy** in the black suit. Reynolds, J.	**Fic**
The **boy** in the striped pajamas. Boyne, J.	**Fic**

BOY MISFITS

Angleberger, T. Darth Paper strikes back	**Fic**
Angleberger, T. The strange case of Origami Yoda	**Fic**
Arnold, E. K. The question of miracles	**Fic**
Kowitt, H. The loser list	**Fic**
Nielsen, S. Word nerd	**Fic**
Rex, A. Cold cereal	**Fic**
Rex, A. Unlucky charms	**Fic**
Silberg, A. Milo	**Fic**
Yee, L. Warp speed	**Fic**

BOY MUSICIANS

Cline-Ransome, L. Leaving Lymon	**Fic**
Boy on the Lion Throne. Kimmel, E. C.	**B**
The **boy** on the wooden box. Leyson, L.	**940.53**

BOY ORPHANS

Almond, D. The boy who swam with piranhas	**Fic**

Auxier, J. Sophie Quire and the last Storyguard	**Fic**
Barratt, M. Joe Rat	**Fic**
Beasley, C. Circus Mirandus	**Fic**
Blackwood, G. L. The Shakespeare stealer	**Fic**
Blackwood, S. Jinx's fire	**Fic**
Blackwood, S. Jinx's magic	**Fic**
Colfer, E. Illegal	**741.5**
Corona, J. Feathers	**741.5**
Dowswell, P. Auslander	**Fic**
Gaiman, N. The graveyard book	**Fic**
Gemeinhart, D. Some kind of courage	**Fic**
Higgins, F. E. The eyeball collector	**Fic**
Hopkinson, D. The great trouble	**Fic**
Hopkinson, D. Into the firestorm	**Fic**
Ibbotson, E. The Ogre of Oglefort	**Fic**
James, H. F. Paper son	**Fic**
Jones, D. W. Enchanted glass	**Fic**
Martin, R. The world before this one	**398.2**
Myklusch, M. Jack Blank and the Imagine Nation	**Fic**
Orlev, U. Run boy run	**Fic**
Park, L. S. A single shard	**Fic**
Philbrick, W. R. The mostly true adventures of Homer P. Figg	**Fic**
Pyron, B. The dogs of winter	**Fic**
Pyron, B. Lucky strike	**Fic**
Russell, P. C. The graveyard book graphic novel	**741.5**
Selznick, B. The invention of Hugo Cabret	**Fic**

BOY POETS

Creech, S. Hate that cat	**Fic**
Creech, S. Love that dog	**Fic**

BOY PRISONERS

Pileggi, L. Prisoner 88	**Fic**
Soontornvat, C. A wish in the dark	**Fic**

BOY PRODIGIES

Baker, M. If you find this	**Fic**
Boy proof. Castellucci, C.	**Fic**

BOY REFUGEES

Applegate, K. Home of the brave	**Fic**
Perkins, M. Bamboo people	**Fic**

BOY SAILORS

Rosen, M. J. Sailing the unknown	**Fic**

BOY SOCCER PLAYERS

Alexander, K. Booked	**Fic**

BOY SOLDIERS

Perkins, M. Bamboo people	**Fic**

BOY SPIES

Gibbs, S. Evil spy school	**Fic**
Gibbs, S. Spy camp	**Fic**
Gibbs, S. Spy school	**Fic**
Gibbs, S. Spy ski school	**Fic**
Stead, R. Liar & spy	**Fic**

BOY SUPERHEROES

Boniface, W. The hero revealed	**Fic**
Boniface, W. The return of Meteor Boy?	**Fic**

BOY THIEVES

Auxier, J. Peter Nimble and his fantastic eyes	**Fic**
Prineas, S. The magic thief	**Fic**

Selznick, B. The invention of Hugo Cabret	**Fic**

BOY WHEELCHAIR USERS

Lloyd, N. A snicker of magic	**Fic**
The **boy** who couldn't sleep and never had to. Pierson, D. C.	**Fic**
The **boy** who dared. Bartoletti, S. C.	**Fic**
The **boy** who fell off the Mayflower. Lynch, P. J.	**B**
The **boy** who harnessed the wind. Kamkwamba, W.	**B**
The **boy** who lost Fairyland. Valente, C. M.	**Fic**
The **boy** who saved baseball. Ritter, J. H.	**Fic**
The **boy** who swam with piranhas. Almond, D.	**Fic**
Boy writers. Fletcher, R. J.	**372.62**
The **boy's** body book. Dunham, K. S.	**612.6**

BOY/GIRL RELATIONS

Babbitt, N. Tuck everlasting	**Fic**
Baskin, N. R. The summer before boys	**Fic**
Gibbs, S. Spy school	**Fic**
Holm, J. L. Middle school is worse than meatloaf	**Fic**
Paterson, K. Bridge to Terabithia	**Fic**
Stead, R. Goodbye stranger	**Fic**
Telgemeier, R. Drama	**741.5**
Vail, R. Well that was awkward	**Fic**

BOYCE, JO ANN ALLEN

Boyce, J. A. A. This promise of change	**379.2**

Boyce, Jo Ann Allen

This promise of change	**379.2**

Boyer, Crispin

Why not?	**031.02**

BOYFRIENDS

Flake, S. Who am I without him?	**Fic**

Boyle, Jordan

Examining geothermal energy	**621.44**

BOYLE, ROBERT, 1627-1691

Sitarski, A. Cold light	**535**

Boyles, Nancy N., 1948-

That's a great answer!	**372.47**

Boyne, John, 1971-

The boy in the striped pajamas	**Fic**

BOYS

Almond, D. The fire-eaters	**Fic**
Avi. Crispin	**Fic**
Boniface, W. The great powers outage	**Fic**
Boniface, W. The hero revealed	**Fic**
Boniface, W. The return of Meteor Boy?	**Fic**
Bradbury, R. The Halloween tree	**Fic**
Cottrell Boyce, F. Sputnik's guide to life on earth	**Fic**
Creech, S. Love that dog	**Fic**
Elphinstone, A. Casper Tock and the Everdark wings	**Fic**
Golding, W. Lord of the flies	**Fic**
Gutman, D. Ray & me	**Fic**
Haddix, M. P. Among the Barons	**Fic**
Haddix, M. P. Among the brave	**Fic**
Lowry, L. Giver quartet	**741.5**
Mercado, N. E. Every man for himself	**Fic**
Pinkwater, D. M. The Neddiad	**Fic**
Pockell, L. 100 great poems for boys	**821**
Scieszka, J. Guys write for Guys Read	**810.8**

Shiga, J. Meanwhile	**741.5**
Silverstein, S. Falling up	**811**
Twain, M. The adventures of Tom Sawyer	**Fic**
Yolen, J. Mightier than the sword	**398.2**

BOYS -- EDUCATION (ELEMENTARY)

Fletcher, R. J. Boy writers	**372.62**

BOYS -- FRIENDSHIP

Bauer, M. D. On my honor	**Fic**
Bradbury, R. Something wicked this way comes	**Fic**
Holt, K. W. When Zachary Beaver came to town	**Fic**

BOYS -- GROWTH

Madaras, L. The "what's happening to my body?" book for boys	**613.9**

BOYS -- IDENTITY

Morris, G. The squire's tale	**Fic**
Orlev, U. Run boy run	**Fic**

BOYS -- INTERPERSONAL RELATIONS

Haddix, M. P. Among the impostors	**Fic**

BOYS AND ANIMALS

Pennypacker, S. Pax	**Fic**

BOYS AND BASEBALL

Gutman, D. Honus and me	**Fic**
Gutman, D. Jim & me	**Fic**
Gutman, D. Ray & me	**Fic**
Gutman, D. Roberto & me	**Fic**
Gutman, D. Satch & me	**Fic**

BOYS AND CATS

Creech, S. Hate that cat	**Fic**

BOYS AND DOGS

Cheng, J. See you in the cosmos	**Fic**
Creech, S. Love that dog	**Fic**
Gemeinhart, D. The honest truth	**Fic**
Hobbs, W. Jason's gold	**Fic**
Jacques, B. The angel's command	**Fic**
Jacques, B. Castaways of the Flying Dutchman	**Fic**
Juster, N. The annotated Phantom tollbooth	**Fic**
Martin, A. M. Everything for a dog	**Fic**
Naylor, P. R. Shiloh	**Fic**
Philbrick, W. R. Zane and the hurricane	**Fic**
Pyron, B. The dogs of winter	**Fic**

BOYS AND DRAGONS

Paolini, C. Eragon	**Fic**
Yolen, J. Dragon's blood	**Fic**

BOYS AND ELEPHANTS

Kadohata, C. A million shades of gray	**Fic**
Kelly, L. Chained	**Fic**

BOYS AND FOXES

Pennypacker, S. Pax	**Fic**

BOYS AND GIANTS

Chase, R. The Jack tales	**398.2**

BOYS AND HORSES

Lewis, C. S. The horse and his boy	**Fic**
Morpurgo, M. War horse	**Fic**

BOYS AND MONSTERS

Harrell, R. Monster on the hill	**741.5**

BOYS AND MOVING

Choldenko, G. Al Capone does my shirts	**Fic**

BOYS AND SPORTS

Green, T. Football genius	**Fic**

BOYS AND WILD ANIMALS

Kipling, R. The jungle book	**Fic**

BOYS AND WOLVES

Beckhorn, S. W. The wolf's boy	**Fic**
Boys girls and other hazardous materials. Wiseman, R.	**Fic**
The **boys** in the back row. Jung, M.	**Fic**
The **boys** in the boat. Brown, D.	**797.12**

BOYS WHO ARE BLIND

Auxier, J. Peter Nimble and his fantastic eyes	**Fic**
Auxier, J. Sophie Quire and the last Storyguard	**Fic**

BOYS WHO ARE DEAF

Dowell, F. O. Dovey Coe	**Fic**
Selznick, B. Wonderstruck	**Fic**

BOYS WHO ARE MUTE

Sloan, H. G. I'll be there	**Fic**
The **boys** who challenged Hitler. Hoose, P. M.	**940.53**

BOYS WITH ADHD

Gantos, J. I am not Joey Pigza	**Fic**
Gantos, J. Joey Pigza loses control	**Fic**
Gantos, J. Joey Pigza swallowed the key	**Fic**
Gantos, J. What would Joey do?	**Fic**

BOYS WITH AMNESIA

Korman, G. Restart	**Fic**

BOYS WITH ASTHMA

Nix, G. Mister Monday	**Fic**

BOYS WITH AUTISM

Baskin, N. R. Anything but typical	**Fic**
Davis, M. Superstar	**Fic**
Morpurgo, M. The day the world stopped turning	**Fic**

BOYS WITH CEREBRAL PALSY

Lewis, G. One white dolphin	**Fic**

BOYS WITH DISABILITIES

Wolkenstein, M. E. Turtle boy	**Fic**

BOYS WITH DISFIGUREMENTS

Corona, J. Feathers	**741.5**
Palacio, R. J. Wonder	**Fic**

BOYS WITH DYSLEXIA

Armstrong, A. W. Whittington	**Fic**

BOYS WITH POLIOMYELITIS

Palacio, R. J. White bird	**741.5**
The **boys'** guide to growing up. Couwenhoven, T.	**613**

BP DEEPWATER HORIZON EXPLOSION AND OIL SPILL, 2010

Bodden, V. The Deepwater Horizon oil spill	**363.11**
Braced. Gerber, A.	**Fic**

BRACES (DENTISTRY)

Telgemeier, R. Smile	**617.6**

Bracken, Alexandra

The darkest minds	**Fic**
Never fade	**Fic**

Bradbury, Jennifer. (Jennifer A.)

Shift	**Fic**

BRADBURY, RAY, 1920-2012

Bankston, J. Ray Bradbury	**B**
Bradbury, Ray, 1920-2012	

Oppenheim, J. Dear Miss Breed — 940.53
BREENDONK (CONCENTRATION CAMP)
Deem, J. M. The prisoners of Breendonk — 940.53
BRER RABBIT
Lester, J. Uncle Remus — 398.2
Breuilly, Elizabeth
Religions of the world — 200
Brewer's dictionary of phrase & fable. Brewer, E. C. — 423
Brewer, Ebenezer Cobham, 1810-1897
Brewer's dictionary of phrase & fable — 423
Brewer, Zac, 1973-
Eighth grade bites — Fic
Brewster, Hugh
The other Mozart — B
Brezenoff, Steven
Brooklyn burning — Fic
Brian's return. Paulsen, G. — Fic
Brian's winter. Paulsen, G. — Fic
Briar Rose. Yolen, J. — Fic
Briar's book. Pierce, T. — Fic
BRIDGE (GAME)
Sachar, L. The cardturner — Fic
Bridge. Jones, P. — Fic
The **bridge** home. Venkatraman, P. — Fic
Bridge to Terabithia. Paterson, K. — Fic
Bridge to the wild. O'Connell, C. — 636.088
BRIDGES
Flanagan, J. The burning bridge — Fic
BRIDGES -- DESIGN AND CONSTRUCTION
Graham, I. Fabulous bridges — 624.2
Prentzas, G. S. The Brooklyn Bridge — 624.2
BRIDGMAN, LAURA DEWEY, 1829-1889
Alexander, S. H. She touched the world — B
A **brief** history of Montmaray. Cooper, M. — Fic
Bright ideas. Rossi, A. — 609.73
Bright lights dark nights. Emond, S. — Fic
Bright, Michael
Darwin's tree of life — 576.8
Bright, Sandra
Examining solar energy — 621.47
Brignull, Irena
The hawkweed prophecy — Fic
Brill, Marlene Targ
Diabetes — 616.4
The **brilliant** fall of Gianna Z. Messner, K. — Fic
Brimner, Larry Dane
Accused! — 345.761
Birmingham Sunday — 323.1196
Black & white — 323.1196
Blacklisted! — 323
Finding a way home — 346.7301
The rain wizard — 979.4
Strike! — 331.8
Twelve days in May — 323.11
We are one — B
BRIN, SERGEY, 1973-
Redding, A. C. Google it — 005.1092

Sapet, K. Google founders — B
Bringing back our deserts. MacCarald, C. — 333.75
Bringing back our freshwater lakes. Amstutz, L. J. — 333.91
Bringing back our oceans. Hand, C. — 333.91
Bringing back our tropical forests. Hand, C. — 333.75
Bristow, Barbara A
Sears list of subject headings — 025.4
Bristow, David (David L.)
The sky sailors — 910.4
BRITAIN, BATTLE OF, GREAT BRITAIN, 1940
Moore, K. The Battle of Britain — 940.54211
BRITISH COLUMBIA
Horvath, P. Everything on a waffle — Fic
Horvath, P. One year in Coal Harbor — Fic
McAllister, I. The salmon bears — 599.786
McAllister, I. The sea wolves — 599.773
Oppel, K. Bloom — Fic
Palana, B. J. British Columbia — 971.1
British Columbia. Palana, B. J. — 971.1
BRITISH IN AFRICA
MacColl, M. Promise the night — Fic
BRITISH IN INDIA
Brahmachari, S. Jasmine skies — Fic
Whelan, G. All my noble dreams and then what happens — Fic
Whelan, G. Small acts of amazing courage — Fic
BRITISH IN THE UNITED STATES
Smith, J. E. Field notes on love — Fic
BRITISH ISLES
Carey, J. L. Dragon's keep — Fic
BRITISH RAJ (1858-1947)
Ruiz Zafon, C. The Midnight Palace — Fic
Sheth, K. Keeping corner — Fic
Venkatraman, P. Climbing the stairs — Fic
Whelan, G. All my noble dreams and then what happens — Fic
Whelan, G. Small acts of amazing courage — Fic
Britt, Fanny
Jane the fox and me — 741.5
Broach, Elise
Shakespeare's secret — Fic
The wolf keepers — Fic
BROADWAY, NEW YORK CITY
Federle, T. Five six seven Nate! — Fic
Broberg, Catherine
Kenya in pictures — 967.62
Brockman, Christian Frank, 1902-
Trees of North America — 582.16
Brody, Jessica
The geography of lost things — Fic
Sky without stars — Fic
The **broken** blade. Durbin, W. — Fic
Broken pride. Hunter, E. — Fic
Broken strings. Walters, E. — Fic
BRONTE FAMILY
Valente, C. M. The Glass Town game — Fic
The **Bronte** sisters. Reef, C. — 920
BRONTE, ANNE, 1820-1849
Reef, C. The Bronte sisters — 920

Valente, C. M. The Glass Town game — Fic

BRONTE, CHARLOTTE, 1816-1855
Reef, C. The Bronte sisters — 920
Valente, C. M. The Glass Town game — Fic

BRONTE, CHARLOTTE, 1816-1855. JANE EYRE
Britt, F. Jane the fox and me — 741.5
Nunn, M. When the ground is hard — Fic

BRONTE, EMILY, 1818-1848
Reef, C. The Bronte sisters — 920
Valente, C. M. The Glass Town game — Fic

BRONTE, PATRICK BRANWELL, 1817-1848
Valente, C. M. The Glass Town game — Fic
Bronx masquerade. Grimes, N. — Fic

BRONX, NEW YORK CITY
Grimes, N. Bronx masquerade — Fic
Lupica, M. Strike zone — Fic
McGuigan, M. A. Morning in a different place — Fic
Bronze and Sunflower. Cao, W. — Fic
The **bronze** key. Black, H. — Fic

BROOKLYN BRIDGE, NEW YORK CITY -- DESIGN AND CONSTRUCTION
Prentzas, G. S. The Brooklyn Bridge — 624.2

BROOKLYN BRIDGE, NEW YORK CITY -- HISTORY
Prentzas, G. S. The Brooklyn Bridge — 624.2
Brooklyn Bridge. Hesse, K. — Fic
The **Brooklyn** Bridge. Prentzas, G. S. — 624.2
Brooklyn burning. Brezenoff, S. — Fic

BROOKLYN, NEW YORK CITY
Avi. Catch you later traitor — Fic
Brezenoff, S. Brooklyn burning — Fic
Gulledge, L. L. Page by Paige — 741.5
Hesse, K. Brooklyn Bridge — Fic
Jackson, T. D. Let me hear a rhyme — Fic
Maldonado, T. Secret Saturdays — Fic
Maldonado, T. Tight — Fic
Margolis, L. Girl's best friend — Fic
Park, L. S. Keeping score — Fic
Reynolds, J. The boy in the black suit — Fic
Reynolds, J. Miles Morales — Fic
Riordan, R. The red pyramid — Fic
Shusterman, N. Antsy does time — Fic
Stead, R. Liar & spy — Fic
Williams-Garcia, R. P.S. be eleven — Fic
Woodson, J. From the notebooks of Melanin Sun — Fic
Yoon, N. The sun is also a star — Fic
Zoboi, I. A. Pride — Fic

Brooks, Martha, 1944-
Mistik Lake — Fic
Queen of hearts — Fic

Brooks, Susie
Get into art — 704.9

Brooks-Young, Susan
Teaching with the tools kids really use — 372.3

Broom, Jenny
Animalium — 590

Brosgol, Vera
Anya's ghost — 741.5

Be prepared — 741.5

Brosius, Peter
Fierce & true — 812
Brother's keeper. Lee, J. — Fic

BROTHERS
Abdul-Jabbar, K. Stealing the game — Fic
Ansari, R. K. S. The missing piece of Charlie O'Reilly — Fic
Black, H. The white cat — Fic
Deuker, C. Golden arm — Fic
Esplin, J. L. 96 miles — Fic
Flores-Scott, P. American road trip — Fic
Funke, C. The Thief Lord — Fic
Giblin, J. C. Good brother bad brother — 920
Green, T. Football hero — Fic
Haddix, M. P. Among the Barons — Fic
Han, J. We'll always have summer — Fic
Herlong, M. The great wide sea — Fic
Hinton, S. E. The outsiders — Fic
Holt, K. A. Knockout — Fic
Horowitz, A. The Greek who stole Christmas — Fic
Johnston, T. Beast rider — Fic
Kinney, J. The long haul — Fic
Kinney, J. Rodrick rules — Fic
Kris. A bag of marbles — 741.5
Levy, D. A. The misadventures of the family Fletcher — Fic
Lu, M. Rebel — Fic
Magoon, K. The rock and the river — Fic
Morpurgo, M. Private Peaceful — Fic
Philbrick, W. R. The mostly true adventures of Homer P. Figg — Fic
Reinhardt, D. The things a brother knows — Fic
Rubens, M. Sons of the 613 — Fic
Sattar, A. Ramayana — 294.5
Sendak, M. My brother's book — Fic
Springstubb, T. Every single second — Fic
Stiefvater, M. Call down the hawk — Fic
Wallace, R. Perpetual check — Fic
Wallace, R. War and watermelon — Fic
Walter, J. My name is not Friday — Fic
Watkins, S. Great Falls — Fic
Williams, M. Now is the time for running — Fic
Williams, S. Bull rider — Fic
Zuckerman, L. A taste for rabbit — Fic

BROTHERS -- DEATH
Charles, T. Becoming Beatriz — Fic
Dooley, S. Free verse — Fic
Flake, S. Bang! — Fic
Hale, S. Enna burning — Fic
Joseph, L. The color of my words — Fic
Rupp, R. After Eli — Fic
Watson, C. Benched — Fic

BROTHERS AND SISTERS
Ansari, R. K. S. The in-between — Fic
Bayard, L. Lucky strikes — Fic
Beaty, A. Cicada summer — Fic
Beaufrand, M. J. Useless Bay — Fic
Benway, R. Far from the tree — Fic

Berlin, E. The puzzling world of Winston Breen	Fic
Bolden, T. Crossing Ebenezer Creek	Fic
Bradley, K. B. The war that saved my life	Fic
Card, O. S. Ender's game	Fic
Carroll, E. In darkling wood	Fic
Carter, C. Forever or a long long time	Fic
Collins, S. Gregor the Overlander	Fic
Dessen, S. Saint Anything	Fic
Dorris, M. Morning Girl	Fic
Dowell, F. O. Dovey Coe	Fic
Dowell, F. O. Shooting the moon	Fic
Dunkle, C. B. The sky inside	Fic
Dunmore, H. The deep	Fic
Dunmore, H. Ingo	Fic
Dunmore, H. The tide knot	Fic
Fletcher, S. Alphabet of dreams	Fic
Freedman, R. We will not be silent	943.086
Freymann-Weyr, G. My heartbeat	Fic
Funaro, G. The alchemist's shadow	Fic
Gaiman, N. Hansel & Gretel	398.20943
Gidwitz, A. The Grimm conclusion	Fic
Giff, P. R. Nory Ryan's song	Fic
Haddix, M. P. Caught	Fic
Haddix, M. P. Children of refuge	Fic
Haddix, M. P. The deceivers	Fic
Haddix, M. P. Risked	Fic
Haddix, M. P. Sabotaged	Fic
Haddix, M. P. Sent	Fic
Hahn, M. D. All the lovely bad ones	Fic
Hahn, M. D. Took	Fic
Hale, N. One trick pony	741.5
Hatke, B. Mighty Jack	741.5
Heider, M. W. The losers at the center of the galaxy	Fic
Hicks, F. E. Friends with boys	741.5
Hirsch, J. Breakaway	Fic
Holm, J. L. Our only May Amelia	Fic
Holm, J. L. Swing it Sunny	741.5
Hopkinson, N. The Chaos	Fic
Horvath, P. My one hundred adventures	Fic
Hunter, E. The sight	Fic
Iserles, I. The taken	Fic
Jacobson, J. Paper things	Fic
Joseph, L. The color of my words	Fic
Joseph, L. Flowers in the sky	Fic
Kadohata, C. The thing about luck	Fic
Kelly, E. E. We dream of space	Fic
Kibuishi, K. Amulet	741.5
Knowles, J. See you at Harry's	Fic
Korman, G. Slacker	Fic
Kuehn, S. Complicit	Fic
L'Engle, M. A wind in the door	Fic
L'Engle, M. A wrinkle in time	Fic
Lai, T. Butterfly yellow	Fic
Lee, M. The gentleman's guide to vice and virtue	Fic
Lord, C. Rules	Fic
Lu, M. The Kingdom of Back	Fic
Magoon, K. Fire in the streets	Fic

Marcus, K. Exposed	Fic
McKay, H. Saffy's angel	Fic
McKernan, V. The devil's paintbox	Fic
Milford, K. Bluecrowne	Fic
Molope, K. L. This book betrays my brother	Fic
Naidoo, B. The other side of truth	Fic
Nelson, T. Ruby electric	Fic
Park, L. S. Storm warning	Fic
Paterson, K. The same stuff as stars	Fic
Peck, R. The teacher's funeral	Fic
Pierpoint, E. The last ride of Caleb O'Toole	Fic
Riordan, R. Vespers rising	Fic
Sage, A. Twilight hauntings	Fic
Sedgwick, M. She is not invisible	Fic
Shusterman, N. Dry	Fic
Simon, F. The monstrous child	Fic
Sleator, W. Oddballs	Fic
Springer, N. The case of the gypsy goodbye	Fic
Starmer, A. The storyteller	Fic
Tarshis, L. The battle of Gettysburg 1863	Fic
Valente, C. M. The Glass Town game	Fic
Vanhee, J. Engines of the broken world	Fic
Voigt, C. Dicey's song	Fic
Walters, E. The money pit mystery	Fic
Warga, J. The shape of thunder	Fic
Watson, J. Beyond the grave	Fic
Watson, J. Nowhere to run	Fic
Wein, E. Black dove white raven	Fic
Woodson, J. Locomotion	811
Woodson, J. Peace Locomotion	Fic
Wrede, P. C. The thirteenth child	Fic
Young, M. Blood red road	Fic

BROTHERS AND SISTERS OF CHILDREN WITH AUTISM

Choldenko, G. Al Capone does my shirts	Fic
Galante, C. The world from up here	Fic
Hautman, P. Slider	Fic

BROTHERS AND SISTERS OF CHILDREN WITH DISABILITIES

Acampora, P. Rachel Spinelli punched me in the face	Fic
Skotko, B. Fasten your seatbelt	616.85
Williams, M. Now is the time for running	Fic

BROTHERS AND SISTERS OF PEOPLE WITH MENTAL ILLNESSES

Alonzo, S. Riding invisible	Fic

BROTHERS AND SISTERS OF SICK CHILDREN

Kadohata, C. Kira-kira	Fic
The **brothers'** war. Lewis, J. P.	811

Brouwer, Sigmund, 1959-

Devil's pass	Fic
Moon mission	629.45

BROWN BEAR

Dumon Tak, B. Soldier bear	Fic
Gish, M. Brown bears	599.784
Brown bears. Gish, M.	599.784
Brown girl dreaming. Woodson, J.	B
Brown v. Board of Education. Rubin, S. G.	344.73

Brown, Christopher C., 1953-
Librarian's guide to online searching — 025.04

Brown, Daniel, 1951-
The boys in the boat — 797.12

Brown, Dee, 1908-2002
Bury my heart at Wounded Knee — 978
Dee Brown's folktales of the Native American retold for our times — 398.2

Brown, Don, 1949-
Drowned City — 363.34
The great American Dust Bowl — 978
In the shadow of the fallen towers — 973.931
Machines that think! — 006.3
Older than dirt — 551.7
A shot in the arm! — 615.3

Brown, Gavin, 1983-
Josh Baxter levels up — Fic

BROWN, HENRY BOX, B. 1816
Weatherford, C. B. Box — B

Brown, Jeffrey, 1975-
Return of the Padawan — 741.5
Star Wars — 741.5

Brown, Jeremy K.
Amelia Earhart — B

BROWN, JOHN, 1800-1859
Marrin, A. A volcano beneath the snow — 973.7

Brown, Jordan
Micro mania — 579.3
Science stunts — 530.078

Brown, Martin, 1959-
Lesser spotted animals — 599

BROWN, OLIVER, 1918-1961
Goldstone, L. Separate no more — 323.1196
Rubin, S. G. Brown v. Board of Education — 344.73

Brown, Robin Terry
Breaking the news — 070.9

Brown, Roslind Varghese
Tunisia — 961.1

Brown, Skila
Caminar — Fic
To stay alive — Fic

Brown, Stephen F.
Catholicism & Orthodox Christianity — 280
Protestantism — 280

Brownlie Bojang, Ali, 1949-
South Africa in our world — 968.06
Sudan in our world — 962.404

BRUCHAC, JOSEPH, 1942-
Bruchac, J. Bowman's store — B

Bruchac, Joseph, 1942-
Bowman's store — B
Code Talker — Fic
Dragon castle — Fic
Killer of enemies — Fic
Walking two worlds — Fic

Brulles, Dina
The cluster grouping handbook — 371.2

A teacher's guide to flexible grouping and collaborative learning — 371.3

BRUSSELS, BELGIUM
Marsh, K. Nowhere boy — Fic

Bruton, Catherine
I predict a riot — Fic

BRYAN, ASHLEY
Bryan, A. Infinite hope — B

Bryan, Ashley
Ashley Bryan's African tales uh-huh — 398.2
Ashley Bryan's puppets — 811
Infinite hope — B

Bryan, Trevor Andrew, 1975-
Art of comprehension — 372.47

Bryant, Howard, 1968-
Legends — 796.357

Bryant, Jennifer
Kaleidoscope eyes — Fic
Ringside 1925 — Fic

Bryant, Megan E.
Oh my gods! — 398.2
She's all that! — 398

Bryce, Celia
Anthem for Jackson Dawes — Fic

Brynie, Faith Hickman, 1946-
101 questions about muscles to stretch your mind and flex your brain — 612.7

Bryson, Bill
A really short history of nearly everything — 500

Bubonic panic. Jarrow, G. — 614.5
Bubonic plague. Person, S. — 614.5

BUCCANEERS
Hanel, R. Pirates — 910.4
Sandler, M. W. The Whydah — 910.4

BUCCANEERS -- HISTORY
Clifford, B. Real pirates — 910.4

Buchanan, Shelly C.
Animal senses — 573.8
Plant reproduction — 575.6

Buchholz, Rachel
How to survive anything — 646.7

Buckey, A. W.
Women and sports — 796.082

Buckley, James
Animals — 590.3
Lou Gehrig — B
Pele — B

Buckley, Susan
Journeys for freedom — 973
Kids make history — 920

Buckley-Archer, Linda
The many lives of John Stone — Fic

Bud not Buddy. Curtis, C. P. — Fic
Buddha. Demi. — B

BUDDHISM
Eckel, M. D. Buddhism — 294.3
Ganeri, A. Buddhism — 294.3

Burt, Jake
  Greetings from witness protection! — Fic

Burton, Bonnie, 1972-
  Girls against girls — 305.235

Burton, Erica
  Race relations — 305.800973

Bury my heart at Wounded Knee. Brown, D. — 978

BUS TRAVEL
  Angleberger, T. Emperor Pickletine rides the bus — Fic
  Baskin, N. R. All we know of love — Fic
  Black, H. Doll bones — Fic
  Law, I. Savvy — Fic

BUSBY, CYLIN
  Busby, C. The year we disappeared — B

Busby, Cylin
  The year we disappeared — B

Bush, Gail
  Indivisible — 811.008

Bushman lives! Pinkwater, D. M. — Fic

Bushman, Claudia L.
  Mormons in America — 289.3

Bushnell, Candace
  Rules for being a girl — Fic

BUSINESS COMPETITION
  Lord, E. Tweet cute — Fic

Business without borders. Andrews, D. — 658

BUSINESSPEOPLE
  Redding, A. C. Google it — 005.1092

BUSING (SCHOOL INTEGRATION)
  Aretha, D. With all deliberate speed — 379.2

Butkus, Mike
  How to draw zombies — 743

Butler, George
  Drawn across borders — 304.8

Butler, Rebecca P.
  Copyright for teachers & librarians in the 21st century — 346.7304

Butter. Lange, E. J. — Fic

BUTTERFLIES
  Gregory, J. From butterfly wings to... display technology — 621.3815
  Harkins, S. S. Design your own butterfly garden — 638
  Pasternak, C. How to raise monarch butterflies — 595.78
  Whalley, P. E. S. Butterfly & moth — 595.78

BUTTERFLIES -- IDENTIFICATION
  Pyle, R. M. The Audubon Society field guide to North American butterflies — 595.78

Butterfly & moth. Whalley, P. E. S. — 595.78

BUTTERFLY GARDENING
  Harkins, S. S. Design your own butterfly garden — 638

Butterfly yellow. Lai, T. — Fic

The **button** war. Avi. — Fic

Buyea, Rob
  Because of Mr. Terupt — Fic

Buzz kill. Fantaskey, B. — Fic

Byars, Betsy Cromer, 1928-2020
  Cracker Jackson — Fic

The dark stairs — Fic
The keeper of the doves — Fic

Byers, Ann
  Saving children from the Holocaust — 940.53
  Trapped — 940.53

Bylines. Macy, S. — B

Byng, Georgia
  Molly Moon's incredible book of hypnotism — Fic

BYRD, RICHARD EVELYN, 1888-1957
  Finkelstein, N. H. Three across — 629.130973

Bystander. Preller, J. — Fic

BYZANTINE CIVILIZATION
  VanVoorst, J. The Byzantine Empire — 949.5

BYZANTINE EMPIRE -- HISTORY
  VanVoorst, J. The Byzantine Empire — 949.5

The **Byzantine** Empire. VanVoorst, J. — 949.5

C

C.S. Lewis. Hamilton, J. — B

CABEZA DE VACA, ALVAR NUNEZ, 1490?-1557
  Lourie, P. On the Texas trail of Cabeza de Vaca — 976.4

CABIN BOYS
  Northrop, M. Polaris — Fic
  Oppel, K. Airborn — Fic

Cabin fever. Kinney, J. — Fic

The **cabinet** of curiosities. Bachmann, S. — Fic

The **Cabinet** of Wonders. Rutkoski, M. — Fic

CABINS
  Sedgwick, M. Revolver — Fic

Cabot, Meg
  All-American girl — Fic
  Black Canary — 741.5
  From the notebooks of a middle school princess — Fic
  The princess diaries — Fic

CACAO
  Frydenborg, K. Chocolate — 338.7

Caddy ever after. McKay, H. — Fic

CADILLAC AUTOMOBILE
  Taylor, M. D. The gold Cadillac — Fic

Caes, Charles J.
  Discovering the speed of light — 535

CAESAR, JULIUS, 100-44 B.C.E
  National Geographic Society. Julius Caesar — B

CAFFEINE
  Scott, C. Caffeine — 362.29

Caffeine. Scott, C. — 362.29

CAFFEINE ADDICTION
  Scott, C. Caffeine — 362.29

The **cage**. Sender, R. M. — 940.53

Cain, Susan
  Quiet power — 155.4

Caine, Rachel, 1962-2020
  Ink and bone — Fic

Calabro, Marian
  The perilous journey of the Donner Party — 979.4

CALAMITY JANE, 1852-1903

Vande Velde, V. The book of Mordred   **Fic**

CAMERAS

Jennings, R. W. Ghost town   **Fic**

Proujansky, A. Go photo!   **770**

Cameron, Sharon, 1970-

The Forgetting   **Fic**

The light in hidden places   **Fic**

Cameron, Sophie

Last bus to Everland   **Fic**

CAMEROON

Sheehan, S. Cameroon   **967.11**

Cameroon. Sheehan, S.   **967.11**

Caminar. Brown, S.   **Fic**

Camo girl. Magoon, K.   **Fic**

CAMP SITES, FACILITIES, ETC

Kinney, J. The deep end   **Fic**

Mass, W. Every soul a star   **Fic**

CAMPAIGN DEBATES -- HISTORY

Burgan, M. TV shapes presidential politics in the Kennedy-Nixon debates   **324.973**

Campbell, Andrew, 1974-

Cosmetic surgery   **617.9**

Organ transplants   **617.954**

Campbell, Jeff

Daisy to the rescue   **636**

Campbell, Margaret Christine

Discovering atoms   **539.7**

Camper, Cathy

Lowriders in space   **741.5**

Lowriders to the center of the Earth   **741.5**

CAMPING

Davis, J. P. Hiking and camping   **796.51**

Smith, J. Tall tales   **741.5**

CAMPS

Gibbs, S. Spy camp   **Fic**

Riordan, R. The lightning thief   **Fic**

Riordan, R. The mark of Athena   **Fic**

Tamaki, M. Unicorn power!   **Fic**

Venditti, R. The lightning thief   **741.5**

Can I see your I.D.? Barton, C.   **001.9**

Can you say catastrophe? Friedman, L. B.   **Fic**

Can't stop won't stop. Chang, J.   **306.4**

CANADA

Brouwer, S. Devil's pass   **Fic**

Curtis, C. P. Elijah of Buxton   **Fic**

Curtis, C. P. The madman of Piney Woods   **Fic**

Durbin, W. The broken blade   **Fic**

Ferry, S. Ontario   **971.3**

Ferry, S. Quebec   **971.4**

Ferry, S. Yukon Territory   **971.91**

Hicks, F. E. Friends with boys   **741.5**

Hobbs, W. Never say die   **Fic**

Hopkinson, N. The Chaos   **Fic**

Horvath, P. Everything on a waffle   **Fic**

Horvath, P. One year in Coal Harbor   **Fic**

Houston, J. James Houston's treasury of Inuit legends   **398.2089**

Johnston, E. K. Prairie fire   **Fic**

Johnston, E. K. The story of Owen   **Fic**

Juby, S. The fashion committee   **Fic**

Korman, G. Notorious   **Fic**

Laws, G. D. Alberta   **971.23**

Laws, G. D. Manitoba   **971.27**

Laws, G. D. The Maritime provinces   **971.5**

Leatherdale, M. B. Urban tribes   **305.897**

Leavitt, M. My book of life by Angel   **Fic**

Mara, W. Canada   **971**

Marshall, K. A. I am still alive   **Fic**

Mayell, M. Newfoundland   **971.8**

McCulloch, A. Jinxed   **Fic**

Miller, S. E. The miracle & tragedy of the Dionne quintuplets   **306.875**

Oppel, K. The Boundless   **Fic**

Oppel, K. Half brother   **Fic**

Ostertag, M. The girl from the sea   **Fic**

Paulsen, G. Brian's winter   **Fic**

Paulsen, G. Hatchet   **Fic**

Sonneborn, L. Canada   **971**

Williams, B. Canada   **971**

CANADA -- HISTORY

Weaver, J. Mirror with a memory   **971.0022**

CANADA -- RACE RELATIONS

Gray Smith, M. Speaking our truth   **971.004**

CANADA -- SOCIAL LIFE AND CUSTOMS

Weaver, J. Mirror with a memory   **971.0022**

CANADA -- SOCIAL LIFE AND CUSTOMS -- 21ST CENTURY

Ellis, D. Off to war   **303.6**

Canada. Mara, W.   **971**

Canada. Sonneborn, L.   **971**

Canada. Williams, B.   **971**

CANADA, NORTHERN -- DESCRIPTION AND TRAVEL

Wallace, M. Inuksuk journey   **917**

CANADIAN PROVINCES

Ferry, S. Ontario   **971.3**

Ferry, S. Quebec   **971.4**

Laws, G. D. Alberta   **971.23**

Laws, G. D. Manitoba   **971.27**

Laws, G. D. The Maritime provinces   **971.5**

Mayell, M. Newfoundland   **971.8**

Palana, B. J. British Columbia   **971.1**

CANALS -- DESIGN AND CONSTRUCTION

Vander Hook, S. Building the Panama Canal   **972.87**

CANALS -- HISTORY

Vander Hook, S. Building the Panama Canal   **972.87**

Canavan, Thomas, 1956-

Super experiments with light and sound   **535.078**

CANCER

Bryce, C. Anthem for Jackson Dawes   **Fic**

Esposito, L. Cancer information for teens   **616.99**

Markle, S. Leukemia   **616.99**

Sonnenblick, J. After ever after   **Fic**

Cancer information for teens. Esposito, L.   **616.99**

CANCER SURVIVORS

Murphy, J. An American plague	**614.5**
Stork, F. X. The last summer of the Death Warriors	**Fic**
Carey, Charles W.	
The Mexican War	**973.6**
Carey, Edward, 1970-	
Heap House	**Fic**
Carey, Janet Lee	
Dragon's keep	**Fic**
CARIBBEAN AREA	
Baptiste, T. The jumbie god's revenge	**Fic**
Baptiste, T. The jumbies	**Fic**
Baptiste, T. Rise of the jumbies	**Fic**
Stevenson, R. L. Treasure Island	**Fic**
Taylor, T. The cay	**Fic**
Taylor, T. Timothy of the cay	**Fic**
Tracy, K. We visit Cuba	**972.91**
Vaughn, C. Steel	**Fic**
Wright, D. K. Cuba	**972.91**
Yomtov, N. Haiti	**972.94**
CARIBBEAN BASIN INITIATIVE COUNTRIES	
Pang, G. Grenada	**972.9845**
CARIBBEAN SEA	
Herlong, M. The great wide sea	**Fic**
Carle, Megan	
Teens cook	**641.5**
Teens cook dessert	**641.8**
Carlisle, Rodney P.	
Exploring space	**629.4**
World War I	**940.3**
CARLOS, JOHN, 1945-	
Smith-Llera, D. Black power salute	**796.48**
Carlson, Laurie M., 1952-	
Harry Houdini for kids	**793.8**
Knit hook and spin	**745.5**
Carlson, Lori M.	
Cool salsa	**811**
Moccasin thunder	**Fic**
Red hot salsa	**811.008**
Carlton, Susan Kaplan	
In the neighborhood of true	**Fic**
Carman, Patrick	
The Crossbones	**Fic**
The Dark Hills divide	**Fic**
Skeleton Creek	**Fic**
Carmichael, L. E. (Lindsey E.)	
Amazing feats of civil engineering	**624**
CARNARVON, GEORGE EDWARD STANHOPE MOLY-	
NEUX HERBERT, EARL OF, 1866-1923	
Lace, W. W. King Tut's curse	**932**
CARNIVALS	
Almond, D. The boy who swam with piranhas	**Fic**
Bradbury, R. Something wicked this way comes	**Fic**
Fusco, K. N. Beholding Bee	**Fic**
Martin, A. M. A corner of the universe	**Fic**
CARNIVOROUS PLANTS	
Aaseng, N. Weird meat-eating plants	**583**
Oppel, K. Bloom	**Fic**

Carriger, Gail	
Curtsies & conspiracies	**Fic**
Etiquette & espionage	**Fic**
Waistcoats & weaponry	**Fic**
Carroll, Emily	
Through the woods	**741.5**
Carroll, Emma, 1970-	
In darkling wood	**Fic**
Carroll, Michael W., 1955-	
Envisioning exoplanets	**523.2**
Carroll, Robert P.	
The Bible	**220.5**
Carry on. Rowell, R.	**Fic**
Carson, Mary Kay	
Alexander Graham Bell	**B**
Alexander Graham Bell for kids	**621.385092**
Animal watching	**590.72**
The bat scientists	**599.4**
Beyond the solar system	**520.9**
Emi and the rhino scientist	**599.66**
Inside Biosphere 2	**304.2**
Inside hurricanes	**551.55**
Inside tornadoes	**551.55**
Mission to Pluto	**629.43**
The park scientists	**333.78**
CARSON, RACHEL, 1907-1964	
Rae, R. Rachel Carson and ecology for kids	**B**
Carson, Rachel, 1907-1964	
The edge of the sea	**578.769**
Carson, Rae	
The bitter kingdom	**Fic**
The crown of embers	**Fic**
The girl of fire and thorns	**Fic**
Walk on Earth a stranger	**Fic**
Carstensen, Angela	
The readers' advisory guide to teen literature	**028.5**
Cart, Michael	
911	**810.8**
Young adult literature	**813.009**
Cartaya, Pablo	
The epic fail of Arturo Zamora	**Fic**
Carter, Ally	
All fall down	**Fic**
Cross my heart and hope to spy	**Fic**
Dear Ally how do you write a book?	**808.02**
Don't judge a girl by her cover	**Fic**
Heist society	**Fic**
I'd tell you I love you but then I'd have to kill you	**Fic**
Only the good spy young	**Fic**
Out of sight out of time	**Fic**
Uncommon criminals	**Fic**
Carter, Caela	
Forever or a long long time	**Fic**
How to be a girl in the world	**Fic**
CARTOGRAPHERS	
Lucier, M. Song of the abyss	**Fic**
CARTOGRAPHY	

CATHOLIC CHURCH -- RELATIONS -- ORTHODOX EASTERN CHURCH -- HISTORY

Brown, S. F. Catholicism & Orthodox Christianity   280

CATHOLIC GIRLS

Cameron, S. The light in hidden places   Fic

CATHOLIC SCHOOLS

Beil, M. D. The ring of Rocamadour   Fic

Edwardson, D. D. My name is not easy   Fic

Henry, K. Heretics anonymous   Fic

Melleby, N. In the role of Brie Hutchens...   Fic

Catholicism & Orthodox Christianity. Brown, S. F.   280

CATHOLICS

Schlitz, L. A. The hired girl   Fic

CATLIN, GEORGE, 1796-1872

Reich, S. Painting the wild frontier   B

Catmull, Katherine

The radiant road   Fic

CATS

Appelt, K. The underneath   Fic

Armstrong, A. W. Whittington   Fic

Arntson, S. The wikkeling   Fic

Clutton-Brock, J. Cat   636.8

Creech, S. Hate that cat   Fic

Drimmer, S. W. Cat breed guide   636.8

Epstein, A. J. Circle of heroes   Fic

Gaiman, N. M is for magic   Fic

Hirsch, A. Cats   599.75

Hunter, E. Code of the clans   Fic

Hunter, E. A dangerous path   Fic

Hunter, E. The darkest hour   Fic

Hunter, E. Dawn   Fic

Hunter, E. Fire and ice   Fic

Hunter, E. Into the wild   Fic

Hunter, E. Rising storm   Fic

Hunter, E. The sight   Fic

Levy, D. A. The family Fletcher takes Rock Island   Fic

Mashima, H. Fairy tail   741.5

Mass, W. A mango-shaped space   Fic

Murdock, C. G. Da Vinci's cat   Fic

Myron, V. Dewey the library cat   636.80092

Pratchett, T. The amazing Maurice and his educated rodents   Fic

Rex, A. The true meaning of Smekday   Fic

Weeks, S. Pie   Fic

CATS -- BEHAVIOR

Hunter, E. Forest of secrets   Fic

CATS -- HEALTH

Laidlaw, R. Cat champions   636.8

Cats. Hirsch, A.   599.75

CATWOMAN (FICTITIOUS CHARACTER)

Maas, S. J. Catwoman   Fic

Catwoman. Maas, S. J.   Fic

Caughey, Melissa

A kid's guide to keeping chickens   636.5

Caught. Haddix, M. P.   Fic

Cause & effect. Nardo, D.   935

Cavanaugh, Nancy J.

This journal belongs to Ratchet   Fic

CAVES

Athans, S. K. Secrets of the sky caves   796.522

Felix, R. Exploring caves   796.52

Soontornvat, C. All thirteen   796.52

Taylor, P. L. The secret of Priest's Grotto   940.53

CAVING

Felix, R. Exploring caves   796.52

Soontornvat, C. All thirteen   796.52

The **cay**. Taylor, T.   Fic

Cece Rios and the Desert of Souls. Rivera, K.   Fic

A **ceiling** made of eggshells. Levine, G. C.   Fic

Celebrate Ramadan. Jeffrey, L. S.   297.3

CELEBRITIES

Amara, P. Awesome Asian Americans   920

Bieber, J. Justin Bieber   782.42164

Croll, J. Bad boys of fashion   391.1

Croll, J. Fashion that changed the world   391.009

Horowitz, A. The Greek who stole Christmas   Fic

Mills, E. Famous in a small town   Fic

Peters, S. T. Groundbreaking guys   920.71

Swartz, C. Who wins?   920

CELEBRITIES -- DEATH

Bragg, G. How they croaked   920

CELEBRITIES -- PERSONAL CONDUCT

Bragg, G. How they choked   920

The **Celestial** Globe. Rutkoski, M.   Fic

CELL CULTURE

Skloot, R. The immortal life of Henrietta Lacks   616

CELL PHONES

San Souci, R. D. Dare to be scared   Fic

Spilsbury, R. The telephone   621.385

CELL PHONES -- SOCIAL ASPECTS

Steffens, B. Thinking critically   384.5

CELLISTS

Forman, G. Where she went   Fic

CELLO

Ganeri, A. Stringed instruments   787

CELLS

Ballard, C. Cells and cell function   571.6

Goddard, J. Inside the human body   612

Green, J. Inside animals   571.1

Cells and cell function. Ballard, C.   571.6

Celtic fairy tales. Philip, N.   398.2

Celtic myth. Harpur, J.   299

CELTS

Green, J. Ancient Celts   936.4

Harpur, J. Celtic myth   299

Hinds, K. Ancient Celts   936.4

Philip, N. Celtic fairy tales   398.2

CEMETERIES

Fleming, C. On the day I died   Fic

Gaiman, N. The graveyard book   Fic

Huey, L. M. Forgotten bones   306.3

Russell, P. C. The graveyard book graphic novel   741.5

CEMETERIES -- HISTORY 18TH CENTURY

Hansen, J. Breaking ground breaking silence   305.5

Heinecke, L. L. Chemistry for kids	540.92

Cheng, Andrea
Etched in clay — B

Cheng, Jack
See you in the cosmos — Fic

CHENNAI, INDIA
Venkatraman, P. A time to dance — Fic

CHEOPS, KING OF EGYPT
Weitzman, D. Pharaoh's boat — 932

CHERNOBYL NUCLEAR ACCIDENT, 1986
Blankman, A. The blackbird girls — Fic
Johnson, R. L. Chernobyl's wild kingdom — 590.9477

Chernobyl's wild kingdom. Johnson, R. L. — 590.9477

CHERNOBYL, UKRAINE
Johnson, R. L. Chernobyl's wild kingdom — 590.9477

CHEROKEE INDIANS -- GOVERNMENT RELATIONS
Marsico, K. The trail of tears — 973.04

CHEROKEE INDIANS -- HISTORY
Elish, D. The Trail of Tears — 973
Vander Hook, S. Trail of Tears — 975.004

CHEROKEE INDIANS -- RELOCATION
Elish, D. The Trail of Tears — 973
Marsico, K. The trail of tears — 973.04
Vander Hook, S. Trail of Tears — 975.004

CHEROKEE INDIANS -- SOCIAL CONDITIONS
Marsico, K. The trail of tears — 973.04

Cherrix, Amy E.
In the shadow of the moon — 629.45

Cherry, Lynne
How we know what we know about our changing climate — 551.6

CHESAPEAKE BAY REGION
Paterson, K. Jacob have I loved — Fic

CHESAPEAKE BAY REGION -- HISTORY
Walker, S. M. Written in bone — 614

CHESS
Basman, M. Chess for kids — 794.1
King, D. Chess — 794.1

CHESS -- HISTORY
King, D. Chess — 794.1

CHESS -- TOURNAMENTS
Wallace, R. Perpetual check — Fic

Chess. King, D. — 794.1

CHESS FOR CHILDREN
Basman, M. Chess for kids — 794.1
King, D. Chess — 794.1

Chess for kids. Basman, M. — 794.1

CHESS PLAYERS
King, D. Chess — 794.1

Chesterman, Charles W. (Charles Wesley), 1913-1991
The Audubon Society field guide to North American rocks and minerals — 552

Chevat, Richie
The omnivore's dilemma — 394.1
Our choice — 363.738
A queer history of the United States for young people — 306.76

Chew on this. Schlosser, E. — 394.1

CHEYENNE INDIANS -- WARS, 1876
Walker, P. R. Remember Little Bighorn — 973.8

Chiang, Mona
Oil spill — 363.738

Chibbaro, Julie
Deadly — Fic

CHICAGO CHILDREN'S CHOIR -- HISTORY
Turck, M. Freedom song — 323.0973

CHICAGO WHITE SOX (BASEBALL TEAM) -- HISTORY
Gutman, D. Shoeless Joe & me — Fic

CHICAGO, ILLINOIS
Ahmed, S. Love hate & other filters — Fic
Ansari, R. K. S. The in-between — Fic
Balliett, B. Chasing Vermeer — Fic
Balliett, B. Hold fast — Fic
Balliett, B. Pieces and players — Fic
Barron, R. Maya and the rising dark — Fic
Cisneros, S. The house on Mango Street — Fic
Cline-Ransome, L. Being Clem — Fic
Cline-Ransome, L. Leaving Lymon — Fic
Colbert, B. The revolution of Birdie Randolph — Fic
Elkeles, S. How to ruin my teenage life — Fic
Foley, J. A. Sorry for your loss — Fic
Kadohata, C. Outside beauty — Fic
Klise, J. The art of secrets — Fic
Magoon, K. Fire in the streets — Fic
Magoon, K. The rock and the river — Fic
Martinez, C. G. Pig park — Fic
Martinez, J. Virtuosity — Fic
Peck, R. Fair weather — Fic
Perez, C. C. The first rule of punk — Fic
Pinkwater, D. M. Bushman lives! — Fic
Polonsky, A. Gracefully Grayson — Fic
Raskin, E. The Westing game — Fic
Rhodes, J. P. Ghost boys — Fic
Valente, C. M. The boy who lost Fairyland — Fic
Zettel, S. Bad luck girl — Fic

CHICAGO, ILLINOIS -- HISTORY -- 19TH CENTURY
Bennie, P. The Great Chicago Fire of 1871 — 977.3

CHICAGO, ILLINOIS -- HISTORY -- TO 1875
Hannigan, K. The Great Chicago Fire — 977.3

CHICAGO, ILLINOIS -- SOCIAL CONDITIONS
Neri, G. Yummy — 741.5

CHICKEN POX
Hoffmann, G. Chickenpox — 616.9

CHICKEN POX -- TREATMENT
Hoffmann, G. Chickenpox — 616.9

Chickenpox. Hoffmann, G. — 616.9

CHICKENS
Caughey, M. A kid's guide to keeping chickens — 636.5

Chief Joseph. Hopping, L. J. — B

CHIKWANINE, MICHEL
Humphreys, J. D. Child soldier — B

CHILD ABUSE
Chaltas, T. Because I am furniture — Fic

Crossan, S. Being Toffee — Fic
Jackson, T. D. Monday's not coming — Fic
Roe, R. A list of cages — Fic
Werlin, N. The rules of survival — Fic

CHILD ABUSE VICTIMS
Gantos, J. Joey Pigza swallowed the key — Fic

CHILD ACTORS AND ACTRESSES
Howland, L. The forget-me-not summer — Fic
Nesbet, A. Daring Darleen queen of the screen — Fic
Shevah, E. Dara Palmer's major drama — Fic

CHILD ADVENTURERS
Kaufman, A. The world between blinks — Fic
Lewis, C. S. The last battle — Fic
Lewis, C. S. The lion the witch and the wardrobe — Fic
Park, L. S. Storm warning — Fic
Riordan, R. The maze of bones — Fic
Riordan, R. Vespers rising — Fic
Watson, J. Beyond the grave — Fic

CHILD ARTISTS
Raczka, B. Before they were famous — 704

CHILD AUTHORS
Stern, R. Brave the page — 808.3

CHILD CASTAWAYS
Golding, W. Lord of the flies — Fic

CHILD CIVIL RIGHTS WORKERS
Beals, M. March forward girl — 379.2

CHILD CUSTODY
Miller, S. E. The miracle & tragedy of the Dionne quintuplets — 306.875
Sumner, J. Tune it out — Fic

CHILD DETECTIVES
Balliett, B. Chasing Vermeer — Fic
Chambliss Bertman, J. The unbreakable code — Fic
Klise, K. Regarding the bathrooms — Fic
Ormsbee, K. The house in Poplar Wood — Fic
Ponti, J. Framed! — Fic
Ponti, J. Trapped! — Fic
Ponti, J. Vanished! — Fic
Pullman, P. Two crafty criminals! — Fic
Turnage, S. The odds of getting even — Fic

CHILD ENVIRONMENTALISTS
Jankeliowitch, A. Kids who are changing the world — 363.7092

CHILD GHOSTS
Almond, D. Kit's wilderness — Fic

CHILD HEROES
Anderson, M. T. Whales on stilts! — Fic
French, S. T. Operation Redwood — Fic
Hicks, F. E. The Nameless City — 741.5
Lapinski, L. The Strangeworlds Travel Agency — Fic

CHILD HOLOCAUST VICTIMS
Boyne, J. The boy in the striped pajamas — Fic

CHILD IMMIGRANTS
Argueta, J. Somos como las nubes — 811
Colfer, E. Illegal — 741.5
Ewald, W. America border culture dreamer — 305.23092
Na, A. A step from heaven — Fic

CHILD JOURNALISTS

Winerip, M. Adam Canfield of the Slash — Fic

CHILD KIDNAPPING VICTIMS
Cooney, C. B. The face on the milk carton — Fic
Cooney, C. B. Janie face to face — Fic
Farmer, N. The Land of the Silver Apples — Fic
Farmer, N. The Sea of Trolls — Fic
Grant, H. The league of beastly dreadfuls — Fic
Pullman, P. The golden compass — Fic
Russell, P. C. Coraline — 741.5

CHILD LABOR
Hopkinson, D. A bandit's tale — Fic
Kelly, L. Chained — Fic
Paterson, K. Bread and roses too — Fic
Polonsky, A. Threads — Fic

CHILD LABOR -- HISTORY
Bartoletti, S. C. Growing up in coal country — 331.3
Bartoletti, S. C. Kids on strike! — 331.892
Burgan, M. Breaker boys — 331.3
Winthrop, E. Counting on Grace — Fic

CHILD LABOR -- LAW AND LEGISLATION -- HISTORY
Bartoletti, S. C. Kids on strike! — 331.892

CHILD LABOR EXPLOITATION
Meloy, C. Under Wildwood — Fic
Paterson, K. Lyddie — Fic
Winthrop, E. Counting on Grace — Fic

CHILD LABOR EXPLOITATION -- HISTORY
Bartoletti, S. C. Kids on strike! — 331.892

CHILD MARRIAGE
Sheth, K. Keeping corner — Fic

CHILD MENTAL HEALTH
Omnigraphics, I. Mental health information for teens — 616.8900835

CHILD MISFITS
Baker, M. If you find this — Fic
Bosch, P. If you're reading this it's too late — Fic
Bosch, P. The name of this book is secret — Fic
Bosch, P. This book is not good for you — Fic
Bosch, P. This isn't what it looks like — Fic
Howe, J. The misfits — Fic
Klages, E. The green glass sea — Fic

CHILD MURDER WITNESSES
Dorisi-Winget, D. A million ways home — Fic

CHILD MURDERERS
Neri, G. Yummy — 741.5

CHILD NEGLECT
Connor, L. Waiting for normal — Fic

CHILD PRISONERS
Duble, K. B. The sacrifice — Fic
Skrypuch, M. F. Making bombs for Hitler — Fic

CHILD PRODIGIES
Yee, L. Millicent Min girl genius — Fic
Zarr, S. The Lucy variations — Fic

CHILD PSYCHOTHERAPY
Telgemeier, R. Guts — 155.4

CHILD REFUGEES
Altman, L. J. Escape teens on the run — 940.53
Argueta, J. Caravan to the North — Fic

Bradman, T. Give me shelter — **Fic**
Colfer, E. Illegal — **741.5**
Ellis, D. Children of war — **305.23086**
Giff, P. R. Lily's crossing — **Fic**
Salazar, A. The land of the cranes — **Fic**
St. John, W. Outcasts united — **796.334092**
Staples, S. F. Under the persimmon tree — **Fic**
Trebincevic, K. World in between — **Fic**
Watkins, Y. K. So far from the bamboo grove — **Fic**
Yousafzai, M. We are displaced — **305.23092**

CHILD SEXUAL ABUSE
Abbott, T. The summer of Owen Todd — **Fic**
Bradley, K. B. Fighting words — **Fic**
Chaltas, T. Because I am furniture — **Fic**
Weeks, S. Jumping the scratch — **Fic**

CHILD SOCIAL ADVOCATES
Wilson, J. One peace — **327.1**
Child soldier. Humphreys, J. D. — **B**

CHILD SOLDIERS
Lewis, G. Gorilla dawn — **Fic**

CHILD SUPERHEROES
Cody, M. Powerless — **Fic**

CHILD TRAFFICKING
Preus, M. West of the moon — **Fic**

CHILD TRAFFICKING VICTIMS
Preus, M. West of the moon — **Fic**

CHILD VAMPIRES
McGrane, M. The accursed vampire — **741.5**

CHILD WIZARDS
Barron, T. A. The lost years of Merlin — **Fic**
Black, H. The bronze key — **Fic**
Black, H. The copper gauntlet — **Fic**
Black, H. The iron trial — **Fic**
Black, H. The silver mask — **Fic**
Le Guin, U. K. A wizard of Earthsea — **Fic**
Nimmo, J. Midnight for Charlie Bone — **Fic**
Rowling, J. K. Harry Potter and the Chamber of Secrets — **Fic**
Rowling, J. K. Harry Potter and the sorcerer's stone — **Fic**
A **child's** introduction to ballet. Lee, L. — **792.8**

CHILD-SEPARATED FATHERS
DiCamillo, K. Raymie Nightingale — **Fic**

CHILDBIRTH
Harris, R. H. It's perfectly normal — **613.9071**
Rand, C. Human reproduction — **612.6**

CHILDHOOD
Herrera, J. F. Laughing out loud I fly — **811**
Lang, L. Lang Lang — **786.2092**
McCann, J. Return of the dapper men — **741.5**
Spinelli, J. Hokey Pokey — **Fic**

CHILDREN
Allison, J. Bad machinery — **741.5**
Buckley, S. Kids make history — **920**
Ellis, D. Three wishes — **956.9405**
French, J. Hitler's daughter — **Fic**
Glasser, D. New kid new scene — **373.18**
Hoose, P. M. We were there too! — **973**
Kerley, B. The world is waiting for you — **910**

Kirkpatrick, K. Snow baby — **910**
Lowry, L. Number the stars — **Fic**
McCann, J. Return of the dapper men — **741.5**
Naidoo, B. Out of bounds — **Fic**
Oppenheim, J. Dear Miss Breed — **940.53**
Paul, C. You are mighty — **306**
Rappaport, D. Beyond courage — **940.53**
Reynolds, J. For every one — **811**
Robinson, A. Young Palestinians speak — **956.95**
Schlitz, L. A. Good masters! Sweet ladies! — **812**
Silverstein, S. Falling up — **811**
Spinelli, J. Hokey Pokey — **Fic**
Thomson, R. Terezin — **940.53**

CHILDREN -- BOOKS AND READING
Bryan, T. A. Art of comprehension — **372.47**
Daniels, H. Literature circles — **371.39**
Daniels, H. Mini-lessons for literature circles — **372.41**
Dorr, C. H. LGBTQAI+ books for children and teens — **028.7**
Farwell, S. M. Supporting reading in grades 6-12 — **428.4071**
Goldsmith, A. Y. Reading the world's stories — **016.80883**
Harvey, S. Strategies that work — **372.47**
Horning, K. T. From cover to cover — **028.1**
Manglik, G. Muslims in story — **809**
Miller, D. The book whisperer — **372.6**
Miller, D. Reading in the wild — **372.4**
Sutton, R. A family of readers — **809**

CHILDREN -- DEATH
Bunting, E. Blackwater — **Fic**
Halls, K. M. Mysteries of the mummy kids — **393**

CHILDREN -- DISEASES
Johnson, A. A cool moonlight — **Fic**

CHILDREN -- DRUG USE
Walker, I. Recreational ritalin — **616.85**

CHILDREN -- FRIENDSHIP
Giff, P. R. Lily's crossing — **Fic**
Konigsburg, E. L. The view from Saturday — **Fic**

CHILDREN -- GROWTH
Loveless, G. Puberty is gross but also really awesome — **612.6**

CHILDREN -- HISTORY 19TH CENTURY
Warren, A. Under siege! — **973.7**

CHILDREN -- HISTORY 20TH CENTURY
Bartoletti, S. C. Hitler Youth — **943.086**

CHILDREN -- INSTITUTIONAL CARE
Frost, H. All he knew — **Fic**

CHILDREN -- INTERPERSONAL RELATIONS
McKay, H. Caddy ever after — **Fic**

CHILDREN -- PHYSIOLOGY
Telgemeier, R. Guts — **155.4**

CHILDREN -- PUNISHMENT
London, A. Proxy — **Fic**

CHILDREN -- SOCIAL CONDITIONS
Buckley, S. Kids make history — **920**

CHILDREN -- SOCIAL LIFE AND CUSTOMS
Buckley, S. Kids make history — **920**
Glasser, D. New kid new scene — **373.18**

Headley, J. C. Return to me	Fic
Henkes, K. Bird Lake moon	Fic
Holt, K. A. Knockout	Fic
McKay, H. Indigo's star	Fic
Murphy, J. Dear Sweet Pea	Fic
Paulsen, G. Brian's return	Fic
Paulsen, G. Brian's winter	Fic
Paulsen, G. Hatchet	Fic
Peterfreund, D. Omega City	Fic
Peters, J. A. Define "normal"	Fic
Preller, J. The courage test	Fic
Stead, R. The list of things that will not change	Fic
Voigt, C. A solitary blue	Fic
West, K. Pivot point	Fic
Youngblood, L. C. Love like sky	Fic

CHILDREN OF DRUG ABUSERS

Juby, S. The fashion committee	Fic
Keplinger, K. Run	Fic
Price, C. Desert Angel	Fic

CHILDREN OF ENVIRONMENTALISTS

Hiaasen, C. Flush	Fic
Children of exile. Haddix, M. P.	Fic

CHILDREN OF IMMIGRANTS

Ewald, W. America border culture dreamer	305.23092
Hesse, K. Brooklyn Bridge	Fic

CHILDREN OF LAWYERS

Thompson, J. The girl from Felony Bay	Fic

CHILDREN OF LGBTQIA PARENTS

Moore, D. B. The stars beneath our feet	Fic
Tamaki, M. Saving Montgomery Sole	Fic
Woodson, J. From the notebooks of Melanin Sun	Fic

**CHILDREN OF MIGRANT FARM WORKERS -- EDUCA-
TION -- HISTORY 20TH CENTURY**

Stanley, J. Children of the Dust Bowl	371.96

CHILDREN OF MILITARY PERSONNEL

Baskin, N. R. The summer before boys	Fic
Dowell, F. O. Shooting the moon	Fic
Ellis, D. Off to war	303.6
Frederick, H. V. Absolutely Truly	Fic
Hughes, D. Missing in action	Fic
Hughes, S. Hero on a bicycle	Fic
Mazer, H. Heroes don't run	Fic
Pennypacker, S. Pax	Fic
Whelan, G. All my noble dreams and then what happens	Fic
Whelan, G. Small acts of amazing courage	Fic
Wiles, D. Countdown	Fic
Yelchin, E. Spy runner	Fic

CHILDREN OF MURDER VICTIMS

Okorafor, N. Ikenga	Fic

CHILDREN OF NAZIS

Boyne, J. The boy in the striped pajamas	Fic

CHILDREN OF PARENTS WITH DISABILITIES

Hiaasen, C. Scat	Fic

CHILDREN OF PEOPLE WITH AIDS

Michael, J. City boy	Fic

CHILDREN OF PEOPLE WITH BREAST CANCER

Lopez, D. Ask my mood ring how I feel	Fic

CHILDREN OF PEOPLE WITH CANCER

Bell, J. Kepler's Dream	Fic
Lopez, D. Ask my mood ring how I feel	Fic
McCall, G. G. Under the mesquite	Fic
Ness, P. A monster calls	Fic
Silver, M. My parent has cancer and it really sucks	616.99
Thompson, H. The language inside	Fic
Trueman, T. Inside out	Fic
Vlahos, L. Life in a fishbowl	Fic
Whitney, D. When you were here	Fic

CHILDREN OF PEOPLE WITH DEPRESSION

Ehrlich, E. Nest	Fic
Hiranandani, V. The whole story of half a girl	Fic
Jones, T. L. Silhouetted by the blue	Fic
King, A. S. The year we fell from space	Fic
Lord, E. When we collided	Fic
Peters, J. A. Define "normal"	Fic

CHILDREN OF PEOPLE WITH DIABETES

Reynolds, J. Patina	Fic

CHILDREN OF PEOPLE WITH MENTAL ILLNESSES

Galante, C. The world from up here	Fic
Harrington, K. Courage for beginners	Fic
Harrington, K. Sure signs of crazy	Fic
Jacobson, J. Small as an elephant	Fic
Lockington, M. For black girls like me	Fic

CHILDREN OF PEOPLE WITH TERMINAL ILLNESSES

Makechnie, A. Ten thousand tries	Fic

CHILDREN OF PHYSICIANS

Agosin, M. I lived on Butterfly Hill	Fic

CHILDREN OF POLICE

Emond, S. Bright lights dark nights	Fic

CHILDREN OF POLITICIANS

Bruton, C. I predict a riot	Fic

CHILDREN OF PREGNANT WOMEN

Burg, A. E. Serafina's promise	Fic

CHILDREN OF PRESIDENTS

Rhatigan, J. White House kids	920

CHILDREN OF PRISONERS

Baskin, N. R. Ruby on the outside	Fic
Connor, L. All rise for the honorable Perry T. Cook	Fic
Hiaasen, C. Flush	Fic
Hitchcock, B. The smell of other people's houses	Fic
Maldonado, T. Secret Saturdays	Fic
Reynolds, J. Ghost	Fic
Shofner, C. Almost paradise	Fic
Zehr, H. What will happen to me?	362.82

CHILDREN OF PRISONERS -- SERVICES FOR

Zehr, H. What will happen to me?	362.82
Children of refuge. Haddix, M. P.	Fic

CHILDREN OF RICH PEOPLE

Bradbury, J. Shift	Fic

CHILDREN OF SCIENTISTS

Fombelle, T. d. Toby alone	Fic
Gray, C. A thousand pieces of you	Fic
Holyoke, P. The Neptune Project	Fic
Klages, E. The green glass sea	Fic
Oppel, K. Half brother	Fic

Stead, R. First light   Fic

CHILDREN OF SEPARATED PARENTS

Hitchcock, B. The smell of other people's houses   Fic

King, A. S. The year we fell from space   Fic

Lupica, M. The batboy   Fic

CHILDREN OF SICK PERSONS

Makechnie, A. Ten thousand tries   Fic

Mann, J. A. What every girl should know   Fic

Sovern, M. J. The meaning of Maggie   Fic

Wolk, L. Echo Mountain   Fic

CHILDREN OF SINGLE PARENTS

Harkrader, L. The adventures of Beanboy   Fic

Hatke, B. Mighty Jack   741.5

Hicks, F. E. One Year at Ellsmere   741.5

Jones, K. Sand dollar summer   Fic

Stead, R. When you reach me   Fic

Vance, A. P. The Heartbreak Messenger   Fic

CHILDREN OF SPIES

Nesbet, A. Cloud and Wallfish   Fic

CHILDREN OF SUFFRAGISTS

Korman, G. Collision course   Fic

CHILDREN OF SUICIDE VICTIMS

Cooper, S. King of shadows   Fic

Ostlere, C. Karma   Fic

Children of the Dust Bowl. Stanley, J.   371.96

Children of the sea. Igarashi, D.   741.5

CHILDREN OF UNEMPLOYED PARENTS

Lubar, D. Character driven   Fic

Trueman, T. Inside out   Fic

CHILDREN OF VETERANS

Keller, J. Back home   Fic

Children of war. Ellis, D.   305.23086

CHILDREN OF WIDOWERS

Austen, C. Walking backward   Fic

Bateson, C. Being Bee   Fic

Black, H. The copper gauntlet   Fic

Black, H. The iron trial   Fic

CHILDREN WHO ARE BLIND

Bender, L. Explaining blindness   617.7

Taylor, T. The cay   Fic

CHILDREN WHO ARE MUTE

Cottrell Boyce, F. Sputnik's guide to life on earth   Fic

Orr, W. Dragonfly song   Fic

CHILDREN WITH ADHD

Van Vleet, C. Eliza Bing is (not) a big fat quitter   Fic

CHILDREN WITH ASPERGER'S SYNDROME

Dowd, S. The London Eye mystery   Fic

Erskine, K. Mockingbird   Fic

Grossberg, B. N. Asperger's rules!   618.92

Martin, A. M. Rain Reign   Fic

CHILDREN WITH AUTISM

Johnson, A. A certain October   Fic

Lord, C. Rules   Fic

Stefanski, D. How to talk to an autistic kid   618.92

CHILDREN WITH AUTISM -- EDUCATION

Grossberg, B. N. Asperger's rules!   618.92

CHILDREN WITH AUTISM -- FAMILY RELATION-SHIPS

Verdick, E. The survival guide for kids with autism spectrum disorders (and their parents)   618.92

CHILDREN WITH AUTISM SPECTRUM DISORDERS

Verdick, E. The survival guide for kids with autism spectrum disorders (and their parents)   618.92

CHILDREN WITH CANCER

Gemeinhart, D. The honest truth   Fic

Harrell, R. Wink   Fic

Loftin, N. Wish girl   Fic

Preller, J. Six innings   Fic

Rivers, K. Love Ish   Fic

CHILDREN WITH CEREBRAL PALSY

Sumner, J. Roll with it   Fic

CHILDREN WITH CHRONIC ILLNESSES

Haydu, C. A. The someday suitcase   Fic

CHILDREN WITH DEPRESSION

Crist, J. J. What to do when you're sad & lonely   618.92

CHILDREN WITH DEVELOPMENTAL DISABILITIES

Giff, P. R. A slip of a girl   Fic

Stefanski, D. How to talk to an autistic kid   618.92

CHILDREN WITH DIABETES

Yohalem, E. The truth according to Blue   Fic

CHILDREN WITH DISABILITIES

Burnett, F. H. The secret garden [Moore ill.]   Fic

Skotko, B. Fasten your seatbelt   616.85

Skrypuch, M. F. One step at a time   618.92

CHILDREN WITH DISABILITIES -- EDUCATION

Maanum, J. L. The general educator's guide to special education   371.9

CHILDREN WITH DOWN SYNDROME

Hobbs, V. The last best days of summer   Fic

CHILDREN WITH EMOTIONAL ILLNESSES

McIntyre, T. The behavior survival guide for kids   649

CHILDREN WITH EPILEPSY

Bender, L. Explaining epilepsy   616.8

CHILDREN WITH LEUKEMIA

Nicholls, S. Ways to live forever   Fic

CHILDREN WITH MENTAL DISABILITIES -- EDUCATION (SECONDARY)

Craig, S. E. Trauma-sensitive schools for the adolescent years   371.92

CHILDREN WITH MENTAL ILLNESSES

Melleby, N. How to become a planet   Fic

CHILDREN WITH TERMINAL ILLNESSES

Nicholls, S. Ways to live forever   Fic

CHILDREN'S ART

Thomson, R. Terezin   940.53

CHILDREN'S BOOKS

Ansberry, K. R. Picture-perfect science lessons expanded 2nd edition   372.3

CHILDREN'S CLUBS

Chmakova, S. Awkward   741.5

CHILDREN'S COSTUMES

Kenney, K. L. Cool costumes   792.02

Children's encyclopedia of American history. King, D.

CHURCHES

Peck, R. A season of gifts — Fic

CIA

Gibbs, S. Charlie Thorne and the last equation — Fic

Gibbs, S. Charlie Thorne and the lost city — Fic

Whyman, M. Goldstrike — Fic

CIA -- HISTORY

Favreau, M. Spies — 327.127304709

Cianciotto, Jason

LGBT youth in America's schools — 371.826

Cicada. Tan, S. — Fic

Cicada summer. Beaty, A. — Fic

CICADAS

Tan, S. Cicada — Fic

CINCINNATI, OHIO

Draper, S. M. Double dutch — Fic

Cinder. Meyer, M. — Fic

CINDERELLA

Whipple, L. If the shoe fits — 811

Circle of heroes. Epstein, A. J. — Fic

Circle of secrets. Little, K. G. — Fic

The **circuit**. Jimenez, F. — Fic

Circulating life. Winner, C. — 615

CIRCULATORY SYSTEM

Gold, J. C. Learning about the circulatory and lymphatic systems — 612.1

Circulatory system. Rose, S. — 612.1

CIRCUS

Beasley, C. Circus Mirandus — Fic

Centore, M. Entertainment industry — 790.1

Howard, J. J. That time I joined the circus — Fic

Kelly, L. Chained — Fic

McCaughrean, G. The kite rider — Fic

Moreci, M. The lost carnival — Fic

Reeve, P. A web of air — Fic

CIRCUS ANIMALS

Laidlaw, R. On parade — 636.088

Circus Mirandus. Beasley, C. — Fic

CIRCUS PERFORMERS

DeWoskin, R. Someday we will fly — Fic

Moreci, M. The lost carnival — Fic

Oppel, K. The Boundless — Fic

Cisneros, Ernesto

Efren divided — Fic

Cisneros, Sandra

The house on Mango Street — Fic

Cities. Reilly, K. M. — 307.1

CITIES AND TOWNS

Fisher, C. The dark city — Fic

Hicks, F. E. The divided earth — 741.5

Hinds, K. The city — 909

Iserles, I. The taken — Fic

Macaulay, D. City — 711

Macaulay, D. Underground — 624

Millard, A. A street through time — 936

Reilly, K. M. Cities — 307.1

Tan, S. Tales from the inner city — Fic

Wagner, H. Nightshade City — Fic

CITIZEN OF THE WORLD (CONCEPT)

Robinson, M. Every human has rights — 323

Citizen scientists. Burns, L. G. — 590.72

CITIZENSHIP

Fleischer, J. Votes of confidence — 324.6

The **city**. Hinds, K. — 909

City. Macaulay, D. — 711

City boy. Michael, J. — Fic

City critters. Read, N. — 591.75

CITY LIFE

Downer, A. Wild animal neighbors — 591.75

Flake, S. You don't even know me — Fic

Fleischman, P. Seedfolks — Fic

Hinds, K. The city — 909

Leatherdale, M. B. Urban tribes — 305.897

Macaulay, D. Underground — 624

Merrill, J. F. The pushcart war — Fic

Onome, L. Like home — Fic

Reilly, K. M. Cities — 307.1

Reynolds, J. Look both ways — Fic

Tan, S. Tales from the inner city — Fic

Thor, A. The lily pond — Fic

CITY LIFE -- HISTORY

Foster, M. Whaleport — 338.3

The **city** of Ember. DuPrau, J. — Fic

City of fire. Yep, L. — Fic

City of orphans. Avi. — Fic

City of saints & thieves. Anderson, N. C. — Fic

City of the plague god. Chadda, S. — Fic

A **city** tossed and broken. Blundell, J. — Fic

CIUDAD JUAREZ, MEXICO

Stork, F. X. Disappeared — Fic

CIVICS

Krull, K. A kids' guide to America's Bill of Rights — 342.73

Levinson, C. Fault lines in the constitution — 342.7302

Panchyk, R. Our Supreme Court — 347.73

CIVICS -- STUDY AND TEACHING

Kaye, C. B. The complete guide to service learning — 370.11

CIVIL DEFENSE

Pope, P. Battling boy — 741.5

CIVIL DISOBEDIENCE

Hasak-Lowy, T. We are power — 303.6

Kirk, A. Understanding Thoreau's Civil disobedience — 818

O'Brien, A. S. After Gandhi — 303.6

CIVIL ENGINEERING

Aaseng, N. Construction — 624

Caney, S. Steven Caney's ultimate building book — 624

Carmichael, L. E. Amazing feats of civil engineering — 624

Graham, I. Fabulous bridges — 624.2

Levy, M. Engineering the city — 624

Macaulay, D. City — 711

Reilly, K. M. Cities — 307.1

CIVIL ENGINEERING -- HISTORY

Aaseng, N. Construction — 624

Sullivan, G. Built to last   **624**

CIVIL ENGINEERS

Carmichael, L. E. Amazing feats of civil engineering   **624**

CIVIL RIGHTS

Anderson, C. One person no vote   **324.6**

Baxter, R. The Bill of Rights   **342.7308**

Bolden, T. Strong voices   **815.08**

Brimner, L. D. Blacklisted!   **323**

Draper, S. M. Stella by starlight   **Fic**

Kimmel, A. C. The Montgomery Bus Boycott   **323.1196**

Krull, K. A kids' guide to America's Bill of Rights   **342.73**

Meersman, E. Majority rule vs. individual rights   **321.8**

Mullenbach, C. Double victory   **940.5308**

Ohnaka, K. Key civil rights laws   **342.73**

Ortiz, V. Dissenter on the bench   **347.73**

Rubin, S. G. Freedom summer   **323.1196**

CIVIL RIGHTS -- HISTORY

Ohnaka, K. Key civil rights laws   **342.73**

Pinkney, A. D. Let it shine   **920**

CIVIL RIGHTS DEMONSTRATIONS

Bausum, A. The March against Fear   **323.1196**

Brimner, L. D. Twelve days in May   **323.11**

CIVIL RIGHTS DEMONSTRATIONS -- HISTORY 20TH CENTURY

Aretha, D. Martin Luther King Jr. and the 1963 March on Washington   **323.092**

Aretha, D. The story of the civil rights March on Washington for Jobs and Freedom in photographs   **975.3**

CIVIL RIGHTS MOVEMENT

Archer, J. They had a dream   **323**

Aretha, D. Martin Luther King Jr. and the 1963 March on Washington   **323.092**

Aretha, D. With all deliberate speed   **379.2**

Bausum, A. Marching to the mountaintop   **323.092**

Beals, M. March forward girl   **379.2**

Bowers, R. The spies of Mississippi   **323.1196**

Boyce, J. A. A. This promise of change   **379.2**

Brimner, L. D. Black & white   **323.1196**

Brimner, L. D. Twelve days in May   **323.11**

Curtis, C. P. The Watsons go to Birmingham 1963   **Fic**

Freedman, R. Freedom walkers   **323.1196**

Goldstone, L. Separate no more   **323.1196**

Kidd, R. Night on fire   **Fic**

Kimmel, A. C. The Montgomery Bus Boycott   **323.1196**

Levinson, C. We've got a job   **323.1196**

Magoon, K. Fire in the streets   **Fic**

Magoon, K. The rock and the river   **Fic**

Nelson, M. How I discovered poetry   **811.54**

Ohnaka, K. Key civil rights laws   **342.73**

Partridge, E. Marching for freedom   **323.1196**

Pinkney, A. D. Loretta Little looks back   **Fic**

Pinkney, A. D. Martin rising   **811**

Powell, P. H. Loving vs. Virginia   **Fic**

Rubin, S. G. Freedom summer   **323.1196**

Shange, N. We troubled the waters   **811**

Smith-Llera, D. Black power salute   **796.48**

Stokes, J. A. Students on strike   **371.829**

Stotts, S. We shall overcome   **782.42162**

Taylor, M. D. All the days past all the days to come   **Fic**

Tougas, S. Birmingham 1963   **323.1196**

Turck, M. Freedom song   **323.0973**

Vaught, S. Things too huge to fix by saying sorry   **Fic**

Venable, R. The civil rights movement   **323.1196**

Watson, B. Freedom Summer for young people   **323.1196**

CIVIL RIGHTS MOVEMENT -- PROTESTS, DEMON-STRATIONS, VIGILS, ETC

Tougas, S. Birmingham 1963   **323.1196**

The **civil** rights movement. Blohm, C. E.   **323.1196**

The **civil** rights movement. Venable, R.   **323.1196**

CIVIL RIGHTS MOVEMENTS -- HISTORY 20TH CENTURY

Blohm, C. E. The civil rights movement   **323.1196**

CIVIL RIGHTS WORKERS

Archer, J. They had a dream   **323**

Brimner, L. D. Black & white   **323.1196**

Mayer, R. H. When the children marched   **323.1196**

Pinkney, A. D. Martin rising   **811**

Rubin, S. G. Freedom summer   **323.1196**

CIVIL SERVICE WORKERS

Black, H. Black heart   **Fic**

CIVIL WAR

Allen, T. B. Mr. Lincoln's high-tech war   **973.7**

Azad, N. The candle and the flame   **Fic**

Beller, S. P. Billy Yank & Johnny Reb   **973.7**

Benoit, P. The surrender at Appomattox   **973.7**

Bolden, T. Emancipation Proclamation   **973.7**

Brown, S. Caminar   **Fic**

Carson, R. The bitter kingdom   **Fic**

Fleischman, P. Bull Run   **Fic**

Gregory, J. Gettysburg   **973.7**

Hernandez, R. E. The Civil War 1840s-1890s   **973.7**

Jarrow, G. Lincoln's flying spies   **973.7**

Keith, H. Rifles for Watie   **Fic**

Lewis, J. P. The brothers' war   **811**

O'Connor, J. What was the Battle of Gettysburg?   **973.7**

Otfinoski, S. The Civil War   **973.7**

Park, L. S. A long walk to water   **Fic**

Pellegrino, M. Journey of dreams   **Fic**

Philbrick, W. R. The mostly true adventures of Homer P. Figg   **Fic**

Rees, B. The Civil War   **973.7**

Reis, R. A. African Americans and the Civil War   **973.7**

Rottman, G. L. The most daring raid of the Civil War   **973.7**

Shepard, R. Now or never!   **973.7**

Silverman, J. Songs and stories of the Civil War   **782.42**

Swanson, J. L. Bloody times   **973.7092**

Tarshis, L. The battle of Gettysburg 1863   **Fic**

Walker, S. M. Deadly aim   **973.7**

Warren, A. Under siege!   **973.7**

The **Civil** War. DK Publishing, I.   **973.7**

The **Civil** War. Otfinoski, S.   **973.7**

The **Civil** War. Rees, B.   **973.7**

The **Civil** War 1840s-1890s. Hernandez, R. E.   **973.7**

CLARK, EUGENIE, 1922-
Lawlor, L. Super women — **509.2**

Clark, Henry, 1952-
What we found in the sofa (and how it saved the world) — **Fic**

CLARK, WILLIAM, 1770-1838
Bertozzi, N. Lewis & Clark — **741.5**
Bodden, V. Through the American West — **917.804**

Clark, William, 1770-1838
Off the map — **917.804**

CLARK, WILLIAM, 1770-1838 ORIGINAL JOURNALS OF THE LEWIS AND CLARK EXPEDITION SELECTIONS
Clark, W. Off the map — **917.804**

CLARKSTON, GEORGIA
St. John, W. Outcasts united — **796.334092**

The **class**. Dowell, F. O. — **Fic**

Class act. Craft, J. — **741.5**

CLASS CONFLICT
Ross, E. Belle epoque — **Fic**

Classic poetry. Rosen, M. — **821.008**

Classical civilization. Nardo, D. — **938**

CLASSICAL MUSIC
Lang, L. Lang Lang — **786.2092**

CLASSICAL MUSIC -- HISTORY AND CRITICISM
Rhodes, J. Playlist — **780.922**

CLASSICS
Adams, R. Watership Down — **Fic**
Alexander, L. The black cauldron — **Fic**
Alexander, L. The book of three — **Fic**
Alexander, L. Taran Wanderer — **Fic**
Almond, D. Skellig — **Fic**
Anderson, L. H. Fever 1793 — **Fic**
Anderson, L. H. Speak — **Fic**
Armstrong, W. H. Sounder — **Fic**
Babbitt, N. Tuck everlasting — **Fic**
Blume, J. Are you there God? It's me Margaret — **Fic**
Bradbury, R. The Halloween tree — **Fic**
Burnett, F. H. The secret garden [Moore ill.] — **Fic**
Cisneros, S. The house on Mango Street — **Fic**
Cleary, B. Dear Mr. Henshaw — **Fic**
Cooney, C. B. The face on the milk carton — **Fic**
Creech, S. Walk two moons — **Fic**
Curtis, C. P. Bud not Buddy — **Fic**
Curtis, C. P. The Watsons go to Birmingham 1963 — **Fic**
Cushman, K. Catherine called Birdy — **Fic**
Cushman, K. The midwife's apprentice — **Fic**
Danziger, P. The cat ate my gymsuit — **Fic**
Dickens, C. A Christmas carol [Lynch ill.] — **Fic**
Duncan, L. I know what you did last summer — **Fic**
Engdahl, S. Enchantress from the stars — **Fic**
Erdrich, L. The birchbark house — **Fic**
Fleischman, S. The whipping boy — **Fic**
Forbes, E. Johnny Tremain — **Fic**
Gantos, J. Joey Pigza swallowed the key — **Fic**
Gipson, F. Old Yeller — **Fic**
Haddix, M. P. Among the hidden — **Fic**
Hamilton, V. The house of Dies Drear — **Fic**

Hesse, K. Letters from Rifka — **Fic**
Hinton, S. E. The outsiders — **Fic**
Homer. The Iliad — **883**
Homer. The Odyssey — **883**
Irving, W. The legend of Sleepy Hollow — **Fic**
Jacques, B. Redwall — **Fic**
Jones, D. W. Howl's moving castle — **Fic**
Keith, H. Rifles for Watie — **Fic**
Kipling, R. The jungle book — **Fic**
Konigsburg, E. L. The view from Saturday — **Fic**
L'Engle, M. A swiftly tilting planet — **Fic**
L'Engle, M. A wind in the door — **Fic**
L'Engle, M. A wrinkle in time — **Fic**
Le Guin, U. K. A wizard of Earthsea — **Fic**
Levine, G. C. Ella enchanted — **Fic**
Lewis, C. S. The horse and his boy — **Fic**
Lewis, C. S. The last battle — **Fic**
Lewis, C. S. The lion the witch and the wardrobe — **Fic**
Lewis, C. S. The magician's nephew — **Fic**
Lewis, C. S. Prince Caspian — **Fic**
Lewis, C. S. The silver chair — **Fic**
Lewis, C. S. The voyage of the Dawn Treader — **Fic**
London, J. The call of the wild — **Fic**
Lowry, L. The giver — **Fic**
Lowry, L. Number the stars — **Fic**
Marsden, J. Tomorrow when the war began — **Fic**
Myers, W. D. Scorpions — **Fic**
Naylor, P. R. Shiloh — **Fic**
O'Brien, R. C. Mrs. Frisby and the rats of NIMH — **Fic**
O'Dell, S. Island of the Blue Dolphins — **Fic**
O'Dell, S. Sing down the moon — **Fic**
O'Dell, S. Streams to the river river to the sea — **Fic**
Paterson, K. Bridge to Terabithia — **Fic**
Paterson, K. The great Gilly Hopkins — **Fic**
Paterson, K. Jacob have I loved — **Fic**
Paterson, K. Lyddie — **Fic**
Paulsen, G. Hatchet — **Fic**
Paulsen, G. Soldier's heart — **Fic**
Pierce, T. Alanna the first adventure — **Fic**
Poe, E. A. Edgar Allan Poe's tales of death and dementia — **Fic**
Pullman, P. The amber spyglass — **Fic**
Pullman, P. The golden compass — **Fic**
Pullman, P. The subtle knife — **Fic**
Raskin, E. The Westing game — **Fic**
Rodgers, M. Freaky Friday — **Fic**
Rowling, J. K. Harry Potter and the Chamber of Secrets — **Fic**
Rowling, J. K. Harry Potter and the deathly hallows — **Fic**
Rowling, J. K. Harry Potter and the goblet of fire — **Fic**
Rowling, J. K. Harry Potter and the Order of the Phoenix — **Fic**
Rowling, J. K. Harry Potter and the prisoner of Azkaban — **Fic**
Rowling, J. K. Harry Potter and the sorcerer's stone — **Fic**
Sachar, L. Holes — **Fic**
Speare, E. G. The witch of Blackbird Pond — **Fic**
Spinelli, J. Maniac Magee — **Fic**
Spinelli, J. Stargirl — **Fic**
Stevenson, R. L. Kidnapped — **Fic**
Stevenson, R. L. Treasure Island — **Fic**

Hinds, G. The Iliad	741.5	O'Neill, K. Princess princess ever after	741.5
Hinds, G. King Lear	741.5	Oseman, A. Heartstopper	741.5
Hinds, G. The merchant of Venice	741.5	Oseman, A. Heartstopper	Fic
Hinds, G. The most excellent and lamentable tragedy of Romeo & Juliet	741.5	Ottaviani, J. Primates	920
		Ottaviani, J. T-minus	629.4
Hinds, G. The Odyssey	741.5	Paige, D. Mera	Fic
Hirsch, A. Cats	599.75	Palacio, R. J. White bird	741.5
Hirsch, A. Dogs	636.7	Pearson, L. Hildafolk	741.5
Hirsch, A. Rocks and minerals	552	Petersen, D. Mouse guard	741.5
Hirsch, A. Trees	582.16	Phelan, M. Around the world	910.4
Holm, J. L. Sunny side up	741.5	Phelan, M. Snow White	741.5
Holm, J. L. Swing it Sunny	741.5	Phelan, M. The storm in the barn	741.5
Horowitz, A. Stormbreaker	741.5	Pope, P. Battling boy	741.5
Hosler, J. The way of the hive	741.5	Reed, M. K. Americus	Fic
Hotta, Y. Hikaru no Go	741.5	Reed, M. K. Dinosaurs	567.9
Howard, A. The crossroads at midnight	Fic	Renier, A. The unsinkable Walker Bean	741.5
Igarashi, D. Children of the sea	741.5	Roman, D. Astronaut Academy	741.5
Jacques, B. Redwall the graphic novel	741.5	Russell, P. C. Coraline	741.5
Jamieson, V. All's faire in middle school	741.5	Russell, P. C. The graveyard book graphic novel	741.5
Jamieson, V. Roller girl	741.5	Schweizer, C. Fix a car!	629.28
Jensen, K. Body talk	306.4	Sfar, J. The little prince	741.5
Johnson, C. G. The Breakaways	741.5	Shen, P. Nothing can possibly go wrong	741.5
Keenan, S. Dogs of war	741.5	Shiga, J. Meanwhile	741.5
Keplinger, K. Poison Ivy	741.5	Shimura, T. Wandering son	741.5
Kibuishi, K. Amulet	741.5	Smith, C. R. The mighty 12	398.2
Kibuishi, K. Explorer	741.5	Smith, J. Out from Boneville	741.5
Kibuishi, K. Flight explorer	741.5	Smith, J. Rose	741.5
Kishimoto, M. Naruto	741.5	Smith, J. Tall tales	741.5
Koch, F. Bats	599.4	Smith, N. The deep & dark blue	741.5
Koch, F. Plagues	614.5	Soo, K. Jellaby	741.5
Landmann, B. The incredible voyage of Ulysses	398.2	Stevenson, N. Lumberjanes	741.5
Larson, H. All summer long	741.5	Stevenson, N. Nimona	741.5
Larson, H. All together now	741.5	Sullivan, T. Escape at 10000 feet	364.1317
Larson, H. Compass south	741.5	Takaya, N. Fruits basket	741.5
Larson, H. A wrinkle in time	741.5	Tamaki, M. Harley Quinn	Fic
Latta, S. L. SMASH!	539.7	Tamaki, M. Skim	741.5
Layne, A. Beetle & the Hollowbones	741.5	Tamaki, M. This one summer	741.5
Lee, T. Outlaw	741.5	Tan, S. The arrival	741.5
Leyh, K. Snapdragon	741.5	Telgemeier, R. Claudia and mean Janine	741.5
Lloyd, M. W. Allergic	741.5	Telgemeier, R. Drama	741.5
Lowry, L. Giver quartet	741.5	Telgemeier, R. Ghosts	741.5
Mashima, H. Fairy tail	741.5	Telgemeier, R. Guts	155.4
McCann, J. Return of the dapper men	741.5	Telgemeier, R. Kristy's great idea	741.5
McCoola, M. Baba Yaga's assistant	741.5	Telgemeier, R. Sisters	306.875
McGrane, M. The accursed vampire	741.5	Telgemeier, R. Smile	617.6
McKinney, L. L. Nubia	741.5	TenNapel, D. Bad Island	741.5
Meconis, D. Queen of the sea	741.5	TenNapel, D. Cardboard	741.5
Medley, L. Castle waiting	741.5	TenNapel, D. Ghostopolis	741.5
Melchior-Durand, S. The golden compass	741.5	Thompson, C. Space dumplins	741.5
Meyer, M. Wires and nerve	741.5	Tolstikova, D. A year without Mom	741.5
Moore, S. Batman	Fic	Varon, S. Bake sale	741.5
Moreci, M. The lost carnival	Fic	Venditti, R. The lightning thief	741.5
Neri, G. Yummy	741.5	Viola, J. Digestive system	612.3
Nicholson, H. Moonshot	741.5	Westerfeld, S. Shay's story	741.5
Nijkamp, M. The oracle code	741.5	Wheeler, A. Another castle	741.5
O'Connor, G. Hephaistos	292	Whitley, J. Princeless	741.5
O'Connor, G. Zeus	292	Wicks, M. Coral reefs	577.5

Landman, T. Hell and high water	**Fic**	
Larocca, R. Red white and whole	**Fic**	
Larson, H. All summer long	**741.5**	
Larson, H. All together now	**741.5**	
Lecesne, J. Absolute brightness	**Fic**	
Lee, H. To kill a mockingbird	**Fic**	
Lloyd, M. W. Allergic	**741.5**	
Lockhart, E. The disreputable history of Frankie Landau-Banks	**Fic**	
Longo, J. What I carry	**Fic**	
Lopez, D. Confetti girl	**Fic**	
Love, D. A. Semiprecious	**Fic**	
Lowry, L. The giver	**Fic**	
Lubar, D. Character driven	**Fic**	
Lundin, B. Ship it	**Fic**	
Lupica, M. Heat	**Fic**	
Makechnie, A. Ten thousand tries	**Fic**	
Marsh, K. Jepp who defied the stars	**Fic**	
Martinez, C. G. Pig park	**Fic**	
Martinez, C. G. The smell of old lady perfume	**Fic**	
Mass, W. Every soul a star	**Fic**	
Mass, W. A mango-shaped space	**Fic**	
McCaffrey, A. Dragon's fire	**Fic**	
McManis, C. W. Indian no more	**Fic**	
McMullan, M. How I found the Strong	**Fic**	
McMullan, M. Sources of light	**Fic**	
Medina, M. Merci Suarez can't dance	**Fic**	
Melleby, N. In the role of Brie Hutchens...	**Fic**	
Mercado, N. E. Every man for himself	**Fic**	
Messner, K. Chirp	**Fic**	
Michael, J. City boy	**Fic**	
Mikaelsen, B. Touching Spirit Bear	**Fic**	
Molope, K. L. This book betrays my brother	**Fic**	
Moriarty, J. Feeling sorry for Celia	**Fic**	
Murdock, C. G. Princess Ben	**Fic**	
Murphy, J. Ramona Blue	**Fic**	
Myers, W. D. Fallen angels	**Fic**	
Myers, W. D. Slam!	**Fic**	
Myers, W. D. Sunrise over Fallujah	**Fic**	
Na, A. A step from heaven	**Fic**	
Na, A. Wait for me	**Fic**	
No such thing as the real world	**Fic**	
Nunn, M. When the ground is hard	**Fic**	
Oaks, J. A. Why I fight	**Fic**	
Onome, L. Like home	**Fic**	
Pancholy, M. The best at it	**Fic**	
Parker, M. Who put this song on?	**Fic**	
Paterson, K. Bread and roses too	**Fic**	
Pearsall, S. The seventh most important thing	**Fic**	
Peck, R. The best man	**Fic**	
Pena, M. d. l. We were here	**Fic**	
Perkins, L. R. Criss cross	**Fic**	
Philippe, B. The field guide to the North American teenager	**Fic**	
Pinkwater, D. M. Bushman lives!	**Fic**	
Pitcher, A. Silence is goldfish	**Fic**	
Plozza, S. Tin heart	**Fic**	
Polisner, G. The pull of gravity	**Fic**	
Preller, J. The courage test	**Fic**	
Quigley, D. Apple in the middle	**Fic**	
Ramee, L. M. A good kind of trouble	**Fic**	
Rhodes, J. P. Ninth Ward	**Fic**	
Ribay, R. Patron saints of nothing	**Fic**	
Rivera, K. Cece Rios and the Desert of Souls	**Fic**	
Rubens, M. Sons of the 613	**Fic**	
Rubin, L. Crying laughing	**Fic**	
Saeed, J. Yara's spring	**Fic**	
Sanchez, A. Bait	**Fic**	
Schlitz, L. A. The hired girl	**Fic**	
Schmidt, G. D. The Wednesday wars	**Fic**	
Sharenow, R. The Berlin Boxing Club	**Fic**	
Silvey, C. Jasper Jones	**Fic**	
Smith, J. E. Field notes on love	**Fic**	
Smith, R. Peak	**Fic**	
Snyder, L. My Jasper June	**Fic**	
Spinelli, J. Hokey Pokey	**Fic**	
Springstubb, T. Every single second	**Fic**	
Stroud, J. Heroes of the valley	**Fic**	
Sugiura, M. It's not like it's a secret	**Fic**	
Taylor, M. D. The land	**Fic**	
Taylor, M. D. The road to Memphis	**Fic**	
Telgemeier, R. Smile	**617.6**	
Temblador, A. Secrets of the Casa Rosada	**Fic**	
Thornburgh, B. Ordinary girls	**Fic**	
Turtschaninoff, M. Maresi	**Fic**	
Umminger, A. American girls	**Fic**	
Ursu, A. Breadcrumbs	**Fic**	
Vawter, V. Copyboy	**Fic**	
Vawter, V. Paperboy	**Fic**	
Voigt, C. Izzy willy-nilly	**Fic**	
Walter, J. My name is not Friday	**Fic**	
Ward, D. Beneath the mask	**Fic**	
Ward, D. Escape the mask	**Fic**	
Watkins, Y. K. So far from the bamboo grove	**Fic**	
Watson, R. Some places more than others	**Fic**	
Watson, R. Watch us rise	**Fic**	
Weil, C. I'm glad I did	**Fic**	
Whelan, G. Homeless bird	**Fic**	
Whitney, D. When you were here	**Fic**	
Wiles, D. The Aurora County All-Stars	**Fic**	
Williams, C. L. The chosen one	**Fic**	
Withers, P. First descent	**Fic**	
Wittlinger, E. Parrotfish	**Fic**	
Woodson, J. After Tupac and D Foster	**Fic**	
Wrede, P. C. The thirteenth child	**Fic**	
Yolen, J. Dragon's blood	**Fic**	
Zaczek, A. Martin McLean middle school queen	**Fic**	
Zindel, P. The pigman	**Fic**	

COMMERCE

Cooke, T. Money and trade	**382**

COMMERCE -- HISTORY

Jenkins, M. The history of money	**332.4**
Commodore Perry in the land of the Shogun. Blumberg, R.	**952**

COMMUNICABLE DISEASES

Aronin, M. Tuberculosis	616.9
Cunningham, K. Flu	614.5
Haelle, T. Vaccination investigation	615.3
Hand, C. Epidemiology	614.4
Jarrow, G. Fatal fever	614.5
Moon, W. K. Past pandemics and COVID-19	614.5
Murphy, J. Invincible microbe	616.9
Person, S. Bubonic plague	614.5
Person, S. Malaria	614.5
Reingold, A. Smallpox	614.5
Rudolph, J. The flu of 1918	614.5
Sonenklar, C. AIDS	616.97

COMMUNICABLE DISEASES -- HISTORY

Barnard, B. Outbreak	614.4
Nardo, D. COVID-19 and other pandemics	614.5

COMMUNICABLE DISEASES -- TRANSMISSION

Aronin, M. Tuberculosis	616.9

COMMUNICATION

Draper, S. M. Out of my mind	Fic
Hitchings, H. The secret life of words	422
Koch, M. Forest talk	581.7

COMMUNISM

Avi. Catch you later traitor	Fic
Brimner, L. D. Blacklisted!	323
Compestine, Y. C. Revolution is not a dinner party	Fic
Kramer, J. K. The story that cannot be told	Fic
Naden, C. J. Mao Zedong and the Chinese Revolution	951.05092
Yelchin, E. Breaking Stalin's nose	Fic

COMMUNISTS

Levine, K. The paper cowboy	Fic

COMMUNITIES

Butler, G. Drawn across borders	304.8
Cartaya, P. The epic fail of Arturo Zamora	Fic
Creech, S. The unfinished angel	Fic
Giff, P. R. Winter sky	Fic
Gulledge, L. L. Will & Whit	Fic
Hirsch, J. The eleventh plague	Fic
Nelson, M. My Seneca village	811
Nicholson, H. Moonshot	741.5
Turnage, S. The ghosts of Tupelo Landing	Fic
Vanderpool, C. Moon over Manifest	Fic

COMMUNITY ACTIVISM

Giles, C. D. Take back the block	Fic
Lady Gaga. Channel kindness	177
Paul, C. You are mighty	306

COMMUNITY AND SCHOOL

Craig, S. E. Trauma-sensitive schools for the adolescent years	371.92

COMMUNITY GARDENING

Fleischman, P. Seedfolks	Fic

COMMUNITY LIFE

Berry, J. All the truth that's in me	Fic
Bryant, J. Ringside 1925	Fic
Nielsen, S. No fixed address	Fic
White, R. Way Down Deep	Fic

COMMUNITY ORGANIZATION

Styron, A. Steal this country	320.0835

COMMUNITY SERVICE (PUNISHMENT)

Pearsall, S. The seventh most important thing	Fic
Sonnenblick, J. Notes from the midnight driver	Fic

COMPARATIVE PSYCHOLOGY

Safina, C. Beyond words	591.56
Comparative religion. Mooney, C.	200.9
Compass south. Larson, H.	741.5

COMPASSION

Bluth, K. The self-compassionate teen	155.5
Lady Gaga. Channel kindness	177
Compestine, Ying Chang	
A banquet for hungry ghosts	Fic
Revolution is not a dinner party	Fic

COMPETITION

Al-Mansour, H. The green bicycle	Fic
Aldredge, B. Sasquatch love and other imaginary things	Fic
Anderson, J. D. One last shot	Fic
Barone, R. Race to the bottom of the Earth	919.89
Camper, C. Lowriders in space	741.5
Chapman, E. Caster	Fic
Collins, S. The Hunger Games	Fic
Collins, S. Mockingjay	Fic
DiCamillo, K. Raymie Nightingale	Fic
Finkelstein, N. H. Three across	629.130973
Furudate, H. Haikyu!!	741.5
Gifford, C. Swimming	797.2
Gifford, C. Track and field	796.42
Gitlin, M. Girls play to win softball	796.357
Grabenstein, C. Mr. Lemoncello's great library race	Fic
Grabenstein, C. Mr. Lemoncello's Library Olympics	Fic
Green, T. Force out	Fic
Gurevich, M. Making the cut	Fic
Ifueko, J. Raybearer	Fic
Johnson, R. L. Battle of the dinosaur bones	560.97309
Juby, S. The fashion committee	Fic
Konigsburg, E. L. The view from Saturday	Fic
Mack, W. C. Athlete vs. mathlete	Fic
Macy, S. Swifter higher stronger	796.48
Martinez, J. Virtuosity	Fic
McDougall, C. Girls play to win track & field	796.42
Munda, R. Fireborne	Fic
Shusterman, N. Scythe	Fic
Smolka, B. Lacrosse	796.34
Stiefvater, M. The Scorpio races	Fic
Wallace, R. Perpetual check	Fic
Young, B. The prettiest	Fic

COMPETITION (BIOLOGY)

Messner, K. Tracking pythons	597.96

COMPETITION IN BOYS

Avi. The button war	Fic

COMPETITION IN GIRLS

DiCamillo, K. Raymie Nightingale	Fic

COMPETITION IN TEENAGERS

Shen, P. Nothing can possibly go wrong	741.5

COMPETITIVE EATING

Nix, G. Lirael daughter of the Clayr	Fic
O'Neill, K. Princess princess ever after	741.5
Oates, J. C. Big Mouth & Ugly Girl	Fic
Oliver, L. The spindlers	Fic
Phelan, M. The storm in the barn	741.5
Skrypuch, M. F. One step at a time	618.92
Smith, I. Half spoon of rice	Fic
Courage for beginners. Harrington, K.	Fic
Courage has no color. Stone, T. L.	940.54

COURAGE IN BOYS

Farmer, N. The house of the scorpion	Fic
Hoobler, D. The ghost in the Tokaido Inn	Fic
Kinney, J. The last straw	Fic
Naylor, P. R. Shiloh	Fic
Smith, I. Half spoon of rice	Fic
Spinelli, J. Wringer	Fic

COURAGE IN CHILDREN

Cline-Ransome, L. Being Clem	Fic
Park, L. S. When my name was Keoko	Fic

COURAGE IN GIRLS

Haddix, M. P. Among the betrayed	Fic
Hesse, K. Letters from Rifka	Fic
Mah, A. Y. Chinese Cinderella and the Secret Dragon Society	Fic
McCoola, M. Baba Yaga's assistant	741.5
McKinley, R. The blue sword	Fic
Oliver, L. The spindlers	Fic
Russell, P. C. Coraline	741.5
Sanderson, B. Skyward	Fic
Wambach, A. Wolfpack	155.3

COURAGE IN MEN

Morpurgo, M. Beowulf	398.2

COURAGE IN TEENAGE BOYS

Bartoletti, S. C. The boy who dared	Fic
Bass, K. Graffiti knight	Fic
Flanagan, J. The battle for Skandia	Fic
Flanagan, J. The emperor of Nihon-ja	Fic
Flanagan, J. Erak's ransom	Fic
Flanagan, J. The kings of Clonmel	Fic
Flanagan, J. The ruins of Gorlan	Fic
Flanagan, J. The siege of Macindaw	Fic
Jinks, C. The genius wars	Fic
Lawrence, I. The smugglers	Fic
Lipsyte, R. The contender	Fic
Wisler, G. C. Red Cap	Fic

COURAGE IN TEENAGE GIRLS

Hale, S. The goose girl	Fic
Matas, C. After the war	Fic
Milford, K. The Boneshaker	Fic
Nix, G. Sabriel	Fic

COURAGE IN TEENAGERS

Gardner, K. Brave enough	Fic
Ibbotson, E. The dragonfly pool	Fic
Nix, G. Abhorsen	Fic
Nix, G. Lirael daughter of the Clayr	Fic
Oates, J. C. Big Mouth & Ugly Girl	Fic

COURAGE IN WOMEN

Del Negro, J. Passion and poison	Fic
Elliott, D. Voices	Fic
Wilson, K. White Rose	Fic
The **courage** test. Preller, J.	Fic
Courage to soar. Biles, S.	B

COURIERS

Vance, A. P. The Heartbreak Messenger	Fic

Courtney, Nadine Jolie, 1980-

All-American Muslim girl	Fic

COURTS

Grisham, J. The abduction	Fic
Grisham, J. The accused	Fic
Marguiles, P. The devil on trial	345.73

COURTS AND COURTIERS

Anderson, M. T. Yvain	741.5
Buckley-Archer, L. The many lives of John Stone	Fic
Goodman, A. The Dark Days Club	Fic
Hartman, R. Shadow scale	Fic
Ifueko, J. Raybearer	Fic
Marsh, K. Jepp who defied the stars	Fic
Nielsen, J. A. The false prince	Fic
Pierce, T. The will of the empress	Fic
Pike, A. Glitter	Fic
Stanley, D. The princess of Cortova	Fic
Zettel, S. A most dangerous deception	Fic

COURTS-MARTIAL AND COURTS OF INQUIRY

Gourley, C. The horrors of Andersonville	973.7

COURTSHIP

Kindl, P. A school for brides	Fic

COURTSHIP OF ANIMALS

Downer, A. The animal mating game	591.56

COUSINS

Chanani, N. Jukebox	Fic
Creech, S. Absolutely normal chaos	Fic
Draper, S. M. The battle of Jericho	Fic
Helgerson, J. Horns and wrinkles	Fic
Hesse, K. Letters from Rifka	Fic
Hiaasen, C. Skink--no surrender	Fic
Kaufman, A. The world between blinks	Fic
Lewis, C. S. The voyage of the Dawn Treader	Fic
Ribay, R. Patron saints of nothing	Fic
Smith, R. Chupacabra	Fic
White, R. Belle Prater's boy	Fic
Wiles, D. Anthem	Fic
Williams-Garcia, R. Like sisters on the homefront	Fic

Couwenhoven, Terri

The boys' guide to growing up	613
Cover-up. Feinstein, J.	Fic

COVERT OPERATIONS

Lerangis, P. The colossus rises	Fic

COVID-19 (DISEASE)

Moon, W. K. Past pandemics and COVID-19	614.5
Nardo, D. COVID-19 and other pandemics	614.5
COVID-19 and other pandemics. Nardo, D.	614.5

COVID-19 PANDEMIC, 2019-

Moon, W. K. Past pandemics and COVID-19	614.5

Coville, Bruce

Hurley, T. Ghostgirl — Fic
Mills, E. Famous in a small town — Fic
Perkins, S. Anna and the French kiss — Fic
Russell, R. R. Tales from a not-so-fabulous life — Fic
Schlitz, L. A. The hired girl — Fic
Simon, F. The monstrous child — Fic
Sones, S. What my mother doesn't know — Fic
Wiseman, R. Boys girls and other hazardous materials — Fic

CRUSHES IN TEENAGERS
Brezenoff, S. Brooklyn burning — Fic
Meyer, S. Twilight — Fic

Crust and spray. Larsen, C. S. — 612.8

Crutcher, Chris
Deadline — Fic

Cryer's cross. McMann, L. — Fic

Crying laughing. Rubin, L. — Fic

CRYOBIOLOGY
Amstutz, L. J. Discover cryobiology — 571.4

CRYOPRESERVATION OF ORGANS, TISSUES, ETC
Amstutz, L. J. Discover cryobiology — 571.4

Cryptocurrencies and the blockchain revolution. January, B. — 332.4

CRYPTOGRAPHY
Bruchac, J. Code Talker — Fic
Gibbs, S. Charlie Thorne and the last equation — Fic
Gibbs, S. Charlie Thorne and the lost city — Fic

CRYPTOZOOLOGY
Halls, K. M. Tales of the cryptids — 001.944
Smith, R. Chupacabra — Fic
Stewart, G. B. Vampires — 001.9

CRYSTALS
Reynolds, T. Rocks crystals and gems — 552

CUBA
Engle, M. The wild book — Fic
Gratz, A. Refugee — Fic
Hayes, J. Dance Nana dance — 398.2
Tracy, K. We visit Cuba — 972.91
Wells, R. My Havana — Fic
Wright, D. K. Cuba — 972.91

CUBA -- HISTORY -- 1959-1990
Smith-Llera, D. Che Guevara's face — 972.9106

Cuba. Wright, D. K. — 972.91

CUBAN AMERICAN GIRLS
Medina, M. Merci Suarez can't dance — Fic

CUBAN AMERICANS
Behar, R. Lucky broken girl — Fic
Cartaya, P. The epic fail of Arturo Zamora — Fic
Lupica, M. Heat — Fic
Moreno, N. Don't date Rosa Santos — Fic
Older, D. J. Thunder run — Fic

CUBAN MISSILE CRISIS, 1962
Stein, R. C. Cuban Missile Crisis — 972.9106
Strasser, T. Fallout — Fic
Wiles, D. Countdown — Fic

Cuban Missile Crisis. Stein, R. C. — 972.9106

CUBANS
Hayes, J. Dance Nana dance — 398.2

Cuckoo song. Hardinge, F. — Fic

Cuevas, Adrianna
The total eclipse of Nestor Lopez — Fic

Culham, Ruth
6+1 traits of writing — 372.62
Traits of writing — 372.6

CULT LEADERS
Flanagan, J. Halt's peril — Fic
Flanagan, J. The kings of Clonmel — Fic
Fukuda, A. X. The prey — Fic

CULTS
Flanagan, J. Halt's peril — Fic
Flanagan, J. The kings of Clonmel — Fic
Fukuda, A. X. The prey — Fic
Johnson, M. The shadow cabinet — Fic
Williams, C. L. The chosen one — Fic

CULTURAL DIFFERENCES
Blumberg, R. Commodore Perry in the land of the Shogun — 952
Johnston, T. Any small goodness — Fic
Lai, T. Inside out & back again — Fic
Larocca, R. Red white and whole — Fic
Stephens, R. D. Henry Chow and other stories from the Asian Canadian Writers' Workshop — Fic

CULTURAL PROPERTY
Kirkpatrick, K. Mysterious bones — 979.7
Walker, S. M. Their skeletons speak — 970.01

Culturally responsive teaching and the brain. Hammond, Z. — 370.117

CULTURE
Bailey, D. Tattoo art around the world — 391.6
Chanani, N. Pashmina — 741.5
Currie, S. African American folklore — 398.08996
Foley, E. El Salvador — 972.84
Gerszak, R. Beyond bullets — 958.1
Heinrichs, A. Sweden — 948.5
Hinds, K. Everyday life in medieval Europe — 909.07
King, D. C. First people — 970.00497
Krasno, R. Cloud weavers — 398.2
Lee, F. Fun with Chinese cooking — 641.595
Mara, W. Poland — 943.8
Moore, W. All about Japan — 952
Moragne, W. New Jersey — 974.9
Nagle, J. Why people get tattoos and other body art — 391.6
Pietrzyk, L. Maryland — 975.2
Schomp, V. The Aztecs — 972
Smelt, R. New Zealand — 993
Sonneborn, L. Kuwait — 953.67
Stefoff, R. Idaho — 979.6
Stefoff, R. Washington — 979.7
Stein, R. C. Ancient Mexico — 972
Stein, R. C. Modern Mexico — 972.08
Yomtov, N. Colombia — 986.1
Yomtov, N. Costa Rica — 972.86

CULTURE CONFLICT
Abdel-Fattah, R. Ten things I hate about me — Fic
Aronson, M. 1968 — 909.82

Baldwin, J. Go tell it on the mountain — Fic

Elkeles, S. How to ruin your boyfriend's reputation — Fic

Myers, W. D. Sunrise over Fallujah — Fic

Ostlere, C. Karma — Fic

Park, L. S. When my name was Keoko — Fic

CULTURE SHOCK

Hiranandani, V. The whole story of half a girl — Fic

Cunningham, Kevin, 1966-

Flu — 614.5

Malaria — 614.5

The **cupcake** queen. Hepler, H. — Fic

CUPCAKES

Bauer, J. Close to famous — Fic

Hepler, H. The cupcake queen — Fic

Varon, S. Bake sale — 741.5

CUPID AND PSYCHE (TALE)

Hearne, B. G. Beauties and beasts — 398.21

Curato, Mike

Flamer — Fic

CURIE FAMILY

Hardyman, R. Pierre and Marie Curie — B

CURIE, MARIE, 1867-1934

Atkins, J. Borrowed names — 811

Krull, K. Marie Curie — B

CURIOSITIES AND WONDERS

Beccaloni, G. Biggest bugs life-size — 595.714

Birmingham, M. Weird zone — 796.1

Boyer, C. Why not? — 031.02

Eaton, G. A history of ambition in 50 hoaxes — 001.9

Etingoff, K. Howling at the moon — 398

Etingoff, K. The science of the beast — 398

Farndon, J. Do not open — 031.02

Grossman, E. What breathes through its butt? — 500

Hawkins, J. Atlantis and other lost worlds — 001.94

Hughes, S. Case closed? — 902

Hulick, K. Strange but true — 001.94

Hussain, S. S. The Arab world thought of it — 909

Johnson, H. Fearsome creatures of the Lumber-woods — 398.2

Kallen, S. A. Vampire history and lore — 398

Karst, K. Area 51 — 358.4

Lake, M. Weird U.S. — 973

Martin, N. Fighting the fangs — 398

National Geographic Kids Almanac 2022 — 031.02

Newquist, H. P. Here there be monsters — 594

Noyes, D. Sideshow — Fic

Nye, B. Bill Nye's great big world of science — 500

O'Meara, S. J. Are you afraid yet? — 001.944

Reynolds, T. Wonders of the world — 031.02

Robson, D. Encounters with vampires — 398

Sanna, E. Pop monsters — 398

Stewart, G. B. Vampires — 001.9

Stewart, S. The psychology of our dark side — 398

Winterbottom, J. Frightlopedia — 031.02

CURIOSITY

Krull, K. Leonardo da Vinci — 509

CURIOSITY IN GIRLS

Byars, B. C. The dark stairs — Fic

A **curious** tale of the in-between. DeStefano, L. — Fic

The **curious** world of Calpurnia Tate. Kelly, J. — Fic

Curran, Robert

The zombie handbook — 398.21

CURRICULUM PLANNING

Harada, V. H. Inquiry learning through librarian-teacher partnerships — 371.14

Currie, Stephen, 1960-

An actor on the Elizabethan stage — 792

African American folklore — 398.08996

Medieval crusades — 909.07

Currie-Mcghee, L. K. (Leanne K.)

Exercise addiction — 616.85

Currier, Katrina Saltonstall, 1969-

Kai's journey to Gold Mountain — Fic

Curse of the forgotten city. Aster, A. — Fic

Curse of the Night Witch. Aster, A. — Fic

CURSES

Anderson, S. The girl who speaks bear — Fic

Aster, A. Curse of the forgotten city — Fic

Aster, A. Curse of the Night Witch — Fic

Black, H. Red glove — Fic

Braswell, L. Part of your world — Fic

Cypess, L. Thornwood — Fic

Flinn, A. A kiss in time — Fic

Funke, C. Fearless — Fic

George, J. D. Princess of the Midnight Ball — Fic

Gratton, T. Strange grace — Fic

Harrison, M. 13 curses — Fic

Kessler, L. Emily Windsnap and the castle in the mist — Fic

Lace, W. W. King Tut's curse — 932

Levine, G. C. Ella enchanted — Fic

Lloyd, N. A snicker of magic — Fic

Lloyd-Jones, E. The bone houses — Fic

Marchetta, M. Finnikin of the rock — Fic

McGrane, M. The accursed vampire — 741.5

McLemore, A. Blanca & Roja — Fic

Medley, L. Castle waiting — 741.5

Morris, P. Ruined — Fic

Napoli, D. J. Beast — Fic

Renier, A. The unsinkable Walker Bean — 741.5

Ryan, P. M. Echo — Fic

Shurtliff, L. Rump — Fic

Stanley, D. The silver bowl — Fic

Tanquary, K. The night parade — Fic

Walsh, P. The Crowfield curse — Fic

Watson, J. Loot — Fic

Werlin, N. Impossible — Fic

Whipple, N. House of ivy and sorrow — Fic

Curtis, Christopher Paul

Bud not Buddy — Fic

Elijah of Buxton — Fic

The madman of Piney Woods — Fic

The Watsons go to Birmingham 1963 — Fic

Curtsies & conspiracies. Carriger, G. — Fic

Cushman, Karen

Catherine called Birdy	Fic
The loud silence of Francine Green	Fic
The midwife's apprentice	Fic
Rodzina	Fic
Cusick, Dawn	
Get the scoop on animal puke	591.5
Cut. McCormick, P.	Fic
Cut from the same cloth. San Souci, R. D.	398.21
CUTTING (SELF-HARM)	
McCormick, P. Cut	Fic
Cybele's secret. Marillier, J.	Fic
CYBER-THRILLERS	
Doctorow, C. Pirate cinema	Fic
Gagnon, M. Don't let go	Fic
Gagnon, M. Don't look now	Fic
Gagnon, M. Don't turn around	Fic
Kincaid, S. J. Insignia	Fic
Kritzer, N. Catfishing on Catnet	Fic
CYBERBULLYING	
Farizan, S. Here to stay	Fic
Kyi, T. L. Eyes & spies	323.44
Littman, S. Backlash	Fic
Scherer, L. S. Cyberbullying	302.34
Cyberbullying. Scherer, L. S.	302.34
CYBERNETICS	
Freedman, J. Robots through history	629.8
CYBORGS	
Meyer, M. Cinder	Fic
Meyer, M. Cress	Fic
Meyer, M. Scarlet	Fic
Rothenberg, J. The Kingdom	Fic
Cyclist bikelist. Robinson, L.	796.6
CYCLOPES (GREEK MYTHOLOGY)	
Hinds, G. The Odyssey	741.5
CYNICISM	
Philippe, B. The field guide to the North American teenager	Fic
Cypess, Leah	
Death sworn	Fic
Thornwood	Fic
Cyprus, Naomi	
Sisters of glass	Fic
CYSTIC FIBROSIS	
Avery, T. Not as we know it	Fic
Miller, P. Cystic fibrosis	616.3
Powell, J. Explaining cystic fibrosis	616.3
Telgemeier, R. Ghosts	741.5
CYSTIC FIBROSIS -- GENETIC ASPECTS	
Giddings, S. Cystic fibrosis	616.3
Cystic fibrosis. Giddings, S.	616.3
Cystic fibrosis. Miller, P.	616.3
CYTOLOGY	
Ballard, C. Cells and cell function	571.6
CZECH REPUBLIC	
Taylor, L. Daughter of smoke and bone	Fic
CZECHOSLOVAKIA	
Polak, M. What world is left	Fic

Rubin, S. G. The cat with the yellow star	940.53
Thomson, R. Terezin	940.53

D

D'Amico, Joan, 1957-	
The coming to America cookbook	641.59
The United States cookbook	641.5973
D'Aulaire, Ingri, 1904-1980	
D'Aulaires' book of Norse myths	293
D'Aulaires' book of Norse myths. D'Aulaire, I.	293
D'Harcourt, Claire, 1960-	
Masterpieces up close	759
D'Lacey, Chris	
Dark fire	Fic
The fire ascending	Fic
The fire eternal	Fic
Fire star	Fic
The fire within	Fic
Fire world	Fic
Icefire	Fic
D-Day. Atkinson, R.	940.54
D-Day. Hopkinson, D.	940.54
Da Vinci's cat. Murdock, C. G.	Fic
DADDY LONGLEGS	
Markle, S. Harvestmen	595.4
DAHL, ROALD	
Dahl, R. Boy	B
Dahl, Roald	
Boy	B
Skin and other stories	Fic
Daily life in colonial America. Nardo, D.	973.2
Daily life in colonial New England. Johnson, C. D.	974
DAIRY PRODUCTS	
Waters, R. My daily diet	613.2
Dairy queen. Murdock, C. G.	Fic
Daisy to the rescue. Campbell, J.	636
Daja's book. Pierce, T.	Fic
Dakin, Glenn	
The Society of Unrelenting Vigilance	Fic
DAKOTA INDIANS -- WARS, 1876	
Walker, P. R. Remember Little Bighorn	973.8
DAKOTA TERRITORY	
Park, L. S. Prairie lotus	Fic
DALAI LAMA	
Kimmel, E. C. Boy on the Lion Throne	B
Dallas, Sandra	
The quilt walk	Fic
Daly, Kathleen N.	
Greek and Roman mythology A to Z	292.1
DAM FAILURES	
Koestler-Grack, R. A. Johnstown flood of 1889	974.8
Philbrick, W. R. Wild river	Fic
DAMASCUS, SYRIA	
Dassu, A. M. Boy everywhere	Fic
Damico, Gina	
Croak	Fic

Lynch, C. Inexcusable — Fic

DATE RAPE DRUGS

Conley, K. A. Date rape drugs — 362.883

Date rape drugs. Conley, K. A. — 362.883

Dateline Troy. Fleischman, P. — 398.2

DATING (SOCIAL CUSTOMS)

Ahmed, S. Love hate & other filters — Fic

Bailey, J. Sex puberty and all that stuff — 613.9

Baskin, N. R. All we know of love — Fic

Bigelow, L. J. Starting from here — Fic

Cooney, C. B. Janie face to face — Fic

Fantaskey, B. Jessica's guide to dating on the dark side — Fic

Flake, S. Who am I without him? — Fic

Giles, L. R. Not so pure and simple — Fic

Johnson, M. The madness underneath — Fic

Johnson, M. Scarlett fever — Fic

Kuhn, S. I love you so mochi — Fic

Levithan, D. Two boys kissing — Fic

Lockhart, E. The disreputable history of Frankie Landau-Banks — Fic

Menon, S. 10 things I hate about Pinky — Fic

Menon, S. There's something about Sweetie — Fic

Moreno, N. Don't date Rosa Santos — Fic

Moskowitz, H. Sick kids in love — Fic

Sones, S. What my girlfriend doesn't know — Fic

Sones, S. What my mother doesn't know — Fic

DATING VIOLENCE

Conley, K. A. Date rape drugs — 362.883

Wright, B. Putting makeup on the fat boy — Fic

Datlow, Ellen

The beastly bride — Fic

The Coyote Road — Fic

Troll's eye view — Fic

DAU, JOHN BUL

Dau, J. B. Lost boy lost girl — B

Dau, John Bul

Lost boy lost girl — B

Daud, Somaiya

Mirage — Fic

Daughter of smoke and bone. Taylor, L. — Fic

Daughter of the pirate king. Levenseller, T. — Fic

Daughter of Xanadu. Yang, D. J. — Fic

Daughters of the desert. Murphy, C. R. — 220.9

DAVE, FL. 1834-1864

Cheng, A. Etched in clay — B

David, Laurie

The down-to-Earth guide to global warming — 363.738

Davies, Nicola, 1958-

Extreme animals — 590

DAVIS, BENJAMIN O., JR., 1912-2002

Earl, S. Benjamin O. Davis Jr. — B

Davis, Daniel K.

Versace — B

DAVIS, JEFFERSON, 1808-1889

Swanson, J. L. Bloody times — 973.7092

Davis, Jennifer Pharr

Hiking and camping — 796.51

Davis, Kenneth C.

In the shadow of Liberty — 920.0092

More deadly than war — 614.5

Strongman — 321.9092

Davis, Mandy

Superstar — Fic

DAVIS, MILES

Orr, T. Miles Davis — B

Davis, Tanita S.

Mare's war — Fic

Davy Crockett. Sanford, W. R. — B

Dawn. Hunter, E. — Fic

Dawson, Eric David

Putting peace first — 303.6

Dawson, Ian

Renaissance medicine — 610

A **day** at the New Amsterdam Theatre. Domenico, G. — 792.09

Day of tears. Lester, J. — Fic

The **day** the world stopped turning. Morpurgo, M. — Fic

Day, Christine, 1993-

I can make this promise — Fic

The sea in winter — Fic

Days of blood & starlight. Taylor, L. — Fic

DAYTON, TENNESSEE

Bryant, J. Ringside 1925 — Fic

De La Bedoyere, Camilla

Balancing work and play — 155.5

Creatures of the night — 591.5

Monsters of the deep — 591.77

De La Cruz, Melissa, 1971-

Never after — Fic

DE LA RENTA, OSCAR

Darraj, S. M. Oscar de la Renta — B

DE LONG, GEORGE W. (GEORGE WASHINGTON), 1844-1881

Wallace, S. N. Bound by ice — 910.4

DE VERE, EDWARD, 17TH EARL OF OXFORD, 1550-1604

Broach, E. Shakespeare's secret — Fic

De-extinction. Hirsch, R. E. — 591.68

DEAD

Damico, G. Croak — Fic

Kwaymullina, A. The things she's seen — Fic

Thornhill, J. I found a dead bird — 306.9

Vande Velde, V. Being dead — Fic

The **dead** girls of Hysteria Hall. Alender, K. — Fic

Dead is the new black. Perez, M. — Fic

Dead little mean girl. Darrows, E. — Fic

Dead voices. Arden, K. — Fic

Dead Wednesday. Spinelli, J. — Fic

Dead zones. Hand, C. — 639.2

DeadEndia. Steele, H. — Fic

Deadliest dinosaurs. Nardo, D. — 567.9

Deadliest mammals. Allman, T. — 599.7

Deadliest reptiles. Hirschmann, K. — 597.9

Deadliest sharks. Abramovitz, M. — 597.3

Deadliest snakes. Hirschmann, K. — 597.96

Bowling, N. Witch born	**Fic**		Helen's eyes	**B**
Scott, M. The alchemyst	**Fic**		**DELAWARE**	
Deem, James M.			Kelly, E. E. We dream of space	**Fic**
Auschwitz	**940.53**		**Delilah** Dirk and the Turkish Lieutenant. Cliff, T.	**741.5**
Bodies from the ash	**937**		**DELIVERY SERVICES**	
Bodies from the bog	**569.9**		Matti, T. Mister orange	**Fic**
Faces from the past	**599.9**		**Dell, Pamela**	
Kristallnacht	**940.53**		Man on the moon	**629.45**
The prisoners of Breendonk	**940.53**		Mississippi	**976.2**
The **deep** & dark blue. Smith, N.	**741.5**		**Dembicki, Matt**	
The **deep**. Dunmore, H.	**Fic**		Trickster	**741.5**
DEEP DIVING			**DEMENTIA**	
Cerullo, M. M. Journey to shark island	**597.309164**		Lord, C. Half a chance	**Fic**
Cerullo, M. M. Searching for Great White Sharks	**597.3**		**Demi**	
Cerullo, M. M. Seeking giant sharks	**597.3**		Buddha	**B**
Cerullo, M. M. Sharks of the deep	**597.3**		Su Dongpo	**B**
Mallory, K. At home beneath the sea	**551.46**		**DEMIGODS**	
The **deep** end. Kinney, J.	**Fic**		Barron, R. Maya and the rising dark	**Fic**
Deep roots. Tate, N.	**582.16**		Riordan, R. The battle of the Labyrinth	**Fic**
Deep sea. Thor, A.	**Fic**		Riordan, R. The blood of Olympus	**Fic**
Deep woods. Caravantes, P.	**B**		Riordan, R. The burning maze	**Fic**
DEEP-SEA SOUNDING			Riordan, R. The dark prophecy	**Fic**
Johnson, R. L. Journey into the deep	**591.77**		Riordan, R. The hidden oracle	**Fic**
Deeper reading. Gallagher, K.	**372.47**		Riordan, R. The house of Hades	**Fic**
Deepest darkest. Ritter, W.	**Fic**		Riordan, R. The last Olympian	**Fic**
Deeplight. Hardinge, F.	**Fic**		Riordan, R. The lightning thief	**Fic**
The **Deepwater** Horizon oil spill. Bodden, V.	**363.11**		Riordan, R. The lost hero	**Fic**
DEER			Riordan, R. The mark of Athena	**Fic**
MacRae, S. Deer hunting	**799.2**		Riordan, R. The sea of monsters	**Fic**
DEER HUNTING			Riordan, R. The son of Neptune	**Fic**
MacRae, S. Deer hunting	**799.2**		Riordan, R. The sword of summer	**Fic**
Deer hunting. MacRae, S.	**799.2**		Riordan, R. The Titan's curse	**Fic**
DEFECATION			Riordan, R. The tower of Nero	**Fic**
Montgomery, H. L. Who gives a poop?	**612.3**		Simon, F. The monstrous child	**Fic**
Define "normal". Peters, J. A.	**Fic**		Venditti, R. The lightning thief	**741.5**
DEFOE, DANIEL, 1661?-1731. ROBINSON CRUSOE			**Demigods** and monsters. Riordan, R.	**813**
Kraske, R. Marooned	**996.1**		**DEMOCRACY -- HISTORY**	
DEFORESTATION			Davis, K. C. Strongman	**321.9092**
Hand, C. Bringing back our tropical forests	**333.75**		**DEMOCRATIC PARTY. NATIONAL CONVENTION, CHICAGO, ILLINOIS, 1968**	
Defries, Cheryl L.			Kaufman, M. T. 1968	**909.82**
Leif Eriksson	**B**		The **demon** in the teahouse. Hoobler, D.	**Fic**
Defy the stars. Gray, C.	**Fic**		The **Demon** King. Chima, C. W.	**Fic**
Degas. Spence, D.	**B**		**DEMON SLAYERS**	
DEGAS, EDGAR, 1834-1917			DasGupta, S. The force of fire	**Fic**
Spence, D. Degas	**B**		Winters, C. Odd & true	**Fic**
Del Negro, Janice			Yee, F. C. The iron will of Genie Lo	**Fic**
Passion and poison	**Fic**		**DEMONIC POSSESSION**	
Delacre, Lulu			Bardugo, L. King of scars	**Fic**
Golden tales	**398.2**		**DEMONS**	
Us in progress	**Fic**		Bardugo, L. King of scars	**Fic**
Delaney, Joseph, 1945-			Goodman, A. The Dark Days Club	**Fic**
The ghost prison	**Fic**		Langrish, K. The shadow hunt	**Fic**
A new darkness	**Fic**		Link, K. Monstrous affections	**Fic**
Revenge of the witch	**Fic**		MacHale, D. J. The lost city of Faar	**Fic**
Delano, Marfe Ferguson			MacHale, D. J. The merchant of death	**Fic**
Earth in the hot seat	**363.738**		MacHale, D. J. The never war	**Fic**
Genius	**B**			

Woods, M. Seven natural wonders of Africa — 960

DESERTS -- SOCIAL LIFE AND CUSTOMS

Hinds, K. The countryside — 909

Deserts inside out. Cohen, M. — 577.54

DESIGN

Kidd, C. Go — 740

Macaulay, D. Mosque — 726

Design it. Arato, R. — 745.2

Design your own butterfly garden. Harkins, S. S. — 638

DESIGNER DRUGS

LeVert, S. Ecstasy — 613.8

Parks, P. J. Bath salts and other synthetic drugs — 362.29

DESIRE

Sendak, M. My brother's book — Fic

DESOTO, HERNANDO, 1500?-1542

Young, J. C. Hernando de Soto — B

Dessen, Sarah

Lock and key — Fic

The moon and more — Fic

Saint Anything — Fic

That summer — Fic

The truth about forever — Fic

What happened to goodbye — Fic

DESSERTS

Carle, M. Teens cook dessert — 641.8

Eboch, M. M. Crave-worthy candy confections with a side of science — 641.86

Destefano, Lauren

A curious tale of the in-between — Fic

Destination moon. Maurer, R. — 629.45

Destination unexpected. Gallo, D. R. — Fic

Destiny's path. Jones, F. — Fic

DETECTIVES

Blake, K. Anna dressed in blood — Fic

Funke, C. The Thief Lord — Fic

Gaiman, N. M is for magic — Fic

Gleason, C. The clockwork scarab — Fic

Hoobler, D. The demon in the teahouse — Fic

Hoobler, D. The ghost in the Tokaido Inn — Fic

Hoobler, D. Seven paths to death — Fic

Hoobler, D. The sword that cut the burning grass — Fic

Landy, D. The faceless ones — Fic

Landy, D. Playing with fire — Fic

Landy, D. Skulduggery Pleasant — Fic

Ritter, W. The dire king — Fic

DETECTOR DOGS

Wadsworth, G. Poop detectives — 636.7

DETERMINATION (PERSONAL QUALITY)

Appelt, K. Keeper — Fic

Donnelly, J. Stepsister — Fic

French, S. T. Operation Redwood — Fic

Jeter, D. The contract — Fic

Park, L. S. When my name was Keoko — Fic

St. John, W. Outcasts united — 796.334092

DETERMINATION IN CHILDREN

French, S. T. Operation Redwood — Fic

DETERMINATION IN GIRLS

Appelt, K. Keeper — Fic

Kadohata, C. Weedflower — Fic

Martinez, C. G. The smell of old lady perfume — Fic

Pierce, T. First test — Fic

Van Vleet, C. Eliza Bing is (not) a big fat quitter — Fic

DETERMINATION IN MEN

Brown, D. The boys in the boat — 797.12

DETERMINATION IN TEENAGE BOYS

Flanagan, J. Halt's peril — Fic

DETERMINATION IN TEENAGE GIRLS

Fusco, K. N. Chasing Augustus — Fic

Qamar, A. Beneath my mother's feet — Fic

Sitomer, A. L. The secret story of Sonia Rodriguez — Fic

Vande Velde, V. Heir apparent — Fic

DETERMINATION IN TEENAGERS

Marsden, J. Tomorrow when the war began — Fic

DETERMINATION IN WOMEN

Sheinkin, S. Born to fly — 797.5

Determined to stay. Sokolower, J. — 305.235

Detrick, Erin

Actor's choice — 808.82

DETROIT TIGERS (BASEBALL TEAM)

Lupica, M. The batboy — Fic

DETROIT, MICHIGAN

Lupica, M. The batboy — Fic

Deuker, Carl

Golden arm — Fic

Gym candy — Fic

Swagger — Fic

DEVELOPING COUNTRIES

Andrews, D. Business without borders — 658

Mulligan, A. Trash — Fic

DEVELOPMENTAL DISABILITIES

Grossberg, B. N. Asperger's rules! — 618.92

Levete, S. Explaining cerebral palsy — 616.8

Rodriguez, A. M. Autism spectrum disorders — 616.85

Royston, A. Explaining Down syndrome — 618.92

Snedden, R. Explaining autism — 616.85

Stefanski, D. How to talk to an autistic kid — 618.92

Tabone, F. Autism spectrum disorder — 616.85

DEVELOPMENTALLY DISABLED CHILDREN -- EDUCATION (SECONDARY)

Mannix, D. Social skills activities for secondary students with special needs — 371.9

DEVELOPMENTALLY DISABLED CHILDREN -- LIFE SKILLS GUIDES

Mannix, D. Social skills activities for secondary students with special needs — 371.9

The **devil** on trial. Marguiles, P. — 345.73

The **devil's** breath. Gilman, D. — Fic

The **devil's** paintbox. McKernan, V. — Fic

Devil's pass. Brouwer, S. — Fic

Devlin, Ivy, 1972-

Low red moon — Fic

DEVON, ENGLAND

Landman, T. Hell and high water — Fic

DEWEY (MARMALADE CAT)

Myron, V. Dewey the library cat	636.80092
Dewey the library cat. Myron, V.	636.80092
Dewoskin, Rachel	
Someday we will fly	Fic
DIABETES	
Ambrose, M. Investigating diabetes	616.4
Brill, M. T. Diabetes	616.4
Williams, A. L. Diabetes information for teens	616.4
Diabetes. Brill, M. T.	616.4
DIABETES IN ADOLESCENCE	
Williams, A. L. Diabetes information for teens	616.4
Diabetes information for teens. Williams, A. L.	616.4
DIAGNOSIS	
Rooney, A. The history of medicine	610.9
DIAKITE, BABA WAGUE	
Diakite, B. W. A gift from childhood	B
Diakite, Baba Wague	
A gift from childhood	B
Diamond boy. Williams, M.	Fic
A **diamond** in the desert. Fitzmaurice, K.	Fic
DIAMOND MINES AND MINING	
Williams, M. Diamond boy	Fic
The **diamond** of Darkhold. DuPrau, J.	Fic
Diamond Willow. Frost, H.	Fic
DIAMONDS	
DuPrau, J. The diamond of Darkhold	Fic
Higgins, F. E. The lunatic's curse	Fic
DIARIES	
Balliett, B. The danger box	Fic
Buckley-Archer, L. The many lives of John Stone	Fic
Clark, W. Off the map	917.804
Frederick, H. V. Yours Truly	Fic
Gale, E. K. The bully book	Fic
Gerszak, R. Beyond bullets	958.1
Goldblatt, M. Twerp	Fic
Levy, D. The year of goodbyes	811
Lugovskaya, N. I want to live	947.084
Rosen, M. J. Sailing the unknown	Fic
Shulman, M. Scrawl	Fic
Sis, P. Tibet	951
Diaries and keepsakes. Turnbull, S.	745.593
DIARISTS	
Adlington, L. J. The diary of Pelly D	Fic
DIARY NOVELS	
Alonzo, S. Riding invisible	Fic
Alvarez, J. Before we were free	Fic
Anderson, J. L. My diary from the edge of the world	Fic
Austen, C. Walking backward	Fic
Blundell, J. A city tossed and broken	Fic
Cabot, M. From the notebooks of a middle school princess	Fic
Cabot, M. The princess diaries	Fic
Carman, P. The Crossbones	Fic
Carman, P. Skeleton Creek	Fic
Chibbaro, J. Deadly	Fic
Cleary, B. Strider	Fic
Cooper, M. A brief history of Montmaray	Fic

Creech, S. Absolutely normal chaos	Fic
Cushman, K. Catherine called Birdy	Fic
Gantos, J. Jack's black book	Fic
Hale, S. Book of a thousand days	Fic
Holm, J. L. Middle school is worse than meatloaf	Fic
Hopkinson, D. The great trouble	Fic
Kinney, J. Cabin fever	Fic
Kinney, J. The deep end	Fic
Kinney, J. Diary of a wimpy kid	Fic
Kinney, J. Dog days	Fic
Kinney, J. Hard luck	Fic
Kinney, J. The last straw	Fic
Kinney, J. The long haul	Fic
Kinney, J. Old school	Fic
Kinney, J. Rodrick rules	Fic
Kinney, J. The third wheel	Fic
Kinney, J. The ugly truth	Fic
Lasky, K. A journey to the New World	Fic
Lavender, W. Aftershocks	Fic
Lloyd, S. The carbon diaries 2015	Fic
McCall, G. G. All the stars denied	Fic
McKissack, P. Nzingha	Fic
Patterson, J. Homeroom diaries	Fic
Pena, M. d. l. We were here	Fic
Pfeffer, S. B. Life as we knew it	Fic
Pierce, T. Bloodhound	Fic
Pierce, T. Mastiff	Fic
Pierce, T. Terrier	Fic
Pinkney, A. D. With the might of angels	Fic
Russell, R. R. Tales from a not-so-fabulous life	Fic
Schlitz, L. A. The hired girl	Fic
Smy, P. Thornhill	Fic
Tamaki, M. Skim	741.5
Van de Ruit, J. Spud	Fic
Walton, J. Words on bathroom walls	Fic
Yee, L. Millicent Min girl genius	Fic
Diary of a wimpy kid. Kinney, J.	Fic
The **diary** of a young girl. Frank, A.	940.53
The **diary** of Ma Yan. Ma, Y.	951.05
The **diary** of Pelly D. Adlington, L. J.	Fic
DIARY WRITING	
Cleary, B. Strider	Fic
Cushman, K. Catherine called Birdy	Fic
Kinney, J. Cabin fever	Fic
Kinney, J. The deep end	Fic
Kinney, J. Diary of a wimpy kid	Fic
Kinney, J. Dog days	Fic
Kinney, J. The last straw	Fic
Kinney, J. Rodrick rules	Fic
Kinney, J. The ugly truth	Fic
Turnbull, S. Diaries and keepsakes	745.593
Walton, J. Words on bathroom walls	Fic
DIARY WRITING FOR CHILDREN	
Kinney, J. Cabin fever	Fic
DIAS, MARLEY (MARLEY EMERSON)	
Dias, M. Marley Dias gets it done	305.23089
Dias, Marley (Marley Emerson)	

Marley Dias gets it done — 305.23089

Diaz, Julio
Tesla model S — 629.22

Dicamillo, Kate
Because of Winn-Dixie — Fic
Beverly right here — Fic
Flora & Ulysses — Fic
The magician's elephant — Fic
Raymie Nightingale — Fic

Dicey's song. Voigt, C. — Fic

Dickens. Rosen, M. — B

DICKENS, CHARLES, 1812-1870
Pratchett, T. Dodger — Fic
Rosen, M. Dickens — B
Warren, A. Charles Dickens and the street children of London — B
Wells, C. Charles Dickens — B

Dickens, Charles, 1812-1870
A Christmas carol [Lynch ill.] — Fic

DICKENS, CHARLES, 1812-1870. CHRISTMAS CAROL
Frederick, H. V. Home for the holidays — Fic

Dicker, Katie
Exercise — 613.7

DICKINSON, EMILY, 1830-1886
Herrera, R. Hope is a ferris wheel — Fic
Yolen, J. The Emily sonnets — 811

Dickinson, Peter, 1927-
The ropemaker — Fic

Dickinson, Terence
Nightwatch — 523.8

Dickmann, Nancy
Using renewable energy — 333.79

Diconsiglio, John
The Mexican-American War — 973.6
Vietnam — 959.704

DICTATORS
Bailey, D. Dictatorship — 321.9
Davis, K. C. Strongman — 321.9092

DICTATORSHIP
Bailey, D. Dictatorship — 321.9
Davis, K. C. Strongman — 321.9092

DICTATORSHIP -- HISTORY
Bailey, D. Dictatorship — 321.9

Dictatorship. Bailey, D. — 321.9

Dictionary for a better world. Latham, I. — 170

Diego. Bernier-Grand, C. T. — B

Diego Rivera. Hillstrom, K. — B

Diego Rivera. Rubin, S. G. — B

Diehn, Gwen, 1943-
Making books that fly fold wrap hide pop up twist & turn — 736

DIET
Etingoff, K. Building a healthy diet with the 5 food groups — 613.2
Hughes, M. S. Plants vs. meats — 641.5
Klimecki, Z. Diet information for teens — 613.2083
Mihaly, C. Diet for a changing climate — 613.2
Rau, D. M. Going vegetarian — 613.2

Traugh, S. M. Vegetarianism — 641.5
Waters, R. My daily diet — 613.2

Diet and disease. Juettner, B. — 613.2

Diet for a changing climate. Mihaly, C. — 613.2

Diet information for teens. Klimecki, Z. — 613.2083

Dietary supplements. Goldsmith, C. — 615.1

DIFFERENCE (PSYCHOLOGY)
Lecesne, J. Absolute brightness — Fic

The **differentiated** instruction book of lists. Fox, J. — 371.9

Differentiated instruction. Blaz, D. — 418

Differentiating instruction with centers in the gifted classroom K-8. Roberts, J. L. — 371.95

DIGESTION
Rose, S. Digestive system — 612.3
Simon, S. Guts — 612.3

DIGESTIVE ORGANS
Donovan, S. Rumble & spew — 612.3
Gold, S. D. Learning about the digestive and excretory systems — 612.3

DIGESTIVE SYSTEM
Cusick, D. Get the scoop on animal puke — 591.5
Donovan, S. Rumble & spew — 612.3
Gold, S. D. Learning about the digestive and excretory systems — 612.3
Rose, S. Digestive system — 612.3
Simon, S. Guts — 612.3
Viola, J. Digestive system — 612.3

Digestive system. Rose, S. — 612.3

Digestive system. Viola, J. — 612.3

Digging for Troy. Rubalcaba, J. — 939

DIGITAL CAMERAS
Turnbull, S. Cool stuff to photograph — 770

DIGITAL CINEMATOGRAPHY
Green, J. Super smart information strategies — 778

DIGITAL CURRENCY
January, B. Cryptocurrencies and the blockchain revolution — 332.4

DIGITAL ELECTRONICS
Gregory, J. From butterfly wings to... display technology — 621.3815

DIGITAL IMAGES
Rabbat, S. Super smart information strategies — 775

DIGITAL MEDIA
Rojas, M. Selfie made — 302.23

DIGITAL PHOTOGRAPHY
Rabbat, S. Super smart information strategies — 775

DILEMMAS
Perkins, M. Tiger boy — Fic
Trueman, T. Stuck in neutral — Fic
Wallace, R. One good punch — Fic
Williams-Garcia, R. Jumped — Fic

DILLINGER, JOHN, 1903-1934
Blumenthal, K. Tommy — 683.4

Dillon, Leo
To every thing there is a season — 223

Dillon, Molly
Yes she can — 973.932

Davis, T. S. Mare's war	**Fic**
Engle, M. Silver people	**Fic**
Goldstone, L. Unpunished murder	**976.3**
Hayes, A. Disability rights movement	**323.3**
Hurt, A. E. Confronting LGBTQ+ discrimination	**306.76**
Jewell, T. This book is anti-racist	**305.800973**
Kendi, I. X. Stamped	**305.800973**
Nevertheless we persisted	**170**
Rodger, M. Racism and prejudice	**305.8**
Shange, N. We troubled the waters	**811**

DISCRIMINATION IN EDUCATION

Howard, G. R. We can't teach what we don't know	**379.2**

DISCRIMINATION IN EDUCATION -- HISTORY 19TH CENTURY

Alexander, E. Miss Crandall's school for young ladies & little misses of color	**811**

DISCRIMINATION IN EDUCATION -- LAW AND LEGISLATION

Goldstone, L. Separate no more	**323.1196**

DISCRIMINATION IN LAW ENFORCEMENT

Behnke, A. Racial profiling	**363.2**

DISCUSSION

Chapin, S. H. Classroom discussions	**372.7**
Hale, M. S. The teacher's guide to leading student-centered discussions	**371.37**

DISEASES

Ambrose, M. Investigating diabetes	**616.4**
Bender, L. Explaining epilepsy	**616.8**
Brill, M. T. Diabetes	**616.4**
Brown, D. A shot in the arm!	**615.3**
Chadda, S. City of the plague god	**Fic**
Cunningham, K. Flu	**614.5**
Cunningham, K. Malaria	**614.5**
Dittmer, L. Parkinson's disease	**616.8**
Evans, M. The adventures of Medical Man	**610**
Goldsmith, C. Hepatitis	**616.3**
Hand, C. Epidemiology	**614.4**
Hyde, N. What is germ theory?	**615**
Jarrow, G. Bubonic panic	**614.5**
Jarrow, G. Fatal fever	**614.5**
Juettner, B. Diet and disease	**613.2**
Jurmain, S. The secret of the yellow death	**614.5**
Keyser, A. Pointe claw	**Fic**
Klosterman, L. Meningitis	**616.8**
Koch, F. Plagues	**614.5**
Kupperberg, P. The influenza pandemic of 1918-1919	**614.5**
Landau, E. Food poisoning and foodborne diseases	**615.9**
Levete, S. Explaining cerebral palsy	**616.8**
Lucier, M. A death-struck year	**Fic**
Markle, S. The case of the vanishing little brown bats	**599.4**
Miller, P. Cystic fibrosis	**616.3**
Murphy, J. Invincible microbe	**616.9**
Newman, P. Ebola	**616.9**
Pierce, T. Briar's book	**Fic**
Powell, J. Explaining cystic fibrosis	**616.3**
Power, R. Wilder girls	**Fic**
Reingold, A. Smallpox	**614.5**
Rooney, A. The history of medicine	**610.9**
Royston, A. Explaining asthma	**616.2**
Sonenklar, C. AIDS	**616.97**
Yancey, D. STDs	**616.95**

DISEASES -- CAUSES

Gardy, J. It's catching	**579.3**

DISEASES -- HISTORY

Nardo, D. COVID-19 and other pandemics	**614.5**

DISEASES -- TREATMENT

Colligan, L. H. Tick-borne illnesses	**616.9**
Evans, M. The adventures of Medical Man	**610**
Younker, J. M. Bleed blister puke and purge	**610.9**

DISEASES AND HISTORY

Lewis, M. L. Cholera	**616.9**
Lewis, M. L. Measles	**614.5**

DISGUISES

Ahdieh, R. Flame in the mist	**Fic**
Burgis, S. The princess who flew with dragons	**Fic**
Gaughen, A. C. Scarlet	**Fic**
Levine, G. C. The lost kingdom of Bamarre	**Fic**
Lim, E. Spin the dawn	**Fic**
Lockhart, E. Genuine fraud	**Fic**
Mashima, H. Fairy tail	**741.5**
Pierce, T. Alanna the first adventure	**Fic**
Smith, N. The deep & dark blue	**741.5**
Stine, R. L. Fear	**Fic**

DISILLUSIONMENT

DiTerlizzi, T. A hero for WondLa	**Fic**
Yelchin, E. Breaking Stalin's nose	**Fic**

DISMAL SWAMP (NORTH CAROLINA AND VIRGINIA)

Burg, A. E. Unbound	**Fic**

DISNEY, WALT, 1901-1966

Finch, C. The art of Walt Disney	**791.43092**
The **disreputable** history of Frankie Landau-Banks. Lockhart, E.	**Fic**
Disrupting thinking. Beers, G. K.	**418**
Dissenter on the bench. Ortiz, V.	**347.73**

DISSENTING OPINIONS

Ortiz, V. Dissenter on the bench	**347.73**

DISTRICT ATTORNEYS

Connor, L. All rise for the honorable Perry T. Cook	**Fic**

Diterlizzi, Tony

The battle for WondLa	**Fic**
A hero for WondLa	**Fic**

DITH PRAN, 1942-2008

Sonneborn, L. The Khmer Rouge	**959.604**

Dittmer, Lori

Parkinson's disease	**616.8**

Divakaruni, Chitra Banerjee, 1956-

The conch bearer	**Fic**

DIVALI

Singh, R. Diwali	**294.5**
Dive! Hopkinson, D.	**940.54**

DIVERS

Dunmore, H. Ingo	**Fic**

DOTS (ART)

Gilberti, F. Yayoi Kusama covered everything in dots and wasn't sorry   **709.2**

DOUBLE AGENTS

Carter, A. Only the good spy young   **Fic**

Double dutch. Draper, S. M.   **Fic**

Double helix. Werlin, N.   **Fic**

Double victory. Mullenbach, C.   **940.5308**

DOUBLEDAY, ABNER, 1819-1893

Gutman, D. Abner & me   **Fic**

Dough boys. Chase, P. J.   **Fic**

DOUGLAS, GABRIELLE, 1995-

Douglas, G. Grace gold and glory   **B**

Douglas, Gabrielle, 1995-

Grace gold and glory   **B**

DOUGLASS, FREDERICK, 1818-1895

Adler, D. A. Frederick Douglass   **B**

Archer, J. They had a dream   **323**

Cline-Ransome, L. Words set me free   **B**

Esty, A. Unbound and unbroken   **B**

Freedman, R. Abraham Lincoln and Frederick Douglass   **973.7092**

Sanders, N. I. Frederick Douglass for kids   **B**

DOVES

Byars, B. C. The keeper of the doves   **Fic**

Dovey Coe. Dowell, F. O.   **Fic**

Dowd, Siobhan

Bog child   **Fic**

The London Eye mystery   **Fic**

Dowell, Frances O'Roark

The class   **Fic**

Dovey Coe   **Fic**

Falling in   **Fic**

The kind of friends we used to be   **Fic**

The second life of Abigail Walker   **Fic**

Shooting the moon   **Fic**

DOWN SYNDROME

Royston, A. Explaining Down syndrome   **618.92**

Skotko, B. Fasten your seatbelt   **616.85**

The **down-to-Earth** guide to global warming. David, L.   **363.738**

Downer, Ann, 1960-

The animal mating game   **591.56**

Elephant talk   **599.67**

Hatching magic   **Fic**

Smart and spineless   **592.13**

Wild animal neighbors   **591.75**

Downham, Jenny

Before I die   **Fic**

Downing, David, 1946-

Apartheid in South Africa   **323.168**

Origins of the Holocaust   **940.53**

The **downstairs** girl. Lee, S.   **Fic**

DOWSERS

Holt, K. W. The water seeker   **Fic**

DOWSING

Holt, K. W. The water seeker   **Fic**

Dowswell, Paul

Auslander   **Fic**

DOYLE, ARTHUR CONAN, SIR, 1859-1930

Noyes, D. The magician and the spirits   **793.8**

Pascal, J. B. Arthur Conan Doyle   **B**

Doyle, Marissa

Bewitching season   **Fic**

Doyle, Roddy, 1958-

A greyhound of a girl   **Fic**

Dr. Frankenstein's human body book. Walker, R.   **611**

Dr. Seuss (Theodor Geisel). Anderson, T.   **B**

DRAFT

Wiles, D. Anthem   **Fic**

DRAG SHOWS

Boteju, T. Kings queens and in-betweens   **Fic**

DRAGON BABIES

Downer, A. Hatching magic   **Fic**

Fletcher, S. Sign of the dove   **Fic**

Dragon castle. Bruchac, J.   **Fic**

Dragon flight. George, J. D.   **Fic**

The **dragon** of Trelian. Knudsen, M.   **Fic**

The **dragon** path. Young, E.   **Fic**

Dragon slippers. George, J. D.   **Fic**

Dragon spear. George, J. D.   **Fic**

Dragon's blood. Yolen, J.   **Fic**

Dragon's fire. McCaffrey, A.   **Fic**

A **dragon's** guide to making your human smarter. Yep, L.   **Fic**

A **dragon's** guide to the care and feeding of humans. Yep, L.   **Fic**

Dragon's keep. Carey, J. L.   **Fic**

Dragon's milk. Fletcher, S.   **Fic**

The **dragon's** tooth. Wilson, N. D.   **Fic**

Dragonflight. McCaffrey, A.   **Fic**

The **dragonfly** pool. Ibbotson, E.   **Fic**

Dragonfly song. Orr, W.   **Fic**

DRAGONS

Blackwood, S. Miss Ellicott's school for the magically minded   **Fic**

Bruchac, J. Dragon castle   **Fic**

Burgis, S. The princess who flew with dragons   **Fic**

Carey, J. L. Dragon's keep   **Fic**

D'Lacey, C. Dark fire   **Fic**

D'Lacey, C. The fire ascending   **Fic**

D'Lacey, C. The fire eternal   **Fic**

D'Lacey, C. Fire star   **Fic**

D'Lacey, C. The fire within   **Fic**

D'Lacey, C. Fire world   **Fic**

D'Lacey, C. Icefire   **Fic**

Downer, A. Hatching magic   **Fic**

Fforde, J. The Eye of Zoltar   **Fic**

Fforde, J. The last dragonslayer   **Fic**

Fletcher, S. Dragon's milk   **Fic**

Fletcher, S. Flight of the Dragon Kyn   **Fic**

George, J. D. Dragon flight   **Fic**

George, J. D. Dragon slippers   **Fic**

George, J. D. Dragon spear   **Fic**

Goodman, A. Eona   **Fic**

Hahn, R. A creature of moonlight — Fic
Hartman, R. Seraphina — Fic
Hartman, R. Shadow scale — Fic
Haskell, M. Handbook for dragon slayers — Fic
Johnson-Shelton, N. The invisible tower — Fic
Johnston, E. K. Prairie fire — Fic
Johnston, E. K. The story of Owen — Fic
Kagawa, J. Talon — Fic
Knudsen, M. The dragon of Trelian — Fic
Le Guin, U. K. Tales from Earthsea — Fic
Le Guin, U. K. A wizard of Earthsea — Fic
Levine, G. C. A tale of Two Castles — Fic
Lewis, C. S. The voyage of the Dawn Treader — Fic
Lin, G. Where the mountain meets the moon — Fic
McCaffrey, A. Dragon's fire — Fic
McCaffrey, A. Dragonflight — Fic
McKinley, R. The hero and the crown — Fic
Munda, R. Fireborne — Fic
Paolini, C. Eragon — Fic
Pasternack, S. Anya and the nightingale — Fic
Rex, A. Champions of breakfast — Fic
Rumford, J. Beowulf a hero's tale retold — 398.2
Smith, J. Rose — 741.5
Sniegoski, T. Quest for the Spark — Fic
Taylor, N. Given — Fic
Tolkien, J. R. R. The hobbit or there and back again — Fic
Wrede, P. C. Calling on dragons — Fic
Wrede, P. C. Dealing with dragons — Fic
Wrede, P. C. Searching for dragons — Fic
Yep, L. City of fire — Fic
Yep, L. A dragon's guide to making your human smarter — Fic
Yep, L. A dragon's guide to the care and feeding of humans — Fic
Yolen, J. Dragon's blood — Fic
Dragonwings. Yep, L. — Fic

DRAKE, FRANCIS, SIR, 1540?-1596
Lacey, J. Island of Thieves — Fic
Drake, Jane, 1954-
Rewilding — 639.9
DRAKE, JOHN FL. 1577-1580
Lacey, J. Island of Thieves — Fic
DRAMA
Blackwood, G. L. The Shakespeare stealer — Fic
Brosius, P. Fierce & true — 812
Chanda, J. Acting out — 812
Detrick, E. Actor's choice — 808.82
Ellis, R. New audition scenes and monologs from contemporary playwrights — 808.82
Fleischman, P. Zap — 812
Hinds, G. King Lear — 741.5
Jennings, C. A. Theatre for young audiences — 812.008
Krueger, S. H. The tempest — 822.3
Levine, K. Hana's suitcase on stage — 940.53
Packer, T. Tales from Shakespeare — 822.3
Ratliff, G. L. Millennium monologs — 792
Schlitz, L. A. Good masters! Sweet ladies! — 812
Sobran, J. A midsummer night's dream — 822.3

Surface, M. H. Short scenes and monologues for middle school actors — 812
Thoms, A. With their eyes — 812
DRAMA -- HISTORY AND CRITICISM
Krueger, S. H. The tempest — 822.3
Sobran, J. A midsummer night's dream — 822.3
Drama. Telgemeier, R. — 741.5
DRAMA 20TH CENTURY
Detrick, E. Actor's choice — 808.82
Ratliff, G. L. Millennium monologs — 792
DRAMA 21ST CENTURY
Ellis, R. New audition scenes and monologs from contemporary playwrights — 808.82
Dramarama. Lockhart, E. — Fic
DRAMATISTS
Perl, E. S. The capybara conspiracy — Fic
DRAMATISTS, ENGLISH 16TH CENTURY
Aliki. William Shakespeare & the Globe — 792
Draper, Sharon M. (Sharon Mills)
The battle of Jericho — Fic
Blended — Fic
Double dutch — Fic
Fire from the rock — Fic
Just another hero — Fic
November blues — Fic
Out of my mind — Fic
Stella by starlight — Fic
Draw 50 endangered animals. Ames, L. J. — 743.6
Draw furries. Hodges, J. — 743.6
DRAWING
Bergin, M. How to draw pets — 743.6
Kowitt, H. The loser list — Fic
Murdock, C. G. Da Vinci's cat — Fic
Pinkwater, D. M. Bushman lives! — Fic
Stephens, J. Heroes! — 741.5
Tan, S. The bird king — 741.64092
Yep, L. A dragon's guide to the care and feeding of humans — Fic
Young, K. R. Doodlebug — Fic
DRAWING -- TECHNIQUE
Ames, L. J. Draw 50 endangered animals — 743.6
Bergin, M. How to draw pets — 743.6
Butkus, M. How to draw zombies — 743
Hart, C. The master guide to drawing anime how to draw original characters from simple templates — 741.5
Hodges, J. Draw furries — 743.6
Masiello, R. Ralph Masiello's ancient Egypt drawing book. — 743
Peot, M. Inkblot — 751.4
Temple, K. Drawing — 741.2
Temple, K. Drawing in color — 741.2
Drawing. Temple, K. — 741.2
Drawing from the city. Behan, T. — B
Drawing in color. Temple, K. — 741.2
Drawn across borders. Butler, G. — 304.8
Dream jobs in math. Hynson, C. — 510.23
The **dream keeper and other poems**. Hughes, L. — 811

Farmer, N. The house of the scorpion — Fic
Pike, A. Glitter — Fic
Drug Enforcement Administration. Newton, M. — 363.25
DRUG INDUSTRY AND TRADE
  Goldsmith, C. Dietary supplements — 615.1
Drug information for teens. Omnigraphics, I. — 613.8
DRUG RESISTANCE IN MICROORGANISMS
  Goldsmith, C. Pandemic — 614.4
  Hirsch, R. E. Microbiomes — 612
DRUG SMUGGLERS
  Gilman, D. Blood sun — Fic
  Hobbs, W. Crossing the wire — Fic
DRUG SMUGGLING
  Horowitz, A. Three of diamonds — Fic
DRUG TRAFFIC
  Martin, C. Drug wars — 363.45
  Newton, M. Drug Enforcement Administration — 363.25
  Quinones, S. Dreamland — 362.29
  Ribay, R. Patron saints of nothing — Fic
DRUG USE
  Allman, T. Drugs — 616.86
  Martin, C. Drug wars — 363.45
Drug wars. Martin, C. — 363.45
DRUGS
  Bjornlund, L. Oxycodone — 615
  Goldsmith, C. Dietary supplements — 615.1
  Gottfried, T. Marijuana — 613.8
  LeVert, S. Ecstasy — 613.8
  Machale, D. J. SYLO — Fic
  Menhard, F. R. Inhalants — 613.8
  Parks, P. J. Bath salts and other synthetic drugs — 362.29
  Patrick, C. Revived — Fic
  Pike, A. Glitter — Fic
  Scott, C. Caffeine — 362.29
DRUGS -- PHYSIOLOGICAL EFFECT
  Omnigraphics, I. Drug information for teens — 613.8
Drugs. Allman, T. — 616.86
DRUM
  Landau, E. Are the drums for you? — 786.9
DRUM SET
  Landau, E. Are the drums for you? — 786.9
DRUMMERS
  Brezenoff, S. Brooklyn burning — Fic
Drums keyboards and other instruments. Witmer, S. — 786
Dry. Shusterman, N. — Fic
Duane, Diane
  So you want to be a wizard — Fic
Duberman, Martin B.
  Paul Robeson — B
Duble, Kathleen Benner
  The sacrifice — Fic
DUBLIN, IRELAND
  Doyle, R. A greyhound of a girl — Fic
Dubosarsky, Ursula, 1961-
  The word snoop — 420.9
DUCT TAPE
  Dobson, J. The duct tape book — 745.5

The **duct** tape book. Dobson, J. — 745.5
The **duel**. St. George, J. — 973.4
DUELING
  Chima, C. W. The warrior heir — Fic
DUELING -- HISTORY 19TH CENTURY
  St. George, J. The duel — 973.4
Duey, Kathleen
  Sacred scars — Fic
  Skin hunger — Fic
Duggleby, John, 1952-
  Story painter — B
Duke Ellington. Stein Crease, S. — B
Duke, Shirley Smith
  You can't wear these genes — 576.5
Dumas, Firoozeh
  It ain't so awful falafel — Fic
The **dumbest** idea ever! Gownley, J. — B
Dumon Tak, Bibi
  Soldier bear — Fic
Duncan, Lois, 1934-2016
  I know what you did last summer — Fic
  Killing Mr. Griffin — Fic
  Locked in time — Fic
  Stranger with my face — Fic
  The third eye — Fic
DUNCAN, TIM, 1976-
  Thornley, S. Tim Duncan — B
Dunham, Kelli S.
  The boy's body book — 612.6
DUNKIRK, FRANCE
  Gallico, P. The snow goose — Fic
Dunkle, Clare B.
  The sky inside — Fic
Dunlap, Susanne Emily
  The musician's daughter — Fic
Dunmore, Helen, 1952-2017
  The deep — Fic
  Ingo — Fic
  The tide knot — Fic
Dunning, Stephen
  Reflections on a gift of watermelon pickle... — 811
Dunstan, Simon
  Entebbe — 967.6104
Duprau, Jeanne
  The city of Ember — Fic
  The diamond of Darkhold — Fic
  The people of Sparks — Fic
  The prophet of Yonwood — Fic
Durbin, William, 1951-
  The broken blade — Fic
Durham, Paul (Paul Joseph), 1972-
  Fork-tongue charmers — Fic
  The Luck Uglies — Fic
Durst, Sarah Beth
  The girl who could not dream — Fic
  Ice — Fic
  Into the Wild — Fic

Charbonneau, J. Independent study	Fic	
Charbonneau, J. The Testing	Fic	
Collins, S. Catching fire	Fic	
Collins, S. The Hunger Games	Fic	
Collins, S. Mockingjay	Fic	
Condie, A. B. Matched	Fic	
Dashner, J. The maze runner	Fic	
Doctorow, C. Pirate cinema	Fic	
DuPrau, J. The city of Ember	Fic	
DuPrau, J. The diamond of Darkhold	Fic	
DuPrau, J. The people of Sparks	Fic	
Dunkle, C. B. The sky inside	Fic	
Falls, K. Inhuman	Fic	
Fisher, C. Sapphique	Fic	
Freitas, D. Unplugged	Fic	
Fukuda, A. X. The prey	Fic	
Gagnon, M. Strangelets	Fic	
Heath, J. The lab	Fic	
Hesse, K. Safekeeping	Fic	
Hirsch, J. The eleventh plague	Fic	
Holyoke, P. The Neptune Project	Fic	
Kade, J. V. Bot Wars	Fic	
London, A. Proxy	Fic	
Lowry, L. Gathering blue	Fic	
Lowry, L. The giver	Fic	
Lowry, L. Giver quartet	741.5	
Lu, M. Champion	Fic	
Lu, M. Legend	Fic	
Lu, M. Prodigy	Fic	
Lu, M. Rebel	Fic	
Marr, M. Shards & ashes	Fic	
Ness, P. The Ask and the Answer	Fic	
Ness, P. The knife of never letting go	Fic	
North, P. Starglass	Fic	
O'Brien, C. M. Birthmarked	Fic	
O'Brien, R. C. Z for Zachariah	Fic	
Orwell, G. Animal farm	Fic	
Price, L. Starters	Fic	
Rossi, V. Under the never sky	Fic	
Unsworth, T. The one safe place	Fic	
Westerfeld, S. Extras	Fic	
Westerfeld, S. Pretties	Fic	
Westerfeld, S. Shatter city	Fic	
Westerfeld, S. Specials	Fic	
Westerfeld, S. Uglies	Fic	
Wiggins, B. Stung	Fic	

E

Eagar, Lindsay	
Hour of the bees	Fic
Race to the bottom of the sea	Fic
Eamer, Claire, 1947-	
Inside your insides	579
What a waste!	363.72
EAR	
Simon, S. Eyes and ears	612.8

EAR -- DISEASES	
Levete, S. Explaining deafness	617.8
Ear nose and throat. Rogers, K.	617.5
EARHART, AMELIA, 1897-1937	
Brown, J. K. Amelia Earhart	B
Fleming, C. Amelia lost	B
Tanaka, S. Amelia Earhart	B
Earl, Rae	
Your brain needs a hug	616.85
Earl, Sari	
Benjamin O. Davis Jr.	B
George Washington	B
Earle, Sylvia A., 1935-	
Extreme ocean	551.46
EARLEY, CHARITY ADAMS, 1918-2002	
Farrell, M. C. Standing up against hate	940.54
Earls, Irene	
Young musicians in world history	780
EARLY AMERICA (1784-1819)	
Anderson, L. H. Fever 1793	Fic
McClafferty, C. K. Buried lives	306.3
Early civilizations. Kelly, K.	610.938
Early Germans. Hinds, K.	936.3
Early medieval times. Malam, J.	940.1
Early national America 1790-1850. McNeese, T.	973.3
EARTH	
Aguilar, D. A. Cosmic catastrophes	520
Allaby, M. National Geographic visual encyclopedia of Earth	550
Brown, D. Older than dirt	551.7
Clark, H. What we found in the sofa (and how it saved the world)	Fic
Goldstein, M. J. Garbage in space	363.72
Mass, W. Pi in the sky	Fic
Nardo, D. The blue marble	525
Nardo, D. Planet under siege	363.738
Oppel, K. Thrive	Fic
Rex, A. The true meaning of Smekday	Fic
Richardson, G. Kaboom!	541
Simon, S. Earth	525
Solway, A. Why is there life on Earth?	576.8
Teague, M. The doom machine	Fic
Young, K. R. Space junk	629.4
EARTH (PLANET)	
National Geographic Partners (U.S.). National Geographic student world atlas	912
EARTH -- INVASIONS	
Grine, C. Animorphs	741.5
Earth. Simon, S.	525
EARTH DAY -- HISTORY	
Peterson, C. Earth Day and the global environmental movement	394.262
Earth Day and the global environmental movement. Peterson, C.	394.262
Earth in the hot seat. Delano, M. F.	363.738
The Earth my butt and other big round things. Mackler, C.	Fic
EARTH SCIENCES	

Angleberger, T. Horton Halfpott or The fiendish mystery of Smugwick Manor or The loosening of M'Lady Luggertuck's corset **Fic**

Atkinson, E. J. I Emma Freke **Fic**

Erskine, K. The absolute value of Mike **Fic**

Grabenstein, C. Mr. Lemoncello's great library race **Fic**

Greenberg, J. The mad potter **738.092**

Heider, M. W. The losers at the center of the galaxy **Fic**

Irving, W. The legend of Sleepy Hollow **Fic**

Jennings, P. Odd weird & little **Fic**

Lindelauf, B. Fing's war **Fic**

Raskin, E. The Westing game **Fic**

Ritter, W. The dire king **Fic**

Snicket, L. "Who could that be at this hour?" **Fic**

Tolan, S. S. Surviving the Applewhites **Fic**

Echevarria, Jana, 1956-
Making content comprehensible for English learners **372.652**

Echo. Ryan, P. M. **Fic**

Echo Mountain. Wolk, L. **Fic**

Eckel, Malcolm David, 1946-
Buddhism **294.3**

ECKFORD, ELIZABETH, 1941-
Tougas, S. Little Rock girl 1957 **379.2**

Eclipse. Meyer, S. **Fic**

Eclipse chaser. Loomis, I. **523.7**

ECO-TERRORISM
Hiaasen, C. Hoot **Fic**
Keplinger, K. Poison Ivy **741.5**

ECOLOGICAL DISTURBANCES -- PREVENTION
Gilman, D. Ice claw **Fic**

ECOLOGY
Berkenkamp, L. Discover the Amazon **613.6**
Buller, L. Ice **577.0911**
Collard, S. B. Fire birds **634.9**
Debbink, A. The wild world handbook **333.95**
Heinrichs, A. The Nile **962**
Latham, D. Amazing biome projects you can build yourself **577**
Lynch, W. Arctic **577.0911**
Marrin, A. Years of dust **978**
Newman, P. Sea otter heroes **599.769**
Parker, S. Seashore **578.769**
Reilly, K. M. Planet Earth **577**
Shusterman, N. Dry **Fic**
Simon, S. Wildfires **574.5**
Tate, N. Deep roots **582.16**
Wechsler, D. Marvels in the muck **578.769**

ECOLOGY -- EXPERIMENTS
VanCleave, J. P. Step-by-step science experiments in ecology **577.078**

ECOLOGY -- RESEARCH
Carson, M. K. Inside Biosphere 2 **304.2**

ECONOMIC HISTORY
Riggs, K. The great recession **330.973**

ECONOMIC POLICY
Bair, S. The bullies of Wall Street **330.973**

ECONOMIC POLICY 1933-1945

Bolden, T. FDR's Alphabet soup **973.917**

ECONOMICS
Gascoigne, I. Papua New Guinea **995.3**
Hopkinson, D. Up before daybreak **331.7**
Scott, E. Dollars and sense **332.024**
Sylvester, K. Follow your money **330**

ECONOMICS -- HISTORY
Blumenthal, K. Six days in October **332.64**

ECONOMICS -- HISTORY 20TH CENTURY
Blumenthal, K. Six days in October **332.64**

ECONOMICS -- RELIGIOUS ASPECTS -- ISLAM
Marshall Cavendish Reference. Modern Muslim societies. **306.6**

ECONOMICS -- SOCIAL ASPECTS
Brown, D. The great American Dust Bowl **978**

ECOSYSTEM MANAGEMENT
Allaby, M. National Geographic visual encyclopedia of Earth **550**

ECSTASY (DRUG)
LeVert, S. Ecstasy **613.8**

Ecstasy. LeVert, S. **613.8**

ECUADOR
Foley, E. Ecuador **986.6**
Kras, S. L. The Galapagos Islands **986.6**

Ecuador. Foley, E. **986.6**

Edda. Kostick, C. **Fic**

EDELWEISS PIRATES (ANTI-NAZI GROUP)
Gaddy, K. R. Flowers in the gutter **940.53**

Edgar Allan Poe's tales of death and dementia. Poe, E. A. **Fic**

Edgar Allan Poe's tales of mystery and madness. Poe, E. A. **Fic**

Edgar, Kathleen J.
Junior worldmark encyclopedia of the states **973.03**

The **edge** of the sea. Carson, R. **578.769**

Edge, Laura B.
Apollo 13 **629.45**

Edible sunlight. Haelle, T. **572**

EDISON, THOMAS A. (THOMAS ALVA), 1847-1931
Hardyman, R. Nikola Tesla and Thomas Edison **621.3092**
Helfand, L. They changed the world **621.3**
Krieg, K. Thomas Edison **B**
Sonneborn, L. The electric light **609**
Woodside, M. Thomas A. Edison **B**

EDITING
Anderson, J. Everyday editing **808**

EDMONDSON FAMILY
Conkling, W. Passenger on the Pearl **306.3**

EDMONSON, EMILY, 1835-1895
Conkling, W. Passenger on the Pearl **306.3**

Edsel, Robert M.
The greatest treasure hunt in history **940.53**

EDUCATION
Nardo, D. Daily life in colonial America **973.2**
Peck, R. The teacher's funeral **Fic**
Pinkney, A. D. The red pencil **Fic**

EDUCATION -- SOCIAL ASPECTS
Minor, C. We got this. **371.82996073**

Nolan, H. A summer of Kings — Fic
Eighth grade bites. Brewer, Z. — Fic
EIGHTH-GRADE BOYS
Herrick, A. The Time Fetch — Fic
EIGHTH-GRADE GIRLS
Bigelow, L. J. Hazel's theory of evolution — Fic
Draper, S. M. Double dutch — Fic
Firestone, C. Dress coded — Fic
Larson, H. All summer long — 741.5
McGuigan, M. A. Morning in a different place — Fic
Young, B. The prettiest — Fic
EIGHTH-GRADERS
Appelt, K. Kissing Tennessee and other stories from the Stardust Dance — Fic
Ellis, A. D. This is what I did — Fic
Hamilton, V. The planet of Junior Brown — Fic
Makechnie, A. Ten thousand tries — Fic
Sonnenblick, J. After ever after — Fic
Einfeld, Jann
Life in the Australian Outback — 994
Einstein adds a new dimension. Hakim, J. — 509
EINSTEIN, ALBERT, 1879-1955
Delano, M. F. Genius — B
Gibbs, S. Charlie Thorne and the last equation — Fic
Haddix, M. P. Caught — Fic
Krull, K. Albert Einstein — B
EINSTEIN-MARIC, MILEVA, 1875-1948
Haddix, M. P. Caught — Fic
Ejaz, Khadija
We visit Oman — 953.53
El Deafo. Bell, C. — B
EL PASO, TEXAS
Martinez, C. G. The smell of old lady perfume — Fic
EL SALVADOR
Argueta, J. Caravan to the North — Fic
Markham, L. The far away brothers — 979.4
EL SALVADOR -- HISTORY
Foley, E. El Salvador — 972.84
El Salvador. Foley, E. — 972.84
ELAINE RACE RIOT, ELAINE, ARK, 1919
Wallace, S. N. Race against time — 976.7
ELDER ABUSE
Crossan, S. Being Toffee — Fic
Eleanor of Aquitaine. Kramer, A. — B
ELEANOR, OF AQUITAINE, QUEEN, CONSORT OF HENRY II, KING OF ENGLAND, 1122?-1204
Kramer, A. Eleanor of Aquitaine — B
ELECTION LAW
Conkling, W. Votes for women! — 324.6
ELECTIONS
Fleischer, J. Votes of confidence — 324.6
Goldstone, L. Stolen justice — 324.6
Jacobs, T. A. Every vote matters — 342.7308
ELECTIVE MUTISM
Beaty, A. Cicada summer — Fic
Hannigan, K. True (--sort of) — Fic
Sloan, H. G. I'll be there — Fic

ELECTORAL REFORM
Goldstone, L. Stolen justice — 324.6
Electric and magnetic phenomena. Galiano, D. — 537
The **electric** light. Sonneborn, L. — 609
ELECTRIC LIGHTING
Collier, J. L. Electricity and the light bulb — 621.32
ELECTRIC LIGHTING -- HISTORY
Sonneborn, L. The electric light — 609
Electric motor experiments. Sobey, E. J. C. — 621.46078
ELECTRIC MOTORS
Sobey, E. J. C. Electric motor experiments — 621.46078
ELECTRIC POWER
Anderson, M. Electricity — 537
ELECTRIC POWER PRODUCTION
Sobey, E. J. C. Solar cell and renewable energy experiments — 621.042078
ELECTRIC VEHICLES
Bearce, S. All about electric and hybrid cars and who's driving them — 629.22
Diaz, J. Tesla model S — 629.22
ELECTRICAL ENGINEERING
Swanson, J. Amazing feats of electrical engineering — 621.3
ELECTRICAL ENGINEERING -- HISTORY
Sonneborn, L. The electric light — 609
ELECTRICAL ENGINEERS
Hardyman, R. Nikola Tesla and Thomas Edison — 621.3092
Swanson, J. Amazing feats of electrical engineering — 621.3
ELECTRICITY
Anderson, M. Electricity — 537
Collier, J. L. Electricity and the light bulb — 621.32
Evans, R. P. Battle of the Ampere — Fic
Evans, R. P. The prisoner of cell 25 — Fic
Evans, R. P. Rise of the Elgen — Fic
Galiano, D. Electric and magnetic phenomena — 537
Sobey, E. J. C. Solar cell and renewable energy experiments — 621.042078
Electricity. Anderson, M. — 537
Electricity and the light bulb. Collier, J. L. — 621.32
ELECTROMAGNETIC WAVES
Bick, I. J. Ashes — Fic
ELECTRONIC COMMERCE
January, B. Cryptocurrencies and the blockchain revolution — 332.4
ELECTRONIC COMMERCE -- MARKETING
Weinick, S. Increasing your tweets likes and ratings — 658.8
ELECTRONIC GAMES INDUSTRY AND TRADE
Rauf, D. Computer game designer — 794.8
ELECTRONIC INFORMATION RESOURCE SEARCHING
Brown, C. C. Librarian's guide to online searching — 025.04
ELECTRONIC RECORDS
Kaufman, A. Illuminae — Fic
ELECTRONICS
Freedman, J. Robots through history — 629.8
Gregory, J. From butterfly wings to... display technology — 621.3815
Kinney, J. Old school — Fic

ELEMENTARY SCHOOL TEACHERS

Buyea, R. Because of Mr. Terupt | Fic
Gutman, D. Miss Daisy is crazy! | Fic
Klise, K. Regarding the sink | Fic

ELEMENTARY SCHOOLS

Gutman, D. Miss Daisy is crazy! | Fic

ELEPHANT BABIES

Applegate, K. The one and only Ivan | Fic
The **elephant** doctor of India. Chodosh, J. | 599.67
The **elephant** in the room. Sloan, H. G. | Fic
The **elephant** scientist. O'Connell, C. | 599.67
Elephant talk. Downer, A. | 599.67

ELEPHANTS

Applegate, K. The one and only Ivan | Fic
Chodosh, J. The elephant doctor of India | 599.67
DiCamillo, K. The magician's elephant | Fic
Hunter, E. Broken pride | Fic
Jacobson, J. Small as an elephant | Fic
Kadohata, C. A million shades of gray | Fic
Kelly, L. Chained | Fic
O'Connell, C. The elephant scientist | 599.67
Safina, C. Beyond words | 591.56

ELEPHANTS -- BEHAVIOR

Downer, A. Elephant talk | 599.67
Elephants and golden thrones. Marx, T. | 951

ELEVEN-YEAR-OLD BOYS

Abbott, T. The summer of Owen Todd | Fic
Armstrong, A. W. Looking for Marco Polo | Fic
Bauer, A. C. E. No castles here | Fic
Byars, B. C. Cracker Jackson | Fic
Corona, J. Feathers | 741.5
Gutman, D. The million dollar shot | Fic
McMullan, M. How I found the Strong | Fic
Nesbet, A. Cloud and Wallfish | Fic
Park, L. S. A long walk to water | Fic
Pullman, P. The book of dust | Fic
Rowling, J. K. Harry Potter and the sorcerer's stone | Fic
Warman, J. The world beneath | Fic
Weeks, S. Jumping the scratch | Fic
Woodruff, E. Dear Austin | Fic
Woodruff, E. The ravenmaster's secret | Fic

ELEVEN-YEAR-OLD GIRLS

Al-Mansour, H. The green bicycle | Fic
Birdsall, J. The Penderwicks at last | Fic
Cavanaugh, N. J. This journal belongs to Ratchet | Fic
Downer, A. Hatching magic | Fic
Dumas, F. It ain't so awful falafel | Fic
Farmer, N. A girl named Disaster | Fic
Holm, J. L. Penny from heaven | Fic
Horvath, P. Everything on a waffle | Fic
Jamieson, V. All's faire in middle school | 741.5
Klages, E. The green glass sea | Fic
Larson, K. Dash | Fic
Lawson, J. Nooks & crannies | Fic
McCrite, K. D. In front of God and everybody | Fic
McKay, H. Forever Rose | Fic
Paterson, K. The great Gilly Hopkins | Fic

Pierce, T. Page | Fic
Sonnichsen, A. L. Red butterfly | Fic
Spratt, R. A. Friday Barnes girl detective | Fic
Uchida, Y. A jar of dreams | Fic
Van Vleet, C. Eliza Bing is (not) a big fat quitter | Fic
Yee, L. Millicent Min girl genius | Fic

ELEVEN-YEAR-OLDS

Mull, B. Wild born | Fic
The **eleventh** plague. Hirsch, J. | Fic

Elias, Marie Louise

Barbados | 972.981

Elie Wiesel. Koestler-Grack, R. A. | B
Elijah of Buxton. Curtis, C. P. | Fic

ELIMINATIVE BEHAVIOR

DiPiazza, F. Remaking the john | 644

ELION, GERTRUDE B.

Lawlor, L. Super women | 509.2

Elish, Dan

Inside the situation room | B
The Trail of Tears | 973

ELITE (SOCIAL SCIENCES)

Brody, J. Sky without stars | Fic
Gelletly, L. Oligarchy | 321
Hinds, K. The palace | 909

ELITISM

Gelletly, L. Oligarchy | 321
Eliza Bing is (not) a big fat quitter. Van Vleet, C. | Fic

ELIZABETH

Adams, S. Elizabeth I | B
Hollihan, K. L. Elizabeth I--the people's queen | B
Elizabeth and Zenobia. Miller, J. | Fic

ELIZABETH I, QUEEN OF ENGLAND, 1533-1603

Bowling, N. Witch born | Fic
Elizabeth I--the people's queen. Hollihan, K. L. | B
Elizabeth I. Adams, S. | B
Elizabethan England. Kallen, S. A. | 942.05

ELIZABETHAN ERA (1558-1603)

Blackwood, G. L. The Shakespeare stealer | Fic
Boecker, V. An assassin's guide to love and treason | Fic
Booth, M. Saving Hamlet | Fic
Bowling, N. Witch born | Fic

Elkeles, Simone

How to ruin a summer vacation | Fic
How to ruin my teenage life | Fic
How to ruin your boyfriend's reputation | Fic
The **ELL** teacher's toolbox. Ferlazzo, L. | 428
Ella enchanted. Levine, G. C. | Fic
Ella Fitzgerald. Stone, T. L. | B

ELLABBAD, MOHIEDDINE, 1940-

Ellabbad, M. The illustrator's notebook | 741.6

Ellabbad, Mohieddine, 1940-

The illustrator's notebook | 741.6

ELLINGTON, DUKE, 1899-1974

Stein Crease, S. Duke Ellington | B

Elliott, David, 1947-

Voices | Fic

Elliott, Laura, 1957-

Sneideman, J. Renewable energy   333.79

ENERGY INDUSTRY AND TRADE
Allen, J. Careers in environmental and energy technology   621.042023
Burgan, M. Energy   621.042

ENERGY PRODUCTION
Lew, K. Goodbye gasoline   621.31
Sneideman, J. Renewable energy   333.79
Walker, N. Harnessing power from the sun   621.47

ENERGY RESOURCE RECOVERY
O'Neal, C. How to use waste energy to heat and light your home   621.1

ENERGY RESOURCES
Bearce, S. How to harness solar power for your home   621.47
Belton, B. How coal is formed   553.2
Conley, K. A. Biofuels   333.95
Dobson, C. Wind power   621.4
Goldstein, M. J. Fuel under fire   338.2
Kidd, J. S. Nuclear power   621.48
Lew, K. Goodbye gasoline   621.31
McPherson, S. S. Arctic thaw   333.79
O'Neal, C. How to use wind power to light and heat your home   621.31
Oxlade, C. Nuclear power   621.48
Rigsby, M. Doable renewables   621.042
Rusch, E. The next wave   621.31
Sneideman, J. Renewable energy   333.79
Squire, A. Hydrofracking   622
Walker, N. Harnessing power from the sun   621.47
Woll, K. Wind energy   333.9

ENGAGED PERSONS
Pierce, T. Mastiff   Fic

ENGAGEMENT
Haddix, M. P. Just Ella   Fic
Han, J. We'll always have summer   Fic
McKay, H. Caddy ever after   Fic
Rutkoski, M. The winner's crime   Fic

Engdahl, Sylvia
Enchantress from the stars   Fic
Military families   355.1

Engineered! Hunt, S.   620

ENGINEERING
Connolly, S. The book of massively epic engineering disasters   624.1
Eboch, C. Amazing feats of mechanical engineering   621.8
Hand, C. Amazing feats of environmental engineering   628
Hunt, S. Engineered!   620
McCulloch, A. Jinxed   Fic
Mercer, B. Junk drawer engineering   620.0078
Rooney, A. Aerospace engineering and the principles of flight   629.1
Rooney, A. Audio engineering and the science of soundwaves   621.389
Sjonger, R. Robotics engineering and our automated world   629.8
Swanson, J. Amazing feats of electrical engineering   621.3

Woolf, A. Buildings   690

ENGINEERING -- EXPERIMENTS
Caney, S. Steven Caney's ultimate building book   624
VanCleave, J. P. Janice VanCleave's engineering for every kid   620.0078

ENGINEERING -- HISTORY
Macaulay, D. Building big   720

ENGINEERING -- STUDY AND TEACHING (ELEMENTARY)
Vasquez, J. A. STEM lesson essentials grades 3-8   372.35

ENGINEERING DESIGN
Macaulay, D. Building big   720

Engineering the city. Levy, M.   624

ENGINEERS
Eboch, C. Amazing feats of mechanical engineering   621.8
Hunt, S. Engineered!   620
Reeve, P. A web of air   Fic

ENGINES
Collier, J. L. Steam engines   621.1
Williams, B. Who invented the automobile?   629.222

Engines of the broken world. Vanhee, J.   Fic

ENGLAND
Allison, J. Bad machinery   741.5
Almond, D. Clay   Fic
Almond, D. Half a creature from the sea   Fic
Almond, D. Kit's wilderness   Fic
Almond, D. Raven summer   Fic
Almond, D. The savage   Fic
Almond, D. Skellig   Fic
Almond, D. Slog's dad   Fic
Angleberger, T. Horton Halfpott or The fiendish mystery of Smugwick Manor or The loosening of M'Lady Luggertuck's corset   Fic
Auxier, J. The night gardener   Fic
Avery, T. Not as we know it   Fic
Avi. The unexpected life of Oliver Cromwell Pitts   Fic
Bedford, M. Flip   Fic
Billingsley, F. Chime   Fic
Blackwood, G. L. The Shakespeare stealer   Fic
Booth, M. Saving Hamlet   Fic
Bray, L. A great and terrible beauty   Fic
Buckley-Archer, L. The many lives of John Stone   Fic
Bunce, E. C. Premeditated Myrtle   Fic
Byng, G. Molly Moon's incredible book of hypnotism   Fic
Carey, E. Heap House   Fic
Carroll, E. In darkling wood   Fic
Cushman, K. Catherine called Birdy   Fic
Cushman, K. The midwife's apprentice   Fic
D'Lacey, C. Dark fire   Fic
Doctorow, C. Pirate cinema   Fic
Doherty, B. The girl who saw lions   Fic
Dowd, S. The London Eye mystery   Fic
Downham, J. Before I die   Fic
Dunmore, H. Ingo   Fic
Dunmore, H. The tide knot   Fic
Elphinstone, A. Casper Tock and the Everdark wings   Fic
Evans, M. Who let the gods out?   Fic

Frederick, H. V. Pies & prejudice	Fic		Springer, N. The case of the missing marquess	Fic
Gaughen, A. C. Scarlet	Fic		Stevens, R. Murder is bad manners	Fic
Gier, K. Emerald green	Fic		Stevens, R. Poison is not polite	Fic
Gier, K. Sapphire blue	Fic		Strange, L. The secret of Nightingale Wood	Fic
Gilman, D. Blood sun	Fic		Stroud, J. The creeping shadow	Fic
Gordon, R. Tunnels	Fic		Stroud, J. The hollow boy	Fic
Haddix, M. P. Sent	Fic		Stroud, J. The screaming staircase	Fic
Hardinge, F. Cuckoo song	Fic		Stroud, J. The whispering skull	Fic
Harrison, M. 13 curses	Fic		Tripp, B. The accidental highwayman	Fic
Harrison, M. 13 secrets	Fic		Valente, C. M. The Glass Town game	Fic
Horowitz, A. The Falcon's Malteser	Fic		Ward, R. The chaos	Fic
Horowitz, A. The Greek who stole Christmas	Fic		Ward, R. Num8ers	Fic
Horowitz, A. Public enemy number two	Fic		Welford, R. Time traveling with a hamster	Fic
Horowitz, A. Raven's gate	Fic		Wood, M. Nightshade	Fic
Horowitz, A. South by southeast	Fic		Wood, M. The poison diaries	Fic
Horowitz, A. Stormbreaker	741.5		Wooding, C. Silver	Fic

Horowitz, A. Three of diamonds	Fic
James, A. The bookwanderers	Fic

ENGLAND -- HISTORY -- 16TH CENTURY

Aliki. William Shakespeare & the Globe	792

Jinks, C. The last bogler	Fic

ENGLAND -- HISTORY -- 17TH CENTURY

Johnson, M. The madness underneath	Fic
Aliki. William Shakespeare & the Globe	792

Johnson, M. The name of the star	Fic

ENGLAND -- HISTORY -- MEDIEVAL PERIOD, 1066-1485

Johnson, M. The shadow cabinet	Fic
Jones, D. W. Enchanted glass	Fic
Schlitz, L. A. Good masters! Sweet ladies!	812
Kindl, P. Keeping the castle	Fic
Williams, M. Chaucer's Canterbury Tales	821

ENGLAND -- RELIGION

Kindl, P. A school for brides	Fic
Schomp, V. The Church	274.2

Lancaster, M. A. Human.4	Fic

ENGLAND -- RULERS

Lawrence, I. The smugglers	Fic
Schomp, V. Victoria and her court	941.081

Lawrence, I. The wreckers	Fic

ENGLAND -- SOCIAL CONDITIONS -- 16TH CENTURY

Lewis, G. One white dolphin	Fic
Kallen, S. A. Elizabethan England	942.05

McKay, H. Caddy ever after	Fic

ENGLAND -- SOCIAL LIFE AND CUSTOMS -- 16TH CENTURY

McKay, H. Forever Rose	Fic
McKay, H. Indigo's star	Fic
Krueger, S. H. The tempest	822.3
McKay, H. Saffy's angel	Fic
Sobran, J. A midsummer night's dream	822.3

McKinley, R. The outlaws of Sherwood	Fic

ENGLAND -- SOCIAL LIFE AND CUSTOMS -- 19TH CENTURY

McNab, A. Avenger	Fic
Moriarty, J. A corner of white	Fic
Harrell, R. Monster on the hill	741.5

ENGLE, MARGARITA

Morpurgo, M. Private Peaceful	Fic
Ness, P. A monster calls	Fic
Engle, M. Soaring earth	B

Engle, Margarita

Nimmo, J. Midnight for Charlie Bone	Fic
Pitcher, A. Silence is goldfish	Fic
Bravo!	920.0092
Pollen, S. The year I didn't eat	Fic
Silver people	Fic
Powell, L. Burn mark	Fic
Soaring earth	B
Pullman, P. The book of dust	Fic
The wild book	Fic
Reeve, P. Fever Crumb	Fic
With a star in my hand	Fic

Rex, A. Unlucky charms	Fic

ENGLISH AS A SECOND LANGUAGE

Riordan, R. The red pyramid	Fic
Ferlazzo, L. The ELL teacher's toolbox	428
Rowling, J. K. Harry Potter and the Chamber of Secrets	Fic
Ferlazzo, L. The ESL/ELL teacher's survival guide	428

Rowling, J. K. Harry Potter and the deathly hallows	Fic

ENGLISH LANGUAGE

Rowling, J. K. Harry Potter and the goblet of fire	Fic
Baldick, C. The Oxford dictionary of literary terms	803
Rowling, J. K. Harry Potter and the Order of the Phoenix	Fic
Brewer, E. C. Brewer's dictionary of phrase & fable	423
Rowling, J. K. Harry Potter and the prisoner of Azkaban	Fic
Janeczko, P. B. Writing winning reports and essays	808
Rowling, J. K. Harry Potter and the sorcerer's stone	Fic
Lewis, C. Thrice told tales	803
Rumford, J. Beowulf a hero's tale retold	398.2
Merriam-Webster, I. Merriam-Webster's intermediate dictionary	423
Russell, C. Songs about a girl	Fic
Russell, P. C. The graveyard book graphic novel	741.5

ENGLISH LANGUAGE -- CHINESE

Sedgwick, M. White crow	Fic
Manser, M. H. Oxford Chinese dictionary	495.1321
Selznick, B. The Marvels	Fic

Alsaid, A. We didn't ask for this — **Fic**
Ball, J. A. Traveling green — **790.1**
Bearce, S. How to harness solar power for your home — **621.47**
Drake, J. Rewilding — **639.9**
Eamer, C. What a waste! — **363.72**
Fleischman, P. Eyes wide open — **363.7**
Fombelle, T. d. Toby alone — **Fic**
Fombelle, T. d. Toby and the secrets of the tree — **Fic**
Gilman, D. The devil's breath — **Fic**
Hoberman, M. A. The tree that time built — **808.81**
Jankeliowitch, A. Kids who are changing the world — **363.7092**
Kaye, C. B. Going blue — **333.91**
Klein, N. How to change everything — **363.738**
Nardo, D. Planet under siege — **363.738**
Nye, N. S. Cast away — **811**
O'Neal, C. How to use waste energy to heat and light your home — **621.1**
O'Neal, C. How to use wind power to light and heat your home — **621.31**
Petronis, L. 47 things you can do for the environment — **333.72**
Rao, A. S. One Earth — **333.72092**
Reilly, K. M. Planet Earth — **577**
Rohmer, H. Heroes of the environment — **920**
Sivertsen, L. Generation green — **640**
Zimmer, M. Solutions for a cleaner greener planet — **577.27**

ENVIRONMENTALISM -- HISTORY
Peterson, C. Earth Day and the global environmental movement — **394.262**

ENVIRONMENTALISTS
Giannella, V. Green Nation revolution — **333.72**
Jankeliowitch, A. Kids who are changing the world — **363.7092**
McPherson, S. S. Hothouse earth — **363.738**
Montgomery, S. Saving the ghost of the mountain — **599.75**
Rao, A. S. One Earth — **333.72092**
Rohmer, H. Heroes of the environment — **920**
Envisioning exoplanets. Carroll, M. W. — **523.2**
Eona. Goodman, A. — **Fic**
Epic. Kostick, C. — **Fic**
Epic adventure Epic treks. Hagglund, B. — **910.9**
Epic climbs. Cleare, J. — **796.522092**
The **epic** crush of Genie Lo. Yee, F. C. — **Fic**
The **epic** fail of Arturo Zamora. Cartaya, P. — **Fic**

EPIC FANTASY
Tolkien, J. R. R. The hobbit or there and back again — **Fic**
Tolkien, J. R. R. The lord of the rings — **Fic**

EPIC FICTION
Sattar, A. Ramayana — **294.5**

EPIC POETRY
Hinds, G. Beowulf — **741.5**
Hinds, G. The Iliad — **741.5**
Homer. The Iliad — **883**
Homer. The Odyssey — **883**
McCaughrean, G. Gilgamesh the hero — **398.2**
Raven, N. Beowulf — **398.2**
Rumford, J. Beowulf a hero's tale retold — **398.2**

Epic voyages. Mundy, R. — **910.4**

EPIDEMICS
Anderson, L. H. Fever 1793 — **Fic**
Aronin, M. Tuberculosis — **616.9**
Bracken, A. Never fade — **Fic**
Chibbaro, J. Deadly — **Fic**
Davis, K. C. More deadly than war — **614.5**
Goldsmith, C. Pandemic — **614.4**
Grant, M. Plague — **Fic**
Hopkinson, D. The great trouble — **Fic**
Howe, K. Conversion — **Fic**
Kupperberg, P. The influenza pandemic of 1918-1919 — **614.5**
Lucier, M. A death-struck year — **Fic**
Moon, W. K. Past pandemics and COVID-19 — **614.5**
Murphy, J. An American plague — **614.5**
Nardo, D. COVID-19 and other pandemics — **614.5**
Newman, P. Ebola — **616.9**
Patent, D. H. Saving the Tasmanian devil — **599.2**
Sangster, C. Last star burning — **Fic**

EPIDEMICS -- HISTORY
Barnard, B. Outbreak — **614.4**
Jarrow, G. Bubonic panic — **614.5**
Jarrow, G. Red madness — **614.5**
Lewis, M. L. Cholera — **616.9**
Lewis, M. L. Measles — **614.5**

EPIDEMIOLOGISTS
Hopkinson, D. The great trouble — **Fic**

EPIDEMIOLOGY
Chibbaro, J. Deadly — **Fic**
Goldsmith, C. Pandemic — **614.4**
Hand, C. Epidemiology — **614.4**
Epidemiology. Hand, C. — **614.4**

EPILEPSY
Bender, L. Explaining epilepsy — **616.8**
Episodes. Ginsberg, B. — **616.858820092**

EPISTOLARY NOVELS
Ali, S. K. Love from A to Z — **Fic**
Cleary, B. Dear Mr. Henshaw — **Fic**
Davis, T. S. Mare's war — **Fic**
Halpern, J. Get well soon — **Fic**
Hesse, K. Letters from Rifka — **Fic**
Kapit, S. Get a grip Vivy Cohen! — **Fic**
Kisner, A. Dear Rachel Maddow — **Fic**
Klise, K. Regarding the fountain — **Fic**
Klise, K. Regarding the sink — **Fic**
Klise, K. Regarding the trees — **Fic**
Lyons, M. E. Letters from a slave boy — **Fic**
Lyons, M. E. Letters from a slave girl — **Fic**
Menon, S. From Twinkle with love — **Fic**
Moriarty, J. Feeling sorry for Celia — **Fic**
Rivers, K. Finding Ruby Starling — **Fic**
Venkatraman, P. The bridge home — **Fic**
Woodruff, E. Dear Austin — **Fic**
Zarr, S. Roomies — **Fic**

Epstein, Adam Jay
Circle of heroes — **Fic**

Ellis, D. Looks like daylight — 970.004
Hest, A. The summer we found the baby — Fic
Hinds, K. Everyday life in medieval Europe — 909.07
Nayeri, D. Everything sad is untrue — Fic
Rylant, C. God went to beauty school — Fic
Everyday life in medieval Europe. Hinds, K. — 909.07
Everyday life in the Renaissance. Hinds, K. — 940.2
Everyday life in the Roman Empire. Hinds, K. — 937
Everything birds of prey. Hoena, B. A. — 598.9
Everything for a dog. Martin, A. M. — Fic
Everything on a waffle. Horvath, P. — Fic
Everything sad is untrue. Nayeri, D. — Fic
Everything you wanted to know about Indians but were afraid to ask. Treuer, A. — 970.1
Everywear. Warwick, E. — 646.4
Eves, Rosalyn
Blood rose rebellion — Fic
Evil genius. Jinks, C. — Fic
Evil spy school. Gibbs, S. — Fic
Evil star. Horowitz, A. — Fic
EVOLUTION
Bright, M. Darwin's tree of life — 576.8
Colson, M. Charles Darwin and Alfred Russel Wallace — 576.8
Gamlin, L. Evolution — 576.8
Hartman, E. Changing life on Earth — 576.8
Hirsch, R. E. Living fossils — 591.3
Holmes, T. Evolution — 576.8
Johnson, S. A. Shaking the foundation — 576.8
Pringle, L. Billions of years amazing changes — 576.8
Stefoff, R. First humans — 569.9
Walker, R. What is the theory of evolution? — 576.8
Winston, R. M. L. Evolution revolution — 576.8
EVOLUTION -- HISTORY
Gamlin, L. Evolution — 576.8
Johnson, S. A. Shaking the foundation — 576.8
Walker, R. What is the theory of evolution? — 576.8
EVOLUTION -- RELIGIOUS ASPECTS
Johnson, S. A. Shaking the foundation — 576.8
EVOLUTION -- RELIGIOUS ASPECTS -- CHRISTIANITY
Schomp, V. The Church — 274.2
EVOLUTION -- STUDY AND TEACHING -- LAW AND LEGISLATION
Bryant, J. Ringside 1925 — Fic
Evolution. Gamlin, L. — 576.8
Evolution. Holmes, T. — 576.8
The **evolution** of Calpurnia Tate. Kelly, J. — Fic
Evolution revolution. Winston, R. M. L. — 576.8
Ewald, Wendy
America border culture dreamer — 305.23092
EXAMINATIONS
Charbonneau, J. Independent study — Fic
Charbonneau, J. The Testing — Fic
Examining geothermal energy. Boyle, J. — 621.44
Examining solar energy. Bright, S. — 621.47
EXCALIBUR (SWORD)

Yancey, R. The extraordinary adventures of Alfred Kropp — Fic
EXCAVATIONS (ARCHAEOLOGY)
Aronson, M. The skull in the rock — 569.9096822
Ball, J. A. National Geographic investigates ancient China — 931
Cooke, T. National Geographic investigates ancient Aztec — 972
Cottman, M. H. Shackles from the deep — 382.4409
Deem, J. M. Bodies from the ash — 937
Gruber, B. National Geographic investigates ancient Inca — 985
Gruber, B. National Geographic investigates ancient Iraq — 935
Hansen, J. Breaking ground breaking silence — 305.5
Harris, N. Ancient Maya — 972.8
Henderson, H. The Leakey family — 599.9092
Huey, L. M. American archaeology uncovers the earliest English colonies — 973.2
Huey, L. M. American archaeology uncovers the Vikings — 948
Kops, D. Palenque — 972
Lace, W. W. King Tut's curse — 932
Liu-Perkins, C. At home in her tomb — 931
Lourie, P. Hidden world of the Aztec — 972
McGee, M. National Geographic investigates ancient Greece — 938
Rubalcaba, J. Digging for Troy — 939
Rubalcaba, J. Every bone tells a story — 930.1
Rubalcaba, J. National Geographic investigates ancient Egypt — 932
Sherrow, V. National Geographic investigates ancient Africa — 960
Vivian, R. G. Chaco Canyon — 978.9
EXCHANGE
January, B. Cryptocurrencies and the blockchain revolution — 332.4
The **exchange** student. Gilmore, K. — Fic
EXCHANGE STUDENTS
Gilmore, K. The exchange student — Fic
Lee, C. The great motion mission — 530
Tan, S. Tales from outer suburbia — Fic
EXCRETION
Klosterman, L. Excretory system — 612.4
Montgomery, H. L. Who gives a poop? — 612.3
EXCRETORY ORGANS
Klosterman, L. Excretory system — 612.4
EXCRETORY SYSTEM
Gold, S. D. Learning about the digestive and excretory systems — 612.3
Excretory system. Klosterman, L. — 612.4
EXECUTIONS AND EXECUTIONERS
Shusterman, N. The toll — Fic
EXERCISE
Aikman, L. Pilates step-by-step — 613.7
Andrus, A. Project you — 155.5
Dicker, K. Exercise — 613.7
Etingoff, K. Building a healthy diet with the 5 food

Carroll, M. W. Envisioning exoplanets	523.2
Kenney, K. L. Exoplanets	523.2
Extreme abilities. Watson, G. F.	612
Extreme animals. Davies, N.	590

EXTREME ENVIRONMENTS

Davies, N. Extreme animals	590
Extreme ocean. Earle, S. A.	551.46
Extreme scientists. Jackson, D. M.	509.2

EXTREME SPORTS

Adamson, T. K. BMX racing	796.6
Birmingham, M. Weird zone	796.1
Fitzpatrick, J. Skateboarding	796.22
Gilman, D. Ice claw	Fic
Hile, L. Surviving extreme sports	796.04
Hobbs, W. Go big or go home	Fic
Schwartz, H. E. Snowboarding	796.939
Extreme survivors. Ridley, K.	591.3
Extreme weather. Shoals, J.	551.55
Extreme wildfire. Thiessen, M.	363.37

EXUDATES AND TRANSUDATES

Larsen, C. S. Crust and spray	612.8

EYE

Auxier, J. Peter Nimble and his fantastic eyes	Fic
Markle, S. Lost sight	617.7
Rutkoski, M. The Cabinet of Wonders	Fic
Simon, S. Eyes and ears	612.8

EYE -- DISEASES AND DEFECTS

Bender, L. Explaining blindness	617.7
An **eye** for art.	708.153
The **Eye** of the Whale. O'Connell, J.	599.5
The **Eye** of Zoltar. Fforde, J.	Fic
The **eyeball** collector. Higgins, F. E.	Fic
Eyes & spies. Kyi, T. L.	323.44
Eyes and ears. Simon, S.	612.8
Eyes of the emperor. Salisbury, G.	Fic
Eyes of the world. Aronson, M.	770
Eyes wide open. Fleischman, P.	363.7
Eyewitness fossil. Taylor, P. D.	560
Eyewitness ocean. MacQuitty, M.	551.46

F

Fabulous bridges. Graham, I.	624.2
The **face** on the milk carton. Cooney, C. B.	Fic
The **faceless** ones. Landy, D.	Fic
Faces from the past. Deem, J. M.	599.9

FACIAL RECONSTRUCTION (ANTHROPOLOGY)

Deem, J. M. Faces from the past	599.9
Fact vs. fiction. LaGarde, J.	370.15

FACTORIES

Haddix, M. P. Uprising	Fic

FACTORIES -- HISTORY

Marrin, A. Flesh & blood so cheap	974.7
Facts about the presidents. Kane, J. N.	973.09

Fagan, Deva

Nightingale	Fic
Fair isn't always equal second edition. Wormeli, R.	371.27

FAIR USE (COPYRIGHT)

Butler, R. P. Copyright for teachers & librarians in the 21st century	346.7304
Russell, C. Complete copyright for K-12 librarians and educators	346.7304
Fair weather. Peck, R.	Fic

FAIRBANKS, ALASKA

Hitchcock, B. The smell of other people's houses	Fic
Fairest. Levine, G. C.	Fic

FAIRIES

Anderson, J. L. Tiger Lily	Fic
Bauer, A. C. E. Come Fall	Fic
Black, H. The Good Neighbors	741.5
Booraem, E. Small persons with wings	Fic
Carroll, E. In darkling wood	Fic
Catmull, K. The radiant road	Fic
Chabon, M. Summerland	Fic
Colfer, C. A tale of magic...	Fic
Colfer, E. Artemis Fowl	741.5
Colfer, E. The Fowl twins	Fic
Coville, B. William Shakespeare's A midsummer night's dream	Fic
De la Cruz, M. Never after	Fic
Fisher, C. The obsidian mirror	Fic
Gaiman, N. Stardust	Fic
Harrison, M. 13 curses	Fic
Harrison, M. 13 secrets	Fic
Levine, G. C. Ella enchanted	Fic
Levine, G. C. The lost kingdom of Bamarre	Fic
Lu, M. The Kingdom of Back	Fic
Marr, M. Ink exchange	Fic
Marr, M. Wicked lovely	Fic
Morrison, M. Grounded	Fic
Pratchett, T. The Wee Free Men	Fic
Rex, A. Champions of breakfast	Fic
Rogerson, M. An enchantment of ravens	Fic
Taylor, L. Blackbringer	Fic
Toro, G. d. Pan's labyrinth	Fic
Trevayne, E. The accidental afterlife of Thomas Marsden	Fic
Tripp, B. The accidental highwayman	Fic
Werlin, N. Extraordinary	Fic
White, K. Paranormalcy	Fic
White, K. Supernaturally	Fic
Yolen, J. Foiled	Fic
Zettel, S. Bad luck girl	Fic

Fairlie, Emily

The magician's bird	Fic
Fairy tail. Mashima, H.	741.5

FAIRY TALE AND FOLKLORE-INSPIRED FICTION

Anderson, S. The girl who speaks bear	Fic
Baptiste, T. The jumbie god's revenge	Fic
Baptiste, T. The jumbies	Fic
Baptiste, T. Rise of the jumbies	Fic
Baratz-Logsted, L. Crazy beautiful	Fic
Barrett, T. The stepsister's tale	Fic
Bashardoust, M. Girls made of snow and glass	Fic
Braswell, L. Part of your world	Fic

Braswell, L. A whole new world	Fic	Ursu, A. Breadcrumbs	Fic
Carroll, E. Through the woods	**741.5**	Vande Velde, V. Cloaked in red	Fic
Chupeco, R. Wicked as you wish	Fic	Vande Velde, V. Frogged	Fic
Cornwell, B. Venturess	Fic	White, K. The Guinevere deception	Fic
Cuevas, A. The total eclipse of Nestor Lopez	Fic	**FAIRY TALES**	
Cypess, L. Thornwood	Fic	Rapunzel and other magic fairy tales	**398.22**
DasGupta, S. The force of fire	Fic	Burns, B. The king with horse's ears and other Irish folk-tales	**398.2**
Datlow, E. Troll's eye view	Fic	Gaiman, N. Hansel & Gretel	**398.20943**
De la Cruz, M. Never after	Fic	Hearne, B. G. Beauties and beasts	**398.21**
Donnelly, J. Stepsister	Fic	Napoli, D. J. Tales from the Arabian nights	**398.2**
Durst, S. B. Ice	Fic	Philip, N. Celtic fairy tales	**398.2**
Durst, S. B. Into the Wild	Fic	**FAIRY TALES IN ART**	
Flinn, A. Beastly	Fic	Tan, S. The singing bones	**730.92**
Flinn, A. Cloaked	Fic	**FAITH**	
Flinn, A. A kiss in time	Fic	Berry, J. The passion of Dolssa	Fic
Gaughen, A. C. Scarlet	Fic	Hautman, P. The obsidian blade	Fic
George, J. D. Princess of the Midnight Ball	Fic	Nicholson, W. Seeker	Fic
Gidwitz, A. The Grimm conclusion	Fic	Rylant, C. A fine white dust	Fic
Gidwitz, A. In a glass Grimmly	Fic	What do you believe?	**200**
Haddix, M. P. Just Ella	Fic	Zarr, S. Once was lost	Fic
Hale, S. Book of a thousand days	Fic	**FAITH (CHRISTIANITY)**	
Hale, S. The goose girl	Fic	Wallace, C. Stories of the saints	**235.2**
Hale, S. Rapunzel's revenge	**741.5**	**FAITH IN WOMEN**	
Hale, S. The storybook of legends	Fic	Elliott, D. Voices	Fic
Healy, C. The hero's guide to saving your kingdom	Fic	The **faithful** spy. Hendrix, J.	**B**
Kemmerer, B. A heart so fierce and broken	Fic	**FAKE NEWS**	
Levine, G. C. Ella enchanted	Fic	Brown, R. T. Breaking the news	**070.9**
Levine, G. C. Fairest	Fic	Miller, M. Fake news	**070.4**
Lin, G. When the sea turned to silver	Fic	Otis, C. L. True or false	**070.4**
Loftin, N. Nightingale's nest	Fic	**FAKE NEWS -- STUDY AND TEACHING**	
Marillier, J. Wildwood dancing	Fic	LaGarde, J. Fact vs. fiction	**370.15**
Mbalia, K. Tristan Strong destroys the world	Fic	**Fake** news. Miller, M.	**070.4**
Mbalia, K. Tristan Strong punches a hole in the sky	Fic	The **Falcon's** Malteser. Horowitz, A.	Fic
McCoola, M. Baba Yaga's assistant	**741.5**	**FALCONERS**	
McKinley, R. Beauty	Fic	Whitman, E. Wildwing	Fic
McKinley, R. The outlaws of Sherwood	Fic	**FALCONRY**	
McKinley, R. Rose daughter	Fic	London, A. Black wings beating	Fic
McNeal, T. Far far away	Fic	London, A. Red skies falling	Fic
Mejia, T. K. Paola Santiago and the river of tears	Fic	**Falkowski, Melissa**	
Messner, K. The seventh wish	Fic	We say #never again	**371.7**
Meyer, M. Cinder	Fic	**Fallen** angels. Myers, W. D.	Fic
Meyer, M. Cress	Fic	**Fallen** Grace. Hooper, M.	Fic
Meyer, M. Scarlet	Fic	**Falling** in. Dowell, F. O.	Fic
Milford, K. The raconteur's commonplace book	Fic	**Falling** up. Silverstein, S.	**811**
Morrison, M. Grounded	Fic	**Fallout.** Strasser, T.	Fic
Napoli, D. J. Beast	Fic	**FALLOUT SHELTERS**	
Napoli, D. J. Bound	Fic	Bodeen, S. A. The compound	Fic
Napoli, D. J. Zel	Fic	Strasser, T. Fallout	Fic
Pattou, E. East	Fic	**Falls, Kat**	
Phelan, M. Snow White	**741.5**	Dark life	Fic
Pratchett, T. The amazing Maurice and his educated rodents	Fic	Inhuman	Fic
		Rip tide	Fic
Shepherd, M. Midnight beauties	Fic	**FALSE ARREST**	
Shulman, P. The Grimm legacy	Fic	Perera, A. Guantanamo boy	Fic
Shurtliff, L. Rump	Fic	**FALSE IMPRISONMENT**	
Stanley, D. Bella at midnight	Fic	Horowitz, A. The Falcon's Malteser	Fic
Thomas, S. The magnolia sword	Fic		

Milford, K. The thief knot — **Fic**
Mobley, J. Katerina's wish — **Fic**
Morpurgo, M. Listen to the moon — **Fic**
Nesbet, A. Cloud and Wallfish — **Fic**
Ollhoff, J. Filling the family tree — **929**
Partridge, E. Dogtag summer — **Fic**
Patterson, J. House of robots — **Fic**
Peck, R. The best man — **Fic**
Peck, R. Fair weather — **Fic**
Polak, M. What world is left — **Fic**
Rodkey, G. The Tapper twins go to war (with each other) — **Fic**
Rosen, M. J. Our farm — **630.9**
Rosen, M. J. The tale of rescue — **Fic**
Rosenberg, M. This is just a test — **Fic**
Roy, J. R. Yellow star — **Fic**
Samphire, P. Secrets of the dragon tomb — **Fic**
Schmidt, G. D. The Wednesday wars — **Fic**
Selznick, B. Wonderstruck — **Fic**
Sheth, K. Keeping corner — **Fic**
Sleator, W. Oddballs — **Fic**
Smith, R. L. Hoodoo — **Fic**
Sones, S. Stop pretending — **Fic**
Soto, G. Help wanted — **Fic**
Sovern, M. J. The meaning of Maggie — **Fic**
Strasser, T. Fallout — **Fic**
Tan, S. The arrival — **741.5**
Thompson, J. The girl from Felony Bay — **Fic**
Tolan, S. S. Surviving the Applewhites — **Fic**
Van de Ruit, J. Spud — **Fic**
Venkatraman, P. Climbing the stairs — **Fic**
Vlahos, L. Life in a fishbowl — **Fic**
Wells, R. My Havana — **Fic**
Whelan, G. All my noble dreams and then what happens — **Fic**
Wiles, D. Countdown — **Fic**
Williams, C. L. The chosen one — **Fic**
Williams-Garcia, R. Gone crazy in Alabama — **Fic**
Williams-Garcia, R. Like sisters on the homefront — **Fic**
Wolk, L. Beyond the bright sea — **Fic**
Wolk, L. Wolf Hollow — **Fic**
Wright, B. Crow — **Fic**
Young, K. R. Hundred percent — **Fic**

FAMILIES -- HISTORY
Hamza, N. Ahmed Aziz's epic year — **Fic**

FAMILIES -- HISTORY 20TH CENTURY
Heuvel, E. A family secret — **741.5**

FAMILIES OF MILITARY PERSONNEL
Flores-Scott, P. American road trip — **Fic**
Holmes, S. Operation Yes — **Fic**

FAMILIES OF MILITARY PERSONNEL -- SERVICES FOR -- EVALUATION
Engdahl, S. Military families — **355.1**

FAMILIES OF MILITARY PERSONNEL -- SOCIAL CONDITIONS
Engdahl, S. Military families — **355.1**

FAMILY AND CHILD ABUSE
Woodson, J. Lena — **Fic**

FAMILY AND MENTAL ILLNESS

Pixley, M. F. Without Tess — **Fic**

FAMILY AND WAR
Jones, M. T. Woodford Brave — **Fic**
Keller, J. Back home — **Fic**

FAMILY BUSINESSES
Cartaya, P. The epic fail of Arturo Zamora — **Fic**
Gregorio, I. W. This is my brain in love — **Fic**
Lesperance, N. The nightmare thief — **Fic**
Messner, K. Chirp — **Fic**
Youngblood, L. C. Forever this summer — **Fic**

FAMILY CURSES
Moreno, N. Don't date Rosa Santos — **Fic**
Stanley, D. The silver bowl — **Fic**

FAMILY FARMS
Bigelow, L. J. Hazel's theory of evolution — **Fic**

FAMILY FEUDS
Appignanesi, R. Romeo and Juliet — **741.5**
Bell, H. Traitor's son — **Fic**
Hinds, G. The most excellent and lamentable tragedy of Romeo & Juliet — **741.5**
Plozza, S. Tin heart — **Fic**
Staples, S. F. Haveli — **Fic**
Walker, S. M. Boundaries — **974.8**
The **family** Fletcher takes Rock Island. Levy, D. A. — **Fic**

FAMILY FORTUNES
Watson, J. Beyond the grave — **Fic**

FAMILY LIFE EDUCATION
Cole, J. Asking about sex & growing up — **649**
Harris, R. H. It's perfectly normal — **613.9071**
Mar, J. The body book for boys — **613**
Murray, C. Sexpectations — **306.70835**
A **family** of readers. Sutton, R. — **809**

FAMILY PROBLEMS
Anderson, J. D. One last shot — **Fic**
Arnold, E. K. Far from fair — **Fic**
Blundell, J. What I saw and how I lied — **Fic**
Bowman, A. D. Starfish — **Fic**
Bradbury, J. Shift — **Fic**
Castellucci, C. Don't cosplay with my heart — **Fic**
Cline-Ransome, L. Leaving Lymon — **Fic**
Dessen, S. Saint Anything — **Fic**
Frost, H. Keesha's house — **Fic**
Grabenstein, C. The island of Dr. Libris — **Fic**
Greenwald, L. My life in pink & green — **Fic**
Grisham, J. The abduction — **Fic**
Hand, C. The last time we say goodbye — **Fic**
Harkrader, L. The adventures of Beanboy — **Fic**
Harrington, K. Courage for beginners — **Fic**
Harrington, K. Sure signs of crazy — **Fic**
Haydu, C. A. Rules for stealing stars — **Fic**
Hepler, H. The cupcake queen — **Fic**
Holm, J. L. Sunny side up — **741.5**
Hughes, D. Search and destroy — **Fic**
Keller, J. Back home — **Fic**
Kelly, E. E. We dream of space — **Fic**
King, A. S. The year we fell from space — **Fic**
Knowles, J. See you at Harry's — **Fic**

Famous in a small town. Mills, E.	Fic	Ostertag, M. The girl from the sea	Fic
FAN CLUBS		Pearson, L. Hildafolk	741.5
Jung, M. Geeks girls and secret identities	Fic	Petersen, D. Mouse guard	741.5
FAN CONVENTIONS		Pope, P. Battling boy	741.5
Jung, M. The boys in the back row	Fic	Renier, A. The unsinkable Walker Bean	741.5
Katcher, B. The improbable theory of Ana and Zak	Fic	Russell, P. C. The graveyard book graphic novel	741.5
Myer, S. Create a costume!	793.93	Smith, J. Out from Boneville	741.5
Fandom. DiPiazza, F.	302.23	Smith, J. Rose	741.5
Fannie never flinched. Farrell, M. C.	B	Smith, J. Tall tales	741.5
FANS (PERSONS)		Smith, N. The deep & dark blue	741.5
DiPiazza, F. Fandom	302.23	Stevenson, N. Lumberjanes	741.5
Ratcliffe, A. A kid's guide to fandom	302.23	Stevenson, N. Nimona	741.5
Fantaskey, Beth		Takaya, N. Fruits basket	741.5
Buzz kill	Fic	TenNapel, D. Cardboard	741.5
Jessica's guide to dating on the dark side	Fic	TenNapel, D. Ghostopolis	741.5
The fantastic body. Bennett, H. J.	612	Venditti, R. The lightning thief	741.5
Fantastic feats and failures.	624.1	Wheeler, A. Another castle	741.5
FANTASY		Whitley, J. Princeless	741.5
Link, K. Steampunk!	Fic	Yolen, J. Foiled	Fic
Mafi, T. Furthermore	Fic	Young, E. The dragon path	Fic
Mafi, T. Whichwood	Fic	**FANTASY FICTION**	
Fantasy. Boos, B.	813	Abbott, T. The forbidden stone	Fic
FANTASY ART		Adams, R. Watership Down	Fic
Boos, B. Fantasy	813	Alexander, L. The black cauldron	Fic
FANTASY BASEBALL (GAME)		Alexander, L. The book of three	Fic
Gutman, D. Babe and me	Fic	Alexander, L. The foundling and other tales of Prydain	Fic
Gutman, D. Jackie and me	Fic	Alexander, L. The golden dream of Carlo Chuchio	Fic
FANTASY CLASSICS		Alexander, L. The iron ring	Fic
Bradbury, R. Something wicked this way comes	Fic	Alexander, L. The remarkable journey of Prince Jen	Fic
Swift, J. Gulliver's travels	Fic	Alexander, L. Taran Wanderer	Fic
Tolkien, J. R. R. The hobbit or there and back again	Fic	Alexander, L. Westmark	Fic
Tolkien, J. R. R. The lord of the rings	Fic	Almond, D. Clay	Fic
FANTASY COMICS		Almond, D. The savage	Fic
Black, H. The Good Neighbors	741.5	Almond, D. Skellig	Fic
Camper, C. Lowriders in space	741.5	Anderson, J. L. My diary from the edge of the world	Fic
Camper, C. Lowriders to the center of the Earth	741.5	Anderson, J. L. Tiger Lily	Fic
Chanani, N. Jukebox	Fic	Anderson, J. D. Standard hero behavior	Fic
Colfer, E. Artemis Fowl	741.5	Anderson, S. The girl who speaks bear	Fic
Collar, O. The red pyramid	741.5	Andrews, C. M. Spindlefish and stars	Fic
Corona, J. Feathers	741.5	Ansari, R. K. S. The missing piece of Charlie O'Reilly	Fic
Gillis, P. B. The last unicorn	741.5	Appelt, K. Keeper	Fic
Harrell, R. Monster on the hill	741.5	Appelt, K. Maybe a fox	Fic
Hatke, B. Mighty Jack	741.5	Appelt, K. The underneath	Fic
Hicks, F. E. The divided earth	741.5	Armstrong, K. Loki's wolves	Fic
Hicks, F. E. The Nameless City	741.5	Armstrong, K. Odin's ravens	Fic
Hicks, F. E. The Stone Heart	741.5	Armstrong, K. A royal guide to monster slaying	Fic
Jacques, B. Redwall the graphic novel	741.5	Arntson, S. The wikkeling	Fic
Kibuishi, K. Amulet	741.5	Aster, A. Curse of the forgotten city	Fic
Layne, A. Beetle & the Hollowbones	741.5	Aster, A. Curse of the Night Witch	Fic
Leyh, K. Snapdragon	741.5	Auxier, J. Peter Nimble and his fantastic eyes	Fic
Mashima, H. Fairy tail	741.5	Auxier, J. Sophie Quire and the last Storyguard	Fic
McCann, J. Return of the dapper men	741.5	Aveyard, V. Red queen	Fic
McCoola, M. Baba Yaga's assistant	741.5	Azad, N. The candle and the flame	Fic
Medley, L. Castle waiting	741.5	Babbitt, N. Tuck everlasting	Fic
Melchior-Durand, S. The golden compass	741.5	Bachmann, S. The cabinet of curiosities	Fic
Moreci, M. The lost carnival	Fic	Baptiste, T. The jumbie god's revenge	Fic
O'Neill, K. Princess princess ever after	741.5	Baptiste, T. The jumbies	Fic

Baptiste, T. Rise of the jumbies	**Fic**	Chima, C. W. The warrior heir	**Fic**
Bardugo, L. King of scars	**Fic**	Chupeco, R. Wicked as you wish	**Fic**
Bardugo, L. Ruin and rising	**Fic**	Colfer, C. A tale of magic...	**Fic**
Bardugo, L. Siege and storm	**Fic**	Colfer, E. Artemis Fowl	**Fic**
Barnhill, K. R. The girl who drank the moon	**Fic**	Colfer, E. The Fowl twins	**Fic**
Barnhill, K. R. The mostly true story of Jack	**Fic**	Collins, S. Gregor the Overlander	**Fic**
Barnhill, K. R. The witch's boy	**Fic**	Connolly, M. Comet rising	**Fic**
Barron, R. Maya and the rising dark	**Fic**	Connolly, M. Hollow dolls	**Fic**
Bashardoust, M. Girls made of snow and glass	**Fic**	Connolly, M. Shadow weaver	**Fic**
Bauer, A. C. E. Come Fall	**Fic**	Constable, K. The singer of all songs	**Fic**
Bauer, A. C. E. No castles here	**Fic**	Cooper, S. King of shadows	**Fic**
Beasley, C. Circus Mirandus	**Fic**	Cornwell, B. Venturess	**Fic**
Bell, H. Traitor's son	**Fic**	Coulthurst, A. Of fire and stars	**Fic**
Berry, J. The Amaranth enchantment	**Fic**	Creech, S. The unfinished angel	**Fic**
Black, H. The bronze key	**Fic**	Croggon, A. The threads of magic	**Fic**
Black, H. The copper gauntlet	**Fic**	Cuevas, A. The total eclipse of Nestor Lopez	**Fic**
Black, H. The iron trial	**Fic**	Cypess, L. Death sworn	**Fic**
Black, H. The silver mask	**Fic**	Cyprus, N. Sisters of glass	**Fic**
Blackburne, L. Midnight thief	**Fic**	D'Lacey, C. Dark fire	**Fic**
Blackburne, L. Rosemarked	**Fic**	D'Lacey, C. The fire ascending	**Fic**
Blackwood, S. Jinx	**Fic**	D'Lacey, C. The fire eternal	**Fic**
Blackwood, S. Jinx's fire	**Fic**	D'Lacey, C. Fire star	**Fic**
Blackwood, S. Jinx's magic	**Fic**	D'Lacey, C. The fire within	**Fic**
Blackwood, S. Miss Ellicott's school for the magically mind-		D'Lacey, C. Fire world	**Fic**
ed	**Fic**	D'Lacey, C. Icefire	**Fic**
Blake, K. Two dark reigns	**Fic**	Dakin, G. The Society of Unrelenting Vigilance	**Fic**
Booraem, E. River magic	**Fic**	DasGupta, S. The force of fire	**Fic**
Booraem, E. Small persons with wings	**Fic**	Datlow, E. The beastly bride	**Fic**
Booraem, E. The unnameables	**Fic**	Datlow, E. The Coyote Road	**Fic**
Booth, M. Saving Hamlet	**Fic**	De la Cruz, M. Never after	**Fic**
Bourne, S. Josephine against the sea	**Fic**	Delaney, J. A new darkness	**Fic**
Bradbury, R. The Halloween tree	**Fic**	Delaney, J. Revenge of the witch	**Fic**
Braswell, L. Part of your world	**Fic**	Dennard, S. Truthwitch	**Fic**
Braswell, L. A whole new world	**Fic**	DiCamillo, K. Flora & Ulysses	**Fic**
Bruchac, J. Dragon castle	**Fic**	DiCamillo, K. The magician's elephant	**Fic**
Bullen, A. Wish	**Fic**	Dickinson, P. The ropemaker	**Fic**
Bunce, E. C. Starcrossed	**Fic**	Divakaruni, C. B. The conch bearer	**Fic**
Burgis, S. The princess who flew with dragons	**Fic**	Donnelly, J. Stepsister	**Fic**
Byng, G. Molly Moon's incredible book of hypnotism	**Fic**	Dowell, F. O. Falling in	**Fic**
Caine, R. Ink and bone	**Fic**	Downer, A. Hatching magic	**Fic**
Caldwell, P. A phoenix first must burn	**Fic**	Doyle, R. A greyhound of a girl	**Fic**
Calejo, R. Charlie Hernandez & the castle of bones	**Fic**	Duane, D. So you want to be a wizard	**Fic**
Carman, P. The Dark Hills divide	**Fic**	Duey, K. Sacred scars	**Fic**
Carroll, E. In darkling wood	**Fic**	Duey, K. Skin hunger	**Fic**
Carson, R. The bitter kingdom	**Fic**	Dunmore, H. The deep	**Fic**
Carson, R. The crown of embers	**Fic**	Dunmore, H. Ingo	**Fic**
Carson, R. The girl of fire and thorns	**Fic**	Dunmore, H. The tide knot	**Fic**
Cashore, K. Fire	**Fic**	Durham, P. Fork-tongue charmers	**Fic**
Cashore, K. Graceling	**Fic**	Durham, P. The Luck Uglies	**Fic**
Cashore, K. Jane unlimited	**Fic**	Durst, S. B. The girl who could not dream	**Fic**
Chabon, M. Summerland	**Fic**	Durst, S. B. Ice	**Fic**
Chadda, S. City of the plague god	**Fic**	Durst, S. B. Into the Wild	**Fic**
Chee, T. The reader	**Fic**	Durst, S. B. Vessel	**Fic**
Chee, T. The speaker	**Fic**	Elphinstone, A. Casper Tock and the Everdark wings	**Fic**
Chee, T. The storyteller	**Fic**	Epstein, A. J. Circle of heroes	**Fic**
Chilton, A. S. The goblin's puzzle	**Fic**	Evans, M. Who let the gods out?	**Fic**
Chima, C. W. The Demon King	**Fic**	Fagan, D. Nightingale	**Fic**

Farrey, B. The Grimjinx rebellion	Fic	George, J. D. Dragon spear	Fic
Farrey, B. The secret of Dreadwillow Carse	Fic	George, J. D. Princess of the Midnight Ball	Fic
Farrey, B. The Shadowhand Covenant	Fic	George, J. D. Tuesdays at the castle	Fic
Farrey, B. The Vengekeep prophecies	Fic	Giles, L. R. The Last Mirror on the Left	Fic
Fawcett, H. Even the darkest stars	Fic	Glaser, M. The book jumper	Fic
Fayers, C. The voyage to Magical North	Fic	Gonzalez, C. D. Moving target	Fic
Ferris, J. Once upon a Marigold	Fic	Goodman, A. Eona	Fic
Ferris, J. Twice upon a Marigold	Fic	Goto, H. Half World	Fic
Fforde, J. The Eye of Zoltar	Fic	Grabenstein, C. The island of Dr. Libris	Fic
Fforde, J. The last dragonslayer	Fic	Graff, L. A tangle of knots	Fic
Fforde, J. The song of the quarkbeast	Fic	Grant, H. The league of beastly dreadfuls	Fic
Fichtelberg, S. Encountering enchantment	016.8093	Grant, M. The trap	Fic
Fisher, C. The dark city	Fic	Gratton, T. Strange grace	Fic
Fisher, C. The hidden Coronet	Fic	Grove, S. E. The crimson skew	Fic
Fisher, C. The lost heiress	Fic	Grove, S. E. The golden specific	Fic
Fisher, C. The obsidian mirror	Fic	Gutman, D. Abner & me	Fic
Fisher, C. Sapphique	Fic	Gutman, D. Babe and me	Fic
Flanagan, J. The battle for Skandia	Fic	Gutman, D. Honus and me	Fic
Flanagan, J. The burning bridge	Fic	Gutman, D. Jackie and me	Fic
Flanagan, J. The emperor of Nihon-ja	Fic	Gutman, D. Jim & me	Fic
Flanagan, J. Erak's ransom	Fic	Gutman, D. Mickey & me	Fic
Flanagan, J. Halt's peril	Fic	Gutman, D. Ray & me	Fic
Flanagan, J. The hunters	Fic	Gutman, D. Roberto & me	Fic
Flanagan, J. The icebound land	Fic	Gutman, D. Satch & me	Fic
Flanagan, J. The invaders	Fic	Gutman, D. Shoeless Joe & me	Fic
Flanagan, J. The kings of Clonmel	Fic	Haddix, M. P. Just Ella	Fic
Flanagan, J. The lost stories	Fic	Hahn, R. A creature of moonlight	Fic
Flanagan, J. The ruins of Gorlan	Fic	Hale, S. Book of a thousand days	Fic
Flanagan, J. The siege of Macindaw	Fic	Hale, S. Enna burning	Fic
Flanagan, J. The sorcerer of the north	Fic	Hale, S. The forgotten sisters	Fic
Flanagan, J. The tournament at Gorlan	Fic	Hale, S. The goose girl	Fic
Fleischman, P. Graven images	Fic	Hale, S. Palace of stone	Fic
Fletcher, C. Ironhand	Fic	Hale, S. The storybook of legends	Fic
Fletcher, C. Silvertongue	Fic	Hardinge, F. Deeplight	Fic
Fletcher, C. Stoneheart	Fic	Hardinge, F. The lost conspiracy	Fic
Fletcher, S. Dragon's milk	Fic	Harrison, M. 13 curses	Fic
Fletcher, S. Flight of the Dragon Kyn	Fic	Harrison, M. 13 secrets	Fic
Fletcher, S. Sign of the dove	Fic	Hartman, R. Seraphina	Fic
Flinn, A. Beastly	Fic	Hartman, R. Shadow scale	Fic
Flinn, A. Cloaked	Fic	Hatfield, R. The Book of Storms	Fic
Flinn, A. A kiss in time	Fic	Haydu, C. A. One jar of magic	Fic
Fombelle, T. d. Toby alone	Fic	Healy, C. The hero's guide to saving your kingdom	Fic
Fombelle, T. d. Toby and the secrets of the tree	Fic	Helgerson, J. Horns and wrinkles	Fic
French, V. The robe of skulls	Fic	Herrick, A. The Time Fetch	Fic
Funke, C. Fearless	Fic	Hoang, V. Girl giant and the Monkey King	Fic
Funke, C. Inkdeath	Fic	Holland, E. The thorn queen	Fic
Funke, C. Inkheart	Fic	Horowitz, A. Evil star	Fic
Funke, C. Inkspell	Fic	Horowitz, A. Necropolis	Fic
Gaiman, N. The graveyard book	Fic	Horowitz, A. Nightrise	Fic
Gaiman, N. M is for magic	Fic	Horowitz, A. Raven's gate	Fic
Gaiman, N. MirrorMask	Fic	Hulme, J. The glitch in sleep	Fic
Gaiman, N. Unnatural creatures	Fic	Hunter, E. Code of the clans	Fic
Gale, E. K. The Zoo at the Edge of the World	Fic	Hunter, E. A dangerous path	Fic
Gallego Garcia, L. The valley of the Wolves	Fic	Hunter, E. The darkest hour	Fic
Gardner, L. Into the woods	Fic	Hunter, E. Dawn	Fic
George, J. D. Dragon flight	Fic	Hunter, E. Fire and ice	Fic
George, J. D. Dragon slippers	Fic	Hunter, E. Forest of secrets	Fic

Ness, P. And the ocean was our sky	Fic	Pratchett, T. The Wee Free Men	Fic
Neumeier, R. The keeper of the mist	Fic	Prineas, S. The magic thief	Fic
Nicholls, S. Season of secrets	Fic	Pullman, P. The amber spyglass	Fic
Nicholson, W. Seeker	Fic	Pullman, P. The book of dust	Fic
Nielsen, J. A. The false prince	Fic	Pullman, P. The golden compass	Fic
Nielsen, J. A. The runaway king	Fic	Pullman, P. Once upon a time in the North	Fic
Nielsen, J. A. The shadow throne	Fic	Pullman, P. The subtle knife	Fic
Nimmo, J. Midnight for Charlie Bone	Fic	Revis, B. Give the dark my love	Fic
Nix, G. Abhorsen	Fic	Rex, A. Champions of breakfast	Fic
Nix, G. Clariel	Fic	Rex, A. Cold cereal	Fic
Nix, G. Goldenhand	Fic	Rex, A. Unlucky charms	Fic
Nix, G. Lirael daughter of the Clayr	Fic	Riggs, R. Hollow City	Fic
Nix, G. Mister Monday	Fic	Riggs, R. Library of souls	Fic
Nix, G. Sabriel	Fic	Riggs, R. A map of days	Fic
Nix, G. To hold the bridge	Fic	Riggs, R. Miss Peregrine's home for peculiar children	Fic
November, S. Firebirds	Fic	Riggs, R. Tales of the Peculiar	Fic
November, S. Firebirds soaring	Fic	Riley, J. Secret origins	Fic
Noyes, D. Gothic!	Fic	Riordan, R. The battle of the Labyrinth	Fic
O'Brien, R. C. Mrs. Frisby and the rats of NIMH	Fic	Riordan, R. The blood of Olympus	Fic
O'Hart, S. The starspun web	Fic	Riordan, R. The burning maze	Fic
O'Neal, E. The false princess	Fic	Riordan, R. The dark prophecy	Fic
Okorafor, N. Akata witch	Fic	Riordan, R. The hammer of Thor	Fic
Oliver, L. Liesl & Po	Fic	Riordan, R. The hidden oracle	Fic
Oliver, L. The magnificent monsters of Cedar Street	Fic	Riordan, R. The house of Hades	Fic
Oliver, L. The spindlers	Fic	Riordan, R. The last Olympian	Fic
Oppel, K. Airborn	Fic	Riordan, R. The lightning thief	Fic
Oppel, K. Silverwing	Fic	Riordan, R. The lost hero	Fic
Orr, W. Dragonfly song	Fic	Riordan, R. The mark of Athena	Fic
Owen, M. The merciful Crow	Fic	Riordan, R. Percy Jackson's Greek gods	Fic
Paolini, C. Eragon	Fic	Riordan, R. The red pyramid	Fic
Park, L. S. Forest of wonders	Fic	Riordan, R. The sea of monsters	Fic
Patterson, J. Best nerds forever	Fic	Riordan, R. The serpent's shadow	Fic
Pattou, E. East	Fic	Riordan, R. The ship of the dead	Fic
Pearson, M. Dance of thieves	Fic	Riordan, R. The son of Neptune	Fic
Pearson, M. Vow of thieves	Fic	Riordan, R. The sword of summer	Fic
Pierce, T. Alanna the first adventure	Fic	Riordan, R. The throne of fire	Fic
Pierce, T. Bloodhound	Fic	Riordan, R. The Titan's curse	Fic
Pierce, T. Briar's book	Fic	Riordan, R. The tower of Nero	Fic
Pierce, T. Daja's book	Fic	Ritter, W. Changeling	Fic
Pierce, T. First test	Fic	Ritter, W. Deepest darkest	Fic
Pierce, T. Lady knight	Fic	Ritter, W. The unready queen	Fic
Pierce, T. Mastiff	Fic	Rivera, K. Cece Rios and the Desert of Souls	Fic
Pierce, T. Melting stones	Fic	Rodgers, M. Freaky Friday	Fic
Pierce, T. Page	Fic	Rogerson, M. An enchantment of ravens	Fic
Pierce, T. Sandry's book	Fic	Rossetti, R. The girl with borrowed wings	Fic
Pierce, T. Squire	Fic	Rowell, R. Carry on	Fic
Pierce, T. Terrier	Fic	Rowell, R. Wayward son	Fic
Pierce, T. Trickster's choice	Fic	Rowling, J. K. Harry Potter and the Chamber of Secrets	Fic
Pierce, T. Tris's book	Fic	Rowling, J. K. Harry Potter and the deathly hallows	Fic
Pierce, T. Wild magic	Fic	Rowling, J. K. Harry Potter and the goblet of fire	Fic
Pierce, T. The will of the empress	Fic	Rowling, J. K. Harry Potter and the Order of the Phoenix	Fic
Pike, A. Earthbound	Fic	Rowling, J. K. Harry Potter and the prisoner of Azkaban	Fic
Pool, K. R. There will come a darkness	Fic	Rowling, J. K. Harry Potter and the sorcerer's stone	Fic
Pratchett, T. The amazing Maurice and his educated rodents	Fic	Rowling, J. K. The tales of Beedle the Bard	Fic
Pratchett, T. I shall wear midnight	Fic	Rutkoski, M. The winner's crime	Fic
Pratchett, T. Only you can save mankind	Fic	Rutkoski, M. The winner's curse	Fic
		Rutkoski, M. The winner's kiss	Fic

Almond, D. The savage — Fic
Blume, J. Tiger eyes — Fic
Cline-Ransome, L. Being Clem — Fic
Duey, K. Skin hunger — Fic
Hautman, P. Road tripped — Fic
Holm, J. L. Penny from heaven — Fic
Howard, J. J. That time I joined the circus — Fic
Ireland, J. Ophie's ghosts — Fic
Kibuishi, K. Amulet — 741.5
Landman, T. Hell and high water — Fic
Maetani, V. E. Ink & ashes — Fic
Marshall, K. A. I am still alive — Fic
McCaughrean, G. The kite rider — Fic
Parkinson, S. Blue like Friday — Fic
Proimos, J. 12 things to do before you crash and burn — Fic
Sedgwick, M. Revolver — Fic
Zarr, S. How to save a life — Fic

FATHERS AND DAUGHTERS

Bourne, S. Josephine against the sea — Fic
Bowling, D. The canyon's edge — Fic
Brody, J. The geography of lost things — Fic
Cabot, M. The princess diaries — Fic
Caletti, D. The last forever — Fic
Cavanaugh, N. J. This journal belongs to Ratchet — Fic
Chanani, N. Jukebox — Fic
Chin, J. Grand Canyon — 557.9132
Danziger, P. The cat ate my gymsuit — Fic
Dessen, S. The moon and more — Fic
Frederick, H. V. Absolutely Truly — Fic
Friedman, A. Two Summers — Fic
George, J. C. Julie — Fic
Giff, P. R. A slip of a girl — Fic
Henkes, K. Protecting Marie — Fic
Hinds, G. King Lear — 741.5
Kadohata, C. Outside beauty — Fic
Lavender, W. Aftershocks — Fic
Lee, H. To kill a mockingbird — Fic
Lopez, D. Confetti girl — Fic
Lupica, M. Miracle on 49th Street — Fic
Mac, C. 10 things I can see from here — Fic
Marillier, J. Cybele's secret — Fic
Marillier, J. Wildwood dancing — Fic
Marks, J. From the desk of Zoe Washington — Fic
Moderow, H. Lily's mountain — Fic
Moriarty, J. Feeling sorry for Celia — Fic
Nelson, T. Ruby electric — Fic
Oliver, L. The magnificent monsters of Cedar Street — Fic
Park, L. S. Prairie lotus — Fic
Peterfreund, D. Omega City — Fic
Pullman, P. The amber spyglass — Fic
Smiley, J. The Georges and the Jewels — Fic
Stanley, D. Bella at midnight — Fic
Thompson, C. Space dumplins — 741.5

FATHERS AND SONS

Alexander, K. The crossover — Fic
Almond, D. Slog's dad — Fic
Anderson, J. D. One last shot — Fic

Avi. The most important thing — Fic
Blackstone, M. Sorry you're lost — Fic
Coates, T. The beautiful struggle — 305.896
Durbin, W. The broken blade — Fic
Green, T. New kid — Fic
Holt, K. W. The water seeker — Fic
Kinney, J. The last straw — Fic
Kipling, R. If — 821
Lubar, D. Character driven — Fic
Lupica, M. The batboy — Fic
Lupica, M. The big field — Fic
Mazer, H. A boy at war — Fic
Napoli, D. J. Beast — Fic
Patterson, J. Ali Cross — Fic
Patterson, J. Like father like son — Fic
Preller, J. The courage test — Fic
Reynolds, J. Ghost — Fic
Robinson, G. Little Brother of War — Fic
Sanderson, B. The dark talent — Fic
Sis, P. Tibet — 951
Taylor, M. D. The land — Fic
Ventrella, K. The secret life of Sam — Fic
Voigt, C. A solitary blue — Fic
Volponi, P. Hurricane song — Fic
Wallace, R. War and watermelon — Fic
Welford, R. Time traveling with a hamster — Fic
Woodson, J. Before the ever after — Fic
Yelchin, E. Breaking Stalin's nose — Fic
Yep, L. Dragonwings — Fic

FATHERS WITH MENTAL ILLNESSES

Nolan, H. Crazy — Fic

Faulk, Michelle

The case of the flesh-eating bacteria — 616.5

Fault lines & tectonic plates. Reilly, K. M. — 551.1

Fault lines in the constitution. Levinson, C. — 342.7302

FAULTS (GEOLOGY)

Reilly, K. M. Fault lines & tectonic plates — 551.1

Faulty heart. Markle, S. — 612.1

FAUNS (ROMAN MYTHOLOGY)

Toro, G. d. Pan's labyrinth — Fic

FAUSTIAN BARGAINS

Gratton, T. Strange grace — Fic
Lu, M. The Kingdom of Back — Fic

Favor, Lesli J.

Eva Peron — B

Favreau, Marc, 1968-

Spies — 327.127304709

Fawcett, Heather (Heather M.)

Even the darkest stars — Fic

Fay, Gail

Sports — 796

Fayers, Claire

The voyage to Magical North — Fic

FBI

Ponti, J. Framed! — Fic
Ponti, J. Trapped! — Fic
Ponti, J. Vanished! — Fic

Sign of the dove	Fic

FLIGHT

Anderson, D. Flight and motion	629.13
Grove, T. Milestones of flight	629.109
Mercer, B. The flying machine book	745.592
Rooney, A. Aerospace engineering and the principles of flight	629.1
Rossetti, R. The girl with borrowed wings	Fic

FLIGHT -- HISTORY

Collins, M. Airborne	629.13
Goldstone, L. Higher steeper faster	629.13
Flight and motion. Anderson, D.	629.13
Flight explorer. Kibuishi, K.	741.5
Flight of the Dragon Kyn. Fletcher, S.	Fic

FLIGHTS

Grove, T. First flight around the world	910.4

FLIGHTS AROUND THE WORLD

Grove, T. First flight around the world	910.4

Flinn, Alex

Beastly	Fic
Cloaked	Fic
A kiss in time	Fic

FLINT, MICHIGAN

Cooper, C. J. Poisoned water	615.9
Curtis, C. P. Bud not Buddy	Fic
Curtis, C. P. The Watsons go to Birmingham 1963	Fic
Flip. Bedford, M.	Fic

FLOODS

Brimner, L. D. The rain wizard	979.4
Koestler-Grack, R. A. Johnstown flood of 1889	974.8
McCaughrean, G. Gilgamesh the hero	398.2
Richards, J. Three rivers rising	Fic
Sweeney, D. The minnow	Fic
Flora & Ulysses. DiCamillo, K.	Fic
Florence Nightingale. Reef, C.	B

FLORENCE, ITALY

Hughes, S. Hero on a bicycle	Fic

FLORES, ERNESTO, 1997-

Markham, L. The far away brothers	979.4

FLORES, RAUL, 1997-

Markham, L. The far away brothers	979.4

Flores-Scott, Patrick

American road trip	Fic

FLORIDA

Baskin, N. R. All we know of love	Fic
Bloor, E. Taken	Fic
Blundell, J. What I saw and how I lied	Fic
Bond, V. Zora and me	Fic
Cartaya, P. The epic fail of Arturo Zamora	Fic
DiCamillo, K. Because of Winn-Dixie	Fic
DiCamillo, K. Beverly right here	Fic
DiCamillo, K. Raymie Nightingale	Fic
Falkowski, M. We say #never again	371.7
Flinn, A. Cloaked	Fic
Gantos, J. Jack's black book	Fic
Gantos, J. The trouble in me	Fic
Hiaasen, C. Flush	Fic

Hiaasen, C. Hoot	Fic
Hiaasen, C. Scat	Fic
Hiaasen, C. Skink--no surrender	Fic
Hodkin, M. The unbecoming of Mara Dyer	Fic
Holm, J. L. Sunny side up	741.5
Howard, J. J. That time I joined the circus	Fic
Jamieson, V. All's faire in middle school	741.5
Konigsburg, E. L. The mysterious edge of the heroic world	Fic
Lerner, S. Parkland speaks	371.7
Lupica, M. The big field	Fic
Medina, M. Merci Suarez can't dance	Fic
Messner, K. Tracking pythons	597.96
Moreno, N. Don't date Rosa Santos	Fic
Orr, T. Florida	975.9
Pyron, B. Lucky strike	Fic
Riggs, R. A map of days	Fic
Sonnichsen, A. L. Red butterfly	Fic
Woods, B. My name is Sally Little Song	Fic

FLORIDA -- HISTORY -- SPANISH COLONY, 1565-1763

Turner, G. T. Fort Mose	975.9
Florida. Orr, T.	975.9

FLORIDA KEYS

Hiaasen, C. Flush	Fic

FLORIDA KEYS NATIONAL MARINE SANCTUARY (FLA)

Mallory, K. At home beneath the sea	551.46

FLOWERS

Willis, K. J. Botanicum	580
Flowers in the gutter. Gaddy, K. R.	940.53
Flowers in the sky. Joseph, L.	Fic
Flu. Cunningham, K.	614.5
The **flu** of 1918. Rudolph, J.	614.5
Flush. Hiaasen, C.	Fic

FLUTE

Landau, E. Is the flute for you?	788.3
Fly girls. Pearson, P. O.	940.54
Fly on the wall. Lai, R.	Fic
Flygirl. Smith, S. L.	Fic

FLYING DUTCHMAN

Jacques, B. Castaways of the Flying Dutchman	Fic
Flying lessons & other stories. Oh, E.	Fic
The **flying** machine book. Mercer, B.	745.592

FLYING MACHINES

Colfer, E. Airman	Fic
Flying machines. Wilgus, A.	629.13
Flying to the moon. Collins, M.	B

FLYING-MACHINES

Graham, I. The science of flight	629.13
Mercer, B. The flying machine book	745.592
Reeve, P. A web of air	Fic
White, R. Cleared for takeoff	629.133

FOG

Ross, J. N. The Fog diver	Fic
The **Fog** diver. Ross, J. N.	Fic

Fogarty, Mignon

Grammar Girl presents the ultimate writing guide for stu-

FOOD CROPS -- SEEDS

Castaldo, N. F. The story of seeds   **581.4**

FOOD HABITS

Augustin, B. The food of Mexico   **394.1**

Ballard, C. Explaining food allergies   **616.97**

Batmanglij, N. Happy Nowruz   **641.595**

Etingoff, K. Building a healthy diet with the 5 food groups   **613.2**

Furgang, A. Salty and sugary snacks   **613.2**

Juettner, B. Diet and disease   **613.2**

Lee, F. Fun with Chinese cooking   **641.595**

Mihaly, C. Diet for a changing climate   **613.2**

Orr, T. The food of China   **394.1**

Schlosser, E. Chew on this   **394.1**

Wagner, L. Cool Chinese & Japanese cooking   **641.595**

Wagner, L. Cool Italian cooking   **641.594**

Wagner, L. Cool Mexican cooking   **641.5972**

FOOD INDUSTRY AND TRADE

Chevat, R. The omnivore's dilemma   **394.1**

Jarrow, G. The poison eaters   **353.9**

Schlosser, E. Chew on this   **394.1**

The **food** of China. Orr, T.   **394.1**

The **food** of Mexico. Augustin, B.   **394.1**

FOOD POISONING

Landau, E. Food poisoning and foodborne diseases   **615.9**

Food poisoning and foodborne diseases. Landau, E.   **615.9**

FOOD PREPARATION

Gold, R. Eat fresh food   **641.5**

Webb, L. S. Holidays of the world cookbook for students   **641.5**

FOOD SAFETY

Jarrow, G. The poison eaters   **353.9**

FOOD SCIENCE

Thornhill, J. Who wants pizza?   **641.3**

FOOD SECURITY

Senker, C. Poverty and hunger   **362.5**

FOOD SUPPLEMENTS

Goldsmith, C. Dietary supplements   **615.1**

FOOD SUPPLY

Chevat, R. The omnivore's dilemma   **394.1**

FOOD VALUES

Chevat, R. The omnivore's dilemma   **394.1**

FOODBORNE DISEASES

Landau, E. Food poisoning and foodborne diseases   **615.9**

FOOLS AND JESTERS

Meyer, M. Heartless   **Fic**

Yolen, J. The queen's own fool   **Fic**

A **foot** in the mouth. Janeczko, P. B.   **821.008**

FOOTBALL

Doeden, M. The Super Bowl   **796.332**

Feinstein, J. Cover-up   **Fic**

Feinstein, J. The rivalry   **Fic**

Feinstein, J. The walk-on   **Fic**

Gigliotti, J. Football   **796.332**

King, W. OCDaniel   **Fic**

Lupica, M. Fantasy league   **Fic**

Stewart, M. Touchdown   **796.33**

Woodson, J. Before the ever after   **Fic**

FOOTBALL -- CORRUPT PRACTICES

Sommers, M. A. The NFL   **362.29**

FOOTBALL -- HISTORY

Bryant, H. Legends   **796.332**

Gilbert, S. The story of the NFL   **796.332**

FOOTBALL -- MATHEMATICAL MODELS

Frederick, S. Football   **796.332**

Football. Frederick, S.   **796.332**

Football. Gigliotti, J.   **796.332**

Football champ. Green, T.   **Fic**

FOOTBALL COACHES

Feinstein, J. The walk-on   **Fic**

FOOTBALL COACHES -- RATING OF

Bryant, H. Legends   **796.332**

FOOTBALL EQUIPMENT

Gigliotti, J. Football   **796.332**

Football genius. Green, T.   **Fic**

Football hero. Green, T.   **Fic**

FOOTBALL INJURIES

Greenwald, T. Game changer   **Fic**

McClafferty, C. K. Fourth down and inches   **617.4**

FOOTBALL PLAYERS

Doeden, M. The Super Bowl   **796.332**

Greenwald, T. Game changer   **Fic**

FOOTBALL PLAYERS -- DRUG USE

Sommers, M. A. The NFL   **362.29**

FOOTBALL PLAYERS -- HEALTH AND HYGIENE

McClafferty, C. K. Fourth down and inches   **617.4**

FOOTBALL PLAYERS -- RATING OF

Bryant, H. Legends   **796.332**

FOOTBALL STORIES

Deuker, C. Gym candy   **Fic**

Feinstein, J. Cover-up   **Fic**

Feinstein, J. The rivalry   **Fic**

Feinstein, J. The walk-on   **Fic**

Green, T. Football champ   **Fic**

Green, T. Football genius   **Fic**

Green, T. Football hero   **Fic**

Greenwald, T. Game changer   **Fic**

Korman, G. Pop   **Fic**

Lupica, M. Fantasy league   **Fic**

Murdock, C. G. Dairy queen   **Fic**

Murdock, C. G. The off season   **Fic**

FOOTBALL TEAMS

Doeden, M. The Super Bowl   **796.332**

Lupica, M. Fantasy league   **Fic**

FOOTBALL TEAMS -- RATING OF

Bryant, H. Legends   **796.332**

FOOTBINDING

Napoli, D. J. Bound   **Fic**

Footnotes. Augustyn, F.   **792.8**

For black girls like me. Lockington, M.   **Fic**

For every one. Reynolds, J.   **811**

For the good of mankind? Wittenstein, V. O.   **174.2**

For white folks who teach in the hood-- and the rest of y'all too. Emdin, C.   **370.9173**

FRESHWATER FISHES

Page, L. M. Peterson field guide to freshwater fishes of North America north of Mexico   **597.17**

FRESNO, CALIFORNIA

Soto, G. Baseball in April and other stories   **Fic**

Fretland Vanvoorst, Jenny, 1972-

Fossils   **560**

Freymann-Weyr, Garret, 1965-

My heartbeat   **Fic**

Frida & Diego. Reef, C.   **759.972**

Frida. Bernier-Grand, C. T.   **B**

Friday Barnes girl detective. Spratt, R. A.   **Fic**

FRIDMAN, YORAM

Orlev, U. Run boy run   **Fic**

Friedman, Aimee

Two Summers   **Fic**

FRIEDMAN, CORY

Patterson, J. Med head   **B**

Friedman, Ina R.

The other victims   **940.53**

Friedman, Laurie B., 1964-

Can you say catastrophe?   **Fic**

Friend, Natasha, 1972-

Bounce   **Fic**

How we roll   **Fic**

Lush   **Fic**

Perfect   **Fic**

FRIENDS -- DEATH

Zindel, P. The pigman   **Fic**

Friends forever. Hale, S.   **302**

Friends forever? Amblard, O.   **158.2**

Friends with boys. Hicks, F. E.   **741.5**

FRIENDS' DEATH

Arnold, E. K. The question of miracles   **Fic**

Barzak, C. The gone away place   **Fic**

Bauer, M. D. On my honor   **Fic**

Draper, S. M. The battle of Jericho   **Fic**

Landmann, B. The fate of Achilles   **883**

McClintock, N. She saidshe saw   **Fic**

Schmidt, G. D. Just like that   **Fic**

FRIENDSHIP

50 Cent. Playground   **Fic**

Abdel-Fattah, R. Where the streets had a name   **Fic**

Acampora, P. Rachel Spinelli punched me in the face   **Fic**

Alifirenka, C. I will always write back   **305.235**

Alvarez, J. Return to sender   **Fic**

Amblard, O. Friends forever?   **158.2**

Anderson, J. D. Posted   **Fic**

Anderson, M. T. Whales on stilts!   **Fic**

Arnold, E. K. The question of miracles   **Fic**

Asher, J. The future of us   **Fic**

Avi. The button war   **Fic**

Balliett, B. Chasing Vermeer   **Fic**

Baratz-Logsted, L. Crazy beautiful   **Fic**

Barnett, M. The terrible two get worse   **Fic**

Barnhill, K. R. The mostly true story of Jack   **Fic**

Baskin, N. R. Ruby on the outside   **Fic**

Bauer, A. C. E. Come Fall   **Fic**

Bean, L. The ship we built   **Fic**

Beil, M. D. The ring of Rocamadour   **Fic**

Benwell, F. The last leaves falling   **Fic**

Bird, J. The brave   **Fic**

Black, H. The copper gauntlet   **Fic**

Black, H. Doll bones   **Fic**

Black, H. The iron trial   **Fic**

Blakemore, M. F. The friendship riddle   **Fic**

Brashares, A. 3 willows   **Fic**

Bray, L. A great and terrible beauty   **Fic**

Broach, E. The wolf keepers   **Fic**

Brown, D. The boys in the boat   **797.12**

Camper, C. Lowriders in space   **741.5**

Camper, C. Lowriders to the center of the Earth   **741.5**

Cao, W. Bronze and Sunflower   **Fic**

Carter, A. Heist society   **Fic**

Chase, P. J. So done   **Fic**

Chase, P. J. Turning point   **Fic**

Chee, T. We are not free   **Fic**

Choldenko, G. Chasing secrets   **Fic**

Cisneros, S. The house on Mango Street   **Fic**

Cohen, M. The Inn Between   **Fic**

Condie, A. B. The Darkdeep   **Fic**

Connolly, M. Shadow weaver   **Fic**

Craft, J. Class act   **741.5**

Cypess, L. Thornwood   **Fic**

Dallas, S. The quilt walk   **Fic**

Dennard, S. Truthwitch   **Fic**

Dessen, S. Saint Anything   **Fic**

DiCamillo, K. Beverly right here   **Fic**

DiCamillo, K. Raymie Nightingale   **Fic**

Dowell, F. O. The kind of friends we used to be   **Fic**

Dowell, F. O. The second life of Abigail Walker   **Fic**

Durham, P. The Luck Uglies   **Fic**

Evans, R. P. Rise of the Elgen   **Fic**

Fagan, D. Nightingale   **Fic**

Federle, T. Five six seven Nate!   **Fic**

Fitzgerald, L. M. Under the egg   **Fic**

Fitzgerald, S. M. The apple tart of hope   **Fic**

Flanagan, J. The hunters   **Fic**

Fraillon, Z. The bone sparrow   **Fic**

Frank, S. Armstrong and Charlie   **Fic**

Frederick, H. V. Dear pen pal   **Fic**

Frederick, H. V. The Mother-Daughter Book Club   **Fic**

Freedman, R. Abraham Lincoln and Frederick Douglass   **973.7092**

Gallico, P. The snow goose   **Fic**

Gibbs, S. Spy ski school   **Fic**

Giles, C. D. Take back the block   **Fic**

Green, T. Force out   **Fic**

Griffin, P. Saving Marty   **Fic**

Hahn, M. D. Closed for the season   **Fic**

Hahn, M. D. One for sorrow   **Fic**

Hale, S. The storybook of legends   **Fic**

Han, J. Shug   **Fic**

Hannigan, K. True (--sort of)   **Fic**

FRIENDSHIP -- RELIGIOUS ASPECTS -- CHRISTIAN-ITY

McCrite, K. D. In front of God and everybody   Fic

The **friendship**. Taylor, M. D.   Fic

A **friendship** for today. McKissack, P.   Fic

FRIENDSHIP IN CHILDREN

Fox, A. Real friends vs. the other kind   177

The **friendship** riddle. Blakemore, M. F.   Fic

Friesner, Esther M.

Nobody's princess   Fic

Nobody's prize   Fic

Sphinx's princess   Fic

Sphinx's queen   Fic

Threads and flames   Fic

Frightlopedia. Winterbottom, J.   031.02

FRIGHTS

Poe, E. A. Edgar Allan Poe's tales of mystery and madness   Fic

FRITZ, JEAN

Fritz, J. Homesick   Fic

Fritz, Jean

Around the world in a hundred years   920

Homesick   Fic

The **frog** scientist. Turner, P. S.   597.8

The **frog** who croaked. Krosoczka, J.   Fic

Frogged. Vande Velde, V.   Fic

FROGS

Bryan, A. Ashley Bryan's African tales uh-huh   398.2

Gidwitz, A. In a glass Grimmly   Fic

Pringle, L. Frogs!   597.8

Vande Velde, V. Frogged   Fic

FROGS -- INFECTIONS

Markle, S. The case of the vanishing golden frogs   597.8

FROGS -- RESEARCH

Turner, P. S. The frog scientist   597.8

Frogs! Pringle, L.   597.8

From a whisper to a rallying cry. Yoo, P.   305.895

From boneshakers to choppers. Smedman, L.   629.227

From butterfly wings to... display technology. Gregory, J.   621.3815

From cover to cover. Horning, K. T.   028.1

From locusts to...automobile anti-collision systems. Mara, W.   629.2

From STEM to STEAM. Sousa, D. A.   372.5

From Texas with love. Gutman, D.   Fic

From the desk of Zoe Washington. Marks, J.   Fic

From the notebooks of a middle school princess. Cabot, M.   Fic

From the notebooks of Melanin Sun. Woodson, J.   Fic

From then to now. Moore, C.   909

From Twinkle with love. Menon, S.   Fic

FROMAN, KYLE, 1976-

Froman, K. In the wings   792.809747

Froman, Kyle, 1976-

In the wings   792.809747

FRONTIER AND PIONEER LIFE

Calabro, M. The perilous journey of the Donner Party   979.4

Dallas, S. The quilt walk   Fic

Erdrich, L. The game of silence   Fic

Freedman, R. In the days of the vaqueros   636.2

Gipson, F. Old Yeller   Fic

Hale, N. Donner dinner party   979.4

Hand, C. My Calamity Jane   Fic

Holm, J. L. Boston Jane   Fic

Holm, J. L. Boston Jane the claim   Fic

Holm, J. L. Boston Jane wilderness days   Fic

Holm, J. L. Our only May Amelia   Fic

Holm, J. L. The trouble with May Amelia   Fic

Holt, K. W. The water seeker   Fic

Larson, K. Hattie Big Sky   Fic

McKernan, V. The devil's paintbox   Fic

Meissner, D. Call of the Klondike   971.9

Miller, B. M. Women of the frontier   978

Olson, T. How to get rich in the California Gold Rush   979.4

Park, L. S. Prairie lotus   Fic

Paulsen, G. Woods runner   Fic

Peterson, C. Birchbark brigade   970.01

Rose, C. S. May B.   Fic

Sheinkin, S. Which way to the wild west?   978

Stefoff, R. The Wild West   978

Tunis, E. Frontier living   973

Wrede, P. C. The thirteenth child   Fic

Frontier living. Tunis, E.   973

Frost, Helen, 1949-

All he knew   Fic

Diamond Willow   Fic

Keesha's house   Fic

FROST, ROBERT, 1874-1963

Caravantes, P. Deep woods   B

Frost, Robert, 1874-1963

Poetry for kids   811

Robert Frost   811

Frozen secrets. Walker, S. M.   919.8

FRUIT

Llewellyn, C. Cooking with fruits and vegetables   641.3

Fruits basket. Takaya, N.   741.5

FRUSTRATION

Wallace, R. Perpetual check   Fic

Wallace, R. Wrestling Sturbridge   Fic

FRUSTRATION IN TEENAGE BOYS

Alonzo, S. Riding invisible   Fic

Wallace, R. Perpetual check   Fic

Wallace, R. Wrestling Sturbridge   Fic

FRY, VARIAN, 1908-1967

McClafferty, C. K. In defiance of Hitler   940.53

Frydenborg, Kay

Chocolate   338.7

The wild horse scientists   599.665

FUEL

Goldstein, M. J. Fuel under fire   338.2

FUEL CELLS

Dickmann, N. Using renewable energy   333.79

Gaiman, N. Stardust	Fic
Glaser, M. The book jumper	Fic
Hulme, J. The glitch in sleep	Fic
Jocelyn, M. Viminy Crowe's comic book	Fic
Kaufman, A. The world between blinks	Fic
Kibuishi, K. Amulet	741.5
Lewis, C. S. The last battle	Fic
Lewis, C. S. The lion the witch and the wardrobe	Fic
Lewis, C. S. The magician's nephew	Fic
Lewis, C. S. Prince Caspian	Fic
Lewis, C. S. The silver chair	Fic
Lewis, C. S. The voyage of the Dawn Treader	Fic
MacHale, D. J. The lost city of Faar	Fic
MacHale, D. J. The merchant of death	Fic
MacHale, D. J. The never war	Fic
MacHale, D. J. The reality bug	Fic
Marillier, J. Wildwood dancing	Fic
Moriarty, J. A corner of white	Fic
Moriarty, J. The cracks in the Kingdom	Fic
Mull, B. Sky raiders	Fic
Mull, B. A world without heroes	Fic
Starmer, A. The storyteller	Fic
Starmer, A. The whisper	Fic
Valente, C. M. The boy who lost Fairyland	Fic
Valente, C. M. The girl who circumnavigated Fairyland in a ship of her own making	Fic
Valente, C. M. The girl who fell beneath Fairyland and led the revels there	Fic
Valente, C. M. The girl who soared over Fairyland and cut the moon in two	Fic
Valente, C. M. The Glass Town game	Fic
Wooding, C. Malice	Fic
Gathering blue. Lowry, L.	Fic
Gaughen, A. C.	
Scarlet	Fic
GAUTAMA BUDDHA	
Demi. Buddha	B
Lee, J. M. I once was a monkey	294.3
Gavin, Jamila	
Tales from India	398.22
GAWAIN (LEGENDARY CHARACTER)	
Morpurgo, M. Sir Gawain and the Green Knight	398.2
GAY AND LESBIAN MOVEMENT	
Chevat, R. A queer history of the United States for young people	306.76
GAY AND LESBIAN MOVEMENT -- HISTORY	
Bausum, A. Stonewall	306.76
Pitman, G. E. The Stonewall Riots	306.76
GAY ATHLETES	
Cronn-Mills, K. LGBTQ+ athletes claim the field	796.086
GAY BOYS	
Bildner, P. A high five for Glenn Burke	Fic
Howe, J. Totally Joe	Fic
Pancholy, M. The best at it	Fic
Telgemeier, R. Drama	741.5
Gay characters in theatre movies and television new roles new attitudes. Seba, J.	791.43

GAY FATHERS	
Stead, R. The list of things that will not change	Fic
GAY MEN -- HISTORY	
Chevat, R. A queer history of the United States for young people	306.76
GAY MEN -- HISTORY 20TH CENTURY	
Pitman, G. E. The Stonewall Riots	306.76
GAY MEN IN MASS MEDIA	
Seba, J. Gay characters in theatre movies and television new roles new attitudes	791.43
GAY STUDENTS	
Cianciotto, J. LGBT youth in America's schools	371.826
GAY TEENAGERS	
Cameron, S. Last bus to Everland	Fic
Finneyfrock, K. The sweet revenge of Celia Door	Fic
Freymann-Weyr, G. My heartbeat	Fic
Gonzales, S. Only mostly devastated	Fic
Huegel, K. LGBTQ	306.76
Konigsberg, B. Openly straight	Fic
Lecesne, J. Absolute brightness	Fic
Lennon, T. When love comes to town	Fic
Levithan, D. Two boys kissing	Fic
Lockhart, E. Dramarama	Fic
Nazemian, A. Like a love story	Fic
Oshiro, M. Anger is a gift	Fic
Savage, D. It gets better	306.76
Stiefvater, M. The dream thieves	Fic
Wright, B. Putting makeup on the fat boy	Fic
GAY TEENAGERS -- COMING OUT	
Huegel, K. LGBTQ	306.76
GAY TEENAGERS -- RELIGIOUS LIFE	
Finke, L. Queerfully and wonderfully made	248.8
GAY TRANSGENDER PERSONS	
McKenna, M. Out!	306.76
Gaya, Ester	
Fungarium	579.5
GAYS IN POPULAR CULTURE	
Seba, J. Gay characters in theatre movies and television new roles new attitudes	791.43
Gee, Joshua	
Encyclopedia horrifica	001.9
GEEKS (COMPUTER ENTHUSIASTS)	
Black, H. Geektastic	Fic
Shen, P. Nothing can possibly go wrong	741.5
Geeks girls and secret identities. Jung, M.	Fic
Geektastic. Black, H.	Fic
GEHRIG, LOU, 1903-1941	
Buckley, J. Lou Gehrig	B
GEISHAS	
Hoobler, D. The demon in the teahouse	Fic
Gelletly, Leeanne	
Monarchy	321
Oligarchy	321
GEM THEFT	
Carter, A. Uncommon criminals	Fic
Gemeinhart, Dan	
The honest truth	Fic

Gettysburg. Gregory, J.	973.7		Winters, C. In the shadow of blackbirds	Fic
GETTYSBURG CAMPAIGN, 1863			Yelchin, E. The haunting of Falcon House	Fic
Gregory, J. Gettysburg	973.7		**Ghost** town. Jennings, R. W.	Fic
O'Connor, J. What was the Battle of Gettysburg?	973.7		**GHOST TOWNS**	
GETTYSBURG, BATTLE OF, 1863			Jennings, R. W. Ghost town	Fic
Gregory, J. Gettysburg	973.7		**Ghostgirl**. Hurley, T.	Fic
O'Connor, J. What was the Battle of Gettysburg?	973.7		**Ghostopolis**. TenNapel, D.	741.5
Tarshis, L. The battle of Gettysburg 1863	Fic		**GHOSTS**	
Gevinson, Tavi			Alender, K. The dead girls of Hysteria Hall	Fic
Rookie on love	Fic		Allison, J. Bad machinery	741.5
GHANA			Almond, D. Kit's wilderness	Fic
Mussi, S. The door of no return	Fic		Ansari, R. K. S. The in-between	Fic
GHANA EMPIRE			Auxier, J. The night gardener	Fic
McKissack, P. The royal kingdoms of Ghana Mali and Song-			Avi. The seer of shadows	Fic
hay	966.2		Balliett, B. Pieces and players	Fic
GHETTOES, AFRICAN AMERICAN			Black, H. Doll bones	Fic
Myers, W. D. Scorpions	Fic		Blake, K. Anna dressed in blood	Fic
GHETTOES, JEWISH			Brosgol, V. Anya's ghost	741.5
Byers, A. Trapped	940.53		Carman, P. The Crossbones	Fic
Gratz, A. Prisoner B-3087	Fic		Carman, P. Skeleton Creek	Fic
Mazzeo, T. J. Irena's children	940.53		Compestine, Y. C. A banquet for hungry ghosts	Fic
Nielsen, J. A. Resistance	Fic		Del Negro, J. Passion and poison	Fic
Yolen, J. Mapping the bones	Fic		Delaney, J. The ghost prison	Fic
Ghost. Reynolds, J.	Fic		Dickens, C. A Christmas carol [Lynch ill.]	Fic
Ghost boys. Rhodes, J. P.	Fic		Fleming, C. On the day I died	Fic
The **ghost** in the Tokaido Inn. Hoobler, D.	Fic		Gaiman, N. The graveyard book	Fic
Ghost moon. Wilson, J.	Fic		Gaiman, N. M is for magic	Fic
Ghost of Spirit Bear. Mikaelsen, B.	Fic		Gee, J. Encyclopedia horrifica	001.9
The **ghost** prison. Delaney, J.	Fic		Grabenstein, C. The crossroads	Fic
GHOST STORIES			Hahn, M. D. All the lovely bad ones	Fic
Alender, K. The dead girls of Hysteria Hall	Fic		Hahn, M. D. Took	Fic
Almond, D. Kit's wilderness	Fic		Hahn, M. D. Wait till Helen comes	Fic
Ansari, R. K. S. The in-between	Fic		Henry, A. The lonely dead	Fic
Arden, K. Dead voices	Fic		Hicks, F. E. Friends with boys	741.5
Auxier, J. The night gardener	Fic		Ireland, J. Ophie's ghosts	Fic
Barzak, C. The gone away place	Fic		Irving, W. The legend of Sleepy Hollow	Fic
Blake, K. Anna dressed in blood	Fic		Johnson, M. The madness underneath	Fic
Compestine, Y. C. A banquet for hungry ghosts	Fic		Johnson, M. The name of the star	Fic
Del Negro, J. Passion and poison	Fic		Johnson, M. The shadow cabinet	Fic
Hahn, M. D. All the lovely bad ones	Fic		Kirby, M. J. A taste for monsters	Fic
Hahn, M. D. One for sorrow	Fic		Lawson, J. Nooks & crannies	Fic
Hahn, M. D. Took	Fic		Layne, A. Beetle & the Hollowbones	741.5
Hahn, M. D. Wait till Helen comes	Fic		Little, K. G. Circle of secrets	Fic
Irving, W. The legend of Sleepy Hollow	Fic		Lukoff, K. Too bright to see	Fic
Jennings, R. W. Ghost town	Fic		Mafi, T. Whichwood	Fic
Lukoff, K. Too bright to see	Fic		McKissack, P. The dark-thirty	Fic
McKissack, P. The dark-thirty	Fic		McNeal, T. Far far away	Fic
Noyes, D. The ghosts of Kerfol	Fic		Milford, K. Ghosts of Greenglass House	Fic
Oh, E. Spirit hunters	Fic		Noyes, D. The ghosts of Kerfol	Fic
San Souci, R. D. Dare to be scared	Fic		Noyes, D. Gothic!	Fic
San Souci, R. D. A terrifying taste of short & shiv-			Noyes, D. The restless dead	Fic
ery	398.25		Oliver, L. Liesl & Po	Fic
Schwartz, A. More scary stories to tell in the dark	Fic		Parkhurst, L. S. The August House book of scary stories	Fic
Schwartz, A. Scary stories 3	Fic		Patterson, J. Best nerds forever	Fic
Smy, P. Thornhill	Fic		Reynolds, J. Long way down	Fic
Tingle, T. How I became a ghost	Fic		Rhodes, J. P. Ghost boys	Fic
Tingle, T. When a ghost talks listen	Fic		Russell, P. C. The graveyard book graphic novel	741.5

San Souci, R. D. Dare to be scared — **Fic**
San Souci, R. D. Haunted houses — **Fic**
San Souci, R. D. A terrifying taste of short & shivery — **398.25**
Schlitz, L. A. Amber and Clay — **Fic**
Schwartz, A. More scary stories to tell in the dark — **Fic**
Schwartz, A. Scary stories 3 — **Fic**
Scieszka, J. Thriller — **Fic**
Shivering, W. Ghosts of Weirdwood — **Fic**
Shulman, P. The Poe estate — **Fic**
Smy, P. Thornhill — **Fic**
Stroud, J. The creeping shadow — **Fic**
Stroud, J. The hollow boy — **Fic**
Stroud, J. The screaming staircase — **Fic**
Stroud, J. The whispering skull — **Fic**
Telep, T. Kiss me deadly — **Fic**
TenNapel, D. Ghostopolis — **741.5**
Tingle, T. How I became a ghost — **Fic**
Tingle, T. When a ghost talks listen — **Fic**
Turnage, S. The ghosts of Tupelo Landing — **Fic**
Vande Velde, V. All Hallows' Eve — **Fic**
Vande Velde, V. Being dead — **Fic**
Winterbottom, J. Frightlopedia — **031.02**
Winters, C. In the shadow of blackbirds — **Fic**
Ghosts. Telgemeier, R. — **741.5**
Ghosts of Greenglass House. Milford, K. — **Fic**
The **ghosts** of Kerfol. Noyes, D. — **Fic**
The **ghosts** of Tupelo Landing. Turnage, S. — **Fic**
Ghosts of war. Smithson, R. — **956.7044**
Ghosts of Weirdwood. Shivering, W. — **Fic**
GHOSTWRITERS
Kephart, B. Undercover — **Fic**
GHOULS AND OGRES
Gidwitz, A. The Grimm conclusion — **Fic**
Ibbotson, E. The Ogre of Oglefort — **Fic**
Noyes, D. Gothic! — **Fic**
Shelley, T. C. The monster who wasn't — **Fic**
Giannella, Valentina
Green Nation revolution — **333.72**
GIANT PANDA
Gish, M. Pandas — **599.789**
Strother, R. Absolute expert — **599.789**
GIANT SQUIDS
Newquist, H. P. Here there be monsters — **594**
GIANTS
Chase, R. The Jack tales — **398.2**
Hatke, B. Mighty Jack — **741.5**
Myklusch, M. Jack Blank and the Imagine Nation — **Fic**
Riordan, R. The blood of Olympus — **Fic**
Riordan, R. The hammer of Thor — **Fic**
Riordan, R. The house of Hades — **Fic**
Riordan, R. The mark of Athena — **Fic**
Riordan, R. The sword of summer — **Fic**
Swift, J. Gulliver's travels — **Fic**
Gibbs, Stuart, 1969-
Belly up — **Fic**
Big game — **Fic**

Charlie Thorne and the last equation — **Fic**
Charlie Thorne and the lost city — **Fic**
Evil spy school — **Fic**
Panda-monium — **Fic**
Poached — **Fic**
Space case — **Fic**
Spaced out — **Fic**
Spy camp — **Fic**
Spy school — **Fic**
Spy ski school — **Fic**
Giblin, James Cross, 1933-
Charles A. Lindbergh — **B**
Good brother bad brother — **920**
The life and death of Adolf Hitler — **B**
The riddle of the Rosetta Stone — **493**
Gibney, Shannon
See no color — **Fic**
Gibson, Karen Bush
Native American history for kids — **970.004**
The Taj Mahal — **954**
Giddings, Sharon
Cystic fibrosis — **616.3**
Gidwitz, Adam
The Grimm conclusion — **Fic**
In a glass Grimmly — **Fic**
Gier, Kerstin
Emerald green — **Fic**
Sapphire blue — **Fic**
Giff, Patricia Reilly., 1935-2021
Genevieve's war — **Fic**
Lily's crossing — **Fic**
Nory Ryan's song — **Fic**
Pictures of Hollis Woods — **Fic**
A slip of a girl — **Fic**
Winter sky — **Fic**
Gifford, Clive
Swimming — **797.2**
Track and field — **796.42**
Why did the Vietnam War happen? — **959.704**
A **gift** from childhood. Diakite, B. W. — **B**
The **gift** of the Magi. Henry, O. — **Fic**
GIFTED BOYS
Colfer, E. Artemis Fowl — **741.5**
Gibbs, S. Spy school — **Fic**
GIFTED CHILDREN
Card, O. S. Ender's game — **Fic**
Dunkle, C. B. The sky inside — **Fic**
Korman, G. Ungifted — **Fic**
Stewart, T. L. The mysterious Benedict Society — **Fic**
Yang, G. L. Secret coders — **741.5**
GIFTED CHILDREN -- EDUCATION
Brulles, D. The cluster grouping handbook — **371.2**
Roberts, J. L. Differentiating instruction with centers in the gifted classroom K-8 — **371.95**
GIFTED CHILDREN -- EDUCATION -- PSYCHOLOGICAL ASPECTS
Galbraith, J. When gifted kids don't have all the an-

swers	371.95	**Gilliland, Ben**		
GIFTED GIRLS		Rocket science for the rest of us		520
Almond, D. My name is Mina	Fic	**Gillis, Peter B.**		
Gibbs, S. Charlie Thorne and the last equation	Fic	The last unicorn		741.5
Gibbs, S. Charlie Thorne and the lost city	Fic	**Gilman, David**		
Jacobson, J. Paper things	Fic	Blood sun		Fic
McCulloch, A. Jinxed	Fic	The devil's breath		Fic
Sovern, M. J. The meaning of Maggie	Fic	Ice claw		Fic
GIFTED TEENAGERS		**Gilmore, Kate**		
Jinks, C. Evil genius	Fic	The exchange student		Fic
Jinks, C. Genius squad	Fic	**Gino, Alex**		
Jinks, C. The genius wars	Fic	Rick		Fic
Kincaid, S. J. Insignia	Fic	**GINSBERG, BLAZE, 1987-**		
Knox, E. Mortal fire	Fic	Ginsberg, B. Episodes		616.858820092
Roy, J. R. Mindblind	Fic	**Ginsberg, Blaze, 1987-**		
Trueman, T. Stuck in neutral	Fic	Episodes		616.858820092
Walden, M. H.I.V.E.	Fic	**GINSBURG, RUTH BADER. 1933-2020**		
GIFTS		Ortiz, V. Dissenter on the bench		347.73
Turnbull, S. Diaries and keepsakes	745.593	**Giovanni, Nikki**		
Gifts from the gods. Lunge-Larsen, L.	401	Ego-tripping and other poems for young people		811
Gigliotti, Jim		On my journey now		782.25
Football	796.332	Paint me like I am		811
Jesse Owens	B	**Gipson, Fred, 1908-1973**		
GILA RIVER RELOCATION CENTER		Old Yeller		Fic
Fitzmaurice, K. A diamond in the desert	Fic	**Giraffe** extinction. Anderson, T.		599.638
Gilbert, Carter Rowell, 1930-		**GIRAFFES**		
National Audubon Society field guide to fishes	597	Anderson, T. Giraffe extinction		599.638
Gilbert, Sara		**Girard, Denis**		
The story of the NFL	796.332	Cassell's French dictionary		443
Gilberti, Fausto, 1970-		**GIRL ADVENTURERS**		
Yayoi Kusama covered everything in dots and wasn't sorry	709.2	DiTerlizzi, T. The battle for WondLa		Fic
		DiTerlizzi, T. A hero for WondLa		Fic
Gilby, Nancy Benovich		Fletcher, S. Dragon's milk		Fic
FIRST robotics	629.8	Gibbs, S. Charlie Thorne and the last equation		Fic
Gilda Joyce psychic investigator. Allison, J.	Fic	Gibbs, S. Charlie Thorne and the lost city		Fic
GILDED AGE (1865-1898)		Helgerson, J. Horns and wrinkles		Fic
Bolden, T. Inventing Victoria	Fic	McKinley, R. The blue sword		Fic
The **Gilded** Age. Telgen, D.	973.8	Pierce, T. Alanna the first adventure		Fic
Giles, Chrystal D.		Weston, R. P. Zorgamazoo		Fic
Take back the block	Fic	**GIRL APPRENTICES**		
Giles, L. R. (Lamar R.)		Jinks, C. How to catch a bogle		Fic
The Last Mirror on the Left	Fic	Jones, D. W. The islands of Chaldea		Fic
Not so pure and simple	Fic	Levine, G. C. A tale of Two Castles		Fic
Overturned	Fic	Reeve, P. Fever Crumb		Fic
Spin	Fic	**GIRL ARTISTS**		
GILGAMESH (LEGENDARY CHARACTER)		Tucker, L. All the Greys on Greene Street		Fic
Chadda, S. City of the plague god	Fic	**GIRL ATHLETES**		
Gilgamesh the hero. McCaughrean, G.	398.2	Klages, E. Out of left field		Fic
Gilles, Renae		**GIRL ATHLETES -- HISTORY**		
Understanding alcohol	613.81	Blumenthal, K. Let me play		796
Understanding screen addiction	616.85	**GIRL AUTHORS**		
Gillespie, Carol Ann		Kramer, J. K. The story that cannot be told		Fic
New Zealand	993	**GIRL BAKERS**		
GILLESPIE, DIZZY, 1917-1993		Bauer, J. Close to famous		Fic
Boone, M. Dizzy Gillespie	B	LaRocca, R. Midsummer's mayhem		Fic
Gillette, Robert H.		Marks, J. From the desk of Zoe Washington		Fic
Escape to Virginia	975.5	**GIRL BALLET DANCERS**		

Pierce, T. Trickster's choice — **Fic**

GIRL STUDENTS
Stevens, R. Poison is not polite — **Fic**

GIRL SUPERHEROES
Hannigan, K. Cape — **Fic**
Hannigan, K. Mask — **Fic**

GIRL THIEVES
Lee, Y. S. A spy in the house — **Fic**

GIRL VIOLINISTS
Wolff, V. E. The Mozart season — **Fic**

GIRL VOLUNTEERS
Cervantes, A. Gaby lost and found — **Fic**

GIRL WARRIORS
Cashore, K. Graceling — **Fic**
Uehashi, N. Moribito II — **Fic**
The **girl** who circumnavigated Fairyland in a ship of her own making. Valente, C. M. — **Fic**
The **girl** who could not dream. Durst, S. B. — **Fic**
The **girl** who drank the moon. Barnhill, K. R. — **Fic**
The **girl** who drew butterflies. Sidman, J. — **B**
The **girl** who fell beneath Fairyland and led the revels there. Valente, C. M. — **Fic**
The **girl** who saw lions. Doherty, B. — **Fic**
The **girl** who soared over Fairyland and cut the moon in two. Valente, C. M. — **Fic**
The **girl** who speaks bear. Anderson, S. — **Fic**
The **girl** with borrowed wings. Rossetti, R. — **Fic**
Girl world. Ottaviano, P. — **155.5**
Girl's best friend. Margolis, L. — **Fic**
Girl's guide to becoming a teen. Pfeifer, K. G. — **613**
The **girl-positive** library. Harlan, M. A. — **028.5**

GIRLFRIENDS
Bourne, S. Josephine against the sea — **Fic**
Girlology's there's something new about you. Holmes, M. — **612.6**

GIRLS
Alvarez, J. Before we were free — **Fic**
Birdsall, J. The Penderwicks — **Fic**
Creech, S. Absolutely normal chaos — **Fic**
Dickinson, P. The ropemaker — **Fic**
Duble, K. B. The sacrifice — **Fic**
Farmer, N. A girl named Disaster — **Fic**
Fraustino, L. R. Don't cramp my style — **Fic**
George, K. O. Swimming upstream — **811**
Hemphill, S. Wicked girls — **Fic**
Holmes, M. Girlology's there's something new about you — **612.6**
Knowles, J. Where the heart is — **Fic**
Ma, Y. The diary of Ma Yan — **951.05**
Martin, A. M. A corner of the universe — **Fic**
McCann, M. R. Girls who rocked the world — **920**
McCann, M. R. More girls who rocked the world — **920.72**
McKissack, P. Nzingha — **Fic**
Meconis, D. Queen of the sea — **741.5**
Natterson, C. F. The care & keeping of you 2 — **613**
Nye, N. S. A maze me — **811**
O'Connor, B. How to steal a dog — **Fic**

Pearson, L. Hildafolk — **741.5**
Roy, J. R. Yellow star — **Fic**
Russell, P. C. Coraline — **741.5**
Sanderson, B. Skyward — **Fic**
Silverstein, S. Falling up — **811**
Smiley, J. The Georges and the Jewels — **Fic**
Soo, K. Jellaby — **741.5**
Staples, S. F. Under the persimmon tree — **Fic**
Watkins, Y. K. So far from the bamboo grove — **Fic**
Weston, R. P. Zorgamazoo — **Fic**
Whitney, D. You don't have to be everything — **808.108**
Woodruff, E. The ravenmaster's secret — **Fic**

GIRLS -- BOOKS AND READING
Harlan, M. A. The girl-positive library — **028.5**

GIRLS -- FAMILY RELATIONSHIPS
Telgemeier, R. Sisters — **306.875**

GIRLS -- FRIENDSHIP
Britt, F. Jane the fox and me — **741.5**
Klages, E. The green glass sea — **Fic**

GIRLS -- HEALTH
Birkemoe, K. Strike a pose — **613.7**
Gravelle, K. The period book — **612.6**

GIRLS -- IDENTITY
Paterson, K. Jacob have I loved — **Fic**

GIRLS -- INTERPERSONAL RELATIONS
George, K. O. Swimming upstream — **811**
Ramee, L. M. A good kind of trouble — **Fic**

GIRLS -- NAMES
Rhuday-Perkovich, O. Two Naomis — **Fic**
Girls against girls. Burton, B. — **305.235**

GIRLS AND ANIMALS
DiCamillo, K. Flora & Ulysses — **Fic**

GIRLS AND CATS
McCulloch, A. Jinxed — **Fic**

GIRLS AND COMPUTERS
Saujani, R. Girls who code — **005.1**

GIRLS AND DEATH
Benjamin, A. The thing about jellyfish — **Fic**

GIRLS AND DOGS
Bauer, J. Almost home — **Fic**
DiCamillo, K. Because of Winn-Dixie — **Fic**
Dorisi-Winget, D. A million ways home — **Fic**
Frost, H. Diamond Willow — **Fic**
Henkes, K. Protecting Marie — **Fic**
Larson, K. Dash — **Fic**
Martin, A. M. Rain Reign — **Fic**
McKay, H. Binny for short — **Fic**
Yohalem, E. The truth according to Blue — **Fic**

GIRLS AND DRAGONS
Burgis, S. The princess who flew with dragons — **Fic**
Downer, A. Hatching magic — **Fic**
Fletcher, S. Sign of the dove — **Fic**
Yep, L. A dragon's guide to making your human smarter — **Fic**

GIRLS AND GHOSTS
DeStefano, L. A curious tale of the in-between — **Fic**
Doyle, R. A greyhound of a girl — **Fic**

GIRLS AND HORSES

Smiley, J. The Georges and the Jewels	Fic
Wilson, D. L. Firehorse	Fic

GIRLS AND PETS

Lloyd, M. W. Allergic	741.5

GIRLS AND SENIOR WOMEN

Giff, P. R. Pictures of Hollis Woods	Fic

GIRLS AND SPORTS

Blumenthal, K. Let me play	796

GIRLS AND WAR

Yep, L. Hiroshima	Fic

GIRLS AND WOLVES

George, J. C. Julie	Fic

GIRLS IN COMAS

Sanderson, B. The dark talent	Fic
Girls made of snow and glass. Bashardoust, M.	Fic
Girls play to win basketball. Robinson, T.	796.323
Girls play to win figure skating. McDougall, C.	796.91
Girls play to win hockey. McMahon, D.	796.962
Girls play to win softball. Gitlin, M.	796.357
Girls play to win track & field. McDougall, C.	796.42
Girls rock. Goodmark, R.	781.66023

GIRLS WHO ARE BLIND

Gantos, J. What would Joey do?	Fic

GIRLS WHO ARE MUTE

Hannigan, K. True (--sort of)	Fic
Langrish, K. The shadow hunt	Fic
Lean, S. A dog called Homeless	Fic
Girls who code. Saujani, R.	005.1

GIRLS WHO HAVE HAD AMPUTATIONS

Voigt, C. Izzy willy-nilly	Fic
Girls who rocked the world. McCann, M. R.	920

GIRLS WITH ADHD

Quinn, P. O. Attention girls!	618.92

GIRLS WITH AMNESIA

Connolly, M. Hollow dolls	Fic

GIRLS WITH AUTISM

Choldenko, G. Al Capone does my shirts	Fic
Hatke, B. Mighty Jack	741.5
Kapit, S. Get a grip Vivy Cohen!	Fic
Martin, A. M. Rain Reign	Fic

GIRLS WITH DISABILITIES

Bowling, D. Insignificant events in the life of a cactus	Fic
Draper, S. M. Out of my mind	Fic
Haskell, M. Handbook for dragon slayers	Fic
Johnson, T. L. Dog driven	Fic
Lowry, L. Gathering blue	Fic
Sumner, J. Roll with it	Fic

GIRLS WITH DISFIGUREMENTS

Yep, L. Hiroshima	Fic

GIRLS WITH DYSLEXIA

Draper, S. M. Double dutch	Fic
Engle, M. The wild book	Fic
Lewis, G. One white dolphin	Fic
Rose, C. S. May B.	Fic

GIRLS WITH LEARNING DISABILITIES

Engle, M. The wild book	Fic
Quinn, P. O. Attention girls!	618.92

GIRLS WITH POLIOMYELITIS

Winters, C. Odd & true	Fic

GIRLS' CLUBS

Telgemeier, R. Claudia and mean Janine	741.5
Telgemeier, R. Kristy's great idea	741.5

GIRLS' SCHOOLS

Alexander, E. Miss Crandall's school for young ladies & little misses of color	811

Gish, Melissa

Alligators	597.98
Armadillos	599.3
Bats	599.4
Beavers	599.37
Bison	599.64
Brown bears	599.784
Gorillas	599.884
Jaguars	599.75
Kangaroos	599.2
Killer whales	599.53
Leopards	599.75
Manatees	599.55
Moose	599.65
Pandas	599.789
Peacocks	598.6
Rhinoceroses	599.66
Sloths	599.3
Whales	599.5

Gitlin, Marty

Billie Jean King	B
Girls play to win softball	796.357
Transgender rights	323.3
U.S. involvement in Vietnam	959.704
Give me shelter. Bradman, T.	Fic
Give me some truth. Gansworth, E. L.	Fic
Give me wings. Lowinger, K.	782.42162
Give the dark my love. Revis, B.	Fic
Given. Taylor, N.	Fic
The giver. Lowry, L.	Fic
Giver quartet. Lowry, L.	741.5

GLADIATORS

Park, L. The Roman gladiators	796

GLADIATORS -- HISTORY

Hanel, R. Gladiators	796.8
Gladiators. Hanel, R.	796.8

Glaser, Mechthild

The book jumper	Fic

GLASS

Jones, D. W. Enchanted glass	Fic
Kassinger, R. Glass	620.1
Glass. Kassinger, R.	620.1

GLASS MANUFACTURE

Kassinger, R. Glass	620.1
The Glass Town game. Valente, C. M.	Fic

Glasser, Debbie

New kid new scene	373.18

Gleason, Carrie, 1973-

Feasting bedbugs mites and ticks	614.4

Gleason, Colleen

    The clockwork scarab   **Fic**

Gleitzman, Morris

    Now   **Fic**

Glenn, Joshua

    Unbored   **790**

Glimmer of hope.   **371.7**

The **glitch** in sleep. Hulme, J.   **Fic**

Glitter. Pike, A.   **Fic**

GLOBAL ENVIRONMENTAL CHANGE

    Allaby, M. National Geographic visual encyclopedia of Earth   **550**

    Burgan, M. Not a drop to drink   **333.91**

    Morris, N. Global warming   **363.738**

    Nardo, D. Planet under siege   **363.738**

    Sneideman, J. Climate change   **577.22**

GLOBAL FINANCIAL CRISIS, 2008-2009

    Bair, S. The bullies of Wall Street   **330.973**

    Riggs, K. The great recession   **330.973**

The **global** refugee crisis. McPherson, S. S.   **362.87**

GLOBAL TEMPERATURE CHANGES

    Baker, S. Climate change in the Arctic   **971.9**

    Delano, M. F. Earth in the hot seat   **363.738**

    Morris, N. Global warming   **363.738**

GLOBAL WARMING

    Baker, S. Climate change in the Arctic   **971.9**

    Bertagna, J. Exodus   **Fic**

    Bow, J. Earth's climate change   **363.738**

    Brown, D. Older than dirt   **551.7**

    Cherry, L. How we know what we know about our changing climate   **551.6**

    Chevat, R. Our choice   **363.738**

    David, L. The down-to-Earth guide to global warming   **363.738**

    Delano, M. F. Earth in the hot seat   **363.738**

    Gore, A. An inconvenient truth   **363.738**

    Heos, B. It's getting hot in here   **363.738**

    Kallen, S. A. Running dry   **333.91**

    Lloyd, S. The carbon diaries 2015   **Fic**

    McPherson, S. S. Hothouse earth   **363.738**

    Morris, N. Global warming   **363.738**

    Nardo, D. Planet under siege   **363.738**

    Reilly, K. M. Planet Earth   **363.7**

    Revkin, A. The North Pole was here   **910**

    Simon, S. Climate action   **363.738**

    Sivertsen, L. Generation green   **640**

    Sneideman, J. Climate change   **577.22**

    Stead, R. First light   **Fic**

GLOBAL WARMING -- ECONOMIC ASPECTS

    McPherson, S. S. Arctic thaw   **333.79**

GLOBAL WARMING -- POLITICAL ASPECTS

    McPherson, S. S. Arctic thaw   **333.79**

Global warming. Morris, N.   **363.738**

GLOBALIZATION

    Mooney, C. Globalization   **303.48**

GLOBALIZATION (ECONOMICS)

    Andrews, D. Business without borders   **658**

    Aronson, M. The real revolution   **973.3**

Globalization. Mooney, C.   **303.48**

GLOBE THEATRE (LONDON, ENGLAND : 1599-1644)

    Aliki. William Shakespeare & the Globe   **792**

    Blackwood, G. L. The Shakespeare stealer   **Fic**

    Booth, M. Saving Hamlet   **Fic**

    Cooper, S. King of shadows   **Fic**

GLOBES

    Rutkoski, M. The Celestial Globe   **Fic**

GMOs. Colson, M.   **660.6**

Go. Kidd, C.   **740**

Go big or go home. Hobbs, W.   **Fic**

Go figure! Ball, J.   **793.74**

Go photo! Proujansky, A.   **770**

Go tell it on the mountain. Baldwin, J.   **Fic**

Goal! Stewart, M.   **796.334**

GOALIES (SOCCER)

    Stewart, M. Goal!   **796.334**

GOBI DESERT EXPLORING EXPEDITIONS

    Armstrong, A. W. Looking for Marco Polo   **Fic**

The **goblin's** puzzle. Chilton, A. S.   **Fic**

GOBLINS

    Anderson, J. D. Standard hero behavior   **Fic**

    Boos, B. Fantasy   **813**

    Chilton, A. S. The goblin's puzzle   **Fic**

    Hatke, B. Mighty Jack   **741.5**

    Layne, A. Beetle & the Hollowbones   **741.5**

    Ritter, W. Changeling   **Fic**

    Ritter, W. Deepest darkest   **Fic**

    Walsh, P. The Crowfield curse   **Fic**

GOD

    Rylant, C. God went to beauty school   **Fic**

GOD (CHRISTIANITY) -- WILL

    Stork, F. X. Marcelo in the real world   **Fic**

God went to beauty school. Rylant, C.   **Fic**

Goddard, Jolyon

    Inside the human body   **612**

Godless. Hautman, P.   **Fic**

GODS AND GODDESSES

    Almond, D. Mouse bird snake wolf   **Fic**

    Boughn, M. Into the world of the dead   **202**

    Durst, S. B. Vessel   **Fic**

    Friesner, E. M. Nobody's princess   **Fic**

    Hardinge, F. Deeplight   **Fic**

    Hovey, K. Ancient voices   **811**

    Pope, P. Battling boy   **741.5**

    Smith, C. R. The mighty 12   **398.2**

    Tchana, K. Changing Woman and her sisters   **398.2**

    Yee, F. C. The iron will of Genie Lo   **Fic**

GODS AND GODDESSES, AFRICAN CARIBBEAN

    Baptiste, T. The jumbie god's revenge   **Fic**

GODS AND GODDESSES, AZTEC

    Camper, C. Lowriders to the center of the Earth   **741.5**

GODS AND GODDESSES, CHINESE

    Yang, G. L. Boxers   **741.5**

GODS AND GODDESSES, EGYPTIAN

    Collar, O. The red pyramid   **741.5**

Lace, W. W. Mummification and death rituals of ancient Egypt 932

Napoli, D. J. Treasury of Egyptian mythology 299

Riordan, R. The red pyramid Fic

Riordan, R. The serpent's shadow Fic

Riordan, R. The throne of fire Fic

GODS AND GODDESSES, GREEK

Bryant, M. E. Oh my gods! 398.2

Bryant, M. E. She's all that! 398

Cross, G. The Iliad Fic

Daly, K. N. Greek and Roman mythology A to Z 292.1

Evans, H. The mythology handbook 292.1

Evans, M. Who let the gods out? Fic

Hinds, G. The Iliad 741.5

Hinds, G. The Odyssey 741.5

Homer. The Odyssey 883

Landmann, B. The fate of Achilles 883

McCaughrean, G. Hercules 398.2

Napoli, D. J. Treasury of Greek mythology 398.2

O'Connor, G. Hephaistos 292

O'Connor, G. Zeus 292

Orr, T. The monsters of Hercules 398.2

Otfinoski, S. All in the family 398.2

Riordan, R. The blood of Olympus Fic

Riordan, R. The burning maze Fic

Riordan, R. The dark prophecy Fic

Riordan, R. The hidden oracle Fic

Riordan, R. The house of Hades Fic

Riordan, R. The last Olympian Fic

Riordan, R. The lost hero Fic

Riordan, R. Percy Jackson's Greek gods Fic

Riordan, R. The sea of monsters Fic

Riordan, R. The son of Neptune Fic

Riordan, R. The tower of Nero Fic

Rylant, C. The beautiful stories of life 398.2

Schlitz, L. A. Amber and Clay Fic

Smith, C. R. The mighty 12 398.2

Turnbull, A. Greek myths 398.2

GODS AND GODDESSES, MAYAN

Voelkel, J. The end of the world club Fic

GODS AND GODDESSES, NORSE

Armstrong, K. Loki's wolves Fic

Armstrong, K. Odin's ravens Fic

D'Aulaire, I. D'Aulaires' book of Norse myths 293

Napoli, D. J. Treasury of Norse mythology 398.2

Riordan, R. The hammer of Thor Fic

Riordan, R. The ship of the dead Fic

Riordan, R. The sword of summer Fic

Simon, F. The monstrous child Fic

GODS AND GODDESSES, ROMAN

Daly, K. N. Greek and Roman mythology A to Z 292.1

GODS AND GODDESSES, SUMERIAN

Chadda, S. City of the plague god Fic

GOGH, VINCENT VAN, 1853-1890

Crispino, E. Van Gogh 759.9492

Whiting, J. Vincent Van Gogh 759.9492

Gogi's gambit. Schrefer, E. Fic

GOH, CHAN HON

Goh, C. H. Beyond the dance B

Goh, Chan Hon

Beyond the dance B

Going blue. Kaye, C. B. 333.91

Going organic. Rau, D. M. 613.2

Going over. Kephart, B. Fic

Going vegetarian. Rau, D. M. 613.2

Gola, Mark

Winning softball for girls 796.357

GOLD

Angliss, S. Gold 669

Carson, R. Walk on Earth a stranger Fic

Lourie, P. Lost treasure of the Inca 986.6

Mills, G. Gold Fic

Shurtliff, L. Rump Fic

Gold. Angliss, S. 669

Gold. Mills, G. Fic

The **gold** Cadillac. Taylor, M. D. Fic

GOLD MINES AND MINING

Condie, A. B. The last voyage of Poe Blythe Fic

Meissner, D. Call of the Klondike 971.9

GOLD MINES AND MINING -- ACCIDENTS

Scott, E. Buried alive! 363.11

GOLD MINES AND MINING -- HISTORY 19TH CENTURY

Olson, T. How to get rich in the California Gold Rush 979.4

GOLD RUSH

Avi. Gold rush girl Fic

Hobbs, W. Jason's gold Fic

Meissner, D. Call of the Klondike 971.9

Olson, T. How to get rich in the California Gold Rush 979.4

Sedgwick, M. Revolver Fic

Sheinkin, S. Which way to the wild west? 978

GOLD RUSH

Carson, R. Walk on Earth a stranger Fic

Gold rush girl. Avi. Fic

GOLD THEFTS

Flanagan, J. The kings of Clonmel Fic

Gold, John Coopersmith

Learning about the circulatory and lymphatic systems 612.1

Gold, Martha V.

Learning about the nervous system 612.8

Gold, Rozanne, 1954-

Eat fresh food 641.5

Gold, Susan Dudley

Learning about the digestive and excretory systems 612.3

Learning about the musculoskeletal system and the skin 612.7

Golda Meir. Blashfield, J. F. B

Goldberg, Enid A.

Grigory Rasputin B

Goldblatt, Mark, 1957-

Twerp Fic

Golden arm. Deuker, C.	Fic
The **golden** compass. Melchior-Durand, S.	741.5
The **golden** compass. Pullman, P.	Fic
The **golden** dream of Carlo Chuchio. Alexander, L.	Fic
The **golden** moon bear. Montgomery, S.	599.78
The **golden** specific. Grove, S. E.	Fic
Golden tales. Delacre, L.	398.2
Goldenhand. Nix, G.	Fic

Golding, William, 1911-1993

Lord of the flies	Fic

Goldsmith, Annette Y

Reading the world's stories	016.80883

Goldsmith, Connie, 1945-

Dietary supplements	615.1
Hepatitis	616.3
Pandemic	614.4
Traumatic brain injury	617.4
Women in the military	355.009

Goldsmith, Francisca

The readers' advisory guide to graphic novels	025.2

Goldstein, Margaret J.

Fuel under fire	338.2
Garbage in space	363.72

Goldstone, Lawrence, 1947-

Higher steeper faster	629.13
Separate no more	323.1196
Stolen justice	324.6
Unpunished murder	976.3

Goldstrike. Whyman, M.	Fic

GOLEM

Love, D. Monstrous devices	Fic
Stroud, J. The golem's eye	Fic
The **golem's** eye. Stroud, J.	Fic

GOLF

Kelley, K. C. Golf	796.352

GOLF -- EQUIPMENT AND SUPPLIES

Kelley, K. C. Golf	796.352
Golf. Kelley, K. C.	796.352

GOLFERS

Kelley, K. C. Golf	796.352
Goliath. Westerfeld, S.	Fic

Golio, Gary

Spirit seeker	B
The **gone** away place. Barzak, C.	Fic
Gone crazy in Alabama. Williams-Garcia, R.	Fic
Gone to the woods. Paulsen, G.	B

Gonzales, S., 1992-

Only mostly devastated	Fic

Gonzalez, Christina Diaz, 1969-

Moving target	Fic

Gooch, Anthony

Cassell's Spanish-English English-Spanish dictionary	463

GOOD AND EVIL

Alexander, L. The black cauldron	Fic
Alexander, L. The book of three	Fic
Alexander, L. The foundling and other tales of Prydain	Fic
Alexander, L. The iron ring	Fic

Alexander, L. Taran Wanderer	Fic
Alston, B. Amari and the night brothers	Fic
Bardugo, L. Ruin and rising	Fic
Barron, R. Maya and the rising dark	Fic
Black, H. The bronze key	Fic
Black, H. The copper gauntlet	Fic
Black, H. The iron trial	Fic
Black, H. The silver mask	Fic
Boniface, W. The great powers outage	Fic
Booraem, E. River magic	Fic
Bradbury, R. Something wicked this way comes	Fic
Bruchac, J. Dragon castle	Fic
Chima, C. W. The Demon King	Fic
Connolly, M. Comet rising	Fic
Connolly, M. Shadow weaver	Fic
D'Lacey, C. Dark fire	Fic
D'Lacey, C. The fire ascending	Fic
D'Lacey, C. Fire world	Fic
Dakin, G. The Society of Unrelenting Vigilance	Fic
Datlow, E. Troll's eye view	Fic
DuPrau, J. The prophet of Yonwood	Fic
Duane, D. So you want to be a wizard	Fic
Elphinstone, A. Casper Tock and the Everdark wings	Fic
Epstein, A. J. Circle of heroes	Fic
Evans, M. Who let the gods out?	Fic
Evans, R. P. Rise of the Elgen	Fic
Gibbs, S. Evil spy school	Fic
Grant, M. Fear	Fic
Grant, M. Lies	Fic
Grant, M. Light	Fic
Grant, M. Plague	Fic
Grant, M. The trap	Fic
Healy, C. The hero's guide to saving your kingdom	Fic
Horowitz, A. Necropolis	Fic
Jacques, B. Mariel of Redwall	Fic
Jacques, B. Martin the Warrior	Fic
Jacques, B. Mattimeo	Fic
Jacques, B. Mossflower	Fic
Jacques, B. Pearls of Lutra	Fic
Jacques, B. Redwall	Fic
Jacques, B. Redwall the graphic novel	741.5
Jacques, B. Salamandastron	Fic
Kenyon, S. Infinity	Fic
L'Engle, M. A wind in the door	Fic
Larson, H. A wrinkle in time	741.5
Lee, S. Convergence	Fic
Lewis, C. S. The horse and his boy	Fic
Lewis, C. S. The last battle	Fic
Lewis, C. S. The lion the witch and the wardrobe	Fic
Lewis, C. S. The magician's nephew	Fic
Lewis, C. S. Prince Caspian	Fic
Lewis, C. S. The silver chair	Fic
Lewis, C. S. The voyage of the Dawn Treader	Fic
Lupica, M. Hero	Fic
Moore, P. V is for villain	Fic
Mull, B. Wild born	Fic
Nix, G. Abhorsen	Fic

Pearson, P. O. Conspiracy 973.924

GOVERNMENT REGULATION

Jarrow, G. The poison eaters 353.9

GOVERNMENT RELATIONS WITH INDIGENOUS PEOPLES

Edwards, J. The history of the American Indians and the reservation 323.1197

Mandell, D. R. King Philip's war 973.2

Philip, N. The great circle 973.04

Stewart, M. The Indian Removal Act 973.04

Gow, Mary

The great philosopher **B**

The great thinker 509.2

The greatest doctor of ancient times 610.938

Measuring the Earth **B**

GOWNLEY, JIMMY

Gownley, J. The dumbest idea ever! **B**

Gownley, Jimmy

The dumbest idea ever! **B**

Grabenstein, Chris

The crossroads Fic

Escape from Mr. Lemoncello's library Fic

The island of Dr. Libris Fic

Mr. Lemoncello's great library race Fic

Mr. Lemoncello's Library Olympics Fic

The smartest kid in the universe Fic

Grabenstein, J. J.

Shine! Fic

Grace gold and glory. Douglas, G. **B**

Gracefully Grayson. Polonsky, A. Fic

Graceling. Cashore, K. Fic

GRADING AND MARKING (STUDENTS)

Stevens, D. D. Introduction to rubrics 371.27

Wormeli, R. Fair isn't always equal second edition 371.27

Graduation day. Charbonneau, J. Fic

Graff, Lisa (Lisa Colleen), 1981-

A tangle of knots Fic

GRAFFITI

Bass, K. Graffiti knight Fic

Gardner, W. You're welcome universe Fic

Kephart, B. Going over Fic

GRAFFITI ARTISTS

Gardner, W. You're welcome universe Fic

Graffiti knight. Bass, K. Fic

Graham, Ian, 1953-

Fabulous bridges 624.2

Robot technology 629.8

The science of flight 629.13

Tremendous tunnels 624.1

You wouldn't want to live without dirt! 631.4

GRAHAM, MARTHA

Freedman, R. Martha Graham **B**

GRAIL

White, T. H. The once and future king Fic

GRAIN

Sobol, R. The life of rice 633.1

GRAMMAR

O'Conner, P. T. Woe is I Jr. 372.61

Grammar Girl presents the ultimate writing guide for students.
Fogarty, M. 428.2

GRAMMAR, COMPARATIVE AND GENERAL

Fogarty, M. Grammar Girl presents the ultimate writing guide for students 428.2

GRAND CANYON

Chin, J. Grand Canyon 557.9132

GRAND CANYON NATIONAL PARK

Chin, J. Grand Canyon 557.9132

Grand Canyon. Chin, J. 557.9132

The **grand** escape. Bascomb, N. 940.4

GRAND PRIX RACING -- HISTORY 20TH CENTURY

Bascomb, N. The racers 796.72092

Grand theft horse. Neri, G. **B**

GRANDDAUGHTERS

Peet, M. Tamar Fic

GRANDFATHER AND CHILD

Almond, D. Kit's wilderness Fic

Levine, G. C. A ceiling made of eggshells Fic

GRANDFATHER AND GRANDDAUGHTER

Eagar, L. Hour of the bees Fic

Fusco, K. N. Chasing Augustus Fic

Gleitzman, M. Now Fic

Harrington, J. N. Catching a storyfish Fic

Medina, M. Merci Suarez can't dance Fic

Walters, E. Broken strings Fic

GRANDFATHER AND GRANDSON

Avi. The most important thing Fic

Beasley, C. Circus Mirandus Fic

Henderson, L. The magic in changing your stars Fic

Korman, G. War stories Fic

Love, D. Monstrous devices Fic

Love, D. The shadow arts Fic

MacLachlan, P. Kindred souls Fic

Morpurgo, M. Half a man Fic

Withers, P. First descent Fic

GRANDFATHERS

Baker, M. If you find this Fic

Brouwer, S. Devil's pass Fic

Bryant, J. Kaleidoscope eyes Fic

Holm, J. L. The fourteenth goldfish Fic

Holm, J. L. Sunny side up 741.5

Holm, J. L. Swing it Sunny 741.5

Love, D. The shadow arts Fic

Walters, E. The money pit mystery Fic

Yep, L. A dragon's guide to making your human smarter Fic

GRANDFATHERS -- DEATH

Riggs, R. A map of days Fic

Riggs, R. Miss Peregrine's home for peculiar children Fic

GRANDIN, TEMPLE

Montgomery, S. Temple Grandin **B**

Sepahban, L. Temple Grandin **B**

GRANDMOTHER AND CHILD

Peck, R. A long way from Chicago Fic

Young, B. Healer of the water monster Fic

GRANDMOTHER AND GRANDDAUGHTER

Sommer, S. Hammerin' Hank Greenberg — **B**

Greenberg, Jan, 1942-
Christo & Jeanne-Claude — **709.2**
Heart to heart — **811**
The mad potter — **738.092**
Meet Cindy Sherman — **770.92**
Runaway girl — **B**
Greenglass House. Milford, K. — **Fic**
GREENHOUSE EFFECT, ATMOSPHERIC
Bow, J. Earth's climate change — **363.738**
Chevat, R. Our choice — **363.738**
Delano, M. F. Earth in the hot seat — **363.738**
McPherson, S. S. Hothouse earth — **363.738**
GREENHOUSE GASES
Simon, S. Climate action — **363.738**
GREENLAND
Stead, R. First light — **Fic**
Greenly, Larry W.
Eugene Bullard — **B**
Greenwald, Lisa
My life in pink & green — **Fic**
Greenwald, Tom, 1962-
Charlie Joe Jackson's guide to summer vacation — **Fic**
Game changer — **Fic**
GREENWICH VILLAGE, NEW YORK CITY
Fitzgerald, L. M. Under the egg — **Fic**
GREENWICH VILLAGE, NEW YORK CITY -- HISTORY
Pitman, G. E. The Stonewall Riots — **306.76**
GREETING CARDS
Turnbull, S. Cards and gifts — **745.594**
Greetings from witness protection! Burt, J. — **Fic**
Gregor the Overlander. Collins, S. — **Fic**
Gregorio, I. W., 1976-
This is my brain in love — **Fic**
Gregory, Josh
From butterfly wings to... display technology — **621.3815**
Gettysburg — **973.7**
Hedgehogs — **599.33**
Sloths — **599.3**
GRENADA
Pang, G. Grenada — **972.9845**
Grenada. Pang, G. — **972.9845**
Greta Thunberg. Marcovitz, H. — **B**
A **greyhound** of a girl. Doyle, R. — **Fic**
Gribbin, Mary
The science of Philip Pullman's His dark materials — **823**
GRIEF
Ali, S. K. Love from A to Z — **Fic**
Almond, D. Slog's dad — **Fic**
Appelt, K. Maybe a fox — **Fic**
Beaty, A. Cicada summer — **Fic**
Blackstone, M. Sorry you're lost — **Fic**
Bowling, D. The canyon's edge — **Fic**
Bullen, A. Wish — **Fic**
Callender, K. Hurricane child — **Fic**
Condie, A. B. The last voyage of Poe Blythe — **Fic**
Cooper, S. King of shadows — **Fic**

Dessen, S. The truth about forever — **Fic**
Doherty, B. The girl who saw lions — **Fic**
Erskine, K. Seeing red — **Fic**
Farrant, N. After Iris — **Fic**
Foxlee, K. The anatomy of wings — **Fic**
Friend, N. Perfect — **Fic**
Han, J. It's not summer without you — **Fic**
Hand, C. The last time we say goodbye — **Fic**
Hardinge, F. Cuckoo song — **Fic**
Harrington, K. Mayday — **Fic**
Hautman, P. Road tripped — **Fic**
Herlong, M. The great wide sea — **Fic**
Horowitz, A. Never say die — **Fic**
Jones, T. L. Silhouetted by the blue — **Fic**
Kadohata, C. Kira-kira — **Fic**
Knowles, J. See you at Harry's — **Fic**
Le Guin, U. K. Powers — **Fic**
Lean, S. A dog called Homeless — **Fic**
Loftin, N. Nightingale's nest — **Fic**
Lord, E. When we collided — **Fic**
Lupica, M. Hero — **Fic**
Nelson, M. Fortune's bones — **811**
Nicholls, S. Season of secrets — **Fic**
Pinkney, A. D. Bird in a box — **Fic**
Polisner, G. The pull of gravity — **Fic**
Polonsky, A. Threads — **Fic**
Reynolds, J. The boy in the black suit — **Fic**
Reynolds, J. Long way down — **Fic**
Rylant, C. Missing May — **Fic**
Selznick, B. The Marvels — **Fic**
Shang, W. W. The way home looks now — **Fic**
Silberberg, A. Milo — **Fic**
Sloan, H. G. The elephant in the room — **Fic**
Sorosiak, C. Wild blue wonder — **Fic**
Sweeney, D. The minnow — **Fic**
Urban, L. The center of everything — **Fic**
Villasante, A. The grief keeper — **Fic**
Watson, C. Benched — **Fic**
Weston, C. Speed of life — **Fic**
Zarr, S. How to save a life — **Fic**
Grief girl. Vincent, E. — **B**
GRIEF IN BOYS
Almond, D. The savage — **Fic**
Almond, D. Slog's dad — **Fic**
Cooper, S. King of shadows — **Fic**
Lupica, M. The only game — **Fic**
Martin, A. M. Everything for a dog — **Fic**
Silberberg, A. Milo — **Fic**
Ventrella, K. The secret life of Sam — **Fic**
GRIEF IN CHILDREN
Blake, A. H. Hazel Bly and the deep blue sea — **Fic**
Cline-Ransome, L. Being Clem — **Fic**
Knowles, J. See you at Harry's — **Fic**
Lukoff, K. Too bright to see — **Fic**
Makechnie, A. Ten thousand tries — **Fic**
Pinkney, A. D. Bird in a box — **Fic**
Rylant, C. Missing May — **Fic**

Gabrielson, C. Kinetic contraptions **621.46**

The **groundbreaking** chance-taking life of George Washington Carver and science & invention in America. Harness, C. **B**

Groundbreaking guys. Peters, S. T. **920.71**

Grounded. Morrison, M. **Fic**

GROUP GAMES

Preller, J. Six innings **Fic**

GROUP HOMES

Chan, G. The disappearance **Fic**

Korman, G. The juvie three **Fic**

GROUP PSYCHOTHERAPY

Nolan, H. Crazy **Fic**

GROUP READING

Daniels, H. Literature circles **371.39**

Daniels, H. Mini-lessons for literature circles **372.41**

GROUP WORK IN EDUCATION

Brulles, D. The cluster grouping handbook **371.2**

Brulles, D. A teacher's guide to flexible grouping and collaborative learning **371.3**

Daniels, H. Literature circles **371.39**

GROUP WORK IN EDUCATION -- EVALUATION

Brulles, D. A teacher's guide to flexible grouping and collaborative learning **371.3**

Grove, S. E.

The crimson skew **Fic**

The golden specific **Fic**

Grove, Tim, 1967-

First flight around the world **910.4**

Milestones of flight **629.109**

Grover, Sharon

Listening to learn **372.4**

Growing schools. Abilock, D. **370.71**

GROWING UP

Black, H. Doll bones **Fic**

Brashares, A. 3 willows **Fic**

Carlson, L. M. Cool salsa **811**

Cisneros, S. The house on Mango Street **Fic**

Gravelle, K. The period book **612.6**

Holmes, M. Girlology's there's something new about you **612.6**

Lai, R. Fly on the wall **Fic**

Lane, K. Pity party **Fic**

Larson, H. All summer long **741.5**

Larson, H. All together now **741.5**

Natterson, C. F. The care & keeping of you 2 **613**

Sleator, W. Oddballs **Fic**

Spinelli, J. Hokey Pokey **Fic**

Stephens, R. D. Henry Chow and other stories from the Asian Canadian Writers' Workshop **Fic**

Tamaki, M. This one summer **741.5**

Thompson, H. Tomo **Fic**

Whitney, D. You don't have to be everything **808.108**

Wiles, D. Countdown **Fic**

Growing up in coal country. Bartoletti, S. C. **331.3**

GROWTH (PSYCHOLOGY)

Johnson, M. 13 little blue envelopes **Fic**

Nye, N. S. A maze me **811**

Oppel, K. Silverwing **Fic**

Schmidt, G. D. The Wednesday wars **Fic**

Spinelli, J. Hokey Pokey **Fic**

Gruber, Beth

National Geographic investigates ancient Inca **985**

National Geographic investigates ancient Iraq **935**

GRUENER, JACK

Gratz, A. Prisoner B-3087 **Fic**

Grundmann, Emmanuelle

When elephants listen with their feet **573.8**

GUANTANAMO BAY DETENTION CAMP

Perera, A. Guantanamo boy **Fic**

GUANTANAMO BAY NAVAL BASE, CUBA

Perera, A. Guantanamo boy **Fic**

Guantanamo boy. Perera, A. **Fic**

Guardian. Lester, J. **Fic**

GUARDIAN AND WARD

Dakin, G. The Society of Unrelenting Vigilance **Fic**

Miller, S. E. The miracle & tragedy of the Dionne quintuplets **306.875**

Rundell, K. Rooftoppers **Fic**

GUARDIAN ANGELS

Anderson, J. L. My diary from the edge of the world **Fic**

Guardians of liberty. Osborne, L. B. **323.44**

GUARDS

Pearson, M. Dance of thieves **Fic**

Turner, M. W. The king of Attolia **Fic**

Ward, D. Beneath the mask **Fic**

Ward, D. Escape the mask **Fic**

GUATEMALA

Brown, S. Caminar **Fic**

Pellegrino, M. Journey of dreams **Fic**

GUERRILLA WARFARE

Elliott, L. Under a war-torn sky **Fic**

Merrill, J. F. The pushcart war **Fic**

GUERRILLAS

Smith-Llera, D. Che Guevara's face **972.9106**

GUEVARA, CHE, 1928-1967

Abrams, D. Ernesto "Che" Guevara **B**

Kallen, S. A. Che Guevara **B**

Miller, C. C. Che Guevara **B**

Smith-Llera, D. Che Guevara's face **972.9106**

Guiberson, Brenda Z.

Feathered dinosaurs **567.9**

GUIDED READING -- STUDY AND TEACHING (ELEMENTARY)

Richardson, J. The next step forward in guided reading **372.41**

GUIDED READING -- STUDY AND TEACHING (MIDDLE SCHOOL)

Richardson, J. The next step forward in guided reading **372.41**

GUIDED READING -- STUDY AND TEACHING (PRESCHOOL)

Richardson, J. The next step forward in guided reading **372.41**

Miller, J. Elizabeth and Zenobia	Fic	Rules for stealing stars	Fic
Noyes, D. The ghosts of Kerfol	Fic	The someday suitcase	Fic
Oh, E. Spirit hunters	Fic	**Hayes, Amy**	
San Souci, R. D. Dare to be scared	Fic	Disability rights movement	323.3
San Souci, R. D. Haunted houses	Fic	**Hayes, Joe**	
Shulman, P. The Poe estate	Fic	Dance Nana dance	398.2
Stroud, J. The screaming staircase	Fic	**HAYES, TYRONE**	
Telgemeier, R. Ghosts	741.5	Turner, P. S. The frog scientist	597.8
Yelchin, E. The haunting of Falcon House	Fic	**Hayles, Marsha**	
Haunted houses. San Souci, R. D.	Fic	Breathing room	Fic
HAUNTED PLACES		**Haywood, John, 1956-**	
Arden, K. Dead voices	Fic	West African kingdoms	966
Carman, P. The Crossbones	Fic	**Haywood, Karen**	
Cohen, M. The Inn Between	Fic	Skeletal system	611
Delaney, J. The ghost prison	Fic	**HAZARDOUS WASTE MANAGEMENT INDUSTRY --**	
Layne, A. Beetle & the Hollowbones	741.5	**VOCATIONAL GUIDANCE**	
Steele, H. DeadEndia	Fic	Harmon, D. E. Jobs in environmental cleanup and emergency	
Turnage, S. The ghosts of Tupelo Landing	Fic	hazmat response	628.023
The **haunting** of Falcon House. Yelchin, E.	Fic	**Hazel** Bly and the deep blue sea. Blake, A. H.	Fic
The **haunting** of Gabriel Ashe. Poblocki, D.	Fic	**Hazel's** theory of evolution. Bigelow, L. J.	Fic
Hausman, Gerald		**HAZING**	
Horses of myth	398.24	Greenwald, T. Game changer	Fic
Hautman, Pete, 1952-		Wiseman, R. Boys girls and other hazardous materials	Fic
All-in	Fic	**He** laughed with his other mouths. Anderson, M. T.	Fic
Blank confession	Fic	**HEAD -- WOUNDS AND INJURIES**	
Godless	Fic	McClafferty, C. K. Fourth down and inches	617.4
The Klaatu terminus	Fic	**HEADACHE**	
The obsidian blade	Fic	Arntson, S. The wikkeling	Fic
Road tripped	Fic	**Headley, Justina Chen, 1968-**	
Slider	Fic	Return to me	Fic
HAVANA, CUBA		**HEADS OF STATE**	
Wells, R. My Havana	Fic	Naden, C. J. Mao Zedong and the Chinese Revolution	
Haveli. Staples, S. F.	Fic	tion	951.05092
HAWAII		**Heads** up psychology. Weeks, M.	150
Bowman, A. D. Summer bird blue	Fic	**Heads** up. Siebert, M.	616.89
Kent, D. Hawaii	996.9	**Heale, Jay**	
Mazer, H. A boy at war	Fic	Madagascar	969.1
Mazer, H. Heroes don't run	Fic	**Healer** of the water monster. Young, B.	Fic
Messner, K. Pearl Harbor	940.54	**HEALERS**	
Salisbury, G. Eyes of the emperor	Fic	Blackburne, L. Rosemarked	Fic
Yep, L. City of fire	Fic	Divakaruni, C. B. The conch bearer	Fic
Hawaii. Kent, D.	996.9	Temblador, A. Secrets of the Casa Rosada	Fic
Hawk & drool. Donovan, S.	612.3	Tingle, T. Spirits dark and light	398.2
HAWKING, STEPHEN, 1942-2018		**Healey, Karen**	
Bankston, J. Stephen Hawking	B	When we wake	Fic
Kenney, K. L. Stephen Hawking	B	**HEALING**	
Hawkins, John		Grant, M. Eve & Adam	Fic
Atlantis and other lost worlds	001.94	Sones, S. Stop pretending	Fic
The **hawkweed** prophecy. Brignull, I.	Fic	Temblador, A. Secrets of the Casa Rosada	Fic
HAWORTH, ENGLAND		**HEALTH**	
Valente, C. M. The Glass Town game	Fic	Allman, T. Drugs	616.86
Hay, Jeff		Andrus, A. Project you	155.5
The Tiananmen Square protests of 1989	951.05	Ashenburg, K. All the dirt	613.4
HAYDN, FRANZ JOSEPH, 1732-1809		Bellenir, E. Fitness information for teens	613.7
Dunlap, S. E. The musician's daughter	Fic	Dicker, K. Exercise	613.7
Haydu, Corey Ann		Donovan, S. Keep your cool!	616.9
One jar of magic	Fic	Dunham, K. S. The boy's body book	612.6

Etingoff, K.   Building a healthy diet with the 5 food groups   **613.2**

Furgang, A. Carbonated beverages   **613.2**

Holmes, M.   Girlology's there's something new about you   **612.6**

Juettner, B. Diet and disease   **613.2**

Klimecki, Z. Diet information for teens   **613.2083**

Kuskowski, A. Cool relaxing   **613.7**

McCoy, K. The teenage body book   **613**

Miller, H. Smoking   **613.85**

Mooney, C. Human movement   **612**

Mooney, C. Junk food junkies   **641.5**

Orr, T. Playing safe eating right   **613**

Rau, D. M. Going organic   **613.2**

Rau, D. M. Going vegetarian   **613.2**

Traugh, S. M. Vegetarianism   **641.5**

Waters, R. My daily diet   **613.2**

Healy, Christopher, 1972-
The hero's guide to saving your kingdom   **Fic**

Heaney, Katie
Girl crushed   **Fic**

Heap House. Carey, E.   **Fic**

HEARING
Simon, S. Eyes and ears   **612.8**

Hearne, Betsy Gould
Beauties and beasts   **398.21**

HEART
Croggon, A. The threads of magic   **Fic**
Murphy, J. Breakthrough!   **617**

HEART -- DISEASES
Markle, S. Faulty heart   **612.1**
Williams, I. Water in May   **Fic**

HEART -- PHYSIOLOGY
Rose, S. Circulatory system   **612.1**

HEART -- SURGERY
Murphy, J. Breakthrough!   **617**
Yount, L. Alfred Blalock Helen Taussig and Vivien Thomas   **617.4**

HEART -- TRANSPLANTATION
Bauer, J. Soar   **Fic**
The **heart** is not a size. Kephart, B.   **Fic**
Heart of a samurai. Preus, M.   **Fic**
A **heart** so fierce and broken. Kemmerer, B.   **Fic**

HEART SURGEONS
Yount, L. Alfred Blalock Helen Taussig and Vivien Thomas   **617.4**

Heart to heart. Greenberg, J.   **811**
The **Heartbreak** Messenger. Vance, A. P.   **Fic**
Heartless. Meyer, M.   **Fic**
Heartstopper. Oseman, A.   **741.5**
Heat. Lupica, M.   **Fic**

Heath, Jack, 1986-
The lab   **Fic**
Remote control   **Fic**

Heaven. Johnson, A.   **Fic**
Hedgehog. Matzke, A. H.   **636.9**
HEDGEHOGS

Gregory, J. Hedgehogs   **599.33**
Matzke, A. H. Hedgehog   **636.9**
Hedgehogs. Gregory, J.   **599.33**

HEDGEHOGS AS PETS
Matzke, A. H. Hedgehog   **636.9**

Heider, Mary Winn
The losers at the center of the galaxy   **Fic**

Heine, Florian
13 architects children should know   **720.92**
Impressionism   **759.05**

Heinecke, Liz Lee
Chemistry for kids   **540.92**

Heinrichs, Ann
The Aztecs   **972**
Maine   **974.1**
Nebraska   **978.2**
Nevada   **979.3**
The Nile   **962**
North Carolina   **975.6**
Sweden   **948.5**

Heir apparent. Vande Velde, V.   **Fic**

HEIRLOOMS
Baker, M. If you find this   **Fic**

HEIRS AND HEIRESSES
Blake, K. Two dark reigns   **Fic**
Fisher, C. The lost heiress   **Fic**
Kemmerer, B. A heart so fierce and broken   **Fic**
Landy, D. Skulduggery Pleasant   **Fic**
Marchetta, M. Finnikin of the rock   **Fic**
Nesbet, A. Daring Darleen queen of the screen   **Fic**
Springer, N. The case of the missing marquess   **Fic**
Yu, M. The Girl King   **Fic**

Heist society. Carter, A.   **Fic**
Helen Keller. Lawlor, L.   **B**

HELEN OF TROY (GREEK MYTHOLOGY)
Friesner, E. M. Nobody's princess   **Fic**
Friesner, E. M. Nobody's prize   **Fic**

Helen's eyes. Delano, M. F.   **B**

Helfand, Lewis
They changed the world   **621.3**

Helgerson, Joseph
Horns and wrinkles   **Fic**

Helget, Nicole Lea, 1976-
Barbarians   **940.1**
Mongols   **950**

HELICOPTERS -- DESIGN AND CONSTRUCTION
Graham, I. The science of flight   **629.13**

HELL
Agard, J. The young inferno   **811**
Horowitz, A. Death and the underworld   **398.28**

Hell and high water. Landman, T.   **Fic**
Hello from 2030. Schutten, J. P.   **303.49**
Hello universe. Kelly, E. E.   **Fic**

Hellweg, Paul
The American Heritage student thesaurus   **428.1**

Help wanted. Soto, G.   **Fic**
HELPFULNESS

Hunter, E. Dawn	Fic	
Jacques, B. Mariel of Redwall	Fic	
Jacques, B. Martin the Warrior	Fic	
Jacques, B. Mattimeo	Fic	
Jacques, B. Mossflower	Fic	
Jacques, B. Pearls of Lutra	Fic	
Jacques, B. Redwall	Fic	
Jacques, B. Redwall the graphic novel	741.5	
Jacques, B. Salamandastron	Fic	
Johnston, E. K. Prairie fire	Fic	
Landmann, B. The fate of Achilles	883	
McCann, M. R. Girls who rocked the world	920	
McCann, M. R. More girls who rocked the world	920.72	
McCaughrean, G. Gilgamesh the hero	398.2	
McKinley, R. The hero and the crown	Fic	
McKinley, R. The outlaws of Sherwood	Fic	
Morpurgo, M. Beowulf	398.2	
Smith, C. R. The mighty 12	398.2	
Smith, J. Tall tales	741.5	
Strasser, T. Price of duty	Fic	
Uehashi, N. Moribito	Fic	
Uehashi, N. Moribito II	Fic	
Winter, J. Peaceful heroes	920	
Yolen, J. Mightier than the sword	398.2	

HEROES AND HEROINES, AFRICAN AMERICAN

Whitley, J. Princeless — 741.5

HEROES AND HEROINES, AMERICAN

San Souci, R. D. Cut from the same cloth — 398.21

HEROES AND HEROINES, GREEK

Bryant, M. E. Oh my gods!	398.2
Bryant, M. E. She's all that!	398
Cross, G. The Iliad	Fic
Daly, K. N. Greek and Roman mythology A to Z	292.1
Evans, H. The mythology handbook	292.1
Fleischman, P. Dateline Troy	398.2
Hinds, G. The Iliad	741.5
Hinds, G. The Odyssey	741.5
Homer. The Odyssey	883
Landmann, B. The incredible voyage of Ulysses	398.2
McCaughrean, G. Hercules	398.2
McCaughrean, G. Odysseus	398.2
McCaughrean, G. Perseus	398.2
Napoli, D. J. Treasury of Greek mythology	398.2
Orr, T. The monsters of Hercules	398.2
Otfinoski, S. All in the family	398.2
Rylant, C. The beautiful stories of life	398.2
Smith, C. R. The mighty 12	398.2

HEROES AND HEROINES, NORSE

Hinds, G. Beowulf	741.5
Raven, N. Beowulf	398.2

HEROES AND HEROINES, ROMAN

Daly, K. N. Greek and Roman mythology A to Z	292.1
Heroes and villains. Horowitz, A.	398.22
Heroes don't run. Mazer, H.	Fic
Heroes of baseball. Lipsyte, R.	920
Heroes of the environment. Rohmer, H.	920
Heroes of the Holocaust. Fishkin, R. L.	940.53

Heroes of the valley. Stroud, J.	Fic
Heroes! Stephens, J.	741.5

HEROIN

Cashin, H. J. The heroin crisis — 362.29

HEROIN ADDICTION

Quinones, S. Dreamland	362.29
The heroin crisis. Cashin, H. J.	362.29

HERRERA, JUAN FELIPE

Herrera, J. F. Laughing out loud I fly — 811

Herrera, Juan Felipe

Laughing out loud I fly	811
Portraits of Hispanic American heroes	920

HERRERA, NICHOLAS, 1964-

Herrera, N. High riders saints and death cars — 709.2

Herrera, Nicholas, 1964-

High riders saints and death cars — 709.2

Herrera, Robin

Hope is a ferris wheel — Fic

Herrick, Amy

The Time Fetch — Fic

HERSHEY, PENNSYLVANIA

Finneyfrock, K. The sweet revenge of Celia Door	Fic
HerStory. Halligan, K.	920

Hesse, Karen

Brooklyn Bridge	Fic
Letters from Rifka	Fic
Out of the dust	Fic
Safekeeping	Fic
Witness	Fic

Hesse, Monica

The war outside — Fic

Hesser, Terry Spencer

Kissing doorknobs — Fic

Hest, Amy

The summer we found the baby — Fic

Hestermann, Josh, 1983-

Zoology for kids — 590

Hestler, Anna

Wales — 942.9

Heuston, Kimberley Burton, 1960-

Mao Zedong — B

Heuvel, Eric, 1960-

A family secret — 741.5

Hewitt, Ben, 1971-

The young adventurer's guide to (almost) everything	796.083
Hey kiddo. Krosoczka, J.	B
Hi-tech clothes. Spilsbury, R.	746.9

Hiaasen, Carl

Flush	Fic
Hoot	Fic
Scat	Fic
Skink--no surrender	Fic
Hiawatha and Megissogwon. Longfellow, H. W.	811

HIAWATHA, ACTIVE 15TH CENTURY

Longfellow, H. W. Hiawatha and Megissogwon — 811

HICKAM, HOMER H., 1943-

Hickam, H. H. Rocket boys — B

Pierce, T. Bloodhound	**Fic**
Pierce, T. First test	**Fic**
Pierce, T. Lady knight	**Fic**
Pierce, T. Mastiff	**Fic**
Pierce, T. Page	**Fic**
Pierce, T. Squire	**Fic**
Pierce, T. Terrier	**Fic**
Pierce, T. Wild magic	**Fic**
Pool, K. R. There will come a darkness	**Fic**
Rogerson, M. An enchantment of ravens	**Fic**
Rutkoski, M. The winner's crime	**Fic**
Rutkoski, M. The winner's curse	**Fic**
Rutkoski, M. The winner's kiss	**Fic**
Sage, A. StarChaser	**Fic**
Tucholke, A. G. The Boneless Mercies	**Fic**
Tucholke, A. G. Seven endless forests	**Fic**
Turner, M. W. A conspiracy of kings	**Fic**
Turner, M. W. The king of Attolia	**Fic**
Turner, M. W. The queen of Attolia	**Fic**
Turner, M. W. Return of the thief	**Fic**
Turner, M. W. Thick as thieves	**Fic**
Turner, M. W. The thief	**Fic**
Zinn, B. Poison	**Fic**
A **high** five for Glenn Burke. Bildner, P.	**Fic**

HIGH INTEREST-LOW VOCABULARY BOOKS

Adams, S. The Iraq War	**956.7044**
Jones, P. Bridge	**Fic**
Martin, M. Extinction!	**576.8**
Watson, C. Benched	**Fic**
Yee, P. Learning to fly	**Fic**
High riders saints and death cars. Herrera, N.	**709.2**

HIGH SCHOOL ATHLETES

Crutcher, C. Deadline	**Fic**
Shen, P. Nothing can possibly go wrong	**741.5**

HIGH SCHOOL ATHLETES -- TRAINING OF

Fay, G. Sports	**796**

HIGH SCHOOL BASKETBALL

Hoose, P. M. Attucks!	**796.323**
Shen, P. Nothing can possibly go wrong	**741.5**

HIGH SCHOOL BASKETBALL PLAYERS

Myers, W. D. Slam!	**Fic**
Volponi, P. Black and white	**Fic**

HIGH SCHOOL DROPOUTS

Blundell, J. Strings attached	**Fic**

HIGH SCHOOL FOOTBALL

Herbach, G. I'm with stupid	**Fic**
Murdock, C. G. The off season	**Fic**

HIGH SCHOOL FOOTBALL PLAYERS

Deuker, C. Gym candy	**Fic**
Feinstein, J. The walk-on	**Fic**
Hand, C. Unearthly	**Fic**
Herbach, G. I'm with stupid	**Fic**
Lynch, C. Inexcusable	**Fic**

HIGH SCHOOL FRESHMEN

Bowling, D. Momentous events in the life of a cactus	**Fic**
Hicks, F. E. Friends with boys	**741.5**

HIGH SCHOOL GIRLS

Peck, R. Are you in the house alone?	**Fic**
Tamaki, M. Skim	**741.5**

HIGH SCHOOL GRADUATES

Brody, J. The geography of lost things	**Fic**
Hughes, D. Search and destroy	**Fic**
Zarr, S. Roomies	**Fic**

HIGH SCHOOL JUNIORS

Draper, S. M. The battle of Jericho	**Fic**

HIGH SCHOOL LIBRARIES

Chance, R. Young adult literature in action	**011.62**

HIGH SCHOOL SENIORS

Bradley, A. 24 girls in 7 days	**Fic**
Draper, S. M. Just another hero	**Fic**
Lubar, D. Character driven	**Fic**
Martin, M. A. To be honest	**Fic**
Mukherjee, S. Gemini	**Fic**
Na, A. Wait for me	**Fic**
Strasser, T. No place	**Fic**
Wallace, R. Wrestling Sturbridge	**Fic**
White, E. E. White House autumn	**Fic**

HIGH SCHOOL SOPHOMORES

Mlynowski, S. Don't even think about it	**Fic**
Zindel, P. The pigman	**Fic**

HIGH SCHOOL STUDENTS

Alsaid, A. We didn't ask for this	**Fic**
Anderson, L. H. Speak	**Fic**
Baratz-Logsted, L. Crazy beautiful	**Fic**
Coy, J. Hoop genius	**796.323**
Duncan, L. Killing Mr. Griffin	**Fic**
Falkowski, M. We say #never again	**371.7**
Farizan, S. Here to stay	**Fic**
Fields, T. After the death of Anna Gonzales	**Fic**
Furudate, H. Haikyu!!	**741.5**
Gallo, D. R. Destination unexpected	**Fic**
Jones, P. Bridge	**Fic**
Kephart, B. Undercover	**Fic**
McCoy, M. I Claudia	**Fic**
Moore, S. Batman	**Fic**
Moriarty, J. Feeling sorry for Celia	**Fic**
Nolan, H. Crazy	**Fic**
Rubin, L. Crying laughing	**Fic**
Thoms, A. With their eyes	**812**

HIGH SCHOOL STUDENTS -- CIVIL RIGHTS

Lusted, M. A. Tinker vs. Des Moines	**342.7308**

HIGH SCHOOL TEACHERS

Bushnell, C. Rules for being a girl	**Fic**
Duncan, L. Killing Mr. Griffin	**Fic**

HIGH SCHOOL TRACK AND FIELD ATHLETICS

Cleary, B. Strider	**Fic**

HIGH SCHOOLS

Alsaid, A. We didn't ask for this	**Fic**
Barnes, J. Perfect cover	**Fic**
Benway, R. Also known as	**Fic**
Bowling, D. Momentous events in the life of a cactus	**Fic**
Boyce, J. A. A. This promise of change	**379.2**
Bushnell, C. Rules for being a girl	**Fic**
Coy, J. Hoop genius	**796.323**

Hinman, Bonnie

  We visit Pakistan — 954.91

Hinton, S. E.

  The outsiders — Fic

HIP-HOP

  Sitomer, A. L. Hip-hop poetry and the classics — 808.1071

HIP-HOP CULTURE

  Chang, J. Can't stop won't stop — 306.4

  Garofoli, W. Hip-hop dancing — 793.3

  Jackson, T. D. Let me hear a rhyme — Fic

HIP-HOP DANCE

  Garofoli, W. Hip-hop dancing — 793.3

Hip-hop dancing. Garofoli, W. — 793.3

Hip-hop poetry and the classics. Sitomer, A. L. — 808.1071

HIPPOCRATES, 460?-377? B.C.E.

  Gow, M. The greatest doctor of ancient times — 610.938

HIPPOPOTAMUS

  Gibbs, S. Belly up — Fic

Hirahara, Naomi, 1962-

  1001 cranes — Fic

Hiranandani, Veera

  The whole story of half a girl — Fic

The **hired** girl. Schlitz, L. A. — Fic

Hiroshima. Burgan, M. — 940.54

Hiroshima. Yep, L. — Fic

HIROSHIMA MAIDENS

  Yep, L. Hiroshima — Fic

HIROSHIMA, JAPAN

  Kadohata, C. A place to belong — Fic

  Yep, L. Hiroshima — Fic

HIROSHIMA, JAPAN -- ATOMIC BOMBING, 1945

  Grant, R. G. Why did Hiroshima happen? — 940.54

HIROSHIMA-SHI (JAPAN) -- HISTORY -- BOMBARD-MENT, 1945

  Burgan, M. Hiroshima — 940.54

Hirsch, Andy, 1987-

  Cats — 599.75

  Dogs — 636.7

  Rocks and minerals — 552

  Trees — 582.16

Hirsch, Jeff

  Breakaway — Fic

  The eleventh plague — Fic

Hirsch, Rebecca E.

  Birds vs. blades? — 578.77

  De-extinction — 591.68

  Living fossils — 591.3

  Microbiomes — 612

  The rock cycle — 552

  Sedimentary rocks — 552

  Soil — 631.4

  Where have all the bees gone? — 595.79

Hirschmann, Kris, 1967-

  Deadliest reptiles — 597.9

  Deadliest snakes — 597.96

  Deadliest spiders — 595.4

  Frankenstein — 823

Medusa — 398.2

His name was Raoul Wallenberg. Borden, L. — B

HISPANIC AMERICAN BOYS

  Cuevas, A. The total eclipse of Nestor Lopez — Fic

HISPANIC AMERICAN CHILDREN

  Soto, G. Baseball in April and other stories — Fic

HISPANIC AMERICAN FAMILIES

  Padian, M. How to build a heart — Fic

HISPANIC AMERICAN GIRLS

  Cervantes, A. Gaby lost and found — Fic

  Lopez, D. Confetti girl — Fic

HISPANIC AMERICAN MEN

  Vourvoulias, S. Nuestra America — 920

HISPANIC AMERICAN TEENAGE BOYS

  Cofer, J. O. Riding low on the streets of gold — Fic

  Jones, P. Bridge — Fic

  Sanchez, A. Bait — Fic

  Wright, B. Putting makeup on the fat boy — Fic

HISPANIC AMERICAN TEENAGE GIRLS

  Cofer, J. O. Riding low on the streets of gold — Fic

  Lopez, D. Ask my mood ring how I feel — Fic

HISPANIC AMERICAN TEENAGERS

  Carlson, L. M. Cool salsa — 811

  Carlson, L. M. Red hot salsa — 811.008

  Cortez, S. You don't have a clue — Fic

  Soto, G. Baseball in April and other stories — Fic

HISPANIC AMERICAN WOMEN

  Alvarez, J. How Tia Lola came to (visit) stay — Fic

  Vourvoulias, S. Nuestra America — 920

HISPANIC AMERICANS

  Carlson, L. M. Cool salsa — 811

  Carlson, L. M. Red hot salsa — 811.008

  Cortez, S. You don't have a clue — Fic

  Delacre, L. Us in progress — Fic

  Engle, M. Bravo! — 920.0092

  Hernandez, R. E. The Civil War 1840s-1890s — 973.7

  Herrera, J. F. Portraits of Hispanic American heroes — 920

  Johnston, T. Any small goodness — Fic

  Martinez, C. G. Pig park — Fic

  Miller-Lachmann, L. Once upon a cuento — Fic

  Vourvoulias, S. Nuestra America — 920

  Williams, I. Water in May — Fic

HISPANIC AMERICANS -- HISTORY

  Petrillo, V. A kid's guide to Latino history — 973

HISPANIC AMERICANS -- HISTORY 19TH CENTURY

  Hernandez, R. E. The Civil War 1840s-1890s — 973.7

HISTORIANS

  McCoy, M. I Claudia — Fic

HISTORIC BUILDINGS

  Fairlie, E. The magician's bird — Fic

  Lewis, J. P. Monumental verses — 811

  Reynolds, T. Wonders of the world — 031.02

HISTORIC DOCUMENTS

  Bolden, T. Emancipation Proclamation — 973.7

  Winkler, A. M. The Cold War — 909.8

HISTORIC SITES

  Eggers, D. Her right foot — 973

Avi. The end of the world and beyond	**Fic**	Curtis, C. P. Elijah of Buxton	**Fic**
Avi. The fighting ground	**Fic**	Curtis, C. P. The madman of Piney Woods	**Fic**
Avi. Gold rush girl	**Fic**	Curtis, C. P. The Watsons go to Birmingham 1963	**Fic**
Avi. Iron thunder	**Fic**	Cushman, K. Catherine called Birdy	**Fic**
Avi. Sophia's war	**Fic**	Cushman, K. The loud silence of Francine Green	**Fic**
Avi. The true confessions of Charlotte Doyle	**Fic**	Cushman, K. The midwife's apprentice	**Fic**
Avi. The unexpected life of Oliver Cromwell Pitts	**Fic**	Cushman, K. Rodzina	**Fic**
Axelrod, A. Your friend in fashion Abby Shapiro	**Fic**	Dallas, S. The quilt walk	**Fic**
Bannen, M. The bird and the blade	**Fic**	Davis, T. S. Mare's war	**Fic**
Barker, M. P. Mending horses	**Fic**	DeWoskin, R. Someday we will fly	**Fic**
Barratt, M. Joe Rat	**Fic**	DiCamillo, K. Beverly right here	**Fic**
Bartoletti, S. C. The boy who dared	**Fic**	DiCamillo, K. Raymie Nightingale	**Fic**
Baskin, N. R. Nine ten	**Fic**	Dorris, M. Morning Girl	**Fic**
Bass, K. Graffiti knight	**Fic**	Dowd, S. Bog child	**Fic**
Bayard, L. Lucky strikes	**Fic**	Dowell, F. O. Shooting the moon	**Fic**
Behar, R. Lucky broken girl	**Fic**	Dowswell, P. Auslander	**Fic**
Berry, J. All the truth that's in me	**Fic**	Draper, S. M. Stella by starlight	**Fic**
Berry, J. The passion of Dolssa	**Fic**	Duble, K. B. The sacrifice	**Fic**
Blackwood, G. L. The Shakespeare stealer	**Fic**	Dumas, F. It ain't so awful falafel	**Fic**
Blankman, A. The blackbird girls	**Fic**	Dumon Tak, B. Soldier bear	**Fic**
Blundell, J. A city tossed and broken	**Fic**	Durbin, W. The broken blade	**Fic**
Blundell, J. Strings attached	**Fic**	Edwardson, D. D. My name is not easy	**Fic**
Blundell, J. What I saw and how I lied	**Fic**	Ehrlich, E. Nest	**Fic**
Boecker, V. An assassin's guide to love and treason	**Fic**	Elliott, D. Voices	**Fic**
Bolden, T. Crossing Ebenezer Creek	**Fic**	Elliott, L. Under a war-torn sky	**Fic**
Bolden, T. Inventing Victoria	**Fic**	Engle, M. The wild book	**Fic**
Bolden, T. Saving Savannah	**Fic**	English, K. Francie	**Fic**
Boyne, J. The boy in the striped pajamas	**Fic**	Erdrich, L. The birchbark house	**Fic**
Bradley, K. B. Jefferson's sons	**Fic**	Erdrich, L. The game of silence	**Fic**
Bradley, K. B. The war that saved my life	**Fic**	Erdrich, L. Makoons	**Fic**
Brashear, A. The incredible true story of the making of the		Erdrich, L. The porcupine year	**Fic**
Eve of Destruction	**Fic**	Erskine, K. Seeing red	**Fic**
Brooks, M. Queen of hearts	**Fic**	Fitzmaurice, K. A diamond in the desert	**Fic**
Brown, S. Caminar	**Fic**	Fleischman, P. Bull Run	**Fic**
Brown, S. To stay alive	**Fic**	Fletcher, S. Alphabet of dreams	**Fic**
Bruchac, J. Code Talker	**Fic**	Forbes, E. Johnny Tremain	**Fic**
Bruchac, J. Walking two worlds	**Fic**	Frank, S. Armstrong and Charlie	**Fic**
Bryant, J. Ringside 1925	**Fic**	Friesner, E. M. Nobody's princess	**Fic**
Budhos, M. T. The long ride	**Fic**	Friesner, E. M. Sphinx's princess	**Fic**
Burg, A. E. All the broken pieces	**Fic**	Friesner, E. M. Sphinx's queen	**Fic**
Burg, A. E. Unbound	**Fic**	Friesner, E. M. Threads and flames	**Fic**
Byars, B. C. The keeper of the doves	**Fic**	Frost, H. All he knew	**Fic**
Cameron, S. The light in hidden places	**Fic**	Fusco, K. N. Beholding Bee	**Fic**
Cao, W. Bronze and Sunflower	**Fic**	Fusco, K. N. The wonder of Charlie Anne	**Fic**
Carlton, S. K. In the neighborhood of true	**Fic**	Gallico, P. The snow goose	**Fic**
Charles, T. Becoming Beatriz	**Fic**	Gansworth, E. L. Give me some truth	**Fic**
Charles, T. Like Vanessa	**Fic**	Gansworth, E. L. If I ever get out of here	**Fic**
Chee, T. We are not free	**Fic**	Gardner, S. The silver blade	**Fic**
Chibbaro, J. Deadly	**Fic**	Gaughen, A. C. Scarlet	**Fic**
Choldenko, G. Al Capone does my shirts	**Fic**	Gemeinhart, D. Some kind of courage	**Fic**
Cline-Ransome, L. Being Clem	**Fic**	Giff, P. R. Genevieve's war	**Fic**
Cline-Ransome, L. Leaving Lymon	**Fic**	Giff, P. R. Lily's crossing	**Fic**
Coats, J. A. The wicked and the just	**Fic**	Giff, P. R. Nory Ryan's song	**Fic**
Cooper, M. A brief history of Montmaray	**Fic**	Giff, P. R. A slip of a girl	**Fic**
Crowder, M. An uninterrupted view of the sky	**Fic**	Goldblatt, M. Twerp	**Fic**
Currier, K. S. Kai's journey to Gold Mountain	**Fic**	Gratz, A. Ground Zero	**Fic**
Curtis, C. P. Bud not Buddy	**Fic**	Gratz, A. Prisoner B-3087	**Fic**

McCaughrean, G. Where the world ends	**Fic**	Pileggi, L. Prisoner 88	**Fic**
McGuigan, M. A. Morning in a different place	**Fic**	Pinkney, A. D. Bird in a box	**Fic**
McKernan, V. The devil's paintbox	**Fic**	Pinkney, A. D. Loretta Little looks back	**Fic**
McKernan, V. Shackleton's stowaway	**Fic**	Pinkney, A. D. With the might of angels	**Fic**
McKinley, R. The outlaws of Sherwood	**Fic**	Powell, P. H. Loving vs. Virginia	**Fic**
McKissack, P. A friendship for today	**Fic**	Pratchett, T. Dodger	**Fic**
McKissack, P. Nzingha	**Fic**	Preus, M. Heart of a samurai	**Fic**
McManis, C. W. Indian no more	**Fic**	Preus, M. Shadow on the mountain	**Fic**
McMullan, M. How I found the Strong	**Fic**	Preus, M. Village of scoundrels	**Fic**
McMullan, M. Sources of light	**Fic**	Rhodes, J. P. Sugar	**Fic**
McMullan, M. When I crossed No-Bob	**Fic**	Richards, J. Three rivers rising	**Fic**
Meyer, L. A. Bloody Jack	**Fic**	Rose, C. S. May B.	**Fic**
Miller, S. E. The lost crown	**Fic**	Rosen, M. J. Sailing the unknown	**Fic**
Miller, S. E. Miss Spitfire	**Fic**	Rosenberg, M. This is just a test	**Fic**
Mobley, J. Katerina's wish	**Fic**	Ross, E. Belle epoque	**Fic**
Morpurgo, M. The day the world stopped turning	**Fic**	Roy, J. R. Yellow star	**Fic**
Morpurgo, M. Private Peaceful	**Fic**	Rundell, K. The wolf wilder	**Fic**
Morpurgo, M. War horse	**Fic**	Ryan, P. M. Echo	**Fic**
Napoli, D. J. Bound	**Fic**	Ryan, P. M. Esperanza rising	**Fic**
Napoli, D. J. Hush	**Fic**	Salisbury, G. Eyes of the emperor	**Fic**
Napoli, D. J. Stones in water	**Fic**	Savit, G. Anna and the Swallow Man	**Fic**
Nazemian, A. Like a love story	**Fic**	Schlitz, L. A. The hired girl	**Fic**
Nelson, V. M. No crystal stair	**Fic**	Schmidt, G. D. Just like that	**Fic**
Nesbet, A. Cloud and Wallfish	**Fic**	Schmidt, G. D. Lizzie Bright and the Buckminster boy	**Fic**
Nesbet, A. Daring Darleen queen of the screen	**Fic**	Schmidt, G. D. The Wednesday wars	**Fic**
Nielsen, J. A. Resistance	**Fic**	Schroder, M. My brother's shadow	**Fic**
Nolan, H. A summer of Kings	**Fic**	Selznick, B. The invention of Hugo Cabret	**Fic**
Northrop, M. Polaris	**Fic**	Selznick, B. The Marvels	**Fic**
Nunn, M. When the ground is hard	**Fic**	Sepetys, R. Between shades of gray	**Fic**
O'Dell, S. Streams to the river river to the sea	**Fic**	Sepetys, R. Salt to the sea	**Fic**
O'Sullivan, J. Between two skies	**Fic**	Shang, W. W. The way home looks now	**Fic**
Odhiambo, E. A. Auma's long run	**Fic**	Sharenow, R. The Berlin Boxing Club	**Fic**
Oppel, K. Half brother	**Fic**	Skrypuch, M. F. Making bombs for Hitler	**Fic**
Orlev, U. Run boy run	**Fic**	Smiley, J. The Georges and the Jewels	**Fic**
Park, L. S. Prairie lotus	**Fic**	Smith, I. Half spoon of rice	**Fic**
Park, L. S. A single shard	**Fic**	Smith, R. L. Hoodoo	**Fic**
Park, L. S. When my name was Keoko	**Fic**	Smith, S. L. Flygirl	**Fic**
Partridge, E. Dogtag summer	**Fic**	Speare, E. G. The witch of Blackbird Pond	**Fic**
Paterson, K. Bread and roses too	**Fic**	Spotswood, J. The radical element	**Fic**
Paterson, K. Lyddie	**Fic**	Stanley, D. Bella at midnight	**Fic**
Paulsen, G. Soldier's heart	**Fic**	Stone, P. The Romeo and Juliet code	**Fic**
Paulsen, G. Woods runner	**Fic**	Strange, L. The secret of Nightingale Wood	**Fic**
Pausewang, G. Dark hours	**Fic**	Tarshis, L. The battle of Gettysburg 1863	**Fic**
Pausewang, G. Traitor	**Fic**	Taylor, M. D. All the days past all the days to come	**Fic**
Pearsall, S. The seventh most important thing	**Fic**	Taylor, M. D. The friendship	**Fic**
Peck, R. Fair weather	**Fic**	Taylor, M. D. The gold Cadillac	**Fic**
Peck, R. A long way from Chicago	**Fic**	Taylor, M. D. The land	**Fic**
Peck, R. A season of gifts	**Fic**	Taylor, M. D. Let the circle be unbroken	**Fic**
Peck, R. The teacher's funeral	**Fic**	Taylor, M. D. The road to Memphis	**Fic**
Peck, R. A year down yonder	**Fic**	Taylor, M. D. Roll of thunder hear my cry	**Fic**
Peet, M. Tamar	**Fic**	Taylor, M. D. The well	**Fic**
Pellegrino, M. Journey of dreams	**Fic**	Thomas, S. The magnolia sword	**Fic**
Perkins, L. R. Criss cross	**Fic**	Thor, A. Deep sea	**Fic**
Philbrick, W. R. The mostly true adventures of Homer P. Figg	**Fic**	Thor, A. A faraway island	**Fic**
		Thor, A. The lily pond	**Fic**
Pierpoint, E. The last ride of Caleb O'Toole	**Fic**	Tingle, T. Danny Blackgoat Navajo prisoner	**Fic**
Pierpoint, E. The secret mission of William Tuck	**Fic**	Tingle, T. How I became a ghost	**Fic**

Tingle, T. When a ghost talks listen	**Fic**	Crew, H. S. Experiencing America's story through fiction	**813**
Tucker, L. All the Greys on Greene Street	**Fic**		
Twain, M. The prince and the pauper	**Fic**	**HISTORICAL GEOGRAPHY**	
Vanderpool, C. Moon over Manifest	**Fic**	Adams, S. The Kingfisher atlas of world history	**909**
Vawter, V. Copyboy	**Fic**	**HISTORICAL MUSEUMS -- DESIGN AND CONSTRUC-**	
Vawter, V. Paperboy	**Fic**	**TION**	
Venkatraman, P. Climbing the stairs	**Fic**	Bolden, T. How to build a museum	**973**
Vernick, S. R. The blood lie	**Fic**	**HISTORICAL MYSTERIES**	
Wallace, R. War and watermelon	**Fic**	Angleberger, T. Horton Halfpott or The fiendish mystery of	
Waller, S. B. A mad wicked folly	**Fic**	Smugwick Manor or The loosening of M'Lady Luggertuck's	
Walrath, D. Like water on stone	**Fic**	corset	**Fic**
Walter, J. My name is not Friday	**Fic**	Bryant, J. Kaleidoscope eyes	**Fic**
Walters, E. Broken strings	**Fic**	Bunce, E. C. Premeditated Myrtle	**Fic**
Warman, J. The world beneath	**Fic**	Choldenko, G. Chasing secrets	**Fic**
Watkins, Y. K. So far from the bamboo grove	**Fic**	Dowell, F. O. Dovey Coe	**Fic**
Wein, E. Black dove white raven	**Fic**	Dunlap, S. E. The musician's daughter	**Fic**
Wells, R. My Havana	**Fic**	Fitzgerald, L. M. The gallery	**Fic**
Whelan, G. All my noble dreams and then what happens	**Fic**	Fombelle, T. d. Between sky and earth	**Fic**
Whelan, G. Small acts of amazing courage	**Fic**	Gleason, C. The clockwork scarab	**Fic**
White, R. The treasure of Way Down Deep	**Fic**	Hoobler, D. The demon in the teahouse	**Fic**
White, R. Way Down Deep	**Fic**	Hoobler, D. The ghost in the Tokaido Inn	**Fic**
Wiechman, K. C. Like a river	**Fic**	Hoobler, D. Seven paths to death	**Fic**
Wiles, D. Anthem	**Fic**	Hoobler, D. The sword that cut the burning grass	**Fic**
Wiles, D. Countdown	**Fic**	Ibbotson, E. The star of Kazan	**Fic**
Wiles, D. Kent State	**Fic**	Landman, T. Hell and high water	**Fic**
Wiles, D. Revolution	**Fic**	Lawson, J. Nooks & crannies	**Fic**
Williams-Garcia, R. Gone crazy in Alabama	**Fic**	Lee, Y. S. The body at the tower	**Fic**
Williams-Garcia, R. One crazy summer	**Fic**	Lee, Y. S. A spy in the house	**Fic**
Williams-Garcia, R. P.S. be eleven	**Fic**	Pullman, P. Two crafty criminals!	**Fic**
Wilson, D. L. Black storm comin'	**Fic**	Ritter, W. The dire king	**Fic**
Wilson, D. L. Firehorse	**Fic**	Sedgwick, M. Revolver	**Fic**
Wilson, K. White Rose	**Fic**	Springer, N. The case of the bizarre bouquets	**Fic**
Winters, C. In the shadow of blackbirds	**Fic**	Springer, N. The case of the cryptic crinoline	**Fic**
Winthrop, E. Counting on Grace	**Fic**	Springer, N. The case of the gypsy goodbye	**Fic**
Wiseman, E. Puppet	**Fic**	Springer, N. The case of the left-handed lady	**Fic**
Wisler, G. C. Red Cap	**Fic**	Springer, N. The case of the missing marquess	**Fic**
Wolf, A. The watch that ends the night	**Fic**	Springer, N. The case of the peculiar pink fan	**Fic**
Wolk, L. Beyond the bright sea	**Fic**	Stevens, R. First class murder	**Fic**
Wolk, L. Echo Mountain	**Fic**	Stevens, R. Murder is bad manners	**Fic**
Wolk, L. Wolf Hollow	**Fic**	Stevens, R. Poison is not polite	**Fic**
Woodruff, E. Dear Austin	**Fic**	Voigt, C. The book of kings	**Fic**
Woodruff, E. The ravenmaster's secret	**Fic**	Voigt, C. The book of lost things	**Fic**
Woods, B. My name is Sally Little Song	**Fic**	Voigt, C. The book of secrets	**Fic**
Woods, B. The unsung hero of Birdsong USA	**Fic**	Weeks, S. Pie	**Fic**
Woodson, J. Feathers	**Fic**	Wegelius, J. The murderer's ape	**Fic**
Wright, B. Crow	**Fic**	Weil, C. I'm glad I did	**Fic**
Yang, D. J. Daughter of Xanadu	**Fic**	Wein, E. The pearl thief	**Fic**
Yelchin, E. Breaking Stalin's nose	**Fic**	Wolf, A. Who killed Christopher Goodman?	**Fic**
Yelchin, E. Spy runner	**Fic**	Zettel, S. A most dangerous deception	**Fic**
Yep, L. Dragonwings	**Fic**	**HISTORICAL ROMANCES**	
Yep, L. Hiroshima	**Fic**	Kindl, P. Keeping the castle	**Fic**
Yep, L. The star maker	**Fic**	**HISTORY**	
Yolen, J. Mapping the bones	**Fic**	Adams, S. The Kingfisher atlas of world history	**909**
Yolen, J. The queen's own fool	**Fic**	Brown, D. Older than dirt	**551.7**
Zail, S. Playing for the commandant	**Fic**	Connolly, S. The Americas and the Pacific	**970.004**
Zusak, M. The book thief	**Fic**	Eaton, G. A history of ambition in 50 hoaxes	**001.9**
HISTORICAL FICTION, AMERICAN		Fritz, J. Around the world in a hundred years	**920**

Preus, M. Village of scoundrels	Fic
Prins, M. Hidden like Anne Frank	**940.53**
Rappaport, D. Beyond courage	**940.53**
Rogasky, B. Smoke and ashes	**940.53**
Sender, R. M. The cage	**940.53**
Sharenow, R. The Berlin Boxing Club	Fic
Taylor, P. L. The secret of Priest's Grotto	**940.53**
Zail, S. Playing for the commandant	Fic

HOLOCAUST (1933-1945) -- CAUSES

Downing, D. Origins of the Holocaust	**940.53**
Rogasky, B. Smoke and ashes	**940.53**

HOLOCAUST (1933-1945) -- CHILDREN

Altman, L. J. Escape teens on the run	**940.53**
Altman, L. J. Hidden teens hidden lives	**940.53**
Altman, L. J. Shattered youth in Nazi Germany	**940.53**
Bartoletti, S. C. Hitler Youth	**943.086**
Boyne, J. The boy in the striped pajamas	Fic
Byers, A. Saving children from the Holocaust	**940.53**
Byers, A. Trapped	**940.53**
Hodge, D. Rescuing the children	**940.53**
Hopkinson, D. We must not forget	**940.53**
Kris. A bag of marbles	**741.5**
Levine, K. Hana's suitcase on stage	**940.53**
Leyson, L. The boy on the wooden box	**940.53**
Mazzeo, T. J. Irena's children	**940.53**
Prins, M. Hidden like Anne Frank	**940.53**
Rubin, S. G. The cat with the yellow star	**940.53**

HOLOCAUST (1933-1945) -- INFLUENCE

Rogasky, B. Smoke and ashes	**940.53**

HOLOCAUST SURVIVORS

Altman, L. J. Hidden teens hidden lives	**940.53**
Bornstein, M. Survivors club	**940.53**
Fitzgerald, L. M. Under the egg	Fic
Friedman, I. R. The other victims	**940.53**
Gratz, A. Prisoner B-3087	Fic
Hoffman, B. N. Liberation	**940.53**
Hopkinson, D. We must not forget	**940.53**
Perl, L. Four perfect pebbles	**940.53**
Roy, J. R. Yellow star	Fic
Rubin, S. G. The cat with the yellow star	**940.53**
Yolen, J. Briar Rose	Fic

HOLOCAUST VICTIMS

Friedman, I. R. The other victims	**940.53**

Holt, K. A.

Knockout	Fic
Redwood and Ponytail	Fic

Holt, Kimberly Willis

The water seeker	Fic
When Zachary Beaver came to town	Fic

HOLY LANCE

Gonzalez, C. D. Moving target	Fic

Holyoke, Nancy

A smart girl's guide money how to make it save it and spend it	**332.024**

Holyoke, Polly

The Neptune Project	Fic

Holzer, Harold

Father Abraham	**B**

HOME (CONCEPT)

Beatty, R. Willa of Dark Hollow	Fic
Cisneros, S. The house on Mango Street	Fic
DiCamillo, K. Beverly right here	Fic
Frost, H. Keesha's house	Fic
McManis, C. W. Indian no more	Fic
Padian, M. How to build a heart	Fic

HOME APPLIANCES

Arato, R. Design it	**745.2**
Home for the holidays. Frederick, H. V.	Fic
Home front. Samuels, C.	**940.53**
Home of the brave. Applegate, K.	Fic

HOME SCHOOLED BOYS

Davis, M. Superstar	Fic
Stead, R. Liar & spy	Fic

HOME SCHOOLED TEENAGE BOYS

Korman, G. Schooled	Fic

HOME SCHOOLED TEENAGE GIRLS

Hicks, F. E. Friends with boys	**741.5**
Martinez, J. Virtuosity	Fic

HOME SCHOOLING

Cavanaugh, N. J. This journal belongs to Ratchet	Fic
Korman, G. Schooled	Fic
Tolan, S. S. Surviving the Applewhites	Fic
Homeboyz. Sitomer, A. L.	Fic
Homecoming. Voigt, C.	Fic
Homeless bird. Whelan, G.	Fic

HOMELESS CHILDREN

Barratt, M. Joe Rat	Fic
Mulligan, A. Trash	Fic
Naidoo, B. The other side of truth	Fic
Phelan, M. Snow White	**741.5**
Pyron, B. The dogs of winter	Fic
Venkatraman, P. The bridge home	Fic

HOMELESS GIRLS

Avi. City of orphans	Fic
Cushman, K. The midwife's apprentice	Fic

HOMELESS PERSONS

Venkatraman, P. The bridge home	Fic
Wolk, L. Wolf Hollow	Fic

HOMELESS TEENAGE GIRLS

Takaya, N. Fruits basket	**741.5**

HOMELESS TEENAGERS

Hamilton, V. The planet of Junior Brown	Fic
Pratchett, T. Dodger	Fic
Schmidt, G. D. Just like that	Fic
Whelan, G. Homeless bird	Fic

HOMELESSNESS

Balliett, B. Hold fast	Fic
Bauer, J. Almost home	Fic
Jacobson, J. Paper things	Fic
Nielsen, S. No fixed address	Fic
O'Connor, B. How to steal a dog	Fic
Strasser, T. No place	Fic

Homer

The Iliad	**883**

America at war	**811.008**
Lives	**811.008**
My America	**811.008**
Pass the poetry please!	**372.64**
Hopkinson, Deborah	
A bandit's tale	**Fic**
D-Day	**940.54**
Dive!	**940.54**
The great trouble	**Fic**
Into the firestorm	**Fic**
Titanic	**910.91**
Up before daybreak	**331.7**
We must not forget	**940.53**
Hopkinson, Nalo	
The Chaos	**Fic**
HOPPER, EDWARD, 1882-1967	
Rubin, S. G. Edward Hopper	**B**
Hopping ahead of climate change. Collard, S. B.	**599.32**
Hopping, Lorraine Jean	
Bone detective	**B**
Chief Joseph	**B**
Horikoshi, Kohei, 1986-	
My hero academia	**741.5**
Horn, Geoffrey	
Environmental engineer	**628**
Hornby, Hugh	
Soccer	**796.334**
Horning, Kathleen T.	
From cover to cover	**028.1**
Horns and wrinkles. Helgerson, J.	**Fic**
Horowitz, Anthony, 1955-	
Death and the underworld	**398.28**
Evil star	**Fic**
The Falcon's Malteser	**Fic**
The Greek who stole Christmas	**Fic**
Heroes and villains	**398.22**
Necropolis	**Fic**
Never say die	**Fic**
Nightrise	**Fic**
Public enemy number two	**Fic**
Raven's gate	**Fic**
South by southeast	**Fic**
Stormbreaker	**741.5**
Three of diamonds	**Fic**
HOROWITZ, ANTHONY, 1955- STORMBREAKER	
Horowitz, A. Stormbreaker	**741.5**
HORROR	
Alender, K. The dead girls of Hysteria Hall	**Fic**
Almond, D. Clay	**Fic**
Arden, K. Dead voices	**Fic**
Auxier, J. The night gardener	**Fic**
Avi. The seer of shadows	**Fic**
Bachmann, S. The cabinet of curiosities	**Fic**
Baptiste, T. The jumbies	**Fic**
Baptiste, T. Rise of the jumbies	**Fic**
Beatty, R. Serafina and the twisted staff	**Fic**
Bick, I. J. Ashes	**Fic**

Black, H. Doll bones	**Fic**
Blake, K. Anna dressed in blood	**Fic**
Bradbury, R. Something wicked this way comes	**Fic**
Carman, P. The Crossbones	**Fic**
Carman, P. Skeleton Creek	**Fic**
Cohen, M. The Inn Between	**Fic**
Del Negro, J. Passion and poison	**Fic**
Delaney, J. The ghost prison	**Fic**
Delaney, J. A new darkness	**Fic**
Delaney, J. Revenge of the witch	**Fic**
Duncan, L. I know what you did last summer	**Fic**
Fleming, C. On the day I died	**Fic**
Fukuda, A. X. The prey	**Fic**
Funaro, G. The alchemist's shadow	**Fic**
Gratton, T. Strange grace	**Fic**
Hahn, M. D. One for sorrow	**Fic**
Hahn, M. D. Took	**Fic**
Hurston, Z. N. The skull talks back and other haunting tales	**Fic**
Kraus, D. At the edge of empire	**Fic**
Link, K. Monstrous affections	**Fic**
Lloyd-Jones, E. The bone houses	**Fic**
Maberry, J. Rot & Ruin	**Fic**
McKissack, P. The dark-thirty	**Fic**
McKissack, P. Porch lies	**Fic**
McMann, L. Cryer's cross	**Fic**
Nix, G. To hold the bridge	**Fic**
Northrop, M. Polaris	**Fic**
Noyes, D. The restless dead	**Fic**
Oh, E. Spirit hunters	**Fic**
Olson, A. N. Ask the bones	**Fic**
Olson, A. N. More bones	**Fic**
Oppel, K. The nest	**Fic**
Oppel, K. This dark endeavor	**Fic**
Parkhurst, L. S. The August House book of scary stories	**Fic**
Poblocki, D. The haunting of Gabriel Ashe	**Fic**
Poe, E. A. Edgar Allan Poe's tales of death and dementia	**Fic**
Poe, E. A. Edgar Allan Poe's tales of mystery and madness	**Fic**
Power, R. Wilder girls	**Fic**
Rich, S. Half-minute horrors	**Fic**
Ruiz Zafon, C. The prince of mist	**Fic**
San Souci, R. D. Dare to be scared	**Fic**
San Souci, R. D. Haunted houses	**Fic**
San Souci, R. D. A terrifying taste of short & shivery	**398.25**
Schwartz, A. More scary stories to tell in the dark	**Fic**
Schwartz, A. Scary stories 3	**Fic**
Schwartz, A. Scary stories to tell in the dark	**398.25**
Scieszka, J. Terrifying tales	**Fic**
Sedgwick, M. White crow	**Fic**
Smith, A. G. Death sentence	**Fic**
Smith, A. G. Lockdown	**Fic**
Smith, A. G. Solitary	**Fic**
Smith, R. L. Hoodoo	**Fic**
Stine, R. L. Fear	**Fic**
Summers, C. This is not a test	**Fic**

Rose, S. Respiratory system — 612.2
Somervill, B. A. The human body — 612
Thomas, M. The how and wow of the human body — 612
Walker, R. Dr. Frankenstein's human body book — 611
Walker, R. Human body — 612
Wicks, M. Human Body Theater — 612
Zuchora-Walske, C. Your head shape reveals your personality! — 610.9

HUMAN BODY -- MICROBIOLOGY
Hirsch, R. E. Microbiomes — 612

HUMAN BODY -- POLITICAL ASPECTS
Jensen, K. Body talk — 306.4

HUMAN BODY -- SOCIAL ASPECTS
Jensen, K. Body talk — 306.4
Human Body Theater. Wicks, M. — 612
Human body. Green, D. — 612
The **human** body. Newquist, H. P. — 610
The **human** body. Somervill, B. A. — 612
Human body. Walker, R. — 612

HUMAN ECOLOGY
Carson, M. K. Inside Biosphere 2 — 304.2
Chevat, R. Our choice — 363.738
Hudak, H. C. Pathways through Africa — 304.2
Hudak, H. C. Pathways through South America — 304.2
Miles, J. C. Pathways through Antarctica — 304.2
Miles, J. C. Pathways through Europe — 304.2
Morganelli, A. Pathways through Australia — 304.2
O'Brien, C. Pathways through North America — 304.2

HUMAN ECOLOGY -- ASIA
Auld, M. Pathways through Asia — 304.2

HUMAN EVOLUTION
Aronson, M. The skull in the rock — 569.9096822
Gamlin, L. Evolution — 576.8
Johnson, S. A. Shaking the foundation — 576.8
Stefoff, R. First humans — 569.9
Stefoff, R. Modern humans — 569.9
Thimmesh, C. Lucy long ago — 569.9
Walker, R. What is the theory of evolution? — 576.8

HUMAN EXPERIMENTATION IN MEDICINE
Gagnon, M. Don't let go — Fic
Gagnon, M. Don't look now — Fic
Gagnon, M. Don't turn around — Fic
LeZotte, A. C. Show me a sign — Fic
Melchior-Durand, S. The golden compass — 741.5
Patterson, J. The angel experiment — Fic
Shiga, J. Meanwhile — 741.5

HUMAN EXPERIMENTATION IN MEDICINE -- HISTORY
Uschan, M. V. The Tuskegee experiments — 174.2
Wittenstein, V. O. For the good of mankind? — 174.2

HUMAN GENOME
Simpson, K. Genetics — 576.5
Human movement. Mooney, C. — 612

HUMAN NATURE
Golding, W. Lord of the flies — Fic
Myers, W. D. Sunrise over Fallujah — Fic
Szpirglas, J. You just can't help it! — 599.9

HUMAN PHYSIOLOGY
Arbuthnott, G. What makes you you? — 572.8
Bennett, H. J. The fantastic body — 612
Goddard, J. Inside the human body — 612
Macaulay, D. The way we work — 612
Newquist, H. P. The human body — 610
Roberts, A. M. The complete human body — 611
Rose, S. Circulatory system — 612.1
Rose, S. Muscular system — 612.7
Rose, S. Nervous system — 612.8
Rose, S. Respiratory system — 612.2
Rose, S. Skeletal system — 612.75
Siy, A. Sneeze! — 612.2
Somervill, B. A. The human body — 612
Thomas, M. The how and wow of the human body — 612
Walker, R. Dr. Frankenstein's human body book — 611
Walker, R. Human body — 612
Wicks, M. Human Body Theater — 612
Zuchora-Walske, C. Your head shape reveals your personality! — 610.9

HUMAN POPULATION GENETICS
Stefoff, R. Modern humans — 569.9

HUMAN REMAINS (ARCHAEOLOGY)
Deem, J. M. Bodies from the bog — 569.9
Deem, J. M. Faces from the past — 599.9
Halls, K. M. Mysteries of the mummy kids — 393
Huey, L. M. Forgotten bones — 306.3
Kirkpatrick, K. Mysterious bones — 979.7
Liu-Perkins, C. At home in her tomb — 931
Rubalcaba, J. Every bone tells a story — 930.1
Walker, S. M. Their skeletons speak — 970.01
Walker, S. M. Written in bone — 614

HUMAN REPRODUCTION
Rand, C. Human reproduction — 612.6
Human reproduction. Rand, C. — 612.6

HUMAN RIGHTS
Amnesty International. Free? — Fic
Gitlin, M. Transgender rights — 323.3
Robinson, M. Every human has rights — 323

HUMAN RIGHTS (INTERNATIONAL LAW)
Robinson, M. Every human has rights — 323

HUMAN SACRIFICE
Barnhill, K. R. The girl who drank the moon — Fic
Gratton, T. Strange grace — Fic
Levine, G. C. Ever — Fic
Orr, W. Dragonfly song — Fic

HUMAN SETTLEMENTS
Armstrong, J. The American story — 973

HUMAN SETTLEMENTS -- HISTORY
Moore, C. From then to now — 909

HUMAN SKIN COLOR
Williams, A. Genesis begins again — Fic

HUMAN SKIN COLOR -- SOCIAL ASPECTS
Nunn, M. When the ground is hard — Fic

HUMAN TRAFFICKING
Polonsky, A. Threads — Fic

HUMAN-ALIEN ENCOUNTERS

HUMOROUS STORIES

Adams, D. The hitchhiker's guide to the galaxy	Fic
Adams, S. J. Sparks	Fic
Anderson, M. T. He laughed with his other mouths	Fic
Anderson, M. T. Whales on stilts!	Fic
Barnes, J. Perfect cover	Fic
Barnett, M. The terrible two	Fic
Barnett, M. The terrible two get worse	Fic
Bird, B. Funny girl	Fic
Birdsall, J. The Penderwicks	Fic
Birdsall, J. The Penderwicks at Point Mouette	Fic
Birdsall, J. The Penderwicks on Gardam Street	Fic
Boniface, W. The great powers outage	Fic
Boniface, W. The hero revealed	Fic
Boniface, W. The return of Meteor Boy?	Fic
Bradley, A. 24 girls in 7 days	Fic
Bray, L. Beauty queens	Fic
Byars, B. C. The dark stairs	Fic
Chao, G. American panda	Fic
Chilton, A. S. The goblin's puzzle	Fic
Clark, H. What we found in the sofa (and how it saved the world)	Fic
Crutcher, C. Deadline	Fic
Ferris, J. Once upon a Marigold	Fic
Ferris, J. Twice upon a Marigold	Fic
Foley, L. K. Remarkable	Fic
French, V. The robe of skulls	Fic
Gantos, J. Jack's black book	Fic
Gantos, J. The trouble in me	Fic
Grabenstein, C. The smartest kid in the universe	Fic
Greenwald, T. Charlie Joe Jackson's guide to summer vacation	Fic
Gutman, D. Miss Daisy is crazy!	Fic
Harper, C. M. Alien encounter	Fic
Healy, C. The hero's guide to saving your kingdom	Fic
Horowitz, A. The Falcon's Malteser	Fic
Horowitz, A. The Greek who stole Christmas	Fic
Horowitz, A. Public enemy number two	Fic
Horowitz, A. South by southeast	Fic
Horowitz, A. Three of diamonds	Fic
Ibbotson, E. The Ogre of Oglefort	Fic
Jennings, P. Odd weird & little	Fic
Jennings, R. W. Ghost town	Fic
Jones, D. W. Howl's moving castle	Fic
Jones, D. W. The tough guide to Fantasyland	Fic
Kim, J. Stand up Yumi Chung!	Fic
Kinney, J. The deep end	Fic
Klise, K. Regarding the bathrooms	Fic
Klise, K. Regarding the fountain	Fic
Klise, K. Regarding the sink	Fic
Klise, K. Regarding the trees	Fic
Koertge, R. Stoner & Spaz	Fic
LaRocca, R. Midsummer's mayhem	Fic
Levy, D. A. The family Fletcher takes Rock Island	Fic
Levy, D. A. This would make a good story someday	Fic
McKissack, P. Porch lies	Fic
Patterson, J. House of robots	Fic

Peck, R. Fair weather	Fic
Peck, R. A season of gifts	Fic
Peck, R. The teacher's funeral	Fic
Perl, E. S. The capybara conspiracy	Fic
Petrucha, S. Teen Inc.	Fic
Pierson, D. C. The boy who couldn't sleep and never had to	Fic
Pinkwater, D. M. Bushman lives!	Fic
Pinkwater, D. M. The Neddiad	Fic
Pratchett, T. The amazing Maurice and his educated rodents	Fic
Pratchett, T. Dodger	Fic
Pratchett, T. I shall wear midnight	Fic
Pratchett, T. Only you can save mankind	Fic
Pratchett, T. The Wee Free Men	Fic
Pullman, P. Two crafty criminals!	Fic
Rex, A. Smek for president!	Fic
Rex, A. The true meaning of Smekday	Fic
Rodgers, M. Freaky Friday	Fic
Rubens, M. Sons of the 613	Fic
Sanderson, B. Alcatraz versus the evil librarians	Fic
Sanderson, B. The dark talent	Fic
Scieszka, J. Funny business	Fic
Shurtliff, L. Rump	Fic
Svingen, A. The ballad of a broken nose	Fic
Teague, M. The doom machine	Fic
Twain, M. The adventures of Tom Sawyer	Fic
Van de Ruit, J. Spud	Fic
Vande Velde, V. Cloaked in red	Fic
Vernon, U. Castle Hangnail	Fic

HUMOROUS WRITING

Marcus, L. S. Funny business	813

HUMPBACK WHALE

O'Connell, J. The Eye of the Whale	599.5

Humphreys, Cathy

Making number talks matter	510.71

Humphreys, Jessica Dee

Child soldier	B
Hundred percent. Young, K. R.	Fic

HUNGARIAN AMERICANS

Carlson, L. M. Harry Houdini for kids	793.8

HUNGARY

Eves, R. Blood rose rebellion	Fic
Wiseman, E. Puppet	Fic

HUNGARY -- INTERETHNIC RELATIONS

Jackson, L. E. B. I have lived a thousand years	940.53

HUNGER

Duey, K. Skin hunger	Fic
Grant, M. Hunger	Fic
Lyons, M. E. Feed the children first	941.5081
Senker, C. Poverty and hunger	362.5
Hunger. Grant, M.	Fic
The Hunger Games. Collins, S.	Fic
Hungry hearts. Chapman, E.	Fic

HUNS -- HISTORY

Hinds, K. Huns	936
Huns. Hinds, K.	936

HYPERACTIVE CHILDREN -- EDUCATION

Rief, S. F. How to reach & teach children & teens with AD-DADHD   **371.94**

HYPNOTICS

Walker, I. Sedatives and hypnotics   **615.7**

HYPNOTISM

Byng, G. Molly Moon's incredible book of hypnotism   **Fic**

I

I am a SEAL Team Six warrior. Wasdin, H. E.   **B**

I am Malala. Yousafzai, M.   **B**

I am not Joey Pigza. Gantos, J.   **Fic**

I am Phoenix. Fleischman, P.   **811**

I am Princess X. Priest, C.   **Fic**

I am Scout. Shields, C. J.   **B**

I am still alive. Marshall, K. A.   **Fic**

I am the darker brother. Adoff, A.   **811**

I and I. Medina, T.   **B**

I can make this promise. Day, C.   **Fic**

I can't keep my own secrets. Fershleiser, R.   **808**

I Claudia. McCoy, M.   **Fic**

I don't want to be crazy. Schutz, S.   **B**

I Emma Freke. Atkinson, E. J.   **Fic**

I feel a little jumpy around you. Nye, N. S.   **808.81**

I found a dead bird. Thornhill, J.   **306.9**

I have lived a thousand years. Jackson, L. E. B.   **940.53**

I know what you did last summer. Duncan, L.   **Fic**

I lived on Butterfly Hill. Agosin, M.   **Fic**

I love you so mochi. Kuhn, S.   **Fic**

I once was a monkey. Lee, J. M.   **294.3**

I predict a riot. Bruton, C.   **Fic**

I read it but I don't get it. Tovani, C.   **428.4**

I robot. Asimov, I.   **Fic**

I shall wear midnight. Pratchett, T.   **Fic**

I too sing America. Clinton, C.   **811**

I want to live. Lugovskaya, N.   **947.084**

I will always write back. Alifirenka, C.   **305.235**

I will plant you a lilac tree. Hillman, L.   **B**

I'd tell you I love you but then I'd have to kill you. Carter, A.   **Fic**

I'll ask you three times are you ok? Nye, N. S.   **811**

I'll be there. Sloan, H. G.   **Fic**

I'll get there it better be worth the trip. Donovan, J.   **Fic**

I'm glad I did. Weil, C.   **Fic**

I'm with stupid. Herbach, G.   **Fic**

I.M. Pei. Rubalcaba, J.   **720.92**

I.M. Pei. Slavicek, L. C.   **B**

Ibbotson, Eva

The dragonfly pool   **Fic**

The Ogre of Oglefort   **Fic**

The star of Kazan   **Fic**

ICE

Pringle, L. Ice!   **338.09**

Ice. Buller, L.   **577.0911**

Ice. Durst, S. B.   **Fic**

Ice breaker. Tanner, L.   **Fic**

Ice claw. Gilman, D.   **Fic**

Ice dogs. Johnson, T. L.   **Fic**

ICE HARVESTING

Pringle, L. Ice!   **338.09**

Ice hockey. Sharp, A. W.   **796.962**

ICE INDUSTRY AND TRADE -- HISTORY

Pringle, L. Ice!   **338.09**

ICE MANUFACTURE

Pringle, L. Ice!   **338.09**

ICE SKATING

McDougall, C. Girls play to win figure skating   **796.91**

Shen, E. L. The comeback   **Fic**

Ice time. McKinley, M.   **796.355**

Ice! Pringle, L.   **338.09**

Iceberg right ahead! McPherson, S. S.   **910.91**

ICEBERGS

Tanner, L. Ice breaker   **Fic**

The icebound land. Flanagan, J.   **Fic**

Icecore. Whyman, M.   **Fic**

Icefall. Kirby, M. J.   **Fic**

Icefire. D'Lacey, C.   **Fic**

ID AL-FITR

Jeffrey, L. S. Celebrate Ramadan   **297.3**

Ida M. Tarbell. McCully, E. A.   **B**

IDAHO

Crutcher, C. Deadline   **Fic**

Hand, C. The how & the why   **Fic**

Kent, D. Idaho   **979.6**

Pileggi, L. Prisoner 88   **Fic**

Reichs, B. Chrysalis   **Fic**

Reichs, B. Genesis   **Fic**

Stefoff, R. Idaho   **979.6**

Idaho. Kent, D.   **979.6**

Idaho. Stefoff, R.   **979.6**

Ideas that changed the world. Ferris, J.   **609**

IDENTICAL TWINS

French, V. The robe of skulls   **Fic**

IDENTITY (PSYCHOLOGY)

Abdel-Fattah, R. Does my head look big in this?   **Fic**

Abdel-Fattah, R. Ten things I hate about me   **Fic**

Alexander, L. Taran Wanderer   **Fic**

Anderson, J. D. Sidekicked   **Fic**

Avi. Crispin   **Fic**

Baldwin, J. Go tell it on the mountain   **Fic**

Barton, C. Can I see your I.D.?   **001.9**

Beatty, R. Serafina and the twisted staff   **Fic**

Bedford, M. Flip   **Fic**

Blumenthal, D. Mafia girl   **Fic**

Boteju, T. Kings queens and in-betweens   **Fic**

Brignull, I. The hawkweed prophecy   **Fic**

Budhos, M. T. The long ride   **Fic**

Cabot, M. The princess diaries   **Fic**

Catmull, K. The radiant road   **Fic**

Chanani, N. Pashmina   **741.5**

Day, C. I can make this promise   **Fic**

Dessen, S. What happened to goodbye   **Fic**

DiTerlizzi, T. A hero for WondLa   **Fic**

Hurwitz, M. W. The summer I saved the world-- in 65 days Fic
Levine, K. The paper cowboy Fic
Mills, E. Famous in a small town Fic
Park, L. S. Project Mulberry Fic
Peck, R. A long way from Chicago Fic
Peck, R. A season of gifts Fic
Peck, R. A year down yonder Fic
Perez, C. C. The first rule of punk Fic
Polonsky, A. Threads Fic
Raskin, E. The Westing game Fic

ILLINOIS -- HISTORY -- 19TH CENTURY
Bennie, P. The Great Chicago Fire of 1871 977.3
Illinois. Burgan, M. 977.3

ILLITERACY
Schmatz, P. Bluefish Fic
Illuminae. Kaufman, A. Fic

ILLUSTRATED BOOKS
Agard, J. The young inferno 811
Almond, D. Half a creature from the sea Fic
Alston, B. Amari and the night brothers Fic
Angleberger, T. Darth Paper strikes back Fic
Angleberger, T. Emperor Pickletine rides the bus Fic
Angleberger, T. Princess Labelmaker to the rescue! Fic
Angleberger, T. The strange case of Origami Yoda Fic
Barnett, M. The terrible two Fic
Barnett, M. The terrible two get worse Fic
Barton, C. Can I see your I.D.? 001.9
Blackburn, S. Philosophers 109
Carey, E. Heap House Fic
Cohen, M. The Inn Between Fic
Cross, G. The Iliad Fic
DiCamillo, K. Flora & Ulysses Fic
Emond, S. Bright lights dark nights Fic
Erdrich, L. Makoons Fic
Gaiman, N. The graveyard book Fic
Gaiman, N. Hansel & Gretel 398.20943
Gaiman, N. MirrorMask Fic
Holm, J. L. Middle school is worse than meatloaf Fic
Ignotofsky, R. Women in sports 796.092
Kinney, J. Cabin fever Fic
Kinney, J. Diary of a wimpy kid Fic
Kinney, J. Dog days Fic
Kinney, J. Hard luck Fic
Kinney, J. The last straw Fic
Kinney, J. The long haul Fic
Kinney, J. Old school Fic
Kinney, J. Rodrick rules Fic
Kinney, J. The third wheel Fic
Kinney, J. The ugly truth Fic
Krosoczka, J. The frog who croaked Fic
Kyi, T. L. Shadow warrior Fic
Lee, S. Convergence Fic
Lin, G. When the sea turned to silver Fic
Messner, K. The Mayflower 974.4
Messner, K. Pearl Harbor 940.54
Moberg, J. Historical animals 590.9

Montgomery, H. L. Who gives a poop? 612.3
Morpurgo, M. Half a man Fic
Napoli, D. J. Tales from the Arabian nights 398.2
Ness, P. A monster calls Fic
Oppel, K. The nest Fic
Park, L. S. The one thing you'd save Fic
Patterson, J. Homeroom diaries Fic
Powell, P. H. Loving vs. Virginia Fic
Rapunzel and other magic fairy tales 398.22
Rex, A. Smek for president! Fic
Rex, A. The true meaning of Smekday Fic
Riggs, R. Hollow City Fic
Riggs, R. Library of souls Fic
Riggs, R. A map of days Fic
Riggs, R. Miss Peregrine's home for peculiar children Fic
Riggs, R. Tales of the Peculiar Fic
Rosen, M. J. The tale of rescue Fic
Ryan, P. M. The dreamer Fic
Saujani, R. Girls who code 005.1
Scarlet, J. Superhero therapy 616.85
Sidman, J. What the heart knows 811
Smy, P. Thornhill Fic
Stevenson, R. My body my choice 362.1988
Stewart, T. L. The secret keepers Fic
Tamaki, M. Unicorn power! Fic
Tan, S. The singing bones 730.92
Tan, S. Tales from outer suburbia Fic
Tan, S. Tales from the inner city Fic
Tate, N. Choosing to live choosing to die 179.7
Townley, R. The blue shoe Fic
Tripp, B. The accidental highwayman Fic
Tucker, L. All the Greys on Greene Street Fic
Vernon, U. Castle Hangnail Fic
Vivat, B. Frazzled Fic
Wegelius, J. The murderer's ape Fic
Yelchin, E. Breaking Stalin's nose Fic
Yolen, J. Bad girls 920
Illustrated dictionary of the Muslim world.. Marshall Cavendish Reference. 297.03

ILLUSTRATION
Tan, S. The bird king 741.64092

ILLUSTRATION OF BOOKS
Artist to artist 741.6
Tan, S. The bird king 741.64092
The **illustrator's** notebook. Ellabbad, M. 741.6

ILLUSTRATORS
Artist to artist 741.6
Ellabbad, M. The illustrator's notebook 741.6
Tan, S. The bird king 741.64092

IMAGE
Westerfeld, S. Extras Fic
Westerfeld, S. Specials Fic
Westerfeld, S. Uglies Fic

IMAGINARY CREATURES
Anderson, J. L. My diary from the edge of the world Fic
Arntson, S. The wikkeling Fic
Avery, T. Not as we know it Fic

Cabot, M. All-American girl — Fic
Cain, S. Quiet power — **155.4**
Carter, A. Only the good spy young — **Fic**
Dowell, F. O. The class — **Fic**
Forman, G. Where she went — **Fic**
Frederick, H. V. Dear pen pal — **Fic**
Frederick, H. V. Home for the holidays — **Fic**
Frederick, H. V. The Mother-Daughter Book Club — **Fic**
Frederick, H. V. Much ado about Anne — **Fic**
Frederick, H. V. Pies & prejudice — **Fic**
Frost, H. Keesha's house — **Fic**
Giles, L. R. Spin — **Fic**
Ginsberg, B. Episodes — **616.858820092**
Green, T. New kid — **Fic**
Greenwald, T. Charlie Joe Jackson's guide to summer vacation — **Fic**
Harris, A. R. Cliques crushes & true friends — **155.5**
Hirahara, N. 1001 cranes — **Fic**
Holt, K. A. Redwood and Ponytail — **Fic**
Horvath, P. One year in Coal Harbor — **Fic**
Jackson, D. M. Every body's talking — **153.6**
Johnson, A. Sweet hereafter — **Fic**
Kade, S. The rules — **Fic**
Kelly, E. E. We dream of space — **Fic**
Mandanna, S. Color outside the lines — **Fic**
Mass, W. Every soul a star — **Fic**
Mercado, N. E. Every man for himself — **Fic**
Metzger, J. G. Will puberty last my whole life? — **613**
Owens, L. L. Frenemies — **155.5**
Pearsall, S. All of the above — **Fic**
Perkins, L. R. Criss cross — **Fic**
Pratchett, T. Nation — **Fic**
Reynolds, J. Look both ways — **Fic**
Stefanski, D. How to talk to an autistic kid — **618.92**
Steffens, B. Thinking critically — **384.5**
Telgemeier, R. Kristy's great idea — **741.5**
Telgemeier, R. Sisters — **306.875**
Teller, J. Nothing — **Fic**
Vawter, V. Paperboy — **Fic**
Ward, R. The chaos — **Fic**
Watkins, C. Addiction — **362.29**
Wells, R. E. Variant — **Fic**
Whittemore, J. Odd girl in — **Fic**
Woodson, J. Harbor me — **Fic**

INTERPERSONAL RELATIONS IN CHILDREN
Fox, A. Real friends vs. the other kind — **177**

INTERRACIAL ADOPTION
Kent, R. Kimchi & calamari — **Fic**
Lockington, M. For black girls like me — **Fic**

INTERRACIAL DATING
Emond, S. Bright lights dark nights — **Fic**

INTERRACIAL FAMILIES
Carter, C. Forever or a long long time — **Fic**
Gibney, S. See no color — **Fic**
Krishnaswami, U. Step up to the plate Maria Singh — **Fic**

INTERRACIAL FRIENDSHIP
Frank, S. Armstrong and Charlie — **Fic**

Fusco, K. N. The wonder of Charlie Anne — **Fic**
Hughes, D. Missing in action — **Fic**
MacColl, M. Promise the night — **Fic**
McGuigan, M. A. Morning in a different place — **Fic**
McKissack, P. A friendship for today — **Fic**
Myracle, L. Luv ya bunches — **Fic**
Park, L. S. Project Mulberry — **Fic**
Schmidt, G. D. Lizzie Bright and the Buckminster boy — **Fic**
Taylor, M. D. The road to Memphis — **Fic**
Taylor, T. The cay — **Fic**
Volponi, P. Black and white — **Fic**
Woodruff, E. Dear Austin — **Fic**
Woodson, J. Feathers — **Fic**

INTERRACIAL MARRIAGE
Brimner, L. D. Finding a way home — **346.7301**
Powell, P. H. Loving vs. Virginia — **Fic**
Taylor, M. D. All the days past all the days to come — **Fic**

INTERRACIAL ROMANCE
Mandanna, S. Color outside the lines — **Fic**
Woodson, J. If you come softly — **Fic**

INTERSECTIONALITY
Mendoza, J. An indigenous peoples' history of the United States for young people — **970.004**
Nijkamp, M. Unbroken — **Fic**
Schatz, K. Rad American women A-Z — **920.72**
Schatz, K. Rad women worldwide — **920**

INTERSEXUALITY
Kuklin, S. Beyond magenta — **306.76**
Interstellar pig. Sleator, W. — **Fic**

INTESTINES
Donovan, S. Rumble & spew — **612.3**
Viola, J. Digestive system — **612.3**
Into the clouds. Olson, T. — **796.522095491**
Into the firestorm. Hopkinson, D. — **Fic**
Into the tall tall grass. Ryon, L. — **Fic**
Into the unknown. Ross, S. — **910.9**
Into the Wild. Durst, S. B. — **Fic**
Into the wild. Hunter, E. — **Fic**
Into the woods. Gardner, L. — **Fic**
Into the world of the dead. Boughn, M. — **202**

INTRIGUE
Carter, A. All fall down — **Fic**
Eves, R. Blood rose rebellion — **Fic**
Hardinge, F. The lost conspiracy — **Fic**
An **introduction** to collection development for school librarians. Kerby, M. — **025.2**
Introduction to rubrics. Stevens, D. D. — **371.27**

INTRODUCTORY CLASSICS
Appignanesi, R. Romeo and Juliet — **741.5**
Hinds, G. The merchant of Venice — **741.5**

INTROVERSION
Cain, S. Quiet power — **155.4**

INTROVERTS
Cain, S. Quiet power — **155.4**
Roat, S. H. How to disappear — **Fic**

INTUITION
Jackson, D. M. Phenomena — **152.1**

Woodruff, E. The ravenmaster's secret — Fic

JACOBS, HARRIET, 1818-1896

Lyons, M. E. Letters from a slave girl — Fic

JACOBS, JANE, 1916-2006

Lang, G. Genius of common sense — B

JACOBS, JOSEPH, B. 1829

Lyons, M. E. Letters from a slave boy — Fic

Jacobs, Thomas A.

Every vote matters — 342.7308

They broke the law you be the judge — 345.73

Jacobson, Jennifer, 1958-

Paper things — Fic

Small as an elephant — Fic

Jacques, Brian

The angel's command — Fic

Castaways of the Flying Dutchman — Fic

Mariel of Redwall — Fic

Martin the Warrior — Fic

Mattimeo — Fic

Mossflower — Fic

Pearls of Lutra — Fic

Redwall — Fic

Redwall the graphic novel — 741.5

Salamandastron — Fic

Jaffe, Nina

The cow of no color — Fic

JAGUAR

Gale, E. K. The Zoo at the Edge of the World — Fic

Gish, M. Jaguars — 599.75

JAILS

Volponi, P. Rikers High — Fic

James Houston's treasury of Inuit legends. Houston, J. — 398.2089

James Monroe. Naden, C. J. — B

James, Anna (Anna Lois)

The bookwanderers — Fic

The lost fairy tales — Fic

James, Helen Foster, 1951-

Paper son — Fic

JAMES, LEBRON

Wetzel, D. LeBron James — B

Yasuda, A. LeBron James — B

JAMESTOWN, VIRGINIA -- HISTORY

Huey, L. M. American archaeology uncovers the earliest English colonies — 973.2

Walker, S. M. Written in bone — 614

Jamieson, Victoria

All's faire in middle school — 741.5

Roller girl — 741.5

When stars are scattered — B

Jane Addams. Fradin, J. B. — B

Jane against the world. Blumenthal, K. — 342.7308

Jane Austen. Reef, C. — B

Jane Goodall and Mary Leakey. Anniss, M. — B

Jane the fox and me. Britt, F. — 741.5

Jane unlimited. Cashore, K. — Fic

Janeczko, Paul B.

The dark game — 327.73

The death of the hat — 808.81

A foot in the mouth — 821.008

A kick in the head — 811.008

The place my words are looking for — 811.008

A poke in the I — 811.008

Requiem — 811

Seeing the blue between — 811

Writing winning reports and essays — 808

Janice VanCleave's engineering for every kid. VanCleave, J. P. — 620.0078

Janie face to face. Cooney, C. B. — Fic

Jankeliowitch, Anne

Kids who are changing the world — 363.7092

January, Brendan, 1972-

Cryptocurrencies and the blockchain revolution — 332.4

Native American art & culture — 704.03

JAPAN

Ahdieh, R. Flame in the mist — Fic

Appignanesi, R. Romeo and Juliet — 741.5

Benwell, F. The last leaves falling — Fic

Bjorklund, R. Japan — 952

Donwerth-Chikamatsu, A. Beyond me — Fic

Furudate, H. Haikyu!! — 741.5

Hoobler, D. The demon in the teahouse — Fic

Hoobler, D. The ghost in the Tokaido Inn — Fic

Hoobler, D. Seven paths to death — Fic

Hoobler, D. The sword that cut the burning grass — Fic

Horikoshi, K. My hero academia — 741.5

Hotta, Y. Hikaru no Go — 741.5

Kadohata, C. A place to belong — Fic

Kuhn, S. I love you so mochi — Fic

Kyi, T. L. Shadow warrior — Fic

Langeland, D. Meltdown — 363.17

Lu, M. Warcross — Fic

Lu, M. Wildcard — Fic

Somervill, B. A. Japan — 952

Thompson, H. The language inside — Fic

Thompson, H. Tomo — Fic

Uehashi, N. Moribito — Fic

Uehashi, N. Moribito II — Fic

Watkins, Y. K. So far from the bamboo grove — Fic

JAPAN -- FOREIGN RELATIONS -- UNITED STATES

Blumberg, R. Commodore Perry in the land of the Shogun — 952

Preus, M. Heart of a samurai — Fic

JAPAN -- HISTORY

Hartz, P. Shinto — 299.5

Niz, X. Samurai — 952

JAPAN -- HISTORY -- 1945-

Grant, R. G. Why did Hiroshima happen? — 940.54

JAPAN -- HISTORY -- TOKUGAWA PERIOD, 1600-1868

Turnbull, S. R. The most daring raid of the samurai — 952

JAPAN -- RELIGION

Hartz, P. Shinto — 299.5

JAPAN -- SOCIAL LIFE AND CUSTOMS

Moore, W. All about Japan — 952

Walters, E. Broken strings	Fic
Weissman, E. B. The length of a string	Fic
Jewish holiday origami. Stern, J.	736
JEWISH HOLIDAYS	
Kimmel, E. A. Wonders and miracles	296.4
JEWISH MEN	
Finkelstein, N. H. Schools of hope	371.829
JEWISH RESISTANCE AND REVOLTS	
Batalion, J. The light of days	940.53
Fishkin, R. L. Heroes of the Holocaust	940.53
Nielsen, J. A. Resistance	Fic
Rappaport, D. Beyond courage	940.53
JEWISH TEENAGE BOYS	
Sharenow, R. The Berlin Boxing Club	Fic
Vernick, S. R. The blood lie	Fic
JEWISH TEENAGE GIRLS	
Alban, A. Anya's war	Fic
Aldredge, B. Sasquatch love and other imaginary things	Fic
DeWoskin, R. Someday we will fly	Fic
Frank, A. The diary of a young girl	940.53
Friesner, E. M. Threads and flames	Fic
Matas, C. After the war	Fic
Nielsen, J. A. Resistance	Fic
Sender, R. M. The cage	940.53
JEWISH TEENAGERS	
Altman, L. J. Escape teens on the run	940.53
Andrews, J. Me and Earl and the dying girl	Fic
Locke, K. It's a whole spiel	Fic
JEWISH TEENAGERS -- HISTORY 20TH CENTURY	
Altman, L. J. Shattered youth in Nazi Germany	940.53
JEWISH WAY OF LIFE	
Locke, K. It's a whole spiel	Fic
Oberman, S. Solomon and the ant	398.2
Rosinsky, N. M. Judaism	296
JEWISH WOMEN	
Batalion, J. The light of days	940.53
Sender, R. M. The cage	940.53
JEWS	
Bornstein, M. Survivors club	940.53
Iturbe, A. The librarian of Auschwitz	Fic
Lowry, L. Number the stars	Fic
North, P. Starglass	Fic
Oberman, S. Solomon and the ant	398.2
Perl, L. Four perfect pebbles	940.53
Preus, M. Village of scoundrels	Fic
Rubens, M. Sons of the 613	Fic
Thor, A. Deep sea	Fic
Yolen, J. Mapping the bones	Fic
JEWS -- PERSECUTIONS	
Deem, J. M. Auschwitz	940.53
Deem, J. M. Kristallnacht	940.53
Frank, A. The diary of a young girl	940.53
Jackson, L. E. B. I have lived a thousand years	940.53
Levine, G. C. A ceiling made of eggshells	Fic
Levy, D. The year of goodbyes	811
Meltzer, M. Rescue	940.53
Nielsen, J. A. Resistance	Fic

Perl, L. Four perfect pebbles	940.53
Wiseman, E. Puppet	Fic
JEWS -- PERSECUTIONS -- HISTORY	
Downing, D. Origins of the Holocaust	940.53
JEWS, CZECH	
Iturbe, A. The librarian of Auschwitz	Fic
Thomson, R. Terezin	940.53
JEWS, DUTCH	
Reiss, J. The upstairs room	Fic
JEWS, EUROPEAN	
Hoffman, B. N. Liberation	940.53
JEWS, EUROPEAN -- HISTORY 20TH CENTURY	
Rogasky, B. Smoke and ashes	940.53
JEWS, EUROPEAN -- RELATIONS WITH GENTILES	
Meltzer, M. Rescue	940.53
JEWS, GERMAN	
Fox, A. L. Ten thousand children	940.53
Gillette, R. H. Escape to Virginia	975.5
JEWS, GERMAN -- HISTORY 1933-1945	
Fox, A. L. Ten thousand children	940.53
JEWS, POLISH	
Batalion, J. The light of days	940.53
Leyson, L. The boy on the wooden box	940.53
Mazzeo, T. J. Irena's children	940.53
Orlev, U. Run boy run	Fic
JEWS, POLISH -- HISTORY	
Altman, L. J. The Warsaw Ghetto Uprising	940.53
JEWS, RUSSIAN	
Lewis, J. P. Self-portrait with seven fingers	811
JEWS, UKRAINIAN -- HISTORY	
Taylor, P. L. The secret of Priest's Grotto	940.53
Jiang, Ji-Li	
Red scarf girl	B
JIANG, JI-LI, 1954-	
Jiang, J. Red scarf girl	B
Jim & me. Gutman, D.	Fic
Jim Thorpe. Labrecque, E.	B
JIMENEZ, FRANCISCO, 1943-	
Jimenez, F. The circuit	Fic
Jimenez, F. Reaching out	Fic
Jimenez, Francisco, 1943-	
Breaking through	Fic
The circuit	Fic
Reaching out	Fic
Jimi Hendrix. Willett, E.	B
Jimmy Choo. Sapet, K.	746.9
Jinks, Catherine	
Evil genius	Fic
Genius squad	Fic
The genius wars	Fic
How to catch a bogle	Fic
The last bogler	Fic
Jinx. Blackwood, S.	Fic
Jinx's fire. Blackwood, S.	Fic
Jinx's magic. Blackwood, S.	Fic

Juettner, Bonnie
Diet and disease   613.2
Jukebox. Chanani, N.   Fic
JUKEBOXES
Chanani, N. Jukebox   Fic
Julie. George, J. C.   Fic
JULIET (FICTITIOUS CHARACTER)
Appignanesi, R. Romeo and Juliet   741.5
Hinds, G. The most excellent and lamentable tragedy of Romeo & Juliet   741.5
Julius Caesar. National Geographic Society.   B
The **jumbie** god's revenge. Baptiste, T.   Fic
The **jumbies**. Baptiste, T.   Fic
The **jumbo** book of art. Luxbacher, I.   702.8
Jumped. Williams-Garcia, R.   Fic
JUMPING ROPE
Bell-Rehwoldt, S. The kids' guide to jumping rope   796.2
JUMPING ROPE -- TOURNAMENTS
Draper, S. M. Double dutch   Fic
JUMPING SPIDERS
Markle, S. Jumping spiders   595.4
Jumping spiders. Markle, S.   595.4
Jumping the scratch. Weeks, S.   Fic
JUNETEENTH
Dolbear, E. Juneteenth   394.263
Juneteenth. Dolbear, E.   394.263
Jung, Mike
The boys in the back row   Fic
Geeks girls and secret identities   Fic
JUNGLE ANIMALS
Kipling, R. The jungle book   Fic
Schrefer, E. Gogi's gambit   Fic
Schrefer, E. Rumi's riddle   Fic
The **jungle** book. Kipling, R.   Fic
JUNGLES
Perkins, M. Bamboo people   Fic
Schrefer, E. Gogi's gambit   Fic
Schrefer, E. Rumi's riddle   Fic
Schrefer, E. Threatened   Fic
JUNIOR HIGH SCHOOL TEACHERS
Danziger, P. The cat ate my gymsuit   Fic
JUNIOR HIGH SCHOOLS
Appelt, K. Kissing Tennessee and other stories from the Stardust Dance   Fic
Danziger, P. The cat ate my gymsuit   Fic
Schmidt, G. D. The Wednesday wars   Fic
Junior worldmark encyclopedia of the states. Edgar, K. J.   973.03
Junk drawer engineering. Mercer, B.   620.0078
JUNK FOOD
Mooney, C. Junk food junkies   641.5
Schlosser, E. Chew on this   394.1
Junk food junkies. Mooney, C.   641.5
Junkyard science. Young, K. R.   628.4
Jurassic poop. Berkowitz, J.   567.9
Jurmain, Suzanne
The forbidden schoolhouse   B

Murder on the Baltimore Express   973.7092
The secret of the yellow death   614.5
Just add water.   546
Just another hero. Draper, S. M.   Fic
Just breathe. Chopra, M.   158.1
Just Ella. Haddix, M. P.   Fic
Just feel. Chopra, M.   152.4
Just like that. Schmidt, G. D.   Fic
Just mercy. Stevenson, B.   340.092
Just pretend. Sharp, T.   B
Just wreck it all. Griffin, N.   Fic
Just write. Myers, W. D.   808.02
JUSTER, NORTON, 1929- PHANTOM TOLLBOOTH
Juster, N. The annotated Phantom tollbooth   Fic
Juster, Norton, 1929-2021
The annotated Phantom tollbooth   Fic
JUSTICE
Friesner, E. M. Sphinx's queen   Fic
Jaffe, N. The cow of no color   Fic
Nelson, P. Left for dead   940.54
Stevenson, B. Just mercy   340.092
Justin Bieber. Bieber, J.   782.42164
JUVENILE CORRECTIONAL INSTITUTIONS
Gemeinhart, D. Scar Island   Fic
Sachar, L. Holes   Fic
JUVENILE CORRECTIONS
Ellis, D. My story starts here   364.36
JUVENILE COURTS
Jacobs, T. A. They broke the law you be the judge   345.73
JUVENILE DELINQUENCY
Ellis, D. My story starts here   364.36
Gantos, J. The trouble in me   Fic
Strasser, T. Boot camp   Fic
Volponi, P. Rikers High   Fic
JUVENILE DELINQUENTS
Ellis, D. My story starts here   364.36
Gemeinhart, D. Scar Island   Fic
Jacobs, T. A. They broke the law you be the judge   345.73
Korman, G. The juvie three   Fic
Kuklin, S. No choirboy   364.66092
Sachar, L. Holes   Fic
Volponi, P. Black and white   Fic
JUVENILE DELINQUENTS (BOYS)
Horowitz, A. Raven's gate   Fic
Mikaelsen, B. Touching Spirit Bear   Fic
Myers, W. D. Lockdown   Fic
Pena, M. d. l. We were here   Fic
JUVENILE DETENTION
Korman, G. The juvie three   Fic
JUVENILE JAILS
Myers, W. D. Lockdown   Fic
JUVENILE JUSTICE SYSTEM
Ellis, D. My story starts here   364.36
Jacobs, T. A. They broke the law you be the judge   345.73
Kuklin, S. No choirboy   364.66092
The **juvie** three. Korman, G.   Fic

K

K2 (PAKISTAN : MOUNTAIN)
Olson, T. Into the clouds   796.522095491
Kaboom! Richardson, G.   541
KABUKI
Hoobler, D. The ghost in the Tokaido Inn   Fic
Kacer, Kathy, 1954-
Hiding Edith   B
KACZYNSKI, THEODORE JOHN, 1942-
Denson, B. The Unabomber   364
Kade, J. V.
Bot Wars   Fic
Kade, Stacey
The rules   Fic
Kadohata, Cynthia
Cracker!   Fic
Half a world away   Fic
Kira-kira   Fic
A million shades of gray   Fic
Outside beauty   Fic
A place to belong   Fic
The thing about luck   Fic
Weedflower   Fic
Kadziolka, Jan
Poland   943.8
Kagawa, Julie
The eternity cure   Fic
The forever song   Fic
The immortal rules   Fic
Talon   Fic
Kagda, Falaq
Hong Kong   951.25
KAHLO, FRIDA
Bernier-Grand, C. T. Frida   B
Reef, C. Frida & Diego   759.972
Kai's journey to Gold Mountain. Currier, K. S.   Fic
Kainen, Dan
Polar   590.911
Kaleidoscope eyes. Bryant, J.   Fic
Kallen, Stuart A., 1955-
The aftermath of the Sandinista Revolution   972.8505
Che Guevara   B
Elizabethan England   942.05
The history of jazz   781.65
The instruments of music   784.19
Pharaohs of Egypt   932.01
Photography   770
Running dry   333.91
The sphinx   398.45
Teen guide to student activism   371.81
Trashing the planet   363.72
Vampire history and lore   398
What is the impact of declining biodiversity?   333.95
KAMKWAMBA, WILLIAM, 1987-
Kamkwamba, W. The boy who harnessed the wind   B
Kamkwamba, William, 1987-

The boy who harnessed the wind   B
Kampung boy. Lat.   B
Kane, Joseph Nathan, Born 1899
Facts about the presidents   973.09
Kanefield, Teri, 1960-
Alexander Hamilton   B
Franklin D. Roosevelt   B
The girl from the tar paper school   B
KANGAROOS
Gish, M. Kangaroos   599.2
KANGAROOS -- BEHAVIOR
Montgomery, S. Quest for the tree kangaroo   599.2
Kangaroos. Gish, M.   599.2
KANSAS
Jennings, R. W. Ghost town   Fic
Kadohata, C. The thing about luck   Fic
Phelan, M. The storm in the barn   741.5
Rose, C. S. May B.   Fic
Vanderpool, C. Moon over Manifest   Fic
Kapit, Sarah
Get a grip Vivy Cohen!   Fic
Kaplan, Paul M.
Lillian Wald   B
Karamanides, Dimitra
Pythagoras   B
KARATE
Pawlett, R. The karate handbook   796.815
The **karate** handbook. Pawlett, R.   796.815
Karl Marx. Rossig, W.   B
Karma. Ostlere, C.   Fic
Karst, Ken
Alien abductions   001.942
Area 51   358.4
Kassinger, Ruth, 1954-
Glass   620.1
Katcher, Brian
The improbable theory of Ana and Zak   Fic
Katerina's wish. Mobley, J.   Fic
Katsoulis, Gregory Scott
Access restricted   Fic
Katz, William Loren
Black Indians   970
Kaufman, Amie
Aurora rising   Fic
Gemina   Fic
Illuminae   Fic
Obsidio   Fic
The world between blinks   Fic
Kaufman, Michael T.
1968   909.82
Kay, Jim
The Great War   Fic
Kay, Katty
The confidence code for girls   155.2
KAYAKING
Levy, D. A. The family Fletcher takes Rock Island   Fic
Withers, P. First descent   Fic

Kent, Zachary

Connecticut — 974.6

KENTUCKY

Byars, B. C. The keeper of the doves — Fic

Henson, H. Dream of Night — Fic

Keplinger, K. Run — Fic

McGarry, K. Only a breath apart — Fic

Patterson, J. Becoming Muhammad Ali — Fic

Santella, A. Kentucky — 976.9

KENTUCKY -- HISTORY

Santella, A. Kentucky — 976.9

Kentucky. Santella, A. — 976.9

KENYA

Anderson, N. C. City of saints & thieves — Fic

Broberg, C. Kenya in pictures — 967.62

MacColl, M. Promise the night — Fic

Odhiambo, E. A. Auma's long run — Fic

Kenya in pictures. Broberg, C. — 967.62

Kenyon, Sherrilyn, 1965-

Infinity — Fic

Kephart, Beth

Going over — Fic

The heart is not a size — Fic

This is the story of you — Fic

Undercover — Fic

Wild blues — Fic

Kepler's Dream. Bell, J. — Fic

KEPLER, JOHANNES, 1571-1630. SOMNIUM

Bell, J. Kepler's Dream — Fic

Keplinger, Kody

Poison Ivy — 741.5

Run — Fic

That's not what happened — Fic

Keppeler, Jill

How gems are formed — 553.8

Kerby, Mona

An introduction to collection development for school librarians — 025.2

Kerley, Barbara

Walt Whitman — B

The world is waiting for you — 910

Kerrigan, Michael, 1959-

Egyptians — 932

Greeks — 938

Mesopotamians — 935

Romans — 937

Kessler, Liz

Emily Windsnap and the castle in the mist — Fic

Emily Windsnap and the land of the midnight sun — Fic

The tail of Emily Windsnap — Fic

When the world was ours — Fic

Key civil rights laws. Ohnaka, K. — 342.73

KEYES, SAMMY (FICTITIOUS CHARACTER)

Van Draanen, W. Sammy Keyes and the hotel thief — Fic

The keys to American history. Panchyk, R. — 973

Keyser, Amber

Pointe claw — Fic

KGB -- HISTORY

Favreau, M. Spies — 327.127304709

Khailova, Ladislava N.

The stories we share — 028.5

Khan, Hena

Amina's song — Fic

Amina's voice — Fic

More to the story — Fic

Khan, Khizr, 1950-

This is our Constitution — 320.973

KHAYRI, BASHIR

Tolan, S. The lemon tree — 956.9405092

The Khmer Rouge. Sonneborn, L. — 959.604

Khorram, Adib

Darius the Great is not okay — Fic

Khoury, Jessica, 1990-

The Mystwick School of Musicraft — Fic

Kibuishi, Kazu, 1978-

Amulet — 741.5

Explorer — 741.5

Flight explorer — 741.5

A kick in the head. Janeczko, P. B. — 811.008

KICKBOXING

Mack, G. Kickboxing — 796.815

Ritschel, J. The kickboxing handbook — 796.815

Kickboxing. Mack, G. — 796.815

The kickboxing handbook. Ritschel, J. — 796.815

A kid's guide to Arab American history. Dennis, Y. W. — 973

A kid's guide to fandom. Ratcliffe, A. — 302.23

A kid's guide to keeping chickens. Caughey, M. — 636.5

A kid's guide to Latino history. Petrillo, V. — 973

Kidd, Chip

Go — 740

Kidd, J. S.

Nuclear power — 621.48

Potent natural medicines — 615

Kidd, Ronald

Night on fire — Fic

KIDD, WILLIAM, D. 1701

Walters, E. The money pit mystery — Fic

Kidder, Tracy

Mountains beyond mountains — 610.92

Kidnapped. Stevenson, R. L. — Fic

KIDNAPPERS

Cooney, C. B. Janie face to face — Fic

Hobbs, W. Take me to the river — Fic

KIDNAPPING

Abbott, T. Wade and the scorpion's claw — Fic

Avi. Gold rush girl — Fic

Balliett, B. Hold fast — Fic

Bayerl, K. A psalm for lost girls — Fic

Blackwood, G. L. The year of the hangman — Fic

Bloor, E. Taken — Fic

Calejo, R. Charlie Hernandez & the castle of bones — Fic

Card, O. S. The lost gate — Fic

Carter, A. Don't judge a girl by her cover — Fic

Chee, T. The reader — Fic

Chee, T. The speaker	Fic	Griffin, P. Skyjacked	Fic
Colfer, E. Artemis Fowl	741.5	Mazer, N. F. The missing girl	Fic
Cyprus, N. Sisters of glass	Fic	Napoli, D. J. Hush	Fic
Durst, S. B. Vessel	Fic	Turner, M. W. A conspiracy of kings	Fic
Eagar, L. Race to the bottom of the sea	Fic	Turner, M. W. Thick as thieves	Fic

Chee, T. The speaker — Fic
Colfer, E. Artemis Fowl — 741.5
Cyprus, N. Sisters of glass — Fic
Durst, S. B. Vessel — Fic
Eagar, L. Race to the bottom of the sea — Fic
Engle, M. The wild book — Fic
Falls, K. Rip tide — Fic
Farmer, N. The Land of the Silver Apples — Fic
Farrey, B. The Grimjinx rebellion — Fic
Farrey, B. The Shadowhand Covenant — Fic
Feinstein, J. Vanishing act — Fic
Fletcher, C. Ironhand — Fic
Funke, C. Inkdeath — Fic
George, J. D. Dragon spear — Fic
Gilman, D. The devil's breath — Fic
Grant, H. The league of beastly dreadfuls — Fic
Grisham, J. The abduction — Fic
Heath, J. Remote control — Fic
Higgins, J. Sure fire — Fic
Johnson, M. The shadow cabinet — Fic
Kephart, B. Wild blues — Fic
Korman, G. The Medusa plot — Fic
Lin, G. When the sea turned to silver — Fic
Lubar, D. True talents — Fic
Mbalia, K. Tristan Strong destroys the world — Fic
Meloy, C. Wildwood — Fic
Milford, K. The thief knot — Fic
Napoli, D. J. Hush — Fic
Nesbet, A. Daring Darleen queen of the screen — Fic
Park, L. S. Trust no one — Fic
Patterson, J. The angel experiment — Fic
Ponti, J. Framed! — Fic
Rex, A. Unlucky charms — Fic
Rivera, K. Cece Rios and the Desert of Souls — Fic
Samphire, P. Secrets of the dragon tomb — Fic
Sattar, A. Ramayana — 294.5
Schlitz, L. A. Splendors and glooms — Fic
Smith, R. Chupacabra — Fic
Springer, N. The case of the cryptic crinoline — Fic
Springer, N. The case of the gypsy goodbye — Fic
Springer, N. The case of the left-handed lady — Fic
Springer, N. The case of the peculiar pink fan — Fic
Stevenson, R. L. Kidnapped — Fic
Tucholke, A. G. Seven endless forests — Fic
Valente, C. M. The Glass Town game — Fic
Vande Velde, V. The book of Mordred — Fic
Wheeler, A. Another castle — 741.5
Young, M. Blood red road — Fic
Zarr, S. Once was lost — Fic

KIDNAPPING INVESTIGATION
Grisham, J. The abduction — Fic
Milford, K. The thief knot — Fic
Springer, N. The case of the left-handed lady — Fic

KIDNAPPING VICTIMS
Bloor, E. Taken — Fic
Chabon, M. Summerland — Fic
Flanagan, J. Erak's ransom — Fic

Griffin, P. Skyjacked — Fic
Mazer, N. F. The missing girl — Fic
Napoli, D. J. Hush — Fic
Turner, M. W. A conspiracy of kings — Fic
Turner, M. W. Thick as thieves — Fic

KIDNEYS
Rogers, K. The kidneys and the renal system — 616.6

KIDNEYS -- DISEASES
Rogers, K. The kidneys and the renal system — 616.6
The **kidneys** and the renal system. Rogers, K. — 616.6
Kids at work. Freedman, R. — B
Kids make history. Buckley, S. — 920
Kids of Kabul. Ellis, D. — 305.235
Kids on strike! Bartoletti, S. C. — 331.892
Kids who are changing the world. Jankeliowitch, A. — 363.7092
A **kids'** guide to America's Bill of Rights. Krull, K. — 342.73
A **kids'** guide to America's first ladies. Krull, K. — 920
The **kids'** guide to balloon twisting. Trusty, B. — 745.594
The **kids'** guide to jumping rope. Bell-Rehwoldt, S. — 796.2

Kiernan, Denise
Signing their rights away — 973.3

KIEVAN RUS
Pasternack, S. Anya and the nightingale — Fic
Killer of enemies. Bruchac, J. — Fic

KILLER WHALE
Gish, M. Killer whales — 599.53
Killer whales. Gish, M. — 599.53
The **killer's** cousin. Werlin, N. — Fic
Killing Mr. Griffin. Duncan, L. — Fic

Kim, Graci
The last fallen star — Fic

Kim, Jessica, 1980-
Stand up Yumi Chung! — Fic

Kim, Melissa
Learning about the endocrine and reproductive systems — 612.4
Kimchi & calamari. Kent, R. — Fic

Kimmel, Allison Crotzer
The Montgomery Bus Boycott — 323.1196

Kimmel, Elizabeth Cody
Boy on the Lion Throne — B

Kimmel, Eric A.
Wonders and miracles — 296.4

Kincaid, S. J.
Insignia — Fic
The **kind** of friends we used to be. Dowell, F. O. — Fic
Kinda like brothers. Booth, C. — Fic
The **kinder** poison. Mae, N. — Fic

KINDERTRANSPORTS (RESCUE OPERATIONS)
Byers, A. Saving children from the Holocaust — 940.53
Hodge, D. Rescuing the children — 940.53

Kindl, Patrice
Keeping the castle — Fic
A school for brides — Fic

KINDNESS
Donwerth-Chikamatsu, A. Beyond me — Fic
Hurwitz, M. W. The summer I saved the world-- in 65

Reece, R. The Korean War	951.904	**Krensky, Stephen**	
The **Korean** War. Reece, R.	951.904	Clara Barton	**B**
KOREANS IN THE UNITED STATES		**Krieg, Katherine**	
Na, A. A step from heaven	Fic	Thomas Edison	**B**
KOREMATSU, FRED, 1919-2005		**Kris, 1972-**	
Atkins, L. Fred Korematsu speaks up	**B**	A bag of marbles	741.5
Korman, Gordon		**Krishnaswami, Uma, 1956-**	
Collision course	Fic	Step up to the plate Maria Singh	Fic
The juvie three	Fic	**Kristallnacht**. Deem, J. M.	940.53
Linked	Fic	**KRISTALLNACHT, 1938**	
The Medusa plot	Fic	Deem, J. M. Kristallnacht	940.53
Notorious	Fic	**Kristoff, Jay**	
Pop	Fic	Lifel1k3	Fic
Restart	Fic	**Kristy's** great idea. Telgemeier, R.	741.5
Schooled	Fic	**Kritzer, Naomi**	
Slacker	Fic	Catfishing on Catnet	Fic
Son of the mob	Fic	**Krok, Lisa**	
Swindle	Fic	Novels in verse for teens	808.83
Ungifted	Fic	**KROSOCZKA, JARRETT**	
War stories	Fic	Krosoczka, J. Hey kiddo	**B**
Zoobreak	Fic	**Krosoczka, Jarrett**	
Kostick, Conor, 1964-		The frog who croaked	Fic
Edda	Fic	Hey kiddo	**B**
Epic	Fic	**Krueger, Susan Heidi**	
Saga	Fic	The tempest	822.3
Kott, Jennifer, 1971-		**Krull, Kathleen, 1952-2021**	
Nicaragua	972.85	Albert Einstein	**B**
Kowitt, Holly		Charles Darwin	**B**
The loser list	Fic	Isaac Newton	**B**
KRAKEN		A kids' guide to America's Bill of Rights	342.73
Newquist, H. P. Here there be monsters	594	A kids' guide to America's first ladies	920
KRAKOW, POLAND		Leonardo da Vinci	509
Gratz, A. Prisoner B-3087	Fic	Lives of the explorers	910.92
Leyson, L. The boy on the wooden box	940.53	Lives of the presidents	973.099
Kramer, Ann, 1946-		Marie Curie	**B**
Eleanor of Aquitaine	**B**	**KRUPNIK, ANASTASIA (FICTITIOUS CHARACTER)**	
Kramer, Barbara		Lowry, L. Anastasia at your service	Fic
Toni Morrison	**B**	Lowry, L. Anastasia Krupnik	Fic
Kramer, J. Kasper		**KU KLUX KLAN**	
The story that cannot be told	Fic	Bartoletti, S. C. They called themselves the K.K.K.	322.4
Kramer, Stephen P.		Bowers, R. Superman versus the Ku Klux Klan	741.5
Hidden worlds	570	Hesse, K. Witness	Fic
Kras, Sara Louise		Draper, S. M. Stella by starlight	Fic
Antigua and Barbuda	972.974	Yang, G. L. Superman smashes the Klan	741.5
The Galapagos Islands	986.6	**KU KLUX KLAN -- HISTORY -- 20TH CENTURY**	
Krashen, Stephen D.		Brimner, L. D. Birmingham Sunday	323.1196
The power of reading	028	McMullan, M. When I crossed No-Bob	Fic
Kraske, Robert		**KUBLAI KHAN, 1216-1294**	
Marooned	996.1	McCaughrean, G. The kite rider	Fic
Krasner, Barbara		Yang, D. J. Daughter of Xanadu	Fic
Russian immigrants	973	**Kuehn, Stephanie**	
Krasno, Rena, 1923-		Complicit	Fic
Cloud weavers	398.2	**Kuhn, Betsy**	
Kraus, Daniel, 1975-		Angels of mercy	940.54
At the edge of empire	Fic	**Kuhn, Sarah**	
KRAUS, DITA, 1929-		I love you so mochi	Fic
Iturbe, A. The librarian of Auschwitz	Fic	**KUIPER BELT**	

Teach like a champion 2.0	373	Cianciotto, J. LGBT youth in America's schools	371.826

Lempp, Jennifer

Math workshop	372.7	

LESBIAN TEENAGERS

Lena. Woodson, J.	Fic

Adams, S. J. Sparks	Fic

Lendler, Ian

Bigelow, L. J. Starting from here	Fic
Boteju, T. Kings queens and in-betweens	Fic

The first dinosaur	560.9	Heaney, K. Girl crushed	Fic
The **length** of a string. Weissman, E. B.	Fic	Huegel, K. LGBTQ	306.76

LENNON, JOHN, 1940-1980

Kisner, A. Dear Rachel Maddow	Fic

Behnke, A. Death of a dreamer	B	Mac, C. 10 things I can see from here	Fic
Burlingame, J. John Lennon	B	Murdock, C. G. The off season	Fic
Partridge, E. John Lennon	B	Murphy, J. Ramona Blue	Fic
Quinn, J. The Beatles	920	Ostertag, M. The girl from the sea	Fic
Rappaport, D. John's secret dreams	B	Talley, R. Pulp	Fic

Lennon, Tom

		Wilkinson, L. Pink	Fic
When love comes to town	Fic	**LESBIANS**	

Leno, Katrina

Holt, K. A. Redwood and Ponytail	Fic

The lost & found	Fic	Melleby, N. In the role of Brie Hutchens...	Fic

LENT

LESBIANS -- HISTORY

Hackney Blackwell, A. Lent Yom Kippur and other Atonement days   **202**

Chevat, R. A queer history of the United States for young
people   **306.76**

Lent Yom Kippur and other Atonement days. Hackney Blackwell, A.   **202**

Lesh, Bruce A.

"Why won't you just tell us the answer?"	973.071

Leon's story. Tillage, L. W.	B

Lesley, Craig

Leon, Vicki

Talking leaves	Fic

Outrageous women of the Middle Ages	920	

Lesperance, Nicole

Leonardo da Vinci. Krull, K.	509	The nightmare thief	Fic

LEONARDO, DA VINCI, 1452-1519

Lessem, Don

Anderson, M. Amazing Leonardo da Vinci inventions you can
build yourself   **620.0092**

National Geographic kids ultimate dinopedia	567.9

Krull, K. Leonardo da Vinci	509	**Lesser** spotted animals. Brown, M.	599

LEONARDO, DA VINCI, 1452-1519. MONA LISA

Lessons and activities for building powerful numeracy. Harris,
P. W.   **372.7**

Barsony, P. The stories of the Mona Lisa	759.06

Lester, Julius

LEOPARD

Day of tears	Fic

Gish, M. Leopards	599.75	Guardian	Fic
Markle, S. The great leopard rescue	599.75	Time's memory	Fic

LEOPARD SEAL

To be a slave	306.3

Snyder, E. Alarming leopard seals	599.79	Uncle Remus	398.2
Leopards. Gish, M.	599.75	**Let** it shine. Pinkney, A. D.	920

Lepore, Jill

Let me hear a rhyme. Jackson, T. D.	Fic

Encounters in the New World	970	**Let** me play. Blumenthal, K.	796

Leppman, Elizabeth J.

Let the circle be unbroken. Taylor, M. D.	Fic

Australia and the Pacific	994	**Let** your voice be heard. Silvey, A.	B

Lerangis, Peter

LETTER WRITING

The colossus rises	Fic	Alifirenka, C. I will always write back	305.235
Lost in babylon	Fic	Axelrod, A. Your friend in fashion Abby Shapiro	Fic
The tomb of shadows	Fic	Friend, N. Lush	Fic

Lerner, Sarah

Hesse, K. Letters from Rifka	Fic

Parkland speaks	371.7	Kapit, S. Get a grip Vivy Cohen!	Fic

LEROUX, CALLIE (FICTITIOUS CHARACTER)

Lyons, M. E. Letters from a slave boy	Fic

Zettel, S. Bad luck girl	Fic	Lyons, M. E. Letters from a slave girl	Fic

LESBIAN GIRLS

Moriarty, J. Feeling sorry for Celia	Fic

Callender, K. Hurricane child	Fic	**LETTERS**	

LESBIAN MOTHERS

Bateson, C. Being Bee	Fic

Blake, A. H. Hazel Bly and the deep blue sea	Fic	Bean, L. The ship we built	Fic
Levy, D. A. This would make a good story someday	Fic	Carroll, E. In darkling wood	Fic
Woodson, J. From the notebooks of Melanin Sun	Fic	Clements, A. Extra credit	Fic

LESBIAN STUDENTS

Johnson, M. 13 little blue envelopes	Fic

Show me a sign	Fic
LGBT youth in America's schools. Cianciotto, J.	371.826
LGBTQ. Huegel, K.	306.76
LGBTQ+ athletes claim the field. Cronn-Mills, K.	796.086
LGBTQAI+ books for children and teens. Dorr, C. H.	028.7

LGBTQIA COMICS

Oseman, A. Heartstopper	741.5
Ostertag, M. The girl from the sea	Fic
Shimura, T. Wandering son	741.5
Steele, H. DeadEndia	Fic

LGBTQIA FICTION

Bean, L. The ship we built	Fic
Bigelow, L. J. Starting from here	Fic
Bildner, P. A high five for Glenn Burke	Fic
Brezenoff, S. Brooklyn burning	Fic
Bunker, L. Zenobia July	Fic
Callender, K. Hurricane child	Fic
Dee, B. Star-crossed	Fic
Donovan, J. I'll get there it better be worth the trip	Fic
Gino, A. Rick	Fic
Howe, J. Totally Joe	Fic
Kisner, A. Dear Rachel Maddow	Fic
Knowles, J. Where the heart is	Fic
Lee, M. The gentleman's guide to vice and virtue	Fic
Lennon, T. When love comes to town	Fic
Levithan, D. The mysterious disappearance of Aidan S.	Fic
Lukoff, K. Too bright to see	Fic
Lundin, B. Ship it	Fic
Mac, C. 10 things I can see from here	Fic
Melleby, N. In the role of Brie Hutchens...	Fic
Murphy, J. Ramona Blue	Fic
Nazemian, A. Like a love story	Fic
Polonsky, A. Gracefully Grayson	Fic
Sanchez, A. Bait	Fic
Smith, N. The deep & dark blue	741.5
Villasante, A. The grief keeper	Fic
Wilkinson, L. Pink	Fic
Wittlinger, E. Parrotfish	Fic
Wright, B. Putting makeup on the fat boy	Fic
Zaczek, A. Martin McLean middle school queen	Fic

LGBTQIA PERSONS

Cronn-Mills, K. LGBTQ+ athletes claim the field	796.086
Dorr, C. H. LGBTQAI+ books for children and teens	028.7
Finke, L. Queerfully and wonderfully made	248.8
Hurt, A. E. Confronting LGBTQ+ discrimination	306.76

LGBTQIA PERSONS -- EDUCATION

Cianciotto, J. LGBT youth in America's schools	371.826

LGBTQIA PERSONS -- LEGAL STATUS, LAWS, ETC

Gitlin, M. Transgender rights	323.3

LGBTQIA RIGHTS

Bausum, A. Stonewall	306.76
Cronn-Mills, K. LGBTQ+ athletes claim the field	796.086
Pitman, G. E. The Stonewall Riots	306.76

LGBTQIA RIGHTS -- HISTORY

Chevat, R. A queer history of the United States for young

people	306.76

LGBTQIA ROMANCES

Gonzales, S. Only mostly devastated	Fic
Heaney, K. Girl crushed	Fic
Konigsberg, B. Openly straight	Fic
Levithan, D. Two boys kissing	Fic
Mandanna, S. Color outside the lines	Fic
Oseman, A. Heartstopper	Fic
Stamper, P. The gravity of us	Fic

LI, MOYING, 1954-

Li, M. Snow falling in spring	B

Li, Moying, 1954-

Snow falling in spring	B

LI, ZHONGMEI, 1966-

Bernstein, R. A girl named Faithful Plum	B
Liar & spy. Stead, R.	Fic

LIBEL AND SLANDER

MacColl, M. Prisoners in the palace	Fic
Liberation. Hoffman, B. N.	940.53
The **librarian** of Auschwitz. Iturbe, A.	Fic
A **librarian's** guide to cultivating an elementary school garden. Mackey, B.	372.35
Librarian's guide to online searching. Brown, C. C.	025.04

LIBRARIANS

Berlin, E. The puzzling world of Winston Breen	Fic
Fitzgerald, L. M. Under the egg	Fic
McQuerry, M. The Peculiars	Fic
Myron, V. Dewey the library cat	636.80092
Oppenheim, J. Dear Miss Breed	940.53
Reed, M. K. Americus	Fic
Sanderson, B. Alcatraz versus the evil librarians	Fic
Sanderson, B. The dark talent	Fic

LIBRARIANS -- LEGAL STATUS, LAWS, ETC

Russell, C. Complete copyright for K-12 librarians and educators	346.7304

LIBRARIES

Caine, R. Ink and bone	Fic
Grabenstein, C. Escape from Mr. Lemoncello's library	Fic
Grabenstein, C. Mr. Lemoncello's great library race	Fic
Grabenstein, C. Mr. Lemoncello's Library Olympics	Fic
Myron, V. Dewey the library cat	636.80092
Ponti, J. Trapped!	Fic

LIBRARIES -- ACTIVITY PROGRAMS

Fitzgerald, K. Successful summer reading programs for all ages	025.5
Phoenix, J. Maximizing the impact of comics in your library	026

LIBRARIES -- CENSORSHIP

Magi, T. J. Intellectual freedom manual	025.2

LIBRARIES -- SPECIAL COLLECTIONS -- AUDIOBOOKS

Grover, S. Listening to learn	372.4

LIBRARIES -- SPECIAL COLLECTIONS -- CHILDREN'S LITERATURE

Smith, K. M. Creating a tween collection	025.2

LIBRARIES -- SPECIAL COLLECTIONS -- COMIC BOOKS, STRIPS, ETC

Mannix, D. Life skills activities for secondary students with special needs **371.91**

Life skills activities for secondary students with special needs. Mannix, D. **371.91**

LIFE SKILLS GUIDES

Bailey, J. Sex puberty and all that stuff **613.9**

Life under occupation. Samuels, C. **940.53**

Lifel1k3. Kristoff, J. **Fic**

LIFT-THE-FLAP BOOKS

D'Harcourt, C. Masterpieces up close **759**

Lifting as we climb. Dionne, E. **323.3**

LIGHT

Caes, C. J. Discovering the speed of light **535**

Canavan, T. Super experiments with light and sound **535.078**

Winterberg, J. Light and its effects **535**

LIGHT -- SPEED -- MEASUREMENT

Caes, C. J. Discovering the speed of light **535**

Light. Grant, M. **Fic**

LIGHT AND DARKNESS

Johnson, A. A cool moonlight **Fic**

Winterberg, J. Light and its effects **535**

Light and its effects. Winterberg, J. **535**

LIGHT BULBS

Collier, J. L. Electricity and the light bulb **621.32**

The **light** in hidden places. Cameron, S. **Fic**

A **light** in the attic. Silverstein, S. **811**

The **light** of days. Batalion, J. **940.53**

LIGHTHOUSE KEEPERS

Gallico, P. The snow goose **Fic**

LIGHTHOUSES

House, K. L. Lighthouses for kids **387.1**

Levy, D. A. The family Fletcher takes Rock Island **Fic**

LIGHTHOUSES -- ACTION PROJECTS FOR CHILDREN

House, K. L. Lighthouses for kids **387.1**

LIGHTHOUSES -- HISTORY

House, K. L. Lighthouses for kids **387.1**

Lighthouses for kids. House, K. L. **387.1**

LIGHTING

Collier, J. L. Electricity and the light bulb **621.32**

LIGHTNING

Pyron, B. Lucky strike **Fic**

Riordan, R. The lightning thief **Fic**

Stewart, M. Inside lightning **551.56**

Venditti, R. The lightning thief **741.5**

The **lightning** thief. Riordan, R. **Fic**

The **lightning** thief. Venditti, R. **741.5**

Like a love story. Nazemian, A. **Fic**

Like a river. Wiechman, K. C. **Fic**

Like father like son. Patterson, J. **Fic**

Like home. Onome, L. **Fic**

Like sisters on the homefront. Williams-Garcia, R. **Fic**

Like Vanessa. Charles, T. **Fic**

Like water on stone. Walrath, D. **Fic**

Lillian Wald. Kaplan, P. M. **B**

LILLIPUTIANS (FICTITIOUS CHARACTERS)

Swift, J. Gulliver's travels **Fic**

The **lily** pond. Thor, A. **Fic**

Lily's crossing. Giff, P. R. **Fic**

Lily's mountain. Moderow, H. **Fic**

Lim, Elizabeth

Spin the dawn **Fic**

Lin, Grace

Starry River of the Sky **Fic**

When the sea turned to silver **Fic**

Where the mountain meets the moon **Fic**

LIN, MAYA YING

Rubin, S. G. Maya Lin **720.92**

Lincoln. Freedman, R. **B**

Lincoln in 3-D. Zeller, B. **973.7092**

Lincoln through the lens. Sandler, M. W. **B**

Lincoln's flying spies. Jarrow, G. **973.7**

Lincoln's grave robbers. Sheinkin, S. **973.7092**

LINCOLN, ABRAHAM, 1809-1865

Allen, T. B. Mr. Lincoln's high-tech war **973.7**

Aronson, B. Abraham Lincoln **B**

Bolden, T. Emancipation Proclamation **973.7**

Fleming, C. The Lincolns **B**

Freedman, R. Abraham Lincoln and Frederick Douglass **973.7092**

Freedman, R. Lincoln **B**

Giblin, J. C. Good brother bad brother **920**

Holzer, H. Father Abraham **B**

Jurmain, S. Murder on the Baltimore Express **973.7092**

Lincoln, A. Abraham Lincoln the writer **B**

Sandler, M. W. Lincoln through the lens **B**

Sheinkin, S. Lincoln's grave robbers **973.7092**

Swanson, J. L. Bloody times **973.7092**

Zeller, B. Lincoln in 3-D **973.7092**

Lincoln, Abraham, 1809-1865

Abraham Lincoln the writer **B**

The **Lincolns**. Fleming, C. **B**

LINDBERGH, CHARLES A. (CHARLES AUGUSTUS), 1902-1974

Finkelstein, N. H. Three across **629.130973**

Fleming, C. The rise and fall of Charles Lindbergh **B**

Giblin, J. C. Charles A. Lindbergh **B**

Lindelauf, Benny, 1964-

Fing's war **Fic**

Nine Open Arms **Fic**

Linder, Rozlyn

The big book of details **372.62**

Lindop, Edmund

America in the 1960s **973.923**

Link, Kelly

Monstrous affections **Fic**

Steampunk! **Fic**

Linked. Korman, G. **Fic**

LINNE, CARL VON, 1707-1778

Beil, K. M. What Linnaeus saw **508.092**

LION

Hague, B. Rise of the lioness **599.757**

Hunter, E. Broken pride **Fic**

Lewis, C. S. The magician's nephew **Fic**

Fletcher, C. Silvertongue	Fic	Stroud, J. The hollow boy	Fic
Fletcher, C. Stoneheart	Fic	Stroud, J. Ptolemy's gate	Fic
Fox, J. S. The charmed children of Rookskill Castle	Fic	Stroud, J. The screaming staircase	Fic
Gier, K. Emerald green	Fic	Stroud, J. The whispering skull	Fic
Gier, K. Sapphire blue	Fic	Trevayne, E. The accidental afterlife of Thomas Marsden	Fic
Gleason, C. The clockwork scarab	Fic	Twain, M. The prince and the pauper	Fic
Goodman, A. The Dark Days Club	Fic	Waller, S. B. A mad wicked folly	Fic
Gordon, R. Tunnels	Fic	Ward, R. The chaos	Fic
Higgins, J. Death run	Fic	Ward, R. Num8ers	Fic
Higgins, J. Sure fire	Fic	Whelan, G. All my noble dreams and then what happens	Fic
Hooper, M. Fallen Grace	Fic	Whelan, G. Small acts of amazing courage	Fic
Hopkinson, D. The great trouble	Fic	Whyman, M. Goldstrike	Fic
Horowitz, A. The Falcon's Malteser	Fic	Wooding, C. Malice	Fic
Horowitz, A. The Greek who stole Christmas	Fic	Woodruff, E. The ravenmaster's secret	Fic
Horowitz, A. Public enemy number two	Fic	Zettel, S. A most dangerous deception	Fic
Horowitz, A. South by southeast	Fic	**LONDON, JACK, 1876-1916**	
Horowitz, A. Three of diamonds	Fic	Lourie, P. Jack London and the Klondike gold rush	**B**
James, A. The bookwanderers	Fic	**London, Jack, 1876-1916**	
Jinks, C. How to catch a bogle	Fic	The call of the wild	Fic
Jinks, C. The last bogler	Fic	**Lone** wolf. Lasky, K.	Fic
Johnson, M. The madness underneath	Fic	**LONELINESS**	
Johnson, M. The name of the star	Fic	Almond, D. My name is Mina	Fic
Johnson, M. The shadow cabinet	Fic	Bauer, M. D. Little dog lost	Fic
Jones, K. Murder magic and what we wore	Fic	Bigelow, L. J. Starting from here	Fic
Kirby, M. J. A taste for monsters	Fic	Delaney, J. Revenge of the witch	Fic
Lee, M. Loki	Fic	Howard, A. The crossroads at midnight	Fic
Lee, Y. S. The body at the tower	Fic	Koertge, R. Strays	Fic
Lee, Y. S. A spy in the house	Fic	Lange, E. J. Butter	Fic
Lloyd, S. The carbon diaries 2015	Fic	O'Dell, S. Island of the Blue Dolphins	Fic
MacColl, M. Prisoners in the palace	Fic	Roat, S. H. How to disappear	Fic
McNab, A. Avenger	Fic	Wittlinger, E. Hard love	Fic
Meloy, M. The apothecary	Fic	**LONELINESS IN BOYS**	
Naidoo, B. The other side of truth	Fic	Delaney, J. Revenge of the witch	Fic
Powell, L. Burn mark	Fic	Martin, A. M. Everything for a dog	Fic
Powell, L. The game of triumphs	Fic	**LONELINESS IN GIRLS**	
Pratchett, T. Dodger	Fic	Almond, D. My name is Mina	Fic
Pullman, P. Two crafty criminals!	Fic	Lord, C. Touch blue	Fic
Reeve, P. Fever Crumb	Fic	Soo, K. Jellaby	**741.5**
Reeve, P. Scrivener's moon	Fic	**LONELINESS IN TEENAGE BOYS**	
Riggs, R. Hollow City	Fic	Koertge, R. Strays	Fic
Riggs, R. Library of souls	Fic	Lange, E. J. Butter	Fic
Rundell, K. Cartwheeling in thunderstorms	Fic	Wittlinger, E. Hard love	Fic
Sands, K. The Blackthorn key	Fic	**LONELINESS IN TEENAGERS**	
Saunders, K. The Whizz Pop Chocolate Shop	Fic	Brooks, M. Queen of hearts	Fic
Schlitz, L. A. Splendors and glooms	Fic	The **lonely** dead. Henry, A.	Fic
Sedgwick, M. She is not invisible	Fic	The **lonely** heart of Maybelle Lane. O'Shaughnessy, K.	Fic
Selznick, B. The Marvels	Fic	**LONERS**	
Shepherd, M. Midnight beauties	Fic	Herrick, A. The Time Fetch	Fic
Springer, N. The case of the bizarre bouquets	Fic	Price, C. Desert Angel	Fic
Springer, N. The case of the cryptic crinoline	Fic	Ramee, L. M. Something to say	Fic
Springer, N. The case of the gypsy goodbye	Fic	Schmatz, P. Bluefish	Fic
Springer, N. The case of the left-handed lady	Fic	**LONG BEACH, CALIFORNIA**	
Springer, N. The case of the missing marquess	Fic	Hughes, D. Search and destroy	Fic
Springer, N. The case of the peculiar pink fan	Fic	The **long** haul. Kinney, J.	Fic
Stroud, J. The amulet of Samarkand	Fic	**LONG ISLAND, NEW YORK**	
Stroud, J. The creeping shadow	Fic	50 Cent. Playground	Fic
Stroud, J. The golem's eye	Fic	Bock, C. Lie	Fic

Hest, A. The summer we found the baby	**Fic**	Kim, J. Stand up Yumi Chung!	**Fic**
Korman, G. Zoobreak	**Fic**	Lu, M. Champion	**Fic**
Preller, J. Bystander	**Fic**	Lu, M. Legend	**Fic**
Schmidt, G. D. The Wednesday wars	**Fic**	Lu, M. Prodigy	**Fic**
Volponi, P. Black and white	**Fic**	Lupica, M. Fantasy league	**Fic**
The **long** ride. Budhos, M. T.	**Fic**	McCoy, M. I Claudia	**Fic**
A **long** walk to water. Park, L. S.	**Fic**	McManis, C. W. Indian no more	**Fic**
Long way down. Reynolds, J.	**Fic**	Nelson, T. Ruby electric	**Fic**
A **long** way from Chicago. Peck, R.	**Fic**	Pinkwater, D. M. The Neddiad	**Fic**
A **long** way from home. Walsh, A.	**Fic**	Riordan, R. The lightning thief	**Fic**
Long, Denise		Umminger, A. American girls	**Fic**
Survivor kid	**613.6**	Whitney, D. When you were here	**Fic**
LONG-DISTANCE ROMANCE		The **loser** list. Kowitt, H.	**Fic**
Smith, J. E. The geography of you and me	**Fic**	The **losers** at the center of the galaxy. Heider, M. W.	**Fic**
LONGEVITY		**LOSS (PSYCHOLOGY)**	
Buckley-Archer, L. The many lives of John Stone	**Fic**	Appelt, K. Maybe a fox	**Fic**
Longfellow, Henry Wadsworth, 1807-1882		Benjamin, A. The thing about jellyfish	**Fic**
Henry Wadsworth Longfellow	**811**	Blackstone, M. Sorry you're lost	**Fic**
Hiawatha and Megissogwon	**811**	Brooks, M. Mistik Lake	**Fic**
Longo, Jennifer		Brown, S. Caminar	**Fic**
What I carry	**Fic**	Caletti, D. The last forever	**Fic**
Look both ways. Reynolds, J.	**Fic**	DeStefano, L. A curious tale of the in-between	**Fic**
Looking at aerial photographs. Belmont, H.	**910**	Ehrlich, E. Nest	**Fic**
Looking at maps. Taylor, B.	**912**	Foley, J. A. Sorry for your loss	**Fic**
Looking back. Lowry, L.	**B**	Henkes, K. Bird Lake moon	**Fic**
Looking for Marco Polo. Armstrong, A. W.	**Fic**	Hesse, K. Out of the dust	**Fic**
Looks like daylight. Ellis, D.	**970.004**	Holczer, T. The secret hum of a daisy	**Fic**
Loomis, Ilima		Jackson, T. D. Monday's not coming	**Fic**
Eclipse chaser	**523.7**	Keplinger, K. That's not what happened	**Fic**
Loos poos and number twos. Hepplewhite, P.	**392.3**	LaFleur, S. M. Love Aubrey	**Fic**
Loot. Watson, J.	**Fic**	Larocca, R. Red white and whole	**Fic**
Lopez, Diana		Leno, K. The lost & found	**Fic**
Ask my mood ring how I feel	**Fic**	Lester, J. Time's memory	**Fic**
Confetti girl	**Fic**	Mazer, H. Heroes don't run	**Fic**
Lord of the flies. Golding, W.	**Fic**	Mbalia, K. Tristan Strong punches a hole in the sky	**Fic**
The **lord** of the rings. Tolkien, J. R. R.	**Fic**	McKay, H. Binny for short	**Fic**
Lord, Cynthia		Moranville, S. B. 27 magic words	**Fic**
Half a chance	**Fic**	Mosier, P. Train I ride	**Fic**
Rules	**Fic**	Nye, N. S. What have you lost?	**808.81**
Touch blue	**Fic**	O'Reilly, J. H. The notations of Cooper Cameron	**Fic**
Lord, Emery		Pearsall, S. The seventh most important thing	**Fic**
When we collided	**Fic**	Pennypacker, S. The summer of the gypsy moths	**Fic**
Lord, Emma		Polonsky, A. Threads	**Fic**
Tweet cute	**Fic**	Reynolds, J. Long way down	**Fic**
Loretta Little looks back. Pinkney, A. D.	**Fic**	Rupp, R. After Eli	**Fic**
LOS ALAMOS, NEW MEXICO		Selznick, B. The Marvels	**Fic**
Blume, J. Tiger eyes	**Fic**	Silver, M. My parent has cancer and it really sucks	**616.99**
Klages, E. The green glass sea	**Fic**	Sitomer, A. L. Homeboyz	**Fic**
LOS ANGELES, CALIFORNIA		Smith, J. E. The geography of you and me	**Fic**
Block, F. L. Love in the time of global warming	**Fic**	Snyder, L. My Jasper June	**Fic**
Castellucci, C. Boy proof	**Fic**	Tan, S. Lost & found	**Fic**
Castellucci, C. Don't cosplay with my heart	**Fic**	Urban, L. The center of everything	**Fic**
Currier, K. S. Kai's journey to Gold Mountain	**Fic**	Valente, C. M. The Glass Town game	**Fic**
Cushman, K. The loud silence of Francine Green	**Fic**	Whitney, D. When you were here	**Fic**
Frank, S. Armstrong and Charlie	**Fic**	**LOSS (PSYCHOLOGY) IN CHILDREN**	
Hirahara, N. 1001 cranes	**Fic**	DiCamillo, K. Raymie Nightingale	**Fic**
Johnston, T. Any small goodness	**Fic**	The **lost** & found. Leno, K.	**Fic**

O'Sullivan, J. Between two skies	Fic	Jarrow, G. Lincoln's flying spies	973.7
Peet, M. Tamar	Fic	**LOWELL, MASSACHUSETTS**	
Talley, R. Pulp	Fic	Paterson, K. Lyddie	Fic
Woodson, J. If you come softly	Fic	**LOWER EAST SIDE, NEW YORK CITY -- SOCIAL CON-**	
Love that dog. Creech, S.	Fic	DITIONS	
LOVE TRIANGLES		Bial, R. Tenement	307.76
Brignull, I. The hawkweed prophecy	Fic	**LOWERY, LYNDA BLACKMON, 1950-**	
Dessen, S. The moon and more	Fic	Lowery, L. B. Turning 15 on the road to freedom	323.1196
Han, J. We'll always have summer	Fic	**Lowery, Lynda Blackmon, 1950-**	
Hautman, P. The Klaatu terminus	Fic	Turning 15 on the road to freedom	323.1196
Irving, W. The legend of Sleepy Hollow	Fic	**Lowinger, Kathy**	
Kagawa, J. Talon	Fic	Give me wings	782.42162
Meyer, S. Eclipse	Fic	**LOWRIDERS**	
Oppel, K. This dark endeavor	Fic	Camper, C. Lowriders in space	741.5
Pike, A. Earthbound	Fic	Camper, C. Lowriders to the center of the Earth	741.5
Love, Ann		**Lowriders** in space. Camper, C.	741.5
Sweet!	641.8	**Lowriders** to the center of the Earth. Camper, C.	741.5
Love, D. Anne		**LOWRY, LOIS**	
Semiprecious	Fic	Lowry, L. Looking back	B
Love, Damien		**Lowry, Lois**	
Monstrous devices	Fic	Anastasia at your service	Fic
The shadow arts	Fic	Anastasia Krupnik	Fic
LOVE, NAT, 1854-1921		Gathering blue	Fic
Bloom, B. L. Nat Love	B	The giver	Fic
A **loved** one with dementia. Rawitt, J.	616.8	Giver quartet	741.5
LOVELACE, ADA KING, COUNTESS OF, 1815-1852		Looking back	B
McCully, E. A. Dreaming in code	B	Number the stars	Fic
Loveless, Gina		Son	Fic
Puberty is gross but also really awesome	612.6	**LOYALISTS (UNITED STATES HISTORY)**	
LOVERS		Anderson, L. H. Chains	Fic
Hinds, G. The most excellent and lamentable tragedy of Ro-		Woodruff, E. George Washington's spy	Fic
meo & Juliet	741.5	**LOYALTY**	
Loving vs. Virginia. Powell, P. H.	Fic	Anderson, J. D. Sidekicked	Fic
LOVING, MILDRED JETER		Charbonneau, J. Graduation day	Fic
Brimner, L. D. Finding a way home	346.7301	Duey, K. Sacred scars	Fic
Powell, P. H. Loving vs. Virginia	Fic	Gray, C. Defy the stars	Fic
LOVING, RICHARD PERRY		Hale, S. Palace of stone	Fic
Brimner, L. D. Finding a way home	346.7301	Hughes, D. Four-Four-Two	Fic
Powell, P. H. Loving vs. Virginia	Fic	Magoon, K. Camo girl	Fic
LOW FANTASY		Pearson, M. Dance of thieves	Fic
Applegate, K. Wishtree	Fic	Pearson, M. Vow of thieves	Fic
Avery, T. Not as we know it	Fic	Ruiz Zafon, C. Marina	Fic
Babbitt, N. Tuck everlasting	Fic	Rutkoski, M. The winner's crime	Fic
DiCamillo, K. Flora & Ulysses	Fic	Rutkoski, M. The winner's curse	Fic
Haydu, C. A. Rules for stealing stars	Fic	Yang, G. L. Saints	741.5
Henderson, L. The magic in changing your stars	Fic	**LOYALTY IN GIRLS**	
LaRocca, R. Midsummer's mayhem	Fic	Magoon, K. Camo girl	Fic
Lackey, L. All the impossible things	Fic	**Lu, Marie, 1984-**	
McKay, H. The time of green magic	Fic	Champion	Fic
Messner, K. The seventh wish	Fic	The Kingdom of Back	Fic
Low red moon. Devlin, I.	Fic	Legend	Fic
LOW TEMPERATURE ENGINEERING		Prodigy	Fic
Healey, K. When we wake	Fic	Rebel	Fic
LOW, JULIETTE GORDON, 1860-1927		Warcross	Fic
Wadsworth, G. First Girl Scout	B	Wildcard	Fic
LOWE, T. S. C. (THADDEUS SOBIESKI COULIN-		The young elites	Fic
COURT), 1832-1913		**Lubar, David**	

M

MA, YAN, 1987-
Ma, Y. The diary of Ma Yan — 951.05
Ma, Yan, 1987-
The diary of Ma Yan — 951.05
Maanum, Jody L.
The general educator's guide to special education — 371.9
Maas, Sarah J.
Catwoman — Fic
Maberry, Jonathan
The orphan army — Fic
Rot & Ruin — Fic
Mac, Carrie, 1975-
10 things I can see from here — Fic
Macaulay, David
Building big — 720
Built to last — 729
City — 711
Mosque — 726
Pyramid — 690
Unbuilding — 690
Underground — 624
The way things work now — 600
The way we work — 612
MACBETH, KING OF SCOTLAND, ACTIVE 11TH CENTURY
Packer, T. Tales from Shakespeare — 822.3
Maccarald, Clara, 1979-
Bringing back our deserts — 333.75
Maccoll, Michaela
Prisoners in the palace — Fic
Promise the night — Fic
Rory's promise — Fic
Maccullough, Carolyn
Once a witch — Fic
Macdonald, Fiona, 1958-
You wouldn't want to live without toilets — 696
Macdonald, Joan Vos
Tanzania — 967.8
Macdonald, Maryann
Odette's secrets — Fic
Machale, D. J.
The lost city of Faar — Fic
The merchant of death — Fic
The never war — Fic
The reality bug — Fic
Machale, D. J.
SYLO — Fic
MACHIAVELLI, NICCOLO, 1469-1527
Scott, M. The alchemyst — Fic
MACHINE LEARNING
Martin, B. S. Big data and machine learning — 005.7
MACHINERY
Link, K. Steampunk! — Fic
Macaulay, D. The way things work now — 600
Mercer, B. The robot book — 629.8
Milford, K. The Boneshaker — Fic
Tomecek, S. Tools and machines — 621.9

MACHINERY -- DESIGN
Kenney, K. L. Folding tech — 736
MACHINERY -- MAINTENANCE AND REPAIR
Miller, M. Modern mechanics — 629.28
Machines that think! Brown, D. — 006.3
Mack, Gail
Kickboxing — 796.815
Mack, W. C., 1972-
Athlete vs. mathlete — Fic
Mackel, Kathryn, 1950-
Boost — Fic
Mackey, Bonnie
A librarian's guide to cultivating an elementary school garden — 372.35
Mackler, Carolyn
The Earth my butt and other big round things — Fic
Maclachlan, Patricia
Kindred souls — Fic
Macleod, D. Peter, 1955-
Four wars of 1812 — 973.5
Macleod, Elizabeth
Bones never lie — 363.25
George Washington Carver — B
Top dogs — 636.7
Macquitty, Miranda
Eyewitness ocean — 551.46
Shark — 597.3
Macrae, Sloan
Deer hunting — 799.2
MACROPHOTOGRAPHY
Siwanowicz, I. Animals up close — 590
Macy, Sue
Breaking through — 796.082
Bylines — B
Sally Ride — B
Swifter higher stronger — 796.48
Wheels of change — 796.6
Mad for ads. Fyvie, E. — 659.1
The mad potter. Greenberg, J. — 738.092
MAD SCIENTIST (CONCEPT)
Anderson, M. T. Whales on stilts! — Fic
Shiga, J. Meanwhile — 741.5
A mad wicked folly. Waller, S. B. — Fic
MADAGASCAR
Heale, J. Madagascar — 969.1
MADAGASCAR -- SOCIAL LIFE AND CUSTOMS
Heale, J. Madagascar — 969.1
Madagascar. Heale, J. — 969.1
Madam C.J. Walker. Hobkirk, L. — B
Madaras, Lynda
The "what's happening to my body?" book for boys — 613.9
The "what's happening to my body?" book for girls — 613.9
Madden, Kerry
Harper Lee — B
MADDOW, RACHEL
Kisner, A. Dear Rachel Maddow — Fic
Madigan, Tim

The burning	**976.6**	Chupeco, R. Wicked as you wish	**Fic**
The **madman** of Piney Woods. Curtis, C. P.	**Fic**	Colfer, C. A tale of magic...	**Fic**
The **madness** underneath. Johnson, M.	**Fic**	Connolly, M. Comet rising	**Fic**
Mae, Natalie		Connolly, M. Hollow dolls	**Fic**
The kinder poison	**Fic**	Connolly, M. Shadow weaver	**Fic**
Maetani, Valynne E.		Cornwell, B. Venturess	**Fic**
Ink & ashes	**Fic**	Coulthurst, A. Of fire and stars	**Fic**
Mafi, Tahereh		Croggon, A. The threads of magic	**Fic**
Furthermore	**Fic**	Cuevas, A. The total eclipse of Nestor Lopez	**Fic**
A very large expanse of sea	**Fic**	Cypess, L. Death sworn	**Fic**
Whichwood	**Fic**	Cyprus, N. Sisters of glass	**Fic**
MAFIA		Dennard, S. Truthwitch	**Fic**
Blumenthal, D. Mafia girl	**Fic**	Divakaruni, C. B. The conch bearer	**Fic**
Blundell, J. Strings attached	**Fic**	Duey, K. Sacred scars	**Fic**
Green, T. Football hero	**Fic**	Dunmore, H. The deep	**Fic**
Higgins, J. Death run	**Fic**	Epstein, A. J. Circle of heroes	**Fic**
Mafia girl. Blumenthal, D.	**Fic**	Eves, R. Blood rose rebellion	**Fic**
Magellan. Bergreen, L.	**910.4**	Fagan, D. Nightingale	**Fic**
MAGELLAN, FERDINAND, 1480?-1521		Farrey, B. The Grimjinx rebellion	**Fic**
Bergreen, L. Magellan	**910.4**	Farrey, B. The Shadowhand Covenant	**Fic**
MAGI		Farrey, B. The Vengekeep prophecies	**Fic**
Fletcher, S. Alphabet of dreams	**Fic**	Fawcett, H. Even the darkest stars	**Fic**
Magi, Trina J		Fforde, J. The song of the quarkbeast	**Fic**
Intellectual freedom manual	**025.2**	Funke, C. Inkdeath	**Fic**
MAGIC		Funke, C. Inkheart	**Fic**
Alexander, L. The foundling and other tales of Prydain	**Fic**	Gaiman, N. M is for magic	**Fic**
Alexander, L. Taran Wanderer	**Fic**	Gaiman, N. Stardust	**Fic**
Anderson, J. L. Tiger Lily	**Fic**	Gallego Garcia, L. The valley of the Wolves	**Fic**
Auxier, J. Peter Nimble and his fantastic eyes	**Fic**	Gardner, S. The silver blade	**Fic**
Auxier, J. Sophie Quire and the last Storyguard	**Fic**	George, J. D. Princess of the Midnight Ball	**Fic**
Azad, N. The candle and the flame	**Fic**	Gillis, P. B. The last unicorn	**741.5**
Baptiste, T. The jumbies	**Fic**	Hatke, B. Mighty Jack	**741.5**
Bardugo, L. Siege and storm	**Fic**	Haydu, C. A. One jar of magic	**Fic**
Barnhill, K. R. The girl who drank the moon	**Fic**	Haydu, C. A. Rules for stealing stars	**Fic**
Barnhill, K. R. The mostly true story of Jack	**Fic**	Helgerson, J. Horns and wrinkles	**Fic**
Barnhill, K. R. The witch's boy	**Fic**	Hoang, V. Girl giant and the Monkey King	**Fic**
Barron, T. A. The lost years of Merlin	**Fic**	James, A. The bookwanderers	**Fic**
Bartlett, C. E. We rule the night	**Fic**	Jones, D. W. Enchanted glass	**Fic**
Beasley, C. Circus Mirandus	**Fic**	Jones, D. W. Howl's moving castle	**Fic**
Berry, J. The Amaranth enchantment	**Fic**	Jones, D. W. The islands of Chaldea	**Fic**
Black, H. The bronze key	**Fic**	Jones, F. Destiny's path	**Fic**
Black, H. The Good Neighbors	**741.5**	Jones, K. Murder magic and what we wore	**Fic**
Black, H. Red glove	**Fic**	Khoury, J. The Mystwick School of Musicraft	**Fic**
Black, H. The silver mask	**Fic**	Knox, E. Mortal fire	**Fic**
Blackwood, S. Jinx	**Fic**	Knudsen, M. The dragon of Trelian	**Fic**
Blackwood, S. Jinx's fire	**Fic**	Lackey, L. All the impossible things	**Fic**
Booraem, E. Small persons with wings	**Fic**	Landy, D. The faceless ones	**Fic**
Braswell, L. Part of your world	**Fic**	Landy, D. Playing with fire	**Fic**
Caldwell, P. A phoenix first must burn	**Fic**	Law, I. Savvy	**Fic**
Carroll, E. In darkling wood	**Fic**	Law, I. Scumble	**Fic**
Carson, R. The bitter kingdom	**Fic**	Law, I. Switch	**Fic**
Carson, R. The crown of embers	**Fic**	Le Guin, U. K. Tales from Earthsea	**Fic**
Carson, R. Walk on Earth a stranger	**Fic**	Le Guin, U. K. Voices	**Fic**
Catmull, K. The radiant road	**Fic**	Lesperance, N. The nightmare thief	**Fic**
Chabon, M. Summerland	**Fic**	Lewis, C. S. The horse and his boy	**Fic**
Chapman, E. Caster	**Fic**	Lewis, C. S. The last battle	**Fic**
Chima, C. W. The warrior heir	**Fic**	Lewis, C. S. The lion the witch and the wardrobe	**Fic**

Lewis, C. S. The magician's nephew	Fic
Lewis, C. S. Prince Caspian	Fic
Lewis, C. S. The silver chair	Fic
Lewis, C. S. The voyage of the Dawn Treader	Fic
Leyh, K. Snapdragon	741.5
Littlewood, K. Bliss	Fic
Maberry, J. The orphan army	Fic
Mae, N. The kinder poison	Fic
Marillier, J. Wildwood dancing	Fic
Marr, M. Wicked lovely	Fic
Mashima, H. Fairy tail	741.5
McCoola, M. Baba Yaga's assistant	741.5
McKinley, R. Water	Fic
Medley, L. Castle waiting	741.5
Messner, K. The seventh wish	Fic
Milford, K. Greenglass House	Fic
Milford, K. The Left-Handed Fate	Fic
Milford, K. The raconteur's commonplace book	Fic
Moriarty, J. A corner of white	Fic
Morrison, M. Grounded	Fic
Mull, B. Sky raiders	Fic
Mull, B. A world without heroes	Fic
Murdock, C. G. Princess Ben	Fic
Neumeier, R. The keeper of the mist	Fic
Nimmo, J. Midnight for Charlie Bone	Fic
Nix, G. Goldenhand	Fic
November, S. Firebirds	Fic
Okorafor, N. Ikenga	Fic
Paolini, C. Eragon	Fic
Park, L. S. Forest of wonders	Fic
Pearson, L. Hildafolk	741.5
Pierce, T. Melting stones	Fic
Pierce, T. Tris's book	Fic
Pierce, T. Wild magic	Fic
Prineas, S. The magic thief	Fic
Pullman, P. The subtle knife	Fic
Rapunzel and other magic fairy tales	398.22
Riley, J. Secret origins	Fic
Riordan, R. The throne of fire	Fic
Ritter, W. Changeling	Fic
Ritter, W. The unready queen	Fic
Rowell, R. Carry on	Fic
Rowling, J. K. The tales of Beedle the Bard	Fic
Ryon, L. Into the tall tall grass	Fic
Sage, A. StarChaser	Fic
Sage, A. Twilight hauntings	Fic
Scott, M. The alchemyst	Fic
Shivering, W. Ghosts of Weirdwood	Fic
Shivering, W. Thieves of Weirdwood	Fic
Shulman, P. The Grimm legacy	Fic
Shurtliff, L. Rump	Fic
Silvera, A. Infinity son	Fic
Smith, R. L. Hoodoo	Fic
Sniegoski, T. Quest for the Spark	Fic
Stanley, D. Bella at midnight	Fic
Stanley, D. The princess of Cortova	Fic
Stewart, T. L. The secret keepers	Fic

Stiefvater, M. Call down the hawk	Fic
Stroud, J. The amulet of Samarkand	Fic
Stroud, J. Ptolemy's gate	Fic
Stroud, J. The ring of Solomon	Fic
Taylor, L. Blackbringer	Fic
TenNapel, D. Cardboard	741.5
Thomas, S. M. The last rabbit	Fic
Trevayne, E. The accidental afterlife of Thomas Marsden	Fic
Vande Velde, V. Tales from the Brothers Grimm and the Sisters Weird	Fic
Vernon, U. Castle Hangnail	Fic
Werlin, N. Impossible	Fic
White, J. A. A path begins	Fic
White, K. The Guinevere deception	Fic
White, T. H. The once and future king	Fic
Wilson, N. D. The dragon's tooth	Fic
Wrede, P. C. Talking to dragons	Fic
Wrede, P. C. The thirteenth child	Fic
Yep, L. City of fire	Fic
Yep, L. A dragon's guide to making your human smarter	Fic
Yep, L. A dragon's guide to the care and feeding of humans	Fic
Yolen, J. Foiled	Fic
Zettel, S. Bad luck girl	Fic
Zinn, B. Poison	Fic

MAGIC (OCCULTISM)
Revis, B. Give the dark my love	Fic
Shepherd, M. Midnight beauties	Fic

MAGIC -- STUDY AND TEACHING
Duey, K. Skin hunger	Fic
Gallego Garcia, L. The valley of the Wolves	Fic
Jennings, M. Magic step-by-step	793.8
Le Guin, U. K. A wizard of Earthsea	Fic
Rowling, J. K. Harry Potter and the Chamber of Secrets	Fic
Rowling, J. K. Harry Potter and the deathly hallows	Fic
Rowling, J. K. Harry Potter and the goblet of fire	Fic
Rowling, J. K. Harry Potter and the Order of the Phoenix	Fic
Rowling, J. K. Harry Potter and the prisoner of Azkaban	Fic
Rowling, J. K. Harry Potter and the sorcerer's stone	Fic

MAGIC CLOAKS
Flinn, A. Cloaked	Fic

MAGIC CLOCKS AND WATCHES
Funaro, G. The alchemist's shadow	Fic
Stewart, T. L. The secret keepers	Fic

MAGIC FLUTES
Gardner, L. Into the woods	Fic

MAGIC GEMS
Fforde, J. The Eye of Zoltar	Fic

MAGIC HAMMERS
Riordan, R. The hammer of Thor	Fic
The magic in changing your stars. Henderson, L.	Fic
Magic Johnson. Roselius, J. C.	B

MAGIC KEYS
Nix, G. Mister Monday	Fic

MAGIC LAMPS
Braswell, L. A whole new world	Fic

MAGIC MIRRORS

Major Impossible. Hale, N.   **B**
Major, John S., 1942-
   Caravan to America   745
MAJORITIES
   Meersman, E. Majority rule vs. individual rights   321.8
Majority rule vs. individual rights. Meersman, E.   321.8
MAKAH INDIANS
   Day, C. The sea in winter   **Fic**
Make it wild! Schofield, J.   790.1
Make lemonade. Wolff, V. E.   **Fic**
Makechnie, Amy
   Ten thousand tries   **Fic**
Maker lab. Challoner, J.   507.8
MAKEUP ARTISTS
   Wright, B. Putting makeup on the fat boy   **Fic**
Making bombs for Hitler. Skrypuch, M. F.   **Fic**
Making books that fly fold wrap hide pop up twist & turn. Diehn, G.   736
Making content comprehensible for English learners. Echevarria, J.   372.652
MAKING FRIENDS
   Amblard, O. Friends forever?   158.2
   Blake, A. H. Hazel Bly and the deep blue sea   **Fic**
   Brosgol, V. Be prepared   741.5
   Glasser, D. New kid new scene   373.18
   Philippe, B. The field guide to the North American teenager   **Fic**
   Ramee, L. M. Something to say   **Fic**
   Yohalem, E. The truth according to Blue   **Fic**
Making number talks matter. Humphreys, C.   510.71
The **making** of America. Johnston, R. D.   973
Making shelter. Champion, N.   613.6
Making the cut. Gurevich, M.   **Fic**
Makoons. Erdrich, L.   **Fic**
Malala Yousafzai and the girls of Pakistan. Aretha, D.   **B**
Malam, John, 1957-
   The birth of modern nations   940.2
   Dinosaur atlas   567.9
   Early medieval times   940.1
Malamander. Taylor, T.   **Fic**
MALARIA
   Cunningham, K. Malaria   614.5
   Person, S. Malaria   614.5
MALARIA -- HISTORY
   Cunningham, K. Malaria   614.5
MALARIA -- PREVENTION
   Person, S. Malaria   614.5
MALARIA -- TRANSMISSION
   Person, S. Malaria   614.5
Malaria. Cunningham, K.   614.5
Malaria. Person, S.   614.5
MALAWI
   Michael, J. City boy   **Fic**
MALAYSIA
   Sapet, K. Jimmy Choo   746.9
Malcolm X and black pride. Sharp, A. W.   **B**
MALCOLM X, 1925-1965

Archer, J. They had a dream   323
Sharp, A. W. Malcolm X and black pride   **B**
MALDIVES
   NgCheong-Lum, R. Maldives   954
Maldives. NgCheong-Lum, R.   954
Maldonado, Torrey
   Secret Saturdays   **Fic**
   Tight   **Fic**
MALE FRIENDSHIP
   Avi. The end of the world and beyond   **Fic**
   Chmakova, S. Crush   741.5
MALI
   Blauer, E. Mali   966.23
Mali. Blauer, E.   966.23
MALI EMPIRE
   McKissack, P. The royal kingdoms of Ghana Mali and Songhay   966.2
Malice. Wooding, C.   **Fic**
MALICIOUS ACCUSATION
   Avi. City of orphans   **Fic**
   Avi. Crispin   **Fic**
   Brimner, L. D. Accused!   345.761
   Friesner, E. M. Sphinx's queen   **Fic**
   Grisham, J. The accused   **Fic**
   Hemphill, S. Wicked girls   **Fic**
   Oates, J. C. Big Mouth & Ugly Girl   **Fic**
Mallory, Kenneth
   At home beneath the sea   551.46
MALNUTRITION
   Jarrow, G. Red madness   614.5
MAMMALOGISTS
   Carson, M. K. The bat scientists   599.4
MAMMALS
   Allman, T. Deadliest mammals   599.7
   Gish, M. Bats   599.4
   Gish, M. Bison   599.64
   Gish, M. Moose   599.65
   Gregory, J. Sloths   599.3
   Koch, F. Bats   599.4
   Matzke, A. H. Hedgehog   636.9
   Montgomery, S. The magnificent migration   591.56
   Montgomery, S. The tapir scientist   599.66
   Patent, D. H. Saving the Tasmanian devil   599.2
   Reed, C. Ferret   636
   Reed, C. Mini Pig   636.4
   Somervill, B. A. Small indian mongoose   599.74
   Swanson, J. Dolphins   599.53
   Taschek, K. Hanging with bats   599.4
MAMMALS -- IDENTIFICATION
   Whitaker, J. O. National Audubon Society field guide to North American mammals   599.097
Mammals of the Northern Hemisphere. Harris, T.   599.168
Mammoth bones and broken stones. Harrison, D. L.   970.01
Man on the moon. Dell, P.   629.45
The **man** who went to the far side of the moon. Schyffert, B. U.   **B**
The **man-eating** tigers of Sundarbans. Montgomery,

The **many** faces of George Washington. McClafferty, C. K. **B**
The **many** lives of John Stone. Buckley-Archer, L. **Fic**
MANZANAR WAR RELOCATION CENTER, CALIFORNIA
    Hannigan, K. Mask **Fic**
    Houston, J. W. Farewell to Manzanar **940.54**
MANZANO, SONIA
    Manzano, S. Becoming Maria **B**
Manzano, Sonia
    Becoming Maria **B**
    The revolution of Evelyn Serrano **Fic**
Mao Zedong. Heuston, K. B. **B**
Mao Zedong. Slavicek, L. C. **B**
Mao Zedong and the Chinese Revolution. Naden, C. J. **951.05092**
MAO, ZEDONG, 1893-1976
    Davis, K. C. Strongman **321.9092**
    Heuston, K. B. Mao Zedong **B**
    Naden, C. J. Mao Zedong and the Chinese Revolution **951.05092**
    Slavicek, L. C. Mao Zedong **B**
MAORI (NEW ZEALAND PEOPLE)
    Jackson, B. New Zealand **993**
MAORI (NEW ZEALAND PEOPLE) -- HISTORY
    Connolly, S. The Americas and the Pacific **970.004**
A **map** of days. Riggs, R. **Fic**
MAPLE
    Frederick, H. V. Yours Truly **Fic**
Mapping the bones. Yolen, J. **Fic**
MAPS
    Grove, S. E. The crimson skew **Fic**
    Grove, S. E. The golden specific **Fic**
    Hoobler, D. Seven paths to death **Fic**
    Jennings, K. Maps and geography **910**
    Levenseller, T. Daughter of the pirate king **Fic**
    Milford, K. Ghosts of Greenglass House **Fic**
    Taylor, B. Looking at maps **912**
Maps and geography. Jennings, K. **910**
Mar, Jonathan
    The body book for boys **613**
Mara, Wil
    Canada **971**
    From locusts to...automobile anti-collision systems **629.2**
    People's Republic of China **951**
    Poland **943.8**
    Space exploration **629.4**
Maraniss, Andrew
    Games of deception **796.48**
    Singled out **B**
    Strong inside **B**
Marcelo in the real world. Stork, F. X. **Fic**
March. Lewis, J. **B**
The **March** against Fear. Bausum, A. **323.1196**
March forward girl. Beals, M. **379.2**
MARCH ON WASHINGTON FOR JOBS AND FREEDOM (1963 : WASHINGTON, D.C.)
    Aretha, D. The story of the civil rights March on Washington

for Jobs and Freedom in photographs **975.3**
Marchetta, Melina, 1965-
    Finnikin of the rock **Fic**
MARCHING BANDS
    Mills, E. Famous in a small town **Fic**
Marching for freedom. Partridge, E. **323.1196**
Marching to the mountaintop. Bausum, A. **323.092**
Marco Polo. Twist, C. **B**
Marcovitz, Hal
    Ancient Greece **938**
    Asthma **616.2**
    Black in America **305.896**
    Greta Thunberg **B**
    Hate crimes **364.15**
    The opioid epidemic **362.29**
Marcus, Kimberly
    Exposed **Fic**
Marcus, Leonard S.
    Funny business **813**
    The wand in the word **813.009**
Mare's war. Davis, T. S. **Fic**
Maresi. Turtschaninoff, M. **Fic**
MARGINALIZED CHILDREN
    Minor, C. We got this. **371.82996073**
MARGINALIZED PEOPLE
    Hudson, W. The talk **305.8**
Margolis, Leslie
    Girl's best friend **Fic**
Marguiles, Phillip
    The devil on trial **345.73**
Marie Curie. Krull, K. **B**
Mariel of Redwall. Jacques, B. **Fic**
MARIJUANA
    Bjornlund, L. Marijuana **362.29**
    Gottfried, T. Marijuana **613.8**
    Wallace, R. One good punch **Fic**
MARIJUANA -- HEALTH ASPECTS
    Clayborne, L. The benefits of medical marijuana **615.7**
MARIJUANA -- LAW AND LEGISLATION
    Bjornlund, L. Marijuana **362.29**
    Clayborne, L. The benefits of medical marijuana **615.7**
    Szumski, B. Is medical marijuana necessary? **615.7**
MARIJUANA -- THERAPEUTIC USE
    Clayborne, L. The benefits of medical marijuana **615.7**
Marijuana. Bjornlund, L. **362.29**
Marijuana. Gottfried, T. **613.8**
MARIJUANA ABUSE
    Bjornlund, L. Marijuana **362.29**
    Gottfried, T. Marijuana **613.8**
Marillier, Juliet
    Cybele's secret **Fic**
    Wildwood dancing **Fic**
Marina. Ruiz Zafon, C. **Fic**
MARINE ANIMALS
    Cerullo, M. M. Journey to shark island **597.309164**
    Cerullo, M. M. Seeking giant sharks **597.3**
    Cerullo, M. M. Sharks of the deep **597.3**

Rhodes, J. P. Black brother black brother **Fic**
Thompson, H. The language inside **Fic**
Trueit, T. S. Massachusetts **974.4**
Werlin, N. The killer's cousin **Fic**
Wolk, L. Beyond the bright sea **Fic**

MASSACHUSETTS -- HISTORY -- NEW PLYMOUTH, 1620-1691
Messner, K. The Mayflower **974.4**
Philbrick, N. The Mayflower and the Pilgrims' new world **973.2**
Massachusetts. Trueit, T. S. **974.4**

MASSACHUSETTS INSTITUTE OF TECHNOLOGY
Chao, G. American panda **Fic**

MASSACRES
Goldstone, L. Unpunished murder **976.3**
The **master** guide to drawing anime how to draw original characters from simple templates. Hart, C. **741.5**
Master of his fate. Tobin, J. **B**
Masterpieces up close. D'Harcourt, C. **759**
Mastiff. Pierce, T. **Fic**
Matas, Carol, 1949-
After the war **Fic**
Matched. Condie, A. B. **Fic**

MATCHMAKING
Condie, A. B. Matched **Fic**
Horvath, P. One year in Coal Harbor **Fic**

MATE SELECTION
Condie, A. B. Matched **Fic**
Irving, W. The legend of Sleepy Hollow **Fic**

MATERIAL CULTURE
Hansen, J. Breaking ground breaking silence **305.5**
Liu-Perkins, C. At home in her tomb **931**
O'Connor, J. The emperor's silent army **931**
Pinkwater, D. M. The Neddiad **Fic**
Whiting, J. Life along the ancient Nile **932.01**
Math doesn't suck. McKellar, D. **510**
Math matters. Chapin, S. H. **372.7**
Math workshop. Lempp, J. **372.7**

MATHEMATICS
Ball, J. Go figure! **793.74**
Bertoletti, J. C. How fashion designers use math **746.9**
Frederick, S. Football **796.332**
Hynson, C. Dream jobs in math **510.23**
McKellar, D. Math doesn't suck **510**
Young, T. Cool math **510**

MATHEMATICS -- HISTORY
Blanchard, A. Arab science and invention in the golden age **509**

MATHEMATICS -- STUDY AND TEACHING
Aungst, G. 5 principles of the modern mathematics classroom **510.71**

MATHEMATICS -- STUDY AND TEACHING (ELEMENTARY)
Chapin, S. H. Classroom discussions **372.7**
Chapin, S. H. Math matters **372.7**
Humphreys, C. Making number talks matter **510.71**
Lempp, J. Math workshop **372.7**

Vasquez, J. A. STEM lesson essentials grades 3-8 **372.35**
MATHEMATICS -- STUDY AND TEACHING (MIDDLE SCHOOL)
Humphreys, C. Making number talks matter **510.71**
McKellar, D. Math doesn't suck **510**

MATHEMATICS FUN
Ball, J. Go figure! **793.74**
Matson, Morgan
Since you've been gone **Fic**

MATTER
Claybourne, A. The nature of matter **530**
Gardner, R. Solids liquids and gases experiments using water air marbles and more **530.078**
Mooney, C. Chemistry **540**

MATTER -- CONSTITUTION
Campbell, M. C. Discovering atoms **539.7**
Manning, P. Atoms molecules and compounds **539.7**

MATTER -- PROPERTIES
Field, A. R. Matter **530**
Matter. Field, A. R. **530**
A **matter** of souls. Patrick, D. L. **Fic**
Mattern, Joanne, 1963-
Benny Goodman **B**
Ralph Lauren **B**
So you want to work in sports? **796**
Matti, Truus, 1961-
Departure time **Fic**
Mister orange **Fic**
Mattimeo. Jacques, B. **Fic**
Matzke, Ann H.
Hedgehog **636.9**
Mini horse **636.1**
Mauled by a bear. Hamilton, S. L. **599.78**
Maurer, Richard, 1950-
Destination moon **629.45**

MAURITANIA
Blauer, E. Mauritania **966.1**
Mauritania. Blauer, E. **966.1**
Maus. Spiegelman, A. **B**

MAUSOLEUM (HALICARNASSUS)
Lerangis, P. The tomb of shadows **Fic**

MAUSOLEUMS
Gibson, K. B. The Taj Mahal **954**

MAWANGDUI SITE (CHINA)
Liu-Perkins, C. At home in her tomb **931**
Maximizing the impact of comics in your library. Phoenix, J. **026**
Maxwell, Lucas
Podcasting with youth **006.7**
May B. Rose, C. S. **Fic**
Maya and the rising dark. Barron, R. **Fic**
Maya Angelou. Angelou, M. **811**
Maya Lin. Rubin, S. G. **720.92**

MAYAN GIRLS
Pellegrino, M. Journey of dreams **Fic**

MAYAS
Croy, A. Ancient Aztec and Maya **972**

Funny you don't look autistic	616.85	Ice time	796.355
Mccrite, K. D. (Kathaleen Deiser)		**Mckinley, Robin**	
In front of God and everybody	Fic	Beauty	Fic
Mcculloch, Amy, 1986-		The blue sword	Fic
Jinxed	Fic	Chalice	Fic
Mccully, Emily Arnold		Fire	Fic
Dreaming in code	B	The hero and the crown	Fic
Ida M. Tarbell	B	The outlaws of Sherwood	Fic
Mccurdy, Michael		Pegasus	Fic
Walden then & now	B	Rose daughter	Fic
Mcdaniel, Lurlene		Water	Fic
Breathless	Fic	**Mckinney, L. L. (Leatrice L.)**	
Hit and run	Fic	Nubia	741.5
Mcdaniel, Melissa, 1964-		**Mckissack, Pat, 1944-2017**	
Arizona	979.1	Black hands white sails	639.2
Mcdonnell, Julia, 1979-		The dark-thirty	Fic
How precious metals form	622	A friendship for today	Fic
Mcdougall, Chros		Nzingha	Fic
Girls play to win figure skating	796.91	Porch lies	Fic
Girls play to win track & field	796.42	The royal kingdoms of Ghana Mali and Songhay	966.2
Jesse Owens	B	**Mclaughlin, Timothy P.**	
Mcgarry, Katie		Walking on Earth & touching the sky	810.8
Only a breath apart	Fic	**Mclemore, Anna-Marie**	
Mcgee, Marni		Blanca & Roja	Fic
National Geographic investigates ancient Greece	938	**Mcmahon, Dave**	
Mcginnis, Mindy		Girls play to win hockey	796.962
Be not far from me	Fic	**Mcmanis, Charlene Willing, 1953-2018**	
Mcginnis, Samuel M		Indian no more	Fic
Peterson field guide to western reptiles and amphibians	597.9	**Mcmann, Lisa**	
		Cryer's cross	Fic
Mcgrane, Madeline		Wake	Fic
The accursed vampire	741.5	**Mcmanus, Sean, 1973-**	
Mcguigan, Mary Ann		How to code in 10 easy lessons	005.13
Morning in a different place	Fic	**MCMULLAN, JAMES, 1934-**	
Mchugh, Erin, 1969-		McMullan, J. Leaving China	B
National parks	333.78	**Mcmullan, James, 1934-**	
Mcintyre, Thomas, 1952-		Leaving China	B
The behavior survival guide for kids	649	**Mcmullan, Margaret**	
MCKAY, CHRISTOPHER P.		How I found the Strong	Fic
Turner, P. S. Life on Earth---and beyond	571.0919	Sources of light	Fic
Mckay, Hilary		When I crossed No-Bob	Fic
Binny for short	Fic	**Mcmullen, Beth, 1969-**	
Caddy ever after	Fic	Mrs. Smith's Spy School for Girls	Fic
Forever Rose	Fic	**Mcnab, Andy, 1959-**	
Indigo's star	Fic	Avenger	Fic
Saffy's angel	Fic	**Mcnab, Chris, 1970-**	
The time of green magic	Fic	50 things you should know about the Vietnam War	959.704
Mckay, Sharon E.		**Mcnamara, Julie**	
Thunder over Kandahar	Fic	Beyond invert & multiply	372.7
Mckellar, Danica		**Mcneal, Tom**	
Math doesn't suck	510	Far far away	Fic
Mckenna, Miles		**Mcneese, Tim**	
Out!	306.76	Civil War battles	973.7
Mckernan, Victoria		Colonial America 1543-1763	973.2
The devil's paintbox	Fic	The Donner Party	979.4
Shackleton's stowaway	Fic	Early national America 1790-1850	973.3
Mckinley, Michael, 1961-		Tito Puente	B

Gow, M. The greatest doctor of ancient times — 610.938
Kent, D. Snake pits talking cures & magic bullets — 616.89
Newquist, H. P. The human body — 610
Rooney, A. The history of medicine — 610.9
Townsend, J. Scalpels stitches + scars — 617
Wittenstein, V. O. For the good of mankind? — 174.2
Younker, J. M. Bleed blister puke and purge — 610.9

MEDICINE -- HISTORY 15TH CENTURY
Dawson, I. Renaissance medicine — 610

MEDICINE -- HISTORY 16TH CENTURY
Dawson, I. Renaissance medicine — 610

MEDICINE SHOWS
Milford, K. The Boneshaker — Fic

MEDICINE, ANCIENT
Kelly, K. Early civilizations — 610.938
Medieval crusades. Currie, S. — 909.07
Medieval Europe. Nardo, D. — 940.1
The medieval knights. Park, L. — 909.07
Medieval life. Langley, A. — 909.07

MEDIEVAL MILITARY HISTORY
Helget, N. L. Mongols — 950

MEDIEVAL PERIOD (476-1492)
Anderson, M. T. Yvain — 741.5
Avi. Crispin — Fic
Berry, J. The passion of Dolssa — Fic
Coats, J. A. The wicked and the just — Fic
Cushman, K. Catherine called Birdy — Fic
Cushman, K. The midwife's apprentice — Fic
Gaughen, A. C. Scarlet — Fic
Haddix, M. P. Sent — Fic
Krull, K. Leonardo da Vinci — 509
Napoli, D. J. Hush — Fic
Pasternack, S. Anya and the nightingale — Fic
Schlitz, L. A. Good masters! Sweet ladies! — 812
Vande Velde, V. The book of Mordred — Fic
Whitman, E. Wildwing — Fic
Williams, M. Chaucer's Canterbury Tales — 821
Yolen, J. The queen's own fool — Fic

MEDIEVAL SCIENCE
Huff, T. E. An age of science and revolutions 1600-1800 — 909

Medina, Meg
Merci Suarez can't dance — Fic

Medina, Tony
I and I — B

MEDITATION
Watson, G. F. Extreme abilities — 612

MEDITATION FOR CHILDREN
Chopra, M. Just breathe — 158.1

MEDITERRANEAN REGION
Friesner, E. M. Nobody's princess — Fic
Friesner, E. M. Nobody's prize — Fic

MEDIUMS
Henry, A. The lonely dead — Fic
McCaughrean, G. The kite rider — Fic

Medley, Linda
Castle waiting — 741.5

MEDUSA (GREEK MYTHOLOGY)

Hirschmann, K. Medusa — 398.2
McCaughrean, G. Perseus — 398.2
Medusa. Hirschmann, K. — 398.2
The Medusa plot. Korman, G. — Fic

Meersman, Erika
Majority rule vs. individual rights — 321.8
Meet Cindy Sherman. Greenberg, J. — 770.92
Meet the dancers. Nathan, A. — 792.802
Megafast motorcycles. Farndon, J. — 629.227

MEGALITHIC MONUMENTS
Aronson, M. If stones could speak — 936.2

Meigs, Cornelia, 1884-1973
Invincible Louisa — B

Meinkoth, Norman August, 1913-
The Audubon Society field guide to North American seashore creatures — 592

MEIR, GOLDA MABOVITZ, 1898-1978
Blashfield, J. F. Golda Meir — B

Meissner, David
Call of the Klondike — 971.9

MEITNER, LISE, 1878-1968
Conkling, W. Radioactive! — 539.7

Mejia, Tehlor Kay
Paola Santiago and the river of tears — Fic

MELBOURNE, VICTORIA
Abdel-Fattah, R. Does my head look big in this? — Fic
Crowley, C. Words in deep blue — Fic
Wood, F. Cloudwish — Fic

Melchior-Durand, Stephane
The golden compass — 741.5

MELIES, GEORGES, 1861-1938
Selznick, B. The invention of Hugo Cabret — Fic

Melleby, Nicole
How to become a planet — Fic
In the role of Brie Hutchens... — Fic

Meloy, Colin
Under Wildwood — Fic
Wildwood — Fic
Wildwood imperium — Fic

Meloy, Maile
The apothecary — Fic
Meltdown. Langeland, D. — 363.17
Melting stones. Pierce, T. — Fic

MELTZER, MILTON, 1915-2009
Meltzer, M. Milton Meltzer — B

Meltzer, Milton, 1915-2009
Milton Meltzer — B
Rescue — 940.53
Memoirs of a teenage amnesiac. Zevin, G. — Fic

MEMORIALS
Rubin, S. G. Maya Lin — 720.92

MEMORIES
Antieau, K. Ruby's imagine — Fic
Keplinger, K. That's not what happened — Fic
Lowry, L. The giver — Fic
Lowry, L. Giver quartet — 741.5
Sís, P. Tibet — 951

Poe, E. A. The raven **811**
Siebert, M. Heads up **616.89**
Strange, L. The secret of Nightingale Wood **Fic**

MENTAL ILLNESS -- CHEMOTHERAPY
Esherick, J. The FDA & psychiatric drugs **615.7**

MENTAL ILLNESS -- HISTORY
Kent, D. Snake pits talking cures & magic bullets **616.89**

MENTAL ILLNESS IN LITERATURE
Richmond, K. J. Mental illness in young adult literature **813**
Mental illness in young adult literature. Richmond, K. J. **813**
Mentor texts. Dorfman, L. R. **372.6**

MENTORING
Watson, R. Piecing me together **Fic**

MENTORS
Anderson, J. D. Sidekicked **Fic**
Mera. Paige, D. **Fic**
Mercado, Nancy E.
Baseball crazy **Fic**
Every man for himself **Fic**

MERCADO, YEHUDI
Mercado, Y. Chunky **B**
Mercado, Yehudi
Chunky **B**

MERCENARIES
Tucholke, A. G. The Boneless Mercies **Fic**
Mercer, Bobby, 1961-
The flying machine book **745.592**
Junk drawer engineering **620.0078**
The robot book **629.8**
The **merchant** of death. MacHale, D. J. **Fic**
The **merchant** of Venice. Hinds, G. **741.5**

MERCHANTS
Marillier, J. Cybele's secret **Fic**
Merci Suarez can't dance. Medina, M. **Fic**
The **merciful** Crow. Owen, M. **Fic**

MERCY
Jaffe, N. The cow of no color **Fic**

MEREDITH, JAMES HOWARD, 1933-
Bausum, A. The March against Fear **323.1196**

MERIAN, MARIA SIBYLLA, 1647-1717
Atkins, J. Finding wonders **Fic**
Sidman, J. The girl who drew butterflies **B**
Merino, Noel
Abortion **362.1988**

MERLIN (LEGENDARY CHARACTER)
Barron, T. A. The lost years of Merlin **Fic**
White, T. H. The once and future king **Fic**
The **mermaid** of Warsaw. Monte, R. **398.2**

MERMAIDS
Appelt, K. Keeper **Fic**
Baptiste, T. Rise of the jumbies **Fic**
Braswell, L. Part of your world **Fic**
Dunmore, H. The deep **Fic**
Dunmore, H. Ingo **Fic**
Dunmore, H. The tide knot **Fic**
Farmer, N. The Islands of the Blessed **Fic**
Kessler, L. Emily Windsnap and the castle in the mist **Fic**

Kessler, L. Emily Windsnap and the land of the midnight sun **Fic**
Kessler, L. The tail of Emily Windsnap **Fic**
McKinley, R. Water **Fic**

MERMEN
Avery, T. Not as we know it **Fic**
Dunmore, H. The deep **Fic**
Dunmore, H. Ingo **Fic**
Dunmore, H. The tide knot **Fic**
McKinley, R. Water **Fic**
Merriam-Webster's intermediate dictionary. Merriam-Webster, I. **423**
Merriam-Webster's school thesaurus.. Merriam-Webster, I. **423**
Merriam-Webster's visual dictionary. Corbeil, J. **423**
Merriam-Webster, Inc
Merriam-Webster's intermediate dictionary **423**
Merriam-Webster's school thesaurus. **423**

MERRICK, JOSEPH CAREY, 1862-1890
Kirby, M. J. A taste for monsters **Fic**
Merrill, Jean Fairbanks
The pushcart war **Fic**

MERRIMACK (FRIGATE)
Avi. Iron thunder **Fic**
The **merry** adventures of Robin Hood. Pyle, H. **398.2**

MERRY-GO-ROUND
Towell, K. Skary childrin and the carousel of sorrow **Fic**

MESOPOTAMIA
Nardo, D. Cause & effect **935**

MESOPOTAMIA -- CIVILIZATION
Kerrigan, M. Mesopotamians **935**

MESOPOTAMIA -- HISTORY
Kerrigan, M. Mesopotamians **935**
O'Neal, C. We visit Iraq **956.7**

MESOPOTAMIA -- HISTORY -- TO 330 B.C.E.
McCaughrean, G. Gilgamesh the hero **398.2**
Mesopotamians. Kerrigan, M. **935**
Messner, Kate
The brilliant fall of Gianna Z **Fic**
Chirp **Fic**
The Mayflower **974.4**
Pearl Harbor **940.54**
The seventh wish **Fic**
Solve this **507.8**
Tracking pythons **597.96**

METAFICTION
Anderson, M. T. He laughed with his other mouths **Fic**
Anderson, M. T. Whales on stilts! **Fic**
Bosch, P. The name of this book is secret **Fic**
Funke, C. Inkdeath **Fic**
Funke, C. Inkheart **Fic**
Funke, C. Inkspell **Fic**
Gidwitz, A. The Grimm conclusion **Fic**
Gidwitz, A. In a glass Grimmly **Fic**
Hale, S. The storybook of legends **Fic**
Maguire, G. Egg & spoon **Fic**
Patterson, J. House of robots **Fic**

MICROSCOPE AND MICROSCOPY -- EXPERIMENTS
Levine, S. The ultimate guide to your microscope — 570.28
MICROSCOPE AND MICROSCOPY -- HISTORY
Kramer, S. P. Hidden worlds — 570
MICROSCOPE AND MICROSCOPY -- TECHNIQUE
Levine, S. The ultimate guide to your microscope — 570.28
MIDDLE AGES
Knight, J. Middle ages — 909.07
Middle ages. Knight, J. — 909.07
MIDDLE EAST
Adams, S. The Iraq War — 956.7044
Azad, N. The candle and the flame — Fic
Cooper, R. Bahrain — 953.65
Elkeles, S. How to ruin a summer vacation — Fic
Higgins, J. Sharp shot — Fic
Owings, L. Israel — 956.94
Samuels, C. Iraq — 956.7
Sonneborn, L. Kuwait — 953.67
Woolf, A. The Arab-Israeli War since 1948 — 956.04
Yomtov, N. Syria — 956.91
MIDDLE EAST -- ANTIQUITIES
Podany, A. H. The ancient Near Eastern world — 939
MIDDLE EAST -- DESCRIPTION AND TRAVEL
Feiler, B. Walking the Bible — 222
MIDDLE EAST -- HISTORY -- 20TH CENTURY
Robinson, A. Young Palestinians speak — 956.95
MIDDLE EAST -- HISTORY -- TO 622
Podany, A. H. The ancient Near Eastern world — 939
MIDDLE EAST -- SOCIAL LIFE AND CUSTOMS
Nye, N. S. 19 varieties of gazelle — 811
MIDDLE EASTERN-INFLUENCED FANTASY
Alexander, L. The golden dream of Carlo Chuchio — Fic
Azad, N. The candle and the flame — Fic
Braswell, L. A whole new world — Fic
Cyprus, N. Sisters of glass — Fic
Mae, N. The kinder poison — Fic
Marillier, J. Cybele's secret — Fic
Napoli, D. J. Beast — Fic
Rossetti, R. The girl with borrowed wings — Fic
Stroud, J. The amulet of Samarkand — Fic
Stroud, J. The golem's eye — Fic
Stroud, J. Ptolemy's gate — Fic
Stroud, J. The ring of Solomon — Fic
The middle passage. Feelings, T. — 704.03
Middle school is worse than meatloaf. Holm, J. L. — Fic
MIDDLE SCHOOL LIBRARIES -- COLLECTION DE-VELOPMENT
Smith, K. M. Creating a tween collection — 025.2
MIDDLE SCHOOL STUDENTS
Anderson, J. D. Posted — Fic
Angleberger, T. Emperor Pickletine rides the bus — Fic
Angleberger, T. Fuzzy — Fic
Angleberger, T. Princess Labelmaker to the rescue! — Fic
Bauer, A. C. E. Come Fall — Fic
Brown, G. Josh Baxter levels up — Fic
Chmakova, S. Brave — 741.5
Chmakova, S. Crush — 741.5

Condie, A. B. The Beast — Fic
De la Cruz, M. Never after — Fic
Dowell, F. O. The class — Fic
Dowell, F. O. Falling in — Fic
George, K. O. Swimming upstream — 811
Gephart, D. How to survive middle school — Fic
Giles, C. D. Take back the block — Fic
Grabenstein, C. The smartest kid in the universe — Fic
Higuera, D. B. Lupe Wong won't dance — Fic
Holm, J. L. Swing it Sunny — 741.5
Holt, K. A. Redwood and Ponytail — Fic
Hotta, Y. Hikaru no Go — 741.5
Hyman, F. Mango Delight — Fic
Johnson, C. G. The Breakaways — 741.5
Johnson, V. The great Greene heist — Fic
Johnson, V. To catch a cheat — Fic
Kelly, E. E. We dream of space — Fic
Kinney, J. The deep end — Fic
Kinney, J. Diary of a wimpy kid — Fic
Kinney, J. Dog days — Fic
Kinney, J. The long haul — Fic
Kinney, J. Old school — Fic
Kinney, J. The ugly truth — Fic
Klise, K. Regarding the bathrooms — Fic
Korman, G. Linked — Fic
Korman, G. Notorious — Fic
Korman, G. Schooled — Fic
Lane, K. Pity party — Fic
Larocca, R. Red white and whole — Fic
Leyh, K. Snapdragon — 741.5
Luddy, K. Spelldown — Fic
Palacio, R. J. Wonder — Fic
Park, L. S. The one thing you'd save — Fic
Patterson, J. Best nerds forever — Fic
Pearsall, S. All of the above — Fic
Philbrick, W. R. Wild river — Fic
Pixley, M. F. Freak — Fic
Shimura, T. Wandering son — 741.5
Vaught, S. Things too huge to fix by saying sorry — Fic
Winerip, M. Adam Canfield of the Slash — Fic
Zaczek, A. Martin McLean middle school queen — Fic
MIDDLE SCHOOL STUDENTS -- BOOKS AND READ-ING
Robb, L. Teaching reading in middle school — 428.4071
Smith, K. M. Creating a tween collection — 025.2
MIDDLE SCHOOL STUDENTS -- PSYCHOLOGY
Fox, A. Real friends vs. the other kind — 177
MIDDLE SCHOOL TEACHERS
Dowell, F. O. The class — Fic
Middle school. Patterson, J. — Fic
MIDDLE SCHOOLS
Abdul-Jabbar, K. Stealing the game — Fic
Angleberger, T. Fuzzy — Fic
Angleberger, T. Princess Labelmaker to the rescue! — Fic
Bigelow, L. J. Hazel's theory of evolution — Fic
Brown, G. Josh Baxter levels up — Fic
Brown, J. Return of the Padawan — 741.5

Brown, J. Star Wars — 741.5

Cabot, M. From the notebooks of a middle school princess — Fic

Chmakova, S. Awkward — 741.5

Chmakova, S. Crush — 741.5

Dee, B. Star-crossed — Fic

Dowell, F. O. The class — Fic

Draper, S. M. Double dutch — Fic

George, K. O. Swimming upstream — 811

Hamza, N. Ahmed Aziz's epic year — Fic

Harrell, R. Wink — Fic

Heider, M. W. The losers at the center of the galaxy — Fic

Holm, J. L. The fourteenth goldfish — Fic

Holm, J. L. Swing it Sunny — 741.5

Jamieson, V. All's faire in middle school — 741.5

Johnson, V. The great Greene heist — Fic

Johnson, V. To catch a cheat — Fic

Jung, M. Geeks girls and secret identities — Fic

Kinney, J. Hard luck — Fic

Kinney, J. Old school — Fic

Kinney, J. The third wheel — Fic

Korman, G. Linked — Fic

Korman, G. Schooled — Fic

Lane, K. Pity party — Fic

Patterson, J. House of robots — Fic

Perl, E. S. The capybara conspiracy — Fic

Ponti, J. Trapped! — Fic

Ponti, J. Vanished! — Fic

Preller, J. Bystander — Fic

Russell, R. R. Tales from a not-so-fabulous life — Fic

Sonnenblick, J. After ever after — Fic

Sovern, M. J. The meaning of Maggie — Fic

Stead, R. Goodbye stranger — Fic

Zaczek, A. Martin McLean middle school queen — Fic

MIDDLE WEST

Barzak, C. The gone away place — Fic

Blashfield, J. F. Iowa — 977.7

McGrane, M. The accursed vampire — 741.5

Peck, R. The teacher's funeral — Fic

Middleman, Amy B.

American Medical Association boys' guide to becoming a teen — 613

MIDLEVEL HEALTH PRACTITIONERS

Strange, C. Physicians assistants & nurses — 610.73

Midnight beauties. Shepherd, M. — Fic

Midnight for Charlie Bone. Nimmo, J. — Fic

The **Midnight** Palace. Ruiz Zafon, C. — Fic

Midnight thief. Blackburne, L. — Fic

A **midsummer** night's dream. Sobran, J. — 822.3

Midsummer's mayhem. LaRocca, R. — Fic

MIDWAY, BATTLE OF, 1942

Torres, J. A. The Battle of Midway — 940.54

The **midwife's** apprentice. Cushman, K. — Fic

Midwinterblood. Sedgwick, M. — Fic

MIDWIVES

Cushman, K. The midwife's apprentice — Fic

O'Brien, C. M. Birthmarked — Fic

MIESCHER, FRIEDRICH, 1844-1895

Dorling Kindersley, I. The DNA book — 572.8

Mieville, China

Railsea — Fic

Mightier than the sword. Yolen, J. — 398.2

The **mighty** 12. Smith, C. R. — 398.2

Mighty Jack. Hatke, B. — 741.5

The **mighty** Mars rovers. Rusch, E. — 523.43

MIGRANT AGRICULTURAL LABORERS

Alvarez, J. Return to sender — Fic

Jimenez, F. Breaking through — Fic

Jimenez, F. The circuit — Fic

Jimenez, F. Reaching out — Fic

Kadohata, C. The thing about luck — Fic

MIGRANT AGRICULTURAL LABORERS -- LABOR UNIONS

Brimner, L. D. Strike! — 331.8

MIGRANT LABOR

Stanley, J. Children of the Dust Bowl — 371.96

Migrant mother. Nardo, D. — 973.917

MIGRANT WORKERS

Brimner, L. D. Strike! — 331.8

Nardo, D. Migrant mother — 973.917

Migration nation. O'Sullivan, J. — 591.56

MIGRATION, INTERNAL

Lawrence, J. The great migration — 759.13

MIGRATIONS OF NATIONS

Helget, N. L. Barbarians — 940.1

Hinds, K. Goths — 936

Mihaly, Christy

Diet for a changing climate — 613.2

Mikaelsen, Ben, 1952-

Ghost of Spirit Bear — Fic

Touching Spirit Bear — Fic

Miles Davis. Orr, T. — B

Miles Morales. Reynolds, J. — Fic

Miles to go for freedom. Osborne, L. B. — 305.896

Miles, John C. (John Christian), 1960-

Pathways through Antarctica — 304.2

Pathways through Europe — 304.2

Miles, Lisa

Ballet spectacular — 792.8

Milestones of flight. Grove, T. — 629.109

Milford, Kate

Bluecrowne — Fic

The Boneshaker — Fic

Ghosts of Greenglass House — Fic

Greenglass House — Fic

The Left-Handed Fate — Fic

The raconteur's commonplace book — Fic

The thief knot — Fic

MILITARY AIRCRAFT

Jackson, R. 101 great bombers — 623.74

Jackson, R. 101 great fighters — 623.74

Mooney, C. Pilotless planes — 623.74

MILITARY ART AND SCIENCE

Torres, J. A. The Battle of Midway — 940.54

Paulsen, G. Woodsong — **796.5**

The **minnow**. Sweeney, D. — **Fic**

Minor, Cornelius
We got this. — **371.82996073**

The **miracle** & tragedy of the Dionne quintuplets. Miller, S. E. — **306.875**

Miracle on 49th Street. Lupica, M. — **Fic**

Miracle on ice. Burgan, M. — **796.962**

MIRACLES
Arnold, E. K. The question of miracles — **Fic**

MIRACLES (CHRISTIANITY)
Connolly, S. New Testament miracles — **226.7**

Mirage. Daud, S. — **Fic**

Mirk, Sarah
You do you — **306.70835**

Mirror with a memory. Weaver, J. — **971.0022**

MirrorMask. Gaiman, N. — **Fic**

MIRRORS
Hughes, N. Refraction — **Fic**

MISADVENTURES
Adams, D. The hitchhiker's guide to the galaxy — **Fic**
Gantos, J. Jack's black book — **Fic**
Lowry, L. Anastasia at your service — **Fic**
Nye, N. S. I'll ask you three times are you ok? — **811**
Rowell, R. Wayward son — **Fic**

The **misadventures** of the family Fletcher. Levy, D. A. — **Fic**

MISBEHAVIOR
Patterson, J. Middle school — **Fic**

MISBEHAVIOR IN BOYS
Patterson, J. Middle school — **Fic**

MISCHIEF
Datlow, E. The Coyote Road — **Fic**
Hargrave, J. Sir John Hargrave's mischief maker's manual — **818**
McKay, H. Forever Rose — **Fic**

MISCHIEF IN BOYS
Twain, M. The adventures of Tom Sawyer — **Fic**

MISCONCEPTIONS
Isabella, J. Hoaxed! — **507**

MISERLINESS
Dickens, C. A Christmas carol [Lynch ill.] — **Fic**

MISFITS (PERSONS)
Anderson, L. H. Speak — **Fic**
Bauer, A. C. E. No castles here — **Fic**
Bean, L. The ship we built — **Fic**
Black, H. Geektastic — **Fic**
Broach, E. Shakespeare's secret — **Fic**
Cameron, S. Last bus to Everland — **Fic**
Dowell, F. O. Falling in — **Fic**
Ellis, A. D. This is what I did — **Fic**
Harrell, R. Wink — **Fic**
Henry, K. Heretics anonymous — **Fic**
Howe, J. Addie on the inside — **Fic**
Howe, J. The misfits — **Fic**
Howe, J. Totally Joe — **Fic**
Jennings, P. Odd weird & little — **Fic**
Kaufman, A. Aurora rising — **Fic**

Magoon, K. Camo girl — **Fic**

Noyes, D. Sideshow — **Fic**

Parker, M. Who put this song on? — **Fic**

Patterson, J. Best nerds forever — **Fic**

Pierce, T. Sandry's book — **Fic**

Pierson, D. C. The boy who couldn't sleep and never had to — **Fic**

Pixley, M. F. Freak — **Fic**

Pratchett, T. Only you can save mankind — **Fic**

Silvey, C. Jasper Jones — **Fic**

Tanner, L. Ice breaker — **Fic**

West, J. A storm of wishes — **Fic**

Wolkenstein, M. E. Turtle boy — **Fic**

Yang, G. L. American born Chinese — **741.5**

The **misfits**. Howe, J. — **Fic**

MISINFORMATION
Brown, R. T. Breaking the news — **070.9**
Miller, M. Fake news — **070.4**
Otis, C. L. True or false — **070.4**

Miss Crandall's school for young ladies & little misses of color. Alexander, E. — **811**

Miss Daisy is crazy! Gutman, D. — **Fic**

Miss Ellicott's school for the magically minded. Blackwood, S. — **Fic**

Miss Peregrine's home for peculiar children. Riggs, R. — **Fic**

Miss Spitfire. Miller, S. E. — **Fic**

MISSILES
Stein, R. C. Cuban Missile Crisis — **972.9106**

MISSING BOYS
Dowd, S. The London Eye mystery — **Fic**
Kelly, E. E. Hello universe — **Fic**
Meloy, C. Wildwood — **Fic**

MISSING CHILDREN
Baptiste, T. Rise of the jumbies — **Fic**
Barnhill, K. R. The mostly true story of Jack — **Fic**
Beaufrand, M. J. Useless Bay — **Fic**
Cooney, C. B. The face on the milk carton — **Fic**
Corona, J. Feathers — **741.5**
DiCamillo, K. The magician's elephant — **Fic**
Duncan, L. The third eye — **Fic**
Dunkle, C. B. The sky inside — **Fic**
Fitzgerald, S. M. The apple tart of hope — **Fic**
Jinks, C. The last bogler — **Fic**
Levithan, D. The mysterious disappearance of Aidan S. — **Fic**
Melchior-Durand, S. The golden compass — **741.5**
Patterson, J. Ali Cross — **Fic**
Starmer, A. The storyteller — **Fic**
Starmer, A. The whisper — **Fic**

The **missing** girl. Mazer, N. F. — **Fic**

MISSING GIRLS
Appelt, K. Maybe a fox — **Fic**
Nimmo, J. Midnight for Charlie Bone — **Fic**
Vernick, S. R. The blood lie — **Fic**

MISSING IN ACTION
Mazer, H. A boy at war — **Fic**

Missing in action. Hughes, D. — **Fic**

Missing May. Rylant, C. — **Fic**

MISSING MEN

Thompson, C. Space dumplins — **741.5**

Tucker, L. All the Greys on Greene Street — **Fic**

MISSING PERSONS

Alston, B. Amari and the night brothers — **Fic**

Anderson, M. T. He laughed with his other mouths — **Fic**

Andrews, C. M. Spindlefish and stars — **Fic**

Ansari, R. K. S. The missing piece of Charlie O'Reilly — **Fic**

Balliett, B. Hold fast — **Fic**

Barron, R. Maya and the rising dark — **Fic**

Black, H. The Good Neighbors — **741.5**

Blackwood, S. Miss Ellicott's school for the magically minded — **Fic**

Chanani, N. Jukebox — **Fic**

Cohen, M. The Inn Between — **Fic**

Doyle, M. Bewitching season — **Fic**

Dunmore, H. The tide knot — **Fic**

Durst, S. B. The girl who could not dream — **Fic**

Evans, L. Horten's miraculous mechanisms — **Fic**

Flinn, A. Cloaked — **Fic**

Fox, J. S. The charmed children of Rookskill Castle — **Fic**

Gibbs, S. Spaced out — **Fic**

Gilman, D. The devil's breath — **Fic**

Goodman, A. The Dark Days Club — **Fic**

Grove, S. E. The golden specific — **Fic**

Haddix, M. P. The deceivers — **Fic**

Hatfield, R. The Book of Storms — **Fic**

Hautman, P. The obsidian blade — **Fic**

Heider, M. W. The losers at the center of the galaxy — **Fic**

Hopkinson, N. The Chaos — **Fic**

Horowitz, A. Never say die — **Fic**

Jackson, T. D. Monday's not coming — **Fic**

Kade, J. V. Bot Wars — **Fic**

King, W. OCDaniel — **Fic**

Klise, K. Regarding the sink — **Fic**

Leavitt, M. My book of life by Angel — **Fic**

Lucier, M. Song of the abyss — **Fic**

Mafi, T. Furthermore — **Fic**

McMullen, B. Mrs. Smith's Spy School for Girls — **Fic**

Meyer, M. Scarlet — **Fic**

Miller, J. Elizabeth and Zenobia — **Fic**

Nolan, H. Crazy — **Fic**

Oliver, L. The magnificent monsters of Cedar Street — **Fic**

Pierce, T. Mastiff — **Fic**

Power, R. Wilder girls — **Fic**

Ritter, W. Deepest darkest — **Fic**

Rundell, K. Rooftoppers — **Fic**

Sedgwick, M. She is not invisible — **Fic**

Springer, N. The case of the bizarre bouquets — **Fic**

Springer, N. The case of the cryptic crinoline — **Fic**

Springer, N. The case of the missing marquess — **Fic**

Stork, F. X. Disappeared — **Fic**

Sullivan, T. Escape at 10000 feet — **364.1317**

Taylor, T. Malamander — **Fic**

Towell, K. Skary childrin and the carousel of sorrow — **Fic**

Wein, E. The pearl thief — **Fic**

Westerfeld, S. Shatter city — **Fic**

Zuckerman, L. A taste for rabbit — **Fic**

MISSING PERSONS INVESTIGATION

Gilman, D. The devil's breath — **Fic**

Horowitz, A. Three of diamonds — **Fic**

Krosoczka, J. The frog who croaked — **Fic**

Springer, N. The case of the bizarre bouquets — **Fic**

Springer, N. The case of the cryptic crinoline — **Fic**

Springer, N. The case of the gypsy goodbye — **Fic**

Springer, N. The case of the missing marquess — **Fic**

Winters, C. Odd & true — **Fic**

The **missing** piece of Charlie O'Reilly. Ansari, R. K. S. — **Fic**

MISSING TEENAGE BOYS

Bradbury, J. Shift — **Fic**

Chan, G. The disappearance — **Fic**

Katcher, B. The improbable theory of Ana and Zak — **Fic**

MISSING TEENAGE GIRLS

Hiaasen, C. Skink--no surrender — **Fic**

MISSING TEENAGERS

McMann, L. Cryer's cross — **Fic**

MISSING WOMEN

Riordan, R. The Titan's curse — **Fic**

Westerfeld, S. So yesterday — **Fic**

Mission control this is Apollo. Chaikin, A. — **629.45**

Mission to Mars. Hartman, E. — **629.45**

Mission to Pluto. Carson, M. K. — **629.43**

Mission unstoppable. Gutman, D. — **Fic**

MISSISSIPPI

Bausum, A. The March against Fear — **323.1196**

Dell, P. Mississippi — **976.2**

McMullan, M. How I found the Strong — **Fic**

McMullan, M. Sources of light — **Fic**

McMullan, M. When I crossed No-Bob — **Fic**

Murphy, J. Ramona Blue — **Fic**

Nelson, M. A wreath for Emmett Till — **811**

Pinkney, A. D. Loretta Little looks back — **Fic**

Robinson, G. Little Brother of War — **Fic**

Taylor, M. D. The friendship — **Fic**

Taylor, M. D. The land — **Fic**

Taylor, M. D. Let the circle be unbroken — **Fic**

Taylor, M. D. The well — **Fic**

Wiles, D. The Aurora County All-Stars — **Fic**

Wiles, D. Revolution — **Fic**

MISSISSIPPI -- HISTORY -- 20TH CENTURY

Rubin, S. G. Freedom summer — **323.1196**

MISSISSIPPI -- POLITICS AND GOVERNMENT -- 1951-

Bowers, R. The spies of Mississippi — **323.1196**

MISSISSIPPI -- RACE RELATIONS

Bowers, R. The spies of Mississippi — **323.1196**

Crowe, C. Getting away with murder — **364.15**

Ribeiro, M. The assassination of Medgar Evers — **976.2**

Mississippi. Dell, P. — **976.2**

MISSISSIPPI FREEDOM PROJECT

Rubin, S. G. Freedom summer — **323.1196**

Watson, B. Freedom Summer for young people — **323.1196**

MISSISSIPPI RIVER

Helgerson, J. Horns and wrinkles — **Fic**

Twain, M. The adventures of Tom Sawyer — **Fic**

MOTHERS -- DEATH

Austen, C. Walking backward	Fic
Blackstone, M. Sorry you're lost	Fic
Blake, A. H. Hazel Bly and the deep blue sea	Fic
Carter, A. All fall down	Fic
Creech, S. Walk two moons	Fic
Ehrlich, E. Nest	Fic
Giff, P. R. A slip of a girl	Fic
Higgins, J. Sure fire	Fic
Lupica, M. Miracle on 49th Street	Fic
Silberberg, A. Milo	Fic

MOTHERS AND DAUGHTERS

Alexander, J. The sweetheart of Prosper County	Fic
Atkins, J. Borrowed names	811
Baskin, N. R. Ruby on the outside	Fic
Cabot, M. Black Canary	741.5
Carter, A. I'd tell you I love you but then I'd have to kill you	Fic
Carter, C. How to be a girl in the world	Fic
Connor, L. Waiting for normal	Fic
Doyle, R. A greyhound of a girl	Fic
Draper, S. M. November blues	Fic
Duble, K. B. The sacrifice	Fic
Durst, S. B. Into the Wild	Fic
Everman, C. H. We belong	Fic
Frederick, H. V. Dear pen pal	Fic
Frederick, H. V. Home for the holidays	Fic
Frederick, H. V. The Mother-Daughter Book Club	Fic
Frederick, H. V. Much ado about Anne	Fic
Frederick, H. V. Pies & prejudice	Fic
Gerber, A. Braced	Fic
Grant, M. Eve & Adam	Fic
Greenwald, L. My life in pink & green	Fic
Haydu, C. A. Rules for stealing stars	Fic
Ibbotson, E. The star of Kazan	Fic
Ifueko, J. Raybearer	Fic
Johnson, V. The Parker inheritance	Fic
Kadohata, C. Outside beauty	Fic
Little, K. G. Circle of secrets	Fic
Love, D. A. Semiprecious	Fic
Martin, M. A. To be honest	Fic
Martinez, J. Virtuosity	Fic
Melleby, N. In the role of Brie Hutchens...	Fic
Napoli, D. J. Zel	Fic
Rodgers, M. Freaky Friday	Fic
Rundell, K. The wolf wilder	Fic
Ryan, P. M. Esperanza rising	Fic
Soo, K. Jellaby	741.5
Springstubb, T. The most perfect thing in the universe	Fic
Sumner, J. Tune it out	Fic
Thornburgh, B. Ordinary girls	Fic

MOTHERS AND SONS

Bird, J. The brave	Fic
Connor, L. All rise for the honorable Perry T. Cook	Fic
Gutman, D. Abner & me	Fic
Jacobson, J. Small as an elephant	Fic
Nielsen, S. No fixed address	Fic

Stevenson, R. L. Treasure Island	Fic
Whitney, D. When you were here	Fic
Yang, G. L. The shadow hero	741.5

MOTHERS WITH MENTAL ILLNESSES

Werlin, N. The rules of survival	Fic

MOTHS

Whalley, P. E. S. Butterfly & moth	595.78

MOTIVATION IN EDUCATION

Aungst, G. 5 principles of the modern mathematics classroom	510.71
Boyles, N. N. That's a great answer!	372.47
Farwell, S. M. Supporting reading in grades 6-12	428.4071
Miller, D. The book whisperer	372.6
Miller, D. Reading in the wild	372.4

MOTOR VEHICLES

Smith, M. Speed machines	629.2

MOTOR VEHICLES -- MODELS

Gabrielson, C. Kinetic contraptions	621.46

MOTORBOATS -- MODELS

Gabrielson, C. Kinetic contraptions	621.46

MOTORCYCLES

Farndon, J. Megafast motorcycles	629.227

MOTORCYCLES -- HISTORY

Smedman, L. From boneshakers to choppers	629.227

MOTORCYCLES, RACING

Farndon, J. Megafast motorcycles	629.227

MOTORCYCLISTS

Smedman, L. From boneshakers to choppers	629.227

MOTORS

Sobey, E. J. C. Electric motor experiments	621.46078

MOTOWN RECORD CORPORATION

Pinkney, A. D. Rhythm ride	781.64409774

MOUNT DENALI (ALASKA)

Moderow, H. Lily's mountain	Fic

MOUNT EVEREST

Berne, E. C. Summiting Everest	796.522
Levy, D. A. Above all else	Fic
Smith, R. Peak	Fic
Taylor-Butler, C. Sacred mountain	954.96

MOUNT OLYMPUS, GREECE

Riordan, R. The last Olympian	Fic

MOUNT RAINIER

Gemeinhart, D. The honest truth	Fic

MOUNT VERNON

McClafferty, C. K. Buried lives	306.3

MOUNTAIN LIFE

Dowell, F. O. Dovey Coe	Fic

MOUNTAIN RESCUE OPERATIONS

Markle, S. Rescues!	363.34

MOUNTAIN STATES

Prentzas, G. S. Wyoming	978.7

MOUNTAINEERING

Athans, S. K. Secrets of the sky caves	796.522
Berne, E. C. Summiting Everest	796.522
Cleare, J. Epic climbs	796.522092
Fawcett, H. Even the darkest stars	Fic
Levy, D. A. Above all else	Fic

Mull, Brandon, 1974-
Sky raiders — Fic
Wild born — Fic
A world without heroes — Fic

Mullenbach, Cheryl
Double victory — 940.5308
Torpedoed! — 940.54

Muller, Melissa, 1967-
Anne Frank — B

Mulligan, Andy
Trash — Fic

Mulroy, Tanya
Mozambique — 967.9

MULTICULTURAL EDUCATION
Hammond, Z. Culturally responsive teaching and the brain — 370.117
Howard, G. R. We can't teach what we don't know — 379.2

MULTICULTURAL ROMANCES
Menon, S. 10 things I hate about Pinky — Fic
Menon, S. There's something about Sweetie — Fic
Menon, S. When Dimple met Rishi — Fic
Moreno, N. Don't date Rosa Santos — Fic
Tamani, L. All the things we never knew — Fic

MULTICULTURALISM
Budhos, M. T. The long ride — Fic
Chapman, E. Hungry hearts — Fic
Latham, I. Dictionary for a better world — 170
Mazer, A. America street — Fic
Moragne, W. New Jersey — 974.9
Nye, N. S. Voices in the air — 811
Smelt, R. New Zealand — 993

MULTIETHNIC NEIGHBORHOODS
Fleischman, P. Seedfolks — Fic

MULTIPLE SCLEROSIS
Sovern, M. J. The meaning of Maggie — Fic

MULTIRACIAL BOYS
Green, T. Baseball genius — Fic
Hughes, D. Missing in action — Fic
Philbrick, W. R. Zane and the hurricane — Fic
Wilson, D. L. Black storm comin' — Fic
Zaczek, A. Martin McLean middle school queen — Fic

MULTIRACIAL CHILDREN
Bradley, K. B. Jefferson's sons — Fic
Hiranandani, V. The whole story of half a girl — Fic
Riordan, R. The red pyramid — Fic
Riordan, R. The serpent's shadow — Fic
Riordan, R. The throne of fire — Fic
Stone, N. Clean getaway — Fic
Wilson, D. L. Black storm comin' — Fic

MULTIRACIAL GIRLS
Budhos, M. T. The long ride — Fic
Cabot, M. From the notebooks of a middle school princess — Fic
Day, C. The sea in winter — Fic
Donwerth-Chikamatsu, A. Beyond me — Fic
Draper, S. M. Blended — Fic
Higuera, D. B. Lupe Wong won't dance — Fic

Hilton, M. Full cicada moon — Fic
Krishnaswami, U. Step up to the plate Maria Singh — Fic
Magoon, K. Camo girl — Fic
Oh, E. Spirit hunters — Fic
Vaught, S. Things too huge to fix by saying sorry — Fic

MULTIRACIAL PERSONS
Katz, W. L. Black Indians — 970
Landman, T. Hell and high water — Fic
Nunn, M. When the ground is hard — Fic
Taylor, M. D. The land — Fic

MULTIRACIAL TEENAGE BOYS
Hobbs, W. Never say die — Fic
Lee, M. The gentleman's guide to vice and virtue — Fic
Pena, M. d. l. We were here — Fic
Reynolds, J. Miles Morales — Fic

MULTIRACIAL TEENAGE GIRLS
Bowman, A. D. Starfish — Fic
Gibney, S. See no color — Fic
Hopkinson, N. The Chaos — Fic
Padian, M. How to build a heart — Fic
Park, L. S. Prairie lotus — Fic
Tamaki, M. Skim — 741.5
Weston, C. Speed of life — Fic
Zoboi, I. A. Pride — Fic

MULTIRACIAL TEENAGE GIRLS -- IDENTITY
Quigley, D. Apple in the middle — Fic

MULTIRACIAL TEENAGERS
Collar, O. The red pyramid — 741.5
Rhodes, J. P. Black brother black brother — Fic

MUMMIES
Berger, M. Mummies of the pharaohs — 932
Halls, K. M. Mysteries of the mummy kids — 393
Lace, W. W. King Tut's curse — 932
Lace, W. W. Mummification and death rituals of ancient Egypt — 932
Manning, P. L. Dinomummy — 567.914
O'Meara, S. J. Are you afraid yet? — 001.944
Perl, L. Mummies tombs and treasure — 932
Scieszka, J. Funny business — Fic
Sloan, C. Mummies — 393
Mummies. Sloan, C. — 393
Mummies of the pharaohs. Berger, M. — 932
Mummies tombs and treasure. Perl, L. — 932
Mummification and death rituals of ancient Egypt. Lace, W. W. — 932

Munda, Rosaria
Fireborne — Fic

Mundy, Robyn
Epic voyages — 910.4

MUNICH UNIVERSITY -- RIOT, 1943
Freedman, R. We will not be silent — 943.086
Wilson, K. White Rose — Fic

MUNICH, GERMANY -- HISTORY -- 20TH CENTURY
Freedman, R. We will not be silent — 943.086

MUNICIPAL ENGINEERING
Levy, M. Engineering the city — 624

MURDER

Angleberger, T. Horton Halfpott or The fiendish mystery of Smugwick Manor or The loosening of M'Lady Luggertuck's corset	Fic	Higgins, F. E. The lunatic's curse	Fic
		Hoobler, D. The demon in the teahouse	Fic
		Hoobler, D. The ghost in the Tokaido Inn	Fic
Balliett, B. Chasing Vermeer	Fic	Hoobler, D. Seven paths to death	Fic
Balliett, B. The danger box	Fic	Hoobler, D. The sword that cut the burning grass	Fic
Balliett, B. Hold fast	Fic	Horowitz, A. The Falcon's Malteser	Fic
Balliett, B. Pieces and players	Fic	Horowitz, A. The Greek who stole Christmas	Fic
Bauer, J. Peeled	Fic	Horowitz, A. Public enemy number two	Fic
Bayerl, K. A psalm for lost girls	Fic	Horowitz, A. South by southeast	Fic
Beatty, R. Willa of Dark Hollow	Fic	Horowitz, A. Three of diamonds	Fic
Beaty, A. Cicada summer	Fic	Howe, K. Conversion	Fic
Beaufrand, M. J. Useless Bay	Fic	Jackson, T. D. Let me hear a rhyme	Fic
Beil, M. D. The ring of Rocamadour	Fic	Jackson, T. D. Monday's not coming	Fic
Beil, M. D. The vanishing violin	Fic	Johnson, M. The hand on the wall	Fic
Bell, J. Kepler's Dream	Fic	Johnson, M. Truly Devious	Fic
Berk, J. The dark days of Hamburger Halpin	Fic	Johnson, M. The vanishing stair	Fic
Berlin, E. The puzzling world of Winston Breen	Fic	Johnson, V. The Parker inheritance	Fic
Broach, E. Shakespeare's secret	Fic	Klise, J. The art of secrets	Fic
Broach, E. The wolf keepers	Fic	Klise, K. Regarding the bathrooms	Fic
Byars, B. C. The dark stairs	Fic	Klise, K. Regarding the fountain	Fic
Chambliss Bertman, J. Book scavenger	Fic	Klise, K. Regarding the sink	Fic
Chambliss Bertman, J. The unbreakable code	Fic	Konigsburg, E. L. The mysterious edge of the heroic world	Fic
Cortez, S. You don't have a clue	Fic	Korman, G. Notorious	Fic
Devlin, I. Low red moon	Fic	Krosoczka, J. The frog who croaked	Fic
Dowd, S. The London Eye mystery	Fic	Lee, Y. S. The body at the tower	Fic
Elston, A. The rules for disappearing	Fic	Lee, Y. S. A spy in the house	Fic
Fairlie, E. The magician's bird	Fic	Levithan, D. The mysterious disappearance of Aidan S.	Fic
Fantaskey, B. Buzz kill	Fic	Margolis, L. Girl's best friend	Fic
Feinstein, J. Change-up	Fic	McClintock, N. Out of tune	Fic
Feinstein, J. Cover-up	Fic	McClintock, N. She said/she saw	Fic
Feinstein, J. Last shot	Fic	Messner, K. Chirp	Fic
Feinstein, J. The rivalry	Fic	Miller, J. Elizabeth and Zenobia	Fic
Feinstein, J. Vanishing act	Fic	Miller, K. Inside the shadow city	Fic
Fitzgerald, L. M. Under the egg	Fic	Mulligan, A. Trash	Fic
Frederick, H. V. Absolutely Truly	Fic	Ormsbee, K. The house in Poplar Wood	Fic
Frederick, H. V. Yours Truly	Fic	Patterson, J. Ali Cross	Fic
Gibbs, S. Belly up	Fic	Patterson, J. Like father like son	Fic
Gibbs, S. Big game	Fic	Ponti, J. Framed!	Fic
Gibbs, S. Panda-monium	Fic	Ponti, J. Trapped!	Fic
Gibbs, S. Poached	Fic	Ponti, J. Vanished!	Fic
Gibbs, S. Space case	Fic	Preus, M. Enchantment Lake	Fic
Gibbs, S. Spaced out	Fic	Priest, C. I am Princess X	Fic
Giles, L. R. Overturned	Fic	Pullman, P. Two crafty criminals!	Fic
Grabenstein, C. Escape from Mr. Lemoncello's library	Fic	Raskin, E. The Westing game	Fic
Grabenstein, C. Mr. Lemoncello's great library race	Fic	Sedgwick, M. Revolver	Fic
Grabenstein, C. Mr. Lemoncello's Library Olympics	Fic	Sedgwick, M. She is not invisible	Fic
Greenwald, T. Game changer	Fic	Snicket, L. "Who could that be at this hour?"	Fic
Grisham, J. The abduction	Fic	Spratt, R. A. Friday Barnes girl detective	Fic
Grisham, J. The accused	Fic	Springer, N. The case of the bizarre bouquets	Fic
Grisham, J. Theodore Boone kid lawyer	Fic	Springer, N. The case of the cryptic crinoline	Fic
Haddix, M. P. The deceivers	Fic	Springer, N. The case of the gypsy goodbye	Fic
Hahn, M. D. Closed for the season	Fic	Springer, N. The case of the left-handed lady	Fic
Hamilton, V. The house of Dies Drear	Fic	Springer, N. The case of the missing marquess	Fic
Hiaasen, C. Scat	Fic	Springer, N. The case of the peculiar pink fan	Fic
Hiaasen, C. Skink--no surrender	Fic	Thompson, J. The girl from Felony Bay	Fic
Higgins, F. E. The black book of secrets	Fic	Tucker, L. All the Greys on Greene Street	Fic
Higgins, F. E. The eyeball collector	Fic		

McHugh, E. National parks — 333.78
National parks. McHugh, E. — 333.78
NATIONAL SELF-DETERMINATION
Sheth, K. Keeping corner — **Fic**
Native American art & culture. January, B. — 704.03
NATIVE AMERICAN ARTISTS
Charleyboy, L. Dreaming in Indian — 700.89
NATIVE AMERICAN AUTHORS
Lesley, C. Talking leaves — **Fic**
NATIVE AMERICAN BOYS
Dorris, M. Sees Behind Trees — **Fic**
Gansworth, E. L. If I ever get out of here — **Fic**
Tingle, T. How I became a ghost — **Fic**
Tingle, T. When a ghost talks listen — **Fic**
NATIVE AMERICAN BOYS WITH VISUAL DISABILITIES
Dorris, M. Sees Behind Trees — **Fic**
NATIVE AMERICAN CHILDREN
Carvell, M. Sweetgrass basket — **Fic**
Ellis, D. Looks like daylight — 970.004
NATIVE AMERICAN DANCERS
Pheasant-Neganigwane, K. Powwow — 394.3
NATIVE AMERICAN FAMILIES
McManis, C. W. Indian no more — **Fic**
Quigley, D. Apple in the middle — **Fic**
NATIVE AMERICAN GIRLS
Carvell, M. Sweetgrass basket — **Fic**
Day, C. I can make this promise — **Fic**
McManis, C. W. Indian no more — **Fic**
O'Dell, S. Island of the Blue Dolphins — **Fic**
O'Dell, S. Zia — **Fic**
Native American history for kids. Gibson, K. B. — 970.004
NATIVE AMERICAN MANHOOD (PSYCHOLOGY)
Dorris, M. Sees Behind Trees — **Fic**
Native American religion. Martin, J. W. — 299
Native American religions. Hartz, P. — 299.7
NATIVE AMERICAN RESIDENTIAL SCHOOLS
Edwardson, D. D. My name is not easy — **Fic**
NATIVE AMERICAN SOLDIERS
Holm, T. Code talkers and warriors — 940.54
Walker, S. M. Deadly aim — 973.7
NATIVE AMERICAN STUDIES
National Museum of the American Indian. Do all Indians live in tipis? — 970.004
NATIVE AMERICAN TEENAGE BOYS
Bell, H. Traitor's son — **Fic**
Bruchac, J. Code Talker — **Fic**
Bruchac, J. Walking two worlds — **Fic**
Robinson, G. Little Brother of War — **Fic**
Tingle, T. Danny Blackgoat Navajo prisoner — **Fic**
NATIVE AMERICAN TEENAGE GIRLS
Anderson, J. L. Tiger Lily — **Fic**
Bruchac, J. Killer of enemies — **Fic**
Creech, S. Walk two moons — **Fic**
Quigley, D. Apple in the middle — **Fic**
Robinson, G. Standing strong — **Fic**
NATIVE AMERICAN TEENAGERS

Carlson, L. M. Moccasin thunder — **Fic**
Gansworth, E. L. Give me some truth — **Fic**
NATIVE AMERICAN WOMEN
Charleyboy, L. #NotYourPrincess — 305.48
O'Dell, S. Streams to the river river to the sea — **Fic**
Sonneborn, L. A to Z of American Indian women — 920.72089
NATIVE AMERICAN WOMEN -- HISTORY
Sonneborn, L. A to Z of American Indian women — 920.72089
NATIVE AMERICANS IN POPULAR CULTURE
National Museum of the American Indian. Do all Indians live in tipis? — 970.004
Treuer, A. Everything you wanted to know about Indians but were afraid to ask — 970.1
Native son. Hart, J. — **B**
Natterson, Cara Familian, 1970-
The care & keeping of you 2 — 613
NATURAL DISASTERS
Aguilar, D. A. Cosmic catastrophes — 520
Aronin, M. Earthquake in Haiti — 972.94
Carson, M. K. Inside hurricanes — 551.55
Donwerth-Chikamatsu, A. Beyond me — **Fic**
Fradin, J. B. Tornado! — 551.55
Fradin, J. B. Volcanoes — 551.21
Hackney Blackwell, A. U-X-L encyclopedia of weather and natural disasters — 551.503
Koestler-Grack, R. A. Johnstown flood of 1889 — 974.8
Langley, A. Hurricanes tsunamis and other natural disasters — 363.34
Philbrick, W. R. Wildfire — **Fic**
Prokos, A. Tornadoes — 551.55
Reilly, K. M. Natural disasters — 550
Rusch, E. Eruption! — 363.34
Rusch, E. Impact! — 551.3
Shoals, J. Extreme weather — 551.55
Silverstein, A. Wildfires — 634.9
Slavicek, L. C. The San Francisco earthquake and fire of 1906 — 979.4
Winchester, S. When the earth shakes — 551.22
NATURAL DISASTERS -- HISTORY
Marrin, A. Years of dust — 978
Natural disasters. Reilly, K. M. — 550
NATURAL FOODS
Rau, D. M. Going organic — 613.2
NATURAL GAS
Squire, A. Hydrofracking — 622
NATURAL GAS -- GEOLOGY
Nagelhout, R. How natural gas is formed — 553.2
NATURAL HISTORY
Beil, K. M. What Linnaeus saw — 508.092
Calhoun, Y. Plant and animal science fair projects revised and expanded using the scientific method — 570.78
Chin, J. Island — 508.866
Heinrichs, A. The Nile — 962
Kras, S. L. The Galapagos Islands — 986.6
Lloyd, C. The nature timeline wallbook — 508
Paquette, A. Two truths and a lie — 508
Woods, M. Seven natural wonders of Africa — 960

Naylor, Phyllis Reynolds
Shiloh — Fic
NAZCA LINES SITE (PERU)
Horowitz, A. Evil star — Fic
Nazemian, Abdi
Like a love story — Fic
NAZI HUNTERS
Bascomb, N. The Nazi hunters — 364.15
The **Nazi** hunters. Bascomb, N. — 364.15
NAZI PLUNDER
Edsel, R. M. The greatest treasure hunt in history — 940.53
Konigsburg, E. L. The mysterious edge of the heroic world — Fic
Nazi saboteurs. Seiple, S. — 940.54
NAZIS
Cameron, S. The light in hidden places — Fic
Deem, J. M. Kristallnacht — 940.53
Fombelle, T. d. Between sky and earth — Fic
Freeman, C. Why did the rise of the Nazis happen? — 943.085
Hannigan, K. Cape — Fic
Heuvel, E. A family secret — 741.5
Napoli, D. J. Stones in water — Fic
Palacio, R. J. White bird — 741.5
Preus, M. Village of scoundrels — Fic
Seiple, S. Nazi saboteurs — 940.54
NAZISM
Bartoletti, S. C. The boy who dared — Fic
Freeman, C. Why did the rise of the Nazis happen? — 943.085
French, J. Hitler's daughter — Fic
Friedman, I. R. The other victims — 940.53
Maraniss, A. Games of deception — 796.48
Wilson, K. White Rose — Fic
NAZISM -- HISTORY
Downing, D. Origins of the Holocaust — 940.53
NAZISM AND CHILDREN
Altman, L. J. Shattered youth in Nazi Germany — 940.53
Bartoletti, S. C. Hitler Youth — 943.086
Bausum, A. Ensnared in the Wolf's Lair — 943.086
NCAA BASKETBALL TOURNAMENT -- HISTORY
Doeden, M. The Final Four — 796.323
NEAR FUTURE
Ahmed, S. Internment — Fic
Bertagna, J. Exodus — Fic
Bloor, E. Taken — Fic
Bruchac, J. Killer of enemies — Fic
Caine, R. Ink and bone — Fic
Falls, K. Inhuman — Fic
Farmer, N. The house of the scorpion — Fic
Gibbs, S. Space case — Fic
Gibbs, S. Spaced out — Fic
Kagawa, J. The immortal rules — Fic
Pike, A. Glitter — Fic
Unsworth, T. The one safe place — Fic
NEAR-DEATH EXPERIENCE
Gagnon, M. Strangelets — Fic
NEAR-EARTH OBJECTS
Goldstein, M. J. Garbage in space — 363.72

Young, K. R. Space junk — 629.4
NEARSIGHTEDNESS
Balliett, B. The danger box — Fic
NEATNESS AND MESSINESS
Morgenstern, J. Organizing from the inside out for teens — 646.7
Walsh, P. It's all too much so get it together — 640
NEBRASKA
Bowman, A. D. Starfish — Fic
Connor, L. All rise for the honorable Perry T. Cook — Fic
Hand, C. The last time we say goodbye — Fic
Heinrichs, A. Nebraska — 978.2
Nebraska. Heinrichs, A. — 978.2
Necropolis. Horowitz, A. — Fic
The **Neddiad.** Pinkwater, D. M. — Fic
NEEDLEWORK
Lisle, A. Sewing school — 646.2
Nefertiti. Lange, B. — B
NEFERTITI, QUEEN OF EGYPT, 14TH CENT. B.C.E.
Friesner, E. M. Sphinx's princess — Fic
Friesner, E. M. Sphinx's queen — Fic
Lange, B. Nefertiti — B
NEIGHBORHOODS
Bruton, C. I predict a riot — Fic
Martinez, C. G. Pig park — Fic
Nelson, M. My Seneca village — 811
Zoboi, I. A. Pride — Fic
NEIGHBORHOODS -- HISTORY 20TH CENTURY
Madigan, T. The burning — 976.6
NEIGHBORS
Acampora, P. Rachel Spinelli punched me in the face — Fic
Birdsall, J. The Penderwicks at Point Mouette — Fic
Bunce, E. C. Premeditated Myrtle — Fic
Gantos, J. The trouble in me — Fic
Haddix, M. P. Remarkables — Fic
Hahn, M. D. Closed for the season — Fic
Hurwitz, M. W. The summer I saved the world-- in 65 days — Fic
Konigsburg, E. L. The mysterious edge of the heroic world — Fic
Larson, K. Hattie Big Sky — Fic
Levine, K. The paper cowboy — Fic
Monninger, J. Whippoorwill — Fic
Padian, M. How to build a heart — Fic
Paulsen, G. Notes from the dog — Fic
Peck, R. A season of gifts — Fic
Poblocki, D. The haunting of Gabriel Ashe — Fic
Raskin, E. The Westing game — Fic
Ruby, L. The clockwork ghost — Fic
Ruby, L. The shadow cipher — Fic
Stead, R. Liar & spy — Fic
Stine, R. L. Fear — Fic
Wells, R. Red moon at Sharpsburg — Fic
Neimark, Anne E.
Mythmaker — B
Nellie Bly. Bankston, J. — B
Nelson Mandela. Gormley, B. — B

Nelson, David Erik
Soldering — 671.5

NELSON, MARILYN, 1946-
Nelson, M. How I discovered poetry — 811.54

Nelson, Marilyn, 1946-
Carver — 811
Fortune's bones — 811
How I discovered poetry — 811.54
My Seneca village — 811
Sweethearts of rhythm — 781.65
A wreath for Emmett Till — 811

Nelson, Peter, 1953-
Left for dead — 940.54

Nelson, Richard E.
The power to prevent suicide — 362.28

Nelson, S. D.
Black Elk's vision — B
Red Cloud — B
Sitting Bull — B

Nelson, Theresa, 1948-
Ruby electric — Fic

Nelson, Vaunda Micheaux
No crystal stair — Fic

NEMO, CAPTAIN (FICTITIOUS CHARACTER)
Verne, J. 20000 leagues under the sea — Fic

NEPAL
Athans, S. K. Secrets of the sky caves — 796.522

NEPAL -- DESCRIPTION AND TRAVEL
Taylor-Butler, C. Sacred mountain — 954.96

NEPHILA MACULATA
Heos, B. Stronger than steel — 595.4

NEPTUNE (ROMAN DEITY)
Kessler, L. Emily Windsnap and the castle in the mist — Fic
Kessler, L. Emily Windsnap and the land of the midnight sun — Fic

The **Neptune** Project. Holyoke, P. — Fic

Neri, Greg
Grand theft horse — B
Yummy — 741.5

NERUDA, PABLO, 1904-1973
Ryan, P. M. The dreamer — Fic

NERVOUS SYSTEM
Gold, M. V. Learning about the nervous system — 612.8
Macaulay, D. The way we work — 612
Mooney, C. The brain — 612.8
Rau, D. M. Freaking out! — 612.8
Rose, S. Nervous system — 612.8

NERVOUS SYSTEM -- DISEASES
Klosterman, L. Meningitis — 616.8
Nervous system. Rose, S. — 612.8

Nesbet, Anne
Cloud and Wallfish — Fic
Daring Darleen queen of the screen — Fic

Ness, Patrick, 1971-
And the ocean was our sky — Fic
The Ask and the Answer — Fic
The knife of never letting go — Fic

A monster calls — Fic
Nest. Ehrlich, E. — Fic
The **nest**. Oppel, K. — Fic

NETHERLANDS
Lindelauf, B. Fing's war — Fic
Lindelauf, B. Nine Open Arms — Fic
Peet, M. Tamar — Fic
Polak, M. What world is left — Fic
Prins, M. Hidden like Anne Frank — 940.53
Reiss, J. The upstairs room — Fic

NETHERLANDS -- COLONIES
Huey, L. M. American archeology uncovers the Dutch colonies — 974.7

Neumeier, Rachel
The keeper of the mist — Fic

NEUROLOGY
Colligan, L. H. Sleep disorders — 616.8
Goldsmith, C. Traumatic brain injury — 617.4

NEUROSCIENCES -- EXPERIMENTS
Chudler, E. H. Brain lab for kids — 612.8

NEVADA
Cohen, M. The Inn Between — Fic
Esplin, J. L. 96 miles — Fic
Heinrichs, A. Nevada — 979.3
Horowitz, A. Nightrise — Fic
Karst, K. Area 51 — 358.4

Nevada. Heinrichs, A. — 979.3
Never after. De la Cruz, M. — Fic
Never fade. Bracken, A. — Fic
Never say die. Hobbs, W. — Fic
Never say die. Horowitz, A. — Fic
Never say genius. Gutman, D. — Fic
The **never** war. MacHale, D. J. — Fic
Nevermore. Lange, K. E. — B
Nevertheless we persisted. — 170

Nevins, Debbie
Bahamas — 972.96

The **new** American Bible. Confraternity of Christian Doctrine. — 220.5205

New audition scenes and monologs from contemporary playwrights. Ellis, R. — 808.82

NEW BABY IN FAMILY
Lowry, L. Anastasia Krupnik — Fic

NEW BRUNSWICK
Laws, G. D. The Maritime provinces — 971.5

NEW BUSINESSES
Rankin, K. Start it up — 658.1

A **new** darkness. Delaney, J. — Fic

NEW DEAL, 1933-1939
Bolden, T. FDR's Alphabet soup — 973.917

NEW ENGLAND
Armstrong, A. W. Whittington — Fic
Hesse, K. Safekeeping — Fic
Jacobson, J. Small as an elephant — Fic
Kirby, M. J. The clockwork three — Fic
Lesperance, N. The nightmare thief — Fic
Lisle, J. T. Quicksand Pond — Fic

Ritter, W. The dire king	Fic
Ritter, W. Jackaby	Fic
Sleator, W. Interstellar pig	Fic
Wasserman, R. The book of blood and shadow	Fic

NEW ENGLAND -- HISTORY

Barker, M. P. Mending horses	Fic

NEW ENGLAND -- HISTORY -- COLONIAL PERIOD, 1600-1775

Johnson, C. D. Daily life in colonial New England	974
Mandell, D. R. King Philip's war	973.2

NEW ENGLAND -- SOCIAL LIFE AND CUSTOMS -- 1600-1775

Johnson, C. D. Daily life in colonial New England	974

NEW EXPERIENCES

Rylant, C. God went to beauty school	Fic
Smith, J. E. Field notes on love	Fic

NEW FRANCE

Worth, R. New France 1534-1763	971.01
New France 1534-1763. Worth, R.	971.01

NEW GUINEA

Montgomery, S. Quest for the tree kangaroo	599.2

NEW HAMPSHIRE

Frederick, H. V. Absolutely Truly	Fic
Frederick, H. V. Yours Truly	Fic
Haydu, C. A. Rules for stealing stars	Fic
Kent, D. New Hampshire	974.2
Lord, C. Half a chance	Fic
Monninger, J. Whippoorwill	Fic
Urban, L. The center of everything	Fic
New Hampshire. Kent, D.	974.2

NEW HORIZONS (SPACECRAFT)

Carson, M. K. Mission to Pluto	629.43

NEW IDENTITIES

Elston, A. The rules for disappearing	Fic

NEW JERSEY

Bryant, J. Kaleidoscope eyes	Fic
Budhos, M. T. Tell us we're home	Fic
DasGupta, S. The force of fire	Fic
Holm, J. L. Penny from heaven	Fic
Hulme, J. The glitch in sleep	Fic
Kent, D. New Jersey	974.9
Kephart, B. This is the story of you	Fic
Lecesne, J. Absolute brightness	Fic
Lubar, D. Character driven	Fic
Melleby, N. How to become a planet	Fic
Moragne, W. New Jersey	974.9
Murdock, C. G. Da Vinci's cat	Fic
Nesbet, A. Daring Darleen queen of the screen	Fic
Rex, A. Champions of breakfast	Fic
Rex, A. Cold cereal	Fic
Sonnenblick, J. After ever after	Fic
Wallace, R. War and watermelon	Fic
Wunder, W. The museum of intangible things	Fic
Zarr, S. Roomies	Fic

NEW JERSEY -- HISTORY -- COLONIAL PERIOD, 1600-1775

Doak, R. S. New Jersey 1609-1776	974.9

NEW JERSEY -- HISTORY -- REVOLUTION, 1775-1783

Doak, R. S. New Jersey 1609-1776	974.9
New Jersey. Kent, D.	974.9
New Jersey. Moragne, W.	974.9
New Jersey 1609-1776. Doak, R. S.	974.9
New kid. Craft, J.	741.5
New kid. Green, T.	Fic
New kid new scene. Glasser, D.	373.18

NEW MEXICO

Bell, J. Kepler's Dream	Fic
Eagar, L. Hour of the bees	Fic
Klages, E. The green glass sea	Fic
Stork, F. X. The last summer of the Death Warriors	Fic
Wells, R. E. Variant	Fic
Wilson, J. Ghost moon	Fic
Wilson, J. Victorio's war	Fic
Young, B. Healer of the water monster	Fic
New moon. Meyer, S.	Fic

NEW NEIGHBORS

Hof, M. Mother number zero	Fic
Mills, E. Famous in a small town	Fic

NEW NETHERLAND -- HISTORY

Huey, L. M. American archeology uncovers the Dutch colonies	974.7

NEW ORLEANS, LOUISIANA

Antieau, K. Ruby's imagine	Fic
Brown, D. Drowned City	363.34
Feinstein, J. Last shot	Fic
Larson, H. Compass south	741.5
Morris, P. Ruined	Fic
Philbrick, W. R. Zane and the hurricane	Fic
Pietras, J. Hurricane Katrina	976
Rhodes, J. P. Ninth Ward	Fic
Vawter, V. Copyboy	Fic
Volponi, P. Hurricane song	Fic
The new Oxford book of war poetry. Stallworthy, J.	808.81
The new republic. Stefoff, R.	973.4

NEW STUDENTS

Anderson, J. D. Posted	Fic
Barnett, M. The terrible two	Fic
Bauer, A. C. E. Come Fall	Fic
Bigelow, L. J. Hazel's theory of evolution	Fic
Brant, W. Zenn diagram	Fic
Broach, E. Shakespeare's secret	Fic
Brown, G. Josh Baxter levels up	Fic
Castellucci, C. Boy proof	Fic
Chmakova, S. Awkward	741.5
Cleary, B. Dear Mr. Henshaw	Fic
Craft, J. New kid	741.5
Davis, M. Superstar	Fic
Ellis, A. D. This is what I did	Fic
Glasser, D. New kid new scene	373.18
Grabenstein, J. J. Shine!	Fic
Green, T. New kid	Fic
Khan, H. More to the story	Fic
Korman, G. Pop	Fic
Mackel, K. Boost	Fic

Myers, W. D. Darius & Twig	Fic
Nazemian, A. Like a love story	Fic
Nelson, V. M. No crystal stair	Fic
Phelan, M. Snow White	741.5
Riordan, R. The hidden oracle	Fic
Riordan, R. The last Olympian	Fic
Riordan, R. The lightning thief	Fic
Riordan, R. The sea of monsters	Fic
Riordan, R. The tower of Nero	Fic
Rodkey, G. The Tapper twins go to war (with each other)	Fic
Rubin, S. G. Wideness and wonder	759.13
Ruby, L. The clockwork ghost	Fic
Ruby, L. The shadow cipher	Fic
Sedgwick, M. She is not invisible	Fic
Selznick, B. Wonderstruck	Fic
Shulman, P. The Grimm legacy	Fic
Silvera, A. Infinity son	Fic
Smith, J. E. The geography of you and me	Fic
Stead, R. Goodbye stranger	Fic
Stead, R. Liar & spy	Fic
Stead, R. When you reach me	Fic
Stephens, J. The fire chronicle	Fic
Tucker, L. All the Greys on Greene Street	Fic
Vail, R. Well that was awkward	Fic
Volponi, P. Rikers High	Fic
Walters, E. Broken strings	Fic
Watson, R. Some places more than others	Fic
Watson, R. Watch us rise	Fic
Weil, C. I'm glad I did	Fic
Westerfeld, S. So yesterday	Fic
Weston, C. Speed of life	Fic
Woodson, J. If you come softly	Fic
Wright, B. Putting makeup on the fat boy	Fic
Yolen, J. Foiled	Fic
Yoon, N. The sun is also a star	Fic
Zoboi, I. A. Pride	Fic

NEW YORK CITY -- ANTIQUITIES

Hansen, J. Breaking ground breaking silence	305.5

NEW YORK CITY -- BUILDINGS

Domenico, G. A day at the New Amsterdam Theatre	792.09

NEW YORK CITY -- HISTORY

Sandler, M. W. Secret subway	388.4

NEW YORK CITY -- HISTORY -- 1898-1951

Marrin, A. Flesh & blood so cheap	974.7
Marsico, K. The Triangle Shirtwaist Factory fire	974.7

NEW YORK CITY -- HISTORY -- 21ST CENTURY

Wachtel, A. September 11	973.931

NEW YORK CITY -- INTELLECTUAL LIFE -- 20TH CENTURY

Hill, L. C. Harlem stomp!	810.9

NEW YORK CITY -- SOCIAL CONDITIONS

Bial, R. Tenement	307.76

NEW YORK CITY -- SOCIAL LIFE AND CUSTOMS

Jarrow, G. Fatal fever	614.5

NEW YORK CITY BALLET

Froman, K. In the wings	792.809747

NEW YORK FOUNDLING HOSPITAL

MacColl, M. Rory's promise	Fic

NEW YORK GIANTS (BASEBALL TEAM)

Gutman, D. Jim & me	Fic

NEW YORK JETS (FOOTBALL TEAM)

Green, T. Football hero	Fic

NEW YORK STATE

Gregorio, I. W. This is my brain in love	Fic

NEW YORK STOCK EXCHANGE

Phelan, M. Snow White	741.5

NEW YORK STOCK EXCHANGE -- HISTORY

Blumenthal, K. Six days in October	332.64
New York. Somervill, B. A.	974.7

NEW ZEALAND

Gillespie, C. A. New Zealand	993
Knox, E. Mortal fire	Fic
Smelt, R. New Zealand	993

NEW ZEALAND -- DESCRIPTION AND TRAVEL

Jackson, B. New Zealand	993

NEW ZEALAND -- SOCIAL LIFE AND CUSTOMS

Jackson, B. New Zealand	993
New Zealand. Gillespie, C. A.	993
New Zealand. Jackson, B.	993
New Zealand. Smelt, R.	993

NEWARK, NEW JERSEY

Charles, T. Becoming Beatriz	Fic
Charles, T. Like Vanessa	Fic
Newfoundland. Mayell, M.	971.8

NEWFOUNDLAND AND LABRADOR

Harlow, J. H. Thunder from the sea	Fic
Mayell, M. Newfoundland	971.8
Walsh, A. A long way from home	Fic

NEWFOUNDLAND AND LABRADOR -- ANTIQUITIES

Huey, L. M. American archaeology uncovers the Vikings	948

NEWFOUNDLAND DOGS

Harlow, J. H. Thunder from the sea	Fic

NEWLYWEDS

Ferris, J. Twice upon a Marigold	Fic

Newman, Patricia, 1958-

Ebola	616.9
Plastic ahoy!	363.738
Sea otter heroes	599.769

Newquist, H. P. (Harvey P.)

The book of blood	612.1
Here there be monsters	594
The human body	610

NEWS MEDIA

Miller, M. Fake news	070.4
Otis, C. L. True or false	070.4

NEWSPAPER CARRIERS

Levine, K. The paper cowboy	Fic
Vawter, V. Paperboy	Fic

NEWSPAPER EMPLOYEES

Vawter, V. Copyboy	Fic

NEWSPAPER VENDORS

Avi. City of orphans	Fic

NEWTON, ISAAC, 1642-1727

Krull, K. Isaac Newton	B

The **nitty-gritty** gardening book. Cornell, K. A.   635.083

Nix, Garth

Abhorsen   Fic

Clariel   Fic

Goldenhand   Fic

Lirael daughter of the Clayr   Fic

Mister Monday   Fic

Sabriel   Fic

To hold the bridge   Fic

NIXON, RICHARD M. (RICHARD MILHOUS), 1913-1994

Burgan, M. TV shapes presidential politics in the Kennedy-Nixon debates   324.973

Pearson, P. O. Conspiracy   973.924

Niz, Xavier

Samurai   952

No castles here. Bauer, A. C. E.   Fic

No choirboy. Kuklin, S.   364.66092

No compromise. Aretha, D.   B

No crystal stair. Nelson, V. M.   Fic

No easy answers. Miller, C. C.   B

No fixed address. Nielsen, S.   Fic

No place. Strasser, T.   Fic

No such thing as the real world.   Fic

No summit out of sight. Romero, J.   796.522092

Noah Webster. Reef, C.   B

NOBILITY

Bunce, E. C. Starcrossed   Fic

Eves, R. Blood rose rebellion   Fic

Goodman, A. The Dark Days Club   Fic

Hale, S. Book of a thousand days   Fic

Higgins, J. Waiting for the queen   Fic

Kindl, P. Keeping the castle   Fic

Napoli, D. J. Zel   Fic

Waller, S. B. A mad wicked folly   Fic

Yolen, J. The queen's own fool   Fic

NOBILITY -- HISTORY 12TH CENTURY

McKinley, R. The outlaws of Sherwood   Fic

Nobody's princess. Friesner, E. M.   Fic

Nobody's prize. Friesner, E. M.   Fic

NOCTURNAL ANIMALS

Matzke, A. H. Hedgehog   636.9

Scott, T. Nocturne   591.5

Taschek, K. Hanging with bats   599.4

de la Bedoyere, C. Creatures of the night   591.5

Nocturne. Scott, T.   591.5

NOGUCHI, ISAMU, 1904-1988

Tiger, C. Isamu Noguchi   B

Nolan, Han

Crazy   Fic

A summer of Kings   Fic

Nomad. Alexander, W.   Fic

NOMADS -- HISTORY

Hinds, K. Huns   936

NONALCOHOLIC DRINKS

Furgang, A. Carbonated beverages   613.2

NONCONFORMISTS

Black, H. Geektastic   Fic

NONCONFORMITY

Spinelli, J. Stargirl   Fic

Nonfiction craft lessons. Portalupi, J.   372.62

Nonfiction mentor texts. Dorfman, L. R.   372.62

NONINDIGENOUS PESTS

Somervill, B. A. Monitor lizard   597.95

NONRENEWABLE NATURAL RESOURCES

Goldstein, M. J. Fuel under fire   338.2

NONSENSE VERSES

Myers, C. Jabberwocky   821

Silverstein, S. Every thing on it   811

Silverstein, S. Falling up   811

NONTRADITIONAL FAMILIES

Levy, D. A. The misadventures of the family Fletcher   Fic

Levy, D. A. This would make a good story someday   Fic

NONVERBAL COMMUNICATION

Jackson, D. M. Every body's talking   153.6

NONVERBAL LEARNING DISABILITIES -- PATIENTS

Price, J. Take control of Asperger's syndrome   618.92

NONVIOLENCE

Hasak-Lowy, T. We are power   303.6

O'Brien, A. S. After Gandhi   303.6

Winter, J. Peaceful heroes   920

Nooks & crannies. Lawson, J.   Fic

The **Norman** conquest of England. Hamilton, J.   942.02

NORMANDY

Atkinson, R. D-Day   940.54

Drez, R. J. Remember D-day   940.54

NORMANDY -- HISTORY

Hamilton, J. The Norman conquest of England   942.02

Hopkinson, D. D-Day   940.54

NORMANDY INVASION, JUNE 6, 1944

Atkinson, R. D-Day   940.54

Drez, R. J. Remember D-day   940.54

Hopkinson, D. D-Day   940.54

NORMANS IN ENGLAND

Hamilton, J. The Norman conquest of England   942.02

NORTH AFRICA

Brown, R. V. Tunisia   961.1

Kuhn, B. Angels of mercy   940.54

NORTH AMERICA

Charleyboy, L. Dreaming in Indian   700.89

Collins, S. Catching fire   Fic

Collins, S. The Hunger Games   Fic

Collins, S. Mockingjay   Fic

Croy, E. United States   973

Deem, J. M. Faces from the past   599.9

O'Sullivan, J. Migration nation   591.56

Sonneborn, L. Canada   971

Williams, B. Canada   971

Zimmermann, K. R. Steam locomotives   625.26

NORTH AMERICA -- CIVILIZATION

Zimmerman, L. J. Exploring the life myth and art of Native Americans   970.004

NORTH AMERICA -- COLONIZATION

Mendoza, J. An indigenous peoples' history of the United States for young people   970.004

Creech, S. Hate that cat	Fic	**NOVELS IN VERSE -- HISTORY AND CRITICISM**	
Creech, S. Love that dog	Fic	Krok, L. Novels in verse for teens	**808.83**
Crossan, S. Being Toffee	Fic	**Novels** in verse for teens. Krok, L.	**808.83**
Crossan, S. One	Fic	**NOVELS-WITHIN-NOVELS**	
Donwerth-Chikamatsu, A. Beyond me	Fic	Talley, R. Pulp	Fic
Elliott, D. Voices	Fic	**November** blues. Draper, S. M.	Fic
Engle, M. Silver people	Fic	**November, Sharyn**	
Engle, M. The wild book	Fic	Firebirds	Fic
Engle, M. With a star in my hand	Fic	Firebirds soaring	Fic
Everman, C. H. We belong	Fic	**NOVITIATE**	
Fields, T. After the death of Anna Gonzales	Fic	Turtschaninoff, M. Maresi	Fic
Fipps, L. Starfish	Fic	**Now.** Gleitzman, M.	Fic
Frost, H. All he knew	Fic	**Now** is the time for running. Williams, M.	Fic
Frost, H. Diamond Willow	Fic	**Now** or never! Shepard, R.	973.7
Frost, H. Keesha's house	Fic	**Nowhere** boy. Marsh, K.	Fic
Giff, P. R. A slip of a girl	Fic	**Nowhere** to run. Watson, J.	Fic
Grimes, N. Bronx masquerade	Fic	**Noyce, Pendred**	
Harrington, J. N. Catching a storyfish	Fic	Remarkable minds	509.2
Hemphill, S. Wicked girls	Fic	**Noyes, Deborah**	
Hesse, K. Out of the dust	Fic	Encyclopedia of the end	306.903
Hesse, K. Witness	Fic	The ghosts of Kerfol	Fic
Hilton, M. Full cicada moon	Fic	Gothic!	Fic
Holt, K. A. Knockout	Fic	A hopeful heart	813
Holt, K. A. Redwood and Ponytail	Fic	The magician and the spirits	793.8
Hopkins, E. Rumble	Fic	The restless dead	Fic
Howe, J. Addie on the inside	Fic	Sideshow	Fic
Koertge, R. Shakespeare makes the playoffs	Fic	**Nubia.** McKinney, L. L.	741.5
Krok, L. Novels in verse for teens	808.83	**NUCLEAR ACCIDENTS**	
Lai, T. Inside out & back again	Fic	Langeland, D. Meltdown	363.17
Leavitt, M. My book of life by Angel	Fic	**NUCLEAR ENGINEERING**	
Macdonald, M. Odette's secrets	Fic	Oxlade, C. Nuclear power	621.48
Marcus, K. Exposed	Fic	**NUCLEAR FISSION**	
McCall, G. G. Under the mesquite	Fic	Conkling, W. Radioactive!	539.7
Myers, W. D. Street love	Fic	**NUCLEAR HOLOCAUST SURVIVORS**	
Park, L. S. The one thing you'd save	Fic	O'Brien, R. C. Z for Zachariah	Fic
Patterson, J. Becoming Muhammad Ali	Fic	**NUCLEAR PHYSICS**	
Pinkney, A. D. The red pencil	Fic	Kidd, J. S. Nuclear power	621.48
Powell, P. H. Loving vs. Virginia	Fic	Latta, S. L. SMASH!	539.7
Reynolds, J. Long way down	Fic	**NUCLEAR PHYSICS -- RESEARCH -- HISTORY**	
Richards, J. Three rivers rising	Fic	Sullivan, E. T. The ultimate weapon	355.8
Rose, C. S. May B.	Fic	**NUCLEAR POWER**	
Rylant, C. God went to beauty school	Fic	Kidd, J. S. Nuclear power	621.48
Salazar, A. The land of the cranes	Fic	Oxlade, C. Nuclear power	621.48
Smith, H. A. Keeping the night watch	Fic	**NUCLEAR POWER PLANTS**	
Sones, S. Stop pretending	Fic	Oxlade, C. Nuclear power	621.48
Sones, S. What my girlfriend doesn't know	Fic	**NUCLEAR POWER PLANTS -- ACCIDENTS**	
Sones, S. What my mother doesn't know	Fic	Blankman, A. The blackbird girls	Fic
Sonnichsen, A. L. Red butterfly	Fic	Langeland, D. Meltdown	363.17
Thompson, H. The language inside	Fic	**NUCLEAR POWER RESEARCH**	
Venkatraman, P. A time to dance	Fic	Sheinkin, S. Bomb	623.4
Walrath, D. Like water on stone	Fic	Sullivan, E. T. The ultimate weapon	355.8
Weston, R. P. Zorgamazoo	Fic	**Nuclear** power. Kidd, J. S.	621.48
Wiles, D. Kent State	Fic	**Nuclear** power. Oxlade, C.	621.48
Wilson, K. White Rose	Fic	**NUCLEAR WARFARE**	
Wolf, A. The watch that ends the night	Fic	L'Engle, M. A swiftly tilting planet	Fic
Wolff, V. E. Make lemonade	Fic	Meloy, M. The apothecary	Fic
Woodson, J. Before the ever after	Fic	**NUCLEAR WEAPONS**	

Brashear, A. The incredible true story of the making of the Eve of Destruction — **Fic**

Nuestra America. Vourvoulias, S. — **920**

Num8ers. Ward, R. — **Fic**

Number the stars. Lowry, L. — **Fic**

NUMBERS

Juster, N. The annotated Phantom tollbooth — **Fic**

NUMERACY -- STUDY AND TEACHING

Harris, P. W. Lessons and activities for building powerful numeracy — **372.7**

Nunn, Malla

When the ground is hard — **Fic**

NUNS

Shofner, C. Almost paradise — **Fic**

NURSES

Gutman, D. Abner & me — **Fic**

Kuhn, B. Angels of mercy — **940.54**

Orenstein, D. G. The secret twin — **Fic**

Sepetys, R. Salt to the sea — **Fic**

Strange, C. Physicians assistants & nurses — **610.73**

NUTRITION

Etingoff, K. Building a healthy diet with the 5 food groups — **613.2**

Goldsmith, C. Dietary supplements — **615.1**

Llewellyn, C. Cooking with fruits and vegetables — **641.3**

Locricchio, M. Teen cuisine new vegetarian — **641.5**

Mihaly, C. Diet for a changing climate — **613.2**

Mooney, C. Junk food junkies — **641.5**

Orr, T. Playing safe eating right — **613**

Parrish, M. Are you what you eat? — **613.2**

Rau, D. M. Going organic — **613.2**

Rau, D. M. Going vegetarian — **613.2**

Thornhill, J. Who wants pizza? — **641.3**

Traugh, S. M. Vegetarianism — **641.5**

Waters, R. My daily diet — **613.2**

NUTRITION -- EXPERIMENTS

Gardner, R. Ace your exercise and nutrition science project — **612.7**

NUTRITION DISORDERS

Juettner, B. Diet and disease — **613.2**

NUTRITIONALLY INDUCED DISEASES

Juettner, B. Diet and disease — **613.2**

Nye, Bill

Bill Nye's great big world of science — **500**

NYE, NAOMI SHIHAB

Nye, N. S. I'll ask you three times are you ok? — **811**

Nye, Naomi Shihab

19 varieties of gazelle — **811**

Cast away — **811**

Habibi — **Fic**

Honeybee — **811**

I feel a little jumpy around you — **808.81**

I'll ask you three times are you ok? — **811**

A maze me — **811**

There is no long distance now — **Fic**

Time you let me in — **811**

Voices in the air — **811**

What have you lost? — **808.81**

Nzingha. McKissack, P. — **Fic**

NZINGHA, QUEEN OF MATAMBA, 1582?-1663

McKissack, P. Nzingha — **Fic**

O

O'BRADY, COLIN ANTARCTICA

Barone, R. Race to the bottom of the Earth — **919.89**

O'Brien, Anne Sibley

After Gandhi — **303.6**

O'Brien, Caragh M.

Birthmarked — **Fic**

O'Brien, Cynthia (Cynthia J.)

Pathways through North America — **304.2**

O'Brien, Robert C.

Mrs. Frisby and the rats of NIMH — **Fic**

Z for Zachariah — **Fic**

O'BRIEN, SOLEDAD, 1966-

Robson, D. Soledad O'Brien — **B**

O'CONNELL, CAITLIN, 1965-

O'Connell, C. Bridge to the wild — **636.088**

O'Connell, C. The elephant scientist — **599.67**

O'Connell, Caitlin, 1965-

Bridge to the wild — **636.088**

The elephant scientist — **599.67**

O'Connell, Jennifer

The Eye of the Whale — **599.5**

O'Conner, Patricia T.

Woe is I Jr. — **372.61**

O'Connor, Barbara

How to steal a dog — **Fic**

O'Connor, George

Hephaistos — **292**

Zeus — **292**

O'Connor, Jane

The emperor's silent army — **931**

O'Connor, Jim

What was the Battle of Gettysburg? — **973.7**

O'Connor, Sheila

Sparrow Road — **Fic**

O'Dell, Scott, 1898-1989

Island of the Blue Dolphins — **Fic**

Sing down the moon — **Fic**

Streams to the river river to the sea — **Fic**

Zia — **Fic**

O'Hart, Sinead

The starspun web — **Fic**

O'Keefe, Sherry

Champion of freedom — **B**

O'KEEFFE, GEORGIA, 1887-1986

Rubin, S. G. Wideness and wonder — **759.13**

O'Meara, Stephen James, 1956-

Are you afraid yet? — **001.944**

O'Neal, Claire

How to use waste energy to heat and light your home — **621.1**

Chiang, M. Oil spill   363.738

OIL SPILLS -- ENVIRONMENTAL ASPECTS
Chiang, M. Oil spill   363.738

OJIBWA GIRLS
Erdrich, L. The birchbark house   Fic
Erdrich, L. The game of silence   Fic

OJIBWA INDIANS
Erdrich, L. The birchbark house   Fic
Erdrich, L. The game of silence   Fic
Erdrich, L. Makoons   Fic
Erdrich, L. The porcupine year   Fic
Treuer, A. Everything you wanted to know about Indians but
were afraid to ask   970.1

OKINAWA ISLAND, JAPAN
Mazer, H. Heroes don't run   Fic

OKLAHOMA
Hesse, K. Out of the dust   Fic
Love, D. A. Semiprecious   Fic
Nayeri, D. Everything sad is untrue   Fic
Orr, T. Oklahoma   976.6
Sumner, J. Roll with it   Fic
Tingle, T. When a ghost talks listen   Fic
Ventrella, K. The secret life of Sam   Fic

Oklahoma. Orr, T.   976.6

Okorafor, Nnedi
Akata witch   Fic
Ikenga   Fic

Old school. Kinney, J.   Fic
The **Old** West. Countryman, E.   978
Old wolf. Avi.   Fic
Old Yeller. Gipson, F.   Fic
Older than dirt. Brown, D.   551.7

Older, Daniel Jose
Thunder run   Fic

OLDUVAI GORGE (TANZANIA) -- ANTIQUITIES
Henderson, H. The Leakey family   599.9092

¡Ole flamenco! Ancona, G.   793.3
Oligarchy. Gelletly, L.   321
Olive's ocean. Henkes, K.   Fic

Oliver, Lauren, 1982-
Liesl & Po   Fic
The magnificent monsters of Cedar Street   Fic
The spindlers   Fic

Ollhoff, Jim, 1959-
Beginning genealogy   929
Collecting primary records   929
DNA   929
Filling the family tree   929
Indian mythology   398.2
Using your research   929

Olson, Arielle North
Ask the bones   Fic
More bones   Fic

Olson, Tod
How to get rich in the California Gold Rush   979.4
Into the clouds   796.522095491
Lost in the Pacific 1942   940.54

OLYMPIC ATHLETES
Burgan, M. Miracle on ice   796.962
Burgan, M. Olympic gold 1936   796.42

OLYMPIC GAMES
Burgan, M. Olympic gold 1936   796.42
Smith-Llera, D. Black power salute   796.48

OLYMPIC GAMES (ANCIENT)
Macy, S. Swifter higher stronger   796.48

OLYMPIC GAMES -- HISTORY
Macy, S. Swifter higher stronger   796.48

OLYMPIC GAMES -- POLITICAL ASPECTS
Maraniss, A. Games of deception   796.48
Olympic gold 1936. Burgan, M.   796.42

OLYMPIC MEDAL WINNERS
Macy, S. Swifter higher stronger   796.48

OLYMPIC PROJECT FOR HUMAN RIGHTS
Smith-Llera, D. Black power salute   796.48

OMAN
Ejaz, K. We visit Oman   953.53
Omega City. Peterfreund, D.   Fic

Omnigraphics, Inc
Abuse and violence information for teens   303.60835
Complementary and alternative medicine information for
teens   610.835
Drug information for teens   613.8
Eating disorders information for teens   616.85
Mental health information for teens   616.8900835
Pregnancy information for teens   618.200835
Sexual health information for teens   613.9071
Sports injuries information for teens   617.1
Stress information for teens   616.9
Tobacco information for teens   613.850835

The **omnivore's** dilemma. Chevat, R.   394.1
On my honor. Bauer, M. D.   Fic
On my journey now. Giovanni, N.   782.25
On parade. Laidlaw, R.   636.088
On the day I died. Fleming, C.   Fic
On the Texas trail of Cabeza de Vaca. Lourie, P. 976.4
On two feet and wings. Kazerooni, A.   B

ONASSIS, JACQUELINE KENNEDY, 1929-1994
Axelrod, A. Your friend in fashion Abby Shapiro   Fic
Once a witch. MacCullough, C.   Fic
The **once** and future king. White, T. H.   Fic
Once upon a cuento. Miller-Lachmann, L.   Fic
Once upon a Marigold. Ferris, J.   Fic
Once upon a time in the North. Pullman, P.   Fic
Once upon an Eid. Ali, S. K.   297.3
Once was lost. Zarr, S.   Fic
One. Crossan, S.   Fic
The **one** and only Ivan. Applegate, K.   Fic
One crazy summer. Williams-Garcia, R.   Fic
One dead spy. Hale, N.   973.3
One Earth. Rao, A. S.   333.72092
One for sorrow. Hahn, M. D.   Fic
One for the Murphys. Hunt, L. M.   Fic
One good punch. Wallace, R.   Fic
One half from the east. Hashimi, N.   Fic

The **other** victims. Friedman, I. R. — 940.53

Otis, Cindy L.
True or false — 070.4

OTOLARYNGOLOGY
Rogers, K. Ear nose and throat — 617.5

Ottaviani, Jim
Primates — 920
T-minus — 629.4

Ottaviano, Patricia
Girl world — 155.5

Our choice. Chevat, R. — 363.738
Our Constitution. Ritchie, D. A. — 342.7302
Our country's first ladies. Bausum, A. — 973.09
Our country's presidents. Bausum, A. — 973.099
Our farm. Rosen, M. J. — 630.9
Our only May Amelia. Holm, J. L. — Fic
Our Supreme Court. Panchyk, R. — 347.73
Our wayward fate. Chao, G. — Fic
Our White House. National Children's Book and Literacy Alliance. — 975.3
Out from Boneville. Smith, J. — 741.5
Out of bounds. Naidoo, B. — Fic
Out of darkness. Freedman, R. — B
Out of Iraq. Wilkes, S. — 305.9
Out of left field. Klages, E. — Fic
Out of line. Grimberg, T. — B
Out of my mind. Draper, S. M. — Fic
Out of sight out of time. Carter, A. — Fic
Out of the dust. Hesse, K. — Fic
Out of the shadows. Waldman, N. — B
Out of tune. McClintock, N. — Fic
Out of wonder. Alexander, K. — 808.1
Out! McKenna, M. — 306.76
Outbreak. Barnard, B. — 614.4
Outcasts united. St. John, W. — 796.334092

OUTDOOR GAMES
Tukey, P. B. Tag toss & run — 790.1922

OUTDOOR LIFE
Hewitt, B. The young adventurer's guide to (almost) everything — 796.083
Paulsen, G. Woodsong — 796.5

OUTDOOR RECREATION
Davis, J. P. Hiking and camping — 796.51
Hewitt, B. The young adventurer's guide to (almost) everything — 796.083
Peterson, J. M. Big game hunting — 799.2

OUTDOOR RECREATION FOR CHILDREN
Hewitt, B. The young adventurer's guide to (almost) everything — 796.083
Schofield, J. Make it wild! — 790.1

OUTER HEBRIDES
McCaughrean, G. Where the world ends — Fic

OUTER SPACE -- EXPLORATION
Carlisle, R. P. Exploring space — 629.4
Woolf, A. The science of spacecraft — 629.47
Outer space. Jennings, K. — 523
Outlaw. Lee, T. — 741.5

OUTLAWS
Barnhill, K. R. The witch's boy — Fic
Falls, K. Dark life — Fic
Falls, K. Rip tide — Fic
Gaughen, A. C. Scarlet — Fic
Lee, T. Outlaw — 741.5
McKinley, R. The outlaws of Sherwood — Fic
Pearson, M. Dance of thieves — Fic
Wilson, J. Ghost moon — Fic
Wilson, J. Victorio's war — Fic

OUTLAWS -- HISTORY 20TH CENTURY
Blumenthal, K. Bonnie and Clyde — 364.15
The **outlaws** of Sherwood. McKinley, R. — Fic
Outrageous women of the Middle Ages. Leon, V. — 920
Outrun the moon. Lee, S. — Fic
Outside beauty. Kadohata, C. — Fic

OUTSIDER ART
Klise, J. The art of secrets — Fic
The **outsiders**. Hinton, S. E. — Fic
Over the mountains. Collier, M. — 557

OVERACHIEVERS
Yee, F. C. The epic crush of Genie Lo — Fic

OVERFISHING
Kurlansky, M. World without fish — 333.95

OVERLAND JOURNEYS TO THE PACIFIC
Brown, S. To stay alive — Fic
Calabro, M. The perilous journey of the Donner Party — 979.4
Hale, N. Donner dinner party — 979.4
McKernan, V. The devil's paintbox — Fic
McNeese, T. The Donner Party — 979.4
Sheinkin, S. Which way to the wild west? — 978

OVERPROTECTIVENESS IN FATHERS
Rossetti, R. The girl with borrowed wings — Fic

OVERPROTECTIVENESS IN MOTHERS
Nielsen, S. Word nerd — Fic
Overturned. Giles, L. R. — Fic

OVERWEIGHT BOYS
Holt, K. W. When Zachary Beaver came to town — Fic
Howe, J. The misfits — Fic

OVERWEIGHT GIRLS
Britt, F. Jane the fox and me — 741.5
Carson, R. The girl of fire and thorns — Fic
Dowell, F. O. The second life of Abigail Walker — Fic
Fipps, L. Starfish — Fic

OVERWEIGHT PERSONS
Manfredi, A. The (other) F word — 306.4

OVERWEIGHT TEENAGE BOYS
50 Cent. Playground — Fic
Berk, J. The dark days of Hamburger Halpin — Fic
Lange, E. J. Butter — Fic

OVERWEIGHT TEENAGE GIRLS
Halpern, J. Get well soon — Fic
Martin, M. A. To be honest — Fic

OVERWEIGHT TEENAGERS
Danziger, P. The cat ate my gymsuit — Fic
Hamilton, V. The planet of Junior Brown — Fic

Paul Robeson. Duberman, M. B.	B	Gish, M. Peacocks	598.6
Paul Robeson. Slavicek, L. C.	B	**Peacocks**. Gish, M.	598.6
PAUL, ALICE, 1885-1977		**Peak**. Smith, R.	Fic
Bausum, A. With courage and cloth	324.6	**PEARCE, STANLEY**	
Kops, D. Alice Paul and the fight for women's rights	B	Meissner, D. Call of the Klondike	971.9
Paul, Caroline		**PEARL (SCHOONER)**	
You are mighty	306	Conkling, W. Passenger on the Pearl	306.3
PAULSEN, GARY		**PEARL HARBOR, ATTACK ON, 1941**	
Brian's return	Fic	Allen, T. B. Remember Pearl Harbor	940.54
Brian's winter	Fic	Haugen, D. M. The attack on Pearl Harbor	940.54
Gone to the woods	B	Hillstrom, L. C. The attack on Pearl Harbor	940.54
Guts	B	Mazer, H. A boy at war	Fic
Hatchet	Fic	Messner, K. Pearl Harbor	940.54
My life in dog years	B	Wukovits, J. F. The bombing of Pearl Harbor	940.54
Notes from the dog	Fic	**PEARL HARBOR, HAWAII**	
Shelf life	Fic	Allen, T. B. Remember Pearl Harbor	940.54
Soldier's heart	Fic	**Pearl** Harbor. Messner, K.	940.54
This side of wild	B	The **pearl** thief. Wein, E.	Fic
The Transall saga	Fic	**PEARLS**	
Woods runner	Fic	Jacques, B. Pearls of Lutra	Fic
Woodsong	796.5	**Pearls** of Lutra. Jacques, B.	Fic
PAULSEN, GARY MINNESOTA		**Pearsall, Shelley**	
Paulsen, G. Woodsong	796.5	All of the above	Fic
Pausewang, Gudrun		The seventh most important thing	Fic
Dark hours	Fic	**Pearson, Luke**	
Traitor	Fic	Hildafolk	741.5
Pawlett, Mark		**Pearson, Mary (Mary E.)**	
The tae kwon do handbook	796.815	The adoration of Jenna Fox	Fic
Pawlett, Raymond		Dance of thieves	Fic
The karate handbook	796.815	Vow of thieves	Fic
Pawlewski, Sarah		**Pearson, P. O'Connell (Patricia O'Connell)**	
Careers	331.7	Conspiracy	973.924
PAWNBROKERS		Fly girls	940.54
Higgins, F. E. The black book of secrets	Fic	**PEARY, MARIE AHNIGHITO, 1893-1978**	
Pax. Pennypacker, S.	Fic	Kirkpatrick, K. Snow baby	910
Payment, Simone		**PEARY, ROBERT E. (ROBERT EDWIN), 1856-1920**	
Robotics careers	629.8	Kirkpatrick, K. Snow baby	910
PEACE		**PECK, JANE (FICTITIOUS CHARACTER)**	
Adams, R. Watership Down	Fic	Holm, J. L. Boston Jane	Fic
Creech, S. The unfinished angel	Fic	Holm, J. L. Boston Jane the claim	Fic
Dawson, E. D. Putting peace first	303.6	Holm, J. L. Boston Jane wilderness days	Fic
Nye, N. S. 19 varieties of gazelle	811	**Peck, Richard, 1934-2018**	
Nye, N. S. Voices in the air	811	Are you in the house alone?	Fic
Wilson, J. One peace	327.1	The best man	Fic
Woodson, J. Peace Locomotion	Fic	Fair weather	Fic
PEACE -- HISTORY		A long way from Chicago	Fic
Winter, J. Peaceful heroes	920	A season of gifts	Fic
PEACE ACTIVISTS		The teacher's funeral	Fic
O'Brien, A. S. After Gandhi	303.6	A year down yonder	Fic
Winter, J. Peaceful heroes	920	The **Peculiars**. McQuerry, M.	Fic
Peace Locomotion. Woodson, J.	Fic	**Pedal** it! Mulder, M.	629.227
PEACE MOVEMENTS		**PEDDLERS**	
Winter, J. Peaceful heroes	920	Barker, M. P. Mending horses	Fic
PEACE-BUILDING		Merrill, J. F. The pushcart war	Fic
Dawson, E. D. Putting peace first	303.6	**Pederson, Charles E.**	
Peaceful heroes. Winter, J.	920	The French & Indian War	940.2
PEACOCKS		**PEDIATRIC CARDIOLOGY -- HISTORY**	

Aronson, M. 1968	**909.82**
Yousafzai, M. We are displaced	**305.23092**

POLITICIANS

Kiernan, D. Signing their rights away	**973.3**
Krull, K. Lives of the presidents	**973.099**

POLITICS AND CULTURE

Fritz, J. Homesick	**Fic**

POLITICS AND LITERATURE

Kirk, A. Understanding Thoreau's Civil disobedience	**818**

Pollen, Samuel

The year I didn't eat	**Fic**

POLLINATION

Hirsch, R. E. Where have all the bees gone?	**595.79**

POLLINATORS

Hirsch, R. E. Where have all the bees gone?	**595.79**

POLLUTION

Burns, L. G. Tracking trash	**551.46**
Goldstein, M. J. Garbage in space	**363.72**
Newman, P. Plastic ahoy!	**363.738**
Reilly, K. M. Planet Earth	**363.7**
Young, K. R. Space junk	**629.4**
Zimmer, M. Solutions for a cleaner greener planet	**577.27**

POLLUTION -- ENVIRONMENTAL ASPECTS

Chiang, M. Oil spill	**363.738**

POLO, MARCO, 1254-1323?

Armstrong, A. W. Looking for Marco Polo	**Fic**
Galloway, P. Adventures on the ancient Silk Road	**950**
Twist, C. Marco Polo	**B**
Yang, D. J. Daughter of Xanadu	**Fic**

Polonsky, Ami

Gracefully Grayson	**Fic**
Threads	**Fic**

POLYGAMY

Williams, C. L. The chosen one	**Fic**

POLYNESIA

NgCheong-Lum, R. Tahiti	**996.2**

POMPEII (EXTINCT CITY)

Deem, J. M. Bodies from the ash	**937**

POMPIDOU ARTS CENTER, PARIS, FRANCE

Harman, A. Modern art explorer	**709.04**

PONDS

Lisle, J. T. Quicksand Pond	**Fic**

Ponti, James

Framed!	**Fic**
Trapped!	**Fic**
Vanished!	**Fic**

PONY EXPRESS

Wilson, D. L. Black storm comin'	**Fic**

Pool, Katy Rose

There will come a darkness	**Fic**

Poop detectives. Wadsworth, G.	**636.7**
Poop happened! Albee, S.	**363.72**

POOR BOYS

Braswell, L. A whole new world	**Fic**
Lee, Y. S. The body at the tower	**Fic**

POOR CHILDREN

Kirby, M. J. The clockwork three	**Fic**

Twain, M. The prince and the pauper	**Fic**

POOR FAMILIES

Armstrong, W. H. Sounder	**Fic**
Barrett, T. The stepsister's tale	**Fic**
Cao, W. Bronze and Sunflower	**Fic**
Mann, J. A. What every girl should know	**Fic**
Rose, C. S. May B.	**Fic**
Wolff, V. E. Make lemonade	**Fic**

POOR GIRLS

Bauer, J. Almost home	**Fic**
Lin, G. Where the mountain meets the moon	**Fic**
Paterson, K. Lyddie	**Fic**
Schmidt, G. D. Lizzie Bright and the Buckminster boy	**Fic**

POOR PEOPLE

Bial, R. Tenement	**307.76**
Henry, O. The gift of the Magi	**Fic**
Landman, T. Hell and high water	**Fic**
Ma, Y. The diary of Ma Yan	**951.05**
Senker, C. Poverty and hunger	**362.5**
Pop. Korman, G.	**Fic**

POP ARTISTS

Gilberti, F. Yayoi Kusama covered everything in dots and wasn't sorry	**709.2**
Pop monsters. Sanna, E.	**398**

POP-UP BOOKS

Green, J. Barron's totally wild fact-packed fold-out animal atlas	**591.9**
Saint-Exupery, A. d. The little prince	**Fic**

Pope, Paul

Battling boy	**741.5**
Popular. Wagenen, M. v.	**155.5**

POPULAR CULTURE

Countryman, E. The Old West	**978**
Croll, J. Fashion that changed the world	**391.009**
DiPiazza, F. Fandom	**302.23**
Ratcliffe, A. A kid's guide to fandom	**302.23**
Sanna, E. Pop monsters	**398**
Stone, T. L. The good the bad and the Barbie	**688.7**

POPULAR MUSIC

Chang, J. Can't stop won't stop	**306.4**
Weil, C. I'm glad I did	**Fic**

POPULAR MUSIC (VOCAL)

Orgill, R. Shout sister shout!	**920**

POPULAR MUSIC -- HISTORY AND CRITICISM

Tsoukanelis, E. A. The Latin music scene	**782.42164**

POPULARITY

Eulberg, E. Revenge of the girl with the great personality	**Fic**
Friend, N. Bounce	**Fic**
Gephart, D. How to survive middle school	**Fic**
Hale, S. Friends forever	**302**
Hobbs, V. The last best days of summer	**Fic**
Hurley, T. Ghostgirl	**Fic**
Johnson, C. G. The Breakaways	**741.5**
Kinney, J. Diary of a wimpy kid	**Fic**
Lundin, B. Ship it	**Fic**
McDaniel, L. Hit and run	**Fic**
Russell, R. R. Tales from a not-so-fabulous life	**Fic**

Spinelli, J. Stargirl — Fic
Wilkinson, L. Pink — Fic
Yee, L. Warp speed — Fic
Yee, P. Learning to fly — Fic

POPULATION -- ENVIRONMENTAL ASPECTS
Kallen, S. A. What is the impact of declining biodiversity? — 333.95

POPULATION CONTROL
Haddix, M. P. Among the hidden — Fic
Porch lies. McKissack, P. — Fic
The **porcupine** year. Erdrich, L. — Fic
The **Port** Chicago 50. Sheinkin, S. — 940.54

PORT-AU-PRINCE (HAITI)
Burg, A. E. Serafina's promise — Fic

Portalupi, Joann
Nonfiction craft lessons — 372.62

PORTLAND, OREGON
Lucier, M. A death-struck year — Fic
Meloy, C. Under Wildwood — Fic
Meloy, C. Wildwood — Fic
Meloy, C. Wildwood imperium — Fic
Watson, R. Piecing me together — Fic
Wolff, V. E. The Mozart season — Fic
Wolff, V. E. Probably still Nick Swansen — Fic

PORTRAIT PHOTOGRAPHY
Berne, E. C. Summiting Everest — 796.522

PORTRAITS
Herrera, J. F. Portraits of Hispanic American heroes — 920
Rogerson, M. An enchantment of ravens — Fic
Portraits of African-American heroes. Bolden, T. — 920
Portraits of Hispanic American heroes. Herrera, J. F. — 920
Portraits of Jewish American heroes. Drucker, M. — 920

PORTUGAL
Blauer, E. Portugal — 946.9
Portugal. Blauer, E. — 946.9

Post, Peggy, 1945-
Emily Post's table manners for kids — 395.5
Emily Post's the guide to good manners for kids — 395.1

POST-APOCALYPSE
Aguirre, A. Enclave — Fic
Bacigalupi, P. The Drowned Cities — Fic
Bacigalupi, P. Ship breaker — Fic
Block, F. L. Love in the time of global warming — Fic
DuPrau, J. The city of Ember — Fic
DuPrau, J. The diamond of Darkhold — Fic
DuPrau, J. The people of Sparks — Fic
Hirsch, J. The eleventh plague — Fic
Hughes, M. P. A crack in the sky — Fic
Lu, M. Champion — Fic
Lu, M. Legend — Fic
Lu, M. Prodigy — Fic
Lu, M. Rebel — Fic
Martin, L. The ark plan — Fic
Mills, G. Gold — Fic
Ross, J. N. The Fog diver — Fic
Rossi, V. Under the never sky — Fic
Wiggins, B. Stung — Fic

POST-COMMUNISM
Langley, A. The collapse of the Soviet Union — 947.085

POST-TRAUMATIC STRESS DISORDER
Barbour, S. Post-traumatic stress disorder — 616.85
Curtis, C. P. The madman of Piney Woods — Fic
Flores-Scott, P. American road trip — Fic
Frederick, H. V. Absolutely Truly — Fic
Hodkin, M. The unbecoming of Mara Dyer — Fic
Kemmerer, B. A heart so fierce and broken — Fic
Paulsen, G. Soldier's heart — Fic
Reinhardt, D. The things a brother knows — Fic
Smithson, R. Ghosts of war — 956.7044
Strasser, T. Price of duty — Fic
Watkins, S. Great Falls — Fic

POST-TRAUMATIC STRESS DISORDER -- TREATMENT
Barbour, S. Post-traumatic stress disorder — 616.85

POST-TRAUMATIC STRESS DISORDER IN CHILDREN
Craig, S. E. Trauma-sensitive schools for the adolescent years — 371.92
Post-traumatic stress disorder. Barbour, S. — 616.85
Posted. Anderson, J. D. — Fic

POSTHUMANISM
Rothenberg, J. The Kingdom — Fic

POSTMORTEM CHANGES
Murray, E. A. Death — 616.07

POSTWAR LIFE
Bolden, T. Saving Savannah — Fic
Hardinge, F. Cuckoo song — Fic
Kadohata, C. A place to belong — Fic

POTATOES -- SOCIAL ASPECTS
Lyons, M. E. Feed the children first — 941.5081
Potent natural medicines. Kidd, J. S. — 615

POTTER, HARRY (FICTITIOUS CHARACTER)
Rowling, J. K. Harry Potter and the Chamber of Secrets — Fic
Rowling, J. K. Harry Potter and the goblet of fire — Fic
Rowling, J. K. Harry Potter and the Order of the Phoenix — Fic
Rowling, J. K. Harry Potter and the prisoner of Azkaban — Fic

POTTERS
Greenberg, J. The mad potter — 738.092
Park, L. S. A single shard — Fic

POTTERY
Park, L. S. A single shard — Fic

POUGHKEEPSIE, NEW YORK
Graff, L. A tangle of knots — Fic

POVERTY
Argueta, J. Somos como las nubes — 811
Barrett, T. The stepsister's tale — Fic
Bayard, L. Lucky strikes — Fic
Cao, W. Bronze and Sunflower — Fic
Crowder, M. An uninterrupted view of the sky — Fic
Deuker, C. Golden arm — Fic
English, K. Francie — Fic
Gansworth, E. L. If I ever get out of here — Fic
Harkrader, L. The adventures of Beanboy — Fic
Hooper, M. Fallen Grace — Fic
Kephart, B. The heart is not a size — Fic

Kidder, T. Mountains beyond mountains	610.92	Pheasant-Neganigwane, K. Powwow	394.3
Leatherdale, M. B. Stormy seas	305.9	**POWWOWS**	
Ma, Y. The diary of Ma Yan	951.05	Pheasant-Neganigwane, K. Powwow	394.3
Mulligan, A. Trash	Fic	Smith, C. L. Ancestor approved	Fic
Myers, W. D. Street love	Fic	**POXVIRUS DISEASES**	
Senker, C. Poverty and hunger	362.5	Reingold, A. Smallpox	614.5
Sharif, M. Poverty and economic inequality	339.4	The **practical** astronomer. Gater, W.	520
Stork, F. X. Disappeared	Fic	**PRACTICAL JOKERS**	
Strasser, T. No place	Fic	Barnett, M. The terrible two	Fic
Uchida, Y. The best bad thing	Fic	Barnett, M. The terrible two get worse	Fic
Venkatraman, P. The bridge home	Fic	Johnson, V. The great Greene heist	Fic
Wolk, L. Echo Mountain	Fic	Johnson, V. To catch a cheat	Fic
Poverty and economic inequality. Sharif, M.	339.4	Korman, G. Ungifted	Fic
Poverty and hunger. Senker, C.	362.5	Whittemore, J. Odd girl in	Fic
POWELL, BARBARA JOHNS, 1935-1991		**PRACTICAL JOKES**	
Kanefield, T. The girl from the tar paper school	B	Barnett, M. The terrible two	Fic
Powell, Jillian		Barnett, M. The terrible two get worse	Fic
Explaining cystic fibrosis	616.3	Hahn, M. D. All the lovely bad ones	Fic
POWELL, JOHN WESLEY, 1834-1902		Hargrave, J. Sir John Hargrave's mischief maker's manual	818
Hale, N. Major Impossible	B	Hirsch, J. The eleventh plague	Fic
Powell, Laura, 1979-		Parkinson, S. Blue like Friday	Fic
Burn mark	Fic	Ponti, J. Vanished!	Fic
The game of triumphs	Fic	Rodkey, G. The Tapper twins go to war (with each other)	Fic
Powell, Patricia Hruby, 1951-		Stroud, J. Heroes of the valley	Fic
Loving vs. Virginia	Fic	Vande Velde, V. All Hallows' Eve	Fic
POWELL, RANSOM J., 1849-1899		Whittemore, J. Odd girl in	Fic
Wisler, G. C. Red Cap	Fic	**PRAGUE, CZECH REPUBLIC**	
Powell, Robert, 1948-		Iturbe, A. The librarian of Auschwitz	Fic
Peterson field guide to reptiles and amphibians of Eastern and Central North America	597.9	Stroud, J. The golem's eye	Fic
		Taylor, L. Daughter of smoke and bone	Fic
POWER (SOCIAL SCIENCES)		Wasserman, R. The book of blood and shadow	Fic
Bardugo, L. Ruin and rising	Fic	**Prairie** fire. Johnston, E. K.	Fic
Bardugo, L. Siege and storm	Fic	**Prairie** lotus. Park, L. S.	Fic
Brody, J. Sky without stars	Fic	**PRAIRIES**	
Friesner, E. M. Sphinx's princess	Fic	Mieville, C. Railsea	Fic
Hicks, F. E. The Stone Heart	741.5	**Pratchett, Terry**	
Hinds, K. The palace	909	The amazing Maurice and his educated rodents	Fic
Le Guin, U. K. Voices	Fic	Dodger	Fic
McCoy, M. I Claudia	Fic	I shall wear midnight	Fic
Munda, R. Fireborne	Fic	Nation	Fic
Stroud, J. The golem's eye	Fic	Only you can save mankind	Fic
Thomas, S. The magnolia sword	Fic	The Wee Free Men	Fic
Turner, M. W. A conspiracy of kings	Fic	**Prazdny, Bronja**	
POWER FAILURES		Bulgaria	949.9
Esplin, J. L. 96 miles	Fic	**PRECIOUS METALS**	
Smith, J. E. The geography of you and me	Fic	McDonnell, J. How precious metals form	622
The **power** of reading. Krashen, S. D.	028	**PRECIOUS STONES**	
The **power** to prevent suicide. Nelson, R. E.	362.28	Callery, S. Rocks minerals & gems	552.0075
Power up blended learning. Tucker, C. R.	371.3	Keppeler, J. How gems are formed	553.8
Power, Rory		Reynolds, T. Rocks crystals and gems	552
Wilder girls	Fic	**PREDATORY ANIMALS**	
Powerless. Cody, M.	Fic	Abramovitz, M. Deadliest sharks	597.3
Powers. Le Guin, U. K.	Fic	Allman, T. Deadliest mammals	599.7
POWNAL, VERMONT		Hirschmann, K. Deadliest reptiles	597.9
Winthrop, E. Counting on Grace	Fic	Hoena, B. A. Everything birds of prey	598.9
Powwow. Pheasant-Neganigwane, K.	394.3	Hunter, E. Broken pride	Fic
POWWOW DANCERS			

MacQuitty, M. Shark | 597.3
Messner, K. Tracking pythons | 597.96

PREDATORY DINOSAURS

Nardo, D. Deadliest dinosaurs | 567.9

PREGNANCY

Banigan, M. Coping with teen pregnancy | 362.7
Draper, S. M. November blues | Fic
Rand, C. Human reproduction | 612.6

PREGNANCY -- PSYCHOLOGICAL ASPECTS

Shantz-Hilkes, C. My girlfriend's pregnant! | 306.874
Pregnancy information for teens. Omnigraphics, I.**618.200835**

PREGNANT TEENAGERS

Draper, S. M. November blues | Fic
Meyer, S. Breaking dawn | Fic
Sepetys, R. Salt to the sea | Fic
Sweeney, D. The minnow | Fic
Werlin, N. Impossible | Fic
Williams, I. Water in May | Fic
Zarr, S. How to save a life | Fic

PREHISTORIC ANIMALS

Bonner, H. When dinos dawned mammals got munched and Pterosaurs took flight | 567.9
Malam, J. Dinosaur atlas | 567.9
Martin, M. Extinction! | 576.8
Nardo, D. Deadliest dinosaurs | 567.9
Reed, M. K. Dinosaurs | 567.9
Ridley, K. Extreme survivors | 591.3
Thimmesh, C. Scaly spotted feathered frilled | 567.9
Turner, A. National Geographic prehistoric mammals | 569
Woodward, J. Dinosaur! | 567.9

PREHISTORIC BOYS

Beckhorn, S. W. The wolf's boy | Fic

PREHISTORIC HUMANS

Aronson, M. The skull in the rock | 569.9096822
Beckhorn, S. W. The wolf's boy | Fic
Buller, L. Ice | 577.0911
Deem, J. M. Bodies from the bog | 569.9
Deem, J. M. Faces from the past | 599.9
Harrison, D. L. Mammoth bones and broken stones | 970.01
Morris, N. Prehistory | 930
Rubalcaba, J. Every bone tells a story | 930.1
Stefoff, R. First humans | 569.9
Stefoff, R. Modern humans | 569.9
Thimmesh, C. Lucy long ago | 569.9
Walker, S. M. Their skeletons speak | 970.01
Prehistory. Morris, N. | 930

PREJUDICE

Ali, S. K. Love from A to Z | Fic
Applegate, K. Wishtree | Fic
Barker, M. P. Mending horses | Fic
Bruchac, J. Walking two worlds | Fic
Bunker, L. Zenobia July | Fic
Coats, J. A. The wicked and the just | Fic
Draper, S. M. Stella by starlight | Fic
Edwardson, D. D. My name is not easy | Fic
Erskine, K. Seeing red | Fic

Frank, S. Armstrong and Charlie | Fic
Fusco, K. N. The wonder of Charlie Anne | Fic
Gutman, D. Jackie and me | Fic
Hesse, K. Witness | Fic
Hughes, D. Four-Four-Two | Fic
Hughes, D. Missing in action | Fic
Jocelyn, M. A big dose of lucky | Fic
Khan, H. Amina's voice | Fic
Krishnaswami, U. Step up to the plate Maria Singh | Fic
Landman, T. Hell and high water | Fic
Larson, K. Hattie Big Sky | Fic
LeZotte, A. C. Show me a sign | Fic
Levine, G. C. The lost kingdom of Bamarre | Fic
Lundin, B. Ship it | Fic
Mafi, T. A very large expanse of sea | Fic
Marcovitz, H. Hate crimes | 364.15
Marsh, K. Nowhere boy | Fic
Martin, A. M. Better to wish | Fic
Mills, W. All we have left | Fic
Murphy, J. Invincible microbe | 616.9
Osborne, L. B. Miles to go for freedom | 305.896
Park, L. S. Prairie lotus | Fic
Reeve, P. Fever Crumb | Fic
Rodger, M. Racism and prejudice | 305.8
Shevah, E. Dara Palmer's major drama | Fic
Smith, S. L. Flygirl | Fic
Speare, E. G. The witch of Blackbird Pond | Fic
Taylor, M. D. The land | Fic
Taylor, T. Timothy of the cay | Fic
Venkatraman, P. Climbing the stairs | Fic
Vernick, S. R. The blood lie | Fic
Wein, E. The pearl thief | Fic
Yep, L. Dragonwings | Fic

PREJUDICES

Burton, E. Race relations | 305.800973
Preller, James
Bystander | Fic
The courage test | Fic
Six innings | Fic

PRELUTSKY, JACK, 1940-

Prelutsky, J. Pizza pigs and poetry | 811
Prelutsky, Jack, 1940-
Pizza pigs and poetry | 811
The Random House book of poetry for children | 811
Premeditated Myrtle. Bunce, E. C. | Fic
Prentzas, G. S.
The Brooklyn Bridge | 624.2
Georgia | 975.8
Wyoming | 978.7

PREP SCHOOL STUDENTS

Woodson, J. If you come softly | Fic

PREP SCHOOLS

Grabenstein, J. J. Shine! | Fic
Monir, A. The girl in the picture | Fic
Reynolds, J. Miles Morales | Fic

PRESCRIPTION DRUGS

Bjornlund, L. Oxycodone | 615

Presenting Buffalo Bill. Fleming, C.   978

PRESIDENTS

Bausum, A. Our country's presidents   973.099

Freedman, R. Abraham Lincoln and Frederick Douglass   973.7092

Higgins, J. First strike   Fic

House, K. L. The White House for kids   975.3

Krull, K. Lives of the presidents   973.099

McClafferty, C. K. Buried lives   306.3

Panchyk, R. The keys to American history   973

Swanson, J. L. Bloody times   973.7092

PRESIDENTS -- ASSASSINATION

O'Reilly, B. Kennedy's last days   973.922092

Swanson, J. L. "The president has been shot!"   973.922092

PRESIDENTS -- ASSASSINATION ATTEMPTS

Cabot, M. All-American girl   Fic

PRESIDENTS -- ATTEMPTED ASSASSINATION

Jurmain, S. Murder on the Baltimore Express   973.7092

PRESIDENTS -- ELECTION 1960

Burgan, M. TV shapes presidential politics in the Kennedy-Nixon debates   324.973

PRESIDENTS -- FAMILY

Rhatigan, J. White House kids   920

PRESIDENTS -- HISTORY

Kane, J. N. Facts about the presidents   973.09

PRESIDENTS -- RELATIONS WITH AFRICAN AMERICANS -- HISTORY

Davis, K. C. In the shadow of Liberty   920.0092

PRESIDENTS -- STAFF

Dillon, M. Yes she can   973.932

PRESIDENTS -- SUCCESSION -- HISTORY 20TH CENTURY

Nardo, D. Assassination and its aftermath   973.922092

PRESIDENTS' SPOUSES

Bausum, A. Our country's first ladies   973.09

Krull, K. A kids' guide to America's first ladies   920

Krull, K. Lives of the presidents   973.099

Moss, C. Become a leader like Michelle Obama   973.932

PRESS

Goodmark, R. Girls rock   781.66023

PRESS AND POLITICS

Osborne, L. B. Guardians of liberty   323.44

PRESTON RIVULETTES (HOCKEY TEAM) -- HISTORY

Adams, C. Queens of the ice   796.962082

PRETEEN BOYS

Aster, A. Curse of the forgotten city   Fic

Aster, A. Curse of the Night Witch   Fic

Bauer, A. C. E. No castles here   Fic

Black, H. The bronze key   Fic

Black, H. The silver mask   Fic

Callender, K. King and the dragonflies   Fic

Dunham, K. S. The boy's body book   612.6

Gemeinhart, D. Some kind of courage   Fic

Gino, A. Rick   Fic

Grabenstein, C. Escape from Mr. Lemoncello's library   Fic

Holt, K. A. Knockout   Fic

Mbalia, K. Tristan Strong destroys the world   Fic

Mbalia, K. Tristan Strong punches a hole in the sky   Fic

Park, L. S. A single shard   Fic

Philbrick, W. R. Wildfire   Fic

Pierpoint, E. The secret mission of William Tuck   Fic

Ritter, W. Changeling   Fic

Ritter, W. Deepest darkest   Fic

Shivering, W. Ghosts of Weirdwood   Fic

Shivering, W. Thieves of Weirdwood   Fic

Starmer, A. The whisper   Fic

Young, B. Healer of the water monster   Fic

PRETEEN GIRLS

Al-Mansour, H. The green bicycle   Fic

Alston, B. Amari and the night brothers   Fic

Blake, A. H. Hazel Bly and the deep blue sea   Fic

Bourne, S. Josephine against the sea   Fic

Connolly, M. Hollow dolls   Fic

Connolly, M. Shadow weaver   Fic

DiTerlizzi, T. The battle for WondLa   Fic

Dowell, F. O. The kind of friends we used to be   Fic

Fitzgerald, L. M. The gallery   Fic

Haddix, M. P. Children of exile   Fic

Hale, S. Friends forever   302

Hilton, M. Full cicada moon   Fic

Hoang, V. Girl giant and the Monkey King   Fic

Holland, E. The thorn queen   Fic

Horvath, P. Northward to the moon   Fic

Kessler, L. Emily Windsnap and the castle in the mist   Fic

Khoury, J. The Mystwick School of Musicraft   Fic

Kim, G. The last fallen star   Fic

LeZotte, A. C. Show me a sign   Fic

Leyh, K. Snapdragon   741.5

Love, D. A. Semiprecious   Fic

Martin, L. The ark plan   Fic

Medina, M. Merci Suarez can't dance   Fic

Melleby, N. How to become a planet   Fic

Messner, K. Chirp   Fic

Milford, K. The thief knot   Fic

Murphy, J. Dear Sweet Pea   Fic

Pratchett, T. The Wee Free Men   Fic

Rivera, K. Cece Rios and the Desert of Souls   Fic

Shen, E. L. The comeback   Fic

White, J. A. A path begins   Fic

Wiles, D. Revolution   Fic

PRETEENS

Hatke, B. Mighty Jack   741.5

Korman, G. Notorious   Fic

Ritter, W. The unready queen   Fic

PRETEENS -- BOOKS AND READING

Smith, K. M. Creating a tween collection   025.2

PRETEENS -- INTERPERSONAL RELATIONS

Larson, H. All together now   741.5

PRETENDING

Bond, V. Zora and me   Fic

Pretties. Westerfeld, S.   Fic

The **prettiest**. Young, B.   Fic

Preus, Margi

Enchantment Lake   Fic

Heart of a samurai	Fic	George, J. D. Dragon flight	Fic
Shadow on the mountain	Fic	George, J. D. Dragon slippers	Fic
Village of scoundrels	Fic	George, J. D. Dragon spear	Fic
West of the moon	Fic	Haddix, M. P. Just Ella	Fic
PREVENTIVE MEDICINE		Haddix, M. P. Sent	Fic
Haelle, T. Vaccination investigation	615.3	Healy, C. The hero's guide to saving your kingdom	Fic
The **prey**. Fukuda, A. X.	Fic	Holland, E. The thorn queen	Fic
Price of duty. Strasser, T.	Fic	Kemmerer, B. A heart so fierce and broken	Fic
Price, Charlie		Lewis, C. S. The horse and his boy	Fic
Desert Angel	Fic	Lewis, C. S. Prince Caspian	Fic
Price, Janet, 1964-		Lewis, C. S. The silver chair	Fic
Take control of Asperger's syndrome	618.92	Maguire, G. Egg & spoon	Fic
Price, Lissa		Meyer, M. Cinder	Fic
Starters	Fic	Napoli, D. J. Beast	Fic
Price, Sean		Napoli, D. J. Bound	Fic
Attila the Hun	**B**	Nielsen, J. A. The false prince	Fic
Benazir Bhutto	**B**	Nix, G. Lirael daughter of the Clayr	Fic
Pride. Zoboi, I. A.	Fic	Rogerson, M. An enchantment of ravens	Fic
PRIDE AND VANITY		Rutkoski, M. The Cabinet of Wonders	Fic
Flinn, A. Beastly	Fic	Saint-Exupery, A. d. The little prince	Fic
Saint-Exupery, A. d. The little prince	Fic	Sfar, J. The little prince	741.5
Taylor, M. D. The gold Cadillac	Fic	Shepherd, M. Midnight beauties	Fic
Priest, Cherie		Stanley, D. Bella at midnight	Fic
I am Princess X	Fic	Turner, M. W. A conspiracy of kings	Fic
PRIESTS		Twain, M. The prince and the pauper	Fic
McKinley, R. Chalice	Fic	Uehashi, N. Moribito	Fic
Sedgwick, M. White crow	Fic	Westerfeld, S. Behemoth	Fic
PRIMATES		Westerfeld, S. Goliath	Fic
Gish, M. Gorillas	599.884	Westerfeld, S. Leviathan	Fic
Ottaviani, J. Primates	920	Wheeler, A. Another castle	741.5
PRIMATES -- RESEARCH		Yelchin, E. The haunting of Falcon House	Fic
Silvey, A. Untamed	599.8	Young, E. The dragon path	Fic
Primates. Ottaviani, J.	920	**Princess** Ben. Murdock, C. G.	Fic
PRIMATOLOGISTS		The **princess** diaries. Cabot, M.	Fic
Ottaviani, J. Primates	920	**Princess** Labelmaker to the rescue! Angleberger, T.	Fic
Silvey, A. Untamed	599.8	The **princess** of Cortova. Stanley, D.	Fic
The **prince** and the pauper. Twain, M.	Fic	**Princess** of the Midnight Ball. George, J. D.	Fic
Prince Caspian. Lewis, C. S.	Fic	**Princess** princess ever after. O'Neill, K.	741.5
The **prince** of mist. Ruiz Zafon, C.	Fic	The **princess** who flew with dragons. Burgis, S.	Fic
PRINCE, LIZ, 1981-		**PRINCESSES**	
Prince, L. Tomboy	**B**	Armstrong, K. A royal guide to monster slaying	Fic
Princeless. Whitley, J.	741.5	Aveyard, V. Red queen	Fic
PRINCES		Bashardoust, M. Girls made of snow and glass	Fic
Alexander, L. The remarkable journey of Prince Jen	Fic	Braswell, L. A whole new world	Fic
Bannen, M. The bird and the blade	Fic	Burgis, S. The princess who flew with dragons	Fic
Berry, J. The Amaranth enchantment	Fic	Cabot, M. From the notebooks of a middle school princess	Fic
Bruchac, J. Dragon castle	Fic	Cabot, M. The princess diaries	Fic
Cashore, K. Graceling	Fic	Carey, J. L. Dragon's keep	Fic
Chupeco, R. Wicked as you wish	Fic	Carson, R. The girl of fire and thorns	Fic
Cornwell, B. Venturess	Fic	Chima, C. W. The Demon King	Fic
Cypess, L. Thornwood	Fic	Coulthurst, A. Of fire and stars	Fic
Durst, S. B. Into the Wild	Fic	Cypess, L. Thornwood	Fic
Fantaskey, B. Jessica's guide to dating on the dark side	Fic	Cyprus, N. Sisters of glass	Fic
Fisher, C. Sapphique	Fic	Farrey, B. The secret of Dreadwillow Carse	Fic
Flanagan, J. The tournament at Gorlan	Fic	Ferris, J. Once upon a Marigold	Fic
Fleischman, S. The whipping boy	Fic	Fletcher, S. Alphabet of dreams	Fic
French, V. The robe of skulls	Fic		

Flinn, A. A kiss in time	Fic	**Prisoner** B-3087. Gratz, A.	Fic
Friesner, E. M. Nobody's princess	Fic	The **prisoner** of cell 25. Evans, R. P.	Fic
Friesner, E. M. Nobody's prize	Fic	**Prisoner** of ice and snow. Lauren, R.	Fic
George, J. D. Princess of the Midnight Ball	Fic	**PRISONERS**	
George, J. D. Tuesdays at the castle	Fic	Avi. The end of the world and beyond	Fic
Haddix, M. P. Just Ella	Fic	Evans, R. P. The prisoner of cell 25	Fic
Hahn, R. A creature of moonlight	Fic	Haddix, M. P. Among the brave	Fic
Hale, S. The forgotten sisters	Fic	Lauren, R. Prisoner of ice and snow	Fic
Hale, S. The goose girl	Fic	Ness, P. And the ocean was our sky	Fic
Hale, S. Palace of stone	Fic	Paulsen, G. Woods runner	Fic
Haskell, M. Handbook for dragon slayers	Fic	Pileggi, L. Prisoner 88	Fic
Ibbotson, E. The Ogre of Oglefort	Fic	Rundell, K. The wolf wilder	Fic
Jones, F. Destiny's path	Fic	Smith, A. G. Death sentence	Fic
Kirby, M. J. Icefall	Fic	Tingle, T. Danny Blackgoat Navajo prisoner	Fic
Knudsen, M. The dragon of Trelian	Fic	Turner, M. W. The queen of Attolia	Fic
McKinley, R. The hero and the crown	Fic	Turner, M. W. The thief	Fic
McKinley, R. Pegasus	Fic	Whyman, M. Icecore	Fic
McKissack, P. Nzingha	Fic	Woodruff, E. The ravenmaster's secret	Fic
Medley, L. Castle waiting	741.5	**PRISONERS FAMILIES**	
Moriarty, J. A corner of white	Fic	Marks, J. From the desk of Zoe Washington	Fic
Murdock, C. G. Princess Ben	Fic	**Prisoners** in the palace. MacColl, M.	Fic
Nielsen, J. A. The runaway king	Fic	The **prisoners** of Breendonk. Deem, J. M.	940.53
Nielsen, J. A. The shadow throne	Fic	**PRISONERS OF WAR**	
O'Neal, E. The false princess	Fic	Bascomb, N. The grand escape	940.4
O'Neill, K. Princess princess ever after	741.5	LaFleur, S. M. Beautiful blue world	Fic
Riggs, R. Tales of the Peculiar	Fic	Pausewang, G. Traitor	Fic
Smith, J. Rose	741.5	**PRISONERS OF WAR -- HISTORY**	
Stanley, D. The princess of Cortova	Fic	Gourley, C. The horrors of Andersonville	973.7
Tripp, B. The accidental highwayman	Fic	**PRISONERS OF WAR, CONFEDERATE**	
Vande Velde, V. Frogged	Fic	Wisler, G. C. Red Cap	Fic
Wheeler, A. Another castle	741.5	**PRISONERS' FAMILIES**	
Whitley, J. Princeless	741.5	Zehr, H. What will happen to me?	362.82
Wrede, P. C. Dealing with dragons	Fic	**PRISONS**	
Wrede, P. C. Searching for dragons	Fic	Connor, L. All rise for the honorable Perry T. Cook	Fic
Yep, L. City of fire	Fic	Crowder, M. An uninterrupted view of the sky	Fic
Zinn, B. Poison	Fic	Delaney, J. The ghost prison	Fic
Prineas, Sarah		Fisher, C. Sapphique	Fic
The magic thief	Fic	Gourley, C. The horrors of Andersonville	973.7
Pringle, Laurence, 1935-		Jinks, C. The last bogler	Fic
Billions of years amazing changes	576.8	Lasky, J. America's prisons	365
Frogs!	597.8	Lauren, R. Prisoner of ice and snow	Fic
Ice!	338.09	Myers, W. D. Monster	Fic
Prins, Marcel, 1962-		Pileggi, L. Prisoner 88	Fic
Hidden like Anne Frank	940.53	Smith, A. G. Lockdown	Fic
PRINTING		Smith, A. G. Solitary	Fic
Bow, J. 3-D printers	621.988	Wiechman, K. C. Like a river	Fic
Koch, M. 3D printing	621.9	**PRIVACY RIGHTS**	
PRISON BOOT CAMPS		Kyi, T. L. Eyes & spies	323.44
Strasser, T. Boot camp	Fic	**PRIVATE INVESTIGATORS**	
PRISON EMPLOYEES		Horowitz, A. Public enemy number two	Fic
Soontornvat, C. A wish in the dark	Fic	Springer, N. The case of the missing marquess	Fic
PRISON GUARDS		**Private** Peaceful. Morpurgo, M.	Fic
Choldenko, G. Al Capone does my shirts	Fic	**PRIVATE SCHOOLS**	
Delaney, J. The ghost prison	Fic	Blumenthal, D. Mafia girl	Fic
Prisoner 88. Pileggi, L.	Fic	Craft, J. Class act	741.5
PRISONER ABUSE		Creech, S. The unfinished angel	Fic
Gourley, C. The horrors of Andersonville	973.7	Crossan, S. One	Fic

Once upon a time in the North   Fic
The subtle knife   Fic
Two crafty criminals!   Fic

PULLMAN, PHILIP, 1946- HIS DARK MATERIALS
Gribbin, M. The science of Philip Pullman's His dark materials   823

Pulp. Talley, R.   Fic

PUMA
Hamilton, S. L. Ambushed by a cougar   599.75

PUMA -- BEHAVIOR
Hamilton, S. L. Ambushed by a cougar   599.75

PUNISHMENT
Duey, K. Skin hunger   Fic
Hale, S. Book of a thousand days   Fic
McCaughrean, G. Hercules   398.2
Shulman, M. Scrawl   Fic

PUNK CULTURE
Peters, J. A. Define "normal"   Fic

PUNK ROCK MUSIC
Perez, C. C. The first rule of punk   Fic

PUNK ROCK MUSICIANS
Winters, B. H. The secret life of Ms. Finkleman   Fic

Puppet. Wiseman, E.   Fic

PUPPET MAKING
Kennedy, J. E. Puppet planet   745.592

Puppet planet. Kennedy, J. E.   745.592

PUPPETEERS
Schlitz, L. A. Splendors and glooms   Fic

PUPPETS
Bryan, A. Ashley Bryan's puppets   811

PURGATORY
Goto, H. Half World   Fic

PURITANISM
Capaccio, G. Religion in colonial America   200.973

PURITANS
Capaccio, G. Religion in colonial America   200.973
Messner, K. The Mayflower   974.4

PURITANS -- HISTORY
Schanzer, R. Witches!   133.4

PURITANS -- HISTORY 18TH CENTURY
Speare, E. G. The witch of Blackbird Pond   Fic

Purperhart, Helen
Yoga exercises for teens   613.7

Purple heart. McCormick, P.   Fic

PURPOSE IN LIFE
Dillon, L. To every thing there is a season   223
Gray, C. Defy the stars   Fic
Mass, W. Jeremy Fink and the meaning of life   Fic
Saint-Exupery, A. d. The little prince   Fic
Sfar, J. The little prince   741.5
Teller, J. Nothing   Fic

The **pushcart** war. Merrill, J. F.   Fic
Put your best foot forward. Schorer, S.   792.8
Putting makeup on the fat boy. Wright, B.   Fic
Putting peace first. Dawson, E. D.   303.6

PUYALLUP ASSEMBLY CENTER (PUYALLUP, WASH.)
Larson, K. Dash   Fic

PUZZLES
Grabenstein, C. Escape from Mr. Lemoncello's library   Fic
Johnson, V. The Parker inheritance   Fic
Ruby, L. The clockwork ghost   Fic
Ruby, L. The shadow cipher   Fic
The **puzzling** world of Winston Breen. Berlin, E.   Fic

Pyle, Howard, 1853-1911
The merry adventures of Robin Hood   398.2

Pyle, Robert Michael
The Audubon Society field guide to North American butterflies   595.78

Pyramid. Macaulay, D.   690

PYRAMIDS
Hautman, P. The Klaatu terminus   Fic

PYRAMIDS -- CONSTRUCTION
Macaulay, D. Pyramid   690

PYRENEES
Gilman, D. Ice claw   Fic

Pyron, Bobbie
The dogs of winter   Fic
Lucky strike   Fic

PYTHAGORAS
Karamanides, D. Pythagoras   B

Pythagoras. Karamanides, D.   B

PYTHONS
Messner, K. Tracking pythons   597.96

PŁASZOW (CONCENTRATION CAMP)
Leyson, L. The boy on the wooden box   940.53

Q

QAIDA (ORGANIZATION)
Hillstrom, K. The September 11 terrorist attacks   973.931
Whyman, M. Goldstrike   Fic

Qamar, Amjed
Beneath my mother's feet   Fic

QATAR
Ali, S. K. Love from A to Z   Fic

Qian, Jifang
Chinese history stories   951

QIN SHI HUANG, EMPEROR OF CHINA, 259-210 B.C.E.
O'Connor, J. The emperor's silent army   931

QUAKERS
Higgins, J. Waiting for the queen   Fic

QUALITY OF LIFE
Savage, D. It gets better   306.76

QUANTUM THEORY
Gribbin, M. The science of Philip Pullman's His dark materials   823
Latta, S. L. SMASH!   539.7

QUARANTINE
Choldenko, G. Chasing secrets   Fic
Falls, K. Inhuman   Fic
Jarrow, G. Fatal fever   614.5
Machale, D. J. SYLO   Fic
Power, R. Wilder girls   Fic

QUARRELING

Valente, C. M. The girl who circumnavigated Fairyland in a ship of her own making **Fic**

Valente, C. M. The girl who fell beneath Fairyland and led the revels there **Fic**

Venditti, R. The lightning thief **741.5**

Weston, R. P. Zorgamazoo **Fic**

Whitley, J. Princeless **741.5**

Wrede, P. C. Searching for dragons **Fic**

Yancey, R. The seal of Solomon **Fic**

Young, B. Healer of the water monster **Fic**

A **quick** & easy guide to theythem pronouns. Bongiovanni, A. **425.55**

Quicksand Pond. Lisle, J. T. **Fic**

Quiet power. Cain, S. **155.4**

Quigley, Dawn, 1970-

Apple in the middle **Fic**

The **quilt** walk. Dallas, S. **Fic**

QUILTING

Dallas, S. The quilt walk **Fic**

Rubin, S. G. The quilts of Gee's Bend **746.4609761**

QUILTS

Rubin, S. G. The quilts of Gee's Bend **746.4609761**

The **quilts** of Gee's Bend. Rubin, S. G. **746.4609761**

Quinn, Jason

The Beatles **920**

Quinn, Patricia O.

Attention girls! **618.92**

Quinones, Sam, 1958-

Dreamland **362.29**

QUINTUPLETS

Beaufrand, M. J. Useless Bay **Fic**

Miller, S. E. The miracle & tragedy of the Dionne quintuplets **306.875**

QUOTATIONS

Kerrigan, M. Egyptians **932**

Kerrigan, M. Greeks **938**

Kerrigan, M. Mesopotamians **935**

Kerrigan, M. Romans **937**

QUOTATIONS, ENGLISH

Bartlett, J. Bartlett's familiar quotations **808.88**

R

R N A

Hall, L. E. DNA and RNA **611**

RA (EGYPTIAN DEITY)

Riordan, R. The throne of fire **Fic**

Raatma, Lucia

Barbara Jordan **B**

Michigan **977.4**

Shirley Chisholm **B**

The Underground Railroad **973.7**

Rabbat, Suzy

Super smart information strategies **775**

RABBITS

Adams, R. Watership Down **Fic**

Lester, J. Uncle Remus **398.2**

Tan, S. Lost & found **Fic**

Thomas, S. M. The last rabbit **Fic**

Zuckerman, L. A taste for rabbit **Fic**

RACCOONS

Appelt, K. The true blue scouts of Sugar Man Swamp **Fic**

Sniegoski, T. Quest for the spark **Fic**

RACE (SOCIAL SCIENCES)

Emdin, C. For white folks who teach in the hood-- and the rest of y'all too **370.9173**

Rodger, M. Racism and prejudice **305.8**

Race against time. Wallace, S. N. **976.7**

RACE AWARENESS

Joseph, F. The Black friend **305.8**

RACE HORSES

Henson, H. Dream of Night **Fic**

RACE RELATIONS

Aretha, D. With all deliberate speed **379.2**

Bausum, A. Marching to the mountaintop **323.092**

Bond, V. Zora and me **Fic**

Bowers, R. Superman versus the Ku Klux Klan **741.5**

Brimner, L. D. Accused! **345.761**

Brimner, L. D. Black & white **323.1196**

Burton, E. Race relations **305.800973**

Draper, S. M. Blended **Fic**

Draper, S. M. Fire from the rock **Fic**

Emond, S. Bright lights dark nights **Fic**

English, K. Francie **Fic**

Erskine, K. Seeing red **Fic**

Frank, S. Armstrong and Charlie **Fic**

Fusco, K. N. The wonder of Charlie Anne **Fic**

Gallagher, J. Policing and race **363.2**

Gray Smith, M. Speaking our truth **971.004**

Hudson, W. The talk **305.8**

Jewell, T. This book is anti-racist **305.800973**

Kendi, I. X. Stamped **305.800973**

Kimmel, A. C. The Montgomery Bus Boycott **323.1196**

Lee, H. To kill a mockingbird **Fic**

Lester, J. Guardian **Fic**

Levine, K. The lions of Little Rock **Fic**

Mazer, A. America street **Fic**

McCall, G. G. All the stars denied **Fic**

McGuigan, M. A. Morning in a different place **Fic**

McMullan, M. Sources of light **Fic**

Nelson, M. How I discovered poetry **811.54**

Patrick, D. L. A matter of souls **Fic**

Pinkney, A. D. With the might of angels **Fic**

Powell, P. H. Loving vs. Virginia **Fic**

Ramee, L. M. A good kind of trouble **Fic**

Rhodes, J. P. Sugar **Fic**

Rodger, M. Racism and prejudice **305.8**

Spinelli, J. Maniac Magee **Fic**

Tougas, S. Little Rock girl 1957 **379.2**

Treuer, A. Everything you wanted to know about Indians but were afraid to ask **970.1**

Vawter, V. Paperboy **Fic**

Wein, E. Black dove white raven **Fic**

Wiles, D. The Aurora County All-Stars **Fic**

Woodson, J. Feathers — **Fic**
Wright, B. Crow — **Fic**

RACE RELATIONS 19TH CENTURY

Bolden, T. Maritcha — **974.7**
Race relations. Burton, E. — **305.800973**
The **race** to save the Lord God Bird. Hoose, P. M. — **598.7**
Race to the bottom of the Earth. Barone, R. — **919.89**
Race to the bottom of the sea. Eagar, L. — **Fic**
The **racers**. Bascomb, N. — **796.72092**
Rachel Carson and ecology for kids. Rae, R. — **B**
Rachel Spinelli punched me in the face. Acampora, P. — **Fic**

RACIAL PROFILING

Behnke, A. Racial profiling — **363.2**
Emond, S. Bright lights dark nights — **Fic**
Marcovitz, H. Black in America — **305.896**
Racial profiling. Behnke, A. — **363.2**

RACING

Gifford, C. Swimming — **797.2**
Smith, M. Speed machines — **629.2**
Spinelli, J. Crash — **Fic**

RACING PILOTS

Sheinkin, S. Born to fly — **797.5**
Racing Savannah. Kenneally, M. — **Fic**

RACISM

Aretha, D. Martin Luther King Jr. and the 1963 March on Washington — **323.092**
Baldwin, J. Go tell it on the mountain — **Fic**
Bausum, A. The March against Fear — **323.1196**
Bock, C. Lie — **Fic**
Bolden, T. Take-off! — **784.4**
Brimner, L. D. Black & white — **323.1196**
Bruchac, J. Walking two worlds — **Fic**
Burton, E. Race relations — **305.800973**
Craft, J. Class act — **741.5**
Craft, J. New kid — **741.5**
Curtis, C. P. The Watsons go to Birmingham 1963 — **Fic**
Dumas, F. It ain't so awful falafel — **Fic**
Engle, M. Silver people — **Fic**
Ewald, W. America border culture dreamer — **305.23092**
Farrell, M. C. Standing up against hate — **940.54**
Gallagher, J. Policing and race — **363.2**
Goldstone, L. Separate no more — **323.1196**
Goldstone, L. Unpunished murder — **976.3**
Hall, M. Great Zimbabwe — **968.91**
Hesse, K. Witness — **Fic**
Howard, G. R. We can't teach what we don't know — **379.2**
Hudson, W. The talk — **305.8**
Jewell, T. This book is anti-racist — **305.800973**
Johnson, V. The Parker inheritance — **Fic**
Joseph, F. The Black friend — **305.8**
Kendi, I. X. Stamped — **305.800973**
Korman, G. Linked — **Fic**
Kwaymullina, A. The things she's seen — **Fic**
Lee, H. To kill a mockingbird — **Fic**
Lester, J. Guardian — **Fic**
Levine, K. The lions of Little Rock — **Fic**
Magoon, K. Fire in the streets — **Fic**

Magoon, K. The rock and the river — **Fic**
Marrin, A. Uprooted — **940.53**
McCall, G. G. All the stars denied — **Fic**
McGuigan, M. A. Morning in a different place — **Fic**
McKissack, P. A friendship for today — **Fic**
McMullan, M. How I found the Strong — **Fic**
McMullan, M. Sources of light — **Fic**
Naidoo, B. Out of bounds — **Fic**
Nelson, M. A wreath for Emmett Till — **811**
Osborne, L. B. Miles to go for freedom — **305.896**
Oshiro, M. Anger is a gift — **Fic**
Patterson, J. Becoming Muhammad Ali — **Fic**
Pinkney, A. D. Loretta Little looks back — **Fic**
Reis, R. A. African Americans and the Civil War — **973.7**
Rhodes, J. P. Black brother black brother — **Fic**
Rhodes, J. P. Ghost boys — **Fic**
Rodger, M. Racism and prejudice — **305.8**
Rubin, S. G. Brown v. Board of Education — **344.73**
Salisbury, G. Eyes of the emperor — **Fic**
Shange, N. We troubled the waters — **811**
Smith, S. L. Flygirl — **Fic**
Spinelli, J. Maniac Magee — **Fic**
Stone, N. Clean getaway — **Fic**
Stone, T. L. Courage has no color — **940.54**
Strasser, T. Fallout — **Fic**
Taylor, M. D. All the days past all the days to come — **Fic**
Taylor, M. D. The friendship — **Fic**
Taylor, M. D. The gold Cadillac — **Fic**
Taylor, M. D. The land — **Fic**
Taylor, M. D. Let the circle be unbroken — **Fic**
Taylor, M. D. The road to Memphis — **Fic**
Taylor, M. D. Roll of thunder hear my cry — **Fic**
Taylor, M. D. The well — **Fic**
Uchida, Y. A jar of dreams — **Fic**
Volponi, P. Black and white — **Fic**
Warman, J. The world beneath — **Fic**
Williams, A. Genesis begins again — **Fic**
Woods, B. The unsung hero of Birdsong USA — **Fic**
Woodson, J. If you come softly — **Fic**
Wright, B. Crow — **Fic**
Yang, G. L. American born Chinese — **741.5**
Yoo, P. From a whisper to a rallying cry — **305.895**

RACISM -- HISTORY

Bartoletti, S. C. They called themselves the K.K.K. — **322.4**
Brimner, L. D. Birmingham Sunday — **323.1196**
Marcovitz, H. Black in America — **305.896**

RACISM -- HISTORY 20TH CENTURY

Crowe, C. Getting away with murder — **364.15**
Madigan, T. The burning — **976.6**

RACISM -- POLITICAL ASPECTS

Anderson, C. One person no vote — **324.6**
Racism and prejudice. Rodger, M. — **305.8**

RACISM IN CRIMINOLOGY

Goldstone, L. Unpunished murder — **976.3**

RACISM IN THE CRIMINAL JUSTICE SYSTEM

Marguiles, P. The devil on trial — **345.73**
The **raconteur's** commonplace book. Milford, K. — **Fic**

Wagner, H. Nightshade City — Fic

RATS -- HISTORY

Marrin, A. Oh rats! — 599.35

RATS AS LABORATORY ANIMALS

O'Brien, R. C. Mrs. Frisby and the rats of NIMH — Fic

RATS AS PETS

Kenney, K. L. Rat — 636.935

Toor, R. Misunderstood — 636.935

Rattlesnake Mesa. Weber, E. N. R. — B

Rau, Dana Meachen, 1971-

Freaking out! — 612.8

Going organic — 613.2

Going vegetarian — 613.2

Rauf, Don

Computer game designer — 794.8

Raven. Garcia, K. — Fic

The **raven.** Poe, E. A. — 811

The **raven** boys. Stiefvater, M. — Fic

The **raven** king. Stiefvater, M. — Fic

Raven summer. Almond, D. — Fic

Raven's gate. Horowitz, A. — Fic

Raven, Nicky

Beowulf — 398.2

The **ravenmaster's** secret. Woodruff, E. — Fic

RAVENS

Avi. Old wolf — Fic

Poe, E. A. The raven — 811

Rawitt, Jean, 1952-

A loved one with dementia — 616.8

Ray & me. Gutman, D. — Fic

Ray Bradbury. Bankston, J. — B

Ray Charles and the birth of soul. Woog, A. — B

Raybearer. Ifueko, J. — Fic

Raymie Nightingale. DiCamillo, K. — Fic

Reaching for the Moon. Johnson, K. G. — B

Reaching out. Jimenez, F. — Fic

Read all about it! Trelease, J. — Fic

Read the world. Ziemke, K. — 372.6

Read, Nicholas, 1956-

City critters — 591.75

The **reader.** Chee, T. — Fic

Readers theatre for middle school boys. Black, A. N. — 812

The **readers'** advisory guide to graphic novels. Goldsmith, F. — 025.2

The **readers'** advisory guide to teen literature. Carstensen, A. — 028.5

READERS' ADVISORY SERVICES

Carstensen, A. The readers' advisory guide to teen literature — 028.5

Goldsmith, F. The readers' advisory guide to graphic novels — 025.2

Krok, L. Novels in verse for teens — 808.83

READERS' THEATRE

Black, A. N. Readers theatre for middle school boys — 812

Readicide. Gallagher, K. — 428.4

READING

Beers, G. K. Disrupting thinking — 418

Bigelow, L. J. Hazel's theory of evolution — Fic

Chee, T. The reader — Fic

Chee, T. The speaker — Fic

Gallagher, K. Readicide — 428.4

Grover, S. Listening to learn — 372.4

Gutman, D. Miss Daisy is crazy! — Fic

Lemov, D. Reading reconsidered — 372.4

Serravallo, J. The reading strategies book — 428.4

READING (ELEMENTARY)

Altieri, J. L. Reading science — 372.35

Bryan, T. A. Art of comprehension — 372.47

Casey, H. K. Literacy learning clubs in grades 4-8 — 372.6

Fountas, I. C. Guided reading — 372.4

Harvey, S. Strategies that work — 372.47

Miller, D. The book whisperer — 372.6

Miller, D. Reading in the wild — 372.4

READING (MIDDLE SCHOOL)

Casey, H. K. Literacy learning clubs in grades 4-8 — 372.6

Gallagher, K. Deeper reading — 372.47

Miller, D. The book whisperer — 372.6

Miller, D. Reading in the wild — 372.4

Robb, L. Teaching reading in middle school — 428.4071

READING (PRIMARY)

Hansen, D. The music and literacy connection — 780

READING (SECONDARY)

Bernadowski, C. Research-based reading strategies in the library for adolescent learners — 428.4071

Farwell, S. M. Supporting reading in grades 6-12 — 428.4071

Gallagher, K. 180 days — 428.4071

Gallagher, K. Deeper reading — 372.47

Tovani, C. I read it but I don't get it — 428.4

READING (SECONDARY) -- COMPUTER-ASSISTED INSTRUCTION

Turner, K. H. Argument in the real world — 808

READING -- PARENT PARTICIPATION

Sutton, R. A family of readers — 809

READING -- REMEDIAL TEACHING

Tovani, C. I read it but I don't get it — 428.4

READING ALOUD

Janeczko, P. B. A foot in the mouth — 821.008

READING COMPREHENSION

Gallagher, K. Deeper reading — 372.47

Harvey, S. Strategies that work — 372.47

Lemov, D. Reading reconsidered — 372.4

Richardson, J. The next step forward in guided reading — 372.41

Tovani, C. I read it but I don't get it — 428.4

READING COMPREHENSION -- STUDY AND TEACHING

Boyles, N. N. That's a great answer! — 372.47

READING COMPREHENSION -- STUDY AND TEACHING (ELEMENTARY)

Bryan, T. A. Art of comprehension — 372.47

Thompson, T. Adventures in graphica — 372.41

Reading in the wild. Miller, D. — 372.4

READING PROMOTION

Gallagher, K. Readicide — 428.4

Bushnell, C. Rules for being a girl	**Fic**	
Buyea, R. Because of Mr. Terupt	**Fic**	
Byars, B. C. Cracker Jackson	**Fic**	
Cabot, M. From the notebooks of a middle school princess	**Fic**	
Caletti, D. The last forever	**Fic**	
Callender, K. King and the dragonflies	**Fic**	
Cartaya, P. The epic fail of Arturo Zamora	**Fic**	
Carter, C. Forever or a long long time	**Fic**	
Castellucci, C. Boy proof	**Fic**	
Castellucci, C. Don't cosplay with my heart	**Fic**	
Cavanaugh, N. J. This journal belongs to Ratchet	**Fic**	
Cervantes, A. Gaby lost and found	**Fic**	
Chaltas, T. Because I am furniture	**Fic**	
Chao, G. American panda	**Fic**	
Chao, G. Our wayward fate	**Fic**	
Charles, T. Like Vanessa	**Fic**	
Chase, P. J. Dough boys	**Fic**	
Chase, P. J. So done	**Fic**	
Chase, P. J. Turning point	**Fic**	
Cheng, J. See you in the cosmos	**Fic**	
Chmakova, S. Awkward	**741.5**	
Chmakova, S. Brave	**741.5**	
Chmakova, S. Crush	**741.5**	
Cisneros, E. Efren divided	**Fic**	
Cleary, B. Dear Mr. Henshaw	**Fic**	
Clements, A. Extra credit	**Fic**	
Connis, D. Suggested reading	**Fic**	
Connor, L. All rise for the honorable Perry T. Cook	**Fic**	
Connor, L. Waiting for normal	**Fic**	
Cooney, C. B. Janie face to face	**Fic**	
Courtney, N. J. All-American Muslim girl	**Fic**	
Creech, S. Absolutely normal chaos	**Fic**	
Creech, S. Hate that cat	**Fic**	
Creech, S. Love that dog	**Fic**	
Creech, S. Walk two moons	**Fic**	
Crossan, S. Being Toffee	**Fic**	
Crossan, S. One	**Fic**	
Crutcher, C. Deadline	**Fic**	
Curato, M. Flamer	**Fic**	
Danziger, P. The cat ate my gymsuit	**Fic**	
Darrows, E. Dead little mean girl	**Fic**	
Davis, M. Superstar	**Fic**	
Day, C. I can make this promise	**Fic**	
Day, C. The sea in winter	**Fic**	
Dee, B. Star-crossed	**Fic**	
Delacre, L. Us in progress	**Fic**	
Dessen, S. Lock and key	**Fic**	
Dessen, S. The moon and more	**Fic**	
Dessen, S. Saint Anything	**Fic**	
Dessen, S. That summer	**Fic**	
Dessen, S. The truth about forever	**Fic**	
Dessen, S. What happened to goodbye	**Fic**	
DiCamillo, K. Because of Winn-Dixie	**Fic**	
Donovan, J. I'll get there it better be worth the trip	**Fic**	
Donwerth-Chikamatsu, A. Beyond me	**Fic**	
Dooley, S. Free verse	**Fic**	

Dowell, F. O. The class	**Fic**	
Dowell, F. O. The kind of friends we used to be	**Fic**	
Downham, J. Before I die	**Fic**	
Draper, S. M. Blended	**Fic**	
Draper, S. M. Just another hero	**Fic**	
Draper, S. M. November blues	**Fic**	
Draper, S. M. Out of my mind	**Fic**	
Efaw, A. Battle dress	**Fic**	
Elkeles, S. How to ruin a summer vacation	**Fic**	
Elkeles, S. How to ruin my teenage life	**Fic**	
Elkeles, S. How to ruin your boyfriend's reputation	**Fic**	
Ellis, A. D. This is what I did	**Fic**	
Elston, A. The rules for disappearing	**Fic**	
Emond, S. Bright lights dark nights	**Fic**	
Emond, S. Winter town	**Fic**	
Erskine, K. The absolute value of Mike	**Fic**	
Erskine, K. Mockingbird	**Fic**	
Esplin, J. L. 96 miles	**Fic**	
Eulberg, E. Revenge of the girl with the great personality	**Fic**	
Farizan, S. Here to stay	**Fic**	
Farrant, N. After Iris	**Fic**	
Federle, T. Five six seven Nate!	**Fic**	
Fields, T. After the death of Anna Gonzales	**Fic**	
Finneyfrock, K. The sweet revenge of Celia Door	**Fic**	
Fipps, L. Starfish	**Fic**	
Firestone, C. Dress coded	**Fic**	
Fitzgerald, S. M. The apple tart of hope	**Fic**	
Flake, S. Bang!	**Fic**	
Flake, S. Who am I without him?	**Fic**	
Flores-Scott, P. American road trip	**Fic**	
Foley, J. A. Sorry for your loss	**Fic**	
Forman, G. Where she went	**Fic**	
Foxlee, K. The anatomy of wings	**Fic**	
Fraillon, Z. The bone sparrow	**Fic**	
Frederick, H. V. Dear pen pal	**Fic**	
Frederick, H. V. Home for the holidays	**Fic**	
Frederick, H. V. The Mother-Daughter Book Club	**Fic**	
Frederick, H. V. Much ado about Anne	**Fic**	
Frederick, H. V. Pies & prejudice	**Fic**	
Freymann-Weyr, G. My heartbeat	**Fic**	
Friedman, A. Two Summers	**Fic**	
Friedman, L. B. Can you say catastrophe?	**Fic**	
Friend, N. Bounce	**Fic**	
Friend, N. Lush	**Fic**	
Friend, N. Perfect	**Fic**	
Frost, H. Keesha's house	**Fic**	
Galante, C. The world from up here	**Fic**	
Gale, E. K. The bully book	**Fic**	
Gantos, J. I am not Joey Pigza	**Fic**	
Gantos, J. Joey Pigza loses control	**Fic**	
Gantos, J. Joey Pigza swallowed the key	**Fic**	
Gantos, J. What would Joey do?	**Fic**	
Gardner, K. Brave enough	**Fic**	
Gardner, W. You're welcome universe	**Fic**	
Gemeinhart, D. The honest truth	**Fic**	
Gephart, D. How to survive middle school	**Fic**	
Gerber, A. Braced	**Fic**	

Keyser, A. Pointe claw	**Fic**	Littman, S. Backlash	**Fic**
Khan, H. Amina's song	**Fic**	Lloyd, M. W. Allergic	**741.5**
Khan, H. Amina's voice	**Fic**	Lockhart, E. The disreputable history of Frankie Landau-	
Khan, H. More to the story	**Fic**	Banks	**Fic**
Khorram, A. Darius the Great is not okay	**Fic**	Lockhart, E. Dramarama	**Fic**
Kim, J. Stand up Yumi Chung!	**Fic**	Lockington, M. For black girls like me	**Fic**
King, A. S. The year we fell from space	**Fic**	Longo, J. What I carry	**Fic**
King, W. OCDaniel	**Fic**	Lopez, D. Ask my mood ring how I feel	**Fic**
Kinney, J. Cabin fever	**Fic**	Lopez, D. Confetti girl	**Fic**
Kinney, J. The deep end	**Fic**	Lord, C. Half a chance	**Fic**
Kinney, J. Diary of a wimpy kid	**Fic**	Lord, C. Rules	**Fic**
Kinney, J. Dog days	**Fic**	Lord, C. Touch blue	**Fic**
Kinney, J. Hard luck	**Fic**	Lord, E. When we collided	**Fic**
Kinney, J. The last straw	**Fic**	Lowry, L. Anastasia at your service	**Fic**
Kinney, J. The long haul	**Fic**	Lowry, L. Anastasia Krupnik	**Fic**
Kinney, J. Old school	**Fic**	Lubar, D. Character driven	**Fic**
Kinney, J. Rodrick rules	**Fic**	Lundin, B. Ship it	**Fic**
Kinney, J. The third wheel	**Fic**	Lupica, M. Miracle on 49th Street	**Fic**
Kinney, J. The ugly truth	**Fic**	Lupica, M. Strike zone	**Fic**
Kisner, A. Dear Rachel Maddow	**Fic**	Lyga, B. The astonishing adventures of Fanboy & Goth	
Knowles, J. Where the heart is	**Fic**	Girl	**Fic**
Koertge, R. Shakespeare makes the playoffs	**Fic**	Lynch, C. Inexcusable	**Fic**
Koertge, R. Stoner & Spaz	**Fic**	Mac, C. 10 things I can see from here	**Fic**
Konigsberg, B. Openly straight	**Fic**	Mack, W. C. Athlete vs. mathlete	**Fic**
Konigsburg, E. L. The view from Saturday	**Fic**	Mackel, K. Boost	**Fic**
Korman, G. The juvie three	**Fic**	Mackler, C. The Earth my butt and other big round	
Korman, G. Linked	**Fic**	things	**Fic**
Korman, G. Pop	**Fic**	Mafi, T. A very large expanse of sea	**Fic**
Korman, G. Restart	**Fic**	Magoon, K. Camo girl	**Fic**
Korman, G. Schooled	**Fic**	Makechnie, A. Ten thousand tries	**Fic**
Korman, G. Slacker	**Fic**	Maldonado, T. Secret Saturdays	**Fic**
Korman, G. Son of the mob	**Fic**	Maldonado, T. Tight	**Fic**
Korman, G. Swindle	**Fic**	Marcus, K. Exposed	**Fic**
Korman, G. Ungifted	**Fic**	Marks, J. From the desk of Zoe Washington	**Fic**
Korman, G. Zoobreak	**Fic**	Marsh, K. Nowhere boy	**Fic**
Kowitt, H. The loser list	**Fic**	Martin, M. A. To be honest	**Fic**
LaBan, E. The Tragedy Paper	**Fic**	Martinez, C. G. Pig park	**Fic**
LaFleur, S. M. Love Aubrey	**Fic**	Martinez, C. G. The smell of old lady perfume	**Fic**
Lai, R. Fly on the wall	**Fic**	Martinez, J. Virtuosity	**Fic**
Lange, E. J. Butter	**Fic**	Mass, W. Every soul a star	**Fic**
Larocca, R. Red white and whole	**Fic**	Mass, W. Jeremy Fink and the meaning of life	**Fic**
Larson, H. All summer long	**741.5**	Mass, W. A mango-shaped space	**Fic**
Larson, H. All together now	**741.5**	Matson, M. Since you've been gone	**Fic**
Lean, S. A dog called Homeless	**Fic**	Mazer, H. Somebody please tell me who I am	**Fic**
Leavitt, M. Calvin	**Fic**	McCall, G. G. Under the mesquite	**Fic**
Leavitt, M. My book of life by Angel	**Fic**	McClintock, N. She saidshe saw	**Fic**
Lecesne, J. Absolute brightness	**Fic**	McCormick, P. Cut	**Fic**
Legrand, C. Some kind of happiness	**Fic**	McDaniel, L. Breathless	**Fic**
Lennon, T. When love comes to town	**Fic**	McDaniel, L. Hit and run	**Fic**
Leno, K. The lost & found	**Fic**	McGarry, K. Only a breath apart	**Fic**
Levithan, D. The mysterious disappearance of Aidan S.	**Fic**	McKay, H. Binny for short	**Fic**
Levithan, D. Two boys kissing	**Fic**	McKay, H. Caddy ever after	**Fic**
Levy, D. A. The family Fletcher takes Rock Island	**Fic**	McKay, H. Forever Rose	**Fic**
Levy, D. A. The misadventures of the family Fletcher	**Fic**	McKay, H. Indigo's star	**Fic**
Levy, D. A. This would make a good story someday	**Fic**	McKay, H. Saffy's angel	**Fic**
Lewis, G. One white dolphin	**Fic**	McKay, S. E. Thunder over Kandahar	**Fic**
Lisle, J. T. Quicksand Pond	**Fic**	Medina, M. Merci Suarez can't dance	**Fic**

Saeed, J. Yara's spring	**Fic**	Trueman, T. Inside out	**Fic**
Salisbury, G. Banjo	**Fic**	Trueman, T. Stuck in neutral	**Fic**
Sanchez, A. Bait	**Fic**	Umminger, A. American girls	**Fic**
Schmatz, P. Bluefish	**Fic**	Urban, L. The center of everything	**Fic**
Schmidt, G. D. Orbiting Jupiter	**Fic**	Vail, R. Well that was awkward	**Fic**
Shaw, S. Safe	**Fic**	Van de Ruit, J. Spud	**Fic**
Shen, E. L. The comeback	**Fic**	Van Draanen, W. The running dream	**Fic**
Shen, P. Nothing can possibly go wrong	**741.5**	Van Vleet, C. Eliza Bing is (not) a big fat quitter	**Fic**
Shevah, E. Dara Palmer's major drama	**Fic**	Vance, A. P. The Heartbreak Messenger	**Fic**
Shofner, C. Almost paradise	**Fic**	Venkatraman, P. The bridge home	**Fic**
Shulman, M. Scrawl	**Fic**	Venkatraman, P. A time to dance	**Fic**
Shusterman, N. Antsy does time	**Fic**	Vivat, B. Frazzled	**Fic**
Shusterman, N. Dry	**Fic**	Vivian, S. The list	**Fic**
Silberberg, A. Milo	**Fic**	Vlahos, L. Life in a fishbowl	**Fic**
Sitomer, A. L. The secret story of Sonia Rodriguez	**Fic**	Voigt, C. Dicey's song	**Fic**
Sloan, H. G. Counting by 7s	**Fic**	Voigt, C. Homecoming	**Fic**
Sloan, H. G. The elephant in the room	**Fic**	Volponi, P. Black and white	**Fic**
Sloan, H. G. I'll be there	**Fic**	Volponi, P. Rikers High	**Fic**
Sloan, H. G. Short	**Fic**	Volponi, P. Rucker Park setup	**Fic**
Snyder, L. My Jasper June	**Fic**	Wallace, R. One good punch	**Fic**
Sones, S. Stop pretending	**Fic**	Wallace, R. Perpetual check	**Fic**
Sones, S. What my girlfriend doesn't know	**Fic**	Wallace, R. Wrestling Sturbridge	**Fic**
Sones, S. What my mother doesn't know	**Fic**	Walton, J. Words on bathroom walls	**Fic**
Sonnenblick, J. After ever after	**Fic**	Warga, J. The shape of thunder	**Fic**
Sonnenblick, J. Notes from the midnight driver	**Fic**	Watkins, S. Great Falls	**Fic**
Sonnenblick, J. Zen and the art of faking it	**Fic**	Watson, R. Piecing me together	**Fic**
Sonnichsen, A. L. Red butterfly	**Fic**	Watson, R. Some places more than others	**Fic**
Sorosiak, C. Wild blue wonder	**Fic**	Watson, R. Watch us rise	**Fic**
Sovern, M. J. The meaning of Maggie	**Fic**	Weaver, W. Saturday night dirt	**Fic**
Spinelli, J. Crash	**Fic**	Weeks, S. Jumping the scratch	**Fic**
Spinelli, J. Maniac Magee	**Fic**	Weissman, E. B. The length of a string	**Fic**
Spinelli, J. Stargirl	**Fic**	Werlin, N. The rules of survival	**Fic**
Spinelli, J. Wringer	**Fic**	Westerfeld, S. So yesterday	**Fic**
Stamper, P. The gravity of us	**Fic**	Weston, C. Speed of life	**Fic**
Staples, S. F. Haveli	**Fic**	White, R. Belle Prater's boy	**Fic**
Stead, R. Goodbye stranger	**Fic**	Whitney, D. When you were here	**Fic**
Stead, R. Liar & spy	**Fic**	Whittemore, J. Odd girl in	**Fic**
Stead, R. The list of things that will not change	**Fic**	Wiles, D. The Aurora County All-Stars	**Fic**
Stone, N. Clean getaway	**Fic**	Wilkinson, L. Pink	**Fic**
Stork, F. X. Marcelo in the real world	**Fic**	Williams, A. Genesis begins again	**Fic**
Strasser, T. Boot camp	**Fic**	Williams, C. L. The chosen one	**Fic**
Strasser, T. No place	**Fic**	Williams, I. Water in May	**Fic**
Strasser, T. Price of duty	**Fic**	Williams, M. Now is the time for running	**Fic**
Sugiura, M. It's not like it's a secret	**Fic**	Williams, S. Bull rider	**Fic**
Sumner, J. Roll with it	**Fic**	Williams-Garcia, R. Jumped	**Fic**
Sumner, J. Tune it out	**Fic**	Williams-Garcia, R. Like sisters on the homefront	**Fic**
Sweeney, D. The minnow	**Fic**	Williamson, V. The fox girl and the white gazelle	**Fic**
Tamaki, M. Saving Montgomery Sole	**Fic**	Winfrey, K. Things Jolie needs to do before she bites it	**Fic**
Tamaki, M. Skim	**741.5**	Wiseman, R. Boys girls and other hazardous materials	**Fic**
Telgemeier, R. Claudia and mean Janine	**741.5**	Wittlinger, E. Hard love	**Fic**
Telgemeier, R. Drama	**741.5**	Wittlinger, E. Parrotfish	**Fic**
Teller, J. Nothing	**Fic**	Wolff, V. E. Make lemonade	**Fic**
Temblador, A. Secrets of the Casa Rosada	**Fic**	Wolff, V. E. The Mozart season	**Fic**
Thompson, H. The language inside	**Fic**	Wolff, V. E. Probably still Nick Swansen	**Fic**
Thornburgh, B. Ordinary girls	**Fic**	Wolkenstein, M. E. Turtle boy	**Fic**
Tolan, S. S. Surviving the Applewhites	**Fic**	Woodson, J. After Tupac and D Foster	**Fic**
Trebincevic, K. World in between	**Fic**	Woodson, J. Before the ever after	**Fic**

Red glove. Black, H. — Fic
Red hot salsa. Carlson, L. M. — 811.008
Red madness. Jarrow, G. — 614.5
Red moon at Sharpsburg. Wells, R. — Fic
The red pencil. Pinkney, A. D. — Fic
The red pyramid. Collar, O. — 741.5
The red pyramid. Riordan, R. — Fic
Red queen. Aveyard, V. — Fic
Red scarf girl. Jiang, J. — B
Red skies falling. London, A. — Fic
Red white and whole. Larocca, R. — Fic
Red white blue and Uncle who? Bateman, T. — 929.9

RED-SIDED GARTER SNAKE
Montgomery, S. The snake scientist — 597.96

Redding, Anna Crowley
Google it — 005.1092

REDEMPTION
Kraus, D. At the edge of empire — Fic
Stevenson, B. Just mercy — 340.092

Rediscovering Easter Island. Pelta, K. — 996.1
Redwall. Jacques, B. — Fic

REDWALL ABBEY (IMAGINARY PLACE)
Jacques, B. Martin the Warrior — Fic
Jacques, B. Mossflower — Fic
Jacques, B. Pearls of Lutra — Fic
Redwall the graphic novel. Jacques, B. — 741.5
Redwood and Ponytail. Holt, K. A. — Fic

Reece, Richard, 1948-
The Korean War — 951.904

Reed, Cristie
Ferret — 636
Mini Pig — 636.4

Reed, M. K.
Americus — Fic
Dinosaurs — 567.9

Reef, Catherine
The Bronte sisters — 920
Florence Nightingale — B
Frida & Diego — 759.972
Jane Austen — B
Noah Webster — B
Sarah Bernhardt — B
Victoria — B

Rees, Bob
The Civil War — 973.7

Reeve, Philip
Fever Crumb — Fic
Scrivener's moon — Fic
A web of air — Fic

Reflections. Jones, D. W. — 823
Reflections on a gift of watermelon pickle.... Dunning, S. — 811
Refraction. Hughes, N. — Fic
Refugee. Gratz, A. — Fic

REFUGEE CAMPS
Pierce, T. Lady knight — Fic

REFUGEES
Agosin, M. I lived on Butterfly Hill — Fic

Alban, A. Anya's war — Fic
Anderson, N. C. City of saints & thieves — Fic
Applegate, K. Wishtree — Fic
Bertagna, J. Exodus — Fic
Butler, G. Drawn across borders — 304.8
DuPrau, J. The people of Sparks — Fic
Fraillon, Z. The bone sparrow — Fic
Gratz, A. Refugee — Fic
Kaufman, A. Illuminae — Fic
Lai, T. Butterfly yellow — Fic
Leatherdale, M. B. Stormy seas — 305.9
Lee, J. Brother's keeper — Fic
McPherson, S. S. The global refugee crisis — 362.87
Naidoo, B. The other side of truth — Fic
Nayeri, D. Everything sad is untrue — Fic
Park, L. S. A long walk to water — Fic
Partridge, E. Boots on the ground — 959.704
Pinkney, A. D. The red pencil — Fic
Preus, M. Village of scoundrels — Fic
Salazar, A. The land of the cranes — Fic
Sepetys, R. Salt to the sea — Fic
Staples, S. F. Under the persimmon tree — Fic
Thompson, H. The language inside — Fic
Thor, A. Deep sea — Fic
Trebincevic, K. World in between — Fic
Villalobos, J. P. The other side — 305.235092
Walsh, A. A long way from home — Fic
Wilkes, S. Out of Iraq — 305.9
Williams, M. Now is the time for running — Fic
Yousafzai, M. We are displaced — 305.23092

REFUGEES, AFGHAN
Walsh, A. A long way from home — Fic

REFUGEES, AFRICAN
St. John, W. Outcasts united — 796.334092

REFUGEES, HUNGARIAN
Giff, P. R. Lily's crossing — Fic

REFUGEES, IRAQI
Ellis, D. Children of war — 305.23086
Wilkes, S. Out of Iraq — 305.9

REFUGEES, JEWISH
Byers, A. Saving children from the Holocaust — 940.53
Fox, A. L. Ten thousand children — 940.53
Hodge, D. Rescuing the children — 940.53
Hoffman, B. N. Liberation — 940.53
Matas, C. After the war — Fic

REFUGEES, SUDANESE
Applegate, K. Home of the brave — Fic
Pinkney, A. D. The red pencil — Fic

REFUGEES, SYRIAN
Dassu, A. M. Boy everywhere — Fic
Marsh, K. Nowhere boy — Fic
Williamson, V. The fox girl and the white gazelle — Fic

REFUSE AND REFUSE DISPOSAL
Kallen, S. A. Trashing the planet — 363.72

Regarding the bathrooms. Klise, K. — Fic
Regarding the fountain. Klise, K. — Fic
Regarding the sink. Klise, K. — Fic

Remarkable. Foley, L. K.   Fic
The **remarkable** journey of Prince Jen. Alexander, L.   Fic
Remarkable journeys. Schoell, W.   B
Remarkable minds. Noyce, P.   509.2
Remarkables. Haddix, M. P.   Fic
REMARRIAGE
   Friend, N. Bounce   Fic
   Stead, R. The list of things that will not change   Fic
Rembrandt. Roberts, R.   B
REMBRANDT HARMENSZOON VAN RIJN, 1606-1669
   Roberts, R. Rembrandt   B
Remember D-day. Drez, R. J.   940.54
Remember Little Bighorn. Walker, P. R.   973.8
Remember Little Rock. Walker, P. R.   379.2
Remember Pearl Harbor. Allen, T. B.   940.54
Remember the Alamo. Walker, P. R.   976.4
REMOTE CONTROL
   Fleischman, P. Zap   812
Remote control. Heath, J.   Fic
REMOTELY OPERATED SUBMERSIBLES
   Spilsbury, R. Robots underwater   623.82
RENAISSANCE (1300-1600)
   Bergreen, L. Magellan   910.4
   Marsh, K. Jepp who defied the stars   Fic
The **Renaissance**. Claybourne, A.   940.2
The **Renaissance** artists. Taylor, D. C.   709.45
Renaissance Europe. Grant, N.   940.2
RENAISSANCE FAIRS
   Jamieson, V. All's faire in middle school   741.5
The **Renaissance** in Europe. Elliott, L.   940.2
Renaissance medicine. Dawson, I.   610
RENAISSANCE SCIENCE
   Krull, K. Leonardo da Vinci   509
RENEWABLE ENERGY INDUSTRY AND TRADE
   Dickmann, N. Using renewable energy   333.79
RENEWABLE ENERGY SOURCES
   Burgan, M. Energy   621.042
   Conley, K. A. Biofuels   333.95
   Dickmann, N. Using renewable energy   333.79
   Lew, K. Goodbye gasoline   621.31
   O'Neal, C. How to use wind power to light and heat your home   621.31
   Rusch, E. The next wave   621.31
   Sneideman, J. Renewable energy   333.79
   Sobey, E. J. C. Solar cell and renewable energy experiments   621.042078
   Walker, N. Harnessing power from the sun   621.47
   Woll, K. Wind energy   333.9
RENEWABLE ENERGY SOURCES -- EXPERIMENTS
   Dobson, C. Wind power   621.4
   Rigsby, M. Doable renewables   621.042
Renewable energy. Sneideman, J.   333.79
Renier, Aaron
   The unsinkable Walker Bean   741.5
RENO, NEVADA
   Horowitz, A. Nightrise   Fic
Repman, Judi

School library management   025.1
REPORT WRITING
   Cornwall, P. Super smart information strategies   372.133
   Janeczko, P. B. Writing winning reports and essays   808
REPORT WRITING -- STUDY AND TEACHING
   Anderson, J. Everyday editing   808
REPRESENTATIVE GOVERNMENT AND REPRESEN-TATION
   Fleischer, J. Votes of confidence   324.6
REPRODUCTION
   Buchanan, S. C. Plant reproduction   575.6
REPRODUCTIVE HEALTH
   Mirk, S. You do you   306.70835
   Omnigraphics, I. Sexual health information for teens   613.9071
REPRODUCTIVE RIGHTS
   Blumenthal, K. Jane against the world   342.7308
   Stevenson, R. My body my choice   362.1988
REPRODUCTIVE SYSTEM
   Gravelle, K. The period book   612.6
Reptile. McCarthy, C.   597.9
REPTILES
   Collard, S. B. Sneed B. Collard III's most fun book ever about lizards   597.95
   Gish, M. Alligators   597.98
   Hirschmann, K. Deadliest reptiles   597.9
   McCarthy, C. Reptile   597.9
   McGinnis, S. M. Peterson field guide to western reptiles and amphibians   597.9
   Powell, R. Peterson field guide to reptiles and amphibians of Eastern and Central North America   597.9
   Somervill, B. A. Monitor lizard   597.95
Republic of Ireland. Wiseman, B.   941.7
Requiem. Janeczko, P. B.   811
Rescue. Meltzer, M.   940.53
RESCUE DOGS
   MacLeod, E. Top dogs   636.7
   Rosen, M. J. The tale of rescue   Fic
RESCUE WORK
   Fowler, W. Counterterrorism in West Africa   966.404
   Lace, W. W. The Indian Ocean tsunami of 2004   909
   Lewis, C. S. The silver chair   Fic
   Markle, S. Rescues!   363.34
RESCUES
   Avi. Gold rush girl   Fic
   Bacigalupi, P. The Drowned Cities   Fic
   Bardugo, L. Wonder Woman   Fic
   Bertozzi, N. Shackleton   919.89
   Campbell, J. Daisy to the rescue   636
   Carson, R. The bitter kingdom   Fic
   Chodosh, J. The elephant doctor of India   599.67
   Curtis, C. P. Elijah of Buxton   Fic
   Cyprus, N. Sisters of glass   Fic
   Durst, S. B. The girl who could not dream   Fic
   Durst, S. B. Ice   Fic
   Flanagan, J. The sorcerer of the north   Fic
   Fletcher, C. Ironhand   Fic

Peet, M. Tamar — Fic
Preus, M. Shadow on the mountain — Fic

Resler, T. J
Dog breed guide — 636.7

RESOURCEFULNESS
Alexander, L. The remarkable journey of Prince Jen — Fic
Friesner, E. M. Sphinx's queen — Fic
Holland, E. The thorn queen — Fic
Levine, G. C. Ella enchanted — Fic
Marsden, J. Tomorrow when the war began — Fic
Stroud, J. The creeping shadow — Fic
Stroud, J. The screaming staircase — Fic
Stroud, J. The whispering skull — Fic

RESOURCEFULNESS IN CHILDREN
DuPrau, J. The city of Ember — Fic

RESOURCEFULNESS IN GIRLS
Giff, P. R. Nory Ryan's song — Fic
Levine, G. C. Ella enchanted — Fic
O'Dell, S. Island of the Blue Dolphins — Fic

RESOURCEFULNESS IN TEENAGE BOYS
Whyman, M. Goldstrike — Fic

RESOURCEFULNESS IN TEENAGE GIRLS
Friesner, E. M. Sphinx's queen — Fic

RESOURCEFULNESS IN TEENAGERS
Marsden, J. Tomorrow when the war began — Fic

RESOURCEFULNESS IN WOMEN
Del Negro, J. Passion and poison — Fic

RESPIRATION
Rose, S. Respiratory system — 612.2

RESPIRATORY ALLERGY
Royston, A. Explaining asthma — 616.2

RESPIRATORY ORGANS
Rose, S. Respiratory system — 612.2
Respiratory system. Rose, S. — 612.2

RESPONSIBILITY
Avi. Iron thunder — Fic
Brown, D. Drowned City — 363.34
Buyea, R. Because of Mr. Terupt — Fic
Engdahl, S. Enchantress from the stars — Fic
Jones, T. L. Silhouetted by the blue — Fic
Korman, G. Slacker — Fic
McCall, G. G. Under the mesquite — Fic

RESPONSIBILITY IN BOYS
Kinney, J. The ugly truth — Fic

RESPONSIBILITY IN TEENAGE BOYS
Jones, P. Bridge — Fic

RESPONSIBILITY IN TEENAGE GIRLS
McCall, G. G. Under the mesquite — Fic
Restart. Korman, G. — Fic

RESTAURANTS
Cartaya, P. The epic fail of Arturo Zamora — Fic
Gregorio, I. W. This is my brain in love — Fic
Klise, K. Regarding the trees — Fic
Turnage, S. Three times lucky — Fic
The **restless** dead. Noyes, D. — Fic

RESTORATION ENGLAND (1660-1688)
Sands, K. The Blackthorn key — Fic

RETIREMENT COMMUNITIES
Holm, J. L. Sunny side up — 741.5
The **return** of Meteor Boy? Boniface, W. — Fic
Return of the dapper men. McCann, J. — 741.5
Return of the Padawan. Brown, J. — 741.5
Return of the thief. Turner, M. W. — Fic
Return to me. Headley, J. C. — Fic
Return to sender. Alvarez, J. — Fic

REUNIONS
Chase, P. J. So done — Fic
Forman, G. Where she went — Fic
Haddix, M. P. Children of exile — Fic
Kessler, L. The tail of Emily Windsnap — Fic
Lai, T. Butterfly yellow — Fic

REVENGE
Ahdieh, R. Flame in the mist — Fic
Anderson, N. C. City of saints & thieves — Fic
Bacigalupi, P. Tool of war — Fic
Baptiste, T. The jumbies — Fic
Blackburne, L. Midnight thief — Fic
Blackburne, L. Rosemarked — Fic
Carter, A. Heist society — Fic
Collins, S. Catching fire — Fic
Condie, A. B. The last voyage of Poe Blythe — Fic
Delaney, J. Revenge of the witch — Fic
Duncan, L. I know what you did last summer — Fic
Finneyfrock, K. The sweet revenge of Celia Door — Fic
Grabenstein, C. The crossroads — Fic
Gray, C. A thousand pieces of you — Fic
Hahn, M. D. One for sorrow — Fic
Hahn, R. A creature of moonlight — Fic
Hale, S. Rapunzel's revenge — 741.5
Hardinge, F. The lost conspiracy — Fic
Harrison, M. 13 secrets — Fic
Higgins, F. E. The eyeball collector — Fic
Hinds, G. The merchant of Venice — 741.5
Korman, G. Swindle — Fic
Landy, D. Skulduggery Pleasant — Fic
Langrish, K. The shadow hunt — Fic
Le Guin, U. K. Voices — Fic
Lu, M. Legend — Fic
Marshall, K. A. I am still alive — Fic
McNeal, T. Far far away — Fic
Meyer, S. Eclipse — Fic
Myracle, L. Luv ya bunches — Fic
Nix, G. Clariel — Fic
Okorafor, N. Ikenga — Fic
Paolini, C. Eragon — Fic
Parker, N. C. Seafire — Fic
Perkins, M. Bamboo people — Fic
Reynolds, J. Long way down — Fic
Rodkey, G. The Tapper twins go to war (with each other) — Fic
Sitomer, A. L. Homeboyz — Fic
Smy, P. Thornhill — Fic
Stork, F. X. The last summer of the Death Warriors — Fic
Stroud, J. The amulet of Samarkand — Fic
Taylor, L. Days of blood & starlight — Fic

Rice, Earle

Charlie Parker — **B**

RICH FAMILIES

Lockhart, E. We were liars — **Fic**

RICH GIRLS

Alegria, M. Estrella's quinceanera — **Fic**

Oppel, K. Airborn — **Fic**

RICH MEN

Kindl, P. Keeping the castle — **Fic**

Sachar, L. The cardturner — **Fic**

RICH PEOPLE

Birdsall, J. The Penderwicks — **Fic**

Cashore, K. Jane unlimited — **Fic**

RICH TEENAGE BOYS

Gagnon, M. Don't look now — **Fic**

Gagnon, M. Don't turn around — **Fic**

Lee, M. The gentleman's guide to vice and virtue — **Fic**

Stiefvater, M. The dream thieves — **Fic**

Stiefvater, M. The raven boys — **Fic**

Stiefvater, M. The raven king — **Fic**

RICH TEENAGE GIRLS

Richards, J. Three rivers rising — **Fic**

RICH TEENAGERS

Monir, A. The girl in the picture — **Fic**

RICH WOMEN

Johnson, M. Suite Scarlett — **Fic**

Rich, Susan

Half-minute horrors — **Fic**

RICHARD I, KING OF ENGLAND, 1157-1199

McKinley, R. The outlaws of Sherwood — **Fic**

RICHARD III, KING OF ENGLAND, 1452-1485

Haddix, M. P. Sent — **Fic**

Richards, Jame

Three rivers rising — **Fic**

RICHARD, DUKE OF YORK, 1472-1483

Haddix, M. P. Sent — **Fic**

Richardson, Gillian

10 plants that shook the world — **581.6**

Kaboom! — **541**

Richardson, Jan

The next step forward in guided reading — **372.41**

Richmond, Kia Jane

Mental illness in young adult literature — **813**

Rick. Gino, A. — **Fic**

RICKENBACKER, EDDIE, 1890-1973

Olson, T. Lost in the Pacific 1942 — **940.54**

The **riddle** of the Rosetta Stone. Giblin, J. C. — **493**

RIDDLES

Abbott, T. Wade and the scorpion's claw — **Fic**

Blakemore, M. F. The friendship riddle — **Fic**

Fletcher, C. Stoneheart — **Fic**

Gonzalez, C. D. Moving target — **Fic**

Johnson, M. The hand on the wall — **Fic**

Werlin, N. Impossible — **Fic**

RIDE, SALLY

Macy, S. Sally Ride — **B**

O'Shaughnessy, T. E. Sally Ride — **B**

Ridge, Yolanda, 1973-

CRISPR — **576.5**

Riding invisible. Alonzo, S. — **Fic**

Riding low on the streets of gold. Cofer, J. O. — **Fic**

Ridley, Kimberly

Extreme survivors — **591.3**

Rief, Sandra F.

How to reach & teach children & teens with ADDAD-HD — **371.94**

Rifles for Watie. Keith, H. — **Fic**

Riggs, Kate

The French Revolution — **944.04**

The great recession — **330.973**

Riggs, Ransom

Hollow City — **Fic**

Library of souls — **Fic**

A map of days — **Fic**

Miss Peregrine's home for peculiar children — **Fic**

Tales of the Peculiar — **Fic**

RIGHT AND WRONG

Bock, C. Lie — **Fic**

Jennings, P. Odd weird & little — **Fic**

Jones, M. T. Woodford Brave — **Fic**

O'Connor, B. How to steal a dog — **Fic**

RIGHT TO DIE

Tate, N. Choosing to live choosing to die — **179.7**

RIGHT TO MEDICAL CARE

Kidder, T. Mountains beyond mountains — **610.92**

RIGHT-WING EXTREMISTS

Miller, M. Exposing hate — **305.5**

RIGHTEOUS GENTILES IN THE HOLOCAUST

Fishkin, R. L. Heroes of the Holocaust — **940.53**

Mazzeo, T. J. Irena's children — **940.53**

McClafferty, C. K. In defiance of Hitler — **940.53**

Meltzer, M. Rescue — **940.53**

Opdyke, I. G. In my hands — **940.53**

Rappaport, D. Beyond courage — **940.53**

Zusak, M. The book thief — **Fic**

Rightfully ours. Hollihan, K. L. — **324.6**

Rigsby, Mike

Amazing rubber band cars — **629.22**

Doable renewables — **621.042**

Rikers High. Volponi, P. — **Fic**

RIKERS ISLAND (NY)

Volponi, P. Rikers High — **Fic**

Riley, James, 1977-

Secret origins — **Fic**

The **ring** of Rocamadour. Beil, M. D. — **Fic**

The **ring** of Solomon. Stroud, J. — **Fic**

RINGS

Beil, M. D. The ring of Rocamadour — **Fic**

Booraem, E. Small persons with wings — **Fic**

Ringside 1925. Bryant, J. — **Fic**

RIO GRANDE

Hobbs, W. Take me to the river — **Fic**

Riordan, Rick

The battle of the Labyrinth — **Fic**

Roberts, Julia L.
Differentiating instruction with centers in the gifted classroom
K-8   **371.95**

Roberts, Russell, 1953-
The Eiffel Tower   **725**
Rembrandt   **B**

Robertson, James I.
Robert E. Lee   **B**

ROBERTSON, OSCAR, 1938-
Hoose, P. M. Attucks!   **796.323**

Robertson, Robbie
Legends icons & rebels   **782.42164**

ROBESON, PAUL, 1898-1976
Duberman, M. B. Paul Robeson   **B**
Rubin, S. G. Sing and shout   **B**
Slavicek, L. C. Paul Robeson   **B**

ROBIN HOOD (LEGENDARY CHARACTER)
Lee, T. Outlaw   **741.5**
McKinley, R. The outlaws of Sherwood   **Fic**
Pyle, H. The merry adventures of Robin Hood   **398.2**
The **robin** makes a laughing sound. Wolf, S.   **598**

Robinet, Harriette Gillem
Walking to the bus-rider blues   **Fic**

ROBINS
Wolf, S. The robin makes a laughing sound   **598**

Robinson, Anthony, 1949 September 8-
Young Palestinians speak   **956.95**

Robinson, Gary, 1950-
Little Brother of War   **Fic**
Standing strong   **Fic**

ROBINSON, JACKIE, 1919-1972
Robinson, S. Promises to keep   **B**

Robinson, Laura
Cyclist bikelist   **796.6**

Robinson, Mary
Every human has rights   **323**

Robinson, Sharon, 1950-
Promises to keep   **B**

Robinson, Tom, 1964-
Girls play to win basketball   **796.323**
The **robot** book. Mercer, B.   **629.8**
Robot experiments. Sobey, E. J. C.   **629.8**
Robot technology. Graham, I.   **629.8**

ROBOTICS
Asimov, I. I robot   **Fic**
Chaffee, J. How to build a prize-winning robot   **629.8**
Gilby, N. B. FIRST robotics   **629.8**
Graham, I. Robot technology   **629.8**
Korman, G. Ungifted   **Fic**
Mercer, B. The robot book   **629.8**
Shea, T. The robotics club   **629.8**
Sjonger, R. Robotics engineering and our automated
world   **629.8**
Sobey, E. J. C. Robot experiments   **629.8**
Spilsbury, L. Robotics   **629.8**
Spilsbury, R. Robots in industry   **629.8**
Spilsbury, R. Robots in medicine   **610.285**

Spilsbury, R. Robots in space   **629.43**
Spilsbury, R. Robots underwater   **623.82**

ROBOTICS -- HISTORY
Freedman, J. Robots through history   **629.8**

ROBOTICS -- VOCATIONAL GUIDANCE
Payment, S. Robotics careers   **629.8**
Robotics. Spilsbury, L.   **629.8**
Robotics careers. Payment, S.   **629.8**
The **robotics** club. Shea, T.   **629.8**
Robotics engineering and our automated world. Sjonger,
R.   **629.8**

ROBOTICS IN MEDICINE
Spilsbury, R. Robots in medicine   **610.285**

ROBOTS
Angleberger, T. Fuzzy   **Fic**
Asimov, I. I robot   **Fic**
Carriger, G. Curtsies & conspiracies   **Fic**
Carriger, G. Etiquette & espionage   **Fic**
Gilby, N. B. FIRST robotics   **629.8**
Graham, I. Robot technology   **629.8**
Gray, C. Defy the stars   **Fic**
Haddix, M. P. In over their heads   **Fic**
Haddix, M. P. Under their skin   **Fic**
Hale, N. One trick pony   **741.5**
Jung, M. Geeks girls and secret identities   **Fic**
Kade, J. V. Bot Wars   **Fic**
Korman, G. Ungifted   **Fic**
Kristoff, J. Lifel1k3   **Fic**
Link, K. Steampunk!   **Fic**
Love, D. Monstrous devices   **Fic**
Love, D. The shadow arts   **Fic**
McCann, J. Return of the dapper men   **741.5**
McCulloch, A. Jinxed   **Fic**
Mercer, B. The robot book   **629.8**
Myklusch, M. Jack Blank and the Imagine Nation   **Fic**
Patterson, J. House of robots   **Fic**
Payment, S. Robotics careers   **629.8**
Roman, D. Astronaut Academy   **741.5**
Selznick, B. The invention of Hugo Cabret   **Fic**
Sjonger, R. Robotics engineering and our automated
world   **629.8**
Spilsbury, L. Robotics   **629.8**
Spilsbury, R. Robots in industry   **629.8**
Spilsbury, R. Robots in medicine   **610.285**
Spilsbury, R. Robots in space   **629.43**
Spilsbury, R. Robots underwater   **623.82**
Woog, A. SCRATCHbot   **629.8**
Yang, G. L. Secret coders   **741.5**

ROBOTS -- BEHAVIOR
Asimov, I. I robot   **Fic**

ROBOTS -- DESIGN AND CONSTRUCTION
Chaffee, J. How to build a prize-winning robot   **629.8**
Shea, T. The robotics club   **629.8**
Sobey, E. J. C. Robot experiments   **629.8**

**ROBOTS -- DESIGN AND CONSTRUCTION -- COMPE-
TITIONS**
Chaffee, J. How to build a prize-winning robot   **629.8**

Ritter, W. The dire king | Fic
Ritter, W. The unready queen | Fic
Shelley, T. C. The monster who wasn't | Fic
Simon, F. The monstrous child | Fic
Stanley, D. The princess of Cortova | Fic
Stanley, D. The silver bowl | Fic
Turner, M. W. A conspiracy of kings | Fic
Turner, M. W. The king of Attolia | Fic
Turner, M. W. Return of the thief | Fic
Turner, M. W. Thick as thieves | Fic
Valente, C. M. The girl who fell beneath Fairyland and led the revels there | Fic
Weitzman, D. Pharaoh's boat | 932

RULERS -- SUCCESSION
Paige, D. Mera | Fic

RULES
Firestone, C. Dress coded | Fic
Hunter, E. Code of the clans | Fic
Patterson, J. Middle school | Fic
The **rules**. Kade, S. | Fic
Rules. Lord, C. | Fic
Rules for being a girl. Bushnell, C. | Fic
The **rules** for disappearing. Elston, A. | Fic
Rules for stealing stars. Haydu, C. A. | Fic
The **rules** of survival. Werlin, N. | Fic
Rumble. Hopkins, E. | Fic
Rumble & spew. Donovan, S. | 612.3
Rumford, James, 1948-
Beowulf a hero's tale retold | 398.2
Rumi's riddle. Schrefer, E. | Fic
Rump. Shurtliff, L. | Fic

RUMPELSTILTSKIN (FICTITIOUS CHARACTER)
Shurtliff, L. Rump | Fic
Run. Keplinger, K. | Fic
Run. Lewis, J. | B
Run boy run. Orlev, U. | Fic

RUNAWAY BOYS
Almond, D. The boy who swam with piranhas | Fic
Avi. The unexpected life of Oliver Cromwell Pitts | Fic
Broach, E. The wolf keepers | Fic
Gemeinhart, D. The honest truth | Fic
Higgins, F. E. The black book of secrets | Fic
Langrish, K. The shadow hunt | Fic
Lin, G. Starry River of the Sky | Fic
Philbrick, W. R. The mostly true adventures of Homer P. Figg | Fic
Selznick, B. The Marvels | Fic
Spinelli, J. Maniac Magee | Fic

RUNAWAY CHILDREN
Funke, C. The Thief Lord | Fic
Selznick, B. Wonderstruck | Fic
Runaway girl. Greenberg, J. | B

RUNAWAY GIRLS
Farmer, N. A girl named Disaster | Fic
Fusco, K. N. Beholding Bee | Fic
Mah, A. Y. Chinese Cinderella and the Secret Dragon Society | Fic

Woodson, J. Lena | Fic
The **runaway** king. Nielsen, J. A. | Fic

RUNAWAY TEENAGE BOYS
Alonzo, S. Riding invisible | Fic
Doctorow, C. Pirate cinema | Fic
Pena, M. d. l. We were here | Fic

RUNAWAY TEENAGE GIRLS
DiCamillo, K. Beverly right here | Fic
Keplinger, K. Run | Fic
McKay, S. E. Thunder over Kandahar | Fic
Umminger, A. American girls | Fic

RUNAWAY TEENAGERS
Bracken, A. The darkest minds | Fic
Hautman, P. Road tripped | Fic
Hitchcock, B. The smell of other people's houses | Fic
Wrede, P. C. Dealing with dragons | Fic

RUNAWAY WIVES, HUSBANDS, ETC
Tucker, L. All the Greys on Greene Street | Fic

RUNAWAYS
Anderson, L. H. Ashes | Fic
Barratt, M. Joe Rat | Fic
Crossan, S. Being Toffee | Fic
Mah, A. Y. Chinese Cinderella and the Secret Dragon Society | Fic
Preller, J. The courage test | Fic
Venkatraman, P. The bridge home | Fic

Rundell, Katherine
Cartwheeling in thunderstorms | Fic
Rooftoppers | Fic
The wolf wilder | Fic

RUNNERS
Reynolds, J. Ghost | Fic
Reynolds, J. Patina | Fic
Smith-Llera, D. Black power salute | 796.48

RUNNING
Gifford, C. Track and field | 796.42
Mason, P. Improving speed | 613.7
McDougall, C. Girls play to win track & field | 796.42
Odhiambo, E. A. Auma's long run | Fic
Spinelli, J. Maniac Magee | Fic
Van Draanen, W. The running dream | Fic
Yee, L. Warp speed | Fic
The **running** dream. Van Draanen, W. | Fic
Running dry. Kallen, S. A. | 333.91

RUNNING RACES
Mae, N. The kinder poison | Fic
Running wild. Watson, G. | 573.7

RUNYON, BRENT
Runyon, B. The burn journals | B
Runyon, Brent
The burn journals | B
Rupp, Rebecca
After Eli | Fic

RURAL BOYS
Moriarty, J. The cracks in the Kingdom | Fic
RURAL FAMILIES
Gallego Garcia, L. The valley of the Wolves | Fic

The **same** stuff as stars. Paterson, K. — Fic
Sammy Keyes and the hotel thief. Van Draanen, W. — Fic
Samphire, Patrick
  Secrets of the dragon tomb — Fic
Samuel Houston. Bodden, V. — B
Samuels, Charlie, 1961-
  Home front — 940.53
  Iraq — 956.7
  Life under occupation — 940.53
  Propaganda — 940.54
  Soldiers — 940.54
SAMURAI
  Ahdieh, R. Flame in the mist — Fic
  Hoobler, D. The demon in the teahouse — Fic
  Hoobler, D. The sword that cut the burning grass — Fic
  Preus, M. Heart of a samurai — Fic
SAMURAI -- HISTORY
  Niz, X. Samurai — 952
  Turnbull, S. R. The most daring raid of the samurai — 952
Samurai. Niz, X. — 952
Samurai rising. Turner, P. S. — B
SAN ANTONIO, TEXAS
  Lopez, D. Ask my mood ring how I feel — Fic
SAN CARLOS INDIAN RESERVATION (ARIZ) -- HISTORY
  Jastrzembski, J. C. The Apache wars — 970.004
SAN DIEGO, CALIFORNIA
  Brimner, L. D. The rain wizard — 979.4
  Heaney, K. Girl crushed — Fic
  Winters, C. In the shadow of blackbirds — Fic
SAN FRANCISCO BAY AREA
  Riordan, R. The tower of Nero — Fic
The **San** Francisco earthquake and fire of 1906. Slavicek, L. C. — 979.4
SAN FRANCISCO EARTHQUAKE AND FIRE, CALIF, 1906
  Blundell, J. A city tossed and broken — Fic
  Lee, S. Outrun the moon — Fic
  Slavicek, L. C. The San Francisco earthquake and fire of 1906 — 979.4
SAN FRANCISCO, CALIFORNIA
  Allison, J. Gilda Joyce psychic investigator — Fic
  Avi. Gold rush girl — Fic
  Blundell, J. A city tossed and broken — Fic
  Bullen, A. Wish — Fic
  Chambliss Bertman, J. Book scavenger — Fic
  Chambliss Bertman, J. The unbreakable code — Fic
  Chanani, N. Jukebox — Fic
  Chee, T. We are not free — Fic
  Choldenko, G. Chasing secrets — Fic
  Grant, M. Eve & Adam — Fic
  Hannigan, K. Mask — Fic
  Hopkinson, D. Into the firestorm — Fic
  Horowitz, A. Never say die — Fic
  Klages, E. Out of left field — Fic
  Lavender, W. Aftershocks — Fic
  Lee, S. Outrun the moon — Fic

  Scott, M. The alchemyst — Fic
  Yep, L. A dragon's guide to making your human smarter — Fic
  Yep, L. A dragon's guide to the care and feeding of humans — Fic
  Yep, L. Dragonwings — Fic
  Yep, L. The star maker — Fic
  Young, K. R. Doodlebug — Fic
  Zarr, S. The Lucy variations — Fic
SAN FRANCISCO, CALIFORNIA -- HISTORY -- 20TH CENTURY
  Slavicek, L. C. The San Francisco earthquake and fire of 1906 — 979.4
SAN GABRIEL MISSION (CALIFORNIA)
  O'Dell, S. Zia — Fic
SAN JOSE MINE ACCIDENT, CHILE, 2010
  Aronson, M. Trapped — 363.11
  Scott, E. Buried alive! — 363.11
San Souci, Robert D.
  Cut from the same cloth — 398.21
  Dare to be scared — Fic
  Haunted houses — Fic
  A terrifying taste of short & shivery — 398.25
SANATORIUMS
  Hayles, M. Breathing room — Fic
Sanchez, Alex, 1957-
  Bait — Fic
SAND
  Sanderson, B. Alcatraz versus the evil librarians — Fic
Sand dollar summer. Jones, K. — Fic
Sanders, Nancy I.
  Frederick Douglass for kids — B
Sanderson, Brandon
  Alcatraz versus the evil librarians — Fic
  The dark talent — Fic
  Skyward — Fic
SANDIFER, ROBERT
  Neri, G. Yummy — 741.5
SANDINISTA NATIONAL LIBERATION FRONT -- HISTORY
  Kallen, S. A. The aftermath of the Sandinista Revolution — 972.8505
Sandler, Martin W.
  1919 — 973.91
  America through the lens — 770
  Apollo 8 — 629.45
  The Dust Bowl through the lens — 973.917
  Imprisoned — 940.53
  Iron rails iron men and the race to link the nation — 385.0979
  Lincoln through the lens — B
  Secret subway — 388.4
  The Whydah — 910.4
Sandry's book. Pierce, T. — Fic
Sands, Crystal
  Women and feminism today — 305.42
Sands, Kevin
  The Blackthorn key — Fic
Sanford, William R. (William Reynolds), 1927-

Gagnon, M. Strangelets	Fic	Kristoff, J. Lifel1k3	Fic
Gaiman, N. M is for magic	Fic	L'Engle, M. A swiftly tilting planet	Fic
Gibbs, S. Space case	Fic	L'Engle, M. A wind in the door	Fic
Gibbs, S. Spaced out	Fic	L'Engle, M. A wrinkle in time	Fic
Gilmore, K. The exchange student	Fic	Lancaster, M. A. Human.4	Fic
Gordon, R. Tunnels	Fic	Lloyd, S. The carbon diaries 2015	Fic
Grant, M. Eve & Adam	Fic	London, A. Proxy	Fic
Grant, M. Fear	Fic	Lowry, L. Gathering blue	Fic
Grant, M. Hunger	Fic	Lowry, L. Son	Fic
Grant, M. Lies	Fic	Lu, M. Champion	Fic
Grant, M. Light	Fic	Lu, M. Legend	Fic
Grant, M. Plague	Fic	Lu, M. Prodigy	Fic
Gray, C. Defy the stars	Fic	Lu, M. Rebel	Fic
Gray, C. A thousand pieces of you	Fic	Lu, M. Warcross	Fic
Haddix, M. P. Among the Barons	Fic	Lu, M. Wildcard	Fic
Haddix, M. P. Among the betrayed	Fic	Lubar, D. Hidden talents	Fic
Haddix, M. P. Among the brave	Fic	Lubar, D. True talents	Fic
Haddix, M. P. Among the enemy	Fic	Maberry, J. The orphan army	Fic
Haddix, M. P. Among the free	Fic	Maberry, J. Rot & Ruin	Fic
Haddix, M. P. Among the hidden	Fic	Machale, D. J. SYLO	Fic
Haddix, M. P. Among the impostors	Fic	Marr, M. Shards & ashes	Fic
Haddix, M. P. Caught	Fic	Martin, L. The ark plan	Fic
Haddix, M. P. Children of exile	Fic	Mass, W. Pi in the sky	Fic
Haddix, M. P. Children of refuge	Fic	McCaffrey, A. Dragon's fire	Fic
Haddix, M. P. The deceivers	Fic	McCaffrey, A. Dragonflight	Fic
Haddix, M. P. Found	Fic	McCulloch, A. Jinxed	Fic
Haddix, M. P. In over their heads	Fic	Meyer, M. Cinder	Fic
Haddix, M. P. Risked	Fic	Meyer, M. Cress	Fic
Haddix, M. P. Sabotaged	Fic	Meyer, M. Scarlet	Fic
Haddix, M. P. Sent	Fic	Mosley, W. 47	Fic
Haddix, M. P. Under their skin	Fic	Murdock, C. G. Da Vinci's cat	Fic
Harper, C. M. Alien encounter	Fic	Ness, P. The Ask and the Answer	Fic
Hautman, P. The Klaatu terminus	Fic	Ness, P. The knife of never letting go	Fic
Hautman, P. The obsidian blade	Fic	Nix, G. To hold the bridge	Fic
Healey, K. When we wake	Fic	North, P. Starglass	Fic
Heath, J. The lab	Fic	November, S. Firebirds	Fic
Heath, J. Remote control	Fic	November, S. Firebirds soaring	Fic
Hirsch, J. The eleventh plague	Fic	O'Brien, C. M. Birthmarked	Fic
Hobbs, W. Go big or go home	Fic	O'Brien, R. C. Z for Zachariah	Fic
Holm, J. L. The fourteenth goldfish	Fic	Oppel, K. Bloom	Fic
Holyoke, P. The Neptune Project	Fic	Oppel, K. Thrive	Fic
Hughes, M. P. A crack in the sky	Fic	Patrick, C. Revived	Fic
Hughes, N. Refraction	Fic	Patterson, J. The angel experiment	Fic
Jinks, C. Evil genius	Fic	Patterson, J. House of robots	Fic
Jinks, C. Genius squad	Fic	Paulsen, G. The Transall saga	Fic
Jinks, C. The genius wars	Fic	Pearson, M. The adoration of Jenna Fox	Fic
Kade, J. V. Bot Wars	Fic	Peterfreund, D. Omega City	Fic
Kade, S. The rules	Fic	Pfeffer, S. B. Life as we knew it	Fic
Katsoulis, G. S. Access restricted	Fic	Pierson, D. C. The boy who couldn't sleep and never had	
Kaufman, A. Aurora rising	Fic	to	Fic
Kaufman, A. Gemina	Fic	Pike, A. Glitter	Fic
Kaufman, A. Illuminae	Fic	Price, L. Starters	Fic
Kaufman, A. Obsidio	Fic	Reeve, P. Fever Crumb	Fic
Kincaid, S. J. Insignia	Fic	Reeve, P. Scrivener's moon	Fic
Kostick, C. Edda	Fic	Reeve, P. A web of air	Fic
Kostick, C. Epic	Fic	Reichs, B. Chrysalis	Fic
Kostick, C. Saga	Fic	Reichs, B. Genesis	Fic

Carson, R. The edge of the sea	**578.769**
Parker, S. Seashore	**578.769**

SEASIDE RESORTS

Taylor, T. Malamander	**Fic**
A **season** of gifts. Peck, R.	**Fic**
Season of secrets. Nicholls, S.	**Fic**

SEASONS

Erdrich, L. The birchbark house	**Fic**
Frost, R. Robert Frost	**811**
Nicholls, S. Season of secrets	**Fic**
Wolf, S. The robin makes a laughing sound	**598**

SEATTLE, WASHINGTON

Day, C. I can make this promise	**Fic**
John, A. Five flavors of Dumb	**Fic**
Katcher, B. The improbable theory of Ana and Zak	**Fic**
McKernan, V. The devil's paintbox	**Fic**
Meyer, S. Breaking dawn	**Fic**
Meyer, S. Eclipse	**Fic**
Priest, C. I am Princess X	**Fic**
Trueman, T. Stuck in neutral	**Fic**

Seba, Jaime

Gay characters in theatre movies and television new roles new attitudes	**791.43**

SECOND CHANCES

Korman, G. The juvie three	**Fic**
Myers, W. D. Dope sick	**Fic**
Plozza, S. Tin heart	**Fic**
The **second** life of Abigail Walker. Dowell, F. O.	**Fic**

SECOND WORLD WAR ERA (1939-1945)

Batalion, J. The light of days	**940.53**
Boyne, J. The boy in the striped pajamas	**Fic**
Bradley, K. B. The war that saved my life	**Fic**
Brooks, M. Queen of hearts	**Fic**
Bruchac, J. Code Talker	**Fic**
Cameron, S. The light in hidden places	**Fic**
Dowswell, P. Auslander	**Fic**
Dumon Tak, B. Soldier bear	**Fic**
Elliott, L. Under a war-torn sky	**Fic**
Farrell, M. C. Standing up against hate	**940.54**
Fitzmaurice, K. A diamond in the desert	**Fic**
Fox, J. S. The charmed children of Rookskill Castle	**Fic**
Frost, H. All he knew	**Fic**
Giff, P. R. Genevieve's war	**Fic**
Gratz, A. Projekt 1065	**Fic**
Hannigan, K. Cape	**Fic**
Hannigan, K. Mask	**Fic**
Hesse, M. The war outside	**Fic**
Hest, A. The summer we found the baby	**Fic**
Hopkinson, D. We must not forget	**940.53**
Iturbe, A. The librarian of Auschwitz	**Fic**
Jones, M. T. Woodford Brave	**Fic**
Kessler, L. When the world was ours	**Fic**
Krishnaswami, U. Step up to the plate Maria Singh	**Fic**
Larson, K. Dash	**Fic**
Lindelauf, B. Fing's war	**Fic**
Lowry, L. Number the stars	**Fic**
Macdonald, M. Odette's secrets	**Fic**

Mah, A. Y. Chinese Cinderella and the Secret Dragon Society	**Fic**
Matti, T. Mister orange	**Fic**
Mazer, H. Heroes don't run	**Fic**
Messner, K. Pearl Harbor	**940.54**
Morpurgo, M. The day the world stopped turning	**Fic**
Napoli, D. J. Stones in water	**Fic**
Nielsen, J. A. Resistance	**Fic**
Palacio, R. J. White bird	**741.5**
Park, L. S. When my name was Keoko	**Fic**
Pausewang, G. Dark hours	**Fic**
Pausewang, G. Traitor	**Fic**
Peet, M. Tamar	**Fic**
Preus, M. Shadow on the mountain	**Fic**
Roy, J. R. Yellow star	**Fic**
Salisbury, G. Eyes of the emperor	**Fic**
Savit, G. Anna and the Swallow Man	**Fic**
Sepetys, R. Salt to the sea	**Fic**
Skrypuch, M. F. Making bombs for Hitler	**Fic**
Smith, S. L. Flygirl	**Fic**
Stone, P. The Romeo and Juliet code	**Fic**
Taylor, M. D. The road to Memphis	**Fic**
Thomas, S. M. The last rabbit	**Fic**
Thor, A. Deep sea	**Fic**
Thor, A. A faraway island	**Fic**
Thor, A. The lily pond	**Fic**
Toro, G. d. Pan's labyrinth	**Fic**
Wilson, K. White Rose	**Fic**
Wolk, L. Wolf Hollow	**Fic**
Yep, L. Hiroshima	**Fic**
Zusak, M. The book thief	**Fic**

SECOND-GRADE BOYS

Gutman, D. Miss Daisy is crazy!	**Fic**

SECRECY

Bean, L. The ship we built	**Fic**
Carlton, S. K. In the neighborhood of true	**Fic**
Fox, J. S. The charmed children of Rookskill Castle	**Fic**
Korman, G. War stories	**Fic**
Oliver, L. The magnificent monsters of Cedar Street	**Fic**
Secret coders. Yang, G. L.	**741.5**

SECRET FRIENDS

Boyne, J. The boy in the striped pajamas	**Fic**
The **secret** garden [Moore ill.]. Burnett, F. H.	**Fic**
The **secret** hum of a daisy. Holczer, T.	**Fic**

SECRET IDENTITY

Abdel-Fattah, R. Ten things I hate about me	**Fic**
Kade, S. The rules	**Fic**
Secret keeper. Perkins, M.	**Fic**
The **secret** keepers. Stewart, T. L.	**Fic**
The **secret** life of Ms. Finkleman. Winters, B. H.	**Fic**
The **secret** life of Sam. Ventrella, K.	**Fic**
The **secret** life of words. Hitchings, H.	**422**
The **secret** mission of William Tuck. Pierpoint, E.	**Fic**
The **secret** of Dreadwillow Carse. Farrey, B.	**Fic**
The **secret** of Nightingale Wood. Strange, L.	**Fic**
The **secret** of Priest's Grotto. Taylor, P. L.	**940.53**
The **secret** of the yellow death. Jurmain, S.	**614.5**

Telgemeier, R. Smile — 617.6
SELF-EXPERIMENTATION IN MEDICINE
Dendy, L. Guinea pig scientists — 616
SELF-FULFILLMENT
Brody, J. The geography of lost things — Fic
Emond, S. Winter town — Fic
Headley, J. C. Return to me — Fic
Kay, K. The confidence code for girls — 155.2
Mass, W. Jeremy Fink and the meaning of life — Fic
Mikaelsen, B. Ghost of Spirit Bear — Fic
Mikaelsen, B. Touching Spirit Bear — Fic
Murdock, C. G. Princess Ben — Fic
Ness, P. A monster calls — Fic
Nicholson, W. Seeker — Fic
Nye, N. S. A maze me — 811
Paterson, K. Jacob have I loved — Fic
Perez, A. H. What can(t) wait — Fic
Rowling, J. K. Harry Potter and the deathly hallows — Fic
SELF-FULFILLMENT IN BOYS
Mass, W. Jeremy Fink and the meaning of life — Fic
SELF-FULFILLMENT IN GIRLS
Nye, N. S. A maze me — 811
SELF-FULFILLMENT IN TEENAGE BOYS
Flinn, A. Beastly — Fic
Mikaelsen, B. Ghost of Spirit Bear — Fic
Mikaelsen, B. Touching Spirit Bear — Fic
Ness, P. A monster calls — Fic
SELF-FULFILLMENT IN TEENAGE GIRLS
Carson, R. The girl of fire and thorns — Fic
Headley, J. C. Return to me — Fic
Murdock, C. G. Princess Ben — Fic
Perez, A. H. What can(t) wait — Fic
Zarr, S. The Lucy variations — Fic
SELF-FULFILLMENT IN TEENAGERS
Emond, S. Winter town — Fic
SELF-HARM
Anderson, L. H. Wintergirls — Fic
SELF-HARM IN TEENAGE GIRLS
McCormick, P. Cut — Fic
SELF-HATE IN TEENAGE GIRLS
Carson, R. The girl of fire and thorns — Fic
SELF-HELP PSYCHOLOGY
Kay, K. The confidence code for girls — 155.2
SELF-HELP PSYCHOLOGY FOR TEENAGERS
Scarlet, J. Superhero therapy — 616.85
Self-image and eating disorders. Smith, R. P. — 616.85
SELF-MANAGEMENT
Crist, J. J. What to do when you're sad & lonely — 618.92
SELF-MANAGEMENT FOR TEENAGERS
Crist, J. J. What to do when you're sad & lonely — 618.92
SELF-PERCEPTION
Bowman, A. D. Starfish — Fic
Holm, J. L. Boston Jane — Fic
Korman, G. Restart — Fic
Pearson, M. The adoration of Jenna Fox — Fic
Rivers, K. The girl in the well is me — Fic
Tamaki, M. Saving Montgomery Sole — Fic

Vande Velde, V. Frogged — Fic
Vivian, S. The list — Fic
SELF-PERCEPTION IN GIRLS
Henkes, K. Olive's ocean — Fic
SELF-PERCEPTION IN TEENAGE BOYS
Myers, W. D. Lockdown — Fic
SELF-PERCEPTION IN TEENAGE GIRLS
Bowman, A. D. Starfish — Fic
Kephart, B. The heart is not a size — Fic
Lockhart, E. The disreputable history of Frankie Landau-Banks — Fic
Mackler, C. The Earth my butt and other big round things — Fic
Ottaviano, P. Girl world — 155.5
Pearson, M. The adoration of Jenna Fox — Fic
Vivian, S. The list — Fic
Westerfeld, S. Pretties — Fic
Zarr, S. Once was lost — Fic
SELF-PERCEPTION IN TEENAGERS
Fonseca, C. The girl guide — 646.700835
Giovanni, N. Paint me like I am — 811
Lyga, B. The astonishing adventures of Fanboy & Goth Girl — Fic
Self-portrait with seven fingers. Lewis, J. P. — 811
SELF-RELIANCE
Giff, P. R. Genevieve's war — Fic
MacColl, M. Prisoners in the palace — Fic
Matson, M. Since you've been gone — Fic
Mlynowski, S. Ten things we did (and probably shouldn't have) — Fic
Oppel, K. Silverwing — Fic
Paterson, K. The same stuff as stars — Fic
Paulsen, G. Brian's return — Fic
Voigt, C. The book of kings — Fic
Voigt, C. The book of lost things — Fic
Voigt, C. The book of secrets — Fic
SELF-RELIANCE IN BOYS
Jacobson, J. Small as an elephant — Fic
Nielsen, S. No fixed address — Fic
SELF-RELIANCE IN GIRLS
Connor, L. Waiting for normal — Fic
Hale, S. Rapunzel's revenge — 741.5
Horvath, P. Everything on a waffle — Fic
Paterson, K. Lyddie — Fic
SELF-RELIANCE IN TEENAGE GIRLS
Lucier, M. A death-struck year — Fic
MacColl, M. Prisoners in the palace — Fic
Mlynowski, S. Ten things we did (and probably shouldn't have) — Fic
Whitley, J. Princeless — 741.5
SELF-RELIANCE IN TEENAGERS
Paulsen, G. Brian's return — Fic
SELF-SACRIFICE
Henry, O. The gift of the Magi — Fic
McKinley, R. Beauty — Fic
Teller, J. Nothing — Fic
SELF-SUFFICIENCY

Shift. Bradbury, J. — Fic

Shiga, Jason
  Meanwhile — 741.5

Shiloh. Naylor, P. R. — Fic

Shimura, Takako, 1973-
  Wandering son — 741.5

Shine! Grabenstein, J. J. — Fic

SHINER, MICHAEL, 1805-1880
  Bolden, T. Capital days — B

SHINTO
  Hartz, P. Shinto — 299.5

SHINTO -- CUSTOMS AND PRACTICES
  Hartz, P. Shinto — 299.5

SHINTO -- HISTORY
  Hartz, P. Shinto — 299.5

Shinto. Hartz, P. — 299.5

Ship breaker. Bacigalupi, P. — Fic

SHIP CAPTAINS
  Condie, A. B. The last voyage of Poe Blythe — Fic
  Parker, N. C. Seafire — Fic
  Pullman, P. Once upon a time in the North — Fic
  Sleator, W. Interstellar pig — Fic

Ship it. Lundin, B. — Fic

The **ship** of the dead. Riordan, R. — Fic

The **ship** we built. Bean, L. — Fic

SHIPPING LINES
  Korman, G. Collision course — Fic

SHIPS
  Farndon, J. Stickmen's guide to watercraft — 623.82
  Kurtz, C. The adventures of a South Pole pig — Fic
  Milford, K. The Left-Handed Fate — Fic
  Ness, P. And the ocean was our sky — Fic
  Northrop, M. Polaris — Fic
  Philbrick, N. Revenge of the whale — 910
  Tanner, L. Ice breaker — Fic
  Walker, S. M. Blizzard of glass — 971.6
  Weitzman, D. Pharaoh's boat — 932

SHIPS, WOODEN
  Weitzman, D. Pharaoh's boat — 932

Shipwreck at the bottom of the world. Armstrong, J. — 919.8

SHIPWRECK SURVIVORS
  Bacigalupi, P. Ship breaker — Fic
  TenNapel, D. Bad Island — 741.5

Shipwrecked! Blumberg, R. — B

SHIPWRECKS
  Adams, S. Titanic — 910.91
  Armstrong, J. Shipwreck at the bottom of the world — 919.8
  Clifford, B. Real pirates — 910.4
  Cottman, M. H. Shackles from the deep — 382.4409
  Hopkinson, D. Titanic — 910.91
  Lawrence, I. The wreckers — Fic
  Marschall, K. Inside the Titanic — 910
  McPherson, S. S. Iceberg right ahead! — 910.91
  Mullenbach, C. Torpedoed! — 940.54
  Philbrick, N. Revenge of the whale — 910
  Ruiz Zafon, C. The prince of mist — Fic
  Sandler, M. W. The Whydah — 910.4

  Taylor, T. The cay — Fic
  TenNapel, D. Bad Island — 741.5
  Wallace, S. N. Bound by ice — 910.4
  Wolf, A. The watch that ends the night — Fic

SHIPWRECKS -- HISTORY
  Tougias, M. The finest hours — 910.91

Shirley Chisholm. Raatma, L. — B

SHIVACK, NADIA
  Shivack, N. Inside out — B

Shivering, William
  Ghosts of Weirdwood — Fic
  Thieves of Weirdwood — Fic

Shoals, James
  Extreme weather — 551.55

Shoeless Joe & me. Gutman, D. — Fic

SHOEMAKERS
  Sapet, K. Jimmy Choo — 746.9
  Townley, R. The blue shoe — Fic

SHOES
  Townley, R. The blue shoe — Fic

SHOES -- REPAIRING
  Flinn, A. Cloaked — Fic

Shofner, Corabel
  Almost paradise — Fic

SHONA (AFRICAN PEOPLE)
  Hall, M. Great Zimbabwe — 968.91
  Williams, M. Diamond boy — Fic

SHOOTING
  Springstubb, T. Every single second — Fic

Shooting the moon. Dowell, F. O. — Fic

SHOPPING MALLS
  Layne, A. Beetle & the Hollowbones — 741.5

SHORE BIRDS
  Hoose, P. M. Moonbird — 598.072

Short. Sloan, H. G. — Fic

SHORT BOYS
  Evans, L. Horten's miraculous mechanisms — Fic

SHORT GIRLS
  Sloan, H. G. Short — Fic

Short scenes and monologues for middle school actors. Surface, M. H. — 812

SHORT STORIES
  Ada, A. F. Yes! We are Latinos — Fic
  Ali, S. K. Once upon an Eid — 297.3
  Almond, D. Half a creature from the sea — Fic
  Amnesty International. Free? — Fic
  Armstrong, J. Shattered — Fic
  Aronson, M. The pick-up game — Fic
  Asimov, I. I robot — Fic
  Avi. The most important thing — Fic
  Bachmann, S. The cabinet of curiosities — Fic
  Bird, B. Funny girl — Fic
  Black, H. Geektastic — Fic
  Bradman, T. Give me shelter — Fic
  Caldwell, P. A phoenix first must burn — Fic
  Carlson, L. M. Moccasin thunder — Fic
  Chapman, E. Hungry hearts — Fic

SINO-JAPANESE CONFLICT, 1937-1945

DeWoskin, R. Someday we will fly — **Fic**

Sir Charlie Chaplin. Fleischman, S. — **B**

Sir Edmund Hillary. Crompton, S. W. — **B**

Sir Gawain and the Green Knight. Morpurgo, M. — **398.2**

Sir John Hargrave's mischief maker's manual. Hargrave, J. — **.818**

SIRENS (MYTHOLOGY)

Orr, T. The sirens — **398.2**

The **sirens**. Orr, T. — **398.2**

Sís, Peter, 1949-

Tibet — **951**

The wall — **B**

The **sisterhood** of the traveling pants. Brashares, A. — **Fic**

SISTERS

Anderson, L. H. Chains — **Fic**

Anderson, N. C. City of saints & thieves — **Fic**

Appelt, K. Maybe a fox — **Fic**

Bernard, R. Find me — **Fic**

Birdsall, J. The Penderwicks — **Fic**

Birdsall, J. The Penderwicks at Point Mouette — **Fic**

Birdsall, J. The Penderwicks on Gardam Street — **Fic**

Blake, K. Two dark reigns — **Fic**

Bradley, K. B. Fighting words — **Fic**

Byars, B. C. The keeper of the doves — **Fic**

Carvell, M. Sweetgrass basket — **Fic**

Cypess, L. Thornwood — **Fic**

Dessen, S. Lock and key — **Fic**

Duble, K. B. The sacrifice — **Fic**

Everman, C. H. We belong — **Fic**

Fletcher, S. Dragon's milk — **Fic**

Giff, P. R. A slip of a girl — **Fic**

Grimes, N. Jazmin's notebook — **Fic**

Hardinge, F. Cuckoo song — **Fic**

Hardinge, F. The lost conspiracy — **Fic**

Harris, T. E. The perfect place — **Fic**

Haydu, C. A. Rules for stealing stars — **Fic**

Hest, A. The summer we found the baby — **Fic**

Hooper, M. Fallen Grace — **Fic**

Katsoulis, G. S. Access restricted — **Fic**

Kelly, E. E. The land of forgotten girls — **Fic**

Lesperance, N. The nightmare thief — **Fic**

MacColl, M. Rory's promise — **Fic**

Marillier, J. Wildwood dancing — **Fic**

Martin, M. A. To be honest — **Fic**

Mazer, N. F. The missing girl — **Fic**

McLemore, A. Blanca & Roja — **Fic**

Messner, K. The seventh wish — **Fic**

Miller, S. E. The lost crown — **Fic**

Moderow, H. Lily's mountain — **Fic**

Paterson, K. Jacob have I loved — **Fic**

Perkins, M. Secret keeper — **Fic**

Pixley, M. F. Freak — **Fic**

Reef, C. The Bronte sisters — **920**

Rivers, K. Finding Ruby Starling — **Fic**

Smith, J. Rose — **741.5**

Smith-Llera, D. Serena vs. Venus — **920**

Sones, S. Stop pretending — **Fic**

Telgemeier, R. Ghosts — **741.5**

Telgemeier, R. Sisters — **306.875**

Thomas, S. M. The last rabbit — **Fic**

Thor, A. Deep sea — **Fic**

Thor, A. A faraway island — **Fic**

Thornburgh, B. Ordinary girls — **Fic**

Tucholke, A. G. Seven endless forests — **Fic**

Umminger, A. American girls — **Fic**

Whitley, J. Princeless — **741.5**

Williams-Garcia, R. One crazy summer — **Fic**

Williams-Garcia, R. P.S. be eleven — **Fic**

Woodson, J. Lena — **Fic**

Youngblood, L. C. Forever this summer — **Fic**

Youngblood, L. C. Love like sky — **Fic**

Yu, M. The Girl King — **Fic**

SISTERS -- DEATH

Bayerl, K. A psalm for lost girls — **Fic**

Bowman, A. D. Summer bird blue — **Fic**

Foxlee, K. The anatomy of wings — **Fic**

Kadohata, C. Kira-kira — **Fic**

Pixley, M. F. Without Tess — **Fic**

Wolff, V. E. Probably still Nick Swansen — **Fic**

SISTERS -- FAMILY RELATIONSHIPS

Winters, C. Odd & true — **Fic**

Sisters. Telgemeier, R. — **306.875**

Sisters of glass. Cypurs, N. — **Fic**

SITA (HINDU DEITY)

Sattar, A. Ramayana — **294.5**

Sita's Ramayana. Arni, S. — **741.5**

Sitarski, Anita

Cold light — **535**

Sitomer, Alan Lawrence

Hip-hop poetry and the classics — **808.1071**

Homeboyz — **Fic**

The secret story of Sonia Rodriguez — **Fic**

SITTING BULL, 1831-1890

Nelson, S. D. Sitting Bull — **B**

Stanley, G. E. Sitting Bull — **B**

Sitting Bull. Nelson, S. D. — **B**

Sitting Bull. Stanley, G. E. — **B**

Sivertsen, Linda, 1964-

Generation green — **640**

Siwanowicz, Igor

Animals up close — **590**

Six days in October. Blumenthal, K. — **332.64**

Six innings. Preller, J. — **Fic**

SIXTEEN-YEAR-OLD BOYS

Berk, J. The dark days of Hamburger Halpin — **Fic**

Bruchac, J. Code Talker — **Fic**

Caine, R. Ink and bone — **Fic**

Draper, S. M. The battle of Jericho — **Fic**

Johnson, A. The first part last — **Fic**

Keith, H. Rifles for Watie — **Fic**

Koertge, R. Strays — **Fic**

Korman, G. Pop — **Fic**

Lawrence, I. The smugglers — **Fic**

London, A. Proxy — **Fic**

Hinds, K. Everyday life in the Roman Empire — 937
Lockhart, E. Genuine fraud — Fic
Maguire, G. Egg & spoon — Fic
Mazer, A. America street — Fic
Munda, R. Fireborne — Fic
Nunn, M. When the ground is hard — Fic
O'Sullivan, J. Between two skies — Fic
Padian, M. How to build a heart — Fic
Richards, J. Three rivers rising — Fic
Ross, E. Belle epoque — Fic
Ryan, P. M. Esperanza rising — Fic
Watson, R. Piecing me together — Fic
Whitman, E. Wildwing — Fic
Wolf, A. The watch that ends the night — Fic

SOCIAL CLASSES -- HISTORY
Nardo, D. Government and social class in colonial America — 973.2

SOCIAL CONFLICT
DuPrau, J. The people of Sparks — Fic
Ellis, D. Three wishes — 956.9405
Grant, M. Hunger — Fic
Hicks, F. E. The divided earth — 741.5

SOCIAL FORECASTING
Schutten, J. P. Hello from 2030 — 303.49

SOCIAL HISTORY
Sandler, M. W. 1919 — 973.91

SOCIAL INDICATORS
Albee, S. Why'd they wear that? — 391.009

SOCIAL ISOLATION
Haddix, M. P. Among the hidden — Fic
Ifueko, J. Raybearer — Fic
Zindel, P. The pigman — Fic

SOCIAL ISOLATION IN CHILDREN
Haddix, M. P. Among the hidden — Fic

SOCIAL JUSTICE
Bush, G. Indivisible — 811.008
Dias, M. Marley Dias gets it done — 305.23089
Latham, I. Dictionary for a better world — 170
Morrow, B. C. Take the mic — Fic
Soontornvat, C. A wish in the dark — Fic
Tamaki, M. Harley Quinn — Fic

SOCIAL MARGINALITY
Black, H. Geektastic — Fic

SOCIAL MEDIA
Lord, E. Tweet cute — Fic
Roat, S. H. How to disappear — Fic
Rojas, M. Selfie made — 302.23
Weinick, S. Increasing your tweets likes and ratings — 658.8

SOCIAL MOVEMENTS
Aronson, M. 1968 — 909.82
Bolden, T. Strong voices — 815.08
Kluger, J. Raise your voice — 303.48
Lerner, S. Parkland speaks — 371.7
Sandler, M. W. 1919 — 973.91
Styron, A. Steal this country — 320.0835

SOCIAL MOVEMENTS -- HISTORY 20TH CENTURY
Hill, L. C. America dreaming — 303.48

SOCIAL PARTICIPATION
Kluger, J. Raise your voice — 303.48

SOCIAL PERCEPTION
Charleyboy, L. #NotYourPrincess — 305.48

SOCIAL PHOBIA
Chmakova, S. Crush — 741.5

SOCIAL PROBLEMS
Bush, G. Indivisible — 811.008
Ness, P. The knife of never letting go — Fic
Paul, C. You are mighty — 306
Peck, R. A long way from Chicago — Fic
Peck, R. A year down yonder — Fic

SOCIAL REFORMERS
Lee, S. The downstairs girl — Fic
Stevenson, B. Just mercy — 340.092

SOCIAL SKILLS
Packer, A. J. How rude! — 395.1

SOCIAL SKILLS -- STUDY AND TEACHING (SECONDARY)
Mannix, D. Social skills activities for secondary students with special needs — 371.9
Social skills activities for secondary students with special needs. Mannix, D. — 371.9

SOCIAL STATUS
Littman, S. Backlash — Fic
Wagenen, M. v. Popular — 155.5

SOCIALISM
Bolden, T. Saving Savannah — Fic

SOCIALITES
Wolf, A. The watch that ends the night — Fic
The **Society** of Unrelenting Vigilance. Dakin, G. — Fic

SOD HOUSES
MacLachlan, P. Kindred souls — Fic

SOFAS
Clark, H. What we found in the sofa (and how it saved the world) — Fic

SOFT DRINKS
Furgang, A. Carbonated beverages — 613.2

SOFTBALL
Gitlin, M. Girls play to win softball — 796.357
Gola, M. Winning softball for girls — 796.357
Lupica, M. The only game — Fic

SOFTBALL FOR CHILDREN
Gitlin, M. Girls play to win softball — 796.357

SOFTBALL FOR WOMEN
Gitlin, M. Girls play to win softball — 796.357
Gola, M. Winning softball for girls — 796.357

SOHO, NEW YORK CITY
Tucker, L. All the Greys on Greene Street — Fic
Soil. Hirsch, R. E. — 631.4

SOIL ECOLOGY
Hirsch, R. E. Soil — 631.4

SOIL EROSION
Hirsch, R. E. Soil — 631.4

SOILS
Abdel-Fattah, R. Where the streets had a name — Fic
Graham, I. You wouldn't want to live without dirt! — 631.4

Hirsch, R. E. Soil   631.4

Sokolower, Jody

Determined to stay   305.235

SOLACE (IMAGINARY PLACE)

Johnson, J. The mark of the dragonfly   Fic

Solar cell and renewable energy experiments. Sobey, E. J.
C.   621.042078

SOLAR ECLIPSES

Loomis, I. Eclipse chaser   523.7

Mass, W. Every soul a star   Fic

SOLAR ENERGY

Bearce, S. How to harness solar power for your
home   621.47

Bright, S. Examining solar energy   621.47

Sobey, E. J. C. Solar cell and renewable energy experiments   621.042078

Walker, N. Harnessing power from the sun   621.47

SOLAR SYSTEM

Aguilar, D. A. Cosmic catastrophes   520

Aldrin, B. Welcome to Mars   523.43

Carson, M. K. Beyond the solar system   520.9

Garlick, M. A. Atlas of the universe   523.1

Green, D. Astronomy   520

Jenkins, M. Exploring space   520.9

Jennings, K. Outer space   523

Kenney, K. L. Exoplanets   523.2

Mara, W. Space exploration   629.4

Miller, R. Natural satellites   520

Mitchell, C. How do astronauts wee in space? 520

Saucier, C. A. P. Explore the cosmos like Neil DeGrasse
Tyson   520.92

Simon, S. The moon   559.9

Stott, C. Space exploration   629.4

SOLDER AND SOLDERING

Nelson, D. E. Soldering   671.5

Soldering. Nelson, D. E.   671.5

Soldier bear. Dumon Tak, B.   Fic

Soldier boys. Hughes, D.   Fic

Soldier X. Wulffson, D. L.   Fic

Soldier's heart. Paulsen, G.   Fic

Soldier's secret. Klass, S. S.   Fic

SOLDIERS

Ambrose, S. E. The good fight   940.53

Avi. The button war   Fic

Bacigalupi, P. Tool of war   Fic

Bascomb, N. The grand escape   940.4

Batten, J. The war to end all wars   940.3

Bausum, A. Stubby the war dog   940.4

Bick, I. J. Ashes   Fic

Blackburne, L. Rosemarked   Fic

Cliff, T. Delilah Dirk and the Turkish Lieutenant 741.5

Dumon Tak, B. Soldier bear   Fic

Elkeles, S. How to ruin your boyfriend's reputation Fic

Ellis, D. Off to war   303.6

Gunderson, J. Conquistadors   970.01

Hale, N. One dead spy   973.3

Hale, S. Enna burning   Fic

Hughes, D. Four-Four-Two   Fic

Hughes, D. Search and destroy   Fic

Hughes, D. Soldier boys   Fic

Hughes, P. Five 4ths of July   Fic

Johnson, A. Sweet hereafter   Fic

Keenan, S. Dogs of war   741.5

Klass, S. S. Soldier's secret   Fic

Kraus, D. At the edge of empire   Fic

LaFleur, S. M. Threads of blue   Fic

Lewis, J. P. And the soldiers sang   Fic

Lynch, C. Casualties of war   Fic

Mazer, H. Somebody please tell me who I am Fic

McCormick, P. Purple heart   Fic

Meyer, M. Wires and nerve   741.5

Morpurgo, M. War horse   Fic

Park, L. S. Keeping score   Fic

Park, L. The Spartan hoplites   938

Partridge, E. Boots on the ground   959.704

Peet, M. Tamar   Fic

Reinhardt, D. The things a brother knows   Fic

Senker, C. The Vietnam War   959.704

Sepetys, R. Salt to the sea   Fic

Smithson, R. Ghosts of war   956.7044

Turner, M. W. The king of Attolia   Fic

Turner, M. W. Thick as thieves   Fic

SOLDIERS -- HISTORY 20TH CENTURY

Samuels, C. Soldiers   940.54

SOLDIERS -- PAY, ALLOWANCES, ETC

Engdahl, S. Military families   355.1

Soldiers. Samuels, C.   940.54

Soledad O'Brien. Robson, D.   B

SOLID WASTE

Eamer, C. What a waste!   363.72

SOLID WASTE DISPOSAL

Carey, E. Heap House   Fic

Eamer, C. What a waste!   363.72

Solids liquids and gases experiments using water air marbles
and more. Gardner, R.   530.078

Solitary. Smith, A. G.   Fic

A **solitary** blue. Voigt, C.   Fic

SOLITARY CONFINEMENT

Smith, A. G. Solitary   Fic

Solomon and the ant. Oberman, S.   398.2

SOLOMON, KING OF ISRAEL

Stroud, J. The ring of Solomon   Fic

Solutions for a cleaner greener planet. Zimmer, M. 577.27

Solve this. Messner, K.   507.8

Solway, Andrew

Why is there life on Earth?   576.8

SOMALIA

Hassig, S. M. Somalia   967.73

Somalia. Hassig, S. M.   967.73

Some kind of courage. Gemeinhart, D.   Fic

Some kind of happiness. Legrand, C.   Fic

Some places more than others. Watson, R.   Fic

Somebody please tell me who I am. Mazer, H. Fic

The **someday** suitcase. Haydu, C. A.   Fic

Someday we will fly. DeWoskin, R.	Fic
Someone like me. Arce, J.	305.48
Somervill, Barbara A.	
Alabama	976.1
The human body	612
Japan	952
Marine biologist	578.77023
Monitor lizard	597.95
New York	974.7
Small indian mongoose	599.74
Texas	976.4
Something to say. Ramee, L. M.	Fic
Something wicked this way comes. Bradbury, R.	Fic
Sometimes it happens. Barnholdt, L.	Fic
SOMME, 1ST BATTLE OF THE, 1916	
Batten, J. The war to end all wars	940.3
Sommer, Shelley	
Hammerin' Hank Greenberg	B
Sommers, Michael A., 1966-	
The NFL	362.29
Somos como las nubes. Argueta, J.	811
Son. Lowry, L.	Fic
The **son** of Neptune. Riordan, R.	Fic
Son of the mob. Korman, G.	Fic
SON THI ANH, TUYET	
Skrypuch, M. F. One step at a time	618.92
Sonenklar, Carol	
AIDS	616.97
Sones, Sonya	
Stop pretending	Fic
What my girlfriend doesn't know	Fic
What my mother doesn't know	Fic
Song of the abyss. Lucier, M.	Fic
The **song** of the quarkbeast. Fforde, J.	Fic
Song, Sok	
Origami accessories	736.982
SONGS	
Stotts, S. We shall overcome	782.42162
Yolen, J. Apple for the teacher	782.42
SONGS -- HISTORY AND CRITICISM	
Murphy, C. R. My country 'tis of thee	782.42
Songs about a girl. Russell, C.	Fic
Songs and stories of the Civil War. Silverman, J.	782.42
SONGWRITERS	
Weil, C. I'm glad I did	Fic
SONGWRITING	
Roy, J. R. Mindblind	Fic
Sonneborn, Liz	
Canada	971
The electric light	609
The end of apartheid in South Africa	968.06
France	944
Jordan	956.95
The Khmer Rouge	959.604
Kuwait	953.67
Mark Twain	B
North Korea	951.93

Pakistan	954.91
Tibet	951
A to Z of American Indian women	920.72089
Sonnenblick, Jordan	
After ever after	Fic
Notes from the midnight driver	Fic
Zen and the art of faking it	Fic
Sonnichsen, A. L.	
Red butterfly	Fic
SONS OF LIBERTY	
Forbes, E. Johnny Tremain	Fic
Sons of the 613. Rubens, M.	Fic
Soo, Kean	
Jellaby	741.5
Soontornvat, Christina	
All thirteen	796.52
A wish in the dark	Fic
Sophia's war. Avi.	Fic
Sophie Quire and the last Storyguard. Auxier, J.	Fic
The **sorcerer** of the north. Flanagan, J.	Fic
Sorosiak, Carlie	
Wild blue wonder	Fic
Sorrow's kitchen. Lyons, M. E.	B
Sorry for your loss. Foley, J. A.	Fic
Sorry you're lost. Blackstone, M.	Fic
Soto, Gary	
Baseball in April and other stories	Fic
A fire in my hands	811
Help wanted	Fic
Local news	Fic
A natural man	811
Sotomayor, Sonia, 1954-	
The beloved world of Sonia Sotomayor	B
SOUL	
Barnhill, K. R. The witch's boy	Fic
Bedford, M. Flip	Fic
Goto, H. Half World	Fic
Oliver, L. The spindlers	Fic
Starmer, A. The storyteller	Fic
SOUL MUSIC -- HISTORY AND CRITICISM	
Mendelson, A. American R & B	781.644
SOUND	
Canavan, T. Super experiments with light and sound	535.078
SOUND -- RECORDING AND REPRODUCING	
Rooney, A. Audio engineering and the science of soundwaves	621.389
SOUND RECORDING INDUSTRY AND TRADE	
Pinkney, A. D. Rhythm ride	781.64409774
Sounder. Armstrong, W. H.	Fic
Sources of light. McMullan, M.	Fic
Sousa, David A.	
From STEM to STEAM	372.5
SOUTH AFRICA	
Aronson, M. The skull in the rock	569.9096822
Brownlie Bojang, A. South Africa in our world	968.06
Molope, K. L. This book betrays my brother	Fic
Naidoo, B. Out of bounds	Fic

SOVIET UNION -- POLITICS AND GOVERNMENT -- 1985-1991

Tolstikova, D. A year without Mom	741.5

SPACE

Abadzis, N. Laika	741.5
Anderson, M. T. He laughed with his other mouths	Fic
Brody, J. Sky without stars	Fic
Garlick, M. A. Atlas of the universe	523.1
Goldstein, M. J. Garbage in space	363.72
Jennings, K. Outer space	523
Jones, T. Ask the astronaut	629.4
Kaufman, A. Aurora rising	Fic
Kibuishi, K. Flight explorer	741.5
Mara, W. Space exploration	629.4
Mass, W. Pi in the sky	Fic
Maurer, R. Destination moon	629.45
Mitchell, C. How do astronauts wee in space?	520
Richardson, G. Kaboom!	541
Roman, D. Astronaut Academy	741.5
Scott, E. Space stars and the beginning of time	522
Siy, A. Voyager's greatest hits	523.4
Stott, C. Space exploration	629.4
Young, K. R. Space junk	629.4

SPACE ACADEMY (U.S. SPACE CAMP (HUNTSVILLE, ALABAMA))

Goodman, S. E. Ultimate field trip 5	629.45

SPACE AND TIME

Ansari, R. K. S. The in-between	Fic
Card, O. S. Pathfinder	Fic
D'Lacey, C. The fire ascending	Fic
Engdahl, S. Enchantress from the stars	Fic
Fletcher, C. Silvertongue	Fic
Gray, C. A thousand pieces of you	Fic
Haddix, M. P. Caught	Fic
Haddix, M. P. Sabotaged	Fic
Haddix, M. P. Sabotaged	Fic
Haddix, M. P. Sent	Fic
Hautman, P. The Klaatu terminus	Fic
Hautman, P. The obsidian blade	Fic
Herrick, A. The Time Fetch	Fic
Hunter, N. Is time travel possible?	530.11
L'Engle, M. A wind in the door	Fic
L'Engle, M. A wrinkle in time	Fic
Larson, H. A wrinkle in time	741.5
MacHale, D. J. The never war	Fic
MacHale, D. J. The reality bug	Fic
Mass, W. Pi in the sky	Fic
O'Hart, S. The starspun web	Fic
Pratchett, T. Only you can save mankind	Fic
Rex, A. Unlucky charms	Fic
Stead, R. When you reach me	Fic
Stephens, J. The emerald atlas	Fic
Stephens, J. The fire chronicle	Fic
Woodruff, E. George Washington's spy	Fic

SPACE BIOLOGY

Turner, P. S. Life on Earth---and beyond	571.0919
Space case. Gibbs, S.	Fic

SPACE COLONIES

Aldrin, B. Welcome to Mars	523.43
Brody, J. Sky without stars	Fic
Card, O. S. Pathfinder	Fic
Emerson, K. Last day on Mars	Fic
Gibbs, S. Space case	Fic
Gibbs, S. Spaced out	Fic
Ness, P. The Ask and the Answer	Fic
Ness, P. The knife of never letting go	Fic

SPACE DEBRIS

Goldstein, M. J. Garbage in space	363.72
Young, K. R. Space junk	629.4
Space dumplins. Thompson, C.	741.5

SPACE ENVIRONMENT

Mitchell, C. How do astronauts wee in space?	520

SPACE EXPLORATION

Aldrin, B. Welcome to Mars	523.43
Bortz, A. B. Seven wonders of space technology	629.4
Brouwer, S. Moon mission	629.45
Carson, M. K. Mission to Pluto	629.43
Chaikin, A. Mission control this is Apollo	629.45
Cherrix, A. E. In the shadow of the moon	629.45
Crompton, S. W. SputnikExplorer 1	629.4
Edge, L. B. Apollo 13	629.45
Garlick, M. A. Atlas of the universe	523.1
Gilliland, B. Rocket science for the rest of us	520
Grove, T. Milestones of flight	629.109
Harris, J. Space exploration	629.4
Hartman, E. Mission to Mars	629.45
Jennings, K. Outer space	523
Jones, T. Ask the astronaut	629.4
Maurer, R. Destination moon	629.45
Rocco, J. How we got to the moon	629.45
Rusch, E. The mighty Mars rovers	523.43
Sandler, M. W. Apollo 8	629.45
Scott, E. Space stars and the beginning of time	522
Siy, A. Voyager's greatest hits	523.4
Spilsbury, R. Robots in space	629.43
Stone, T. L. Almost astronauts	629.450092
Stott, C. Space exploration	629.4

SPACE EXPLORATION -- HISTORY

Jenkins, M. Exploring space	520.9
Space exploration. Harris, J.	629.4
Space exploration. Mara, W.	629.4
Space exploration. Stott, C.	629.4

SPACE FLIGHT

Abadzis, N. Laika	741.5
Adams, D. The hitchhiker's guide to the galaxy	Fic
Carson, M. K. Mission to Pluto	629.43
Dell, P. Man on the moon	629.45
Edge, L. B. Apollo 13	629.45
Goodman, S. E. How do you burp in space?	629.45
Holden, H. M. The coolest job in the universe	629.44
Kaufman, A. Gemina	Fic
Kaufman, A. Illuminae	Fic
Kaufman, A. Obsidio	Fic
Mara, W. Space exploration	629.4

SPIRITUALITY

Hautman, P. Godless **Fic**

Nicholson, H. Moonshot **741.5**

Schlitz, L. A. Amber and Clay **Fic**

SPIRITUALS (SONGS)

Giovanni, N. On my journey now **782.25**

SPIRITUALS (SONGS) -- HISTORY AND CRITICISM

Cooper, M. L. Slave spirituals and the Jubilee Singers **782.42162**

Splendors and glooms. Schlitz, L. A. **Fic**

SPOILED CHILDREN

Fleischman, S. The whipping boy **Fic**

SPOILED TEENAGE BOYS

London, A. Proxy **Fic**

SPOKANE COUNTY (WASH)

Dorisi-Winget, D. A million ways home **Fic**

SPORTS

Allison, J. Bad machinery **741.5**

Armstrong, J. The American story **973**

Berman, L. The greatest moments in sports **796**

Birmingham, M. Weird zone **796.1**

Bryant, H. Legends **796.357**

Burleigh, R. Hoops **811**

Connolly, S. The book of wildly spectacular sports science **507.8**

Coy, J. Hoop genius **796.323**

Doeden, M. Coming up clutch **796.0973**

Ellis, C. Wrestling **796.812**

Fitzpatrick, J. Skateboarding **796.22**

Gifford, C. Track and field **796.42**

Gigliotti, J. Football **796.332**

Gitlin, M. Girls play to win softball **796.357**

Ignotofsky, R. Women in sports **796.092**

Jennings, M. Soccer step-by-step **796.334**

Labrecque, E. Basketball **796.323**

Lipsyte, R. Heroes of baseball **920**

Mason, P. Improving endurance **613.7**

Mason, P. Improving flexibility **613.7**

Mason, P. Improving speed **613.7**

Mason, P. Improving strength and power **613.7**

McDougall, C. Girls play to win track & field **796.42**

McMahon, D. Girls play to win hockey **796.962**

Myers, C. Jabberwocky **821**

Rand, C. Graphing sports **796**

Savage, J. Top 25 hockey skills tips and tricks **796.962**

Smolka, B. Lacrosse **796.34**

Weighill, D. The big book of soccer **796.334**

Yancey, D. Basketball **796.323**

Zuckerman, G. Rising above **796**

Zweig, E. Soccer **796.334**

SPORTS -- CORRUPT PRACTICES

Feinstein, J. Change-up **Fic**

Feinstein, J. Cover-up **Fic**

Myers, W. D. Hoops **Fic**

SPORTS -- HISTORY

Kelley, K. C. Golf **796.352**

Macy, S. Breaking through **796.082**

McKinley, M. Ice time **796.355**

Thorn, J. First pitch **796.357**

SPORTS -- PSYCHOLOGICAL ASPECTS

Afremow, J. A. The young champion's mind **796**

SPORTS -- TECHNOLOGICAL INNOVATIONS

Swanson, J. Super gear **688.7**

SPORTS -- VOCATIONAL GUIDANCE

Howell, B. Sports **796**

Mattern, J. So you want to work in sports? **796**

Sports. Fay, G. **796**

Sports. Howell, B. **796**

SPORTS BETTING

Myers, W. D. Hoops **Fic**

SPORTS CAMPS

Lupica, M. Summer ball **Fic**

SPORTS CARS

Woods, B. Hottest sports cars **629.222**

SPORTS COMICS

Jamieson, V. Roller girl **741.5**

Johnson, C. G. The Breakaways **741.5**

SPORTS COVER-UPS

Feinstein, J. Cover-up **Fic**

SPORTS EQUIPMENT

Lakin, P. Bicycles **629.227**

Lakin, P. Skateboards **796.22**

Swanson, J. Super gear **688.7**

SPORTS FICTION

Alexander, K. The crossover **Fic**

Anderson, J. D. One last shot **Fic**

Aronson, M. The pick-up game **Fic**

Bauer, J. Soar **Fic**

Deuker, C. Golden arm **Fic**

Deuker, C. Gym candy **Fic**

Deuker, C. Swagger **Fic**

Feinstein, J. Change-up **Fic**

Feinstein, J. Cover-up **Fic**

Feinstein, J. Last shot **Fic**

Feinstein, J. The rivalry **Fic**

Feinstein, J. Vanishing act **Fic**

Feinstein, J. The walk-on **Fic**

Green, T. Baseball genius **Fic**

Green, T. Football champ **Fic**

Green, T. Football genius **Fic**

Green, T. Football hero **Fic**

Green, T. Force out **Fic**

Green, T. New kid **Fic**

Greenwald, T. Game changer **Fic**

Gutman, D. The million dollar shot **Fic**

Jeter, D. The contract **Fic**

Klages, E. Out of left field **Fic**

Korman, G. Pop **Fic**

Lipsyte, R. The contender **Fic**

Lupica, M. The batboy **Fic**

Lupica, M. The big field **Fic**

Lupica, M. Fantasy league **Fic**

Lupica, M. Heat **Fic**

Lupica, M. Miracle on 49th Street **Fic**

Lupica, M. The only game	**Fic**	
Lupica, M. Play makers	**Fic**	
Lupica, M. Strike zone	**Fic**	
Lupica, M. Summer ball	**Fic**	
Mack, W. C. Athlete vs. mathlete	**Fic**	
Murdock, C. G. Dairy queen	**Fic**	
Murdock, C. G. The off season	**Fic**	
Preller, J. Six innings	**Fic**	
Shen, E. L. The comeback	**Fic**	
Wallace, R. Wrestling Sturbridge	**Fic**	
Weaver, W. Saturday night dirt	**Fic**	

SPORTS FOR WOMEN -- HISTORY

Buckey, A. W. Women and sports — **796.082**

SPORTS INJURIES

Day, C. The sea in winter	**Fic**
Greenwald, T. Game changer	**Fic**
Gutman, D. Ray & me	**Fic**
McClafferty, C. K. Fourth down and inches	**617.4**
Murdock, C. G. The off season	**Fic**
Omnigraphics, I. Sports injuries information for teens	**617.1**

Sports injuries information for teens. Omnigraphics, I. — **617.1**

SPORTS JOURNALISM

Feinstein, J. The rivalry — **Fic**

SPORTS RIVALRY

Shen, E. L. The comeback — **Fic**

SPORTS SCIENCES

Connolly, S. The book of wildly spectacular sports science	**507.8**
Sharp, A. W. Ice hockey	**796.962**
Slade, S. Basketball	**796.323**
Swanson, J. Super gear	**688.7**
Yancey, D. Basketball	**796.323**

SPORTS UPSETS

Doeden, M. Coming up clutch — **796.0973**

SPORTSWRITERS

Feinstein, J. Change-up	**Fic**
Feinstein, J. Last shot	**Fic**
Feinstein, J. The rivalry	**Fic**
Feinstein, J. Vanishing act	**Fic**

Spotswood, Jessica

The radical element — **Fic**

Spratt, R. A.

Friday Barnes girl detective — **Fic**

SPRING BREAK

Stone, N. Clean getaway — **Fic**

Springer, Nancy

The case of the bizarre bouquets	**Fic**
The case of the cryptic crinoline	**Fic**
The case of the gypsy goodbye	**Fic**
The case of the left-handed lady	**Fic**
The case of the missing marquess	**Fic**
The case of the peculiar pink fan	**Fic**

Springstubb, Tricia

Every single second	**Fic**
The most perfect thing in the universe	**Fic**

SPRINTING

Reynolds, J. Ghost — **Fic**

Spud. Van de Ruit, J. — **Fic**

Sputnik/Explorer 1. Crompton, S. W. — **629.4**

SPUTNIKS -- HISTORY

Miller, R. Satellites — **629.44**

Sputnik's guide to life on earth. Cottrell Boyce, F. — **Fic**

camp. Gibbs, S. — **Fic**

SPY COMICS

Horowitz, A. Stormbreaker — **741.5**

SPY FICTION

Barnes, J. Perfect cover	**Fic**
Benway, R. Also known as	**Fic**
Carter, A. Cross my heart and hope to spy	**Fic**
Carter, A. Don't judge a girl by her cover	**Fic**
Carter, A. I'd tell you I love you but then I'd have to kill you	**Fic**
Carter, A. Only the good spy young	**Fic**
Carter, A. Out of sight out of time	**Fic**
Gibbs, S. Charlie Thorne and the last equation	**Fic**
Gibbs, S. Charlie Thorne and the lost city	**Fic**
Gibbs, S. Evil spy school	**Fic**
Gibbs, S. Spy camp	**Fic**
Gibbs, S. Spy school	**Fic**
Gibbs, S. Spy ski school	**Fic**
Gratz, A. Projekt 1065	**Fic**
Higgins, J. Death run	**Fic**
Higgins, J. First strike	**Fic**
Higgins, J. Sharp shot	**Fic**
Higgins, J. Sure fire	**Fic**
Horowitz, A. Never say die	**Fic**
Horowitz, A. Stormbreaker	**Fic**
McMullen, B. Mrs. Smith's Spy School for Girls	**Fic**
McNab, A. Avenger	**Fic**
Yelchin, E. Spy runner	**Fic**

A **spy** in the house. Lee, Y. S. — **Fic**

Spy runner. Yelchin, E. — **Fic**

Spy school. Gibbs, S. — **Fic**

Spy ski school. Gibbs, S. — **Fic**

SQUIDS

Newquist, H. P. Here there be monsters — **594**

Squire. Pierce, T. — **Fic**

The **squire's** tale. Morris, G. — **Fic**

Squire, Ann

Hydrofracking — **622**

SQUIRES

Pierce, T. Squire — **Fic**

SQUIRRELS

DiCamillo, K. Flora & Ulysses — **Fic**

ST LUCIA

Orr, T. Saint Lucia — **972.9843**

ST PETERSBURG, RUSSIA

Yelchin, E. The haunting of Falcon House — **Fic**

ST THOMAS, VIRGIN ISLANDS

Callender, K. Hurricane child — **Fic**

St. George, Judith, 1931-

The duel — **973.4**

St. John, Warren
Outcasts united   796.334092
STAGED DEATHS
Owen, M. The merciful Crow   Fic
Staging a play. Underwood, D.   792.02
STALIN, JOSEPH, 1879-1953
Davis, K. C. Strongman   321.9092
STALKERS
Mazer, N. F. The missing girl   Fic
STALKING
Peck, R. Are you in the house alone?   Fic
Stallworthy, Jon
The new Oxford book of war poetry   808.81
Stamped. Kendi, I. X.   305.800973
Stamper, Phil
The gravity of us   Fic
Stand up Yumi Chung! Kim, J.   Fic
STAND-UP COMEDY
Becker, H. Funny business   792.7028
Kim, J. Stand up Yumi Chung!   Fic
Rubin, L. Crying laughing   Fic
Standard hero behavior. Anderson, J. D.   Fic
STANDARDIZED TESTS
Angleberger, T. Princess Labelmaker to the rescue!   Fic
McPherson, S. S. Stressed out in school?   371.7
STANDING ROCK RESERVATION, NORTH DAKOTA
Robinson, G. Standing strong   Fic
Standing strong. Robinson, G.   Fic
Standing up against hate. Farrell, M. C.   940.54
Stanley, Diane
Bard of Avon   B
Bella at midnight   Fic
The princess of Cortova   Fic
The silver bowl   Fic
Stanley, George Edward
Sitting Bull   B
Stanley, Jerry, 1941-
Children of the Dust Bowl   371.96
Staples, Suzanne Fisher
Haveli   Fic
Under the persimmon tree   Fic
The **star** maker. Yep, L.   Fic
The **star** of Kazan. Ibbotson, E.   Fic
STAR WARS CHARACTERS
Brown, J. Return of the Padawan   741.5
Brown, J. Star Wars   741.5
Reynolds, D. W. Star Wars   791.4375
STAR WARS FICTION
Brown, J. Return of the Padawan   741.5
Brown, J. Star Wars   741.5
STAR WARS FILMS
Reynolds, D. W. Star Wars   791.4375
Star Wars. Brown, J.   741.5
Star Wars. Reynolds, D. W.   791.4375
Star-crossed. Dee, B.   Fic
StarChaser. Sage, A.   Fic
Starcrossed. Bunce, E. C.   Fic

Stardust. Gaiman, N.   Fic
Starfish. Bowman, A. D.   Fic
Starfish. Fipps, L.   Fic
Stargirl. Spinelli, J.   Fic
Starglass. North, P.   Fic
Starmer, Aaron, 1976-
The storyteller   Fic
The whisper   Fic
STARR, RINGO, 1940-
Quinn, J. The Beatles   920
Roberts, J. The Beatles   B
Starry River of the Sky. Lin, G.   Fic
Starry-eyed. Michael, T.   Fic
STARS
Dickinson, T. Nightwatch   523.8
Green, D. Astronomy   520
The **stars** beneath our feet. Moore, D. B.   Fic
The **starspun** web. O'Hart, S.   Fic
Start it up. Rankin, K.   658.1
Starters. Price, L.   Fic
Starting from here. Bigelow, L. J.   Fic
STATE-SPONSORED TERRORISM
Compestine, Y. C. Revolution is not a dinner party   Fic
Lugovskaya, N. I want to live   947.084
Naidoo, B. Out of bounds   Fic
Pellegrino, M. Journey of dreams   Fic
Sonneborn, L. The Khmer Rouge   959.604
STATES' RIGHTS (AMERICAN POLITICS) -- HISTORY
Bowers, R. The spies of Mississippi   323.1196
STATISTICS -- GRAPHIC METHODS
Rand, C. Graphing sports   796
STATUE OF LIBERTY (NEW YORK, NY) -- HISTORY
Eggers, D. Her right foot   973
STATUES
Fleischman, P. Graven images   Fic
Fletcher, C. Ironhand   Fic
Fletcher, C. Silvertongue   Fic
Fletcher, C. Stoneheart   Fic
Lewis, J. P. Monumental verses   811
Snicket, L. "Who could that be at this hour?"   Fic
STDs. Yancey, D.   616.95
Stead, Rebecca
First light   Fic
Goodbye stranger   Fic
Liar & spy   Fic
The list of things that will not change   Fic
When you reach me   Fic
Steal this country. Styron, A.   320.0835
STEALING
Avi. The button war   Fic
Balliett, B. The danger box   Fic
Beil, M. D. The vanishing violin   Fic
Blackwood, G. L. The Shakespeare stealer   Fic
Flanagan, J. The invaders   Fic
Gaiman, N. MirrorMask   Fic
Green, T. Baseball genius   Fic
Korman, G. Zoobreak   Fic

Robinson, G. Standing strong   Fic

SUICIDE

Appignanesi, R. Romeo and Juliet   741.5

Asher, J. Thirteen reasons why   Fic

Fields, T. After the death of Anna Gonzales   Fic

Foxlee, K. The anatomy of wings   Fic

Littman, S. Backlash   Fic

SUICIDE -- PREVENTION

Chandler, M. Understanding suicide   362.28

Nelson, R. E. The power to prevent suicide   362.28

SUICIDE VICTIMS

Asher, J. Thirteen reasons why   Fic

Fields, T. After the death of Anna Gonzales   Fic

Suite Scarlett. Johnson, M.   Fic

SULLIVAN, ANNIE, 1866-1936

Delano, M. F. Helen's eyes   B

Miller, S. E. Miss Spitfire   Fic

Sullivan, Edward T., 1966-

The ultimate weapon   355.8

Sullivan, George, 1927-

Berenice Abbott photographer   B

Built to last   624

Geronimo   B

Tom Thumb   B

Sullivan, Tom

Escape at 10000 feet   364.1317

SUMATRAN RHINOCEROS

Carson, M. K. Emi and the rhino scientist   599.66

SUMER -- RULERS

McCaughrean, G. Gilgamesh the hero   398.2

SUMMER

Abbott, T. The summer of Owen Todd   Fic

Brashares, A. 3 willows   Fic

Chase, P. J. So done   Fic

Dessen, S. That summer   Fic

Gibbs, S. Spy camp   Fic

Harrington, K. Sure signs of crazy   Fic

Henkes, K. Olive's ocean   Fic

Holm, J. L. Sunny side up   741.5

Horvath, P. My one hundred adventures   Fic

Howe, J. Also known as Elvis   Fic

Howland, L. The forget-me-not summer   Fic

Hurwitz, M. W. The summer I saved the world-- in 65 days   Fic

Jones, M. T. Woodford Brave   Fic

Larson, H. All summer long   741.5

Lee, C. The great motion mission   530

Levy, D. A. The family Fletcher takes Rock Island   Fic

Lisle, J. T. Quicksand Pond   Fic

Menon, S. 10 things I hate about Pinky   Fic

Sloan, H. G. Short   Fic

Snyder, L. My Jasper June   Fic

Tamaki, M. This one summer   741.5

Tanquary, K. The night parade   Fic

Wein, E. The pearl thief   Fic

Summer ball. Lupica, M.   Fic

The **summer** before boys. Baskin, N. R.   Fic

Summer bird blue. Bowman, A. D.   Fic

SUMMER CAMPS

Brosgol, V. Be prepared   741.5

Curato, M. Flamer   Fic

Greenwald, T. Charlie Joe Jackson's guide to summer vacation   Fic

Stevenson, N. Lumberjanes   741.5

SUMMER EMPLOYMENT

Buckley-Archer, L. The many lives of John Stone   Fic

Hobbs, W. Leaving Protection   Fic

Knowles, J. Where the heart is   Fic

The **summer** I saved the world-- in 65 days. Hurwitz, M. W.   Fic

A **summer** of Kings. Nolan, H.   Fic

The **summer** of Owen Todd. Abbott, T.   Fic

The **summer** of the gypsy moths. Pennypacker, S.   Fic

SUMMER READING PROGRAMS

Fitzgerald, K. Successful summer reading programs for all ages   025.5

SUMMER ROMANCE

Gonzales, S. Only mostly devastated   Fic

Han, J. It's not summer without you   Fic

SUMMER SCHOOLS

Booth, C. Kinda like brothers   Fic

The **summer** we found the baby. Hest, A.   Fic

Summerland. Chabon, M.   Fic

Summers, Courtney

This is not a test   Fic

Summiting Everest. Berne, E. C.   796.522

Sumner, Jamie

Roll with it   Fic

Tune it out   Fic

SUN

Green, D. Astronomy   520

Johnson, A. A cool moonlight   Fic

The **sun** is also a star. Yoon, N.   Fic

Sundance, Kyra

101 dog tricks kids edition   636.7

SUNDARBANS (BANGLADESH AND INDIA)

Montgomery, S. The man-eating tigers of Sundarbans   599.756

Perkins, M. Tiger boy   Fic

SUNDARBANS TIGER RESERVE

Montgomery, S. The man-eating tigers of Sundarbans   599.756

Sunny side up. Holm, J. L.   741.5

Sunrise over Fallujah. Myers, W. D.   Fic

The **Super** Bowl. Doeden, M.   796.332

Super bug encyclopedia. Woodward, J.   595.7

Super experiments with light and sound. Canavan, T.   535.078

Super gear. Swanson, J.   688.7

Super smart information strategies. Cornwall, P.   372.133

Super smart information strategies. Green, J.   778

Super smart information strategies. Rabbat, S.   775

Super women. Lawlor, L.   509.2

SUPERBIKES

Farndon, J. Megafast motorcycles   629.227

SUPERCOMPUTERS

Black, P. J. Urban outlaws — Fic

SUPERHERO COMICS

Cabot, M. Black Canary — 741.5
Garcia, K. Raven — Fic
Horikoshi, K. My hero academia — 741.5
Keplinger, K. Poison Ivy — 741.5
McKinney, L. L. Nubia — 741.5
Moore, S. Batman — Fic
Moreci, M. The lost carnival — Fic
Nijkamp, M. The oracle code — 741.5
Paige, D. Mera — Fic
Pope, P. Battling boy — 741.5
Tamaki, M. Harley Quinn — Fic
Yang, G. L. The shadow hero — 741.5
Yang, G. L. Superman smashes the Klan — 741.5

SUPERHERO STORIES

Anderson, J. D. Minion — Fic
Anderson, J. D. Sidekicked — Fic
Bardugo, L. Wonder Woman — Fic
Boniface, W. The great powers outage — Fic
Boniface, W. The hero revealed — Fic
Boniface, W. The return of Meteor Boy? — Fic
Cody, M. Powerless — Fic
Hannigan, K. Cape — Fic
Hannigan, K. Mask — Fic
Jung, M. Geeks girls and secret identities — Fic
Lee, M. Loki — Fic
Lee, S. Convergence — Fic
Lupica, M. Hero — Fic
Maas, S. J. Catwoman — Fic
Moore, P. V is for villain — Fic
Myklusch, M. Jack Blank and the Imagine Nation — Fic
Reynolds, J. Miles Morales — Fic
Stohl, M. Forever red — 741.5
Superhero therapy. Scarlet, J. — 616.85

SUPERHEROES

Anderson, J. D. Minion — Fic
Anderson, J. D. Sidekicked — Fic
Boniface, W. The great powers outage — Fic
Boniface, W. The hero revealed — Fic
Boniface, W. The return of Meteor Boy? — Fic
Cody, M. Powerless — Fic
DiCamillo, K. Flora & Ulysses — Fic
Horikoshi, K. My hero academia — 741.5
Jung, M. Geeks girls and secret identities — Fic
Maas, S. J. Catwoman — Fic
Moore, P. V is for villain — Fic
Myklusch, M. Jack Blank and the Imagine Nation — Fic
Riley, J. Secret origins — Fic
Stephens, J. Heroes! — 741.5
Yang, G. L. The shadow hero — 741.5

SUPERHUMAN ABILITIES

Anderson, S. The girl who speaks bear — Fic
Aveyard, V. Red queen — Fic
Cabot, M. Black Canary — 741.5
Carson, R. Walk on Earth a stranger — Fic

Chapman, E. Caster — Fic
Coulthurst, A. Of fire and stars — Fic
Evans, R. P. The prisoner of cell 25 — Fic
Law, I. Switch — Fic
Okorafor, N. Ikenga — Fic
Watson, G. F. Extreme abilities — 612

SUPERMAN (COMIC BOOK SERIES)

Bowers, R. Superman versus the Ku Klux Klan — 741.5
Superman smashes the Klan. Yang, G. L. — 741.5
Superman versus the Ku Klux Klan. Bowers, R. — 741.5

SUPERNATURAL

Almond, D. Clay — Fic
Alston, B. Amari and the night brothers — Fic
Armstrong, K. Loki's wolves — Fic
Bauer, A. C. E. Come Fall — Fic
Bauer, J. Peeled — Fic
Beatty, R. Serafina and the twisted staff — Fic
Beccia, C. Monstrous — 001.944
Bedford, M. Flip — Fic
Billingsley, F. Chime — Fic
Black, H. The Good Neighbors — 741.5
Black, H. Welcome to Bordertown — Fic
Brewer, Z. Eighth grade bites — Fic
Buckley-Archer, L. The many lives of John Stone — Fic
Carman, P. Skeleton Creek — Fic
Chan, G. The disappearance — Fic
Cody, M. Powerless — Fic
Condie, A. B. The Beast — Fic
Condie, A. B. The Darkdeep — Fic
Connolly, M. Hollow dolls — Fic
D'Lacey, C. Dark fire — Fic
D'Lacey, C. The fire eternal — Fic
D'Lacey, C. The fire within — Fic
D'Lacey, C. Fire world — Fic
D'Lacey, C. Icefire — Fic
Damico, G. Croak — Fic
Datlow, E. The beastly bride — Fic
Delaney, J. A new darkness — Fic
Gaiman, N. The graveyard book — Fic
Garcia, K. Beautiful creatures — Fic
Garcia, K. Beautiful darkness — Fic
Grant, M. Fear — Fic
Grant, M. Hunger — Fic
Grant, M. Lies — Fic
Grant, M. Light — Fic
Grant, M. Plague — Fic
Hand, C. Unearthly — Fic
Hardinge, F. Cuckoo song — Fic
Hatfield, R. The Book of Storms — Fic
Hodkin, M. The unbecoming of Mara Dyer — Fic
Hopkinson, N. The Chaos — Fic
Horowitz, A. Necropolis — Fic
Howard, A. The crossroads at midnight — Fic
Hulick, K. Strange but true — 001.94
Hurston, Z. N. The skull talks back and other haunting tales — Fic
Jinks, C. How to catch a bogle — Fic

Appelt, K. The underneath	Fic	Long, D. Survivor kid	613.6
Beckhorn, S. W. The wolf's boy	Fic	Maberry, J. Rot & Ruin	Fic
Bertagna, J. Exodus	Fic	McCaffrey, A. Dragonflight	Fic
Bick, I. J. Ashes	Fic	McClintock, N. Taken	Fic
Block, F. L. Love in the time of global warming	Fic	McGinnis, M. Be not far from me	Fic
Bodeen, S. A. The compound	Fic	Mooney, C. Surviving in cold places	363.34092
Bowling, D. The canyon's edge	Fic	Napoli, D. J. Beast	Fic
Bray, L. Beauty queens	Fic	O'Dell, S. Island of the Blue Dolphins	Fic
Brown, S. To stay alive	Fic	Palacio, R. J. White bird	741.5
Calabro, M. The perilous journey of the Donner Party	979.4	Park, L. S. A long walk to water	Fic
Champion, N. Finding food and water	613.6	Paulsen, G. The Transall saga	Fic
Champion, N. Finding your way	613.6	Pfeffer, S. B. Life as we knew it	Fic
Champion, N. In an emergency	613.6	Philbrick, W. R. Wild river	Fic
Champion, N. Making shelter	613.6	Philbrick, W. R. Wildfire	Fic
Charbonneau, J. Graduation day	Fic	Power, R. Wilder girls	Fic
Charbonneau, J. Independent study	Fic	Pratchett, T. Nation	Fic
Charbonneau, J. The Testing	Fic	Price, C. Desert Angel	Fic
Colfer, E. Illegal	741.5	Reichs, B. Chrysalis	Fic
Collins, S. Catching fire	Fic	Reichs, B. Genesis	Fic
Collins, S. The Hunger Games	Fic	Rose, C. S. May B.	Fic
Collins, S. Mockingjay	Fic	Ross, J. N. The Fog diver	Fic
Cushman, K. Rodzina	Fic	Saeed, J. Yara's spring	Fic
DuPrau, J. The city of Ember	Fic	Sanderson, B. Skyward	Fic
DuPrau, J. The diamond of Darkhold	Fic	Sangster, C. Last star burning	Fic
Durst, S. B. Vessel	Fic	Schrefer, E. Threatened	Fic
Emerson, K. Last day on Mars	Fic	Sepetys, R. Between shades of gray	Fic
Esplin, J. L. 96 miles	Fic	Shusterman, N. Dry	Fic
Falls, K. Inhuman	Fic	Sloan, H. G. I'll be there	Fic
Flake, S. Bang!	Fic	Smith, R. Peak	Fic
Gagnon, M. Strangelets	Fic	Soontornvat, C. All thirteen	796.52
Gemeinhart, D. Scar Island	Fic	Springstubb, T. The most perfect thing in the universe	Fic
Gibbs, S. Spy camp	Fic	Unsworth, T. The one safe place	Fic
Giff, P. R. Nory Ryan's song	Fic	Verne, J. 20000 leagues under the sea	Fic
Grant, M. Fear	Fic	Voigt, C. Homecoming	Fic
Grant, M. Light	Fic	Volponi, P. Hurricane song	Fic
Grant, M. Plague	Fic	Wells, R. E. Variant	Fic
Gratz, A. Refugee	Fic	Williams, M. Diamond boy	Fic
Griffin, P. Skyjacked	Fic	Wooding, C. Silver	Fic
Haddix, M. P. Among the Barons	Fic	**SURVIVAL (AFTER AIRPLANE ACCIDENTS, SHIPWRECKS, ETC)**	
Hagglund, B. Epic adventure Epic treks	910.9	Armstrong, J. Shipwreck at the bottom of the world	919.8
Hesse, K. Safekeeping	Fic	Aronson, M. Trapped	363.11
Hicks, F. E. The Nameless City	741.5	Bertozzi, N. Shackleton	919.89
Hile, L. Surviving extreme sports	796.04	Bodeen, S. A. The raft	Fic
Hirsch, J. The eleventh plague	Fic	Bray, L. Beauty queens	Fic
Hobbs, W. Never say die	Fic	Buchholz, R. How to survive anything	646.7
Hopkinson, D. Titanic	910.91	Golding, W. Lord of the flies	Fic
Hopkinson, D. We must not forget	940.53	Kraske, R. Marooned	996.1
Howe, P. Waggit's tale	Fic	Lawrence, I. The wreckers	Fic
Hughes, M. P. A crack in the sky	Fic	Markle, S. Rescues!	363.34
Johnson, T. L. Ice dogs	Fic	McKernan, V. Shackleton's stowaway	Fic
Kadohata, C. A million shades of gray	Fic	Mullenbach, C. Torpedoed!	940.54
Kenyon, S. Infinity	Fic	Nelson, P. Left for dead	940.54
LaFleur, S. M. Beautiful blue world	Fic	Olson, T. Lost in the Pacific 1942	940.54
Lasky, K. Lone wolf	Fic	Paulsen, G. Brian's winter	Fic
Lee, J. Brother's keeper	Fic	Paulsen, G. Hatchet	Fic
Lee, S. Outrun the moon	Fic	Taylor, T. The cay	Fic

Timothy of the cay | **Fic**

Taylor, Thomas, 1973-
Malamander | **Fic**

Taylor-Butler, Christine
Sacred mountain | **954.96**

Tchana, Katrin
Changing Woman and her sisters | **398.2**

Teach like a champion 2.0. Lemov, D. | **373**

TEACHER EFFECTIVENESS
Lemov, D. Teach like a champion 2.0 | **373**
Minor, C. We got this. | **371.82996073**

The **teacher's** funeral. Peck, R. | **Fic**

A **teacher's** guide to flexible grouping and collaborative learning. Brulles, D. | **371.3**

The **teacher's** guide to leading student-centered discussions. Hale, M. S. | **371.37**

TEACHER-STUDENT RELATIONSHIPS
Avi. Nothing but the truth a documentary novel | **Fic**
Buyea, R. Because of Mr. Terupt | **Fic**
Creech, S. Love that dog | **Fic**
Miller, S. E. Miss Spitfire | **Fic**
Schmidt, G. D. The Wednesday wars | **Fic**
Volponi, P. Rikers High | **Fic**

TEACHERS
Anderson, J. D. Ms. Bixby's last day | **Fic**
Duncan, L. Killing Mr. Griffin | **Fic**
Heider, M. W. The losers at the center of the galaxy | **Fic**
Holmes, S. Operation Yes | **Fic**
Irving, W. The legend of Sleepy Hollow | **Fic**

TEACHERS -- IN-SERVICE TRAINING
Abilock, D. Growing schools | **370.71**
Tucker, C. R. Power up blended learning | **371.3**

TEACHERS -- LEGAL STATUS, LAWS, ETC
Butler, R. P. Copyright for teachers & librarians in the 21st century | **346.7304**

TEACHERS -- TRAINING OF
Abilock, D. Growing schools | **370.71**
Brooks-Young, S. Teaching with the tools kids really use | **372.3**

TEACHING -- AIDS AND DEVICES
Beers, G. K. Disrupting thinking | **418**

TEACHING -- METHODOLOGY
Williams, Y. R. Teaching U.S. history beyond the textbook | **973.071**

TEACHING -- SOCIAL ASPECTS
Hammond, Z. Culturally responsive teaching and the brain | **370.117**

Teaching adolescent writers. Gallagher, K. | **808**

Teaching literacy skills to adolescents using Coretta Scott King Award winners. Bernadowski, C. | **428**

Teaching phonics & word study in the intermediate grades. Blevins, W. | **372.46**

Teaching reading in middle school. Robb, L. | **428.4071**

TEACHING TEAMS
Harada, V. H. Inquiry learning through librarian-teacher partnerships | **371.14**

Teaching U.S. history beyond the textbook. Williams, Y. | R. | **973.071**

Teaching with the tools kids really use. Brooks-Young, S. | **372.3**

Teague, Mark
The doom machine | **Fic**

Team moon. Thimmesh, C. | **629.45**

TEAMWORK (SPORTS)
Furudate, H. Haikyu!! | **741.5**
Lupica, M. Play makers | **Fic**

TECHNOLOGICAL FORECASTING
Schutten, J. P. Hello from 2030 | **303.49**

TECHNOLOGICAL INNOVATIONS
Allen, T. B. Mr. Lincoln's high-tech war | **973.7**
Bearce, S. All about electric and hybrid cars and who's driving them | **629.22**
Graham, I. Robot technology | **629.8**
Gregory, J. From butterfly wings to... display technology | **621.3815**
Helfand, L. They changed the world | **621.3**
Hughes, S. Case closed? | **902**
Lancaster, M. A. Human.4 | **Fic**
Lee, D. Biomimicry | **608**
Mercer, B. The robot book | **629.8**
Oxlade, C. Gaming technology | **794.8**
Sjonger, R. Robotics engineering and our automated world | **629.8**
Spilsbury, R. Hi-tech clothes | **746.9**
White, R. Cleared for takeoff | **629.133**

TECHNOLOGICAL INNOVATIONS -- HISTORY
Heinrichs, A. The Aztecs | **972**

TECHNOLOGICAL LITERACY -- STANDARDS
Brooks-Young, S. Teaching with the tools kids really use | **372.3**

TECHNOLOGICAL LITERACY -- STUDY AND TEACHING
Abilock, D. Growing schools | **370.71**

TECHNOLOGY
Bortz, A. B. Seven wonders of space technology | **629.4**
Brown, D. Machines that think! | **006.3**
Fisher, C. The dark city | **Fic**
Graham, I. Robot technology | **629.8**
Hale, N. One trick pony | **741.5**
Hulme, J. The glitch in sleep | **Fic**
Kenney, K. L. Folding tech | **736**
Kritzer, N. Catfishing on Catnet | **Fic**
Macaulay, D. The way things work now | **600**
Nardo, D. The medical revolution | **610.285**
Oxlade, C. Gaming technology | **794.8**
Reeve, P. Scrivener's moon | **Fic**
Slavin, B. Transformed | **670**
Spilsbury, L. Robotics | **629.8**
Wood, M. B. The science of science fiction | **500**

TECHNOLOGY -- HISTORY
Ferris, J. Ideas that changed the world | **609**
Mooney, C. The Industrial Revolution | **330.9**

TECHNOLOGY -- HISTORY 19TH CENTURY
Allen, T. B. Mr. Lincoln's high-tech war | **973.7**

TECHNOLOGY -- STUDY AND TEACHING (ELEMENTARY)

Vasquez, J. A. STEM lesson essentials grades 3-8 — 372.35

TECHNOLOGY AND CHILDREN

Steffens, B. Thinking critically — 384.5

Tecumseh. Zimmerman, D. J. — B

TECUMSEH, SHAWNEE CHIEF, 1768-1813

Zimmerman, D. J. Tecumseh — B

TEDDY BEARS

Hesse, K. Brooklyn Bridge — Fic

TEEN CHICK LIT

Abdel-Fattah, R. Does my head look big in this? — Fic
Abdel-Fattah, R. Ten things I hate about me — Fic
Barnholdt, L. Sometimes it happens — Fic
Brashares, A. 3 willows — Fic
Brashares, A. The sisterhood of the traveling pants — Fic
Cabot, M. All-American girl — Fic
Cabot, M. The princess diaries — Fic
Carter, A. Heist society — Fic
Carter, A. Uncommon criminals — Fic
Dessen, S. The moon and more — Fic
Elkeles, S. How to ruin a summer vacation — Fic
Elkeles, S. How to ruin my teenage life — Fic
Elkeles, S. How to ruin your boyfriend's reputation — Fic
Eulberg, E. Revenge of the girl with the great personality — Fic
Hepler, H. The cupcake queen — Fic
Johnson, M. 13 little blue envelopes — Fic
Johnson, M. Scarlett fever — Fic
Johnson, M. Suite Scarlett — Fic
Kenneally, M. Racing Savannah — Fic
Kuhn, S. I love you so mochi — Fic
Lockhart, E. The disreputable history of Frankie Landau-Banks — Fic
Lockhart, E. Dramarama — Fic
Lord, E. Tweet cute — Fic
Mackler, C. The Earth my butt and other big round things — Fic
Mills, E. Famous in a small town — Fic
Mlynowski, S. Ten things we did (and probably shouldn't have) — Fic
Moreno, N. Don't date Rosa Santos — Fic
Moriarty, J. Feeling sorry for Celia — Fic
Perkins, S. Anna and the French kiss — Fic
Teen cuisine new vegetarian. Locricchio, M. — 641.5
Teen guide to student activism. Kallen, S. A. — 371.81
Teen Inc. Petrucha, S. — Fic
Teen manners. Senning, C. P. — 395.1
A **teen's** guide to gut health. Warren, R. M. — 641.5

TEENAGE ABUSE VICTIMS

Engle, M. Silver people — Fic
Roe, R. A list of cages — Fic

TEENAGE ACTORS AND ACTRESSES

Belli, M. L. Acting for young actors — 792.02
Brosius, P. Fierce & true — 812
Lockhart, E. Dramarama — Fic

TEENAGE ADVENTURERS

Lerangis, P. The colossus rises — Fic

Lerangis, P. Lost in babylon — Fic
Lerangis, P. The tomb of shadows — Fic
Stevenson, R. L. Kidnapped — Fic
Stroud, J. Heroes of the valley — Fic
Wrede, P. C. Talking to dragons — Fic

TEENAGE APPRENTICES

Farmer, N. The Islands of the Blessed — Fic
Farmer, N. The Land of the Silver Apples — Fic
Fisher, C. The dark city — Fic
Fisher, C. The hidden Coronet — Fic
Fisher, C. The lost heiress — Fic
Flanagan, J. The battle for Skandia — Fic
Flanagan, J. The burning bridge — Fic
Flanagan, J. The icebound land — Fic
Flanagan, J. The lost stories — Fic
Flanagan, J. The ruins of Gorlan — Fic
Forbes, E. Johnny Tremain — Fic
O'Brien, C. M. Birthmarked — Fic
Shusterman, N. Scythe — Fic
Stroud, J. The golem's eye — Fic

TEENAGE ARTISTS

Brant, W. Zenn diagram — Fic
Sones, S. What my girlfriend doesn't know — Fic
Waller, S. B. A mad wicked folly — Fic

TEENAGE ATHLETES

Afremow, J. A. The young champion's mind — 796
Deuker, C. Gym candy — Fic
McDaniel, L. Breathless — Fic
McDaniel, L. Hit and run — Fic
Myers, W. D. Hoops — Fic
Robinson, G. Little Brother of War — Fic
Wallace, R. Wrestling Sturbridge — Fic

TEENAGE ATHLETES -- TRAINING OF

Fay, G. Sports — 796

TEENAGE AUTHORS

Myers, W. D. Darius & Twig — Fic

TEENAGE BASEBALL PLAYERS

Koertge, R. Shakespeare makes the playoffs — Fic

TEENAGE BASKETBALL PLAYERS

Aronson, M. The pick-up game — Fic
Deuker, C. Swagger — Fic
Tamani, L. All the things we never knew — Fic
The **teenage** body book. McCoy, K. — 613

TEENAGE BOY ADVENTURERS

Gilman, D. Blood sun — Fic
Gilman, D. Ice claw — Fic
Riordan, R. The battle of the Labyrinth — Fic
Riordan, R. The last Olympian — Fic
Riordan, R. The sea of monsters — Fic
Riordan, R. The Titan's curse — Fic

TEENAGE BOY DETECTIVES

Horowitz, A. The Falcon's Malteser — Fic
Horowitz, A. The Greek who stole Christmas — Fic
Horowitz, A. Public enemy number two — Fic
Horowitz, A. South by southeast — Fic
Horowitz, A. Three of diamonds — Fic

TEENAGE BOY DIVERS

Evans, R. P. Battle of the Ampere	**Fic**
Fitzmaurice, K. A diamond in the desert	**Fic**
Flake, S. You don't even know me	**Fic**
Flanagan, J. The battle for Skandia	**Fic**
Flanagan, J. The burning bridge	**Fic**
Flanagan, J. The siege of Macindaw	**Fic**
Furudate, H. Haikyu!!	**741.5**
Gaddy, K. R. Flowers in the gutter	**940.53**
Gantos, J. The trouble in me	**Fic**
Gardner, S. The silver blade	**Fic**
Giles, L. R. Not so pure and simple	**Fic**
Gilman, D. Ice claw	**Fic**
Golding, W. Lord of the flies	**Fic**
Gordon, R. Tunnels	**Fic**
Gratz, A. Ground Zero	**Fic**
Gutman, D. Abner & me	**Fic**
Haddix, M. P. Among the free	**Fic**
Hahn, M. D. Took	**Fic**
Hautman, P. The Klaatu terminus	**Fic**
Hinton, S. E. The outsiders	**Fic**
Hobbs, W. Crossing the wire	**Fic**
Horikoshi, K. My hero academia	**741.5**
Horowitz, A. Evil star	**Fic**
Horowitz, A. South by southeast	**Fic**
Hughes, N. Refraction	**Fic**
Jennings, R. W. Ghost town	**Fic**
Kincaid, S. J. Insignia	**Fic**
Koertge, R. Shakespeare makes the playoffs	**Fic**
Korman, G. Son of the mob	**Fic**
Lawrence, I. The smugglers	**Fic**
Lawrence, I. The wreckers	**Fic**
Lee, S. Convergence	**Fic**
Lennon, T. When love comes to town	**Fic**
Marsh, K. Jepp who defied the stars	**Fic**
Mass, W. Pi in the sky	**Fic**
Mazer, H. Heroes don't run	**Fic**
Mercado, N. E. Every man for himself	**Fic**
Moreci, M. The lost carnival	**Fic**
Moriarty, J. The cracks in the Kingdom	**Fic**
Mussi, S. The door of no return	**Fic**
Myers, W. D. Dope sick	**Fic**
Nicholson, W. Seeker	**Fic**
Oaks, J. A. Why I fight	**Fic**
Orenstein, D. G. The secret twin	**Fic**
Paulsen, G. Brian's return	**Fic**
Paulsen, G. Notes from the dog	**Fic**
Paulsen, G. Soldier's heart	**Fic**
Perkins, L. R. As easy as falling off the face of the earth	**Fic**
Petrucha, S. Teen Inc.	**Fic**
Pinkwater, D. M. Bushman lives!	**Fic**
Pollen, S. The year I didn't eat	**Fic**
Pratchett, T. Dodger	**Fic**
Preller, J. Bystander	**Fic**
Preus, M. Heart of a samurai	**Fic**
Proimos, J. 12 things to do before you crash and burn	**Fic**
Riggs, R. Hollow City	**Fic**
Riggs, R. Library of souls	**Fic**

Riordan, R. The ship of the dead	**Fic**
Romero, J. No summit out of sight	**796.522092**
Sachar, L. Small steps	**Fic**
Schrefer, E. Threatened	**Fic**
Schroder, M. My brother's shadow	**Fic**
Scieszka, J. Guys write for Guys Read	**810.8**
Silvera, A. Infinity son	**Fic**
Silvey, C. Jasper Jones	**Fic**
Sonnenblick, J. Notes from the midnight driver	**Fic**
Sonnenblick, J. Zen and the art of faking it	**Fic**
Soto, G. Help wanted	**Fic**
Spinelli, J. Dead Wednesday	**Fic**
Stork, F. X. The last summer of the Death Warriors	**Fic**
Stork, F. X. Marcelo in the real world	**Fic**
Strasser, T. Boot camp	**Fic**
Strasser, T. No place	**Fic**
Svingen, A. The ballad of a broken nose	**Fic**
Tripp, B. The accidental highwayman	**Fic**
Volponi, P. Rucker Park setup	**Fic**
Walton, J. Words on bathroom walls	**Fic**
Werlin, N. The rules of survival	**Fic**
Wilson, J. Victorio's war	**Fic**
Yolen, J. Dragon's blood	**Fic**
Yolen, J. Mightier than the sword	**398.2**

TEENAGE BOYS -- DEATH

Sorosiak, C. Wild blue wonder	**Fic**

TEENAGE BOYS -- FRIENDSHIP

Lubar, D. Hidden talents	**Fic**
Rylant, C. A fine white dust	**Fic**
Wisler, G. C. Red Cap	**Fic**

TEENAGE BOYS -- GROWTH

Madaras, L. The "what's happening to my body?" book for boys	**613.9**
Middleman, A. B. American Medical Association boys' guide to becoming a teen	**613**

TEENAGE BOYS -- HEALTH

Mar, J. The body book for boys	**613**

TEENAGE BOYS -- INTERPERSONAL RELATIONS

Mar, J. The body book for boys	**613**

TEENAGE BOYS -- PHYSIOLOGY

Couwenhoven, T. The boys' guide to growing up	**613**
Metzger, J. G. Will puberty last my whole life?	**613**

TEENAGE BOYS WITH ADHD

Roe, R. A list of cages	**Fic**

TEENAGE BOYS WITH DISABILITIES

Baratz-Logsted, L. Crazy beautiful	**Fic**
Berk, J. The dark days of Hamburger Halpin	**Fic**
Forbes, E. Johnny Tremain	**Fic**
Koertge, R. Stoner & Spaz	**Fic**
Trueman, T. Stuck in neutral	**Fic**

TEENAGE BOYS WITH MENTAL ILLNESSES

Leavitt, M. Calvin	**Fic**
Walton, J. Words on bathroom walls	**Fic**

TEENAGE CARTOONISTS

Sharenow, R. The Berlin Boxing Club	**Fic**

TEENAGE CHILDREN OF ALCOHOLICS

Donovan, J. I'll get there it better be worth the trip	**Fic**

Lee, Y. S. The body at the tower	Fic	Cushman, K. Catherine called Birdy	Fic
Lee, Y. S. A spy in the house	Fic	Cushman, K. The loud silence of Francine Green	Fic
Lloyd-Jones, E. The bone houses	Fic	Dessen, S. The truth about forever	Fic
MacColl, M. Prisoners in the palace	Fic	Doherty, B. The girl who saw lions	Fic
Meyer, L. A. Bloody Jack	Fic	Duane, D. So you want to be a wizard	Fic
Nix, G. Abhorsen	Fic	Duncan, L. Locked in time	Fic
Nix, G. Lirael daughter of the Clayr	Fic	Duncan, L. Stranger with my face	Fic
Powell, L. The game of triumphs	Fic	Dunlap, S. E. The musician's daughter	Fic
Price, L. Starters	Fic	Elkeles, S. How to ruin a summer vacation	Fic
Stiefvater, M. The Scorpio races	Fic	Elkeles, S. How to ruin my teenage life	Fic
Sweeney, D. The minnow	Fic	Ellis, D. My name is Parvana	Fic
Takaya, N. Fruits basket	741.5	Fawcett, H. Even the darkest stars	Fic
Zettel, S. A most dangerous deception	Fic	Fforde, J. The song of the quarkbeast	Fic
Zink, M. Prophecy of the sisters	Fic	Fletcher, S. Alphabet of dreams	Fic

TEENAGE GIRL PHOTOGRAPHERS

		Fonseca, C. The girl guide	646.700835
Marcus, K. Exposed	Fic	Fraustino, L. R. Don't cramp my style	Fic
Russell, C. Songs about a girl	Fic	Freitas, D. Unplugged	Fic

TEENAGE GIRL PIANISTS

		Friedman, L. B. Can you say catastrophe?	Fic
Zarr, S. The Lucy variations	Fic	Funke, C. Inkspell	Fic

TEENAGE GIRL PSYCHICS

		Gevinson, T. Rookie on love	Fic
Cashore, K. Fire	Fic	Gratz, A. Ground Zero	Fic
Headley, J. C. Return to me	Fic	Griffin, N. Just wreck it all	Fic

TEENAGE GIRL SINGERS

		Grove, S. E. The crimson skew	Fic
Levine, G. C. Fairest	Fic	Halpern, J. Get well soon	Fic

TEENAGE GIRL SOCIAL ADVOCATES

		Hand, C. The how & the why	Fic
Dias, M. Marley Dias gets it done	305.23089	Harrison, M. 13 secrets	Fic

TEENAGE GIRL SOLDIERS

		Haskell, M. Handbook for dragon slayers	Fic
Yang, D. J. Daughter of Xanadu	Fic	Hemphill, S. Wicked girls	Fic

TEENAGE GIRL/GIRL RELATIONS

		Hesse, M. The war outside	Fic
Coulthurst, A. Of fire and stars	Fic	Hicks, F. E. One Year at Ellsmere	741.5
Keplinger, K. Poison Ivy	741.5	Ibbotson, E. The dragonfly pool	Fic
Villasante, A. The grief keeper	Fic	Iturbe, A. The librarian of Auschwitz	Fic

TEENAGE GIRLS

		Jennings, J. Being Jazz	306.76
Abdel-Fattah, R. Does my head look big in this?	Fic	Johnson, M. 13 little blue envelopes	Fic
Alexander, J. The sweetheart of Prosper County	Fic	Johnson, M. Truly Devious	Fic
Allison, J. Gilda Joyce psychic investigator	Fic	Johnson, M. The vanishing stair	Fic
Anderson, L. H. Fever 1793	Fic	Johnson, T. L. Dog driven	Fic
Anderson, L. H. Speak	Fic	Kephart, B. Undercover	Fic
Avi. Sophia's war	Fic	Keplinger, K. Poison Ivy	741.5
Barnes, J. Perfect cover	Fic	Kindl, P. Keeping the castle	Fic
Benway, R. Also known as	Fic	Kindl, P. A school for brides	Fic
Berry, J. The Amaranth enchantment	Fic	Kritzer, N. Catfishing on Catnet	Fic
Berry, J. The passion of Dolssa	Fic	Lavender, W. Aftershocks	Fic
Blundell, J. A city tossed and broken	Fic	Lee, Y. S. The body at the tower	Fic
Blundell, J. What I saw and how I lied	Fic	Levine, G. C. Fairest	Fic
Booraem, E. River magic	Fic	Littman, S. Backlash	Fic
Bracken, A. Never fade	Fic	Lockhart, E. The disreputable history of Frankie Landau-	
Bray, L. A great and terrible beauty	Fic	Banks	Fic
Brooks, M. Mistik Lake	Fic	Loughead, D. Cleavage	Fic
Budhos, M. T. Ask me no questions	Fic	Luddy, K. Spelldown	Fic
Bushnell, C. Rules for being a girl	Fic	Mackel, K. Boost	Fic
Cabot, M. Black Canary	741.5	Mae, N. The kinder poison	Fic
Carey, J. L. Dragon's keep	Fic	Mazer, N. F. The missing girl	Fic
Carter, A. Cross my heart and hope to spy	Fic	McClintock, N. Taken	Fic
Castellucci, C. Boy proof	Fic	McGuigan, M. A. Morning in a different place	Fic
Castellucci, C. Don't cosplay with my heart	Fic	McKinney, L. L. Nubia	741.5
Cooper, M. A brief history of Montmaray	Fic	McMullan, M. Sources of light	Fic

Goodman, A. Eona — Fic
John, A. Five flavors of Dumb — Fic
Venkatraman, P. A time to dance — Fic

TEENAGE GIRLS WITH EATING DISORDERS
Anderson, L. H. Wintergirls — Fic
Friend, N. Perfect — Fic

TEENAGE GIRLS WITH LEUKEMIA
Andrews, J. Me and Earl and the dying girl — Fic
Downham, J. Before I die — Fic

TEENAGE GIRLS WITH MENTAL ILLNESSES
Lord, E. When we collided — Fic
Sones, S. Stop pretending — Fic

TEENAGE HACKERS
Bernard, R. Find me — Fic
Lu, M. Warcross — Fic
Lu, M. Wildcard — Fic

TEENAGE HEROES AND HEROINES
Flanagan, J. The battle for Skandia — Fic
Flanagan, J. The burning bridge — Fic
Flanagan, J. The emperor of Nihon-ja — Fic
Flanagan, J. Erak's ransom — Fic
Flanagan, J. Halt's peril — Fic
Flanagan, J. The icebound land — Fic
Flanagan, J. The kings of Clonmel — Fic
Flanagan, J. The lost stories — Fic
Flanagan, J. The ruins of Gorlan — Fic
Flanagan, J. The siege of Macindaw — Fic
Flanagan, J. The sorcerer of the north — Fic
Larson, H. A wrinkle in time — 741.5
MacHale, D. J. The lost city of Faar — Fic
MacHale, D. J. The merchant of death — Fic
MacHale, D. J. The never war — Fic
MacHale, D. J. The reality bug — Fic
Mull, B. A world without heroes — Fic
Pope, P. Battling boy — 741.5

TEENAGE HOUSEHOLD EMPLOYEES
Coats, J. A. The wicked and the just — Fic

TEENAGE IMMIGRANTS
Budhos, M. T. Tell us we're home — Fic
Carlson, L. M. Cool salsa — 811
Carlson, L. M. Red hot salsa — 811.008
Cofer, J. O. Riding low on the streets of gold — Fic
Friesner, E. M. Threads and flames — Fic
Joseph, L. Flowers in the sky — Fic
Villalobos, J. P. The other side — 305.235092
Yee, P. Learning to fly — Fic

TEENAGE JOURNALISTS
Bauer, J. Peeled — Fic
Fantaskey, B. Buzz kill — Fic
Feinstein, J. Change-up — Fic
Feinstein, J. Cover-up — Fic
Feinstein, J. The rivalry — Fic
Feinstein, J. Vanishing act — Fic
Khan, H. More to the story — Fic

TEENAGE KIDNAPPING VICTIMS
Card, O. S. The lost gate — Fic
Daud, S. Mirage — Fic

Stevenson, R. L. Kidnapped — Fic
Walden, M. H.I.V.E. — Fic
Ward, D. Escape the mask — Fic
Yancey, R. The seal of Solomon — Fic

TEENAGE MAGICIANS
Pierce, T. Melting stones — Fic
Stroud, J. Ptolemy's gate — Fic

TEENAGE MISFITS
Black, H. Geektastic — Fic
Castellucci, C. Boy proof — Fic
Holt, K. W. When Zachary Beaver came to town — Fic
Lubar, D. Hidden talents — Fic
Lubar, D. True talents — Fic
Lyga, B. The astonishing adventures of Fanboy & Goth Girl — Fic
Oates, J. C. Big Mouth & Ugly Girl — Fic
Pierce, T. Briar's book — Fic
Pierce, T. Daja's book — Fic
Pierce, T. Sandry's book — Fic
Pierce, T. Tris's book — Fic

TEENAGE MOTHERS
Williams-Garcia, R. Like sisters on the homefront — Fic

TEENAGE MOUNTAINEERS
Smith, R. Peak — Fic

TEENAGE MURDER SUSPECTS
Myers, W. D. Monster — Fic

TEENAGE MURDER VICTIMS
Hahn, M. D. Mister Death's blue-eyed girls — Fic
Wolf, A. Who killed Christopher Goodman? — Fic

TEENAGE MURDER WITNESSES
Gilman, D. Ice claw — Fic
Johnson, M. The name of the star — Fic
McClintock, N. She saidshe saw — Fic

TEENAGE MURDERERS
Hautman, P. Blank confession — Fic

TEENAGE MUSICIANS
Brezenoff, S. Brooklyn burning — Fic
Gansworth, E. L. Give me some truth — Fic
Hamilton, V. The planet of Junior Brown — Fic
Martinez, J. Virtuosity — Fic
Sloan, H. G. I'll be there — Fic

TEENAGE NONCONFORMISTS
Cushman, K. The loud silence of Francine Green — Fic
Westerfeld, S. Specials — Fic

TEENAGE ORPHANS
Chee, T. The storyteller — Fic
Jocelyn, M. A big dose of lucky — Fic
Munda, R. Fireborne — Fic
Petrucha, S. Teen Inc. — Fic
Ruiz Zafon, C. The Midnight Palace — Fic

TEENAGE PARENTS
Banigan, M. Coping with teen pregnancy — 362.7
Johnson, A. The first part last — Fic
Omnigraphics, I. Pregnancy information for teens — 618.200835

TEENAGE PHOTOGRAPHERS
Foley, J. A. Sorry for your loss — Fic

Mazer, H. Heroes don't run — **Fic**
Mazer, H. The last mission — **Fic**
Morpurgo, M. Private Peaceful — **Fic**
Paulsen, G. Soldier's heart — **Fic**
Salisbury, G. Eyes of the emperor — **Fic**
Wiechman, K. C. Like a river — **Fic**
Wisler, G. C. Red Cap — **Fic**
Wulffson, D. L. Soldier X — **Fic**

TEENAGE SPIES
Barnes, J. Perfect cover — **Fic**
Benway, R. Also known as — **Fic**
Boecker, V. An assassin's guide to love and treason — **Fic**
Bunce, E. C. Starcrossed — **Fic**
Carter, A. Cross my heart and hope to spy — **Fic**
Carter, A. Don't judge a girl by her cover — **Fic**
Carter, A. I'd tell you I love you but then I'd have to kill you — **Fic**
Carter, A. Only the good spy young — **Fic**
Carter, A. Out of sight out of time — **Fic**
Gratz, A. Projekt 1065 — **Fic**
Heath, J. The lab — **Fic**
Heath, J. Remote control — **Fic**
Horowitz, A. Never say die — **Fic**
Horowitz, A. Stormbreaker — **741.5**
Keith, H. Rifles for Watie — **Fic**

TEENAGE SUPERHEROES
Dakin, G. The Society of Unrelenting Vigilance — **Fic**
Lupica, M. Hero — **Fic**
Pope, P. Battling boy — **741.5**
Reynolds, J. Miles Morales — **Fic**

TEENAGE TRAVELERS
Johnson, M. 13 little blue envelopes — **Fic**

TEENAGE VAMPIRES
Brewer, Z. Eighth grade bites — **Fic**
Fantaskey, B. Jessica's guide to dating on the dark side — **Fic**
Meyer, S. Breaking dawn — **Fic**
Meyer, S. Eclipse — **Fic**
Meyer, S. Twilight — **Fic**

TEENAGE VOLUNTEERS
Kallen, S. A. Teen guide to student activism — **371.81**
Kephart, B. The heart is not a size — **Fic**
Thompson, H. The language inside — **Fic**

TEENAGE WEREWOLVES
Devlin, I. Low red moon — **Fic**
Meyer, S. Eclipse — **Fic**
Meyer, S. New moon — **Fic**

TEENAGE WITCHES
Garcia, K. Beautiful chaos — **Fic**
Garcia, K. Beautiful creatures — **Fic**
Garcia, K. Beautiful darkness — **Fic**
MacCullough, C. Once a witch — **Fic**
Pratchett, T. I shall wear midnight — **Fic**

TEENAGE WIZARDS
Card, O. S. The lost gate — **Fic**
Duane, D. So you want to be a wizard — **Fic**
Pierce, T. Briar's book — **Fic**
Pierce, T. Daja's book — **Fic**

Pierce, T. Sandry's book — **Fic**
Pierce, T. Tris's book — **Fic**
Rowling, J. K. Harry Potter and the deathly hallows — **Fic**
Rowling, J. K. Harry Potter and the goblet of fire — **Fic**

TEENAGERS
Adlington, L. J. The diary of Pelly D — **Fic**
Alifirenka, C. I will always write back — **305.235**
Anderson, M. T. Feed — **Fic**
Aspromonte, J. ADHD — **616.85**
Bradley, A. 24 girls in 7 days — **Fic**
Brashares, A. The sisterhood of the traveling pants — **Fic**
Brashear, A. The incredible true story of the making of the Eve of Destruction — **Fic**
Bryant, J. Kaleidoscope eyes — **Fic**
Carlson, L. M. Cool salsa — **811**
Carlson, L. M. Red hot salsa — **811.008**
Castellucci, C. Boy proof — **Fic**
Chee, T. We are not free — **Fic**
Cofer, J. O. Riding low on the streets of gold — **Fic**
Cortez, S. You don't have a clue — **Fic**
Detrick, E. Actor's choice — **808.82**
Doyle, M. Bewitching season — **Fic**
Duncan, L. I know what you did last summer — **Fic**
Duncan, L. Killing Mr. Griffin — **Fic**
Earl, R. Your brain needs a hug — **616.85**
Elkeles, S. How to ruin a summer vacation — **Fic**
Ellis, A. D. This is what I did — **Fic**
Ellis, D. Three wishes — **956.9405**
Fershleiser, R. I can't keep my own secrets — **808**
Fields, T. After the death of Anna Gonzales — **Fic**
Flanagan, J. The battle for Skandia — **Fic**
Flanagan, J. The siege of Macindaw — **Fic**
Fleming, C. On the day I died — **Fic**
Frost, H. Keesha's house — **Fic**
Gagnon, M. Strangelets — **Fic**
Gallo, D. R. Destination unexpected — **Fic**
Gardner, S. The silver blade — **Fic**
Giovanni, N. Paint me like I am — **811**
Halpern, J. Get well soon — **Fic**
Hinton, S. E. The outsiders — **Fic**
Hirsch, J. Breakaway — **Fic**
Hoose, P. M. We were there too! — **973**
Kagawa, J. Talon — **Fic**
Kephart, B. Undercover — **Fic**
Lavender, W. Aftershocks — **Fic**
Lecesne, J. Absolute brightness — **Fic**
Lee, C. The great motion mission — **530**
Leno, K. The lost & found — **Fic**
Levy, D. A. Above all else — **Fic**
Lyga, B. The astonishing adventures of Fanboy & Goth Girl — **Fic**
Markham, L. The far away brothers — **979.4**
Mazer, N. F. The missing girl — **Fic**
McNab, A. Avenger — **Fic**
Mercado, N. E. Every man for himself — **Fic**
Michael, T. Starry-eyed — **Fic**
Morgenstern, J. Organizing from the inside out for

Vail, R. Well that was awkward — Fic

TEXTILE CRAFTS

Carlson, L. M. Knit hook and spin — 745.5

Lisle, A. Sewing school — 646.2

TEXTILE FABRICS

Albee, S. Why'd they wear that? — 391.009

TEXTILE MILLS

Paterson, K. Lyddie — Fic

THAILAND

Sobol, R. The life of rice — 633.1

Soontornvat, C. All thirteen — 796.52

THANATOS (GREEK DEITY)

Evans, M. Who let the gods out? — Fic

Thank you for coming to my TED talk. Anderson, C. — 808.5

THARP, MARIE

Lawlor, L. Super women — 509.2

That summer. Dessen, S. — Fic

That time I joined the circus. Howard, J. J. — Fic

That's a great answer! Boyles, N. N. — 372.47

That's not what happened. Keplinger, K. — Fic

THE WEST (UNITED STATES)

Cushman, K. Rodzina — Fic

Fleming, C. Presenting Buffalo Bill — 978

Hale, N. Donner dinner party — 979.4

Hale, S. Rapunzel's revenge — 741.5

Hand, C. My Calamity Jane — Fic

Kent, D. Idaho — 979.6

McKernan, V. The devil's paintbox — Fic

Pierpoint, E. The last ride of Caleb O'Toole — Fic

Sheinkin, S. Which way to the wild west? — 978

Wilson, D. L. Black storm comin' — Fic

THE WEST (UNITED STATES) -- DESCRIPTION AND TRAVEL

McNeese, T. The Donner Party — 979.4

THE WEST (UNITED STATES) -- EXPLORATION

Bertozzi, N. Lewis & Clark — 741.5

Bodden, V. Through the American West — 917.804

THE WEST (UNITED STATES) -- HISTORY

Ehrlich, A. Wounded Knee — 970.004

THE WEST (UNITED STATES) -- HISTORY -- 19TH CENTURY

Brown, D. Bury my heart at Wounded Knee — 978

Miller, B. M. Women of the frontier — 978

Stefoff, R. The Wild West — 978

THE WEST (UNITED STATES) -- SOCIAL LIFE AND CUSTOMS -- 19TH CENTURY

Tunis, E. Frontier living — 973

THEATER

Blackwood, G. L. The Shakespeare stealer — Fic

Boecker, V. An assassin's guide to love and treason — Fic

Booth, M. Saving Hamlet — Fic

Dee, B. Star-crossed — Fic

Federle, T. Five six seven Nate! — Fic

Fleischman, P. Zap — 812

Henderson, L. The magic in changing your stars — Fic

Johnson, M. Suite Scarlett — Fic

Jones, T. L. Silhouetted by the blue — Fic

Kenney, K. L. Cool costumes — 792.02

Perl, E. S. The capybara conspiracy — Fic

Polonsky, A. Gracefully Grayson — Fic

Schumacher, T. How does the show go on? — 792.02

Selznick, B. The Marvels — Fic

Sloan, H. G. Short — Fic

Telgemeier, R. Drama — 741.5

Tolan, S. S. Surviving the Applewhites — Fic

THEATER -- HISTORY

Krueger, S. H. The tempest — 822.3

Sobran, J. A midsummer night's dream — 822.3

THEATER -- HISTORY 16TH CENTURY

Aliki. William Shakespeare & the Globe — 792

Currie, S. An actor on the Elizabethan stage — 792

THEATER -- PRODUCTION AND DIRECTION

Bezdecheck, B. Directing — 792.602

Domenico, G. A day at the New Amsterdam Theatre — 792.09

Schumacher, T. How does the show go on? — 792.02

Underwood, D. Staging a play — 792.02

THEATERS

Aliki. William Shakespeare & the Globe — 792

Domenico, G. A day at the New Amsterdam Theatre — 792.09

Mann, E. The Roman Colosseum — 937

THEATERS -- RECONSTRUCTION

Aliki. William Shakespeare & the Globe — 792

Theatre for young audiences. Jennings, C. A. — 812.008

Their skeletons speak. Walker, S. M. — 970.01

Theodore Boone kid lawyer. Grisham, J. — Fic

Theodore Roosevelt. Cooper, M. L. — B

Theodore Roosevelt. Fitzpatrick, B. — B

Theoharis, Jeanne

The rebellious life of Mrs. Rosa Parks — B

There is no long distance now. Nye, N. S. — Fic

There will come a darkness. Pool, K. R. — Fic

There's something about Sweetie. Menon, S. — Fic

THERESIENSTADT (CONCENTRATION CAMP)

Janeczko, P. B. Requiem — 811

Levine, K. Hana's suitcase on stage — 940.53

Polak, M. What world is left — Fic

Rubin, S. G. The cat with the yellow star — 940.53

Thomson, R. Terezin — 940.53

They broke the law you be the judge. Jacobs, T. A. — 345.73

They call me a hero. Hernandez, D. — B

They called themselves the K.K.K.. Bartoletti, S. C. — 322.4

They changed the world. Helfand, L. — 621.3

They had a dream. Archer, J. — 323

They wore what?! Platt, R. — 391.009

Thick as thieves. Turner, M. W. — Fic

The **thief**. Turner, M. W. — Fic

The **thief** knot. Milford, K. — Fic

The **Thief** Lord. Funke, C. — Fic

Thieret, John W.

National Audubon Society field guide to North American wildflowers — 582.13

Thiessen, Mark

Extreme wildfire — 363.37

THIEVES

teens — 646.7

TIME MEASUREMENTS

Formichelli, L. Timekeeping — 529

The **time** of green magic. McKay, H. — Fic

A **time** to dance. Venkatraman, P. — Fic

TIME TRAVEL

Bradbury, R. The Halloween tree — Fic

Chabon, M. Summerland — Fic

Colfer, E. The reluctant assassin — Fic

Emerson, K. Last day on Mars — Fic

Fisher, C. The obsidian mirror — Fic

Gleason, C. The clockwork scarab — Fic

Gutman, D. Roberto & me — Fic

Haddix, M. P. Found — Fic

Haddix, M. P. Remarkables — Fic

Hautman, P. The Klaatu terminus — Fic

Hautman, P. The obsidian blade — Fic

Hunter, N. Is time travel possible? — 530.11

L'Engle, M. A swiftly tilting planet — Fic

L'Engle, M. A wrinkle in time — Fic

MacCullough, C. Once a witch — Fic

MacHale, D. J. The never war — Fic

Milford, K. Bluecrowne — Fic

Murdock, C. G. Da Vinci's cat — Fic

Paulsen, G. The Transall saga — Fic

Rex, A. Smek for president! — Fic

Riggs, R. Tales of the Peculiar — Fic

Wood, M. B. The science of science fiction — 500

TIME TRAVEL (PAST)

Booth, M. Saving Hamlet — Fic

Bosch, P. This isn't what it looks like — Fic

Card, O. S. Pathfinder — Fic

Chanani, N. Jukebox — Fic

Cooper, S. King of shadows — Fic

Gier, K. Emerald green — Fic

Gier, K. Sapphire blue — Fic

Gutman, D. Abner & me — Fic

Gutman, D. Babe and me — Fic

Gutman, D. Honus and me — Fic

Gutman, D. Jackie and me — Fic

Gutman, D. Jim & me — Fic

Gutman, D. Mickey & me — Fic

Gutman, D. Ray & me — Fic

Gutman, D. Satch & me — Fic

Gutman, D. Shoeless Joe & me — Fic

Haddix, M. P. Caught — Fic

Haddix, M. P. Risked — Fic

Haddix, M. P. Sabotaged — Fic

Haddix, M. P. Sent — Fic

Henderson, L. The magic in changing your stars — Fic

Riggs, R. A map of days — Fic

Riggs, R. Miss Peregrine's home for peculiar children — Fic

Stephens, J. The emerald atlas — Fic

Stephens, J. The fire chronicle — Fic

Vaughn, C. Steel — Fic

Welford, R. Time traveling with a hamster — Fic

Whitman, E. Wildwing — Fic

Woodruff, E. George Washington's spy — Fic

Time traveling with a hamster. Welford, R. — Fic

Time you let me in. Nye, N. S. — 811

Time's memory. Lester, J. — Fic

Timekeeping. Formichelli, L. — 529

Timothy of the cay. Taylor, T. — Fic

Tin heart. Plozza, S. — Fic

Tingle, Tim

Danny Blackgoat Navajo prisoner — Fic

How I became a ghost — Fic

Spirits dark and light — 398.2

When a ghost talks listen — Fic

Tinker vs. Des Moines. Lusted, M. A. — 342.7308

TINKER, JOHN FREDERICK

Lusted, M. A. Tinker vs. Des Moines — 342.7308

TINY TIM (FICTITIOUS CHARACTER)

Dickens, C. A Christmas carol [Lynch ill.] — Fic

The **Titan's** curse. Riordan, R. — Fic

TITANIC (STEAMSHIP)

Adams, S. Titanic — 910.91

Hopkinson, D. Titanic — 910.91

Korman, G. Collision course — Fic

Marschall, K. Inside the Titanic — 910

McPherson, S. S. Iceberg right ahead! — 910.91

Wolf, A. The watch that ends the night — Fic

Titanic. Adams, S. — 910.91

Titanic. Hopkinson, D. — 910.91

TITANS (MYTHOLOGY)

Riordan, R. The last Olympian — Fic

Tito Puente. McNeese, T. — B

To be a slave. Lester, J. — 306.3

To be honest. Martin, M. A. — Fic

To catch a cheat. Johnson, V. — Fic

To dare mighty things. Rappaport, D. — B

To every thing there is a season. Dillon, L. — 223

To hold the bridge. Nix, G. — Fic

To kill a mockingbird. Lee, H. — Fic

To stay alive. Brown, S. — Fic

To the moon. Bodden, V. — 629.45

To the mountaintop! Hunter-Gault, C. — B

To the South Pole. Bodden, V. — B

A **to** Z of American Indian women. Sonneborn, L. — 920.72089

TOADS

Pringle, L. Frogs! — 597.8

TOBACCO

Chandler, M. Understanding tobacco — 613.85

Espejo, R. Tobacco and smoking — 362.29

Miller, H. Smoking — 613.85

Tobacco and smoking. Espejo, R. — 362.29

Tobacco information for teens. Omnigraphics, I. — 613.850835

TOBACCO USE -- HEALTH ASPECTS

Omnigraphics, I. Tobacco information for teens — 613.850835

Tobin, James, 1956-

Master of his fate — B

Toby alone. Fombelle, T. d. — Fic

Toby and the secrets of the tree. Fombelle, T. d. — Fic

Today the world is watching you the Little Rock Nine and

TUBERCULOSIS -- PREVENTION

Aronin, M. Tuberculosis — 616.9

Tuberculosis. Aronin, M. — 616.9

TUBMAN, HARRIET, 1820?-1913

Adler, D. A. Harriet Tubman and the Underground Railroad — B

Allen, T. B. Harriet Tubman secret agent — B

Hale, N. The underground abductor — B

Pinkney, A. D. Let it shine — 920

Tucholke, April Genevieve

The Boneless Mercies — Fic

Seven endless forests — Fic

Tuck everlasting. Babbitt, N. — Fic

Tucker, Catlin R.

Blended learning in action — 371.3

Power up blended learning — 371.3

Tucker, Laura, 1973-

All the Greys on Greene Street — Fic

TUDOR PERIOD (1485-1603)

Blackwood, G. L. The Shakespeare stealer — Fic

Boecker, V. An assassin's guide to love and treason — Fic

Meconis, D. Queen of the sea — 741.5

Twain, M. The prince and the pauper — Fic

Tuesdays at the castle. George, J. D. — Fic

Tukey, Paul Boardway

Tag toss & run — 790.1922

TULSA, OKLAHOMA -- RACE RELATIONS

Madigan, T. The burning — 976.6

Tuminelly, Nancy, 1952-

Cool meat-free recipes — 641.5

TUMORS

Patent, D. H. Saving the Tasmanian devil — 599.2

TUNDRA ECOLOGY

Bow, J. Tundras inside out — 577.5

TUNDRAS

Bow, J. Tundras inside out — 577.5

Tundras inside out. Bow, J. — 577.5

Tune it out. Sumner, J. — Fic

Tunis, Edwin, 1897-1973

Frontier living — 973

TUNISIA

Brown, R. V. Tunisia — 961.1

Tunisia. Brown, R. V. — 961.1

TUNNELING

Graham, I. Tremendous tunnels — 624.1

Tunnell, Michael O.

Candy bomber — B

TUNNELS

Gordon, R. Tunnels — Fic

Graham, I. Tremendous tunnels — 624.1

Tunnels. Gordon, R. — Fic

Tupac Shakur. Harris, A. R. — B

Turck, Mary

Freedom song — 323.0973

TURKEY

Cliff, T. Delilah Dirk and the Turkish Lieutenant — 741.5

Laroche, A. We visit Turkey — 956.1

Marillier, J. Cybele's secret — Fic

Walrath, D. Like water on stone — Fic

TURKEY -- HISTORY

Laroche, A. We visit Turkey — 956.1

TURKEYS

Hutto, J. When I was a turkey — 598.6

Scieszka, J. Funny business — Fic

Turnage, Sheila

The ghosts of Tupelo Landing — Fic

The odds of getting even — Fic

Three times lucky — Fic

Turnbull, Ann

Greek myths — 398.2

Turnbull, Stephanie

Cards and gifts — 745.594

Cool stuff to make with paper — 745.54

Cool stuff to photograph — 770

Diaries and keepsakes — 745.593

Turnbull, Stephen R.

The most daring raid of the samurai — 952

Turner, Alan, 1947-

National Geographic prehistoric mammals — 569

Turner, Glennette Tilley

Fort Mose — 975.9

Turner, Kate, 1967-

Australia — 994

Turner, Kristen Hawley

Argument in the real world — 808

Turner, Megan Whalen

A conspiracy of kings — Fic

The king of Attolia — Fic

The queen of Attolia — Fic

Return of the thief — Fic

Thick as thieves — Fic

The thief — Fic

Turner, Pamela S.

Crow smarts — 598.8

The dolphins of Shark Bay — 599.53

The frog scientist — 597.8

A life in the wild — B

Life on Earth---and beyond — 571.0919

Project seahorse — 597

Samurai rising — B

Turning 15 on the road to freedom. Lowery, L. B. — 323.1196

Turning point. Chase, P. J. — Fic

Turtle boy. Wolkenstein, M. E. — Fic

Turtle Island. Yellowhorn, E. — 970.1

TURTLES

Pinkwater, D. M. The Neddiad — Fic

Turtschaninoff, Maria, 1977-

Maresi — Fic

TUSCARORA INDIANS

Gansworth, E. L. Give me some truth — Fic

Gansworth, E. L. If I ever get out of here — Fic

TUSCARORA NATION RESERVATION (NY)

Gansworth, E. L. Give me some truth — Fic

Gansworth, E. L. If I ever get out of here — Fic

Strange, L. The secret of Nightingale Wood	Fic
Tanner, L. Ice breaker	Fic
Tolstikova, D. A year without Mom	741.5
Vernon, U. Castle Hangnail	Fic
Weissman, E. B. The length of a string	Fic
White, J. A. A path begins	Fic
Wiles, D. Revolution	Fic
Winthrop, E. Counting on Grace	Fic
Wolk, L. Beyond the bright sea	Fic
Young, K. R. Hundred percent	Fic

TWELVE-YEAR-OLDS

Haddix, M. P. Under their skin	Fic
Jones, K. Sand dollar summer	Fic
Larson, H. Compass south	741.5

Twerp. Goldblatt, M.	Fic
Twice upon a Marigold. Ferris, J.	Fic
Twilight. Meyer, S.	Fic
Twilight hauntings. Sage, A.	Fic

TWIN BROTHERS

Alexander, K. The crossover	Fic
Avery, T. Not as we know it	Fic
Barnhill, K. R. The witch's boy	Fic
Colfer, E. The Fowl twins	Fic
Erdrich, L. Makoons	Fic
Grant, M. Hunger	Fic
Heath, J. Remote control	Fic
Horowitz, A. Nightrise	Fic
Mack, W. C. Athlete vs. mathlete	Fic
Markham, L. The far away brothers	979.4
Menon, S. From Twinkle with love	Fic
Mills, G. Gold	Fic
Oppel, K. This dark endeavor	Fic
Ormsbee, K. The house in Poplar Wood	Fic
Ritter, W. Changeling	Fic
Ritter, W. Deepest darkest	Fic
Silvera, A. Infinity son	Fic

TWIN BROTHERS AND SISTERS

Armstrong, K. A royal guide to monster slaying	Fic
Gutman, D. From Texas with love	Fic
Gutman, D. License to thrill	Fic
Gutman, D. Mission unstoppable	Fic
Gutman, D. Never say genius	Fic
Haddix, M. P. In over their heads	Fic
Haddix, M. P. Under their skin	Fic
Higgins, J. Death run	Fic
Higgins, J. First strike	Fic
Higgins, J. Sharp shot	Fic
Higgins, J. Sure fire	Fic
Kagawa, J. Talon	Fic
London, A. Black wings beating	Fic
London, A. Red skies falling	Fic
Margolis, L. Girl's best friend	Fic
Rex, A. Cold cereal	Fic
Rodkey, G. The Tapper twins go to war (with each other)	Fic
Ruby, L. The clockwork ghost	Fic
Ruby, L. The shadow cipher	Fic

Ruiz Zafon, C. The Midnight Palace	Fic
Saunders, K. The Whizz Pop Chocolate Shop	Fic
Scott, M. The alchemyst	Fic
Walrath, D. Like water on stone	Fic
Watson, J. Loot	Fic
Young, M. Blood red road	Fic

TWIN SISTERS

Billingsley, F. Chime	Fic
Bullen, A. Wish	Fic
Crossan, S. One	Fic
Lauren, R. Prisoner of ice and snow	Fic
Rivers, K. Finding Ruby Starling	Fic
Ryon, L. Into the tall tall grass	Fic
Zink, M. Prophecy of the sisters	Fic

TWIN SISTERS -- DEATH

Farrant, N. After Iris	Fic

TWINS

Duncan, L. Stranger with my face	Fic
Foley, L. K. Remarkable	Fic
Funaro, G. The alchemist's shadow	Fic
Larson, H. Compass south	741.5
London, A. Black wings beating	Fic
Paterson, K. Jacob have I loved	Fic
Smith, N. The deep & dark blue	741.5
Westerfeld, S. Shatter city	Fic
Yolen, J. Mapping the bones	Fic

Twist, Clint

Marco Polo	B

Two boys kissing. Levithan, D.	Fic
Two crafty criminals! Pullman, P.	Fic
Two dark reigns. Blake, K.	Fic
Two Naomis. Rhuday-Perkovich, O.	Fic
Two Summers. Friedman, A.	Fic
Two truths and a lie. Paquette, A.	508

TYPHOID FEVER

Chibbaro, J. Deadly	Fic
Jarrow, G. Fatal fever	614.5

TYPHOID MARY, 1869-1938

Bartoletti, S. C. Terrible Typhoid Mary	B
Chibbaro, J. Deadly	Fic
Jarrow, G. Fatal fever	614.5

TYSON, NEIL DEGRASSE

Saucier, C. A. P. Explore the cosmos like Neil DeGrasse Tyson	520.92

U

U S STATES -- POLITICS AND GOVERNMENT 19TH CENTURY

Osborne, L. B. Traveling the freedom road	973.7
U-X-L encyclopedia of weather and natural disasters. Hackney Blackwell, A.	551.503

U.S. CUSTOMS AND BORDER PROTECTION

Weir, W. Border patrol	363.28

U.S. IMMIGRATION AND CUSTOMS ENFORCEMENT

Lupica, M. Strike zone	Fic
U.S. involvement in Vietnam. Gitlin, M.	959.704

UNDERGROUND CITIES
Miller, K. Inside the shadow city   Fic

UNDERGROUND CONSTRUCTION
Graham, I. Tremendous tunnels   624.1
Macaulay, D. Underground   624

UNDERGROUND NEWSPAPERS
Preus, M. Shadow on the mountain   Fic

UNDERGROUND RAILROAD
Hamilton, V. The house of Dies Drear   Fic
Raatma, L. The Underground Railroad   973.7
Shange, N. Freedom's a-calling me   811
Williams, C. The Underground Railroad   973.7
Woodruff, E. Dear Austin   Fic
The **Underground** Railroad. Raatma, L.   973.7
The **Underground** Railroad. Williams, C.   973.7

UNDERGROUND UTILITY LINES
Macaulay, D. Underground   624
The **underneath**. Appelt, K.   Fic

UNDERSEA COLONIES
Falls, K. Dark life   Fic
Falls, K. Rip tide   Fic
Holyoke, P. The Neptune Project   Fic
Understanding addiction. Hudak, H. C.   616.85
Understanding alcohol. Gilles, R.   613.81
Understanding Hinduism. Nardo, D.   294.5
Understanding Islam. Radley, G.   297
Understanding obesity. Chandler, M.   618.92
Understanding screen addiction. Gilles, R.   616.85
Understanding suicide. Chandler, M.   362.28
Understanding the Declaration of Independence. Driver, S. S.   973.3
Understanding Thoreau's Civil disobedience. Kirk, A.   818
Understanding tobacco. Chandler, M.   613.85

UNDERTAKERS
Hooper, M. Fallen Grace   Fic

UNDERWATER ARCHAEOLOGY
Cottman, M. H. Shackles from the deep   382.4409
McGee, M. National Geographic investigates ancient Greece   938

UNDERWATER CITIES
MacHale, D. J. The lost city of Faar   Fic

UNDERWATER EXPLORATION
Earle, S. A. Extreme ocean   551.46
Mallory, K. At home beneath the sea   551.46
Verne, J. 20000 leagues under the sea   Fic

UNDERWATER PHOTOGRAPHY
Cerullo, M. M. Journey to shark island   597.309164
Cerullo, M. M. Searching for Great White Sharks   597.3
Cerullo, M. M. Seeking giant sharks   597.3

Underwood, Deborah
Staging a play   792.02

UNDOCUMENTED IMMIGRANTS
Alexander, W. Ambassador   Fic
Alexander, W. Nomad   Fic
Arce, J. Someone like me   305.48
Bausum, A. Denied detained deported   325.73
Budhos, M. T. Ask me no questions   Fic
Cervantes, A. Gaby lost and found   Fic
Cisneros, E. Efren divided   Fic
Gallagher, J. Thinking critically   364.1
Johnston, T. Beast rider   Fic
Markham, L. The far away brothers   979.4
Sitomer, A. L. The secret story of Sonia Rodriguez   Fic
Villasante, A. The grief keeper   Fic
Yoon, N. The sun is also a star   Fic

UNDOCUMENTED WORKERS
Hobbs, W. Crossing the wire   Fic
Jimenez, F. The circuit   Fic
Unearthly. Hand, C.   Fic
The **unexpected** life of Oliver Cromwell Pitts. Avi.   Fic
The **unfinished** angel. Creech, S.   Fic
Ungifted. Korman, G.   Fic

UNHAPPINESS
Johnson, A. Sweet hereafter   Fic
The **unholy** crusade. Lace, W. W.   949.5
Unicorn power! Tamaki, M.   Fic

UNICORNS
Gillis, P. B. The last unicorn   741.5
L'Engle, M. A swiftly tilting planet   Fic
Laskow, S. The very short entirely true history of unicorns   398.24
O'Neill, K. Princess princess ever after   741.5
Tamaki, M. Unicorn power!   Fic

UNIDENTIFIED FLYING OBJECTS -- SIGHTINGS AND ENCOUNTERS
Karst, K. Alien abductions   001.942

UNINHABITED COMBAT AERIAL VEHICLES
Mooney, C. Pilotless planes   623.74
An **uninterrupted** view of the sky. Crowder, M.   Fic

UNION PACIFIC RAILROAD -- HISTORY -- 19TH CENTURY
Sandler, M. W. Iron rails iron men and the race to link the nation   385.0979

UNION SOLDIERS
Beller, S. P. Billy Yank & Johnny Reb   973.7
Keith, H. Rifles for Watie   Fic
Shepard, R. Now or never!   973.7
Wiechman, K. C. Like a river   Fic

UNITED ARAB EMIRATES
King, D. C. United Arab Emirates   953.57
United Arab Emirates. King, D. C.   953.57

UNITED FARM WORKERS UNION -- HISTORY
Brimner, L. D. Strike!   331.8

UNITED NATIONS. GENERAL ASSEMBLY. UNIVERSAL DECLARATION OF HUMAN RIGHTS
Amnesty International. Free?   Fic

UNITED SERVICE ORGANIZATIONS (U.S.)
Bolden, T. Take-off!   784.4

UNITED STATES
Alifirenka, C. I will always write back   305.235
Anderson, L. H. Ashes   Fic
Anderson, L. H. Chains   Fic
Avi. The end of the world and beyond   Fic
Avi. The fighting ground   Fic

UNITED STATES -- POLITICS AND GOVERNMENT -- 1933-1945

Bolden, T. FDR's Alphabet soup — 973.917

UNITED STATES -- POLITICS AND GOVERNMENT -- 1969-1974

Pearson, P. O. Conspiracy — 973.924

Sheinkin, S. Most dangerous — 959.704

UNITED STATES -- POLITICS AND GOVERNMENT -- 2001-2009

Mason, P. The Iraq War — 956.7044

Sutherland, J. The ten-year century — 973.93

UNITED STATES -- POLITICS AND GOVERNMENT -- 2009-2017

Dillon, M. Yes she can — 973.932

UNITED STATES -- POLITICS AND GOVERNMENT -- 20TH CENTURY

Burgan, M. TV shapes presidential politics in the Kennedy-Nixon debates — 324.973

UNITED STATES -- RACE RELATIONS

Bartoletti, S. C. They called themselves the K.K.K. — 322.4

Blohm, C. E. The civil rights movement — 323.1196

Brimner, L. D. Finding a way home — 346.7301

Currie, S. African American folklore — 398.08996

Edwards, J. The history of the American Indians and the reservation — 323.1197

Gallagher, J. Policing and race — 363.2

Goldstone, L. Separate no more — 323.1196

Jewell, T. This book is anti-racist — 305.800973

Joseph, F. The Black friend — 305.8

King, M. L. The words of Martin Luther King Jr. — 323.4

Osborne, L. B. Miles to go for freedom — 305.896

Philip, N. The great circle — 973.04

Pinkney, A. D. Let it shine — 920

Stewart, M. The Indian Removal Act — 973.04

Venable, R. The civil rights movement — 323.1196

UNITED STATES -- RACE RELATIONS -- HISTORY

Davis, K. C. In the shadow of Liberty — 920.0092

Katz, W. L. Black Indians — 970

Kendi, I. X. Stamped — 305.800973

Marcovitz, H. Black in America — 305.896

UNITED STATES -- RACE RELATIONS -- HISTORY -- 20TH CENTURY

Madigan, T. The burning — 976.6

Mullenbach, C. Double victory — 940.5308

Watson, B. Freedom Summer for young people — 323.1196

UNITED STATES -- RELIGION

Bushman, C. L. Mormons in America — 289.3

Haugen, D. M. Religion in America — 200.973

UNITED STATES -- RELIGION -- TO 1800

Capaccio, G. Religion in colonial America — 200.973

UNITED STATES -- RELIGIOUS LIFE AND CUSTOMS

Mann, G. S. Buddhists Hindus and Sikhs in America — 294

UNITED STATES -- SOCIAL CONDITIONS

Buckley, S. Kids make history — 920

Colman, P. Rosie the riveter — 331.4

UNITED STATES -- SOCIAL CONDITIONS -- 20TH CENTURY

Bausum, A. Unraveling freedom — 940.3

UNITED STATES -- SOCIAL CONDITIONS -- 21ST CENTURY

Corrigan, J. The 2000s decade in photos — 973.93

UNITED STATES -- SOCIAL CONDITIONS -- COLONIAL PERIOD, 1600-1775

Capaccio, G. The countryside in colonial America — 973.2

UNITED STATES -- SOCIAL LIFE AND CUSTOMS

Armstrong, J. The American story — 973

Buckley, S. Kids make history — 920

Chevat, R. A queer history of the United States for young people — 306.76

UNITED STATES -- SOCIAL LIFE AND CUSTOMS -- 20TH CENTURY

Nathan, A. Yankee doodle gals — 940.54

Nelson, M. Sweethearts of rhythm — 781.65

Oppenheim, J. Dear Miss Breed — 940.53

UNITED STATES -- SOCIAL LIFE AND CUSTOMS -- 21ST CENTURY

Atkin, S. B. Gunstories — 363.33

Ellis, D. Off to war — 303.6

UNITED STATES -- SOCIAL LIFE AND CUSTOMS -- COLONIAL PERIOD, 1600-1775

Capaccio, G. The countryside in colonial America — 973.2

UNITED STATES -- SOCIAL LIFE AND CUSTOMS -- TO 1775

Clancy Steer, D. Colonial America — 391

Nardo, D. Daily life in colonial America — 973.2

UNITED STATES -- TERRITORIAL EXPANSION

Sheinkin, S. Which way to the wild west? — 978

Stewart, M. The Indian Removal Act — 973.04

UNITED STATES ARMED FORCES -- AFRICAN AMERICANS

Farrell, M. C. Standing up against hate — 940.54

UNITED STATES ARMED FORCES -- MILITARY LIFE

Goldsmith, C. Women in the military — 355.009

UNITED STATES ARMED FORCES -- WOMEN

Farrell, M. C. Standing up against hate — 940.54

Goldsmith, C. Women in the military — 355.009

UNITED STATES ARMY -- HISTORY -- CIVIL WAR, 1861-1865

Keith, H. Rifles for Watie — Fic

UNITED STATES CIVIL WAR, 1861-1865

Beller, S. P. Billy Yank & Johnny Reb — 973.7

Benoit, P. The surrender at Appomattox — 973.7

Fleischman, P. Bull Run — Fic

Gregory, J. Gettysburg — 973.7

Hernandez, R. E. The Civil War 1840s-1890s — 973.7

Lewis, J. P. The brothers' war — 811

O'Connor, J. What was the Battle of Gettysburg? — 973.7

Older, D. J. Thunder run — Fic

Otfinoski, S. The Civil War — 973.7

Rees, B. The Civil War — 973.7

Rottman, G. L. The most daring raid of the Civil War — 973.7

Shepard, R. Now or never! — 973.7

Silverman, J. Songs and stories of the Civil War — 782.42

Esherick, J. The FDA & psychiatric drugs	615.7
Jarrow, G. The poison eaters	353.9

UNITED STATES. MARINE CORPS

Mazer, H. Heroes don't run	Fic

UNITED STATES. MARINE CORPS -- INDIAN TROOPS

Bruchac, J. Code Talker	Fic

UNITED STATES. MARSHALS SERVICE

Newton, M. U.S. marshals	363.28

UNITED STATES. NATIONAL AERONAUTICS AND SPACE ADMINISTRATION

Maurer, R. Destination moon	629.45
Ottaviani, J. T-minus	629.4
Rhuday-Perkovich, O. Above and beyond	629.40973
Rocco, J. How we got to the moon	629.45
Stamper, P. The gravity of us	Fic
Thimmesh, C. Team moon	629.45

UNITED STATES. NATIONAL AERONAUTICS AND SPACE ADMINISTRATION -- HISTORY

Rhuday-Perkovich, O. Above and beyond	629.40973

UNITED STATES. NATIONAL AERONAUTICS AND SPACE ADMINISTRATION -- OFFICIALS AND EMPLOYEES

Edwards, S. B. Hidden human computers	510.92

UNITED STATES. NATIONAL INSTITUTE OF MENTAL HEALTH

O'Brien, R. C. Mrs. Frisby and the rats of NIMH	Fic

UNITED STATES. NAVY -- AFRICAN AMERICANS -- HISTORY -- 20TH CENTURY

Sheinkin, S. The Port Chicago 50	940.54

UNITED STATES. SECRET SERVICE

Ryan, B. The Secret Service	363.28

UNITED STATES. SUPREME COURT

Blumenthal, K. Jane against the world	342.7308
Brimner, L. D. Finding a way home	346.7301
Cates, D. Plessy v. Ferguson segregation and the separate but equal policy	342.7308
Goldstone, L. Unpunished murder	976.3
Jacobs, T. A. Every vote matters	342.7308
Panchyk, R. Our Supreme Court	347.73

UNITED STATES. SUPREME COURT -- JUSTICES

Ortiz, V. Dissenter on the bench	347.73

UNIVERSITIES AND COLLEGES

Charbonneau, J. Independent study	Fic
Charbonneau, J. The Testing	Fic
Melchior-Durand, S. The golden compass	741.5
Wrede, P. C. The thirteenth child	Fic

UNIVERSITY OF MISSISSIPPI -- HISTORY

Vaught, S. Things too huge to fix by saying sorry	Fic

UNIVERSITY OF OXFORD

Pullman, P. The book of dust: la belle sauvage	Fic
Pullman, P. The book of dust: the secret commonwealth	Fic

UNIVERSITY OF WASHINGTON -- ROWING -- HISTORY

Brown, D. The boys in the boat	797.12
Unlikely pairs. Raczka, B.	750
Unlucky charms. Rex, A.	Fic

The **unnameables**. Booraem, E.	Fic
Unnatural creatures. Gaiman, N.	Fic
The **unofficial** LEGO builder's guide. Bedford, A.	790.133
Unofficial Minecraft lab for kids. Miller, J.	793.93
Unplugged. Freitas, D.	Fic
Unpunished murder. Goldstone, L.	976.3
Unraveling freedom. Bausum, A.	940.3
The **unready** queen. Ritter, W.	Fic

UNREQUITED LOVE

Anderson, J. L. Tiger Lily	Fic
The **unsinkable** Walker Bean. Renier, A.	741.5
The **unsung** hero of Birdsong USA. Woods, B.	Fic

Unsworth, Tania

The one safe place	Fic
Untamed. Silvey, A.	599.8
Up before daybreak. Hopkinson, D.	331.7
Up from slavery. Washington, B. T.	B
Upon the head of the goat. Siegal, A.	B

UPPER CLASS

Gelletly, L. Oligarchy	321
Hinds, K. The palace	909

UPPER EAST SIDE, NEW YORK CITY

Beil, M. D. The ring of Rocamadour	Fic
Beil, M. D. The vanishing violin	Fic
Uprising. Haddix, M. P.	Fic
Uprooted. Marrin, A.	940.53
The **upstairs** room. Reiss, J.	Fic

UPWARD MOBILITY

Bolden, T. Inventing Victoria	Fic
Urban 'street' art. Wood, A.	709.173

URBAN ANIMALS

Downer, A. Wild animal neighbors	591.75
Read, N. City critters	591.75

URBAN ANTHROPOLOGY

Millard, A. A street through time	936

URBAN ARCHAEOLOGY

Millard, A. A street through time	936

URBAN ECOLOGY

Downer, A. Wild animal neighbors	591.75

URBAN EDUCATION

Emdin, C. For white folks who teach in the hood-- and the rest of y'all too	370.9173

URBAN FANTASY

Black, H. Black heart	Fic
Black, H. The Good Neighbors	741.5
Black, H. Red glove	Fic
Black, H. Welcome to Bordertown	Fic
Black, H. The white cat	Fic
Brewer, Z. Eighth grade bites	Fic
Card, O. S. The lost gate	Fic
Catmull, K. The radiant road	Fic
Chupeco, R. Wicked as you wish	Fic
Damico, G. Croak	Fic
Gier, K. Emerald green	Fic
Gier, K. Sapphire blue	Fic
Hopkinson, N. The Chaos	Fic
Kagawa, J. The eternity cure	Fic

V

V is for villain. Moore, P. — Fic

The **vacation**. Horvath, P. — Fic

VACATION HOMES

Han, J. It's not summer without you — Fic

O'Reilly, J. H. The notations of Cooper Cameron — Fic

VACATIONS

Arden, K. Dead voices — Fic

Birdsall, J. The Penderwicks at Point Mouette — Fic

Horvath, P. The vacation — Fic

VACCINATION

Brown, D. A shot in the arm! — 615.3

Hutchison, P. The debate about vaccines — 615.3

Nardo, D. How vaccines changed the world — 615.3

VACCINATION -- HISTORY

Haelle, T. Vaccination investigation — 615.3

Vaccination investigation. Haelle, T. — 615.3

VACCINES

Brown, D. A shot in the arm! — 615.3

Haelle, T. Vaccination investigation — 615.3

Hutchison, P. The debate about vaccines — 615.3

Nardo, D. How vaccines changed the world — 615.3

Wiggins, B. Stung — Fic

VAIL, COLORADO

Gibbs, S. Spy ski school — Fic

Vail, Rachel

Well that was awkward — Fic

Valente, Catherynne M., 1979-

The boy who lost Fairyland — Fic

The girl who circumnavigated Fairyland in a ship of her own making — Fic

The girl who fell beneath Fairyland and led the revels there — Fic

The girl who soared over Fairyland and cut the moon in two — Fic

The Glass Town game — Fic

VALENTINE'S DAY

Kinney, J. The third wheel — Fic

Valentino. Reis, R. A. — B

VALENTINO, 1932-

Reis, R. A. Valentino — B

VALHALLA

Armstrong, K. Odin's ravens — Fic

VALLEY FORGE, PENNSYLVANIA

Anderson, L. H. Forge — Fic

VALLEY OF THE KINGS, EGYPT -- ANTIQUITIES

Berger, M. Mummies of the pharaohs — 932

Lace, W. W. King Tut's curse — 932

The **valley** of the Wolves. Gallego Garcia, L. — Fic

VALLEYS

Smith, J. Rose — 741.5

VALMIKI

Arni, S. Sita's Ramayana — 741.5

VALMIKI. RAMAYANA

Ganeri, A. The Ramayana and Hinduism — 294.5

VAMPIRE FILMS -- HISTORY AND CRITICISM

Woog, A. Vampires in the movies — 791.43

Vampire history and lore. Kallen, S. A. — 398

VAMPIRE SLAYERS

Gleason, C. The clockwork scarab — Fic

Kenyon, S. Infinity — Fic

VAMPIRES

Brewer, Z. Eighth grade bites — Fic

Etingoff, K. Howling at the moon — 398

Etingoff, K. The science of the beast — 398

Fukuda, A. X. The prey — Fic

Gee, J. Encyclopedia horrifica — 001.9

Indovino, S. C. Transsylvania and beyond — 398

Kagawa, J. The eternity cure — Fic

Kagawa, J. The forever song — Fic

Kagawa, J. The immortal rules — Fic

Kallen, S. A. Vampire history and lore — 398

Kenyon, S. Infinity — Fic

Link, K. Monstrous affections — Fic

Martin, N. Fighting the fangs — 398

Meyer, S. Twilight — Fic

Newquist, H. P. The book of blood — 612.1

Noyes, D. Gothic! — Fic

O'Meara, S. J. Are you afraid yet? — 001.944

Robson, D. Encounters with vampires — 398

Rowell, R. Wayward son — Fic

Sanna, E. Pop monsters — 398

Stewart, G. B. Vampires — 001.9

Stewart, S. The psychology of our dark side — 398

Vande Velde, V. All Hallows' Eve — Fic

White, K. Supernaturally — Fic

Woog, A. Vampires in the movies — 791.43

VAMPIRES -- HISTORY

Kallen, S. A. Vampire history and lore — 398

Robson, D. Encounters with vampires — 398

Vampires. Stewart, G. B. — 001.9

Vampires in the movies. Woog, A. — 791.43

Van Allsburg, Chris

The chronicles of Harris Burdick — Fic

Van De Ruit, John

Spud — Fic

Van Draanen, Wendelin

The running dream — Fic

Sammy Keyes and the hotel thief — Fic

Van Gogh. Crispino, E. — 759.9492

Van Natta, Don, 1964-

Wonder girl — B

Van Vleet, Carmella

Eliza Bing is (not) a big fat quitter — Fic

Vance, Alexander P. (Alexander Phillip), 1978-

The Heartbreak Messenger — Fic

Vancleave, Janice Pratt

Janice VanCleave's engineering for every kid — 620.0078

Step-by-step science experiments in biology — 570.78

Step-by-step science experiments in ecology — 577.078

VANCOUVER, BRITISH COLUMBIA

Leavitt, M. My book of life by Angel — Fic

Mac, C. 10 things I can see from here — Fic

Nielsen, S. No fixed address	Fic	ian	641.5
Nielsen, S. Word nerd	Fic	**VEGETARIAN FOODS**	
Oppel, K. Bloom	Fic	Hughes, M. S. Plants vs. meats	641.5
VANDALISM		**VEGETARIANISM**	
Kinney, J. Cabin fever	Fic	Hughes, M. S. Plants vs. meats	641.5
Korman, G. Linked	Fic	Rau, D. M. Going vegetarian	613.2
Onome, L. Like home	Fic	Traugh, S. M. Vegetarianism	641.5
Voigt, C. The book of secrets	Fic	Warren, R. M. The smart girl's guide to going vegetar-	
Vande Velde, Vivian		ian	641.5
All Hallows' Eve	Fic	Vegetarianism. Traugh, S. M.	641.5
Being dead	Fic	**VEGETARIANS**	
The book of Mordred	Fic	Rau, D. M. Going vegetarian	613.2
Cloaked in red	Fic	**VEHICLES**	
Frogged	Fic	Smith, M. Speed machines	629.2
Heir apparent	Fic	**Venable, Rose**	
Tales from the Brothers Grimm and the Sisters Weird	Fic	The civil rights movement	323.1196
Vander Hook, Sue, 1949-		**Vendittelli, Marie**	
Building the Panama Canal	972.87	The fashion book	741.6
Trail of Tears	975.004	**Venditti, Robert**	
Vanderpool, Clare		The lightning thief	741.5
Moon over Manifest	Fic	The **Vengekeep** prophecies. Farrey, B.	Fic
Vanhee, Jason		**VENICE, ITALY**	
Engines of the broken world	Fic	Armstrong, A. W. Looking for Marco Polo	Fic
Vanished! Ponti, J.	Fic	Funke, C. The Thief Lord	Fic
Vanishing act. Feinstein, J.	Fic	Hinds, G. The merchant of Venice	741.5
The **vanishing** stair. Johnson, M.	Fic	**Venkatraman, Padma**	
The **vanishing** violin. Beil, M. D.	Fic	The bridge home	Fic
Vanvoorst, Jennifer, 1972-		Climbing the stairs	Fic
The ancient Maya	972.81	A time to dance	Fic
The Byzantine Empire	949.5	**Ventrella, Kim**	
Variant. Wells, R. E.	Fic	The secret life of Sam	Fic
VARIATION (BIOLOGY)		**VENTRILOQUISTS**	
Ballard, C. Plant variation and classification	580.1	Alexander, L. Westmark	Fic
Varmer, Hjordis		**Venturess.** Cornwell, B.	Fic
Hans Christian Andersen	B	**Vera** Wang. Petrillo, L.	B
Varon, Sara		**Verdi** for kids. Bauer, H.	B
Bake sale	741.5	**VERDI, GIUSEPPE, 1813-1901**	
Vasco da Gama. Calvert, P.	B	Bauer, H. Verdi for kids	B
Vasquez, Jo Anne, 1943-		**Verdick, Elizabeth**	
STEM lesson essentials grades 3-8	372.35	The survival guide for kids with autism spectrum disorders	
Vaughan, Jenny, 1947-		(and their parents)	618.92
Who discovered DNA?	572.8	**VERMEER, JOHANNES, 1632-1675**	
Vaughn, Carrie		Balliett, B. Chasing Vermeer	Fic
Steel	Fic	**Vermond, Kira**	
Vaught, Susan, 1965-		Half-truths and brazen lies	177
Things too huge to fix by saying sorry	Fic	**VERMONT**	
Vawter, Vince		Alvarez, J. How Tia Lola came to (visit) stay	Fic
Copyboy	Fic	Alvarez, J. Return to sender	Fic
Paperboy	Fic	Appelt, K. Maybe a fox	Fic
VEDDER, AMY		Arden, K. Dead voices	Fic
Ebersole, R. Gorilla mountain	B	Hahn, M. D. All the lovely bad ones	Fic
VEGETABLES		Hesse, K. Witness	Fic
Llewellyn, C. Cooking with fruits and vegetables	641.3	Hilton, M. Full cicada moon	Fic
VEGETARIAN COOKING		Johnson, M. The hand on the wall	Fic
Locricchio, M. Teen cuisine new vegetarian	641.5	Johnson, M. Truly Devious	Fic
Tuminelly, N. Cool meat-free recipes	641.5	Johnson, M. The vanishing stair	Fic
Warren, R. M. The smart girl's guide to going vegetar-		LaFleur, S. M. Love Aubrey	Fic

Messner, K. The brilliant fall of Gianna Z   **Fic**
Messner, K. Chirp   **Fic**
Winthrop, E. Counting on Grace   **Fic**

VERNE, JULES, 1828-1905
Schoell, W. Remarkable journeys   **B**

Verne, Jules, 1828-1905
20000 leagues under the sea   **Fic**

Vernick, Shirley Reva
The blood lie   **Fic**

Vernon, Ursula
Castle Hangnail   **Fic**

VERONA, ITALY
Hinds, G. The most excellent and lamentable tragedy of Romeo & Juliet   **741.5**

Versace. Davis, D. K.   **B**

VERSACE, GIANNI, 1946-1997
Davis, D. K. Versace   **B**

VERSAILLES, FRANCE
Pike, A. Glitter   **Fic**

A **very** large expanse of sea. Mafi, T.   **Fic**
The **very** short entirely true history of unicorns. Laskow, S.   **398.24**

Vespers rising. Riordan, R.   **Fic**
Vessel. Durst, S. B.   **Fic**

VETERANS
Curtis, C. P. The madman of Piney Woods   **Fic**
Partridge, E. Boots on the ground   **959.704**
Strasser, T. Price of duty   **Fic**
Watkins, S. Great Falls   **Fic**

VETERINARIANS
Chodosh, J. The elephant doctor of India   **599.67**
Frydenborg, K. The wild horse scientists   **599.665**
Jackson, D. M. ER vets   **636.089**
Kelly, J. The curious world of Calpurnia Tate   **Fic**

VETERINARY EMERGENCIES
Jackson, D. M. ER vets   **636.089**

VETERINARY MEDICINE
Wilson, D. L. Firehorse   **Fic**

VETERINARY MEDICINE -- HISTORY
Jackson, D. M. ER vets   **636.089**

VEY, MICHAEL (FICTITIOUS CHARACTER)
Evans, R. P. Battle of the Ampere   **Fic**

VICES
Yep, L. The rainbow people   **398.2**

VICKSBURG, MISSISSIPPI -- HISTORY -- SIEGE, 1863
Warren, A. Under siege!   **973.7**

VICTIMS OF TERRORISM
Brown, D. In the shadow of the fallen towers   **973.931**
Thoms, A. With their eyes   **812**
Wachtel, A. September 11   **973.931**

VICTORIA
Gleitzman, M. Now   **Fic**
Victoria. Reef, C.   **B**
Victoria and her court. Schomp, V.   **941.081**

VICTORIA, BRITISH COLUMBIA
Oppel, K. Half brother   **Fic**

VICTORIA, QUEEN OF GREAT BRITAIN, 1819-1901

MacColl, M. Prisoners in the palace   **Fic**
Reef, C. Victoria   **B**
Schomp, V. Victoria and her court   **941.081**

VICTORIAN ERA (1837-1901)
Angleberger, T. Horton Halfpott or The fiendish mystery of Smugwick Manor or The loosening of M'Lady Luggertuck's corset   **Fic**
Barratt, M. Joe Rat   **Fic**
Bray, L. A great and terrible beauty   **Fic**
Bunce, E. C. Premeditated Myrtle   **Fic**
Carey, E. Heap House   **Fic**
Carriger, G. Curtsies & conspiracies   **Fic**
Carriger, G. Etiquette & espionage   **Fic**
Carriger, G. Waistcoats & weaponry   **Fic**
Eves, R. Blood rose rebellion   **Fic**
Gaiman, N. Stardust   **Fic**
Gleason, C. The clockwork scarab   **Fic**
Hooper, M. Fallen Grace   **Fic**
Hopkinson, D. The great trouble   **Fic**
Jinks, C. How to catch a bogle   **Fic**
Jinks, C. The last bogler   **Fic**
Kirby, M. J. A taste for monsters   **Fic**
Lee, Y. S. The body at the tower   **Fic**
Lee, Y. S. A spy in the house   **Fic**
Pratchett, T. Dodger   **Fic**
Pullman, P. Two crafty criminals!   **Fic**
Schlitz, L. A. Splendors and glooms   **Fic**
Springer, N. The case of the bizarre bouquets   **Fic**
Springer, N. The case of the cryptic crinoline   **Fic**
Springer, N. The case of the gypsy goodbye   **Fic**
Springer, N. The case of the left-handed lady   **Fic**
Springer, N. The case of the missing marquess   **Fic**
Springer, N. The case of the peculiar pink fan   **Fic**
Trevayne, E. The accidental afterlife of Thomas Marsden   **Fic**
Victorio's war. Wilson, J.   **Fic**
Video game developer. Jozefowicz, C.   **794.8**

VIDEO GAMERS
Brown, G. Josh Baxter levels up   **Fic**
Korman, G. Slacker   **Fic**

VIDEO GAMES
Adams, S. S. Crash course in gaming   **794.8**
Avi. Old wolf   **Fic**
Gallaway, B. Game on!   **025.2**
Johnson-Shelton, N. The invisible tower   **Fic**

VIDEO GAMES -- DESIGN -- VOCATIONAL GUIDANCE
Jozefowicz, C. Video game developer   **794.8**

VIDEO GAMES -- HISTORY
Hansen, D. Game on!   **794.8**

VIDEO GAMES -- SOCIAL ASPECTS
Haugen, H. M. Video games   **794.8**

VIDEO GAMES -- TECHNOLOGICAL INNOVATIONS
Oxlade, C. Gaming technology   **794.8**

VIDEO GAMES AND BOYS
Brown, G. Josh Baxter levels up   **Fic**
Kinney, J. Dog days   **Fic**

VIDEO GAMES INDUSTRY AND TRADE
Hansen, D. Game on!   **794.8**

Horowitz, A. Heroes and villains	398.22
Moore, P. V is for villain	Fic
Nimmo, J. Midnight for Charlie Bone	Fic
Pratchett, T. I shall wear midnight	Fic
Ruiz Zafon, C. The Midnight Palace	Fic
Walden, M. H.I.V.E.	Fic

Villalobos, Juan Pablo, 1973-
The other side — 305.235092

Villasante, Alexandra
The grief keeper — Fic

Viminy Crowe's comic book. Jocelyn, M. — Fic

VIMY RIDGE, BATTLE OF, 1917
Batten, J. The war to end all wars — 940.3

Vincent Van Gogh. Whiting, J. — 759.9492

VINCENT, ERIN
Vincent, E. Grief girl — B

Vincent, Zu, 1952-
Catherine the Great — B

VINTAGE CLOTHING
Rogers, B. Costumes accessories props and stage illusions made easy — 646.4

Viola, Jason
Digestive system — 612.3

VIOLENCE

Brown, S. Caminar	Fic
Haugen, H. M. Video games	794.8
Kidd, R. Night on fire	Fic
Martin, C. Drug wars	363.45
Miller, M. Exposing hate	305.5
Neri, G. Yummy	741.5
Price, C. Desert Angel	Fic
Sitomer, A. L. Homeboyz	Fic
Wilson, J. Ghost moon	Fic
Wilson, J. Written in blood	Fic
Yousafzai, M. We are displaced	305.23092

VIOLENCE -- HISTORY 20TH CENTURY
Madigan, T. The burning — 976.6

VIOLENCE AGAINST AFRICAN-AMERICANS
Taylor, M. D. The road to Memphis — Fic

VIOLENCE AGAINST WOMEN
Byars, B. C. Cracker Jackson — Fic

VIOLENCE AND DRUGS
Martin, C. Drug wars — 363.45

VIOLENCE AND GUNS
Doeden, M. Gun violence — 363.33
Reynolds, J. Long way down — Fic

VIOLENCE IN GANGS
Atkin, S. B. Gunstories — 363.33

VIOLENCE IN MEN
Chaltas, T. Because I am furniture — Fic
Sloan, H. G. I'll be there — Fic

VIOLENCE IN SCHOOLS
Draper, S. M. Just another hero — Fic
Williams-Garcia, R. Jumped — Fic

VIOLENCE IN TEENAGE BOYS
Lynch, C. Inexcusable — Fic

VIOLENCE IN VIDEO GAMES

Haugen, H. M. Video games — 794.8

VIOLENT CRIMES
Doeden, M. Gun violence — 363.33
Miller, M. Exposing hate — 305.5

VIOLIN
Beil, M. D. The vanishing violin — Fic
Ganeri, A. Stringed instruments — 787
Landau, E. Is the violin for you? — 787.2

VIOLINISTS
Landau, E. Is the violin for you? — 787.2
McClintock, N. Out of tune — Fic

VIRGIN ISLANDS OF THE UNITED STATES
Callender, K. Hurricane child — Fic

VIRGINIA

Bayard, L. Lucky strikes	Fic
Black, H. The copper gauntlet	Fic
Black, H. The iron trial	Fic
Bradley, K. B. Jefferson's sons	Fic
Brimner, L. D. Finding a way home	346.7301
Card, O. S. The lost gate	Fic
Erskine, K. Mockingbird	Fic
Erskine, K. Seeing red	Fic
Gibbs, S. Spy school	Fic
Giles, L. R. The Last Mirror on the Left	Fic
Giles, L. R. Not so pure and simple	Fic
Hahn, M. D. Closed for the season	Fic
Harris, T. E. The perfect place	Fic
Kent, D. Virginia	975.5
LaFleur, S. M. Love Aubrey	Fic
Lester, J. Time's memory	Fic
Pinkney, A. D. With the might of angels	Fic
Powell, P. H. Loving vs. Virginia	Fic
Rosenberg, M. This is just a test	Fic
Watkins, S. Great Falls	Fic
Wolf, A. Who killed Christopher Goodman?	Fic

VIRGINIA -- ANTIQUITIES
Huey, L. M. American archaeology uncovers the earliest English colonies — 973.2

VIRGINIA -- HISTORY
McClafferty, C. K. Buried lives — 306.3

VIRGINIA -- HISTORY -- 20TH CENTURY
Stokes, J. A. Students on strike — 371.829

Virginia. Kent, D. — 975.5

VIRGINITY
Giles, L. R. Not so pure and simple — Fic
Lubar, D. Character driven — Fic

VIRTUAL COMMUNITY
Kritzer, N. Catfishing on Catnet — Fic

VIRTUAL REALITY
Freitas, D. Unplugged — Fic
Kincaid, S. J. Insignia — Fic
MacHale, D. J. The reality bug — Fic

VIRTUAL REALITY GAMES
Lu, M. Warcross — Fic
Lu, M. Wildcard — Fic
Vande Velde, V. Heir apparent — Fic

VIRTUES

W

Wachtel, Alan

Maraniss, A. Strong inside	B
Wallace, Rich	
Babe conquers the world	B
Blood Brother	B
One good punch	Fic
Perpetual check	Fic
War and watermelon	Fic
Wrestling Sturbridge	Fic
Wallace, Sandra Neil	
Bound by ice	910.4
Race against time	976.7
Wallace, Virginia, 1938-	
Collaborating for inquiry-based learning	371.3
WALLENBERG, RAOUL, 1912-1947	
Borden, L. His name was Raoul Wallenberg	B
Waller, Sharon Biggs, 1966-	
A mad wicked folly	Fic
WALLS	
Carman, P. The Dark Hills divide	Fic
Gaiman, N. Stardust	Fic
Walrath, Dana	
Like water on stone	Fic
Walsh, Alice, 1958-	
A long way from home	Fic
Walsh, Pat, 1954-	
The Crowfield curse	Fic
Walsh, Peter, 1956-	
It's all too much so get it together	640
WALT DISNEY COMPANY	
Finch, C. The art of Walt Disney	791.43092
Schumacher, T. How does the show go on?	792.02
Walt Whitman. Kerley, B.	B
Walter Wick's optical tricks Anniversary ed.. Wick, W.	Wick, W. 152.14
Walter, Jon, 1964-	
My name is not Friday	Fic
Walters, Eric, 1957-	
Broken strings	Fic
The money pit mystery	Fic
Walton, Julia, 1986-	
Words on bathroom walls	Fic
Wambach, Abby, 1980-	
Wolfpack	155.3
WAMPANOAG INDIANS	
Messner, K. The Mayflower	974.4
WAMPANOAG INDIANS -- HISTORY	
Mandell, D. R. King Philip's war	973.2
The **wand** in the word. Marcus, L. S.	813.009
Wandering son. Shimura, T.	741.5
WANG, VERA	
Petrillo, L. Vera Wang	B
WAR	
Almond, D. Raven summer	Fic
Ambrose, S. E. The good fight	940.53
Armstrong, J. Shattered	Fic
Barber, N. World War I	940.3
Bradley, K. B. The war that saved my life	Fic

Brown, S. Caminar	Fic
Bruchac, J. Code Talker	Fic
Dassu, A. M. Boy everywhere	Fic
DiConsiglio, J. The Mexican-American War	973.6
DiConsiglio, J. Vietnam	959.704
Dowell, F. O. Shooting the moon	Fic
Drez, R. J. Remember D-day	940.54
Ellis, D. Children of war	305.23086
Ellis, D. Kids of Kabul	305.235
Ellis, D. Off to war	303.6
Gifford, C. Why did the Vietnam War happen?	959.704
Grant, R. G. Why did World War I happen?	940.3
Hartman, R. Shadow scale	Fic
Hinds, G. The Iliad	741.5
Hopkins, L. B. America at war	811.008
Keenan, S. Dogs of war	741.5
Kincaid, S. J. Insignia	Fic
Korman, G. War stories	Fic
Langley, A. The Plains Indian wars 1864-1890	978.004
Lewis, J. P. And the soldiers sang	Fic
Lindelauf, B. Fing's war	Fic
Mason, P. The Iraq War	956.7044
McNab, C. 50 things you should know about the Vietnam War	959.704
Morpurgo, M. Listen to the moon	Fic
Nye, N. S. 19 varieties of gazelle	811
Partridge, E. Boots on the ground	959.704
Rees, B. The Civil War	973.7
Riggs, K. The French Revolution	944.04
Samuels, C. Home front	940.53
Samuels, C. Life under occupation	940.53
Samuels, C. Propaganda	940.54
Samuels, C. Soldiers	940.54
Sanderson, B. Skyward	Fic
Schroder, M. My brother's shadow	Fic
Senker, C. The Vietnam War	959.704
Senker, C. Why did World War II happen?	940.53
Smithson, R. Ghosts of war	956.7044
Strasser, T. Price of duty	Fic
Sutherland, J. The ten-year century	973.93
Swain, G. World War I	940.3
Wells, R. Red moon at Sharpsburg	Fic
Wilkes, S. Out of Iraq	305.9
Woolf, A. The Arab-Israeli War since 1948	956.04
WAR -- MORAL AND ETHICAL ASPECTS	
Rubin, S. G. The cat with the yellow star	940.53
Walker, P. R. Remember Little Bighorn	973.8
WAR -- PSYCHOLOGICAL ASPECTS	
Bradman, T. Give me shelter	Fic
WAR -- RELIGIOUS ASPECTS	
Currie, S. Medieval crusades	909.07
Lace, W. W. The unholy crusade	949.5
WAR AND SOCIETY	
Armstrong, J. Shattered	Fic
Bartlett, C. E. We rule the night	Fic
Bradman, T. Give me shelter	Fic
Fleischman, P. Dateline Troy	398.2

Wet cement. Raczka, B.   811
WETLAND ECOLOGY
    Bow, J. Wetlands inside out   **577.68**
WETLANDS
    Bow, J. Wetlands inside out   **577.68**
Wetlands inside out. Bow, J.   **577.68**
Wetzel, Dan
    LeBron James   **B**
Whaam! Rubin, S. G.   **B**
The **whale** scientists. Hodgkins, F.   **599.5**
WHALE SHARK
    Cerullo, M. M. Seeking giant sharks   **597.3**
    Markle, S. The great shark rescue   **597.3**
Whaleport. Foster, M.   **338.3**
WHALERS
    Foster, M. Whaleport   **338.3**
    McKissack, P. Black hands white sails   **639.2**
WHALES
    Anderson, M. T. Whales on stilts!   **Fic**
    Gish, M. Killer whales   **599.53**
    Gish, M. Whales   **599.5**
    Hodgkins, F. The whale scientists   **599.5**
    Hoyt, E. Encyclopedia of whales dolphins and porpoises **599**
    Lockwood, S. Whales   **599.5**
    Lourie, P. Whaling season   **599.5**
    Ness, P. And the ocean was our sky   **Fic**
    O'Connell, J. The Eye of the Whale   **599.5**
    Philbrick, N. Revenge of the whale   **910**
    Safina, C. Beyond words   **591.56**
    Siebert, C. The secret world of whales   **599.5**
WHALES -- STRANDING
    Hodgkins, F. The whale scientists   **599.5**
Whales. Gish, M.   **599.5**
Whales. Lockwood, S.   **599.5**
Whales on stilts! Anderson, M. T.   **Fic**
WHALING
    Hodgkins, F. The whale scientists   **599.5**
    Philbrick, N. Revenge of the whale   **910**
WHALING -- HISTORY
    Foster, M. Whaleport   **338.3**
    McKissack, P. Black hands white sails   **639.2**
Whaling season. Lourie, P.   **599.5**
Whalley, Paul Ernest Sutton
    Butterfly & moth   **595.78**
WHARTON, EDITH, 1862-1937
    Wooldridge, C. N. The brave escape of Edith Wharton   **B**
What a beast! Kelly, S.   **398**
What a kick. Berne, E. C.   **796.334**
What a scientist sees. Rice, D.   **500**
What a waste! Eamer, C.   **363.72**
What breathes through its butt? Grossman, E.   **500**
What can(t) wait. Perez, A. H.   **Fic**
What do you believe?   **200**
What every girl should know. Mann, J. A.   **Fic**
What happened to goodbye. Dessen, S.   **Fic**
What have you lost? Nye, N. S.   **808.81**
What I carry. Longo, J.   **Fic**

What I saw and how I lied. Blundell, J.   **Fic**
What is anxiety disorder? Mooney, C.   **616.85**
What is germ theory? Hyde, N.   **615**
What is the impact of declining biodiversity? Kallen, S. A.   **333.95**
What is the theory of evolution? Walker, R.   **576.8**
What Linnaeus saw. Beil, K. M.   **508.092**
What makes us a family? Lynette, R.   **306.85**
What makes you you? Arbuthnott, G.   **572.8**
What my girlfriend doesn't know. Sones, S.   **Fic**
What my mother doesn't know. Sones, S.   **Fic**
What the heart knows. Sidman, J.   **811**
What they found. Myers, W. D.   **Fic**
What to do when you're sad & lonely. Crist, J. J.   **618.92**
What was the Battle of Gettysburg? O'Connor, J.   **973.7**
What we found in the sofa (and how it saved the world). Clark, H.   **Fic**
What will happen to me? Zehr, H.   **362.82**
What world is left. Polak, M.   **Fic**
What would Joey do? Gantos, J.   **Fic**
The **what's** happening to my body? book for girls. Madaras, L.   **613.9**
Wheeler, Andrew, 1976-
    Another castle   **741.5**
Wheels of change. Macy, S.   **796.6**
Whelan, Gloria
    All my noble dreams and then what happens   **Fic**
    Homeless bird   **Fic**
    Small acts of amazing courage   **Fic**
When a friend dies. Gootman, M. E.   **155.9**
When a ghost talks listen. Tingle, T.   **Fic**
When Dimple met Rishi. Menon, S.   **Fic**
When dinos dawned mammals got munched and Pterosaurs took flight. Bonner, H.   **567.9**
When elephants listen with their feet. Grundmann, E.   **573.8**
When gifted kids don't have all the answers. Galbraith, J.   **371.95**
When I crossed No-Bob. McMullan, M.   **Fic**
When I was a soldier. Zenatti, V.   **B**
When I was a turkey. Hutto, J.   **598.6**
When love comes to town. Lennon, T.   **Fic**
When lunch fights back. Johnson, R. L.   **591.47**
When my name was Keoko. Park, L. S.   **Fic**
When stars are scattered. Jamieson, V.   **B**
When the black girl sings. Wright, B.   **Fic**
When the children marched. Mayer, R. H.   **323.1196**
When the earth shakes. Winchester, S.   **551.22**
When the ground is hard. Nunn, M.   **Fic**
When the sea turned to silver. Lin, G.   **Fic**
When the world was ours. Kessler, L.   **Fic**
When we collided. Lord, E.   **Fic**
When we wake. Healey, K.   **Fic**
When you reach me. Stead, R.   **Fic**
When you were here. Whitney, D.   **Fic**
When Zachary Beaver came to town. Holt, K. W.   **Fic**
Where have all the bees gone? Hirsch, R. E.   **595.79**
Where she went. Forman, G.   **Fic**

Champion, N. Making shelter — 613.6
Farmer, N. A girl named Disaster — Fic
Hobbs, W. Jason's gold — Fic
Johnson, T. L. Dog driven — Fic
Levy, D. A. Above all else — Fic
Long, D. Survivor kid — 613.6
Marshall, K. A. I am still alive — Fic
McCaughrean, G. Where the world ends — Fic
McClintock, N. Taken — Fic
McGinnis, M. Be not far from me — Fic
Mikaelsen, B. Touching Spirit Bear — Fic
Paulsen, G. Brian's return — Fic
Paulsen, G. Brian's winter — Fic
Paulsen, G. Hatchet — Fic
Paulsen, G. The Transall saga — Fic
Schrefer, E. Endangered — Fic
Wildfire. Philbrick, W. R. — Fic

WILDFIRE FIGHTERS -- JUVENILE LITERATURE
Thiessen, M. Extreme wildfire — 363.37

WILDFIRES
Collard, S. B. Fire birds — 634.9
Gleitzman, M. Now — Fic
Philbrick, W. R. Wildfire — Fic
Reilly, K. M. Natural disasters — 550
Silverstein, A. Wildfires — 634.9
Simon, S. Wildfires — 574.5

**WILDFIRES -- PREVENTION AND CONTROL -- JUVE-
NILE LITERATURE**
Thiessen, M. Extreme wildfire — 363.37
Wildfires. Silverstein, A. — 634.9
Wildfires. Simon, S. — 574.5

WILDLIFE
Castaldo, N. F. Polar bear rescue — 599.786
Chin, J. Island — 508.866
Cotton, K. Counting lions — 591.68
Gascoigne, I. Papua New Guinea — 995.3
Green, J. Barron's totally wild fact-packed fold-out animal atlas — 591.9
Heinrichs, A. The Nile — 962
Hestermann, J. Zoology for kids — 590
Johnson, R. L. Chernobyl's wild kingdom — 590.9477
Kras, S. L. The Galapagos Islands — 986.6
Lynch, W. Arctic — 577.0911
Peterson, J. M. Big game hunting — 799.2
Smelt, R. New Zealand — 993

WILDLIFE CONSERVATION
Anderson, T. Giraffe extinction — 599.638
Carson, M. K. Emi and the rhino scientist — 599.66
Castaldo, N. F. Back from the brink — 333.95
Coey, J. Animal hospital — 639.9
Drake, J. Rewilding — 639.9
Farley, T. Wild at heart — 599.665
Gilmore, K. The exchange student — Fic
Hague, B. Rise of the lioness — 599.757
Hiaasen, C. Hoot — Fic
Hiaasen, C. Scat — Fic
Hoose, P. M. The race to save the Lord God Bird — 598.7

Houston, D. Bulu African wonder dog — 636.7
Markle, S. The case of the vanishing golden frogs — 597.8
Markle, S. The great leopard rescue — 599.75
Markle, S. The great shark rescue — 597.3
Pobst, S. Animals on the edge — 333.95
Sobol, R. Breakfast in the rainforest — 599.884
Turner, P. S. Crow smarts — 598.8

WILDLIFE CONSERVATIONISTS
Farley, T. Wild at heart — 599.665
Frydenborg, K. The wild horse scientists — 599.665
Montgomery, S. Saving the ghost of the mountain — 599.75

WILDLIFE HABITATS
McCarthy, C. Reptile — 597.9
Pobst, S. Animals on the edge — 333.95
Wildlife of the world. Ambrose, J. — 591

WILDLIFE PHOTOGRAPHERS
Cerullo, M. M. Journey to shark island — 597.309164
Cerullo, M. M. Searching for Great White Sharks — 597.3
Cerullo, M. M. Sharks of the deep — 597.3

WILDLIFE REFUGES
Houston, D. Bulu African wonder dog — 636.7
Laidlaw, R. Saving lives & changing hearts — 333.95

WILDLIFE REINTRODUCTION
Drake, J. Rewilding — 639.9

WILDLIFE RESCUE
Coey, J. Animal hospital — 639.9
Halls, K. M. Saving the Baghdad Zoo — 590.73
Lewis, G. One white dolphin — Fic
Markle, S. The case of the vanishing golden frogs — 597.8
Markle, S. The great leopard rescue — 599.75
Markle, S. The great shark rescue — 597.3

WILDLIFE RESEARCHERS
Walker, S. M. Frozen secrets — 919.8

WILDLIFE VETERINARIANS
Chodosh, J. The elephant doctor of India — 599.67
Wildwing. Whitman, E. — Fic
Wildwood. Meloy, C. — Fic
Wildwood dancing. Marillier, J. — Fic
Wildwood imperium. Meloy, C. — Fic
Wiles, Deborah
Anthem — Fic
The Aurora County All-Stars — Fic
Countdown — Fic
Kent State — Fic
Revolution — Fic

WILEY, HARVEY WASHINGTON, 1844-1930
Jarrow, G. The poison eaters — 353.9
Wilgus, Alison
Flying machines — 629.13

WILHELM GUSTLOFF (SHIP)
Sepetys, R. Salt to the sea — Fic
Wilkes, Sybella
Out of Iraq — 305.9

WILKINS, MAURICE, 1916-2004
Dorling Kindersley, I. The DNA book — 572.8
Wilkinson, Lili, 1981-
Pink — Fic

Winkler, Allan M., 1945-

The Cold War — 909.8

The **winner's** crime. Rutkoski, M. — Fic

The **winner's** curse. Rutkoski, M. — Fic

The **winner's** kiss. Rutkoski, M. — Fic

Winner, Cherie

Circulating life — 615

WINNING AND LOSING

Hautman, P. All-in — Fic

Hoose, P. M. Attucks! — 796.323

Winning lacrosse for girls. Swissler, B. — 796.347082

Winning soccer for girls. Crisfield, D. — 796.334

Winning softball for girls. Gola, M. — 796.357

Winning track and field for girls. Housewright, E. — 796.42

Winning volleyball for girls. Crisfield, D. — 796.325082

Winston, Robert M. L.

Evolution revolution — 576.8

WINTER

Armstrong, A. W. Whittington — Fic

Kirby, M. J. Icefall — Fic

Paulsen, G. Brian's winter — Fic

Petersen, D. Mouse guard — 741.5

WINTER OLYMPIC MEDAL WINNERS

McKinley, M. Ice time — 796.355

Winter sky. Giff, P. R. — Fic

WINTER SPORTS

McDougall, C. Girls play to win figure skating — 796.91

Schwartz, H. E. Snowboarding — 796.939

Woods, B. Snowmobile racers — 796.94

WINTER SURVIVAL

Mooney, C. Surviving in cold places — 363.34092

Winter town. Emond, S. — Fic

Winter, Jonah, 1962-

Peaceful heroes — 920

Winterberg, Jenna

Light and its effects — 535

Winterbottom, Julie

Frightlopedia — 031.02

Wintergirls. Anderson, L. H. — Fic

Winters, Ben H.

The secret life of Ms. Finkleman — Fic

Winters, Cat

In the shadow of blackbirds — Fic

Odd & true — Fic

Winters, Eleanor

Calligraphy for kids — 745.6

Winthrop, Elizabeth

Counting on Grace — Fic

Wires and nerve. Meyer, M. — 741.5

WIRZ, HENRY, 1823-1865

Gourley, C. The horrors of Andersonville — 973.7

WISCONSIN

Atkinson, E. J. I Emma Freke — Fic

Blashfield, J. F. Wisconsin — 977.5

Henkes, K. Bird Lake moon — Fic

Herbach, G. I'm with stupid — Fic

Khan, H. Amina's voice — Fic

Murdock, C. G. Dairy queen — Fic

Murdock, C. G. The off season — Fic

Wisconsin. Blashfield, J. F. — 977.5

Wisdom tales from around the world. Forest, H. — 398.2

Wiseman, Blaine

Republic of Ireland — 941.7

Wiseman, Eva, 1947-

Puppet — Fic

Wiseman, Rosalind, 1969-

Boys girls and other hazardous materials — Fic

Wish. Bullen, A. — Fic

Wish girl. Loftin, N. — Fic

A **wish** in the dark. Soontornvat, C. — Fic

WISHING AND WISHES

Bullen, A. Wish — Fic

Messner, K. The seventh wish — Fic

Mobley, J. Katerina's wish — Fic

Scieszka, J. Thriller — Fic

Wees, A. The waking forest — Fic

West, J. A storm of wishes — Fic

Wood, F. Cloudwish — Fic

Wishtree. Applegate, K. — Fic

Wisler, G. Clifton

Red Cap — Fic

Witch born. Bowling, N. — Fic

The **witch** of Blackbird Pond. Speare, E. G. — Fic

The **witch's** boy. Barnhill, K. R. — Fic

WITCHCRAFT

Bowling, N. Witch born — Fic

Okorafor, N. Akata witch — Fic

Speare, E. G. The witch of Blackbird Pond — Fic

Vernon, U. Castle Hangnail — Fic

Whipple, N. House of ivy and sorrow — Fic

WITCHCRAFT -- HISTORY

Schanzer, R. Witches! — 133.4

WITCHES

Barnhill, K. R. The girl who drank the moon — Fic

Barnhill, K. R. The witch's boy — Fic

Blackwood, S. Miss Ellicott's school for the magically minded — Fic

Bowling, N. Witch born — Fic

Brignull, I. The hawkweed prophecy — Fic

Cuevas, A. The total eclipse of Nestor Lopez — Fic

Delaney, J. A new darkness — Fic

Delaney, J. Revenge of the witch — Fic

Dennard, S. Truthwitch — Fic

Flinn, A. Cloaked — Fic

Ford, C. Stickman Odyssey — Fic

Fox, J. S. The charmed children of Rookskill Castle — Fic

French, V. The robe of skulls — Fic

Gaiman, N. Hansel & Gretel — 398.20943

Gratton, T. Strange grace — Fic

Hahn, M. D. Took — Fic

Healy, C. The hero's guide to saving your kingdom — Fic

Hemphill, S. Wicked girls — Fic

Herrick, A. The Time Fetch — Fic

Horowitz, A. Raven's gate — Fic

Kim, G. The last fallen star	Fic	A **wizard** of Earthsea. Le Guin, U. K.		Fic
Layne, A. Beetle & the Hollowbones	741.5	**WIZARDS**		
Lewis, C. S. The lion the witch and the wardrobe	Fic	Alexander, L. The black cauldron		Fic
Lewis, C. S. The magician's nephew	Fic	Barron, T. A. The lost years of Merlin		Fic
Lewis, C. S. The silver chair	Fic	Blackwood, S. Jinx		Fic
Leyh, K. Snapdragon	741.5	Blackwood, S. Jinx's fire		Fic
MacCullough, C. Once a witch	Fic	Blackwood, S. Jinx's magic		Fic
Maguire, G. Egg & spoon	Fic	Booraem, E. River magic		Fic
McCoola, M. Baba Yaga's assistant	741.5	Chima, C. W. The Demon King		Fic
McGrane, M. The accursed vampire	741.5	Chima, C. W. The warrior heir		Fic
Medley, L. Castle waiting	741.5	Constable, K. The singer of all songs		Fic
Morrison, M. Grounded	Fic	Dickinson, P. The ropemaker		Fic
Okorafor, N. Akata witch	Fic	Downer, A. Hatching magic		Fic
Owen, M. The merciful Crow	Fic	Duey, K. Sacred scars		Fic
Powell, L. Burn mark	Fic	Epstein, A. J. Circle of heroes		Fic
Pratchett, T. I shall wear midnight	Fic	Fayers, C. The voyage to Magical North		Fic
Pratchett, T. The Wee Free Men	Fic	Ferris, J. Twice upon a Marigold		Fic
Renier, A. The unsinkable Walker Bean	741.5	Fforde, J. The Eye of Zoltar		Fic
Sage, A. StarChaser	Fic	Fforde, J. The last dragonslayer		Fic
Schlitz, L. A. Splendors and glooms	Fic	Fforde, J. The song of the quarkbeast		Fic
Shepherd, M. Midnight beauties	Fic	Gallego Garcia, L. The valley of the Wolves		Fic
Stephens, J. The emerald atlas	Fic	Ibbotson, E. The Ogre of Oglefort		Fic
Tingle, T. Spirits dark and light	398.2	Jones, D. W. Howl's moving castle		Fic
Vernon, U. Castle Hangnail	Fic	Jones, D. W. The islands of Chaldea		Fic
Wees, A. The waking forest	Fic	Landy, D. The faceless ones		Fic
Welsh, M. L. Mistress of the Storm	Fic	Le Guin, U. K. Tales from Earthsea		Fic
Whipple, N. House of ivy and sorrow	Fic	Mashima, H. Fairy tail		741.5
Witches! Schanzer, R.	133.4	McKinley, R. The hero and the crown		Fic
With a banjo on my knee. Ellis, R. M.	787	McKinley, R. Pegasus		Fic
With a mighty hand. Ehrlich, A.	221.9	Morris, G. The squire's tale		Fic
With a star in my hand. Engle, M.	Fic	Mull, B. A world without heroes		Fic
With all deliberate speed. Aretha, D.	379.2	Nix, G. Abhorsen		Fic
With courage and cloth. Bausum, A.	324.6	Nix, G. Sabriel		Fic
With the might of angels. Pinkney, A. D.	Fic	Noyes, D. Gothic!		Fic
With their eyes. Thoms, A.	812	O'Neal, E. The false princess		Fic
Withers, Pam		Pierce, T. Briar's book		Fic
First descent	Fic	Pierce, T. Daja's book		Fic
Without Tess. Pixley, M. F.	Fic	Pierce, T. Sandry's book		Fic
Witmer, Scott		Pierce, T. Tris's book		Fic
Drums keyboards and other instruments	786	Pierce, T. Wild magic		Fic
Guitars & bass	787.87	Prineas, S. The magic thief		Fic
Managing your band	781.66068	Rowell, R. Carry on		Fic
Witness. Hesse, K.	Fic	Rowell, R. Wayward son		Fic
WITNESSES		Rowling, J. K. The tales of Beedle the Bard		Fic
Van Draanen, W. Sammy Keyes and the hotel thief	Fic	Sage, A. StarChaser		Fic
WITNESSES -- PROTECTION		Stroud, J. The ring of Solomon		Fic
Burt, J. Greetings from witness protection!	Fic	Tolkien, J. R. R. The hobbit or there and back again		Fic
Elston, A. The rules for disappearing	Fic	Vande Velde, V. The book of Mordred		Fic
Wittenstein, Vicki O., 1954-		White, T. H. The once and future king		Fic
For the good of mankind?	174.2	Wrede, P. C. Calling on dragons		Fic
Wittlinger, Ellen		Wrede, P. C. Dealing with dragons		Fic
Hard love	Fic	Wrede, P. C. Searching for dragons		Fic
Parrotfish	Fic	Wrede, P. C. Talking to dragons		Fic
Wittmann, Kelly		**WIZARDS' APPRENTICES**		
Botswana	968.83	Blackwood, S. Jinx's magic		Fic
WITWATERSRAND REGION, SOUTH AFRICA		Fayers, C. The voyage to Magical North		Fic
Aronson, M. The skull in the rock	569.9096822	Knudsen, M. The dragon of Trelian		Fic

O'Neal, E. The false princess — Fic
Pierce, T. The will of the empress — Fic
Prineas, S. The magic thief — Fic
Sage, A. StarChaser — Fic
Woe is I Jr.. O'Conner, P. T. — 372.61
Woelfle, Gretchen
  The wind at work — 621.4
Wolf Hollow. Wolk, L. — Fic
The **wolf** keepers. Broach, E. — Fic
WOLF PUPS
  Lasky, K. Lone wolf — Fic
WOLF SPIDERS
  Markle, S. Wolf spiders — 595.4
Wolf spiders. Markle, S. — 595.4
The **wolf** wilder. Rundell, K. — Fic
The **wolf's** boy. Beckhorn, S. W. — Fic
Wolf, Allan
  The watch that ends the night — Fic
  Who killed Christopher Goodman? — Fic
Wolf, Laurie Goldrich
  Recyclo-gami — 745.5
Wolf, Sallie
  The robin makes a laughing sound — 598
Wolff, Virginia Euwer
  Make lemonade — Fic
  The Mozart season — Fic
  Probably still Nick Swansen — Fic
Wolfpack. Wambach, A. — 155.3
Wolk, Lauren, 1956-
  Beyond the bright sea — Fic
  Echo Mountain — Fic
  Wolf Hollow — Fic
Wolkenstein, M. Evan
  Turtle boy — Fic
Woll, Kris
  Wind energy — 333.9
WOLVES
  Avi. Old wolf — Fic
  Broach, E. The wolf keepers — Fic
  Gardner, L. Into the woods — Fic
  Hirsch, A. Dogs — 636.7
  Johnson-Shelton, N. The invisible tower — Fic
  Lasky, K. Lone wolf — Fic
  London, J. The call of the wild — Fic
  McAllister, I. The sea wolves — 599.773
  Rundell, K. The wolf wilder — Fic
  Vande Velde, V. Cloaked in red — Fic
A **woman** in the House and Senate. Cooper, I. — 320.082
WOMEN
  Bausum, A. Our country's first ladies — 973.09
  Chin-Lee, C. Amelia to Zora — 920
  Del Negro, J. Passion and poison — Fic
  Halligan, K. HerStory — 920
  Harrison, V. Little dreamers — 920
  Jackson, L. E. B. I have lived a thousand years — 940.53
  Krull, K. A kids' guide to America's first ladies — 920
  Langley, W. Women of the wind — 920

Leon, V. Outrageous women of the Middle Ages — 920
McCann, M. R. Girls who rocked the world — 920
McCann, M. R. More girls who rocked the world — 920.72
Noyce, P. Remarkable minds — 509.2
Noyes, D. A hopeful heart — 813
Nye, N. S. I feel a little jumpy around you — 808.81
Qamar, A. Beneath my mother's feet — Fic
Reef, C. The Bronte sisters — 920
Roberts, C. Founding mothers — 973.3
San Souci, R. D. Cut from the same cloth — 398.21
Schatz, K. Rad American women A-Z — 920.72
Schatz, K. Rad women worldwide — 920
Schwartz, H. E. Women of the U.S. Air Force — 358.4
Sonneborn, L. A to Z of American Indian women — 920.72089
Spotswood, J. The radical element — Fic
Staples, S. F. Haveli — Fic
Staples, S. F. Under the persimmon tree — Fic
Swaby, R. Trailblazers — 920
Tchana, K. Changing Woman and her sisters — 398.2
Yolen, J. Bad girls — 920
Zuckerman, G. Rising above — 796
WOMEN -- EMPLOYMENT -- HISTORY 20TH CENTURY
  Colman, P. Rosie the riveter — 331.4
WOMEN -- HISTORY
  Leon, V. Outrageous women of the Middle Ages — 920
  Yolen, J. Sea queens — 910.4
WOMEN -- HISTORY 19TH CENTURY
  Bray, L. A great and terrible beauty — Fic
WOMEN -- INTERPERSONAL RELATIONS
  Holm, J. L. Boston Jane the claim — Fic
  Holm, J. L. Boston Jane wilderness days — Fic
WOMEN -- POLITICAL ACTIVITY
  Cooper, I. A woman in the House and Senate — 320.082
  Dillon, M. Yes she can — 973.932
WOMEN -- POLITICAL ACTIVITY -- HISTORY
  Roberts, C. Founding mothers — 973.3
WOMEN -- SOCIAL CONDITIONS
  Chambers, V. Finish the fight! — 324.6
WOMEN -- SUFFRAGE
  Chambers, V. Finish the fight! — 324.6
  Sandler, M. W. 1919 — 973.91
WOMEN -- SUFFRAGE -- HISTORY
  Bausum, A. With courage and cloth — 324.6
  Conkling, W. Votes for women! — 324.6
  Hollihan, K. L. Rightfully ours — 324.6
  Zimet, S. Roses and radicals — 324.6
WOMEN ADVENTURERS
  Cliff, T. Delilah Dirk and the Turkish Lieutenant — 741.5
WOMEN AIR PILOTS
  MacColl, M. Promise the night — Fic
WOMEN AIRFORCE SERVICE PILOTS (U.S.)
  Nathan, A. Yankee doodle gals — 940.54
  Pearson, P. O. Fly girls — 940.54
  Smith, S. L. Flygirl — Fic
Women and feminism today. Sands, C. — 305.42
WOMEN AND SPORTS

WORLD WAR II

Allen, T. B. Remember Pearl Harbor	940.54
Altman, L. J. Hidden teens hidden lives	940.53
Ambrose, S. E. The good fight	940.53
Atkinson, R. D-Day	940.54
Atwood, K. J. Women heroes of World War II	940.54
Bradley, K. B. The war that saved my life	Fic
Byers, A. Saving children from the Holocaust	940.53
Byers, A. Trapped	940.53
Cornioley, P. W. Code name Pauline	940.54
Deem, J. M. Auschwitz	940.53
Deem, J. M. The prisoners of Breendonk	940.53
Drez, R. J. Remember D-day	940.54
Dumon Tak, B. Soldier bear	Fic
Freedman, R. We will not be silent	943.086
Friedman, I. R. The other victims	940.53
Frost, H. All he knew	Fic
Gaddy, K. R. Flowers in the gutter	940.53
Giff, P. R. Genevieve's war	Fic
Grant, R. G. Why did Hiroshima happen?	940.54
Hannigan, K. Cape	Fic
Hannigan, K. Mask	Fic
Hoffman, B. N. Liberation	940.53
Hoose, P. M. The boys who challenged Hitler	940.53
Hopkinson, D. D-Day	940.54
Hopkinson, D. Dive!	940.54
Houston, J. W. Farewell to Manzanar	940.54
Hughes, D. Four-Four-Two	Fic
Hughes, D. Soldier boys	Fic
Hughes, S. Hero on a bicycle	Fic
Jackson, L. E. B. I have lived a thousand years	940.53
Kadohata, C. Weedflower	Fic
Kessler, L. When the world was ours	Fic
Kuhn, B. Angels of mercy	940.54
Langley, A. World War II	940.53
Larson, K. Dash	Fic
Lowry, L. Number the stars	Fic
Macdonald, M. Odette's secrets	Fic
Maraniss, A. Games of deception	796.48
Matti, T. Mister orange	Fic
Mazer, H. A boy at war	Fic
Messner, K. Pearl Harbor	940.54
Morpurgo, M. The day the world stopped turning	Fic
Mullenbach, C. Torpedoed!	940.54
Napoli, D. J. Stones in water	Fic
Nardo, D. Hitler in Paris	943.086
Nelson, P. Left for dead	940.54
Olson, T. Lost in the Pacific 1942	940.54
Oppenheim, J. Dear Miss Breed	940.53
Peet, M. Tamar	Fic
Preus, M. Shadow on the mountain	Fic
Preus, M. Village of scoundrels	Fic
Prins, M. Hidden like Anne Frank	940.53
Reiss, J. The upstairs room	Fic
Rubin, S. G. The cat with the yellow star	940.53
Samuels, C. Soldiers	940.54
Savit, G. Anna and the Swallow Man	Fic

Seiple, S. Nazi saboteurs	940.54
Sender, R. M. The cage	940.53
Senker, C. Why did World War II happen?	940.53
Sepetys, R. Salt to the sea	Fic
Sheinkin, S. Bomb	623.4
Silver Line (Organization). Voices from the Second World War	940.5309
Stone, P. The Romeo and Juliet code	Fic
Stone, T. L. Courage has no color	940.54
Thomson, R. Terezin	940.53
Thor, A. A faraway island	Fic
Thor, A. The lily pond	Fic
Torres, J. A. The Battle of Midway	940.54
Watkins, Y. K. So far from the bamboo grove	Fic
Weatherford, C. B. You can fly	811
Wulffson, D. L. Soldier X	Fic
Yep, L. Hiroshima	Fic

WORLD WAR II -- AERIAL OPERATIONS

Elliott, L. Under a war-torn sky	Fic
Mazer, H. The last mission	Fic

WORLD WAR II -- AERIAL OPERATIONS, AMERICAN

Pearson, P. O. Fly girls	940.54

WORLD WAR II -- AFRICAN AMERICAN PARTICIPATION

Sheinkin, S. The Port Chicago 50	940.54

WORLD WAR II -- AFRICAN AMERICANS

Farrell, M. C. Standing up against hate	940.54
Mullenbach, C. Double victory	940.5308

WORLD WAR II -- CAUSES

Wukovits, J. F. The bombing of Pearl Harbor	940.54

WORLD WAR II -- CHILDREN

Altman, L. J. Hidden teens hidden lives	940.53
Bausum, A. Ensnared in the Wolf's Lair	943.086
Byers, A. Trapped	940.53
Dowswell, P. Auslander	Fic
Giff, P. R. Lily's crossing	Fic
Heuvel, E. A family secret	741.5
Pausewang, G. Dark hours	Fic
Skrypuch, M. F. Making bombs for Hitler	Fic

WORLD WAR II -- CONFISCATIONS AND CONTRIBUTIONS

Edsel, R. M. The greatest treasure hunt in history	940.53

WORLD WAR II -- CRYPTOGRAPHY

Holm, T. Code talkers and warriors	940.54

WORLD WAR II -- ECONOMIC ASPECTS

Colman, P. Rosie the riveter	331.4
Samuels, C. Home front	940.53

WORLD WAR II -- HISTORY

Callery, S. World War II	940.53

WORLD WAR II -- JAPANESE AMERICANS

Chee, T. We are not free	Fic
Kent, D. The tragic history of the Japanese-American internment camps	940.53
Marrin, A. Uprooted	940.53
Sandler, M. W. Imprisoned	940.53

WORLD WAR II -- JEWS

Frank, A. The diary of a young girl	940.53

The **year** we fell from space. King, A. S. — Fic
A **year** without Mom. Tolstikova, D. — 741.5
Years of dust. Marrin, A. — 978
Yee, F. C.
  The epic crush of Genie Lo — Fic
  The iron will of Genie Lo — Fic
Yee, Lisa
  Millicent Min girl genius — Fic
  Warp speed — Fic
Yee, Paul
  Learning to fly — Fic
Yelchin, Eugene
  Breaking Stalin's nose — Fic
  The haunting of Falcon House — Fic
  Spy runner — Fic
YELLOW FEVER
  Anderson, L. H. Fever 1793 — Fic
  Murphy, J. An American plague — 614.5
YELLOW FEVER -- DIAGNOSIS
  Jurmain, S. The secret of the yellow death — 614.5
Yellow star. Roy, J. R. — Fic
Yellowhorn, Eldon, 1956-
  Turtle Island — 970.1
YELNATS, STANLEY (FICTITIOUS CHARACTER)
  Sachar, L. Holes — Fic
YELTSIN, BORIS NIKOLAYEVICH, 1931-2007
  Langley, A. The collapse of the Soviet Union — 947.085
YEMEN (REPUBLIC)
  O'Neal, C. We visit Yemen — 953.3
YEMEN (REPUBLIC) -- HISTORY
  O'Neal, C. We visit Yemen — 953.3
Yep, Laurence, 1948-
  City of fire — Fic
  A dragon's guide to making your human smarter — Fic
  A dragon's guide to the care and feeding of humans — Fic
  Dragonwings — Fic
  Hiroshima — Fic
  The lost garden — B
  The rainbow people — 398.2
  The star maker — Fic
Yes she can. Dillon, M. — 973.932
Yes! We are Latinos. Ada, A. F. — Fic
YETI
  Harper, C. M. Alien encounter — Fic
  Valente, C. M. The girl who soared over Fairyland and cut the moon in two — Fic
Ynes Mexia. Anema, D. — B
YODA (FICTITIOUS CHARACTER)
  Angleberger, T. Darth Paper strikes back — Fic
  Angleberger, T. The strange case of Origami Yoda — Fic
YOGA
  Birkemoe, K. Strike a pose — 613.7
  Purperhart, H. Yoga exercises for teens — 613.7
  Rissman, R. Yoga for your mind and body — 613.7
Yoga exercises for teens. Purperhart, H. — 613.7
YOGA FOR CHILDREN
  Gates, M. This moment is your life (and so is this

one) — 613.7
Yoga for your mind and body. Rissman, R. — 613.7
Yohalem, Eve
  The truth according to Blue — Fic
Yolen, Jane
  Animal stories — 591
  Apple for the teacher — 782.42
  Bad girls — 920
  Briar Rose — Fic
  Dragon's blood — Fic
  The Emily sonnets — 811
  Foiled — Fic
  Mapping the bones — Fic
  Mightier than the sword — 398.2
  The queen's own fool — Fic
  Sea queens — 910.4
YOM KIPPUR
  Hackney Blackwell, A. Lent Yom Kippur and other Atonement days — 202
Yomtov, Nelson
  Bolivia — 984
  China — 951
  Colombia — 986.1
  Costa Rica — 972.86
  Haiti — 972.94
  Iraq — 956.7
  Syria — 956.91
Yoo, Paula
  From a whisper to a rallying cry — 305.895
Yoon, Nicola
  The sun is also a star — Fic
YORKSHIRE, ENGLAND
  Allison, J. Bad machinery — 741.5
  Burnett, F. H. The secret garden [Moore ill.] — Fic
  Horowitz, A. Raven's gate — Fic
  Kindl, P. A school for brides — Fic
YORKSHIRE, ENGLAND -- HISTORY -- 19TH CENTURY
  Reef, C. The Bronte sisters — 920
You. Benoit, C. — Fic
You are enough. Petro-Roy, J. — 616.85
You are mighty. Paul, C. — 306
You can fly. Weatherford, C. B. — 811
You can't wear these genes. Duke, S. S. — 576.5
You do you. Mirk, S. — 306.70835
You don't even know me. Flake, S. — Fic
You don't have a clue. Cortez, S. — Fic
You don't have to be everything. Whitney, D. — 808.108
You just can't help it! Szpirglas, J. — 599.9
You wouldn't want to live without dirt! Graham, I. — 631.4
You wouldn't want to live without gravity! Rooney, A. — 531
You wouldn't want to live without toilets. MacDonald, F. — 696
You're welcome universe. Gardner, W. — Fic
YOUNG ADULT FICTION, AMERICAN
  Crew, H. S. Experiencing America's story through fic-

tion 813

YOUNG ADULT FICTION, AMERICAN -- HISTORY AND CRITICISM

Cart, M. Young adult literature 813.009

YOUNG ADULT FICTION, AMERICAN 21ST CENTURY -- HISTORY AND CRITICISM

Richmond, K. J. Mental illness in young adult literature 813

YOUNG ADULT LITERATURE

Carstensen, A. The readers' advisory guide to teen literature 028.5

Chance, R. Young adult literature in action 011.62

YOUNG ADULT LITERATURE -- HISTORY AND CRITICISM

Cart, M. Young adult literature 813.009

Young adult literature in action. Chance, R. 011.62

YOUNG ADULT LITERATURE, AMERICAN

Chance, R. Young adult literature in action 011.62

Khailova, L. N. The stories we share 028.5

YOUNG ADULT LITERATURE, AMERICAN -- STUDY AND TEACHING (SECONDARY)

Bernadowski, C. Teaching literacy skills to adolescents using Coretta Scott King Award winners 428

Young adult literature. Cart, M. 813.009

YOUNG ADULTS

Nye, N. S. There is no long distance now Fic

YOUNG ADULTS -- BOOKS AND READING

Chance, R. Young adult literature in action 011.62

Sutton, R. A family of readers 809

YOUNG ADULTS' LIBRARIES -- ACTIVITY PROGRAMS

Krok, L. Novels in verse for teens 808.83

The **young** adventurer's guide to (almost) everything. Hewitt, B. 796.083

The **young** champion's mind. Afremow, J. A. 796

The **young** elites. Lu, M. Fic

The **young** inferno. Agard, J. 811

YOUNG MEN

Crisler, C. L. Tough boy sonatas 811

Hinds, G. The merchant of Venice 741.5

Hughes, D. Search and destroy Fic

Mercado, N. E. Every man for himself Fic

Morpurgo, M. War horse Fic

Scieszka, J. Guys write for Guys Read 810.8

Strasser, T. No place Fic

Young musicians in world history. Earls, I. 780

Young Palestinians speak. Robinson, A. 956.95

A **young** patriot. Murphy, J. B

YOUNG WOMEN

Bolden, T. Inventing Victoria Fic

Constable, K. The singer of all songs Fic

Dillon, M. Yes she can 973.932

Holm, J. L. Boston Jane Fic

Friesner, E. M. Nobody's princess Fic

Friesner, E. M. Nobody's prize Fic

Holm, J. L. Boston Jane the claim Fic

Holm, J. L. Boston Jane wilderness days Fic

Pierce, T. The will of the empress Fic

Pullman, P. The book of dust Fic

Talley, R. Pulp Fic

Uehashi, N. Moribito Fic

Uehashi, N. Moribito II Fic

Whitney, D. You don't have to be everything 808.108

Young, Brian

Healer of the water monster Fic

Young, Brigit

The prettiest Fic

Young, Ed

Beyond the great mountains 811

Young, Ethan, 1983-

The dragon path Fic

Young, Jeff C., 1948-

Hernando de Soto B

Inspiring African-American inventors 608.996

Young, Karen Romano

Across the wide ocean 623.89

Best science fair workshops -- bug science 595.7078

Doodlebug Fic

Hundred percent Fic

Junkyard science 628.4

Space junk 629.4

Young, Marilyn B.

The Vietnam War 959.704

Young, Moira

Blood red road Fic

Young, Tracie

Cool math 510

Youngblood, Leslie C.

Forever this summer Fic

Love like sky Fic

YOUNGER BROTHERS AND SISTERS

Lord, C. Rules Fic

Nelson, T. Ruby electric Fic

Younker, J. Marin

Bleed blister puke and purge 610.9

Yount, Lisa

Alfred Blalock Helen Taussig and Vivien Thomas 617.4

The father of anatomy B

Nikola Tesla B

Rosalind Franklin B

Your brain needs a hug. Earl, R. 616.85

Your friend in fashion Abby Shapiro. Axelrod, A. Fic

Your head shape reveals your personality! Zuchora-Walske, C. 610.9

Your own Sylvia. Hemphill, S. Fic

Yours Truly. Frederick, H. V. Fic

YOUSAFZAI, MALALA, 1997-

Aretha, D. Malala Yousafzai and the girls of Pakistan B

Yousafzai, M. I am Malala B

Yousafzai, Malala, 1997-

I am Malala B

We are displaced 305.23092

YOUTH -- ALCOHOL USE

Bellenir, K. Alcohol information for teens 613.81

YOUTH -- BOOKS AND READING

APPENDIX

APPENDIX

The following charts list Newbery medalists in the collection and their locations in the Classified Collection. Newbery titles with both an author and illustrator are listed under the illustrator's name with a reference to the author's name, under which the book's entry can be found

Newbery Medal titles

Author/Illustrator	Title	Dewey Location
Alexander, K.	*The crossover*	**Fic**
Applegate, K.	*The one and only Ivan*	**Fic**
Armstrong, W. H.	*Sounder*	**Fic**
Avi.	*Crispin: the cross of lead*	**Fic**
Barnhill, K.	*The girl who drank the moon*	**Fic**
Brink, C. R.	*Caddie Woodlawn*	**Fic**
Cleary, B.	*Dear Mr. Henshaw*	**Fic**
Cooper, S.	*The grey king*	**Fic**
Craft, Jerry	*New kid*	**741.5**
Creech, S.	*Walk two moons*	**Fic**
Curtis, C. P.	*Bud, not Buddy*	**Fic**
Cushman, K.	*The midwife's apprentice*	**Fic**
DiCamillo, K.	*Flora and Ulysses*	**Fic**
DiCamillo, K.	*The tale of Despereaux*	**Fic**
Du Bois, W. P.	*The twenty-one balloons*	**Fic**
Estes, E.	*Ginger Pye*	**Fic**
Field, R.	*Hitty: her first hundred years*	**Fic**
Fleischman, P.	*Joyful noise: poems for two voices*	**811**
Fleischman, S.	*The whipping boy*	**Fic**
Freedman, R.	*Lincoln: a photobiography*	**B**
Gaiman, N.	*The graveyard book*	**Fic**
Gantos, J.	*Dead end in Norvelt*	**Fic**
Hamilton, V.	*M.C. Higgins, the great*	**Fic**
Henry, M.	*King of the wind*	**Fic**
Hesse, K.	*Out of the dust*	**Fic**
Kadohata, C.	*Kira-Kira*	**Fic**
Keith, H.	*Rifles for Watie*	**Fic**
Keller, Tae	*When you trap a tiger*	**Fic**
Kelly, Erin Entrada	*Hello universe*	**Fic**
Konigsburg, E. L.	*From the mixed-up files of Mrs. Basil E. Frankweiler*	**Fic**
Konigsburg, E. L.	*The view from Saturday*	**Fic**
Krumgold, J.	*Onion John*	**Fic**
L'Engle, M.	*A wrinkle in time*	**Fic**
Lowry, L.	*The giver*	**Fic**
Lowry, L.	*Number the stars*	**Fic**
MacLachlan, P.	*Sarah, plain and tall*	**Fic**

Medina, Meg	*Merci Suárez changes gears*	**Fic**
Naylor, P. R.	*Shiloh*	**Fic**
Neville, E. C.	*It's like this, Cat*	**Fic**
O'Brien, R. C.	*Mrs. Frisby and the rats of NIMH*	**Fic**
O'Dell, S.	*Island of the Blue Dolphins*	**Fic**
Park, L. S.	*A single shard*	**Fic**
Paterson, K.	*Bridge to Terabithia*	**Fic**
Patron, S.	*The higher power of Lucky*	**Fic**
Peck, R.	*A year down yonder*	**Fic**
Pena, Matt de la	*Last stop on Market Street*	**E**
Perkins, L. R.	*Criss cross*	**Fic**
Raskin, E.	*The Westing game*	**Fic**
Rylant, C.	*Missing May*	**Fic**
Sachar, L.	*Holes*	**Fic**
Sawyer, R.	*Roller skates*	**Fic**
Schlitz, L. A.	*Good masters! Sweet ladies!*	**812**
Seredy, K.	*The white stag*	**Fic**
Speare, E. G.	*The bronze bow*	**Fic**
Speare, E. G.	*The witch of Blackbird Pond*	**Fic**
Sperry, A.	*Call it courage*	**Fic**
Spinelli, J.	*Maniac Magee*	**Fic**
Stead, R.	*When you reach me*	**Fic**
Taylor, M. D.	*Roll of thunder, hear my cry*	**Fic**
Treviño, E. B. d.	*I, Juan de Pareja*	**Fic**
Vanderpool, C.	*Moon over Manifest*	**Fic**
Vining, E. G.	*Adam of the road*	**Fic**
Voigt, C.	*Dicey's song*	**Fic**
Willard, N.	*A visit to William Blake's inn*	**811**